## RECIPROCALS OF BASIC FUNCTIONS

18. $$\int \frac{1}{1 \pm \sin u}\, du = \tan u \mp \sec u + C$$

19. $$\int \frac{1}{1 \pm \cos u}\, du = -\cot u \pm \csc u + C$$

20. $$\int \frac{1}{1 \pm \tan u}\, du = \tfrac{1}{2}(u \pm \ln|\cos u \pm \sin u|) + C$$

21. $$\int \frac{1}{\sin u \cos u}\, du = \ln|\tan u| + C$$

22. $$\int \frac{1}{1 \pm \cot u}\, du = \tfrac{1}{2}(u \mp \ln|\sin u \pm \cos u|) + C$$

23. $$\int \frac{1}{1 \pm \sec u}\, du = u + \cot u \mp \csc u + C$$

24. $$\int \frac{1}{1 \pm \csc u}\, du = u - \tan u \pm \sec u + C$$

25. $$\int \frac{1}{1 \pm e^u}\, du = u - \ln(1 \pm e^u) + C$$

## POWERS OF TRIGONOMETRIC FUNCTIONS

26. $$\int \sin^2 u\, du = \tfrac{1}{2}u - \tfrac{1}{4}\sin 2u + C$$

27. $$\int \cos^2 u\, du = \tfrac{1}{2}u + \tfrac{1}{4}\sin 2u + C$$

28. $$\int \tan^2 u\, du = \tan u - u + C$$

29. $$\int \sin^n u\, du = -\frac{1}{n}\sin^{n-1} u \cos u + \frac{n-1}{n}\int \sin^{n-2} u\, du$$

30. $$\int \cos^n u\, du = \frac{1}{n}\cos^{n-1} u \sin u + \frac{n-1}{n}\int \cos^{n-2} u\, du$$

31. $$\int \tan^n u\, du = \frac{1}{n-1}\tan^{n-1} u - \int \tan^{n-2} u\, du$$

32. $$\int \cot^2 u\, du = -\cot u - u + C$$

33. $$\int \sec^2 u\, du = \tan u + C$$

34. $$\int \csc^2 u\, du = -\cot u + C$$

35. $$\int \cot^n u\, du = -\frac{1}{n-1}\cot^{n-1} u - \int \cot^{n-2} u\, du$$

36. $$\int \sec^n u\, du = \frac{1}{n-1}\sec^{n-2} u \tan u + \frac{n-2}{n-1}\int \sec^{n-2} u\, du$$

37. $$\int \csc^n u\, du = -\frac{1}{n-1}\csc^{n-2} u \cot u + \frac{n-2}{n-1}\int \csc^{n-2} u\, du$$

## PRODUCTS OF TRIGONOMETRIC FUNCTIONS

38. $$\int \sin mu \sin nu\, du = -\frac{\sin(m+n)u}{2(m+n)} + \frac{\sin(m-n)u}{2(m-n)} + C$$

39. $$\int \cos mu \cos nu\, du = \frac{\sin(m+n)u}{2(m+n)} + \frac{\sin(m-n)u}{2(m-n)} + C$$

40. $$\int \sin mu \cos nu\, du = -\frac{\cos(m+n)u}{2(m+n)} - \frac{\cos(m-n)u}{2(m-n)} + C$$

41. $$\int \sin^m u \cos^n u\, du = -\frac{\sin^{m-1} u \cos^{n+1} u}{m+n} + \frac{m-1}{m+n}\int \sin^{m-2} u \cos^n u\, du$$
$$= \frac{\sin^{m+1} u \cos^{n-1} u}{m+n} + \frac{n-1}{m+n}\int \sin^m u \cos^{n-2} u\, du$$

## PRODUCTS OF TRIGONOMETRIC AND EXPONENTIAL FUNCTIONS

42. $$\int e^{au}\sin bu\, du = \frac{e^{au}}{a^2+b^2}(a\sin bu - b\cos bu) + C$$

43. $$\int e^{au}\cos bu\, du = \frac{e^{au}}{a^2+b^2}(a\cos bu + b\sin bu) + C$$

## POWERS OF *u* MULTIPLYING OR DIVIDING BASIC FUNCTIONS

44. $$\int u \sin u\, du = \sin u - u\cos u + C$$

45. $$\int u \cos u\, du = \cos u + u\sin u + C$$

46. $$\int u^2 \sin u\, du = 2u\sin u + (2-u^2)\cos u + C$$

47. $$\int u^2 \cos u\, du = 2u\cos u + (u^2-2)\sin u + C$$

48. $$\int u^n \sin u\, du = -u^n \cos u + n\int u^{n-1}\cos u\, du$$

49. $$\int u^n \cos u\, du = u^n \sin u - n\int u^{n-1}\sin u\, du$$

50. $$\int u^n \ln u\, du = \frac{u^{n+1}}{(n+1)^2}[(n+1)\ln u - 1] + C$$

51. $$\int ue^u\, du = e^u(u-1) + C$$

52. $$\int u^n e^u\, du = u^n e^u - n\int u^{n-1}e^u\, du$$

53. $$\int u^n a^u\, du = \frac{u^n a^u}{\ln a} - \frac{n}{\ln a}\int u^{n-1}a^u\, du + C$$

54. $$\int \frac{e^u\, du}{u^n} = -\frac{e^u}{(n-1)u^{n-1}} + \frac{1}{n-1}\int \frac{e^u\, du}{u^{n-1}}$$

55. $$\int \frac{a^u\, du}{u^n} = -\frac{a^u}{(n-1)u^{n-1}} + \frac{\ln a}{n-1}\int \frac{a^u\, du}{u^{n-1}}$$

56. $$\int \frac{du}{u\ln u} = \ln|\ln u| + C$$

## POLYNOMIALS MULTIPLYING BASIC FUNCTIONS

57. $$\int p(u)e^{au}\, du = \frac{1}{a}p(u)e^{au} - \frac{1}{a^2}p'(u)e^{au} + \frac{1}{a^3}p''(u)e^{au} - \cdots$$ [signs alternate: $+ - + - \cdots$]

58. $$\int p(u)\sin au\, du = -\frac{1}{a}p(u)\cos au + \frac{1}{a^2}p'(u)\sin au + \frac{1}{a^3}p''(u)\cos au - \cdots$$ [signs alternate in pairs after first term: $+ + - - + + - - \cdots$]

59. $$\int p(u)\cos au\, du = \frac{1}{a}p(u)\sin au + \frac{1}{a^2}p'(u)\cos au - \frac{1}{a^3}p''(u)\sin au - \cdots$$ [signs alternate in pairs: $+ + - - + + - - \cdots$]

# FOR THE STUDENT

Calculus provides a way of viewing and analyzing the physical world. As with all mathematics courses, calculus involves equations and formulas. However, if you successfully learn to use all the formulas and solve all of the problems in the text but do not master the underlying *ideas*, you will have missed the most important part of calculus. If you master these ideas, you will have a widely applicable tool that goes far beyond textbook exercises.

Before starting your studies, you may find it helpful to leaf through this text to get a general feeling for its different parts:

- The opening page of each chapter gives you an overview of what that chapter is about, and the opening page of each section within a chapter gives you an overview of what that section is about. To help you locate specific information, sections are subdivided into topics that are marked with a box like this ■.
- Each section ends with a set of exercises. The answers to most odd-numbered exercises appear in the back of the book. If you find that your answer to an exercise does not match that in the back of the book, do not assume immediately that yours is incorrect—there may be more than one way to express the answer. For example, if your answer is $\sqrt{2}/2$ and the text answer is $1/\sqrt{2}$, then both are correct since your answer can be obtained by "rationalizing" the text answer. In general, if your answer does not match that in the text, then your best first step is to look for an algebraic manipulation or a trigonometric identity that might help you determine if the two answers are equivalent. If the answer is in the form of a decimal approximation, then your answer might differ from that in the text because of a difference in the number of decimal places used in the computations.
- The section exercises include regular exercises and four special categories: *Quick Check*, *Focus on Concepts*, *True/False*, and *Writing*.
  - The *Quick Check* exercises are intended to give you quick feedback on whether you understand the key ideas in the section; they involve relatively little computation, and have answers provided at the end of the exercise set.
  - The *Focus on Concepts* exercises, as their name suggests, key in on the main ideas in the section.
  - *True/False* exercises focus on key ideas in a different way. You must decide whether the statement is true in *all possible circumstances*, in which case you would declare it to be "true," or whether there are some circumstances in which it is not true, in which case you would declare it to be "false." In each such exercise you are asked to "Explain your answer." You might do this by noting a theorem in the text that shows the statement to be true or by finding a particular example in which the statement is not true.
  - *Writing* exercises are intended to test your ability to explain mathematical ideas in words rather than relying solely on numbers and symbols. All exercises requiring writing should be answered in complete, correctly punctuated logical sentences—not with fragmented phrases and formulas.
- Each chapter ends with two additional sets of exercises: *Chapter Review Exercises*, which, as the name suggests, is a select set of exercises that provide a review of the main concepts and techniques in the chapter, and *Making Connections*, in which exercises require you to draw on and combine various ideas developed throughout the chapter.
- Your instructor may choose to incorporate technology in your calculus course. Exercises whose solution involves the use of some kind of technology are tagged with icons to alert you and your instructor. Those exercises tagged with the icon ⌒ require graphing technology—either a graphing calculator or a computer program that can graph equations. Those exercises tagged with the icon C require a computer algebra system (CAS) such as *Mathematica*, *Maple*, or available on some graphing calculators.
- Inside the front and back covers of the text you will find endpapers that contain useful formulas.
- Five summary appendices are included at the end of the text, surveying key definitions and facts from trigonometry, general functions, and inverse functions. More detailed versions of these appendices, as well as eleven additional appendices that supply further support and/or extend the text, are available in web versions.
- The ideas in this text were created by real people with interesting personalities and backgrounds. Pictures and biographical sketches of many of these people appear throughout the book.
- Notes in the margin are intended to clarify or comment on important points in the text.

## A Word of Encouragement

As you work your way through this text you will find some ideas that you understand immediately, some that you don't understand until you have read them several times, and others that you do not seem to understand, even after several readings. Do not become discouraged—some ideas are intrinsically difficult and take time to "percolate." You may well find that a hard idea becomes clear later when you least expect it.

## Web Sites for this Text

**www.antontextbooks.com**

**www.wiley.com/go/global/anton**

Carlos Fernandez/Getty Images

11th EDITION

# CALCULUS

## EARLY TRANSCENDENTALS


- **HOWARD ANTON** *Drexel University*
- **IRL BIVENS** *Davidson College*
- **STEPHEN DAVIS** *Davidson College*


WILEY

JOHN WILEY & SONS, INC.

**Vice President & Director:** Laurie Rosatone
**Acquisitions Editor:** Shannon Corliss
**Sponsoring Editor:** Jennifer Brady
**Freelance Project Editor:** Anne Scanlan-Rohrer
**Marketing Manager:** John LaVacca III
**Senior Product Designer:** David Dietz
**Product Design Manager:** Thomas Kulesa
**Market Solutions Assistant:** Ryann Dannelly
**Production Services:** Carol Sawyer/The Perfect Proof
**Senior Content Manager:** Karoline Luciano/Valerie Zaborski
**Senior Production Editor:** Laura Abrams
**Senior Designer:** Maureen Eide
**Photo Editor:** James Russiello
**Cover Photo:** Carlos Fernandez/Getty Images

**Sunrise Icon:** AlexSava / iStockphoto

This book was set in LaTeX by MPS Limited, and printed and bound by RR Donnelley.The cover was printed by RR Donnelley.

This book is printed on acid-free paper.



ISBN 978-1-118-88382-2

Printed in the United States of America

10 9 8 7 6 5 4 3 2 1

## About HOWARD ANTON

Howard Anton obtained his B.A. from Lehigh University, his M.A. from the University of Illinois, and his Ph.D. from the Polytechnic University of Brooklyn, all in mathematics. In the early 1960s he worked for Burroughs Corporation and Avco Corporation at Cape Canaveral, Florida, where he was involved with the manned space program. In 1968 he joined the Mathematics Department at Drexel University, where he taught full time until 1983. Since that time he has been an Emeritus Professor at Drexel and has devoted the majority of his time to textbook writing and activities for mathematical associations. Dr. Anton was president of the EPADEL section of the Mathematical Association of America (MAA), served on the Board of Governors of that organization, and guided the creation of the student chapters of the MAA. He has published numerous research papers in functional analysis, approximation theory, and topology, as well as pedagogical papers. He is best known for his textbooks in mathematics, which are among the most widely used in the world. There are currently more than one hundred versions of his books, including translations into Spanish, Arabic, Portuguese, Italian, Indonesian, French, Japanese, Chinese, Hebrew, and German. His textbook in linear algebra has won both the Textbook Excellence Award and the McGuffey Award from the Textbook Author's Association. For relaxation, Dr. Anton enjoys traveling and photography.

## About IRL BIVENS

Irl C. Bivens, a recipient of the George Polya Award and the Merten M. Hasse Prize for Expository Writing in Mathematics, received his A.B. from Pfeiffer College and his Ph.D. from the University of North Carolina at Chapel Hill, both in mathematics. Since 1982 he has taught at Davidson College, where he currently holds the position of professor of mathematics. A typical academic year sees him teaching courses in calculus, complex analysis, and the history of mathematics. He has published numerous articles on undergraduate mathematics, as well as research papers in differential geometry. Past service to the MAA includes membership on the editorial boards of *The College Mathematics Journal,* the Problem Book series, Dolciani Mathematical Expositions, along with service on awards committees for expository writing. For recreation, he enjoys swimming, juggling, and the exploration of mathematical legerdemain.

## About STEPHEN DAVIS

Stephen L. Davis received his B.A. from Lindenwood College and his Ph.D. from Rutgers University in mathematics. Having previously taught at Rutgers University and Ohio State University, Dr. Davis joined the faculty at Davidson College in 1981, where he is currently a professor of mathematics. He regularly teaches calculus, linear algebra, abstract algebra, and computer science. Professor Davis has published numerous articles on calculus reform and testing, as well as research papers on finite group theory. Professor Davis has held several offices in the Southeastern section of the MAA, including chair and secretary-treasurer, and has represented the section on the MAA Board of Governors. He has been involved in the grading of the Advanced Placement Calculus Exam since 1988 and began a four-year term as Chief Reader in 2015. He is also webmaster for the North Carolina Association of Advanced Placement Mathematics Teachers and is actively involved in nurturing mathematically talented high school students through leadership in the Charlotte Mathematics Club. For relaxation, he plays basketball, travels, and occasionally juggles. Professor Davis and his wife Elisabeth have three children, Laura, Anne, and James, all former calculus students.

*To*
**my wife Pat and my children: Brian, David, and Lauren**

*In Memory of*
**my mother Shirley**
**my father Benjamin**
**my thesis advisor and inspiration, George Bachman**
**my benefactor in my time of need, Stephen Girard (1750–1831)**
*—HA*

*To*
**my son Robert**
*—IB*

*To*
**my wife Elisabeth**
**my children: Laura, Anne, and James**
*—SD*

# PREFACE

This eleventh edition of *Calculus* maintains those aspects of previous editions that have led to the series' success—we continue to strive for student comprehension without sacrificing mathematical accuracy, and the exercise sets are carefully constructed to avoid unhappy surprises that can derail a calculus class.

All of the changes to the eleventh edition were carefully reviewed by outstanding teachers comprised of both users and nonusers of the previous edition. The charge of this committee was to ensure that all changes did not alter those aspects of the text that attracted users of the tenth edition and at the same time provide freshness to the new edition that would attract new users.

## NEW TO THIS EDITION

- Most of the pre-calculus material in the 10th edition Chapter 0 has been moved to Appendices, and the remaining Chapter 0 material is merged into Chapter 1.
- Some prose in other areas of the text has been tightened to enhance clarity and student understanding.
- New applied exercises have been added to the book and some existing applied exercises have been updated.

## OTHER FEATURES

**Flexibility** This edition has a built-in flexibility that is designed to serve a broad spectrum of calculus philosophies—from traditional to "reform." Technology can be emphasized or not, and the order of many topics can be permuted freely to accommodate each instructor's specific needs.

**Rigor** The challenge of writing a good calculus book is to strike the right balance between rigor and clarity. Our goal is to present precise mathematics to the fullest extent possible in an introductory treatment. Where clarity and rigor conflict, we choose clarity; however, we believe it to be important that the student understand the difference between a careful proof and an informal argument, so we have informed the reader when the arguments being presented are informal or motivational. Theory involving $\epsilon$-$\delta$ arguments appears in separate sections so that they can be covered or not, as preferred by the instructor.

**Rule of Four** The "rule of four" refers to presenting concepts from the verbal, algebraic, visual, and numerical points of view. In keeping with current pedagogical philosophy, we used this approach whenever appropriate.

**Visualization** This edition makes extensive use of modern computer graphics to clarify concepts and to develop the student's ability to visualize mathematical objects, particularly those in 3-space. For those students who are working with graphing technology, there are many exercises that are designed to develop the student's ability to generate and analyze mathematical curves and surfaces.

**Quick Check Exercises** Each exercise set begins with approximately five exercises (answers included) that are designed to provide students with an immediate assessment of whether they have mastered key ideas from the section. They require a minimum of computation and are answered by filling in the blanks.

**Focus on Concepts Exercises** Each exercise set contains a clearly identified group of problems that focus on the main ideas of the section.

**Technology Exercises** Most sections include exercises that are designed to be solved using either a graphing calculator or a computer algebra system such as *Mathematica*, *Maple*, or the open source program *Sage*. These exercises are marked with an icon for easy identification.

**Applicability of Calculus** One of the primary goals of this text is to link calculus to the real world and the student's own experience. This theme is carried through in the examples and exercises.

**Career Preparation** This text is written at a mathematical level that will prepare students for a wide variety of careers that require a sound mathematics background, including engineering, the various sciences, and business.

**Trigonometry Summary and Review** Deficiencies in trigonometry plague many students, so we have included a substantial trigonometry review in Appendices A and J.

**Appendix on Polynomial Equations** Because many calculus students are weak in solving polynomial equations, we have included an appendix (Appendix H) that reviews the Factor Theorem, the Remainder Theorem, and procedures for finding rational roots.

**Principles of Integral Evaluation** The traditional Techniques of Integration is entitled "Principles of Integral Evaluation" to reflect its more modern approach to the material. The chapter emphasizes general methods and the role of technology rather than specific tricks for evaluating complicated or obscure integrals.

**Historical Notes** The biographies and historical notes have been a hallmark of this text from its first edition and have been maintained. All of the biographical materials have been distilled from standard sources with the goal of capturing and bringing to life for the student the personalities of history's greatest mathematicians.

**Margin Notes and Warnings** These appear in the margins throughout the text to clarify or expand on the text exposition or to alert the reader to some pitfall.

# SUPPLEMENTS

The **Student Solutions Manual** provides detailed solutions to the odd-numbered exercises in the text. The structure of the step-by-step solutions matches those of the worked examples in the textbook. The Student Solutions Manual is also provided in digital format to students in *WileyPLUS*.

Volume I (Calculus: Early Transcendental) ISBN: 978-1-119-14781-7
Volume II (Calculus: Late Transcendental) ISBN: 978-1-119-19366-1

**The Student Study Guide** is available for download from the book companion Web site at www.wiley.com/college/anton or at www.howardanton.com and to users of *WileyPLUS*.

The **Instructor's Solutions Manual** contains detailed solutions to all of the exercises in the text. The Instructor's Solutions Manual is also available in PDF format on the password-protected Instructor Companion Site at www.wiley.com/college/anton or at www.howardanton.com and in *WileyPLUS*.

ISBN: 978-1-119-14782-4

The **Instructor's Manual** suggests time allocations and teaching plans for each section in the text. Most of the teaching plans contain a bulleted list of key points to emphasize. The discussion of each section concludes with a sample homework assignment. The Instructor's Manual is available in PDF format on the password-protected Instructor Companion Site at www.wiley.com/college/anton or at www.howardanton.com and in *WileyPLUS*.

The **Web Projects (Expanding the Calculus Horizon)** referenced in the text can also be downloaded from the companion Web sites and from *WileyPLUS*.

Instructors can also access the following materials from either the book companion site or *WileyPLUS*:

- The **Printable Test Bank** features questions and answers for every section of the text.
- **PowerPoint lecture slides** cover the major concepts and themes of each section of the book. Personal-Response System questions ("Clicker Questions") appear at the end of each PowerPoint presentation and provide an easy way to gauge classroom understanding.
- **Additional calculus content** covers analytic geometry in calculus, mathematical modeling with differential equations and parametric equations, as well as an introduction to linear algebra.

## *WileyPLUS*

*WileyPLUS*, Wiley's digital-learning environment, is loaded with all of the supplements listed on the previous page, and also features the following:

- **Homework management tools**, which easily allow you to assign and grade algorithmic questions, as well as gauge student comprehension.
- **Algorithmic** questions with randomized numeric values and an answer-entry palette for symbolic notation are provided online though *WileyPLUS*. Students can click on "help" buttons for hints, link to the relevant section of the text, show their work or query their instructor using a white board, or see a step-by-step solution (depending on instructor-selecting settings).
- **QuickStart** predesigned reading and homework assignments. Use them as-is or customize them to fit the needs of your classroom.
- The **e-book**, which is an exact version of the print text but also features hyperlinks to questions, definitions, and supplements for quicker and easier support.
- **Guided Online (GO) Tutorial Exercises** that prompt students to build solutions step by step. Rather than simply grading an exercise answer as wrong, GO tutorial problems show students precisely where they are making a mistake.
- **Are You Ready?** quizzes gauge student mastery of chapter concepts and techniques and provide feedback on areas that require further attention.
- **ORION Algebra and Trigonometry Refresher** provides students with an opportunity to brush up on the material necessary to master calculus, as well as to determine areas that require further review.

***WileyPLUS.*** Learn more at www.wileyplus.com.

# ACKNOWLEDGMENTS

It has been our good fortune to have the advice and guidance of many talented people whose knowledge and skills have enhanced this book in many ways. We wish to thank John Wiley and Sons, in particular Shannon Corliss and Jennifer Brady for their dedication in preparing this edition. We would also like to thank Carol Sawyer for her amazing work on the text layout.

Furthermore for their valuable help we thank the following people.

## Reviewers of the Eleventh Edition

Jay Abramson, *Arizona State University*
Gerardo Aladro, *Florida International University*
Theodore M. Alper, *Online High School of Stanford University*
Mahboub Baccouch, *University of Nebraska Omaha*
Jeffery J. Boats, *University of Detroit Mercy*
Tom Bella, *University of Rhode Island*
Michael Boardman, *Pacific University*
Charles W. Bock, *Philadelphia University*
Olguta Buse, *Indiana University at Purdue University Indianapolis*
Christopher Butler, *Case Western Reserve University*
Thomas Cassidy, *Bucknell University*
Manning G. Collier, *University of Mary Washington*
Charles L. Cooper, *University of Central Omaha*
John Davis, *Baylor University*
Madhu Motha, *Butler County Community College*
Bharath Narayanan, *Pennsylvania State University*
Deborah Doucette, *Erie Community College*
Judith Downey, *University of Nebraska Omaha*
Raluca Dumitru, *University of North Florida*
Mark Dunster, *San Diego State University*
Catherine Famiglietti, *University of California, Irvine*
Jennifer Galovich, *St. John's University*
William Girton, *Florida Tech*
Frank Gonzalez, *Saddleback College*
William Hamill, *University of Tulsa*
Rita Hibschweiler, *University of New Hampshire*
Derek Hiley, *Cuyahoga Community College*
Randall Holmes, *Boise State University*
Dragos Hrimiuc, *University of Alberta*
Cindy J. Parsons, *Pennsylvania State University*
Bin Jiang, *Portland State University*
Clarence Johnson, *Cuyahoga Community College*
Jim E. Jones, *Florida Tech*
Ron Jorgensen, *Milwaukee School of Engineering*
Uwe Kaiser, *Boise State University*
Kristi Karber, *University of Central Omaha*
Michael Kouritzin, *University of Alberta*
M. Paul Latiolais, *Portland State University*
Douglas Lloyd, *Golden West College*
Lew Ludwig, *Denison University*
Paolo Mantero, *University of California, Riverside*
William McGovern, *University of Washington*
Thomas Milligan, *University of Central Oklahoma*
Carla Monticelli, *Camden County College*
Laura Moore-Mueller, *Green River Community College*
Jeanette Palmiter, *Portland State University*
Cynthia Piez, *University of Idaho*
Emma Previato, *Boston University*
Ferdinand Rivera, *San Jose State University*
Joan Rosebush, *University of Vermont*
Hossein Rostami, *Philadelphia University*
Nathan Ryan, *Bucknell University*
Ronda Sander, *University of South Carolina*
Jonathan Scott, *Cleveland State University*
Eugene Schlereth, *University of Tennessee Chattanooga*
Mark Serebransky, *Camden County College*
Qin Sheng, *Baylor University*
Slobodan Simic', *San Jose State University*
Satyanand Singh, *New York City College of Technology*
Adi Tcaciuc, *MacEwan University*
Michael Tom, *Louisiana State University*
Brian VanPelt, *Cuyahoga Community College*
Stephanie Van Rhein, *University of Missouri, Kansas City*
Kathy Vranicar, *University of Nebraska Omaha*
Belinda Wang, *University of Toronto*
Anna Wlodarczyk, *Florida International University*
Nataliya Zadorozhna, *MacEwan University*
Constance Ziemian, *Bucknell University*
Diane Zych, *Erie Community College*

## Reviewers and Contributors of the Tenth Edition

Frederick Adkins, *Indiana University of Pennsylvania*
Gerardo Aladro, *Florida International University*
Mike Albanese, *Central Piedmont Community College*
Faiz Al-Rubaee, *University of North Florida*
Mahboub Baccouch, *University of Nebraska at Omaha*
Jim Brandt, *Southern Utah University*
Elizabeth Brown, *James Madison University*
Michael Brown, *San Diego Mesa College*
Christopher Butler, *Case Western Reserve University*
Nick Bykov, *San Joaquin Delta College*
Jamylle Carter, *Diablo Valley College*
Hongwei Chen, *Christopher Newport University*
David A. Clark, *Randolph-Macon College*
Dominic P. Clemence, *North Carolina Agricultural and Technical State University*
Michael Cohen, *Hofstra University*
Hugh Cornell, *Salt Lake Community College*
Kyle Costello, *Salt Lake Community College*
Walter Czarnec, *Framingham State University*
Michael Daniel, *Drexel University*
Judith Downey, *University of Nebraska, Omaha*
Artur Elezi, *American University*
David James Ellingson, *Napa Valley College*
Elaine B. Fitt, *Bucks County Community College*
Greg Gibson, *North Carolina Agricultural and Technical State University*
Yvonne A. Greenbaun, *Mercer County Community College*
Jerome I. Heaven, *Indiana Tech*
Derek Hiley, *Cuyahoga Community College*
John Khoury, *Brevard Community College*
Kathryn Lesh, *Union College*
Eric Matsuoka, *Leeward Community College*
Ted Nirgiotis, *Diablo Valley College*
Mihaela Poplicher, *University of Cincinnati*
Adrian R. Ranic, *Erie Community College–North*
Thomas C. Redd, *North Carolina Agricultural and Technical State University*
R. A. Rock, *Daniel Webster College*
John Paul Roop, *North Carolina Agricultural and Technical State University*
Philippe Rukimbira, *Florida International University*
Joseph P. Rusinko, *Winthrop University*
Susan W. Santolucito, *Delgado Community College, City Park*
Dee Dee Shaulis, *University of Colorado at Boulder*
Michael D. Shaw, *Florida Institute of Technology*
Jennifer Siegel, *Broward College–Central Campus*
Thomas W. Simpson, *University of South Carolina Union*
Maria Siopsis, *Maryville College*
Mark A. Smith, *Miami University, Ohio*
James Sochacki, *James Madison University*
Kelly Stady, *Cuyahoga Community College*
Alan Taylor, *Union College*
Kathy Vranicar, *University of Nebraska, Omaha*
Anke Walz, *Kutztown University*
Zhi-Qiang Wang, *Utah State University*
Tom Wells, *Delta College*
Greg Wisloski, *Indiana University of Pennsylvania*

We would also like to thank Thomas Polaski and Roger Lipsett for their accuracy check of the eleventh edition. Thanks also to Tamas Wiandt for revising the solutions manuals and Jennifer Blue for accuracy checking those solutions. We also appreciate the feedback we received from Mark Dunster, Cecelia Knoll, and Michael Rosenthal on selected *WileyPLUS* problems.

# CONTENTS

# THE ROOTS OF CALCULUS

Today's exciting applications of calculus have roots that can be traced to the work of the Greek mathematician Archimedes, but the actual discovery of the fundamental principles of calculus was made independently by Isaac Newton (English) and Gottfried Leibniz (German) in the late seventeenth century. The work of Newton and Leibniz was motivated by four major classes of scientific and mathematical problems of the time:

- Find the tangent line to a general curve at a given point.
- Find the area of a general region, the length of a general curve, and the volume of a general solid.
- Find the maximum or minimum value of a quantity—for example, the maximum and minimum distances of a planet from the Sun, or the maximum range attainable for a projectile by varying its angle of fire.
- Given a formula for the distance traveled by a body in any specified amount of time, find the velocity and acceleration of the body at any instant. Conversely, given a formula that specifies the acceleration of velocity at any instant, find the distance traveled by the body in a specified period of time.

Newton and Leibniz found a fundamental relationship between the problem of finding a tangent line to a curve and the problem of determining the area of a region. Their realization of this connection is considered to be the "discovery of calculus." Though Newton saw how these two problems are related ten years before Leibniz did, Leibniz published his work twenty years before Newton. This situation led to a stormy debate over who was the rightful discoverer of calculus. The debate engulfed Europe for half a century, with the scientists of the European continent supporting Leibniz and those from England supporting Newton. The conflict was extremely unfortunate because Newton's inferior notation badly hampered scientific development in England, and the Continent in turn lost the benefit of Newton's discoveries in astronomy and physics for nearly fifty years. In spite of it all, Newton and Leibniz were sincere admirers of each other's work.

*[Image: Public domain image from http://commons.wikimedia.org/wiki/File:Hw-newton.jpg. Image provided courtesy of the University of Texas Libraries, The University of Texas at Austin.]*

## ISAAC NEWTON (1642–1727)

Newton was born in the village of Woolsthorpe, England. His father died before he was born and his mother raised him on the family farm. As a youth he showed little evidence of his later brilliance, except for an unusual talent with mechanical devices—he apparently built a working water clock and a toy flour mill powered by a mouse. In 1661 he entered Trinity College in Cambridge with a deficiency in geometry. Fortunately, Newton caught the eye of Isaac Barrow, a gifted mathematician and teacher. Under Barrow's guidance Newton immersed himself in mathematics and science, but he graduated without any special distinction. Because the bubonic plague was spreading rapidly through London, Newton returned to his home in Woolsthorpe and stayed there during the years of 1665 and 1666. In those two momentous years the entire framework of modern science was miraculously created in Newton's mind. He discovered calculus, recognized the underlying principles of planetary motion and gravity, and determined that "white" sunlight was composed of all colors, red to violet. For whatever reasons he kept his discoveries to himself. In 1667 he returned to Cambridge to obtain his Master's degree and upon graduation became a teacher at Trinity. Then in 1669 Newton succeeded his teacher, Isaac Barrow, to the Lucasian chair of mathematics at Trinity, one of the most honored chairs of mathematics in the world.

Thereafter, brilliant discoveries flowed from Newton steadily. He formulated the law of gravitation and used it to explain the motion of the moon, the planets, and the tides; he formulated basic theories of light, thermodynamics, and hydrodynamics; and he devised and constructed the first modern reflecting telescope. Throughout his life Newton was hesitant to publish his major discoveries, revealing them only to a select circle of friends, perhaps because of a fear of criticism or controversy. In 1687, only after intense coaxing by the astronomer, Edmond Halley (discoverer of Halley's comet), did Newton publish his masterpiece, *Philosophiae Naturalis Principia Mathematica* (The Mathematical Principles of Natural Philosophy). This work is generally considered to be the most important and influential scientific book ever written. In it Newton explained the workings of the solar system and formulated the basic laws of motion, which to this day are fundamental in engineering and physics. However, not even the pleas of his friends could convince Newton to publish his discovery of calculus. Only after Leibniz published his results did Newton relent and publish his own work on calculus.

After twenty-five years as a professor, Newton suffered depression and a nervous breakdown. He gave up research in 1695 to accept a position as warden and later master of the London mint. During the twenty-five years that he worked at the mint, he did virtually no scientific or mathematical work. He was knighted in 1705 and on his death was buried in Westminster Abbey with all the honors his country could bestow. It is interesting to note that Newton was a learned theologian who viewed the primary value of his work to be its support of the existence of God. Throughout his life he worked passionately to date biblical events by relating them to astronomical phenomena. He was so consumed with this passion that he spent years searching the Book of Daniel for clues to the end of the world and the geography of hell.

Newton described his brilliant accomplishments as follows: "I seem to have been only like a boy playing on the seashore and diverting myself in now and then finding a smoother pebble or prettier shell than ordinary, whilst the great ocean of truth lay all undiscovered before me."

[*Image: Public domain image from http://commons.wikimedia.org/wiki/ File:Gottfried_Wilhelm_von_ Leibniz.jpg*]

## GOTTFRIED WILHELM LEIBNIZ (1646–1716)

This gifted genius was one of the last people to have mastered most major fields of knowledge—an impossible accomplishment in our own era of specialization. He was an expert in law, religion, philosophy, literature, politics, geology, metaphysics, alchemy, history, and mathematics.

Leibniz was born in Leipzig, Germany. His father, a professor of moral philosophy at the University of Leipzig, died when Leibniz was six years old. The precocious boy then gained access to his father's library and began reading voraciously on a wide range of subjects, a habit that he maintained throughout his life. At age fifteen he entered the University of Leipzig as a law student and by the age of twenty received a doctorate from the University of Altdorf. Subsequently, Leibniz followed a career in law and international politics, serving as counsel to kings and princes. During his numerous foreign missions, Leibniz came in contact with outstanding mathematicians and scientists who stimulated his interest in mathematics—most notably, the physicist Christian Huygens. In mathematics Leibniz was self-taught, learning the subject by reading papers and journals. As a result of this fragmented mathematical education, Leibniz often rediscovered the results of others, and this helped to fuel the debate over the discovery of calculus.

Leibniz never married. He was moderate in his habits, quick-tempered but easily appeased, and charitable in his judgment of other people's work.

In spite of his great achievements, Leibniz never received the honors showered on Newton, and he spent his final years as a lonely embittered man. At his funeral there was one mourner, his secretary. An eyewitness stated, "He was buried more like a robber than what he really was—an ornament of his country."

Kevin Morroun and William O'Nieal

*Air resistance prevents the velocity of a skydiver from increasing indefinitely. The velocity approaches a limit, called the "terminal velocity."*

# 1 LIMITS AND CONTINUITY

The development of calculus in the seventeenth century by Newton and Leibniz provided scientists with their first real understanding of what is meant by an "instantaneous rate of change" such as velocity and acceleration. Once the idea was understood conceptually, efficient computational methods followed, and science took a quantum leap forward. The fundamental building block on which rates of change rest is the concept of a "limit," an idea that is so important that all other calculus concepts are now based on it.

In this chapter we will develop the concept of a limit in stages, proceeding from an informal, intuitive notion to a precise mathematical definition. We will also develop theorems and procedures for calculating limits, and use limits to study "continuous" curves. We will conclude by studying continuity and other properties of trigonometric, inverse trigonometric, logarithmic, and exponential functions.

## 1.1 LIMITS (AN INTUITIVE APPROACH)

*The concept of a "limit" is the fundamental building block on which all calculus concepts are based. In this section we will study limits informally, with the goal of developing an intuitive feel for the basic ideas. In the next three sections we will focus on computational methods and precise definitions.*

Many of the ideas of calculus originated with the following two geometric problems:

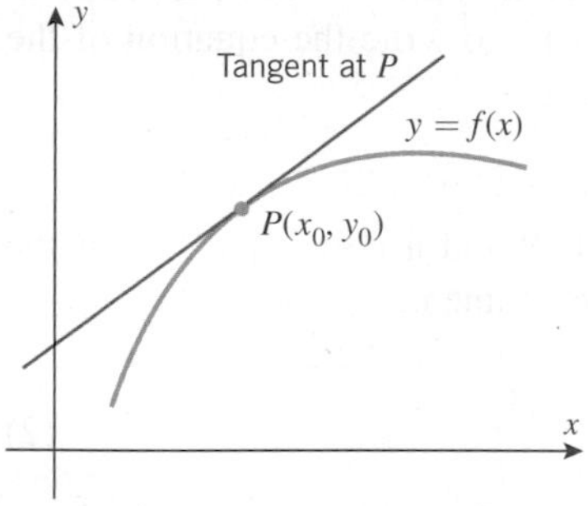


▲ **Figure 1.1.1**

**THE TANGENT LINE PROBLEM** Given a function $f$ and a point $P(x_0, y_0)$ on its graph, find an equation of the line that is tangent to the graph at $P$ (Figure 1.1.1).

**THE AREA PROBLEM** Given a function $f$, find the area between the graph of $f$ and an interval $[a, b]$ on the $x$-axis (Figure 1.1.2).

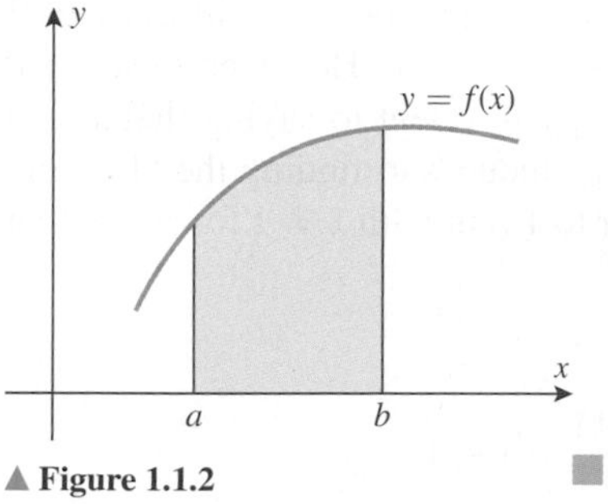


▲ **Figure 1.1.2**

Traditionally, that portion of calculus arising from the tangent line problem is called ***differential calculus*** and that arising from the area problem is called ***integral calculus***. However, we will see later that the tangent line and area problems are so closely related that the distinction between differential and integral calculus is somewhat artificial.

### TANGENT LINES AND LIMITS

In plane geometry, a line is called *tangent* to a circle if it meets the circle at precisely one point (Figure 1.1.3*a*). Although this definition is adequate for circles, it is not appropriate for more general curves. For example, in Figure 1.1.3*b*, the line meets the curve exactly once but is obviously not what we would regard to be a tangent line; and in Figure 1.1.3*c*, the line appears to be tangent to the curve, yet it intersects the curve more than once.

To obtain a definition of a tangent line that applies to curves other than circles, we must view tangent lines another way. For this purpose, suppose that we are interested in the tangent line at a point $P$ on a curve in the $xy$-plane and that $Q$ is any point that lies on

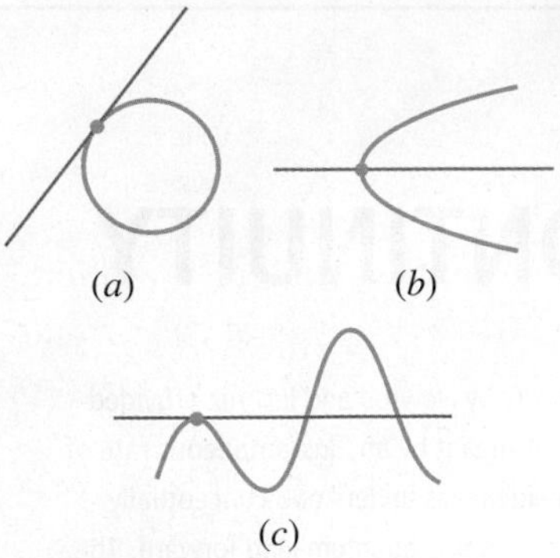

▲ Figure 1.1.3

the curve and is different from $P$. The line through $P$ and $Q$ is called a ***secant line*** for the curve at $P$. Intuition suggests that if we move the point $Q$ along the curve toward $P$, then the secant line will rotate toward a *limiting position*. The line in this limiting position is what we will consider to be the ***tangent line*** at $P$ (Figure 1.1.4*a*). As suggested by Figure 1.1.4*b*, this new concept of a tangent line coincides with the traditional concept when applied to circles.

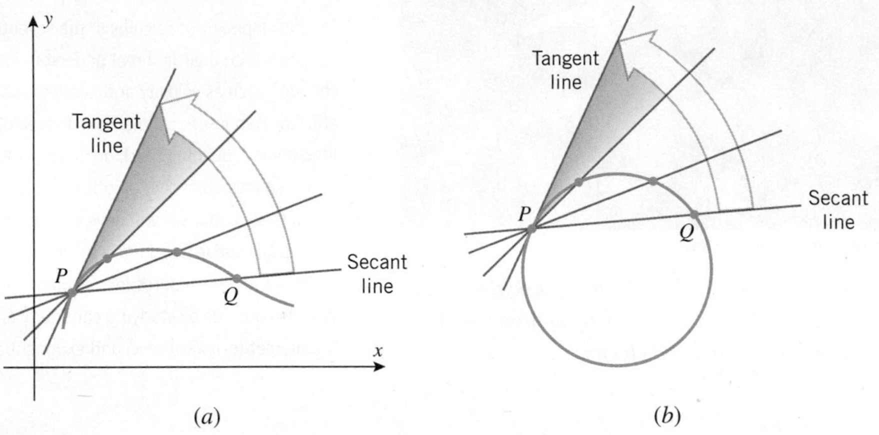


► Figure 1.1.4

► **Example 1** Find an equation for the tangent line to the parabola $y = x^2$ at the point $P(1, 1)$.

***Solution.*** If we can find the slope $m_{\tan}$ of the tangent line at $P$, then we can use the point $P$ and the point-slope formula for a line (Web Appendix H) to write the equation of the tangent line as

$$y - 1 = m_{\tan}(x - 1) \tag{1}$$

To find the slope $m_{\tan}$, consider the secant line through $P$ and a point $Q(x, x^2)$ on the parabola that is distinct from $P$. The slope $m_{\sec}$ of this secant line is

Why are we requiring that $P$ and $Q$ be distinct?

$$m_{\sec} = \frac{x^2 - 1}{x - 1} \tag{2}$$

Figure 1.1.4*a* suggests that if we now let $Q$ move along the parabola, getting closer and closer to $P$, then the limiting position of the secant line through $P$ and $Q$ will coincide with that of the tangent line at $P$. This in turn suggests that the value of $m_{\sec}$ will get closer and closer to the value of $m_{\tan}$ as $P$ moves toward $Q$ along the curve. However, to say that $Q(x, x^2)$ gets closer and closer to $P(1, 1)$ is algebraically equivalent to saying that $x$ gets closer and closer to 1. Thus, the problem of finding $m_{\tan}$ reduces to finding the "limiting value" of $m_{\sec}$ in Formula (2) as $x$ gets closer and closer to 1 (but with $x \neq 1$ to ensure that $P$ and $Q$ remain distinct).

We can rewrite (2) as

$$m_{\sec} = \frac{x^2 - 1}{x - 1} = \frac{(x - 1)(x + 1)}{(x - 1)} = x + 1$$

where the cancellation of the factor $(x - 1)$ is allowed because $x \neq 1$. It is now evident that $m_{\sec}$ gets closer and closer to 2 as $x$ gets closer and closer to 1. Thus, $m_{\tan} = 2$ and (1) implies that the equation of the tangent line is

$$y - 1 = 2(x - 1) \quad \text{or equivalently} \quad y = 2x - 1$$

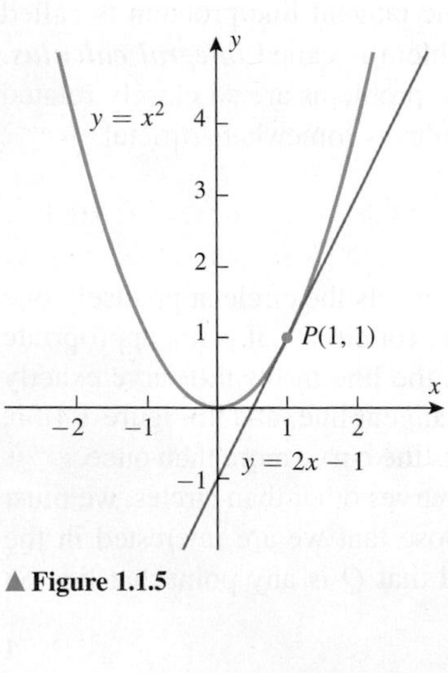


▲ Figure 1.1.5

Figure 1.1.5 shows the graph of $y = x^2$ and this tangent line. ◄

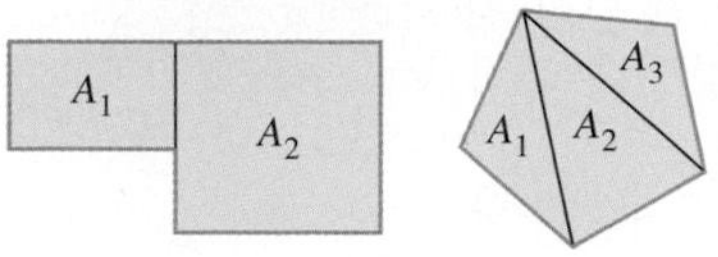


▲ **Figure 1.1.6**

## AREAS AND LIMITS

Just as the general notion of a tangent line leads to the concept of *limit*, so does the general notion of area. For plane regions with straight-line boundaries, areas can often be calculated by subdividing the region into rectangles or triangles and adding the areas of the constituent parts (Figure 1.1.6). However, for regions with curved boundaries, such as that in Figure 1.1.7*a*, a more general approach is needed. One such approach is to begin by approximating the area of the region by inscribing a number of rectangles of equal width under the curve and adding the areas of these rectangles (Figure 1.1.7*b*). Intuition suggests that if we repeat that approximation process using more and more rectangles, then the rectangles will tend to fill in the gaps under the curve, and the approximations will get closer and closer to the exact area under the curve (Figure 1.1.7*c*). This suggests that we can define the area under the curve to be the limiting value of these approximations. This idea will be considered in detail later, but the point to note here is that once again the concept of a limit comes into play.

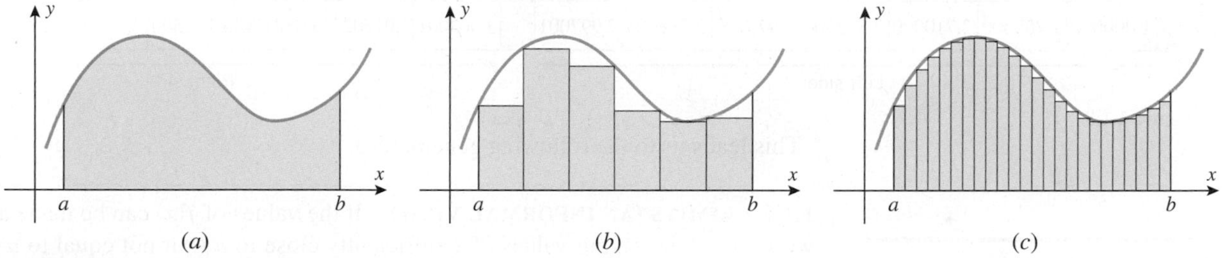


▲ **Figure 1.1.7**

## DECIMALS AND LIMITS

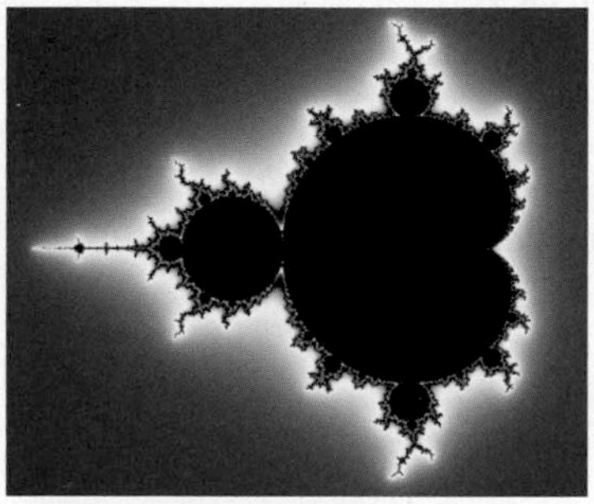

Andreas Nilsson/Shutterstock

*This figure shows a region called the* ***Mandelbrot Set****. It illustrates how complicated a region in the plane can be and why the notion of area requires careful definition.*

Limits also arise in the familiar context of decimals. For example, the decimal expansion of the fraction $\frac{1}{3}$ is

$$\frac{1}{3} = 0.33333\ldots \tag{3}$$

in which the dots indicate that the digit 3 repeats indefinitely. Although you may not have thought about decimals in this way, we can write (3) as

$$\frac{1}{3} = 0.33333\ldots = 0.3 + 0.03 + 0.003 + 0.0003 + 0.00003 + \cdots \tag{4}$$

which is a sum with "infinitely many" terms. As we will discuss in more detail later, we interpret (4) to mean that the succession of finite sums

$$0.3,\ 0.3 + 0.03,\ 0.3 + 0.03 + 0.003,\ 0.3 + 0.03 + 0.003 + 0.0003, \ldots$$

gets closer and closer to a limiting value of $\frac{1}{3}$ as more and more terms are included. Thus, limits even occur in the familiar context of decimal representations of real numbers.

## LIMITS

Now that we have seen how limits arise in various ways, let us focus on the limit concept itself.

The most basic use of limits is to describe how a function behaves as the independent variable approaches a given value. For example, let us examine the behavior of the function

$$f(x) = x^2 - x + 1$$

for $x$-values closer and closer to 2. It is evident from the graph and table in Figure 1.1.8 that the values of $f(x)$ get closer and closer to 3 as values of $x$ are selected closer and closer to 2 on either the left or the right side of 2. We describe this by saying that the "limit of $x^2 - x + 1$ is 3 as $x$ approaches 2 from either side," and we write

$$\lim_{x \to 2} (x^2 - x + 1) = 3 \tag{5}$$

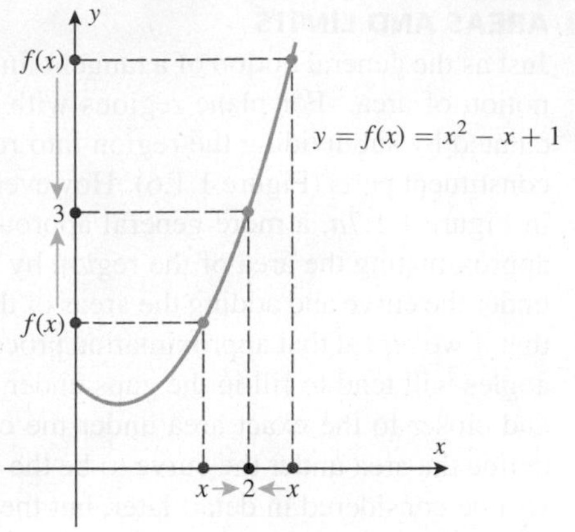


| $x$ | 1.0 | 1.5 | 1.9 | 1.95 | 1.99 | 1.995 | 1.999 | 2 | 2.001 | 2.005 | 2.01 | 2.05 | 2.1 | 2.5 | 3.0 |
|---|---|---|---|---|---|---|---|---|---|---|---|---|---|---|---|
| $f(x)$ | 1.000000 | 1.750000 | 2.710000 | 2.852500 | 2.970100 | 2.985025 | 2.997001 | | 3.003001 | 3.015025 | 3.030100 | 3.152500 | 3.310000 | 4.750000 | 7.000000 |

Left side → ← Right side

▲ **Figure 1.1.8**

This leads us to the following general idea.

**1.1.1 LIMITS (AN INFORMAL VIEW)** If the values of $f(x)$ can be made as close as we like to $L$ by taking values of $x$ sufficiently close to $a$ (but not equal to $a$), then we write

$$\lim_{x\to a} f(x) = L \tag{6}$$

which is read "the limit of $f(x)$ as $x$ approaches $a$ is $L$" or "$f(x)$ approaches $L$ as $x$ approaches $a$." The expression in (6) can also be written as

$$f(x)\to L \quad \text{as} \quad x\to a \tag{7}$$

Since $x$ is required to be different from $a$ in (6), the value of $f$ at $a$, or even whether $f$ is defined at $a$, has no bearing on the limit $L$. The limit describes the behavior of $f$ *close to* $a$ but not *at* $a$.

▶ **Example 2** Use numerical evidence to make a conjecture about the value of

$$\lim_{x\to 1} \frac{x-1}{\sqrt{x}-1} \tag{8}$$

***Solution.*** Although the function

$$f(x) = \frac{x-1}{\sqrt{x}-1} \tag{9}$$

is undefined at $x = 1$, this has no bearing on the limit. Table 1.1.1 shows sample $x$-values approaching 1 from the left side and from the right side. In both cases the corresponding values of $f(x)$, calculated to six decimal places, appear to get closer and closer to 2, and hence we conjecture that

$$\lim_{x\to 1} \frac{x-1}{\sqrt{x}-1} = 2$$

This is consistent with the graph of $f$ shown in Figure 1.1.9. In the next section we will show how to obtain this result algebraically. ◀

**TECHNOLOGY MASTERY**

Use a graphing utility to generate the graph of the equation $y = f(x)$ for the function in (9). Find a window containing $x = 1$ in which all values of $f(x)$ are within 0.5 of $y = 2$ and one in which all values of $f(x)$ are within 0.1 of $y = 2$.

**Table 1.1.1**

| $x$ | 0.99 | 0.999 | 0.9999 | 0.99999 | | 1.00001 | 1.0001 | 1.001 | 1.01 |
|---|---|---|---|---|---|---|---|---|---|
| $f(x)$ | 1.994987 | 1.999500 | 1.999950 | 1.999995 | | 2.000005 | 2.000050 | 2.000500 | 2.004988 |

Left side → ← Right side

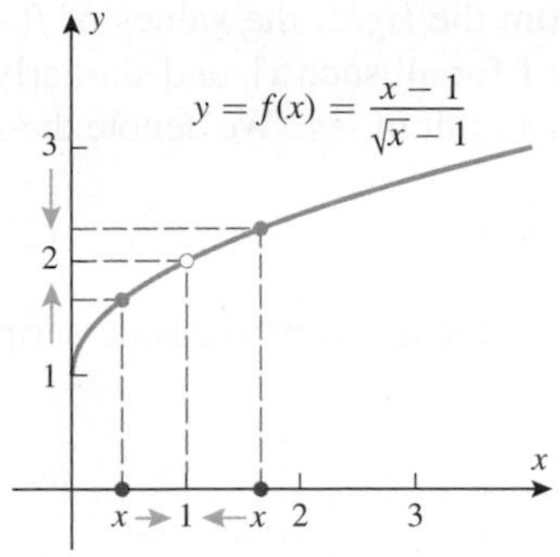


▲ **Figure 1.1.9**

Use numerical evidence to determine whether the limit in (11) changes if $x$ is measured in degrees.

**Table 1.1.2**

| $x$ (RADIANS) | $y = \dfrac{\sin x}{x}$ |
|---|---|
| ±1.0 | 0.84147 |
| ±0.9 | 0.87036 |
| ±0.8 | 0.89670 |
| ±0.7 | 0.92031 |
| ±0.6 | 0.94107 |
| ±0.5 | 0.95885 |
| ±0.4 | 0.97355 |
| ±0.3 | 0.98507 |
| ±0.2 | 0.99335 |
| ±0.1 | 0.99833 |
| ±0.01 | 0.99998 |

▶ **Example 3** Use numerical evidence to make a conjecture about the value of

$$\lim_{x \to 0} \frac{\sin x}{x} \tag{10}$$

***Solution.*** With the help of a calculating utility set in radian mode, we obtain Table 1.1.2. The data in the table suggest that

$$\lim_{x \to 0} \frac{\sin x}{x} = 1 \tag{11}$$

The result is consistent with the graph of $f(x) = (\sin x)/x$ shown in Figure 1.1.10. Later in this chapter we will give a geometric argument to prove that our conjecture is correct. ◀

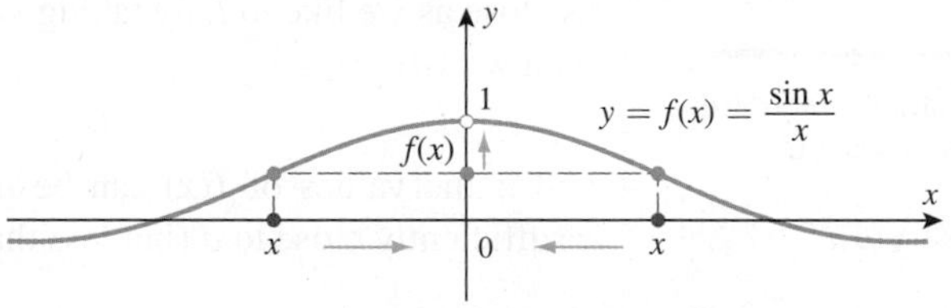


▶ **Figure 1.1.10**

## SAMPLING PITFALLS

Numerical evidence can sometimes lead to incorrect conclusions about limits because of roundoff error or because the sample values chosen do not reveal the true limiting behavior. For example, one might *incorrectly* conclude from Table 1.1.3 that

$$\lim_{x \to 0} \sin\left(\frac{\pi}{x}\right) = 0$$

The fact that this is not correct is evidenced by the graph of $f$ in Figure 1.1.11. The graph reveals that the values of $f$ oscillate between $-1$ and 1 with increasing rapidity as $x \to 0$ and hence do not approach a limit. The data in the table deceived us because the $x$-values selected all happened to be $x$-intercepts for $f(x)$. This points out the need for having alternative methods for corroborating limits conjectured from numerical evidence.

**Table 1.1.3**

| $x$ | $\frac{\pi}{x}$ | $f(x) = \sin\left(\frac{\pi}{x}\right)$ |
|---|---|---|
| $x = \pm 1$ | $\pm\pi$ | $\sin(\pm\pi) = 0$ |
| $x = \pm 0.1$ | $\pm 10\pi$ | $\sin(\pm 10\pi) = 0$ |
| $x = \pm 0.01$ | $\pm 100\pi$ | $\sin(\pm 100\pi) = 0$ |
| $x = \pm 0.001$ | $\pm 1000\pi$ | $\sin(\pm 1000\pi) = 0$ |
| $x = \pm 0.0001$ | $\pm 10{,}000\pi$ | $\sin(\pm 10{,}000\pi) = 0$ |
| ⋮ | ⋮ | ⋮ |

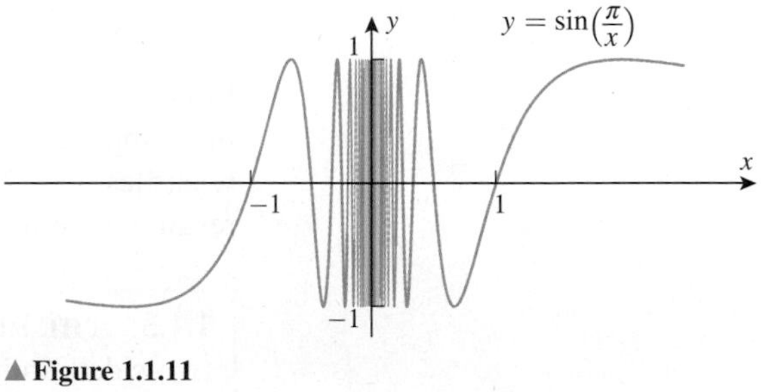


▲ **Figure 1.1.11**

## ONE-SIDED LIMITS

The limit in (6) is called a ***two-sided limit*** because it requires the values of $f(x)$ to get closer and closer to $L$ as values of $x$ are taken from *either* side of $x = a$. However, some functions exhibit different behaviors on the two sides of an $x$-value $a$, in which case it is necessary to distinguish whether values of $x$ near $a$ are on the left side or on the right side of $a$ for purposes of investigating limiting behavior. For example, consider the function

$$f(x) = \frac{|x|}{x} = \begin{cases} 1, & x > 0 \\ -1, & x < 0 \end{cases} \tag{12}$$

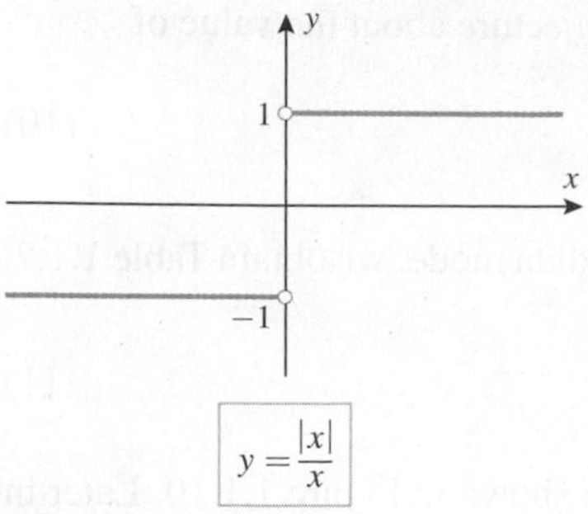


▲ **Figure 1.1.12**

As with two-sided limits, the one-sided limits in (14) and (15) can also be written as

$$f(x) \to L \quad \text{as} \quad x \to a^+$$

and

$$f(x) \to L \quad \text{as} \quad x \to a^-$$

respectively.

which is graphed in Figure 1.1.12. As $x$ approaches 0 from the *right*, the values of $f(x)$ approach a limit of 1 [in fact, the values of $f(x)$ are exactly 1 for all such $x$], and similarly, as $x$ approaches 0 from the *left*, the values of $f(x)$ approach a limit of $-1$. We denote these limits by writing

$$\lim_{x \to 0^+} \frac{|x|}{x} = 1 \quad \text{and} \quad \lim_{x \to 0^-} \frac{|x|}{x} = -1 \tag{13}$$

With this notation, the superscript "+" indicates a limit from the right and the superscript "−" indicates a limit from the left.

This leads to the general idea of a ***one-sided limit***.

**1.1.2 ONE-SIDED LIMITS (AN INFORMAL VIEW)** If the values of $f(x)$ can be made as close as we like to $L$ by taking values of $x$ sufficiently close to $a$ (but greater than $a$), then we write

$$\lim_{x \to a^+} f(x) = L \tag{14}$$

and if the values of $f(x)$ can be made as close as we like to $L$ by taking values of $x$ sufficiently close to $a$ (but less than $a$), then we write

$$\lim_{x \to a^-} f(x) = L \tag{15}$$

Expression (14) is read "the limit of $f(x)$ as $x$ approaches $a$ from the right is $L$" or "$f(x)$ approaches $L$ as $x$ approaches $a$ from the right." Similarly, expression (15) is read "the limit of $f(x)$ as $x$ approaches $a$ from the left is $L$" or "$f(x)$ approaches $L$ as $x$ approaches $a$ from the left."

## THE RELATIONSHIP BETWEEN ONE-SIDED LIMITS AND TWO-SIDED LIMITS

In general, there is no guarantee that a function $f$ will have a two-sided limit at a given point $a$; that is, the values of $f(x)$ may not get closer and closer to any *single* real number $L$ as $x \to a$. In this case we say that

$$\lim_{x \to a} f(x) \quad \textbf{\textit{does not exist}}$$

Similarly, the values of $f(x)$ may not get closer and closer to a single real number $L$ as $x \to a^+$ or as $x \to a^-$. In these cases we say that

$$\lim_{x \to a^+} f(x) \quad \textbf{\textit{does not exist}}$$

or that

$$\lim_{x \to a^-} f(x) \quad \textbf{\textit{does not exist}}$$

In order for the two-sided limit of a function $f(x)$ to exist at a point $a$, the values of $f(x)$ must approach some real number $L$ as $x$ approaches $a$, and this number must be the same regardless of whether $x$ approaches $a$ from the left or the right. This suggests the following result, which we state without formal proof.

**1.1.3 THE RELATIONSHIP BETWEEN ONE-SIDED AND TWO-SIDED LIMITS** The two-sided limit of a function $f(x)$ exists at $a$ if and only if both of the one-sided limits exist at $a$ and have the same value; that is,

$$\lim_{x \to a} f(x) = L \quad \text{if and only if} \quad \lim_{x \to a^-} f(x) = L = \lim_{x \to a^+} f(x)$$

▶ **Example 4** Explain why

$$\lim_{x \to 0} \frac{|x|}{x}$$

does not exist.

***Solution.*** As $x$ approaches 0, the values of $f(x) = |x|/x$ approach $-1$ from the left and approach 1 from the right [see (13)]. Thus, the one-sided limits at 0 are not the same. ◀

**▶ Example 5** For the functions in Figure 1.1.13, find the one-sided and two-sided limits at $x = a$ if they exist.

***Solution.*** The functions in all three figures have the same one-sided limits as $x \to a$, since the functions are identical, except at $x = a$. These limits are

$$\lim_{x \to a^+} f(x) = 3 \quad \text{and} \quad \lim_{x \to a^-} f(x) = 1$$

In all three cases the two-sided limit does not exist as $x \to a$ because the one-sided limits are not equal. ◀

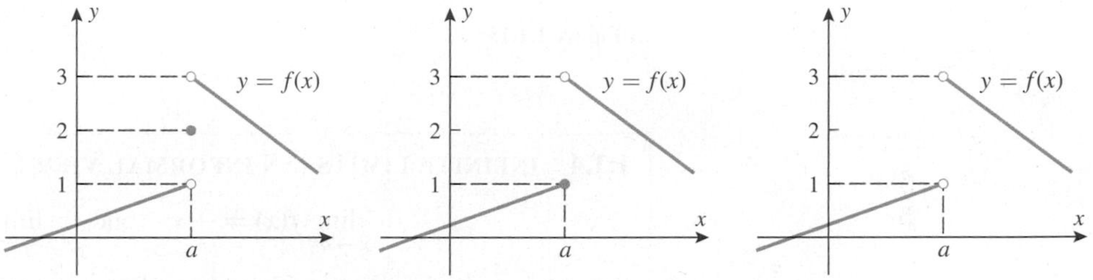


▶ Figure 1.1.13

**▶ Example 6** For the functions in Figure 1.1.14, find the one-sided and two-sided limits at $x = a$ if they exist.

***Solution.*** As in the preceding example, the value of $f$ at $x = a$ has no bearing on the limits as $x \to a$, so in all three cases we have

$$\lim_{x \to a^+} f(x) = 2 \quad \text{and} \quad \lim_{x \to a^-} f(x) = 2$$

Since the one-sided limits are equal, the two-sided limit exists and

$$\lim_{x \to a} f(x) = 2 \;◀$$

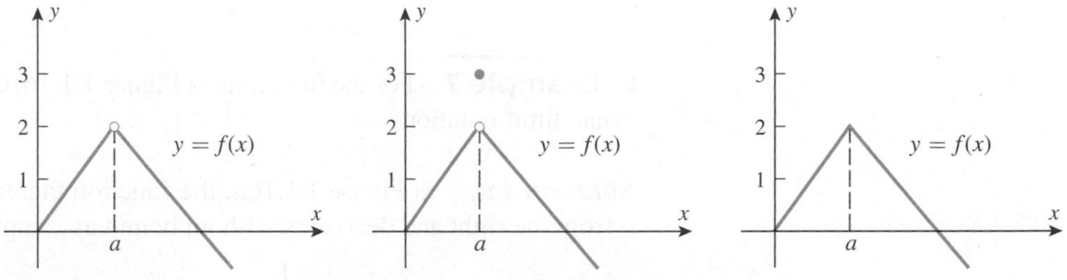


▲ Figure 1.1.14

## INFINITE LIMITS

Sometimes one-sided or two-sided limits fail to exist because the values of the function increase or decrease without bound. For example, consider the behavior of $f(x) = 1/x$ for values of $x$ near 0. It is evident from the table and graph in Figure 1.1.15 that as $x$-values are taken closer and closer to 0 from the right, the values of $f(x) = 1/x$ are positive and increase without bound; and as $x$-values are taken closer and closer to 0 from the left, the values of $f(x) = 1/x$ are negative and decrease without bound. We describe these limiting behaviors by writing

$$\lim_{x \to 0^+} \frac{1}{x} = +\infty \quad \text{and} \quad \lim_{x \to 0^-} \frac{1}{x} = -\infty$$

The symbols $+\infty$ and $-\infty$ here are *not* real numbers; they simply describe particular ways in which the limits fail to exist. Do not make the mistake of manipulating these symbols using rules of algebra. For example, it is *incorrect* to write $(+\infty) - (+\infty) = 0$.

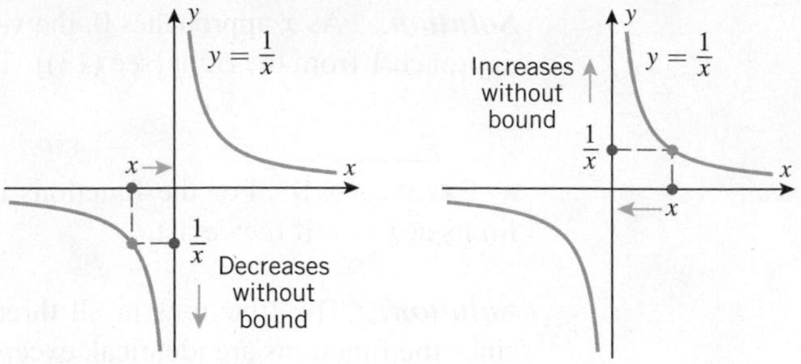


| $x$ | −1 | −0.1 | −0.01 | −0.001 | −0.0001 | 0 | 0.0001 | 0.001 | 0.01 | 0.1 | 1 |
|---|---|---|---|---|---|---|---|---|---|---|---|
| $\frac{1}{x}$ | −1 | −10 | −100 | −1000 | −10,000 | | 10,000 | 1000 | 100 | 10 | 1 |

Left side → ← Right side

▲ **Figure 1.1.15**

**1.1.4 INFINITE LIMITS (AN INFORMAL VIEW)** The expressions

$$\lim_{x\to a^-} f(x) = +\infty \quad \text{and} \quad \lim_{x\to a^+} f(x) = +\infty$$

denote that $f(x)$ increases without bound as $x$ approaches $a$ from the left and from the right, respectively. If both are true, then we write

$$\lim_{x\to a} f(x) = +\infty$$

Similarly, the expressions

$$\lim_{x\to a^-} f(x) = -\infty \quad \text{and} \quad \lim_{x\to a^+} f(x) = -\infty$$

denote that $f(x)$ decreases without bound as $x$ approaches $a$ from the left and from the right, respectively. If both are true, then we write

$$\lim_{x\to a} f(x) = -\infty$$

▶ **Example 7** For the functions in Figure 1.1.16, describe the limits at $x = a$ in appropriate limit notation.

***Solution (a).*** In Figure 1.1.16$a$, the function increases without bound as $x$ approaches $a$ from the right and decreases without bound as $x$ approaches $a$ from the left. Thus,

$$\lim_{x\to a^+} \frac{1}{x-a} = +\infty \quad \text{and} \quad \lim_{x\to a^-} \frac{1}{x-a} = -\infty$$

***Solution (b).*** In Figure 1.1.16$b$, the function increases without bound as $x$ approaches $a$ from both the left and right. Thus,

$$\lim_{x\to a} \frac{1}{(x-a)^2} = \lim_{x\to a^+} \frac{1}{(x-a)^2} = \lim_{x\to a^-} \frac{1}{(x-a)^2} = +\infty$$

***Solution (c).*** In Figure 1.1.16$c$, the function decreases without bound as $x$ approaches $a$ from the right and increases without bound as $x$ approaches $a$ from the left. Thus,

$$\lim_{x\to a^+} \frac{-1}{x-a} = -\infty \quad \text{and} \quad \lim_{x\to a^-} \frac{-1}{x-a} = +\infty$$

***Solution (d).*** In Figure 1.1.16*d*, the function decreases without bound as $x$ approaches $a$ from both the left and right. Thus,

$$\lim_{x\to a}\frac{-1}{(x-a)^2}=\lim_{x\to a^+}\frac{-1}{(x-a)^2}=\lim_{x\to a^-}\frac{-1}{(x-a)^2}=-\infty \blacktriangleleft$$

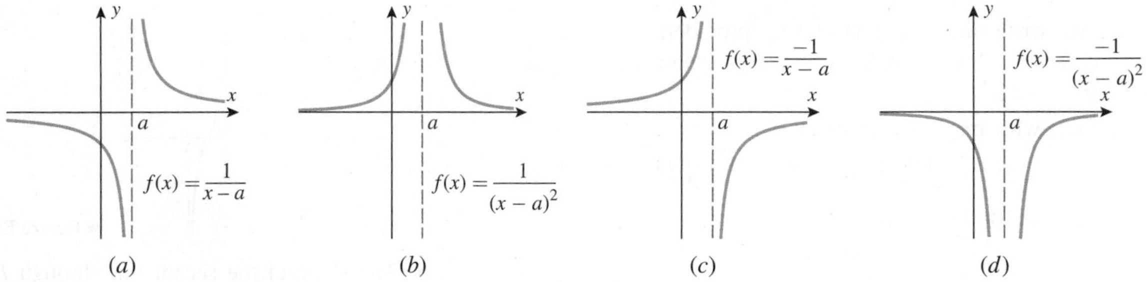


▲ **Figure 1.1.16**

## VERTICAL ASYMPTOTES

Figure 1.1.17 illustrates geometrically what happens when any of the following situations occur:

$$\lim_{x\to a^-} f(x)=+\infty,\quad \lim_{x\to a^+} f(x)=+\infty,\quad \lim_{x\to a^-} f(x)=-\infty,\quad \lim_{x\to a^+} f(x)=-\infty$$

In each case the graph of $y=f(x)$ either rises or falls without bound, squeezing closer and closer to the vertical line $x=a$ as $x$ approaches $a$ from the side indicated in the limit. The line $x=a$ is called a ***vertical asymptote*** of the curve $y=f(x)$ (from the Greek word *asymptotos*, meaning "nonintersecting").

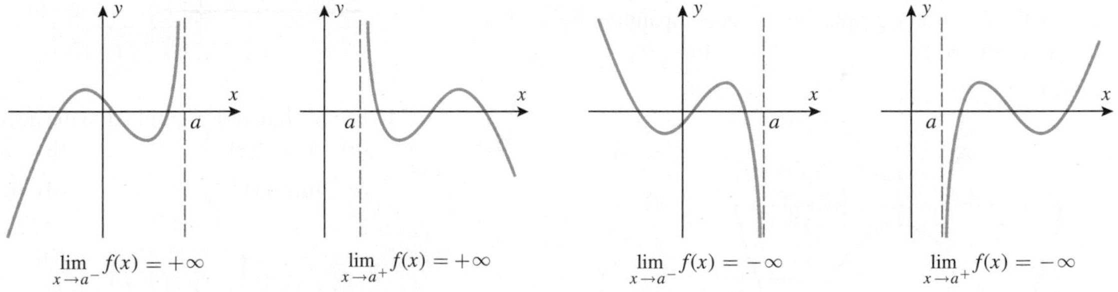


▲ **Figure 1.1.17**

In general, the graph of a single function can display a wide variety of limits.

▶ **Example 8** For the function $f$ graphed in Figure 1.1.18, find

(a) $\lim_{x\to -2^-} f(x)$ (b) $\lim_{x\to -2^+} f(x)$ (c) $\lim_{x\to 0^-} f(x)$ (d) $\lim_{x\to 0^+} f(x)$
(e) $\lim_{x\to 4^-} f(x)$ (f) $\lim_{x\to 4^+} f(x)$ (g) the vertical asymptotes of the graph of $f$.

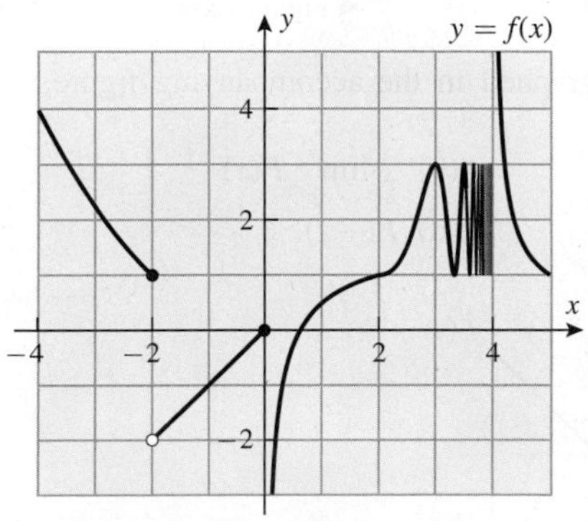


▲ **Figure 1.1.18**

***Solution (a) and (b).***

$$\lim_{x\to -2^-} f(x)=1=f(-2) \quad\text{and}\quad \lim_{x\to -2^+} f(x)=-2$$

***Solution (c) and (d).***

$$\lim_{x\to 0^-} f(x)=0=f(0) \quad\text{and}\quad \lim_{x\to 0^+} f(x)=-\infty$$

***Solution (e) and (f).***

$$\lim_{x\to 4^-} f(x) \text{ does not exist due to oscillation} \quad\text{and}\quad \lim_{x\to 4^+} f(x)=+\infty$$

***Solution (g).*** The $y$-axis and the line $x=4$ are vertical asymptotes for the graph of $f$. ◀

## ✓QUICK CHECK EXERCISES 1.1 *(See page 13 for answers.)*

1. We write $\lim_{x\to a} f(x) = L$ provided the values of ________ can be made as close to ________ as desired, by taking values of ________ sufficiently close to ________ but not ________.

2. We write $\lim_{x\to a^-} f(x) = +\infty$ provided ________ increases without bound, as ________ approaches ________ from the left.

3. State what must be true about
$$\lim_{x\to a^-} f(x) \quad \text{and} \quad \lim_{x\to a^+} f(x)$$
in order for it to be the case that
$$\lim_{x\to a} f(x) = L$$

4. Use the accompanying graph of $y = f(x)$ $(-\infty < x < 3)$ to determine the limits.
(a) $\lim_{x\to 0} f(x) =$ ________
(b) $\lim_{x\to 2^-} f(x) =$ ________
(c) $\lim_{x\to 2^+} f(x) =$ ________
(d) $\lim_{x\to 3^-} f(x) =$ ________

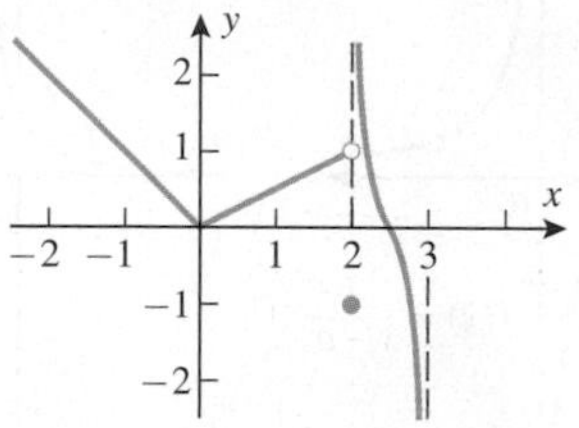


◀ Figure Ex-4

5. The slope of the secant line through $P(2, 4)$ and $Q(x, x^2)$ on the parabola $y = x^2$ is $m_{\text{sec}} = x + 2$. It follows that the slope of the tangent line to this parabola at the point $P$ is ________.

## EXERCISE SET 1.1 Graphing Utility C CAS

**1–10** In these exercises, make reasonable assumptions about the graph of the indicated function outside of the region depicted. ■

1. For the function $g$ graphed in the accompanying figure, find
(a) $\lim_{x\to 0^-} g(x)$ (b) $\lim_{x\to 0^+} g(x)$
(c) $\lim_{x\to 0} g(x)$ (d) $g(0)$.

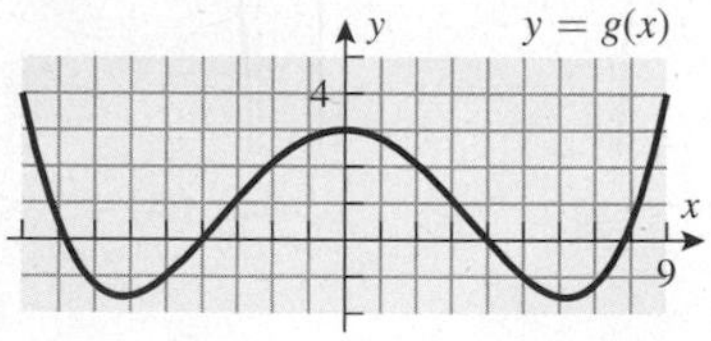


◀ Figure Ex-1

2. For the function $G$ graphed in the accompanying figure, find
(a) $\lim_{x\to 0^-} G(x)$ (b) $\lim_{x\to 0^+} G(x)$
(c) $\lim_{x\to 0} G(x)$ (d) $G(0)$.

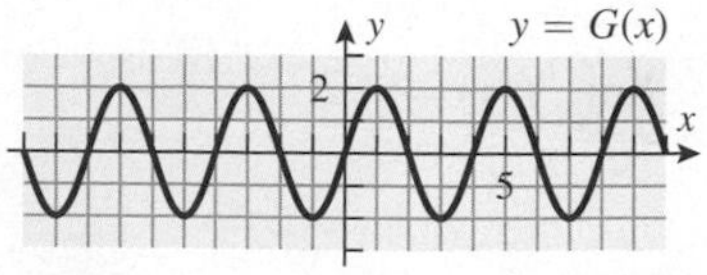


◀ Figure Ex-2

3. For the function $f$ graphed in the accompanying figure, find
(a) $\lim_{x\to 3^-} f(x)$ (b) $\lim_{x\to 3^+} f(x)$
(c) $\lim_{x\to 3} f(x)$ (d) $f(3)$.

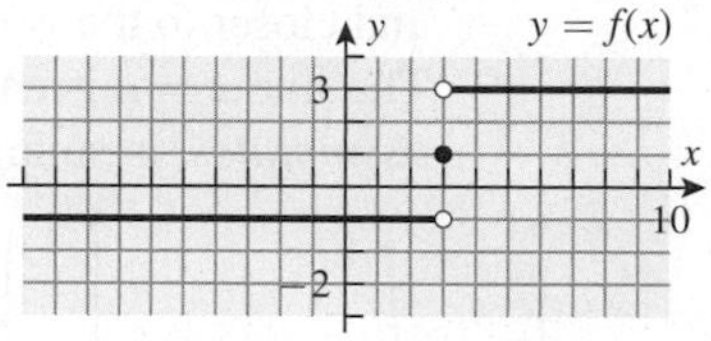


◀ Figure Ex-3

4. For the function $f$ graphed in the accompanying figure, find
(a) $\lim_{x\to 2^-} f(x)$ (b) $\lim_{x\to 2^+} f(x)$
(c) $\lim_{x\to 2} f(x)$ (d) $f(2)$.

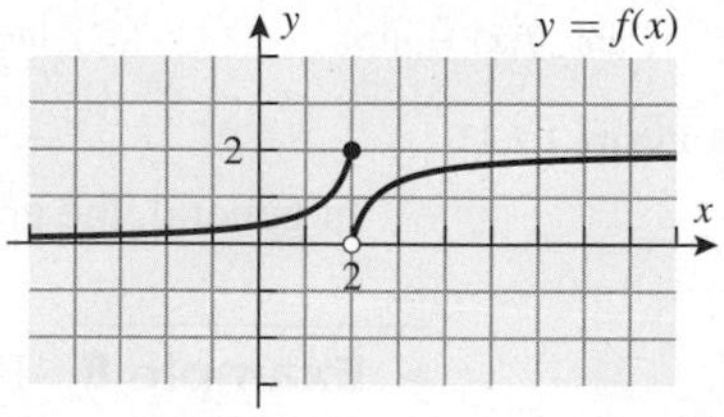


◀ Figure Ex-4

5. For the function $F$ graphed in the accompanying figure, find
(a) $\lim_{x\to -2^-} F(x)$ (b) $\lim_{x\to -2^+} F(x)$
(c) $\lim_{x\to -2} F(x)$ (d) $F(-2)$.

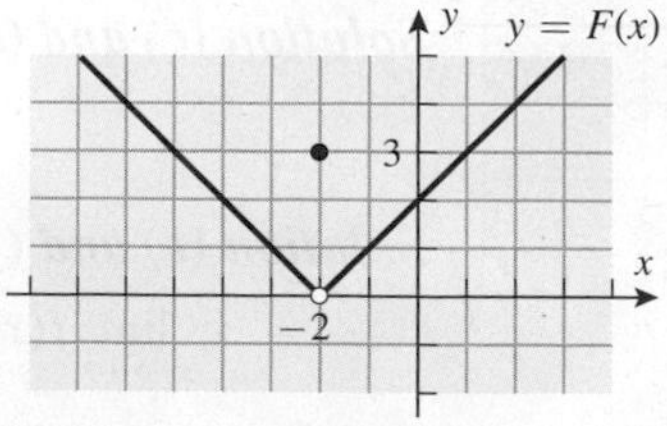


◀ Figure Ex-5

**6.** For the function $G$ graphed in the accompanying figure, find
(a) $\lim_{x\to 0^-} G(x)$ (b) $\lim_{x\to 0^+} G(x)$
(c) $\lim_{x\to 0} G(x)$ (d) $G(0)$.

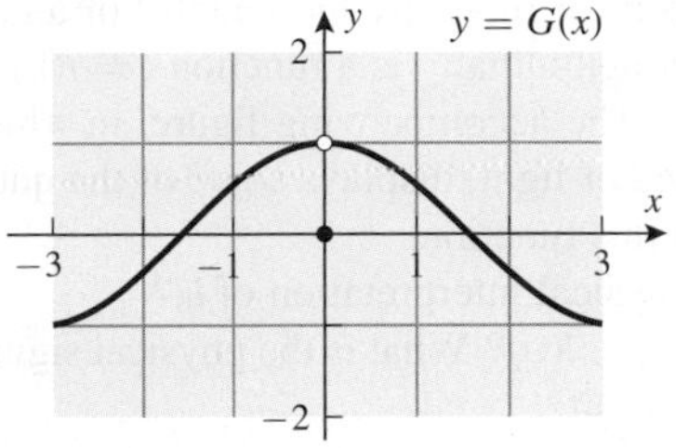


◀ **Figure Ex-6**

**7.** For the function $f$ graphed in the accompanying figure, find
(a) $\lim_{x\to 3^-} f(x)$ (b) $\lim_{x\to 3^+} f(x)$
(c) $\lim_{x\to 3} f(x)$ (d) $f(3)$.

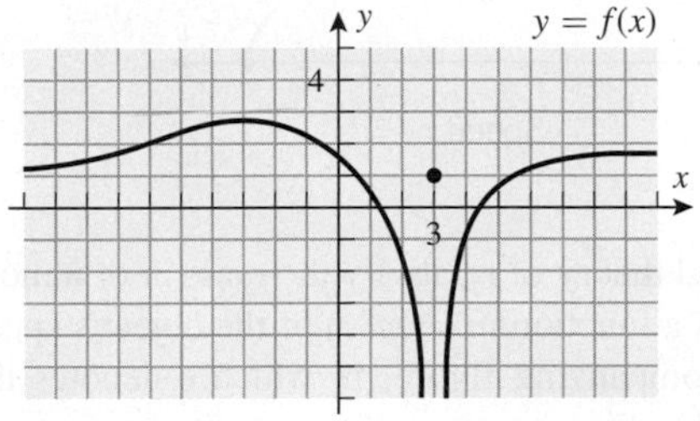


◀ **Figure Ex-7**

**8.** For the function $\phi$ graphed in the accompanying figure, find
(a) $\lim_{x\to 4^-} \phi(x)$ (b) $\lim_{x\to 4^+} \phi(x)$
(c) $\lim_{x\to 4} \phi(x)$ (d) $\phi(4)$.

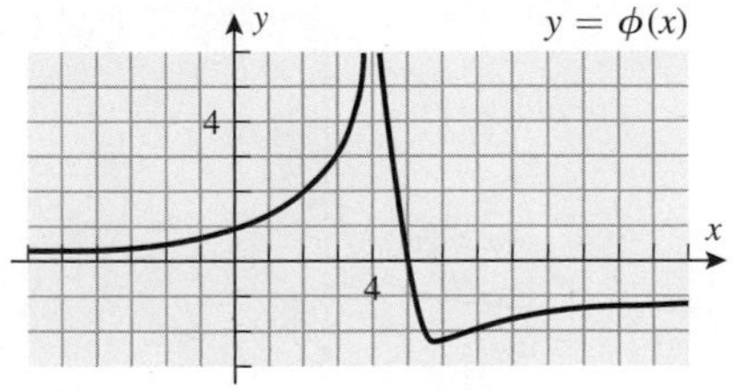


◀ **Figure Ex-8**

**9.** For the function $f$ graphed in the accompanying figure, find
(a) $\lim_{x\to -2} f(x)$ (b) $\lim_{x\to 0^-} f(x)$
(c) $\lim_{x\to 0^+} f(x)$ (d) $\lim_{x\to 2^-} f(x)$
(e) $\lim_{x\to 2^+} f(x)$
(f) the vertical asymptotes of the graph of $f$.

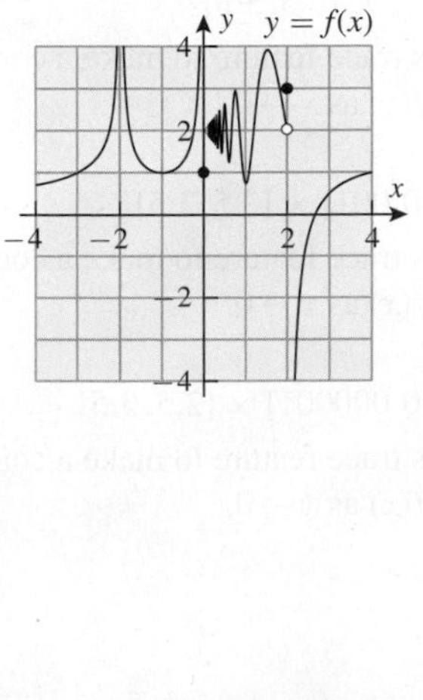


◀ **Figure Ex-9**

**10.** For the function $f$ graphed in the accompanying figure, find
(a) $\lim_{x\to -2^-} f(x)$ (b) $\lim_{x\to -2^+} f(x)$ (c) $\lim_{x\to 0^-} f(x)$
(d) $\lim_{x\to 0^+} f(x)$ (e) $\lim_{x\to 2^-} f(x)$ (f) $\lim_{x\to 2^+} f(x)$
(g) the vertical asymptotes of the graph of $f$.

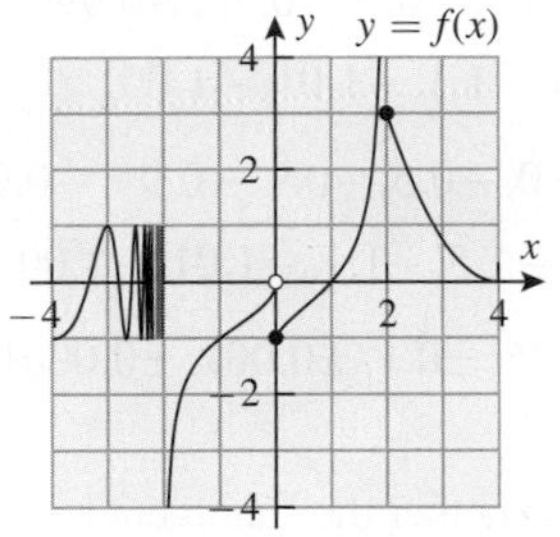


◀ **Figure Ex-10**

**11–12** (i) Complete the table and make a guess about the limit indicated. (ii) Confirm your conclusions about the limit by graphing a function over an appropriate interval. [*Note:* For the trigonometric functions, be sure to put your calculating and graphing utilities in radian mode.] ■

**11.** $f(x) = \dfrac{\sin 2x}{x}$; $\lim_{x\to 0} f(x)$

| $x$ | −0.1 | −0.01 | −0.001 | 0.001 | 0.01 | 0.1 |
|---|---|---|---|---|---|---|
| $f(x)$ | | | | | | |

▲ **Table Ex-11**

**12.** $f(x) = \dfrac{\cos x - 1}{x^2}$; $\lim_{x\to 0} f(x)$

| $x$ | −0.5 | −0.05 | −0.005 | 0.005 | 0.05 | 0.5 |
|---|---|---|---|---|---|---|
| $f(x)$ | | | | | | |

▲ **Table Ex-12**

**13–16** (i) Make a guess at the limit (if it exists) by evaluating the function at the specified $x$-values. (ii) Confirm your conclusions about the limit by graphing the function over an appropriate interval. (iii) If you have a CAS, then use it to find the limit. [*Note:* For the trigonometric functions, be sure to put your calculating and graphing utilities in radian mode.] ■

**13.** (a) $\lim_{x\to 1} \dfrac{x-1}{x^3-1}$; $x = 2, 1.5, 1.1, 1.01, 1.001, 0, 0.5, 0.9, 0.99, 0.999$

(b) $\lim_{x\to 1^+} \dfrac{x+1}{x^3-1}$; $x = 2, 1.5, 1.1, 1.01, 1.001, 1.0001$

(c) $\lim_{x\to 1^-} \dfrac{x+1}{x^3-1}$; $x = 0, 0.5, 0.9, 0.99, 0.999, 0.9999$

**14.** (a) $\lim_{x\to 0} \dfrac{\sqrt{x+1}-1}{x}$; $x = \pm 0.25, \pm 0.1, \pm 0.001, \pm 0.0001$

(b) $\lim_{x\to 0^+} \dfrac{\sqrt{x+1}+1}{x}$; $x = 0.25, 0.1, 0.001, 0.0001$

(*cont.*)

(c) $\lim_{x\to 0^-} \frac{\sqrt{x+1}+1}{x}$; $x = -0.25, -0.1, -0.001, -0.0001$

**15.** (a) $\lim_{x\to 0} \frac{\sin 3x}{x}$; $x = \pm 0.25, \pm 0.1, \pm 0.001, \pm 0.0001$

(b) $\lim_{x\to -1} \frac{\cos x}{x+1}$; $x = 0, -0.5, -0.9, -0.99, -0.999, -1.5, -1.1, -1.01, -1.001$

**16.** (a) $\lim_{x\to -1} \frac{\tan(x+1)}{x+1}$; $x = 0, -0.5, -0.9, -0.99, -0.999, -1.5, -1.1, -1.01, -1.001$

(b) $\lim_{x\to 0} \frac{\sin(5x)}{\sin(2x)}$; $x = \pm 0.25, \pm 0.1, \pm 0.001, \pm 0.0001$

**17–20 True–False** Determine whether the statement is true or false. Explain your answer. ■

**17.** If $f(a) = L$, then $\lim_{x\to a} f(x) = L$.

**18.** If $\lim_{x\to a} f(x)$ exists, then so do $\lim_{x\to a^-} f(x)$ and $\lim_{x\to a^+} f(x)$.

**19.** If $\lim_{x\to a^-} f(x)$ and $\lim_{x\to a^+} f(x)$ exist, then so does $\lim_{x\to a} f(x)$.

**20.** If $\lim_{x\to a^+} f(x) = +\infty$, then $f(a)$ is undefined.

**21–26** Sketch a possible graph for a function $f$ with the specified properties. (Many different solutions are possible.) ■

**21.** (i) the domain of $f$ is $[-1, 1]$
(ii) $f(-1) = f(0) = f(1) = 0$
(iii) $\lim_{x\to -1^+} f(x) = \lim_{x\to 0} f(x) = \lim_{x\to 1^-} f(x) = 1$

**22.** (i) the domain of $f$ is $[-2, 1]$
(ii) $f(-2) = f(0) = f(1) = 0$
(iii) $\lim_{x\to -2^+} f(x) = 2$, $\lim_{x\to 0} f(x) = 0$, and $\lim_{x\to 1^-} f(x) = 1$

**23.** (i) the domain of $f$ is $(-\infty, 0]$
(ii) $f(-2) = f(0) = 1$
(iii) $\lim_{x\to -2} f(x) = +\infty$

**24.** (i) the domain of $f$ is $(0, +\infty)$
(ii) $f(1) = 0$
(iii) the $y$-axis is a vertical asymptote for the graph of $f$
(iv) $f(x) < 0$ if $0 < x < 1$

**25.** (i) $f(-3) = f(0) = f(2) = 0$
(ii) $\lim_{x\to -2^-} f(x) = +\infty$ and $\lim_{x\to -2^+} f(x) = -\infty$
(iii) $\lim_{x\to 1} f(x) = +\infty$

**26.** (i) $f(-1) = 0$, $f(0) = 1$, $f(1) = 0$
(ii) $\lim_{x\to -1^-} f(x) = 0$ and $\lim_{x\to -1^+} f(x) = +\infty$
(iii) $\lim_{x\to 1^-} f(x) = 1$ and $\lim_{x\to 1^+} f(x) = +\infty$

**27–30** Modify the argument of Example 1 to find the equation of the tangent line to the specified graph at the point given. ■

**27.** the graph of $y = x^2$ at $(-1, 1)$

**28.** the graph of $y = x^2$ at $(0, 0)$

**29.** the graph of $y = x^4$ at $(1, 1)$

**30.** the graph of $y = x^4$ at $(-1, 1)$

**FOCUS ON CONCEPTS**

**31.** In the special theory of relativity the length $l$ of a narrow rod moving longitudinally is a function $l = l(v)$ of the rod's speed $v$. The accompanying figure, in which $c$ denotes the speed of light, displays some of the qualitative features of this function.
(a) What is the physical interpretation of $l_0$?
(b) What is $\lim_{v\to c^-} l(v)$? What is the physical significance of this limit?

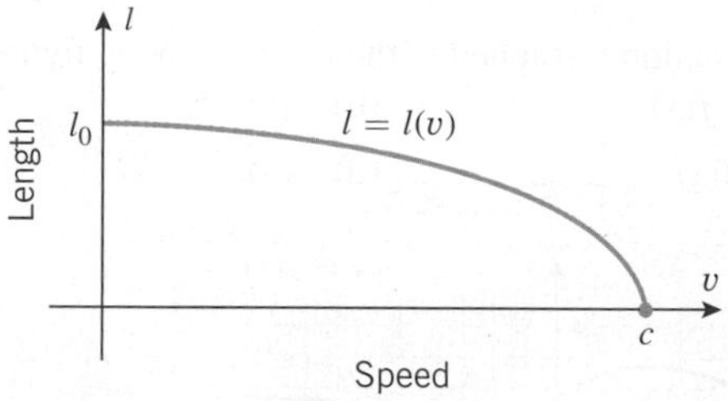


▲ **Figure Ex-31**

**32.** In the special theory of relativity the mass $m$ of a moving object is a function $m = m(v)$ of the object's speed $v$. The accompanying figure, in which $c$ denotes the speed of light, displays some of the qualitative features of this function.
(a) What is the physical interpretation of $m_0$?
(b) What is $\lim_{v\to c^-} m(v)$? What is the physical significance of this limit?

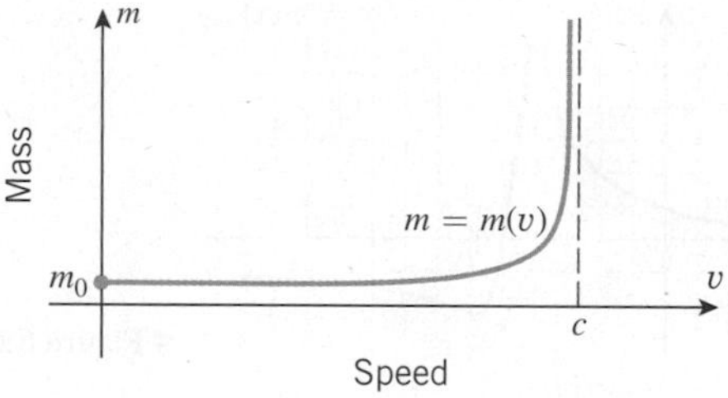


▲ **Figure Ex-32**

**33.** Let
$$f(x) = \left(1 + x^2\right)^{1.1/x^2}$$
(a) Graph $f$ in the window
$$[-1, 1] \times [2.5, 3.5]$$
and use the calculator's trace feature to make a conjecture about the limit of $f(x)$ as $x\to 0$.
(b) Graph $f$ in the window
$$[-0.001, 0.001] \times [2.5, 3.5]$$
and use the calculator's trace feature to make a conjecture about the limit of $f(x)$ as $x\to 0$.
(c) Graph $f$ in the window
$$[-0.000001, 0.000001] \times [2.5, 3.5]$$
and use the calculator's trace feature to make a conjecture about the limit of $f(x)$ as $x\to 0$.

(cont.)

(d) Later we will be able to show that

$$\lim_{x\to 0}\left(1+x^2\right)^{1.1/x^2} \approx 3.00416602$$

What flaw do your graphs reveal about using numerical evidence (as revealed by the graphs you obtained) to make conjectures about limits?

34. **Writing** Two students are discussing the limit of $\sqrt{x}$ as $x$ approaches 0. One student maintains that the limit is 0, while the other claims that the limit does not exist. Write a short paragraph that discusses the pros and cons of each student's position.

35. **Writing** Given a function $f$ and a real number $a$, explain informally why

$$\lim_{x\to 0} f(x+a) = \lim_{x\to a} f(x)$$

(Here "equality" means that either both limits exist and are equal or that both limits fail to exist.)

✓ QUICK CHECK ANSWERS 1.1 1. $f(x)$; $L$; $x$; $a$; $a$ 2. $f(x)$; $x$; $a$ 3. Both one-sided limits must exist and equal $L$. 4. (a) 0 (b) 1 (c) $+\infty$ (d) $-\infty$ 5. 4

## 1.2 COMPUTING LIMITS

*In this section we will discuss techniques for computing limits of many functions. We base these results on the informal development of the limit concept discussed in the preceding section. A more formal derivation of these results is possible after Section 1.4.*

### SOME BASIC LIMITS

Our strategy for finding limits algebraically has two parts:

- First we will obtain the limits of some simple functions.
- Then we will develop a repertoire of theorems that will enable us to use the limits of those simple functions as building blocks for finding limits of more complicated functions.

We start with the following basic results, which are illustrated in Figure 1.2.1.

**1.2.1 THEOREM** *Let a and k be real numbers.*

(a) $\lim_{x\to a} k = k$ (b) $\lim_{x\to a} x = a$ (c) $\lim_{x\to 0^-} \frac{1}{x} = -\infty$ (d) $\lim_{x\to 0^+} \frac{1}{x} = +\infty$

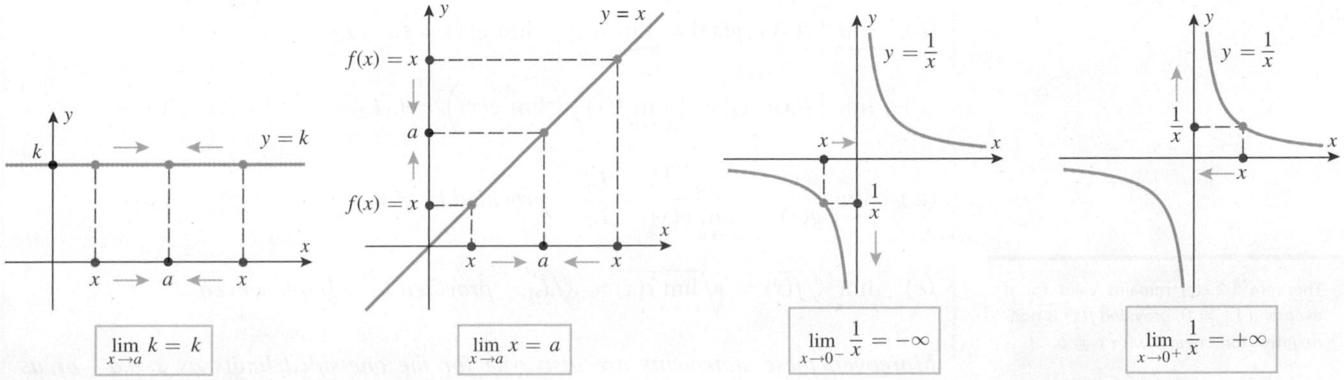


▲ Figure 1.2.1

The following examples explain these results further.

▶ **Example 1** If $f(x) = k$ is a constant function, then the values of $f(x)$ remain fixed at $k$ as $x$ varies, which explains why $f(x) \to k$ as $x \to a$ for all values of $a$. For example,

$$\lim_{x \to -25} 3 = 3, \qquad \lim_{x \to 0} 3 = 3, \qquad \lim_{x \to \pi} 3 = 3 \blacktriangleleft$$

Do not confuse the algebraic size of a number with its closeness to zero. For positive numbers, the smaller the number the closer it is to zero, but for negative numbers, the larger the number the closer it is to zero. For example, $-2$ is larger than $-4$, but it is closer to zero.

▶ **Example 2** If $f(x) = x$, then as $x \to a$ it must also be true that $f(x) \to a$. For example,

$$\lim_{x \to 0} x = 0, \qquad \lim_{x \to -2} x = -2, \qquad \lim_{x \to \pi} x = \pi \blacktriangleleft$$

▶ **Example 3** You should know from your experience with fractions that for a fixed nonzero numerator, the closer the denominator is to zero, the larger the absolute value of the fraction. This fact and the data in Table 1.2.1 suggest why $1/x \to +\infty$ as $x \to 0^+$ and why $1/x \to -\infty$ as $x \to 0^-$. ◀

**Table 1.2.1**

| | VALUES | | | | | | CONCLUSION |
|---|---|---|---|---|---|---|---|
| $x$<br>$1/x$ | $-1$<br>$-1$ | $-0.1$<br>$-10$ | $-0.01$<br>$-100$ | $-0.001$<br>$-1000$ | $-0.0001$<br>$-10{,}000$ | $\cdots$<br>$\cdots$ | As $x \to 0^-$ the value of $1/x$ decreases without bound. |
| $x$<br>$1/x$ | $1$<br>$1$ | $0.1$<br>$10$ | $0.01$<br>$100$ | $0.001$<br>$1000$ | $0.0001$<br>$10{,}000$ | $\cdots$<br>$\cdots$ | As $x \to 0^+$ the value of $1/x$ increases without bound. |

The following theorem, parts of which are proved in Web Appendix L, will be our basic tool for finding limits algebraically.

**1.2.2 THEOREM** *Let a be a real number, and suppose that*

$$\lim_{x \to a} f(x) = L_1 \quad \text{and} \quad \lim_{x \to a} g(x) = L_2$$

*That is, the limits exist and have values $L_1$ and $L_2$, respectively. Then:*

(*a*) $\lim_{x \to a} [f(x) + g(x)] = \lim_{x \to a} f(x) + \lim_{x \to a} g(x) = L_1 + L_2$

(*b*) $\lim_{x \to a} [f(x) - g(x)] = \lim_{x \to a} f(x) - \lim_{x \to a} g(x) = L_1 - L_2$

(*c*) $\lim_{x \to a} [f(x)g(x)] = \left(\lim_{x \to a} f(x)\right)\left(\lim_{x \to a} g(x)\right) = L_1 L_2$

(*d*) $\lim_{x \to a} \dfrac{f(x)}{g(x)} = \dfrac{\lim_{x \to a} f(x)}{\lim_{x \to a} g(x)} = \dfrac{L_1}{L_2}$, *provided* $L_2 \neq 0$

(*e*) $\lim_{x \to a} \sqrt[n]{f(x)} = \sqrt[n]{\lim_{x \to a} f(x)} = \sqrt[n]{L_1}$, *provided* $L_1 > 0$ *if n is even.*

*Moreover, these statements are also true for the one-sided limits as $x \to a^-$ or as $x \to a^+$.*

Theorem 1.2.2(e) remains valid for $n$ even and $L_1 = 0$, provided $f(x)$ is nonnegative for $x$ near $a$ with $x \neq a$.

This theorem can be stated informally as follows:

(*a*) *The limit of a sum is the sum of the limits.*
(*b*) *The limit of a difference is the difference of the limits.*
(*c*) *The limit of a product is the product of the limits.*
(*d*) *The limit of a quotient is the quotient of the limits, provided the limit of the denominator is not zero.*
(*e*) *The limit of an nth root is the nth root of the limit.*

For the special case of part (*c*) in which $f(x) = k$ is a constant function, we have

$$\lim_{x\to a}(kg(x)) = \lim_{x\to a} k \cdot \lim_{x\to a} g(x) = k \lim_{x\to a} g(x) \tag{1}$$

and similarly for one-sided limits. This result can be rephrased as follows:

*A constant factor can be moved through a limit symbol.*

Although parts (*a*) and (*c*) of Theorem 1.2.2 are stated for two functions, the results hold for any finite number of functions. Moreover, the various parts of the theorem can be used in combination to reformulate expressions involving limits.

**▶ Example 4**

$$\lim_{x\to a}[f(x) - g(x) + 2h(x)] = \lim_{x\to a} f(x) - \lim_{x\to a} g(x) + 2\lim_{x\to a} h(x)$$

$$\lim_{x\to a}[f(x)g(x)h(x)] = \left(\lim_{x\to a} f(x)\right)\left(\lim_{x\to a} g(x)\right)\left(\lim_{x\to a} h(x)\right)$$

$$\lim_{x\to a}[f(x)]^3 = \left(\lim_{x\to a} f(x)\right)^3$$ Take $g(x) = h(x) = f(x)$ in the last equation.

$$\lim_{x\to a}[f(x)]^n = \left(\lim_{x\to a} f(x)\right)^n$$ The extension of Theorem 1.2.2(*c*) in which there are *n* factors, each of which is $f(x)$

$$\lim_{x\to a} x^n = \left(\lim_{x\to a} x\right)^n = a^n$$ Apply the previous result with $f(x) = x$. ◀

## LIMITS OF POLYNOMIALS AND RATIONAL FUNCTIONS AS $x \to a$

**▶ Example 5** Find $\lim_{x\to 5}(x^2 - 4x + 3)$.

***Solution.***

$$\lim_{x\to 5}(x^2 - 4x + 3) = \lim_{x\to 5} x^2 - \lim_{x\to 5} 4x + \lim_{x\to 5} 3$$ Theorem 1.2.2(*a*), (*b*)

$$= \lim_{x\to 5} x^2 - 4\lim_{x\to 5} x + \lim_{x\to 5} 3$$ A constant can be moved through a limit symbol.

$$= 5^2 - 4(5) + 3$$ The last part of Example 4

$$= 8$$ ◀

Observe that in Example 5 the limit of the polynomial $p(x) = x^2 - 4x + 3$ as $x\to 5$ turned out to be the same as $p(5)$. This is not an accident. The next result shows that, in general, the limit of a polynomial $p(x)$ as $x\to a$ is the same as the value of the polynomial at $a$. Knowing this fact allows us to reduce the computation of limits of polynomials to simply evaluating the polynomial at the appropriate point.

**1.2.3 THEOREM** *For any polynomial*

$$p(x) = c_0 + c_1x + \cdots + c_nx^n$$

*and any real number a,*

$$\lim_{x \to a} p(x) = c_0 + c_1a + \cdots + c_na^n = p(a)$$

**PROOF**

$$\begin{aligned}\lim_{x \to a} p(x) &= \lim_{x \to a} (c_0 + c_1x + \cdots + c_nx^n)\\ &= \lim_{x \to a} c_0 + \lim_{x \to a} c_1x + \cdots + \lim_{x \to a} c_nx^n\\ &= \lim_{x \to a} c_0 + c_1 \lim_{x \to a} x + \cdots + c_n \lim_{x \to a} x^n\\ &= c_0 + c_1a + \cdots + c_na^n = p(a) \quad \blacksquare\end{aligned}$$

▶ **Example 6** Find $\lim_{x \to 1} (x^7 - 2x^5 + 1)^{35}$.

***Solution.*** The function involved is a polynomial (why?), so the limit can be obtained by evaluating this polynomial at $x = 1$. This yields

$$\lim_{x \to 1} (x^7 - 2x^5 + 1)^{35} = 0 \quad ◀$$

Recall that a rational function is a ratio of two polynomials. The following example illustrates how Theorems 1.2.2(*d*) and 1.2.3 can sometimes be used in combination to compute limits of rational functions.

▶ **Example 7** Find $\lim_{x \to 2} \dfrac{5x^3 + 4}{x - 3}$.

***Solution.***

$$\begin{aligned}\lim_{x \to 2} \frac{5x^3 + 4}{x - 3} &= \frac{\lim_{x \to 2} (5x^3 + 4)}{\lim_{x \to 2} (x - 3)} && \boxed{\text{Theorem 1.2.2}(d)}\\ &= \frac{5 \cdot 2^3 + 4}{2 - 3} = -44 && \boxed{\text{Theorem 1.2.3}} \quad ◀\end{aligned}$$

The method used in the last example will not work for rational functions in which the limit of the denominator is zero because Theorem 1.2.2(*d*) is not applicable. There are two cases of this type to be considered—the case where the limit of the denominator is zero and the limit of the numerator is not, and the case where the limits of the numerator and denominator are both zero. If the limit of the denominator is zero but the limit of the numerator is not, then one can prove that the limit of the rational function does not exist and that one of the following situations occurs:

- The limit may be $-\infty$ from one side and $+\infty$ from the other.
- The limit may be $+\infty$.
- The limit may be $-\infty$.

Figure 1.2.2 illustrates these three possibilities graphically for rational functions of the form $1/(x - a)$, $1/(x - a)^2$, and $-1/(x - a)^2$.

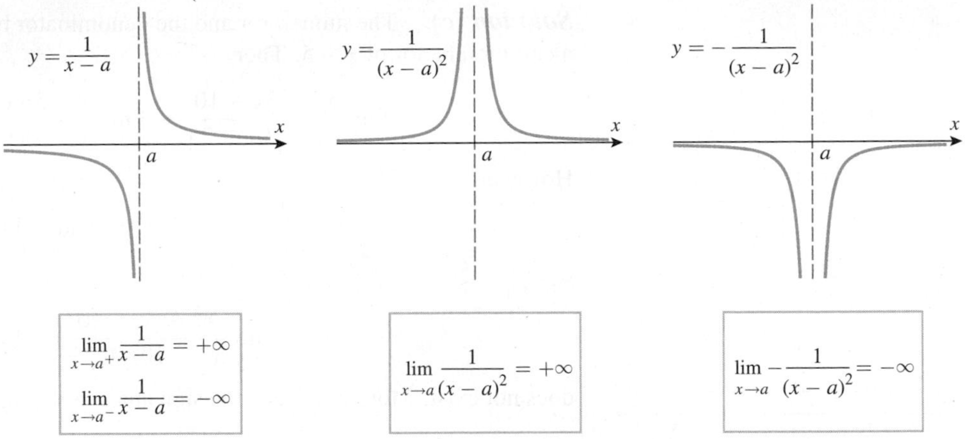


▲ **Figure 1.2.2**

▶ **Example 8** Find

$$\text{(a)} \lim_{x\to 4^+} \frac{2-x}{(x-4)(x+2)} \qquad \text{(b)} \lim_{x\to 4^-} \frac{2-x}{(x-4)(x+2)} \qquad \text{(c)} \lim_{x\to 4} \frac{2-x}{(x-4)(x+2)}$$

***Solution.*** In all three parts the limit of the numerator is $-2$, and the limit of the denominator is 0, so the limit of the ratio does not exist. To be more specific than this, we need to analyze the sign of the ratio. The sign of the ratio, which is given in Figure 1.2.3, is determined by the signs of $2-x$, $x-4$, and $x+2$. (The method of test points, discussed in Web Appendix F, provides a way of finding the sign of the ratio here.) It follows from this figure that as $x$ approaches 4 from the right, the ratio is always negative; and as $x$ approaches 4 from the left, the ratio is eventually positive. Thus,

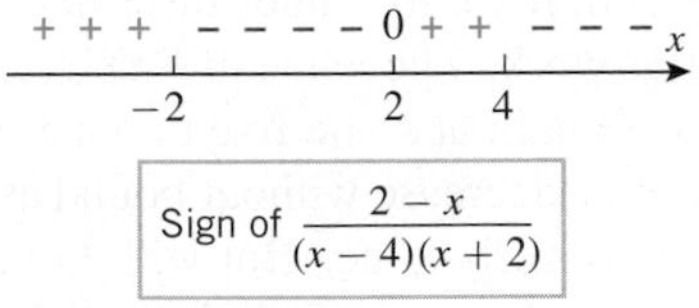


▲ **Figure 1.2.3**

$$\lim_{x\to 4^+} \frac{2-x}{(x-4)(x+2)} = -\infty \quad \text{and} \quad \lim_{x\to 4^-} \frac{2-x}{(x-4)(x+2)} = +\infty$$

Because the one-sided limits have opposite signs, all we can say about the two-sided limit is that it does not exist. ◀

In the case where $p(x)/q(x)$ is a rational function for which $p(a) = 0$ and $q(a) = 0$, the numerator and denominator must have one or more common factors of $x - a$. In this case the limit of $p(x)/q(x)$ as $x \to a$ can be found by canceling all common factors of $x - a$ and using one of the methods already considered to find the limit of the simplified function. Here is an example.

In Example 9(a), the simplified function $x - 3$ is defined at $x = 3$, but the original function is not. However, this has no effect on the limit as *x approaches* 3 since the two functions are identical if $x \neq 3$ (Exercise 50).

▶ **Example 9** Find

$$\text{(a)} \lim_{x\to 3} \frac{x^2-6x+9}{x-3} \qquad \text{(b)} \lim_{x\to -4} \frac{2x+8}{x^2+x-12} \qquad \text{(c)} \lim_{x\to 5} \frac{x^2-3x-10}{x^2-10x+25}$$

***Solution (a).*** The numerator and the denominator both have a zero at $x = 3$, so there is a common factor of $x - 3$. Then

$$\lim_{x\to 3} \frac{x^2-6x+9}{x-3} = \lim_{x\to 3} \frac{(x-3)^2}{x-3} = \lim_{x\to 3} (x-3) = 0$$

***Solution (b).*** The numerator and the denominator both have a zero at $x = -4$, so there is a common factor of $x - (-4) = x + 4$. Then

$$\lim_{x\to -4} \frac{2x+8}{x^2+x-12} = \lim_{x\to -4} \frac{2(x+4)}{(x+4)(x-3)} = \lim_{x\to -4} \frac{2}{x-3} = -\frac{2}{7}$$

***Solution (c).*** The numerator and the denominator both have a zero at $x = 5$, so there is a common factor of $x - 5$. Then

$$\lim_{x \to 5} \frac{x^2 - 3x - 10}{x^2 - 10x + 25} = \lim_{x \to 5} \frac{(x-5)(x+2)}{(x-5)(x-5)} = \lim_{x \to 5} \frac{x+2}{x-5}$$

However,

$$\lim_{x \to 5} (x+2) = 7 \neq 0 \quad \text{and} \quad \lim_{x \to 5} (x-5) = 0$$

so

$$\lim_{x \to 5} \frac{x^2 - 3x - 10}{x^2 - 10x + 25} = \lim_{x \to 5} \frac{x+2}{x-5}$$

does not exist. More precisely, the sign analysis in Figure 1.2.4 implies that

$$\lim_{x \to 5^+} \frac{x^2 - 3x - 10}{x^2 - 10x + 25} = \lim_{x \to 5^+} \frac{x+2}{x-5} = +\infty$$

and

$$\lim_{x \to 5^-} \frac{x^2 - 3x - 10}{x^2 - 10x + 25} = \lim_{x \to 5^-} \frac{x+2}{x-5} = -\infty \blacktriangleleft$$

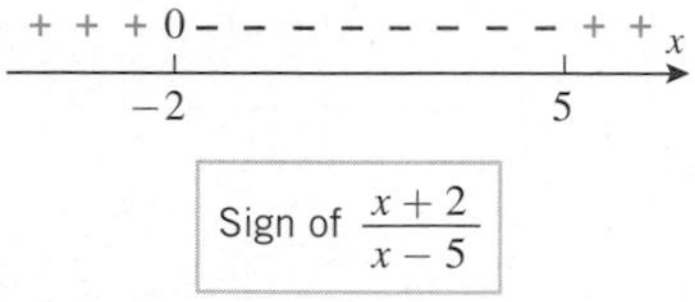


▲ **Figure 1.2.4**

Discuss the logical errors in the following statement: An indeterminate form of type $0/0$ must have a limit of zero because zero divided by anything is zero.

A quotient $f(x)/g(x)$ in which the numerator and denominator both have a limit of zero as $x \to a$ is called an ***indeterminate form of type* 0/0**. The problem with such limits is that it is difficult to tell by inspection whether the limit exists, and, if so, its value. Informally stated, this is because there are two conflicting influences at work. The value of $f(x)/g(x)$ would tend to zero as $f(x)$ approached zero if $g(x)$ were to remain at some fixed nonzero value, whereas the value of this ratio would tend to increase or decrease without bound as $g(x)$ approached zero if $f(x)$ were to remain at some fixed nonzero value. But with both $f(x)$ and $g(x)$ approaching zero, the behavior of the ratio depends on precisely how these conflicting tendencies offset one another for the particular $f$ and $g$.

Sometimes, limits of indeterminate forms of type $0/0$ can be found by algebraic simplification, as in the last example, but frequently this will not work and other methods must be used. We will study such methods in later sections.

The following theorem summarizes our observations about limits of rational functions.

**1.2.4 THEOREM** *Let*

$$f(x) = \frac{p(x)}{q(x)}$$

*be a rational function, and let a be any real number.*

*(a) If $q(a) \neq 0$, then $\lim_{x \to a} f(x) = f(a)$.*

*(b) If $q(a) = 0$ but $p(a) \neq 0$, then $\lim_{x \to a} f(x)$ does not exist.*

## LIMITS INVOLVING RADICALS

▶ **Example 10** Find $\lim_{x \to 1} \frac{x - 1}{\sqrt{x} - 1}$.

***Solution.*** In Example 2 of Section 1.1 we used numerical evidence to conjecture that this limit is 2. Here we will confirm this algebraically. Since this limit is an indeterminate form of type 0/0, we will need to devise some strategy for making the limit (if it exists) evident. One such strategy is to rationalize the denominator of the function. This yields

$$\frac{x-1}{\sqrt{x}-1} = \frac{(x-1)(\sqrt{x}+1)}{(\sqrt{x}-1)(\sqrt{x}+1)} = \frac{(x-1)(\sqrt{x}+1)}{x-1} = \sqrt{x}+1 \quad (x \neq 1)$$

Confirm the limit in Example 10 by factoring the numerator.

Therefore,

$$\lim_{x\to 1} \frac{x-1}{\sqrt{x}-1} = \lim_{x\to 1}(\sqrt{x}+1) = 2 \blacktriangleleft$$

## LIMITS OF PIECEWISE-DEFINED FUNCTIONS

For functions that are defined piecewise, a two-sided limit at a point where the formula changes is best obtained by first finding the one-sided limits at that point.

**▶ Example 11** Let

$$f(x) = \begin{cases} 1/(x+2), & x < -2 \\ x^2 - 5, & -2 < x \leq 3 \\ \sqrt{x+13}, & x > 3 \end{cases}$$

Find

$$\text{(a)} \lim_{x\to -2} f(x) \quad \text{(b)} \lim_{x\to 0} f(x) \quad \text{(c)} \lim_{x\to 3} f(x)$$

***Solution (a).*** We will determine the stated two-sided limit by first considering the corresponding one-sided limits. For each one-sided limit, we must use that part of the formula that is applicable on the interval over which $x$ varies. For example, as $x$ approaches $-2$ from the left, the applicable part of the formula is

$$f(x) = \frac{1}{x+2}$$

and as $x$ approaches $-2$ from the right, the applicable part of the formula near $-2$ is

$$f(x) = x^2 - 5$$

Thus,

$$\lim_{x\to -2^-} f(x) = \lim_{x\to -2^-} \frac{1}{x+2} = -\infty$$

$$\lim_{x\to -2^+} f(x) = \lim_{x\to -2^+} (x^2 - 5) = (-2)^2 - 5 = -1$$

from which it follows that $\lim_{x\to -2} f(x)$ does not exist.

***Solution (b).*** The applicable part of the formula is $f(x) = x^2 - 5$ on both sides of 0, so there is no need to consider one-sided limits here. We see directly that

$$\lim_{x\to 0} f(x) = \lim_{x\to 0} (x^2 - 5) = 0^2 - 5 = -5$$

***Solution (c).*** Using the applicable parts of the formula for $f(x)$, we obtain

$$\lim_{x\to 3^-} f(x) = \lim_{x\to 3^-} (x^2 - 5) = 3^2 - 5 = 4$$

$$\lim_{x\to 3^+} f(x) = \lim_{x\to 3^+} \sqrt{x+13} = \sqrt{\lim_{x\to 3^+}(x+13)} = \sqrt{3+13} = 4$$

Since the one-sided limits are equal, we have

$$\lim_{x\to 3} f(x) = 4$$

We note that the limit calculations in parts (a), (b), and (c) are consistent with the graph of $f$ shown in Figure 1.2.5. ◀

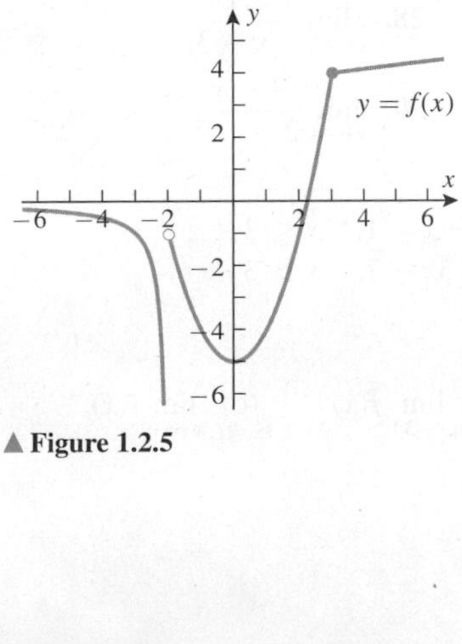


▲ Figure 1.2.5

## ✓QUICK CHECK EXERCISES 1.2 *(See page 21 for answers.)*

1. In each part, find the limit by inspection.
   (a) $\lim_{x\to 8} 7 =$ ______ (b) $\lim_{y\to 3^+} 12y =$ ______
   (c) $\lim_{x\to 0^-} \dfrac{x}{|x|} =$ ______ (d) $\lim_{w\to 5} \dfrac{w}{|w|} =$ ______
   (e) $\lim_{z\to 1^-} \dfrac{1}{1-z} =$ ______

2. Given that $\lim_{x\to a} f(x) = 1$ and $\lim_{x\to a} g(x) = 2$, find the limits.
   (a) $\lim_{x\to a} [3f(x) + 2g(x)] =$ ______
   (b) $\lim_{x\to a} \dfrac{2f(x)+1}{1-f(x)g(x)} =$ ______
   (c) $\lim_{x\to a} \dfrac{\sqrt{f(x)+3}}{g(x)} =$ ______

3. Find the limits.
   (a) $\lim_{x\to -1} (x^3 + x^2 + x)^{101} =$ ______
   (b) $\lim_{x\to 2^-} \dfrac{(x-1)(x-2)}{x+1} =$ ______
   (c) $\lim_{x\to -1^+} \dfrac{(x-1)(x-2)}{x+1} =$ ______
   (d) $\lim_{x\to 4} \dfrac{x^2-16}{x-4} =$ ______

4. Let
$$f(x) = \begin{cases} x+1, & x \le 1 \\ x-1, & x > 1 \end{cases}$$
   Find the limits that exist.
   (a) $\lim_{x\to 1^-} f(x) =$ ______
   (b) $\lim_{x\to 1^+} f(x) =$ ______
   (c) $\lim_{x\to 1} f(x) =$ ______

## EXERCISE SET 1.2

1. Given that
$$\lim_{x\to a} f(x) = 2, \quad \lim_{x\to a} g(x) = -4, \quad \lim_{x\to a} h(x) = 0$$
   find the limits.
   (a) $\lim_{x\to a} [f(x) + 2g(x)]$
   (b) $\lim_{x\to a} [h(x) - 3g(x) + 1]$
   (c) $\lim_{x\to a} [f(x)g(x)]$ (d) $\lim_{x\to a} [g(x)]^2$
   (e) $\lim_{x\to a} \sqrt[3]{6+f(x)}$ (f) $\lim_{x\to a} \dfrac{2}{g(x)}$

2. Use the graphs of $f$ and $g$ in the accompanying figure to find the limits that exist. If the limit does not exist, explain why.
   (a) $\lim_{x\to 2} [f(x) + g(x)]$ (b) $\lim_{x\to 0} [f(x) + g(x)]$
   (c) $\lim_{x\to 0^+} [f(x) + g(x)]$ (d) $\lim_{x\to 0^-} [f(x) + g(x)]$
   (e) $\lim_{x\to 2} \dfrac{f(x)}{1+g(x)}$ (f) $\lim_{x\to 2} \dfrac{1+g(x)}{f(x)}$
   (g) $\lim_{x\to 0^+} \sqrt{f(x)}$ (h) $\lim_{x\to 0^-} \sqrt{f(x)}$

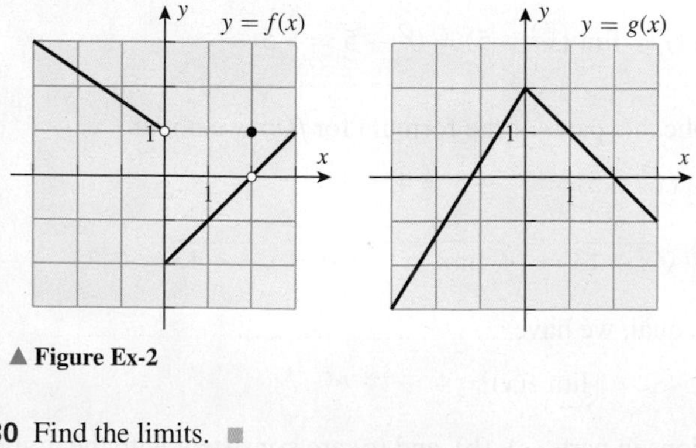


▲ Figure Ex-2

**3–30** Find the limits. ■

3. $\lim_{x\to 2} x(x-1)(x+1)$
4. $\lim_{x\to 3} x^3 - 3x^2 + 9x$
5. $\lim_{x\to 3} \dfrac{x^2-2x}{x+1}$
6. $\lim_{x\to 0} \dfrac{6x-9}{x^3-12x+3}$
7. $\lim_{x\to 1^+} \dfrac{x^4-1}{x-1}$
8. $\lim_{t\to -2} \dfrac{t^3+8}{t+2}$
9. $\lim_{x\to -1} \dfrac{x^2+6x+5}{x^2-3x-4}$
10. $\lim_{x\to 2} \dfrac{x^2-4x+4}{x^2+x-6}$
11. $\lim_{x\to -1} \dfrac{2x^2+x-1}{x+1}$
12. $\lim_{x\to 1} \dfrac{3x^2-x-2}{2x^2+x-3}$
13. $\lim_{t\to 2} \dfrac{t^3+3t^2-12t+4}{t^3-4t}$
14. $\lim_{t\to 1} \dfrac{t^3+t^2-5t+3}{t^3-3t+2}$
15. $\lim_{x\to 3^+} \dfrac{x}{x-3}$
16. $\lim_{x\to 3^-} \dfrac{x}{x-3}$
17. $\lim_{x\to 3} \dfrac{x}{x-3}$
18. $\lim_{x\to 2^+} \dfrac{x}{x^2-4}$
19. $\lim_{x\to 2^-} \dfrac{x}{x^2-4}$
20. $\lim_{x\to 2} \dfrac{x}{x^2-4}$
21. $\lim_{y\to 6^+} \dfrac{y+6}{y^2-36}$
22. $\lim_{y\to 6^-} \dfrac{y+6}{y^2-36}$
23. $\lim_{y\to 6} \dfrac{y+6}{y^2-36}$
24. $\lim_{x\to 4^+} \dfrac{3-x}{x^2-2x-8}$
25. $\lim_{x\to 4^-} \dfrac{3-x}{x^2-2x-8}$
26. $\lim_{x\to 4} \dfrac{3-x}{x^2-2x-8}$
27. $\lim_{x\to 2^+} \dfrac{1}{|2-x|}$
28. $\lim_{x\to 3^-} \dfrac{1}{|x-3|}$
29. $\lim_{x\to 9} \dfrac{x-9}{\sqrt{x}-3}$
30. $\lim_{y\to 4} \dfrac{4-y}{2-\sqrt{y}}$

31. Let
$$f(x) = \begin{cases} x-1, & x \le 3 \\ 3x-7, & x > 3 \end{cases}$$
   Find
   (a) $\lim_{x\to 3^-} f(x)$ (b) $\lim_{x\to 3^+} f(x)$ (c) $\lim_{x\to 3} f(x)$.

**32.** Let

$$g(t) = \begin{cases} t-2, & t<0 \\ t^2, & 0 \le t \le 2 \\ 2t, & t>2 \end{cases}$$

Find
(a) $\lim_{t\to 0} g(t)$ (b) $\lim_{t\to 1} g(t)$ (c) $\lim_{t\to 2} g(t)$.

**33–36 True–False** Determine whether the statement is true or false. Explain your answer. ■

**33.** If $\lim_{x\to a} f(x)$ and $\lim_{x\to a} g(x)$ exist, then so does $\lim_{x\to a}[f(x)+g(x)]$.

**34.** If $\lim_{x\to a} g(x) = 0$ and $\lim_{x\to a} f(x)$ exists, then $\lim_{x\to a}[f(x)/g(x)]$ does not exist.

**35.** If $\lim_{x\to a} f(x)$ and $\lim_{x\to a} g(x)$ both exist and are equal, then $\lim_{x\to a}[f(x)/g(x)] = 1$.

**36.** If $f(x)$ is a rational function and $x = a$ is in the domain of $f$, then $\lim_{x\to a} f(x) = f(a)$.

**37–38** First rationalize the numerator and then find the limit. ■

**37.** $\lim_{x\to 0} \dfrac{\sqrt{x+4}-2}{x}$ **38.** $\lim_{x\to 0} \dfrac{\sqrt{x^2+4}-2}{x}$

**39.** Let

$$f(x) = \frac{x^3-1}{x-1}$$

(a) Find $\lim_{x\to 1} f(x)$.
(b) Sketch the graph of $y = f(x)$.

**40.** Let

$$f(x) = \begin{cases} \dfrac{x^2-9}{x+3}, & x \ne -3 \\ k, & x = -3 \end{cases}$$

(a) Find $k$ so that $f(-3) = \lim_{x\to -3} f(x)$.
(b) With $k$ assigned the value $\lim_{x\to -3} f(x)$, show that $f(x)$ can be expressed as a polynomial.

**FOCUS ON CONCEPTS**

**41.** (a) Explain why the following calculation is incorrect.

$$\lim_{x\to 0^+}\left(\frac{1}{x}-\frac{1}{x^2}\right) = \lim_{x\to 0^+}\frac{1}{x} - \lim_{x\to 0^+}\frac{1}{x^2}$$
$$= +\infty - (+\infty) = 0$$

(b) Show that $\lim_{x\to 0^+}\left(\dfrac{1}{x}-\dfrac{1}{x^2}\right) = -\infty$.

**42.** (a) Explain why the following argument is incorrect.

$$\lim_{x\to 0}\left(\frac{1}{x}-\frac{2}{x^2+2x}\right) = \lim_{x\to 0}\frac{1}{x}\left(1-\frac{2}{x+2}\right)$$
$$= \infty \cdot 0 = 0$$

(b) Show that $\lim_{x\to 0}\left(\dfrac{1}{x}-\dfrac{2}{x^2+2x}\right) = \dfrac{1}{2}$.

**43.** Find all values of $a$ such that

$$\lim_{x\to 1}\left(\frac{1}{x-1}-\frac{a}{x^2-1}\right)$$

exists and is finite.

**44.** (a) Explain informally why

$$\lim_{x\to 0^-}\left(\frac{1}{x}+\frac{1}{x^2}\right) = +\infty$$

(b) Verify the limit in part (a) algebraically.

**45.** Let $p(x)$ and $q(x)$ be polynomials, with $q(x_0) = 0$. Discuss the behavior of the graph of $y = p(x)/q(x)$ in the vicinity of $x = x_0$. Give examples to support your conclusions.

**46.** Suppose that $f$ and $g$ are two functions such that $\lim_{x\to a} f(x)$ exists but $\lim_{x\to a}[f(x)+g(x)]$ does not exist. Use Theorem 1.2.2 to prove that $\lim_{x\to a} g(x)$ does not exist.

**47.** Suppose that $f$ and $g$ are two functions such that both $\lim_{x\to a} f(x)$ and $\lim_{x\to a}[f(x)+g(x)]$ exist. Use Theorem 1.2.2 to prove that $\lim_{x\to a} g(x)$ exists.

**48.** Suppose that $f$ and $g$ are two functions such that

$$\lim_{x\to a} g(x) = 0 \quad \text{and} \quad \lim_{x\to a}\frac{f(x)}{g(x)}$$

exists. Use Theorem 1.2.2 to prove that $\lim_{x\to a} f(x) = 0$.

**49. Writing** According to Newton's Law of Universal Gravitation, the gravitational force of attraction between two masses is inversely proportional to the square of the distance between them. What results of this section are useful in describing the gravitational force of attraction between the masses as they get closer and closer together?

**50. Writing** Suppose that $f$ and $g$ are two functions that are equal except at a finite number of points and that $a$ denotes a real number. Explain informally why both

$$\lim_{x\to a} f(x) \quad \text{and} \quad \lim_{x\to a} g(x)$$

exist and are equal, or why both limits fail to exist. Write a short paragraph that explains the relationship of this result to the use of "algebraic simplification" in the evaluation of a limit.

✓ **QUICK CHECK ANSWERS 1.2** 1. (a) 7 (b) 36 (c) −1 (d) 1 (e) $+\infty$ 2. (a) 7 (b) −3 (c) 1 3. (a) −1 (b) 0 (c) $+\infty$ (d) 8 4. (a) 2 (b) 0 (c) does not exist

# 1.3 LIMITS AT INFINITY; END BEHAVIOR OF A FUNCTION

*Up to now we have been concerned with limits that describe the behavior of a function $f(x)$ as $x$ approaches some real number $a$. In this section we will be concerned with the behavior of $f(x)$ as $x$ increases or decreases without bound.*

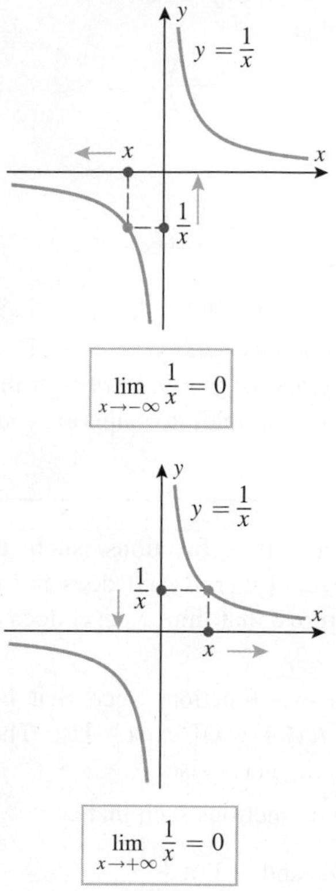


▲ Figure 1.3.1

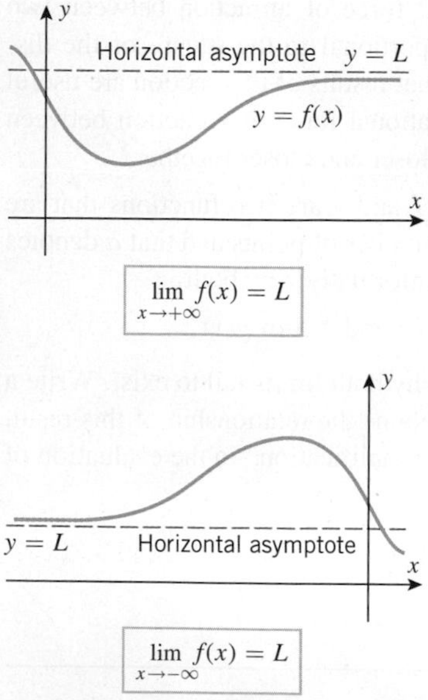


▲ Figure 1.3.2

## LIMITS AT INFINITY AND HORIZONTAL ASYMPTOTES

If the values of a variable $x$ increase without bound, then we write $x \to +\infty$, and if the values of $x$ decrease without bound, then we write $x \to -\infty$. The behavior of a function $f(x)$ as $x$ increases without bound or decreases without bound is sometimes called the ***end behavior*** of the function. For example,

$$\lim_{x \to -\infty} \frac{1}{x} = 0 \quad \text{and} \quad \lim_{x \to +\infty} \frac{1}{x} = 0 \tag{1–2}$$

are illustrated numerically in Table 1.3.1 and geometrically in Figure 1.3.1.

**Table 1.3.1**

| | VALUES | | | | | | CONCLUSION |
|---|---|---|---|---|---|---|---|
| $x$ | −1 | −10 | −100 | −1000 | −10,000 | ··· | As $x \to -\infty$ the value of $1/x$ increases toward zero. |
| $1/x$ | −1 | −0.1 | −0.01 | −0.001 | −0.0001 | ··· | |
| $x$ | 1 | 10 | 100 | 1000 | 10,000 | ··· | As $x \to +\infty$ the value of $1/x$ decreases toward zero. |
| $1/x$ | 1 | 0.1 | 0.01 | 0.001 | 0.0001 | ··· | |

In general, we will use the following notation.

**1.3.1 LIMITS AT INFINITY (AN INFORMAL VIEW)** If the values of $f(x)$ eventually get as close as we like to a number $L$ as $x$ increases without bound, then we write

$$\lim_{x \to +\infty} f(x) = L \quad \text{or} \quad f(x) \to L \text{ as } x \to +\infty \tag{3}$$

Similarly, if the values of $f(x)$ eventually get as close as we like to a number $L$ as $x$ decreases without bound, then we write

$$\lim_{x \to -\infty} f(x) = L \quad \text{or} \quad f(x) \to L \text{ as } x \to -\infty \tag{4}$$

Figure 1.3.2 illustrates the end behavior of a function $f$ when

$$\lim_{x \to +\infty} f(x) = L \quad \text{or} \quad \lim_{x \to -\infty} f(x) = L$$

In the first case the graph of $f$ eventually comes as close as we like to the line $y = L$ as $x$ increases without bound, and in the second case it eventually comes as close as we like to the line $y = L$ as $x$ decreases without bound. If either limit holds, we call the line $y = L$ a ***horizontal asymptote*** for the graph of $f$.

▶ **Example 1** It follows from (1) and (2) that $y = 0$ is a horizontal asymptote for the graph of $f(x) = 1/x$ in both the positive and negative directions. This is consistent with the graph of $y = 1/x$ shown in Figure 1.3.1. ◀

## LIMIT LAWS FOR LIMITS AT INFINITY

It can be shown that the limit laws in Theorem 1.2.2 carry over without change to limits at $+\infty$ and $-\infty$. Moreover, it follows by the same argument used in Section 1.2 that if $n$ is a positive integer, then

$$\lim_{x\to+\infty} (f(x))^n = \left(\lim_{x\to+\infty} f(x)\right)^n \qquad \lim_{x\to-\infty} (f(x))^n = \left(\lim_{x\to-\infty} f(x)\right)^n \tag{5–6}$$

provided the indicated limit of $f(x)$ exists. It also follows that constants can be moved through the limit symbols for limits at infinity:

$$\lim_{x\to+\infty} kf(x) = k \lim_{x\to+\infty} f(x) \qquad \lim_{x\to-\infty} kf(x) = k \lim_{x\to-\infty} f(x) \tag{7–8}$$

provided the indicated limit of $f(x)$ exists.

Finally, if $f(x) = k$ is a constant function, then the values of $f$ do not change as $x\to+\infty$ or as $x\to-\infty$, so

$$\lim_{x\to+\infty} k = k \qquad \lim_{x\to-\infty} k = k \tag{9–10}$$

▶ **Example 2** It follows from (1), (2), (5), and (6) that if $n$ is a positive integer, then

$$\lim_{x\to+\infty} \frac{1}{x^n} = \left(\lim_{x\to+\infty} \frac{1}{x}\right)^n = 0 \quad \text{and} \quad \lim_{x\to-\infty} \frac{1}{x^n} = \left(\lim_{x\to-\infty} \frac{1}{x}\right)^n = 0 \blacktriangleleft$$

## INFINITE LIMITS AT INFINITY

Limits at infinity, like limits at a real number $a$, can fail to exist for various reasons. One such possibility is that the values of $f(x)$ increase or decrease without bound as $x\to+\infty$ or as $x\to-\infty$. We will use the following notation to describe this situation.

**1.3.2 INFINITE LIMITS AT INFINITY (AN INFORMAL VIEW)** If the values of $f(x)$ increase without bound as $x\to+\infty$ or as $x\to-\infty$, then we write

$$\lim_{x\to+\infty} f(x) = +\infty \quad \text{or} \quad \lim_{x\to-\infty} f(x) = +\infty$$

as appropriate; and if the values of $f(x)$ decrease without bound as $x\to+\infty$ or as $x\to-\infty$, then we write

$$\lim_{x\to+\infty} f(x) = -\infty \quad \text{or} \quad \lim_{x\to-\infty} f(x) = -\infty$$

as appropriate.

## LIMITS OF $x^n$ AS $x\to\pm\infty$

Figure 1.3.3 illustrates the end behavior of the polynomials $x^n$ for $n = 1, 2, 3$, and 4. These are special cases of the following general results:

$$\lim_{x\to+\infty} x^n = +\infty, \quad n = 1, 2, 3, \ldots \qquad \lim_{x\to-\infty} x^n = \begin{cases} -\infty, & n = 1, 3, 5, \ldots \\ +\infty, & n = 2, 4, 6, \ldots \end{cases} \tag{11–12}$$

Multiplying $x^n$ by a positive real number does not affect limits (11) and (12), but multiplying by a negative real number reverses the sign.

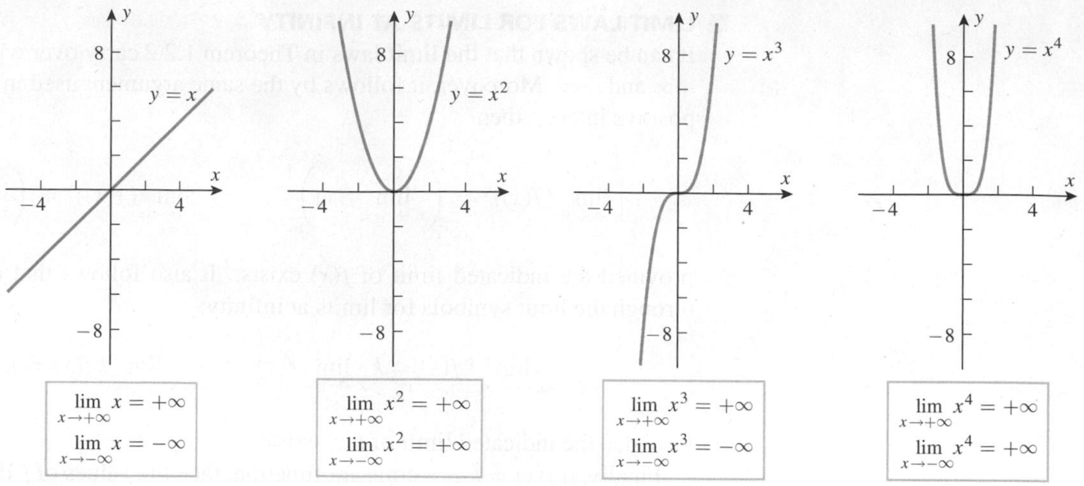


▲ Figure 1.3.3

**▶ Example 3**

$$\lim_{x\to+\infty} 2x^5 = +\infty, \qquad \lim_{x\to-\infty} 2x^5 = -\infty$$

$$\lim_{x\to+\infty} -7x^6 = -\infty, \qquad \lim_{x\to-\infty} -7x^6 = -\infty \blacktriangleleft$$

## LIMITS OF POLYNOMIALS AS $x \to \pm\infty$

There is a useful principle about polynomials which, expressed informally, states:

*The end behavior of a polynomial matches the end behavior of its highest degree term.*

More precisely, if $c_n \neq 0$, then

$$\lim_{x\to-\infty} (c_0 + c_1x + \cdots + c_nx^n) = \lim_{x\to-\infty} c_nx^n \tag{13}$$

$$\lim_{x\to+\infty} (c_0 + c_1x + \cdots + c_nx^n) = \lim_{x\to+\infty} c_nx^n \tag{14}$$

We can motivate these results by factoring out the highest power of $x$ from the polynomial and examining the limit of the factored expression. Thus,

$$c_0 + c_1x + \cdots + c_nx^n = x^n\left(\frac{c_0}{x^n} + \frac{c_1}{x^{n-1}} + \cdots + c_n\right)$$

As $x \to -\infty$ or $x \to +\infty$, it follows from Example 2 that all of the terms with positive powers of $x$ in the denominator approach 0, so (13) and (14) are certainly plausible.

**▶ Example 4**

$$\lim_{x\to-\infty} (7x^5 - 4x^3 + 2x - 9) = \lim_{x\to-\infty} 7x^5 = -\infty$$

$$\lim_{x\to-\infty} (-4x^8 + 17x^3 - 5x + 1) = \lim_{x\to-\infty} -4x^8 = -\infty \blacktriangleleft$$

## LIMITS OF RATIONAL FUNCTIONS AS $x \to \pm\infty$

One technique for determining the end behavior of a rational function is to divide each term in the numerator and denominator by the highest power of $x$ that occurs in the denominator, after which the limiting behavior can be determined using results we have already established. Here are some examples.

**▶ Example 5** Find $\displaystyle\lim_{x\to+\infty} \frac{3x+5}{6x-8}$.

***Solution.*** Divide each term in the numerator and denominator by the highest power of $x$ that occurs in the denominator, namely, $x^1 = x$. We obtain

$$\lim_{x\to+\infty}\frac{3x+5}{6x-8} = \lim_{x\to+\infty}\frac{3+\frac{5}{x}}{6-\frac{8}{x}} \quad \boxed{\text{Divide each term by } x.}$$

$$= \frac{\lim\limits_{x\to+\infty}\left(3+\frac{5}{x}\right)}{\lim\limits_{x\to+\infty}\left(6-\frac{8}{x}\right)} \quad \boxed{\text{Limit of a quotient is the quotient of the limits.}}$$

$$= \frac{\lim\limits_{x\to+\infty} 3 + \lim\limits_{x\to+\infty}\frac{5}{x}}{\lim\limits_{x\to+\infty} 6 - \lim\limits_{x\to+\infty}\frac{8}{x}} \quad \boxed{\text{Limit of a sum is the sum of the limits.}}$$

$$= \frac{3+5\lim\limits_{x\to+\infty}\frac{1}{x}}{6-8\lim\limits_{x\to+\infty}\frac{1}{x}} = \frac{3+0}{6-0} = \frac{1}{2} \quad \boxed{\text{A constant can be moved through a limit symbol; Formulas (2) and (9).}}$$ ◀

► **Example 6** Find

$$\text{(a)} \lim_{x\to-\infty}\frac{4x^2-x}{2x^3-5} \qquad \text{(b)} \lim_{x\to+\infty}\frac{5x^3-2x^2+1}{1-3x}$$

***Solution (a).*** Divide each term in the numerator and denominator by the highest power of $x$ that occurs in the denominator, namely, $x^3$. We obtain

$$\lim_{x\to-\infty}\frac{4x^2-x}{2x^3-5} = \lim_{x\to-\infty}\frac{\frac{4}{x}-\frac{1}{x^2}}{2-\frac{5}{x^3}} \quad \boxed{\text{Divide each term by } x^3.}$$

$$= \frac{\lim\limits_{x\to-\infty}\left(\frac{4}{x}-\frac{1}{x^2}\right)}{\lim\limits_{x\to-\infty}\left(2-\frac{5}{x^3}\right)} \quad \boxed{\text{Limit of a quotient is the quotient of the limits.}}$$

$$= \frac{\lim\limits_{x\to-\infty}\frac{4}{x} - \lim\limits_{x\to-\infty}\frac{1}{x^2}}{\lim\limits_{x\to-\infty} 2 - \lim\limits_{x\to-\infty}\frac{5}{x^3}} \quad \boxed{\text{Limit of a difference is the difference of the limits.}}$$

$$= \frac{4\lim\limits_{x\to-\infty}\frac{1}{x} - \lim\limits_{x\to-\infty}\frac{1}{x^2}}{2-5\lim\limits_{x\to-\infty}\frac{1}{x^3}} = \frac{0-0}{2-0} = 0 \quad \boxed{\text{A constant can be moved through a limit symbol; Formula (10) and Example 2.}}$$

***Solution (b).*** Divide each term in the numerator and denominator by the highest power of $x$ that occurs in the denominator, namely, $x^1 = x$. We obtain

$$\lim_{x\to+\infty}\frac{5x^3-2x^2+1}{1-3x} = \lim_{x\to+\infty}\frac{5x^2-2x+\frac{1}{x}}{\frac{1}{x}-3} \tag{15}$$

In this case we cannot argue that the limit of the quotient is the quotient of the limits because the limit of the numerator does not exist. However, we have

$$\lim_{x\to+\infty} 5x^2-2x = +\infty, \qquad \lim_{x\to+\infty}\frac{1}{x} = 0, \qquad \lim_{x\to+\infty}\left(\frac{1}{x}-3\right) = -3$$

Thus, the numerator on the right side of (15) approaches $+\infty$ and the denominator has a finite *negative* limit. We conclude from this that the quotient approaches $-\infty$; that is,

$$\lim_{x\to+\infty}\frac{5x^3-2x^2+1}{1-3x}=\lim_{x\to+\infty}\frac{5x^2-2x+\dfrac{1}{x}}{\dfrac{1}{x}-3}=-\infty \blacktriangleleft$$

## A QUICK METHOD FOR FINDING LIMITS OF RATIONAL FUNCTIONS AS $x\to+\infty$ OR $x\to-\infty$

Since the end behavior of a polynomial matches the end behavior of its highest degree term, one can reasonably conclude:

> *The end behavior of a rational function matches the end behavior of the quotient of the highest degree term in the numerator divided by the highest degree term in the denominator.*

**▶ Example 7** Use the preceding observation to compute the limits in Examples 5 and 6.

***Solution.***

$$\lim_{x\to+\infty}\frac{3x+5}{6x-8}=\lim_{x\to+\infty}\frac{3x}{6x}=\lim_{x\to+\infty}\frac{1}{2}=\frac{1}{2}$$

$$\lim_{x\to-\infty}\frac{4x^2-x}{2x^3-5}=\lim_{x\to-\infty}\frac{4x^2}{2x^3}=\lim_{x\to-\infty}\frac{2}{x}=0$$

$$\lim_{x\to+\infty}\frac{5x^3-2x^2+1}{1-3x}=\lim_{x\to+\infty}\frac{5x^3}{(-3x)}=\lim_{x\to+\infty}\left(-\frac{5}{3}x^2\right)=-\infty \blacktriangleleft$$

## LIMITS INVOLVING RADICALS

**▶ Example 8** Find

$$\text{(a)}\ \lim_{x\to+\infty}\frac{\sqrt{x^2+2}}{3x-6}\qquad\text{(b)}\ \lim_{x\to-\infty}\frac{\sqrt{x^2+2}}{3x-6}$$

In both parts it would be helpful to manipulate the function so that the powers of $x$ are transformed to powers of $1/x$. This can be achieved in both cases by dividing the numerator and denominator by $|x|$ and using the fact that $\sqrt{x^2}=|x|$.

***Solution (a).*** As $x\to+\infty$, the values of $x$ under consideration are positive, so we can replace $|x|$ by $x$ where helpful. We obtain

$$\lim_{x\to+\infty}\frac{\sqrt{x^2+2}}{3x-6}=\lim_{x\to+\infty}\frac{\dfrac{\sqrt{x^2+2}}{|x|}}{\dfrac{3x-6}{|x|}}=\lim_{x\to+\infty}\frac{\dfrac{\sqrt{x^2+2}}{\sqrt{x^2}}}{\dfrac{3x-6}{x}}$$

$$=\lim_{x\to+\infty}\frac{\sqrt{1+\dfrac{2}{x^2}}}{3-\dfrac{6}{x}}=\frac{\lim\limits_{x\to+\infty}\sqrt{1+\dfrac{2}{x^2}}}{\lim\limits_{x\to+\infty}\left(3-\dfrac{6}{x}\right)}$$

$$=\frac{\sqrt{\lim\limits_{x\to+\infty}\left(1+\dfrac{2}{x^2}\right)}}{\lim\limits_{x\to+\infty}\left(3-\dfrac{6}{x}\right)}=\frac{\sqrt{\left(\lim\limits_{x\to+\infty}1\right)+\left(2\lim\limits_{x\to+\infty}\dfrac{1}{x^2}\right)}}{\left(\lim\limits_{x\to+\infty}3\right)-\left(6\lim\limits_{x\to+\infty}\dfrac{1}{x}\right)}$$

$$=\frac{\sqrt{1+(2\cdot 0)}}{3-(6\cdot 0)}=\frac{1}{3}$$

**TECHNOLOGY MASTERY**

It follows from Example 8 that the function

$$f(x)=\frac{\sqrt{x^2+2}}{3x-6}$$

has an asymptote of $y=\frac{1}{3}$ in the positive direction and an asymptote of $y=-\frac{1}{3}$ in the negative direction. Confirm this using a graphing utility.

***Solution (b).*** As $x\to-\infty$, the values of $x$ under consideration are negative, so we can replace $|x|$ by $-x$ where helpful. We obtain

$$\lim_{x\to-\infty}\frac{\sqrt{x^2+2}}{3x-6}=\lim_{x\to-\infty}\frac{\dfrac{\sqrt{x^2+2}}{|x|}}{\dfrac{3x-6}{|x|}}=\lim_{x\to-\infty}\frac{\dfrac{\sqrt{x^2+2}}{\sqrt{x^2}}}{\dfrac{3x-6}{(-x)}}$$

$$=\lim_{x\to-\infty}\frac{\sqrt{1+\dfrac{2}{x^2}}}{-3+\dfrac{6}{x}}=-\frac{1}{3} \blacktriangleleft$$

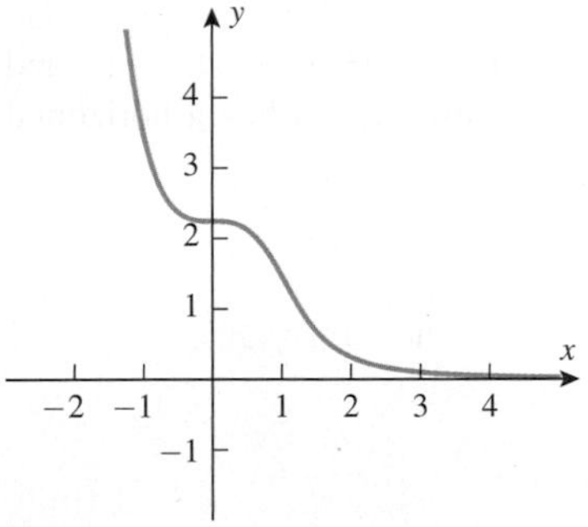

$y=\sqrt{x^6+5}-x^3$

(a)

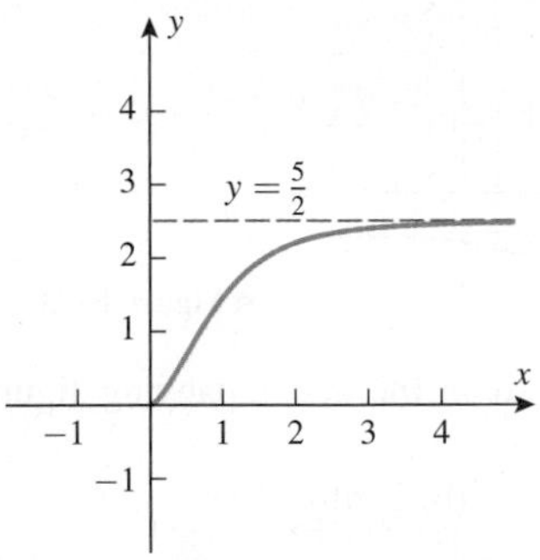

$y=\sqrt{x^6+5x^3}-x^3, x\geq 0$

(b)

▲ **Figure 1.3.4**

We noted in Section 1.1 that the standard rules of algebra do not apply to the symbols $+\infty$ and $-\infty$. Part (b) of Example 9 illustrates this. The terms $\sqrt{x^6+5x^3}$ and $x^3$ both approach $+\infty$ as $x\to+\infty$, but their difference does not approach 0.

▶ **Example 9** Find

(a) $\lim_{x\to+\infty}(\sqrt{x^6+5}-x^3)$ (b) $\lim_{x\to+\infty}(\sqrt{x^6+5x^3}-x^3)$

***Solution.*** Graphs of the functions $f(x)=\sqrt{x^6+5}-x^3$, and $g(x)=\sqrt{x^6+5x^3}-x^3$ for $x\geq 0$, are shown in Figure 1.3.4. From the graphs we might conjecture that the requested limits are 0 and $\frac{5}{2}$, respectively. To confirm this, we treat each function as a fraction with a denominator of 1 and rationalize the numerator.

$$\lim_{x\to+\infty}(\sqrt{x^6+5}-x^3)=\lim_{x\to+\infty}(\sqrt{x^6+5}-x^3)\left(\frac{\sqrt{x^6+5}+x^3}{\sqrt{x^6+5}+x^3}\right)$$

$$=\lim_{x\to+\infty}\frac{(x^6+5)-x^6}{\sqrt{x^6+5}+x^3}=\lim_{x\to+\infty}\frac{5}{\sqrt{x^6+5}+x^3}$$

$$=\lim_{x\to+\infty}\frac{\dfrac{5}{x^3}}{\sqrt{1+\dfrac{5}{x^6}}+1}$$

$\sqrt{x^6}=x^3$ for $x>0$

$$=\frac{0}{\sqrt{1+0}+1}=0$$

$$\lim_{x\to+\infty}(\sqrt{x^6+5x^3}-x^3)=\lim_{x\to+\infty}(\sqrt{x^6+5x^3}-x^3)\left(\frac{\sqrt{x^6+5x^3}+x^3}{\sqrt{x^6+5x^3}+x^3}\right)$$

$$=\lim_{x\to+\infty}\frac{(x^6+5x^3)-x^6}{\sqrt{x^6+5x^3}+x^3}=\lim_{x\to+\infty}\frac{5x^3}{\sqrt{x^6+5x^3}+x^3}$$

$$=\lim_{x\to+\infty}\frac{5}{\sqrt{1+\dfrac{5}{x^3}}+1}$$

$\sqrt{x^6}=x^3$ for $x>0$

$$=\frac{5}{\sqrt{1+0}+1}=\frac{5}{2} \blacktriangleleft$$

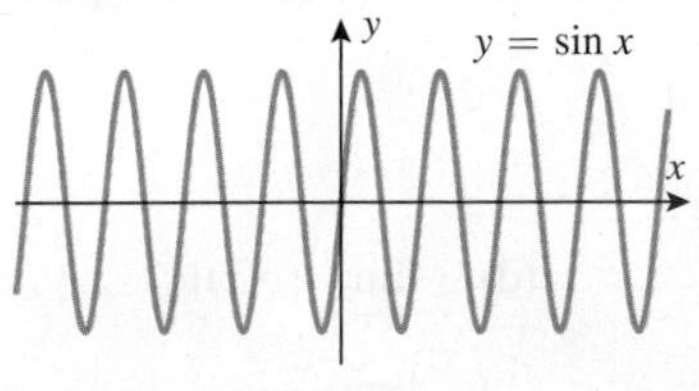

There is no limit as $x\to+\infty$ or $x\to-\infty$.

▲ **Figure 1.3.5**

## END BEHAVIOR OF TRIGONOMETRIC FUNCTIONS

Consider the function $f(x)=\sin x$ that is graphed in Figure 1.3.5. For this function the limits as $x\to+\infty$ and as $x\to-\infty$ fail to exist not because $f(x)$ increases or decreases without bound, but rather because the values vary between $-1$ and 1 without approaching some specific real number. In general, the trigonometric functions fail to have limits as $x\to+\infty$ and as $x\to-\infty$ because of periodicity. There is no specific notation to denote this kind of behavior.

## ✓ QUICK CHECK EXERCISES 1.3 *(See page 30 for answers.)*

**1.** Find the limits.

(a) $\lim_{x\to+\infty} (-2x) =$ ______

(b) $\lim_{x\to-\infty} \dfrac{x}{|x|} =$ ______

(c) $\lim_{x\to-\infty} (3 - x) =$ ______

(d) $\lim_{x\to+\infty} \left(5 - \dfrac{1}{x}\right) =$ ______

**2.** Find the limits that exist.

(a) $\lim_{x\to-\infty} \dfrac{2x^2 + x}{4x^2 - 3} =$ ______

(b) $\lim_{x\to+\infty} \dfrac{1}{2 + \sin x} =$ ______

**3.** Given that

$$\lim_{x\to+\infty} f(x) = 2 \quad \text{and} \quad \lim_{x\to+\infty} g(x) = -3$$

find the limits that exist.

(a) $\lim_{x\to+\infty} [3f(x) - g(x)] =$ ______

(b) $\lim_{x\to+\infty} \dfrac{f(x)}{g(x)} =$ ______

(c) $\lim_{x\to+\infty} \dfrac{2f(x) + 3g(x)}{3f(x) + 2g(x)} =$ ______

(d) $\lim_{x\to+\infty} \sqrt{10 - f(x)g(x)} =$ ______

**4.** Consider the graphs of $y = 1/(x + 1)$, $y = x/(x + 1)$, and $y = x^2/(x + 1)$. Which of these graphs has a horizontal asymptote?

## EXERCISE SET 1.3 ⌂ Graphing Utility

**1–4** In these exercises, make reasonable assumptions about the end behavior of the indicated function. ■

**1.** For the function $g$ graphed in the accompanying figure, find
(a) $\lim_{x\to-\infty} g(x)$ (b) $\lim_{x\to+\infty} g(x)$.

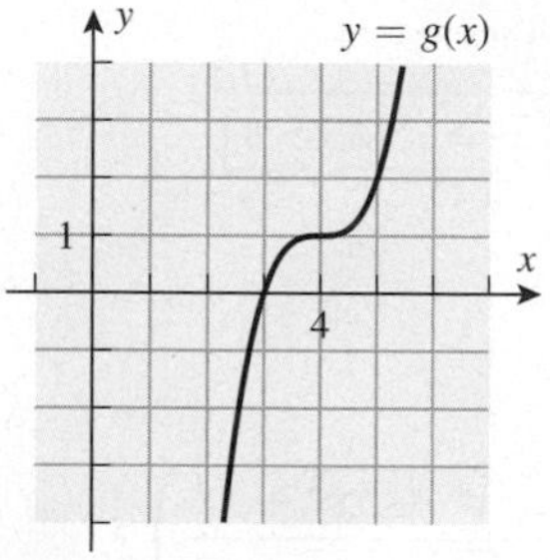


◀ **Figure Ex-1**

**2.** For the function $\phi$ graphed in the accompanying figure, find
(a) $\lim_{x\to-\infty} \phi(x)$ (b) $\lim_{x\to+\infty} \phi(x)$.

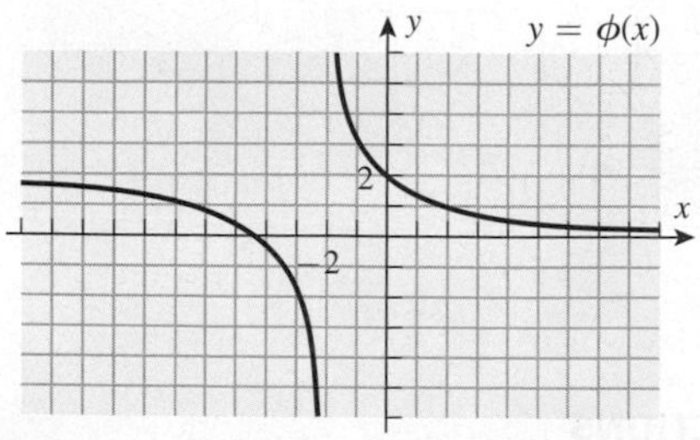


◀ **Figure Ex-2**

**3.** For the function $\phi$ graphed in the accompanying figure, find
(a) $\lim_{x\to-\infty} \phi(x)$ (b) $\lim_{x\to+\infty} \phi(x)$.

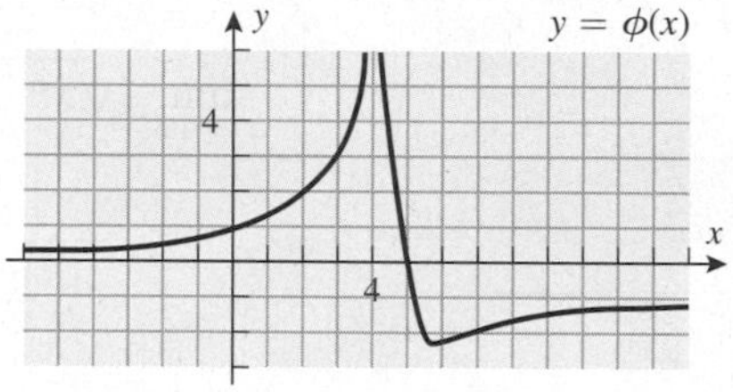


◀ **Figure Ex-3**

**4.** For the function $G$ graphed in the accompanying figure, find
(a) $\lim_{x\to-\infty} G(x)$ (b) $\lim_{x\to+\infty} G(x)$.

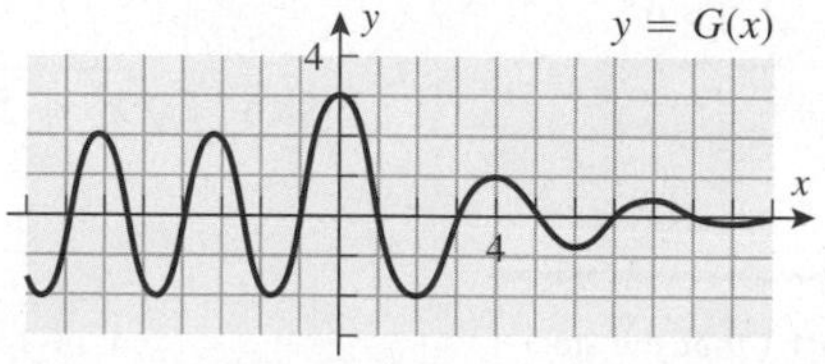


◀ **Figure Ex-4**

**5.** Given that

$$\lim_{x\to+\infty} f(x) = 3, \quad \lim_{x\to+\infty} g(x) = -5, \quad \lim_{x\to+\infty} h(x) = 0$$

find the limits that exist. If the limit does not exist, explain why.

(a) $\lim_{x\to+\infty} [f(x) + 3g(x)]$

(b) $\lim_{x\to+\infty} [h(x) - 4g(x) + 1]$

(c) $\lim_{x\to+\infty} [f(x)g(x)]$

(d) $\lim_{x\to+\infty} [g(x)]^2$

(e) $\lim_{x\to+\infty} \sqrt[3]{5 + f(x)}$

(f) $\lim_{x\to+\infty} \dfrac{3}{g(x)}$

(g) $\lim_{x\to+\infty} \dfrac{3h(x) + 4}{x^2}$

(h) $\lim_{x\to+\infty} \dfrac{6f(x)}{5f(x) + 3g(x)}$

6. Given that
$$\lim_{x\to-\infty} f(x) = 7 \quad \text{and} \quad \lim_{x\to-\infty} g(x) = -6$$
find the limits that exist. If the limit does not exist, explain why.

(a) $\lim_{x\to-\infty} [2f(x) - g(x)]$ (b) $\lim_{x\to-\infty} [6f(x) + 7g(x)]$

(c) $\lim_{x\to-\infty} [x^2 + g(x)]$ (d) $\lim_{x\to-\infty} [x^2 g(x)]$

(e) $\lim_{x\to-\infty} \sqrt[3]{f(x)g(x)}$ (f) $\lim_{x\to-\infty} \frac{g(x)}{f(x)}$

(g) $\lim_{x\to-\infty} \left[f(x) + \frac{g(x)}{x}\right]$ (h) $\lim_{x\to-\infty} \frac{xf(x)}{(2x+3)g(x)}$

7. Complete the table and make a guess about the limit indicated.
$$f(x) = \frac{\sqrt{x^2+x}}{x+1} \qquad \lim_{x\to+\infty} f(x)$$

| $x$ | 10 | 100 | 1000 | 10,000 | 100,000 | 1,000,000 |
|---|---|---|---|---|---|---|
| $f(x)$ | | | | | | |

8. Complete the table and make a guess about the limit indicated.
$$f(x) = \frac{\sqrt{x^2+x}}{x+1} \qquad \lim_{x\to-\infty} f(x)$$

| $x$ | −10 | −100 | −1000 | −10,000 | −100,000 | −1,000,000 |
|---|---|---|---|---|---|---|
| $f(x)$ | | | | | | |

**9–32** Find the limits. ■

9. $\lim_{x\to+\infty} (1 + 2x - 3x^5)$

10. $\lim_{x\to+\infty} (2x^3 - 100x + 5)$

11. $\lim_{x\to+\infty} \sqrt{x}$

12. $\lim_{x\to-\infty} \sqrt{5-x}$

13. $\lim_{x\to+\infty} \frac{3x+1}{2x-5}$

14. $\lim_{x\to+\infty} \frac{5x^2-4x}{2x^2+3}$

15. $\lim_{y\to-\infty} \frac{3}{y+4}$

16. $\lim_{x\to+\infty} \frac{1}{x-12}$

17. $\lim_{x\to-\infty} \frac{x-2}{x^2+2x+1}$

18. $\lim_{x\to+\infty} \frac{5x^2+7}{3x^2-x}$

19. $\lim_{x\to+\infty} \frac{7-6x^5}{x+3}$

20. $\lim_{t\to-\infty} \frac{5-2t^3}{t^2+1}$

21. $\lim_{t\to+\infty} \frac{6-t^3}{7t^3+3}$

22. $\lim_{x\to-\infty} \frac{x+4x^3}{1-x^2+7x^3}$

23. $\lim_{x\to+\infty} \sqrt[3]{\frac{2+3x-5x^2}{1+8x^2}}$

24. $\lim_{s\to+\infty} \sqrt[3]{\frac{3s^7-4s^5}{2s^7+1}}$

25. $\lim_{x\to-\infty} \frac{\sqrt{5x^2-2}}{x+3}$

26. $\lim_{x\to+\infty} \frac{\sqrt{5x^2-2}}{x+3}$

27. $\lim_{y\to-\infty} \frac{2-y}{\sqrt{7+6y^2}}$

28. $\lim_{y\to+\infty} \frac{2-y}{\sqrt{7+6y^2}}$

29. $\lim_{x\to-\infty} \frac{\sqrt{3x^4+x}}{x^2-8}$

30. $\lim_{x\to+\infty} \frac{\sqrt{3x^4+x}}{x^2-8}$

31. $\lim_{x\to+\infty} (\sqrt{x^2+3} - x)$

32. $\lim_{x\to+\infty} (\sqrt{x^2-3x} - x)$

**33–36 True–False** Determine whether the statement is true or false. Explain your answer. ■

33. By subtraction, $\lim_{x\to+\infty} (x^2 - 1000x) = \infty - \infty = 0$.

34. If $y = L$ is a horizontal asymptote for the curve $y = f(x)$, then
$$\lim_{x\to-\infty} f(x) = L \quad \text{and} \quad \lim_{x\to+\infty} f(x) = L$$

35. If $y = L$ is a horizontal asymptote for the curve $y = f(x)$, then it is possible for the graph of $f$ to intersect the line $y = L$ infinitely many times.

36. If a rational function $p(x)/q(x)$ has a horizontal asymptote, then the degree of $p(x)$ must equal the degree of $q(x)$.

**FOCUS ON CONCEPTS**

37. Assume that a particle is accelerated by a constant force. The two curves $v = n(t)$ and $v = e(t)$ in the accompanying figure provide velocity versus time curves for the particle as predicted by classical physics and by the special theory of relativity, respectively. The parameter $c$ represents the speed of light. Using the language of limits, describe the differences in the long-term predictions of the two theories.

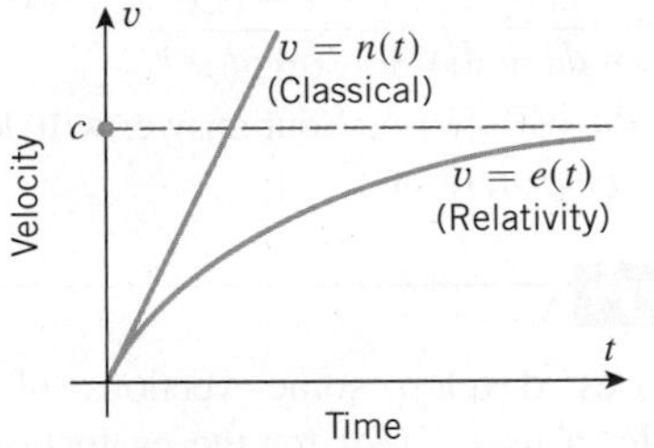


◄ **Figure Ex-37**

38. Let $T = f(t)$ denote the temperature of a baked potato $t$ minutes after it has been removed from a hot oven. The accompanying figure shows the temperature versus time curve for the potato, where $r$ is the temperature of the room.

(a) What is the physical significance of $\lim_{t\to 0^+} f(t)$?

(b) What is the physical significance of $\lim_{t\to+\infty} f(t)$?

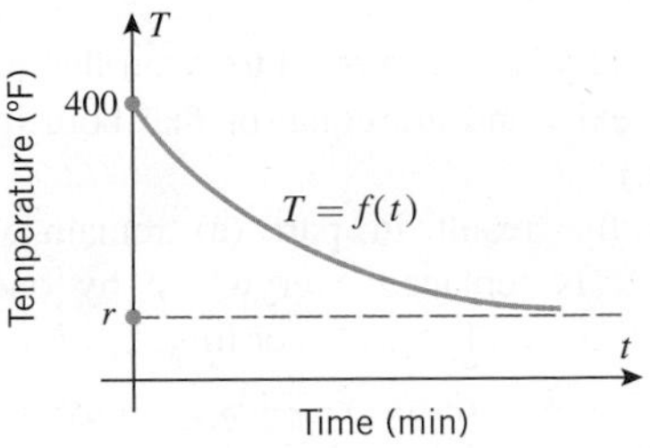


◄ **Figure Ex-38**

39. Let
$$f(x) = \begin{cases} 2x^2 + 5, & x < 0 \\ \dfrac{3-5x^3}{1+4x+x^3}, & x \geq 0 \end{cases}$$

(cont.)

Find
(a) $\lim_{x \to -\infty} f(x)$ (b) $\lim_{x \to +\infty} f(x)$.

**40.** Let

$$g(t) = \begin{cases} \dfrac{2+3t}{5t^2+6}, & t < 1{,}000{,}000 \\ \dfrac{\sqrt{36t^2-100}}{5-t}, & t > 1{,}000{,}000 \end{cases}$$

Find
(a) $\lim_{t \to -\infty} g(t)$ (b) $\lim_{t \to +\infty} g(t)$.

**41.** Discuss the limits of $p(x) = (1-x)^n$ as $x \to +\infty$ and $x \to -\infty$ for positive integer values of $n$.

**42.** In each part, find examples of polynomials $p(x)$ and $q(x)$ that satisfy the stated condition and such that $p(x) \to +\infty$ and $q(x) \to +\infty$ as $x \to +\infty$.
(a) $\lim_{x \to +\infty} \dfrac{p(x)}{q(x)} = 1$ (b) $\lim_{x \to +\infty} \dfrac{p(x)}{q(x)} = 0$
(c) $\lim_{x \to +\infty} \dfrac{p(x)}{q(x)} = +\infty$ (d) $\lim_{x \to +\infty} [p(x) - q(x)] = 3$

**43.** (a) Do any of the trigonometric functions $\sin x$, $\cos x$, $\tan x$, $\cot x$, $\sec x$, and $\csc x$ have horizontal asymptotes?
(b) Do any of the trigonometric functions have vertical asymptotes? Where?

**44.** Find
$$\lim_{x \to +\infty} \frac{c_0 + c_1 x + \cdots + c_n x^n}{d_0 + d_1 x + \cdots + d_m x^m}$$
where $c_n \neq 0$ and $d_m \neq 0$. [*Hint:* Your answer will depend on whether $m < n$, $m = n$, or $m > n$.]

**FOCUS ON CONCEPTS**

**45–46** These exercises develop some versions of the ***substitution principle***, a useful tool for the evaluation of limits. ■

**45.** (a) Suppose $g(x) \to +\infty$ as $x \to +\infty$. Given any function $f(x)$, explain why we can evaluate $\lim_{x \to +\infty} f[g(x)]$ by substituting $t = g(x)$ and writing
$$\lim_{x \to +\infty} f[g(x)] = \lim_{t \to +\infty} f(t)$$
(Here, "equality" is interpreted to mean that either both limits exist and are equal or that both limits fail to exist.)
(b) Why does the result in part (a) remain valid if $\lim_{x \to +\infty}$ is replaced everywhere by one of $\lim_{x \to -\infty}$, $\lim_{x \to c}$, $\lim_{x \to c^-}$, or $\lim_{x \to c^+}$?

**46.** (a) Suppose $g(x) \to -\infty$ as $x \to +\infty$. Given any function $f(x)$, explain why we can evaluate $\lim_{x \to +\infty} f[g(x)]$ by substituting $t = g(x)$ and writing
$$\lim_{x \to +\infty} f[g(x)] = \lim_{t \to -\infty} f(t)$$
(Here, "equality" is interpreted to mean that either both limits exist and are equal or that both limits fail to exist.)
(b) Why does the result in part (a) remain valid if $\lim_{x \to +\infty}$ is replaced everywhere by one of $\lim_{x \to -\infty}$, $\lim_{x \to c}$, $\lim_{x \to c^-}$, or $\lim_{x \to c^+}$?

**47–50** Given that
$$\lim_{x \to -\infty} f(x) = 0 \quad \text{and} \quad \lim_{x \to +\infty} f(x) = +\infty$$
evaluate the limit using an appropriate substitution. ■

**47.** $\lim_{x \to 0^+} f(1/x)$ **48.** $\lim_{x \to 0^-} f(1/x)$

**49.** $\lim_{x \to 0^+} f(\csc x)$ **50.** $\lim_{x \to 0^-} f(\csc x)$

**51–55** The notion of an asymptote can be extended to include curves as well as lines. Specifically, we say that curves $y = f(x)$ and $y = g(x)$ are ***asymptotic as*** $x \to +\infty$ provided
$$\lim_{x \to +\infty} [f(x) - g(x)] = 0$$
and are ***asymptotic as*** $x \to -\infty$ provided
$$\lim_{x \to -\infty} [f(x) - g(x)] = 0$$
In these exercises, determine a simpler function $g(x)$ such that $y = f(x)$ is asymptotic to $y = g(x)$ as $x \to +\infty$ or $x \to -\infty$. Use a graphing utility to generate the graphs of $y = f(x)$ and $y = g(x)$ and identify all vertical asymptotes. ■

**51.** $f(x) = \dfrac{x^2 - 2}{x - 2}$ [*Hint:* Divide $x - 2$ into $x^2 - 2$.]

**52.** $f(x) = \dfrac{x^3 - x + 3}{x}$ **53.** $f(x) = \dfrac{-x^3 + 3x^2 + x - 1}{x - 3}$

**54.** $f(x) = \dfrac{x^5 - x^3 + 3}{x^2 - 1}$ **55.** $f(x) = \sin x + \dfrac{1}{x - 1}$

**56. Writing** In some models for learning a skill (e.g., juggling), it is assumed that the skill level for an individual increases with practice but cannot become arbitrarily high. How do the concepts of this section apply to such a model?

**57. Writing** In some population models it is assumed that a given ecological system possesses a ***carrying capacity*** $L$. Populations greater than the carrying capacity tend to decline toward $L$, while populations less than the carrying capacity tend to increase toward $L$. Explain why these assumptions are reasonable, and discuss how the concepts of this section apply to such a model.

✓ **QUICK CHECK ANSWERS 1.3** 1. (a) $-\infty$ (b) $-1$ (c) $+\infty$ (d) 5 2. (a) $\frac{1}{2}$ (b) does not exist 3. (a) 9 (b) $-\frac{2}{3}$ (c) does not exist (d) 4 4. The graphs of $y = 1/(x+1)$ and $y = x/(x+1)$ have horizontal asymptotes.

## 1.4 LIMITS (DISCUSSED MORE RIGOROUSLY)

*In the previous sections of this chapter we focused on the discovery of values of limits, either by sampling selected x-values or by applying limit theorems that were stated without proof. Our main goal in this section is to define the notion of a limit precisely, thereby making it possible to establish limits with certainty and to prove theorems about them. This will also provide us with a deeper understanding of some of the more subtle properties of functions.*

### MOTIVATION FOR THE DEFINITION OF A TWO-SIDED LIMIT

The statement $\lim_{x\to a} f(x) = L$ can be interpreted informally to mean that we can make the value of $f(x)$ as close as we like to the real number $L$ by making the value of $x$ sufficiently close to $a$. It is our goal to make the informal phrases "as close as we like to $L$" and "sufficiently close to $a$" mathematically precise.

To do this, consider the function $f$ graphed in Figure 1.4.1$a$ for which $f(x)\to L$ as $x\to a$. For visual simplicity we have drawn the graph of $f$ to be increasing on an open interval containing $a$, and we have intentionally placed a hole in the graph at $x = a$ to emphasize that $f$ need not be defined at $x = a$ to have a limit there.

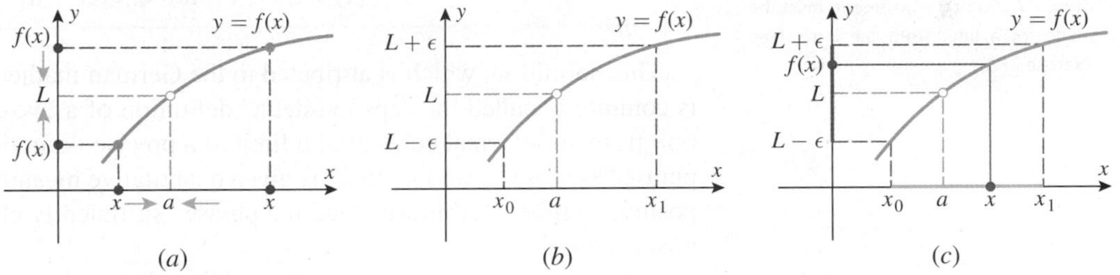


▲ **Figure 1.4.1**

Next, let us choose any positive number $\epsilon$ and ask how close $x$ must be to $a$ in order for the values of $f(x)$ to be within $\epsilon$ units of $L$. We can answer this geometrically by drawing horizontal lines from the points $L + \epsilon$ and $L - \epsilon$ on the $y$-axis until they meet the curve $y = f(x)$, and then drawing vertical lines from those points on the curve to the $x$-axis (Figure 1.4.1$b$). As indicated in the figure, let $x_0$ and $x_1$ be the points where those vertical lines intersect the $x$-axis.

Now imagine that $x$ gets closer and closer to $a$ (from either side). Eventually, $x$ will lie inside the interval $(x_0, x_1)$, which is marked in green in Figure 1.4.1$c$; and when this happens, the value of $f(x)$ will fall between $L - \epsilon$ and $L + \epsilon$, marked in red in the figure. Thus, we conclude:

*If $f(x)\to L$ as $x\to a$, then for any positive number $\epsilon$, we can find an open interval $(x_0, x_1)$ on the x-axis that contains a and has the property that for each x in that interval (except possibly for $x = a$), the value of $f(x)$ is between $L - \epsilon$ and $L + \epsilon$.*

What is important about this result is that it holds no matter how small we make $\epsilon$. However, making $\epsilon$ smaller and smaller forces $f(x)$ *closer and closer* to $L$—which is precisely the concept we were trying to capture mathematically.

Observe that in Figure 1.4.1 the interval $(x_0, x_1)$ extends farther on the right side of $a$ than on the left side. However, for many purposes it is preferable to have an interval that extends the same distance on both sides of $a$. For this purpose, let us choose any positive number $\delta$ that is smaller than both $x_1 - a$ and $a - x_0$, and consider the interval

$$(a - \delta, a + \delta)$$

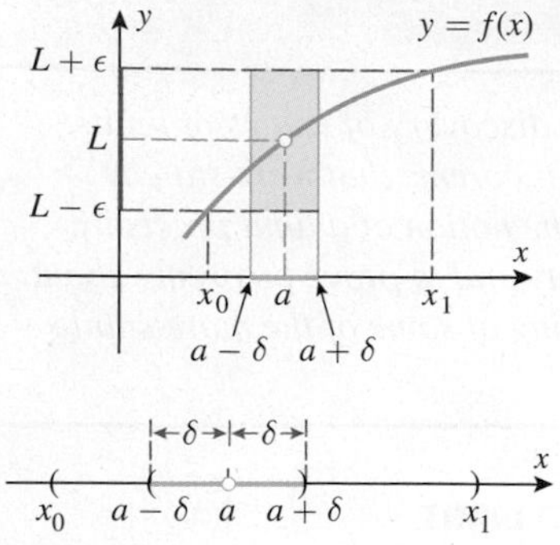


▲ **Figure 1.4.2**

This interval extends the same distance $\delta$ on both sides of $a$ and lies inside of the interval $(x_0, x_1)$ (Figure 1.4.2). Moreover, the condition

$$L - \epsilon < f(x) < L + \epsilon \tag{1}$$

holds for every $x$ in this interval (except possibly $x = a$), since this condition holds on the larger interval $(x_0, x_1)$.

Since (1) can be expressed as

$$|f(x) - L| < \epsilon$$

and the condition that $x$ lies in the interval $(a - \delta, a + \delta)$, but $x \neq a$, can be expressed as

$$0 < |x - a| < \delta$$

we are led to the following precise definition of a two-sided limit.

The definitions of one-sided limits require minor adjustments to Definition 1.4.1. For example, for a limit from the right we need only assume that $f(x)$ is defined on an interval $(a, b)$ extending to the right of $a$ and that the $\epsilon$ condition is met for $x$ in an interval $a < x < a + \delta$ extending to the right of $a$. A similar adjustment must be made for a limit from the left. (See Exercise 27.)

**1.4.1 LIMIT DEFINITION** Let $f(x)$ be defined for all $x$ in some open interval containing the number $a$, with the possible exception that $f(x)$ need not be defined at $a$. We will write

$$\lim_{x \to a} f(x) = L$$

if given any number $\epsilon > 0$ we can find a number $\delta > 0$ such that

$$|f(x) - L| < \epsilon \quad \text{if} \quad 0 < |x - a| < \delta$$

This definition, which is attributed to the German mathematician Karl Weierstrass and is commonly called the "epsilon-delta" definition of a two-sided limit, makes the transition from an informal concept of a limit to a precise definition. Specifically, the informal phrase "as close as we like to $L$" is given quantitative meaning by our ability to choose the positive number $\epsilon$ arbitrarily, and the phrase "sufficiently close to $a$" is quantified by the positive number $\delta$.

In the preceding sections we illustrated various numerical and graphical methods for *guessing* at limits. Now that we have a precise definition to work with, we can actually confirm the validity of those guesses with mathematical proof. Here is a typical example of such a proof.

▶ **Example 1** Use Definition 1.4.1 to prove that $\lim_{x \to 2} (3x - 5) = 1$.

***Solution.*** We must show that given any positive number $\epsilon$, we can find a positive number $\delta$ such that

$$|\underbrace{(3x - 5)}_{f(x)} - \underbrace{1}_{L}| < \epsilon \quad \text{if} \quad 0 < |x - \underbrace{2}_{a}| < \delta \tag{2}$$

**Karl Weierstrass (1815–1897)** Weierstrass, the son of a customs officer, was born in Ostenfelde, Germany. As a youth Weierstrass showed outstanding skills in languages and mathematics. However, at the urging of his dominant father, Weierstrass entered the law and commerce program at the University of Bonn. To the chagrin of his family, the rugged and congenial young man concentrated instead on fencing and beer drinking. Four years later he returned home without a degree. In 1839 Weierstrass entered the Academy of Münster to study for a career in secondary education, and he met and studied under an excellent mathematician named Christof Gudermann. Gudermann's ideas greatly influenced the work of Weierstrass. After receiving his teaching certificate, Weierstrass spent the next 15 years in secondary education teaching German, geography, and mathematics. In addition, he taught handwriting to small children. During this period much of Weierstrass's mathematical work was ignored because he was a secondary schoolteacher and not a college professor. Then, in 1854, he published a paper of major importance that created a sensation in the mathematics world and catapulted him to international fame overnight. He was immediately given an honorary Doctorate at the University of Königsberg and began a new career in college teaching at the University of Berlin in 1856. In 1859 the strain of his mathematical research caused a temporary nervous breakdown and led to spells of dizziness that plagued him for the rest of his life. Weierstrass was a brilliant teacher and his classes overflowed with multitudes of auditors. In spite of his fame, he never lost his early beer-drinking congeniality and was always in the company of students, both ordinary and brilliant. Weierstrass was acknowledged as the leading mathematical analyst in the world. He and his students opened the door to the modern school of mathematical analysis.

*[Image: © Universitätsbibliothek der Humboldt-Universität zu Berlin, Porträtsammlung: Weierstraß, Karl]*

There are two things to do. First, we must *discover* a value of $\delta$ for which this statement holds, and then we must *prove* that the statement holds for that $\delta$. For the discovery part we begin by simplifying (2) and writing it as

$$|3x - 6| < \epsilon \quad \text{if} \quad 0 < |x - 2| < \delta$$

Next we will rewrite this statement in a form that will facilitate the discovery of an appropriate $\delta$:

$$\begin{aligned} 3|x - 2| &< \epsilon \quad \text{if} \quad 0 < |x - 2| < \delta \\ |x - 2| &< \epsilon/3 \quad \text{if} \quad 0 < |x - 2| < \delta \end{aligned} \tag{3}$$

It should be self-evident that this last statement holds if $\delta = \epsilon/3$, which completes the discovery portion of our work. Now we need to prove that (2) holds for this choice of $\delta$. However, statement (2) is equivalent to (3), and (3) holds with $\delta = \epsilon/3$, so (2) also holds with $\delta = \epsilon/3$. This proves that $\lim_{x\to 2} (3x - 5) = 1$. ◀

**REMARK** This example illustrates the general form of a limit proof: We *assume* that we are given a positive number $\epsilon$, and we try to *prove* that we can find a positive number $\delta$ such that

$$|f(x) - L| < \epsilon \quad \text{if} \quad 0 < |x - a| < \delta \tag{4}$$

This is done by first discovering $\delta$, and then proving that the discovered $\delta$ works. Since the argument has to be general enough to work for all positive values of $\epsilon$, the quantity $\delta$ has to be expressed as a function of $\epsilon$. In Example 1 we found the function $\delta = \epsilon/3$ by some simple algebra; however, most limit proofs require a little more algebraic and logical ingenuity. Thus, if you find our ensuing discussion of "$\epsilon$-$\delta$" proofs challenging, do not become discouraged; the concepts and techniques are intrinsically difficult. In fact, a precise understanding of limits evaded the finest mathematical minds for more than 150 years after the basic concepts of calculus were discovered.

▶ **Example 2** Prove that $\lim_{x\to 0^+} \sqrt{x} = 0$.

***Solution.*** Note that the domain of $\sqrt{x}$ is $0 \le x$, so it is valid to discuss the limit as $x\to 0^+$. We must show that given $\epsilon > 0$, there exists a $\delta > 0$ such that

$$|\sqrt{x} - 0| < \epsilon \quad \text{if} \quad 0 < x - 0 < \delta$$

or more simply,

$$\sqrt{x} < \epsilon \quad \text{if} \quad 0 < x < \delta \tag{5}$$

But, by squaring both sides of the inequality $\sqrt{x} < \epsilon$, we can rewrite (5) as

$$x < \epsilon^2 \quad \text{if} \quad 0 < x < \delta \tag{6}$$

It should be self-evident that (6) is true if $\delta = \epsilon^2$; and since (6) is a reformulation of (5), we have shown that (5) holds with $\delta = \epsilon^2$. This proves that $\lim_{x\to 0^+} \sqrt{x} = 0$. ◀

In Example 2 the limit from the left and the two-sided limit do not exist at $x = 0$ because $\sqrt{x}$ is defined only for nonnegative values of $x$.

## THE VALUE OF $\delta$ IS NOT UNIQUE

In preparation for our next example, we note that the value of $\delta$ in Definition 1.4.1 is not unique; once we have found a value of $\delta$ that fulfills the requirements of the definition, then any *smaller* positive number $\delta_1$ will also fulfill those requirements. That is, if it is true that

$$|f(x) - L| < \epsilon \quad \text{if} \quad 0 < |x - a| < \delta$$

then it will also be true that

$$|f(x) - L| < \epsilon \quad \text{if} \quad 0 < |x - a| < \delta_1$$

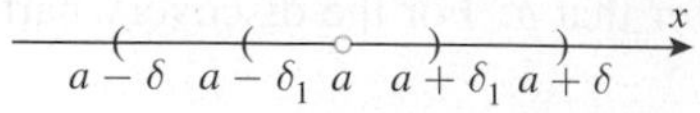


▲ Figure 1.4.3

This is because $\{x : 0 < |x - a| < \delta_1\}$ is a subset of $\{x : 0 < |x - a| < \delta\}$ (Figure 1.4.3), and hence if $|f(x) - L| < \epsilon$ is satisfied for all $x$ in the larger set, then it will automatically be satisfied for all $x$ in the subset. Thus, in Example 1, where we used $\delta = \epsilon/3$, we could have used any smaller value of $\delta$ such as $\delta = \epsilon/4$, $\delta = \epsilon/5$, or $\delta = \epsilon/6$.

▶ **Example 3** Prove that $\lim_{x\to 3} x^2 = 9$.

***Solution.*** We must show that given any positive number $\epsilon$, we can find a positive number $\delta$ such that

$$|x^2 - 9| < \epsilon \quad \text{if} \quad 0 < |x - 3| < \delta \tag{7}$$

Because $|x - 3|$ occurs on the right side of this "if statement," it will be helpful to factor the left side to introduce a factor of $|x - 3|$. This yields the following alternative form of (7):

$$|x + 3||x - 3| < \epsilon \quad \text{if} \quad 0 < |x - 3| < \delta \tag{8}$$

If you are wondering how we knew to make the restriction $\delta \le 1$, as opposed to $\delta \le 5$ or $\delta \le \frac{1}{2}$, for example, the answer is that 1 is merely a convenient choice—any restriction of the form $\delta \le c$ would work equally well.

We wish to bound the factor $|x + 3|$. If we knew, for example, that $\delta \le 1$, then we would have $-1 < x - 3 < 1$, so $5 < x + 3 < 7$, and consequently $|x + 3| < 7$. Thus, if $\delta \le 1$ and $0 < |x - 3| < \delta$, then

$$|x + 3||x - 3| < 7\delta$$

It follows that (8) will be satisfied for any positive $\delta$ such that $\delta \le 1$ and $7\delta < \epsilon$. We can achieve this by taking $\delta$ to be the minimum of the numbers 1 and $\epsilon/7$, which is sometimes written as $\delta = \min(1, \epsilon/7)$. This proves that $\lim_{x\to 3} x^2 = 9$. ◀

## LIMITS AS $x \to \pm\infty$

In Section 1.3 we discussed the limits

$$\lim_{x\to +\infty} f(x) = L \quad \text{and} \quad \lim_{x\to -\infty} f(x) = L$$

from an intuitive point of view. The first limit can be interpreted to mean that we can make the value of $f(x)$ as close as we like to $L$ by taking $x$ sufficiently large, and the second can be interpreted to mean that we can make the value of $f(x)$ as close as we like to $L$ by taking $x$ sufficiently far to the left of 0. These ideas are captured in the following definitions and are illustrated in Figure 1.4.4.

**1.4.2 DEFINITION** Let $f(x)$ be defined for all $x$ in some infinite open interval extending in the positive $x$-direction. We will write

$$\lim_{x\to +\infty} f(x) = L$$

if given any number $\epsilon > 0$, there corresponds a positive number $N$ such that

$$|f(x) - L| < \epsilon \quad \text{if} \quad x > N$$

**1.4.3 DEFINITION** Let $f(x)$ be defined for all $x$ in some infinite open interval extending in the negative $x$-direction. We will write

$$\lim_{x\to -\infty} f(x) = L$$

if given any number $\epsilon > 0$, there corresponds a negative number $N$ such that

$$|f(x) - L| < \epsilon \quad \text{if} \quad x < N$$

To see how these definitions relate to our informal concepts of these limits, suppose that $f(x) \to L$ as $x \to +\infty$, and for a given $\epsilon$ let $N$ be the positive number described in Definition 1.4.2. If $x$ is allowed to increase indefinitely, then eventually $x$ will lie in the interval

$(N, +\infty)$, which is marked in green in Figure 1.4.4*a*; when this happens, the value of $f(x)$ will fall between $L - \epsilon$ and $L + \epsilon$, marked in red in the figure. Since this is true for all positive values of $\epsilon$ (no matter how small), we can force the values of $f(x)$ as close as we like to $L$ by making $N$ sufficiently large. This agrees with our informal concept of this limit. Similarly, Figure 1.4.4*b* illustrates Definition 1.4.3.

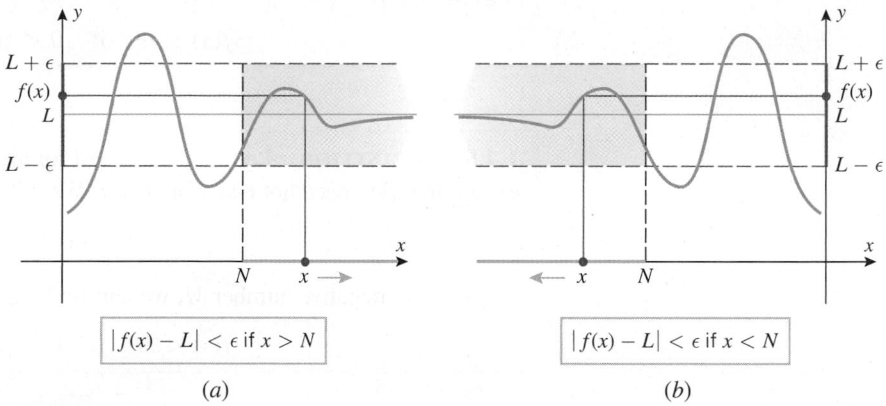


▲ **Figure 1.4.4**

▶ **Example 4** Prove that $\lim\limits_{x \to +\infty} \dfrac{1}{x} = 0$.

***Solution.*** Applying Definition 1.4.2 with $f(x) = 1/x$ and $L = 0$, we must show that given $\epsilon > 0$, we can find a number $N > 0$ such that

$$\left|\frac{1}{x} - 0\right| < \epsilon \quad \text{if} \quad x > N \tag{9}$$

Because $x \to +\infty$ we can assume that $x > 0$. Thus, we can eliminate the absolute values in this statement and rewrite it as

$$\frac{1}{x} < \epsilon \quad \text{if} \quad x > N$$

or, on taking reciprocals,

$$x > \frac{1}{\epsilon} \quad \text{if} \quad x > N \tag{10}$$

It is self-evident that $N = 1/\epsilon$ satisfies this requirement, and since (10) and (9) are equivalent for $x > 0$, the proof is complete. ◀

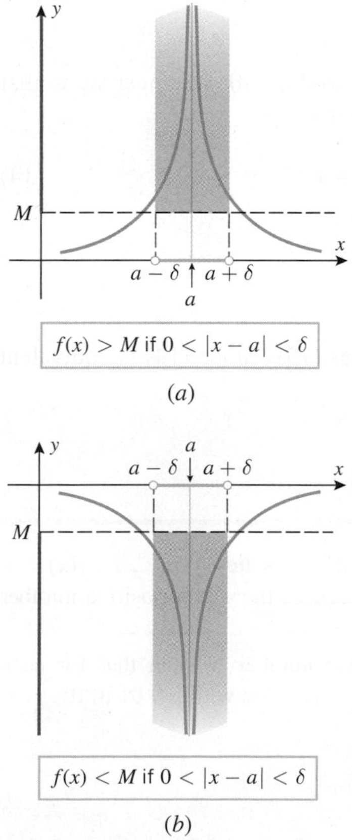


▲ **Figure 1.4.5**

## INFINITE LIMITS

In Section 1.1 we discussed limits of the following type from an intuitive viewpoint:

$$\lim_{x \to a} f(x) = +\infty, \qquad \lim_{x \to a} f(x) = -\infty \tag{11}$$

$$\lim_{x \to a^+} f(x) = +\infty, \qquad \lim_{x \to a^+} f(x) = -\infty \tag{12}$$

$$\lim_{x \to a^-} f(x) = +\infty, \qquad \lim_{x \to a^-} f(x) = -\infty \tag{13}$$

Recall that each of these expressions describes a particular way in which the limit fails to exist. The $+\infty$ indicates that the limit fails to exist because $f(x)$ increases without bound, and the $-\infty$ indicates that the limit fails to exist because $f(x)$ decreases without bound. These ideas are captured more precisely in the following definitions and are illustrated in Figure 1.4.5.

**1.4.4 DEFINITION** Let $f(x)$ be defined for all $x$ in some open interval containing $a$, except that $f(x)$ need not be defined at $a$. We will write

$$\lim_{x \to a} f(x) = +\infty$$

if given any positive number $M$, we can find a number $\delta > 0$ such that $f(x)$ satisfies

$$f(x) > M \quad \text{if} \quad 0 < |x - a| < \delta$$

**1.4.5 DEFINITION** Let $f(x)$ be defined for all $x$ in some open interval containing $a$, except that $f(x)$ need not be defined at $a$. We will write

$$\lim_{x \to a} f(x) = -\infty$$

if given any negative number $M$, we can find a number $\delta > 0$ such that $f(x)$ satisfies

$$f(x) < M \quad \text{if} \quad 0 < |x - a| < \delta$$

To see how these definitions relate to our informal concepts of these limits, suppose that $f(x) \to +\infty$ as $x \to a$, and for a given $M$ let $\delta$ be the corresponding positive number described in Definition 1.4.4. Next, imagine that $x$ gets closer and closer to $a$ (from either side). Eventually, $x$ will lie in the interval $(a - \delta, a + \delta)$, which is marked in green in Figure 1.4.5*a*; when this happens the value of $f(x)$ will be greater than $M$, marked in red in the figure. Since this is true for any positive value of $M$ (no matter how large), we can force the values of $f(x)$ to be as large as we like by making $x$ sufficiently close to $a$. This agrees with our informal concept of this limit. Similarly, Figure 1.4.5*b* illustrates Definition 1.4.5.

How would you define these limits?

$$\lim_{x \to a^+} f(x) = +\infty \qquad \lim_{x \to a^+} f(x) = -\infty$$
$$\lim_{x \to a^-} f(x) = +\infty \qquad \lim_{x \to a^-} f(x) = -\infty$$
$$\lim_{x \to +\infty} f(x) = +\infty \qquad \lim_{x \to +\infty} f(x) = -\infty$$
$$\lim_{x \to -\infty} f(x) = +\infty \qquad \lim_{x \to -\infty} f(x) = -\infty$$

► **Example 5** Prove that $\lim_{x \to 0} \dfrac{1}{x^2} = +\infty$.

***Solution.*** Applying Definition 1.4.4 with $f(x) = 1/x^2$ and $a = 0$, we must show that given a number $M > 0$, we can find a number $\delta > 0$ such that

$$\frac{1}{x^2} > M \quad \text{if} \quad 0 < |x - 0| < \delta \tag{14}$$

or, on taking reciprocals and simplifying,

$$x^2 < \frac{1}{M} \quad \text{if} \quad 0 < |x| < \delta \tag{15}$$

But $x^2 < 1/M$ if $|x| < 1/\sqrt{M}$, so that $\delta = 1/\sqrt{M}$ satisfies (15). Since (14) is equivalent to (15), the proof is complete. ◄

## ✓QUICK CHECK EXERCISES 1.4 (See page 40 for answers.)

1. The definition of a two-sided limit states: $\lim_{x \to a} f(x) = L$ if given any number ______ there is a number ______ such that $|f(x) - L| < \epsilon$ if ______.
2. Suppose that $f(x)$ is a function such that for any given $\epsilon > 0$, the condition $0 < |x - 1| < \epsilon/2$ guarantees that $|f(x) - 5| < \epsilon$. What limit results from this property?
3. Suppose that $\epsilon$ is any positive number. Find the largest value of $\delta$ such that $|5x - 10| < \epsilon$ if $0 < |x - 2| < \delta$.
4. The definition of limit at $+\infty$ states: $\lim_{x \to +\infty} f(x) = L$ if given any number ______ there is a positive number ______ such that $|f(x) - L| < \epsilon$ if ______.
5. Find the smallest positive number $N$ such that for each $x > N$, the value of $f(x) = 1/\sqrt{x}$ is within 0.01 of 0.

## EXERCISE SET 1.4 Graphing Utility

1. (a) Find the largest open interval, centered at the origin on the $x$-axis, such that for each $x$ in the interval the value of the function $f(x) = x + 2$ is within 0.1 unit of the number $f(0) = 2$.
   (b) Find the largest open interval, centered at $x = 3$, such that for each $x$ in the interval the value of the function $f(x) = 4x - 5$ is within 0.01 unit of the number $f(3) = 7$.
   (c) Find the largest open interval, centered at $x = 4$, such that for each $x$ in the interval the value of the function $f(x) = x^2$ is within 0.001 unit of the number $f(4) = 16$.

2. In each part, find the largest open interval, centered at $x = 0$, such that for each $x$ in the interval the value of $f(x) = 2x + 3$ is within $\epsilon$ units of the number $f(0) = 3$.
   (a) $\epsilon = 0.1$ (b) $\epsilon = 0.01$
   (c) $\epsilon = 0.0012$

3. (a) Find the values of $x_0$ and $x_1$ in the accompanying figure.
   (b) Find a positive number $\delta$ such that $|\sqrt{x} - 2| < 0.05$ if $0 < |x - 4| < \delta$.

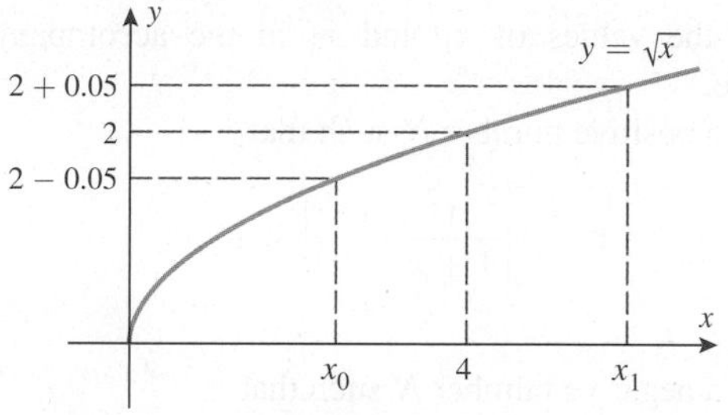


*Not drawn to scale*

▲ **Figure Ex-3**

4. (a) Find the values of $x_0$ and $x_1$ in the accompanying figure.
   (b) Find a positive number $\delta$ such that $|(1/x) - 1| < 0.1$ if $0 < |x - 1| < \delta$.

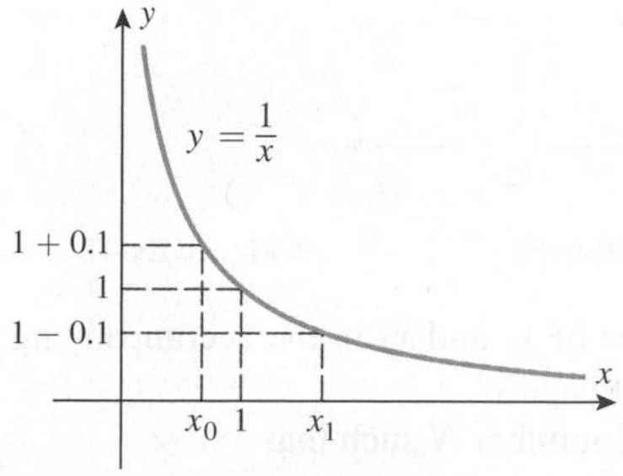


*Not drawn to scale* ◀ **Figure Ex-4**

5. Generate the graph of $f(x) = x^3 - 4x + 5$ with a graphing utility, and use the graph to find a number $\delta$ such that $|f(x) - 2| < 0.05$ if $0 < |x - 1| < \delta$. [*Hint:* Show that the inequality $|f(x) - 2| < 0.05$ can be rewritten as $1.95 < x^3 - 4x + 5 < 2.05$, and estimate the values of $x$ for which $x^3 - 4x + 5 = 1.95$ and $x^3 - 4x + 5 = 2.05$.]

6. Use the method of Exercise 5 to find a number $\delta$ such that $|\sqrt{5x + 1} - 4| < 0.5$ if $0 < |x - 3| < \delta$.

7. Let $f(x) = x + \sqrt{x}$ with $L = \lim_{x \to 1} f(x)$ and let $\epsilon = 0.2$. Use a graphing utility and its trace feature to find a positive number $\delta$ such that $|f(x) - L| < \epsilon$ if $0 < |x - 1| < \delta$.

8. Let $f(x) = (\sin 2x)/x$ and use a graphing utility to conjecture the value of $L = \lim_{x \to 0} f(x)$. Then let $\epsilon = 0.1$ and use the graphing utility and its trace feature to find a positive number $\delta$ such that $|f(x) - L| < \epsilon$ if $0 < |x| < \delta$.

**9–16** A positive number $\epsilon$ and the limit $L$ of a function $f$ at $a$ are given. Find a number $\delta$ such that $|f(x) - L| < \epsilon$ if $0 < |x - a| < \delta$. ■

9. $\lim_{x \to 4} 2x = 8$; $\epsilon = 0.1$
10. $\lim_{x \to 3} (5x - 2) = 13$; $\epsilon = 0.01$
11. $\lim_{x \to 3} \dfrac{x^2 - 9}{x - 3} = 6$; $\epsilon = 0.05$
12. $\lim_{x \to -1/2} \dfrac{4x^2 - 1}{2x + 1} = -2$; $\epsilon = 0.05$
13. $\lim_{x \to 2} x^3 = 8$; $\epsilon = 0.001$
14. $\lim_{x \to 4} \sqrt{x} = 2$; $\epsilon = 0.001$
15. $\lim_{x \to 5} \dfrac{1}{x} = \dfrac{1}{5}$; $\epsilon = 0.05$
16. $\lim_{x \to 0} |x| = 0$; $\epsilon = 0.05$

**17–26** Use Definition 1.4.1 to prove that the limit is correct. ■

17. $\lim_{x \to 2} 3 = 3$
18. $\lim_{x \to 4} (x + 2) = 6$
19. $\lim_{x \to 5} 3x = 15$
20. $\lim_{x \to -1} (7x + 5) = -2$
21. $\lim_{x \to 0} \dfrac{2x^2 + x}{x} = 1$
22. $\lim_{x \to -3} \dfrac{x^2 - 9}{x + 3} = -6$
23. $\lim_{x \to 1} f(x) = 3$, where $f(x) = \begin{cases} x + 2, & x \neq 1 \\ 10, & x = 1 \end{cases}$
24. $\lim_{x \to 2} f(x) = 5$, where $f(x) = \begin{cases} 9 - 2x, & x \neq 2 \\ 49, & x = 2 \end{cases}$
25. $\lim_{x \to 0} |x| = 0$
26. $\lim_{x \to 2} f(x) = 5$, where $f(x) = \begin{cases} 9 - 2x, & x < 2 \\ 3x - 1, & x > 2 \end{cases}$

**FOCUS ON CONCEPTS**

27. Give rigorous definitions of $\lim_{x \to a^+} f(x) = L$ and $\lim_{x \to a^-} f(x) = L$.

28. Consider the statement that $\lim_{x \to a} |f(x) - L| = 0$.
    (a) Using Definition 1.4.1, write down precisely what this limit statement means.

*(cont.)*

(b) Explain why your answer to part (a) shows that
$$\lim_{x\to a} |f(x) - L| = 0 \quad \text{if and only if} \quad \lim_{x\to a} f(x) = L$$

**29.** (a) Show that
$$|(3x^2 + 2x - 20) - 300| = |3x + 32| \cdot |x - 10|$$
(b) Find an upper bound for $|3x + 32|$ if $x$ satisfies $|x - 10| < 1$.
(c) Fill in the blanks to complete a proof that
$$\lim_{x\to 10} [3x^2 + 2x - 20] = 300$$
Suppose that $\epsilon > 0$. Set $\delta = \min(1, \_\_\_\_\_)$ and assume that $0 < |x - 10| < \delta$. Then
$$\begin{aligned}\left|(3x^2 + 2x - 20) - 300\right| &= |3x + 32| \cdot |x - 10| \\ &< \_\_\_\_\_ \cdot |x - 10| \\ &< \_\_\_\_\_ \cdot \_\_\_\_\_ \\ &= \epsilon\end{aligned}$$

**30.** (a) Show that
$$\left|\frac{28}{3x + 1} - 4\right| = \left|\frac{12}{3x + 1}\right| \cdot |x - 2|$$
(b) Is $|12/(3x + 1)|$ bounded if $|x - 2| < 4$? If not, explain; if so, give a bound.
(c) Is $|12/(3x + 1)|$ bounded if $|x - 2| < 1$? If not, explain; if so, give a bound.
(d) Fill in the blanks to complete a proof that
$$\lim_{x\to 2} \left[\frac{28}{3x + 1}\right] = 4$$
Suppose that $\epsilon > 0$. Set $\delta = \min(1, \_\_\_\_\_)$ and assume that $0 < |x - 2| < \delta$. Then
$$\begin{aligned}\left|\frac{28}{3x + 1} - 4\right| &= \left|\frac{12}{3x + 1}\right| \cdot |x - 2| \\ &< \_\_\_\_\_ \cdot |x - 2| \\ &< \_\_\_\_\_ \cdot \_\_\_\_\_ \\ &= \epsilon\end{aligned}$$

**31–36** Use Definition 1.4.1 to prove that the stated limit is correct. In each case, to show that $\lim_{x\to a} f(x) = L$, factor $|f(x) - L|$ in the form
$$|f(x) - L| = |\text{“something”}| \cdot |x - a|$$
and then bound the size of |“something”| by putting restrictions on the size of $\delta$. ■

**31.** $\lim_{x\to 1} 2x^2 = 2$ [*Hint:* Assume $\delta \le 1$.]

**32.** $\lim_{x\to 3} (x^2 + x) = 12$ [*Hint:* Assume $\delta \le 1$.]

**33.** $\lim_{x\to -2} \frac{1}{x + 1} = -1$

**34.** $\lim_{x\to 1/2} \frac{2x + 3}{x} = 8$

**35.** $\lim_{x\to 4} \sqrt{x} = 2$

**36.** $\lim_{x\to 2} x^3 = 8$

**37.** Let
$$f(x) = \begin{cases} 0, & \text{if } x \text{ is rational} \\ x, & \text{if } x \text{ is irrational} \end{cases}$$
Use Definition 1.4.1 to prove that $\lim_{x\to 0} f(x) = 0$.

**38.** Let
$$f(x) = \begin{cases} 0, & \text{if } x \text{ is rational} \\ 1, & \text{if } x \text{ is irrational} \end{cases}$$
Use Definition 1.4.1 to prove that $\lim_{x\to 0} f(x)$ does not exist. [*Hint:* Assume $\lim_{x\to 0} f(x) = L$ and apply Definition 1.4.1 with $\epsilon = \frac{1}{2}$ to conclude that $|1 - L| < \frac{1}{2}$ and $|L| = |0 - L| < \frac{1}{2}$. Then show $1 \le |1 - L| + |L|$ and derive a contradiction.]

**39.** (a) Find the smallest positive number $N$ such that for each $x$ in the interval $(N, +\infty)$, the value of the function $f(x) = 1/x^2$ is within 0.1 unit of $L = 0$.
(b) Find the smallest positive number $N$ such that for each $x$ in the interval $(N, +\infty)$, the value of $f(x) = x/(x + 1)$ is within 0.01 unit of $L = 1$.
(c) Find the largest negative number $N$ such that for each $x$ in the interval $(-\infty, N)$, the value of the function $f(x) = 1/x^3$ is within 0.001 unit of $L = 0$.
(d) Find the largest negative number $N$ such that for each $x$ in the interval $(-\infty, N)$, the value of the function $f(x) = x/(x + 1)$ is within 0.01 unit of $L = 1$.

**40.** In each part, find the smallest positive value of $N$ such that for each $x$ in the interval $(N, +\infty)$, the function $f(x) = 1/x^3$ is within $\epsilon$ units of the number $L = 0$.
(a) $\epsilon = 0.1$ (b) $\epsilon = 0.01$ (c) $\epsilon = 0.001$

**41.** (a) Find the values of $x_1$ and $x_2$ in the accompanying figure.
(b) Find a positive number $N$ such that
$$\left|\frac{x^2}{1 + x^2} - 1\right| < \epsilon$$
for $x > N$.
(c) Find a negative number $N$ such that
$$\left|\frac{x^2}{1 + x^2} - 1\right| < \epsilon$$
for $x < N$.

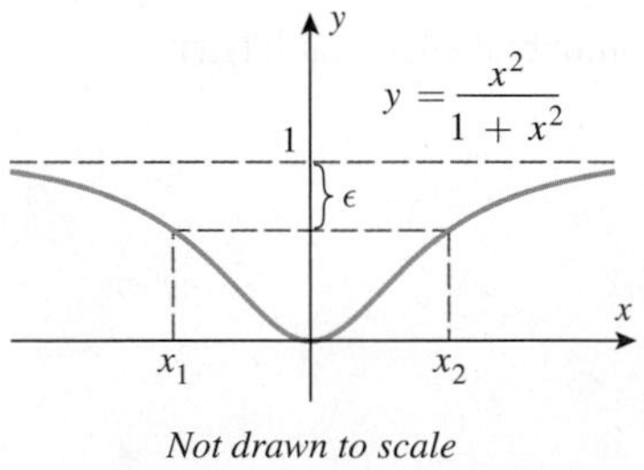


**Figure Ex-41**

**42.** (a) Find the values of $x_1$ and $x_2$ in the accompanying figure on the next page.
(b) Find a positive number $N$ such that
$$\left|\frac{1}{\sqrt[3]{x}} - 0\right| = \left|\frac{1}{\sqrt[3]{x}}\right| < \epsilon$$
for $x > N$.
(c) Find a negative number $N$ such that
$$\left|\frac{1}{\sqrt[3]{x}} - 0\right| = \left|\frac{1}{\sqrt[3]{x}}\right| < \epsilon$$
for $x < N$.

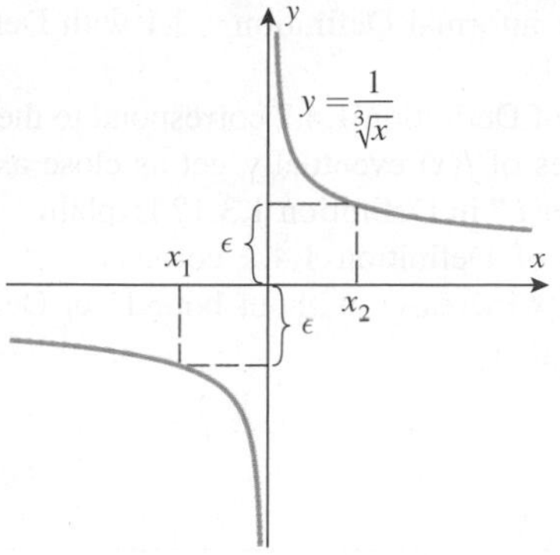


◄ Figure Ex-42

**43–46** A positive number $\epsilon$ and the limit $L$ of a function $f$ at $+\infty$ are given. Find a positive number $N$ such that if $x > N$ then $|f(x) - L| < \epsilon$. ■

**43.** $\lim_{x\to+\infty} \frac{1}{x^2} = 0;\ \epsilon = 0.01$

**44.** $\lim_{x\to+\infty} \frac{1}{x+2} = 0;\ \epsilon = 0.005$

**45.** $\lim_{x\to+\infty} \frac{x}{x+1} = 1;\ \epsilon = 0.001$

**46.** $\lim_{x\to+\infty} \frac{4x-1}{2x+5} = 2;\ \epsilon = 0.1$

**47–50** A positive number $\epsilon$ and the limit $L$ of a function $f$ at $-\infty$ are given. Find a negative number $N$ such that $|f(x) - L| < \epsilon$ if $x < N$. ■

**47.** $\lim_{x\to-\infty} \frac{1}{x+2} = 0;\ \epsilon = 0.005$

**48.** $\lim_{x\to-\infty} \frac{1}{x^2} = 0;\ \epsilon = 0.01$

**49.** $\lim_{x\to-\infty} \frac{4x-1}{2x+5} = 2;\ \epsilon = 0.1$

**50.** $\lim_{x\to-\infty} \frac{x}{x+1} = 1;\ \epsilon = 0.001$

**51–56** Use Definition 1.4.2 or 1.4.3 to prove that the stated limit is correct. ■

**51.** $\lim_{x\to+\infty} \frac{1}{x^2} = 0$

**52.** $\lim_{x\to+\infty} \frac{1}{x+2} = 0$

**53.** $\lim_{x\to-\infty} \frac{4x-1}{2x+5} = 2$

**54.** $\lim_{x\to-\infty} \frac{x}{x+1} = 1$

**55.** $\lim_{x\to+\infty} \frac{2\sqrt{x}}{\sqrt{x}-1} = 2$

**56.** $\lim_{x\to-\infty} \frac{\sqrt[3]{x}}{\sqrt[3]{x}+2} = 1$

**57.** (a) Find the largest open interval, centered at the origin on the $x$-axis, such that for each $x$ in the interval, other than the center, the values of $f(x) = 1/x^2$ are greater than 100.

(b) Find the largest open interval, centered at $x = 1$, such that for each $x$ in the interval, other than the center, the values of the function $f(x) = 1/|x - 1|$ are greater than 1000.

(c) Find the largest open interval, centered at $x = 3$, such that for each $x$ in the interval, other than the center, the values of the function $f(x) = -1/(x-3)^2$ are less than $-1000$.

(d) Find the largest open interval, centered at the origin on the $x$-axis, such that for each $x$ in the interval, other than the center, the values of $f(x) = -1/x^4$ are less than $-10{,}000$.

**58.** In each part, find the largest open interval centered at $x = 1$, such that for each $x$ in the interval, other than the center, the value of $f(x) = 1/(x-1)^2$ is greater than $M$.
(a) $M = 10$ (b) $M = 1000$ (c) $M = 100{,}000$

**59–64** Use Definition 1.4.4 or 1.4.5 to prove that the stated limit is correct. ■

**59.** $\lim_{x\to 3} \frac{1}{(x-3)^2} = +\infty$

**60.** $\lim_{x\to 3} \frac{-1}{(x-3)^2} = -\infty$

**61.** $\lim_{x\to 0} \frac{1}{|x|} = +\infty$

**62.** $\lim_{x\to 1} \frac{1}{|x-1|} = +\infty$

**63.** $\lim_{x\to 0} \left(-\frac{1}{x^4}\right) = -\infty$

**64.** $\lim_{x\to 0} \frac{1}{x^4} = +\infty$

**65–70** Use the definitions in Exercise 27 to prove that the stated one-sided limit is correct. ■

**65.** $\lim_{x\to 2^+} (x+1) = 3$

**66.** $\lim_{x\to 1^-} (3x+2) = 5$

**67.** $\lim_{x\to 4^+} \sqrt{x-4} = 0$

**68.** $\lim_{x\to 0^-} \sqrt{-x} = 0$

**69.** $\lim_{x\to 2^+} f(x) = 2$, where $f(x) = \begin{cases} x, & x > 2 \\ 3x, & x \le 2 \end{cases}$

**70.** $\lim_{x\to 2^-} f(x) = 6$, where $f(x) = \begin{cases} x, & x > 2 \\ 3x, & x \le 2 \end{cases}$

**71–74** Write out the definition for the corresponding limit in the marginal note on page 36, and use your definition to prove that the stated limit is correct. ■

**71.** (a) $\lim_{x\to 1^+} \frac{1}{1-x} = -\infty$ (b) $\lim_{x\to 1^-} \frac{1}{1-x} = +\infty$

**72.** (a) $\lim_{x\to 0^+} \frac{1}{x} = +\infty$ (b) $\lim_{x\to 0^-} \frac{1}{x} = -\infty$

**73.** (a) $\lim_{x\to+\infty} (x+1) = +\infty$ (b) $\lim_{x\to-\infty} (x+1) = -\infty$

**74.** (a) $\lim_{x\to+\infty} (x^2-3) = +\infty$ (b) $\lim_{x\to-\infty} (x^3+5) = -\infty$

**75.** According to Ohm's law, when a voltage of $V$ volts is applied across a resistor with a resistance of $R$ ohms, a current of $I = V/R$ amperes flows through the resistor.

(a) How much current flows if a voltage of 3.0 volts is applied across a resistance of 7.5 ohms?

(b) If the resistance varies by $\pm 0.1$ ohm, and the voltage remains constant at 3.0 volts, what is the resulting range of values for the current?

(c) If temperature variations cause the resistance to vary by $\pm\delta$ from its value of 7.5 ohms, and the voltage remains constant at 3.0 volts, what is the resulting range of values for the current?

(d) If the current is not allowed to vary by more than $\epsilon = \pm 0.001$ ampere at a voltage of 3.0 volts, what variation of $\pm\delta$ from the value of 7.5 ohms is allowable?

(e) Certain alloys become ***superconductors*** as their temperature approaches absolute zero ($-273^\circ$C), meaning that their resistance approaches zero. If the voltage remains constant, what happens to the current in a superconductor as $R \to 0^+$?

**76. Writing** Compare informal Definition 1.1.1 with Definition 1.4.1.
(a) What portions of Definition 1.4.1 correspond to the expression "values of $f(x)$ can be made as close as we like to $L$" in Definition 1.1.1? Explain.
(b) What portions of Definition 1.4.1 correspond to the expression "taking values of $x$ sufficiently close to $a$ (but not equal to $a$)" in Definition 1.1.1? Explain.

**77. Writing** Compare informal Definition 1.3.1 with Definition 1.4.2.
(a) What portions of Definition 1.4.2 correspond to the expression "values of $f(x)$ eventually get as close as we like to a number $L$" in Definition 1.3.1? Explain.
(b) What portions of Definition 1.4.2 correspond to the expression "as $x$ increases without bound" in Definition 1.3.1? Explain.

✓ **QUICK CHECK ANSWERS 1.4** 1. $\epsilon > 0$; $\delta > 0$; $0 < |x - a| < \delta$ 2. $\lim_{x\to 1} f(x) = 5$ 3. $\delta = \epsilon/5$ 4. $\epsilon > 0$; $N$; $x > N$ 5. $N = 10{,}000$

# 1.5 CONTINUITY

*A thrown baseball cannot vanish at some point and reappear someplace else to continue its motion. Thus, we perceive the path of the ball as an unbroken curve. In this section, we translate "unbroken curve" into a precise mathematical formulation called continuity, and develop some fundamental properties of continuous curves.*

Joseph Helfenberger/iStockphoto

*A baseball moves along a "continuous" trajectory after leaving the pitcher's hand.*

## DEFINITION OF CONTINUITY

Intuitively, the graph of a function can be described as a "continuous curve" if it has no breaks or holes. To make this idea more precise we need to understand what properties of a function can cause breaks or holes. Referring to Figure 1.5.1, we see that the graph of a function has a break or hole if any of the following conditions occur:

- The function $f$ is undefined at $c$ (Figure 1.5.1$a$).
- The limit of $f(x)$ does not exist as $x$ approaches $c$ (Figures 1.5.1$b$, 1.5.1$c$).
- The value of the function and the value of the limit at $c$ are different (Figure 1.5.1$d$).

This suggests the following definition.

The third condition in Definition 1.5.1 actually implies the first two, since it is tacitly understood in the statement

$$\lim_{x\to c} f(x) = f(c)$$

that the limit exists and the function is defined at $c$. Thus, when we want to establish continuity at $c$ our usual procedure will be to verify the third condition only.

**1.5.1 DEFINITION** A function $f$ is said to be ***continuous at $x = c$*** provided the following conditions are satisfied:

1. $f(c)$ is defined.
2. $\lim_{x\to c} f(x)$ exists.
3. $\lim_{x\to c} f(x) = f(c)$.

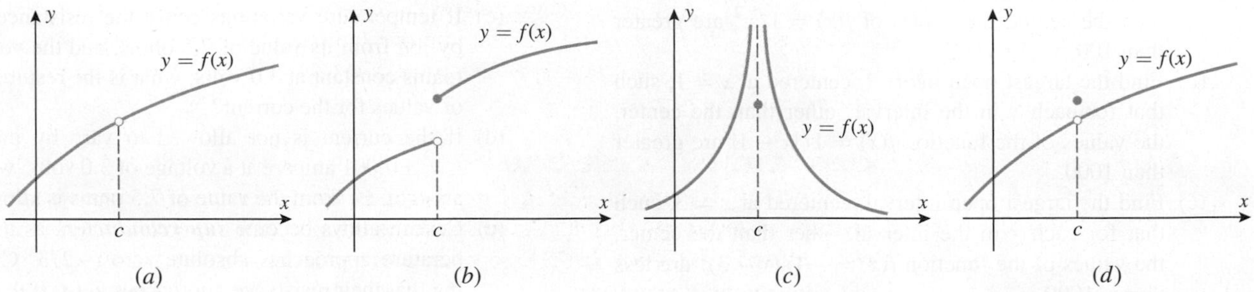


▲ **Figure 1.5.1**

If one or more of the conditions of this definition fails to hold, then we will say that $f$ has a ***discontinuity at $x = c$***. Each function drawn in Figure 1.5.1 illustrates a discontinuity at $x = c$. In Figure 1.5.1*a*, the function is not defined at $c$, violating the first condition of Definition 1.5.1. In Figure 1.5.1*b*, the one-sided limits of $f(x)$ as $x$ approaches $c$ both exist but are not equal. Thus, $\lim_{x\to c} f(x)$ does not exist, and this violates the second condition of Definition 1.5.1. We will say that a function like that in Figure 1.5.1*b* has a ***jump discontinuity*** at $c$. In Figure 1.5.1*c*, the one-sided limits of $f(x)$ as $x$ approaches $c$ are infinite. Thus, $\lim_{x\to c} f(x)$ does not exist, and this violates the second condition of Definition 1.5.1. We will say that a function like that in Figure 1.5.1*c* has an ***infinite discontinuity*** at $c$. In Figure 1.5.1*d*, the function is defined at $c$ and $\lim_{x\to c} f(x)$ exists, but these two values are not equal, violating the third condition of Definition 1.5.1. We will say that a function like that in Figure 1.5.1*d* has a ***removable discontinuity*** at $c$. Exercises 33 and 34 help to explain why discontinuities of this type are given this name.

▶ **Example 1** Determine whether the following functions are continuous at $x = 2$.

$$f(x) = \frac{x^2 - 4}{x - 2}, \qquad g(x) = \begin{cases} \dfrac{x^2-4}{x-2}, & x \neq 2 \\ 3, & x = 2, \end{cases} \qquad h(x) = \begin{cases} \dfrac{x^2-4}{x-2}, & x \neq 2 \\ 4, & x = 2 \end{cases}$$

***Solution.*** In each case we must determine whether the limit of the function as $x\to 2$ is the same as the value of the function at $x = 2$. In all three cases the functions are identical, except at $x = 2$, and hence all three have the same limit at $x = 2$, namely,

$$\lim_{x\to 2} f(x) = \lim_{x\to 2} g(x) = \lim_{x\to 2} h(x) = \lim_{x\to 2} \frac{x^2-4}{x-2} = \lim_{x\to 2} (x+2) = 4$$

The function $f$ is undefined at $x = 2$, and hence is not continuous at $x = 2$ (Figure 1.5.2*a*). The function $g$ is defined at $x = 2$, but its value there is $g(2) = 3$, which is not the same as the limit as $x$ approaches 2; hence, $g$ is also not continuous at $x = 2$ (Figure 1.5.2*b*). The value of the function $h$ at $x = 2$ is $h(2) = 4$, which is the same as the limit as $x$ approaches 2; hence, $h$ is continuous at $x = 2$ (Figure 1.5.2*c*). (Note that the function $h$ could have been written more simply as $h(x) = x + 2$, but we wrote it in piecewise form to emphasize its relationship to $f$ and $g$.) ◀

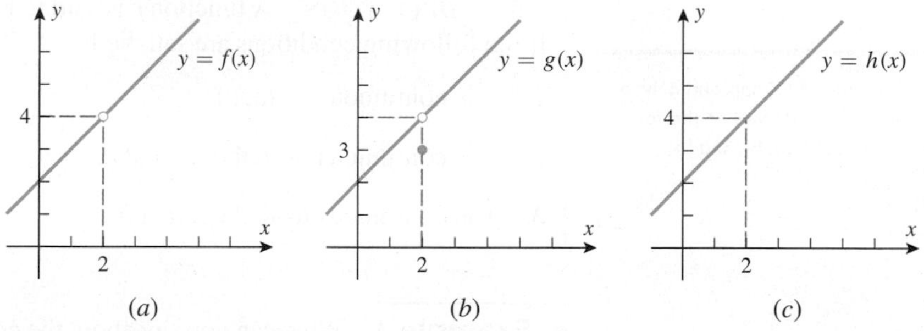


▲ **Figure 1.5.2**

Shannon Faulk/DreamPictures/Getty Images

*A poor connection in a transmission cable can cause a discontinuity in the electrical signal it carries.*

## CONTINUITY IN APPLICATIONS

In applications, discontinuities often signal the occurrence of important physical events. For example, Figure 1.5.3*a* is a graph of voltage versus time for an underground cable that is accidentally cut by a work crew at time $t = t_0$ (the voltage drops to zero when the line is cut). Figure 1.5.3*b* shows the graph of inventory versus time for a company that restocks its warehouse to $y_1$ units when the inventory falls to $y_0$ units. The discontinuities occur at those times when restocking occurs.

## CONTINUITY ON AN INTERVAL

If a function $f$ is continuous at each number in an open interval $(a, b)$, then we say that $f$ is ***continuous on $(a, b)$***. This definition applies to infinite open intervals of the form $(a, +\infty)$, $(-\infty, b)$, and $(-\infty, +\infty)$. In the case where $f$ is continuous on $(-\infty, +\infty)$, we will say that $f$ is ***continuous everywhere***.

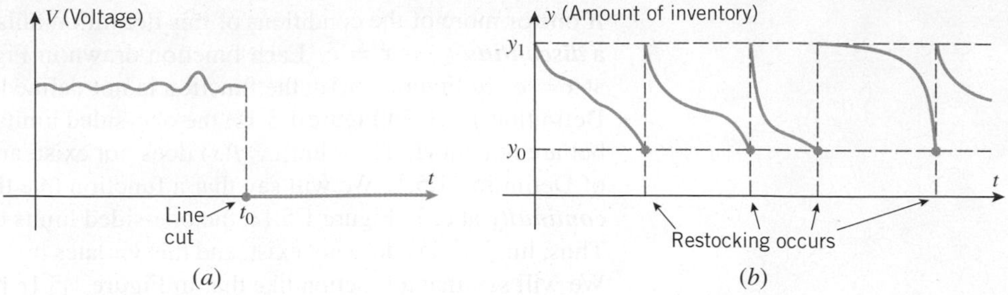


▲ **Figure 1.5.3**

Because Definition 1.5.1 involves a two-sided limit, that definition does not generally apply at the endpoints of a closed interval $[a, b]$ or at the endpoint of an interval of the form $[a, b)$, $(a, b]$, $(-\infty, b]$, or $[a, +\infty)$. To remedy this problem, we will agree that a function is continuous at an endpoint of an interval if its value at the endpoint is equal to the appropriate one-sided limit at that endpoint. For example, the function graphed in Figure 1.5.4 is continuous at the right endpoint of the interval $[a, b]$ because

$$\lim_{x\to b^-} f(x) = f(b)$$

but it is not continuous at the left endpoint because

$$\lim_{x\to a^+} f(x) \neq f(a)$$

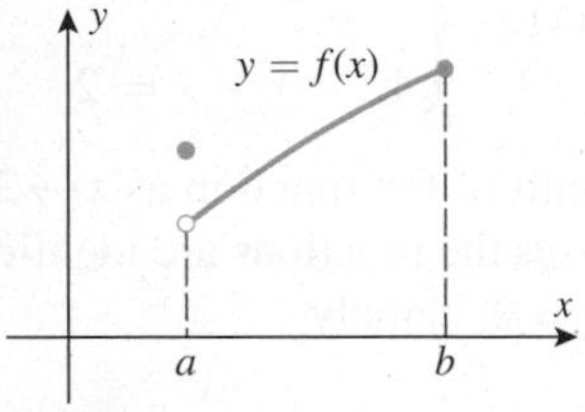


▲ **Figure 1.5.4**

In general, we will say a function $f$ is ***continuous from the left*** at $c$ if

$$\lim_{x\to c^-} f(x) = f(c)$$

and is ***continuous from the right*** at $c$ if

$$\lim_{x\to c^+} f(x) = f(c)$$

Using this terminology we define continuity on a closed interval as follows.

**1.5.2 DEFINITION** A function $f$ is said to be ***continuous on a closed interval*** $[a, b]$ if the following conditions are satisfied:

1. $f$ is continuous on $(a, b)$.
2. $f$ is continuous from the right at $a$.
3. $f$ is continuous from the left at $b$.

Modify Definition 1.5.2 appropriately so that it applies to intervals of the form $[a, +\infty)$, $(-\infty, b]$, $(a, b]$, and $[a, b)$.

▶ **Example 2** What can you say about the continuity of the function $f(x) = \sqrt{9 - x^2}$?

***Solution.*** Because the natural domain of this function is the closed interval $[-3, 3]$, we will need to investigate the continuity of $f$ on the open interval $(-3, 3)$ and at the two endpoints. If $c$ is any point in the interval $(-3, 3)$, then it follows from Theorem 1.2.2(*e*) that

$$\lim_{x\to c} f(x) = \lim_{x\to c} \sqrt{9 - x^2} = \sqrt{\lim_{x\to c} (9 - x^2)} = \sqrt{9 - c^2} = f(c)$$

which proves $f$ is continuous at each point in the interval $(-3, 3)$. The function $f$ is also continuous at the endpoints since

$$\lim_{x\to 3^-} f(x) = \lim_{x\to 3^-} \sqrt{9 - x^2} = \sqrt{\lim_{x\to 3^-} (9 - x^2)} = 0 = f(3)$$

$$\lim_{x\to -3^+} f(x) = \lim_{x\to -3^+} \sqrt{9 - x^2} = \sqrt{\lim_{x\to -3^+} (9 - x^2)} = 0 = f(-3)$$

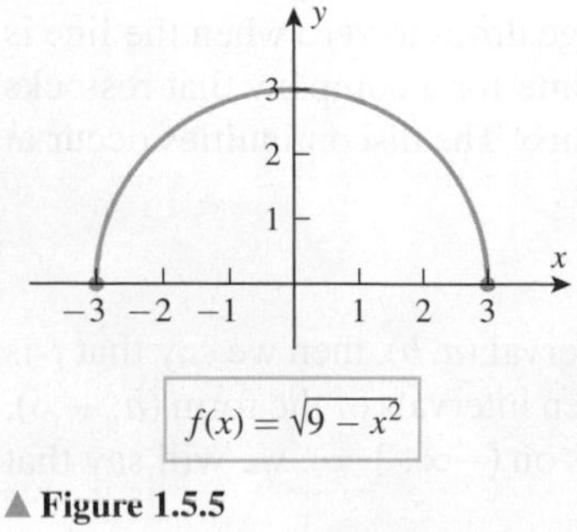


▲ **Figure 1.5.5**

Thus, $f$ is continuous on the closed interval $[-3, 3]$ (Figure 1.5.5). ◀

## SOME PROPERTIES OF CONTINUOUS FUNCTIONS

The following theorem, which is a consequence of Theorem 1.2.2, will enable us to reach conclusions about the continuity of functions that are obtained by adding, subtracting, multiplying, and dividing continuous functions.

> **1.5.3 THEOREM** *If the functions $f$ and $g$ are continuous at $c$, then*
>
> (a) $f + g$ *is continuous at* $c$.
>
> (b) $f - g$ *is continuous at* $c$.
>
> (c) $fg$ *is continuous at* $c$.
>
> (d) $f/g$ *is continuous at* $c$ *if* $g(c) \neq 0$ *and has a discontinuity at* $c$ *if* $g(c) = 0$.

We will prove part (*d*). The remaining proofs are similar and will be left to the exercises.

**PROOF** First, consider the case where $g(c) = 0$. In this case $f(c)/g(c)$ is undefined, so the function $f/g$ has a discontinuity at $c$.

Next, consider the case where $g(c) \neq 0$. To prove that $f/g$ is continuous at $c$, we must show that

$$\lim_{x \to c} \frac{f(x)}{g(x)} = \frac{f(c)}{g(c)} \tag{1}$$

Since $f$ and $g$ are continuous at $c$,

$$\lim_{x \to c} f(x) = f(c) \quad \text{and} \quad \lim_{x \to c} g(x) = g(c)$$

Thus, by Theorem 1.2.2(*d*)

$$\lim_{x \to c} \frac{f(x)}{g(x)} = \frac{\lim_{x \to c} f(x)}{\lim_{x \to c} g(x)} = \frac{f(c)}{g(c)}$$

which proves (1). ■

## CONTINUITY OF POLYNOMIALS AND RATIONAL FUNCTIONS

The general procedure for showing that a function is continuous everywhere is to show that it is continuous at an *arbitrary* point. For example, we know from Theorem 1.2.3 that if $p(x)$ is a polynomial and $a$ is *any* real number, then

$$\lim_{x \to a} p(x) = p(a)$$

This shows that polynomials are continuous everywhere. Moreover, since rational functions are ratios of polynomials, it follows from part (*d*) of Theorem 1.5.3 that rational functions are continuous at points other than the zeros of the denominator, and at these zeros they have discontinuities. Thus, we have the following result.

> **1.5.4 THEOREM**
>
> (a) *A polynomial is continuous everywhere.*
>
> (b) *A rational function is continuous at every point where the denominator is nonzero, and has discontinuities at the points where the denominator is zero.*

**TECHNOLOGY MASTERY**

If you use a graphing utility to generate the graph of the equation in Example 3, there is a good chance you will see the discontinuity at $x = 2$ but not at $x = 3$. Try it, and explain what you think is happening.

► **Example 3** For what values of $x$ is there a discontinuity in the graph of

$$y = \frac{x^2 - 9}{x^2 - 5x + 6}?$$

***Solution.*** The function being graphed is a rational function, and hence is continuous at every number where the denominator is nonzero. Solving the equation

$$x^2 - 5x + 6 = 0$$

yields discontinuities at $x = 2$ and at $x = 3$ (Figure 1.5.6). ◄

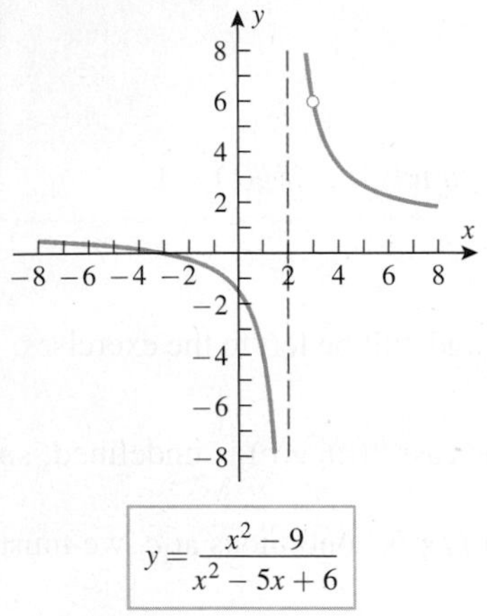


▲ **Figure 1.5.6**

► **Example 4** Show that $|x|$ is continuous everywhere.

***Solution.*** We can write $|x|$ as

$$|x| = \begin{cases} x & \text{if } x > 0 \\ 0 & \text{if } x = 0 \\ -x & \text{if } x < 0 \end{cases}$$

so $|x|$ is the same as the polynomial $x$ on the interval $(0, +\infty)$ and is the same as the polynomial $-x$ on the interval $(-\infty, 0)$. But polynomials are continuous everywhere, so $x = 0$ is the only possible discontinuity for $|x|$. Since $|0| = 0$, to prove the continuity at $x = 0$ we must show that

$$\lim_{x \to 0} |x| = 0 \tag{2}$$

Because the piecewise formula for $|x|$ changes at 0, it will be helpful to consider the one-sided limits at 0 rather than the two-sided limit. We obtain

$$\lim_{x \to 0^+} |x| = \lim_{x \to 0^+} x = 0 \quad \text{and} \quad \lim_{x \to 0^-} |x| = \lim_{x \to 0^-} (-x) = 0$$

Thus, (2) holds and $|x|$ is continuous at $x = 0$ (Figure 1.5.7). ◄

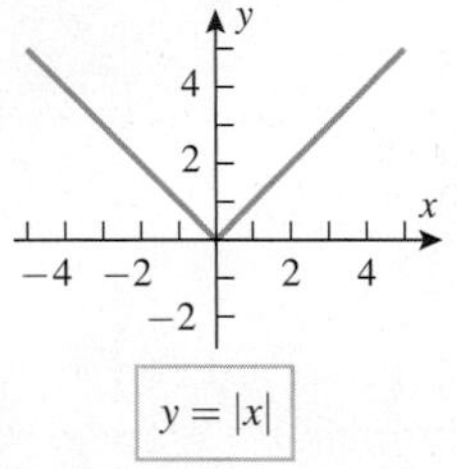


▲ **Figure 1.5.7**

## CONTINUITY OF COMPOSITIONS

The following theorem, whose proof is given in Web Appendix L, will be useful for calculating limits of compositions of functions.

In words, Theorem 1.5.5 states that a limit symbol can be moved through a function sign provided the limit of the expression inside the function sign exists and the function is continuous at this limit.

**1.5.5 THEOREM** *If $\lim_{x \to c} g(x) = L$ and if the function $f$ is continuous at $L$, then $\lim_{x \to c} f(g(x)) = f(L)$. That is,*

$$\lim_{x \to c} f(g(x)) = f\left(\lim_{x \to c} g(x)\right)$$

*This equality remains valid if $\lim_{x \to c}$ is replaced everywhere by one of $\lim_{x \to c^+}$, $\lim_{x \to c^-}$, $\lim_{x \to +\infty}$, or $\lim_{x \to -\infty}$.*

In the special case of this theorem where $f(x) = |x|$, the fact that $|x|$ is continuous everywhere allows us to write

$$\lim_{x \to c} |g(x)| = \left|\lim_{x \to c} g(x)\right| \tag{3}$$

provided $\lim_{x \to c} g(x)$ exists. Thus, for example,

$$\lim_{x \to 3} |5 - x^2| = \left|\lim_{x \to 3} (5 - x^2)\right| = |-4| = 4$$

The following theorem is concerned with the continuity of compositions of functions; the first part deals with continuity at a specific number and the second with continuity everywhere.

**1.5.6 THEOREM**

(a) *If the function g is continuous at c, and the function f is continuous at g(c), then the composition $f \circ g$ is continuous at c.*

(b) *If the function g is continuous everywhere and the function f is continuous everywhere, then the composition $f \circ g$ is continuous everywhere.*

**PROOF** We will prove part (*a*) only; the proof of part (*b*) can be obtained by applying part (*a*) at an arbitrary number *c*. To prove that $f \circ g$ is continuous at *c*, we must show that the value of $f \circ g$ and the value of its limit are the same at $x = c$. But this is so, since we can write

$$\lim_{x \to c} (f \circ g)(x) = \lim_{x \to c} f(g(x)) = f\left(\lim_{x \to c} g(x)\right) = f(g(c)) = (f \circ g)(c) \quad \blacksquare$$

Theorem 1.5.5 | g is continuous at c.

Can the absolute value of a function that is not continuous everywhere be continuous everywhere? Justify your answer.

We know from Example 4 that the function $|x|$ is continuous everywhere. Thus, if $g(x)$ is continuous at *c*, then by part (*a*) of Theorem 1.5.6, the function $|g(x)|$ must also be continuous at *c*; and, more generally, if $g(x)$ is continuous everywhere, then so is $|g(x)|$. Stated informally:

*The absolute value of a continuous function is continuous.*

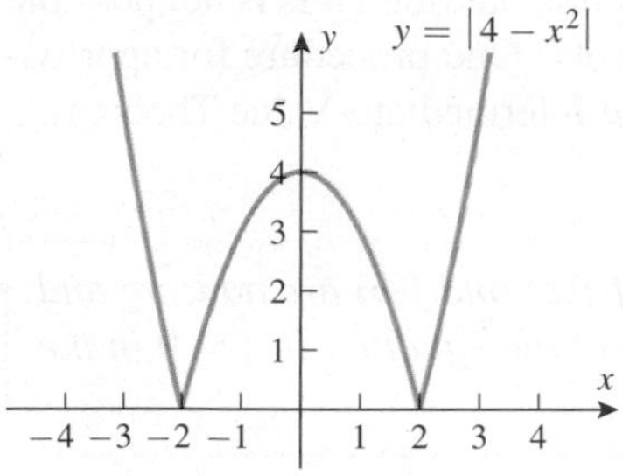

▲ Figure 1.5.8

For example, the polynomial $g(x) = 4 - x^2$ is continuous everywhere, so we can conclude that the function $|4 - x^2|$ is also continuous everywhere (Figure 1.5.8).

## CONTINUITY OF INVERSE FUNCTIONS

Since the graphs of a one-to-one function *f* and its inverse $f^{-1}$ are reflections of one another about the line $y = x$, it is clear geometrically that if the graph of *f* has no breaks or holes in it, then neither does the graph of $f^{-1}$. This, and the fact that the range of *f* is the domain of $f^{-1}$, suggests the following result, which we state without formal proof.

To paraphrase Theorem 1.5.7, *the inverse of a continuous function is continuous.*

**1.5.7 THEOREM** *If f is a one-to-one function that is continuous at each point of its domain, then $f^{-1}$ is continuous at each point of its domain; that is, $f^{-1}$ is continuous at each point in the range of f.*

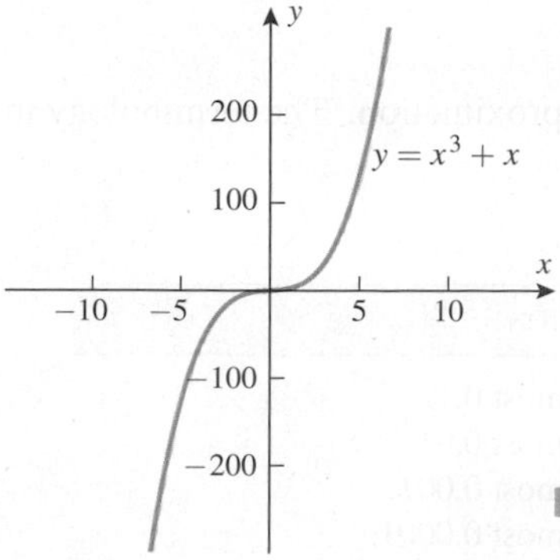

▲ Figure 1.5.9

▶ **Example 5** Show that the function $f(x) = x^3 + x$ has an inverse. Is $f^{-1}$ continuous at each point in $(-\infty, +\infty)$?

***Solution.*** Note that *f* is increasing for all *x* (why?), so *f* is one-to-one and has an inverse. Also notice that *f* is continuous everywhere since it is a polynomial. From Figure 1.5.9 we infer that the range of *f* is $(-\infty, +\infty)$, so the domain of $f^{-1}$ is also $(-\infty, +\infty)$. Although a formula for $f^{-1}(x)$ cannot be found easily, we can use Theorem 1.5.7 to conclude that $f^{-1}$ is continuous on $(-\infty, +\infty)$. ◀

## THE INTERMEDIATE-VALUE THEOREM

Figure 1.5.10 shows the graph of a function that is continuous on the closed interval $[a, b]$. The figure suggests that if we draw any horizontal line $y = k$, where *k* is between $f(a)$ and $f(b)$, then that line will cross the curve $y = f(x)$ at least once over the interval $[a, b]$. Stated in numerical terms, if *f* is continuous on $[a, b]$, then the function *f* must take on

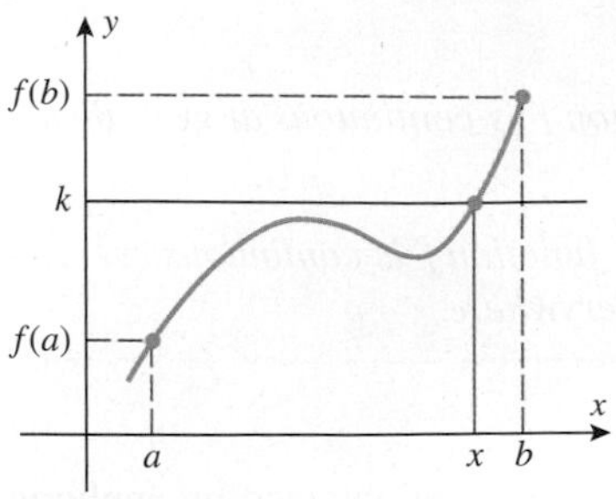

▲ Figure 1.5.10

every value $k$ between $f(a)$ and $f(b)$ at least once as $x$ varies from $a$ to $b$. For example, the polynomial $p(x) = x^5 - x + 3$ has a value of 3 at $x = 1$ and a value of 33 at $x = 2$. Thus, it follows from the continuity of $p$ that the equation $x^5 - x + 3 = k$ has at least one solution in the interval $[1, 2]$ for every value of $k$ between 3 and 33. This idea is stated more precisely in the following theorem.

> **1.5.8 THEOREM** (*Intermediate-Value Theorem*) *If $f$ is continuous on a closed interval $[a, b]$ and $k$ is any number between $f(a)$ and $f(b)$, inclusive, then there is at least one number $x$ in the interval $[a, b]$ such that $f(x) = k$.*

Although this theorem is intuitively obvious, its proof depends on a mathematically precise development of the real number system, which is beyond the scope of this text.

## APPROXIMATING ROOTS USING THE INTERMEDIATE-VALUE THEOREM

A variety of problems can be reduced to solving an equation $f(x) = 0$ for its roots. Sometimes it is possible to solve for the roots exactly using algebra, but often this is not possible and one must settle for decimal approximations of the roots. One procedure for approximating roots is based on the following consequence of the Intermediate-Value Theorem.

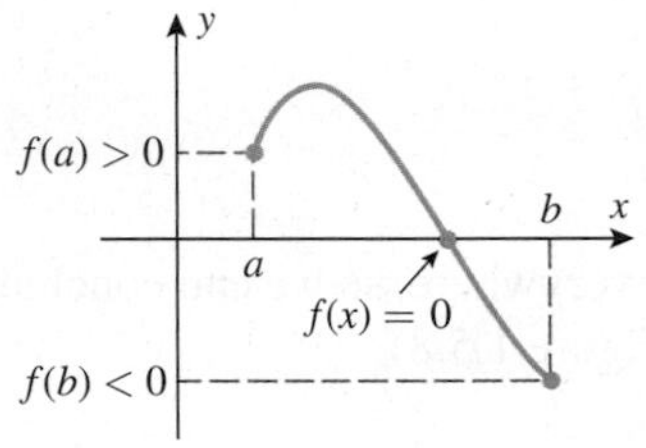

▲ Figure 1.5.11

> **1.5.9 THEOREM** *If $f$ is continuous on $[a, b]$, and if $f(a)$ and $f(b)$ are nonzero and have opposite signs, then there is at least one solution of the equation $f(x) = 0$ in the interval $(a, b)$.*

This result, which is illustrated in Figure 1.5.11, can be proved as follows.

**PROOF** Since $f(a)$ and $f(b)$ have opposite signs, 0 is between $f(a)$ and $f(b)$. Thus, by the Intermediate-Value Theorem there is at least one number $x$ in the interval $[a, b]$ such that $f(x) = 0$. However, $f(a)$ and $f(b)$ are nonzero, so $x$ must lie in the interval $(a, b)$, which completes the proof. ■

Before we illustrate how this theorem can be used to approximate roots, it will be helpful to discuss some standard terminology for describing errors in approximations. If $x$ is an approximation to a quantity $x_0$, then we call

$$\epsilon = |x - x_0|$$

the ***absolute error*** or (less precisely) the ***error*** in the approximation. The terminology in Table 1.5.1 is used to describe the size of such errors.

**Table 1.5.1**

| ERROR | DESCRIPTION |
|---|---|
| $\|x - x_0\| \le 0.1$ | $x$ approximates $x_0$ with an error of at most 0.1. |
| $\|x - x_0\| \le 0.01$ | $x$ approximates $x_0$ with an error of at most 0.01. |
| $\|x - x_0\| \le 0.001$ | $x$ approximates $x_0$ with an error of at most 0.001. |
| $\|x - x_0\| \le 0.0001$ | $x$ approximates $x_0$ with an error of at most 0.0001. |
| $\|x - x_0\| \le 0.5$ | $x$ approximates $x_0$ to the nearest integer. |
| $\|x - x_0\| \le 0.05$ | $x$ approximates $x_0$ to 1 decimal place (i.e., to the nearest tenth). |
| $\|x - x_0\| \le 0.005$ | $x$ approximates $x_0$ to 2 decimal places (i.e., to the nearest hundredth). |
| $\|x - x_0\| \le 0.0005$ | $x$ approximates $x_0$ to 3 decimal places (i.e., to the nearest thousandth). |

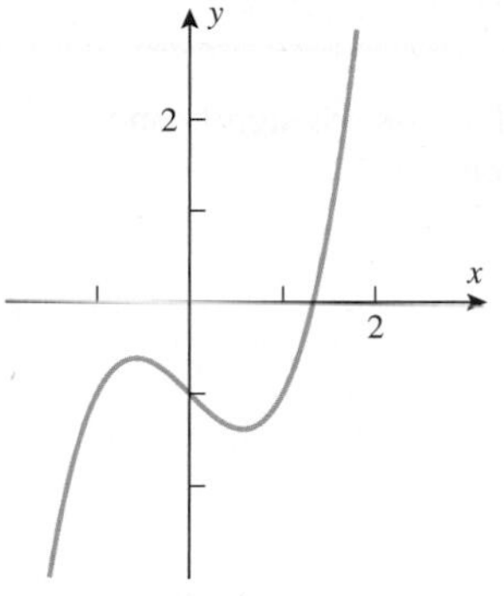


▲ **Figure 1.5.12**

► **Example 6** The equation
$$x^3 - x - 1 = 0$$
cannot be solved algebraically very easily because the left side has no simple factors. However, if we graph $p(x) = x^3 - x - 1$ with a graphing utility (Figure 1.5.12), then we are led to conjecture that there is one real root and that this root lies inside the interval $[1, 2]$. The existence of a root in this interval is also confirmed by Theorem 1.5.9, since $p(1) = -1$ and $p(2) = 5$ have opposite signs. Approximate this root to two decimal-place accuracy.

***Solution.*** Our objective is to approximate the unknown root $x_0$ with an error of at most 0.005. It follows that if we can find an interval of length 0.01 that contains the root, then the midpoint of that interval will approximate the root with an error of at most $\frac{1}{2}(0.01) = 0.005$, which will achieve the desired accuracy.

We know that the root $x_0$ lies in the interval $[1, 2]$. However, this interval has length 1, which is too large. We can pinpoint the location of the root more precisely by dividing the interval $[1, 2]$ into 10 equal parts and evaluating $p$ at the points of subdivision using a calculating utility (Table 1.5.2). In this table $p(1.3)$ and $p(1.4)$ have opposite signs, so we know that the root lies in the interval $[1.3, 1.4]$. This interval has length 0.1, which is still too large, so we repeat the process by dividing the interval $[1.3, 1.4]$ into 10 parts and evaluating $p$ at the points of subdivision; this yields Table 1.5.3, which tells us that the root is inside the interval $[1.32, 1.33]$ (Figure 1.5.13). Since this interval has length 0.01, its midpoint 1.325 will approximate the root with an error of at most 0.005. Thus, $x_0 \approx 1.325$ to two decimal-place accuracy. ◄

**Table 1.5.2**

| $x$ | 1 | 1.1 | 1.2 | 1.3 | 1.4 | 1.5 | 1.6 | 1.7 | 1.8 | 1.9 | 2 |
|---|---|---|---|---|---|---|---|---|---|---|---|
| $p(x)$ | −1 | −0.77 | −0.47 | −0.10 | 0.34 | 0.88 | 1.50 | 2.21 | 3.03 | 3.96 | 5 |

**Table 1.5.3**

| $x$ | 1.3 | 1.31 | 1.32 | 1.33 | 1.34 | 1.35 | 1.36 | 1.37 | 1.38 | 1.39 | 1.4 |
|---|---|---|---|---|---|---|---|---|---|---|---|
| $p(x)$ | −0.103 | −0.062 | −0.020 | 0.023 | 0.066 | 0.110 | 0.155 | 0.201 | 0.248 | 0.296 | 0.344 |

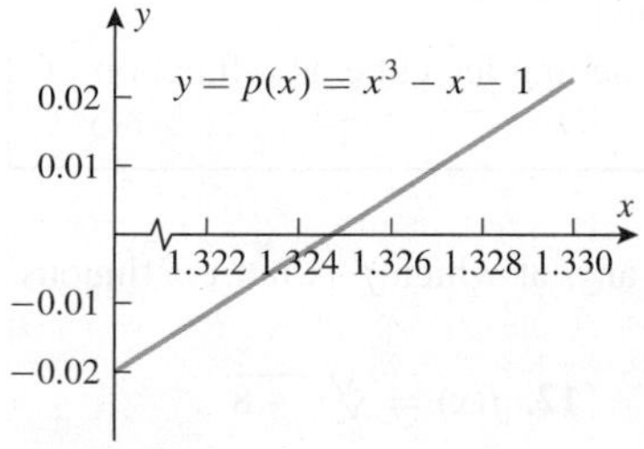


▲ **Figure 1.5.13**

**REMARK**

To say that $x$ approximates $x_0$ to $n$ decimal places does *not* mean that the first $n$ decimal places of $x$ and $x_0$ will be the same when the numbers are rounded to $n$ decimal places. For example, $x = 1.084$ approximates $x_0 = 1.087$ to two decimal places because $|x - x_0| = 0.003$ $(< 0.005)$. However, if we round these values to two decimal places, then we obtain $x \approx 1.08$ and $x_0 \approx 1.09$. Thus, if you approximate a number to $n$ decimal places, then you should display that approximation to at least $n + 1$ decimal places to preserve the accuracy.

**TECHNOLOGY MASTERY**

Use a graphing or calculating utility to show that the root $x_0$ in Example 6 can be approximated as $x_0 \approx 1.3245$ to three decimal-place accuracy.

## ✓ QUICK CHECK EXERCISES 1.5

*(See page 50 for answers.)*

1. What three conditions are satisfied if $f$ is continuous at $x = c$?
2. Suppose that $f$ and $g$ are continuous functions such that $f(2) = 1$ and $\lim_{x \to 2} [f(x) + 4g(x)] = 13$. Find
   (a) $g(2)$
   (b) $\lim_{x \to 2} g(x)$.
3. Suppose that $f$ and $g$ are continuous functions such that $\lim_{x \to 3} g(x) = 5$ and $f(3) = -2$. Find $\lim_{x \to 3} [f(x)/g(x)]$.
4. For what values of $x$, if any, is the function
$$f(x) = \frac{x^2 - 16}{x^2 - 5x + 4}$$
discontinuous?
5. Suppose that a function $f$ is continuous everywhere and that $f(-2) = 3$, $f(-1) = -1$, $f(0) = -4$, $f(1) = 1$, and $f(2) = 5$. Does the Intermediate-Value Theorem guarantee that $f$ has a root on the following intervals?
   (a) $[-2, -1]$ (b) $[-1, 0]$ (c) $[-1, 1]$ (d) $[0, 2]$

## EXERCISE SET 1.5 Graphing Utility

**1–4** Let $f$ be the function whose graph is shown. On which of the following intervals, if any, is $f$ continuous?
(a) $[1, 3]$ (b) $(1, 3)$ (c) $[1, 2]$
(d) $(1, 2)$ (e) $[2, 3]$ (f) $(2, 3)$
For each interval on which $f$ is not continuous, indicate which conditions for the continuity of $f$ do not hold. ■

**1.**

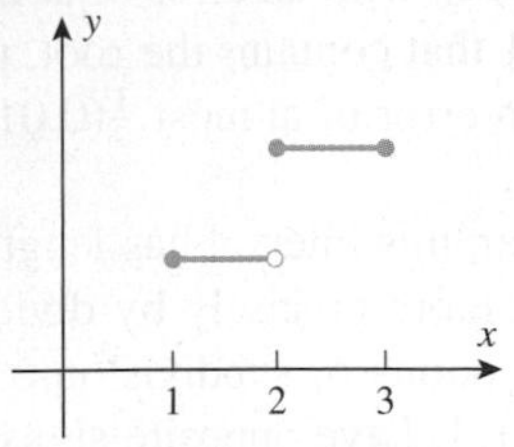


**2.**

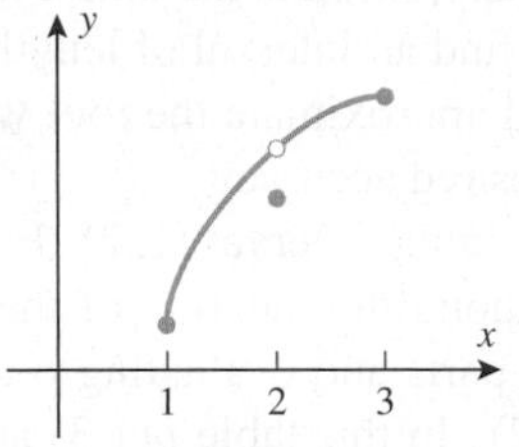


**3.**

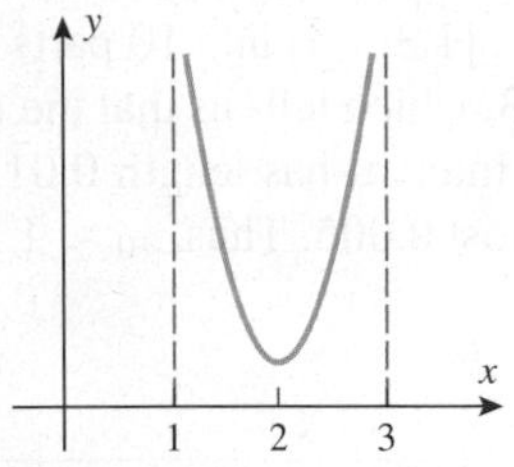


**4.**

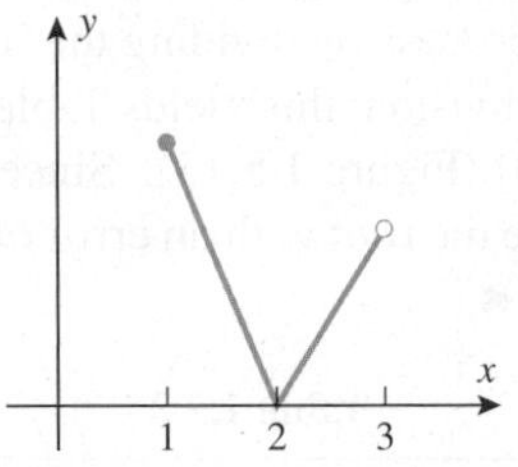


**5.** Consider the functions

$$f(x) = \begin{cases} 1, & x \neq 4 \\ -1, & x = 4 \end{cases} \quad \text{and} \quad g(x) = \begin{cases} 4x - 10, & x \neq 4 \\ -6, & x = 4 \end{cases}$$

In each part, is the given function continuous at $x = 4$?
(a) $f(x)$ (b) $g(x)$ (c) $-g(x)$ (d) $|f(x)|$
(e) $f(x)g(x)$ (f) $g(f(x))$ (g) $g(x) - 6f(x)$

**6.** Consider the functions

$$f(x) = \begin{cases} 1, & 0 \leq x \\ 0, & x < 0 \end{cases} \quad \text{and} \quad g(x) = \begin{cases} 0, & 0 \leq x \\ 1, & x < 0 \end{cases}$$

In each part, is the given function continuous at $x = 0$?
(a) $f(x)$ (b) $g(x)$ (c) $f(-x)$ (d) $|g(x)|$
(e) $f(x)g(x)$ (f) $g(f(x))$ (g) $f(x) + g(x)$

**FOCUS ON CONCEPTS**

**7.** In each part sketch the graph of a function $f$ that satisfies the stated conditions.
(a) $f$ is continuous everywhere except at $x = 3$, at which point it is continuous from the right.
(b) $f$ has a two-sided limit at $x = 3$, but it is not continuous at $x = 3$.
(c) $f$ is not continuous at $x = 3$, but if its value at $x = 3$ is changed from $f(3) = 1$ to $f(3) = 0$, it becomes continuous at $x = 3$.
(d) $f$ is continuous on the interval $[0, 3)$ and is defined on the closed interval $[0, 3]$; but $f$ is not continuous on the interval $[0, 3]$.

**8.** The accompanying figure models the concentration $C$ of medication in the bloodstream of a patient over a 48-hour period of time. Discuss the significance of the discontinuities in the graph.

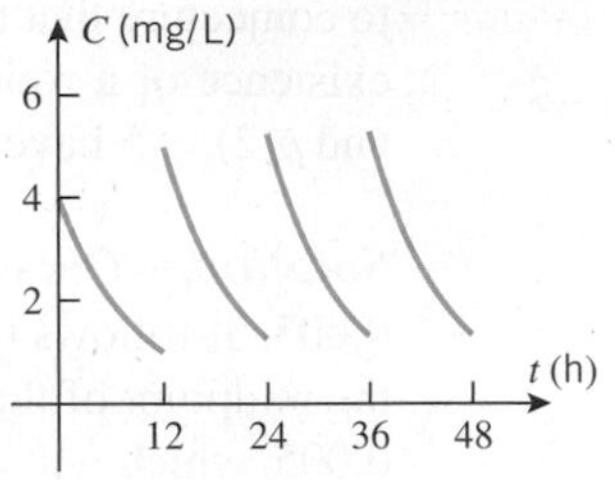


◀ **Figure Ex-8**

**9.** A student parking lot at a university charges \$2.00 for the first half hour (or any part) and \$1.00 for each subsequent half hour (or any part) up to a daily maximum of \$10.00.
(a) Sketch a graph of cost as a function of the time parked.
(b) Discuss the significance of the discontinuities in the graph to a student who parks there.

**10.** In each part determine whether the function is continuous or not, and explain your reasoning.
(a) The Earth's population as a function of time.
(b) Your exact height as a function of time.
(c) The cost of a taxi ride in your city as a function of the distance traveled.
(d) The volume of a melting ice cube as a function of time.

**11–22** Find values of $x$, if any, at which $f$ is not continuous. ■

**11.** $f(x) = 5x^4 - 3x + 7$

**12.** $f(x) = \sqrt[3]{x - 8}$

**13.** $f(x) = \dfrac{x + 2}{x^2 + 4}$

**14.** $f(x) = \dfrac{x + 2}{x^2 - 4}$

**15.** $f(x) = \dfrac{x}{2x^2 + x}$

**16.** $f(x) = \dfrac{2x + 1}{4x^2 + 4x + 5}$

**17.** $f(x) = \dfrac{3}{x} + \dfrac{x - 1}{x^2 - 1}$

**18.** $f(x) = \dfrac{5}{x} + \dfrac{2x}{x + 4}$

**19.** $f(x) = \dfrac{x^2 + 6x + 9}{|x| + 3}$

**20.** $f(x) = \left|4 - \dfrac{8}{x^4 + x}\right|$

**21.** $f(x) = \begin{cases} 2x + 3, & x \leq 4 \\ 7 + \dfrac{16}{x}, & x > 4 \end{cases}$

**22.** $f(x) = \begin{cases} \dfrac{3}{x - 1}, & x \neq 1 \\ 3, & x = 1 \end{cases}$

**23–28 True–False** Determine whether the statement is true or false. Explain your answer. ■

**23.** If $f(x)$ is continuous at $x = c$, then so is $|f(x)|$.

**24.** If $|f(x)|$ is continuous at $x = c$, then so is $f(x)$.

**25.** If $f$ and $g$ are discontinuous at $x = c$, then so is $f + g$.

**26.** If $f$ and $g$ are discontinuous at $x = c$, then so is $fg$.

**27.** If $\sqrt{f(x)}$ is continuous at $x = c$, then so is $f(x)$.

**28.** If $f(x)$ is continuous at $x = c$, then so is $\sqrt{f(x)}$.

**29–30** Find a value of the constant $k$, if possible, that will make the function continuous everywhere. ■

**29.** (a) $f(x) = \begin{cases} 7x - 2, & x \le 1 \\ kx^2, & x > 1 \end{cases}$

(b) $f(x) = \begin{cases} kx^2, & x \le 2 \\ 2x + k, & x > 2 \end{cases}$

**30.** (a) $f(x) = \begin{cases} 9 - x^2, & x \ge -3 \\ k/x^2, & x < -3 \end{cases}$

(b) $f(x) = \begin{cases} 9 - x^2, & x \ge 0 \\ k/x^2, & x < 0 \end{cases}$

**31.** Find values of the constants $k$ and $m$, if possible, that will make the function $f$ continuous everywhere.

$$f(x) = \begin{cases} x^2 + 5, & x > 2 \\ m(x + 1) + k, & -1 < x \le 2 \\ 2x^3 + x + 7, & x \le -1 \end{cases}$$

**32.** On which of the following intervals is

$$f(x) = \frac{1}{\sqrt{x - 2}}$$

continuous?

(a) $[2, +\infty)$ (b) $(-\infty, +\infty)$ (c) $(2, +\infty)$ (d) $[1, 2)$

**33–36** A function $f$ is said to have a ***removable discontinuity*** at $x = c$ if $\lim_{x \to c} f(x)$ exists but $f$ is not continuous at $x = c$, either because $f$ is not defined at $c$ or because the definition for $f(c)$ differs from the value of the limit. This terminology will be needed in these exercises. ■

**33.** (a) Sketch the graph of a function with a removable discontinuity at $x = c$ for which $f(c)$ is undefined.

(b) Sketch the graph of a function with a removable discontinuity at $x = c$ for which $f(c)$ is defined.

**34.** (a) The terminology *removable discontinuity* is appropriate because a removable discontinuity of a function $f$ at $x = c$ can be "removed" by redefining the value of $f$ appropriately at $x = c$. What value for $f(c)$ removes the discontinuity?

(b) Show that the following functions have removable discontinuities at $x = 1$, and sketch their graphs.

$$f(x) = \frac{x^2 - 1}{x - 1} \quad \text{and} \quad g(x) = \begin{cases} 1, & x > 1 \\ 0, & x = 1 \\ 1, & x < 1 \end{cases}$$

(c) What values should be assigned to $f(1)$ and $g(1)$ to remove the discontinuities?

**35–36** Find the values of $x$ (if any) at which $f$ is not continuous, and determine whether each such value is a removable discontinuity. ■

**35.** (a) $f(x) = \dfrac{|x|}{x}$ (b) $f(x) = \dfrac{x^2 + 3x}{x + 3}$

(c) $f(x) = \dfrac{x - 2}{|x| - 2}$

**36.** (a) $f(x) = \dfrac{x^2 - 4}{x^3 - 8}$ (b) $f(x) = \begin{cases} 2x - 3, & x \le 2 \\ x^2, & x > 2 \end{cases}$

(c) $f(x) = \begin{cases} 3x^2 + 5, & x \ne 1 \\ 6, & x = 1 \end{cases}$

**37.** (a) Use a graphing utility to generate the graph of the function $f(x) = (x + 3)/(2x^2 + 5x - 3)$, and then use the graph to make a conjecture about the number and locations of all discontinuities.

(b) Check your conjecture by factoring the denominator.

**38.** (a) Use a graphing utility to generate the graph of the function $f(x) = x/(x^3 - x + 2)$, and then use the graph to make a conjecture about the number and locations of all discontinuities.

(b) Use the Intermediate-Value Theorem to approximate the locations of all discontinuities to two decimal places.

**39.** Prove that $f(x) = x^{3/5}$ is continuous everywhere, carefully justifying each step.

**40.** Prove that $f(x) = 1/\sqrt{x^4 + 7x^2 + 1}$ is continuous everywhere, carefully justifying each step.

**41.** Prove:

(a) part (*a*) of Theorem 1.5.3

(b) part (*b*) of Theorem 1.5.3

(c) part (*c*) of Theorem 1.5.3.

**42.** Prove part (*b*) of Theorem 1.5.4.

**43.** (a) Use Theorem 1.5.5 to prove that if $f$ is continuous at $x = c$, then $\lim_{h \to 0} f(c + h) = f(c)$.

(b) Prove that if $\lim_{h \to 0} f(c + h) = f(c)$, then $f$ is continuous at $x = c$. [*Hint:* What does this limit tell you about the continuity of $g(h) = f(c + h)$?]

(c) Conclude from parts (a) and (b) that $f$ is continuous at $x = c$ if and only if $\lim_{h \to 0} f(c + h) = f(c)$.

**44.** Prove: If $f$ and $g$ are continuous on $[a, b]$, and $f(a) > g(a)$, $f(b) < g(b)$, then there is at least one solution of the equation $f(x) = g(x)$ in $(a, b)$. [*Hint:* Consider $f(x) - g(x)$.]

**FOCUS ON CONCEPTS**

**45.** Give an example of a function $f$ that is defined on a closed interval, and whose values at the endpoints have opposite signs, but for which the equation $f(x) = 0$ has no solution in the interval.

**46.** Let $f$ be the function whose graph is shown in Exercise 2. For each interval, determine (i) whether the hypothesis of the Intermediate-Value Theorem is satisfied, and (ii) whether the conclusion of the Intermediate-Value Theorem is satisfied.

(a) $[1, 2]$ (b) $[2, 3]$ (c) $[1, 3]$

**47.** Show that the equation $x^3 + x^2 - 2x = 1$ has at least one solution in the interval $[-1, 1]$.

**48.** Prove: If $p(x)$ is a polynomial of odd degree, then the equation $p(x) = 0$ has at least one real solution.

**49.** The accompanying figure on the next page shows the graph of the equation $y = x^4 + x - 1$. Use the method of

Example 6 to approximate the $x$-intercepts with an error of at most 0.05.

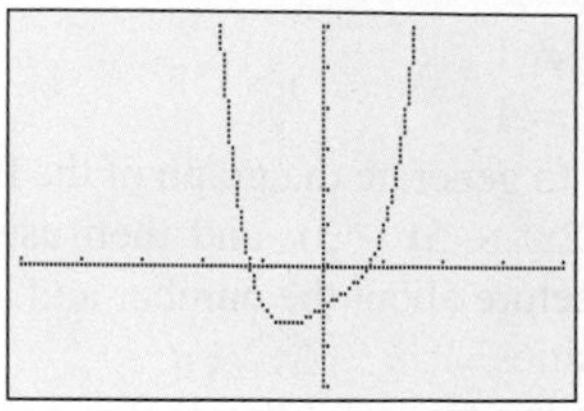

$[-5, 4] \times [-3, 6]$
$x$Scl = 1, $y$Scl = 1

◀ **Figure Ex-49**

**50.** The accompanying figure shows the graph of the equation $y = 5 - x - x^4$. Use the method of Example 6 to approximate the roots of the equation $5 - x - x^4 = 0$ to two decimal-place accuracy.

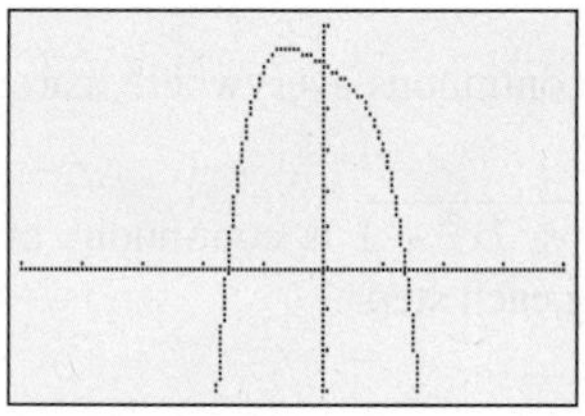

$[-5, 4] \times [-3, 6]$
$x$Scl = 1, $y$Scl = 1

◀ **Figure Ex-50**

**51.** Use the fact that $\sqrt{5}$ is a solution of $x^2 - 5 = 0$ to approximate $\sqrt{5}$ with an error of at most 0.005.

**52.** A sprinter, who is timed with a stopwatch, runs a hundred yard dash in 10 s. The stopwatch is reset to 0, and the sprinter is timed jogging back to the starting block. Show that there is at least one point on the track at which the reading on the stopwatch during the sprint is the same as the reading during the return jog. [*Hint:* Use the result in Exercise 44.]

**53.** Prove that there exist points on opposite sides of the equator that are at the same temperature. [*Hint:* Consider the accompanying figure, which shows a view of the equator from a point above the North Pole. Assume that the temperature $T(\theta)$ is a continuous function of the angle $\theta$, and consider the function $f(\theta) = T(\theta + \pi) - T(\theta)$.]

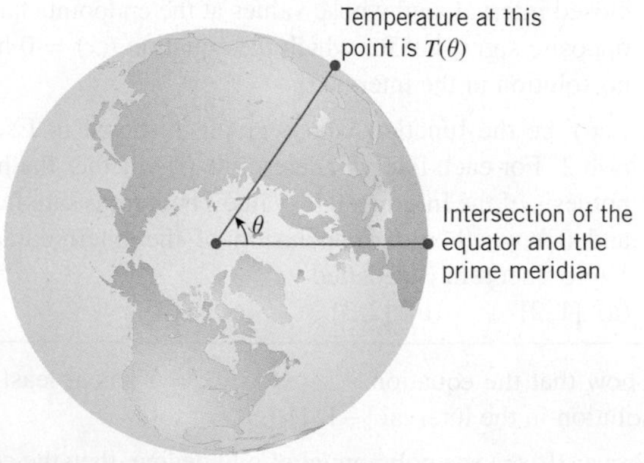


▲ **Figure Ex-53**

**54.** Let $R$ denote an elliptical region in the $xy$-plane, and define $f(z)$ to be the area within $R$ that is on, or to the left of, the vertical line $x = z$. Prove that $f$ is a continuous function of $z$. [*Hint:* Assume the ellipse is between the horizontal lines $y = a$ and $y = b$, $a < b$. Argue that $|f(z_1) - f(z_2)| \leq (b - a) \cdot |z_1 - z_2|$.]

**55.** Let $R$ denote an elliptical region in the plane. For any line $L$, prove there is a line perpendicular to $L$ that divides $R$ in half by area. [*Hint:* Introduce coordinates so that $L$ is the $x$-axis. Use the result in Exercise 54 and the Intermediate-Value Theorem.]

**56.** Suppose that $f$ is continuous on the interval [0, 1] and that $0 \leq f(x) \leq 1$ for all $x$ in this interval.
(a) Sketch the graph of $y = x$ together with a possible graph for $f$ over the interval [0, 1].
(b) Use the Intermediate-Value Theorem to help prove that there is at least one number $c$ in the interval [0, 1] such that $f(c) = c$.

**57.** Let $f(x) = x^6 + 3x + 5, x \geq 0$. Show that $f$ is an invertible function and that $f^{-1}$ is continuous on $[5, +\infty)$.

**58.** Suppose that $f$ is an invertible function, $f(0) = 0$, $f$ is continuous at 0, and $\lim_{x\to 0} f(x)/x$ exists. Given that $L = \lim_{x\to 0} f(x)/x$, show

$$\lim_{x\to 0} \frac{x}{f^{-1}(x)} = L$$

[*Hint:* Apply Theorem 1.5.5 to the composition $h \circ g$, where

$$h(x) = \begin{cases} f(x)/x, & x \neq 0 \\ L, & x = 0 \end{cases}$$

and $g(x) = f^{-1}(x)$.]

**59. Writing** It is often assumed that changing physical quantities, such as the height of a falling object or the weight of a melting snowball, are continuous functions of time. Use specific examples to discuss the merits of this assumption.

**60. Writing** The Intermediate-Value Theorem is an example of what is known as an "existence theorem." In your own words, describe how to recognize an existence theorem, and discuss some of the ways in which an existence theorem can be useful.

✓ **QUICK CHECK ANSWERS 1.5** **1.** $f(c)$ is defined; $\lim_{x\to c} f(x)$ exists; $\lim_{x\to c} f(x) = f(c)$ **2.** (a) 3 (b) 3 **3.** $-2/5$ **4.** $x = 1, 4$ **5.** (a) yes (b) no (c) yes (d) yes

# 1.6 CONTINUITY OF TRIGONOMETRIC FUNCTIONS

*In this section we will discuss the continuity properties of trigonometric functions. We will also discuss some important limits involving such functions.*

## CONTINUITY OF TRIGONOMETRIC FUNCTIONS

Recall from trigonometry that the graphs of $\sin x$ and $\cos x$ are drawn as continuous curves. We will not formally prove that these functions are continuous, but we can motivate this fact by letting $c$ be a fixed angle in radian measure and $x$ a variable angle in radian measure. If, as illustrated in Figure 1.6.1, the angle $x$ approaches the angle $c$, then the point $P(\cos x, \sin x)$ moves along the unit circle toward $Q(\cos c, \sin c)$, and the coordinates of $P$ approach the corresponding coordinates of $Q$. This implies that

$$\lim_{x\to c} \sin x = \sin c \quad \text{and} \quad \lim_{x\to c} \cos x = \cos c \tag{1}$$

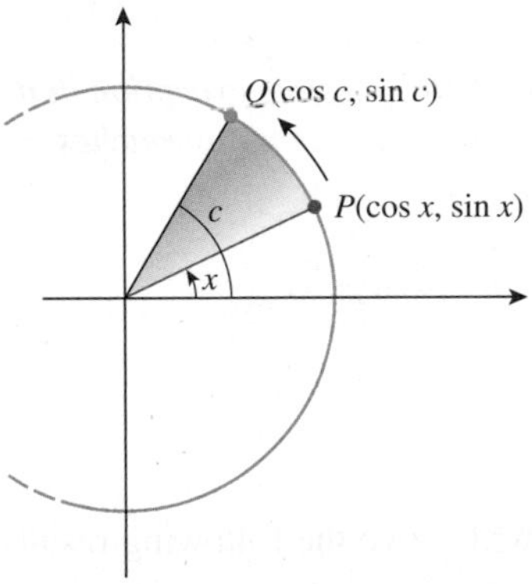


As $x$ approaches $c$ the point $P$ approaches the point $Q$.

▲ Figure 1.6.1

Thus, $\sin x$ and $\cos x$ are continuous at the arbitrary point $c$; that is, these functions are continuous everywhere.

The formulas in (1) can be used to find limits of the remaining trigonometric functions by expressing them in terms of $\sin x$ and $\cos x$; for example, if $\cos c \neq 0$, then

$$\lim_{x\to c} \tan x = \lim_{x\to c} \frac{\sin x}{\cos x} = \frac{\sin c}{\cos c} = \tan c$$

Thus, we are led to the following theorem.

**1.6.1 THEOREM** *If $c$ is any number in the natural domain of the stated trigonometric function, then*

$$\lim_{x\to c} \sin x = \sin c \qquad \lim_{x\to c} \cos x = \cos c \qquad \lim_{x\to c} \tan x = \tan c$$

$$\lim_{x\to c} \csc x = \csc c \qquad \lim_{x\to c} \sec x = \sec c \qquad \lim_{x\to c} \cot x = \cot c$$

Theorem 1.6.1 implies that the six basic trigonometric functions are continuous on their domains. In particular, $\sin x$ and $\cos x$ are continuous everywhere.

► **Example 1** Find the limit

$$\lim_{x\to 1} \cos\left(\frac{x^2-1}{x-1}\right)$$

***Solution.*** Since the cosine function is continuous everywhere, it follows from Theorem 1.5.5 that

$$\lim_{x\to 1} \cos(g(x)) = \cos\left(\lim_{x\to 1} g(x)\right)$$

provided $\lim_{x\to 1} g(x)$ exists. Thus,

$$\lim_{x\to 1} \cos\left(\frac{x^2-1}{x-1}\right) = \lim_{x\to 1} \cos(x+1) = \cos\left(\lim_{x\to 1}(x+1)\right) = \cos 2 \;◄$$

## OBTAINING LIMITS BY SQUEEZING

In Section 1.1 we used numerical evidence to conjecture that

$$\lim_{x\to 0} \frac{\sin x}{x} = 1 \tag{2}$$

However, this limit is not easy to establish with certainty. The limit is an indeterminate form of type $0/0$, and there is no simple algebraic manipulation that one can perform to obtain the limit. Later in the text we will develop general methods for finding limits of indeterminate forms, but in this particular case we can use a technique called *squeezing*.

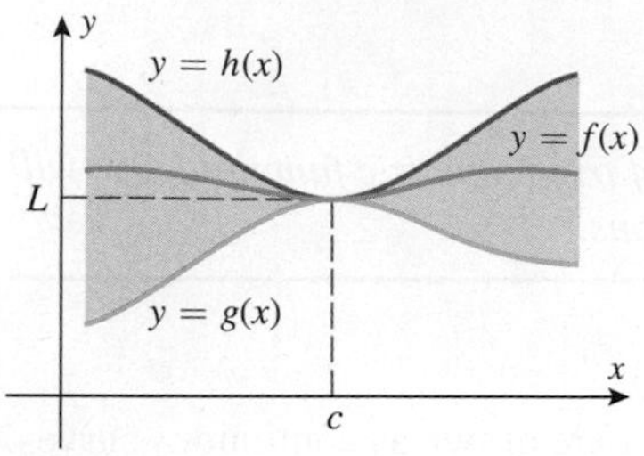

▲ Figure 1.6.2

The method of squeezing is used to prove that $f(x) \to L$ as $x \to c$ by "trapping" or "squeezing" $f$ between two functions, $g$ and $h$, whose limits as $x \to c$ are known with *certainty* to be $L$. As illustrated in Figure 1.6.2, this forces $f$ to have a limit of $L$ as well. This is the idea behind the following theorem, which we state without proof.

The Squeezing Theorem also holds for one-sided limits and limits at $+\infty$ and $-\infty$. How do you think the hypotheses would change in those cases?

**1.6.2 THEOREM (*The Squeezing Theorem*)** *Let $f$, $g$, and $h$ be functions satisfying*

$$g(x) \le f(x) \le h(x)$$

*for all $x$ in some open interval containing the number $c$, with the possible exception that the inequalities need not hold at $c$. If $g$ and $h$ have the same limit as $x$ approaches $c$, say*

$$\lim_{x\to c} g(x) = \lim_{x\to c} h(x) = L$$

*then $f$ also has this limit as $x$ approaches $c$, that is,*

$$\lim_{x\to c} f(x) = L$$

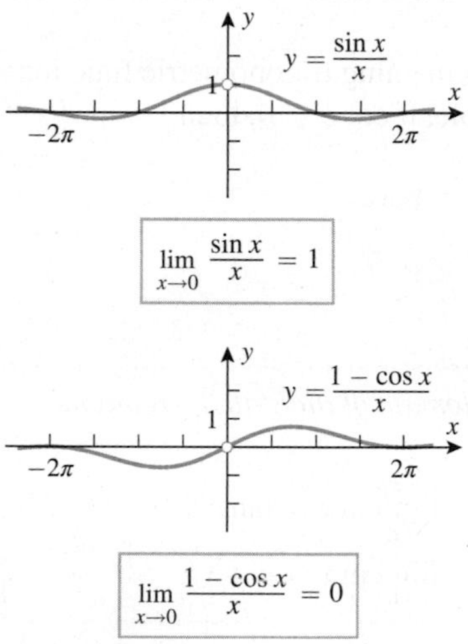

▲ Figure 1.6.3

To illustrate how the Squeezing Theorem works, we will prove the following results, which are illustrated in Figure 1.6.3.

**1.6.3 THEOREM**

$$(a)\quad \lim_{x\to 0} \frac{\sin x}{x} = 1 \qquad (b)\quad \lim_{x\to 0} \frac{1-\cos x}{x} = 0$$

**PROOF** (*a*) In this proof we will interpret $x$ as an angle in radian measure, and we will assume to start that $0 < x < \pi/2$. As illustrated in Figure 1.6.4, the area of a sector with central angle $x$ and radius 1 lies between the areas of two triangles, one with area $\frac{1}{2}\tan x$ and the other with area $\frac{1}{2}\sin x$. Since the sector has area $\frac{1}{2}x$ (see marginal note), it follows that

$$\frac{1}{2}\tan x \ge \frac{1}{2}x \ge \frac{1}{2}\sin x$$

Multiplying through by $2/(\sin x)$ and using the fact that $\sin x > 0$ for $0 < x < \pi/2$, we obtain

$$\frac{1}{\cos x} \ge \frac{x}{\sin x} \ge 1$$

Next, taking reciprocals reverses the inequalities, so we obtain

$$\cos x \le \frac{\sin x}{x} \le 1 \tag{3}$$

which squeezes the function $(\sin x)/x$ between the functions $\cos x$ and 1. Although we derived these inequalities by assuming that $0 < x < \pi/2$, they also hold for $-\pi/2 < x < 0$ [since replacing $x$ by $-x$ and using the identities $\sin(-x) = -\sin x$ and $\cos(-x) = \cos x$ leaves (3) unchanged]. Finally, since

$$\lim_{x\to 0} \cos x = 1 \quad \text{and} \quad \lim_{x\to 0} 1 = 1$$

the Squeezing Theorem implies that

$$\lim_{x\to 0} \frac{\sin x}{x} = 1$$

Recall that the area $A$ of a sector of radius $r$ and central angle $\theta$ is

$$A = \frac{1}{2}r^2\theta$$

This can be derived from the relationship

$$\frac{A}{\pi r^2} = \frac{\theta}{2\pi}$$

which states that the area of the sector is to the area of the circle as the central angle of the sector is to the central angle of the circle.

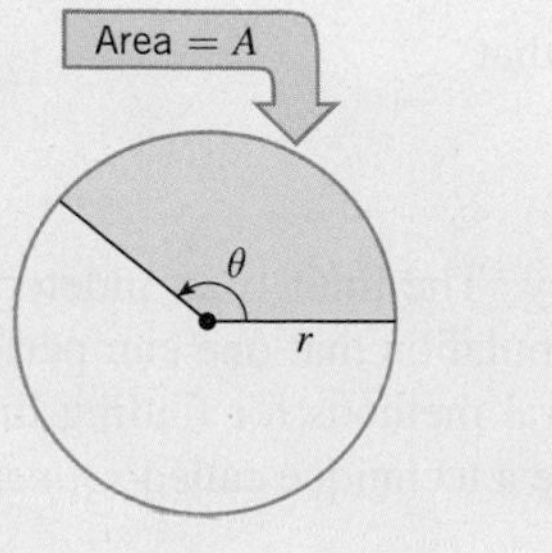

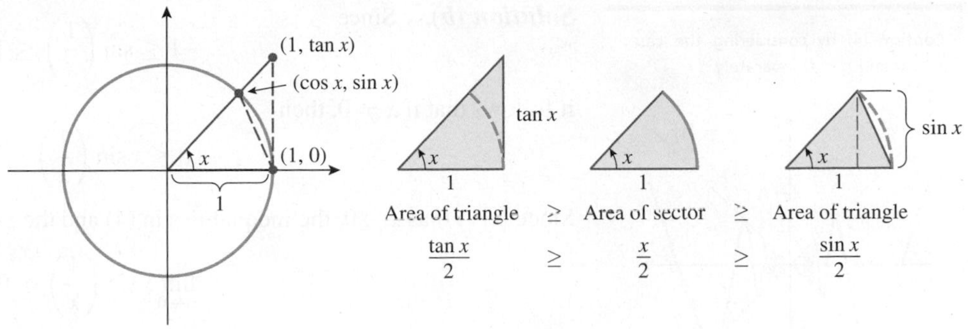


▶ Figure 1.6.4

PROOF (*b*) For this proof we will use the limit in part (*a*), the continuity of the sine function, and the trigonometric identity $\sin^2 x = 1 - \cos^2 x$. We obtain

$$\lim_{x\to 0}\frac{1-\cos x}{x} = \lim_{x\to 0}\left[\frac{1-\cos x}{x}\cdot\frac{1+\cos x}{1+\cos x}\right] = \lim_{x\to 0}\frac{\sin^2 x}{(1+\cos x)x}$$

$$= \left(\lim_{x\to 0}\frac{\sin x}{x}\right)\left(\lim_{x\to 0}\frac{\sin x}{1+\cos x}\right) = (1)\left(\frac{0}{1+1}\right) = 0 \ \blacksquare$$

▶ **Example 2** Find

$$\text{(a)}\ \lim_{x\to 0}\frac{\tan x}{x} \qquad \text{(b)}\ \lim_{\theta\to 0}\frac{\sin 2\theta}{\theta} \qquad \text{(c)}\ \lim_{x\to 0}\frac{\sin 3x}{\sin 5x}$$

***Solution (a).***

$$\lim_{x\to 0}\frac{\tan x}{x} = \lim_{x\to 0}\left(\frac{\sin x}{x}\cdot\frac{1}{\cos x}\right) = \left(\lim_{x\to 0}\frac{\sin x}{x}\right)\left(\lim_{x\to 0}\frac{1}{\cos x}\right) = (1)(1) = 1$$

***Solution (b).*** The trick is to multiply and divide by 2, which will make the denominator the same as the argument of the sine function [just as in Theorem 1.6.3(*a*)]:

$$\lim_{\theta\to 0}\frac{\sin 2\theta}{\theta} = \lim_{\theta\to 0} 2\cdot\frac{\sin 2\theta}{2\theta} = 2\lim_{\theta\to 0}\frac{\sin 2\theta}{2\theta}$$

Now make the substitution $x = 2\theta$, and use the fact that $x\to 0$ as $\theta\to 0$. This yields

$$\lim_{\theta\to 0}\frac{\sin 2\theta}{\theta} = 2\lim_{\theta\to 0}\frac{\sin 2\theta}{2\theta} = 2\lim_{x\to 0}\frac{\sin x}{x} = 2(1) = 2$$

***Solution (c).***

$$\lim_{x\to 0}\frac{\sin 3x}{\sin 5x} = \lim_{x\to 0}\frac{\dfrac{\sin 3x}{x}}{\dfrac{\sin 5x}{x}} = \lim_{x\to 0}\frac{3\cdot\dfrac{\sin 3x}{3x}}{5\cdot\dfrac{\sin 5x}{5x}} = \frac{3\cdot 1}{5\cdot 1} = \frac{3}{5} \ \blacktriangleleft$$

**TECHNOLOGY MASTERY**

Use a graphing utility to confirm the limits in Example 2, and if you have a CAS, use it to obtain the limits.

▶ **Example 3** Discuss the limits

$$\text{(a)}\ \lim_{x\to 0}\sin\left(\frac{1}{x}\right) \qquad \text{(b)}\ \lim_{x\to 0} x\sin\left(\frac{1}{x}\right)$$

***Solution (a).*** Let us view $1/x$ as an angle in radian measure. As $x\to 0^+$, the angle $1/x$ approaches $+\infty$, so the values of $\sin(1/x)$ keep oscillating between $-1$ and 1 without approaching a limit. Similarly, as $x\to 0^-$, the angle $1/x$ approaches $-\infty$, so again the values of $\sin(1/x)$ keep oscillating between $-1$ and 1 without approaching a limit. These conclusions are consistent with the graph shown in Figure 1.6.5. Note that the oscillations become more and more rapid as $x\to 0$ because $1/x$ increases (or decreases) more and more rapidly as $x$ approaches 0.

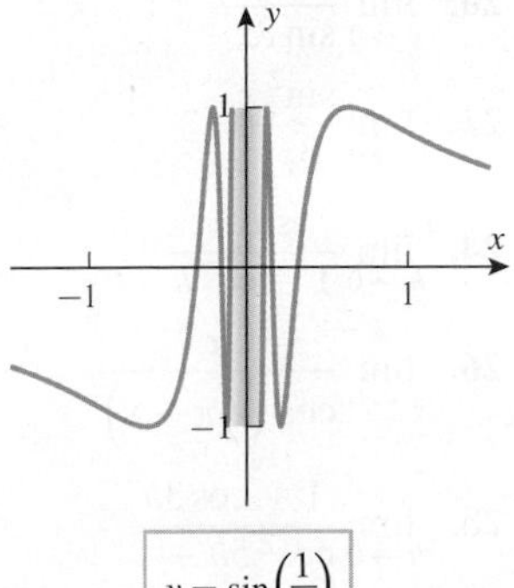


▲ Figure 1.6.5

Confirm (4) by considering the cases $x > 0$ and $x < 0$ separately.

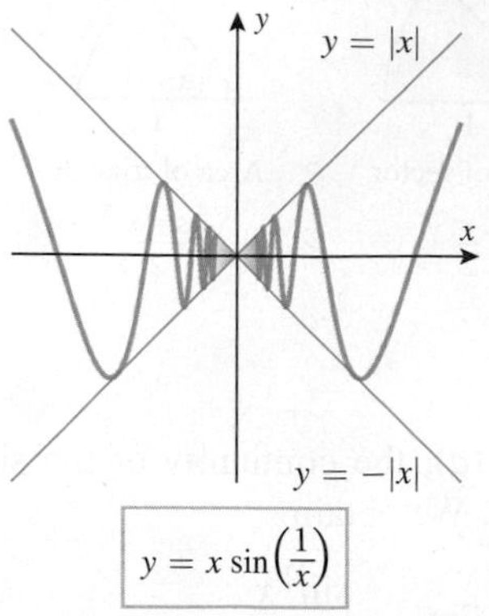


▲ **Figure 1.6.6**

***Solution (b).*** Since

$$-1 \leq \sin\left(\frac{1}{x}\right) \leq 1$$

it follows that if $x \neq 0$, then

$$-|x| \leq x \sin\left(\frac{1}{x}\right) \leq |x| \tag{4}$$

Since $|x| \to 0$ as $x \to 0$, the inequalities in (4) and the Squeezing Theorem imply that

$$\lim_{x\to 0} x \sin\left(\frac{1}{x}\right) = 0$$

This is consistent with the graph shown in Figure 1.6.6. ◄

**REMARK** It follows from part (b) of this example that the function

$$f(x) = \begin{cases} x\sin(1/x), & x \neq 0 \\ 0, & x = 0 \end{cases}$$

is continuous at $x = 0$, since the value of the function and the value of the limit are the same at 0. This shows that the behavior of a function can be very complex in the vicinity of $x = c$, even though the function is continuous at $c$.

## ✓ QUICK CHECK EXERCISES 1.6 *(See page 56 for answers.)*

1. In each part, is the given function continuous on the interval $[0, \pi/2)$?
   (a) $\sin x$ (b) $\cos x$ (c) $\tan x$ (d) $\csc x$
2. Evaluate
   (a) $\lim_{x\to 0} \dfrac{\sin x}{x}$
   (b) $\lim_{x\to 0} \dfrac{1-\cos x}{x}$.
3. Suppose a function $f$ has the property that for all real numbers $x$
   $$3 - |x| \leq f(x) \leq 3 + |x|$$
   From this we can conclude that $f(x) \to$ ______ as $x \to$ ______.

## EXERCISE SET 1.6 Graphing Utility

**1–8** Find the discontinuities, if any. ■

1. $f(x) = \sin(x^2 - 2)$
2. $f(x) = \cos\left(\dfrac{x}{x-\pi}\right)$
3. $f(x) = |\cot x|$
4. $f(x) = \sec x$
5. $f(x) = \csc x$
6. $f(x) = \dfrac{1}{1+\sin^2 x}$
7. $f(x) = \dfrac{1}{1-2\sin x}$
8. $f(x) = \sqrt{2+\tan^2 x}$

**9–10** In each part, use Theorem 1.5.6(*b*) to show that the function is continuous everywhere. ■

9. (a) $\sin(x^3 + 7x + 1)$ (b) $|\sin x|$
   (c) $\cos^3(x+1)$
10. (a) $|3 + \sin 2x|$ (b) $\sin(\sin x)$
    (c) $\cos^5 x - 2\cos^3 x + 1$

**11–32** Find the limits. ■

11. $\lim_{x\to +\infty} \cos\left(\dfrac{1}{x}\right)$
12. $\lim_{x\to +\infty} \sin\left(\dfrac{\pi x}{2-3x}\right)$
13. $\lim_{\theta\to 0} \dfrac{\sin 3\theta}{\theta}$
14. $\lim_{h\to 0} \dfrac{\sin h}{2h}$
15. $\lim_{x\to 0} \dfrac{x^2 - 3\sin x}{x}$
16. $\lim_{x\to 0} \dfrac{2 - \cos 3x - \cos 4x}{x}$
17. $\lim_{\theta\to 0^+} \dfrac{\sin\theta}{\theta^2}$
18. $\lim_{\theta\to 0} \dfrac{\sin^2\theta}{\theta}$
19. $\lim_{x\to 0} \dfrac{\tan 7x}{\sin 3x}$
20. $\lim_{x\to 0} \dfrac{\sin 6x}{\sin 8x}$
21. $\lim_{x\to 0^+} \dfrac{\sin x}{\sqrt[5]{x}}$
22. $\lim_{x\to 0} \dfrac{\sin^2 x}{3x^2}$
23. $\lim_{x\to 0} \dfrac{\sin x^2}{x}$
24. $\lim_{h\to 0} \dfrac{\sin h}{1-\cos h}$
25. $\lim_{t\to 0} \dfrac{t^2}{1-\cos^2 t}$
26. $\lim_{x\to 0} \dfrac{x}{\cos\left(\frac{1}{2}\pi - x\right)}$
27. $\lim_{\theta\to 0} \dfrac{\theta^2}{1-\cos\theta}$
28. $\lim_{h\to 0} \dfrac{1-\cos 3h}{\cos^2 5h - 1}$
29. $\lim_{x\to 0^+} \sin\left(\dfrac{1}{x}\right)$
30. $\lim_{x\to 0} \dfrac{\tan 3x^2 + \sin^2 5x}{x^2}$

**31.** $\lim_{x\to 0} \dfrac{\tan ax}{\sin bx}, \quad (a \neq 0, b \neq 0)$

**32.** $\lim_{x\to 0} \dfrac{\sin^2(kx)}{x}, \quad k \neq 0$

**33–34** (a) Complete the table and make a guess about the limit indicated. (b) Find the exact value of the limit. ■

**33.** $f(x) = \dfrac{\sin(x-5)}{x^2-25}; \ \lim_{x\to 5} f(x)$

| $x$ | 4 | 4.5 | 4.9 | 5.1 | 5.5 | 6 |
|---|---|---|---|---|---|---|
| $f(x)$ | | | | | | |

◀ Table Ex-33

**34.** $f(x) = \dfrac{\sin(x^2+3x+2)}{x+2}; \ \lim_{x\to -2} f(x)$

| $x$ | −2.1 | −2.01 | −2.001 | −1.999 | −1.99 | −1.9 |
|---|---|---|---|---|---|---|
| $f(x)$ | | | | | | |

▲ Table Ex-34

**35–38 True–False** Determine whether the statement is true or false. Explain your answer. ■

**35.** Suppose that for all real numbers $x$, a function $f$ satisfies

$$|f(x)+5| \leq |x+1|$$

Then $\lim_{x\to -1} f(x) = -5$.

**36.** For $0 < x < \pi/2$, the graph of $y = \sin x$ lies below the graph of $y = x$ and above the graph of $y = x\cos x$.

**37.** The function

$$f(x) = \begin{cases} x\sin(1/x), & x \neq 0 \\ 0, & x = 0 \end{cases}$$

is continuous everywhere.

**38.** Suppose that $M$ is a positive number and that for all real numbers $x$, a function $f$ satisfies

$$-M \leq f(x) \leq M$$

Then

$$\lim_{x\to 0} xf(x) = 0 \quad \text{and} \quad \lim_{x\to +\infty} \frac{f(x)}{x} = 0$$

**FOCUS ON CONCEPTS**

**39.** In an attempt to verify that $\lim_{x\to 0} (\sin x)/x = 1$, a student constructs the accompanying table.
(a) What mistake did the student make?
(b) What is the exact value of the limit illustrated by this table?

| $x$ | −0.01 | −0.001 | 0.001 | 0.01 |
|---|---|---|---|---|
| $(\sin x)/x$ | 0.017453 | 0.017453 | 0.017453 | 0.017453 |

▲ Table Ex-39

**40.** In the circle in the accompanying figure, a central angle of measure $\theta$ radians subtends a chord of length $c(\theta)$ and a circular arc of length $s(\theta)$. Based on your intuition, what would you conjecture is the value of $\lim_{\theta\to 0^+} c(\theta)/s(\theta)$? Verify your conjecture by computing the limit.

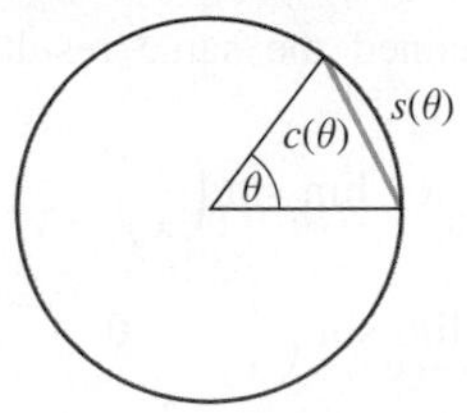


◀ Figure Ex-40

**41.** Find a nonzero value for the constant $k$ that makes

$$f(x) = \begin{cases} \dfrac{\tan kx}{x}, & x < 0 \\ 3x + 2k^2, & x \geq 0 \end{cases}$$

continuous at $x = 0$.

**42.** Is

$$f(x) = \begin{cases} \dfrac{\sin x}{|x|}, & x \neq 0 \\ 1, & x = 0 \end{cases}$$

continuous at $x = 0$? Explain.

**43.** In parts (a)–(c), find the limit by making the indicated substitution.

(a) $\lim_{x\to +\infty} x\sin\dfrac{1}{x}; \quad t = \dfrac{1}{x}$

(b) $\lim_{x\to -\infty} x\left(1 - \cos\dfrac{1}{x}\right); \quad t = \dfrac{1}{x}$

(c) $\lim_{x\to \pi} \dfrac{\pi - x}{\sin x}; \quad t = \pi - x$

**44.** Find $\lim_{x\to 2} \dfrac{\cos(\pi/x)}{x-2}$. $\left[\textit{Hint:} \text{ Let } t = \dfrac{\pi}{2} - \dfrac{\pi}{x}.\right]$

**45.** Find $\lim_{x\to 1} \dfrac{\sin(\pi x)}{x-1}$.

**46.** Find $\lim_{x\to \pi/4} \dfrac{\tan x - 1}{x - \pi/4}$.

**FOCUS ON CONCEPTS**

**47.** Use the Squeezing Theorem to show that

$$\lim_{x\to 0} x\cos\frac{50\pi}{x} = 0$$

and illustrate the principle involved by using a graphing utility to graph the equations $y = |x|$, $y = -|x|$, and $y = x\cos(50\pi/x)$ on the same screen in the window $[-1, 1] \times [-1, 1]$.

**48.** Use the Squeezing Theorem to show that

$$\lim_{x\to 0} x^2 \sin\left(\frac{50\pi}{\sqrt[3]{x}}\right) = 0$$

and illustrate the principle involved by using a graphing utility to graph the equations $y = x^2$, $y = -x^2$, and $y = x^2\sin(50\pi/\sqrt[3]{x})$ on the same screen in the window $[-0.5, 0.5] \times [-0.25, 0.25]$.

**49.** In Example 3 we used the Squeezing Theorem to prove that

$$\lim_{x\to 0} x \sin\left(\frac{1}{x}\right) = 0$$

Why couldn't we have obtained the same result by writing

$$\lim_{x\to 0} x \sin\left(\frac{1}{x}\right) = \lim_{x\to 0} x \cdot \lim_{x\to 0} \sin\left(\frac{1}{x}\right)$$

$$= 0 \cdot \lim_{x\to 0} \sin\left(\frac{1}{x}\right) = 0?$$

**50.** Sketch the graphs of the curves $y = 1 - x^2$, $y = \cos x$, and $y = f(x)$, where $f$ is a function that satisfies the inequalities

$$1 - x^2 \le f(x) \le \cos x$$

for all $x$ in the interval $(-\pi/2, \pi/2)$. What can you say about the limit of $f(x)$ as $x \to 0$? Explain.

**51.** Sketch the graphs of the curves $y = 1/x$, $y = -1/x$, and $y = f(x)$, where $f$ is a function that satisfies the inequalities

$$-\frac{1}{x} \le f(x) \le \frac{1}{x}$$

for all $x$ in the interval $[1, +\infty)$. What can you say about the limit of $f(x)$ as $x \to +\infty$? Explain your reasoning.

**52.** Draw pictures analogous to Figure 1.6.2 that illustrate the Squeezing Theorem for limits of the forms $\lim_{x\to+\infty} f(x)$ and $\lim_{x\to-\infty} f(x)$.

**53.** (a) Use the Intermediate-Value Theorem to show that the equation $x = \cos x$ has at least one solution in the interval $[0, \pi/2]$.
(b) Show graphically that there is exactly one solution in the interval.
(c) Approximate the solution to three decimal places.

**54.** (a) Use the Intermediate-Value Theorem to show that the equation $x + \sin x = 1$ has at least one solution in the interval $[0, \pi/6]$.
(b) Show graphically that there is exactly one solution in the interval.
(c) Approximate the solution to three decimal places.

**55.** In the study of falling objects near the surface of the Earth, the ***acceleration g due to gravity*** is commonly taken to be a constant 9.8 m/s$^2$. However, the elliptical shape of the Earth and other factors cause variations in this value that depend on latitude. The following formula, known as the World Geodetic System 1984 (WGS 84) Ellipsoidal Gravity Formula, is used to predict the value of $g$ at a latitude of $\phi$ degrees (either north or south of the equator):

$$g = 9.7803253359 \frac{1 + 0.0019318526461 \sin^2 \phi}{\sqrt{1 - 0.0066943799901 \sin^2 \phi}} \text{ m/s}^2$$

(a) Use a graphing utility to graph the curve $y = g(\phi)$ for $0° \le \phi \le 90°$. What do the values of $g$ at $\phi = 0°$ and at $\phi = 90°$ tell you about the WGS 84 ellipsoid model for the Earth?
(b) Show that $g = 9.8$ m/s$^2$ somewhere between latitudes of $38°$ and $39°$.

**56. Writing** In your own words, explain the *practical value* of the Squeezing Theorem.

**57. Writing** A careful examination of the proof of Theorem 1.6.3 raises the issue of whether the proof might actually be a circular argument! Read the article "A Circular Argument" by Fred Richman in the March 1993 issue of *The College Mathematics Journal*, and write a short report on the author's principal points.

✓ **QUICK CHECK ANSWERS 1.6** 1. (a) yes (b) yes (c) yes (d) no 2. (a) 1 (b) 0 3. 3; 0

## 1.7 INVERSE TRIGONOMETRIC FUNCTIONS

*A common problem in trigonometry is to find an angle x using a known value of* sin $x$, cos $x$, *or some other trigonometric function. Problems of this type involve the computation of inverse trigonometric functions. In this section we will study these functions from the viewpoint of general inverse functions. A discussion of general inverse functions is in Appendix E.*

### INVERSE TRIGONOMETRIC FUNCTIONS

The six basic trigonometric functions do not have inverses because their graphs repeat periodically and hence do not pass the horizontal line test. To circumvent this problem we will restrict the domains of the trigonometric functions to produce one-to-one functions and then define the "inverse trigonometric functions" to be the inverses of these restricted functions. The top part of Figure 1.7.1 shows geometrically how these restrictions are made for $\sin x$, $\cos x$, $\tan x$, and $\sec x$, and the bottom part of the figure shows the graphs of the corresponding inverse functions

$$\sin^{-1} x, \quad \cos^{-1} x, \quad \tan^{-1} x, \quad \sec^{-1} x$$

(also denoted by $\arcsin x$, $\arccos x$, $\arctan x$, and $\operatorname{arcsec} x$). Inverses of $\cot x$ and $\csc x$ are of lesser importance and will be considered in the exercises.

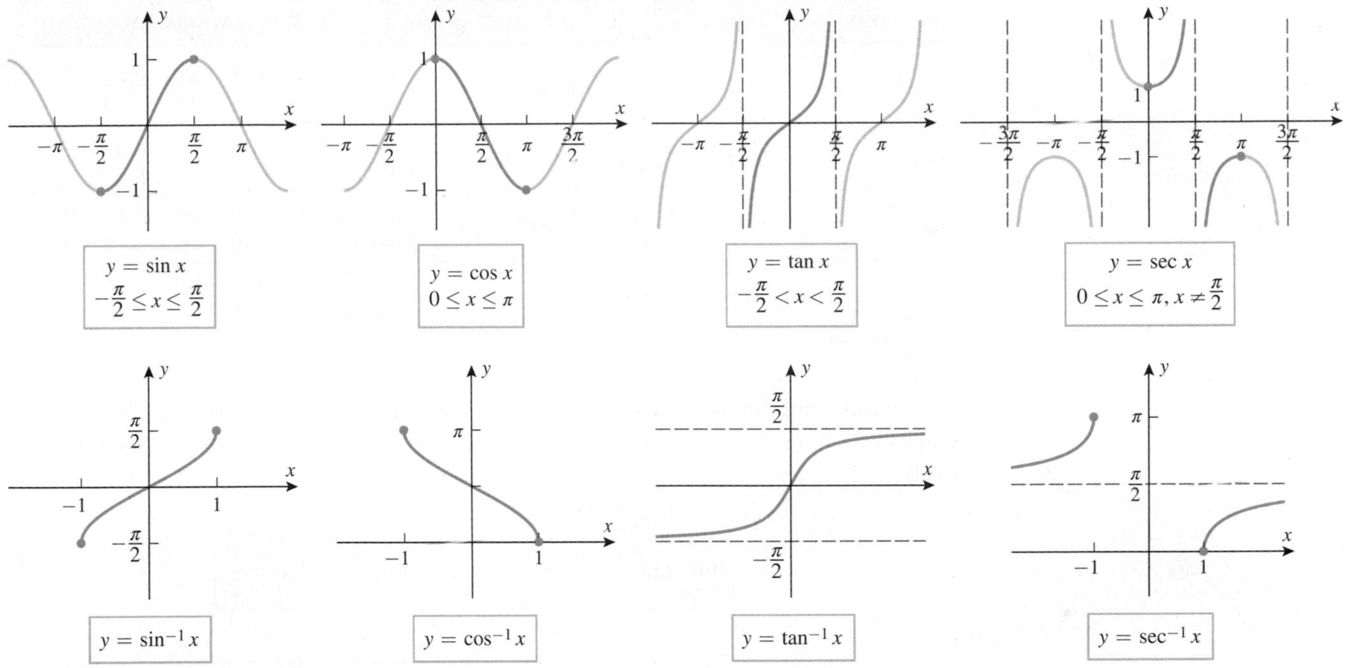


▲ **Figure 1.7.1**

If you have trouble visualizing the correspondence between the top and bottom parts of Figure 1.7.1, keep in mind that a reflection about $y = x$ converts vertical lines into horizontal lines, and vice versa; and it converts $x$-intercepts into $y$-intercepts, and vice versa.

The following formal definitions summarize the preceding discussion.

**1.7.1 DEFINITION** The ***inverse sine function***, denoted by $\sin^{-1}$, is defined to be the inverse of the restricted sine function

$$\sin x, \quad -\pi/2 \le x \le \pi/2$$

**1.7.2 DEFINITION** The ***inverse cosine function***, denoted by $\cos^{-1}$, is defined to be the inverse of the restricted cosine function

$$\cos x, \quad 0 \le x \le \pi$$

**1.7.3 DEFINITION** The ***inverse tangent function***, denoted by $\tan^{-1}$, is defined to be the inverse of the restricted tangent function

$$\tan x, \quad -\pi/2 < x < \pi/2$$

**1.7.4 DEFINITION*** The ***inverse secant function***, denoted by $\sec^{-1}$, is defined to be the inverse of the restricted secant function

$$\sec x, \quad 0 \le x \le \pi \text{ with } x \ne \pi/2$$

**WARNING**

The notations $\sin^{-1} x$, $\cos^{-1} x$, ... are reserved exclusively for the inverse trigonometric functions and are not used for reciprocals of the trigonometric functions. If we want to express the reciprocal $1/\sin x$ using an exponent, we would write $(\sin x)^{-1}$ and *never* $\sin^{-1} x$.

Table 1.7.1 summarizes the basic properties of the inverse trigonometric functions we have considered. You should confirm that the domains and ranges listed in this table are consistent with the graphs shown in Figure 1.7.1.

*There is no universal agreement on the definition of $\sec^{-1} x$, and some mathematicians prefer to restrict the domain of $\sec x$ so that $0 \le x < \pi/2$ or $\pi \le x < 3\pi/2$, which was the definition used in some earlier editions of this text. Each definition has advantages and disadvantages, but we will use the current definition to conform with the conventions used by the CAS programs *Mathematica*, *Maple*, and *Sage*.

**Table 1.7.1**
PROPERTIES OF INVERSE TRIGONOMETRIC FUNCTIONS

| FUNCTION | DOMAIN | RANGE | BASIC RELATIONSHIPS |
|---|---|---|---|
| $\sin^{-1}$ | $[-1, 1]$ | $[-\pi/2, \pi/2]$ | $\sin^{-1}(\sin x) = x$ if $-\pi/2 \le x \le \pi/2$<br>$\sin(\sin^{-1} x) = x$ if $-1 \le x \le 1$ |
| $\cos^{-1}$ | $[-1, 1]$ | $[0, \pi]$ | $\cos^{-1}(\cos x) = x$ if $0 \le x \le \pi$<br>$\cos(\cos^{-1} x) = x$ if $-1 \le x \le 1$ |
| $\tan^{-1}$ | $(-\infty, +\infty)$ | $(-\pi/2, \pi/2)$ | $\tan^{-1}(\tan x) = x$ if $-\pi/2 < x < \pi/2$<br>$\tan(\tan^{-1} x) = x$ if $-\infty < x < +\infty$ |
| $\sec^{-1}$ | $(-\infty, -1] \cup [1, +\infty)$ | $[0, \pi/2) \cup (\pi/2, \pi]$ | $\sec^{-1}(\sec x) = x$ if $0 \le x \le \pi, x \ne \pi/2$<br>$\sec(\sec^{-1} x) = x$ if $\lvert x\rvert \ge 1$ |

The following limits can be readily seen from the geometric relationships between the graphs of $y = \tan^{-1} x$ and $y = \sec^{-1} x$ and the graphs of $y = \tan x$ and $y = \sec x$, respectively.

$$\lim_{x\to-\infty} \tan^{-1} x = -\frac{\pi}{2} \qquad \lim_{x\to+\infty} \tan^{-1} x = \frac{\pi}{2} \tag{1–2}$$

$$\lim_{x\to-\infty} \sec^{-1} x = \lim_{x\to+\infty} \sec^{-1} x = \frac{\pi}{2} \tag{3}$$

## CONTINUITY OF INVERSE TRIGONOMETRIC FUNCTIONS

**▸ Example 1** Use Theorem 1.5.7 to prove that $\sin^{-1} x$ is continuous on the interval $[-1, 1]$.

***Solution.*** By definition, $\sin^{-1} x$ is the inverse of the restricted sine function whose domain is the interval $[-\pi/2, \pi/2]$ and whose range is the interval $[-1, 1]$. Since $\sin x$ is continuous on the interval $[-\pi/2, \pi/2]$, Theorem 1.5.7 implies $\sin^{-1} x$ is continuous on the interval $[-1, 1]$. ◂

Arguments similar to the solution of Example 1 show that each of the inverse trigonometric functions is continuous at each point of its domain.

**▸ Example 2** Where is the function $f(x) = \dfrac{\sec^{-1} x}{\pi + 4\tan^{-1} x}$ continuous?

***Solution.*** The fraction will be continuous at all points where the numerator and denominator are both continuous and the denominator is nonzero. Since $\sec^{-1} x$ is continuous on its domain, the numerator is continuous if $x \le -1$ or $x \ge 1$. Since $\tan^{-1} x$ is continuous everywhere, the denominator is continuous everywhere, so the fraction will be continuous at all points where the denominator is nonzero and either $x \le -1$ or $x \ge 1$. Note that $\pi + 4\tan^{-1} x = 0$ if $x = \tan(-\pi/4) = -1$. Thus, $f$ is continuous on the intervals $(-\infty, -1)$ and $[1, +\infty)$. ◂

## EVALUATING INVERSE TRIGONOMETRIC FUNCTIONS

A common problem in trigonometry is to find an angle whose sine is known. For example, you might want to find an angle $x$ in radian measure such that

$$\sin x = \tfrac{1}{2} \tag{4}$$

and, more generally, for a given value of $y$ in the interval $-1 \le y \le 1$ you might want to solve the equation

$$\sin x = y \tag{5}$$

Because $\sin x$ repeats periodically, this equation has infinitely many solutions for $x$; however, if we solve this equation as

$$x = \sin^{-1} y$$

then we isolate the specific solution that lies in the interval $[-\pi/2, \pi/2]$, since this is the range of the inverse sine. For example, Figure 1.7.2 shows four solutions of Equation (4), namely, $-11\pi/6$, $-7\pi/6$, $\pi/6$, and $5\pi/6$. Of these, $\pi/6$ is the solution in the interval $[-\pi/2, \pi/2]$, so

$$\sin^{-1}\left(\tfrac{1}{2}\right) = \pi/6 \tag{6}$$

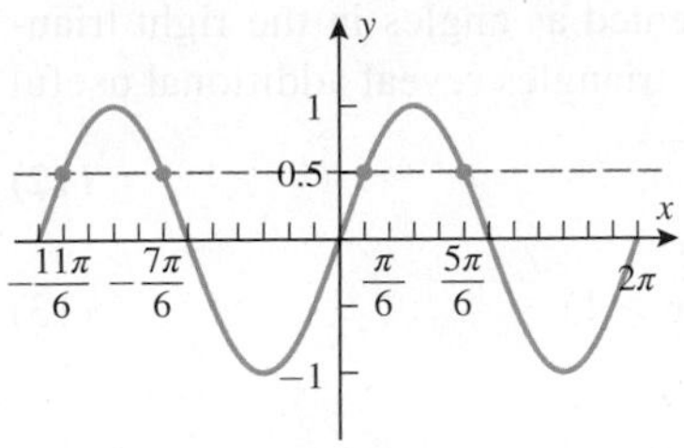


▲ **Figure 1.7.2**

**TECHNOLOGY MASTERY**

Refer to the documentation for your calculating utility to determine how to calculate inverse sines, inverse cosines, and inverse tangents; and then confirm Equation (6) numerically by showing that

$$\sin^{-1}(0.5) \approx 0.523598775598\ldots \approx \pi/6$$

In general, if we view $x = \sin^{-1} y$ as an angle in radian measure whose sine is $y$, then the restriction $-\pi/2 \le x \le \pi/2$ imposes the geometric requirement that the angle $x$ in standard position terminate in either the first or fourth quadrant or on an axis adjacent to those quadrants.

If $x = \cos^{-1} y$ is viewed as an angle in radian measure whose cosine is $y$, in what possible quadrants can $x$ lie? Answer the same question for

$$x = \tan^{-1} y \quad \text{and} \quad x = \sec^{-1} y$$

► **Example 3** Find exact values of

$$\text{(a) } \sin^{-1}(1/\sqrt{2}) \qquad \text{(b) } \sin^{-1}(-1)$$

by inspection, and confirm your results numerically using a calculating utility.

***Solution (a).*** Because $\sin^{-1}(1/\sqrt{2}) > 0$, we can view $x = \sin^{-1}(1/\sqrt{2})$ as that angle in the first quadrant such that $\sin\theta = 1/\sqrt{2}$. Thus, $\sin^{-1}(1/\sqrt{2}) = \pi/4$. You can confirm this with your calculating utility by showing that $\sin^{-1}(1/\sqrt{2}) \approx 0.785 \approx \pi/4$.

***Solution (b).*** Because $\sin^{-1}(-1) < 0$, we can view $x = \sin^{-1}(-1)$ as an angle in the fourth quadrant (or an adjacent axis) such that $\sin x = -1$. Thus, $\sin^{-1}(-1) = -\pi/2$. You can confirm this with your calculating utility by showing that $\sin^{-1}(-1) \approx -1.57 \approx -\pi/2$. ◄

**TECHNOLOGY MASTERY**

Most calculators do not provide a direct method for calculating inverse secants. In such situations the identity

$$\sec^{-1} x = \cos^{-1}(1/x) \tag{7}$$

is useful (Exercise 30). Use this formula to show that

$$\sec^{-1}(2.25) \approx 1.11 \quad \text{and} \quad \sec^{-1}(-2.25) \approx 2.03$$

If you have a calculating utility (such as a CAS) that can find $\sec^{-1} x$ directly, use it to check these values.

## IDENTITIES FOR INVERSE TRIGONOMETRIC FUNCTIONS

If we interpret $\sin^{-1} x$ as an angle in radian measure whose sine is $x$, and if that angle is *nonnegative*, then we can represent $\sin^{-1} x$ geometrically as an angle in a right triangle in which the hypotenuse has length 1 and the side opposite to the angle $\sin^{-1} x$ has length $x$ (Figure 1.7.3*a*). Moreover, the unlabeled acute angle in Figure 1.7.3*a* is $\cos^{-1} x$, since the cosine of that angle is $x$, and the unlabeled side in that figure has length $\sqrt{1-x^2}$ by the Theorem of Pythagoras (Figure 1.7.3*b*). This triangle motivates a number of useful identities involving inverse trigonometric functions that are valid for $-1 \le x \le 1$; for example,

$$\sin^{-1} x + \cos^{-1} x = \frac{\pi}{2} \tag{8}$$

$$\cos(\sin^{-1} x) = \sqrt{1-x^2} \tag{9}$$

$$\sin(\cos^{-1} x) = \sqrt{1-x^2} \tag{10}$$

$$\tan(\sin^{-1} x) = \frac{x}{\sqrt{1-x^2}} \tag{11}$$

There is little to be gained by memorizing these identities. What is important is the mastery of the *method* used to obtain them.

In a similar manner, $\tan^{-1} x$ and $\sec^{-1} x$ can be represented as angles in the right triangles shown in Figures 1.7.3*c* and 1.7.3*d* (verify). Those triangles reveal additional useful identities; for example,

$$\sec(\tan^{-1} x) = \sqrt{1+x^2} \tag{12}$$

$$\sin(\sec^{-1} x) = \frac{\sqrt{x^2-1}}{x} \quad (x \geq 1) \tag{13}$$

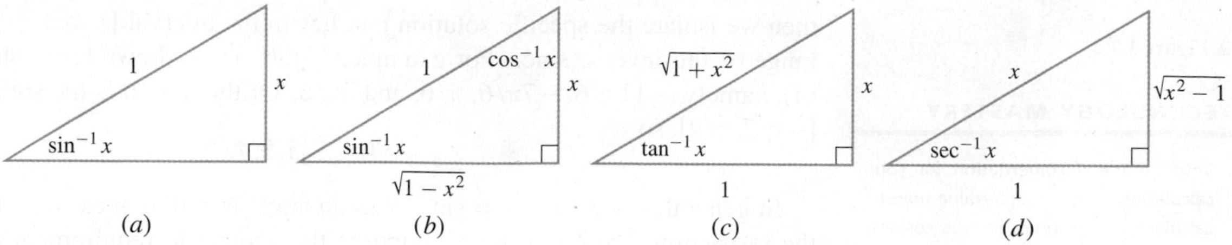


▲ **Figure 1.7.3**

**REMARK** The triangle technique does not always produce the most general form of an identity. For example, in Exercise 41 we will ask you to derive the following extension of Formula (13) that is valid for $x \leq -1$ as well as $x \geq 1$:

$$\sin(\sec^{-1} x) = \frac{\sqrt{x^2-1}}{|x|} \quad (|x| \geq 1) \tag{14}$$

Referring to Figure 1.7.1, observe that the inverse sine and inverse tangent are odd functions; that is,

$$\sin^{-1}(-x) = -\sin^{-1}(x) \quad \text{and} \quad \tan^{-1}(-x) = -\tan^{-1}(x) \tag{15–16}$$

▶ **Example 4** Figure 1.7.4 shows a computer-generated graph of $y = \sin^{-1}(\sin x)$. One might think that this graph should be the line $y = x$, since $\sin^{-1}(\sin x) = x$. Why isn't it?

***Solution.*** The relationship $\sin^{-1}(\sin x) = x$ is valid on the interval $-\pi/2 \leq x \leq \pi/2$, so we can say with certainty that the graphs of $y = \sin^{-1}(\sin x)$ and $y = x$ coincide on this interval (which is confirmed by Figure 1.7.4). However, outside of this interval the relationship $\sin^{-1}(\sin x) = x$ does not hold. For example, if the quantity $x$ lies in the interval $\pi/2 \leq x \leq 3\pi/2$, then the quantity $x - \pi$ lies in the interval $-\pi/2 \leq x \leq \pi/2$, so

$$\sin^{-1}[\sin(x-\pi)] = x - \pi$$

Thus, by using the identity $\sin(x - \pi) = -\sin x$ and the fact that $\sin^{-1}$ is an odd function, we can express $\sin^{-1}(\sin x)$ as

$$\sin^{-1}(\sin x) = \sin^{-1}[-\sin(x-\pi)] = -\sin^{-1}[\sin(x-\pi)] = -(x-\pi)$$

This shows that on the interval $\pi/2 \leq x \leq 3\pi/2$ the graph of $y = \sin^{-1}(\sin x)$ coincides with the line $y = -(x - \pi)$, which has slope $-1$ and an $x$-intercept at $x = \pi$. This agrees with Figure 1.7.4. ◀

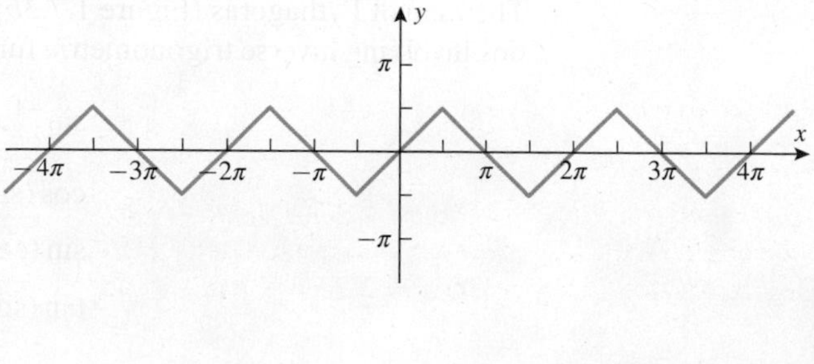


▶ **Figure 1.7.4**

## ✓ QUICK CHECK EXERCISES 1.7 (See page 63 for answers.)

1. State the domain and range for $f(x) = \cos^{-1} 2x$.
2. State the domain and range for $f(x) = \tan^{-1} 2x$.
3. In each part, determine the exact value without using a calculating utility.
   (a) $\sin^{-1}(-1) =$ ______
   (b) $\tan^{-1}(1) =$ ______
   (c) $\sin^{-1}\left(\frac{1}{2}\sqrt{3}\right) =$ ______
   (d) $\cos^{-1}\left(\frac{1}{2}\right) =$ ______
   (e) $\sec^{-1}(-2) =$ ______
4. In each part, determine the exact value without using a calculating utility.
   (a) $\sin^{-1}(\sin \pi/7) =$ ______
   (b) $\sin^{-1}(\sin 5\pi/7) =$ ______
   (c) $\tan^{-1}(\tan 13\pi/6) =$ ______
   (d) $\cos^{-1}(\cos 12\pi/7) =$ ______

## EXERCISE SET 1.7 Graphing Utility

**1–4** Determine where $f$ is continuous. ■

**1.** $f(x) = \sin^{-1} 2x$ **2.** $f(x) = 2x\cos^{-1}(\sqrt{2x})$

**3.** $f(x) = 2x\dfrac{\sqrt{\tan^{-1} x}}{x^2 - 9}$ **4.** $f(x) = \dfrac{\sin^{-1}(1/x)}{x}$

**5.** Given that $\theta = \tan^{-1}\left(\frac{4}{3}\right)$, find the exact values of $\sin\theta$, $\cos\theta$, $\cot\theta$, $\sec\theta$, and $\csc\theta$.

**6.** Given that $\theta = \sec^{-1} 2.6$, find the exact values of $\sin\theta$, $\cos\theta$, $\tan\theta$, $\cot\theta$, and $\csc\theta$.

**7.** For which values of $x$ is it true that
(a) $\cos^{-1}(\cos x) = x$ (b) $\cos(\cos^{-1} x) = x$
(c) $\tan^{-1}(\tan x) = x$ (d) $\tan(\tan^{-1} x) = x$?

**8–9** Find the exact value of the given quantity. ■

**8.** $\sec\left[\sin^{-1}\left(-\frac{3}{4}\right)\right]$ **9.** $\sin\left[2\cos^{-1}\left(\frac{3}{5}\right)\right]$

**10–11** Complete the identities using the triangle method (Figure 1.7.3). ■

**10.** (a) $\sin(\cos^{-1} x) = ?$ (b) $\tan(\cos^{-1} x) = ?$
(c) $\csc(\tan^{-1} x) = ?$ (d) $\sin(\tan^{-1} x) = ?$

**11.** (a) $\cos(\tan^{-1} x) = ?$ (b) $\tan(\cos^{-1} x) = ?$
(c) $\sin(\sec^{-1} x) = ?$ (d) $\cot(\sec^{-1} x) = ?$

**12.** (a) Use a calculating utility set to radian measure to make tables of values of $y = \sin^{-1} x$ and $y = \cos^{-1} x$ for $x = -1, -0.8, -0.6, \ldots, 0, 0.2, \ldots, 1$. Round your answers to two decimal places.
(b) Plot the points obtained in part (a), and use the points to sketch the graphs of $y = \sin^{-1} x$ and $y = \cos^{-1} x$. Confirm that your sketches agree with those in Figure 1.7.1.
(c) Use your graphing utility to graph $y = \sin^{-1} x$ and $y = \cos^{-1} x$; confirm that the graphs agree with those in Figure 1.7.1.

**13.** In each part, sketch the graph and check your work with a graphing utility.
(a) $y = \sin^{-1} 2x$ (b) $y = \tan^{-1} \frac{1}{2}x$

**14.** The ***law of cosines*** states that

$$c^2 = a^2 + b^2 - 2ab\cos\theta$$

where $a$, $b$, and $c$ are the lengths of the sides of a triangle and $\theta$ is the angle formed by sides $a$ and $b$. Find $\theta$, to the nearest degree, for the triangle with $a = 2$, $b = 3$, and $c = 4$

**15–16** Use a calculating utility to approximate the solution of each equation. Where radians are used, express your answer to four decimal places, and where degrees are used, express it to the nearest tenth of a degree. [*Note:* In each part, the solution is not in the range of the relevant inverse trigonometric function.] ■

**15.** (a) $\sin x = 0.37$, $\pi/2 < x < \pi$
(b) $\sin\theta = -0.61$, $180° < \theta < 270°$

**16.** (a) $\cos x = -0.85$, $\pi < x < 3\pi/2$
(b) $\cos\theta = 0.23$, $-90° < \theta < 0°$

### FOCUS ON CONCEPTS

**17.** (a) Use a calculating utility to evaluate the expressions $\sin^{-1}(\sin^{-1} 0.25)$ and $\sin^{-1}(\sin^{-1} 0.9)$, and explain what you think is happening in the second calculation.
(b) For what values of $x$ in the interval $-1 \le x \le 1$ will your calculating utility produce a real value for the function $\sin^{-1}(\sin^{-1} x)$?

**18.** A soccer player kicks a ball with an initial speed of 14 m/s at an angle $\theta$ with the horizontal (see the accompanying figure). The ball lands 18 m down the field. If air resistance is neglected, then the ball will have a parabolic trajectory and the horizontal range $R$ will be given by

$$R = \frac{v^2}{g}\sin 2\theta$$

where $v$ is the initial speed of the ball and $g$ is the acceleration due to gravity. Using $g = 9.8\ \text{m/s}^2$, approximate two values of $\theta$, to the nearest degree, at which the ball could have been kicked. Which angle results in the shorter time of flight? Why?

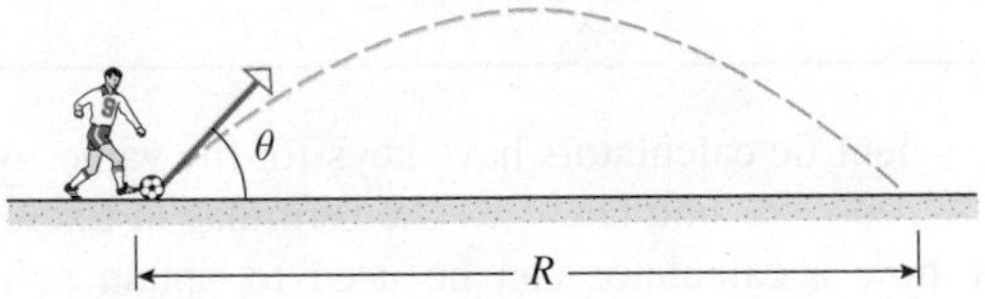


▲ **Figure Ex-18**

**19–20** Find the limits. ■

**19.** $\lim_{x\to+\infty} \sin^{-1}\left(\frac{x}{1-2x}\right)$ **20.** $\lim_{x\to+\infty} \cos(2\tan^{-1} x)$

**21–23 True–False** Determine whether the statement is true or false. Explain your answer. ■

**21.** By definition, $\sin^{-1}(\sin x) = x$ for all real numbers $x$.

**22.** The range of the inverse tangent function is the interval $-\frac{1}{2}\pi \le y \le \frac{1}{2}\pi$.

**23.** The graph of $y = \sec^{-1} x$ has a horizontal asymptote.

**24.** Suppose that $f$ is an invertible function, $f(0) = 0$, $f$ is continuous at 0, and $\lim_{x\to 0}(f(x)/x)$ exists. Given that $L = \lim_{x\to 0}(f(x)/x)$, show

$$\lim_{x\to 0} \frac{x}{f^{-1}(x)} = L$$

[*Hint:* Apply Theorem 1.5.5 to the composition $h \circ g$, where

$$h(x) = \begin{cases} f(x)/x, & x \ne 0 \\ L, & x = 0 \end{cases}$$

and $g(x) = f^{-1}(x)$.]

**25–28** Apply the result of Exercise 24, if needed, to find the limits. ■

**25.** $\lim_{x\to 0} \frac{x}{\sin^{-1} x}$ **26.** $\lim_{x\to 0} \frac{\tan^{-1} x}{x}$

**27.** $\lim_{x\to 0} \frac{\sin^{-1} 5x}{x}$ **28.** $\lim_{x\to 1} \frac{\sin^{-1}(x-1)}{x^2-1}$

**FOCUS ON CONCEPTS**

**29–30** The function $\cot^{-1} x$ is defined to be the inverse of the restricted cotangent function

$$\cot x, \quad 0 < x < \pi$$

and the function $\csc^{-1} x$ is defined to be the inverse of the restricted cosecant function

$$\csc x, \quad -\pi/2 \le x \le \pi/2, \quad x \ne 0$$

Use these definitions in these and in all subsequent exercises that involve these functions. ■

**29.** (a) Sketch the graphs of $\cot^{-1} x$ and $\csc^{-1} x$.
(b) Find the domain and range of $\cot^{-1} x$ and $\csc^{-1} x$.

**30.** Show that

(a) $\cot^{-1} x = \begin{cases} \tan^{-1}(1/x), & \text{if } x > 0 \\ \pi + \tan^{-1}(1/x), & \text{if } x < 0 \end{cases}$

(b) $\sec^{-1} x = \cos^{-1}\frac{1}{x}$, if $|x| \ge 1$

(c) $\csc^{-1} x = \sin^{-1}\frac{1}{x}$, if $|x| \ge 1$.

**31.** Most scientific calculators have keys for the values of only $\sin^{-1} x$, $\cos^{-1} x$, and $\tan^{-1} x$. The formulas in Exercise 30 show how a calculator can be used to obtain values of $\cot^{-1} x$, $\sec^{-1} x$, and $\csc^{-1} x$ for positive values of $x$. Use these formulas and a calculator to find numerical values for each of the following inverse trigonometric functions. Express your answers in degrees, rounded to the nearest tenth of a degree.
(a) $\cot^{-1} 0.7$ (b) $\sec^{-1} 1.2$ (c) $\csc^{-1} 2.3$

**32.** A camera is positioned $x$ feet from the base of a missile launching pad (see the accompanying figure). If a missile of length $a$ feet is launched vertically, show that when the base of the missile is $b$ feet above the camera lens, the angle $\theta$ subtended at the lens by the missile is

$$\theta = \cot^{-1}\frac{x}{a+b} - \cot^{-1}\frac{x}{b}$$

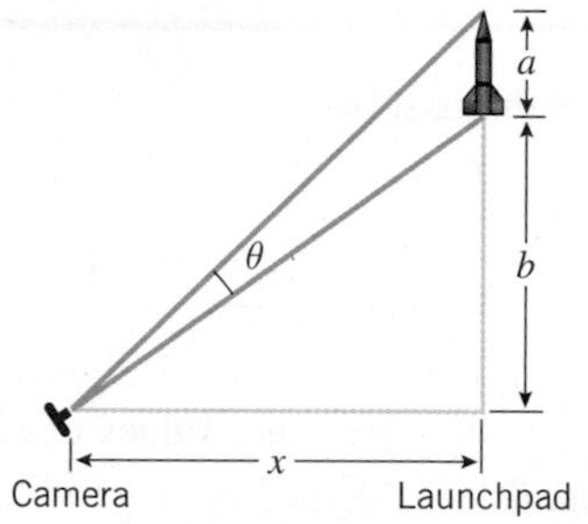


**Figure Ex-32**

**33.** The number of hours of daylight on a given day at a given point on the Earth's surface depends on the latitude $\lambda$ of the point, the angle $\gamma$ through which the Earth has moved in its orbital plane during the time period from the vernal equinox (March 21), and the angle of inclination $\phi$ of the Earth's axis of rotation measured from ecliptic north ($\phi \approx 23.45°$). The number of hours of daylight $h$ can be approximated by the formula

$$h = \begin{cases} 24, & D \ge 1 \\ 12 + \frac{2}{15}\sin^{-1} D, & |D| < 1 \\ 0, & D \le -1 \end{cases}$$

where

$$D = \frac{\sin\phi \sin\gamma \tan\lambda}{\sqrt{1 - \sin^2\phi \sin^2\gamma}}$$

and $\sin^{-1} D$ is in degree measure. Given that Fairbanks, Alaska, is located at a latitude of $\lambda = 65°$ N and also that $\gamma = 90°$ on June 20 and $\gamma = 270°$ on December 20, approximate
(a) the maximum number of daylight hours at Fairbanks to one decimal place
(b) the minimum number of daylight hours at Fairbanks to one decimal place.

***Source:*** This problem was adapted from *TEAM, A Path to Applied Mathematics*, The Mathematical Association of America, Washington, D.C., 1985.

**34.** An Earth-observing satellite has horizon sensors that can measure the angle $\theta$ shown in the accompanying figure on the next page. Let $R$ be the radius of the Earth (assumed spherical) and $h$ the distance between the satellite and the Earth's surface.

(a) Show that $\sin\theta = \frac{R}{R+h}$.
(b) Find the angle $\theta$, to the nearest degree, for a satellite that is 10,000 km from the Earth's surface (use $R = 6378$ km).

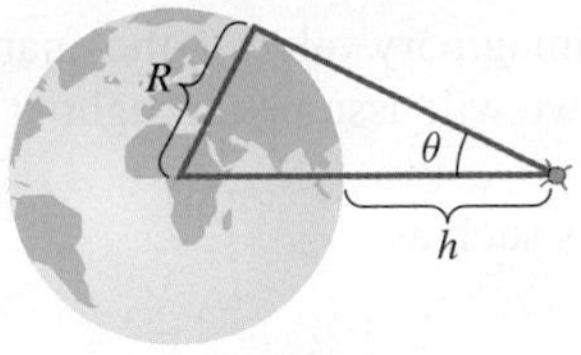


Figure Ex-34

**35.** An airplane is flying at a constant height of 3000 ft above water at a speed of 400 ft/s. The pilot is to release a survival package so that it lands in the water at a sighted point $P$. If air resistance is neglected, then the package will follow a parabolic trajectory whose equation relative to the coordinate system in the accompanying figure is

$$y = 3000 - \frac{g}{2v^2}x^2$$

where $g$ is the acceleration due to gravity and $v$ is the speed of the airplane. Using $g = 32$ ft/s$^2$, find the "line of sight" angle $\theta$, to the nearest degree, that will result in the package hitting the target point.

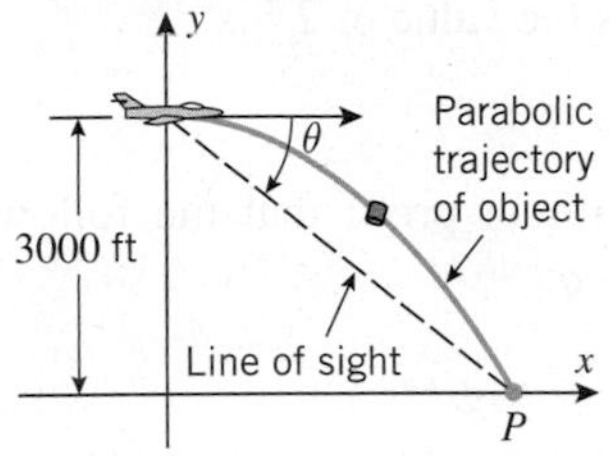


Figure Ex-35

**36.** Prove:
(a) $\sin^{-1}(-x) = -\sin^{-1} x$
(b) $\tan^{-1}(-x) = -\tan^{-1} x$.

**37.** Prove:
(a) $\cos^{-1}(-x) = \pi - \cos^{-1} x$
(b) $\sec^{-1}(-x) = \pi - \sec^{-1} x$.

**38.** Prove:
(a) $\sin^{-1} x = \tan^{-1} \dfrac{x}{\sqrt{1-x^2}} \quad (|x| < 1)$
(b) $\cos^{-1} x = \dfrac{\pi}{2} - \tan^{-1} \dfrac{x}{\sqrt{1-x^2}} \quad (|x| < 1)$.

**39.** Prove:

$$\tan^{-1} x + \tan^{-1} y = \tan^{-1}\left(\frac{x+y}{1-xy}\right)$$

provided $-\pi/2 < \tan^{-1} x + \tan^{-1} y < \pi/2$. [*Hint:* Use an identity for $\tan(\alpha + \beta)$.]

**40.** Use the result in Exercise 39 to show that
(a) $\tan^{-1} \frac{1}{2} + \tan^{-1} \frac{1}{3} = \pi/4$
(b) $2\tan^{-1} \frac{1}{3} + \tan^{-1} \frac{1}{7} = \pi/4$.

**41.** Use identities (7) and (10) to obtain identity (14).

**42. Writing** Let $\theta = \tan^{-1}(-3/4)$ and explain why the triangle in the accompanying figure may be used to evaluate $\sin\theta$ and $\cos\theta$. More generally, suppose that $q$ denotes a rational number and that $\theta = \tan^{-1} q$ or that $\theta = \sin^{-1} q$. Find right triangles, with at least two sides labeled by integers, that may be used to evaluate $\sin\theta$ and $\cos\theta$.

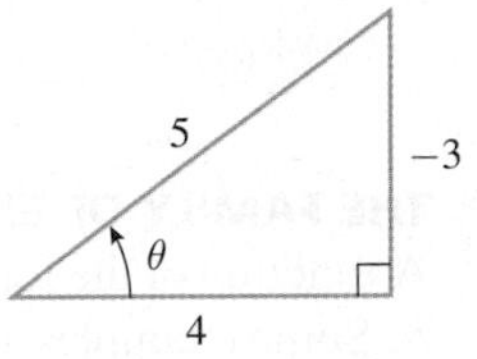


Figure Ex-42

✓ **QUICK CHECK ANSWERS 1.7** 1. domain: $[-1/2, 1/2]$; range: $[0, \pi]$ 2. domain: $(-\infty, +\infty)$; range: $(-\pi/2, \pi/2)$ 3. (a) $-\pi/2$ (b) $\pi/4$ (c) $\pi/3$ (d) $\pi/3$ (e) $2\pi/3$ 4. (a) $\pi/7$ (b) $2\pi/7$ (c) $\pi/6$ (d) $2\pi/7$

# 1.8 EXPONENTIAL AND LOGARITHMIC FUNCTIONS

*When logarithms were introduced in the seventeenth century as a computational tool, they provided scientists of that period computing power that was previously unimaginable. Although computers and calculators have replaced logarithm tables for numerical calculations, the logarithmic functions have wide-ranging applications in mathematics and science. In this section we will review some properties of exponents and logarithms and then develop results about exponential and logarithmic functions.*

## IRRATIONAL EXPONENTS

Recall from algebra that if $b$ is a nonzero real number, then nonzero *integer* powers of $b$ are defined by

$$b^n = \underbrace{b \times b \times \cdots \times b}_{n \text{ factors}} \quad \text{and} \quad b^{-n} = \frac{1}{b^n}$$

and if $n = 0$, then $b^0 = 1$. Also, if $p/q$ is a positive *rational* number expressed in lowest terms, then

$$b^{p/q} = \sqrt[q]{b^p} = (\sqrt[q]{b})^p \quad \text{and} \quad b^{-p/q} = \frac{1}{b^{p/q}}$$

If $b$ is negative, then some fractional powers of $b$ will have imaginary values—the quantity $(-2)^{1/2} = \sqrt{-2}$, for example. To avoid this complication, we will assume throughout this section that $b > 0$, even if it is not stated explicitly.

There are various methods for defining *irrational* powers such as

$$2^{\pi}, \quad 3^{\sqrt{2}}, \quad \pi^{-\sqrt{7}}$$

One approach is to define irrational powers of $b$ via successive approximations using rational powers of $b$. For example, to define $2^{\pi}$ consider the decimal representation of $\pi$:

$$3.1415926\ldots$$

From this decimal we can form a sequence of rational numbers that gets closer and closer to $\pi$, namely,

$$3.1, \quad 3.14, \quad 3.141, \quad 3.1415, \quad 3.14159$$

and from these we can form a sequence of *rational* powers of 2:

$$2^{3.1}, \quad 2^{3.14}, \quad 2^{3.141}, \quad 2^{3.1415}, \quad 2^{3.14159}$$

Since the exponents of the terms in this sequence get successively closer to $\pi$, it seems plausible that the terms themselves will get successively closer to some number. It is that number that we *define* to be $2^{\pi}$. This is illustrated in Table 1.8.1, which we generated using a calculator. The table suggests that to four decimal places the value of $2^{\pi}$ is

$$2^{\pi} \approx 8.8250 \tag{1}$$

**Table 1.8.1**

| $x$ | $2^x$ |
|---|---|
| 3 | 8.000000 |
| 3.1 | 8.574188 |
| 3.14 | 8.815241 |
| 3.141 | 8.821353 |
| 3.1415 | 8.824411 |
| 3.14159 | 8.824962 |
| 3.141592 | 8.824974 |
| 3.1415926 | 8.824977 |

**TECHNOLOGY MASTERY**

Use a calculating utility to verify the results in Table 1.8.1, and then verify (1) by using the utility to compute $2^{\pi}$ directly.

With this notion for irrational powers, we remark without proof that the following familiar laws of exponents hold for all real values of $p$ and $q$:

$$b^p b^q = b^{p+q}, \quad \frac{b^p}{b^q} = b^{p-q}, \quad (b^p)^q = b^{pq}$$

## THE FAMILY OF EXPONENTIAL FUNCTIONS

A function of the form $f(x) = b^x$, where $b > 0$, is called an ***exponential function with base b***. Some examples are

$$f(x) = 2^x, \quad f(x) = \left(\tfrac{1}{2}\right)^x, \quad f(x) = \pi^x$$

Note that an exponential function has a constant base and variable exponent. Thus, functions such as $f(x) = x^2$ and $f(x) = x^{\pi}$ would *not* be classified as exponential functions, since they have a variable base and a constant exponent.

Figure 1.8.1 illustrates that the graph of $y = b^x$ has one of three general forms, depending on the value of $b$. The graph of $y = b^x$ has the following properties:

- The graph passes through (0, 1) because $b^0 = 1$.
- If $b > 1$, the value of $b^x$ increases as $x$ increases. As you traverse the graph of $y = b^x$ from left to right, the values of $b^x$ increase indefinitely. If you traverse the graph from right to left, the values of $b^x$ decrease toward zero but never reach zero. Thus, the $x$-axis is a horizontal asymptote of the graph of $b^x$.
- If $0 < b < 1$, the value of $b^x$ decreases as $x$ increases. As you traverse the graph of $y = b^x$ from left to right, the values of $b^x$ decrease toward zero but never reach zero. Thus, the $x$-axis is a horizontal asymptote of the graph of $b^x$. If you traverse the graph from right to left, the values of $b^x$ increase indefinitely.
- If $b = 1$, then the value of $b^x$ is constant.

Some typical members of the family of exponential functions are graphed in Figure 1.8.2. This figure illustrates that the graph of $y = (1/b)^x$ is the reflection of the graph of $y = b^x$ about the $y$-axis. This is because replacing $x$ by $-x$ in the equation $y = b^x$ yields

$$y = b^{-x} = (1/b)^x$$

The figure also conveys that for $b > 1$, the larger the base $b$, the more rapidly the function $f(x) = b^x$ increases for $x > 0$.

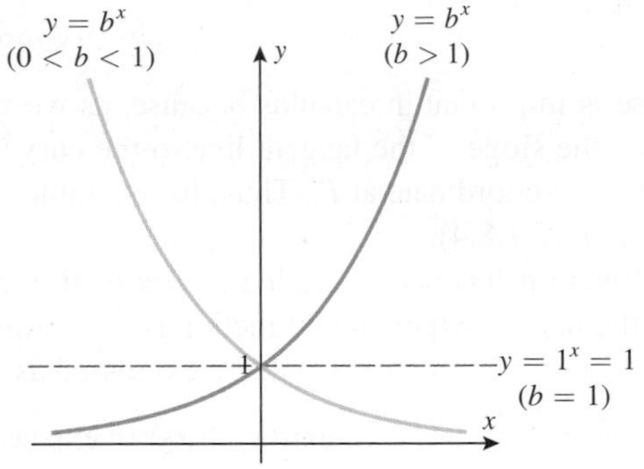


▲ **Figure 1.8.1**

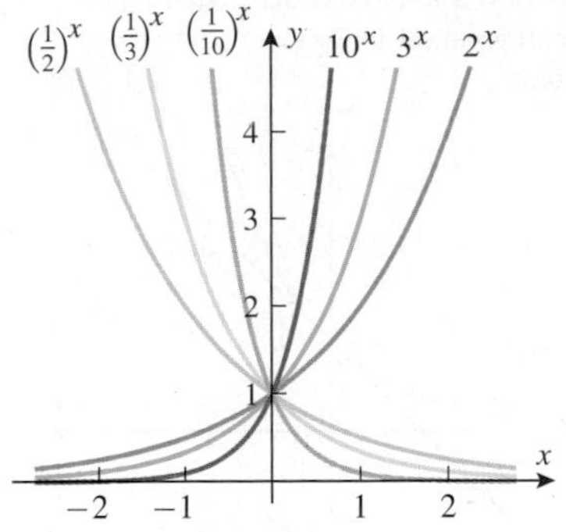


▲ **Figure 1.8.2** The family $y = b^x$ $(b > 0)$

Since it is not our objective in this section to develop the properties of exponential functions in rigorous mathematical detail, we will simply observe without proof that the following properties of exponential functions are consistent with the graphs shown in Figures 1.8.1 and 1.8.2.

> **1.8.1 THEOREM** *If $b > 0$ and $b \neq 1$, then:*
>
> (a) *The function $f(x) = b^x$ is defined for all real values of $x$, so its natural domain is $(-\infty, +\infty)$.*
>
> (b) *The function $f(x) = b^x$ is continuous on the interval $(-\infty, +\infty)$, and its range is $(0, +\infty)$.*

▶ **Example 1** Sketch the graph of the function $f(x) = 1 - 2^x$ and find its domain and range.

***Solution.*** Start with a graph of $y = 2^x$. Reflect this graph across the $x$-axis to obtain the graph of $y = -2^x$, then translate that graph upward by 1 unit to obtain the graph of $y = 1 - 2^x$ (Figure 1.8.3). The dashed line in the third part of Figure 1.8.3 is a horizontal asymptote for the graph. You should be able to see from the graph that the domain of $f$ is $(-\infty, +\infty)$ and the range is $(-\infty, 1)$. ◀

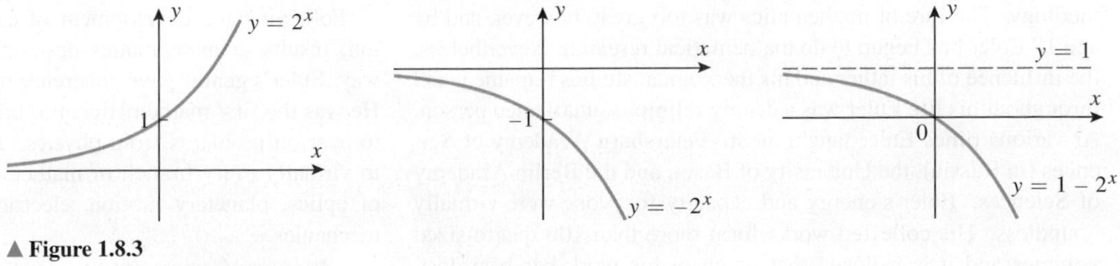


▲ **Figure 1.8.3**

## THE NATURAL EXPONENTIAL FUNCTION

The use of the letter $e$ is in honor of the Swiss mathematician Leonhard Euler who is credited with recognizing the mathematical importance of this constant.

Among all possible bases for exponential functions there is one particular base that plays a special role in calculus. That base, denoted by the letter $e$, is a certain irrational number whose value to six decimal places is

$$e \approx 2.718282 \tag{2}$$

This base is important in calculus because, as we will prove later, $b = e$ is the only base for which the slope of the tangent line to the curve $y = b^x$ at any point $P$ on the curve is equal to the $y$-coordinate at $P$. Thus, for example, the tangent line to $y = e^x$ at $(0, 1)$ has slope 1 (Figure 1.8.4).

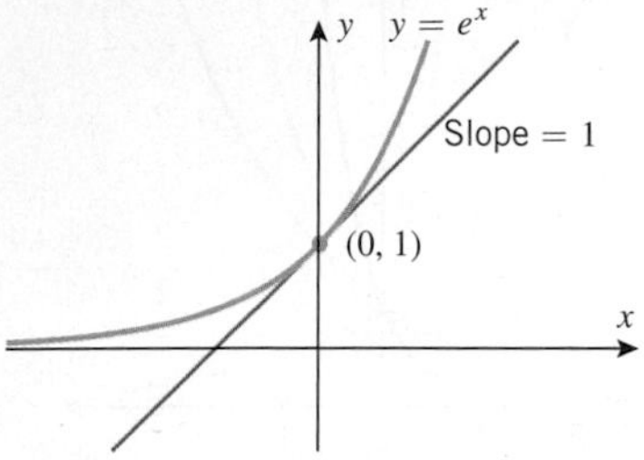


▲ **Figure 1.8.4** The tangent line to the graph of $y = e^x$ at $(0, 1)$ has slope 1.

The function $f(x) = e^x$ is called the ***natural exponential function***. To simplify typography, the natural exponential function is sometimes written as $\exp(x)$, in which case the relationship $e^{x_1+x_2} = e^{x_1}e^{x_2}$ would be expressed as

$$\exp(x_1 + x_2) = \exp(x_1)\exp(x_2)$$

**TECHNOLOGY MASTERY** Your technology utility should have keys or commands for approximating $e$ and for graphing the natural exponential function. Read your documentation on how to do this and use your utility to confirm (2) and to generate the graphs in Figures 1.8.2 and 1.8.4.

The constant $e$ also arises in the context of the graph of the equation

$$y = \left(1 + \frac{1}{x}\right)^x \tag{3}$$

As suggested by Figure 1.8.5 and Table 1.8.2, $y = e$ is a horizontal asymptote of this graph, and the limits

$$\lim_{x\to+\infty}\left(1 + \frac{1}{x}\right)^x = e \quad \text{and} \quad \lim_{x\to-\infty}\left(1 + \frac{1}{x}\right)^x = e \tag{4–5}$$

are satisfied. These limits can be derived from the limit

$$\lim_{x\to 0}(1 + x)^{1/x} = e \tag{6}$$

which is sometimes taken as the definition of $e$.

**Leonhard Euler (1707–1783)** Euler was probably the most prolific mathematician who ever lived. It has been said that "Euler wrote mathematics as effortlessly as most men breathe." He was born in Basel, Switzerland, and was the son of a Protestant minister who had himself studied mathematics. Euler's genius developed early. He attended the University of Basel, where by age 16 he obtained both a Bachelor of Arts degree and a Master's degree in philosophy. While at Basel, Euler had the good fortune to be tutored one day a week in mathematics by a distinguished mathematician, Johann Bernoulli. At the urging of his father, Euler then began to study theology. The lure of mathematics was too great, however, and by age 18 Euler had begun to do mathematical research. Nevertheless, the influence of his father and his theological studies remained, and throughout his life Euler was a deeply religious, unaffected person. At various times Euler taught at St. Petersburg Academy of Sciences (in Russia), the University of Basel, and the Berlin Academy of Sciences. Euler's energy and capacity for work were virtually boundless. His collected works form more than 100 quarto-sized volumes and it is believed that much of his work has been lost. What is particularly astonishing is that Euler was blind for the last 17 years of his life, and this was one of his most productive periods! Euler's flawless memory was phenomenal. Early in his life he memorized the entire *Aeneid* by Virgil, and at age 70 he could not only recite the entire work but could also state the first and last sentence on each page of the book from which he memorized the work. His ability to solve problems in his head was beyond belief. He worked out in his head major problems of lunar motion that baffled Isaac Newton and once did a complicated calculation in his head to settle an argument between two students whose computations differed in the fiftieth decimal place.

Following the development of calculus by Leibniz and Newton, results in mathematics developed rapidly in a disorganized way. Euler's genius gave coherence to the mathematical landscape. He was the first mathematician to bring the full power of calculus to bear on problems from physics. He made major contributions to virtually every branch of mathematics as well as to the theory of optics, planetary motion, electricity, magnetism, and general mechanics.

*[Image: http://commons.wikimedia.org/wiki/File:Leonhard_Euler_by_Handmann_.png]*

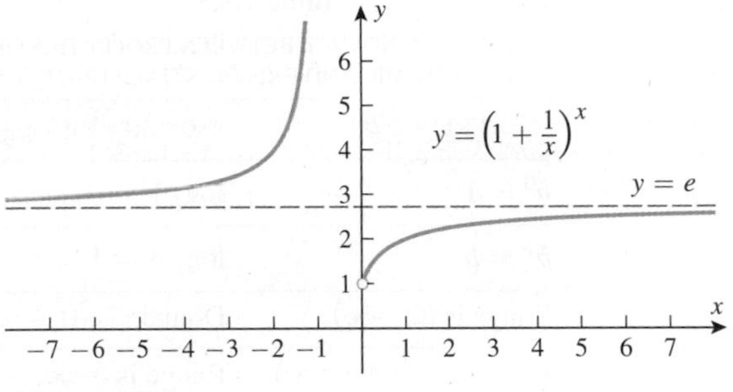


▲ **Figure 1.8.5**

**Table 1.8.2**

THE VALUES OF $(1 + 1/x)^x$ APPROACH $e$ AS $x \to +\infty$

| $x$ | $1 + \frac{1}{x}$ | $\left(1 + \frac{1}{x}\right)^x$ |
|---|---|---|
| 1 | 2 | ≈2.000000 |
| 10 | 1.1 | 2.593742 |
| 100 | 1.01 | 2.704814 |
| 1000 | 1.001 | 2.716924 |
| 10,000 | 1.0001 | 2.718146 |
| 100,000 | 1.00001 | 2.718268 |
| 1,000,000 | 1.000001 | 2.718280 |

## LOGARITHMIC FUNCTIONS

Recall from algebra that a logarithm is an exponent. More precisely, if $b > 0$ and $b \neq 1$, then for a positive value of $x$ the expression

$$\log_b x$$

(read "the logarithm to the base $b$ of $x$") denotes that exponent to which $b$ must be raised to produce $x$. Thus, for example,

> Logarithms with base 10 are called ***common logarithms*** and are often written without explicit reference to the base. Thus, the symbol $\log x$ generally denotes $\log_{10} x$.

$$\log_{10} 100 = 2, \quad \log_{10}(1/1000) = -3, \quad \log_2 16 = 4, \quad \log_b 1 = 0, \quad \log_b b = 1$$

$10^2 = 100$ | $10^{-3} = 1/1000$ | $2^4 = 16$ | $b^0 = 1$ | $b^1 = b$

We call the function $f(x) = \log_b x$ the ***logarithmic function with base b***.

Logarithmic functions can also be viewed as inverses of exponential functions. To see why this is so, observe from Figure 1.8.1 that if $b > 0$ and $b \neq 1$, then the graph of $f(x) = b^x$ passes the horizontal line test, so $b^x$ has an inverse. We can find a formula for this inverse with $x$ as the independent variable by solving the equation

$$x = b^y$$

for $y$ as a function of $x$. But this equation states that $y$ is the logarithm to the base $b$ of $x$, so it can be rewritten as

$$y = \log_b x$$

Thus, we have established part $(a)$ of the following theorem. Theorem 1.5.7 then implies part $(b)$.

> **1.8.2 THEOREM** *Let $b > 0$, $b \neq 1$.*
>
> *(a) The functions $b^x$ and $\log_b x$ are inverse functions.*
>
> *(b) The function $\log_b x$ is continuous on $(0, +\infty)$.*

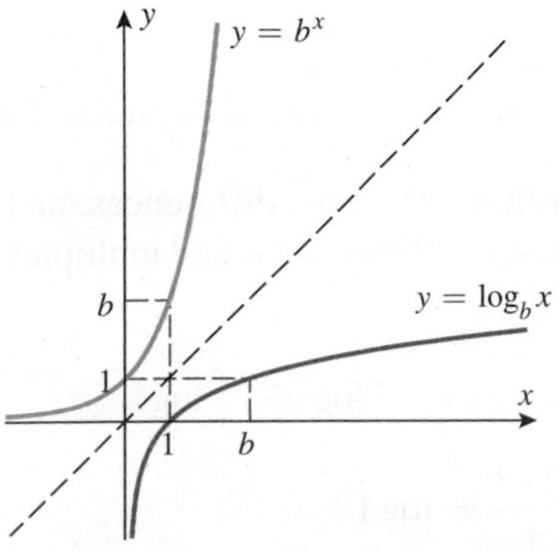


▲ **Figure 1.8.6**

It follows from this theorem that the graphs of $y = b^x$ and $y = \log_b x$ are reflections of one another about the line $y = x$ (see Figure 1.8.6 for the case where $b > 1$). Figure 1.8.7 shows the graphs of $y = \log_b x$ for various values of $b$. Observe that they all pass through the point $(1, 0)$.

The most important logarithm function in applications is the one with base $e$. This is called the ***natural logarithm function*** because the function $\log_e x$ is the inverse of the natural exponential function $e^x$. It is standard to denote the natural logarithm of $x$ by $\ln x$ (read "ell en of $x$"), rather than $\log_e x$. For example,

$$\ln 1 = 0, \quad \ln e = 1, \quad \ln 1/e = -1, \quad \ln(e^2) = 2$$

Since $e^0 = 1$ | Since $e^1 = e$ | Since $e^{-1} = 1/e$ | Since $e^2 = e^2$

In general,

$$y = \ln x \quad \text{if and only if} \quad x = e^y$$

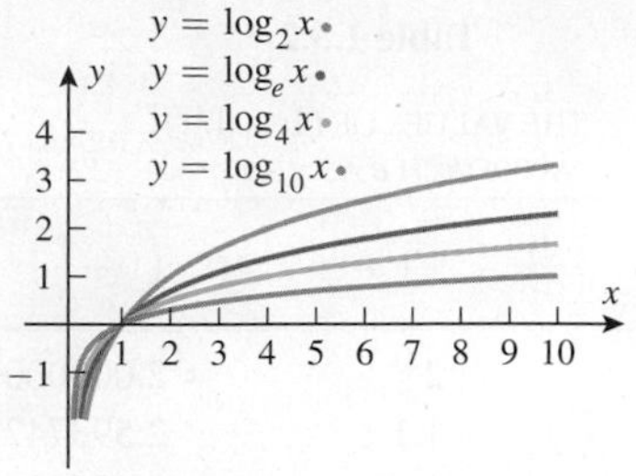


▲ **Figure 1.8.7** The family $y = \log_b x\ (b > 1)$

As shown in Table 1.8.3, the inverse relationship between $b^x$ and $\log_b x$ produces a correspondence between some basic properties of those functions.

**Table 1.8.3**

CORRESPONDENCE BETWEEN PROPERTIES OF LOGARITHMIC AND EXPONENTIAL FUNCTIONS

| PROPERTY OF $b^x$ | PROPERTY OF $\log_b x$ |
|---|---|
| $b^0 = 1$ | $\log_b 1 = 0$ |
| $b^1 = b$ | $\log_b b = 1$ |
| Range is $(0, +\infty)$ | Domain is $(0, +\infty)$ |
| Domain is $(-\infty, +\infty)$ | Range is $(-\infty, +\infty)$ |
| $x$-axis is a horizontal asymptote | $y$-axis is a vertical asymptote |

It also follows from the cancellation properties of inverse functions that

$$\log_b (b^x) = x \quad \text{for all real values of } x$$
$$b^{\log_b x} = x \quad \text{for } x > 0 \tag{7}$$

In the special case where $b = e$, these equations become

$$\ln (e^x) = x \quad \text{for all real values of } x$$
$$e^{\ln x} = x \quad \text{for } x > 0 \tag{8}$$

**TECHNOLOGY MASTERY**

Use your graphing utility to generate the graphs of $y = \ln x$ and $y = \log x$.

In words, the functions $b^x$ and $\log_b x$ cancel out the effect of one another when composed in either order; for example,

$$\log 10^x = x, \quad 10^{\log x} = x, \quad \ln e^x = x, \quad e^{\ln x} = x, \quad \ln e^5 = 5, \quad e^{\ln \pi} = \pi$$

## SOLVING EQUATIONS INVOLVING EXPONENTIALS AND LOGARITHMS

You should be familiar with the following properties of logarithms from your earlier studies.

**1.8.3 THEOREM** (*Algebraic Properties of Logarithms*) *If $b > 0, b \neq 1, a > 0, c > 0$, and $r$ is any real number, then:*

(*a*) $\log_b(ac) = \log_b a + \log_b c$ — Product property

(*b*) $\log_b(a/c) = \log_b a - \log_b c$ — Quotient property

(*c*) $\log_b(a^r) = r \log_b a$ — Power property

(*d*) $\log_b(1/c) = -\log_b c$ — Reciprocal property

**WARNING**

Expressions of the form $\log_b (u + v)$ and $\log_b (u - v)$ have no useful simplifications. In particular,

$$\log_b (u + v) \neq \log_b (u) + \log_b (v)$$
$$\log_b (u - v) \neq \log_b (u) - \log_b (v)$$

These properties are often used to expand a single logarithm into sums, differences, and multiples of other logarithms and, conversely, to condense sums, differences, and multiples of logarithms into a single logarithm. For example,

$$\log \frac{xy^5}{\sqrt{z}} = \log xy^5 - \log \sqrt{z} = \log x + \log y^5 - \log z^{1/2} = \log x + 5 \log y - \tfrac{1}{2} \log z$$

$$5 \log 2 + \log 3 - \log 8 = \log 32 + \log 3 - \log 8 = \log \frac{32 \cdot 3}{8} = \log 12$$

$$\tfrac{1}{3} \ln x - \ln (x^2 - 1) + 2 \ln (x + 3) = \ln x^{1/3} - \ln (x^2 - 1) + \ln (x + 3)^2 = \ln \frac{\sqrt[3]{x}(x + 3)^2}{x^2 - 1}$$

An equation of the form $\log_b x = k$ can be solved for $x$ by rewriting it in the exponential form $x = b^k$, and an equation of the form $b^x = k$ can be solved by rewriting it in the logarithm form $x = \log_b k$. Alternatively, the equation $b^x = k$ can be solved by taking *any* logarithm of both sides (but usually log or ln) and applying part (*c*) of Theorem 1.8.3. These ideas are illustrated in the following example.

▶ **Example 2** Find $x$ such that

$$\text{(a) } \log x = \sqrt{2} \qquad \text{(b) } \ln(x+1) = 5 \qquad \text{(c) } 5^x = 7$$

***Solution (a).*** Converting the equation to exponential form yields

$$x = 10^{\sqrt{2}} \approx 25.95$$

***Solution (b).*** Converting the equation to exponential form yields

$$x + 1 = e^5 \quad \text{or} \quad x = e^5 - 1 \approx 147.41$$

***Solution (c).*** Converting the equation to logarithmic form yields

$$x = \log_5 7 \approx 1.21$$

Alternatively, taking the natural logarithm of both sides and using the power property of logarithms yields

$$x \ln 5 = \ln 7 \quad \text{or} \quad x = \frac{\ln 7}{\ln 5} \approx 1.21 \blacktriangleleft$$

pete stopher/Getty Images

*Power to satellites can be supplied by batteries, fuel cells, solar cells, or radioisotope devices.*

▶ **Example 3** A satellite that requires 7 watts of power to operate at full capacity is equipped with a radioisotope power supply whose power output $P$ in watts is given by the equation

$$P = 75e^{-t/125}$$

where $t$ is the time in days that the supply is used. How long can the satellite operate at full capacity?

***Solution.*** The power $P$ will fall to 7 watts when

$$7 = 75e^{-t/125}$$

The solution for $t$ is as follows:

$$\begin{aligned} 7/75 &= e^{-t/125} \\ \ln(7/75) &= \ln(e^{-t/125}) \\ \ln(7/75) &= -t/125 \\ t &= -125 \ln(7/75) \approx 296.4 \end{aligned}$$

so the satellite can operate at full capacity for about 296 days. ◀

Here is a more complicated example.

▶ **Example 4** Solve $\dfrac{e^x - e^{-x}}{2} = 1$ for $x$.

***Solution.*** Multiplying both sides of the given equation by 2 yields

$$e^x - e^{-x} = 2$$

or equivalently,

$$e^x - \frac{1}{e^x} = 2$$

Multiplying through by $e^x$ yields

$$e^{2x} - 1 = 2e^x \quad \text{or} \quad e^{2x} - 2e^x - 1 = 0$$

This is really a quadratic equation in disguise, as can be seen by rewriting it in the form

$$(e^x)^2 - 2e^x - 1 = 0$$

and letting $u = e^x$ to obtain

$$u^2 - 2u - 1 = 0$$

Solving for $u$ by the quadratic formula yields

$$u = \frac{2 \pm \sqrt{4+4}}{2} = \frac{2 \pm \sqrt{8}}{2} = 1 \pm \sqrt{2}$$

or, since $u = e^x$,

$$e^x = 1 \pm \sqrt{2}$$

But $e^x$ cannot be negative, so we discard the negative value $1 - \sqrt{2}$; thus,

$$e^x = 1 + \sqrt{2}$$

$$\ln e^x = \ln(1 + \sqrt{2})$$

$$x = \ln(1 + \sqrt{2}) \approx 0.881 \blacktriangleleft$$

## CHANGE OF BASE FORMULA FOR LOGARITHMS

Scientific calculators generally have no keys for evaluating logarithms with bases other than 10 or $e$. However, this is not a serious deficiency because it is possible to express a logarithm with any base in terms of logarithms with any other base (see Exercise 42). For example, the following formula expresses a logarithm with base $b$ in terms of natural logarithms:

$$\log_b x = \frac{\ln x}{\ln b} \tag{9}$$

We can derive this result by letting $y = \log_b x$, from which it follows that $b^y = x$. Taking the natural logarithm of both sides of this equation we obtain $y \ln b = \ln x$, from which (9) follows.

▶ **Example 5** Use a calculating utility to evaluate $\log_2 5$ by expressing this logarithm in terms of natural logarithms.

***Solution.*** From (9) we obtain

$$\log_2 5 = \frac{\ln 5}{\ln 2} \approx 2.321928 \blacktriangleleft$$

## LOGARITHMIC SCALES IN SCIENCE AND ENGINEERING

Logarithms are used in science and engineering to deal with quantities whose units vary over an excessively wide range of values. For example, the "loudness" of a sound can be measured by its ***intensity*** $I$ (in watts per square meter), which is related to the energy transmitted by the sound wave—the greater the intensity, the greater the transmitted energy, and the louder the sound is perceived by the human ear. However, intensity units are unwieldy because they vary over an enormous range. For example, a sound at the threshold of human hearing has an intensity of about $10^{-12}$ W/m$^2$, a close whisper has an intensity that is about 100 times the hearing threshold, and a jet engine at 50 meters has an intensity that is about $10{,}000{,}000{,}000{,}000 = 10^{13}$ times the hearing threshold. To see how logarithms can be used to reduce this wide spread, observe that if

$$y = \log x$$

then increasing $x$ by a *factor* of 10 *adds* 1 unit to $y$ since

$$\log 10x = \log 10 + \log x = 1 + y$$

Physicists and engineers take advantage of this property by measuring loudness in terms of the ***sound level*** $\beta$, which is defined by

$$\beta = 10 \log (I/I_0)$$

where $I_0 = 10^{-12}$ W/m$^2$ is a reference intensity close to the threshold of human hearing. The units of $\beta$ are ***decibels*** (dB), named in honor of the telephone inventor Alexander Graham Bell. With this scale of measurement, *multiplying* the intensity $I$ by a factor of 10 *adds* 10 dB to the sound level $\beta$ (verify). This results in a more tractable scale than intensity for measuring sound loudness (Table 1.8.4). Some other familiar logarithmic scales are the ***Richter scale*** used to measure earthquake intensity and the **pH** ***scale*** used to measure acidity in chemistry, both of which are discussed in the exercises.

**Table 1.8.4**

| $\beta$ (dB) | $I/I_0$ |
|---|---|
| 0 | $10^0 = 1$ |
| 10 | $10^1 = 10$ |
| 20 | $10^2 = 100$ |
| 30 | $10^3 = 1000$ |
| 40 | $10^4 = 10{,}000$ |
| 50 | $10^5 = 100{,}000$ |
| ⋮ | ⋮ |
| 120 | $10^{12} = 1{,}000{,}000{,}000{,}000$ |

Mooneydriver/iStockphoto

*The roar of a space shuttle near the launchpad would damage your hearing without ear protection.*

▶ **Example 6** A space shuttle taking off generates a sound level of 150 dB near the launchpad. A person exposed to this level of sound would experience severe physical injury. By comparison, a car horn at 1 meter has a sound level of 110 dB, near the threshold of pain for many people. What is the ratio of sound intensity of a space shuttle takeoff to that of a car horn?

***Solution.*** Let $I_1$ and $\beta_1$ (= 150 dB) denote the sound intensity and sound level of the space shuttle taking off, and let $I_2$ and $\beta_2$ (= 110 dB) denote the sound intensity and sound level of a car horn. Then

$$\begin{aligned}
I_1/I_2 &= (I_1/I_0)/(I_2/I_0) \\
\log (I_1/I_2) &= \log (I_1/I_0) - \log (I_2/I_0) \\
10 \log (I_1/I_2) &= 10 \log (I_1/I_0) - 10 \log (I_2/I_0) = \beta_1 - \beta_2 \\
10 \log (I_1/I_2) &= 150 - 110 = 40 \\
\log (I_1/I_2) &= 4
\end{aligned}$$

Thus, $I_1/I_2 = 10^4$, which tells us that the sound intensity of the space shuttle taking off is 10,000 times greater than a car horn! ◀

## EXPONENTIAL AND LOGARITHMIC GROWTH

The growth patterns of $e^x$ and $\ln x$ illustrated in Table 1.8.5 are worth noting. Both functions increase as $x$ increases, but they increase in dramatically different ways—the value of $e^x$ increases extremely rapidly and that of $\ln x$ increases extremely slowly. For example, the value of $e^x$ at $x = 10$ is over 22,000, but at $x = 1000$ the value of $\ln x$ has not even reached 7.

**Table 1.8.5**

| $x$ | $e^x$ | $\ln x$ |
|---|---|---|
| 1 | 2.72 | 0.00 |
| 2 | 7.39 | 0.69 |
| 3 | 20.09 | 1.10 |
| 4 | 54.60 | 1.39 |
| 5 | 148.41 | 1.61 |
| 6 | 403.43 | 1.79 |
| 7 | 1096.63 | 1.95 |
| 8 | 2980.96 | 2.08 |
| 9 | 8103.08 | 2.20 |
| 10 | 22026.47 | 2.30 |
| 100 | $2.69 \times 10^{43}$ | 4.61 |
| 1000 | $1.97 \times 10^{434}$ | 6.91 |

A function $f$ is said to ***increase without bound*** as $x$ increases if the values of $f(x)$ eventually exceed any specified positive number $M$ (no matter how large) as $x$ increases indefinitely. Table 1.8.5 strongly suggests that $f(x) = e^x$ increases without bound, which is consistent with the fact that the range of this function is $(0, +\infty)$. Indeed, if we choose any positive number $M$, then we will have $e^x = M$ when $x = \ln M$, and since the values of $e^x$ increase as $x$ increases, we will have

$$e^x > M \quad \text{if} \quad x > \ln M$$

(Figure 1.8.8). It is not clear from Table 1.8.5 whether $\ln x$ increases without bound as $x$ increases because the values grow so slowly, but we know this to be so since the range of this function is $(-\infty, +\infty)$. To see this algebraically, let $M$ be any positive number. We will have $\ln x = M$ when $x = e^M$, and since the values of $\ln x$ increase as $x$ increases, we will have

$$\ln x > M \quad \text{if} \quad x > e^M$$

(Figure 1.8.9).

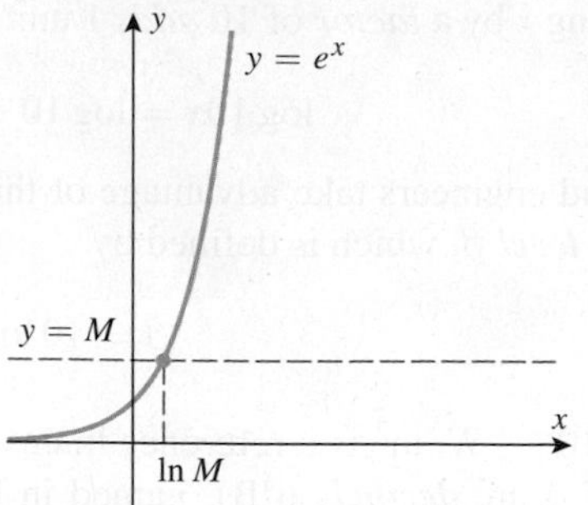


▲ **Figure 1.8.8** The value of $y = e^x$ will exceed an arbitrary positive value of $M$ when $x > \ln M$.

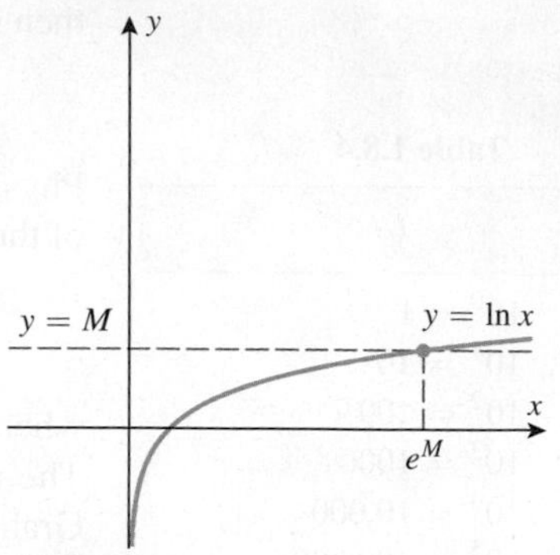


▲ **Figure 1.8.9** The value of $y = \ln x$ will exceed an arbitrary positive value of $M$ when $x > e^M$.

In summary,

$$\lim_{x\to+\infty} e^x = +\infty \qquad \lim_{x\to+\infty} \ln x = +\infty \tag{10–11}$$

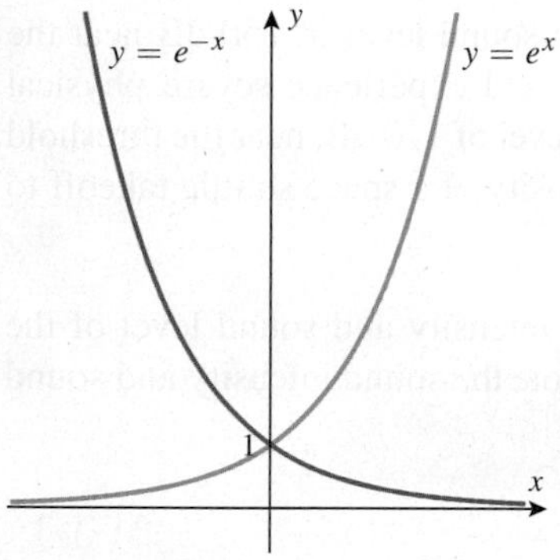


▲ **Figure 1.8.10**

The following limits can be deduced numerically by constructing appropriate tables of values (verify):

$$\lim_{x\to-\infty} e^x = 0 \qquad \lim_{x\to 0^+} \ln x = -\infty \tag{12–13}$$

The following limits can be deduced numerically, but they can be seen more readily by noting that the graph of $y = e^{-x}$ is the reflection about the $y$-axis of the graph of $y = e^x$ (Figure 1.8.10):

$$\lim_{x\to+\infty} e^{-x} = 0 \qquad \lim_{x\to-\infty} e^{-x} = +\infty \tag{14–15}$$

## ✓ QUICK CHECK EXERCISES 1.8 *(See page 75 for answers.)*

1. The function $y = \left(\frac{1}{2}\right)^x$ has domain ______ and range ______.
2. The function $y = \ln(1 - x)$ has domain ______ and range ______.
3. Express as a power of 4:
   (a) 1 (b) 2 (c) $\frac{1}{16}$ (d) $\sqrt{8}$ (e) 5.
4. Solve each equation for $x$.
   (a) $e^x = \frac{1}{2}$ (b) $10^{3x} = 1{,}000{,}000$
   (c) $7e^{3x} = 56$
5. Solve each equation for $x$.
   (a) $\ln x = 3$ (b) $\log(x - 1) = 2$
   (c) $2\log x - \log(x + 1) = \log 4 - \log 3$

## EXERCISE SET 1.8 ▭ Graphing Utility

**1–2** Simplify the expression without using a calculating utility. ■

1. (a) $-8^{2/3}$ (b) $(-8)^{2/3}$ (c) $8^{-2/3}$
2. (a) $2^{-4}$ (b) $4^{1.5}$ (c) $9^{-0.5}$

**3–4** Use a calculating utility to approximate the expression. Round your answer to four decimal places. ■

3. (a) $2^{1.57}$ (b) $5^{-2.1}$
4. (a) $\sqrt[5]{24}$ (b) $\sqrt[8]{0.6}$

**5–6** Find the exact value of the expression without using a calculating utility. ■

5. (a) $\log_2 16$ (b) $\log_2\left(\frac{1}{32}\right)$
   (c) $\log_4 4$ (d) $\log_9 3$
6. (a) $\log_{10}(0.001)$ (b) $\log_{10}(10^4)$
   (c) $\ln(e^3)$ (d) $\ln(\sqrt{e})$

**7–8** Use a calculating utility to approximate the expression. Round your answer to four decimal places. ■

7. (a) $\log 23.2$ (b) $\ln 0.74$
8. (a) $\log 0.3$ (b) $\ln \pi$

**9–10** Use the logarithm properties in Theorem 1.8.3 to rewrite the expression in terms of $r$, $s$, and $t$, where $r = \ln a$, $s = \ln b$, and $t = \ln c$. ■

**9.** (a) $\ln a^2\sqrt{bc}$ (b) $\ln \dfrac{b}{a^3c}$

**10.** (a) $\ln \dfrac{\sqrt[3]{c}}{ab}$ (b) $\ln \sqrt{\dfrac{ab^3}{c^2}}$

**11–12** Expand the logarithm in terms of sums, differences, and multiples of simpler logarithms. ■

**11.** (a) $\log(10x\sqrt{x-3})$ (b) $\ln \dfrac{x^2\sin^3 x}{\sqrt{x^2+1}}$

**12.** (a) $\log \dfrac{\sqrt[3]{x+2}}{\cos 5x}$ (b) $\ln \sqrt{\dfrac{x^2+1}{x^3+5}}$

**13–15** Rewrite the expression as a single logarithm. ■

**13.** $4\log 2 - \log 3 + \log 16$

**14.** $\frac{1}{2}\log x - 3\log(\sin 2x) + 2$

**15.** $2\ln(x+1) + \frac{1}{3}\ln x - \ln(\cos x)$

**16–23** Solve for $x$ without using a calculating utility. ■

**16.** $\log_{10}(1+x) = 3$

**17.** $\log_{10}(\sqrt{x}) = -1$

**18.** $\ln(x^2) = 4$

**19.** $\ln(1/x) = -2$

**20.** $\log_3(3^x) = 7$

**21.** $\log_5(5^{2x}) = 8$

**22.** $\ln 4x - 3\ln(x^2) = \ln 2$

**23.** $\ln(1/x) + \ln(2x^3) = \ln 3$

**24–29** Solve for $x$ without using a calculating utility. Use the natural logarithm anywhere that logarithms are needed. ■

**24.** $3^x = 2$

**25.** $5^{-2x} = 3$

**26.** $3e^{-2x} = 5$

**27.** $2e^{3x} = 7$

**28.** $e^x - 2xe^x = 0$

**29.** $xe^{-x} + 2e^{-x} = 0$

**30.** Solve $e^{-2x} - 3e^{-x} = -2$ for $x$ without using a calculating utility. [*Hint:* Rewrite the equation as a quadratic equation in $u = e^{-x}$.]

**FOCUS ON CONCEPTS**

**31–34** In each part, identify the domain and range of the function, and then sketch the graph of the function without using a graphing utility. ■

**31.** (a) $f(x) = \left(\frac{1}{2}\right)^{x-1} - 1$ (b) $g(x) = \ln|x|$

**32.** (a) $f(x) = 1 + \ln(x-2)$ (b) $g(x) = 3 + e^{x-2}$

**33.** (a) $f(x) = \ln(x^2)$ (b) $g(x) = e^{-x^2}$

**34.** (a) $f(x) = 1 - e^{-x+1}$ (b) $g(x) = 3\ln\sqrt[3]{x-1}$

**35–38 True–False** Determine whether the statement is true or false. Explain your answer. ■

**35.** The function $y = x^3$ is an exponential function.

**36.** The graph of the exponential function with base $b$ passes through the point $(0, 1)$.

**37.** The natural logarithm function is the logarithmic function with base $e$.

**38.** The domain of a logarithmic function is the interval $x > 1$.

**39.** Use a calculating utility and the change of base formula (9) to find the values of $\log_2 7.35$ and $\log_5 0.6$, rounded to four decimal places.

**40–41** Graph the functions on the same screen of a graphing utility. [Use the change of base formula (9), where needed.] ■

**40.** $\ln x,\ e^x,\ \log x,\ 10^x$

**41.** $\log_2 x,\ \ln x,\ \log_5 x,\ \log x$

**42.** (a) Derive the general change of base formula

$$\log_b x = \frac{\log_a x}{\log_a b}$$

(b) Use the result in part (a) to find the exact value of $(\log_2 81)(\log_3 32)$ without using a calculating utility.

**43.** Use a graphing utility to estimate the two points of intersection of the graphs of $y = 1.3^x$ and $y = \log_{1.3} x$.

**44.** Use a graphing utility to estimate the two points of intersection of the graphs of $y = 0.6^{(x^2)}$ and $y = \log_{0.6}(x^2)$.

**FOCUS ON CONCEPTS**

**45.** (a) Is the curve in the accompanying figure the graph of an exponential function? Explain your reasoning.

(b) Find the equation of an exponential function that passes through the point $(4, 2)$.

(c) Find the equation of an exponential function that passes through the point $\left(2, \frac{1}{4}\right)$.

(d) Use a graphing utility to generate the graph of an exponential function that passes through the point $(2, 5)$.

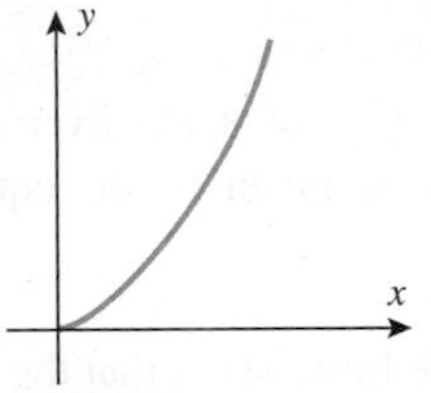


**Figure Ex-45**

**46.** (a) Make a conjecture about the general shape of the graph of $y = \log(\log x)$, and sketch the graph of this equation and $y = \log x$ in the same coordinate system.

(b) Check your work in part (a) with a graphing utility.

**47.** Find the fallacy in the following "proof" that $\frac{1}{8} > \frac{1}{4}$. Multiply both sides of the inequality $3 > 2$ by $\log \frac{1}{2}$ to get

$$3\log\tfrac{1}{2} > 2\log\tfrac{1}{2}$$

$$\log\left(\tfrac{1}{2}\right)^3 > \log\left(\tfrac{1}{2}\right)^2$$

$$\log\tfrac{1}{8} > \log\tfrac{1}{4}$$

$$\tfrac{1}{8} > \tfrac{1}{4}$$

**48.** Prove the four algebraic properties of logarithms in Theorem 1.8.3.

**49–56** Find the limits. ■

**49.** $\lim_{x\to-\infty} \frac{1-e^x}{1+e^x}$ **50.** $\lim_{x\to+\infty} \frac{1-e^x}{1+e^x}$

**51.** $\lim_{x\to+\infty} \frac{e^x+e^{-x}}{e^x-e^{-x}}$ **52.** $\lim_{x\to-\infty} \frac{e^x+e^{-x}}{e^x-e^{-x}}$

**53.** $\lim_{x\to+\infty} \ln\left(\frac{2}{x^2}\right)$ **54.** $\lim_{x\to0^+} \ln\left(\frac{2}{x^2}\right)$

**55.** $\lim_{x\to+\infty} \frac{(x+1)^x}{x^x}$ **56.** $\lim_{x\to+\infty} \left(1+\frac{1}{x}\right)^{-x}$

**57–64** Evaluate the limit using an appropriate substitution. (See Exercises 45–46 of Section 1.3.) ■

**57.** $\lim_{x\to0^+} e^{1/x}$ **58.** $\lim_{x\to0^-} e^{1/x}$

**59.** $\lim_{x\to0^+} e^{\csc x}$ **60.** $\lim_{x\to0^-} e^{\csc x}$

**61.** $\lim_{x\to+\infty} \frac{\ln 2x}{\ln 3x}$ [*Hint:* $t=\ln x$]

**62.** $\lim_{x\to+\infty} [\ln(x^2-1)-\ln(x+1)]$ [*Hint:* $t=x-1$]

**63.** $\lim_{x\to+\infty} \left(1-\frac{1}{x}\right)^{-x}$ [*Hint:* $t=-x$]

**64.** $\lim_{x\to+\infty} \left(1+\frac{2}{x}\right)^{x}$ [*Hint:* $t=x/2$]

**65.** Let $f(x)=b^x$, where $0<b$. Use the substitution principle to verify the asymptotic behavior of $f$ that is illustrated in Figure 1.8.1. [*Hint:* $f(x)=b^x=(e^{\ln b})^x=e^{(\ln b)x}$]

**66.** Prove that $\lim_{x\to0}(1+x)^{1/x}=e$ by completing parts (a) and (b).

(a) Use Equation (4) and the substitution $t=1/x$ to prove that $\lim_{x\to0^+}(1+x)^{1/x}=e$.

(b) Use Equation (5) and the substitution $t=1/x$ to prove that $\lim_{x\to0^-}(1+x)^{1/x}=e$.

**67.** Suppose that the speed $v$ (in ft/s) of a skydiver $t$ seconds after leaping from a plane is given by the equation $v=190(1-e^{-0.168t})$.

(a) Graph $v$ versus $t$.

(b) By evaluating an appropriate limit, show that the graph of $v$ versus $t$ has a horizontal asymptote $v=c$ for an appropriate constant $c$.

(c) What is the physical significance of the constant $c$ in part (b)?

**68.** The population $p$ of the United States (in millions) in year $t$ can be modeled by the function

$$p(t)=\frac{525}{1+1.1e^{-0.02225(t-1990)}}$$

(a) Based on this model, what was the U.S. population in 1990?

(b) Plot $p$ versus $t$ for the 200-year period from 1950 to 2150.

(c) By evaluating an appropriate limit, show that the graph of $p$ versus $t$ has a horizontal asymptote $p=c$ for an appropriate constant $c$.

(d) What is the significance of the constant $c$ in part (c) for the population predicted by this model?

**69.** (a) Compute the (approximate) values of the terms in the sequence

$$1.01^{101},\ 1.001^{1001},\ 1.0001^{10001},\ 1.00001^{100001},\ 1.000001^{1000001},\ 1.0000001^{10000001}\ \ldots$$

What number do these terms appear to be approaching?

(b) Use Equation (4) to verify your answer in part (a).

(c) Let $1\le a\le 9$ denote a positive integer. What number is approached more and more closely by the terms in the following sequence?

$$1.01^{a0a},\ 1.001^{a00a},\ 1.0001^{a000a},\ 1.00001^{a0000a},\ 1.000001^{a00000a},\ 1.0000001^{a000000a}\ \ldots$$

(The powers are positive integers that begin and end with the digit $a$ and have 0's in the remaining positions.)

**70.** Let $f(x)=\left(1+\frac{1}{x}\right)^x$.

(a) Prove the identity

$$f(-x)=\frac{x}{x-1}\cdot f(x-1)$$

(b) Use Equation (4) and the identity from part (a) to prove Equation (5).

**71.** If equipment in the satellite of Example 3 requires 15 watts to operate correctly, what is the operational lifetime of the power supply?

**72.** The equation $Q=12e^{-0.055t}$ gives the mass $Q$ in grams of radioactive potassium-42 that will remain from some initial quantity after $t$ hours of radioactive decay.

(a) How many grams were there initially?

(b) How many grams remain after 4 hours?

(c) How long will it take to reduce the amount of radioactive potassium-42 to half of the initial amount?

**73.** The acidity of a substance is measured by its pH value, which is defined by the formula

$$\text{pH}=-\log[H^+]$$

where the symbol $[H^+]$ denotes the concentration of hydrogen ions measured in moles per liter. Distilled water has a pH of 7; a substance is called *acidic* if it has pH $<7$ and *basic* if it has pH $>7$. Find the pH of each of the following substances and state whether it is acidic or basic.

| | SUBSTANCE | $[H^+]$ |
|---|---|---|
| (a) | Arterial blood | $3.9\times10^{-8}$ mol/L |
| (b) | Tomatoes | $6.3\times10^{-5}$ mol/L |
| (c) | Milk | $4.0\times10^{-7}$ mol/L |
| (d) | Coffee | $1.2\times10^{-6}$ mol/L |

**74.** Use the definition of pH in Exercise 73 to find $[H^+]$ in a solution having a pH equal to

(a) 2.44 (b) 8.06.

**75.** The perceived loudness $\beta$ of a sound in decibels (dB) is related to its intensity $I$ in watts per square meter ($W/m^2$) by the equation

$$\beta = 10 \log (I/I_0)$$

where $I_0 = 10^{-12}\ W/m^2$. Damage to the average ear occurs at 90 dB or greater. Find the decibel level of each of the following sounds and state whether it will cause ear damage.

| | SOUND | $I$ |
|---|---|---|
| (a) | Jet aircraft (from 50 ft) | $1.0 \times 10^2\ W/m^2$ |
| (b) | Amplified rock music | $1.0\ W/m^2$ |
| (c) | Garbage disposal | $1.0 \times 10^{-4}\ W/m^2$ |
| (d) | TV (mid volume from 10 ft) | $3.2 \times 10^{-5}\ W/m^2$ |

**76–78** Use the definition of the decibel level of a sound (see Exercise 75). ■

**76.** If one sound is three times as intense as another, how much greater is its decibel level?

**77.** According to one source, the noise inside a moving automobile is about 70 dB, whereas an electric blender generates 93 dB. Find the ratio of the intensity of the noise of the blender to that of the automobile.

**78.** Suppose that the intensity level of an echo is $\frac{2}{3}$ the intensity level of the original sound. If each echo results in another echo, how many echoes will be heard from a 120 dB sound given that the average human ear can hear a sound as low as 10 dB?

**79.** On the ***Richter scale***, the magnitude $M$ of an earthquake is related to the released energy $E$ in joules (J) by the equation

$$\log E = 4.4 + 1.5M$$

(a) Find the energy $E$ of the 1906 San Francisco earthquake that registered $M = 8.2$ on the Richter scale.
(b) If the released energy of one earthquake is 10 times that of another, how much greater is its magnitude on the Richter scale?

**80.** Suppose that the magnitudes of two earthquakes differ by 1 on the Richter scale. Find the ratio of the released energy of the larger earthquake to that of the smaller earthquake. [*Note:* See Exercise 79 for terminology.]

✓ **QUICK CHECK ANSWERS 1.8** 1. $(-\infty, +\infty)$; $(0, +\infty)$ 2. $(-\infty, 1)$; $(-\infty, +\infty)$ 3. (a) $4^0$ (b) $4^{1/2}$ (c) $4^{-2}$ (d) $4^{3/4}$ (e) $4^{\log_4 5}$ 4. (a) $\ln \frac{1}{2} = -\ln 2$ (b) 2 (c) $\ln 2$ 5. (a) $e^3$ (b) 101 (c) 2

## CHAPTER 1 REVIEW EXERCISES

Graphing Utility  C CAS

**1.** For the function $f$ graphed in the accompanying figure, find the limit if it exists.

(a) $\lim_{x\to 1} f(x)$ (b) $\lim_{x\to 2} f(x)$ (c) $\lim_{x\to 3} f(x)$
(d) $\lim_{x\to 4} f(x)$ (e) $\lim_{x\to +\infty} f(x)$ (f) $\lim_{x\to -\infty} f(x)$
(g) $\lim_{x\to 3^+} f(x)$ (h) $\lim_{x\to 3^-} f(x)$ (i) $\lim_{x\to 0} f(x)$

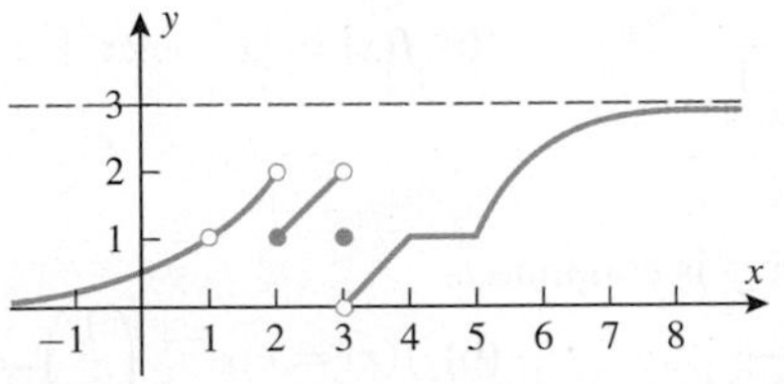


◀ **Figure Ex-1**

**2.** In each part, complete the table and make a conjecture about the value of the limit indicated. Confirm your conjecture by finding the limit analytically.

(a) $f(x) = \dfrac{x-2}{x^2-4}$; $\lim_{x\to 2^+} f(x)$

| $x$ | 2.00001 | 2.0001 | 2.001 | 2.01 | 2.1 | 2.5 |
|---|---|---|---|---|---|---|
| $f(x)$ | | | | | | |

(b) $f(x) = \dfrac{\tan 4x}{x}$; $\lim_{x\to 0} f(x)$

| $x$ | −0.01 | −0.001 | −0.0001 | 0.0001 | 0.001 | 0.01 |
|---|---|---|---|---|---|---|
| $f(x)$ | | | | | | |

**3.** (a) Approximate the value for the limit

$$\lim_{x\to 0} \frac{3^x - 2^x}{x}$$

to three decimal places by constructing an appropriate table of values.
(b) Confirm your approximation using graphical evidence.

C **4.** Approximate

$$\lim_{x\to 3} \frac{2^x - 8}{x - 3}$$

both by looking at a graph and by calculating values for some appropriate choices of $x$. Compare your answer with the value produced by a CAS.

**5–10** Find the limits. ■

**5.** $\lim_{x\to -1} \dfrac{x^3 - x^2}{x - 1}$

**6.** $\lim_{x\to 1} \dfrac{x^3 - x^2}{x - 1}$

**7.** $\lim_{x\to -3} \dfrac{3x+9}{x^2+4x+3}$ **8.** $\lim_{x\to 2^-} \dfrac{x+2}{x-2}$

**9.** $\lim_{x\to +\infty} \dfrac{(2x-1)^5}{(3x^2+2x-7)(x^3-9x)}$

**10.** $\lim_{x\to 0} \dfrac{\sqrt{x^2+4}-2}{x^2}$

**11.** In each part, find the horizontal asymptotes, if any.
(a) $y = \dfrac{2x-7}{x^2-4x}$ (b) $y = \dfrac{x^3-x^2+10}{3x^2-4x}$
(c) $y = \dfrac{2x^2-6}{x^2+5x}$

**12.** In each part, find $\lim_{x\to a} f(x)$, if it exists, where $a$ is replaced by $0, 5^+, -5^-, -5, 5, -\infty$, and $+\infty$.
(a) $f(x) = \sqrt{5-x}$
(b) $f(x) = \begin{cases} (x-5)/|x-5|, & x \neq 5 \\ 0, & x = 5 \end{cases}$

**13–20** Find the limits. ■

**13.** $\lim_{x\to 0} \dfrac{\sin 3x}{\tan 3x}$ **14.** $\lim_{x\to 0} \dfrac{x \sin x}{1-\cos x}$

**15.** $\lim_{x\to 0} \dfrac{3x - \sin(kx)}{x}, \quad k \neq 0$

**16.** $\lim_{\theta\to 0} \tan\left(\dfrac{1-\cos\theta}{\theta}\right)$

**17.** $\lim_{t\to \pi/2^+} e^{\tan t}$ **18.** $\lim_{\theta\to 0^+} \ln(\sin 2\theta) - \ln(\tan\theta)$

**19.** $\lim_{x\to +\infty} \left(1+\dfrac{3}{x}\right)^{-x}$ **20.** $\lim_{x\to +\infty} \left(1+\dfrac{a}{x}\right)^{bx}, \quad a, b > 0$

**21.** If \$1000 is invested in an account that pays 7% interest compounded $n$ times each year, then in 10 years there will be $1000(1+0.07/n)^{10n}$ dollars in the account. How much money will be in the account in 10 years if the interest is compounded quarterly ($n = 4$)? Monthly ($n = 12$)? Daily ($n = 365$)? Determine the amount of money that will be in the account in 10 years if the interest is compounded *continuously*, that is, as $n \to +\infty$.

**22.** (a) Write a paragraph or two that describes how the limit of a function can fail to exist at $x = a$, and accompany your description with some specific examples.
(b) Write a paragraph or two that describes how the limit of a function can fail to exist as $x \to +\infty$ or $x \to -\infty$, and accompany your description with some specific examples.
(c) Write a paragraph or two that describes how a function can fail to be continuous at $x = a$, and accompany your description with some specific examples.

**23.** (a) Find a formula for a rational function that has a vertical asymptote at $x = 1$ and a horizontal asymptote at $y = 2$.
(b) Check your work by using a graphing utility to graph the function.

**24.** Paraphrase the $\epsilon$-$\delta$ definition for $\lim_{x\to a} f(x) = L$ in terms of a graphing utility viewing window centered at the point $(a, L)$.

**25.** Suppose that $f(x)$ is a function and that for any given $\epsilon > 0$, the condition $0 < |x-2| < \frac{3}{4}\epsilon$ guarantees that $|f(x) - 5| < \epsilon$.
(a) What limit is described by this statement?
(b) Find a value of $\delta$ such that $0 < |x-2| < \delta$ guarantees that $|8f(x) - 40| < 0.048$.

**26.** The limit

$$\lim_{x\to 0} \frac{\sin x}{x} = 1$$

ensures that there is a number $\delta$ such that

$$\left|\frac{\sin x}{x} - 1\right| < 0.001$$

if $0 < |x| < \delta$. Estimate the largest such $\delta$.

**27.** In each part, a positive number $\epsilon$ and the limit $L$ of a function $f$ at $a$ are given. Find a number $\delta$ such that $|f(x) - L| < \epsilon$ if $0 < |x-a| < \delta$.
(a) $\lim_{x\to 2} (4x-7) = 1; \ \epsilon = 0.01$
(b) $\lim_{x\to 3/2} \dfrac{4x^2-9}{2x-3} = 6; \ \epsilon = 0.05$
(c) $\lim_{x\to 4} x^2 = 16; \ \epsilon = 0.001$

**28.** Use Definition 1.4.1 to prove the stated limits are correct.
(a) $\lim_{x\to 2} (4x-7) = 1$ (b) $\lim_{x\to 3/2} \dfrac{4x^2-9}{2x-3} = 6$

**29.** Suppose that $f$ is continuous at $x_0$ and that $f(x_0) > 0$. Give either an $\epsilon$-$\delta$ proof or a convincing verbal argument to show that there must be an open interval containing $x_0$ on which $f(x) > 0$.

**30.** (a) Let

$$f(x) = \frac{\sin x - \sin 1}{x-1}$$

Approximate $\lim_{x\to 1} f(x)$ by graphing $f$ and calculating values for some appropriate choices of $x$.
(b) Use the identity

$$\sin\alpha - \sin\beta = 2\sin\frac{\alpha-\beta}{2}\cos\frac{\alpha+\beta}{2}$$

to find the exact value of $\lim_{x\to 1} f(x)$.

**31.** Find values of $x$, if any, at which the given function is not continuous.
(a) $f(x) = \dfrac{x}{x^2-1}$ (b) $f(x) = |x^3 - 2x^2|$
(c) $f(x) = \dfrac{x+3}{|x^2+3x|}$

**32.** Determine where $f$ is continuous.
(a) $f(x) = \dfrac{x}{|x|-3}$ (b) $f(x) = \cos^{-1}\left(\dfrac{1}{x}\right)$
(c) $f(x) = e^{\ln x}$

**33.** Suppose that

$$f(x) = \begin{cases} -x^4+3, & x \leq 2 \\ x^2+9, & x > 2 \end{cases}$$

Is $f$ continuous everywhere? Justify your conclusion.

**34.** One dictionary describes a continuous function as "one whose value at each point is closely approached by its values at neighboring points."

*(cont.)*

(a) How would you explain the meaning of the terms "neighboring points" and "closely approached" to a nonmathematician?
(b) Write a paragraph that explains why the dictionary definition is consistent with Definition 1.5.1.

**35.** Show that the conclusion of the Intermediate-Value Theorem may be false if $f$ is not continuous on the interval $[a, b]$.

**36.** Suppose that $f$ is continuous on the interval $[0, 1]$, that $f(0) = 2$, and that $f$ has no zeros in the interval. Prove that $f(x) > 0$ for all $x$ in $[0, 1]$.

**37.** Show that the equation $x^4 + 5x^3 + 5x - 1 = 0$ has at least two real solutions in the interval $[-6, 2]$.

**38.** In each part, find $f^{-1}(x)$ if the inverse exists.
(a) $f(x) = (e^x)^2 + 1$
(b) $f(x) = \sin\left(\dfrac{1-2x}{x}\right), \quad \dfrac{2}{4+\pi} \le x \le \dfrac{2}{4-\pi}$
(c) $f(x) = \dfrac{1}{1 + 3\tan^{-1} x}$

**39.** In each part, find the exact numerical value of the given expression.
(a) $\cos[\cos^{-1}(4/5) + \sin^{-1}(5/13)]$
(b) $\sin[\sin^{-1}(4/5) + \cos^{-1}(5/13)]$

**40.** In each part, sketch the graph, and check your work with a graphing utility.
(a) $f(x) = 3\sin^{-1}(x/2)$
(b) $f(x) = \cos^{-1} x - \pi/2$
(c) $f(x) = 2\tan^{-1}(-3x)$
(d) $f(x) = \cos^{-1} x + \sin^{-1} x$

**41.** Suppose that the graph of $y = \log x$ is drawn with equal scales of 1 inch per unit in both the $x$- and $y$-directions. If a bug wants to walk along the graph until it reaches a height of 5 ft above the $x$-axis, how many miles to the right of the origin will it have to travel?

**42.** Suppose that the graph of $y = 10^x$ is drawn with equal scales of 1 inch per unit in both the $x$- and $y$-directions. If a bug wants to walk along the graph until it reaches a height of 100 mi above the $x$-axis, how many feet to the right of the origin will it have to travel?

**43.** Express the following function as a rational function of $x$:
$$3\ln\left(e^{2x}(e^x)^3\right) + 2\exp(\ln 1)$$

**44.** Suppose that $y = Ce^{kt}$, where $C$ and $k$ are constants, and let $Y = \ln y$. Show that the graph of $Y$ versus $t$ is a line, and state its slope and $Y$-intercept.

**45.** (a) Sketch the curves $y = \pm e^{-x/2}$ and $y = e^{-x/2}\sin 2x$ for $-\pi/2 \le x \le 3\pi/2$ in the same coordinate system, and check your work using a graphing utility.
(b) Find all $x$-intercepts of the curve $y = e^{-x/2}\sin 2x$ in the stated interval, and find the $x$-coordinates of all points where this curve intersects the curves $y = \pm e^{-x/2}$.

**46.** Suppose that a package of medical supplies is dropped from a helicopter straight down by parachute into a remote area. The velocity $v$ (in feet per second) of the package $t$ seconds after it is released is given by $v = 24.61(1 - e^{-1.3t})$.
(a) Graph $v$ versus $t$.
(b) Show that the graph has a horizontal asymptote $v = c$.
(c) The constant $c$ is called the ***terminal velocity***. Explain what the terminal velocity means in practical terms.
(d) Can the package actually reach its terminal velocity? Explain.
(e) How long does it take for the package to reach 98% of its terminal velocity?

**47.** A breeding group of 20 bighorn sheep is released in a protected area in Colorado. It is expected that with careful management the number of sheep, $N$, after $t$ years will be given by the formula
$$N = \frac{220}{1 + 10(0.83^t)}$$
and that the sheep population will be able to maintain itself without further supervision once the population reaches a size of 80.
(a) Graph $N$ versus $t$.
(b) How many years must the state of Colorado maintain a program to care for the sheep?
(c) How many bighorn sheep can the environment in the protected area support? [*Hint:* Examine the graph of $N$ versus $t$ for large values of $t$.]

**48.** An oven is preheated and then remains at a constant temperature. A potato is placed in the oven to bake. Suppose that the temperature $T$ (in °F) of the potato $t$ minutes later is given by $T = 400 - 325(0.97^t)$. The potato will be considered done when its temperature is anywhere between 260°F and 280°F.
(a) During what interval of time would the potato be considered done?
(b) How long does it take for the difference between the potato and oven temperatures to be cut in half?

**49.** (a) Show that the graphs of $y = \ln x$ and $y = x^{0.2}$ intersect.
(b) Approximate the solution(s) of the equation $\ln x = x^{0.2}$ to three decimal places.

**50.** (a) Show that for $x > 0$ and $k \ne 0$ the equations
$$x^k = e^x \quad \text{and} \quad \frac{\ln x}{x} = \frac{1}{k}$$
have the same solutions.
(b) Use the graph of $y = (\ln x)/x$ to determine the values of $k$ for which the equation $x^k = e^x$ has two distinct positive solutions.
(c) Estimate the positive solution(s) of $x^8 = e^x$.

**51.** Consider $f(x) = x^2\tan x + \ln x, 0 < x < \pi/2$.
(a) Explain why $f$ is one-to-one.
(b) Use a graphing utility to generate the graph of $f$. Then sketch the graphs of $f$ and $f^{-1}$ together. What are the asymptotes for each graph?

## CHAPTER 1 MAKING CONNECTIONS

In Section 1.1 we developed the notion of a tangent line to a graph at a given point by considering it as a limiting position of secant lines through that point (Figure 1.1.4*a*). In these exercises we will develop an analogous idea in which secant lines are replaced by "secant circles" and the tangent line is replaced by a "tangent circle" (called the ***osculating circle***). We begin with the graph of $y = x^2$.

**1.** Recall that there is a unique circle through any three noncollinear points in the plane. For any positive real number $x$, consider the unique "secant circle" that passes through the fixed point $O(0, 0)$ and the variable points $Q(-x, x^2)$ and $P(x, x^2)$ (see the accompanying figure). Use plane geometry to explain why the center of this circle is the intersection of the $y$-axis and the perpendicular bisector of segment $OP$.

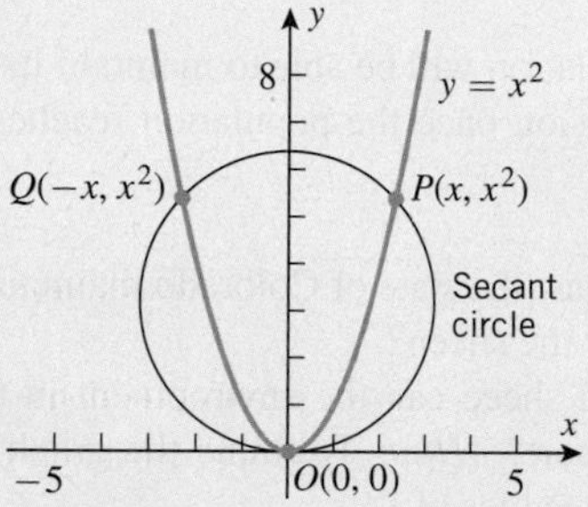


Figure Ex-1

**2.** (a) Let $(0, C(x))$ denote the center of the circle in Exercise 1 and show that

$$C(x) = \tfrac{1}{2}x^2 + \tfrac{1}{2}$$

(b) Show that as $x \to 0^+$, the secant circles approach a limiting position given by the circle that passes through the origin and is centered at $\left(0, \tfrac{1}{2}\right)$. As shown in the accompanying figure, this circle is the osculating circle to the graph of $y = x^2$ at the origin.

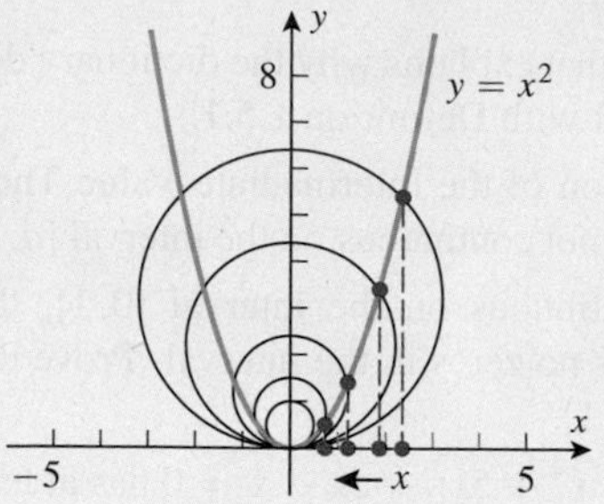


Figure Ex-2

**3.** Show that if we replace the curve $y = x^2$ by the curve $y = f(x)$, where $f$ is an even function, then the formula for $C(x)$ becomes

$$C(x) = \frac{1}{2}\left[f(0) + f(x) + \frac{x^2}{f(x) - f(0)}\right]$$

[Here we assume that $f(x) \neq f(0)$ for positive values of $x$ close to 0.] If $\lim_{x\to 0^+} C(x) = L \neq f(0)$, then we define the osculating circle to the curve $y = f(x)$ at $(0, f(0))$ to be the unique circle through $(0, f(0))$ with center $(0, L)$. If $C(x)$ does not have a finite limit different from $f(0)$ as $x \to 0^+$, then we say that the curve has no osculating circle at $(0, f(0))$.

**4.** In each part, determine the osculating circle to the curve $y = f(x)$ at $(0, f(0))$, if it exists.

(a) $f(x) = 4x^2$
(b) $f(x) = x^2 \cos x$
(c) $f(x) = |x|$
(d) $f(x) = x \sin x$
(e) $f(x) = \cos x$
(f) $f(x) = x^2 g(x)$, where $g(x)$ is an even continuous function with $g(0) \neq 0$
(g) $f(x) = x^4$

Henglein and Steets/Getty Images

*One of the crowning achievements of calculus is its ability to capture continuous motion mathematically, allowing that motion to be analyzed instant by instant.*

# 2 THE DERIVATIVE

Many real-world phenomena involve changing quantities—the speed of a rocket, the inflation of currency, the number of bacteria in a culture, the shock intensity of an earthquake, the voltage of an electrical signal, and so forth. In this chapter we will develop the concept of a "derivative," which is the mathematical tool for studying the rate at which one quantity changes relative to another. The study of rates of change is closely related to the geometric concept of a tangent line to a curve, so we will also be discussing the general definition of a tangent line and methods for finding its slope and equation.

## 2.1 TANGENT LINES AND RATES OF CHANGE

*In this section we will discuss three ideas: tangent lines to curves, the velocity of an object moving along a line, and the rate at which one variable changes relative to another. Our goal is to show how these seemingly unrelated ideas are, in actuality, closely linked.*

### TANGENT LINES

In Example 1 of Section 1.1 we used an informal argument to find the equation of a tangent line to a curve. However, at that stage in the text we did not have a precise definition of a tangent line. Now that limits have been defined precisely we can give a mathematical definition of the tangent line to a curve $y = f(x)$ at a point $P(x_0, f(x_0))$ on the curve. As illustrated in Figure 2.1.1, the slope $m_{PQ}$ of the secant line through $P$ and a second point $Q(x, f(x))$ on the graph of $f$ is

$$m_{PQ} = \frac{f(x) - f(x_0)}{x - x_0}$$

If we let $x$ approach $x_0$, then the point $Q$ will move along the curve and approach the point $P$. Suppose the slope $m_{PQ}$ of the secant line through $P$ and $Q$ approaches a limit as $x \to x_0$. In that case we can take the value of the limit to be the slope $m_{\tan}$ of the tangent line at $P$. Thus, we make the following definition.

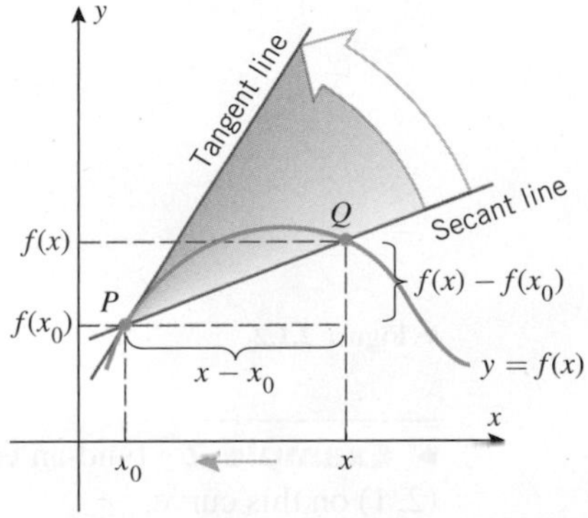


▶ Figure 2.1.1

**2.1.1 DEFINITION** Suppose that $x_0$ is in the domain of the function $f$. The ***tangent line*** to the curve $y = f(x)$ at the point $P(x_0, f(x_0))$ is the line with equation

$$y - f(x_0) = m_{\tan}(x - x_0)$$

where

$$m_{\tan} = \lim_{x \to x_0} \frac{f(x) - f(x_0)}{x - x_0} \tag{1}$$

provided the limit exists. For simplicity, we will also call this the tangent line to $y = f(x)$ at $x_0$.

**▶ Example 1** Use Definition 2.1.1 to find an equation for the tangent line to the parabola $y = x^2$ at the point $P(1, 1)$, and confirm the result agrees with that obtained in Example 1 of Section 1.1.

***Solution.*** Applying Formula (1) with $f(x) = x^2$ and $x_0 = 1$, we have

$$\begin{aligned} m_{\tan} &= \lim_{x \to 1} \frac{f(x) - f(1)}{x - 1} \\ &= \lim_{x \to 1} \frac{x^2 - 1}{x - 1} \\ &= \lim_{x \to 1} \frac{(x-1)(x+1)}{x - 1} = \lim_{x \to 1} (x + 1) = 2 \end{aligned}$$

Thus, the tangent line to $y = x^2$ at $(1, 1)$ has equation

$$y - 1 = 2(x - 1) \quad \text{or equivalently} \quad y = 2x - 1$$

which agrees with Example 1 of Section 1.1. ◀

There is an alternative way of expressing Formula (1) that is commonly used. If we let $h$ denote the difference

$$h = x - x_0$$

then the statement that $x \to x_0$ is equivalent to the statement $h \to 0$, so we can rewrite (1) in terms of $x_0$ and $h$ as

$$m_{\tan} = \lim_{h \to 0} \frac{f(x_0 + h) - f(x_0)}{h} \tag{2}$$

Formulas (1) and (2) for $m_{\tan}$ usually lead to indeterminate forms of type $0/0$, so you will generally need to perform algebraic simplifications or use other methods to determine limits of such indeterminate forms.

Figure 2.1.2 shows how Formula (2) expresses the slope of the tangent line as a limit of slopes of secant lines.

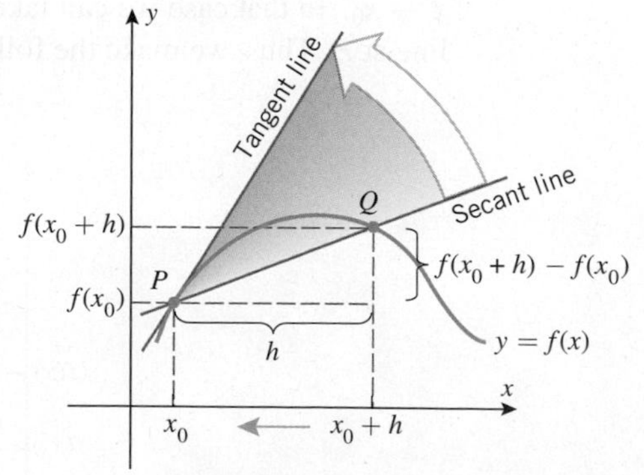


▶ **Figure 2.1.2**

**▶ Example 2** Find an equation for the tangent line to the curve $y = 2/x$ at the point $(2, 1)$ on this curve.

***Solution.*** First, we will find the slope of the tangent line by applying Formula (2) with $f(x) = 2/x$ and $x_0 = 2$. This yields

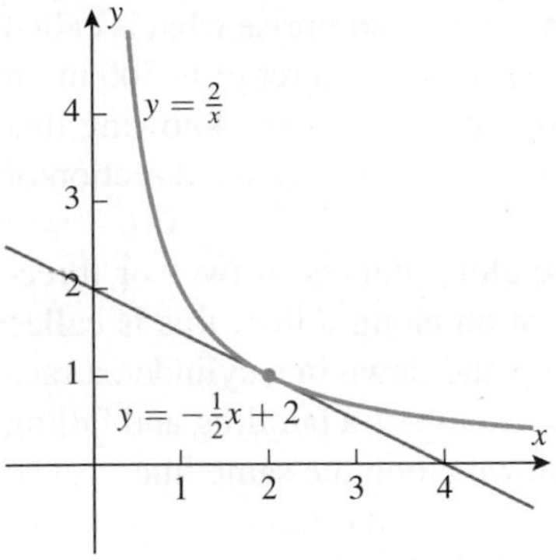


▲ **Figure 2.1.3**

$$\begin{aligned} m_{\tan} &= \lim_{h\to 0} \frac{f(2+h)-f(2)}{h} \\ &= \lim_{h\to 0} \frac{\dfrac{2}{2+h}-1}{h} = \lim_{h\to 0} \frac{\left(\dfrac{2-(2+h)}{2+h}\right)}{h} \\ &= \lim_{h\to 0} \frac{-h}{h(2+h)} = -\left(\lim_{h\to 0} \frac{1}{2+h}\right) = -\frac{1}{2} \end{aligned}$$

Thus, an equation of the tangent line at (2, 1) is

$$y - 1 = -\tfrac{1}{2}(x-2) \quad \text{or equivalently} \quad y = -\tfrac{1}{2}x + 2$$

(see Figure 2.1.3). ◄

▶ **Example 3** Find the slopes of the tangent lines to the curve $y = \sqrt{x}$ at $x_0 = 1$, $x_0 = 4$, and $x_0 = 9$.

***Solution.*** We could compute each of these slopes separately, but it will be more efficient to find the slope for a general value of $x_0$ and then substitute the specific numerical values. Proceeding in this way we obtain

$$\begin{aligned} m_{\tan} &= \lim_{h\to 0} \frac{f(x_0+h)-f(x_0)}{h} \\ &= \lim_{h\to 0} \frac{\sqrt{x_0+h}-\sqrt{x_0}}{h} \\ &= \lim_{h\to 0} \frac{\sqrt{x_0+h}-\sqrt{x_0}}{h} \cdot \frac{\sqrt{x_0+h}+\sqrt{x_0}}{\sqrt{x_0+h}+\sqrt{x_0}} \\ &= \lim_{h\to 0} \frac{x_0+h-x_0}{h(\sqrt{x_0+h}+\sqrt{x_0})} \\ &= \lim_{h\to 0} \frac{h}{h(\sqrt{x_0+h}+\sqrt{x_0})} \\ &= \lim_{h\to 0} \frac{1}{\sqrt{x_0+h}+\sqrt{x_0}} = \frac{1}{2\sqrt{x_0}} \end{aligned}$$

Rationalize the numerator to help eliminate the indeterminate form of the limit.

The slopes at $x_0 = 1, 4,$ and 9 can now be obtained by substituting these values into our general formula for $m_{\tan}$. Thus,

$$\text{slope at } x_0 = 1: \frac{1}{2\sqrt{1}} = \frac{1}{2}$$

$$\text{slope at } x_0 = 4: \frac{1}{2\sqrt{4}} = \frac{1}{4}$$

$$\text{slope at } x_0 = 9: \frac{1}{2\sqrt{9}} = \frac{1}{6}$$

(see Figure 2.1.4). ◄

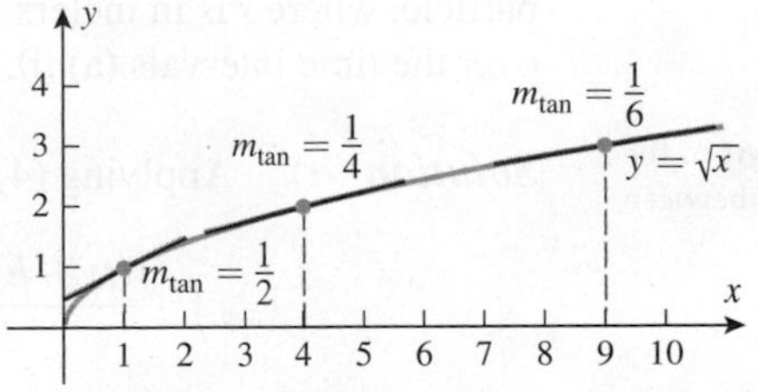


▶ **Figure 2.1.4**

## VELOCITY

Carlos E. Santa Maria/iStockphoto

*The velocity of an airplane describes its speed and direction.*

One of the important themes in calculus is the study of motion. To describe the motion of an object completely, one must specify its ***speed*** (how fast it is going) and the direction in which it is moving. The speed and the direction of motion together comprise what is called the ***velocity*** of the object. For example, knowing that the speed of an aircraft is 500 mi/h tells us how fast it is going, but not which way it is moving. In contrast, knowing that the velocity of the aircraft is 500 mi/h *due south* pins down the speed and the direction of motion.

Later, we will study the motion of objects that move along curves in two- or three-dimensional space, but for now we will only consider motion along a line; this is called ***rectilinear motion***. Some examples are a piston moving up and down in a cylinder, a race car moving along a straight track, an object dropped from the top of a building and falling straight down, a ball thrown straight up and then falling down along the same line, and so forth.

For computational purposes we will assume that a particle in rectilinear motion moves along a coordinate line that we will call the $s$-axis. A plot of the $s$-coordinate of the particle versus the elapsed time $t$ is called the ***position versus time curve*** for the particle. Figure 2.1.5 shows two typical position versus time curves. The first is for a car that moves in the positive direction along the $s$-axis and the second is for a ball that is thrown straight up in the positive direction of an $s$-axis from some initial height $s_0$.

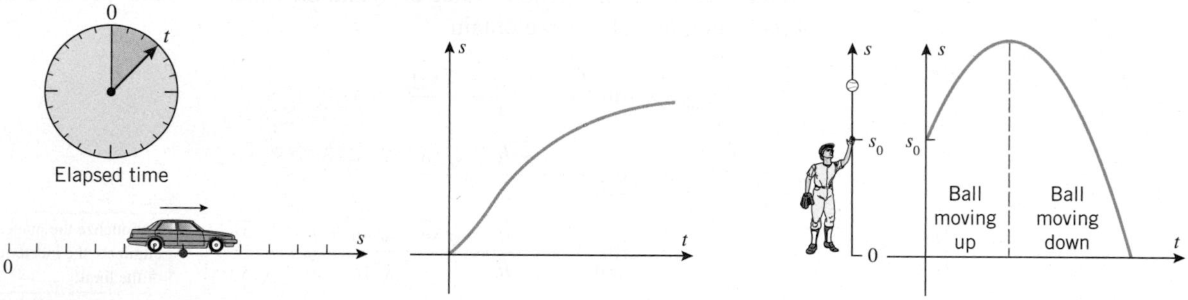


Car moves only in the positive direction. Position versus time curve Position versus time curve

▲ **Figure 2.1.5**

If a particle in rectilinear motion moves along an $s$-axis so that its position coordinate function of the elapsed time $t$ is

$$s = f(t) \tag{3}$$

then $f$ is called the ***position function of the particle***; the graph of (3) is the position versus time curve. The ***average velocity*** of the particle over a time interval $[t_0, t_0 + h]$, $h > 0$, is defined to be

Show that (4) is also correct for a time interval $[t_0 + h, t_0]$, $h < 0$.

$$v_{\text{ave}} = \frac{\text{change in position}}{\text{time elapsed}} = \frac{f(t_0 + h) - f(t_0)}{h} \tag{4}$$

The change in position

$$f(t_0 + h) - f(t_0)$$

is also called the ***displacement*** of the particle over the time interval between $t_0$ and $t_0 + h$.

▶ **Example 4** Suppose that $s = f(t) = 1 + 5t - 2t^2$ is the position function of a particle, where $s$ is in meters and $t$ is in seconds. Find the average velocities of the particle over the time intervals (a) $[0, 2]$ and (b) $[2, 3]$.

***Solution (a).*** Applying (4) with $t_0 = 0$ and $h = 2$, we see that the average velocity is

$$v_{\text{ave}} = \frac{f(t_0 + h) - f(t_0)}{h} = \frac{f(2) - f(0)}{2} = \frac{3 - 1}{2} = \frac{2}{2} = 1 \text{ m/s}$$

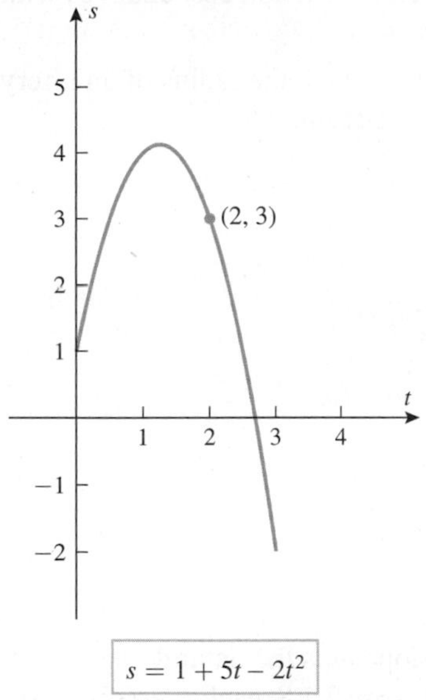


▲ Figure 2.1.6

***Solution (b).*** Applying (4) with $t_0 = 2$ and $h = 1$, we see that the average velocity is

$$v_{\text{ave}} = \frac{f(t_0 + h) - f(t_0)}{h} = \frac{f(3) - f(2)}{1} = \frac{-2 - 3}{1} = \frac{-5}{1} = -5 \text{ m/s} \blacktriangleleft$$

For a particle in rectilinear motion, average velocity describes its behavior over an *interval* of time. We are also interested in the particle's "instantaneous velocity," its speed and direction at a specific *instant* $t = t_0$ in time. Average velocities over small time intervals between $t = t_0$ and $t = t_0 + h$ can be viewed as approximations to this instantaneous velocity. If these average velocities have a limit as $h$ approaches 0, then we can take that limit to be the instantaneous velocity of the particle at time $t_0$. Here is an example.

▶ **Example 5** Consider the particle in Example 4, whose position function is

$$s = f(t) = 1 + 5t - 2t^2$$

The position of the particle at time $t = 2$ s is $s = 3$ m (Figure 2.1.6). Find the particle's instantaneous velocity at time $t = 2$ s.

**Table 2.1.1**

| TIME INTERVAL | AVERAGE VELOCITY (m/s) |
|---|---|
| $2.0 \le t \le 3.0$ | −5 |
| $2.0 \le t \le 2.1$ | −3.2 |
| $2.0 \le t \le 2.01$ | −3.02 |
| $2.0 \le t \le 2.001$ | −3.002 |
| $2.0 \le t \le 2.0001$ | −3.0002 |

***Solution.*** Table 2.1.1 displays the average velocity of the particle over a succession of smaller and smaller time intervals. The table suggests that the instantaneous velocity at time $t = 2$ s is $-3$ m/s. To confirm this analytically, we start by computing the object's average velocity over a general time interval between $t = 2$ and $t = 2 + h$ using Formula (4):

$$v_{\text{ave}} = \frac{f(2 + h) - f(2)}{h} = \frac{[1 + 5(2 + h) - 2(2 + h)^2] - 3}{h}$$

The object's instantaneous velocity at time $t = 2$ is calculated as a limit as $h \to 0$:

$$\begin{aligned}
\text{instantaneous velocity} &= \lim_{h \to 0} \frac{[1 + 5(2 + h) - 2(2 + h)^2] - 3}{h} \\
&= \lim_{h \to 0} \frac{-2 + (10 + 5h) - (8 + 8h + 2h^2)}{h} \\
&= \lim_{h \to 0} \frac{-3h - 2h^2}{h} = \lim_{h \to 0} (-3 - 2h) = -3
\end{aligned}$$

This confirms our numerical conjecture that the instantaneous velocity after 2 s is $-3$ m/s. ◀

Note the negative values for the velocities in Example 5. This is consistent with the fact that the object is moving in the negative direction along the $s$-axis.

Consider a particle in rectilinear motion with position function $s = f(t)$. Motivated by Example 5, we define the ***instantaneous velocity*** $v_{\text{inst}}$ of the particle at time $t_0$ to be the limit as $h \to 0$ of the average velocities $v_{\text{ave}}$ in Equation (4):

$$v_{\text{inst}} = \lim_{h \to 0} v_{\text{ave}} = \lim_{h \to 0} \frac{f(t_0 + h) - f(t_0)}{h} \tag{5}$$

Geometrically, the average velocity $v_{\text{ave}}$ between $t = t_0$ and $t = t_0 + h$ is the slope of the secant line through points $P(t_0, f(t_0))$ and $Q(t_0 + h, f(t_0 + h))$ on the position versus time curve, and the instantaneous velocity $v_{\text{inst}}$ at time $t_0$ is the slope of the tangent line to the position versus time curve at the point $P(t_0, f(t_0))$ (Figure 2.1.7).

Confirm the solution to Example 4(b) by computing the slope of an appropriate secant line.

## SLOPES AND RATES OF CHANGE

Velocity can be viewed as *rate of change*—the rate of change of position with respect to time. Rates of change occur in other applications as well. For example:

- A microbiologist might be interested in the rate at which the number of bacteria in a colony changes with time.
- An engineer might be interested in the rate at which the length of a metal rod changes with temperature.

- An economist might be interested in the rate at which production cost changes with the quantity of a product that is manufactured.
- A medical researcher might be interested in the rate at which the radius of an artery changes with the concentration of alcohol in the bloodstream.

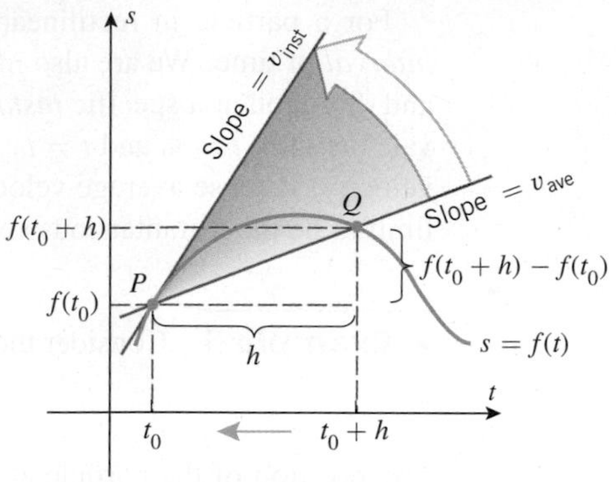


▶ Figure 2.1.7

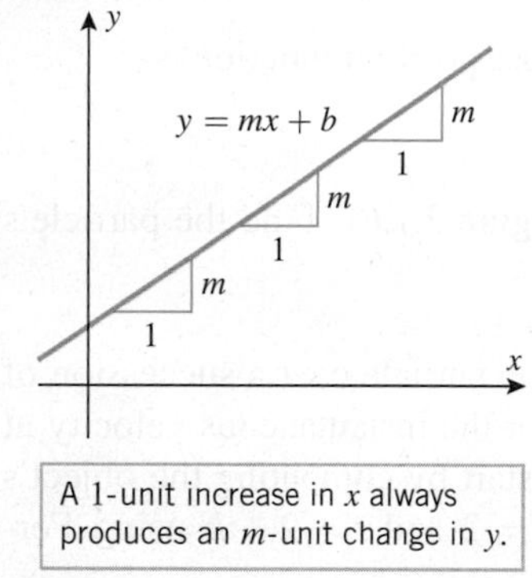


▲ Figure 2.1.8

When $y$ is a linear function of $x$, say $y = mx + b$, the slope $m$ is the natural measure of the rate of change of $y$ with respect to $x$. As illustrated in Figure 2.1.8, each 1-unit increase in $x$ anywhere along the line produces an $m$-unit change in $y$, so we see that $y$ changes at a constant rate with respect to $x$ along the line and that $m$ measures this rate of change.

Although the rate of change of $y$ with respect to $x$ is constant along a nonvertical line $y = mx + b$, this is not true for a general curve $y = f(x)$ (Figure 2.1.9). As with velocity, we need to distinguish between the average rate of change over an interval and the instantaneous rate of change at a specific point.

If $y = f(x)$, then we define the ***average rate of change of y with respect to x over the interval*** $[x_0, x_1]$ to be

$$r_{\text{ave}} = \frac{f(x_1) - f(x_0)}{x_1 - x_0} \tag{6}$$

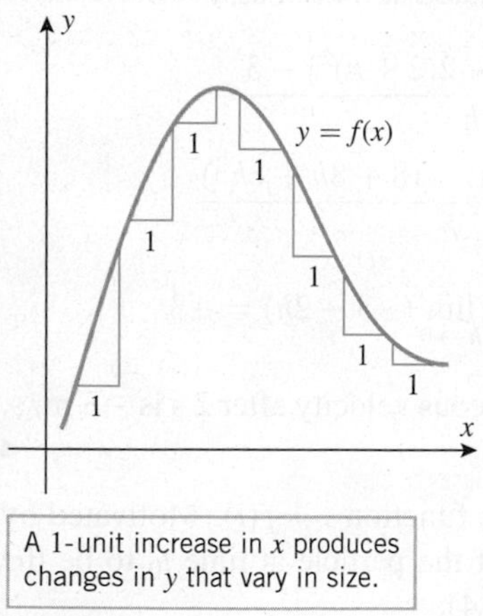


▲ Figure 2.1.9

and we define the ***instantaneous rate of change of y with respect to x at*** $x_0$ to be

$$r_{\text{inst}} = \lim_{x_1 \to x_0} \frac{f(x_1) - f(x_0)}{x_1 - x_0} \tag{7}$$

Geometrically, the average rate of change of $y$ with respect to $x$ over the interval $[x_0, x_1]$ is the slope of the secant line through the points $P(x_0, f(x_0))$ and $Q(x_1, f(x_1))$ (Figure 2.1.10), and the instantaneous rate of change of $y$ with respect to $x$ at $x_0$ is the slope of the tangent line at the point $P(x_0, f(x_0))$ (since it is the limit of the slopes of the secant lines through $P$).

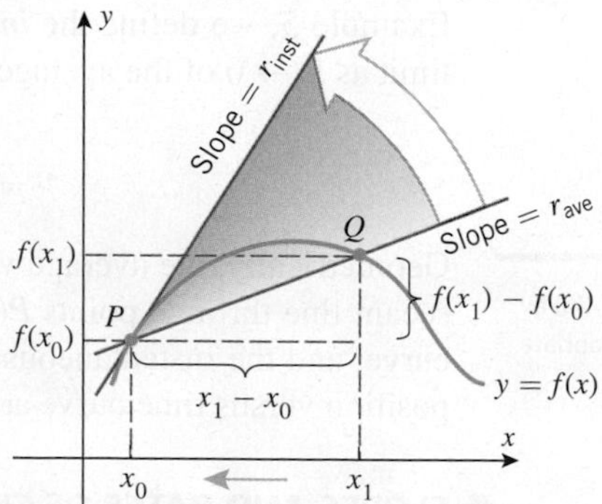


▶ Figure 2.1.10

If desired, we can let $h = x_1 - x_0$, and rewrite (6) and (7) as

$$r_{\text{ave}} = \frac{f(x_0 + h) - f(x_0)}{h} \tag{8}$$

$$r_{\text{inst}} = \lim_{h \to 0} \frac{f(x_0 + h) - f(x_0)}{h} \tag{9}$$

► **Example 6** Let $y = x^2 + 1$.

(a) Find the average rate of change of $y$ with respect to $x$ over the interval $[3, 5]$.
(b) Find the instantaneous rate of change of $y$ with respect to $x$ when $x = -4$.

***Solution (a).*** We will apply Formula (6) with $f(x) = x^2 + 1$, $x_0 = 3$, and $x_1 = 5$. This yields

$$r_{\text{ave}} = \frac{f(x_1) - f(x_0)}{x_1 - x_0} = \frac{f(5) - f(3)}{5 - 3} = \frac{26 - 10}{2} = 8$$

Thus, $y$ increases an average of 8 units per unit increase in $x$ over the interval $[3, 5]$.

***Solution (b).*** We will apply Formula (7) with $f(x) = x^2 + 1$ and $x_0 = -4$. This yields

$$r_{\text{inst}} = \lim_{x_1 \to x_0} \frac{f(x_1) - f(x_0)}{x_1 - x_0} = \lim_{x_1 \to -4} \frac{f(x_1) - f(-4)}{x_1 - (-4)} = \lim_{x_1 \to -4} \frac{(x_1^2 + 1) - 17}{x_1 + 4}$$

$$= \lim_{x_1 \to -4} \frac{x_1^2 - 16}{x_1 + 4} = \lim_{x_1 \to -4} \frac{(x_1 + 4)(x_1 - 4)}{x_1 + 4} = \lim_{x_1 \to -4} (x_1 - 4) = -8$$

Thus, a small increase in $x$ from $x = -4$ will produce approximately an 8-fold decrease in $y$. ◄

Perform the calculations in Example 6 using Formulas (8) and (9).

## RATES OF CHANGE IN APPLICATIONS

In applied problems, changing the units of measurement can change the slope of a line, so it is essential to include the units when calculating the slope and describing rates of change. The following example illustrates this.

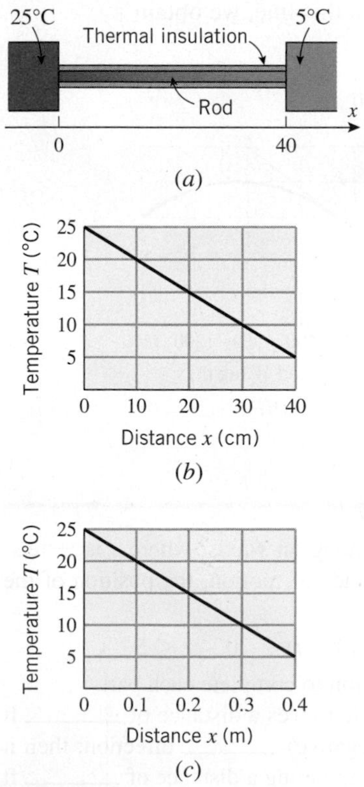


▲ **Figure 2.1.11**

► **Example 7** Suppose that a uniform rod of length 40 cm (= 0.4 m) is thermally insulated around the lateral surface and that the exposed ends of the rod are held at constant temperatures of 25°C and 5°C, respectively (Figure 2.1.11*a*). It is shown in physics that under appropriate conditions the graph of the temperature $T$ versus the distance $x$ from the left-hand end of the rod will be a straight line. Parts (*b*) and (*c*) of Figure 2.1.11 show two such graphs: one in which $x$ is measured in centimeters and one in which it is measured in meters. The slopes in the two cases are

$$m = \frac{5 - 25}{40 - 0} = \frac{-20}{40} = -0.5 \qquad (10)$$

$$m = \frac{5 - 25}{0.4 - 0} = \frac{-20}{0.4} = -50 \qquad (11)$$

The slope in (10) implies that the temperature *decreases* at a rate of 0.5°C per centimeter of distance from the left end of the rod, and the slope in (11) implies that the temperature decreases at a rate of 50°C per meter of distance from the left end of the rod. The two statements are equivalent physically, even though the slopes differ. ◄

In general, the units for a rate of change of $y$ with respect to $x$ are obtained by "dividing" the units of $y$ by the units of $x$ and then simplifying according to the standard rules of algebra. Here are some examples:

- If $y$ is in degrees Fahrenheit (°F) and $x$ is in inches (in), then a rate of change of $y$ with respect to $x$ has units of degrees Fahrenheit per inch (°F/in).
- If $y$ is in feet per second (ft/s) and $x$ is in seconds (s), then a rate of change of $y$ with respect to $x$ has units of feet per second per second (ft/s/s), which would usually be written as ft/s$^2$.

- If $y$ is in newton-meters (N·m) and $x$ is in meters (m), then a rate of change of $y$ with respect to $x$ has units of newtons (N), since N·m/m = N.
- If $y$ is in foot-pounds (ft·lb) and $x$ is in hours (h), then a rate of change of $y$ with respect to $x$ has units of foot-pounds per hour (ft·lb/h).

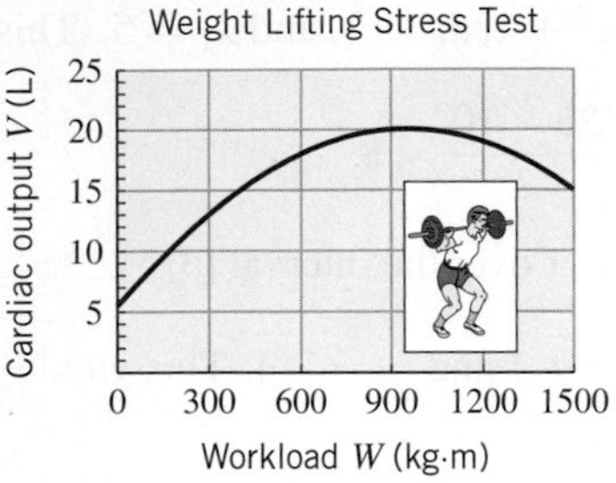

▲ **Figure 2.1.12**

▶ **Example 8** The limiting factor in athletic endurance is cardiac output, that is, the volume of blood that the heart can pump per unit of time during an athletic competition. Figure 2.1.12 shows a stress-test graph of cardiac output $V$ in liters (L) of blood versus workload $W$ in kilogram-meters (kg·m) for 1 minute of weight lifting. This graph illustrates the known medical fact that cardiac output increases with the workload, but after reaching a peak value begins to decrease.

(a) Use the secant line shown in Figure 2.1.13*a* to estimate the average rate of change of cardiac output with respect to workload as the workload increases from 300 to 1200 kg·m.

(b) Use the line segment shown in Figure 2.1.13*b* to estimate the instantaneous rate of change of cardiac output with respect to workload at the point where the workload is 300 kg·m.

***Solution (a).*** Using the estimated points (300, 13) and (1200, 19) to find the slope of the secant line, we obtain

$$r_{\text{ave}} \approx \frac{19-13}{1200-300} \approx 0.0067 \frac{\text{L}}{\text{kg}\cdot\text{m}}$$

This means that on average a 1-unit increase in workload produced a 0.0067 L increase in cardiac output over the interval.

***Solution (b).*** We estimate the slope of the cardiac output curve at $W = 300$ by sketching a line that appears to meet the curve at $W = 300$ with slope equal to that of the curve (Figure 2.1.13*b*). Estimating points (0, 7) and (900, 25) on this line, we obtain

$$r_{\text{inst}} \approx \frac{25-7}{900-0} = 0.02 \frac{\text{L}}{\text{kg}\cdot\text{m}}$$ ◀

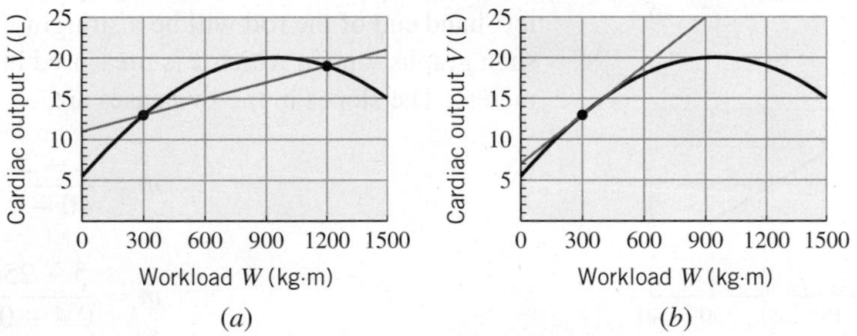

▶ **Figure 2.1.13**

## ✓ QUICK CHECK EXERCISES 2.1 *(See page 89 for answers.)*

1. The slope $m_{\tan}$ of the tangent line to the curve $y = f(x)$ at the point $P(x_0, f(x_0))$ is given by
$$m_{\tan} = \lim_{x \to x_0} \underline{\qquad\qquad} = \lim_{h \to 0} \underline{\qquad\qquad}$$

2. The tangent line to the curve $y = (x-1)^2$ at the point $(-1, 4)$ has equation $4x + y = 0$. Thus, the value of the limit
$$\lim_{x \to -1} \frac{x^2 - 2x - 3}{x + 1}$$
is ______.

3. A particle is moving along an $s$-axis, where $s$ is in feet. During the first 5 seconds of motion, the position of the particle is given by
$$s = 10 - (3 - t)^2, \quad 0 \le t \le 5$$
Use this position function to complete each part.
(a) Initially, the particle moves a distance of ______ ft in the (positive/negative) ______ direction; then it reverses direction, traveling a distance of ______ ft during the remainder of the 5-second period.
(b) The average velocity of the particle over the 5-second period is ______.

4. Let $s = f(t)$ be the equation of a position versus time curve for a particle in rectilinear motion, where $s$ is in meters and $t$ is in seconds. Assume that $s = -1$ when $t = 2$ and that the instantaneous velocity of the particle at this instant is 3 m/s. The equation of the tangent line to the position versus time curve at time $t = 2$ is ______.

5. Suppose that $y = x^2 + x$.
   (a) The average rate of change of $y$ with respect to $x$ over the interval $2 \le x \le 5$ is ______.
   (b) The instantaneous rate of change of $y$ with respect to $x$ at $x = 2$, $r_{\text{inst}}$, is given by the limit ______.

## EXERCISE SET 2.1

1. The accompanying figure shows the position versus time curve for an elevator that moves upward a distance of 60 m and then discharges its passengers.
   (a) Estimate the instantaneous velocity of the elevator at $t = 10$ s.
   (b) Sketch a velocity versus time curve for the motion of the elevator for $0 \le t \le 20$.

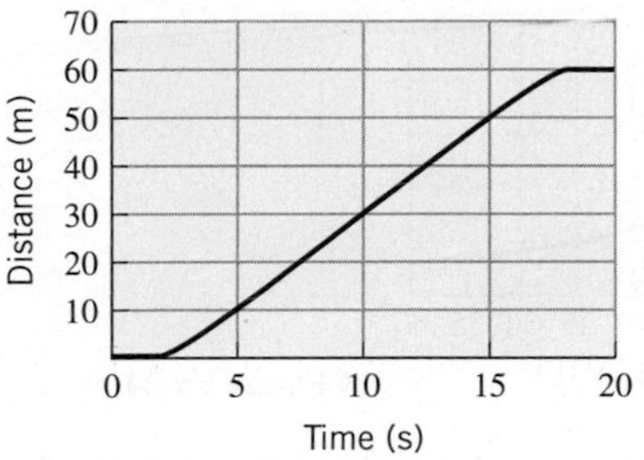

◀ **Figure Ex-1**

2. The accompanying figure shows the position versus time curve for an automobile over a period of time of 10 s. Use the line segments shown in the figure to estimate the instantaneous velocity of the automobile at time $t = 4$ s and again at time $t = 8$ s.

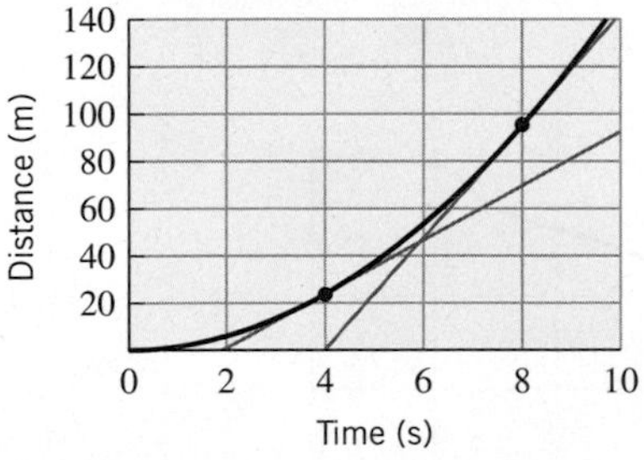

◀ **Figure Ex-2**

3. The accompanying figure shows the position versus time curve for a certain particle moving along a straight line. Estimate each of the following from the graph:
   (a) the average velocity over the interval $0 \le t \le 3$
   (b) the values of $t$ at which the instantaneous velocity is zero
   (c) the values of $t$ at which the instantaneous velocity is either a maximum or a minimum
   (d) the instantaneous velocity when $t = 3$ s.

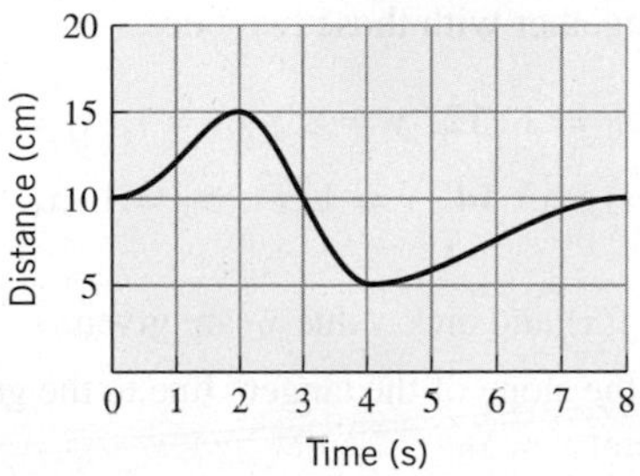

◀ **Figure Ex-3**

4. The accompanying figure shows the position versus time curves of four different particles moving on a straight line. For each particle, determine whether its instantaneous velocity is increasing or decreasing with time.

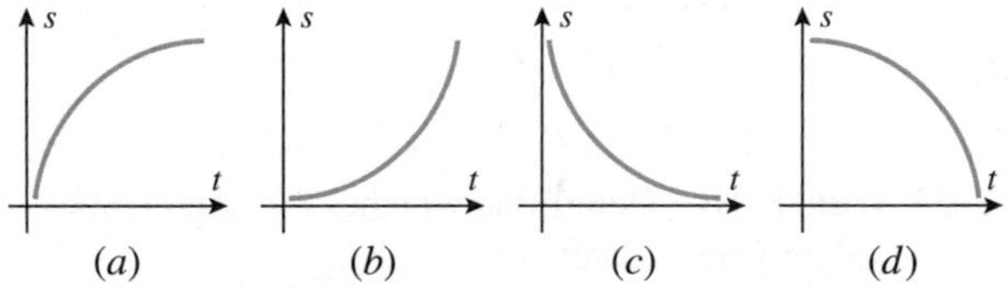

▲ **Figure Ex-4**

**FOCUS ON CONCEPTS**

5. If a particle moves at constant velocity, what can you say about its position versus time curve?

6. An automobile, initially at rest, begins to move along a straight track. The velocity increases steadily until suddenly the driver sees a concrete barrier in the road and applies the brakes sharply at time $t_0$. The car decelerates rapidly, but it is too late—the car crashes into the barrier at time $t_1$ and instantaneously comes to rest. Sketch a position versus time curve that might represent the motion of the car. Indicate how characteristics of your curve correspond to the events of this scenario.

**7–10** For each exercise, sketch a curve and a line $L$ satisfying the stated conditions. ■

7. $L$ is tangent to the curve and intersects the curve in at least two points.

8. $L$ intersects the curve in exactly one point, but $L$ is not tangent to the curve.

9. $L$ is tangent to the curve at two different points.

10. $L$ is tangent to the curve at two different points and intersects the curve at a third point.

**11–14** A function $y = f(x)$ and values of $x_0$ and $x_1$ are given.

(a) Find the average rate of change of $y$ with respect to $x$ over the interval $[x_0, x_1]$.

(b) Find the instantaneous rate of change of $y$ with respect to $x$ at the specified value of $x_0$.

(c) Find the instantaneous rate of change of $y$ with respect to $x$ at an arbitrary value of $x_0$.

(d) The average rate of change in part (a) is the slope of a certain secant line, and the instantaneous rate of change in part (b) is the slope of a certain tangent line. Sketch the graph of $y = f(x)$ together with those two lines. ■

**11.** $y = 2x^2;\ x_0 = 0,\ x_1 = 1$ **12.** $y = x^3;\ x_0 = 1,\ x_1 = 2$

**13.** $y = 1/x;\ x_0 = 2,\ x_1 = 3$ **14.** $y = 1/x^2;\ x_0 = 1,\ x_1 = 2$

**15–18** A function $y = f(x)$ and an $x$-value $x_0$ are given.

(a) Find a formula for the slope of the tangent line to the graph of $f$ at a general point $x = x_0$.

(b) Use the formula obtained in part (a) to find the slope of the tangent line for the given value of $x_0$. ■

**15.** $f(x) = x^2 - 1;\ x_0 = -1$

**16.** $f(x) = x^2 + 3x + 2;\ x_0 = 2$

**17.** $f(x) = x + \sqrt{x};\ x_0 = 1$

**18.** $f(x) = 1/\sqrt{x};\ x_0 = 4$

**19–22 True–False** Determine whether the statement is true or false. Explain your answer. ■

**19.** If $\lim_{x \to 1} \dfrac{f(x) - f(1)}{x - 1} = 3$, then $\lim_{h \to 0} \dfrac{f(1 + h) - f(1)}{h} = 3$.

**20.** A tangent line to a curve $y = f(x)$ is a particular kind of secant line to the curve.

**21.** The velocity of an object represents a change in the object's position.

**22.** A 50-foot horizontal metal beam is supported on either end by concrete pillars and a weight is placed on the middle of the beam. If $f(x)$ models how many inches the center of the beam sags when the weight measures $x$ tons, then the units of the rate of change of $y = f(x)$ with respect to $x$ are inches/ton.

**23.** Suppose that the outside temperature versus time curve over a 24-hour period is as shown in the accompanying figure.

(a) Estimate the maximum temperature and the time at which it occurs.

(b) The temperature rise is fairly linear from 8 A.M. to 2 P.M. Estimate the rate at which the temperature is increasing during this time period.

(c) Estimate the time at which the temperature is decreasing most rapidly. Estimate the instantaneous rate of change of temperature with respect to time at this instant.

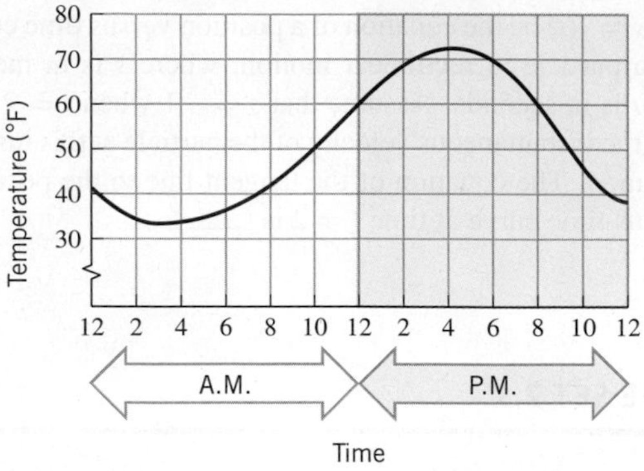


▲ **Figure Ex-23**

**24.** The accompanying figure shows the graph of the pressure $p$ in atmospheres (atm) versus the volume $V$ in liters (L) of 1 mole of an ideal gas at a constant temperature of 300 K (kelvins). Use the line segments shown in the figure to estimate the rate of change of pressure with respect to volume at the points where $V = 10$ L and $V = 25$ L.

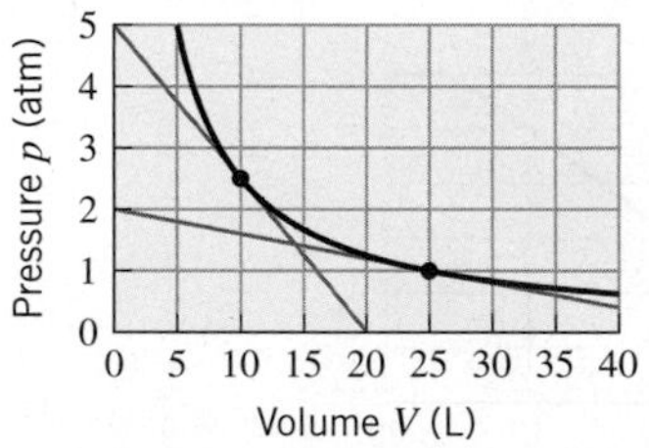


◀ **Figure Ex-24**

**25.** The accompanying figure shows the graph of the height $h$ in centimeters versus the age $t$ in years of an individual from birth to age 20.

(a) When is the growth rate greatest?

(b) Estimate the growth rate at age 5.

(c) At approximately what age between 10 and 20 is the growth rate greatest? Estimate the growth rate at this age.

(d) Draw a rough graph of the growth rate versus age.

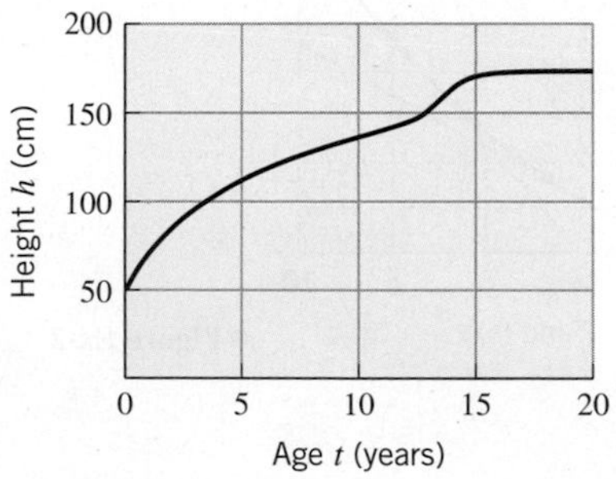


◀ **Figure Ex-25**

**26.** An object is released from rest (its initial velocity is zero) from the Empire State Building at a height of 1250 ft above street level (Figure Ex-26 on the next page). The height of the object can be modeled by the position function $s = f(t) = 1250 - 16t^2$.

(a) Verify that the object is still falling at $t = 5$ s.

(b) Find the average velocity of the object over the time interval from $t = 5$ to $t = 6$ s.

(c) Find the object's instantaneous velocity at time $t = 5$ s.

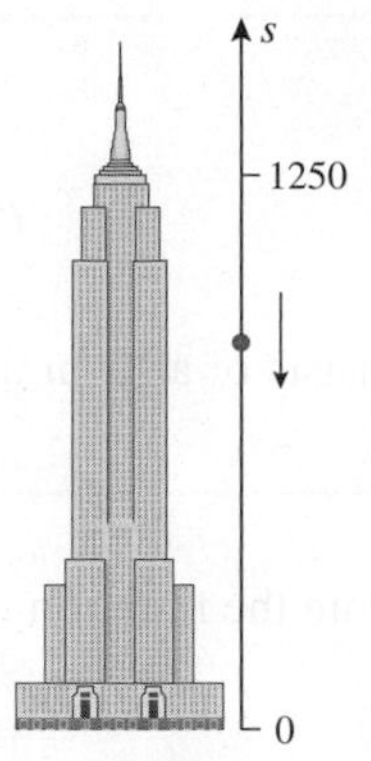

◀ **Figure Ex-26**

**27.** During the first 40 s of a rocket flight, the rocket is propelled straight up so that in $t$ seconds it reaches a height of $s = 0.3t^3$ ft.
(a) How high does the rocket travel in 40 s?
(b) What is the average velocity of the rocket during the first 40 s?
(c) What is the average velocity of the rocket during the first 1000 ft of its flight?
(d) What is the instantaneous velocity of the rocket at the end of 40 s?

**28.** An automobile is driven down a straight highway such that after $0 \le t \le 12$ seconds it is $s = 4.5t^2$ feet from its initial position.
(a) Find the average velocity of the car over the interval [0, 12].
(b) Find the instantaneous velocity of the car at $t = 6$.

**29.** A robot moves in the positive direction along a straight line so that after $t$ minutes its distance is $s = 6t^4$ feet from the origin.
(a) Find the average velocity of the robot over the interval [2, 4].
(b) Find the instantaneous velocity at $t = 2$.

**30. Writing** Discuss how the tangent line to the graph of a function $y = f(x)$ at a point $P(x_0, f(x_0))$ is defined in terms of secant lines to the graph through point $P$.

**31. Writing** A particle is in rectilinear motion during the time interval $0 \le t \le 2$. Explain the connection between the instantaneous velocity of the particle at time $t = 1$ and the average velocities of the particle during portions of the interval $0 \le t \le 2$.

**✓ QUICK CHECK ANSWERS 2.1** 1. $\dfrac{f(x)-f(x_0)}{x-x_0}$; $\dfrac{f(x_0+h)-f(x_0)}{h}$ 2. −4 3. (a) 9; positive; 4 (b) 1 ft/s 4. $s = 3t - 7$
5. (a) 8 (b) $\lim_{x\to 2} \dfrac{(x^2+x)-6}{x-2}$ or $\lim_{h\to 0} \dfrac{[(2+h)^2+(2+h)]-6}{h}$

# 2.2 THE DERIVATIVE FUNCTION

*In this section we will discuss the concept of a "derivative," which is the primary mathematical tool that is used to calculate and study rates of change.*

## DEFINITION OF THE DERIVATIVE FUNCTION

In the last section we showed that if the limit

$$\lim_{h\to 0} \frac{f(x_0+h)-f(x_0)}{h}$$

exists, then it can be interpreted either as the slope of the tangent line to the curve $y = f(x)$ at $x = x_0$ or as the instantaneous rate of change of $y$ with respect to $x$ at $x = x_0$ [see Formulas (2) and (9) of that section]. This limit is so important that it has a special notation:

$$f'(x_0) = \lim_{h\to 0} \frac{f(x_0+h)-f(x_0)}{h} \tag{1}$$

You can think of $f'$ (read "$f$ prime") as a function whose input is $x_0$ and whose output is the number $f'(x_0)$ that represents either the slope of the tangent line to $y = f(x)$ at $x = x_0$ or the instantaneous rate of change of $y$ with respect to $x$ at $x = x_0$. To emphasize this function point of view, we will replace $x_0$ by $x$ in (1) and make the following definition.

The expression

$$\frac{f(x+h)-f(x)}{h}$$

that appears in (2) is commonly called the *difference quotient*.

**2.2.1 DEFINITION** The function $f'$ defined by the formula

$$f'(x) = \lim_{h\to 0} \frac{f(x+h)-f(x)}{h} \qquad (2)$$

is called the ***derivative of f with respect to x***. The domain of $f'$ consists of all $x$ in the domain of $f$ for which the limit exists.

The term "derivative" is used because the function $f'$ is *derived* from the function $f$ by a limiting process.

**▶ Example 1** Find the derivative with respect to $x$ of $f(x) = x^2$, and use it to find the equation of the tangent line to $y = x^2$ at $x = 2$.

***Solution.*** It follows from (2) that

$$\begin{aligned} f'(x) &= \lim_{h\to 0} \frac{f(x+h)-f(x)}{h} = \lim_{h\to 0} \frac{(x+h)^2 - x^2}{h} \\ &= \lim_{h\to 0} \frac{x^2 + 2xh + h^2 - x^2}{h} = \lim_{h\to 0} \frac{2xh + h^2}{h} \\ &= \lim_{h\to 0} (2x + h) = 2x \end{aligned}$$

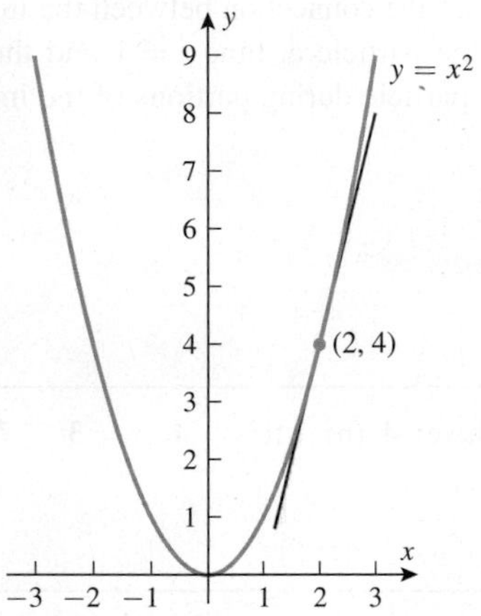

▲ Figure 2.2.1

Thus, the slope of the tangent line to $y = x^2$ at $x = 2$ is $f'(2) = 4$. Since $y = 4$ if $x = 2$, the point-slope form of the tangent line is

$$y - 4 = 4(x - 2)$$

which we can rewrite in slope-intercept form as $y = 4x - 4$ (Figure 2.2.1). ◀

The function $f'$ is a "slope-producing function" since the value of $f'(x)$ at $x = x_0$ is the slope of the tangent line to the graph of $f$ at $x = x_0$. This aspect of the derivative is illustrated in Figure 2.2.2, which shows the graphs of $f(x) = x^2$ and its derivative $f'(x) = 2x$ (obtained in Example 1). The figure illustrates that the values of $f'(x) = 2x$ at $x = -2, 0$, and 2 correspond to the slopes of the tangent lines to the graph of $f(x) = x^2$ at those values of $x$.

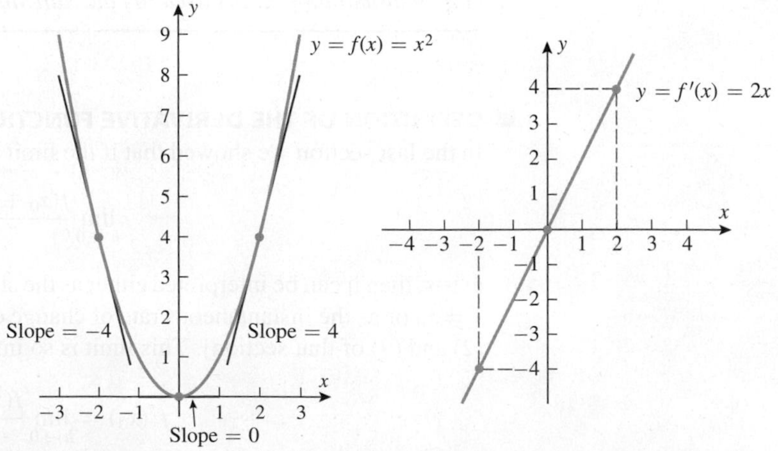

▶ Figure 2.2.2

In general, if $f'(x)$ is defined at $x = x_0$, then the point-slope form of the equation of the tangent line to the graph of $y = f(x)$ at $x = x_0$ may be found using the following steps.

***Finding an Equation for the Tangent Line to $y = f(x)$ at $x = x_0$.***

**Step 1.** Evaluate $f(x_0)$; the point of tangency is $(x_0, f(x_0))$.

**Step 2.** Find $f'(x)$ and evaluate $f'(x_0)$, which is the slope $m$ of the line.

**Step 3.** Substitute the value of the slope $m$ and the point $(x_0, f(x_0))$ into the point-slope form of the line

$$y - f(x_0) = f'(x_0)(x - x_0)$$

or, equivalently,

$$y = f(x_0) + f'(x_0)(x - x_0) \tag{3}$$

► **Example 2**

In Solution (a), the binomial formula is used to expand $(x+h)^3$. This formula may be found on the front endpaper.

(a) Find the derivative with respect to $x$ of $f(x) = x^3 - x$.

(b) Graph $f$ and $f'$ together, and discuss the relationship between the two graphs.

***Solution (a).***

$$\begin{aligned} f'(x) &= \lim_{h\to 0} \frac{f(x+h) - f(x)}{h} \\ &= \lim_{h\to 0} \frac{[(x+h)^3 - (x+h)] - [x^3 - x]}{h} \\ &= \lim_{h\to 0} \frac{[x^3 + 3x^2h + 3xh^2 + h^3 - x - h] - [x^3 - x]}{h} \\ &= \lim_{h\to 0} \frac{3x^2h + 3xh^2 + h^3 - h}{h} \\ &= \lim_{h\to 0} [3x^2 + 3xh + h^2 - 1] = 3x^2 - 1 \end{aligned}$$

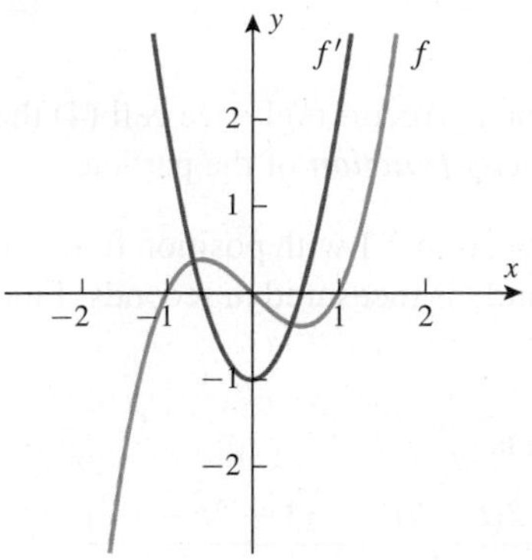

▲ **Figure 2.2.3**

***Solution (b).*** Since $f'(x)$ can be interpreted as the slope of the tangent line to the graph of $y = f(x)$ at $x$, it follows that $f'(x)$ is positive where the tangent line has positive slope, is negative where the tangent line has negative slope, and is zero where the tangent line is horizontal. We leave it for you to verify that this is consistent with the graphs of $f(x) = x^3 - x$ and $f'(x) = 3x^2 - 1$ shown in Figure 2.2.3. ◄

► **Example 3** At each value of $x$, the tangent line to a line $y = mx + b$ coincides with the line itself (Figure 2.2.4), and hence all tangent lines have slope $m$. This suggests geometrically that if $f(x) = mx + b$, then $f'(x) = m$ for all $x$. This is confirmed by the following computations:

$$\begin{aligned} f'(x) &= \lim_{h\to 0} \frac{f(x+h) - f(x)}{h} \\ &= \lim_{h\to 0} \frac{[m(x+h) + b] - [mx + b]}{h} \\ &= \lim_{h\to 0} \frac{mh}{h} = \lim_{h\to 0} m = m \end{aligned}$$ ◄

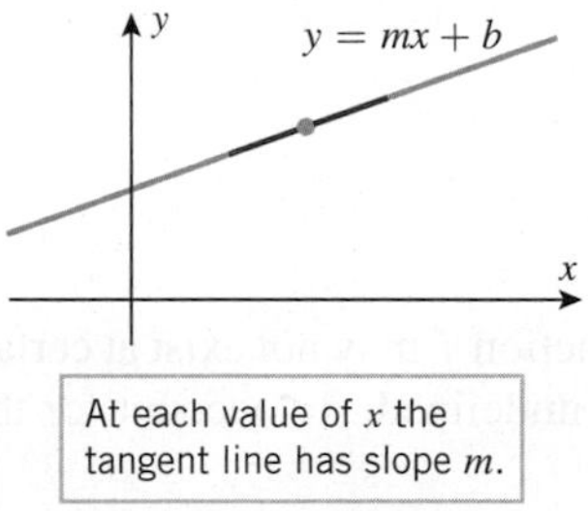

▲ **Figure 2.2.4**

► **Example 4**

The result in Example 3 is consistent with our earlier observation that the rate of change of $y$ with respect to $x$ along a line $y = mx + b$ is constant and that constant is $m$.

(a) Find the derivative with respect to $x$ of $f(x) = \sqrt{x}$.

(b) Find the slope of the tangent line to $y = \sqrt{x}$ at $x = 9$.

(c) Find the limits of $f'(x)$ as $x \to 0^+$ and as $x \to +\infty$, and explain what those limits say about the graph of $f$.

***Solution (a).*** Recall from Example 3 of Section 2.1 that the slope of the tangent line to $y = \sqrt{x}$ at $x = x_0$ is given by $m_{\tan} = 1/(2\sqrt{x_0})$. Thus, $f'(x) = 1/(2\sqrt{x})$.

***Solution (b).*** The slope of the tangent line at $x = 9$ is $f'(9)$. From part (a), this slope is $f'(9) = 1/(2\sqrt{9}) = \frac{1}{6}$.

***Solution (c).*** The graphs of $f(x) = \sqrt{x}$ and $f'(x) = 1/(2\sqrt{x})$ are shown in Figure 2.2.5. Observe that $f'(x) > 0$ if $x > 0$, which means that all tangent lines to the graph of $y = \sqrt{x}$ have positive slope at all points in this interval. Since

$$\lim_{x\to 0^+} \frac{1}{2\sqrt{x}} = +\infty \quad \text{and} \quad \lim_{x\to +\infty} \frac{1}{2\sqrt{x}} = 0$$

the graph of $f$ becomes more and more vertical as $x \to 0^+$ and more and more horizontal as $x \to +\infty$. ◀

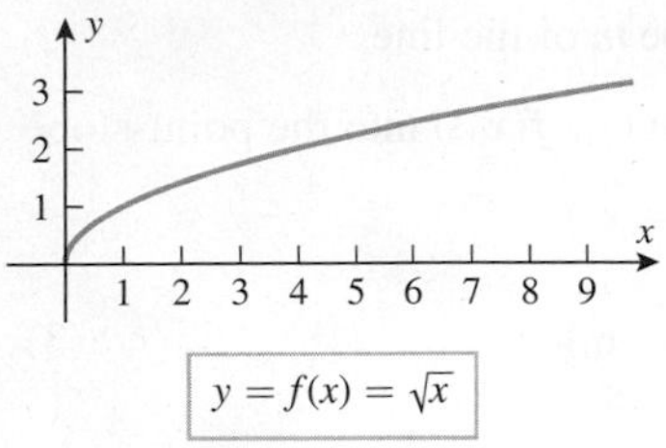


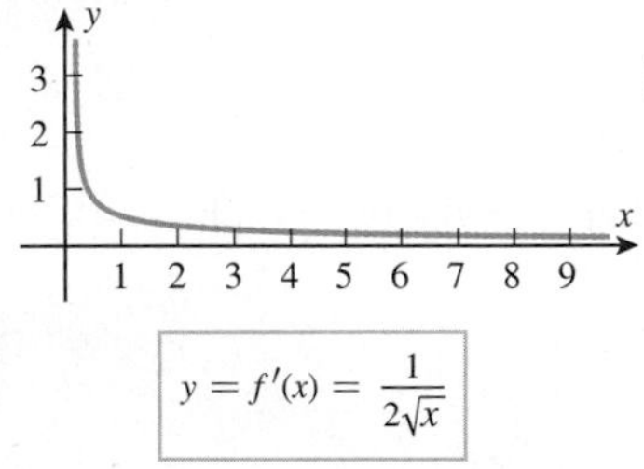


▲ **Figure 2.2.5**

## COMPUTING INSTANTANEOUS VELOCITY

It follows from Formula (5) of Section 2.1 (with $t$ replacing $t_0$) that if $s = f(t)$ is the position function of a particle in rectilinear motion, then the instantaneous velocity at an arbitrary time $t$ is given by

$$v_{\text{inst}} = \lim_{h\to 0} \frac{f(t+h) - f(t)}{h}$$

Since the right side of this equation is the derivative of the function $f$ (with $t$ rather than $x$ as the independent variable), it follows that if $f(t)$ is the position function of a particle in rectilinear motion, then the function

$$v(t) = f'(t) = \lim_{h\to 0} \frac{f(t+h) - f(t)}{h} \tag{4}$$

represents the instantaneous velocity of the particle at time $t$. Accordingly, we call (4) the ***instantaneous velocity function*** or, more simply, the ***velocity function*** of the particle.

▶ **Example 5** Recall the particle from Example 4 of Section 2.1 with position function $s = f(t) = 1 + 5t - 2t^2$. Here $f(t)$ is measured in meters and $t$ is measured in seconds. Find the velocity function of the particle.

***Solution.*** It follows from (4) that the velocity function is

$$\begin{aligned} v(t) &= \lim_{h\to 0} \frac{f(t+h) - f(t)}{h} = \lim_{h\to 0} \frac{[1 + 5(t+h) - 2(t+h)^2] - [1 + 5t - 2t^2]}{h} \\ &= \lim_{h\to 0} \frac{-2[t^2 + 2th + h^2 - t^2] + 5h}{h} = \lim_{h\to 0} \frac{-4th - 2h^2 + 5h}{h} \\ &= \lim_{h\to 0} (-4t - 2h + 5) = 5 - 4t \end{aligned}$$

where the units of velocity are meters per second. ◀

## DIFFERENTIABILITY

It is possible that the limit that defines the derivative of a function $f$ may not exist at certain points in the domain of $f$. At such points the derivative is undefined. To account for this possibility we make the following definition.

**2.2.2 DEFINITION** A function $f$ is said to be ***differentiable at*** $x_0$ if the limit

$$f'(x_0) = \lim_{h\to 0} \frac{f(x_0 + h) - f(x_0)}{h} \tag{5}$$

exists. If $f$ is differentiable at each point of the open interval $(a, b)$, then we say that it is ***differentiable on*** $(a, b)$, and similarly for open intervals of the form $(a, +\infty)$, $(-\infty, b)$, and $(-\infty, +\infty)$. In the last case we say that $f$ is ***differentiable everywhere***.

Geometrically, a function $f$ is differentiable at $x_0$ if the graph of $f$ has a tangent line at $x_0$. Thus, $f$ is not differentiable at any point $x_0$ where the secant lines from $P(x_0, f(x_0))$ to points $Q(x, f(x))$ distinct from $P$ do not approach a unique *nonvertical* limiting position as $x \to x_0$. Figure 2.2.6 illustrates two common ways in which a function that is continuous at $x_0$ can fail to be differentiable at $x_0$. These can be described informally as

- corner points
- points of vertical tangency

At a corner point, the slopes of the secant lines have different limits from the left and from the right, and hence the *two-sided* limit that defines the derivative does not exist (Figure 2.2.7). At a point of vertical tangency the slopes of the secant lines approach $+\infty$ or $-\infty$ from the left and from the right (Figure 2.2.8), so again the limit that defines the derivative does not exist.

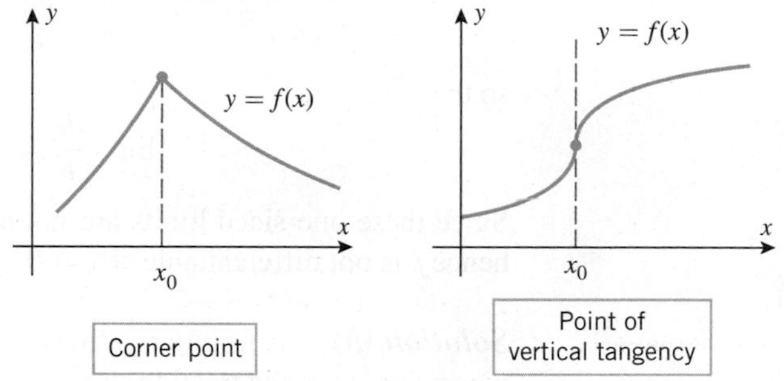


▶ **Figure 2.2.6**

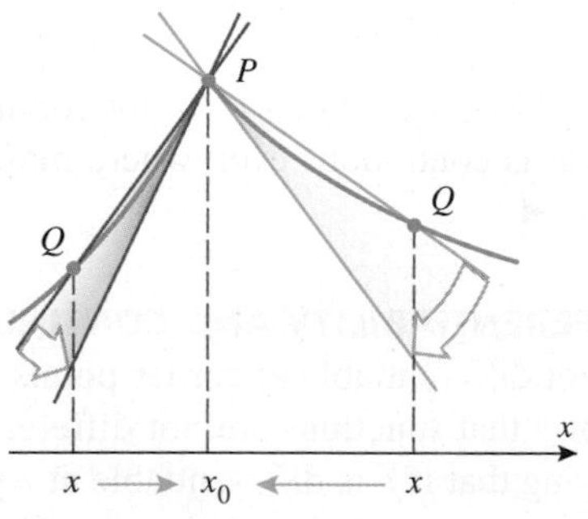


▲ **Figure 2.2.7**

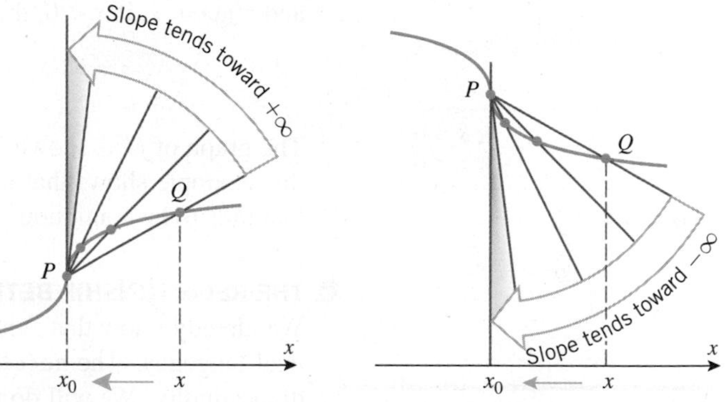


▲ **Figure 2.2.8**

There are other less obvious circumstances under which a function may fail to be differentiable. (See Exercise 49, for example.)

Differentiability at $x_0$ can also be described informally in terms of the behavior of the graph of $f$ under increasingly stronger magnification at the point $P(x_0, f(x_0))$ (Figure 2.2.9). If $f$ is differentiable at $x_0$, then under sufficiently strong magnification at $P$ the graph looks like a nonvertical line (the tangent line); if a corner point occurs at $x_0$, then no matter how great the magnification at $P$ the corner persists and the graph never looks like a nonvertical line; and if vertical tangency occurs at $x_0$, then the graph of $f$ looks like a vertical line under sufficiently strong magnification at $P$.

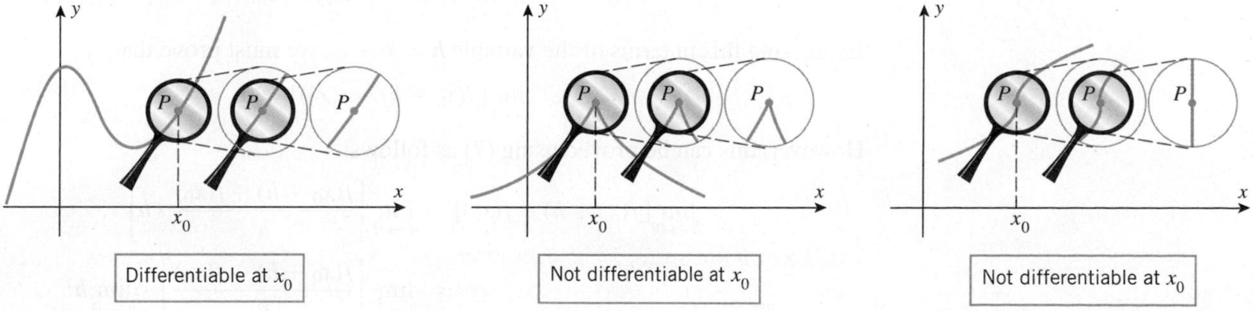


▲ **Figure 2.2.9**

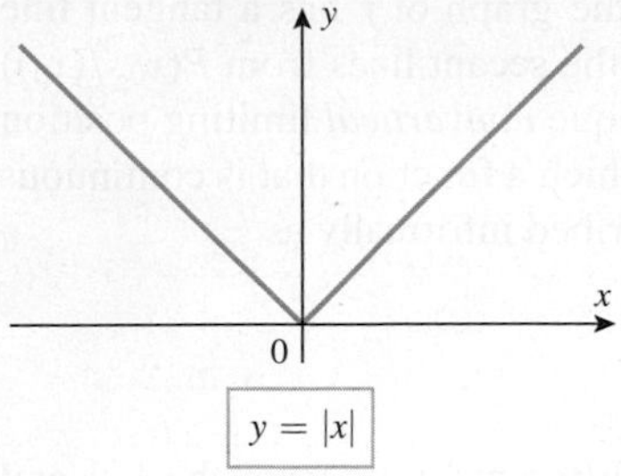


▲ Figure 2.2.10

**▶ Example 6** The graph of $y = |x|$ in Figure 2.2.10 has a corner at $x = 0$, which implies that $f(x) = |x|$ is not differentiable at $x = 0$.

(a) Prove that $f(x) = |x|$ is not differentiable at $x = 0$ by showing that the limit in Definition 2.2.2 does not exist at $x = 0$.

(b) Find a formula for $f'(x)$.

***Solution (a).*** From Formula (5) with $x_0 = 0$, the value of $f'(0)$, if it were to exist, would be given by

$$f'(0) = \lim_{h\to 0} \frac{f(0+h) - f(0)}{h} = \lim_{h\to 0} \frac{f(h) - f(0)}{h} = \lim_{h\to 0} \frac{|h| - |0|}{h} = \lim_{h\to 0} \frac{|h|}{h} \tag{6}$$

But

$$\frac{|h|}{h} = \begin{cases} 1, & h > 0 \\ -1, & h < 0 \end{cases}$$

so that

$$\lim_{h\to 0^-} \frac{|h|}{h} = -1 \quad \text{and} \quad \lim_{h\to 0^+} \frac{|h|}{h} = 1$$

Since these one-sided limits are not equal, the two-sided limit in (5) does not exist, and hence $f$ is not differentiable at $x = 0$.

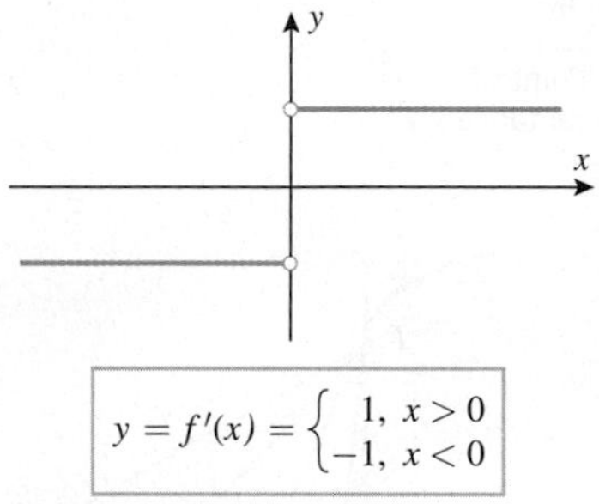


▲ Figure 2.2.11

***Solution (b).*** A formula for the derivative of $f(x) = |x|$ can be obtained by writing $|x|$ in piecewise form and treating the cases $x > 0$ and $x < 0$ separately. If $x > 0$, then $f(x) = x$ and $f'(x) = 1$; if $x < 0$, then $f(x) = -x$ and $f'(x) = -1$. Thus,

$$f'(x) = \begin{cases} 1, & x > 0 \\ -1, & x < 0 \end{cases}$$

The graph of $f'$ is shown in Figure 2.2.11. Observe that $f'$ is not continuous at $x = 0$, so this example shows that a function that is continuous everywhere may have a derivative that fails to be continuous everywhere. ◀

## THE RELATIONSHIP BETWEEN DIFFERENTIABILITY AND CONTINUITY

We already know that functions are not differentiable at corner points and points of vertical tangency. The next theorem shows that functions are not differentiable at points of discontinuity. We will do this by proving that if $f$ is differentiable at a point, then it must be continuous at that point.

> A theorem that says "If statement $A$ is true, then statement $B$ is true" is equivalent to the theorem that says "If statement $B$ is not true, then statement $A$ is not true." The two theorems are called ***contrapositive forms*** of one another. Thus, Theorem 2.2.3 can be rewritten in contrapositive form as "If a function $f$ is not continuous at $x_0$, then $f$ is not differentiable at $x_0$."

**2.2.3 THEOREM** *If a function $f$ is differentiable at $x_0$, then $f$ is continuous at $x_0$.*

**PROOF** We are given that $f$ is differentiable at $x_0$, so it follows from (5) that $f'(x_0)$ exists and is given by

$$f'(x_0) = \lim_{h\to 0}\left[\frac{f(x_0+h) - f(x_0)}{h}\right] \tag{7}$$

To show that $f$ is continuous at $x_0$, we must show that $\lim_{x\to x_0} f(x) = f(x_0)$ or, equivalently,

$$\lim_{x\to x_0} [f(x) - f(x_0)] = 0$$

Expressing this in terms of the variable $h = x - x_0$, we must prove that

$$\lim_{h\to 0} [f(x_0+h) - f(x_0)] = 0$$

However, this can be proved using (7) as follows:

$$\begin{aligned} \lim_{h\to 0} [f(x_0+h) - f(x_0)] &= \lim_{h\to 0}\left[\frac{f(x_0+h) - f(x_0)}{h} \cdot h\right] \\ &= \lim_{h\to 0}\left[\frac{f(x_0+h) - f(x_0)}{h}\right] \cdot \lim_{h\to 0} h \\ &= f'(x_0) \cdot 0 = 0 \ \blacksquare \end{aligned}$$

**WARNING**

The converse of Theorem 2.2.3 is false; that is, *a function may be continuous at a point but not differentiable at that point.* This occurs, for example, at corner points of continuous functions. For instance, $f(x) = |x|$ is continuous at $x = 0$ but not differentiable there (Example 6).

The relationship between continuity and differentiability was of great historical significance in the development of calculus. In the early nineteenth century mathematicians believed that if a continuous function had many points of nondifferentiability, these points, like the tips of a sawblade, would have to be separated from one another and joined by smooth curve segments (Figure 2.2.12). This misconception was corrected by a series of discoveries beginning in 1834. In that year a Bohemian priest, philosopher, and mathematician named Bernhard Bolzano discovered a procedure for constructing a continuous function that is not differentiable at any point. Later, in 1860, the great German mathematician Karl Weierstrass (biography on p. 32) produced the first formula for such a function. The graphs of such functions are impossible to draw; it is as if the corners are so numerous that any segment of the curve, when suitably enlarged, reveals more corners. The discovery of these functions was important in that it made mathematicians distrustful of their geometric intuition and more reliant on precise mathematical proof. Recently, such functions have started to play a fundamental role in the study of geometric objects called ***fractals***. Fractals have revealed an order to natural phenomena that were previously dismissed as random and chaotic.

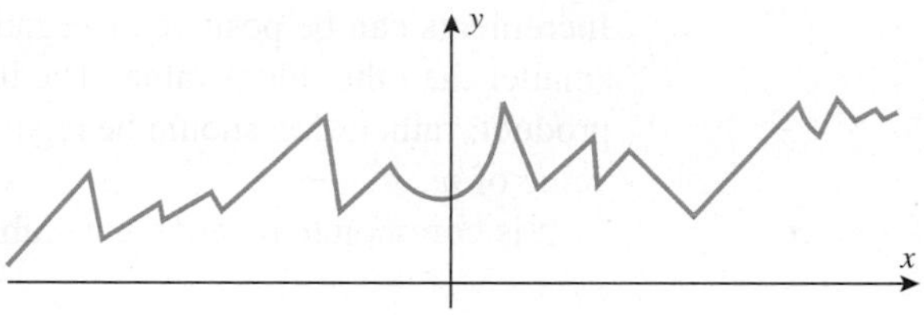


▶ **Figure 2.2.12**

## DERIVATIVES AT THE ENDPOINTS OF AN INTERVAL

If a function $f$ is defined on a closed interval $[a, b]$ but not outside that interval, then $f'$ is not defined at the endpoints of the interval because derivatives are two-sided limits. To deal with this we define ***left-hand derivatives*** and ***right-hand derivatives*** by

$$f'_-(x) = \lim_{h\to 0^-} \frac{f(x+h) - f(x)}{h} \quad \text{and} \quad f'_+(x) = \lim_{h\to 0^+} \frac{f(x+h) - f(x)}{h}$$

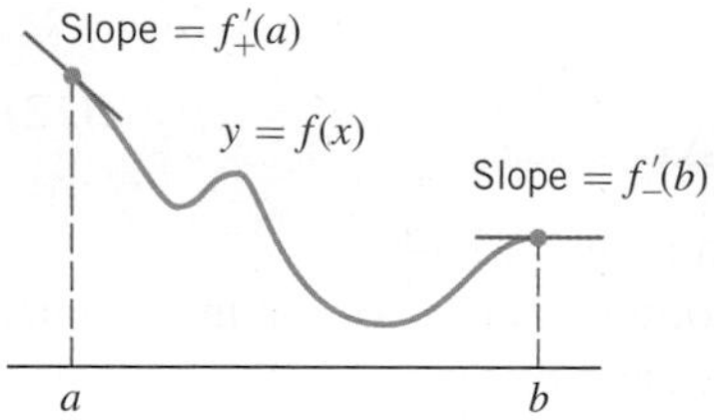


▲ **Figure 2.2.13**

respectively. These are called ***one-sided derivatives***. Geometrically, $f'_-(x)$ is the limit of the slopes of the secant lines as $x$ is approached from the left and $f'_+(x)$ is the limit of the slopes of the secant lines as $x$ is approached from the right. For a closed interval $[a, b]$, we will understand the derivative at the left endpoint to be $f'_+(a)$ and at the right endpoint to be $f'_-(b)$ (Figure 2.2.13).

In general, we will say that $f$ is ***differentiable*** on an interval of the form $[a, b]$, $[a, +\infty)$, $(-\infty, b]$, $[a, b)$, or $(a, b]$ if it is differentiable at all points inside the interval and the appropriate one-sided derivative exists at each included endpoint.

It can be proved that a function $f$ is continuous from the left at those points where the left-hand derivative exists and is continuous from the right at those points where the right-hand derivative exists.

**Bernhard Bolzano (1781–1848)** Bolzano, the son of an art dealer, was born in Prague, Bohemia (Czech Republic). He was educated at the University of Prague, and eventually won enough mathematical fame to be recommended for a mathematics chair there. However, Bolzano became an ordained Roman Catholic priest, and in 1805 he was appointed to a chair of Philosophy at the University of Prague. Bolzano was a man of great human compassion; he spoke out for educational reform, he voiced the right of individual conscience over government demands, and he lectured on the absurdity of war and militarism. His views so disenchanted Emperor Franz I of Austria that the emperor pressed the Archbishop of Prague to have Bolzano recant his statements. Bolzano refused and was then forced to retire in 1824 on a small pension. Bolzano's main contribution to mathematics was philosophical. His work helped convince mathematicians that sound mathematics must ultimately rest on rigorous proof rather than intuition. In addition to his work in mathematics, Bolzano investigated problems concerning space, force, and wave propagation.

[*Image: Juulijs/Fotolia*]

## OTHER DERIVATIVE NOTATIONS

The process of finding a derivative is called ***differentiation***. You can think of differentiation as an *operation* on functions that associates a function $f'$ with a function $f$. When the independent variable is $x$, the differentiation operation is also commonly denoted by

$$f'(x) = \frac{d}{dx}[f(x)] \quad \text{or} \quad f'(x) = D_x[f(x)]$$

In the case where there is a dependent variable $y = f(x)$, the derivative is also commonly denoted by

$$f'(x) = y'(x) \quad \text{or} \quad f'(x) = \frac{dy}{dx}$$

Later, the symbols $dy$ and $dx$ will be given specific meanings. However, for the time being do not regard $dy/dx$ as a ratio, but rather as a single symbol denoting the derivative.

With the above notations, the value of the derivative at a point $x_0$ can be expressed as

$$f'(x_0) = \frac{d}{dx}[f(x)]\bigg|_{x=x_0}, \quad f'(x_0) = D_x[f(x)]|_{x=x_0}, \quad f'(x_0) = y'(x_0), \quad f'(x_0) = \frac{dy}{dx}\bigg|_{x=x_0}$$

If a variable $w$ changes from some initial value $w_0$ to some final value $w_1$, then the final value minus the initial value is called an ***increment*** in $w$ and is denoted by

$$\Delta w = w_1 - w_0 \tag{8}$$

Increments can be positive or negative, depending on whether the final value is larger or smaller than the initial value. The increment symbol in (8) should not be interpreted as a product; rather, $\Delta w$ should be regarded as a single symbol representing the change in the value of $w$.

It is common to regard the variable $h$ in the derivative formula

$$f'(x) = \lim_{h\to 0} \frac{f(x+h) - f(x)}{h} \tag{9}$$

as an increment $\Delta x$ in $x$ and write (9) as

$$f'(x) = \lim_{\Delta x\to 0} \frac{f(x+\Delta x) - f(x)}{\Delta x} \tag{10}$$

Moreover, if $y = f(x)$, then the numerator in (10) can be regarded as the increment

$$\Delta y = f(x+\Delta x) - f(x) \tag{11}$$

in which case

$$\frac{dy}{dx} = \lim_{\Delta x\to 0} \frac{\Delta y}{\Delta x} = \lim_{\Delta x\to 0} \frac{f(x+\Delta x) - f(x)}{\Delta x} \tag{12}$$

The geometric interpretations of $\Delta x$ and $\Delta y$ are shown in Figure 2.2.14.

Sometimes it is desirable to express derivatives in a form that does not use increments at all. For example, if we let $w = x + h$ in Formula (9), then $w \to x$ as $h \to 0$, so we can rewrite that formula as

$$f'(x) = \lim_{w\to x} \frac{f(w) - f(x)}{w - x} \tag{13}$$

(Compare Figures 2.2.14 and 2.2.15.)

When letters other than $x$ and $y$ are used for the independent and dependent variables, the derivative notations must be adjusted accordingly. Thus, for example, if $s = f(t)$ is the position function for a particle in rectilinear motion, then the velocity function $v(t)$ in (4) can be expressed as

$$v(t) = \frac{ds}{dt} = \lim_{\Delta t\to 0} \frac{\Delta s}{\Delta t} = \lim_{\Delta t\to 0} \frac{f(t+\Delta t) - f(t)}{\Delta t} \tag{14}$$

Newton and Leibniz each used a different notation when they published their discoveries of calculus, thereby creating a notational divide between Britain and the European continent that lasted for more than 50 years. The ***Leibniz notation*** $dy/dx$ eventually prevailed because it reflects the underlying concepts in a natural way, the equation

$$\frac{dy}{dx} = \lim_{\Delta x\to 0} \frac{\Delta y}{\Delta x}$$

being one example.

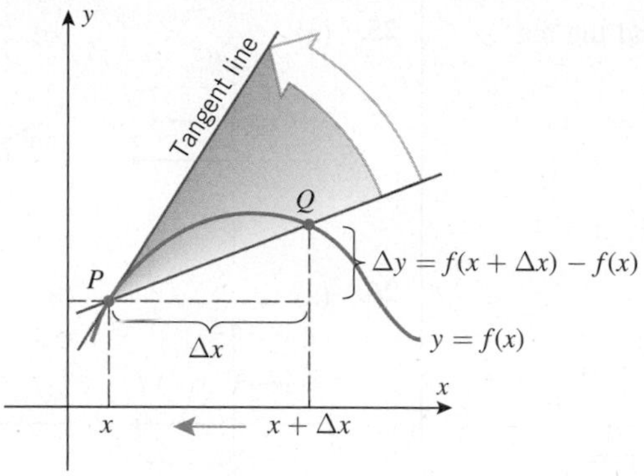


$$\frac{dy}{dx} = \lim_{\Delta x \to 0} \frac{\Delta y}{\Delta x}$$

▲ **Figure 2.2.14**

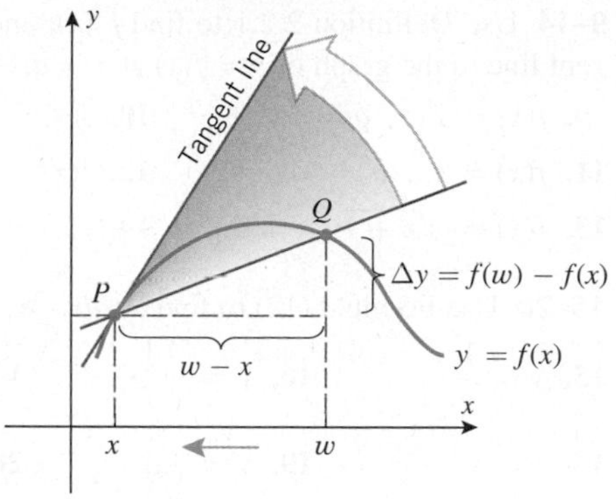


$$f'(x) = \lim_{w \to x} \frac{f(w) - f(x)}{w - x}$$

▲ **Figure 2.2.15**

## ✓ QUICK CHECK EXERCISES 2.2 *(See page 100 for answers.)*

**1.** The function $f'(x)$ is defined by the formula

$$f'(x) = \lim_{h \to 0} \underline{\qquad\qquad}$$

**2.** (a) The derivative of $f(x) = x^2$ is $f'(x) =$ ________.
(b) The derivative of $f(x) = \sqrt{x}$ is $f'(x) =$ ________.

**3.** Suppose that the line $2x + 3y = 5$ is tangent to the graph of $y = f(x)$ at $x = 1$. The value of $f(1)$ is ________ and the value of $f'(1)$ is ________.

**4.** Which theorem guarantees us that if

$$\lim_{h \to 0} \frac{f(x_0 + h) - f(x_0)}{h}$$

exists, then $\lim_{x \to x_0} f(x) = f(x_0)$?

## EXERCISE SET 2.2 Graphing Utility

**1.** Use the graph of $y = f(x)$ in the accompanying figure to estimate the value of $f'(1)$, $f'(3)$, $f'(5)$, and $f'(6)$.

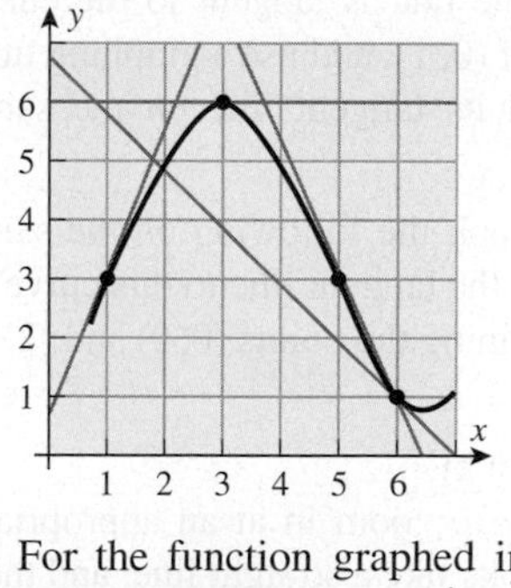

◀ **Figure Ex-1**

**2.** For the function graphed in the accompanying figure, arrange the numbers 0, $f'(-3)$, $f'(0)$, $f'(2)$, and $f'(4)$ in increasing order.

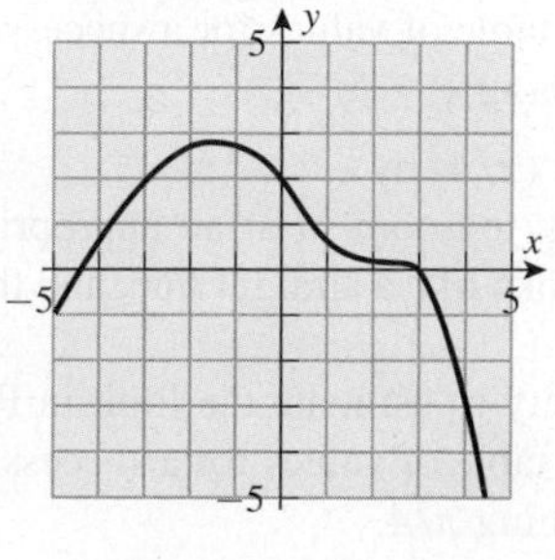

◀ **Figure Ex-2**

**FOCUS ON CONCEPTS**

**3.** (a) If you are given an equation for the tangent line at the point $(a, f(a))$ on a curve $y = f(x)$, how would you go about finding $f'(a)$?
(b) Given that the tangent line to the graph of $y = f(x)$ at the point (2, 5) has the equation $y = 3x - 1$, find $f'(2)$.
(c) For the function $y = f(x)$ in part (b), what is the instantaneous rate of change of $y$ with respect to $x$ at $x = 2$?

**4.** Given that the tangent line to $y = f(x)$ at the point (1, 2) passes through the point $(-1, -1)$, find $f'(1)$.

**5.** Sketch the graph of a function $f$ for which $f(0) = -1$, $f'(0) = 0$, $f'(x) < 0$ if $x < 0$, and $f'(x) > 0$ if $x > 0$.

**6.** Sketch the graph of a function $f$ for which $f(0) = 0$, $f'(0) = 0$, and $f'(x) > 0$ if $x < 0$ or $x > 0$.

**7.** Given that $f(3) = -1$ and $f'(3) = 5$, find an equation for the tangent line to the graph of $y = f(x)$ at $x = 3$.

**8.** Given that $f(-2) = 3$ and $f'(-2) = -4$, find an equation for the tangent line to the graph of $y = f(x)$ at $x = -2$.

**9–14** Use Definition 2.2.1 to find $f'(x)$, and then find the tangent line to the graph of $y = f(x)$ at $x = a$. ■

**9.** $f(x) = 2x^2;\ a = 1$
**10.** $f(x) = 1/x^2;\ a = -1$
**11.** $f(x) = x^3;\ a = 0$
**12.** $f(x) = 2x^3 + 1;\ a = -1$
**13.** $f(x) = \sqrt{x+1};\ a = 8$
**14.** $f(x) = \sqrt{2x+1};\ a = 4$

**15–20** Use Formula (12) to find $dy/dx$. ■

**15.** $y = \dfrac{1}{x}$
**16.** $y = \dfrac{1}{x+1}$
**17.** $y = x^2 - x$
**18.** $y = x^4$
**19.** $y = \dfrac{1}{\sqrt{x}}$
**20.** $y = \dfrac{1}{\sqrt{x-1}}$

**21–22** Use Definition 2.2.1 (with appropriate change in notation) to obtain the derivative requested. ■

**21.** Find $f'(t)$ if $f(t) = 4t^2 + t$.

**22.** Find $dV/dr$ if $V = \frac{4}{3}\pi r^3$.

**FOCUS ON CONCEPTS**

**23.** Match the graphs of the functions shown in (a)–(f) with the graphs of their derivatives in (A)–(F).

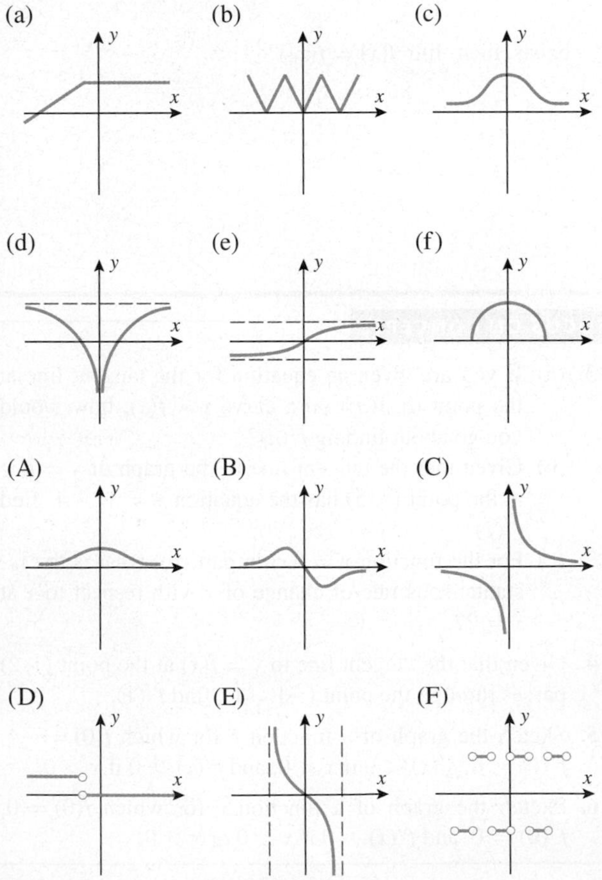


**24.** Let $f(x) = \sqrt{1-x^2}$. Use a geometric argument to find $f'(\sqrt{2}/2)$.

**25–26** Sketch the graph of the derivative of the function whose graph is shown. ■

**25.**

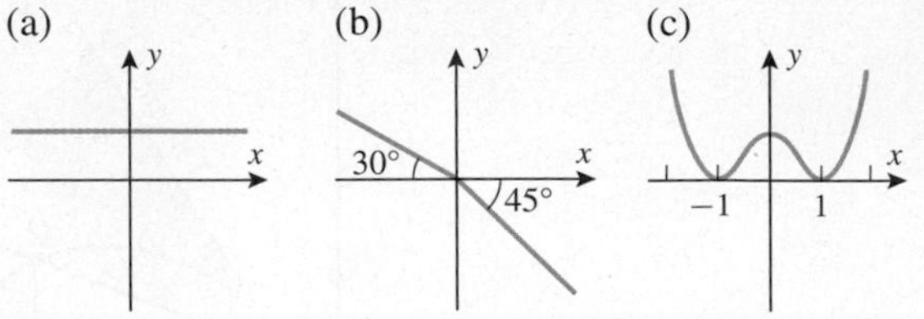


**26.**

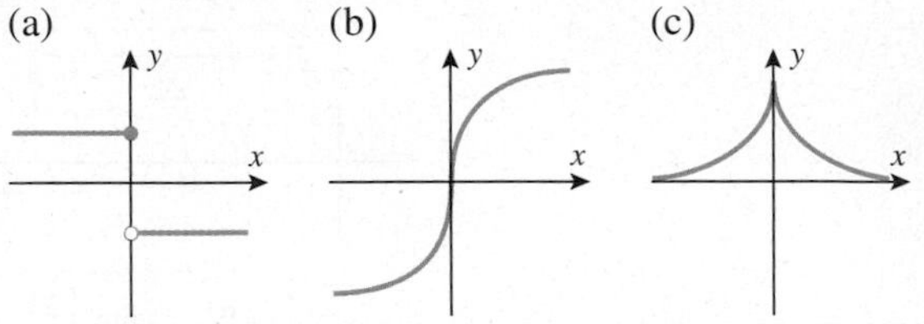


**27–30 True–False** Determine whether the statement is true or false. Explain your answer. ■

**27.** If a curve $y = f(x)$ has a horizontal tangent line at $x = a$, then $f'(a)$ is not defined.

**28.** If the tangent line to the graph of $y = f(x)$ at $x = -2$ has negative slope, then $f'(-2) < 0$.

**29.** If a function $f$ is continuous at $x = 0$, then $f$ is differentiable at $x = 0$.

**30.** If a function $f$ is differentiable at $x = 0$, then $f$ is continuous at $x = 0$.

**31–32** The given limit represents $f'(a)$ for some function $f$ and some number $a$. Find $f(x)$ and $a$ in each case. ■

**31.** (a) $\displaystyle\lim_{\Delta x \to 0} \frac{\sqrt{1+\Delta x} - 1}{\Delta x}$ (b) $\displaystyle\lim_{x_1 \to 3} \frac{x_1^2 - 9}{x_1 - 3}$

**32.** (a) $\displaystyle\lim_{h \to 0} \frac{\cos(\pi + h) + 1}{h}$ (b) $\displaystyle\lim_{x \to 1} \frac{x^7 - 1}{x - 1}$

**33.** Find $dy/dx|_{x=1}$, given that $y = 1 - x^2$.

**34.** Find $dy/dx|_{x=-2}$, given that $y = (x+2)/x$.

**35.** Find an equation for the line that is tangent to the curve $y = x^3 - 2x + 1$ at the point $(0, 1)$, and use a graphing utility to graph the curve and its tangent line on the same screen.

**36.** Use a graphing utility to graph the following on the same screen: the curve $y = x^2/4$, the tangent line to this curve at $x = 1$, and the secant line joining the points $(0, 0)$ and $(2, 1)$ on this curve.

**37.** Let $f(x) = 2^x$. Estimate $f'(1)$ by
(a) using a graphing utility to zoom in at an appropriate point until the graph looks like a straight line, and then estimating the slope
(b) using a calculating utility to estimate the limit in Formula (13) by making a table of values for a succession of values of $w$ approaching 1.

**38.** Let $f(x) = \sin x$. Estimate $f'(\pi/4)$ by
(a) using a graphing utility to zoom in at an appropriate point until the graph looks like a straight line, and then estimating the slope
(b) using a calculating utility to estimate the limit in Formula (13) by making a table of values for a succession of values of $w$ approaching $\pi/4$.

**39–40** The function $f$ whose graph is shown below has values as given in the accompanying table.

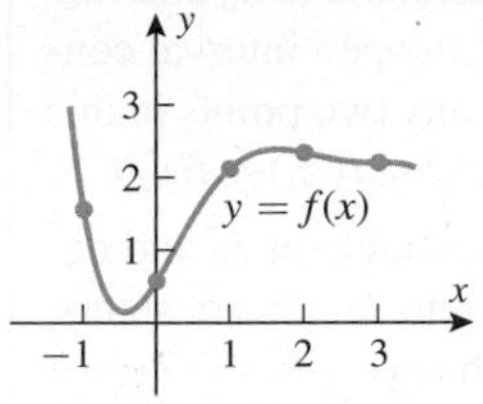


| $x$ | −1 | 0 | 1 | 2 | 3 |
|---|---|---|---|---|---|
| $f(x)$ | 1.56 | 0.58 | 2.12 | 2.34 | 2.2 |

**39.** (a) Use data from the table to calculate the difference quotients

$$\frac{f(3)-f(1)}{3-1}, \quad \frac{f(2)-f(1)}{2-1}, \quad \frac{f(2)-f(0)}{2-0}$$

(b) Using the graph of $y = f(x)$, indicate which difference quotient in part (a) best approximates $f'(1)$ and which difference quotient gives the worst approximation to $f'(1)$.

**40.** Use data from the table to approximate the derivative values.
(a) $f'(0.5)$ (b) $f'(2.5)$

**FOCUS ON CONCEPTS**

**41.** Suppose that the cost of drilling $x$ feet for an oil well is $C = f(x)$ dollars.
(a) What are the units of $f'(x)$?
(b) In practical terms, what does $f'(x)$ mean in this case?
(c) What can you say about the sign of $f'(x)$?
(d) Estimate the cost of drilling an additional foot, starting at a depth of 300 ft, given that $f'(300) = 1000$.

**42.** A paint manufacturing company estimates that it can sell $g = f(p)$ gallons of paint at a price of $p$ dollars per gallon.
(a) What are the units of $dg/dp$?
(b) In practical terms, what does $dg/dp$ mean in this case?
(c) What can you say about the sign of $dg/dp$?
(d) Given that $dg/dp|_{p=10} = -100$, what can you say about the effect of increasing the price from \$10 per gallon to \$11 per gallon?

**43.** It is a fact that when a flexible rope is wrapped around a rough cylinder, a small force of magnitude $F_0$ at one end can resist a large force of magnitude $F$ at the other end. The size of $F$ depends on the angle $\theta$ through which the rope is wrapped around the cylinder (see the accompanying figure). The figure shows the graph of $F$ (in pounds) versus $\theta$ (in radians), where $F$ is the magnitude of the force that can be resisted by a force with magnitude $F_0 = 10$ lb for a certain rope and cylinder.
(a) Estimate the values of $F$ and $dF/d\theta$ when the angle $\theta = 10$ radians.
(b) It can be shown that the force $F$ satisfies the equation $dF/d\theta = \mu F$, where the constant $\mu$ is called the ***coefficient of friction***. Use the results in part (a) to estimate the value of $\mu$.

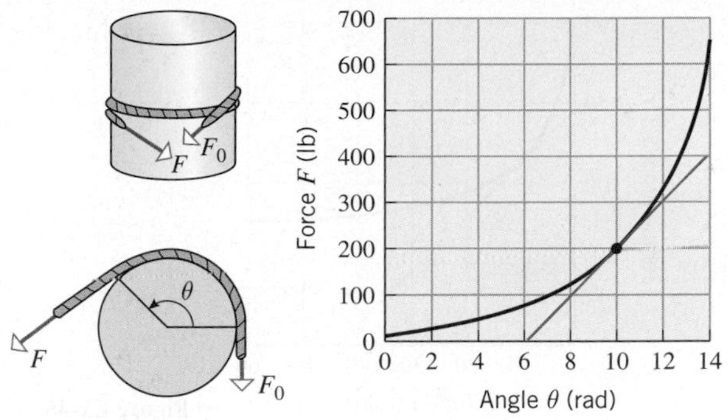

▲ **Figure Ex-43**

**44.** The accompanying figure shows the velocity versus time curve for a rocket in outer space where the only significant force on the rocket is from its engines. It can be shown that the mass $M(t)$ (in slugs) of the rocket at time $t$ seconds satisfies the equation

$$M(t) = \frac{T}{dv/dt}$$

where $T$ is the thrust (in lb) of the rocket's engines and $v$ is the velocity (in ft/s) of the rocket. The thrust of the first stage of a *Saturn V* rocket is $T = 7{,}680{,}982$ lb. Use this value of $T$ and the line segment in the figure to estimate the mass of the rocket at time $t = 100$.

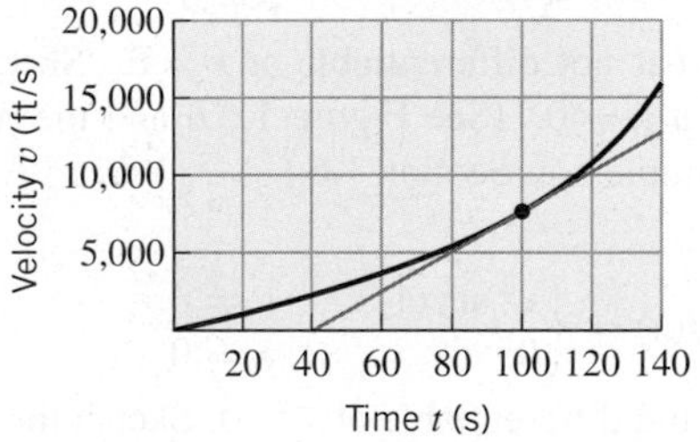

◀ **Figure Ex-44**

**45.** According to ***Newton's Law of Cooling***, the rate of change of an object's temperature is proportional to the difference between the temperature of the object and that of the surrounding medium. The accompanying figure on the next page shows the graph of the temperature $T$ (in degrees Fahrenheit) versus time $t$ (in minutes) for a cup of coffee, initially with a temperature of 200° F, that is allowed to cool in a room with a constant temperature of 75° F.
(a) Estimate $T$ and $dT/dt$ when $t = 10$ min.
(b) Newton's Law of Cooling can be expressed as

$$\frac{dT}{dt} = k(T - T_0)$$

where $k$ is the constant of proportionality and $T_0$ is the temperature (assumed constant) of the surrounding medium. Use the results in part (a) to estimate the value of $k$.

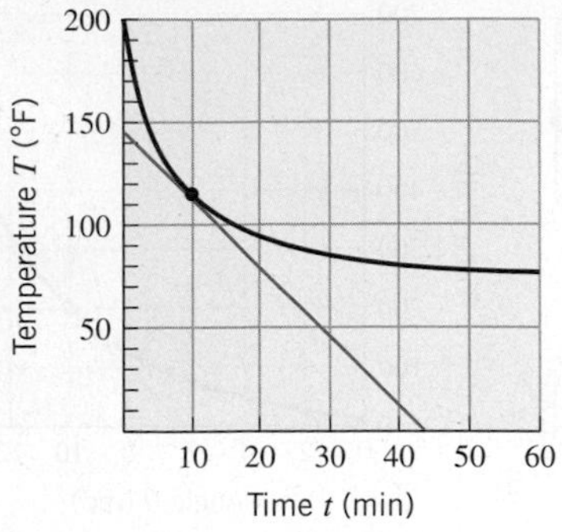


◀ **Figure Ex-45**

**46.** Show that $f(x)$ is continuous but not differentiable at the indicated point. Sketch the graph of $f$.
(a) $f(x) = \sqrt[3]{x}$, $x = 0$
(b) $f(x) = \sqrt[3]{(x-2)^2}$, $x = 2$

**47.** Show that

$$f(x) = \begin{cases} x^2+1, & x \le 1 \\ 2x, & x > 1 \end{cases}$$

is continuous and differentiable at $x = 1$. Sketch the graph of $f$.

**48.** Show that

$$f(x) = \begin{cases} x^2+2, & x \le 1 \\ x+2, & x > 1 \end{cases}$$

is continuous but not differentiable at $x = 1$. Sketch the graph of $f$.

**49.** Show that

$$f(x) = \begin{cases} x\sin(1/x), & x \ne 0 \\ 0, & x = 0 \end{cases}$$

is continuous but not differentiable at $x = 0$. Sketch the graph of $f$ near $x = 0$. (See Figure 1.6.6 and the remark following Example 3 in Section 1.6.)

**50.** Show that

$$f(x) = \begin{cases} x^2\sin(1/x), & x \ne 0 \\ 0, & x = 0 \end{cases}$$

is continuous and differentiable at $x = 0$. Sketch the graph of $f$ near $x = 0$.

**FOCUS ON CONCEPTS**

**51.** Suppose that a function $f$ is differentiable at $x_0$ and that $f'(x_0) > 0$. Prove that there exists an open interval containing $x_0$ such that if $x_1$ and $x_2$ are any two points in this interval with $x_1 < x_0 < x_2$, then $f(x_1) < f(x_0) < f(x_2)$.

**52.** Suppose that a function $f$ is differentiable at $x_0$ and define $g(x) = f(mx+b)$, where $m$ and $b$ are constants. Prove that if $x_1$ is a point at which $mx_1 + b = x_0$, then $g(x)$ is differentiable at $x_1$ and $g'(x_1) = mf'(x_0)$.

**53.** Suppose that a function $f$ is differentiable at $x = 0$ with $f(0) = f'(0) = 0$, and let $y = mx$, $m \ne 0$, denote any line of nonzero slope through the origin.
(a) Prove that there exists an open interval containing 0 such that for all nonzero $x$ in this interval $|f(x)| < \left|\frac{1}{2}mx\right|$. [*Hint:* Let $\epsilon = \frac{1}{2}|m|$ and apply Definition 1.4.1 to (5) with $x_0 = 0$.]
(b) Conclude from part (a) and the triangle inequality that there exists an open interval containing 0 such that $|f(x)| < |f(x) - mx|$ for all $x$ in this interval.
(c) Explain why the result obtained in part (b) may be interpreted to mean that the tangent line to the graph of $f$ at the origin is the best *linear* approximation to $f$ at that point.

**54.** Suppose that $f$ is differentiable at $x_0$. Modify the argument of Exercise 53 to prove that the tangent line to the graph of $f$ at the point $P(x_0, f(x_0))$ provides the best linear approximation to $f$ at $P$. [*Hint:* Suppose that $y = f(x_0) + m(x - x_0)$ is any line through $P(x_0, f(x_0))$ with slope $m \ne f'(x_0)$. Apply Definition 1.4.1 to (5) with $x = x_0 + h$ and $\epsilon = \frac{1}{2}|f'(x_0) - m|$.]

**55. Writing** Write a paragraph that explains what it means for a function to be differentiable. Include examples of functions that are not differentiable as well as examples of functions that are differentiable.

**56. Writing** Explain the relationship between continuity and differentiability.

✓ **QUICK CHECK ANSWERS 2.2** 1. $\dfrac{f(x+h)-f(x)}{h}$ 2. (a) $2x$ (b) $\dfrac{1}{2\sqrt{x}}$ 3. 1; $-\frac{2}{3}$ 4. Theorem 2.2.3: If $f$ is differentiable at $x_0$, then $f$ is continuous at $x_0$.

## 2.3 INTRODUCTION TO TECHNIQUES OF DIFFERENTIATION

*In the last section we defined the derivative of a function f as a limit, and we used that limit to calculate a few simple derivatives. In this section we will develop some important theorems that will enable us to calculate derivatives more efficiently.*

### DERIVATIVE OF A CONSTANT

The simplest kind of function is a constant function $f(x) = c$. Since the graph of $f$ is a horizontal line of slope 0, the tangent line to the graph of $f$ has slope 0 for every $x$;

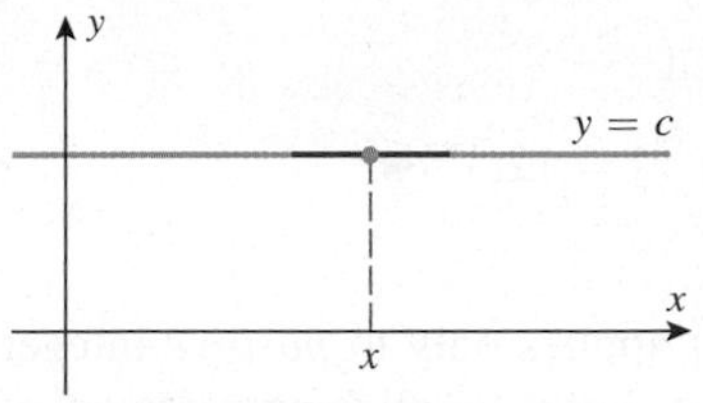


The tangent line to the graph of $f(x) = c$ has slope 0 for all $x$.

▲ **Figure 2.3.1**

and hence we can see geometrically that $f'(x) = 0$ (Figure 2.3.1). We can also see this algebraically since

$$f'(x) = \lim_{h\to 0} \frac{f(x+h) - f(x)}{h} = \lim_{h\to 0} \frac{c-c}{h} = \lim_{h\to 0} 0 = 0$$

Thus, we have established the following result.

> **2.3.1 THEOREM** *The derivative of a constant function is 0; that is, if c is any real number, then*
>
> $$\frac{d}{dx}[c] = 0 \qquad (1)$$

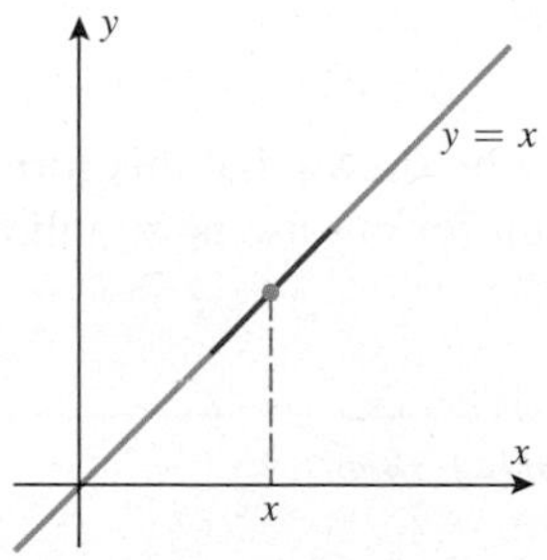


The tangent line to the graph of $f(x) = x$ has slope 1 for all $x$.

▲ **Figure 2.3.2**

### ▶ Example 1

$$\frac{d}{dx}[1] = 0, \quad \frac{d}{dx}[-3] = 0, \quad \frac{d}{dx}[\pi] = 0, \quad \frac{d}{dx}[-\sqrt{2}] = 0 \ ◀$$

## DERIVATIVES OF POWER FUNCTIONS

The simplest power function is $f(x) = x$. Since the graph of $f$ is a line of slope 1, it follows from Example 3 of Section 2.2 that $f'(x) = 1$ for all $x$ (Figure 2.3.2). In other words,

$$\frac{d}{dx}[x] = 1 \qquad (2)$$

Example 1 of Section 2.2 shows that the power function $f(x) = x^2$ has derivative $f'(x) = 2x$. From Example 2 in that section one can infer that the power function $f(x) = x^3$ has derivative $f'(x) = 3x^2$. That is,

$$\frac{d}{dx}[x^2] = 2x \quad \text{and} \quad \frac{d}{dx}[x^3] = 3x^2 \qquad (3\text{–}4)$$

These results are special cases of the following more general result.

> **2.3.2 THEOREM (*The Power Rule*)** *If n is a positive integer, then*
>
> $$\frac{d}{dx}[x^n] = nx^{n-1} \qquad (5)$$

Verify that Formulas (2), (3), and (4) are the special cases of (5) in which $n = 1$, 2, and 3.

**PROOF** Let $f(x) = x^n$. Thus, from the definition of a derivative and the binomial formula for expanding the expression $(x+h)^n$, we obtain

$$\frac{d}{dx}[x^n] = f'(x) = \lim_{h\to 0} \frac{f(x+h) - f(x)}{h} = \lim_{h\to 0} \frac{(x+h)^n - x^n}{h}$$

$$= \lim_{h\to 0} \frac{\left[x^n + nx^{n-1}h + \dfrac{n(n-1)}{2!}x^{n-2}h^2 + \cdots + nxh^{n-1} + h^n\right] - x^n}{h}$$

$$= \lim_{h\to 0} \frac{nx^{n-1}h + \dfrac{n(n-1)}{2!}x^{n-2}h^2 + \cdots + nxh^{n-1} + h^n}{h}$$

$$= \lim_{h\to 0} \left[nx^{n-1} + \frac{n(n-1)}{2!}x^{n-2}h + \cdots + nxh^{n-2} + h^{n-1}\right]$$

$$= nx^{n-1} + 0 + \cdots + 0 + 0$$

$$= nx^{n-1} \ ■$$

The binomial formula can be found on the front endpaper of the text. Replacing $y$ by $h$ in this formula yields the identity used in the proof of Theorem 2.3.2.

**▶ Example 2**

$$\frac{d}{dx}[x^4] = 4x^3, \quad \frac{d}{dx}[x^5] = 5x^4, \quad \frac{d}{dt}[t^{12}] = 12t^{11} \blacktriangleleft$$

Although our proof of the power rule in Formula (5) applies only to *positive* integer powers of $x$, it is not difficult to show that the same formula holds for all integer powers of $x$ (Exercise 84). Also, we saw in Example 4 of Section 2.2 that

$$\frac{d}{dx}[\sqrt{x}] = \frac{1}{2\sqrt{x}} \tag{6}$$

which can be expressed as

$$\frac{d}{dx}[x^{1/2}] = \frac{1}{2}x^{-1/2} = \frac{1}{2}x^{(1/2)-1}$$

Thus, Formula (5) is valid for $n = \frac{1}{2}$, as well. In fact, it can be shown that this formula holds for any real exponent. We state this more general result for our use now, although we won't be prepared to prove it until Chapter 3.

**2.3.3 THEOREM (*Extended Power Rule*)** *If $r$ is any real number, then*

$$\frac{d}{dx}[x^r] = rx^{r-1} \tag{7}$$

In words, *to differentiate a power function, decrease the constant exponent by one and multiply the resulting power function by the original exponent.*

**▶ Example 3**

$$\frac{d}{dx}[x^\pi] = \pi x^{\pi-1}$$

$$\frac{d}{dx}\left[\frac{1}{x}\right] = \frac{d}{dx}[x^{-1}] = (-1)x^{-1-1} = -x^{-2} = -\frac{1}{x^2}$$

$$\frac{d}{dw}\left[\frac{1}{w^{100}}\right] = \frac{d}{dw}[w^{-100}] = -100w^{-101} = -\frac{100}{w^{101}}$$

$$\frac{d}{dx}[x^{4/5}] = \frac{4}{5}x^{(4/5)-1} = \frac{4}{5}x^{-1/5}$$

$$\frac{d}{dx}[\sqrt[3]{x}] = \frac{d}{dx}[x^{1/3}] = \frac{1}{3}x^{-2/3} = \frac{1}{3\sqrt[3]{x^2}} \blacktriangleleft$$

## DERIVATIVE OF A CONSTANT TIMES A FUNCTION

Formula (8) can also be expressed in function notation as

$$(cf)' = cf'$$

**2.3.4 THEOREM (*Constant Multiple Rule*)** *If $f$ is differentiable at $x$ and $c$ is any real number, then $cf$ is also differentiable at $x$ and*

$$\frac{d}{dx}[cf(x)] = c\frac{d}{dx}[f(x)] \tag{8}$$

**PROOF**

$$\begin{aligned}\frac{d}{dx}[cf(x)] &= \lim_{h\to 0}\frac{cf(x+h)-cf(x)}{h}\\ &= \lim_{h\to 0} c\left[\frac{f(x+h)-f(x)}{h}\right]\\ &= c\lim_{h\to 0}\frac{f(x+h)-f(x)}{h}\\ &= c\frac{d}{dx}[f(x)] \quad \blacksquare\end{aligned}$$

A constant factor can be moved through a limit sign.

In words, *a constant factor can be moved through a derivative sign.*

### ▶ Example 4

$$\frac{d}{dx}[4x^8] = 4\frac{d}{dx}[x^8] = 4[8x^7] = 32x^7$$

$$\frac{d}{dx}[-x^{12}] = (-1)\frac{d}{dx}[x^{12}] = -12x^{11}$$

$$\frac{d}{dx}\left[\frac{\pi}{x}\right] = \pi\frac{d}{dx}[x^{-1}] = \pi(-x^{-2}) = -\frac{\pi}{x^2} \quad ◀$$

## DERIVATIVES OF SUMS AND DIFFERENCES

**2.3.5 THEOREM** (***Sum and Difference Rules***) *If f and g are differentiable at x, then so are $f+g$ and $f-g$ and*

$$\frac{d}{dx}[f(x)+g(x)] = \frac{d}{dx}[f(x)] + \frac{d}{dx}[g(x)] \tag{9}$$

$$\frac{d}{dx}[f(x)-g(x)] = \frac{d}{dx}[f(x)] - \frac{d}{dx}[g(x)] \tag{10}$$

Formulas (9) and (10) can also be expressed as

$$(f+g)' = f' + g'$$
$$(f-g)' = f' - g'$$

**PROOF** Formula (9) can be proved as follows:

$$\begin{aligned}\frac{d}{dx}[f(x)+g(x)] &= \lim_{h\to 0}\frac{[f(x+h)+g(x+h)]-[f(x)+g(x)]}{h}\\ &= \lim_{h\to 0}\frac{[f(x+h)-f(x)]+[g(x+h)-g(x)]}{h}\\ &= \lim_{h\to 0}\frac{f(x+h)-f(x)}{h} + \lim_{h\to 0}\frac{g(x+h)-g(x)}{h}\\ &= \frac{d}{dx}[f(x)] + \frac{d}{dx}[g(x)]\end{aligned}$$

The limit of a sum is the sum of the limits.

Formula (10) can be proved in a similar manner or, alternatively, by writing $f(x)-g(x)$ as $f(x)+(-1)g(x)$ and then applying Formulas (8) and (9). ■

In words, *the derivative of a sum equals the sum of the derivatives*, and *the derivative of a difference equals the difference of the derivatives.*

**▶ Example 5**

$$\frac{d}{dx}[2x^6 + x^{-9}] = \frac{d}{dx}[2x^6] + \frac{d}{dx}[x^{-9}] = 12x^5 + (-9)x^{-10} = 12x^5 - 9x^{-10}$$

$$\frac{d}{dx}\left[\frac{\sqrt{x} - 2x}{\sqrt{x}}\right] = \frac{d}{dx}[1 - 2\sqrt{x}]$$

$$= \frac{d}{dx}[1] - \frac{d}{dx}[2\sqrt{x}] = 0 - 2\left(\frac{1}{2\sqrt{x}}\right) = -\frac{1}{\sqrt{x}}$$

See Formula (6). ◀

Although Formulas (9) and (10) are stated for sums and differences of two functions, they can be extended to any finite number of functions. For example, by grouping and applying Formula (9) twice we obtain

$$(f + g + h)' = [(f + g) + h]' = (f + g)' + h' = f' + g' + h'$$

As illustrated in the following example, the constant multiple rule together with the extended versions of the sum and difference rules can be used to differentiate any polynomial.

**▶ Example 6** Find $dy/dx$ if $y = 3x^8 - 2x^5 + 6x + 1$.

***Solution.***

$$\frac{dy}{dx} = \frac{d}{dx}[3x^8 - 2x^5 + 6x + 1]$$

$$= \frac{d}{dx}[3x^8] - \frac{d}{dx}[2x^5] + \frac{d}{dx}[6x] + \frac{d}{dx}[1]$$

$$= 24x^7 - 10x^4 + 6 \blacktriangleleft$$

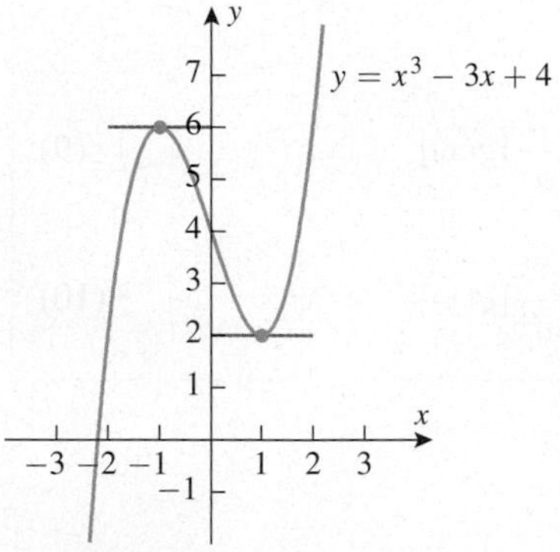


▲ Figure 2.3.3

**▶ Example 7** At what points, if any, does the graph of $y = x^3 - 3x + 4$ have a horizontal tangent line?

***Solution.*** Horizontal tangent lines have slope zero, so we must find those values of $x$ for which $y'(x) = 0$. Differentiating yields

$$y'(x) = \frac{d}{dx}[x^3 - 3x + 4] = 3x^2 - 3$$

Thus, horizontal tangent lines occur at those values of $x$ for which $3x^2 - 3 = 0$, that is, if $x = -1$ or $x = 1$. The corresponding points on the curve $y = x^3 - 3x + 4$ are $(-1, 6)$ and $(1, 2)$ (see Figure 2.3.3). ◀

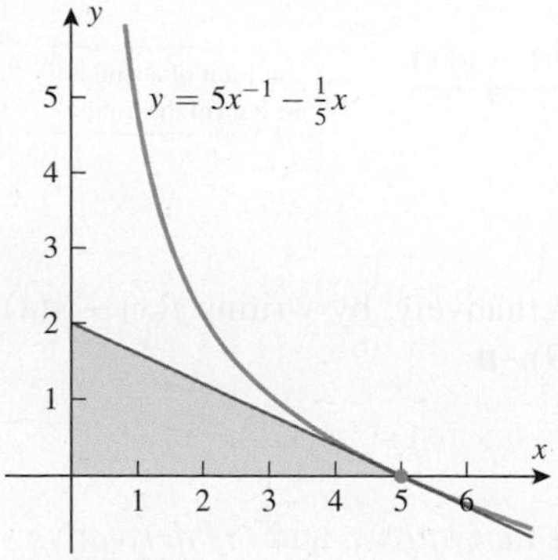


▲ Figure 2.3.4

**▶ Example 8** Find the area of the triangle formed from the coordinate axes and the tangent line to the curve $y = 5x^{-1} - \frac{1}{5}x$ at the point $(5, 0)$.

***Solution.*** Since the derivative of $y$ with respect to $x$ is

$$y'(x) = \frac{d}{dx}\left[5x^{-1} - \frac{1}{5}x\right] = \frac{d}{dx}[5x^{-1}] - \frac{d}{dx}\left[\frac{1}{5}x\right] = -5x^{-2} - \frac{1}{5}$$

the slope of the tangent line at the point $(5, 0)$ is $y'(5) = -\frac{2}{5}$. Thus, the equation of the tangent line at this point is

$$y - 0 = -\frac{2}{5}(x - 5) \quad \text{or equivalently} \quad y = -\frac{2}{5}x + 2$$

Since the $y$-intercept of this line is 2, the right triangle formed from the coordinate axes and the tangent line has legs of length 5 and 2, so its area is $\frac{1}{2}(5)(2) = 5$ (Figure 2.3.4). ◀

## HIGHER DERIVATIVES

The derivative $f'$ of a function $f$ is itself a function and hence may have a derivative of its own. If $f'$ is differentiable, then its derivative is denoted by $f''$ and is called the ***second derivative*** of $f$. As long as we have differentiability, we can continue the process of differentiating to obtain third, fourth, fifth, and even higher derivatives of $f$. These successive derivatives are denoted by

$$f', \quad f'' = (f')', \quad f''' = (f'')', \quad f^{(4)} = (f''')', \quad f^{(5)} = (f^{(4)})', \ldots$$

If $y = f(x)$, then successive derivatives can also be denoted by

$$y', \quad y'', \quad y''', \quad y^{(4)}, \quad y^{(5)}, \ldots$$

Other common notations are

$$y' = \frac{dy}{dx} = \frac{d}{dx}[f(x)]$$

$$y'' = \frac{d^2y}{dx^2} = \frac{d}{dx}\left[\frac{d}{dx}[f(x)]\right] = \frac{d^2}{dx^2}[f(x)]$$

$$y''' = \frac{d^3y}{dx^3} = \frac{d}{dx}\left[\frac{d^2}{dx^2}[f(x)]\right] = \frac{d^3}{dx^3}[f(x)]$$

$$\vdots \qquad\qquad\qquad\qquad \vdots$$

These are called, in succession, the *first derivative*, the *second derivative*, the *third derivative*, and so forth. The number of times that $f$ is differentiated is called the ***order*** of the derivative. A general $n$th order derivative can be denoted by

$$\frac{d^ny}{dx^n} = f^{(n)}(x) = \frac{d^n}{dx^n}[f(x)] \tag{11}$$

and the value of a general $n$th order derivative at a specific point $x = x_0$ can be denoted by

$$\left.\frac{d^ny}{dx^n}\right|_{x=x_0} = f^{(n)}(x_0) = \left.\frac{d^n}{dx^n}[f(x)]\right|_{x=x_0} \tag{12}$$

► **Example 9** If $f(x) = 3x^4 - 2x^3 + x^2 - 4x + 2$, then

$$\begin{aligned}
f'(x) &= 12x^3 - 6x^2 + 2x - 4 \\
f''(x) &= 36x^2 - 12x + 2 \\
f'''(x) &= 72x - 12 \\
f^{(4)}(x) &= 72 \\
f^{(5)}(x) &= 0 \\
&\vdots \\
f^{(n)}(x) &= 0 \quad (n \geq 5)
\end{aligned}$$ ◄

We will discuss the significance of second derivatives and those of higher order in later sections.

## ✓ QUICK CHECK EXERCISES 2.3 (See page 108 for answers.)

**1.** In each part, determine $f'(x)$.
(a) $f(x) = \sqrt{6}$ (b) $f(x) = \sqrt{6}x$
(c) $f(x) = 6\sqrt{x}$ (d) $f(x) = \sqrt{6x}$

**2.** In parts (a)–(d), determine $f'(x)$.
(a) $f(x) = x^3 + 5$ (b) $f(x) = x^2(x^3 + 5)$
(c) $f(x) = \dfrac{x^3 + 5}{2}$ (d) $f(x) = \dfrac{x^3 + 5}{x^2}$

**3.** The slope of the tangent line to the curve $y = x^2 + 4x + 7$ at $x = 1$ is ______.

**4.** If $f(x) = 3x^3 - 3x^2 + x + 1$, then $f''(x) =$ ______.

## EXERCISE SET 2.3 Graphing Utility

**1–8** Find $dy/dx$. ■

1. $y = 4x^7$
2. $y = -3x^{12}$
3. $y = 3x^8 + 2x + 1$
4. $y = \frac{1}{2}(x^4 + 7)$
5. $y = \pi^3$
6. $y = \sqrt{2}x + (1/\sqrt{2})$
7. $y = -\frac{1}{3}(x^7 + 2x - 9)$
8. $y = \dfrac{x^2 + 1}{5}$

**9–16** Find $f'(x)$. ■

9. $f(x) = x^{-3} + \dfrac{1}{x^7}$
10. $f(x) = \sqrt{x} + \dfrac{1}{x}$
11. $f(x) = -3x^{-8} + 2\sqrt{x}$
12. $f(x) = 7x^{-6} - 5\sqrt{x}$
13. $f(x) = x^e + \dfrac{1}{x^{\sqrt{10}}}$
14. $f(x) = \sqrt[3]{\dfrac{8}{x}}$
15. $f(x) = (3x^2 + 1)^2$
16. $f(x) = ax^3 + bx^2 + cx + d$ $(a, b, c, d$ constant)

**17–18** Find $y'(1)$. ■

17. $y = 5x^2 - 3x + 1$
18. $y = \dfrac{x^{3/2} + 2}{x}$

**19–20** Find $dx/dt$. ■

19. $x = t^2 - t$
20. $x = \dfrac{t^2 + 1}{3t}$

**21–24** Find $dy/dx|_{x=1}$. ■

21. $y = 1 + x + x^2 + x^3 + x^4 + x^5$
22. $y = \dfrac{1 + x + x^2 + x^3 + x^4 + x^5 + x^6}{x^3}$
23. $y = (1 - x)(1 + x)(1 + x^2)(1 + x^4)$
24. $y = x^{24} + 2x^{12} + 3x^8 + 4x^6$

**25–26** Approximate $f'(1)$ by considering the difference quotient

$$\frac{f(1 + h) - f(1)}{h}$$

for values of $h$ near 0, and then find the exact value of $f'(1)$ by differentiating. ■

25. $f(x) = x^3 - 3x + 1$
26. $f(x) = \dfrac{1}{x^2}$

**27–28** Use a graphing utility to estimate the value of $f'(1)$ by zooming in on the graph of $f$, and then compare your estimate to the exact value obtained by differentiating. ■

27. $f(x) = \dfrac{x^2 + 1}{x}$
28. $f(x) = \dfrac{x + 2x^{3/2}}{\sqrt{x}}$

**29–32** Find the indicated derivative. ■

29. $\dfrac{d}{dt}[16t^2]$
30. $\dfrac{dC}{dr}$, where $C = 2\pi r$
31. $V'(r)$, where $V = \pi r^3$
32. $\dfrac{d}{d\alpha}[2\alpha^{-1} + \alpha]$

**33–36 True–False** Determine whether the statement is true or false. Explain your answer. ■

33. If $f$ and $g$ are differentiable at $x = 2$, then
$$\left.\frac{d}{dx}[f(x) - 8g(x)]\right|_{x=2} = f'(2) - 8g'(2)$$
34. If $f(x)$ is a cubic polynomial, then $f'(x)$ is a quadratic polynomial.
35. If $f'(2) = 5$, then
$$\left.\frac{d}{dx}[4f(x) + x^3]\right|_{x=2} = \left.\frac{d}{dx}[4f(x) + 8]\right|_{x=2} = 4f'(2) = 20$$
36. If $f(x) = x^2(x^4 - x)$, then
$$f''(x) = \frac{d}{dx}[x^2] \cdot \frac{d}{dx}[x^4 - x] = 2x(4x^3 - 1)$$
37. A spherical balloon is being inflated.
    (a) Find a general formula for the instantaneous rate of change of the volume $V$ with respect to the radius $r$, given that $V = \frac{4}{3}\pi r^3$.
    (b) Find the rate of change of $V$ with respect to $r$ at the instant when the radius is $r = 5$.
38. Find $\dfrac{d}{d\lambda}\left[\dfrac{\lambda\lambda_0 + \lambda^6}{2 - \lambda_0}\right]$ $(\lambda_0$ is constant).
39. Find an equation of the tangent line to the graph of $y = f(x)$ at $x = -3$ if $f(-3) = 2$ and $f'(-3) = 5$.
40. Find an equation of the tangent line to the graph of $y = f(x)$ at $x = 2$ if $f(2) = -2$ and $f'(2) = -1$.

**41–42** Find $d^2y/dx^2$. ■

41. (a) $y = 7x^3 - 5x^2 + x$ (b) $y = 12x^2 - 2x + 3$
    (c) $y = \dfrac{x + 1}{x}$ (d) $y = (5x^2 - 3)(7x^3 + x)$
42. (a) $y = 4x^7 - 5x^3 + 2x$ (b) $y = 3x + 2$
    (c) $y = \dfrac{3x - 2}{5x}$ (d) $y = (x^3 - 5)(2x + 3)$

**43–44** Find $y'''$. ■

43. (a) $y = x^{-5} + x^5$ (b) $y = 1/x$
    (c) $y = ax^3 + bx + c$ $(a, b, c$ constant)
44. (a) $y = 5x^2 - 4x + 7$ (b) $y = 3x^{-2} + 4x^{-1} + x$
    (c) $y = ax^4 + bx^2 + c$ $(a, b, c$ constant)
45. Find
    (a) $f'''(2)$, where $f(x) = 3x^2 - 2$
    (b) $\left.\dfrac{d^2y}{dx^2}\right|_{x=1}$, where $y = 6x^5 - 4x^2$
    (c) $\left.\dfrac{d^4}{dx^4}[x^{-3}]\right|_{x=1}$.
46. Find
    (a) $y'''(0)$, where $y = 4x^4 + 2x^3 + 3$
    (b) $\left.\dfrac{d^4y}{dx^4}\right|_{x=1}$, where $y = \dfrac{6}{x^4}$.
47. Show that $y = x^3 + 3x + 1$ satisfies $y''' + xy'' - 2y' = 0$.
48. Show that if $x \neq 0$, then $y = 1/x$ satisfies the equation $x^3y'' + x^2y' - xy = 0$.

**49–50** Use a graphing utility to make rough estimates of the locations of all horizontal tangent lines, and then find their exact locations by differentiating. ■

**49.** $y = \frac{1}{3}x^3 - \frac{3}{2}x^2 + 2x$ **50.** $y = \dfrac{x^2 + 9}{x}$

**FOCUS ON CONCEPTS**

**51.** Find a function $y = ax^2 + bx + c$ whose graph has an $x$-intercept of 1, a $y$-intercept of $-2$, and a tangent line with a slope of $-1$ at the $y$-intercept.

**52.** Find $k$ if the curve $y = x^2 + k$ is tangent to the line $y = 2x$.

**53.** Find the $x$-coordinate of the point on the graph of $y = x^2$ where the tangent line is parallel to the secant line that cuts the curve at $x = -1$ and $x = 2$.

**54.** Find the $x$-coordinate of the point on the graph of $y = \sqrt{x}$ where the tangent line is parallel to the secant line that cuts the curve at $x = 1$ and $x = 4$.

**55.** Find the coordinates of all points on the graph of $y = 1 - x^2$ at which the tangent line passes through the point $(2, 0)$.

**56.** Show that any two tangent lines to the parabola $y = ax^2$, $a \neq 0$, intersect at a point that is on the vertical line halfway between the points of tangency.

**57.** Suppose that $L$ is the tangent line at $x = x_0$ to the graph of the cubic equation $y = ax^3 + bx$. Find the $x$-coordinate of the point where $L$ intersects the graph a second time.

**58.** Show that the segment cut off by the coordinate axes from any tangent line to the graph of $y = 1/x$ is bisected by the point of tangency.

**59.** Show that the triangle that is formed by any tangent line to the graph of $y = 1/x$, $x > 0$, and the coordinate axes has an area of 2 square units.

**60.** Find conditions on $a$, $b$, $c$, and $d$ so that the graph of the polynomial $f(x) = ax^3 + bx^2 + cx + d$ has
(a) exactly two horizontal tangents
(b) exactly one horizontal tangent
(c) no horizontal tangents.

**61.** Newton's Law of Universal Gravitation states that the magnitude $F$ of the force exerted by a point with mass $M$ on a point with mass $m$ is

$$F = \frac{GmM}{r^2}$$

where $G$ is a constant and $r$ is the distance between the points. Assuming that the points are moving, find a formula for the instantaneous rate of change of $F$ with respect to $r$.

**62.** In the temperature range between $0°$C and $700°$C the resistance $R$ [in ohms $(\Omega)$] of a certain platinum resistance thermometer is given by

$$R = 10 + 0.04124T - 1.779 \times 10^{-5}T^2$$

where $T$ is the temperature in degrees Celsius. Where in the interval from $0°$C to $700°$C is the resistance of the thermometer most sensitive and least sensitive to temperature changes? [*Hint:* Consider the size of $dR/dT$ in the interval $0 \le T \le 700$.]

**63.** A stuntman estimates the time $T$ in seconds for him to fall $x$ meters by $T = 0.453\sqrt{x}$. Use this formula to find the instantaneous rate of change of $T$ with respect to $x$ when $x = 9$ meters.

**64.** The mean orbital radius $r$ (in units of $10^5$ km) of a moon of Saturn can be modeled by the equation $r = 1.93t^{2/3}$, where $t$ is the time in (Earth) days for the moon to complete one orbit about the planet. Use this model to estimate the instantaneous rate of change of $r$ with respect to $t$ when $t = 0.602$ day (the orbital period of Saturn's moon Atlas).

**65–66** Use a graphing utility to make rough estimates of the intervals on which $f'(x) > 0$, and then find those intervals exactly by differentiating. ■

**65.** $f(x) = x - \dfrac{1}{x}$ **66.** $f(x) = x^3 - 3x$

**67–70** You are asked in these exercises to determine whether a piecewise-defined function $f$ is differentiable at a value $x = x_0$, where $f$ is defined by different formulas on different sides of $x_0$. You may use without proof the following result, which is a consequence of the Mean-Value Theorem (discussed in Section 4.8). ***Theorem.*** *Let $f$ be continuous at $x_0$ and suppose that $\lim_{x\to x_0} f'(x)$ exists. Then $f$ is differentiable at $x_0$, and $f'(x_0) = \lim_{x\to x_0} f'(x)$.* ■

**67.** Show that

$$f(x) = \begin{cases} x^2 + x + 1, & x \le 1 \\ 3x, & x > 1 \end{cases}$$

is continuous at $x = 1$. Determine whether $f$ is differentiable at $x = 1$. If so, find the value of the derivative there. Sketch the graph of $f$.

**68.** Let

$$f(x) = \begin{cases} x^2 - 16x, & x < 9 \\ \sqrt{x}, & x \ge 9 \end{cases}$$

Is $f$ continuous at $x = 9$? Determine whether $f$ is differentiable at $x = 9$. If so, find the value of the derivative there.

**69.** Let

$$f(x) = \begin{cases} x^2, & x \le 1 \\ \sqrt{x}, & x > 1 \end{cases}$$

Determine whether $f$ is differentiable at $x = 1$. If so, find the value of the derivative there.

**70.** Let

$$f(x) = \begin{cases} x^3 + \frac{1}{16}, & x < \frac{1}{2} \\ \frac{3}{4}x^2, & x \ge \frac{1}{2} \end{cases}$$

Determine whether $f$ is differentiable at $x = \frac{1}{2}$. If so, find the value of the derivative there.

**71.** Find all points where $f$ fails to be differentiable. Justify your answer.
(a) $f(x) = |3x - 2|$ (b) $f(x) = |x^2 - 4|$

**72.** In each part, compute $f'$, $f''$, $f'''$, and then state the formula for $f^{(n)}$.
(a) $f(x) = 1/x$ (b) $f(x) = 1/x^2$
[*Hint:* The expression $(-1)^n$ has a value of 1 if $n$ is even and $-1$ if $n$ is odd. Use this expression in your answer.]

**73.** (a) Prove:

$$\frac{d^2}{dx^2}[cf(x)] = c\frac{d^2}{dx^2}[f(x)]$$

$$\frac{d^2}{dx^2}[f(x)+g(x)] = \frac{d^2}{dx^2}[f(x)] + \frac{d^2}{dx^2}[g(x)]$$

(b) Do the results in part (a) generalize to $n$th derivatives? Justify your answer.

**74.** Let $f(x) = x^8 - 2x + 3$; find

$$\lim_{w\to 2} \frac{f'(w) - f'(2)}{w - 2}$$

**75.** (a) Find $f^{(n)}(x)$ if $f(x) = x^n, n = 1, 2, 3, \ldots$.
(b) Find $f^{(n)}(x)$ if $f(x) = x^k$ and $n > k$, where $k$ is a positive integer.
(c) Find $f^{(n)}(x)$ if

$$f(x) = a_0 + a_1x + a_2x^2 + \cdots + a_nx^n$$

**76.** (a) Prove: If $f''(x)$ exists for each $x$ in $(a, b)$, then both $f$ and $f'$ are continuous on $(a, b)$.
(b) What can be said about the continuity of $f$ and its derivatives if $f^{(n)}(x)$ exists for each $x$ in $(a, b)$?

**77.** Let $f(x) = (mx + b)^n$, where $m$ and $b$ are constants and $n$ is an integer. Use the result of Exercise 52 in Section 2.2 to prove that $f'(x) = nm(mx + b)^{n-1}$.

**78–79** Verify the result of Exercise 77 for $f(x)$. ■

**78.** $f(x) = (2x + 3)^2$ **79.** $f(x) = (3x - 1)^3$

**80–83** Use the result of Exercise 77 to compute the derivative of the given function $f(x)$. ■

**80.** $f(x) = \dfrac{1}{x - 1}$

**81.** $f(x) = \dfrac{3}{(2x + 1)^2}$

**82.** $f(x) = \dfrac{x}{x + 1}$

**83.** $f(x) = \dfrac{2x^2 + 4x + 3}{x^2 + 2x + 1}$

**84.** The purpose of this exercise is to extend the power rule (Theorem 2.3.2) to any integer exponent. Let $f(x) = x^n$, where $n$ is any integer. If $n > 0$, then $f'(x) = nx^{n-1}$ by Theorem 2.3.2.
(a) Show that the conclusion of Theorem 2.3.2 holds in the case $n = 0$.
(b) Suppose that $n < 0$ and set $m = -n$ so that

$$f(x) = x^n = x^{-m} = \frac{1}{x^m}$$

Use Definition 2.2.1 and Theorem 2.3.2 to show that

$$\frac{d}{dx}\left[\frac{1}{x^m}\right] = -mx^{m-1} \cdot \frac{1}{x^{2m}}$$

and conclude that $f'(x) = nx^{n-1}$.

✓ **QUICK CHECK ANSWERS 2.3** 1. (a) 0 (b) $\sqrt{6}$ (c) $3/\sqrt{x}$ (d) $\sqrt{6}/(2\sqrt{x})$ 2. (a) $3x^2$ (b) $5x^4 + 10x$ (c) $\frac{3}{2}x^2$ (d) $1 - 10x^{-3}$ 3. 6 4. $18x - 6$

## 2.4 THE PRODUCT AND QUOTIENT RULES

*In this section we will develop techniques for differentiating products and quotients of functions whose derivatives are known.*

### ■ DERIVATIVE OF A PRODUCT

You might be tempted to conjecture that the derivative of a product of two functions is the product of their derivatives. However, a simple example will show this to be false. Consider the functions

$$f(x) = x \quad \text{and} \quad g(x) = x^2$$

The product of their derivatives is

$$f'(x)g'(x) = (1)(2x) = 2x$$

but their product is $h(x) = f(x)g(x) = x^3$, so the derivative of the product is

$$h'(x) = 3x^2$$

Thus, the derivative of the product is not equal to the product of the derivatives. The correct relationship, which is credited to Leibniz, is given by the following theorem.

**2.4.1 THEOREM (*The Product Rule*)** *If $f$ and $g$ are differentiable at $x$, then so is the product $f \cdot g$, and*

$$\frac{d}{dx}[f(x)g(x)] = f(x)\frac{d}{dx}[g(x)] + g(x)\frac{d}{dx}[f(x)] \tag{1}$$

Formula (1) can also be expressed as

$$(f \cdot g)' = f \cdot g' + g \cdot f'$$

PROOF Whereas the proofs of the derivative rules in the last section were straightforward applications of the derivative definition, a key step in this proof involves adding and subtracting the quantity $f(x+h)g(x)$ to the numerator in the derivative definition. This yields

$$\begin{aligned}
\frac{d}{dx}[f(x)g(x)] &= \lim_{h\to 0}\frac{f(x+h)\cdot g(x+h) - f(x)\cdot g(x)}{h} \\
&= \lim_{h\to 0}\frac{f(x+h)g(x+h) - f(x+h)g(x) + f(x+h)g(x) - f(x)g(x)}{h} \\
&= \lim_{h\to 0}\left[f(x+h)\cdot\frac{g(x+h)-g(x)}{h} + g(x)\cdot\frac{f(x+h)-f(x)}{h}\right] \\
&= \lim_{h\to 0} f(x+h)\cdot\lim_{h\to 0}\frac{g(x+h)-g(x)}{h} + \lim_{h\to 0} g(x)\cdot\lim_{h\to 0}\frac{f(x+h)-f(x)}{h} \\
&= \left[\lim_{h\to 0} f(x+h)\right]\frac{d}{dx}[g(x)] + \left[\lim_{h\to 0} g(x)\right]\frac{d}{dx}[f(x)] \\
&= f(x)\frac{d}{dx}[g(x)] + g(x)\frac{d}{dx}[f(x)]
\end{aligned}$$

[*Note:* In the last step $f(x+h)\to f(x)$ as $h\to 0$ because $f$ is continuous at $x$ by Theorem 2.2.3. Also, $g(x)\to g(x)$ as $h\to 0$ because $g(x)$ does not involve $h$ and hence is treated as constant for the limit.] ■

In words, *the derivative of a product of two functions is the first function times the derivative of the second plus the second function times the derivative of the first.*

▶ **Example 1** Find $dy/dx$ if $y = (4x^2 - 1)(7x^3 + x)$.

***Solution.*** There are two methods that can be used to find $dy/dx$. We can either use the product rule or we can multiply out the factors in $y$ and then differentiate. We will give both methods.

**Method 1.** *(Using the Product Rule)*

$$\begin{aligned}
\frac{dy}{dx} &= \frac{d}{dx}[(4x^2-1)(7x^3+x)] \\
&= (4x^2-1)\frac{d}{dx}[7x^3+x] + (7x^3+x)\frac{d}{dx}[4x^2-1] \\
&= (4x^2-1)(21x^2+1) + (7x^3+x)(8x) = 140x^4 - 9x^2 - 1
\end{aligned}$$

**Method 2.** *(Multiplying First)*

$$y = (4x^2-1)(7x^3+x) = 28x^5 - 3x^3 - x$$

Thus,

$$\frac{dy}{dx} = \frac{d}{dx}[28x^5 - 3x^3 - x] = 140x^4 - 9x^2 - 1$$

which agrees with the result obtained using the product rule. ◀

▶ **Example 2** Find $ds/dt$ if $s = (1+t)\sqrt{t}$.

***Solution.*** Applying the product rule yields

$$\begin{aligned}\frac{ds}{dt} &= \frac{d}{dt}[(1+t)\sqrt{t}] \\ &= (1+t)\frac{d}{dt}[\sqrt{t}] + \sqrt{t}\frac{d}{dt}[1+t] \\ &= \frac{1+t}{2\sqrt{t}} + \sqrt{t} = \frac{1+3t}{2\sqrt{t}}\end{aligned}$$ ◀

## DERIVATIVE OF A QUOTIENT

Just as the derivative of a product is not generally the product of the derivatives, so the derivative of a quotient is not generally the quotient of the derivatives. The correct relationship is given by the following theorem.

**2.4.2 THEOREM (*The Quotient Rule*)** *If $f$ and $g$ are both differentiable at $x$ and if $g(x) \neq 0$, then $f/g$ is differentiable at $x$ and*

$$\frac{d}{dx}\left[\frac{f(x)}{g(x)}\right] = \frac{g(x)\dfrac{d}{dx}[f(x)] - f(x)\dfrac{d}{dx}[g(x)]}{[g(x)]^2} \qquad (2)$$

Formula (2) can also be expressed as

$$\left(\frac{f}{g}\right)' = \frac{g \cdot f' - f \cdot g'}{g^2}$$

**PROOF**

$$\frac{d}{dx}\left[\frac{f(x)}{g(x)}\right] = \lim_{h\to 0}\frac{\dfrac{f(x+h)}{g(x+h)} - \dfrac{f(x)}{g(x)}}{h} = \lim_{h\to 0}\frac{f(x+h)\cdot g(x) - f(x)\cdot g(x+h)}{h\cdot g(x)\cdot g(x+h)}$$

Adding and subtracting $f(x)\cdot g(x)$ in the numerator yields

$$\begin{aligned}\frac{d}{dx}\left[\frac{f(x)}{g(x)}\right] &= \lim_{h\to 0}\frac{f(x+h)\cdot g(x) - f(x)\cdot g(x) - f(x)\cdot g(x+h) + f(x)\cdot g(x)}{h\cdot g(x)\cdot g(x+h)} \\ &= \lim_{h\to 0}\frac{\left[g(x)\cdot\dfrac{f(x+h)-f(x)}{h}\right] - \left[f(x)\cdot\dfrac{g(x+h)-g(x)}{h}\right]}{g(x)\cdot g(x+h)} \\ &= \frac{\lim\limits_{h\to 0} g(x)\cdot\lim\limits_{h\to 0}\dfrac{f(x+h)-f(x)}{h} - \lim\limits_{h\to 0} f(x)\cdot\lim\limits_{h\to 0}\dfrac{g(x+h)-g(x)}{h}}{\lim\limits_{h\to 0} g(x)\cdot\lim\limits_{h\to 0} g(x+h)} \\ &= \frac{\left[\lim\limits_{h\to 0} g(x)\right]\cdot\dfrac{d}{dx}[f(x)] - \left[\lim\limits_{h\to 0} f(x)\right]\cdot\dfrac{d}{dx}[g(x)]}{\lim\limits_{h\to 0} g(x)\cdot\lim\limits_{h\to 0} g(x+h)} \\ &= \frac{g(x)\dfrac{d}{dx}[f(x)] - f(x)\dfrac{d}{dx}[g(x)]}{[g(x)]^2}\end{aligned}$$

[See the note at the end of the proof of Theorem 2.4.1 for an explanation of the last step.] ■

In words, *the derivative of a quotient of two functions is the denominator times the derivative of the numerator minus the numerator times the derivative of the denominator, all divided by the denominator squared.*

Sometimes it is better to simplify a function first than to apply the quotient rule immediately. For example, it is easier to differentiate

$$f(x) = \frac{x^{3/2} + x}{\sqrt{x}}$$

by rewriting it as

$$f(x) = x + \sqrt{x}$$

as opposed to using the quotient rule.

**▸ Example 3** Find $y'(x)$ for $y = \dfrac{x^3 + 2x^2 - 1}{x + 5}$.

***Solution.*** Applying the quotient rule yields

$$\begin{aligned}
\frac{dy}{dx} = \frac{d}{dx}\left[\frac{x^3 + 2x^2 - 1}{x + 5}\right] &= \frac{(x+5)\dfrac{d}{dx}[x^3 + 2x^2 - 1] - (x^3 + 2x^2 - 1)\dfrac{d}{dx}[x+5]}{(x+5)^2} \\
&= \frac{(x+5)(3x^2 + 4x) - (x^3 + 2x^2 - 1)(1)}{(x+5)^2} \\
&= \frac{(3x^3 + 19x^2 + 20x) - (x^3 + 2x^2 - 1)}{(x+5)^2} \\
&= \frac{2x^3 + 17x^2 + 20x + 1}{(x+5)^2} \quad ◀
\end{aligned}$$

**▸ Example 4** Let $f(x) = \dfrac{x^2 - 1}{x^4 + 1}$.

(a) Graph $y = f(x)$, and use your graph to make rough estimates of the locations of all horizontal tangent lines.

(b) By differentiating, find the exact locations of the horizontal tangent lines.

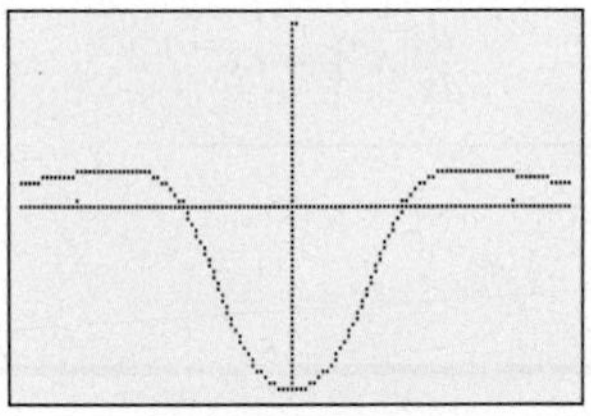

$[-2.5, 2.5] \times [-1, 1]$
$x\text{Scl} = 1, y\text{Scl} = 1$

$y = \dfrac{x^2 - 1}{x^4 + 1}$

▲ **Figure 2.4.1**

***Solution (a).*** In Figure 2.4.1 we have shown the graph of the equation $y = f(x)$ in the window $[-2.5, 2.5] \times [-1, 1]$. This graph suggests that horizontal tangent lines occur at $x = 0, x \approx 1.5$, and $x \approx -1.5$.

***Solution (b).*** To find the exact locations of the horizontal tangent lines, we must find the points where $dy/dx = 0$. We start by finding $dy/dx$:

$$\begin{aligned}
\frac{dy}{dx} = \frac{d}{dx}\left[\frac{x^2 - 1}{x^4 + 1}\right] &= \frac{(x^4 + 1)\dfrac{d}{dx}[x^2 - 1] - (x^2 - 1)\dfrac{d}{dx}[x^4 + 1]}{(x^4 + 1)^2} \\
&= \frac{(x^4 + 1)(2x) - (x^2 - 1)(4x^3)}{(x^4 + 1)^2} \\
&= \frac{-2x^5 + 4x^3 + 2x}{(x^4 + 1)^2} = -\frac{2x(x^4 - 2x^2 - 1)}{(x^4 + 1)^2}
\end{aligned}$$

The differentiation is complete. The rest is simplification.

Now we will set $dy/dx = 0$ and solve for $x$. We obtain

$$-\frac{2x(x^4 - 2x^2 - 1)}{(x^4 + 1)^2} = 0$$

The solutions of this equation are the values of $x$ for which the numerator is 0, that is,

$$2x(x^4 - 2x^2 - 1) = 0$$

The first factor yields the solution $x = 0$. Other solutions can be found by solving the equation

$$x^4 - 2x^2 - 1 = 0$$

This can be treated as a quadratic equation in $x^2$ and solved by the quadratic formula. This yields

$$x^2 = \frac{2 \pm \sqrt{8}}{2} = 1 \pm \sqrt{2}$$

Derive the following rule for differentiating a reciprocal:

$$\left(\frac{1}{g}\right)' = -\frac{g'}{g^2}$$

Use it to find the derivative of

$$f(x) = \frac{1}{x^2+1}$$

The minus sign yields imaginary values of $x$, which we ignore since they are not relevant to the problem. The plus sign yields the solutions

$$x = \pm\sqrt{1+\sqrt{2}}$$

In summary, horizontal tangent lines occur at

$$x = 0, \quad x = \sqrt{1+\sqrt{2}} \approx 1.55, \quad \text{and} \quad x = -\sqrt{1+\sqrt{2}} \approx -1.55$$

which is consistent with the rough estimates that we obtained graphically in part (a). ◄

## SUMMARY OF DIFFERENTIATION RULES

The following table summarizes the differentiation rules that we have encountered thus far.

**Table 2.4.1**

RULES FOR DIFFERENTIATION

| | | | |
|---|---|---|---|
| $\frac{d}{dx}[c] = 0$ | $(f+g)' = f' + g'$ | $(f \cdot g)' = f \cdot g' + g \cdot f'$ | $\left(\frac{1}{g}\right)' = -\frac{g'}{g^2}$ |
| $(cf)' = cf'$ | $(f-g)' = f' - g'$ | $\left(\frac{f}{g}\right)' = \frac{g \cdot f' - f \cdot g'}{g^2}$ | $\frac{d}{dx}[x^r] = rx^{r-1}$ |

## ✓ QUICK CHECK EXERCISES 2.4

(See page 113 for answers.)

1. (a) $\frac{d}{dx}[x^2 f(x)] =$ ______ (b) $\frac{d}{dx}\left[\frac{f(x)}{x^2+1}\right] =$ ______
(c) $\frac{d}{dx}\left[\frac{x^2+1}{f(x)}\right] =$ ______

2. Find $F'(1)$ given that $f(1) = -1$, $f'(1) = 2$, $g(1) = 3$, and $g'(1) = -1$.
(a) $F(x) = 2f(x) - 3g(x)$ (b) $F(x) = [f(x)]^2$
(c) $F(x) = f(x)g(x)$ (d) $F(x) = f(x)/g(x)$

## EXERCISE SET 2.4

Graphing Utility

**1–4** Compute the derivative of the given function $f(x)$ by (a) multiplying and then differentiating and (b) using the product rule. Verify that (a) and (b) yield the same result. ■

1. $f(x) = (x+1)(2x-1)$
2. $f(x) = (3x^2-1)(x^2+2)$
3. $f(x) = (x^2+1)(x^2-1)$
4. $f(x) = (x+1)(x^2-x+1)$

**5–20** Find $f'(x)$. ■

5. $f(x) = (3x^2+6)\left(2x - \frac{1}{4}\right)$
6. $f(x) = (2-x-3x^3)(7+x^5)$
7. $f(x) = (x^3+7x^2-8)(2x^{-3}+x^{-4})$
8. $f(x) = \left(\frac{1}{x} + \frac{1}{x^2}\right)(3x^3+27)$
9. $f(x) = (x-2)(x^2+2x+4)$
10. $f(x) = (x^2+x)(x^2-x)$
11. $f(x) = \frac{3x+4}{x^2+1}$
12. $f(x) = \frac{x-2}{x^4+x+1}$
13. $f(x) = \frac{x^2}{3x-4}$
14. $f(x) = \frac{2x^2+5}{3x-4}$
15. $f(x) = \frac{(2\sqrt{x}+1)(x-1)}{x+3}$
16. $f(x) = (2\sqrt{x}+1)\left(\frac{2-x}{x^2+3x}\right)$
17. $f(x) = (2x+1)\left(1+\frac{1}{x}\right)(x^{-3}+7)$
18. $f(x) = x^{-5}(x^2+2x)(4-3x)(2x^9+1)$
19. $f(x) = (x^7+2x-3)^3$
20. $f(x) = (x^2+1)^4$

**21–24** Find $dy/dx|_{x=1}$. ■

21. $y = \frac{2x-1}{x+3}$
22. $y = \frac{4x+1}{x^2-5}$
23. $y = \left(\frac{3x+2}{x}\right)(x^{-5}+1)$
24. $y = (2x^7-x^2)\left(\frac{x-1}{x+1}\right)$

**25–26** Use a graphing utility to estimate the value of $f'(1)$ by zooming in on the graph of $f$, and then compare your estimate to the exact value obtained by differentiating. ■

25. $f(x) = \frac{x}{x^2+1}$
26. $f(x) = \frac{x^2-1}{x^2+1}$

**27.** Find $g'(4)$ given that $f(4) = 3$ and $f'(4) = -5$.
(a) $g(x) = \sqrt{x}f(x)$ (b) $g(x) = \dfrac{f(x)}{x}$

**28.** Find $g'(3)$ given that $f(3) = -2$ and $f'(3) = 4$.
(a) $g(x) = 3x^2 - 5f(x)$ (b) $g(x) = \dfrac{2x+1}{f(x)}$

**29.** In parts (a)–(d), $F(x)$ is expressed in terms of $f(x)$ and $g(x)$. Find $F'(2)$ given that $f(2) = -1$, $f'(2) = 4$, $g(2) = 1$, and $g'(2) = -5$.
(a) $F(x) = 5f(x) + 2g(x)$ (b) $F(x) = f(x) - 3g(x)$
(c) $F(x) = f(x)g(x)$ (d) $F(x) = f(x)/g(x)$

**30.** Find $F'(\pi)$ given that $f(\pi) = 10$, $f'(\pi) = -1$, $g(\pi) = -3$, and $g'(\pi) = 2$.
(a) $F(x) = 6f(x) - 5g(x)$ (b) $F(x) = x(f(x) + g(x))$
(c) $F(x) = 2f(x)g(x)$ (d) $F(x) = \dfrac{f(x)}{4 + g(x)}$

**31–36** Find all values of $x$ at which the tangent line to the given curve satisfies the stated property. ■

**31.** $y = \dfrac{x^2 - 1}{x + 2}$; horizontal **32.** $y = \dfrac{x^2 + 1}{x - 1}$; horizontal

**33.** $y = \dfrac{x^2 + 1}{x + 1}$; parallel to the line $y = x$

**34.** $y = \dfrac{x + 3}{x + 2}$; perpendicular to the line $y = x$

**35.** $y = \dfrac{1}{x + 4}$; passes through the origin

**36.** $y = \dfrac{2x + 5}{x + 2}$; $y$-intercept 2

**FOCUS ON CONCEPTS**

**37.** (a) What should it mean to say that two curves intersect at right angles?
(b) Show that the curves $y = 1/x$ and $y = 1/(2 - x)$ intersect at right angles.

**38.** Find all values of $a$ such that the curves $y = a/(x - 1)$ and $y = x^2 - 2x + 1$ intersect at right angles.

**39.** Find a general formula for $F''(x)$ if $F(x) = xf(x)$ and $f$ and $f'$ are differentiable at $x$.

**40.** Suppose that the function $f$ is differentiable everywhere and $F(x) = xf(x)$.
(a) Express $F'''(x)$ in terms of $x$ and derivatives of $f$.
(b) For $n \geq 2$, conjecture a formula for $F^{(n)}(x)$.

**41.** A manufacturer of athletic footwear finds that the sales of their ZipStride brand running shoes is a function $f(p)$ of the selling price $p$ (in dollars) for a pair of shoes. Suppose that $f(120) = 9000$ pairs of shoes and $f'(120) = -60$ pairs of shoes per dollar. The revenue that the manufacturer will receive for selling $f(p)$ pairs of shoes at $p$ dollars per pair is $R(p) = p \cdot f(p)$. Find $R'(120)$. What impact would a small increase in price have on the manufacturer's revenue?

**42.** Solve the problem in Exercise 41 under the assumption that $f(120) = 9000$ and $f'(120) = -80$.

**43.** Use the quotient rule (Theorem 2.4.2) to derive the formula for the derivative of $f(x) = x^{-n}$, where $n$ is a positive integer.

✓ **QUICK CHECK ANSWERS 2.4** 1. (a) $x^2f'(x) + 2xf(x)$ (b) $\dfrac{(x^2+1)f'(x) - 2xf(x)}{(x^2+1)^2}$ (c) $\dfrac{2xf(x) - (x^2+1)f'(x)}{[f(x)^2]}$
2. (a) 7 (b) −4 (c) 7 (d) $\frac{5}{9}$

## 2.5 DERIVATIVES OF TRIGONOMETRIC FUNCTIONS

*The main objective of this section is to obtain formulas for the derivatives of the six basic trigonometric functions. If needed, you will find a review of trigonometric functions in Appendix A.*

We will assume in this section that the variable $x$ in the trigonometric functions $\sin x$, $\cos x$, $\tan x$, $\cot x$, $\sec x$, and $\csc x$ is measured in radians. Also, we will need the limits in Theorem 1.6.3, but restated as follows using $h$ rather than $x$ as the variable:

$$\lim_{h \to 0} \frac{\sin h}{h} = 1 \quad \text{and} \quad \lim_{h \to 0} \frac{1 - \cos h}{h} = 0 \qquad (1\text{–}2)$$

Let us start with the problem of differentiating $f(x) = \sin x$. Using the definition of the derivative we obtain

$$
\begin{aligned}
f'(x) &= \lim_{h\to 0} \frac{f(x+h) - f(x)}{h} \\
&= \lim_{h\to 0} \frac{\sin(x+h) - \sin x}{h} \\
&= \lim_{h\to 0} \frac{\sin x \cos h + \cos x \sin h - \sin x}{h} && \text{By the addition formula for sine} \\
&= \lim_{h\to 0} \left[\sin x \left(\frac{\cos h - 1}{h}\right) + \cos x \left(\frac{\sin h}{h}\right)\right] \\
&= \lim_{h\to 0} \left[\cos x \left(\frac{\sin h}{h}\right) - \sin x \left(\frac{1 - \cos h}{h}\right)\right] && \text{Algebraic reorganization} \\
&= \lim_{h\to 0} \cos x \cdot \lim_{h\to 0} \frac{\sin h}{h} - \lim_{h\to 0} \sin x \cdot \lim_{h\to 0} \frac{1 - \cos h}{h} \\
&= \left(\lim_{h\to 0} \cos x\right)(1) - \left(\lim_{h\to 0} \sin x\right)(0) && \text{Formulas (1) and (2)} \\
&= \lim_{h\to 0} \cos x = \cos x && \text{$\cos x$ does not involve the variable $h$ and hence is treated as a constant in the limit computation.}
\end{aligned}
$$

Formulas (1) and (2) and the derivation of Formulas (3) and (4) are only valid if $h$ and $x$ are in radians. See Exercise 49 for how Formulas (3) and (4) change when $x$ is measured in degrees.

Thus, we have shown that

$$\frac{d}{dx}[\sin x] = \cos x \tag{3}$$

In the exercises we will ask you to use the same method to derive the following formula for the derivative of $\cos x$:

$$\frac{d}{dx}[\cos x] = -\sin x \tag{4}$$

► **Example 1** Find $dy/dx$ if $y = x \sin x$.

***Solution.*** Using Formula (3) and the product rule we obtain

$$
\begin{aligned}
\frac{dy}{dx} &= \frac{d}{dx}[x \sin x] \\
&= x \frac{d}{dx}[\sin x] + \sin x \frac{d}{dx}[x] \\
&= x \cos x + \sin x \quad ◄
\end{aligned}
$$

► **Example 2** Find $dy/dx$ if $y = \dfrac{\sin x}{1 + \cos x}$.

***Solution.*** Using the quotient rule together with Formulas (3) and (4) we obtain

$$
\begin{aligned}
\frac{dy}{dx} &= \frac{(1 + \cos x) \cdot \frac{d}{dx}[\sin x] - \sin x \cdot \frac{d}{dx}[1 + \cos x]}{(1 + \cos x)^2} \\
&= \frac{(1 + \cos x)(\cos x) - (\sin x)(-\sin x)}{(1 + \cos x)^2} \\
&= \frac{\cos x + \cos^2 x + \sin^2 x}{(1 + \cos x)^2} = \frac{\cos x + 1}{(1 + \cos x)^2} = \frac{1}{1 + \cos x} \quad ◄
\end{aligned}
$$

Since Formulas (3) and (4) are valid only if $x$ is in radians, the same is true for Formulas (5)–(8).

The derivatives of the remaining trigonometric functions are

$$\frac{d}{dx}[\tan x] = \sec^2 x \qquad \frac{d}{dx}[\sec x] = \sec x \tan x \tag{5–6}$$

$$\frac{d}{dx}[\cot x] = -\csc^2 x \qquad \frac{d}{dx}[\csc x] = -\csc x \cot x \tag{7–8}$$

These can all be obtained using the definition of the derivative, but it is easier to use Formulas (3) and (4) and apply the quotient rule to the relationships

$$\tan x = \frac{\sin x}{\cos x}, \quad \cot x = \frac{\cos x}{\sin x}, \quad \sec x = \frac{1}{\cos x}, \quad \csc x = \frac{1}{\sin x}$$

For example,

$$\frac{d}{dx}[\tan x] = \frac{d}{dx}\left[\frac{\sin x}{\cos x}\right] = \frac{\cos x \cdot \frac{d}{dx}[\sin x] - \sin x \cdot \frac{d}{dx}[\cos x]}{\cos^2 x}$$

$$= \frac{\cos x \cdot \cos x - \sin x \cdot (-\sin x)}{\cos^2 x} = \frac{\cos^2 x + \sin^2 x}{\cos^2 x} = \frac{1}{\cos^2 x} = \sec^2 x$$

When finding the value of a derivative at a specific point $x = x_0$, it is important to substitute $x_0$ *after* the derivative is obtained. Thus, in Example 3 we made the substitution $x = \pi/4$ after $f''$ was calculated. What would have happened had we *incorrectly* substituted $x = \pi/4$ into $f'(x)$ before calculating $f''$?

► **Example 3** Find $f''(\pi/4)$ if $f(x) = \sec x$.

$$f'(x) = \sec x \tan x$$

$$f''(x) = \sec x \cdot \frac{d}{dx}[\tan x] + \tan x \cdot \frac{d}{dx}[\sec x]$$

$$= \sec x \cdot \sec^2 x + \tan x \cdot \sec x \tan x$$

$$= \sec^3 x + \sec x \tan^2 x$$

Thus,

$$f''(\pi/4) = \sec^3(\pi/4) + \sec(\pi/4)\tan^2(\pi/4)$$

$$= (\sqrt{2})^3 + (\sqrt{2})(1)^2 = 3\sqrt{2} \quad ◄$$

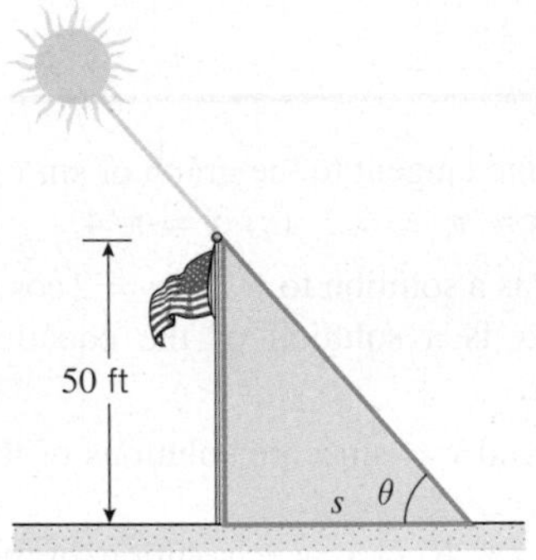

▲ **Figure 2.5.1**

► **Example 4** On a sunny day, a 50 ft flagpole casts a shadow that changes with the angle of elevation of the Sun. Let $s$ be the length of the shadow and $\theta$ the angle of elevation of the Sun (Figure 2.5.1). Find the rate at which the length of the shadow is changing with respect to $\theta$ when $\theta = 45°$. Express your answer in units of feet/degree.

***Solution.*** The variables $s$ and $\theta$ are related by $\tan\theta = 50/s$ or, equivalently,

$$s = 50 \cot\theta \tag{9}$$

If $\theta$ is measured in radians, then Formula (7) is applicable, which yields

$$\frac{ds}{d\theta} = -50\csc^2\theta$$

which is the rate of change of shadow length with respect to the elevation angle $\theta$ in units of feet/radian. When $\theta = 45°$ (or equivalently $\theta = \pi/4$ radians), we obtain

$$\left.\frac{ds}{d\theta}\right|_{\theta=\pi/4} = -50\csc^2(\pi/4) = -100 \text{ feet/radian}$$

Converting radians (rad) to degrees (deg) yields

$$-100\,\frac{\text{ft}}{\text{rad}} \cdot \frac{\pi}{180}\,\frac{\text{rad}}{\text{deg}} = -\frac{5}{9}\pi\,\frac{\text{ft}}{\text{deg}} \approx -1.75 \text{ ft/deg}$$

Thus, when $\theta = 45°$, the shadow length is decreasing (because of the minus sign) at an approximate rate of 1.75 ft/deg increase in the angle of elevation. ◄

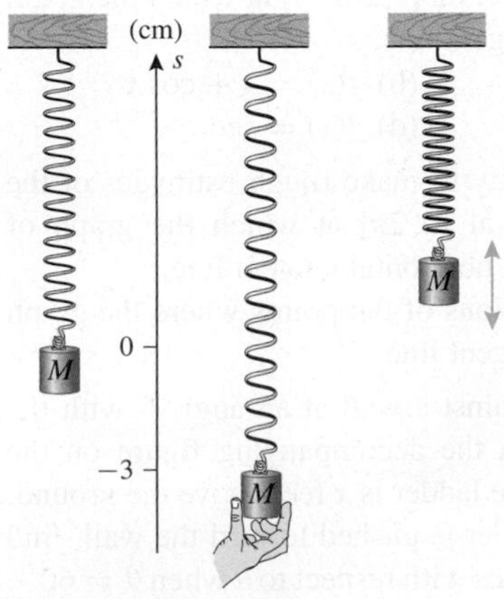

▲ **Figure 2.5.2**

► **Example 5** As illustrated in Figure 2.5.2, suppose that a spring with an attached mass is stretched 3 cm beyond its rest position and released at time $t = 0$. Assuming that

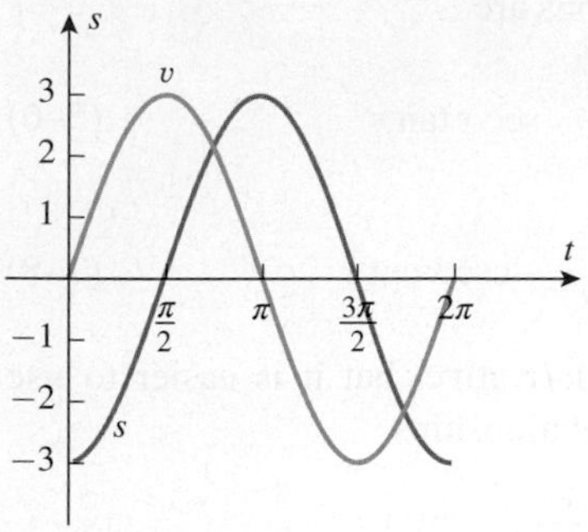


▲ Figure 2.5.3

the position function of the top of the attached mass is

$$s = -3\cos t \tag{10}$$

where $s$ is in centimeters and $t$ is in seconds, find the velocity function and discuss the motion of the attached mass.

***Solution.*** The velocity function is

$$v = \frac{ds}{dt} = \frac{d}{dt}[-3\cos t] = 3\sin t$$

Figure 2.5.3 shows the graphs of the position and velocity functions. The position function tells us that the top of the mass oscillates between a low point of $s = -3$ and a high point of $s = 3$ with one complete oscillation occuring every $2\pi$ seconds [the period of (10)]. The top of the mass is moving up (the positive $s$-direction) when $v$ is positive, is moving down when $v$ is negative, and is at a high or low point when $v = 0$. Thus, for example, the top of the mass moves up from time $t = 0$ to time $t = \pi$, at which time it reaches the high point $s = 3$ and then moves down until time $t = 2\pi$, at which time it reaches the low point of $s = -3$. The motion then repeats periodically. ◄

In Example 5, the top of the mass has its maximum speed when it passes through its rest position. Why? What is that maximum speed?

## ✓ QUICK CHECK EXERCISES 2.5 

(See page 118 for answers.)

1. Find $dy/dx$.
   (a) $y = \sin x$ (b) $y = \cos x$
   (c) $y = \tan x$ (d) $y = \sec x$
2. Find $f'(x)$ and $f'(\pi/3)$ if $f(x) = \sin x \cos x$.
3. Use a derivative to evaluate each limit.
   (a) $\lim_{h\to 0} \frac{\sin\left(\frac{\pi}{2}+h\right)-1}{h}$ (b) $\lim_{h\to 0} \frac{\csc(x+h)-\csc x}{h}$

## EXERCISE SET 2.5 

Graphing Utility

**1–18** Find $f'(x)$. ■

1. $f(x) = 4\cos x + 2\sin x$
2. $f(x) = \frac{5}{x^2} + \sin x$
3. $f(x) = -4x^2 \cos x$
4. $f(x) = 2\sin^2 x$
5. $f(x) = \frac{5-\cos x}{5+\sin x}$
6. $f(x) = \frac{\sin x}{x^2 + \sin x}$
7. $f(x) = \sec x - \sqrt{2}\tan x$
8. $f(x) = (x^2+1)\sec x$
9. $f(x) = 4\csc x - \cot x$
10. $f(x) = \cos x - x\csc x$
11. $f(x) = \sec x \tan x$
12. $f(x) = \csc x \cot x$
13. $f(x) = \frac{\cot x}{1+\csc x}$
14. $f(x) = \frac{\sec x}{1+\tan x}$
15. $f(x) = \sin^2 x + \cos^2 x$
16. $f(x) = \sec^2 x - \tan^2 x$
17. $f(x) = \frac{\sin x \sec x}{1 + x\tan x}$
18. $f(x) = \frac{(x^2+1)\cot x}{3 - \cos x \csc x}$

**19–24** Find $d^2y/dx^2$. ■

19. $y = x\cos x$
20. $y = \csc x$
21. $y = x\sin x - 3\cos x$
22. $y = x^2\cos x + 4\sin x$
23. $y = \sin x \cos x$
24. $y = \tan x$
25. Find the equation of the line tangent to the graph of $\tan x$ at
    (a) $x = 0$ (b) $x = \pi/4$ (c) $x = -\pi/4$.
26. Find the equation of the line tangent to the graph of $\sin x$ at
    (a) $x = 0$ (b) $x = \pi$ (c) $x = \pi/4$.
27. (a) Show that $y = x\sin x$ is a solution to $y'' + y = 2\cos x$.
    (b) Show that $y = x\sin x$ is a solution of the equation $y^{(4)} + y'' = -2\cos x$.
28. (a) Show that $y = \cos x$ and $y = \sin x$ are solutions of the equation $y'' + y = 0$.
    (b) Show that $y = A\sin x + B\cos x$ is a solution of the equation $y'' + y = 0$ for all constants $A$ and $B$.
29. Find all values in the interval $[-2\pi, 2\pi]$ at which the graph of $f$ has a horizontal tangent line.
    (a) $f(x) = \sin x$ (b) $f(x) = x + \cos x$
    (c) $f(x) = \tan x$ (d) $f(x) = \sec x$
30. (a) Use a graphing utility to make rough estimates of the values in the interval $[0, 2\pi]$ at which the graph of $y = \sin x \cos x$ has a horizontal tangent line.
    (b) Find the exact locations of the points where the graph has a horizontal tangent line.
31. A 10 ft ladder leans against a wall at an angle $\theta$ with the horizontal, as shown in the accompanying figure on the next page. The top of the ladder is $x$ feet above the ground. If the bottom of the ladder is pushed toward the wall, find the rate at which $x$ changes with respect to $\theta$ when $\theta = 60°$. Express the answer in units of feet/degree.

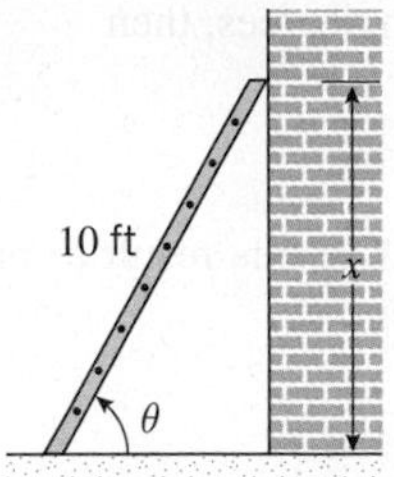


◀ **Figure Ex-31**

**32.** An airplane is flying on a horizontal path at a height of 3800 ft, as shown in the accompanying figure. At what rate is the distance $s$ between the airplane and the fixed point $P$ changing with respect to $\theta$ when $\theta = 30°$? Express the answer in units of feet/degree.

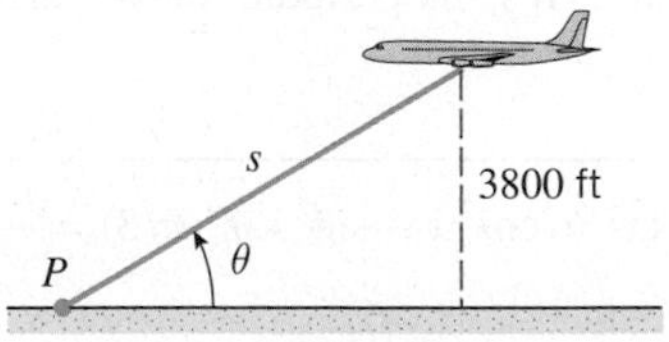


◀ **Figure Ex-32**

**33.** A scarchlight is trained on the side of a tall building. As the light rotates, the spot it illuminates moves up and down the side of the building. That is, the distance $D$ between ground level and the illuminated spot on the side of the building is a function of the angle $\theta$ formed by the light beam and the horizontal (see the accompanying figure). If the searchlight is located 50 m from the building, find the rate at which $D$ is changing with respect to $\theta$ when $\theta = 45°$. Express your answer in units of meters/degree.

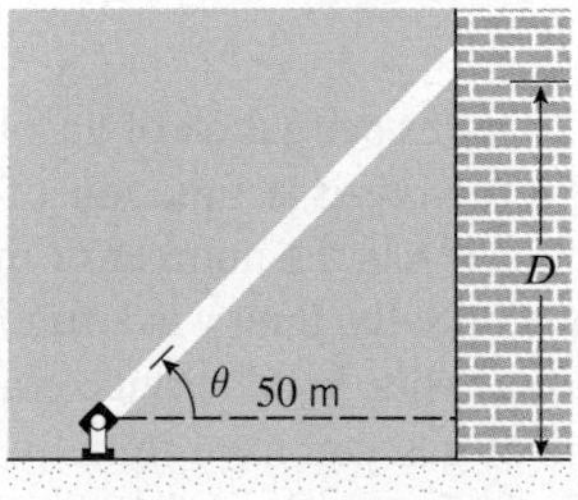


◀ **Figure Ex-33**

**34.** An Earth-observing satellite can see only a portion of the Earth's surface. The satellite has horizon sensors that can detect the angle $\theta$ shown in the accompanying figure. Let $r$ be the radius of the Earth (assumed spherical) and $h$ the distance of the satellite from the Earth's surface.

(a) Show that $h = r(\csc\theta - 1)$.

(b) Using $r = 6378$ km, find the rate at which $h$ is changing with respect to $\theta$ when $\theta = 30°$. Express the answer in units of kilometers/degree.

**Source:** Adapted from *Space Mathematics*, NASA, 1985.

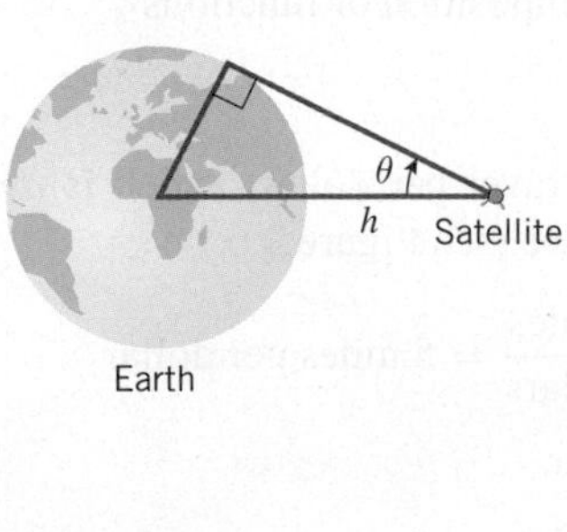


◀ **Figure Ex-34**

**35–38 True–False** Determine whether the statement is true or false. Explain your answer. ■

**35.** If $g(x) = f(x)\sin x$, then $g'(x) = f'(x)\cos x$.

**36.** If $g(x) = f(x)\sin x$, then $g'(0) = f(0)$.

**37.** If $f(x)\cos x = \sin x$, then $f'(x) = \sec^2 x$.

**38.** Suppose that $g(x) = f(x)\sec x$, where $f(0) = 8$ and $f'(0) = -2$. Then

$$g'(0) = \lim_{h\to 0} \frac{f(h)\sec h - f(0)}{h} = \lim_{h\to 0} \frac{8(\sec h - 1)}{h}$$

$$= 8 \cdot \frac{d}{dx}[\sec x]\bigg|_{x=0} = 8 \sec 0 \tan 0 = 0$$

**39–40** Make a conjecture about the derivative by calculating the first few derivatives and observing the resulting pattern. ■

**39.** $\dfrac{d^{87}}{dx^{87}}[\sin x]$ **40.** $\dfrac{d^{100}}{dx^{100}}[\cos x]$

**41.** Let $f(x) = \cos x$. Find all positive integers $n$ for which $f^{(n)}(x) = \sin x$.

**42.** Let $f(x) = \sin x$. Find all positive integers $n$ for which $f^{(n)}(x) = \sin x$.

**FOCUS ON CONCEPTS**

**43.** In each part, determine where $f$ is differentiable.

(a) $f(x) = \sin x$ (b) $f(x) = \cos x$

(c) $f(x) = \tan x$ (d) $f(x) = \cot x$

(e) $f(x) = \sec x$ (f) $f(x) = \csc x$

(g) $f(x) = \dfrac{1}{1 + \cos x}$ (h) $f(x) = \dfrac{1}{\sin x \cos x}$

(i) $f(x) = \dfrac{\cos x}{2 - \sin x}$

**44.** (a) Derive Formula (4) using the definition of a derivative.

(b) Use Formulas (3) and (4) to obtain (7).

(c) Use Formula (4) to obtain (6).

(d) Use Formula (3) to obtain (8).

**45.** Use Formula (1), the alternative form for the definition of derivative given in Formula (13) of Section 2.2, that is,

$$f'(x) = \lim_{w\to x} \frac{f(w) - f(x)}{w - x}$$

and the difference identity

$$\sin\alpha - \sin\beta = 2\sin\left(\frac{\alpha - \beta}{2}\right)\cos\left(\frac{\alpha + \beta}{2}\right)$$

to show that $\dfrac{d}{dx}[\sin x] = \cos x$.

**46.** Follow the directions of Exercise 45 using the difference identity

$$\cos\alpha - \cos\beta = -2\sin\left(\frac{\alpha - \beta}{2}\right)\sin\left(\frac{\alpha + \beta}{2}\right)$$

to show that $\dfrac{d}{dx}[\cos x] = -\sin x$.

**47.** (a) Show that $\lim_{h\to 0} \frac{\tan h}{h} = 1$.
(b) Use the result in part (a) to help derive the formula for the derivative of $\tan x$ directly from the definition of a derivative.

**48.** Without using any trigonometric identities, find

$$\lim_{x\to 0} \frac{\tan(x+y) - \tan y}{x}$$

[*Hint:* Relate the given limit to the definition of the derivative of an appropriate function of $y$.]

**49.** The derivative formulas for $\sin x$, $\cos x$, $\tan x$, $\cot x$, $\sec x$, and $\csc x$ were obtained under the assumption that $x$ is measured in radians. If $x$ is measured in degrees, then

$$\lim_{x\to 0} \frac{\sin x}{x} = \frac{\pi}{180}$$

(See Exercise 39 of Section 1.6). Use this result to prove that if $x$ is measured in degrees, then

(a) $\frac{d}{dx}[\sin x] = \frac{\pi}{180}\cos x$

(b) $\frac{d}{dx}[\cos x] = -\frac{\pi}{180}\sin x$.

**50. Writing** Suppose that $f$ is a function that is differentiable everywhere. Explain the relationship, if any, between the periodicity of $f$ and that of $f'$. That is, if $f$ is periodic, must $f'$ also be periodic? If $f'$ is periodic, must $f$ also be periodic?

✓ **QUICK CHECK ANSWERS 2.5** 1. (a) $\cos x$ (b) $-\sin x$ (c) $\sec^2 x$ (d) $\sec x \tan x$ 2. $f'(x) = \cos^2 x - \sin^2 x$, $f'(\pi/3) = -\frac{1}{2}$
3. (a) $\left.\frac{d}{dx}[\sin x]\right|_{x=\pi/2} = 0$ (b) $\frac{d}{dx}[\csc x] = -\csc x \cot x$

## 2.6 THE CHAIN RULE

*In this section we will derive a formula that expresses the derivative of a composition $f \circ g$ in terms of the derivatives of $f$ and $g$. This formula will enable us to differentiate complicated functions using known derivatives of simpler functions.*

### DERIVATIVES OF COMPOSITIONS

Comstock Images/Getty Images
*The cost of a car trip is a combination of fuel efficiency and the cost of gasoline.*

Suppose you are traveling to school in your car, which gets 20 miles per gallon of gasoline. The number of miles you can travel in your car without refueling is a function of the number of gallons of gas you have in the gas tank. In symbols, if $y$ is the number of miles you can travel and $u$ is the number of gallons of gas you have initially, then $y$ is a function of $u$, or $y = f(u)$. As you continue your travels, you note that your local service station is selling gasoline for \$4 per gallon. The number of gallons of gas you have initially is a function of the amount of money you spend for that gas. If $x$ is the number of dollars you spend on gas, then $u = g(x)$. Now 20 miles per gallon is the rate at which your mileage changes with respect to the amount of gasoline you use, so

$$f'(u) = \frac{dy}{du} = 20 \text{ miles per gallon}$$

Similarly, since gasoline costs \$4 per gallon, each dollar you spend will give you 1/4 of a gallon of gas, and

$$g'(x) = \frac{du}{dx} = \frac{1}{4} \text{ gallons per dollar}$$

Notice that the number of miles you can travel is also a function of the number of dollars you spend on gasoline. This fact is expressible as the composition of functions

$$y = f(u) = f(g(x))$$

You might be interested in how many miles you can travel per dollar, which is $dy/dx$. Intuition suggests that rates of change multiply in this case (see Figure 2.6.1), so

$$\frac{dy}{dx} = \frac{dy}{du}\cdot\frac{du}{dx} = \frac{20 \text{ miles}}{1 \text{ gallon}}\cdot\frac{1 \text{ gallon}}{4 \text{ dollars}} = \frac{20 \text{ miles}}{4 \text{ dollars}} = 5 \text{ miles per dollar}$$

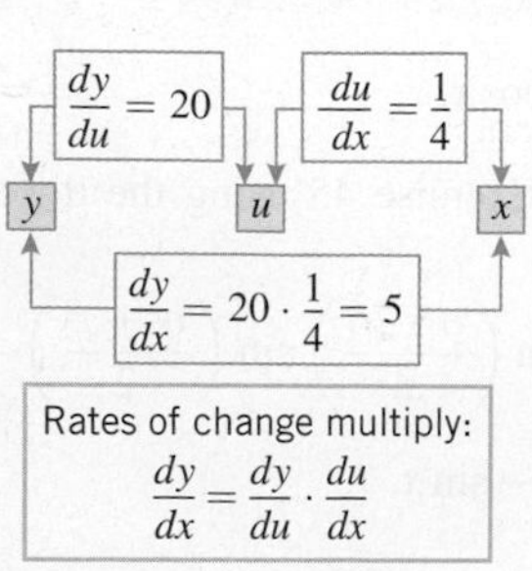


▲ **Figure 2.6.1**

The following theorem, the proof of which is given in Web Appendix L, formalizes the preceding ideas.

**2.6.1 THEOREM (*The Chain Rule*)** *If g is differentiable at x and f is differentiable at g(x), then the composition f ∘ g is differentiable at x. Moreover, if*

$$y = f(g(x)) \quad \text{and} \quad u = g(x)$$

*then* $y = f(u)$ *and*

$$\frac{dy}{dx} = \frac{dy}{du} \cdot \frac{du}{dx} \tag{1}$$

The name "chain rule" is appropriate because the desired derivative is obtained by a two-link "chain" of simpler derivatives.

Formula (1) is easy to remember because the left side is exactly what results if we "cancel" the *du*'s on the right side. This "canceling" device provides a good way of deducing the correct form of the chain rule when different variables are used. For example, if $w$ is a function of $x$ and $x$ is a function of $t$, then the chain rule takes the form

$$\frac{dw}{dt} = \frac{dw}{dx} \cdot \frac{dx}{dt}$$

▶ **Example 1** Find $dy/dx$ if $y = \cos(x^3)$.

***Solution.*** Let $u = x^3$ and express $y$ as $y = \cos u$. Applying Formula (1) yields

$$\begin{aligned}
\frac{dy}{dx} &= \frac{dy}{du} \cdot \frac{du}{dx} \\
&= \frac{d}{du}[\cos u] \cdot \frac{d}{dx}[x^3] \\
&= (-\sin u) \cdot (3x^2) \\
&= (-\sin(x^3)) \cdot (3x^2) = -3x^2 \sin(x^3) \blacktriangleleft
\end{aligned}$$

▶ **Example 2** Find $dw/dt$ if $w = \tan x$ and $x = 4t^3 + t$.

***Solution.*** In this case the chain rule computations take the form

$$\begin{aligned}
\frac{dw}{dt} &= \frac{dw}{dx} \cdot \frac{dx}{dt} \\
&= \frac{d}{dx}[\tan x] \cdot \frac{d}{dt}[4t^3 + t] \\
&= (\sec^2 x) \cdot (12t^2 + 1) \\
&= [\sec^2(4t^3 + t)] \cdot (12t^2 + 1) = (12t^2 + 1)\sec^2(4t^3 + t) \blacktriangleleft
\end{aligned}$$

## AN ALTERNATIVE VERSION OF THE CHAIN RULE

Formula (1) for the chain rule can be unwieldy in some problems because it involves so many variables. As you become more comfortable with the chain rule, you may want to dispense with writing out the dependent variables by expressing (1) in the form

$$\frac{d}{dx}[f(g(x))] = (f \circ g)'(x) = f'(g(x))g'(x) \tag{2}$$

Confirm that (2) is an alternative version of (1) by letting $y = f(g(x))$ and $u = g(x)$.

A convenient way to remember this formula is to call $f$ the "outside function" and $g$ the "inside function" in the composition $f(g(x))$ and then express (2) in words as:

*The derivative of f(g(x)) is the derivative of the outside function evaluated at the inside function times the derivative of the inside function.*

$$\frac{d}{dx}[f(g(x))] = \underbrace{f'(g(x))}_{\text{Derivative of the outside function evaluated at the inside function}} \cdot \underbrace{g'(x)}_{\text{Derivative of the inside function}}$$

**▶ Example 3** (*Example 1 revisited*) Find $h'(x)$ if $h(x) = \cos(x^3)$.

***Solution.*** We can think of $h$ as a composition $f(g(x))$ in which $g(x) = x^3$ is the inside function and $f(x) = \cos x$ is the outside function. Thus, Formula (2) yields

$$h'(x) = \underbrace{f'(g(x))}_{\text{Derivative of the outside function evaluated at the inside function}} \cdot \underbrace{g'(x)}_{\text{Derivative of the inside function}}$$

$$= f'(x^3) \cdot 3x^2$$

$$= -\sin(x^3) \cdot 3x^2 = -3x^2 \sin(x^3)$$

which agrees with the result obtained in Example 1. ◀

**▶ Example 4**

$$\frac{d}{dx}[\tan^2 x] = \frac{d}{dx}[(\tan x)^2] = \underbrace{(2\tan x)}_{\text{Derivative of the outside function evaluated at the inside function}} \cdot \underbrace{(\sec^2 x)}_{\text{Derivative of the inside function}} = 2\tan x \sec^2 x$$

$$\frac{d}{dx}\left[\sqrt{x^2+1}\right] = \underbrace{\frac{1}{2\sqrt{x^2+1}}}_{\text{Derivative of the outside function evaluated at the inside function}} \cdot \underbrace{2x}_{\text{Derivative of the inside function}} = \frac{x}{\sqrt{x^2+1}}$$

See Formula (6) of Section 2.3. ◀

## GENERALIZED DERIVATIVE FORMULAS

There is a useful third variation of the chain rule that strikes a middle ground between Formulas (1) and (2). If we let $u = g(x)$ in (2), then we can rewrite that formula as

$$\frac{d}{dx}[f(u)] = f'(u)\frac{du}{dx} \tag{3}$$

This result, called the ***generalized derivative formula*** for $f$, provides a way of using the derivative of $f(x)$ to produce the derivative of $f(u)$, where $u$ is a function of $x$. Table 2.6.1 gives some examples of this formula.

**Table 2.6.1**

GENERALIZED DERIVATIVE FORMULAS

$$\frac{d}{dx}[u^r] = ru^{r-1}\frac{du}{dx}$$

| | |
|---|---|
| $\frac{d}{dx}[\sin u] = \cos u \frac{du}{dx}$ | $\frac{d}{dx}[\cos u] = -\sin u \frac{du}{dx}$ |
| $\frac{d}{dx}[\tan u] = \sec^2 u \frac{du}{dx}$ | $\frac{d}{dx}[\cot u] = -\csc^2 u \frac{du}{dx}$ |
| $\frac{d}{dx}[\sec u] = \sec u \tan u \frac{du}{dx}$ | $\frac{d}{dx}[\csc u] = -\csc u \cot u \frac{du}{dx}$ |

**▶ Example 5** Find

(a) $\frac{d}{dx}[\sin(2x)]$ (b) $\frac{d}{dx}[\tan(x^2+1)]$ (c) $\frac{d}{dx}\left[\sqrt{x^3+\csc x}\right]$

(d) $\frac{d}{dx}[x^2-x+2]^{3/4}$ (e) $\frac{d}{dx}\left[(1+x^5\cot x)^{-8}\right]$

***Solution (a).*** Taking $u = 2x$ in the generalized derivative formula for $\sin u$ yields

$$\frac{d}{dx}[\sin(2x)] = \frac{d}{dx}[\sin u] = \cos u\frac{du}{dx} = \cos 2x \cdot \frac{d}{dx}[2x] = \cos 2x \cdot 2 = 2\cos 2x$$

***Solution (b).*** Taking $u = x^2 + 1$ in the generalized derivative formula for $\tan u$ yields

$$\begin{aligned}\frac{d}{dx}[\tan(x^2+1)] &= \frac{d}{dx}[\tan u] = \sec^2 u\frac{du}{dx}\\ &= \sec^2(x^2+1)\cdot\frac{d}{dx}[x^2+1] = \sec^2(x^2+1)\cdot 2x\\ &= 2x\sec^2(x^2+1)\end{aligned}$$

***Solution (c).*** Taking $u = x^3 + \csc x$ in the generalized derivative formula for $\sqrt{u}$ yields

$$\begin{aligned}\frac{d}{dx}\left[\sqrt{x^3+\csc x}\right] &= \frac{d}{dx}[\sqrt{u}] = \frac{1}{2\sqrt{u}}\frac{du}{dx} = \frac{1}{2\sqrt{x^3+\csc x}}\cdot\frac{d}{dx}[x^3+\csc x]\\ &= \frac{1}{2\sqrt{x^3+\csc x}}\cdot(3x^2-\csc x\cot x) = \frac{3x^2-\csc x\cot x}{2\sqrt{x^3+\csc x}}\end{aligned}$$

***Solution (d).*** Taking $u = x^2 - x + 2$ in the generalized derivative formula for $u^{3/4}$ yields

$$\begin{aligned}\frac{d}{dx}[x^2-x+2]^{3/4} &= \frac{d}{dx}[u^{3/4}] = \frac{3}{4}u^{-1/4}\frac{du}{dx}\\ &= \frac{3}{4}(x^2-x+2)^{-1/4}\cdot\frac{d}{dx}[x^2-x+2]\\ &= \frac{3}{4}(x^2-x+2)^{-1/4}(2x-1)\end{aligned}$$

***Solution (e).*** Taking $u = 1 + x^5\cot x$ in the generalized derivative formula for $u^{-8}$ yields

$$\begin{aligned}\frac{d}{dx}\left[(1+x^5\cot x)^{-8}\right] &= \frac{d}{dx}[u^{-8}] = -8u^{-9}\frac{du}{dx}\\ &= -8(1+x^5\cot x)^{-9}\cdot\frac{d}{dx}[1+x^5\cot x]\\ &= -8(1+x^5\cot x)^{-9}\cdot[x^5(-\csc^2 x)+5x^4\cot x]\\ &= (8x^5\csc^2 x - 40x^4\cot x)(1+x^5\cot x)^{-9} \blacktriangleleft\end{aligned}$$

Sometimes you will have to make adjustments in notation or apply the chain rule more than once to calculate a derivative.

**▶ Example 6** Find

(a) $\frac{d}{dx}\left[\sin(\sqrt{1+\cos x})\right]$ (b) $\frac{d\mu}{dt}$ if $\mu = \sec\sqrt{\omega t}$ ($\omega$ constant)

***Solution (a).*** Taking $u = \sqrt{1+\cos x}$ in the generalized derivative formula for $\sin u$ yields

$$\frac{d}{dx}\left[\sin(\sqrt{1+\cos x})\right] = \frac{d}{dx}[\sin u] = \cos u \frac{du}{dx}$$
$$= \cos(\sqrt{1+\cos x}) \cdot \frac{d}{dx}\left[\sqrt{1+\cos x}\right]$$
$$= \cos(\sqrt{1+\cos x}) \cdot \frac{-\sin x}{2\sqrt{1+\cos x}}$$
$$= -\frac{\sin x \cos(\sqrt{1+\cos x})}{2\sqrt{1+\cos x}}$$

We used the generalized derivative formula for $\sqrt{u}$ with $u = 1 + \cos x$.

***Solution (b).***

$$\frac{d\mu}{dt} = \frac{d}{dt}[\sec\sqrt{\omega t}] = \sec\sqrt{\omega t}\tan\sqrt{\omega t}\frac{d}{dt}[\sqrt{\omega t}]$$

We used the generalized derivative formula for $\sec u$ with $u = \sqrt{\omega t}$.

$$= \sec\sqrt{\omega t}\tan\sqrt{\omega t}\frac{\omega}{2\sqrt{\omega t}}$$

We used the generalized derivative formula for $\sqrt{u}$ with $u = \omega t$. ◀

## DIFFERENTIATING USING COMPUTER ALGEBRA SYSTEMS

Even with the chain rule and other differentiation rules, some derivative computations can be tedious to perform. For complicated derivatives, engineers and scientists often use computer algebra systems such as *Mathematica*, *Maple*, or *Sage*. For example, although we have all the mathematical tools to compute

$$\frac{d}{dx}\left[\frac{(x^2+1)^{10}\sin^3(\sqrt{x})}{\sqrt{1+\csc x}}\right] \tag{4}$$

by hand, the computation is sufficiently involved that it may be more efficient (and less error-prone) to use a computer algebra system.

**TECHNOLOGY MASTERY**

If you have a CAS, use it to perform the differentiation in (4).

## ✓QUICK CHECK EXERCISES 2.6

(See page 125 for answers.)

1. The chain rule states that the derivative of the composition of two functions is the derivative of the ________ function evaluated at the ________ function times the derivative of the ________ function.
2. If $y$ is a differentiable function of $u$, and $u$ is a differentiable function of $x$, then
$$\frac{dy}{dx} = \_\_\_\_\_\_\_\_ \cdot \_\_\_\_\_\_\_\_$$
3. Find $dy/dx$.
(a) $y = (x^2+5)^{10}$ (b) $y = \sqrt{1+6x}$
4. Find $dy/dx$.
(a) $y = \sin(3x+2)$ (b) $y = (x^2\tan x)^4$
5. Suppose that $f(2) = 3$, $f'(2) = 4$, $g(3) = 6$, and $g'(3) = -5$. Evaluate
(a) $h'(2)$, where $h(x) = g(f(x))$
(b) $k'(3)$, where $k(x) = f\left(\frac{1}{3}g(x)\right)$.

## EXERCISE SET 2.6

Graphing Utility  C CAS

1. Given that
$$f'(0) = 2, \quad g(0) = 0 \quad \text{and} \quad g'(0) = 3$$
find $(f \circ g)'(0)$.
2. Given that
$$f'(9) = 5, \quad g(2) = 9 \quad \text{and} \quad g'(2) = -3$$
find $(f \circ g)'(2)$.
3. Let $f(x) = x^5$ and $g(x) = 2x - 3$.
(a) Find $(f \circ g)(x)$ and $(f \circ g)'(x)$.
(b) Find $(g \circ f)(x)$ and $(g \circ f)'(x)$.
4. Let $f(x) = 5\sqrt{x}$ and $g(x) = 4 + \cos x$.
(a) Find $(f \circ g)(x)$ and $(f \circ g)'(x)$.
(b) Find $(g \circ f)(x)$ and $(g \circ f)'(x)$.

**FOCUS ON CONCEPTS**

**5.** Given the following table of values, find the indicated derivatives in parts (a) and (b).

| $x$ | $f(x)$ | $f'(x)$ | $g(x)$ | $g'(x)$ |
|---|---|---|---|---|
| 3 | 5 | −2 | 5 | 7 |
| 5 | 3 | −1 | 12 | 4 |

(a) $F'(3)$, where $F(x) = f(g(x))$
(b) $G'(3)$, where $G(x) = g(f(x))$

**6.** Given the following table of values, find the indicated derivatives in parts (a) and (b).

| $x$ | $f(x)$ | $f'(x)$ | $g(x)$ | $g'(x)$ |
|---|---|---|---|---|
| −1 | 2 | 3 | 2 | −3 |
| 2 | 0 | 4 | 1 | −5 |

(a) $F'(-1)$, where $F(x) = f(g(x))$
(b) $G'(-1)$, where $G(x) = g(f(x))$

**7–26** Find $f'(x)$. ■

**7.** $f(x) = (x^3 + 2x)^{37}$
**8.** $f(x) = (3x^2 + 2x - 1)^6$
**9.** $f(x) = \left(x^3 - \dfrac{7}{x}\right)^{-2}$
**10.** $f(x) = \dfrac{1}{(x^5 - x + 1)^9}$
**11.** $f(x) = \dfrac{4}{(3x^2 - 2x + 1)^3}$
**12.** $f(x) = \sqrt{x^3 - 2x + 5}$
**13.** $f(x) = \sqrt{4 + \sqrt{3x}}$
**14.** $f(x) = \sqrt[3]{12 + \sqrt{x}}$
**15.** $f(x) = \sin\left(\dfrac{1}{x^2}\right)$
**16.** $f(x) = \tan\sqrt{x}$
**17.** $f(x) = 4\cos^5 x$
**18.** $f(x) = 4x + 5\sin^4 x$
**19.** $f(x) = \cos^2(3\sqrt{x})$
**20.** $f(x) = \tan^4(x^3)$
**21.** $f(x) = 2\sec^2(x^7)$
**22.** $f(x) = \cos^3\left(\dfrac{x}{x+1}\right)$
**23.** $f(x) = \sqrt{\cos(5x)}$
**24.** $f(x) = \sqrt{3x - \sin^2(4x)}$
**25.** $f(x) = [x + \csc(x^3 + 3)]^{-3}$
**26.** $f(x) = [x^4 - \sec(4x^2 - 2)]^{-4}$

**27–40** Find $dy/dx$. ■

**27.** $y = x^3\sin^2(5x)$
**28.** $y = \sqrt{x}\tan^3(\sqrt{x})$
**29.** $y = x^5\sec(1/x)$
**30.** $y = \dfrac{\sin x}{\sec(3x + 1)}$
**31.** $y = \cos(\cos x)$
**32.** $y = \sin(\tan 3x)$
**33.** $y = \cos^3(\sin 2x)$
**34.** $y = \dfrac{1 + \csc(x^2)}{1 - \cot(x^2)}$
**35.** $y = (5x + 8)^7(1 - \sqrt{x})^6$
**36.** $y = (x^2 + x)^5\sin^8 x$
**37.** $y = \left(\dfrac{x - 5}{2x + 1}\right)^3$
**38.** $y = \left(\dfrac{1 + x^2}{1 - x^2}\right)^{17}$
**39.** $y = \dfrac{(2x + 3)^3}{(4x^2 - 1)^8}$
**40.** $y = [1 + \sin^3(x^5)]^{12}$

C **41–42** Use a CAS to find $dy/dx$. ■

**41.** $y = [x\sin 2x + \tan^4(x^7)]^5$

**42.** $y = \tan^4\left(2 + \dfrac{(7 - x)\sqrt{3x^2 + 5}}{x^3 + \sin x}\right)$

**43–50** Find an equation for the tangent line to the graph at the specified value of $x$. ■

**43.** $y = x\cos 3x,\ x = \pi$
**44.** $y = \sin(1 + x^3),\ x = -3$
**45.** $y = \sec^3\left(\dfrac{\pi}{2} - x\right),\ x = -\dfrac{\pi}{2}$
**46.** $y = \left(x - \dfrac{1}{x}\right)^3,\ x = 2$
**47.** $y = \tan(4x^2),\ x = \sqrt{\pi}$
**48.** $y = 3\cot^4 x,\ x = \dfrac{\pi}{4}$
**49.** $y = x^2\sqrt{5 - x^2},\ x = 1$
**50.** $y = \dfrac{x}{\sqrt{1 - x^2}},\ x = 0$

**51–54** Find $d^2y/dx^2$. ■

**51.** $y = x\cos(5x) - \sin^2 x$
**52.** $y = \sin(3x^2)$
**53.** $y = \dfrac{1 + x}{1 - x}$
**54.** $y = x\tan\left(\dfrac{1}{x}\right)$

**55–58** Find the indicated derivative. ■

**55.** $y = \cot^3(\pi - \theta)$; find $\dfrac{dy}{d\theta}$.

**56.** $\lambda = \left(\dfrac{au + b}{cu + d}\right)^6$; find $\dfrac{d\lambda}{du}$ ($a, b, c, d$ constants).

**57.** $\dfrac{d}{d\omega}[a\cos^2\pi\omega + b\sin^2\pi\omega]$ ($a, b$ constants)

**58.** $x = \csc^2\left(\dfrac{\pi}{3} - y\right)$; find $\dfrac{dx}{dy}$.

**59.** (a) Use a graphing utility to obtain the graph of the function $f(x) = x\sqrt{4 - x^2}$.
(b) Use the graph in part (a) to make a rough sketch of the graph of $f'$.
(c) Find $f'(x)$, and then check your work in part (b) by using the graphing utility to obtain the graph of $f'$.
(d) Find the equation of the tangent line to the graph of $f$ at $x = 1$, and graph $f$ and the tangent line together.

**60.** (a) Use a graphing utility to obtain the graph of the function $f(x) = \sin x^2\cos x$ over the interval $[-\pi/2, \pi/2]$.
(b) Use the graph in part (a) to make a rough sketch of the graph of $f'$ over the interval.
(c) Find $f'(x)$, and then check your work in part (b) by using the graphing utility to obtain the graph of $f'$ over the interval.
(d) Find the equation of the tangent line to the graph of $f$ at $x = 1$, and graph $f$ and the tangent line together over the interval.

**61–64 True–False** Determine whether the statement is true or false. Explain your answer. ■

**61.** If $y = f(x)$, then $\frac{d}{dx}[\sqrt{y}] = \sqrt{f'(x)}$.

**62.** If $y = f(u)$ and $u = g(x)$, then $dy/dx = f'(x) \cdot g'(x)$.

**63.** If $y = \cos[g(x)]$, then $dy/dx = -\sin[g'(x)]$.

**64.** If $y = \sin^3(3x^3)$, then $dy/dx = 27x^2 \sin^2(3x^3)\cos(3x^3)$.

**65.** If an object suspended from a spring is displaced vertically from its equilibrium position by a small amount and released, and if the air resistance and the mass of the spring are ignored, then the resulting oscillation of the object is called ***simple harmonic motion***. Under appropriate conditions the displacement $y$ from equilibrium in terms of time $t$ is given by

$$y = A\cos\omega t$$

where $A$ is the initial displacement at time $t = 0$, and $\omega$ is a constant that depends on the mass of the object and the stiffness of the spring (see the accompanying figure). The constant $|A|$ is called the ***amplitude*** of the motion and $\omega$ the ***angular frequency***.

(a) Show that

$$\frac{d^2y}{dt^2} = -\omega^2 y$$

(b) The ***period*** $T$ is the time required to make one complete oscillation. Show that $T = 2\pi/\omega$.

(c) The ***frequency*** $f$ of the vibration is the number of oscillations per unit time. Find $f$ in terms of the period $T$.

(d) Find the amplitude, period, and frequency of an object that is executing simple harmonic motion given by $y = 0.6\cos 15t$, where $t$ is in seconds and $y$ is in centimeters.

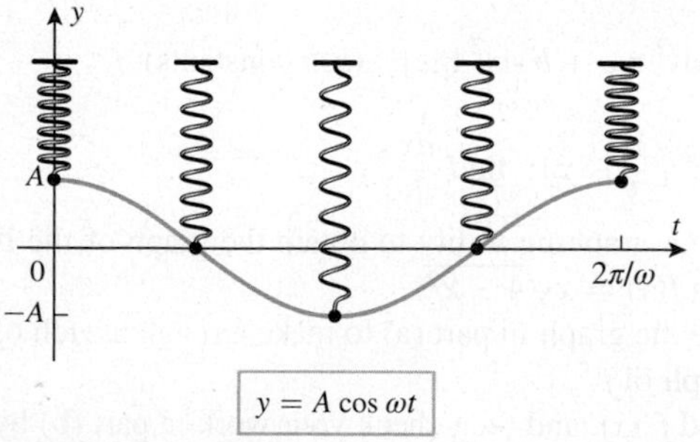


▲ **Figure Ex-65**

**66.** Find the value of the constant $A$ so that $y = A\sin 3t$ satisfies the equation

$$\frac{d^2y}{dt^2} + 2y = 4\sin 3t$$

**FOCUS ON CONCEPTS**

**67.** Use the graph of the function $f$ in the accompanying figure to evaluate

$$\frac{d}{dx}\left[\sqrt{x+f(x)}\right]\Bigg|_{x=-1}$$

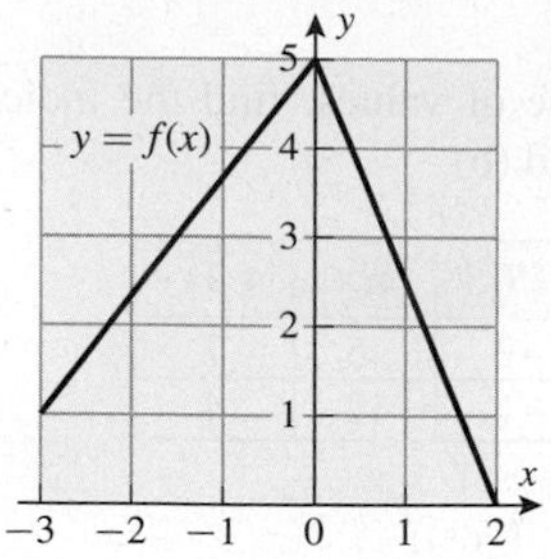


◀ **Figure Ex-67**

**68.** Using the function $f$ in Exercise 67, evaluate

$$\frac{d}{dx}[f(2\sin x)]\Bigg|_{x=\pi/6}$$

**69.** The accompanying figure shows the graph of atmospheric pressure $p$ (lb/in²) versus the altitude $h$ (mi) above sea level.

(a) From the graph and the tangent line at $h = 2$ shown on the graph, estimate the values of $p$ and $dp/dh$ at an altitude of 2 mi.

(b) If the altitude of a space vehicle is increasing at the rate of 0.3 mi/s at the instant when it is 2 mi above sea level, how fast is the pressure changing with time at this instant?

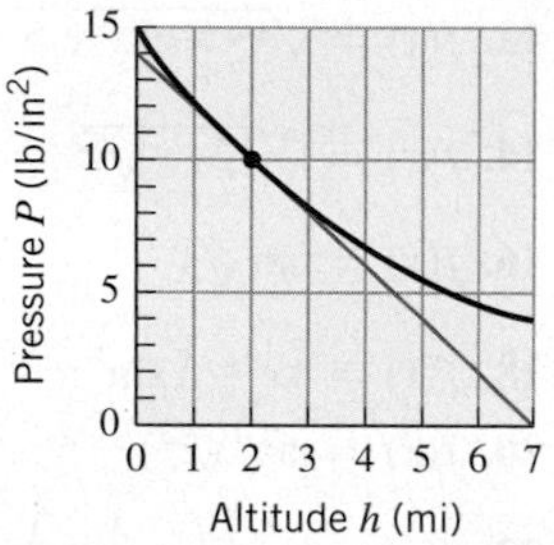


◀ **Figure Ex-69**

**70.** The force $F$ (in pounds) acting at an angle $\theta$ with the horizontal that is needed to drag a crate weighing $W$ pounds along a horizontal surface at a constant velocity is given by

$$F = \frac{\mu W}{\cos\theta + \mu\sin\theta}$$

where $\mu$ is a constant called the ***coefficient of sliding friction*** between the crate and the surface (see the accompanying figure). Suppose that the crate weighs 150 lb and that $\mu = 0.3$.

(a) Find $dF/d\theta$ when $\theta = 30°$. Express the answer in units of pounds/degree.

(b) Find $dF/dt$ when $\theta = 30°$ if $\theta$ is decreasing at the rate of $0.5°$/s at this instant.

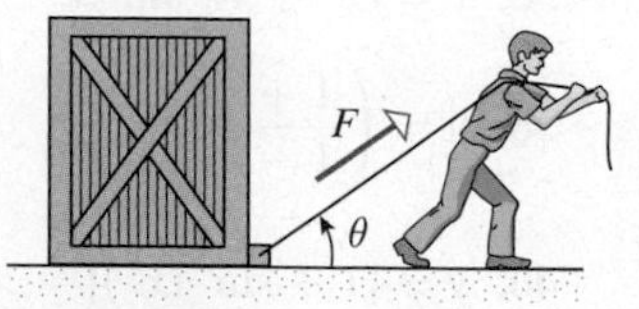


◀ **Figure Ex-70**

**71.** Recall that
$$\frac{d}{dx}(|x|) = \begin{cases} 1, & x > 0 \\ -1, & x < 0 \end{cases}$$
Use this result and the chain rule to find
$$\frac{d}{dx}(|\sin x|)$$
for nonzero $x$ in the interval $(-\pi, \pi)$.

**72.** Use the derivative formula for $\sin x$ and the identity
$$\cos x = \sin\left(\frac{\pi}{2} - x\right)$$
to obtain the derivative formula for $\cos x$.

**73.** Let
$$f(x) = \begin{cases} x \sin \dfrac{1}{x}, & x \neq 0 \\ 0, & x = 0 \end{cases}$$
(a) Show that $f$ is continuous at $x = 0$.
(b) Use Definition 2.2.1 to show that $f'(0)$ does not exist.
(c) Find $f'(x)$ for $x \neq 0$.
(d) Determine whether $\lim_{x\to 0} f'(x)$ exists.

**74.** Let
$$f(x) = \begin{cases} x^2 \sin \dfrac{1}{x}, & x \neq 0 \\ 0, & x = 0 \end{cases}$$
(a) Show that $f$ is continuous at $x = 0$.
(b) Use Definition 2.2.1 to find $f'(0)$.
(c) Find $f'(x)$ for $x \neq 0$.
(d) Show that $f'$ is not continuous at $x = 0$.

**75.** Given the following table of values, find the indicated derivatives in parts (a) and (b).

| $x$ | $f(x)$ | $f'(x)$ |
|---|---|---|
| 2 | 1 | 7 |
| 8 | 5 | −3 |

(a) $g'(2)$, where $g(x) = [f(x)]^3$
(b) $h'(2)$, where $h(x) = f(x^3)$

**76.** Given that $f'(x) = \sqrt{3x+4}$ and $g(x) = x^2 - 1$, find $F'(x)$ if $F(x) = f(g(x))$.

**77.** Given that $f'(x) = \dfrac{x}{x^2+1}$ and $g(x) = \sqrt{3x-1}$, find $F'(x)$ if $F(x) = f(g(x))$.

**78.** Find $f'(x^2)$ if $\dfrac{d}{dx}[f(x^2)] = x^2$.

**79.** Find $\dfrac{d}{dx}[f(x)]$ if $\dfrac{d}{dx}[f(3x)] = 6x$.

**80.** Recall that a function $f$ is ***even*** if $f(-x) = f(x)$ and ***odd*** if $f(-x) = -f(x)$, for all $x$ in the domain of $f$. Assuming that $f$ is differentiable, prove:
(a) $f'$ is odd if $f$ is even
(b) $f'$ is even if $f$ is odd.

**81.** Draw some pictures to illustrate the results in Exercise 80, and write a paragraph that gives an informal explanation of why the results are true.

**82.** Let $y = f_1(u)$, $u = f_2(v)$, $v = f_3(w)$, and $w = f_4(x)$. Express $dy/dx$ in terms of $dy/du$, $dw/dx$, $du/dv$, and $dv/dw$.

**83.** Find a formula for
$$\frac{d}{dx}[f(g(h(x)))]$$

**84. Writing** The "co" in "cosine" comes from "complementary," since the cosine of an angle is the sine of the complementary angle, and vice versa:
$$\cos x = \sin\left(\frac{\pi}{2} - x\right) \quad \text{and} \quad \sin x = \cos\left(\frac{\pi}{2} - x\right)$$
Suppose that we define a function $g$ to be a *cofunction* of a function $f$ if
$$g(x) = f\left(\frac{\pi}{2} - x\right) \quad \text{for all } x$$
Thus, cosine and sine are cofunctions of each other, as are cotangent and tangent, and also cosecant and secant. If $g$ is the cofunction of $f$, state a formula that relates $g'$ and the cofunction of $f'$. Discuss how this relationship is exhibited by the derivatives of the cosine, cotangent, and cosecant functions.

**✓ QUICK CHECK ANSWERS 2.6** 1. outside; inside; inside 2. $\dfrac{dy}{du} \cdot \dfrac{du}{dx}$ 3. (a) $10(x^2+5)^9 \cdot 2x = 20x(x^2+5)^9$ (b) $\dfrac{1}{2\sqrt{1+6x}} \cdot 6 = \dfrac{3}{\sqrt{1+6x}}$ 4. (a) $3\cos(3x+2)$ (b) $4(x^2\tan x)^3(2x\tan x + x^2\sec^2 x)$ 5. (a) $g'(f(2))f'(2) = -20$ (b) $f'\left(\frac{1}{3}g(3)\right) \cdot \frac{1}{3}g'(3) = -\dfrac{20}{3}$

## CHAPTER 2 REVIEW EXERCISES

Graphing Utility  C CAS

**1.** Explain the difference between average and instantaneous rates of change, and discuss how they are calculated.

**2.** In parts (a)–(d), use the function $y = \frac{1}{2}x^2$.
(a) Find the average rate of change of $y$ with respect to $x$ over the interval [3, 4].
(b) Find the instantaneous rate of change of $y$ with respect to $x$ at $x = 3$.

(cont.)

(c) Find the instantaneous rate of change of $y$ with respect to $x$ at a general $x$-value.
(d) Sketch the graph of $y = \frac{1}{2}x^2$ together with the secant line whose slope is given by the result in part (a), and indicate graphically the slope of the tangent line that corresponds to the result in part (b).

**3.** Complete each part for the function $f(x) = x^2 + 1$.
(a) Find the slope of the tangent line to the graph of $f$ at a general $x$-value.
(b) Find the slope of the tangent line to the graph of $f$ at $x = 2$.

**4.** A car is traveling on a straight road that is 120 mi long. For the first 100 mi the car travels at an average velocity of 50 mi/h. Show that no matter how fast the car travels for the final 20 mi it cannot bring the average velocity up to 60 mi/h for the entire trip.

**5.** At time $t = 0$ a car moves into the passing lane to pass a slow-moving truck. The average velocity of the car from $t = 1$ to $t = 1 + h$ is

$$v_{\text{ave}} = \frac{3(h+1)^{2.5} + 580h - 3}{10h}$$

Estimate the instantaneous velocity of the car at $t = 1$, where time is in seconds and distance is in feet.

**6.** A skydiver jumps from an airplane. Suppose that the distance she falls during the first $t$ seconds before her parachute opens is $s(t) = 976((0.835)^t - 1) + 176t$, where $s$ is in feet. Graph $s$ versus $t$ for $0 \le t \le 20$, and use your graph to estimate the instantaneous velocity at $t = 15$.

**7.** A particle moves on a line away from its initial position so that after $t$ hours it is $s = 3t^2 + t$ miles from its initial position.
(a) Find the average velocity of the particle over the interval [1, 3].
(b) Find the instantaneous velocity at $t = 1$.

**8.** State the definition of a derivative, and give two interpretations of it.

**9.** Use the definition of a derivative to find $dy/dx$, and check your answer by calculating the derivative using appropriate derivative formulas.
(a) $y = \sqrt{9 - 4x}$ (b) $y = \dfrac{x}{x+1}$

**10.** Suppose that $f(x) = \begin{cases} x^2 - 1, & x \le 1 \\ k(x-1), & x > 1. \end{cases}$
For what values of $k$ is $f$
(a) continuous? (b) differentiable?

**11.** The accompanying figure shows the graph of $y = f'(x)$ for an unspecified function $f$.
(a) For what values of $x$ does the curve $y = f(x)$ have a horizontal tangent line?
(b) Over what intervals does the curve $y = f(x)$ have tangent lines with positive slope?
(c) Over what intervals does the curve $y = f(x)$ have tangent lines with negative slope?
(d) Given that $g(x) = f(x)\sin x$, find $g''(0)$.

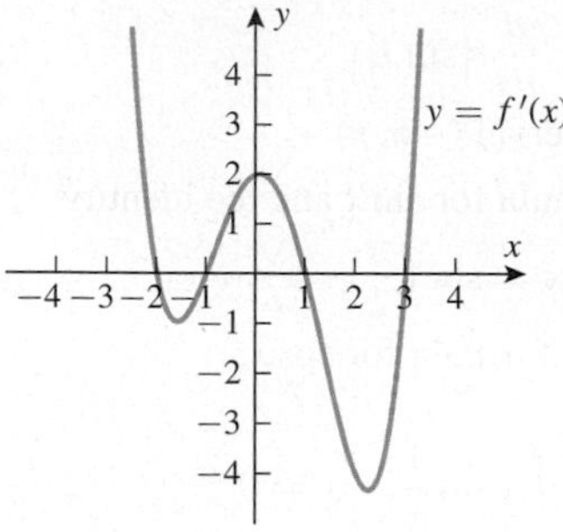


◀ **Figure Ex-11**

**12.** Sketch the graph of a function $f$ for which $f(0) = 1$, $f'(0) = 0$, $f'(x) > 0$ if $x < 0$, and $f'(x) < 0$ if $x > 0$.

**13.** According to the U.S. Bureau of the Census, the estimated and projected midyear world population, $N$, in billions for the years 1950, 1975, 2000, 2025, and 2050 was 2.555, 4.088, 6.080, 7.841, and 9.104, respectively. Although the increase in population is not a continuous function of the time $t$, we can apply the ideas in this section if we are willing to approximate the graph of $N$ versus $t$ by a continuous curve, as shown in the accompanying figure.
(a) Use the tangent line at $t = 2000$ shown in the figure to approximate the value of $dN/dt$ there. Interpret your result as a rate of change.
(b) The instantaneous ***growth rate*** is defined as

$$\frac{dN/dt}{N}$$

Use your answer to part (a) to approximate the instantaneous growth rate at the start of the year 2000. Express the result as a percentage and include the proper units.

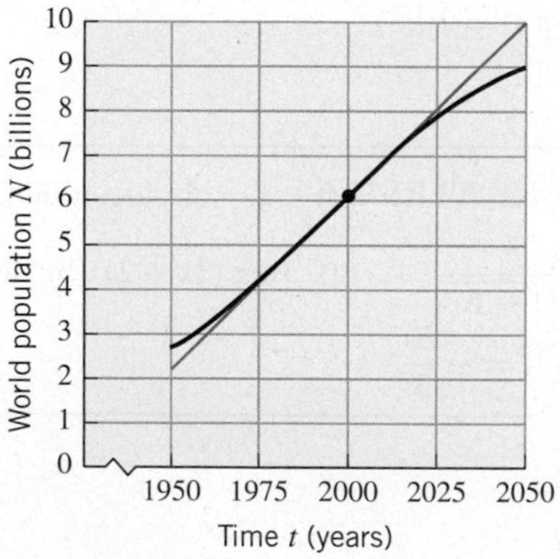


◀ **Figure Ex-13**

**14.** Use a graphing utility to graph the function

$$f(x) = |x^4 - x - 1| - x$$

and estimate the values of $x$ where the derivative of this function does not exist.

C **15–18** (a) Use a CAS to find $f'(x)$ via Definition 2.2.1; (b) check the result by finding the derivative by hand; (c) use the CAS to find $f''(x)$. ■

**15.** $f(x) = x^2 \sin x$  **16.** $f(x) = \sqrt{x} + \cos^2 x$

**17.** $f(x) = \dfrac{2x^2 - x + 5}{3x + 2}$  **18.** $f(x) = \dfrac{\tan x}{1 + x^2}$

**19.** The amount of water in a tank $t$ minutes after it has started to drain is given by $W = 100(t - 15)^2$ gal.
(a) At what rate is the water running out at the end of 5 min?
(b) What is the average rate at which the water flows out during the first 5 min?

**20.** Use the formula $V = l^3$ for the volume of a cube of side $l$ to find
(a) the average rate at which the volume of a cube changes with $l$ as $l$ increases from $l = 2$ to $l = 4$
(b) the instantaneous rate at which the volume of a cube changes with $l$ when $l = 5$.

**21–22** Zoom in on the graph of $f$ on an interval containing $x = x_0$ until the graph looks like a straight line. Estimate the slope of this line and then check your answer by finding the exact value of $f'(x_0)$. ■

**21.** (a) $f(x) = x^2 - 1,\ x_0 = 1.8$
(b) $f(x) = \dfrac{x^2}{x - 2},\ x_0 = 3.5$

**22.** (a) $f(x) = x^3 - x^2 + 1,\ x_0 = 2.3$
(b) $f(x) = \dfrac{x}{x^2 + 1},\ x_0 = -0.5$

**23.** Suppose that a function $f$ is differentiable at $x = 1$ and

$$\lim_{h \to 0} \frac{f(1 + h)}{h} = 5$$

Find $f(1)$ and $f'(1)$.

**24.** Suppose that a function $f$ is differentiable at $x = 2$ and

$$\lim_{x \to 2} \frac{x^3 f(x) - 24}{x - 2} = 28$$

Find $f(2)$ and $f'(2)$.

**25.** Find the equations of all lines through the origin that are tangent to the curve $y = x^3 - 9x^2 - 16x$.

**26.** Find all values of $x$ for which the tangent line to the curve $y = 2x^3 - x^2$ is perpendicular to the line $x + 4y = 10$.

**27.** Let $f(x) = x^2$. Show that for any distinct values of $a$ and $b$, the slope of the tangent line to $y = f(x)$ at $x = \frac{1}{2}(a + b)$ is equal to the slope of the secant line through the points $(a, a^2)$ and $(b, b^2)$. Draw a picture to illustrate this result.

**28.** In each part, evaluate the expression given that $f(1) = 1$, $g(1) = -2$, $f'(1) = 3$, and $g'(1) = -1$.
(a) $\left.\dfrac{d}{dx}[f(x)g(x)]\right|_{x=1}$  (b) $\left.\dfrac{d}{dx}\left[\dfrac{f(x)}{g(x)}\right]\right|_{x=1}$
(c) $\left.\dfrac{d}{dx}\left[\sqrt{f(x)}\right]\right|_{x=1}$  (d) $\dfrac{d}{dx}[f(1)g'(1)]$

**29–32** Find $f'(x)$. ■

**29.** (a) $f(x) = x^8 - 3\sqrt{x} + 5x^{-3}$
(b) $f(x) = (2x + 1)^{101}(5x^2 - 7)$

**30.** (a) $f(x) = \sin x + 2\cos^3 x$
(b) $f(x) = (1 + \sec x)(x^2 - \tan x)$

**31.** (a) $f(x) = \sqrt{3x + 1}(x - 1)^2$
(b) $f(x) = \left(\dfrac{3x + 1}{x^2}\right)^3$

**32.** (a) $f(x) = \cot\left(\dfrac{\csc 2x}{x^3 + 5}\right)$  (b) $f(x) = \dfrac{1}{2x + \sin^3 x}$

**33–34** Find the values of $x$ at which the curve $y = f(x)$ has a horizontal tangent line. ■

**33.** $f(x) = (2x + 7)^6(x - 2)^5$  **34.** $f(x) = \dfrac{(x - 3)^4}{x^2 + 2x}$

**35.** Find all lines that are simultaneously tangent to the graph of $y = x^2 + 1$ and to the graph of $y = -x^2 - 1$.

**36.** (a) Let $n$ denote an even positive integer. Generalize the result of Exercise 35 by finding all lines that are simultaneously tangent to the graph of $y = x^n + n - 1$ and to the graph of $y = -x^n - n + 1$.
(b) Let $n$ denote an odd positive integer. Are there any lines that are simultaneously tangent to the graph of $y = x^n + n - 1$ and to the graph of $y = -x^n - n + 1$? Explain.

**37.** Find all values of $x$ for which the line that is tangent to $y = 3x - \tan x$ is parallel to the line $y - x = 2$.

**38.** Approximate the values of $x$ at which the tangent line to the graph of $y = x^3 - \sin x$ is horizontal.

**39.** Suppose that $f(x) = M \sin x + N \cos x$ for some constants $M$ and $N$. If $f(\pi/4) = 3$ and $f'(\pi/4) = 1$, find an equation for the tangent line to $y = f(x)$ at $x = 3\pi/4$.

**40.** Suppose that $f(x) = M \tan x + N \sec x$ for some constants $M$ and $N$. If $f(\pi/4) = 2$ and $f'(\pi/4) = 0$, find an equation for the tangent line to $y = f(x)$ at $x = 0$.

**41.** Suppose that $f'(x) = 2x \cdot f(x)$ and $f(2) = 5$.
(a) Find $g'(\pi/3)$ if $g(x) = f(\sec x)$.
(b) Find $h'(2)$ if $h(x) = [f(x)/(x - 1)]^4$.

## CHAPTER 2 MAKING CONNECTIONS

**1.** Suppose that $f$ is a function with the properties (i) $f$ is differentiable everywhere, (ii) $f(x+y)=f(x)f(y)$ for all values of $x$ and $y$, (iii) $f(0)\neq 0$, and (iv) $f'(0)=1$.
(a) Show that $f(0)=1$. [*Hint:* Consider $f(0+0)$.]
(b) Show that $f(x)>0$ for all values of $x$. [*Hint:* First show that $f(x)\neq 0$ for any $x$ by considering $f(x-x)$.]
(c) Use the definition of derivative (Definition 2.2.1) to show that $f'(x)=f(x)$ for all values of $x$.

**2.** Suppose that $f$ and $g$ are functions each of which has the properties (i)–(iv) in Exercise 1.
(a) Show that $y=f(2x)$ satisfies the equation $y'=2y$ in two ways: using property (ii), and by directly applying the chain rule (Theorem 2.6.1).
(b) If $k$ is any constant, show that $y=f(kx)$ satisfies the equation $y'=ky$.
(c) Find a value of $k$ such that $y=f(x)g(x)$ satisfies the equation $y'=ky$.
(d) If $h=f/g$, find $h'(x)$. Make a conjecture about the relationship between $f$ and $g$.

**3.** (a) Apply the product rule (Theorem 2.4.1) twice to show that if $f$, $g$, and $h$ are differentiable functions, then $f\cdot g\cdot h$ is differentiable and

$$(f\cdot g\cdot h)'=f'\cdot g\cdot h+f\cdot g'\cdot h+f\cdot g\cdot h'$$

(b) Suppose that $f, g, h$, and $k$ are differentiable functions. Derive a formula for $(f\cdot g\cdot h\cdot k)'$.
(c) Based on the result in part (a), make a conjecture about a formula differentiating a product of $n$ functions. Prove your formula using induction.

**4.** (a) Apply the quotient rule (Theorem 2.4.2) twice to show that if $f$, $g$, and $h$ are differentiable functions, then $(f/g)/h$ is differentiable where it is defined and

$$[(f/g)/h]'=\frac{f'\cdot g\cdot h-f\cdot g'\cdot h-f\cdot g\cdot h'}{g^2h^2}$$

(b) Derive the derivative formula of part (a) by first simplifying $(f/g)/h$ and then applying the quotient and product rules.
(c) Apply the quotient rule (Theorem 2.4.2) twice to derive a formula for $[f/(g/h)]'$.
(d) Derive the derivative formula of part (c) by first simplifying $f/(g/h)$ and then applying the quotient and product rules.

**5.** Assume that $h(x)=f(x)/g(x)$ is differentiable. Derive the quotient rule formula for $h'(x)$ (Theorem 2.4.2) in two ways:
(a) Write $h(x)=f(x)\cdot[g(x)]^{-1}$ and use the product and chain rules (Theorems 2.4.1 and 2.6.1) to differentiate $h$.
(b) Write $f(x)=h(x)\cdot g(x)$ and use the product rule to derive a formula for $h'(x)$.

## EXPANDING THE CALCULUS HORIZON

To learn how derivatives can be used in the field of robotics, see the module entitled **Robotics** at:

www.wiley.com/college/anton

# 3

# TOPICS IN DIFFERENTIATION

William Davies/iStockphoto

*The growth and decline of animal populations and natural resources can be modeled using basic functions studied in calculus.*

We begin this chapter by extending the process of differentiation to functions that are either difficult or impossible to differentiate directly. Next we will develop a number of new derivative formulas that include the derivatives of logarithmic, exponential, and inverse trigonometric functions. Later in the chapter, we will consider some applications of the derivative. These will include some new methods for finding rates of change as well as the use of linear functions to approximate nonlinear functions. Finally, we will discuss L'Hôpital's rule, a powerful tool for evaluating limits.

## 3.1 IMPLICIT DIFFERENTIATION

*In this section we will describe a method for differentiating functions that are not expressed in the form $y = f(x)$.*

### FUNCTIONS DEFINED EXPLICITLY AND IMPLICITLY

An equation of the form $y = f(x)$ is said to define $y$ ***explicitly*** as a function of $x$. However, sometimes functions are defined by equations not of this form. For example, the equation

$$yx + y + 1 = x \tag{1}$$

defines $y$ as a function of $x$ since it can be rewritten as

$$y = \frac{x-1}{x+1}$$

We say that (1) defines $y$ ***implicitly*** as a function of $x$, the function being

$$f(x) = \frac{x-1}{x+1}$$

An equation in $x$ and $y$ can implicitly define more than one function of $x$. For example, if we solve the equation of the circle

$$x^2 + y^2 = 1 \tag{2}$$

for $y$ in terms of $x$, we obtain $y = \pm\sqrt{1-x^2}$, so we have found two functions that are defined implicitly by (2), namely,

$$f_1(x) = \sqrt{1-x^2} \quad \text{and} \quad f_2(x) = -\sqrt{1-x^2} \tag{3}$$

The graphs of these functions are the upper and lower semicircles of the circle $x^2 + y^2 = 1$ (Figure 3.1.1). This leads us to the following definition.

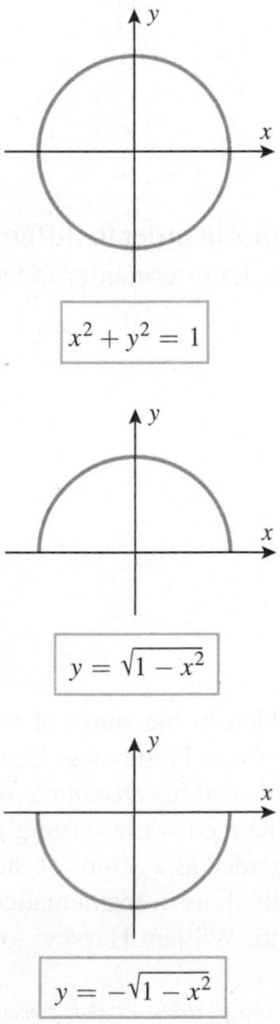


▲ **Figure 3.1.1**

> **3.1.1 DEFINITION** We will say that a given equation in $x$ and $y$ defines the function $f$ ***implicitly*** if the graph of $y = f(x)$ coincides with a portion of the graph of the equation.

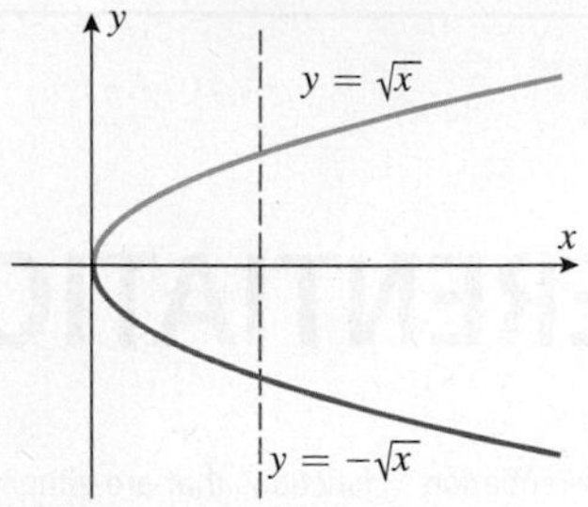


▲ **Figure 3.1.2** The graph of $x = y^2$ does not pass the vertical line test, but the graphs of $y = \sqrt{x}$ and $y = -\sqrt{x}$ do.

► **Example 1** The graph of $x = y^2$ is not the graph of a function of $x$, since it does not pass the vertical line test (Figure 3.1.2). However, if we solve this equation for $y$ in terms of $x$, we obtain the equations $y = \sqrt{x}$ and $y = -\sqrt{x}$, whose graphs pass the vertical line test and are portions of the graph of $x = y^2$ (Figure 3.1.2). Thus, the equation $x = y^2$ implicitly defines the functions

$$f_1(x) = \sqrt{x} \quad \text{and} \quad f_2(x) = -\sqrt{x}$$ ◄

Although it was easy in Example 1 to solve the equation $x = y^2$ for $y$ in terms of $x$, it is difficult or impossible to do this for some equations. For example, the equation

$$x^3 + y^3 = 3xy \tag{4}$$

can be solved for $y$ in terms of $x$, but the resulting formulas are too complicated to be practical. Other equations, such as $\sin(xy) = y$, cannot be solved for $y$ in terms of $x$. Thus, even though an equation may define one or more functions of $x$, it may not be possible or practical to find explicit formulas for those functions.

Fortunately, CAS programs, such as *Mathematica* and *Maple*, have "implicit plotting" capabilities that can graph equations such as (4). The graph of this equation, which is called the ***Folium of Descartes***, is shown in Figure 3.1.3*a*. Parts (*b*) and (*c*) of the figure show the graphs (in blue) of two functions that are defined implicitly by (4).

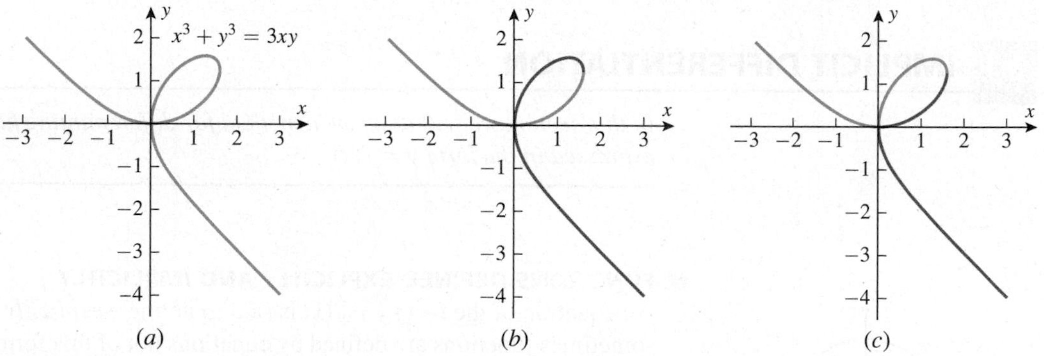


▲ **Figure 3.1.3**

## IMPLICIT DIFFERENTIATION

In general, it is not necessary to solve an equation for $y$ in terms of $x$ in order to differentiate the functions defined implicitly by the equation. To illustrate this, let us consider the simple equation

$$xy = 1 \tag{5}$$

One way to find $dy/dx$ is to rewrite this equation as

$$y = \frac{1}{x} \tag{6}$$

from which it follows that

$$\frac{dy}{dx} = -\frac{1}{x^2} \tag{7}$$

**René Descartes (1596–1650)** Descartes, a French aristocrat, was the son of a government official. He graduated from the University of Poitiers with a law degree at age 20. After a brief probe into the pleasures of Paris he became a military engineer, first for the Dutch Prince of Nassau and then for the German Duke of Bavaria. It was during his service as a soldier that Descartes began to pursue mathematics seriously and develop his analytic geometry. After the wars, he returned to Paris where he stalked the city as an eccentric, wearing a sword in his belt and a plumed hat. He lived in leisure, seldom arose before 11 A.M., and dabbled in the study of human physiology, philosophy, glaciers, meteors, and rainbows. He eventually moved to Holland, where he published his *Discourse on the Method*, and finally to Sweden where he died while serving as tutor to Queen Christina. Descartes is regarded as a genius of the first magnitude. In addition to major contributions in mathematics and philosophy he is considered, along with William Harvey, to be a founder of modern physiology.

*[Image: Georgios Kollidas/Shutterstock]*

Another way to obtain this derivative is to differentiate both sides of (5) *before* solving for $y$ in terms of $x$, treating $y$ as a (temporarily unspecified) differentiable function of $x$. With this approach we obtain

$$\frac{d}{dx}[xy] = \frac{d}{dx}[1]$$

$$x\frac{d}{dx}[y] + y\frac{d}{dx}[x] = 0$$

The product rule was used here because $y$ is a function of $x$.

$$x\frac{dy}{dx} + y = 0$$

$$\frac{dy}{dx} = -\frac{y}{x}$$

If we now substitute (6) into the last expression, we obtain

$$\frac{dy}{dx} = -\frac{1}{x^2}$$

which agrees with Equation (7). This method of obtaining derivatives is called ***implicit differentiation***.

▶ **Example 2** Use implicit differentiation to find $dy/dx$ if $5y^2 + \sin y = x^2$.

$$\frac{d}{dx}[5y^2 + \sin y] = \frac{d}{dx}[x^2]$$

$$5\frac{d}{dx}[y^2] + \frac{d}{dx}[\sin y] = 2x$$

$$5\left(2y\frac{dy}{dx}\right) + (\cos y)\frac{dy}{dx} = 2x$$

The chain rule was used here because $y$ is a function of $x$.

$$10y\frac{dy}{dx} + (\cos y)\frac{dy}{dx} = 2x$$

Solving for $dy/dx$ we obtain

$$\frac{dy}{dx} = \frac{2x}{10y + \cos y} \tag{8}$$

Note that this formula involves both $x$ and $y$. ◀

▶ **Example 3** Use implicit differentiation to find $d^2y/dx^2$ if $4x^2 - 2y^2 = 9$.

***Solution.*** Differentiating both sides of $4x^2 - 2y^2 = 9$ with respect to $x$ yields

$$8x - 4y\frac{dy}{dx} = 0$$

from which we obtain

$$\frac{dy}{dx} = \frac{2x}{y} \tag{9}$$

Differentiating both sides of (9) yields

$$\frac{d^2y}{dx^2} = \frac{(y)(2) - (2x)(dy/dx)}{y^2} \tag{10}$$

Substituting (9) into (10) and simplifying using the original equation, we obtain

$$\frac{d^2y}{dx^2} = \frac{2y - 2x(2x/y)}{y^2} = \frac{2y^2 - 4x^2}{y^3} = -\frac{9}{y^3}$$ ◀

In Examples 2 and 3, the resulting formulas for $dy/dx$ involved both $x$ and $y$. This is not an impediment to finding slopes and equations of tangent lines provided the $x$- and $y$-coordinates of the point of tangency are known.

**▶ Example 4** Find the slopes of the tangent lines to the curve $y^2 - x + 1 = 0$ at the points $(2, -1)$ and $(2, 1)$.

***Solution.*** Differentiating implicitly yields

$$\frac{d}{dx}[y^2 - x + 1] = \frac{d}{dx}[0]$$

$$\frac{d}{dx}[y^2] - \frac{d}{dx}[x] + \frac{d}{dx}[1] = \frac{d}{dx}[0]$$

$$2y\frac{dy}{dx} - 1 = 0$$

$$\frac{dy}{dx} = \frac{1}{2y}$$

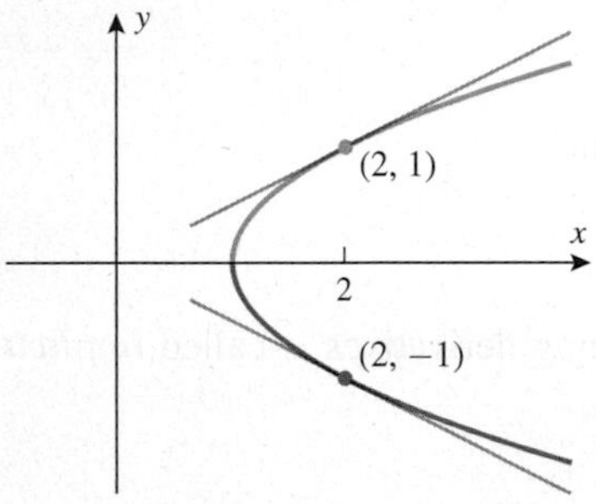

▲ **Figure 3.1.4**

At $(2, -1)$ we have $y = -1$, and at $(2, 1)$ we have $y = 1$, so the slopes of the tangent lines to the curve at those points are (Figure 3.1.4)

$$\left.\frac{dy}{dx}\right|_{\substack{x=2\\y=-1}} = -\frac{1}{2} \quad \text{and} \quad \left.\frac{dy}{dx}\right|_{\substack{x=2\\y=1}} = \frac{1}{2} \blacktriangleleft$$

**▶ Example 5**

(a) Use implicit differentiation to find $dy/dx$ for the Folium of Descartes $x^3 + y^3 = 3xy$.

(b) Find an equation for the tangent line to the Folium of Descartes at the point $\left(\frac{3}{2}, \frac{3}{2}\right)$.

(c) At what point(s) in the first quadrant is the tangent line to the Folium of Descartes horizontal?

Formula (11) cannot be evaluated at $(0, 0)$ and hence provides no information about the nature of the Folium of Descartes at the origin. Based on the graphs in Figure 3.1.3, what can you say about the differentiability of the implicitly defined functions graphed in blue in parts (*b*) and (*c*) of the figure?

***Solution (a).*** Differentiating implicitly yields

$$\frac{d}{dx}[x^3 + y^3] = \frac{d}{dx}[3xy]$$

$$3x^2 + 3y^2\frac{dy}{dx} = 3x\frac{dy}{dx} + 3y$$

$$x^2 + y^2\frac{dy}{dx} = x\frac{dy}{dx} + y$$

$$(y^2 - x)\frac{dy}{dx} = y - x^2$$

$$\frac{dy}{dx} = \frac{y - x^2}{y^2 - x} \tag{11}$$

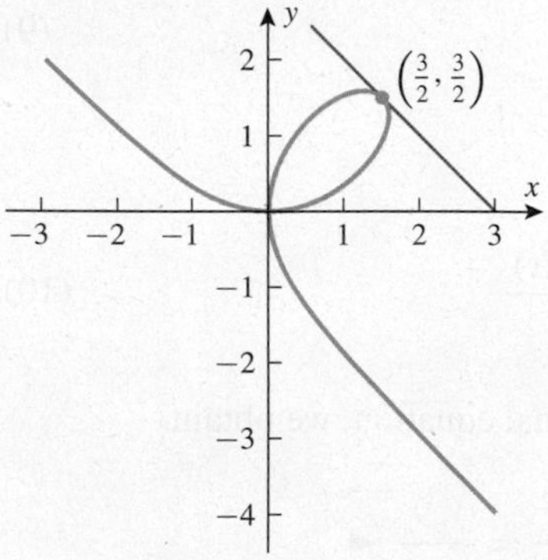

▲ **Figure 3.1.5**

***Solution (b).*** At the point $\left(\frac{3}{2}, \frac{3}{2}\right)$, we have $x = \frac{3}{2}$ and $y = \frac{3}{2}$, so from (11) the slope $m_{\tan}$ of the tangent line at this point is

$$m_{\tan} = \left.\frac{dy}{dx}\right|_{\substack{x=3/2\\y=3/2}} = \frac{(3/2) - (3/2)^2}{(3/2)^2 - (3/2)} = -1$$

Thus, the equation of the tangent line at the point $\left(\frac{3}{2}, \frac{3}{2}\right)$ is

$$y - \tfrac{3}{2} = -1\left(x - \tfrac{3}{2}\right) \quad \text{or} \quad x + y = 3$$

which is consistent with Figure 3.1.5.

***Solution (c).*** The tangent line is horizontal at the points where $dy/dx = 0$, and from (11) this occurs only where $y - x^2 = 0$ or

$$y = x^2 \tag{12}$$

Substituting this expression for $y$ in the equation $x^3 + y^3 = 3xy$ for the curve yields

$$x^3 + (x^2)^3 = 3x^3$$
$$x^6 - 2x^3 = 0$$
$$x^3(x^3 - 2) = 0$$

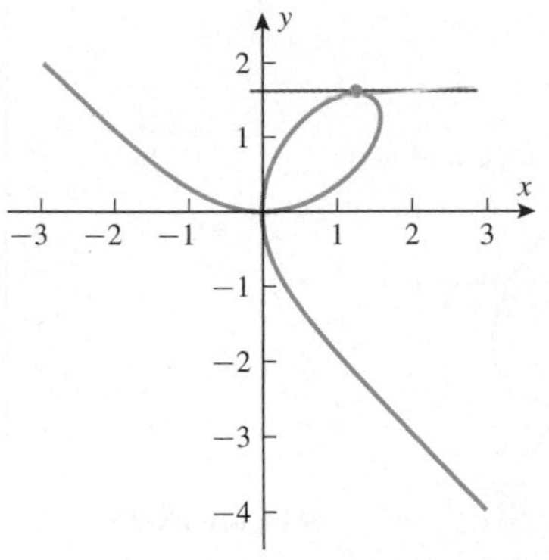

▲ **Figure 3.1.6**

whose solutions are $x = 0$ and $x = 2^{1/3}$. From (12), the solutions $x = 0$ and $x = 2^{1/3}$ yield the points $(0, 0)$ and $(2^{1/3}, 2^{2/3})$, respectively. Of these two, only $(2^{1/3}, 2^{2/3})$ is in the first quadrant. Substituting $x = 2^{1/3}, y = 2^{2/3}$ into (11) yields

$$\left.\frac{dy}{dx}\right|_{\substack{x=2^{1/3}\\ y=2^{2/3}}} = \frac{0}{2^{4/3} - 2^{2/3}} = 0$$

We conclude that $(2^{1/3}, 2^{2/3}) \approx (1.26, 1.59)$ is the only point on the Folium of Descartes in the first quadrant at which the tangent line is horizontal (Figure 3.1.6). ◀

## NECESSARY CONDITIONS FOR IMPLICIT DIFFERENTIATION

When using implicit differentiation to find $dy/dx$, we usually make two assumptions:

- The variable $y$ represents a function of $x$ that is defined implicitly by the given equation.
- The function defined implicitly is *differentiable*.

However, if either assumption is incorrect, then the resulting calculations may be nonsense. For example, it would be meaningless to apply implicit differentiation to the equation

$$x^2 + y^2 + 1 = 0 \tag{13}$$

because there are no real values of $x$ and $y$ that satisfy (13) (why?). Hence (13) does not define any real functions implicitly.

Questions about the differentiability of an implicitly defined function can sometimes be correctly answered with the help of a graph. For example, the function graphed in Figure 3.1.3*b* appears to be differentiable everywhere and the function graphed in Figure 3.1.3*c* seems to be differentiable everywhere except at $x = 0$. In general, it can be difficult to determine analytically whether functions defined implicitly are differentiable, so we will leave such matters for more advanced courses.

## ✓QUICK CHECK EXERCISES 3.1 (See page 135 for answers.)

1. The equation $xy + 2y = 1$ defines implicitly the function $y =$ ______.
2. Use implicit differentiation to find $dy/dx$ for $x^2 - y^3 = xy$.
3. The slope of the tangent line to the graph of $x + y + xy = 3$ at $(1, 1)$ is ______.
4. Use implicit differentiation to find $d^2y/dx^2$ for $\sin y = x$.

## EXERCISE SET 3.1 [C] CAS

**1–2**
(a) Find $dy/dx$ by differentiating implicitly.
(b) Solve the equation for $y$ as a function of $x$, and find $dy/dx$ from that equation.
(c) Confirm that the two results are consistent by expressing the derivative in part (a) as a function of $x$ alone. ■

**1.** $x + xy - 2x^3 = 2$ **2.** $\sqrt{y} - \sin x = 2$

**3–12** Find $dy/dx$ by implicit differentiation. ■

**3.** $x^2 + y^2 = 100$ **4.** $x^3 + y^3 = 3xy^2$

**5.** $x^2y + 3xy^3 - x = 3$ **6.** $x^3y^2 - 5x^2y + x = 1$

**7.** $\dfrac{1}{\sqrt{x}} + \dfrac{1}{\sqrt{y}} = 1$ **8.** $x^2 = \dfrac{x+y}{x-y}$

**9.** $\sin(x^2y^2) = x$ **10.** $\cos(xy^2) = y$

**11.** $\tan^3(xy^2 + y) = x$ **12.** $\dfrac{xy^3}{1 + \sec y} = 1 + y^4$

**13–18** Find $d^2y/dx^2$ by implicit differentiation. ■

**13.** $2x^2 - 3y^2 = 4$ **14.** $x^3 + y^3 = 1$

**15.** $x^3y^3 - 4 = 0$ **16.** $xy + y^2 = 2$

**17.** $y + \sin y = x$ **18.** $x\cos y = y$

**19–20** Find the slope of the tangent line to the curve at the given points in two ways: first by solving for $y$ in terms of $x$ and differentiating and then by implicit differentiation. ■

**19.** $x^2 + y^2 = 1$; $(1/2, \sqrt{3}/2), (1/2, -\sqrt{3}/2)$

**20.** $y^2 - x + 1 = 0$; $(10, 3), (10, -3)$

**21–24 True–False** Determine whether the statement is true or false. Explain your answer. ■

**21.** If an equation in $x$ and $y$ defines a function $y = f(x)$ implicitly, then the graph of the equation and the graph of $f$ are identical.

**22.** The function

$$f(x) = \begin{cases} \sqrt{1-x^2}, & 0 < x \le 1 \\ -\sqrt{1-x^2}, & -1 \le x \le 0 \end{cases}$$

is defined implicitly by the equation $x^2 + y^2 = 1$.

**23.** The function $|x|$ is not defined implicitly by the equation $(x+y)(x-y) = 0$.

**24.** If $y$ is defined implicitly as a function of $x$ by the equation $x^2 + y^2 = 1$, then $dy/dx = -x/y$.

**25–28** Use implicit differentiation to find the slope of the tangent line to the curve at the specified point, and check that your answer is consistent with the accompanying graph. ■

**25.** $x^4 + y^4 = 16$; $(1, \sqrt[4]{15})$ [*Lamé's special quartic*]

**26.** $y^3 + yx^2 + x^2 - 3y^2 = 0$; $(0, 3)$ [*trisectrix*]

**27.** $2(x^2 + y^2)^2 = 25(x^2 - y^2)$; $(3, 1)$ [*lemniscate*]

**28.** $x^{2/3} + y^{2/3} = 4$; $(-1, 3\sqrt{3})$ [*four-cusped hypocycloid*]

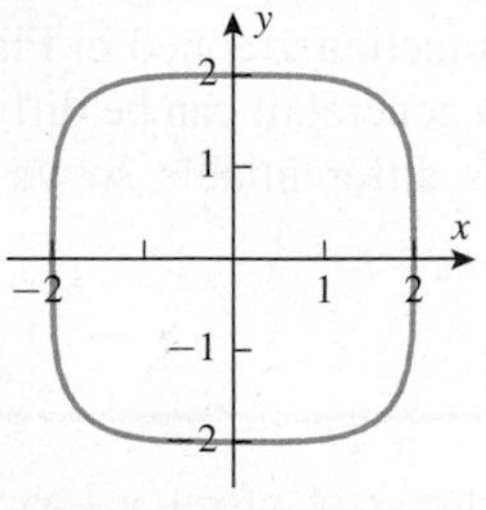

▲ Figure Ex-25

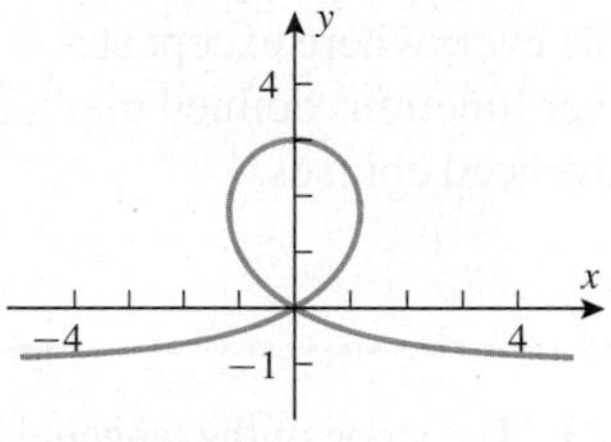

▲ Figure Ex-26

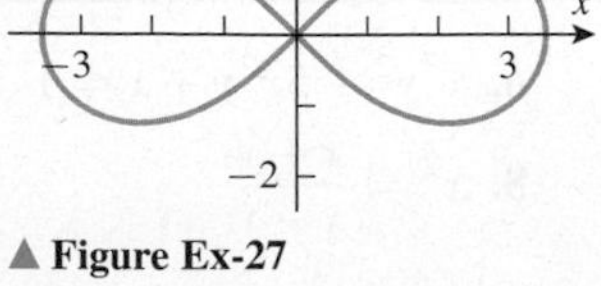

▲ Figure Ex-27

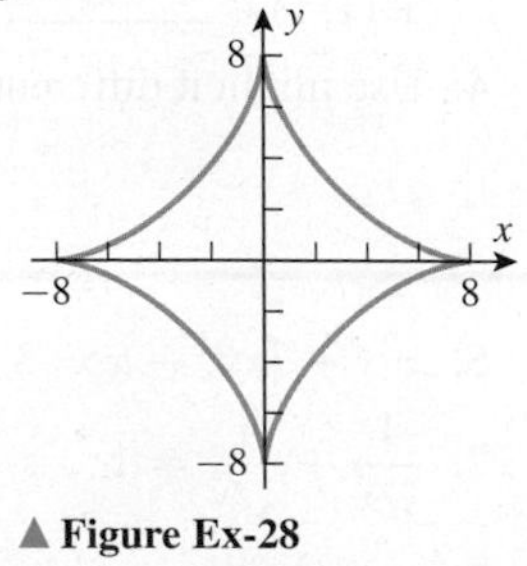

▲ Figure Ex-28

**29–32** Use implicit differentiation to find the specified derivative. ■

**29.** $a^4 - t^4 = 6a^2t$; $da/dt$ **30.** $\sqrt{u} + \sqrt{v} = 5$; $du/dv$

**31.** $a^2\omega^2 + b^2\lambda^2 = 1$ ($a, b$ constants); $d\omega/d\lambda$

**32.** $y = \sin x$; $dx/dy$

**FOCUS ON CONCEPTS**

**33.** As shown in the accompanying figure, it appears that the ellipse $x^2 + xy + y^2 = 3$ has horizontal tangent lines at the points of intersection of the ellipse and the line $y = -2x$. Use implicit differentiation to explain why this is the case.

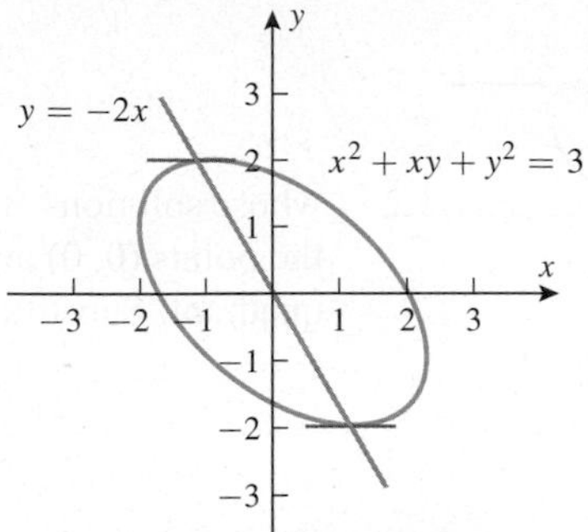

◀ Figure Ex-33

**34.** (a) A student claims that the ellipse $x^2 - xy + y^2 = 1$ has a horizontal tangent line at the point $(1, 1)$. Without doing any computations, explain why the student's claim must be incorrect.

(b) Find all points on the ellipse $x^2 - xy + y^2 = 1$ at which the tangent line is horizontal.

C **35.** (a) Use the implicit plotting capability of a CAS to graph the equation $y^4 + y^2 = x(x-1)$.

(b) Use implicit differentiation to help explain why the graph in part (a) has no horizontal tangent lines.

(c) Solve the equation $y^4 + y^2 = x(x-1)$ for $x$ in terms of $y$ and explain why the graph in part (a) consists of two parabolas.

**36.** Use implicit differentiation to find all points on the graph of $y^4 + y^2 = x(x-1)$ at which the tangent line is vertical.

**37.** Find the values of $a$ and $b$ for the curve $x^2y + ay^2 = b$ if the point $(1, 1)$ is on its graph and the tangent line at $(1, 1)$ has the equation $4x + 3y = 7$.

**38.** At what point(s) is the tangent line to the curve $y^3 = 2x^2$ perpendicular to the line $x + 2y - 2 = 0$?

**39–40** Two curves are said to be ***orthogonal*** if their tangent lines are perpendicular at each point of intersection, and two families of curves are said to be ***orthogonal trajectories*** of one another if each member of one family is orthogonal to each member of the other family. This terminology is used in these exercises. ■

**39.** The accompanying figure on the next page shows some typical members of the families of circles $x^2 + (y-c)^2 = c^2$ (black curves) and $(x-k)^2 + y^2 = k^2$ (gray curves). Show that these families are orthogonal trajectories of one another. [*Hint:* For the tangent lines to be perpendicular at a point of intersection, the slopes of those tangent lines must be negative reciprocals of one another.]

**40.** The accompanying figure on the next page shows some typical members of the families of hyperbolas $xy = c$ (black curves) and $x^2 - y^2 = k$ (gray curves), where $c \ne 0$ and $k \ne 0$. Use the hint in Exercise 39 to show that these families are orthogonal trajectories of one another.

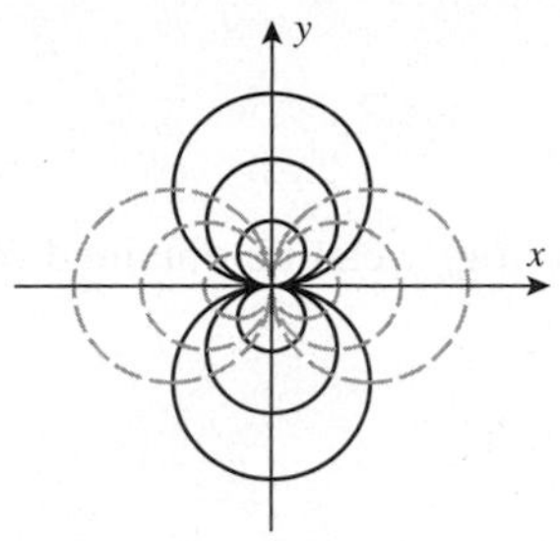

▲ Figure Ex-39

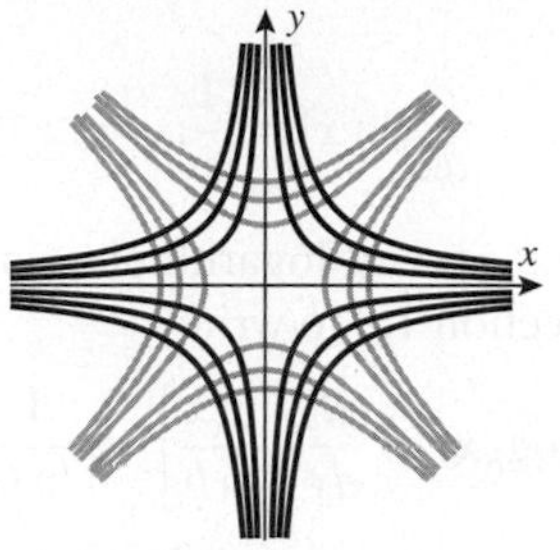

▲ Figure Ex-40

C **41.** (a) Use the implicit plotting capability of a CAS to graph the curve $C$ whose equation is $x^3 - 2xy + y^3 = 0$.
(b) Use the graph in part (a) to estimate the $x$-coordinates of a point in the first quadrant that is on $C$ and at which the tangent line to $C$ is parallel to the $x$-axis.
(c) Find the exact value of the $x$-coordinate in part (b).

C **42.** (a) Use the implicit plotting capability of a CAS to graph the curve $C$ whose equation is $x^3 - 2xy + y^3 = 0$.
(b) Use the graph to guess the coordinates of a point in the first quadrant that is on $C$ and at which the tangent line to $C$ is parallel to the line $y = -x$.
(c) Use implicit differentiation to verify your conjecture in part (b).

**43.** Find $dy/dx$ if

$$2y^3t + t^3y = 1 \quad \text{and} \quad \frac{dt}{dx} = \frac{1}{\cos t}$$

**44.** Find equations for two lines through the origin that are tangent to the ellipse $2x^2 - 4x + y^2 + 1 = 0$.

**45. Writing** Write a paragraph that compares the concept of an *explicit* definition of a function with that of an *implicit* definition of a function.

**46. Writing** A student asks: "Suppose implicit differentiation yields an undefined expression at a point. Does this mean that $dy/dx$ is undefined at that point?" Using the equation $x^2 - 2xy + y^2 = 0$ as a basis for your discussion, write a paragraph that answers the student's question.

✓ QUICK CHECK ANSWERS 3.1 1. $\dfrac{1}{x+2}$ 2. $\dfrac{dy}{dx} = \dfrac{2x-y}{x+3y^2}$ 3. $-1$ 4. $\dfrac{d^2y}{dx^2} = \sec^2 y \tan y$

## 3.2 DERIVATIVES OF LOGARITHMIC FUNCTIONS

*In this section we will obtain derivative formulas for logarithmic functions, and we will introduce a new method for differentiating algebraic functions.*

### DERIVATIVES OF LOGARITHMIC FUNCTIONS

We will establish that $f(x) = \ln x$ is differentiable for $x > 0$ by applying the derivative definition to $f(x)$. To evaluate the resulting limit, we will need the fact that $\ln x$ is continuous for $x > 0$ [Theorem 1.8.2(*b*)], and we will need the limit

$$\lim_{v \to 0} (1 + v)^{1/v} = e \tag{1}$$

that was given in Formula (6) of Section 1.8 (with $x$ rather than $v$ as the variable). Using the definition of the derivative, we obtain

$$\begin{aligned}
\frac{d}{dx}[\ln x] &= \lim_{h \to 0} \frac{\ln(x+h) - \ln x}{h} \\
&= \lim_{h \to 0} \frac{1}{h} \ln\left(\frac{x+h}{x}\right) && \text{The quotient property of logarithms in Theorem 1.8.3} \\
&= \lim_{h \to 0} \frac{1}{h} \ln\left(1 + \frac{h}{x}\right) \\
&= \lim_{v \to 0} \frac{1}{vx} \ln(1 + v) && \text{Let } v = h/x \text{ and note that } v \to 0 \text{ if and only if } h \to 0. \\
&= \frac{1}{x} \lim_{v \to 0} \frac{1}{v} \ln(1 + v) && x \text{ is fixed in this limit computation, so } 1/x \text{ can be moved through the limit sign.} \\
&= \frac{1}{x} \lim_{v \to 0} \ln(1 + v)^{1/v} && \text{The power property of logarithms in Theorem 1.8.3} \\
&= \frac{1}{x} \ln\left[\lim_{v \to 0} (1 + v)^{1/v}\right] && \ln x \text{ is continuous on } (0, +\infty) \text{ so we can move the limit through the function symbol.} \\
&= \frac{1}{x} \ln e \\
&= \frac{1}{x} && \text{Since } \ln e = 1
\end{aligned}$$

Thus,

$$\frac{d}{dx}[\ln x] = \frac{1}{x}, \quad x > 0 \tag{2}$$

A derivative formula for the general logarithmic function $\log_b x$ can be obtained from (2) by using Formula (9) of Section 1.8 to write

$$\frac{d}{dx}[\log_b x] = \frac{d}{dx}\left[\frac{\ln x}{\ln b}\right] = \frac{1}{\ln b}\frac{d}{dx}[\ln x]$$

It follows from this that

$$\frac{d}{dx}[\log_b x] = \frac{1}{x \ln b}, \quad x > 0 \tag{3}$$

Note that, among all possible bases, the base $b = e$ produces the simplest formula for the derivative of $\log_b x$. This is one of the reasons why the natural logarithm function is preferred over other logarithms in calculus.

### ▶ Example 1

(a) Figure 3.2.1 shows the graph of $y = \ln x$ and its tangent lines at the points $x = \frac{1}{2}, 1, 3,$ and 5. Find the slopes of those tangent lines.

(b) Does the graph of $y = \ln x$ have any horizontal tangent lines? Use the derivative of $\ln x$ to justify your answer.

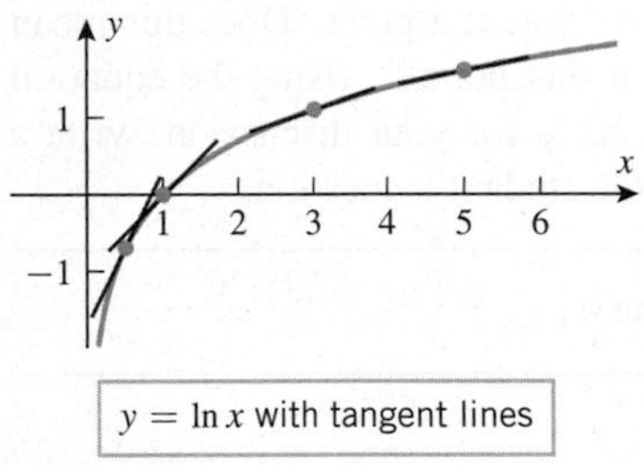


▲ **Figure 3.2.1**

***Solution (a).*** From (2), the slopes of the tangent lines at the points $x = \frac{1}{2}, 1, 3,$ and 5 are $1/x = 2, 1, \frac{1}{3},$ and $\frac{1}{5}$, respectively, which is consistent with Figure 3.2.1.

***Solution (b).*** It does not appear from the graph of $y = \ln x$ that there are any horizontal tangent lines. This is confirmed by the fact that $dy/dx = 1/x$ is not equal to zero for any real value of $x$. ◀

If $u$ is a differentiable function of $x$, and if $u(x) > 0$, then applying the chain rule to (2) and (3) produces the following generalized derivative formulas:

$$\frac{d}{dx}[\ln u] = \frac{1}{u} \cdot \frac{du}{dx} \quad \text{and} \quad \frac{d}{dx}[\log_b u] = \frac{1}{u \ln b} \cdot \frac{du}{dx} \tag{4–5}$$

### ▶ Example 2 Find $\dfrac{d}{dx}[\ln(x^2 + 1)]$.

***Solution.*** Using (4) with $u = x^2 + 1$ we obtain

$$\frac{d}{dx}[\ln(x^2 + 1)] = \frac{1}{x^2 + 1} \cdot \frac{d}{dx}[x^2 + 1] = \frac{1}{x^2 + 1} \cdot 2x = \frac{2x}{x^2 + 1} \quad ◀$$

When possible, the properties of logarithms in Theorem 1.8.3 should be used to convert products, quotients, and exponents into sums, differences, and constant multiples *before* differentiating a function involving logarithms.

### ▶ Example 3

$$\begin{aligned}\frac{d}{dx}\left[\ln\left(\frac{x^2 \sin x}{\sqrt{1 + x}}\right)\right] &= \frac{d}{dx}\left[2\ln x + \ln(\sin x) - \frac{1}{2}\ln(1 + x)\right] \\ &= \frac{2}{x} + \frac{\cos x}{\sin x} - \frac{1}{2(1 + x)} \\ &= \frac{2}{x} + \cot x - \frac{1}{2 + 2x} \quad ◀\end{aligned}$$

Figure 3.2.2 shows the graph of $f(x) = \ln|x|$. This function is important because it "extends" the domain of the natural logarithm function in the sense that the values of $\ln|x|$

and $\ln x$ are the same for $x > 0$, but $\ln|x|$ is defined for all nonzero values of $x$, and $\ln x$ is only defined for positive values of $x$.

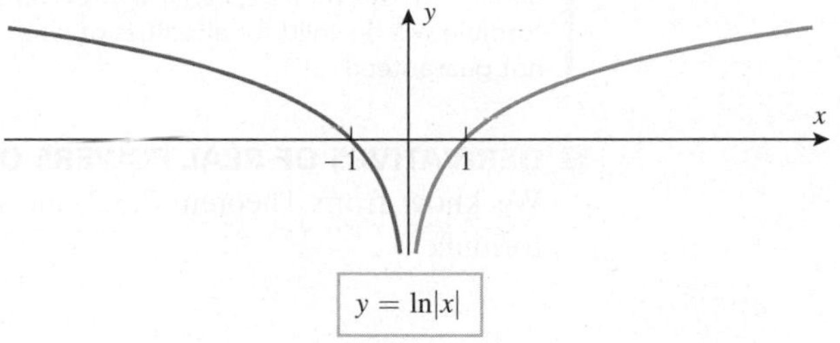


▶ **Figure 3.2.2**

The derivative of $\ln|x|$ for $x \neq 0$ can be obtained by considering the cases $x > 0$ and $x < 0$ separately:

**Case $x > 0$.** In this case $|x| = x$, so

$$\frac{d}{dx}[\ln|x|] = \frac{d}{dx}[\ln x] = \frac{1}{x}$$

**Case $x < 0$.** In this case $|x| = -x$, so it follows from (4) that

$$\frac{d}{dx}[\ln|x|] = \frac{d}{dx}[\ln(-x)] = \frac{1}{(-x)} \cdot \frac{d}{dx}[-x] = \frac{1}{x}$$

Since the same formula results in both cases, we have shown that

$$\frac{d}{dx}[\ln|x|] = \frac{1}{x} \quad \text{if } x \neq 0 \tag{6}$$

▶ **Example 4** From (6) and the chain rule,

$$\frac{d}{dx}[\ln|\sin x|] = \frac{1}{\sin x} \cdot \frac{d}{dx}[\sin x] = \frac{\cos x}{\sin x} = \cot x \blacktriangleleft$$

## LOGARITHMIC DIFFERENTIATION

We now consider a technique called ***logarithmic differentiation*** that is useful for differentiating functions that are composed of products, quotients, and powers.

▶ **Example 5** The derivative of

$$y = \frac{x^2\sqrt[3]{7x-14}}{(1+x^2)^4} \tag{7}$$

is messy to calculate directly. However, if we first take the natural logarithm of both sides and then use its properties, we can write

$$\ln y = 2\ln x + \tfrac{1}{3}\ln(7x-14) - 4\ln(1+x^2)$$

Differentiating both sides with respect to $x$ yields

$$\frac{1}{y}\frac{dy}{dx} = \frac{2}{x} + \frac{7/3}{7x-14} - \frac{8x}{1+x^2}$$

Thus, on solving for $dy/dx$ and using (7) we obtain

$$\frac{dy}{dx} = \frac{x^2\sqrt[3]{7x-14}}{(1+x^2)^4}\left[\frac{2}{x} + \frac{1}{3x-6} - \frac{8x}{1+x^2}\right] \blacktriangleleft$$

**REMARK** Since $\ln y$ is only defined for $y > 0$, the computations in Example 5 are only valid for $x > 2$ (verify). However, using the fact that the expression for the derivative of $\ln y$ is the same as that for $\ln|y|$, it can be shown that the formula obtained for $dy/dx$ is valid for $x < 2$ as well as $x > 2$ (Exercise 59). In general, whenever a derivative $dy/dx$ is obtained by logarithmic differentiation, the resulting derivative formula will be valid for all values of $x$ for which $y \neq 0$. It may be valid at those points as well, but it is not guaranteed.

## DERIVATIVES OF REAL POWERS OF x

We know from Theorem 2.3.2 and Exercise 84 in Section 2.3, that the differentiation formula

$$\frac{d}{dx}[x^r] = rx^{r-1} \tag{8}$$

holds for constant integer values of $r$. We will now use logarithmic differentiation to show that this formula holds if $r$ is *any* real number (rational or irrational). In our computations we will assume that $x^r$ is a differentiable function and that the familiar laws of exponents hold for real exponents.

In the next section we will discuss differentiating functions that have exponents which are not constant.

Let $y = x^r$, where $r$ is a real number. The derivative $dy/dx$ can be obtained by logarithmic differentiation as follows:

$$\ln|y| = \ln|x^r| = r\ln|x|$$

$$\frac{d}{dx}[\ln|y|] = \frac{d}{dx}[r\ln|x|]$$

$$\frac{1}{y}\frac{dy}{dx} = \frac{r}{x}$$

$$\frac{dy}{dx} = \frac{r}{x}y = \frac{r}{x}x^r = rx^{r-1}$$

## ✓ QUICK CHECK EXERCISES 3.2 (See page 139 for answers.)

1. The equation of the tangent line to the graph of $y = \ln x$ at $x = e^2$ is ________.
2. Find $dy/dx$.
   (a) $y = \ln 3x$ (b) $y = \ln\sqrt{x}$
   (c) $y = \log(1/|x|)$
3. Use logarithmic differentiation to find the derivative of
$$f(x) = \frac{\sqrt{x+1}}{\sqrt[3]{x-1}}$$
4. $\displaystyle\lim_{h\to 0}\frac{\ln(1+h)}{h} =$ ________

## EXERCISE SET 3.2

**1–26** Find $dy/dx$. ■

1. $y = \ln 5x$
2. $y = \ln\dfrac{x}{3}$
3. $y = \ln|1+x|$
4. $y = \ln(2+\sqrt{x})$
5. $y = \ln|x^2-1|$
6. $y = \ln|x^3-7x^2-3|$
7. $y = \ln\left(\dfrac{x}{1+x^2}\right)$
8. $y = \ln\left|\dfrac{1+x}{1-x}\right|$
9. $y = \ln x^2$
10. $y = (\ln x)^3$
11. $y = \sqrt{\ln x}$
12. $y = \ln\sqrt{x}$
13. $y = x\ln x$
14. $y = x^3\ln x$
15. $y = x^2\log_2(3-2x)$
16. $y = x[\log_2(x^2-2x)]^3$
17. $y = \dfrac{x^2}{1+\log x}$
18. $y = \dfrac{\log x}{1+\log x}$
19. $y = \ln(\ln x)$
20. $y = \ln(\ln(\ln x))$
21. $y = \ln(\tan x)$
22. $y = \ln(\cos x)$
23. $y = \cos(\ln x)$
24. $y = \sin^2(\ln x)$
25. $y = \log(\sin^2 x)$
26. $y = \log(1-\sin^2 x)$

**27–30** Use the method of Example 3 to help perform the indicated differentiation. ■

27. $\dfrac{d}{dx}[\ln((x-1)^3(x^2+1)^4)]$
28. $\dfrac{d}{dx}[\ln((\cos^2 x)\sqrt{1+x^4})]$
29. $\dfrac{d}{dx}\left[\ln\dfrac{\cos x}{\sqrt{4-3x^2}}\right]$
30. $\dfrac{d}{dx}\left[\ln\sqrt{\dfrac{x-1}{x+1}}\right]$

**31–34 True–False** Determine whether the statement is true or false. Explain your answer. ■

**31.** The slope of the tangent line to the graph of $y = \ln x$ at $x = a$ approaches infinity as $a \to 0^+$.

**32.** If $\lim_{x\to+\infty} f'(x) = 0$, then the graph of $y = f(x)$ has a horizontal asymptote.

**33.** The derivative of $\ln |x|$ is an odd function.

**34.** We have

$$\frac{d}{dx}((\ln x)^2) = \frac{d}{dx}(2(\ln x)) = \frac{2}{x}$$

**35–38** Find $dy/dx$ using logarithmic differentiation. ■

**35.** $y = x\sqrt[3]{1+x^2}$ **36.** $y = \sqrt[5]{\dfrac{x-1}{x+1}}$

**37.** $y = \dfrac{(x^2-8)^{1/3}\sqrt{x^3+1}}{x^6-7x+5}$ **38.** $y = \dfrac{\sin x \cos x \tan^3 x}{\sqrt{x}}$

**39.** Find
(a) $\dfrac{d}{dx}[\log_x e]$ (b) $\dfrac{d}{dx}[\log_x 2]$.

**40.** Find
(a) $\dfrac{d}{dx}[\log_{(1/x)} e]$ (b) $\dfrac{d}{dx}[\log_{(\ln x)} e]$.

**41–44** Find the equation of the tangent line to the graph of $y = f(x)$ at $x = x_0$. ■

**41.** $f(x) = \ln x$; $x_0 = e^{-1}$ **42.** $f(x) = \log x$; $x_0 = 10$

**43.** $f(x) = \ln(-x)$; $x_0 = -e$ **44.** $f(x) = \ln|x|$; $x_0 = -2$

**FOCUS ON CONCEPTS**

**45.** (a) Find the equation of a line through the origin that is tangent to the graph of $y = \ln x$.
(b) Explain why the $y$-intercept of a tangent line to the curve $y = \ln x$ must be 1 unit less than the $y$-coordinate of the point of tangency.

**46.** Use logarithmic differentiation to verify the product and quotient rules. Explain what properties of $\ln x$ are important for this verification.

**47.** Find a formula for the area $A(w)$ of the triangle bounded by the tangent line to the graph of $y = \ln x$ at $P(w, \ln w)$, the horizontal line through $P$, and the $y$-axis.

**48.** Find a formula for the area $A(w)$ of the triangle bounded by the tangent line to the graph of $y = \ln x^2$ at $P(w, \ln w^2)$, the horizontal line through $P$, and the $y$-axis.

**49.** Verify that $y = \ln(x + e)$ satisfies $dy/dx = e^{-y}$, with $y = 1$ when $x = 0$.

**50.** Verify that $y = -\ln(e^2 - x)$ satisfies $dy/dx = e^y$, with $y = -2$ when $x = 0$.

**51.** Find a function $f$ such that $y = f(x)$ satisfies $dy/dx = e^{-y}$, with $y = 0$ when $x = 0$.

**52.** Find a function $f$ such that $y = f(x)$ satisfies $dy/dx = e^y$, with $y = -\ln 2$ when $x = 0$.

**53–55** Find the limit by interpreting the expression as an appropriate derivative. ■

**53.** (a) $\displaystyle\lim_{x\to 0} \frac{\ln(1+3x)}{x}$ (b) $\displaystyle\lim_{x\to 0} \frac{\ln(1-5x)}{x}$

**54.** (a) $\displaystyle\lim_{\Delta x\to 0} \frac{\ln(e^2+\Delta x)-2}{\Delta x}$ (b) $\displaystyle\lim_{w\to 1} \frac{\ln w}{w-1}$

**55.** (a) $\displaystyle\lim_{x\to 0} \frac{\ln(\cos x)}{x}$ (b) $\displaystyle\lim_{h\to 0} \frac{(1+h)^{\sqrt{2}}-1}{h}$

**56.** Modify the derivation of Equation (2) to give another proof of Equation (3).

**57.** Let $p$ denote the number of paramecia in a nutrient solution $t$ days after the start of an experiment, and assume that $p$ is defined implicitly as a function of $t$ by the equation

$$0 = \ln p + 0.83 - \ln(2.3 - 0.0046p) - 2.3t$$

Use implicit differentiation to show that the rate of change of $p$ with respect to $t$ satisfies the equation

$$\frac{dp}{dt} = 0.0046p(500 - p)$$

**58.** One model for the spread of information over time $t$ is given by

$$\ln y - \ln(1 - y) = \alpha t$$

where $y$ is the fraction of the population with the information and $\alpha > 0$ is a constant. Find an expression for $dy/dt$ and explain why $y$ is growing most rapidly at the moment when half the population has the information.

**59.** Show that the formula for $dy/dx$ obtained in the solution to Example 5 is also valid for $x < 2$. (*Hint:* First take the log of the absolute value of each side of Equation (7) and simplify the right-hand side using properties of the log and absolute value functions. Then differentiate.)

**60. Writing** Review the derivation of the formula

$$\frac{d}{dx}[\ln x] = \frac{1}{x}$$

and then write a paragraph that discusses all the ingredients (theorems, limit properties, etc.) that are needed for this derivation.

**61. Writing** Write a paragraph that explains how logarithmic differentiation can replace a difficult differentiation computation with a simpler computation.

✓ **QUICK CHECK ANSWERS 3.2** 1. $y = \dfrac{x}{e^2} + 1$ 2. (a) $\dfrac{dy}{dx} = \dfrac{1}{x}$ (b) $\dfrac{dy}{dx} = \dfrac{1}{2x}$ (c) $\dfrac{dy}{dx} = -\dfrac{1}{x\ln 10}$
3. $\dfrac{\sqrt{x+1}}{\sqrt[3]{x-1}}\left[\dfrac{1}{2(x+1)} - \dfrac{1}{3(x-1)}\right]$ 4. 1

# 3.3 DERIVATIVES OF EXPONENTIAL AND INVERSE TRIGONOMETRIC FUNCTIONS

See Appendix E for a review of one-to-one functions and inverse functions.

*In this section we will use the derivative of a one-to-one function to obtain the derivative of its inverse function. This will yield derivative formulas for exponential functions from the derivative formulas for logarithmic functions and derivative formulas for inverse trigonometric functions from the derivative formulas for trigonometric functions.*

Our first goal in this section is to obtain a formula relating the derivative of an inverse function $f^{-1}$ to the derivative of an invertible function $f$.

▶ **Example 1** Suppose that $f$ is a one-to-one differentiable function such that $f(2) = 1$ and $f'(2) = \frac{3}{4}$. Then the tangent line to $y = f(x)$ at the point (2, 1) has equation

$$y - 1 = \tfrac{3}{4}(x - 2)$$

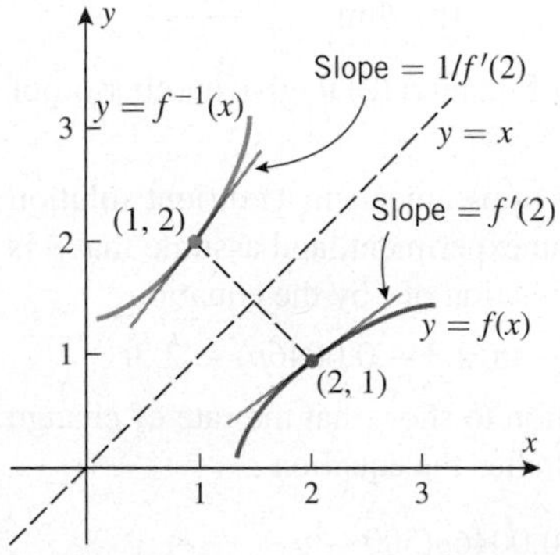

▲ **Figure 3.3.1**

The tangent line to $y = f^{-1}(x)$ at the point (1, 2) is the reflection about the line $y = x$ of the tangent line to $y = f(x)$ at the point (2, 1) (Figure 3.3.1), and its equation can be obtained by interchanging $x$ and $y$:

$$x - 1 = \tfrac{3}{4}(y - 2) \quad \text{or} \quad y - 2 = \tfrac{4}{3}(x - 1)$$

Notice that the slope of the tangent line to $y = f^{-1}(x)$ at $x = 1$ is the reciprocal of the slope of the tangent line to $y = f(x)$ at $x = 2$. That is,

$$(f^{-1})'(1) = \frac{1}{f'(2)} = \frac{4}{3} \blacktriangleleft \tag{1}$$

Since $2 = f^{-1}(1)$ for the function $f$ in Example 1, it follows that $f'(2) = f'(f^{-1}(1))$. Thus, Formula (1) can also be expressed as

$$(f^{-1})'(1) = \frac{1}{f'(f^{-1}(1))}$$

In general, if $f$ is a differentiable and one-to-one function, then

$$(f^{-1})'(x) = \frac{1}{f'(f^{-1}(x))} \tag{2}$$

provided $f'(f^{-1}(x)) \neq 0$.

Formula (2) can be confirmed using implicit differentiation. The equation $y = f^{-1}(x)$ is equivalent to $x = f(y)$. Differentiating with respect to $x$ we obtain

$$1 = \frac{d}{dx}[x] = \frac{d}{dx}[f(y)] = f'(y) \cdot \frac{dy}{dx}$$

so that

$$\frac{dy}{dx} = \frac{1}{f'(y)} = \frac{1}{f'(f^{-1}(x))}$$

Also from $x = f(y)$ we have $dx/dy = f'(y)$, which gives the following alternative version of Formula (2):

$$\frac{dy}{dx} = \frac{1}{dx/dy} \tag{3}$$

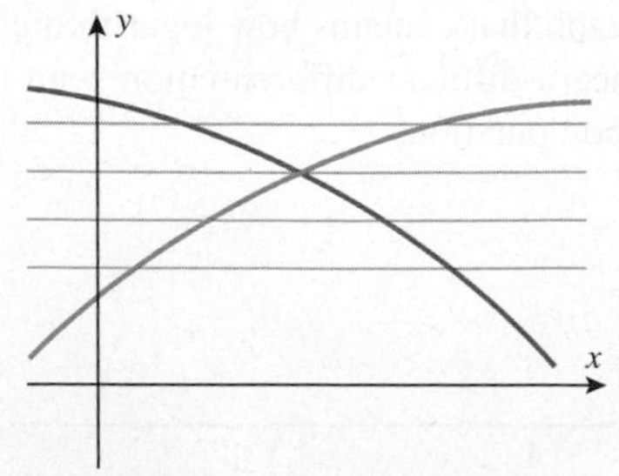

▲ **Figure 3.3.2** The graph of an increasing function (blue) or a decreasing function (purple) is cut at most once by any horizontal line.

## INCREASING OR DECREASING FUNCTIONS ARE ONE-TO-ONE

If the graph of a function $f$ is always increasing or always decreasing over the domain of $f$, then a horizontal line will cut the graph of $f$ in at most one point (Figure 3.3.2), so $f$ must have an inverse function. We will prove in the next chapter that $f$ is increasing on any interval on which $f'(x) > 0$ (since the graph has positive slope) and that $f$ is decreasing on any interval on which $f'(x) < 0$ (since the graph has negative slope). These intuitive observations, together with Formula (2), suggest the following theorem, which we state without formal proof.

**3.3.1 THEOREM** *Suppose that the domain of a function $f$ is an open interval on which $f'(x) > 0$ or on which $f'(x) < 0$. Then $f$ is one-to-one, $f^{-1}(x)$ is differentiable at all values of $x$ in the range of $f$, and the derivative of $f^{-1}(x)$ is given by Formula (2).*

▶ **Example 2** Consider the function $f(x) = x^5 + x + 1$.

(a) Show that $f$ is one-to-one on the interval $(-\infty, +\infty)$.

(b) Find a formula for the derivative of $f^{-1}$.

(c) Compute $(f^{-1})'(1)$.

In general, once it is established that $f^{-1}$ is differentiable, one has the option of calculating the derivative of $f^{-1}$ using Formula (2) or (3), or by differentiating implicitly, as in Example 2.

***Solution (a).*** Since

$$f'(x) = 5x^4 + 1 > 0$$

for all real values of $x$, it follows from Theorem 3.3.1 that $f$ is one-to-one on the interval $(-\infty, +\infty)$.

***Solution (b).*** Let $y = f^{-1}(x)$. Differentiating $x = f(y) = y^5 + y + 1$ implicitly with respect to $x$ yields

$$\frac{d}{dx}[x] = \frac{d}{dx}[y^5 + y + 1]$$

$$1 = (5y^4 + 1)\frac{dy}{dx}$$

$$\frac{dy}{dx} = \frac{1}{5y^4 + 1} \tag{4}$$

We cannot solve $x = y^5 + y + 1$ for $y$ in terms of $x$, so we leave the expression for $dy/dx$ in Equation (4) in terms of $y$.

***Solution (c).*** From Equation (4),

$$(f^{-1})'(1) = \left.\frac{dy}{dx}\right|_{x=1} = \left.\frac{1}{5y^4 + 1}\right|_{x=1}$$

Thus, we need to know the value of $y = f^{-1}(x)$ at $x = 1$, which we can obtain by solving the equation $f(y) = 1$ for $y$. This equation is $y^5 + y + 1 = 1$, which, by inspection, is satisfied by $y = 0$. Thus,

$$(f^{-1})'(1) = \left.\frac{1}{5y^4 + 1}\right|_{y=0} = 1 \quad ◀$$

## DERIVATIVES OF EXPONENTIAL FUNCTIONS

Our next objective is to show that the general exponential function $b^x$ $(b > 0, b \neq 1)$ is differentiable everywhere and to find its derivative. To do this, we will use the fact that $b^x$ is the inverse of the function $f(x) = \log_b x$. We will assume that $b > 1$. With this assumption we have $\ln b > 0$, so

$$f'(x) = \frac{d}{dx}[\log_b x] = \frac{1}{x \ln b} > 0 \quad \text{for all } x \text{ in the interval } (0, +\infty)$$

It now follows from Theorem 3.3.1 that $f^{-1}(x) = b^x$ is differentiable for all $x$ in the range of $f(x) = \log_b x$. But we know from Table 1.8.3 that the range of $\log_b x$ is $(-\infty, +\infty)$, so we have established that $b^x$ is differentiable everywhere.

To obtain a derivative formula for $b^x$ we rewrite $y = b^x$ as

$$x = \log_b y$$

and differentiate implicitly using Formula (5) of Section 3.2 to obtain

$$1 = \frac{1}{y \ln b} \cdot \frac{dy}{dx}$$

Solving for $dy/dx$ and replacing $y$ by $b^x$ we have

$$\frac{dy}{dx} = y \ln b = b^x \ln b$$

Thus, we have shown that

$$\frac{d}{dx}[b^x] = b^x \ln b \tag{5}$$

How does the derivation of Formula (5) change if $0 < b < 1$?

In the special case where $b = e$ we have $\ln e = 1$, so that (5) becomes

$$\frac{d}{dx}[e^x] = e^x \tag{6}$$

It follows from (5) and (6) that $b = e$ is the only base for which the slope of the tangent line to the curve $y = b^x$ at any point $P$ on the curve is the $y$-coordinate at $P$. Verify this statement.

Moreover, if $u$ is a differentiable function of $x$, then it follows from (5) and (6) that

$$\frac{d}{dx}[b^u] = b^u \ln b \cdot \frac{du}{dx} \quad \text{and} \quad \frac{d}{dx}[e^u] = e^u \cdot \frac{du}{dx} \tag{7–8}$$

It is important to distinguish between differentiating an exponential function $b^x$ (variable exponent and constant base) and a power function $x^b$ (variable base and constant exponent). For example, compare the derivative

$$\frac{d}{dx}[x^2] = 2x$$

to the derivative of $2^x$ in Example 3.

▶ **Example 3** The following computations use Formulas (7) and (8).

$$\frac{d}{dx}[2^x] = 2^x \ln 2$$

$$\frac{d}{dx}[e^{-2x}] = e^{-2x} \cdot \frac{d}{dx}[-2x] = -2e^{-2x}$$

$$\frac{d}{dx}[e^{x^3}] = e^{x^3} \cdot \frac{d}{dx}[x^3] = 3x^2 e^{x^3}$$

$$\frac{d}{dx}[e^{\cos x}] = e^{\cos x} \cdot \frac{d}{dx}[\cos x] = -(\sin x)e^{\cos x}$$ ◀

Functions of the form $f(x) = u^v$ in which $u$ and $v$ are *nonconstant* functions of $x$ are neither exponential functions nor power functions. Functions of this form can be differentiated using logarithmic differentiation.

▶ **Example 4** Use logarithmic differentiation to find $\frac{d}{dx}[(x^2+1)^{\sin x}]$.

***Solution.*** Setting $y = (x^2+1)^{\sin x}$ we have

$$\ln y = \ln[(x^2+1)^{\sin x}] = (\sin x)\ln(x^2+1)$$

Differentiating both sides with respect to $x$ yields

$$\frac{1}{y}\frac{dy}{dx} = \frac{d}{dx}[(\sin x)\ln(x^2+1)]$$

$$= (\sin x)\frac{1}{x^2+1}(2x) + (\cos x)\ln(x^2+1)$$

Thus,

$$\frac{dy}{dx} = y\left[\frac{2x \sin x}{x^2+1} + (\cos x)\ln(x^2+1)\right]$$

$$= (x^2+1)^{\sin x}\left[\frac{2x \sin x}{x^2+1} + (\cos x)\ln(x^2+1)\right]$$ ◀

## DERIVATIVES OF THE INVERSE TRIGONOMETRIC FUNCTIONS

To obtain formulas for the derivatives of the inverse trigonometric functions, we will need to use some of the identities given in Formulas (8) to (14) of Section 1.7. Rather than memorize those identities, we recommend that you review the "triangle technique" that we used to obtain them.

To begin, consider the function $\sin^{-1} x$. If we let $f(x) = \sin x\,(-\pi/2 \le x \le \pi/2)$, then it follows from Formula (2) that $f^{-1}(x) = \sin^{-1} x$ will be differentiable at any point $x$ where $\cos(\sin^{-1} x) \ne 0$. This is equivalent to the condition

$$\sin^{-1} x \ne -\frac{\pi}{2} \quad \text{and} \quad \sin^{-1} x \ne \frac{\pi}{2}$$

so it follows that $\sin^{-1} x$ is differentiable on the interval $(-1, 1)$.

A derivative formula for $\sin^{-1} x$ on $(-1, 1)$ can be obtained by using Formula (2) or (3) or by differentiating implicitly. We will use the latter method. Rewriting the equation $y = \sin^{-1} x$ as $x = \sin y$ and differentiating implicitly with respect to $x$, we obtain

Observe that $\sin^{-1} x$ is only differentiable on the interval $(-1, 1)$, even though its domain is $[-1, 1]$. This is because the graph of $y = \sin x$ has horizontal tangent lines at the points $(\pi/2, 1)$ and $(-\pi/2, -1)$, so the graph of $y = \sin^{-1} x$ has vertical tangent lines at $x = \pm 1$.

$$\frac{d}{dx}[x] = \frac{d}{dx}[\sin y]$$

$$1 = \cos y \cdot \frac{dy}{dx}$$

$$\frac{dy}{dx} = \frac{1}{\cos y} = \frac{1}{\cos(\sin^{-1} x)}$$

At this point we have succeeded in obtaining the derivative; however, this derivative formula can be simplified using the identity indicated in Figure 3.3.3. This yields

$$\frac{dy}{dx} = \frac{1}{\sqrt{1 - x^2}}$$

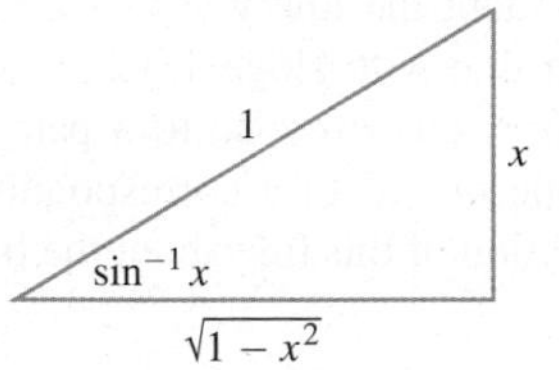


$\cos(\sin^{-1} x) = \sqrt{1 - x^2}$

▲ Figure 3.3.3

Thus, we have shown that

$$\frac{d}{dx}[\sin^{-1} x] = \frac{1}{\sqrt{1 - x^2}} \qquad (-1 < x < 1)$$

More generally, if $u$ is a differentiable function of $x$, then the chain rule produces the following generalized version of this formula:

$$\frac{d}{dx}[\sin^{-1} u] = \frac{1}{\sqrt{1 - u^2}}\frac{du}{dx} \qquad (-1 < u < 1)$$

The method used to derive this formula can be used to obtain generalized derivative formulas for the remaining inverse trigonometric functions. The following is a complete list of these formulas, each of which is valid on the natural domain of the function that multiplies $du/dx$.

$$\frac{d}{dx}[\sin^{-1} u] = \frac{1}{\sqrt{1 - u^2}}\frac{du}{dx} \qquad \frac{d}{dx}[\cos^{-1} u] = -\frac{1}{\sqrt{1 - u^2}}\frac{du}{dx} \qquad (9\text{–}10)$$

$$\frac{d}{dx}[\tan^{-1} u] = \frac{1}{1 + u^2}\frac{du}{dx} \qquad \frac{d}{dx}[\cot^{-1} u] = -\frac{1}{1 + u^2}\frac{du}{dx} \qquad (11\text{–}12)$$

$$\frac{d}{dx}[\sec^{-1} u] = \frac{1}{|u|\sqrt{u^2 - 1}}\frac{du}{dx} \qquad \frac{d}{dx}[\csc^{-1} u] = -\frac{1}{|u|\sqrt{u^2 - 1}}\frac{du}{dx} \qquad (13\text{–}14)$$

The appearance of $|u|$ in (13) and (14) will be explained in Exercise 64.

► **Example 5** Find $dy/dx$ if

(a) $y = \sin^{-1}(x^3)$ (b) $y = \sec^{-1}(e^x)$

***Solution (a).*** From (9)

$$\frac{dy}{dx} = \frac{1}{\sqrt{1 - (x^3)^2}}(3x^2) = \frac{3x^2}{\sqrt{1 - x^6}}$$

***Solution (b).*** From (13)

$$\frac{dy}{dx} = \frac{1}{e^x\sqrt{(e^x)^2-1}}\frac{d}{dx}(e^x) = \frac{1}{\sqrt{e^{2x}-1}}$$ ◀

## ✓QUICK CHECK EXERCISES 3.3 *(See page 146 for answers.)*

1. Suppose that a one-to-one function $f$ has tangent line $y = 5x + 3$ at the point $(1, 8)$. Evaluate $(f^{-1})'(8)$.
2. In each case, from the given derivative, determine whether the function $f$ is invertible.
   (a) $f'(x) = x^2 + 1$ (b) $f'(x) = x^2 - 1$
   (c) $f'(x) = \sin x$ (d) $f'(x) = \frac{\pi}{2} + \tan^{-1} x$
3. Evaluate the derivative.
   (a) $\frac{d}{dx}[e^x]$ (b) $\frac{d}{dx}[7^x]$
   (c) $\frac{d}{dx}[\cos(e^x + 1)]$ (d) $\frac{d}{dx}[e^{3x-2}]$
4. Let $f(x) = e^{x^3+x}$. Use $f'(x)$ to verify that $f$ is one-to-one.

## EXERCISE SET 3.3 Graphing Utility

**FOCUS ON CONCEPTS**

1. Let $f(x) = x^5 + x^3 + x$.
   (a) Show that $f$ is one-to-one and confirm that $f(1) = 3$.
   (b) Find $(f^{-1})'(3)$.
2. Let $f(x) = x^3 + 2e^x$.
   (a) Show that $f$ is one-to-one and confirm that $f(0) = 2$.
   (b) Find $(f^{-1})'(2)$.

**3–4** Find $(f^{-1})'(x)$ using Formula (2), and check your answer by differentiating $f^{-1}$ directly. ■

3. $f(x) = 2/(x + 3)$
4. $f(x) = \ln(2x + 1)$

**5–6** Determine whether the function $f$ is one-to-one by examining the sign of $f'(x)$. ■

5. (a) $f(x) = x^2 + 8x + 1$
   (b) $f(x) = 2x^5 + x^3 + 3x + 2$
   (c) $f(x) = 2x + \sin x$
   (d) $f(x) = \left(\frac{1}{2}\right)^x$
6. (a) $f(x) = x^3 + 3x^2 - 8$
   (b) $f(x) = x^5 + 8x^3 + 2x - 1$
   (c) $f(x) = \frac{x}{x+1}$
   (d) $f(x) = \log_b x, \quad 0 < b < 1$

**7–10** Find the derivative of $f^{-1}$ by using Formula (3), and check your result by differentiating implicitly. ■

7. $f(x) = 5x^3 + x - 7$
8. $f(x) = 1/x^2, \quad x > 0$
9. $f(x) = 2x^5 + x^3 + 1$
10. $f(x) = 5x - \sin 2x, \quad -\frac{\pi}{4} < x < \frac{\pi}{4}$

**FOCUS ON CONCEPTS**

11. Complete each part to establish that the reflection of a point $P(a, b)$ about the line $y = x$ is the point $Q(b, a)$.
    (a) Prove that if $P$ is not on the line $y = x$, then $P$ and $Q$ are distinct, and the line $\overleftrightarrow{PQ}$ is perpendicular to the line $y = x$.
    (b) Prove that if $P$ is not on the line $y = x$, the midpoint of segment $PQ$ is on the line $y = x$.
    (c) Carefully explain what it means geometrically to reflect $P$ about the line $y = x$.
    (d) Use the results of parts (a)–(c) to prove that $Q$ is the reflection of $P$ about the line $y = x$.
12. Prove that the reflection about the line $y = x$ of a line with slope $m, m \neq 0$, is a line with slope $1/m$. [*Hint:* Apply the result of the previous exercise to a pair of points on the line of slope $m$ and to a corresponding pair of points on the reflection of this line about the line $y = x$.]
13. Suppose that $f$ and $g$ are increasing functions. Determine which of the functions $f(x) + g(x)$, $f(x)g(x)$, and $f(g(x))$ must also be increasing.
14. Suppose that $f$ and $g$ are one-to-one functions. Determine which of the functions $f(x) + g(x)$, $f(x)g(x)$, and $f(g(x))$ must also be one-to-one.

**15–26** Find $dy/dx$. ■

15. $y = e^{7x}$
16. $y = e^{-5x^2}$
17. $y = x^3e^x$
18. $y = e^{1/x}$
19. $y = \frac{e^x - e^{-x}}{e^x + e^{-x}}$
20. $y = \sin(e^x)$
21. $y = e^{x\tan x}$
22. $y = \frac{e^x}{\ln x}$
23. $y = e^{(x-e^{3x})}$
24. $y = \exp(\sqrt{1 + 5x^3})$
25. $y = \ln(1 - xe^{-x})$
26. $y = \ln(\cos e^x)$

**27–30** Find $f'(x)$ by Formula (7) and then by logarithmic differentiation. ■

27. $f(x) = 2^x$
28. $f(x) = 3^{-x}$
29. $f(x) = \pi^{\sin x}$
30. $f(x) = \pi^{x\tan x}$

**31–35** Find $dy/dx$ using the method of logarithmic differentiation. ■

31. $y = (x^3 - 2x)^{\ln x}$
32. $y = x^{\sin x}$
33. $y = (\ln x)^{\tan x}$
34. $y = (x^2 + 3)^{\ln x}$

**35.** $y = (\ln x)^{\ln x}$

**36.** (a) Explain why Formula (5) cannot be used to find $(d/dx)[x^x]$.
(b) Find this derivative by logarithmic differentiation.

**37–42** Find $dy/dx$ using any method. ■

**37.** $y = (x^3 - 2x^2 + 1)e^x$ **38.** $y = (2x^2 - 2x + 1)e^{2x}$

**39.** $y = (x^2 + \sqrt{x})3^x$ **40.** $y = (x^3 + \sqrt[3]{x})5^x$

**41.** $y = 4^{3\sin x - e^x}$ **42.** $y = 2^{\cos x + \ln x}$

**43–58** Find $dy/dx$. ■

**43.** $y = \sin^{-1}(3x)$ **44.** $y = \cos^{-1}\left(\frac{x+1}{2}\right)$

**45.** $y = \sin^{-1}(1/x)$ **46.** $y = \cos^{-1}(\cos x)$

**47.** $y = \tan^{-1}(x^3)$ **48.** $y = \sec^{-1}(x^5)$

**49.** $y = (\tan x)^{-1}$ **50.** $y = \dfrac{1}{\tan^{-1} x}$

**51.** $y = e^x \sec^{-1} x$ **52.** $y = \ln(\cos^{-1} x)$

**53.** $y = \sin^{-1} x + \cos^{-1} x$ **54.** $y = x^2(\sin^{-1} x)^3$

**55.** $y = \sec^{-1} x + \csc^{-1} x$ **56.** $y = \csc^{-1}(e^x)$

**57.** $y = \cot^{-1}(\sqrt{x})$ **58.** $y = \sqrt{\cot^{-1} x}$

**59–62 True–False** Determine whether the statement is true or false. Explain your answer. ■

**59.** If a function $y = f(x)$ satisfies $dy/dx = y$, then $y = e^x$.

**60.** If $y = f(x)$ is a function such that $dy/dx$ is a rational function, then $f(x)$ is also a rational function.

**61.** $\dfrac{d}{dx}(\log_b |x|) = \dfrac{1}{x \ln b}$

**62.** We can conclude from the derivatives of $\sin^{-1} x$ and $\cos^{-1} x$ that $\sin^{-1} x + \cos^{-1} x$ is constant.

**63.** (a) Use Formula (2) to prove that
$$\left.\frac{d}{dx}[\cot^{-1} x]\right|_{x=0} = -1$$
(b) Use part (a) above, part (a) of Exercise 30 in Section 1.7, and the chain rule to show that
$$\frac{d}{dx}[\cot^{-1} x] = -\frac{1}{1+x^2}$$
for $-\infty < x < +\infty$.
(c) Conclude from part (b) that
$$\frac{d}{dx}[\cot^{-1} u] = -\frac{1}{1+u^2}\frac{du}{dx}$$
for $-\infty < u < +\infty$.

**64.** (a) Use part (c) of Exercise 30 in Section 1.7 and the chain rule to show that
$$\frac{d}{dx}[\csc^{-1} x] = -\frac{1}{|x|\sqrt{x^2-1}}$$
for $1 < |x|$.
(b) Conclude from part (a) that
$$\frac{d}{dx}[\csc^{-1} u] = -\frac{1}{|u|\sqrt{u^2-1}}\frac{du}{dx}$$
for $1 < |u|$.
(c) Use Equation (8) in Section 1.7 and parts (b) and (c) of Exercise 30 in that section to show that if $|x| \geq 1$, then $\sec^{-1} x + \csc^{-1} x = \pi/2$. Conclude from part (a) that
$$\frac{d}{dx}[\sec^{-1} x] = \frac{1}{|x|\sqrt{x^2-1}}$$
(d) Conclude from part (c) that
$$\frac{d}{dx}[\sec^{-1} u] = \frac{1}{|u|\sqrt{x^2-1}}\frac{du}{dx}$$

**65–66** Find $dy/dx$ by implicit differentiation. ■

**65.** $x^3 + x\tan^{-1} y = e^y$ **66.** $\sin^{-1}(xy) = \cos^{-1}(x - y)$

**67.** (a) Show that $f(x) = x^3 - 3x^2 + 2x$ is not one-to-one on $(-\infty, +\infty)$.
(b) Find the largest value of $k$ such that $f$ is one-to-one on the interval $(-k, k)$.

**68.** (a) Show that the function $f(x) = x^4 - 2x^3$ is not one-to-one on $(-\infty, +\infty)$.
(b) Find the smallest value of $k$ such that $f$ is one-to-one on the interval $[k, +\infty)$.

**69.** Let $f(x) = x^4 + x^3 + 1$, $0 \leq x \leq 2$.
(a) Show that $f$ is one-to-one.
(b) Let $g(x) = f^{-1}(x)$ and define $F(x) = f(2g(x))$. Find an equation for the tangent line to $y = F(x)$ at $x = 3$.

**70.** Let $f(x) = \dfrac{\exp(4 - x^2)}{x}$, $x > 0$.
(a) Show that $f$ is one-to-one.
(b) Let $g(x) = f^{-1}(x)$ and define $F(x) = f([g(x)]^2)$. Find $f'\left(\frac{1}{2}\right)$.

**71.** Show that for any constants $A$ and $k$, the function $y = Ae^{kt}$ satisfies the equation $dy/dt = ky$.

**72.** Show that for any constants $A$ and $B$, the function
$$y = Ae^{2x} + Be^{-4x}$$
satisfies the equation
$$y'' + 2y' - 8y = 0$$

**73.** Show that
(a) $y = xe^{-x}$ satisfies the equation $xy' = (1 - x)y$.
(b) $y = xe^{-x^2/2}$ satisfies the equation $xy' = (1 - x^2)y$.

**74.** Suppose that a new car is purchased for \$20,000 and depreciates by 15% each year.
(a) Explain why the dollar value $V$ of the car $t$ years after the date of purchase can be modeled by the function $V = 20{,}000(0.85)^t$.
(b) For the model in part (a) determine how rapidly the car is losing value (in dollars per year) 5 years after the date of purchase.

**75.** Suppose that the percentage of U.S. households with broadband Internet access is modeled by the equation
$$P(t) = \frac{5300}{53 + 47e^{-0.182t}}$$
where $P(t)$ is the percentage $t$ years after an initial survey result made in the year 2007.
(a) Use a graphing utility to graph the function $P(t)$.
(b) In words, explain what happens to the percentage over time. Check your conclusion by finding $\lim_{t\to+\infty} P(t)$.

*(cont.)*

(c) In words, what happens to the *rate* of population growth over time? Check your conclusion by graphing $P'(t)$.

**76.** Suppose that the population of oxygen-dependent bacteria in a pond is modeled by the equation

$$P(t) = \frac{60}{5 + 7e^{-t}}$$

where $P(t)$ is the population (in billions) $t$ days after an initial observation at time $t = 0$.

(a) Use a graphing utility to graph the function $P(t)$.

(b) In words, explain what happens to the population over time. Check your conclusion by finding $\lim_{t\to+\infty} P(t)$.

(c) In words, what happens to the *rate* of population growth over time? Check your conclusion by graphing $P'(t)$.

**77–82** Find the limit by interpreting the expression as an appropriate derivative. ■

**77.** $\lim_{x\to 0} \frac{e^{3x} - 1}{x}$  **78.** $\lim_{x\to 0} \frac{\exp(x^2) - 1}{x}$

**79.** $\lim_{h\to 0} \frac{10^h - 1}{h}$  **80.** $\lim_{h\to 0} \frac{\tan^{-1}(1+h) - \pi/4}{h}$

**81.** $\lim_{\Delta x\to 0} \frac{9\left[\sin^{-1}\left(\frac{\sqrt{3}}{2} + \Delta x\right)\right]^2 - \pi^2}{\Delta x}$

**82.** $\lim_{w\to 2} \frac{3\sec^{-1} w - \pi}{w - 2}$

**83.** Suppose that a steel ball bearing is released within a vat of fluid and begins to sink. According to one model, the speed $v(t)$ (in m/s) of the ball bearing $t$ seconds after its release is given by the formula

$$v(t) = \frac{9.8}{k}(1 - e^{-kt})$$

where $k$ is a positive constant that corresponds to the resistance the fluid offers against the motion of the bearing. (The smaller the value of $k$, the weaker will be the resistance.) For $t$ fixed, determine the limiting value of the speed as $k \to 0^+$, and give a physical interpretation of the limit.

✓ **QUICK CHECK ANSWERS 3.3** 1. $\frac{1}{5}$ 2. (a) yes (b) no (c) no (d) yes 3. (a) $e^x$ (b) $7^x \ln 7$ (c) $-e^x \sin(e^x + 1)$ (d) $3e^{3x-2}$ 4. $f'(x) = e^{x^3+x} \cdot (3x^2 + 1) > 0$ for all $x$

## 3.4 RELATED RATES

*In this section we will study related rates problems. In such problems one finds the rate at which a quantity is changing using other quantities whose rates of change are known.*

### DIFFERENTIATING EQUATIONS TO RELATE RATES

Figure 3.4.1 shows a liquid draining through a conical filter. As the liquid drains, its volume $V$, height $h$, and radius $r$ are functions of the elapsed time $t$, and at each instant these variables are related by the equation

$$V = \frac{\pi}{3} r^2 h$$

To find the rate of change of the volume $V$ with respect to the time $t$, we can differentiate both sides of this equation with respect to $t$ to obtain

$$\frac{dV}{dt} = \frac{\pi}{3}\left[r^2\frac{dh}{dt} + h\left(2r\frac{dr}{dt}\right)\right] = \frac{\pi}{3}\left(r^2\frac{dh}{dt} + 2rh\frac{dr}{dt}\right)$$

Thus, to find $dV/dt$ at a specific time $t$ we need to have values for $r$, $h$, $dh/dt$, and $dr/dt$ at that time. This is called a ***related rates problem*** because an unknown rate of change is related to other variables whose values and whose rates of change are known or can be found in some way. Let us begin with a simple example.

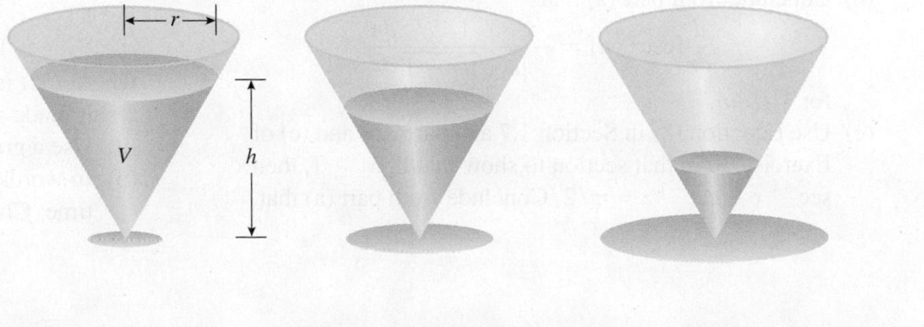


▶ **Figure 3.4.1**

▶ **Example 1** Suppose that $x$ and $y$ are differentiable functions of $t$ and are related by the equation $y = x^3$. Find $dy/dt$ at time $t = 1$ if $x = 2$ and $dx/dt = 4$ at time $t = 1$.

***Solution.*** Differentiating both sides of the equation $y = x^3$ with respect to $t$ yields

$$\frac{dy}{dt} = \frac{d}{dt}[x^3] = 3x^2\frac{dx}{dt}$$

Thus, the value of $dy/dt$ at time $t = 1$ is

$$\left.\frac{dy}{dt}\right|_{t=1} = 3(2)^2\left.\frac{dx}{dt}\right|_{t=1} = 12 \cdot 4 = 48 \blacktriangleleft$$

dehooks/Depositphotos
*Oil spill from a ruptured tanker.*

▶ **Example 2** Assume that oil spilled from a ruptured tanker spreads in a circular pattern whose radius increases at a constant rate of 2 ft/s. How fast is the area of the spill increasing when the radius of the spill is 60 ft?

***Solution.*** Let

$t$ = number of seconds elapsed from the time of the spill
$r$ = radius of the spill in feet after $t$ seconds
$A$ = area of the spill in square feet after $t$ seconds

(Figure 3.4.2). We know the rate at which the radius is increasing, and we want to find the rate at which the area is increasing at the instant when $r = 60$; that is, we want to find

$$\left.\frac{dA}{dt}\right|_{r=60} \quad \text{given that} \quad \frac{dr}{dt} = 2 \text{ ft/s}$$

Since $A$ is the area of a circle of radius $r$,

$$A = \pi r^2 \tag{1}$$

Differentiating both sides of (1) with respect to $t$ yields

$$\frac{dA}{dt} = 2\pi r\frac{dr}{dt} \tag{2}$$

Thus, when $r = 60$ the area of the spill is increasing at the rate of

$$\left.\frac{dA}{dt}\right|_{r=60} = 2\pi(60)(2) = 240\pi \text{ ft}^2/\text{s} \approx 754 \text{ ft}^2/\text{s} \blacktriangleleft$$

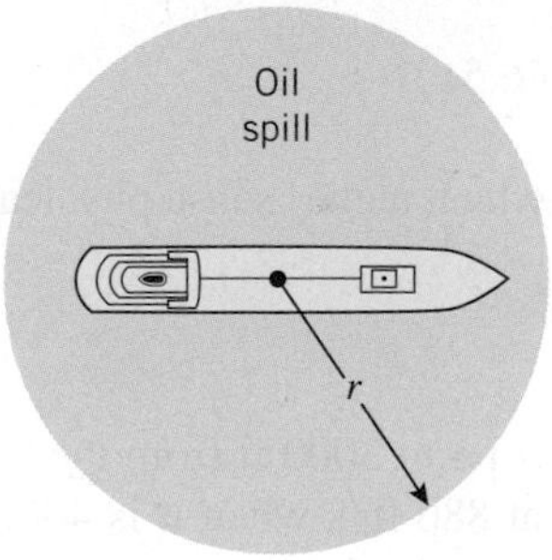


▲ **Figure 3.4.2**

With some minor variations, the method used in Example 2 can be used to solve a variety of related rates problems. We can break the method down into five steps.

***A Strategy for Solving Related Rates Problems***

**Step 1.** Assign letters to all quantities that vary with time and any others that seem relevant to the problem. Give a definition for each letter.

**Step 2.** Identify the rates of change that are known and the rate of change that is to be found. Interpret each rate as a derivative.

**Step 3.** Find an equation that relates the variables whose rates of change were identified in Step 2. To do this, it will often be helpful to draw an appropriately labeled figure that illustrates the relationship.

**Step 4.** Differentiate both sides of the equation obtained in Step 3 with respect to time to produce a relationship between the known rates of change and the unknown rate of change.

**Step 5.** *After* completing Step 4, substitute all known values for the rates of change and the variables, and then solve for the unknown rate of change.

**WARNING**

We have italicized the word "After" in Step 5 because it is a common error to substitute numerical values before performing the differentiation. For instance, in Example 2 had we substituted the known value of $r = 60$ in (1) before differentiating, we would have obtained $dA/dt = 0$, which is obviously incorrect.

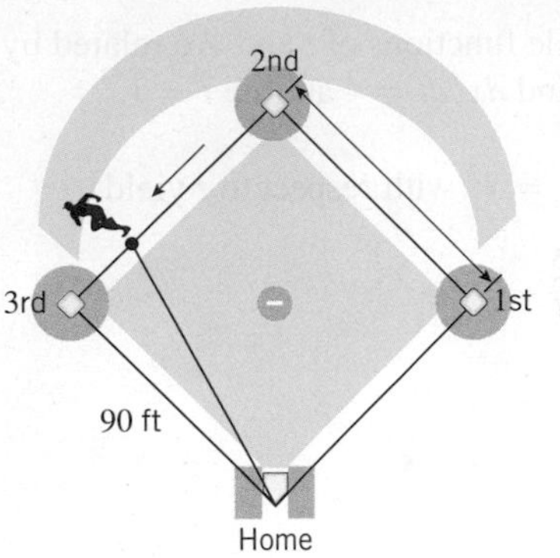


▲ **Figure 3.4.3**

The quantity

$$\left.\frac{dx}{dt}\right|_{x=20}$$

is negative because $x$ is decreasing with respect to $t$.

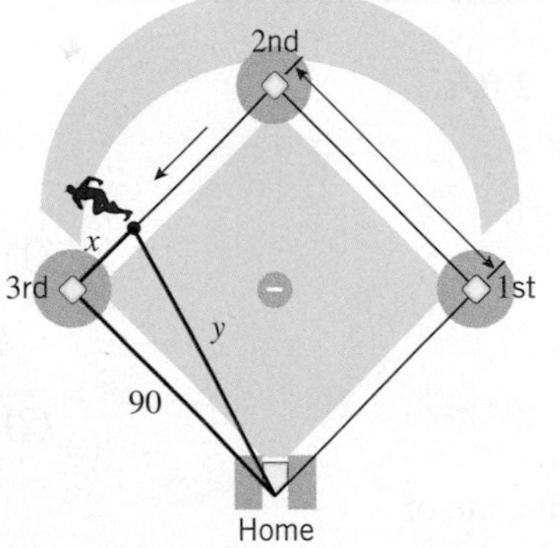


▲ **Figure 3.4.4**

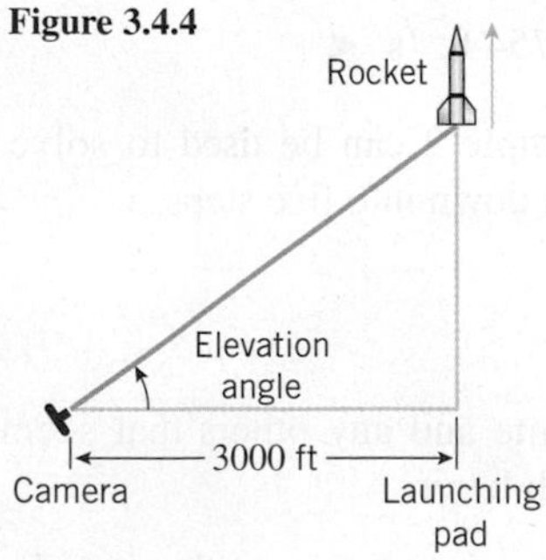


▲ **Figure 3.4.5**

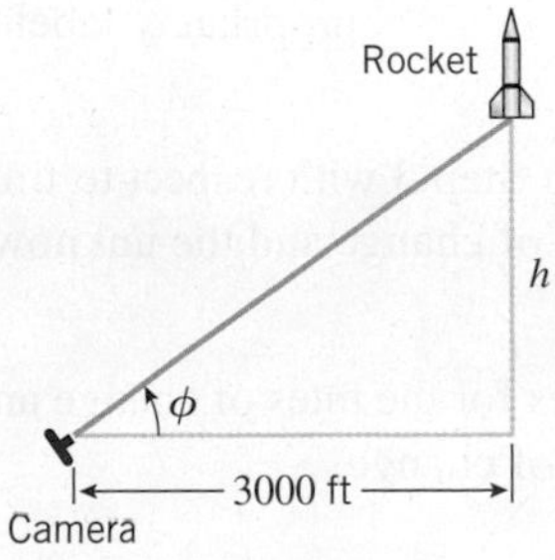


▲ **Figure 3.4.6**

▶ **Example 3** A baseball diamond is a square whose sides are 90 ft long (Figure 3.4.3). Suppose that a player running from second base to third base has a speed of 30 ft/s at the instant when he is 20 ft from third base. At what rate is the player's distance from home plate changing at that instant?

***Solution.*** We are given a constant speed with which the player is approaching third base, and we want to find the rate of change of the distance between the player and home plate at a particular instant. Thus, let

$t$ = number of seconds since the player left second base
$x$ = distance in feet from the player to third base
$y$ = distance in feet from the player to home plate

(Figure 3.4.4). Thus, we want to find

$$\left.\frac{dy}{dt}\right|_{x=20} \quad \text{given that} \quad \left.\frac{dx}{dt}\right|_{x=20} = -30 \text{ ft/s}$$

As suggested by Figure 3.4.4, the variables $x$ and $y$ are related by the Theorem of Pythagoras:

$$x^2 + 90^2 = y^2 \tag{3}$$

Differentiating both sides of this equation with respect to $t$ yields

$$2x\frac{dx}{dt} = 2y\frac{dy}{dt}$$

from which we obtain

$$\frac{dy}{dt} = \frac{x}{y}\frac{dx}{dt} \tag{4}$$

When $x = 20$, it follows from (3) that

$$y = \sqrt{20^2 + 90^2} = \sqrt{8500} = 10\sqrt{85}$$

so that (4) yields

$$\left.\frac{dy}{dt}\right|_{x=20} = \frac{20}{10\sqrt{85}}(-30) = -\frac{60}{\sqrt{85}} \approx -6.51 \text{ ft/s}$$

The negative sign in the answer tells us that $y$ is decreasing, which makes sense physically from Figure 3.4.4. ◀

▶ **Example 4** Figure 3.4.5 shows a camera mounted at a point 3000 ft from the base of a rocket launching pad. If the rocket is rising vertically at 880 ft/s when it is 4000 ft above the launching pad, how fast must the camera elevation angle change at that instant to keep the camera aimed at the rocket?

***Solution.*** Let

$t$ = number of seconds elapsed from the time of launch
$\phi$ = camera elevation angle in radians after $t$ seconds
$h$ = height of the rocket in feet after $t$ seconds

(Figure 3.4.6). At each instant the rate at which the camera elevation angle must change is $d\phi/dt$, and the rate at which the rocket is rising is $dh/dt$. We want to find

$$\left.\frac{d\phi}{dt}\right|_{h=4000} \quad \text{given that} \quad \left.\frac{dh}{dt}\right|_{h=4000} = 880 \text{ ft/s}$$

From Figure 3.4.6 we see that

$$\tan\phi = \frac{h}{3000} \tag{5}$$

Differentiating both sides of (5) with respect to $t$ yields

$$(\sec^2 \phi)\frac{d\phi}{dt} = \frac{1}{3000}\frac{dh}{dt} \tag{6}$$

When $h = 4000$, it follows that

$$(\sec \phi)\Big|_{h=4000} = \frac{5000}{3000} = \frac{5}{3}$$

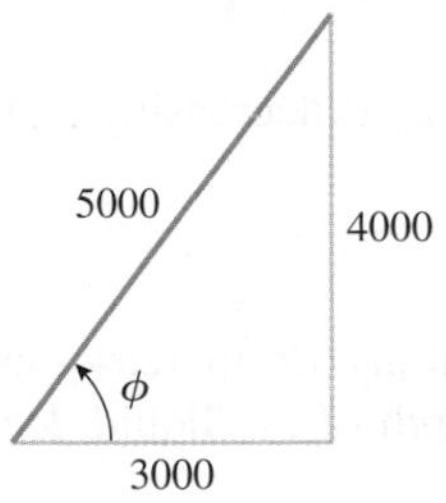


▲ **Figure 3.4.7**

(see Figure 3.4.7), so that from (6)

$$\left(\frac{5}{3}\right)^2 \frac{d\phi}{dt}\Big|_{h=4000} = \frac{1}{3000} \cdot 880 = \frac{22}{75}$$

$$\frac{d\phi}{dt}\Big|_{h=4000} = \frac{22}{75} \cdot \frac{9}{25} = \frac{66}{625} \approx 0.11 \text{ rad/s} \approx 6.05 \text{ deg/s} \blacktriangleleft$$

▶ **Example 5** Suppose that liquid is to be cleared of sediment by allowing it to drain through a conical filter that is 16 cm high and has a radius of 4 cm at the top (Figure 3.4.8). Suppose also that the liquid is forced out of the cone at a constant rate of 2 $\text{cm}^3/\text{min}$.

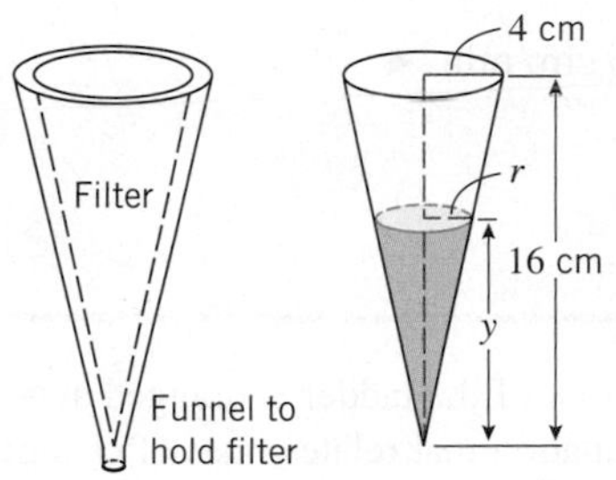


▲ **Figure 3.4.8**

(a) Do you think that the depth of the liquid will decrease at a constant rate? Give a verbal argument that justifies your conclusion.

(b) Find a formula that expresses the rate at which the depth of the liquid is changing in terms of the depth, and use that formula to determine whether your conclusion in part (a) is correct.

(c) At what rate is the depth of the liquid changing at the instant when the liquid in the cone is 8 cm deep?

***Solution (a).*** For the volume of liquid to decrease by a *fixed amount*, it requires a greater decrease in depth when the cone is close to empty than when it is almost full (Figure 3.4.9). This suggests that for the volume to decrease at a constant rate, the depth must decrease at an increasing rate.

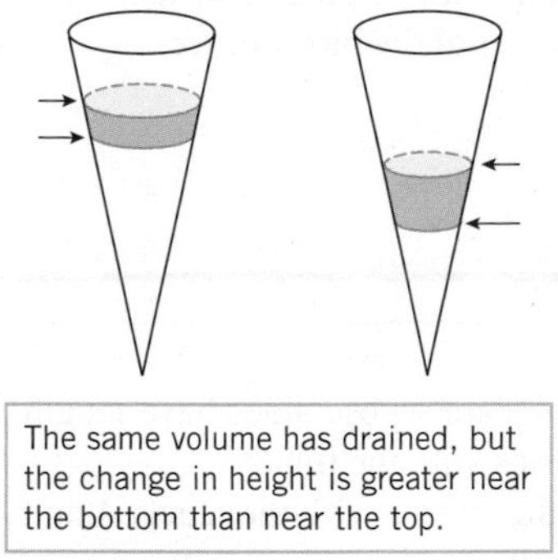


▲ **Figure 3.4.9**

***Solution (b).*** Let

$t$ = time elapsed from the initial observation (min)
$V$ = volume of liquid in the cone at time $t$ ($\text{cm}^3$)
$y$ = depth of the liquid in the cone at time $t$ (cm)
$r$ = radius of the liquid surface at time $t$ (cm)

(Figure 3.4.8). At each instant the rate at which the volume of liquid is changing is $dV/dt$, and the rate at which the depth is changing is $dy/dt$. We want to express $dy/dt$ in terms of $y$ given that $dV/dt$ has a constant value of $dV/dt = -2$. (We must use a minus sign here because $V$ *decreases* as $t$ increases.)

From the formula for the volume of a cone, the volume $V$, the radius $r$, and the depth $y$ are related by

$$V = \tfrac{1}{3}\pi r^2 y \tag{7}$$

If we differentiate both sides of (7) with respect to $t$, the right side will involve the quantity $dr/dt$. Since we have no direct information about $dr/dt$, it is desirable to eliminate $r$ from (7) before differentiating. This can be done using similar triangles. From Figure 3.4.8 we see that

$$\frac{r}{y} = \frac{4}{16} \quad \text{or} \quad r = \frac{1}{4}y$$

Substituting this expression in (7) gives

$$V = \frac{\pi}{48}y^3 \tag{8}$$

Differentiating both sides of (8) with respect to $t$ we obtain

$$\frac{dV}{dt} = \frac{\pi}{48}\left(3y^2\frac{dy}{dt}\right)$$

or

$$\frac{dy}{dt} = \frac{16}{\pi y^2}\frac{dV}{dt} = \frac{16}{\pi y^2}(-2) = -\frac{32}{\pi y^2} \tag{9}$$

which expresses $dy/dt$ in terms of $y$. The minus sign tells us that $y$ is decreasing with time, and

$$\left|\frac{dy}{dt}\right| = \frac{32}{\pi y^2}$$

tells us how fast $y$ is decreasing. From this formula we see that $|dy/dt|$ increases as $y$ decreases, which confirms our conjecture in part (a) that the depth of the liquid decreases more quickly as the liquid drains through the filter.

***Solution (c).*** The rate at which the depth is changing when the depth is 8 cm can be obtained from (9) with $y = 8$:

$$\left.\frac{dy}{dt}\right|_{y=8} = -\frac{32}{\pi(8^2)} = -\frac{1}{2\pi} \approx -0.16 \text{ cm/min} \blacktriangleleft$$

## ✓ QUICK CHECK EXERCISES 3.4

(See page 153 for answers.)

1. If $A = x^2$ and $\dfrac{dx}{dt} = 3$, find $\left.\dfrac{dA}{dt}\right|_{x=10}$.
2. If $A = x^2$ and $\dfrac{dA}{dt} = 3$, find $\left.\dfrac{dx}{dt}\right|_{x=10}$.
3. A 10-foot ladder stands on a horizontal floor and leans against a vertical wall. Use $x$ to denote the distance along the floor from the wall to the foot of the ladder, and use $y$ to denote the distance along the wall from the floor to the top of the ladder. If the foot of the ladder is dragged away from the wall, find an equation that relates rates of change of $x$ and $y$ with respect to time.
4. Suppose that a block of ice in the shape of a right circular cylinder melts so that it retains its cylindrical shape. Find an equation that relates the rates of change of the volume ($V$), height ($h$), and radius ($r$) of the block of ice.

## EXERCISE SET 3.4

**1–4** Both $x$ and $y$ denote functions of $t$ that are related by the given equation. Use this equation and the given derivative information to find the specified derivative. ■

1. Equation: $y = 3x + 5$.
   (a) Given that $dx/dt = 2$, find $dy/dt$ when $x = 1$.
   (b) Given that $dy/dt = -1$, find $dx/dt$ when $x = 0$.
2. Equation: $x + 4y = 3$.
   (a) Given that $dx/dt = 1$, find $dy/dt$ when $x = 2$.
   (b) Given that $dy/dt = 4$, find $dx/dt$ when $x = 3$.
3. Equation: $4x^2 + 9y^2 = 1$.
   (a) Given that $dx/dt = 3$, find $dy/dt$ when $(x, y) = \left(\frac{1}{2\sqrt{2}}, \frac{1}{3\sqrt{2}}\right)$.
   (b) Given that $dy/dt = 8$, find $dx/dt$ when $(x, y) = \left(\frac{1}{3}, -\frac{\sqrt{5}}{9}\right)$.
4. Equation: $x^2 + y^2 = 2x + 4y$.
   (a) Given that $dx/dt = -5$, find $dy/dt$ when $(x, y) = (3, 1)$.
   (b) Given that $dy/dt = 6$, find $dx/dt$ when $(x, y) = (1 + \sqrt{2}, 2 + \sqrt{3})$.

**FOCUS ON CONCEPTS**

5. Let $A$ be the area of a square whose sides have length $x$, and assume that $x$ varies with the time $t$.
   (a) Draw a picture of the square with the labels $A$ and $x$ placed appropriately.
   (b) Write an equation that relates $A$ and $x$.
   (c) Use the equation in part (b) to find an equation that relates $dA/dt$ and $dx/dt$.
   (d) At a certain instant the sides are 3 ft long and increasing at a rate of 2 ft/min. How fast is the area increasing at that instant?
6. In parts (a)–(d), let $A$ be the area of a circle of radius $r$, and assume that $r$ increases with the time $t$.
   (a) Draw a picture of the circle with the labels $A$ and $r$ placed appropriately.
   (b) Write an equation that relates $A$ and $r$.
   (c) Use the equation in part (b) to find an equation that relates $dA/dt$ and $dr/dt$.
   (d) At a certain instant the radius is 5 cm and increasing at the rate of 2 cm/s. How fast is the area increasing at that instant?

**7.** Let $V$ be the volume of a cylinder having height $h$ and radius $r$, and assume that $h$ and $r$ vary with time.
(a) How are $dV/dt$, $dh/dt$, and $dr/dt$ related?
(b) At a certain instant, the height is 6 in and increasing at 1 in/s, while the radius is 10 in and decreasing at 1 in/s. How fast is the volume changing at that instant? Is the volume increasing or decreasing at that instant?

**8.** Let $l$ be the length of a diagonal of a rectangle whose sides have lengths $x$ and $y$, and assume that $x$ and $y$ vary with time.
(a) How are $dl/dt$, $dx/dt$, and $dy/dt$ related?
(b) If $x$ increases at a constant rate of $\frac{1}{2}$ ft/s and $y$ decreases at a constant rate of $\frac{1}{4}$ ft/s, how fast is the size of the diagonal changing when $x = 3$ ft and $y = 4$ ft? Is the diagonal increasing or decreasing at that instant?

**9.** Let $\theta$ (in radians) be an acute angle in a right triangle, and let $x$ and $y$, respectively, be the lengths of the sides adjacent to and opposite $\theta$. Suppose also that $x$ and $y$ vary with time.
(a) How are $d\theta/dt$, $dx/dt$, and $dy/dt$ related?
(b) At a certain instant, $x = 2$ units and is increasing at 1 unit/s, while $y = 2$ units and is decreasing at $\frac{1}{4}$ unit/s. How fast is $\theta$ changing at that instant? Is $\theta$ increasing or decreasing at that instant?

**10.** Suppose that $z = x^3y^2$, where both $x$ and $y$ are changing with time. At a certain instant when $x = 1$ and $y = 2$, $x$ is decreasing at the rate of 2 units/s, and $y$ is increasing at the rate of 3 units/s. How fast is $z$ changing at this instant? Is $z$ increasing or decreasing?

**11.** The minute hand of a certain clock is 4 in long. Starting from the moment when the hand is pointing straight up, how fast is the area of the sector that is swept out by the hand increasing at any instant during the next revolution of the hand?

**12.** A stone dropped into a still pond sends out a circular ripple whose radius increases at a constant rate of 3 ft/s. How rapidly is the area enclosed by the ripple increasing at the end of 10 s?

**13.** Oil spilled from a ruptured tanker spreads in a circle whose area increases at a constant rate of 6 mi$^2$/h. How fast is the radius of the spill increasing when the area is 9 mi$^2$?

**14.** A spherical balloon is inflated so that its volume is increasing at the rate of 3 ft$^3$/min. How fast is the diameter of the balloon increasing when the radius is 1 ft?

**15.** A spherical balloon is to be deflated so that its radius decreases at a constant rate of 15 cm/min. At what rate must air be removed when the radius is 9 cm?

**16.** A 17 ft ladder is leaning against a wall. If the bottom of the ladder is pulled along the ground away from the wall at a constant rate of 5 ft/s, how fast will the top of the ladder be moving down the wall when it is 8 ft above the ground?

**17.** A 13 ft ladder is leaning against a wall. If the top of the ladder slips down the wall at a rate of 2 ft/s, how fast will the foot be moving away from the wall when the top is 5 ft above the ground?

**18.** A 10 ft plank is leaning against a wall. If at a certain instant the bottom of the plank is 2 ft from the wall and is being pushed toward the wall at the rate of 6 in/s, how fast is the acute angle that the plank makes with the ground increasing?

**19.** A softball diamond is a square whose sides are 60 ft long. Suppose that a player running from first to second base has a speed of 25 ft/s at the instant when she is 10 ft from second base. At what rate is the player's distance from home plate changing at that instant?

**20.** A rocket, rising vertically, is tracked by a radar station that is on the ground 5 mi from the launchpad. How fast is the rocket rising when it is 4 mi high and its distance from the radar station is increasing at a rate of 2000 mi/h?

**21.** For the camera and rocket shown in Figure 3.4.5, at what rate is the camera-to-rocket distance changing when the rocket is 4000 ft up and rising vertically at 880 ft/s?

**22.** For the camera and rocket shown in Figure 3.4.5, at what rate is the rocket rising when the elevation angle is $\pi/4$ radians and increasing at a rate of 0.2 rad/s?

**23.** A satellite is in an elliptical orbit around the Earth. Its distance $r$ (in miles) from the center of the Earth is given by

$$r = \frac{4995}{1 + 0.12\cos\theta}$$

where $\theta$ is the angle measured from the point on the orbit nearest the Earth's surface (see the accompanying figure).
(a) Find the altitude of the satellite at ***perigee*** (the point nearest the surface of the Earth) and at ***apogee*** (the point farthest from the surface of the Earth). Use 3960 mi as the radius of the Earth.
(b) At the instant when $\theta$ is 120°, the angle $\theta$ is increasing at the rate of 2.7°/min. Find the altitude of the satellite and the rate at which the altitude is changing at this instant. Express the rate in units of mi/min.

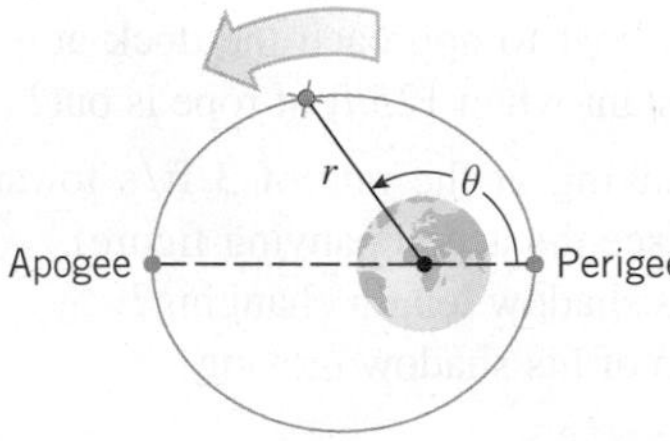

**Figure Ex-23**

**24.** An aircraft is flying horizontally at a constant height of 4000 ft above a fixed observation point (see the accompanying figure on the next page). At a certain instant the angle of elevation $\theta$ is 30° and decreasing, and the speed of the aircraft is 300 mi/h.
(a) How fast is $\theta$ decreasing at this instant? Express the result in units of deg/s.
(b) How fast is the distance between the aircraft and the observation point changing at this instant? Express the result in units of ft/s. Use 1 mi = 5280 ft.

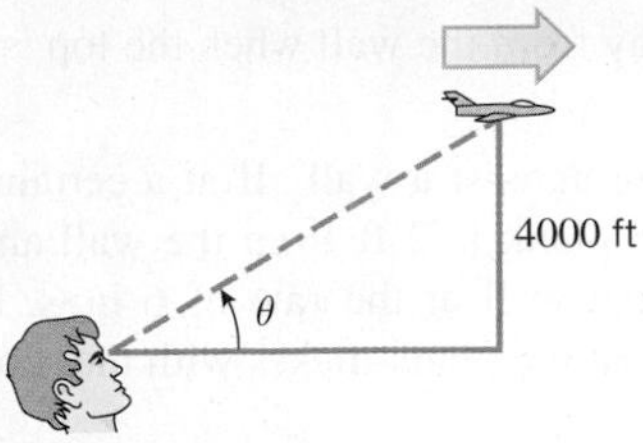


◀ **Figure Ex-24**

**25.** A conical water tank with vertex down has a radius of 10 ft at the top and is 24 ft high. If water flows into the tank at a rate of 20 $\text{ft}^3/\text{min}$, how fast is the depth of the water increasing when the water is 16 ft deep?

**26.** Grain pouring from a chute at the rate of 8 $\text{ft}^3/\text{min}$ forms a conical pile whose height is always twice its radius. How fast is the height of the pile increasing at the instant when the pile is 6 ft high?

**27.** Sand pouring from a chute forms a conical pile whose height is always equal to the diameter. If the height increases at a constant rate of 5 ft/min, at what rate is sand pouring from the chute when the pile is 10 ft high?

**28.** Wheat is poured through a chute at the rate of 10 $\text{ft}^3/\text{min}$ and falls in a conical pile whose bottom radius is always half the altitude. How fast will the circumference of the base be increasing when the pile is 8 ft high?

**29.** An aircraft is climbing at a $30^\circ$ angle to the horizontal. How fast is the aircraft gaining altitude if its speed is 500 mi/h?

**30.** A boat is pulled into a dock by means of a rope attached to a pulley on the dock (see the accompanying figure). The rope is attached to the bow of the boat at a point 10 ft below the pulley. If the rope is pulled through the pulley at a rate of 20 ft/min, at what rate will the boat be approaching the dock when 125 ft of rope is out?

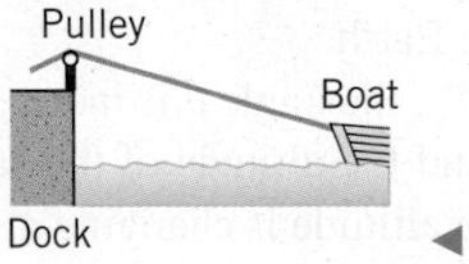


◀ **Figure Ex-30**

**31.** For the boat in Exercise 30, how fast must the rope be pulled if we want the boat to approach the dock at a rate of 12 ft/min at the instant when 125 ft of rope is out?

**32.** A man 6 ft tall is walking at the rate of 3 ft/s toward a streetlight 18 ft high (see the accompanying figure).
(a) At what rate is his shadow length changing?
(b) How fast is the tip of his shadow moving?

◀ **Figure Ex-32**

**33.** A beacon that makes one revolution every 10 s is located on a ship anchored 4 kilometers from a straight shoreline. How fast is the beam moving along the shoreline when it makes an angle of $45^\circ$ with the shore?

**34.** An aircraft is flying at a constant altitude with a constant speed of 600 mi/h. An antiaircraft missile is fired on a straight line perpendicular to the flight path of the aircraft so that it will hit the aircraft at a point $P$ (see the accompanying figure). At the instant the aircraft is 2 mi from the impact point $P$ the missile is 4 mi from $P$ and flying at 1200 mi/h. At that instant, how rapidly is the distance between missile and aircraft decreasing?

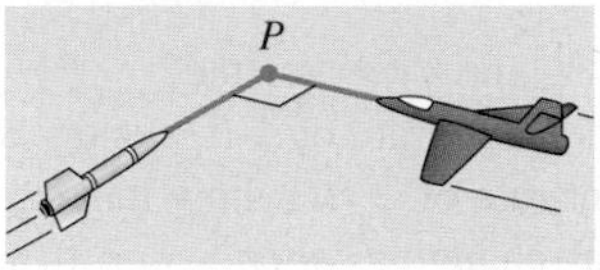


◀ **Figure Ex-34**

**35.** Solve Exercise 34 under the assumption that the angle between the flight paths is $120^\circ$ instead of the assumption that the paths are perpendicular. [*Hint:* Use the law of cosines.]

**36.** A police helicopter is flying due north at 100 mi/h and at a constant altitude of $\frac{1}{2}$ mi. Below, a car is traveling west on a highway at 75 mi/h. At the moment the helicopter crosses over the highway the car is 2 mi east of the helicopter.
(a) How fast is the distance between the car and helicopter changing at the moment the helicopter crosses the highway?
(b) Is the distance between the car and helicopter increasing or decreasing at that moment?

**37.** A particle is moving along the curve whose equation is
$$\frac{xy^3}{1+y^2} = \frac{8}{5}$$
Assume that the $x$-coordinate is increasing at the rate of 6 units/s when the particle is at the point $(1, 2)$.
(a) At what rate is the $y$-coordinate of the point changing at that instant?
(b) Is the particle rising or falling at that instant?

**38.** A point $P$ is moving along the curve whose equation is $y = \sqrt{x^3 + 17}$. When $P$ is at $(2, 5)$, $y$ is increasing at the rate of 2 units/s. How fast is $x$ changing?

**39.** A point $P$ is moving along the line whose equation is $y = 2x$. How fast is the distance between $P$ and the point $(3, 0)$ changing at the instant when $P$ is at $(3, 6)$ if $x$ is decreasing at the rate of 2 units/s at that instant?

**40.** A point $P$ is moving along the curve whose equation is $y = \sqrt{x}$. Suppose that $x$ is increasing at the rate of 4 units/s when $x = 3$.
(a) How fast is the distance between $P$ and the point $(2, 0)$ changing at this instant?
(b) How fast is the angle of inclination of the line segment from $P$ to $(2, 0)$ changing at this instant?

**41.** A particle is moving along the curve $y = x/(x^2 + 1)$. Find all values of $x$ at which the rate of change of $x$ with respect to time is three times that of $y$. [Assume that $dx/dt$ is never zero.]

**42.** A new design for a wind turbine adjusts the length of the turbine blade to keep the generated power constant even if the wind speed changes by a small amount. Assume that the power $P$ (in watts) generated by the turbine can be expressed as $P = 0.87\ell^2\nu^3$, where $\ell$ is the length of the blade in meters and $\nu$ is the speed of the wind in meters per second. Suppose the wind speed is increasing at a constant rate of 0.01 m/s$^2$ and that the length of the blade adjusts to keep the generated power constant. Determine how quickly $\ell$ is changing at the moment when $\ell = 16$ and $\nu = 4$.

**43.** The ***thin lens equation*** in physics is

$$\frac{1}{s} + \frac{1}{S} = \frac{1}{f}$$

where $s$ is the object distance from the lens, $S$ is the image distance from the lens, and $f$ is the focal length of the lens. Suppose that a certain lens has a focal length of 6 cm and that an object is moving toward the lens at the rate of 2 cm/s. How fast is the image distance changing at the instant when the object is 10 cm from the lens? Is the image moving away from the lens or toward the lens?

**44.** Water is stored in a cone-shaped reservoir (vertex down). Assuming the water evaporates at a rate proportional to the surface area exposed to the air, show that the depth of the water will decrease at a constant rate that does not depend on the dimensions of the reservoir.

**45.** A meteor enters the Earth's atmosphere and burns up at a rate that, at each instant, is proportional to its surface area. Assuming that the meteor is always spherical, show that the radius decreases at a constant rate.

**46.** On a certain clock the minute hand is 4 in long and the hour hand is 3 in long. How fast is the distance between the tips of the hands changing at 9 o'clock?

**47.** Coffee is poured at a uniform rate of 20 cm$^3$/s into a cup whose inside is shaped like a truncated cone (see the accompanying figure). If the upper and lower radii of the cup are 4 cm and 2 cm and the height of the cup is 6 cm, how fast will the coffee level be rising when the coffee is halfway up? [*Hint:* Extend the cup downward to form a cone.]

◀ **Figure Ex-47**

✓ **QUICK CHECK ANSWERS 3.4** 1. 60 2. $\frac{3}{20}$ 3. $x\frac{dx}{dt} + y\frac{dy}{dt} = 0$ 4. $\frac{dV}{dt} = 2\pi rh\frac{dr}{dt} + \pi r^2\frac{dh}{dt}$

## 3.5 LOCAL LINEAR APPROXIMATION; DIFFERENTIALS

*In this section we will use derivatives to approximate nonlinear functions by linear functions. Also, up to now we have interpreted dy/dx as simply a notation for the derivative. In this section we will define the quantities dx and dy themselves, thereby allowing us to interpret dy/dx as an actual ratio.*

Recall from Section 2.2 that if a function $f$ is differentiable at $x_0$, then a sufficiently magnified portion of the graph of $f$ centered at the point $P(x_0, f(x_0))$ takes on the appearance of a straight line segment. Figure 3.5.1 illustrates this at several points on the graph of $y = x^2 + 1$. For this reason, a function that is differentiable at $x_0$ is sometimes said to be ***locally linear*** at $x_0$.

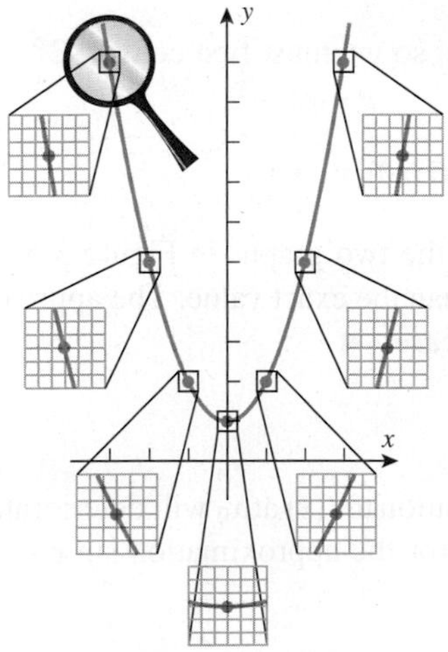


Magnifying portions of the graph of $y = x^2 + 1$

▲ **Figure 3.5.1**

The line that best approximates the graph of $f$ in the vicinity of $P(x_0, f(x_0))$ is the tangent line to the graph of $f$ at $x_0$, given by the equation

$$y = f(x_0) + f'(x_0)(x - x_0)$$

[see Formula (3) of Section 2.2]. Thus, for values of $x$ near $x_0$ we can approximate values of $f(x)$ by

$$f(x) \approx f(x_0) + f'(x_0)(x - x_0) \tag{1}$$

This is called the ***local linear approximation*** of $f$ at $x_0$. This formula can also be expressed in terms of the increment $\Delta x = x - x_0$ as

$$f(x_0 + \Delta x) \approx f(x_0) + f'(x_0)\Delta x \tag{2}$$

▶ **Example 1**

(a) Find the local linear approximation of $f(x) = \sqrt{x}$ at $x_0 = 1$.

(b) Use the local linear approximation obtained in part (a) to approximate $\sqrt{1.1}$, and compare your approximation to the result produced directly by a calculating utility.

***Solution (a).*** Since $f'(x) = 1/(2\sqrt{x})$, it follows from (1) that the local linear approximation of $\sqrt{x}$ at a point $x_0$ is

$$\sqrt{x} \approx \sqrt{x_0} + \frac{1}{2\sqrt{x_0}}(x - x_0)$$

Thus, the local linear approximation at $x_0 = 1$ is

$$\sqrt{x} \approx 1 + \tfrac{1}{2}(x - 1) \tag{3}$$

The graphs of $y = \sqrt{x}$ and the local linear approximation $y = 1 + \frac{1}{2}(x - 1)$ are shown in Figure 3.5.2.

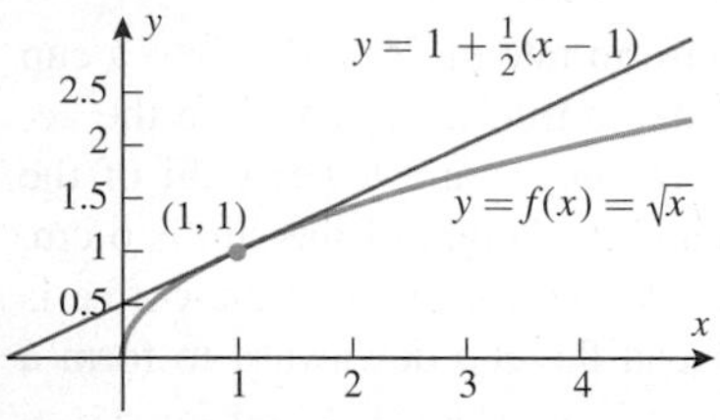


▲ **Figure 3.5.2**

***Solution (b).*** Applying (3) with $x = 1.1$ yields

$$\sqrt{1.1} \approx 1 + \tfrac{1}{2}(1.1 - 1) = 1.05$$

Since the tangent line $y = 1 + \frac{1}{2}(x - 1)$ in Figure 3.5.2 lies above the graph of $f(x) = \sqrt{x}$, we would expect this approximation to be slightly too large. This expectation is confirmed by the approximation $\sqrt{1.1} \approx 1.04881$. ◄

Examples 1 and 2 illustrate important ideas and are not meant to suggest that you should use local linear approximations for computations that your calculating utility can perform. The main application of local linear approximation is in modeling problems where it is useful to replace complicated functions by simpler ones.

### ▶ Example 2

(a) Find the local linear approximation of $f(x) = \sin x$ at $x_0 = 0$.

(b) Use the local linear approximation obtained in part (a) to approximate $\sin 2^\circ$, and compare your approximation to the result produced directly by your calculating device.

***Solution (a).*** Since $f'(x) = \cos x$, it follows from (1) that the local linear approximation of $\sin x$ at a point $x_0$ is

$$\sin x \approx \sin x_0 + (\cos x_0)(x - x_0)$$

Thus, the local linear approximation at $x_0 = 0$ is

$$\sin x \approx \sin 0 + (\cos 0)(x - 0)$$

which simplifies to

$$\sin x \approx x \tag{4}$$

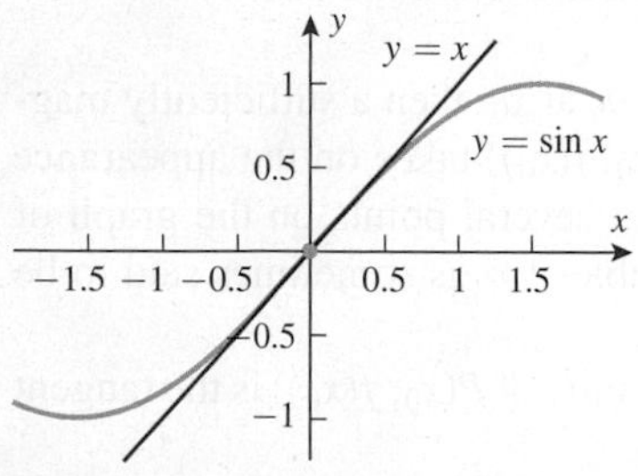


▲ **Figure 3.5.3**

***Solution (b).*** The variable $x$ in (4) is in radian measure, so we must first convert $2^\circ$ to radians before we can apply this approximation. Since

$$2^\circ = 2\left(\frac{\pi}{180}\right) = \frac{\pi}{90} \approx 0.0349066 \text{ radian}$$

it follows from (4) that $\sin 2^\circ \approx 0.0349066$. Comparing the two graphs in Figure 3.5.3, we would expect this approximation to be slightly larger than the exact value. The approximation $\sin 2^\circ \approx 0.0348995$ shows that this is indeed the case. ◄

## ■ ERROR IN LOCAL LINEAR APPROXIMATIONS

As a general rule, the accuracy of the local linear approximation to $f(x)$ at $x_0$ will deteriorate as $x$ gets progressively farther from $x_0$. To illustrate this for the approximation $\sin x \approx x$ in Example 2, let us graph the function

$$E(x) = |\sin x - x|$$

which is the absolute value of the error in the approximation (Figure 3.5.4).

In Figure 3.5.4, the graph shows how the absolute error in the local linear approximation of $\sin x$ increases as $x$ moves progressively farther from 0 in either the positive or negative direction. The graph also tells us that for values of $x$ between the two vertical lines, the absolute error does not exceed 0.01. Thus, for example, we could use the local linear approximation $\sin x \approx x$ for all values of $x$ in the interval $-0.35 < x < 0.35$ (radians) with confidence that the approximation is within $\pm 0.01$ of the exact value.

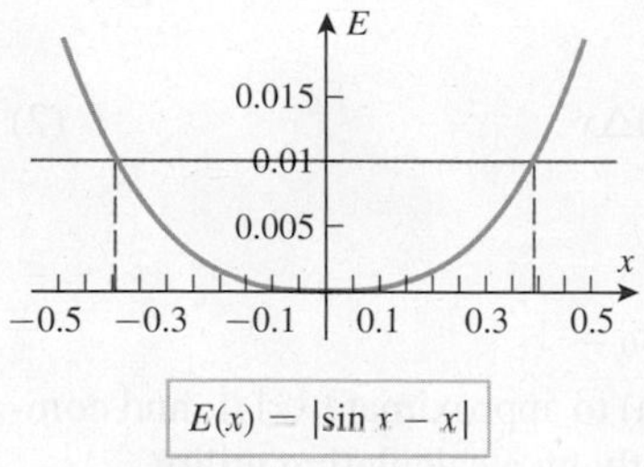


▲ **Figure 3.5.4**

## DIFFERENTIALS

Up to now we have interpreted $dy/dx$ as a single entity representing the derivative of $y$ with respect to $x$; the symbols "$dy$" and "$dx$," which are called ***differentials***, have had no meanings attached to them. Our next goal is to define these symbols in such a way that $dy/dx$ can be treated as an actual ratio. To do this, assume that $f$ is differentiable at a point $x$, *define* $dx$ to be an independent variable that can have any real value, and *define* $dy$ by the formula

$$dy = f'(x)\,dx \tag{5}$$

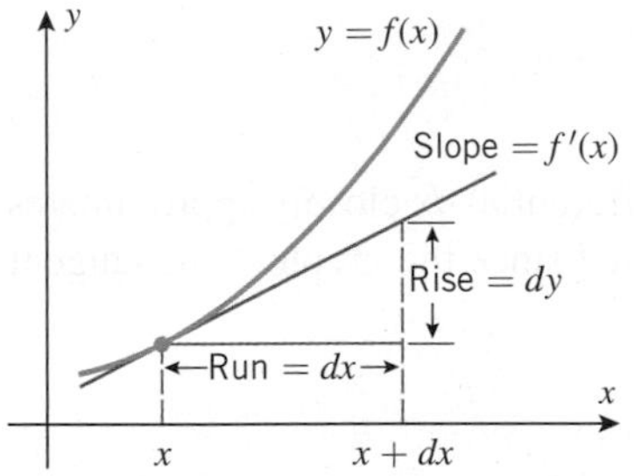


▲ **Figure 3.5.5**

If $dx \neq 0$, then we can divide both sides of (5) by $dx$ to obtain

$$\frac{dy}{dx} = f'(x) \tag{6}$$

This achieves our goal of defining $dy$ and $dx$ so their ratio is $f'(x)$. Formula (5) is said to express (6) in ***differential form***.

To interpret (5) geometrically, note that $f'(x)$ is the slope of the tangent line to the graph of $f$ at $x$. The differentials $dy$ and $dx$ can be viewed as a corresponding rise and run of this tangent line (Figure 3.5.5).

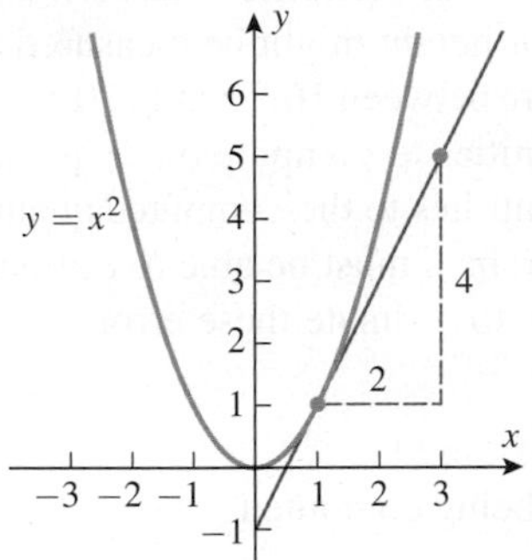


▲ **Figure 3.5.6**

▶ **Example 3** Express the derivative with respect to $x$ of $y = x^2$ in differential form, and discuss the relationship between $dy$ and $dx$ at $x = 1$.

***Solution.*** The derivative of $y$ with respect to $x$ is $dy/dx = 2x$, which can be expressed in differential form as

$$dy = 2x\,dx$$

When $x = 1$ this becomes

$$dy = 2\,dx$$

This tells us that if we travel along the tangent line to the curve $y = x^2$ at $x = 1$, then a change of $dx$ units in $x$ produces a change of $2\,dx$ units in $y$. Thus, for example, a run of $dx = 2$ units produces a rise of $dy = 4$ units along the tangent line (Figure 3.5.6). ◀

It is important to understand the distinction between the increment $\Delta y$ and the differential $dy$. To see the difference, let us assign the independent variables $dx$ and $\Delta x$ the same value, so $dx = \Delta x$. Then $\Delta y$ represents the change in $y$ that occurs when we start at $x$ and travel *along the curve* $y = f(x)$ until we have moved $\Delta x\,(= dx)$ units in the $x$-direction, while $dy$ represents the change in $y$ that occurs if we start at $x$ and travel *along the tangent line* until we have moved $dx\,(= \Delta x)$ units in the $x$-direction (Figure 3.5.7).

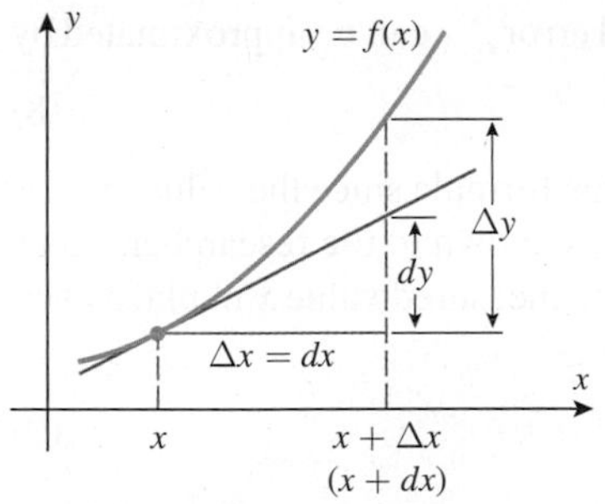


▲ **Figure 3.5.7**

▶ **Example 4** Let $y = \sqrt{x}$.

(a) Find formulas for $\Delta y$ and $dy$.

(b) Evaluate $\Delta y$ and $dy$ at $x = 4$ with $dx = \Delta x = 3$. Then make a sketch of $y = \sqrt{x}$, showing the values of $\Delta y$ and $dy$ in the picture.

***Solution (a).*** With $y = f(x) = \sqrt{x}$ we obtain

$$\Delta y = f(x + \Delta x) - f(x) = \sqrt{x + \Delta x} - \sqrt{x}$$

and

$$\frac{dy}{dx} = \frac{1}{2\sqrt{x}}, \quad \text{so} \quad dy = \frac{1}{2\sqrt{x}}\,dx$$

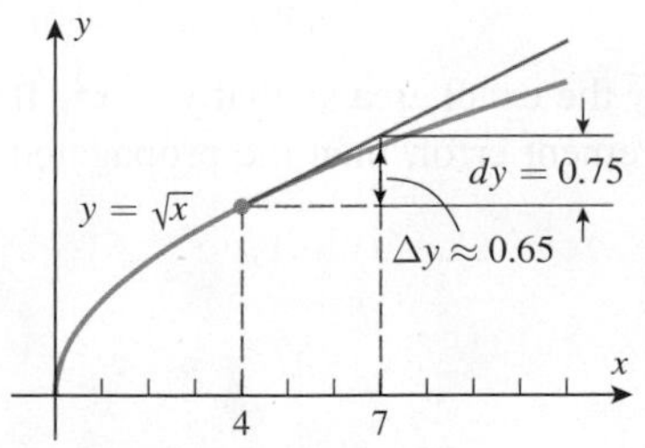


▲ **Figure 3.5.8**

***Solution (b).*** At $x = 4$ with $dx = \Delta x = 3$,

$$\Delta y = \sqrt{7} - \sqrt{4} \approx 0.65$$

and

$$dy = \frac{1}{2\sqrt{4}}(3) = \frac{3}{4} = 0.75$$

Figure 3.5.8 shows the curve $y = \sqrt{x}$ together with $\Delta y$ and $dy$. ◀

## LOCAL LINEAR APPROXIMATION FROM THE DIFFERENTIAL POINT OF VIEW

Although $\Delta y$ and $dy$ are generally different, the differential $dy$ will be a good approximation of $\Delta y$ provided $dx = \Delta x$ is close to 0. To see this, recall from Section 2.2 that

$$f'(x) = \lim_{\Delta x \to 0} \frac{\Delta y}{\Delta x}$$

It follows that if $\Delta x$ is close to 0, then we will have $f'(x) \approx \Delta y/\Delta x$ or, equivalently,

$$\Delta y \approx f'(x)\Delta x$$

If we agree to let $dx = \Delta x$, then we can rewrite this as

$$\Delta y \approx f'(x)\,dx = dy \tag{7}$$

In words, this states that for values of $dx$ near zero the differential $dy$ closely approximates the increment $\Delta y$ (Figure 3.5.7). But this is to be expected since the graph of the tangent line at $x$ is the local linear approximation of the graph of $f$.

## ERROR PROPAGATION

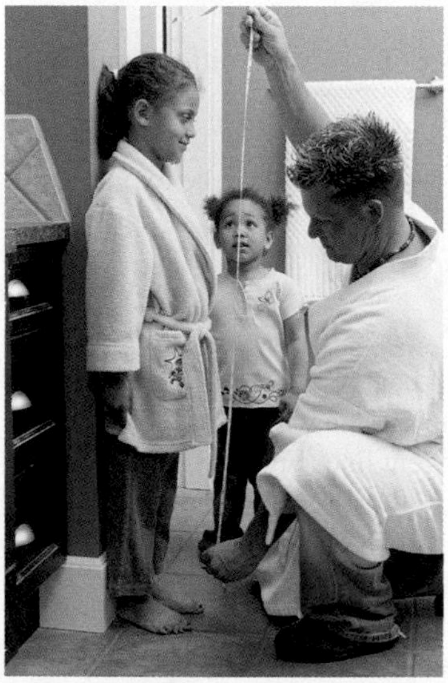

Wave Royalty Free/Science Source Images

*Real-world measurements inevitably have small errors.*

In real-world applications, small errors in measured quantities will invariably occur. These measurement errors are of importance in scientific research—all scientific measurements come with measurement errors included. For example, your height might be measured as $170 \pm 0.5$ cm, meaning that your exact height lies somewhere between 169.5 and 170.5 cm. Researchers often must use these inexactly measured quantities to compute other quantities, thereby *propagating* the errors from the measured quantitites to the computed quantities. This phenomenon is called ***error propagation***. Researchers must be able to estimate errors in the computed quantities. Our goal is to show how to estimate these errors using differentials. For this purpose, suppose

$x_0$ is the exact value of the quantity being measured
$y_0 = f(x_0)$ is the exact value of the quantity being computed
$x$ is the measured value of $x_0$
$y = f(x)$ is the computed value of $y$

We define

$dx\ (= \Delta x) = x - x_0$ to be the ***measurement error*** of $x$
$\Delta y = f(x) - f(x_0)$ to be the ***propagated error*** of $y$

It follows from (7) with $x_0$ replacing $x$ that the propagated error $\Delta y$ can be approximated by

$$\Delta y \approx dy = f'(x_0)\,dx \tag{8}$$

Unfortunately, there is a practical difficulty in applying this formula since the value of $x_0$ is unknown. (Keep in mind that only the measured value $x$ is known to the researcher.) This being the case, it is standard practice in research to use the measured value $x$ in place of $x_0$ in (8) and use the approximation

$$\Delta y \approx dy = f'(x)\,dx \tag{9}$$

for the propagated error.

> Note that measurement error is positive if the measured value is greater than the exact value and is negative if it is less than the exact value. The sign of the propagated error conveys similar information.

**▶ Example 5** Suppose that the side of a square is measured with a ruler to be 10 inches with a measurement error of at most $\pm\frac{1}{32}$ in. Estimate the error in the computed area of the square.

> Explain why an error estimate of at most $\pm\frac{1}{32}$ inch is reasonable for a ruler that is calibrated in sixteenths of an inch.

***Solution.*** Let $x$ denote the exact length of a side and $y$ the exact area so that $y = x^2$. It follows from (9) with $f(x) = x^2$ that if $dx$ is the measurement error, then the propagated error $\Delta y$ can be approximated as

$$\Delta y \approx dy = 2x\,dx$$

Substituting the measured value $x = 10$ into this equation yields

$$dy = 20\,dx \tag{10}$$

But to say that the measurement error is at most $\pm\frac{1}{32}$ means that

$$-\frac{1}{32} \le dx \le \frac{1}{32}$$

Multiplying these inequalities through by 20 and applying (10) yields

$$20\left(-\tfrac{1}{32}\right) \le dy \le 20\left(\tfrac{1}{32}\right) \quad \text{or equivalently} \quad -\tfrac{5}{8} \le dy \le \tfrac{5}{8}$$

Thus, the propagated error in the area is estimated to be within $\pm\frac{5}{8}$ in$^2$. ◀

If the true value of a quantity is $q$ and a measurement or calculation produces an error $\Delta q$, then $\Delta q/q$ is called the ***relative error*** in the measurement or calculation; when expressed as a percentage, $\Delta q/q$ is called the ***percentage error***. As a practical matter, the true value $q$ is usually unknown, so that the measured or calculated value of $q$ is used instead; and the relative error is approximated by $dq/q$.

▶ **Example 6** The diameter of a polyurethane sphere is measured with percentage error within $\pm 0.4\%$. Estimate the percentage error in the calculated volume of the sphere.

***Solution.*** A sphere of diameter $x$ has radius $r = x/2$ and volume

$$V = \frac{4}{3}\pi r^3 = \frac{4}{3}\pi\left(\frac{x}{2}\right)^3 = \frac{1}{6}\pi x^3$$

ssuaphoto/iStockphoto

*Polyurethane spheres are used in the maintenance of oil and gas pipelines.*

Therefore

$$\frac{dV}{dx} = \frac{1}{2}\pi x^2 \quad \text{and} \quad dV = \frac{1}{2}\pi x^2\,dx$$

The relative error in $V$ is then approximately

$$\frac{dV}{V} = \frac{\frac{1}{2}\pi x^2\,dx}{\frac{1}{6}\pi x^3} = 3\,\frac{dx}{x} \tag{11}$$

We are given that the percentage error in the measured value of $x$ is within $\pm 0.4\%$, which means that

$$-0.004 \le \frac{dx}{x} \le 0.004$$

Multiplying these inequalities through by 3 and applying (11) yields

$$-0.012 \le \frac{dV}{V} \le 0.012$$

Thus, we estimate the percentage error in the calculated value of $V$ to be within $\pm 1.2\%$. ◀

## MORE NOTATION; DIFFERENTIAL FORMULAS

The symbol $df$ is another common notation for the differential of a function $y = f(x)$. For example, if $f(x) = \sin x$, then we can write $df = \cos x\,dx$. We can also view the symbol "$d$" as an *operator* that acts on a function to produce the corresponding differential. For example, $d[x^2] = 2x\,dx$, $d[\sin x] = \cos x\,dx$, and so on. All of the general rules of differentiation then have corresponding differential versions:

| DERIVATIVE FORMULA | DIFFERENTIAL FORMULA |
|---|---|
| $\frac{d}{dx}[c] = 0$ | $d[c] = 0$ |
| $\frac{d}{dx}[cf] = c\frac{df}{dx}$ | $d[cf] = c\,df$ |
| $\frac{d}{dx}[f+g] = \frac{df}{dx} + \frac{dg}{dx}$ | $d[f+g] = df + dg$ |
| $\frac{d}{dx}[fg] = f\frac{dg}{dx} + g\frac{df}{dx}$ | $d[fg] = f\,dg + g\,df$ |
| $\frac{d}{dx}\left[\frac{f}{g}\right] = \frac{g\frac{df}{dx} - f\frac{dg}{dx}}{g^2}$ | $d\left[\frac{f}{g}\right] = \frac{g\,df - f\,dg}{g^2}$ |

For example,

$$\begin{aligned} d[x^2 \sin x] &= (x^2 \cos x + 2x \sin x)\,dx \\ &= x^2(\cos x\,dx) + (2x\,dx)\sin x \\ &= x^2 d[\sin x] + (\sin x)\,d[x^2] \end{aligned}$$

illustrates the differential version of the product rule.

## ✓ QUICK CHECK EXERCISES 3.5 (See page 160 for answers.)

1. The local linear approximation of $f$ at $x_0$ uses the ______ line to the graph of $y = f(x)$ at $x = x_0$ to approximate values of ______ for values of $x$ near ______.

2. Find an equation for the local linear approximation to $y = 5 - x^2$ at $x_0 = 2$.

3. Let $y = 5 - x^2$. Find $dy$ and $\Delta y$ at $x = 2$ with $dx = \Delta x = 0.1$.

4. The intensity of light from a light source is a function $I = f(x)$ of the distance $x$ from the light source. Suppose that a small gemstone is measured to be 10 m from a light source, $f(10) = 0.2\ \text{W/m}^2$, and $f'(10) = -0.04\ \text{W/m}^3$. If the distance $x = 10$ m was obtained with a measurement error within $\pm 0.05$ m, estimate the percentage error in the calculated intensity of the light on the gemstone.

## EXERCISE SET 3.5 Graphing Utility

1. (a) Use Formula (1) to obtain the local linear approximation of $x^3$ at $x_0 = 1$.
   (b) Use Formula (2) to rewrite the approximation obtained in part (a) in terms of $\Delta x$.
   (c) Use the result obtained in part (a) to approximate $(1.02)^3$, and confirm that the formula obtained in part (b) produces the same result.

2. (a) Use Formula (1) to obtain the local linear approximation of $1/x$ at $x_0 = 2$.
   (b) Use Formula (2) to rewrite the approximation obtained in part (a) in terms of $\Delta x$.
   (c) Use the result obtained in part (a) to approximate $1/2.05$, and confirm that the formula obtained in part (b) produces the same result.

**FOCUS ON CONCEPTS**

3. (a) Find the local linear approximation of the function $f(x) = \sqrt{1+x}$ at $x_0 = 0$, and use it to approximate $\sqrt{0.9}$ and $\sqrt{1.1}$.
   (b) Graph $f$ and its tangent line at $x_0$ together, and use the graphs to illustrate the relationship between the exact values and the approximations of $\sqrt{0.9}$ and $\sqrt{1.1}$.

4. A student claims that whenever a local linear approximation is used to approximate the square root of a number, the approximation is too large.
   (a) Write a few sentences that make the student's claim precise, and justify this claim geometrically.
   (b) Verify the student's claim algebraically using approximation (1).

**5–10** Confirm that the stated formula is the local linear approximation at $x_0 = 0$. ■

5. $(1+x)^{15} \approx 1 + 15x$

6. $\dfrac{1}{\sqrt{1-x}} \approx 1 + \frac{1}{2}x$

7. $\tan x \approx x$

8. $\dfrac{1}{1+x} \approx 1 - x$

9. $e^x \approx 1 + x$

10. $\ln(1+x) \approx x$

**11–16** Confirm that the stated formula is the local linear approximation of $f$ at $x_0 = 1$, where $\Delta x = x - 1$. ■

11. $f(x) = x^4$; $(1+\Delta x)^4 \approx 1 + 4\Delta x$

12. $f(x) = \sqrt{x}$; $\sqrt{1+\Delta x} \approx 1 + \frac{1}{2}\Delta x$

13. $f(x) = \dfrac{1}{2+x}$; $\dfrac{1}{3+\Delta x} \approx \dfrac{1}{3} - \dfrac{1}{9}\Delta x$

14. $f(x) = (4+x)^3$; $(5+\Delta x)^3 \approx 125 + 75\Delta x$

**15.** $\tan^{-1}x$; $\tan^{-1}(1+\Delta x) \approx \frac{\pi}{4} + \frac{1}{2}\Delta x$

**16.** $\sin^{-1}\left(\frac{x}{2}\right)$; $\sin^{-1}\left(\frac{1}{2} + \frac{1}{2}\Delta x\right) \approx \frac{\pi}{6} + \frac{1}{\sqrt{3}}\Delta x$

**17–20** Confirm that the formula is the local linear approximation at $x_0 = 0$, and use a graphing utility to estimate an interval of $x$-values on which the error is at most $\pm 0.1$. ■

**17.** $\sqrt{x+3} \approx \sqrt{3} + \frac{1}{2\sqrt{3}}x$ **18.** $\frac{1}{\sqrt{9-x}} \approx \frac{1}{3} + \frac{1}{54}x$

**19.** $\tan 2x \approx 2x$ **20.** $\frac{1}{(1+2x)^5} \approx 1 - 10x$

**21.** (a) Use the local linear approximation of $\sin x$ at $x_0 = 0$ obtained in Example 2 to approximate $\sin 1^\circ$, and compare the approximation to the result produced directly by your calculating device.
(b) How would you choose $x_0$ to approximate $\sin 44^\circ$?
(c) Approximate $\sin 44^\circ$; compare the approximation to the result produced directly by your calculating device.

**22.** (a) Use the local linear approximation of $\tan x$ at $x_0 = 0$ to approximate $\tan 2^\circ$, and compare the approximation to the result produced directly by your calculating device.
(b) How would you choose $x_0$ to approximate $\tan 61^\circ$?
(c) Approximate $\tan 61^\circ$; compare the approximation to the result produced directly by your calculating device.

**23–33** Use an appropriate local linear approximation to estimate the value of the given quantity. ■

**23.** $(3.02)^4$ **24.** $(1.97)^3$ **25.** $\sqrt{65}$
**26.** $\sqrt{24}$ **27.** $\sqrt{80.9}$ **28.** $\sqrt{36.03}$
**29.** $\sin 0.1$ **30.** $\tan 0.2$ **31.** $\cos 31^\circ$
**32.** $\ln(1.01)$ **33.** $\tan^{-1}(0.99)$

**FOCUS ON CONCEPTS**

**34.** The approximation $(1+x)^k \approx 1 + kx$ is commonly used by engineers for quick calculations.
(a) Derive this result, and use it to make a rough estimate of $(1.001)^{37}$.
(b) Compare your estimate to that produced directly by your calculating device.
(c) If $k$ is a positive integer, how is the approximation $(1+x)^k \approx 1 + kx$ related to the expansion of $(1+x)^k$ using the binomial theorem?

**35.** Use the approximation $(1+x)^k \approx 1 + kx$, along with some mental arithmetic to show that $\sqrt[3]{8.24} \approx 2.02$ and $4.08^{3/2} \approx 8.24$.

**36.** Referring to the accompanying figure, suppose that the angle of elevation of the top of the building, as measured from a point 500 ft from its base, is found to be $\theta = 6^\circ$. Use an appropriate local linear approximation, along with some mental arithmetic to show that the building is about 52 ft high.

◀ **Figure Ex-36**

**37.** (a) Let $y = 1/x$. Find $dy$ and $\Delta y$ at $x = 1$ with $dx = \Delta x = -0.5$.
(b) Sketch the graph of $y = 1/x$, showing $dy$ and $\Delta y$ in the picture.

**38.** (a) Let $y = \sqrt{x}$. Find $dy$ and $\Delta y$ at $x = 9$ with $dx = \Delta x = -1$.
(b) Sketch the graph of $y = \sqrt{x}$, showing $dy$ and $\Delta y$ in the picture.

**39–42** Find formulas for $dy$ and $\Delta y$. ■

**39.** $y = x^3$ **40.** $y = 8x - 4$
**41.** $y = x^2 - 2x + 1$ **42.** $y = \sin x$

**43–46** Find the differential $dy$. ■

**43.** (a) $y = 4x^3 - 7x^2$ (b) $y = x\cos x$
**44.** (a) $y = 1/x$ (b) $y = 5\tan x$
**45.** (a) $y = x\sqrt{1-x}$ (b) $y = (1+x)^{-17}$
**46.** (a) $y = \frac{1}{x^3 - 1}$ (b) $y = \frac{1-x^3}{2-x}$

**47–50 True–False** Determine whether the statement is true or false. Explain your answer. ■

**47.** A differential $dy$ is defined to be a very small change in $y$.

**48.** The error in approximation (2) is the same as the error in approximation (7).

**49.** A local linear approximation to a function can never be identically equal to the function.

**50.** A local linear approximation to a nonconstant function can never be constant.

**51–54** Use the differential $dy$ to approximate $\Delta y$ when $x$ changes as indicated. ■

**51.** $y = \sqrt{3x-2}$; from $x = 2$ to $x = 2.03$

**52.** $y = \sqrt{x^2+8}$; from $x = 1$ to $x = 0.97$

**53.** $y = \frac{x}{x^2+1}$; from $x = 2$ to $x = 1.96$

**54.** $y = x\sqrt{8x+1}$; from $x = 3$ to $x = 3.05$

**55.** The side of a square is measured to be 10 ft, with a possible error of $\pm 0.1$ ft.
(a) Use differentials to estimate the error in the calculated area.
(b) Estimate the percentage errors in the side and the area.

**56.** The side of a cube is measured to be 25 cm, with a possible error of $\pm 1$ cm.
(a) Use differentials to estimate the error in the calculated volume.
(b) Estimate the percentage errors in the side and volume.

**57.** The hypotenuse of a right triangle is known to be 10 in exactly, and one of the acute angles is measured to be $30^\circ$, with a possible error of $\pm 1^\circ$.
(a) Use differentials to estimate the errors in the sides opposite and adjacent to the measured angle.
(b) Estimate the percentage errors in the sides.

**58.** One side of a right triangle is known to be 25 cm exactly. The angle opposite to this side is measured to be 60°, with a possible error of ±0.5°.
(a) Use differentials to estimate the errors in the adjacent side and the hypotenuse.
(b) Estimate the percentage errors in the adjacent side and hypotenuse.

**59.** The electrical resistance $R$ of a certain wire is given by $R = k/r^2$, where $k$ is a constant and $r$ is the radius of the wire. Assuming that the radius $r$ has a possible error of ±5%, use differentials to estimate the percentage error in $R$. (Assume $k$ is exact.)

**60.** A long high-voltage power line is 18 feet above the ground. The electric current in the line generates a magnetic field whose magnitude $F$ (in microtesla) is given by $F = 36/L$, where $L$ is the (perpendicular) distance to the line in feet. Suppose that a new regulation requires the power line to be raised everywhere by 0.9 ft. Use a differential to estimate the decrease in the value of $F$ at a point on the ground directly beneath the line.

**61.** The area of a right triangle with a hypotenuse of $H$ is calculated using the formula $A = \frac{1}{4}H^2 \sin 2\theta$, where $\theta$ is one of the acute angles. Use differentials to approximate the error in calculating $A$ if $H = 4$ cm (exactly) and $\theta$ is measured to be 30°, with a possible error of ±15′.

**62.** The side of a square is measured with a possible percentage error of ±1%. Use differentials to estimate the percentage error in the area.

**63.** The side of a cube is measured with a possible percentage error of ±2%. Use differentials to estimate the percentage error in the volume.

**64.** The volume of a sphere is to be computed from a measured value of its radius. Estimate the maximum permissible percentage error in the measurement if the percentage error in the volume must be kept within ±3%. ($V = \frac{4}{3}\pi r^3$ is the volume of a sphere of radius $r$.)

**65.** The area of a circle is to be computed from a measured value of its diameter. Estimate the maximum permissible percentage error in the measurement if the percentage error in the area must be kept within ±1%.

**66.** A steel cube with 1-inch sides is coated with 0.01 inch of copper. Use differentials to estimate the volume of copper in the coating. [*Hint:* Let $\Delta V$ be the change in the volume of the cube.]

**67.** A metal rod 15 cm long and 5 cm in diameter is to be covered (except for the ends) with insulation that is 0.1 cm thick. Use differentials to estimate the volume of insulation. [*Hint:* Let $\Delta V$ be the change in volume of the rod.]

**68.** The time required for one complete oscillation of a pendulum is called its ***period***. If $L$ is the length of the pendulum and the oscillation is small, then the period is given by $P = 2\pi\sqrt{L/g}$, where $g$ is the constant acceleration due to gravity. Use differentials to show that the percentage error in $P$ is approximately half the percentage error in $L$.

**69.** The magnitude $R$ of an earthquake on the Richter scale is related to the amplitude $A$ of the shock wave by the equation

$$R = \log_{10}\left(\frac{A}{A_0}\right)$$

where $A_0$ is a small positive constant. (Originally, $A_0$ was the smallest possible amplitude that could be detected.) Use differentials to show that for a small change in $A$ the change in $R$ can be approximated by multiplying the relative change $\Delta A/A$ in amplitude by 0.4343.

**70.** Suppose that the time $T$ (in days) for a cancerous tumor to double in volume (in cm$^3$) is given by

$$T = \frac{10 \ln 2}{\ln V_1 - \ln V_0} \quad (V_0 < V_1)$$

where $V_0$ is the volume of the tumor when it's first observed and $V_1$ denotes its volume 10 days later. Assume that $V_0$ is correctly measured to be 20 cm$^3$ and $V_1$ is measured to be 33 cm$^3$ with a measurement error of at most ±0.4 cm$^3$. Estimate the error in the computed value of $T$.

**71. Writing** Explain why the local linear approximation of a function value is equivalent to the use of a differential to approximate a change in the function.

**72. Writing** The local linear approximation

$$\sin x \approx x$$

is known as the *small angle approximation* and has both practical and theoretical applications. Do some research on some of these applications, and write a short report on the results of your investigations.

✓ **QUICK CHECK ANSWERS 3.5** 1. tangent; $f(x)$; $x_0$ 2. $y = 1 + (-4)(x - 2)$ or $y = -4x + 9$ 3. $dy = -0.4$, $\Delta y = -0.41$ 4. within ±1%

## 3.6 L'HÔPITAL'S RULE; INDETERMINATE FORMS

*In this section we will discuss a general method for using derivatives to find limits. This method will enable us to establish limits with certainty that earlier in the text we were only able to conjecture using numerical or graphical evidence. The method that we will discuss in this section is an extremely powerful tool that is used internally by many computer programs to calculate limits of various types.*

## INDETERMINATE FORMS OF TYPE 0/0

Recall that a limit of the form

$$\lim_{x\to a} \frac{f(x)}{g(x)} \tag{1}$$

in which $f(x)\to 0$ and $g(x)\to 0$ as $x\to a$ is called an ***indeterminate form of type* 0/0**. Some examples encountered earlier in the text are

$$\lim_{x\to 1} \frac{x^2-1}{x-1} = 2, \quad \lim_{x\to 0} \frac{\sin x}{x} = 1, \quad \lim_{x\to 0} \frac{1-\cos x}{x} = 0$$

The first limit was obtained algebraically by factoring the numerator and canceling the common factor of $x-1$, and the second two limits were obtained using geometric methods. However, there are many indeterminate forms for which neither algebraic nor geometric methods will produce the limit, so we need to develop a more general method.

To motivate such a method, suppose that (1) is an indeterminate form of type 0/0 in which $f'$ and $g'$ are continuous at $x=a$ and $g'(a)\neq 0$. Since $f$ and $g$ can be closely approximated by their local linear approximations near $a$, it is reasonable to expect that

$$\lim_{x\to a} \frac{f(x)}{g(x)} = \lim_{x\to a} \frac{f(a)+f'(a)(x-a)}{g(a)+g'(a)(x-a)} \tag{2}$$

Since we are assuming that $f'$ and $g'$ are continuous at $x=a$, we have

$$\lim_{x\to a} f'(x) = f'(a) \quad \text{and} \quad \lim_{x\to a} g'(x) = g'(a)$$

and since the differentiability of $f$ and $g$ at $x=a$ implies the continuity of $f$ and $g$ at $x=a$, we have

$$f(a) = \lim_{x\to a} f(x) = 0 \quad \text{and} \quad g(a) = \lim_{x\to a} g(x) = 0$$

Thus, we can rewrite (2) as

$$\lim_{x\to a} \frac{f(x)}{g(x)} = \lim_{x\to a} \frac{f'(a)(x-a)}{g'(a)(x-a)} = \lim_{x\to a} \frac{f'(a)}{g'(a)} = \lim_{x\to a} \frac{f'(x)}{g'(x)} \tag{3}$$

This result, called ***L'Hôpital's rule***, converts the given indeterminate form into a limit involving derivatives that is often easier to evaluate.

Although we motivated (3) by assuming that $f$ and $g$ have continuous derivatives at $x=a$ and that $g'(a)\neq 0$, the result is true under less stringent conditions and is also valid for one-sided limits and limits at $+\infty$ and $-\infty$. The proof of the following precise statement of L'Hôpital's rule is omitted.

**3.6.1 THEOREM** (*L'Hôpital's Rule for Form* 0/0) *Suppose that $f$ and $g$ are differentiable functions on an open interval containing $x=a$, except possibly at $x=a$, and that*

$$\lim_{x\to a} f(x) = 0 \quad \textit{and} \quad \lim_{x\to a} g(x) = 0$$

*If $\lim_{x\to a}[f'(x)/g'(x)]$ exists, or if this limit is $+\infty$ or $-\infty$, then*

$$\lim_{x\to a} \frac{f(x)}{g(x)} = \lim_{x\to a} \frac{f'(x)}{g'(x)}$$

*Moreover, this statement is also true in the case of a limit as $x\to a^-, x\to a^+, x\to -\infty$, or as $x\to +\infty$.*

**WARNING**

Note that in L'Hôpital's rule the numerator and denominator are differentiated individually. This is *not* the same as differentiating $f(x)/g(x)$.

In the examples that follow we will apply L'Hôpital's rule using the following three-step process:

*Applying L'Hôpital's Rule*

**Step 1.** Check that the limit of $f(x)/g(x)$ is an indeterminate form of type $0/0$.

**Step 2.** Differentiate $f$ and $g$ separately.

**Step 3.** Find the limit of $f'(x)/g'(x)$. If this limit is finite, $+\infty$, or $-\infty$, then it is equal to the limit of $f(x)/g(x)$.

▶ **Example 1** Find the limit

$$\lim_{x\to 2}\frac{x^2-4}{x-2}$$

using L'Hôpital's rule, and check the result by factoring.

***Solution.*** The numerator and denominator have a limit of 0, so the limit is an indeterminate form of type $0/0$. Applying L'Hôpital's rule yields

$$\lim_{x\to 2}\frac{x^2-4}{x-2}=\lim_{x\to 2}\frac{\frac{d}{dx}[x^2-4]}{\frac{d}{dx}[x-2]}=\lim_{x\to 2}\frac{2x}{1}=4$$

This agrees with the computation

$$\lim_{x\to 2}\frac{x^2-4}{x-2}=\lim_{x\to 2}\frac{(x-2)(x+2)}{x-2}=\lim_{x\to 2}(x+2)=4 \;◀$$

The limit in Example 1 can be interpreted as the limit form of a certain derivative. Use that derivative to evaluate the limit.

▶ **Example 2** In each part confirm that the limit is an indeterminate form of type $0/0$, and evaluate it using L'Hôpital's rule.

(a) $\lim_{x\to 0}\frac{\sin 2x}{x}$ (b) $\lim_{x\to \pi/2}\frac{1-\sin x}{\cos x}$ (c) $\lim_{x\to 0}\frac{e^x-1}{x^3}$

(d) $\lim_{x\to 0^-}\frac{\tan x}{x^2}$ (e) $\lim_{x\to 0}\frac{1-\cos x}{x^2}$ (f) $\lim_{x\to +\infty}\frac{x^{-4/3}}{\sin(1/x)}$

***Solution (a).*** The numerator and denominator have a limit of 0, so the limit is an indeterminate form of type $0/0$. Applying L'Hôpital's rule yields

$$\lim_{x\to 0}\frac{\sin 2x}{x}=\lim_{x\to 0}\frac{\frac{d}{dx}[\sin 2x]}{\frac{d}{dx}[x]}=\lim_{x\to 0}\frac{2\cos 2x}{1}=2$$

Observe that this result agrees with that obtained by substitution in Example 2(b) of Section 1.6.

**Guillaume François Antoine de L'Hôpital (1661–1704)** French mathematician. L'Hôpital, born to parents of the French high nobility, held the title of Marquis de Sainte-Mesme Comte d'Autrement. He showed mathematical talent quite early and at age 15 solved a difficult problem about cycloids posed by Pascal. As a young man he served briefly as a cavalry officer, but resigned because of nearsightedness. In his own time he gained fame as the author of the first textbook ever published on differential calculus, *L'Analyse des Infiniment Petits pour l'Intelligence des Lignes Courbes* (1696). L'Hôpital's rule appeared for the first time in that book. Actually, L'Hôpital's rule and most of the material in the calculus text were due to John Bernoulli, who was L'Hôpital's teacher. L'Hôpital dropped his plans for a book on integral calculus when Leibniz informed him that he intended to write such a text. L'Hôpital was apparently generous and personable, and his many contacts with major mathematicians provided the vehicle for disseminating major discoveries in calculus throughout Europe.

*[Image: Engraving by G. Edelinck, 1695, after Foucher/Wellcome Library, London]*

**WARNING**

Applying L'Hôpital's rule to limits that are not indeterminate forms can produce incorrect results. For example, the computation

$$\lim_{x\to 0}\frac{x+6}{x+2} = \lim_{x\to 0}\frac{\dfrac{d}{dx}[x+6]}{\dfrac{d}{dx}[x+2]} = \lim_{x\to 0}\frac{1}{1} = 1$$

is ***not valid***, since the limit is not an indeterminate form. The correct result is

$$\lim_{x\to 0}\frac{x+6}{x+2} = \frac{0+6}{0+2} = 3$$

***Solution (b).*** The numerator and denominator have a limit of 0, so the limit is an indeterminate form of type $0/0$. Applying L'Hôpital's rule yields

$$\lim_{x\to\pi/2}\frac{1-\sin x}{\cos x} = \lim_{x\to\pi/2}\frac{\dfrac{d}{dx}[1-\sin x]}{\dfrac{d}{dx}[\cos x]} = \lim_{x\to\pi/2}\frac{-\cos x}{-\sin x} = \frac{0}{-1} = 0$$

***Solution (c).*** The numerator and denominator have a limit of 0, so the limit is an indeterminate form of type $0/0$. Applying L'Hôpital's rule yields

$$\lim_{x\to 0}\frac{e^x-1}{x^3} = \lim_{x\to 0}\frac{\dfrac{d}{dx}[e^x-1]}{\dfrac{d}{dx}[x^3]} = \lim_{x\to 0}\frac{e^x}{3x^2} = +\infty$$

***Solution (d).*** The numerator and denominator have a limit of 0, so the limit is an indeterminate form of type $0/0$. Applying L'Hôpital's rule yields

$$\lim_{x\to 0^-}\frac{\tan x}{x^2} = \lim_{x\to 0^-}\frac{\sec^2 x}{2x} = -\infty$$

***Solution (e).*** The numerator and denominator have a limit of 0, so the limit is an indeterminate form of type $0/0$. Applying L'Hôpital's rule yields

$$\lim_{x\to 0}\frac{1-\cos x}{x^2} = \lim_{x\to 0}\frac{\sin x}{2x}$$

Since the new limit is another indeterminate form of type $0/0$, we apply L'Hôpital's rule again:

$$\lim_{x\to 0}\frac{1-\cos x}{x^2} = \lim_{x\to 0}\frac{\sin x}{2x} = \lim_{x\to 0}\frac{\cos x}{2} = \frac{1}{2}$$

***Solution (f).*** The numerator and denominator have a limit of 0, so the limit is an indeterminate form of type $0/0$. Applying L'Hôpital's rule yields

$$\lim_{x\to+\infty}\frac{x^{-4/3}}{\sin(1/x)} = \lim_{x\to+\infty}\frac{-\frac{4}{3}x^{-7/3}}{(-1/x^2)\cos(1/x)} = \lim_{x\to+\infty}\frac{\frac{4}{3}x^{-1/3}}{\cos(1/x)} = \frac{0}{1} = 0 \blacktriangleleft$$

## INDETERMINATE FORMS OF TYPE $\infty/\infty$

When we want to indicate that the limit (or a one-sided limit) of a function is $+\infty$ or $-\infty$ without being specific about the sign, we will say that the limit is $\infty$. For example,

$$\lim_{x\to a^+} f(x) = \infty \quad \text{means} \quad \lim_{x\to a^+} f(x) = +\infty \quad \text{or} \quad \lim_{x\to a^+} f(x) = -\infty$$

$$\lim_{x\to +\infty} f(x) = \infty \quad \text{means} \quad \lim_{x\to +\infty} f(x) = +\infty \quad \text{or} \quad \lim_{x\to +\infty} f(x) = -\infty$$

$$\lim_{x\to a} f(x) = \infty \quad \text{means} \quad \lim_{x\to a^+} f(x) = \pm\infty \quad \text{and} \quad \lim_{x\to a^-} f(x) = \pm\infty$$

The limit of a ratio, $f(x)/g(x)$, in which the numerator has limit $\infty$ and the denominator has limit $\infty$ is called an ***indeterminate form of type*** $\infty/\infty$. The following version of L'Hôpital's rule, which we state without proof, can often be used to evaluate limits of this type.

**3.6.2 THEOREM** (*L'Hôpital's Rule for Form* $\infty/\infty$) *Suppose that f and g are differentiable functions on an open interval containing $x = a$, except possibly at $x = a$, and that*

$$\lim_{x\to a} f(x) = \infty \quad \textit{and} \quad \lim_{x\to a} g(x) = \infty$$

*If* $\lim_{x\to a}[f'(x)/g'(x)]$ *exists, or if this limit is* $+\infty$ *or* $-\infty$*, then*

$$\lim_{x\to a}\frac{f(x)}{g(x)} = \lim_{x\to a}\frac{f'(x)}{g'(x)}$$

*Moreover, this statement is also true in the case of a limit as* $x\to a^-, x\to a^+, x\to -\infty$*, or as* $x\to +\infty$*.*

▶ **Example 3** In each part confirm that the limit is an indeterminate form of type $\infty/\infty$ and apply L'Hôpital's rule.

$$\text{(a)}\ \lim_{x\to+\infty}\frac{x}{e^x} \qquad \text{(b)}\ \lim_{x\to 0^+}\frac{\ln x}{\csc x}$$

***Solution (a).*** The numerator and denominator both have a limit of $+\infty$, so we have an indeterminate form of type $\infty/\infty$. Applying L'Hôpital's rule yields

$$\lim_{x\to+\infty}\frac{x}{e^x} = \lim_{x\to+\infty}\frac{1}{e^x} = 0$$

***Solution (b).*** The numerator has a limit of $-\infty$ and the denominator has a limit of $+\infty$, so we have an indeterminate form of type $\infty/\infty$. Applying L'Hôpital's rule yields

$$\lim_{x\to 0^+}\frac{\ln x}{\csc x} = \lim_{x\to 0^+}\frac{1/x}{-\csc x\cot x} \tag{4}$$

This last limit is again an indeterminate form of type $\infty/\infty$. Moreover, any additional applications of L'Hôpital's rule will yield powers of $1/x$ in the numerator and expressions involving $\csc x$ and $\cot x$ in the denominator; thus, repeated application of L'Hôpital's rule simply produces new indeterminate forms. We must try something else. The last limit in (4) can be rewritten as

$$\lim_{x\to 0^+}\left(-\frac{\sin x}{x}\tan x\right) = -\lim_{x\to 0^+}\frac{\sin x}{x}\cdot\lim_{x\to 0^+}\tan x = -(1)(0) = 0$$

Thus,

$$\lim_{x\to 0^+}\frac{\ln x}{\csc x} = 0 \ ◀$$

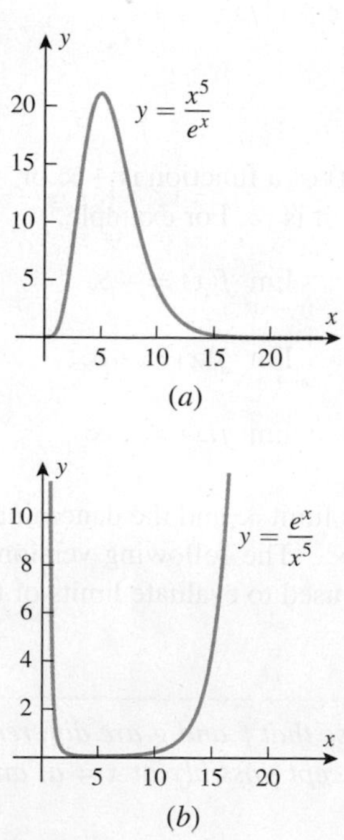

▲ **Figure 3.6.1**

## ANALYZING THE GROWTH OF EXPONENTIAL FUNCTIONS USING L'HÔPITAL'S RULE

If $n$ is any positive integer, then $x^n\to+\infty$ as $x\to+\infty$. Such integer powers of $x$ are sometimes used as "measuring sticks" to describe how rapidly other functions grow. For example, we know that $e^x\to+\infty$ as $x\to+\infty$ and that the growth of $e^x$ is very rapid (Table 1.8.5); however, the growth of $x^n$ is also rapid when $n$ is a high power, so it is reasonable to ask whether high powers of $x$ grow more or less rapidly than $e^x$. One way to investigate this is to examine the behavior of the ratio $x^n/e^x$ as $x\to+\infty$. For example, Figure 3.6.1*a* shows the graph of $y = x^5/e^x$. This graph suggests that $x^5/e^x\to 0$ as $x\to+\infty$, and this implies that the growth of the function $e^x$ is sufficiently rapid that its values eventually overtake those of $x^5$ and force the ratio toward zero. Stated informally, "$e^x$ eventually grows more rapidly than $x^5$." The same conclusion could have been reached by putting $e^x$ on top and examining the behavior of $e^x/x^5$ as $x\to+\infty$ (Figure 3.6.1*b*). In this case the values of $e^x$ eventually overtake those of $x^5$ and force the ratio toward $+\infty$. More generally, we can use L'Hôpital's rule to show that $e^x$ *eventually grows more rapidly than any positive integer power of* $x$, that is,

$$\lim_{x\to+\infty}\frac{x^n}{e^x} = 0 \quad\text{and}\quad \lim_{x\to+\infty}\frac{e^x}{x^n} = +\infty \tag{5–6}$$

Both limits are indeterminate forms of type $\infty/\infty$ that can be evaluated using L'Hôpital's rule. For example, to establish (5), we will need to apply L'Hôpital's rule $n$ times. For this purpose, observe that successive differentiations of $x^n$ reduce the exponent by 1 each time, thus producing a constant for the $n$th derivative. For example, the successive derivatives of $x^3$ are $3x^2$, $6x$, and 6. In general, the $n$th derivative of $x^n$ is $n(n-1)(n-2)\cdots 1 = n!$ (verify).* Thus, applying L'Hôpital's rule $n$ times to (5) yields

$$\lim_{x\to+\infty}\frac{x^n}{e^x} = \lim_{x\to+\infty}\frac{n!}{e^x} = 0$$

Limit (6) can be established similarly.

## INDETERMINATE FORMS OF TYPE $0 \cdot \infty$

Thus far we have discussed indeterminate forms of type $0/0$ and $\infty/\infty$. However, these are not the only possibilities; in general, the limit of an expression that has one of the forms

$$\frac{f(x)}{g(x)},\quad f(x)\cdot g(x),\quad f(x)^{g(x)},\quad f(x)-g(x),\quad f(x)+g(x)$$

is called an *indeterminate form* if the limits of $f(x)$ and $g(x)$ individually exert conflicting influences on the limit of the entire expression. For example, the limit

$$\lim_{x\to 0^+} x\ln x$$

is an ***indeterminate form of type*** $0\cdot\infty$ because the limit of the first factor is 0, the limit of the second factor is $-\infty$, and these two limits exert conflicting influences on the product. On the other hand, the limit

$$\lim_{x\to+\infty}[\sqrt{x}(1-x^2)]$$

is not an indeterminate form because the first factor has a limit of $+\infty$, the second factor has a limit of $-\infty$, and these influences work together to produce a limit of $-\infty$ for the product.

Indeterminate forms of type $0\cdot\infty$ can sometimes be evaluated by rewriting the product as a ratio, and then applying L'Hôpital's rule for indeterminate forms of type $0/0$ or $\infty/\infty$.

**WARNING**

It is tempting to argue that an indeterminate form of type $0\cdot\infty$ has value 0 since "zero times anything is zero." However, this is fallacious since $0\cdot\infty$ is not a product of numbers, but rather a statement about limits. For example, here are two indeterminate forms of type $0\cdot\infty$ whose limits are *not* zero:

$$\lim_{x\to 0}\left(x\cdot\frac{1}{x}\right) = \lim_{x\to 0} 1 = 1$$

$$\lim_{x\to 0^+}\left(\sqrt{x}\cdot\frac{1}{x}\right) = \lim_{x\to 0^+}\left(\frac{1}{\sqrt{x}}\right) = +\infty$$

▶ **Example 4** Evaluate

(a) $\lim_{x\to 0^+} x\ln x$  (b) $\lim_{x\to\pi/4}(1-\tan x)\sec 2x$

***Solution (a).*** The factor $x$ has a limit of 0 and the factor $\ln x$ has a limit of $-\infty$, so the stated problem is an indeterminate form of type $0\cdot\infty$. There are two possible approaches: we can rewrite the limit as

$$\lim_{x\to 0^+}\frac{\ln x}{1/x} \quad\text{or}\quad \lim_{x\to 0^+}\frac{x}{1/\ln x}$$

the first being an indeterminate form of type $\infty/\infty$ and the second an indeterminate form of type $0/0$. However, the first form is the preferred initial choice because the derivative of $1/x$ is less complicated than the derivative of $1/\ln x$. That choice yields

$$\lim_{x\to 0^+} x\ln x = \lim_{x\to 0^+}\frac{\ln x}{1/x} = \lim_{x\to 0^+}\frac{1/x}{-1/x^2} = \lim_{x\to 0^+}(-x) = 0$$

***Solution (b).*** The stated problem is an indeterminate form of type $0\cdot\infty$. We will convert it to an indeterminate form of type $0/0$:

$$\lim_{x\to\pi/4}(1-\tan x)\sec 2x = \lim_{x\to\pi/4}\frac{1-\tan x}{1/\sec 2x} = \lim_{x\to\pi/4}\frac{1-\tan x}{\cos 2x}$$

$$= \lim_{x\to\pi/4}\frac{-\sec^2 x}{-2\sin 2x} = \frac{-2}{-2} = 1 \;◀$$

*Recall that for $n \geq 1$ the expression $n!$, read ***n-factorial***, denotes the product of the first $n$ positive integers.

## INDETERMINATE FORMS OF TYPE $\infty - \infty$

A limit problem that leads to one of the expressions

$$(+\infty) - (+\infty), \quad (-\infty) - (-\infty),$$
$$(+\infty) + (-\infty), \quad (-\infty) + (+\infty)$$

is called an ***indeterminate form of type*** $\infty - \infty$. Such limits are indeterminate because the two terms exert conflicting influences on the expression: one pushes it in the positive direction and the other pushes it in the negative direction. However, limit problems that lead to one of the expressions

$$(+\infty) + (+\infty), \quad (+\infty) - (-\infty),$$
$$(-\infty) + (-\infty), \quad (-\infty) - (+\infty)$$

are not indeterminate, since the two terms work together (those on the top produce a limit of $+\infty$ and those on the bottom produce a limit of $-\infty$).

Indeterminate forms of type $\infty - \infty$ can sometimes be evaluated by combining the terms and manipulating the result to produce an indeterminate form of type $0/0$ or $\infty/\infty$.

▶ **Example 5** Evaluate $\lim\limits_{x\to 0^+} \left(\dfrac{1}{x} - \dfrac{1}{\sin x}\right)$.

***Solution.*** Both terms have a limit of $+\infty$, so the stated problem is an indeterminate form of type $\infty - \infty$. Combining the two terms yields

$$\lim_{x\to 0^+} \left(\frac{1}{x} - \frac{1}{\sin x}\right) = \lim_{x\to 0^+} \frac{\sin x - x}{x \sin x}$$

which is an indeterminate form of type $0/0$. Applying L'Hôpital's rule twice yields

$$\lim_{x\to 0^+} \frac{\sin x - x}{x\sin x} = \lim_{x\to 0^+} \frac{\cos x - 1}{\sin x + x\cos x}$$
$$= \lim_{x\to 0^+} \frac{-\sin x}{\cos x + \cos x - x\sin x} = \frac{0}{2} = 0 \ ◀$$

## INDETERMINATE FORMS OF TYPE $0^0$, $\infty^0$, $1^\infty$

Limits of the form

$$\lim f(x)^{g(x)}$$

can give rise to ***indeterminate forms of the types*** $0^0$, $\infty^0$, ***and*** $1^\infty$. (The interpretations of these symbols should be clear.) For example, the limit

$$\lim_{x\to 0^+} (1+x)^{1/x}$$

whose value we know to be $e$ [see Formula (1) of Section 3.2] is an indeterminate form of type $1^\infty$. It is indeterminate because the expressions $1 + x$ and $1/x$ exert two conflicting influences: the first approaches 1, which drives the expression toward 1, and the second approaches $+\infty$, which drives the expression toward $+\infty$.

Indeterminate forms of types $0^0$, $\infty^0$, and $1^\infty$ can sometimes be evaluated by first introducing a dependent variable

$$y = f(x)^{g(x)}$$

and then computing the limit of $\ln y$. Since

$$\ln y = \ln [f(x)^{g(x)}] = g(x) \cdot \ln [f(x)]$$

the limit of $\ln y$ will be an indeterminate form of type $0 \cdot \infty$ (verify), which can be evaluated by methods we have already studied. Once the limit of $\ln y$ is known, it is a straightforward matter to determine the limit of $y = f(x)^{g(x)}$, as we will illustrate in the next example.

▶ **Example 6** Find $\lim\limits_{x\to 0} (1 + \sin x)^{1/x}$.

***Solution.*** As discussed above, we begin by introducing a dependent variable

$$y = (1 + \sin x)^{1/x}$$

and taking the natural logarithm of both sides:

$$\ln y = \ln(1+\sin x)^{1/x} = \frac{1}{x}\ln(1+\sin x) = \frac{\ln(1+\sin x)}{x}$$

Thus,

$$\lim_{x\to 0} \ln y = \lim_{x\to 0} \frac{\ln(1+\sin x)}{x}$$

which is an indeterminate form of type 0/0, so by L'Hôpital's rule

$$\lim_{x\to 0} \ln y = \lim_{x\to 0} \frac{\ln(1+\sin x)}{x} = \lim_{x\to 0} \frac{(\cos x)/(1+\sin x)}{1} = 1$$

Since we have shown that $\ln y \to 1$ as $x \to 0$, the continuity of the exponential function implies that $e^{\ln y} \to e^1$ as $x \to 0$, and this implies that $y \to e$ as $x \to 0$. Thus,

$$\lim_{x\to 0} (1+\sin x)^{1/x} = e \blacktriangleleft$$

## ✓ QUICK CHECK EXERCISES 3.6 *(See page 169 for answers.)*

1. In each part, does L'Hôpital's rule apply to the given limit?
   (a) $\lim_{x\to 1} \dfrac{2x-2}{x^3+x-2}$ (b) $\lim_{x\to 0} \dfrac{\cos x}{x}$
   (c) $\lim_{x\to 0} \dfrac{e^{2x}-1}{\tan x}$

2. Evaluate each of the limits in Quick Check Exercise 1.

3. Using L'Hôpital's rule, $\lim_{x\to +\infty} \dfrac{e^x}{500x^2} =$ ______.

## EXERCISE SET 3.6 Graphing Utility C CAS

**1–2** Evaluate the given limit without using L'Hôpital's rule, and then check that your answer is correct using L'Hôpital's rule. ■

1. (a) $\lim_{x\to 2} \dfrac{x^2-4}{x^2+2x-8}$ (b) $\lim_{x\to +\infty} \dfrac{2x-5}{3x+7}$

2. (a) $\lim_{x\to 0} \dfrac{\sin x}{\tan x}$ (b) $\lim_{x\to 1} \dfrac{x^2-1}{x^3-1}$

**3–6 True–False** Determine whether the statement is true or false. Explain your answer. ■

3. L'Hôpital's rule does not apply to $\lim_{x\to -\infty} \dfrac{\ln x}{x}$.

4. For any polynomial $p(x)$, $\lim_{x\to +\infty} \dfrac{p(x)}{e^x} = 0$.

5. If $n$ is chosen sufficiently large, then $\lim_{x\to +\infty} \dfrac{(\ln x)^n}{x} = +\infty$.

6. $\lim_{x\to 0^+} (\sin x)^{1/x} = 0$

**7–45** Find the limits. ■

7. $\lim_{x\to 0} \dfrac{e^x-1}{\sin x}$

8. $\lim_{x\to 0} \dfrac{\sin 2x}{\sin 5x}$

9. $\lim_{\theta\to 0} \dfrac{\tan\theta}{\theta}$

10. $\lim_{t\to 0} \dfrac{te^t}{1-e^t}$

11. $\lim_{x\to \pi^+} \dfrac{\sin x}{x-\pi}$

12. $\lim_{x\to 0^+} \dfrac{\sin x}{x^2}$

13. $\lim_{x\to +\infty} \dfrac{\ln x}{x}$

14. $\lim_{x\to +\infty} \dfrac{e^{3x}}{x^2}$

15. $\lim_{x\to 0^+} \dfrac{\cot x}{\ln x}$

16. $\lim_{x\to 0^+} \dfrac{1-\ln x}{e^{1/x}}$

17. $\lim_{x\to +\infty} \dfrac{x^{100}}{e^x}$

18. $\lim_{x\to 0^+} \dfrac{\ln(\sin x)}{\ln(\tan x)}$

19. $\lim_{x\to 0} \dfrac{\sin^{-1} 2x}{x}$

20. $\lim_{x\to 0} \dfrac{x-\tan^{-1} x}{x^3}$

21. $\lim_{x\to +\infty} xe^{-x}$

22. $\lim_{x\to \pi^-} (x-\pi)\tan \frac{1}{2}x$

23. $\lim_{x\to +\infty} x \sin \dfrac{\pi}{x}$

24. $\lim_{x\to 0^+} \tan x \ln x$

25. $\lim_{x\to \pi/2^-} \sec 3x \cos 5x$

26. $\lim_{x\to \pi} (x-\pi)\cot x$

27. $\lim_{x\to +\infty} (1-3/x)^x$

28. $\lim_{x\to 0} (1+2x)^{-3/x}$

29. $\lim_{x\to 0} (e^x+x)^{1/x}$

30. $\lim_{x\to +\infty} (1+a/x)^{bx}$

31. $\lim_{x\to 1} (2-x)^{\tan[(\pi/2)x]}$

32. $\lim_{x\to +\infty} [\cos(2/x)]^{x^2}$

33. $\lim_{x\to 0} (\csc x - 1/x)$

34. $\lim_{x\to 0} \left(\dfrac{1}{x^2} - \dfrac{\cos 3x}{x^2}\right)$

35. $\lim_{x\to +\infty} (\sqrt{x^2+x} - x)$

36. $\lim_{x\to 0} \left(\dfrac{1}{x} - \dfrac{1}{e^x-1}\right)$

37. $\lim_{x\to +\infty} [x - \ln(x^2+1)]$

38. $\lim_{x\to +\infty} [\ln x - \ln(1+x)]$

39. $\lim_{x\to 0^+} x^{\sin x}$

40. $\lim_{x\to 0^+} (e^{2x}-1)^x$

41. $\lim_{x\to 0^+} \left[-\dfrac{1}{\ln x}\right]^x$

42. $\lim_{x\to +\infty} x^{1/x}$

43. $\lim_{x\to +\infty} (\ln x)^{1/x}$

44. $\lim_{x\to 0^+} (-\ln x)^x$

45. $\lim_{x\to \pi/2^-} (\tan x)^{(\pi/2)-x}$

46. Show that for any positive integer $n$
    (a) $\lim_{x\to +\infty} \dfrac{\ln x}{x^n} = 0$ (b) $\lim_{x\to +\infty} \dfrac{x^n}{\ln x} = +\infty$.

**FOCUS ON CONCEPTS**

**47.** (a) Find the error in the following calculation:

$$\lim_{x\to 1}\frac{x^3-x^2+x-1}{x^3-x^2}=\lim_{x\to 1}\frac{3x^2-2x+1}{3x^2-2x}$$
$$=\lim_{x\to 1}\frac{6x-2}{6x-2}=1$$

(b) Find the correct limit.

**48.** (a) Find the error in the following calculation:

$$\lim_{x\to 2}\frac{e^{3x^2-12x+12}}{x^4-16}=\lim_{x\to 2}\frac{(6x-12)e^{3x^2-12x+12}}{4x^3}=0$$

(b) Find the correct limit.

**49–52** Make a conjecture about the limit by graphing the function involved with a graphing utility; then check your conjecture using L'Hôpital's rule. ■

**49.** $\lim_{x\to+\infty}\dfrac{\ln(\ln x)}{\sqrt{x}}$ **50.** $\lim_{x\to 0^+} x^x$

**51.** $\lim_{x\to 0^+}(\sin x)^{3/\ln x}$ **52.** $\lim_{x\to(\pi/2)^-}\dfrac{4\tan x}{1+\sec x}$

**53–56** Make a conjecture about the equations of horizontal asymptotes, if any, by graphing the equation with a graphing utility; then check your answer using L'Hôpital's rule. ■

**53.** $y=\ln x - e^x$ **54.** $y = x-\ln(1+2e^x)$

**55.** $y=(\ln x)^{1/x}$ **56.** $y=\left(\dfrac{x+1}{x+2}\right)^x$

**57.** Limits of the type

$$0/\infty,\quad \infty/0,\quad 0^\infty,\quad \infty\cdot\infty,\quad +\infty+(+\infty),$$
$$+\infty-(-\infty),\quad -\infty+(-\infty),\quad -\infty-(+\infty)$$

are *not* indeterminate forms. Find the following limits by inspection.

(a) $\lim_{x\to 0^+}\dfrac{x}{\ln x}$ (b) $\lim_{x\to+\infty}\dfrac{x^3}{e^{-x}}$

(c) $\lim_{x\to(\pi/2)^-}(\cos x)^{\tan x}$ (d) $\lim_{x\to 0^+}(\ln x)\cot x$

(e) $\lim_{x\to 0^+}\left(\dfrac{1}{x}-\ln x\right)$ (f) $\lim_{x\to-\infty}(x+x^3)$

**58.** There is a myth that circulates among beginning calculus students which states that all indeterminate forms of types $0^0$, $\infty^0$, and $1^\infty$ have value 1 because "anything to the zero power is 1" and "1 to any power is 1." The fallacy is that $0^0, \infty^0$, and $1^\infty$ are not powers of numbers, but rather descriptions of limits. The following examples, which were suggested by Prof. Jack Staib of Drexel University, show that such indeterminate forms can have any positive real value:

(a) $\lim_{x\to 0^+}[x^{(\ln a)/(1+\ln x)}]=a$ (form $0^0$)

(b) $\lim_{x\to+\infty}[x^{(\ln a)/(1+\ln x)}]=a$ (form $\infty^0$)

(c) $\lim_{x\to 0}[(x+1)^{(\ln a)/x}]=a$ (form $1^\infty$).

Verify these results.

**59–62** Verify that L'Hôpital's rule is of no help in finding the limit; then find the limit, if it exists, by some other method. ■

**59.** $\lim_{x\to+\infty}\dfrac{x+\sin 2x}{x}$ **60.** $\lim_{x\to+\infty}\dfrac{2x-\sin x}{3x+\sin x}$

**61.** $\lim_{x\to+\infty}\dfrac{x(2+\sin 2x)}{x+1}$ **62.** $\lim_{x\to+\infty}\dfrac{x(2+\sin x)}{x^2+1}$

**63.** The accompanying schematic diagram represents an electrical circuit consisting of an electromotive force that produces a voltage $V$, a resistor with resistance $R$, and an inductor with inductance $L$. It is shown in electrical circuit theory that if the voltage is first applied at time $t=0$, then the current $I$ flowing through the circuit at time $t$ is given by

$$I=\frac{V}{R}(1-e^{-Rt/L})$$

What is the effect on the current at a fixed time $t$ if the resistance approaches 0 (i.e., $R\to 0^+$)?

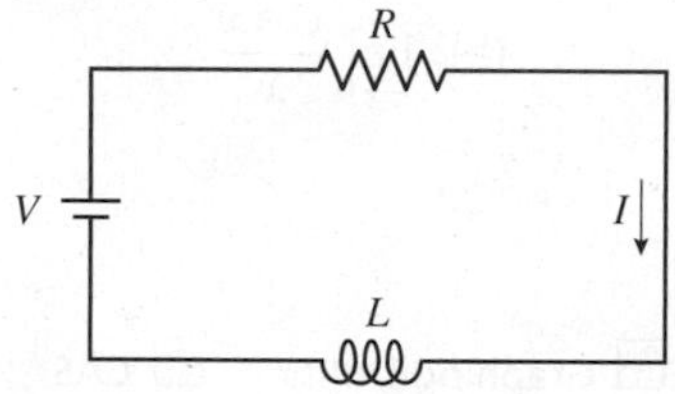


◀ **Figure Ex-63**

**64.** (a) Show that $\lim_{x\to\pi/2}(\pi/2-x)\tan x=1$.

(b) Show that

$$\lim_{x\to\pi/2}\left(\frac{1}{\pi/2-x}-\tan x\right)=0$$

(c) It follows from part (b) that the approximation

$$\tan x\approx\frac{1}{\pi/2-x}$$

should be good for values of $x$ near $\pi/2$. Use a calculator to find $\tan x$ and $1/(\pi/2-x)$ for $x=1.57$; compare the results.

C **65.** (a) Use a CAS to show that if $k$ is a positive constant, then

$$\lim_{x\to+\infty}x(k^{1/x}-1)=\ln k$$

(b) Confirm this result using L'Hôpital's rule. [*Hint:* Express the limit in terms of $t=1/x$.]

(c) If $n$ is a positive integer, then it follows from part (a) with $x=n$ that the approximation

$$n(\sqrt[n]{k}-1)\approx\ln k$$

should be good when $n$ is large. Use this result and the square root key on a calculator to approximate the values of $\ln 0.3$ and $\ln 2$ with $n=1024$, then compare the values obtained with values of the logarithms generated directly from the calculator. [*Hint:* The $n$th roots for which $n$ is a power of 2 can be obtained as successive square roots.]

**66.** Find all values of $k$ and $l$ such that

$$\lim_{x\to 0}\frac{k+\cos lx}{x^2}=-4$$

**FOCUS ON CONCEPTS**

**67.** Let $f(x) = x^2 \sin(1/x)$.
(a) Are the limits $\lim_{x\to 0^+} f(x)$ and $\lim_{x\to 0^-} f(x)$ indeterminate forms?
(b) Use a graphing utility to generate the graph of $f$, and use the graph to make conjectures about the limits in part (a).
(c) Use the Squeezing Theorem (1.6.2) to confirm that your conjectures in part (b) are correct.

**68.** (a) Explain why L'Hôpital's rule does not apply to the problem
$$\lim_{x\to 0} \frac{x^2 \sin(1/x)}{\sin x}$$
(b) Find the limit.

**69.** Find $\lim_{x\to 0^+} \frac{x \sin(1/x)}{\sin x}$ if it exists.

**70.** Suppose that functions $f$ and $g$ are differentiable at $x = a$ and that $f(a) = g(a) = 0$. If $g'(a) \neq 0$, show that
$$\lim_{x\to a} \frac{f(x)}{g(x)} = \frac{f'(a)}{g'(a)}$$
without using L'Hôpital's rule. [*Hint:* Divide the numerator and denominator of $f(x)/g(x)$ by $x - a$ and use the definitions for $f'(a)$ and $g'(a)$.]

**71. Writing** Were we to use L'Hôpital's rule to evaluate either
$$\lim_{x\to 0} \frac{\sin x}{x} \quad \text{or} \quad \lim_{x\to +\infty} \left(1 + \frac{1}{x}\right)^x$$
we could be accused of circular reasoning. Explain why.

**72. Writing** Exercise 58 shows that the indeterminate forms $0^0$ and $\infty^0$ can assume any positive real value. However, it is often the case that these indeterminate forms have value 1. Read the article "Indeterminate Forms of Exponential Type" by John Baxley and Elmer Hayashi in the June–July 1978 issue of *The American Mathematical Monthly*, and write a short report on why this is the case.

**✓ QUICK CHECK ANSWERS 3.6** 1. (a) yes (b) no (c) yes 2. (a) $\frac{1}{2}$ (b) does not exist (c) 2 3. $+\infty$

## CHAPTER 3 REVIEW EXERCISES

Graphing Utility

**1–2** (a) Find $dy/dx$ by differentiating implicitly. (b) Solve the equation for $y$ as a function of $x$, and find $dy/dx$ from that equation. (c) Confirm that the two results are consistent by expressing the derivative in part (a) as a function of $x$ alone. ■

**1.** $x^3 + xy - 2x = 1$ **2.** $xy = x - y$

**3–6** Find $dy/dx$ by implicit differentiation. ■

**3.** $\frac{1}{y} + \frac{1}{x} = 1$ **4.** $x^3 - y^3 = 6xy$

**5.** $\sec(xy) = y$ **6.** $x^2 = \frac{\cot y}{1 + \csc y}$

**7–8** Find $d^2y/dx^2$ by implicit differentiation. ■

**7.** $3x^2 - 4y^2 = 7$ **8.** $2xy - y^2 = 3$

**9.** Use implicit differentiation to find the slope of the tangent line to the curve $y = x\tan(\pi y/2)$, $x > 0$, $y > 0$ (***the quadratrix of Hippias***) at the point $\left(\frac{1}{2}, \frac{1}{2}\right)$.

**10.** At what point(s) is the tangent line to the curve $y^2 = 2x^3$ perpendicular to the line $4x - 3y + 1 = 0$?

**11.** Prove that if $P$ and $Q$ are two distinct points on the rotated ellipse $x^2 + xy + y^2 = 4$ such that $P$, $Q$, and the origin are collinear, then the tangent lines to the ellipse at $P$ and $Q$ are parallel.

**12.** Find the coordinates of the point in the first quadrant at which the tangent line to the curve $x^3 - xy + y^3 = 0$ is parallel to the $x$-axis.

**13.** Find the coordinates of the point in the first quadrant at which the tangent line to the curve $x^3 - xy + y^3 = 0$ is parallel to the $y$-axis.

**14.** Use implicit differentiation to show that the equation of the tangent line to the curve $y^2 = kx$ at $(x_0, y_0)$ is
$$y_0 y = \tfrac{1}{2}k(x + x_0)$$

**15–16** Find $dy/dx$ by first using algebraic properties of the natural logarithm function. ■

**15.** $y = \ln\left(\frac{(x+1)(x+2)^2}{(x+3)^3(x+4)^4}\right)$ **16.** $y = \ln\left(\frac{\sqrt{x}\sqrt[3]{x+1}}{\sin x \sec x}\right)$

**17–34** Find $dy/dx$. ■

**17.** $y = \ln 2x$ **18.** $y = (\ln x)^2$

**19.** $y = \sqrt[3]{\ln x + 1}$ **20.** $y = \ln(\sqrt[3]{x + 1})$

**21.** $y = \log(\ln x)$ **22.** $y = \frac{1 + \log x}{1 - \log x}$

**23.** $y = \ln(x^{3/2}\sqrt{1 + x^4})$ **24.** $y = \ln\left(\frac{\sqrt{x}\cos x}{1 + x^2}\right)$

**25.** $y = e^{\ln(x^2+1)}$ **26.** $y = \ln\left(\frac{1 + e^x + e^{2x}}{1 - e^{3x}}\right)$

**27.** $y = 2xe^{\sqrt{x}}$ **28.** $y = \frac{a}{1 + be^{-x}}$

**29.** $y = \frac{1}{\pi}\tan^{-1} 2x$ **30.** $y = 2^{\sin^{-1} x}$

**31.** $y = x^{(e^x)}$

**32.** $y = (1+x)^{1/x}$

**33.** $y = \sec^{-1}(2x+1)$

**34.** $y = \sqrt{\cos^{-1} x^2}$

**35–36** Find $dy/dx$ using logarithmic differentiation. ■

**35.** $y = \dfrac{x^3}{\sqrt{x^2+1}}$

**36.** $y = \sqrt[3]{\dfrac{x^2-1}{x^2+1}}$

**37.** (a) Make a conjecture about the shape of the graph of $y = \frac{1}{2}x - \ln x$, and draw a rough sketch.
(b) Check your conjecture by graphing the equation over the interval $0 < x < 5$ with a graphing utility.
(c) Show that the slopes of the tangent lines to the curve at $x = 1$ and $x = e$ have opposite signs.
(d) What does part (c) imply about the existence of a horizontal tangent line to the curve? Explain.
(e) Find the exact $x$-coordinates of all horizontal tangent lines to the curve.

**38.** Recall from Section 1.8 that the loudness $\beta$ of a sound in decibels (dB) is given by $\beta = 10\log(I/I_0)$, where $I$ is the intensity of the sound in watts per square meter (W/m$^2$) and $I_0$ is a constant that is approximately the intensity of a sound at the threshold of human hearing. Find the rate of change of $\beta$ with respect to $I$ at the point where
(a) $I/I_0 = 10$ (b) $I/I_0 = 100$ (c) $I/I_0 = 1000$.

**39.** A particle is moving along the curve $y = x\ln x$. Find all values of $x$ at which the rate of change of $y$ with respect to time is three times that of $x$. [Assume that $dx/dt$ is never zero.]

**40.** Find the equation of the tangent line to the graph of $y = \ln(5 - x^2)$ at $x = 2$.

**41.** Find the value of $b$ so that the line $y = x$ is tangent to the graph of $y = \log_b x$. Confirm your result by graphing both $y = x$ and $y = \log_b x$ in the same coordinate system.

**42.** In each part, find the value of $k$ for which the graphs of $y = f(x)$ and $y = \ln x$ share a common tangent line at their point of intersection. Confirm your result by graphing $y = f(x)$ and $y = \ln x$ in the same coordinate system.
(a) $f(x) = \sqrt{x} + k$ (b) $f(x) = k\sqrt{x}$

**43.** If $f$ and $g$ are inverse functions and $f$ is differentiable on its domain, must $g$ be differentiable on its domain? Give a reasonable informal argument to support your answer.

**44.** In each part, find $(f^{-1})'(x)$ using Formula (2) of Section 3.3, and check your answer by differentiating $f^{-1}$ directly.
(a) $f(x) = 3/(x+1)$ (b) $f(x) = \sqrt{e^x}$

**45.** Find a point on the graph of $y = e^{3x}$ at which the tangent line passes through the origin.

**46.** Show that the rate of change of $y = 5000e^{1.07x}$ is proportional to $y$.

**47.** Show that the rate of change of $y = 3^{2x}5^{7x}$ is proportional to $y$.

**48.** The equilibrium constant $k$ of a balanced chemical reaction changes with the absolute temperature $T$ according to the law
$$k = k_0 \exp\left(-\frac{q(T-T_0)}{2T_0T}\right)$$
where $k_0$, $q$, and $T_0$ are constants. Find the rate of change of $k$ with respect to $T$.

**49.** Show that the function $y = e^{ax}\sin bx$ satisfies
$$y'' - 2ay' + (a^2 + b^2)y = 0$$
for any real constants $a$ and $b$.

**50.** Show that the function $y = \tan^{-1} x$ satisfies
$$y'' = -2\sin y \cos^3 y$$

**51.** Suppose that the population of deer on an island is modeled by the equation
$$P(t) = \frac{95}{5 - 4e^{-t/4}}$$
where $P(t)$ is the number of deer $t$ weeks after an initial observation at time $t = 0$.
(a) Use a graphing utility to graph the function $P(t)$.
(b) In words, explain what happens to the population over time. Check your conclusion by finding $\lim_{t\to+\infty} P(t)$.
(c) In words, what happens to the *rate* of population growth over time? Check your conclusion by graphing $P'(t)$.

**52.** In each part, find each limit by interpreting the expression as an appropriate derivative.
(a) $\displaystyle\lim_{h\to 0} \frac{(1+h)^\pi - 1}{h}$ (b) $\displaystyle\lim_{x\to e} \frac{1 - \ln x}{(x-e)\ln x}$

**53.** Suppose that $\lim f(x) = \pm\infty$ and $\lim g(x) = \pm\infty$. In each of the four possible cases, state whether $\lim\,[f(x) - g(x)]$ is an indeterminate form, and give a reasonable informal argument to support your answer.

**54.** (a) Under what conditions will a limit of the form
$$\lim_{x\to a}\,[f(x)/g(x)]$$
be an indeterminate form?
(b) If $\lim_{x\to a} g(x) = 0$, must $\lim_{x\to a}\,[f(x)/g(x)]$ be an indeterminate form? Give some examples to support your answer.

**55–58** Evaluate the given limit. ■

**55.** $\displaystyle\lim_{x\to+\infty} (e^x - x^2)$

**56.** $\displaystyle\lim_{x\to 1} \sqrt{\frac{\ln x}{x^4 - 1}}$

**57.** $\displaystyle\lim_{x\to 0} \frac{x^2 e^x}{\sin^2 3x}$

**58.** $\displaystyle\lim_{x\to 0} \frac{a^x - 1}{x}, \quad a > 0$

**59.** An oil slick on a lake is surrounded by a floating circular containment boom. As the boom is pulled in, the circular containment area shrinks. If the boom is pulled in at the rate of 5 m/min, at what rate is the containment area shrinking when the containment area has a diameter of 100 m?

**60.** The hypotenuse of a right triangle is growing at a constant rate of $a$ centimeters per second and one leg is decreasing at a constant rate of $b$ centimeters per second. How fast is the acute angle between the hypotenuse and the other leg changing at the instant when both legs are 1 cm?

**61.** In each part, use the given information to find $\Delta x$, $\Delta y$, and $dy$.
(a) $y = 1/(x-1)$; $x$ decreases from 2 to 1.5.
(b) $y = \tan x$; $x$ increases from $-\pi/4$ to 0.
(c) $y = \sqrt{25 - x^2}$; $x$ increases from 0 to 3.

**62.** Use an appropriate local linear approximation to estimate the value of $\cot 46°$, and compare your answer to the value obtained with a calculating device.

**63.** The base of the Great Pyramid at Giza is a square that is 230 m on each side.
(a) As illustrated in the accompanying figure, suppose that an archaeologist standing at the center of a side measures the angle of elevation of the apex to be $\phi = 51°$ with an error of $\pm 0.5°$. What can the archaeologist reasonably say about the height of the pyramid?
(b) Use differentials to estimate the allowable error in the elevation angle that will ensure that the error in calculating the height is at most $\pm 5$ m.

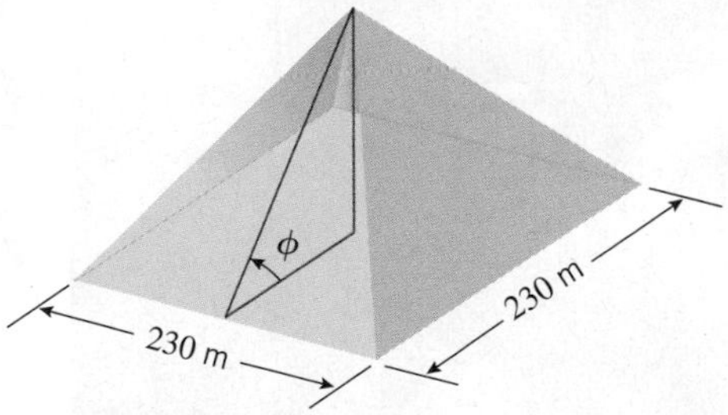

▲ **Figure Ex-63**

## CHAPTER 3 MAKING CONNECTIONS

In these exercises we explore an application of exponential functions to radioactive decay, and we consider another approach to computing the derivative of the natural exponential function.

**1.** Consider a simple model of radioactive decay. We assume that given any quantity of a radioactive element, the fraction of the quantity that decays over a period of time will be a constant that depends on only the particular element and the length of the time period. We choose a time parameter $-\infty < t < +\infty$ and let $A = A(t)$ denote the amount of the element remaining at time $t$. We also choose units of measure such that the initial amount of the element is $A(0) = 1$, and we let $b = A(1)$ denote the amount at time $t = 1$. Prove that the function $A(t)$ has the following properties.

(a) $A(-t) = \dfrac{1}{A(t)}$ [*Hint:* For $t > 0$, you can interpret $A(t)$ as the fraction of any given amount that remains after a time period of length $t$.]

(b) $A(s + t) = A(s) \cdot A(t)$ [*Hint:* First consider positive $s$ and $t$. For the other cases use the property in part (a).]

(c) If $n$ is any nonzero integer, then

$$A\left(\frac{1}{n}\right) = (A(1))^{1/n} = b^{1/n}$$

(d) If $m$ and $n$ are integers with $n \neq 0$, then

$$A\left(\frac{m}{n}\right) = (A(1))^{m/n} = b^{m/n}$$

(e) Assuming that $A(t)$ is a continuous function of $t$, then $A(t) = b^t$. [*Hint:* Prove that if two continuous functions agree on the set of rational numbers, then they are equal.]

(f) If we replace the assumption that $A(0) = 1$ by the condition $A(0) = A_0$, prove that $A = A_0 b^t$.

**2.** Refer to Figure 1.8.5.
(a) Make the substitution $h = 1/x$ and conclude that

$$(1+h)^{1/h} < e < (1-h)^{-1/h} \quad \text{for } h > 0$$

and

$$(1-h)^{-1/h} < e < (1+h)^{1/h} \quad \text{for } h < 0$$

(b) Use the inequalities in part (a) and the Squeezing Theorem to prove that

$$\lim_{h \to 0} \frac{e^h - 1}{h} = 1$$

(c) Explain why the limit in part (b) confirms Figure 1.8.4.
(d) Use the limit in part (b) to prove that

$$\frac{d}{dx}(e^x) = e^x$$

Tomasz Wyszolmirski/iStockphoto

*Derivatives can help to find the most cost-effective location for an offshore oil-drilling rig.*

# 4 THE DERIVATIVE IN GRAPHING AND APPLICATIONS

In this chapter we will study various applications of the derivative. For example, we will use methods of calculus to analyze functions and their graphs. In the process, we will show how calculus and graphing utilities, working together, can provide most of the important information about the behavior of functions. Another important application of the derivative will be in the solution of optimization problems. For example, if time is the main consideration in a problem, we might be interested in finding the quickest way to perform a task, and if cost is the main consideration, we might be interested in finding the least expensive way to perform a task. Mathematically, optimization problems can be reduced to finding the largest or smallest value of a function on some interval, and determining where the largest or smallest value occurs. Using the derivative, we will develop the mathematical tools necessary for solving such problems. We will also use the derivative to study the motion of a particle moving along a line, and we will show how the derivative can help us to approximate solutions of equations.

## 4.1 ANALYSIS OF FUNCTIONS I: INCREASE, DECREASE, AND CONCAVITY

*Although graphing utilities are useful for determining the general shape of a graph, many problems require more precision than graphing utilities are capable of producing. The purpose of this section is to develop mathematical tools that can be used to determine the exact shape of a graph and the precise locations of its key features.*

### INCREASING AND DECREASING FUNCTIONS

The terms *increasing*, *decreasing*, and *constant* are used to describe the behavior of a function as we travel left to right along its graph. For example, the function graphed in Figure 4.1.1 can be described as increasing to the left of $x = 0$, decreasing from $x = 0$ to $x = 2$, increasing from $x = 2$ to $x = 4$, and constant to the right of $x = 4$.

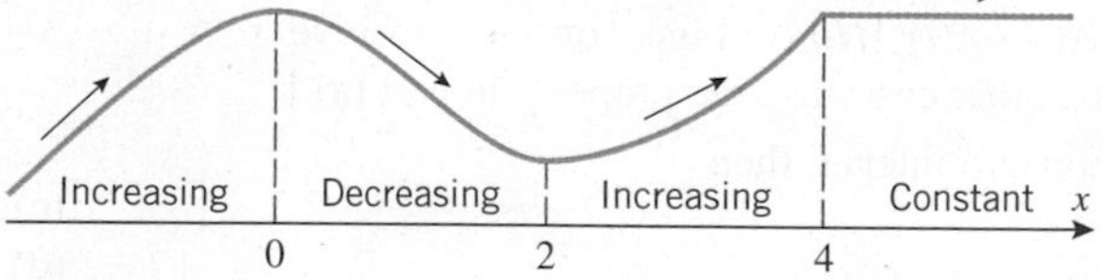


▶ **Figure 4.1.1**

The following definition, which is illustrated in Figure 4.1.2, expresses these intuitive ideas precisely.

The definitions of "increasing," "decreasing," and "constant" describe the behavior of a function on an *interval* and not at a point. In particular, it is not inconsistent to say that the function in Figure 4.1.1 is decreasing on the interval $[0, 2]$ and increasing on the interval $[2, 4]$.

**4.1.1 DEFINITION** Let $f$ be defined on an interval, and let $x_1$ and $x_2$ denote points in that interval.

(a) $f$ is ***increasing*** on the interval if $f(x_1) < f(x_2)$ whenever $x_1 < x_2$.

(b) $f$ is ***decreasing*** on the interval if $f(x_1) > f(x_2)$ whenever $x_1 < x_2$.

(c) $f$ is ***constant*** on the interval if $f(x_1) = f(x_2)$ for all points $x_1$ and $x_2$.

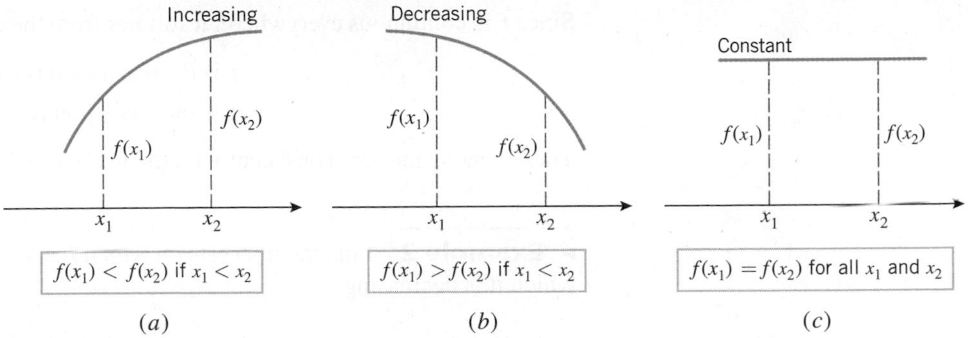


▶ **Figure 4.1.2**

Figure 4.1.3 suggests that a differentiable function $f$ is increasing on any interval where each tangent line to its graph has positive slope, is decreasing on any interval where each tangent line to its graph has negative slope, and is constant on any interval where each tangent line to its graph has zero slope. This intuitive observation suggests the following important theorem that will be proved in Section 4.8.

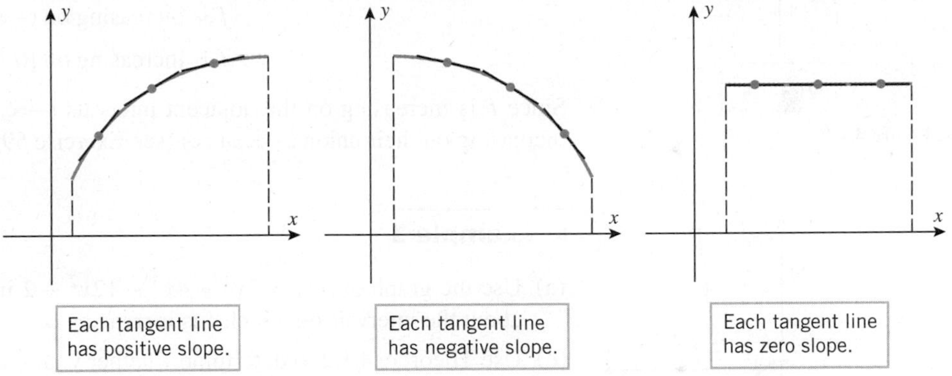


▶ **Figure 4.1.3**

> **4.1.2 THEOREM** *Let $f$ be a function that is continuous on a closed interval $[a, b]$ and differentiable on the open interval $(a, b)$.*
>
> (a) *If $f'(x) > 0$ for every value of $x$ in $(a, b)$, then $f$ is increasing on $[a, b]$.*
>
> (b) *If $f'(x) < 0$ for every value of $x$ in $(a, b)$, then $f$ is decreasing on $[a, b]$.*
>
> (c) *If $f'(x) = 0$ for every value of $x$ in $(a, b)$, then $f$ is constant on $[a, b]$.*

Observe that the derivative conditions in Theorem 4.1.2 are only required to hold *inside* the interval $[a, b]$, even though the conclusions apply to the entire interval.

Although stated for closed intervals, Theorem 4.1.2 is applicable on any interval on which $f$ is continuous. For example, if $f$ is continuous on $[a, +\infty)$ and $f'(x) > 0$ on $(a, +\infty)$, then $f$ is increasing on $[a, +\infty)$; and if $f$ is continuous on $(-\infty, +\infty)$ and $f'(x) < 0$ on $(-\infty, +\infty)$, then $f$ is decreasing on $(-\infty, +\infty)$.

▶ **Example 1** Find the intervals on which $f(x) = x^2 - 4x + 3$ is increasing and the intervals on which it is decreasing.

***Solution.*** The graph of $f$ in Figure 4.1.4 suggests that $f$ is decreasing for $x \leq 2$ and increasing for $x \geq 2$. To confirm this, we analyze the sign of $f'$. The derivative of $f$ is

$$f'(x) = 2x - 4 = 2(x - 2)$$

It follows that

$$f'(x) < 0 \quad \text{if} \quad x < 2$$
$$f'(x) > 0 \quad \text{if} \quad 2 < x$$

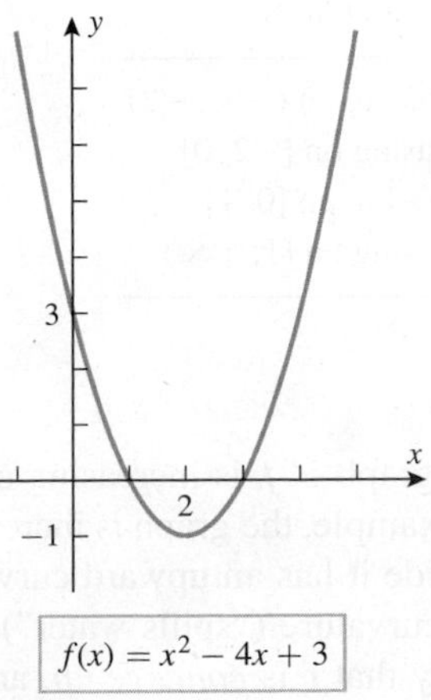


▲ **Figure 4.1.4**

Since $f$ is continuous everywhere, it follows from the comment after Theorem 4.1.2 that

$$f \text{ is decreasing on } (-\infty, 2]$$
$$f \text{ is increasing on } [2, +\infty)$$

These conclusions are consistent with the graph of $f$ in Figure 4.1.4. ◀

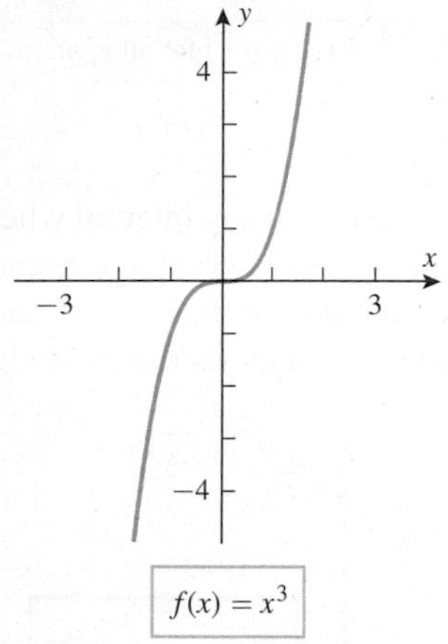


▲ Figure 4.1.5

**▶ Example 2** Find the intervals on which $f(x) = x^3$ is increasing and the intervals on which it is decreasing.

***Solution.*** The graph of $f$ in Figure 4.1.5 suggests that $f$ is increasing over the entire $x$-axis. To confirm this, we differentiate $f$ to obtain $f'(x) = 3x^2$. Thus,

$$f'(x) > 0 \quad \text{if} \quad x < 0$$
$$f'(x) > 0 \quad \text{if} \quad 0 < x$$

Since $f$ is continuous everywhere,

$$f \text{ is increasing on } (-\infty, 0]$$
$$f \text{ is increasing on } [0, +\infty)$$

Since $f$ is increasing on the adjacent intervals $(-\infty, 0]$ and $[0, +\infty)$, it follows that $f$ is increasing on their union $(-\infty, +\infty)$ (see Exercise 59). ◀

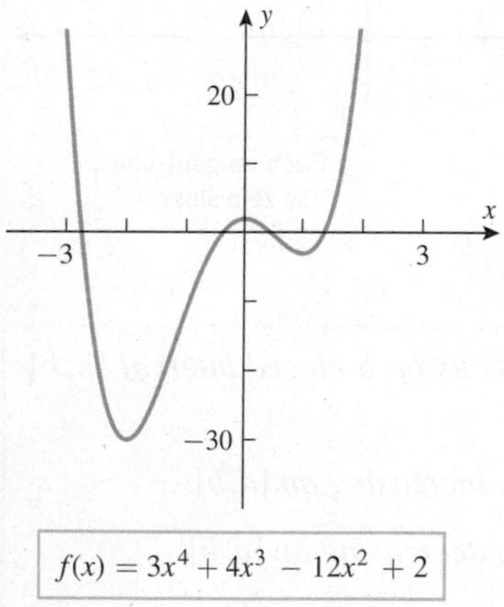


▲ Figure 4.1.6

**▶ Example 3**

(a) Use the graph of $f(x) = 3x^4 + 4x^3 - 12x^2 + 2$ in Figure 4.1.6 to make a conjecture about the intervals on which $f$ is increasing or decreasing.

(b) Use Theorem 4.1.2 to determine whether your conjecture is correct.

***Solution (a).*** The graph suggests that the function $f$ is decreasing if $x \leq -2$, increasing if $-2 \leq x \leq 0$, decreasing if $0 \leq x \leq 1$, and increasing if $x \geq 1$.

***Solution (b).*** Differentiating $f$ we obtain

$$f'(x) = 12x^3 + 12x^2 - 24x = 12x(x^2 + x - 2) = 12x(x + 2)(x - 1)$$

The sign analysis of $f'$ in Table 4.1.1 can be obtained using the method of test points discussed in Web Appendix F. The conclusions in Table 4.1.1 confirm the conjecture in part (a). ◀

**Table 4.1.1**

| INTERVAL | $(12x)(x+2)(x-1)$ | $f'(x)$ | CONCLUSION |
|---|---|---|---|
| $x < -2$ | $(-)(-)(-)$ | $-$ | $f$ is decreasing on $(-\infty, -2]$ |
| $-2 < x < 0$ | $(-)(+)(-)$ | $+$ | $f$ is increasing on $[-2, 0]$ |
| $0 < x < 1$ | $(+)(+)(-)$ | $-$ | $f$ is decreasing on $[0, 1]$ |
| $1 < x$ | $(+)(+)(+)$ | $+$ | $f$ is increasing on $[1, +\infty)$ |

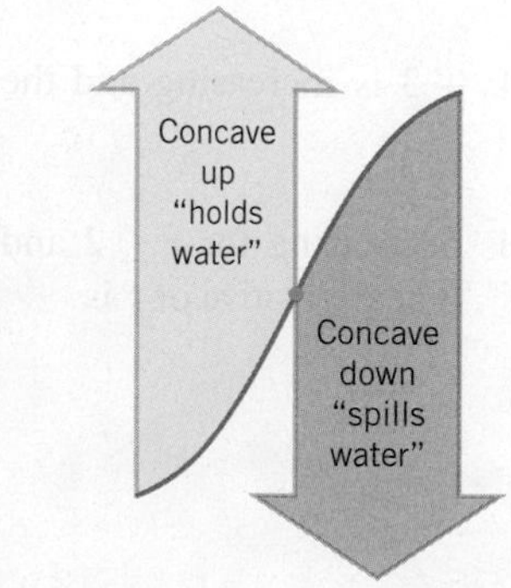


▲ Figure 4.1.7

## ■ CONCAVITY

Although the sign of the derivative of $f$ reveals where the graph of $f$ is increasing or decreasing, it does not reveal the direction of *curvature*. For example, the graph is increasing on both sides of the point in Figure 4.1.7, but on the left side it has an upward curvature ("holds water") and on the right side it has a downward curvature ("spills water"). On intervals where the graph of $f$ has upward curvature we say that $f$ is *concave up*, and on intervals where the graph has downward curvature we say that $f$ is *concave down*.

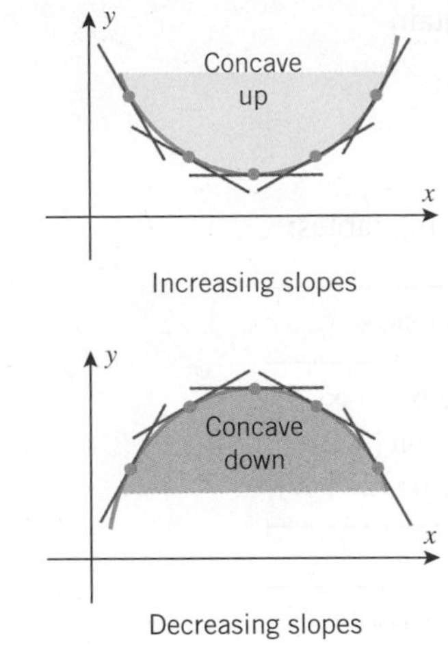


▲ **Figure 4.1.8**

Figure 4.1.8 suggests two ways to characterize the concavity of a differentiable function $f$ on an open interval:

- $f$ is concave up on an open interval if its tangent lines have increasing slopes on that interval and is concave down if they have decreasing slopes.
- $f$ is concave up on an open interval if its graph lies above its tangent lines on that interval and is concave down if it lies below its tangent lines.

Our formal definition for "concave up" and "concave down" corresponds to the first of these characterizations.

> **4.1.3 DEFINITION** If $f$ is differentiable on an open interval, then $f$ is said to be ***concave up*** on the open interval if $f'$ is increasing on that interval, and $f$ is said to be ***concave down*** on the open interval if $f'$ is decreasing on that interval.

Since the slopes of the tangent lines to the graph of a differentiable function $f$ are the values of its derivative $f'$, it follows from Theorem 4.1.2 (applied to $f'$ rather than $f$) that $f'$ will be increasing on intervals where $f''$ is positive and that $f'$ will be decreasing on intervals where $f''$ is negative. Thus, we have the following theorem.

> **4.1.4 THEOREM** *Let $f$ be twice differentiable on an open interval.*
>
> (*a*) *If $f''(x) > 0$ for every value of $x$ in the open interval, then $f$ is concave up on that interval.*
>
> (*b*) *If $f''(x) < 0$ for every value of $x$ in the open interval, then $f$ is concave down on that interval.*

▶ **Example 4** Figure 4.1.4 suggests that the function $f(x) = x^2 - 4x + 3$ is concave up on the interval $(-\infty, +\infty)$. This is consistent with Theorem 4.1.4, since $f'(x) = 2x - 4$ and $f''(x) = 2$, so

$$f''(x) > 0 \quad \text{on the interval } (-\infty, +\infty)$$

Also, Figure 4.1.5 suggests that $f(x) = x^3$ is concave down on the interval $(-\infty, 0)$ and concave up on the interval $(0, +\infty)$. This agrees with Theorem 4.1.4, since $f'(x) = 3x^2$ and $f''(x) = 6x$, so

$$f''(x) < 0 \quad \text{if } x < 0 \quad \text{and} \quad f''(x) > 0 \quad \text{if } x > 0 \blacktriangleleft$$

## INFLECTION POINTS

We see from Example 4 and Figure 4.1.5 that the graph of $f(x) = x^3$ changes from concave down to concave up at $x = 0$. Points where a curve changes from concave up to concave down or vice versa are of special interest, so there is some terminology associated with them.

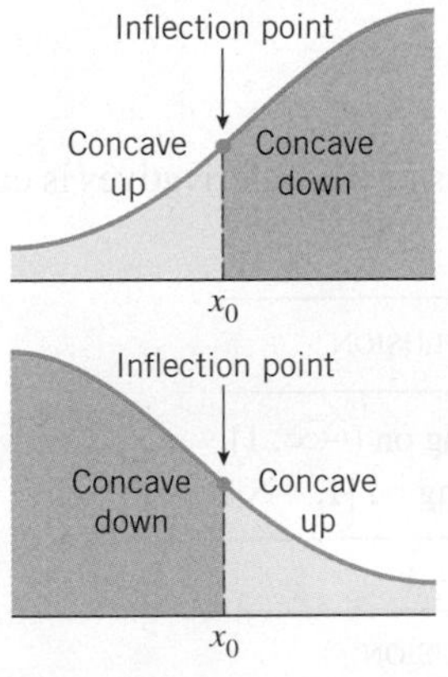


▲ **Figure 4.1.9**

> **4.1.5 DEFINITION** If $f$ is continuous on an open interval containing a value $x_0$, and if $f$ changes the direction of its concavity at the point $(x_0, f(x_0))$, then we say that $f$ has an ***inflection point at $x_0$***, and we call the point $(x_0, f(x_0))$ on the graph of $f$ an ***inflection point*** of $f$ (Figure 4.1.9).

▶ **Example 5** Figure 4.1.10 shows the graph of the function $f(x) = x^3 - 3x^2 + 1$. Use the first and second derivatives of $f$ to determine the intervals on which $f$ is increasing, decreasing, concave up, and concave down. Locate all inflection points and confirm that your conclusions are consistent with the graph.

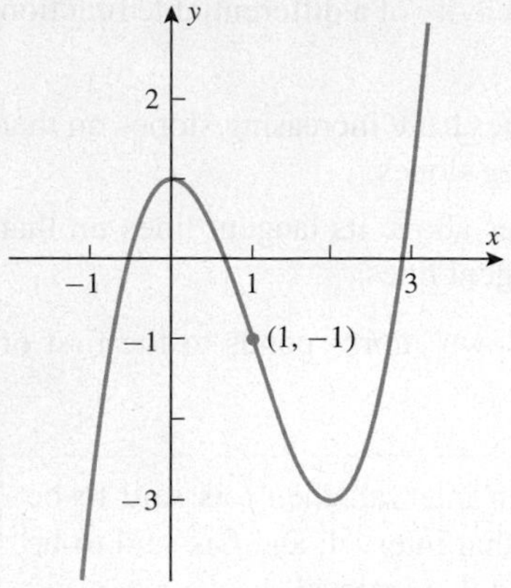


$f(x) = x^3 - 3x^2 + 1$

▲ **Figure 4.1.10**

***Solution.*** Calculating the first two derivatives of $f$ we obtain

$$f'(x) = 3x^2 - 6x = 3x(x-2)$$
$$f''(x) = 6x - 6 = 6(x-1)$$

The sign analysis of these derivatives is shown in the following tables:

| INTERVAL | $(3x)(x-2)$ | $f'(x)$ | CONCLUSION |
|---|---|---|---|
| $x < 0$ | $(-)(-)$ | $+$ | $f$ is increasing on $(-\infty, 0]$ |
| $0 < x < 2$ | $(+)(-)$ | $-$ | $f$ is decreasing on $[0, 2]$ |
| $x > 2$ | $(+)(+)$ | $+$ | $f$ is increasing on $[2, +\infty)$ |

| INTERVAL | $6(x-1)$ | $f''(x)$ | CONCLUSION |
|---|---|---|---|
| $x < 1$ | $(-)$ | $-$ | $f$ is concave down on $(-\infty, 1)$ |
| $x > 1$ | $(+)$ | $+$ | $f$ is concave up on $(1, +\infty)$ |

The second table shows that there is an inflection point at $x = 1$, since $f$ changes from concave down to concave up at that point. The inflection point is $(1, f(1)) = (1, -1)$. All of these conclusions are consistent with the graph of $f$. ◀

One can correctly guess from Figure 4.1.10 that the function $f(x) = x^3 - 3x^2 + 1$ has an inflection point at $x = 1$ without actually computing derivatives. However, sometimes changes in concavity are so subtle that calculus is essential to confirm their existence and identify their location. Here is an example.

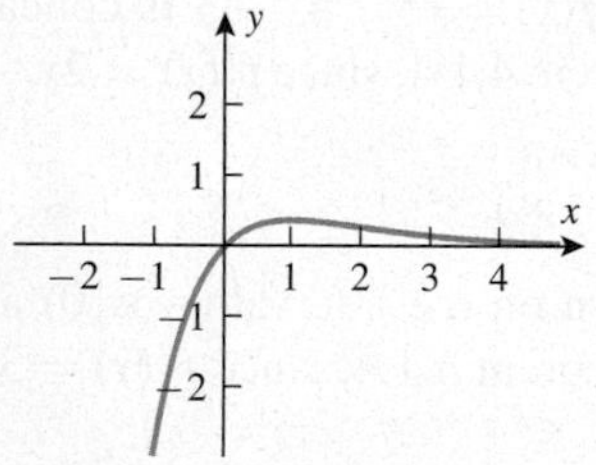


$f(x) = xe^{-x}$

▲ **Figure 4.1.11**

▶ **Example 6** Figure 4.1.11 suggests that the function $f(x) = xe^{-x}$ has an inflection point but its exact location is not evident from the graph in this figure. Use the first and second derivatives of $f$ to determine the intervals on which $f$ is increasing, decreasing, concave up, and concave down. Locate all inflection points.

***Solution.*** Calculating the first two derivatives of $f$ we obtain (verify)

$$f'(x) = (1-x)e^{-x}$$
$$f''(x) = (x-2)e^{-x}$$

Keeping in mind that $e^{-x}$ is positive for all $x$, the sign analysis of these derivatives is easily determined:

| INTERVAL | $(1-x)(e^{-x})$ | $f'(x)$ | CONCLUSION |
|---|---|---|---|
| $x < 1$ | $(+)(+)$ | $+$ | $f$ is increasing on $(-\infty, 1]$ |
| $x > 1$ | $(-)(+)$ | $-$ | $f$ is decreasing on $[1, +\infty)$ |

| INTERVAL | $(x-2)(e^{-x})$ | $f''(x)$ | CONCLUSION |
|---|---|---|---|
| $x < 2$ | $(-)(+)$ | $-$ | $f$ is concave down on $(-\infty, 2)$ |
| $x > 2$ | $(+)(+)$ | $+$ | $f$ is concave up on $(2, +\infty)$ |

The second table shows that there is an inflection point at $x = 2$, since $f$ changes from concave down to concave up at that point. All of these conclusions are consistent with the graph of $f$. ◀

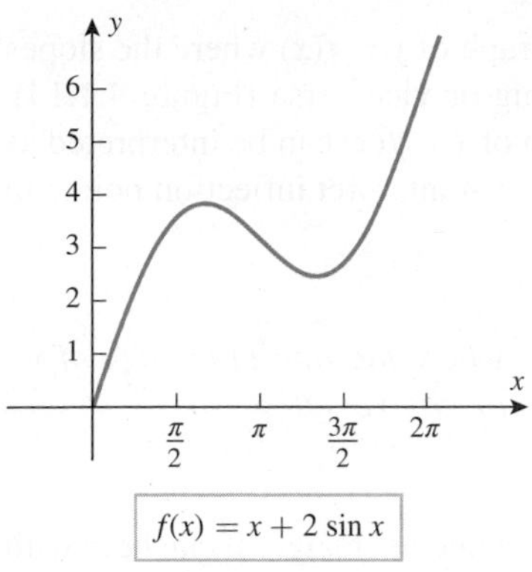


▲ **Figure 4.1.12**

The signs in the two tables of Example 7 can be obtained either using the method of test points or using the unit circle definition of the sine and cosine functions.

► **Example 7** Figure 4.1.12 shows the graph of the function $f(x) = x + 2\sin x$ over the interval $[0, 2\pi]$. Use the first and second derivatives of $f$ to determine where $f$ is increasing, decreasing, concave up, and concave down. Locate all inflection points and confirm that your conclusions are consistent with the graph.

***Solution.*** Calculating the first two derivatives of $f$ we obtain

$$f'(x) = 1 + 2\cos x$$
$$f''(x) = -2\sin x$$

Since $f'$ is a continuous function, it changes sign on the interval $(0, 2\pi)$ only at points where $f'(x) = 0$ (why?). These values are solutions of the equation

$$1 + 2\cos x = 0 \quad \text{or equivalently} \quad \cos x = -\tfrac{1}{2}$$

There are two solutions of this equation in the interval $(0, 2\pi)$, namely, $x = 2\pi/3$ and $x = 4\pi/3$ (verify). Similarly, $f''$ is a continuous function, so its sign changes in the interval $(0, 2\pi)$ will occur only at values of $x$ for which $f''(x) = 0$. These values are solutions of the equation

$$-2\sin x = 0$$

There is one solution of this equation in the interval $(0, 2\pi)$, namely, $x = \pi$. With the help of these "sign transition points" we obtain the sign analysis shown in the following tables:

| INTERVAL | $f'(x) = 1 + 2\cos x$ | CONCLUSION |
|---|---|---|
| $0 < x < 2\pi/3$ | + | $f$ is increasing on $[0, 2\pi/3]$ |
| $2\pi/3 < x < 4\pi/3$ | – | $f$ is decreasing on $[2\pi/3, 4\pi/3]$ |
| $4\pi/3 < x < 2\pi$ | + | $f$ is increasing on $[4\pi/3, 2\pi]$ |

| INTERVAL | $f''(x) = -2\sin x$ | CONCLUSION |
|---|---|---|
| $0 < x < \pi$ | – | $f$ is concave down on $(0, \pi)$ |
| $\pi < x < 2\pi$ | + | $f$ is concave up on $(\pi, 2\pi)$ |

The second table shows that there is an inflection point at $x = \pi$, since $f$ changes from concave down to concave up at that point. All of these conclusions are consistent with the graph of $f$. ◄

In the preceding examples the inflection points of $f$ occurred wherever $f''(x) = 0$. However, this is not always the case. Here is a specific example.

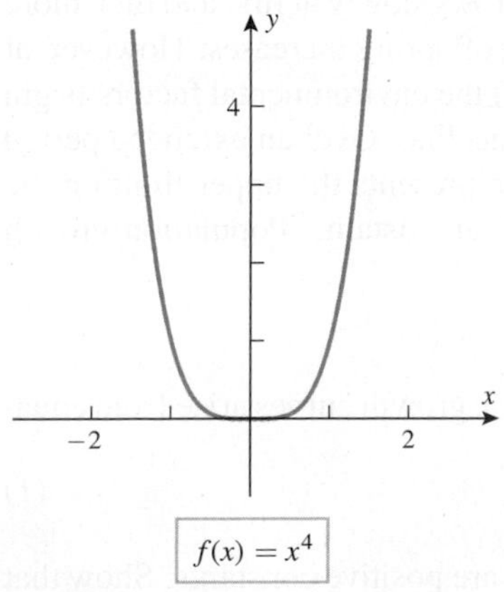


▲ **Figure 4.1.13**

► **Example 8** Find the inflection points, if any, of $f(x) = x^4$.

***Solution.*** Calculating the first two derivatives of $f$ we obtain

$$f'(x) = 4x^3$$
$$f''(x) = 12x^2$$

Since $f''(x)$ is positive for $x < 0$ and for $x > 0$, the function $f$ is concave up on the interval $(-\infty, 0)$ and on the interval $(0, +\infty)$. Thus, there is no change in concavity and hence no inflection point at $x = 0$, even though $f''(0) = 0$ (Figure 4.1.13). ◄

We will see later that if a function $f$ has an inflection point at $x = x_0$ and $f''(x_0)$ exists, then $f''(x_0) = 0$. Also, we will see in Section 4.3 that an inflection point may also occur where $f''(x)$ is not defined.

Give an argument to show that the function $f(x) = x^4$ graphed in Figure 4.1.13 is concave up on the interval $(-\infty, +\infty)$.

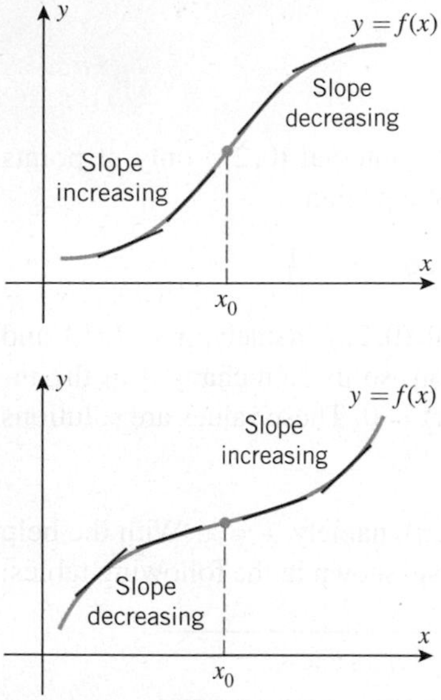

▲ **Figure 4.1.14**

## INFLECTION POINTS IN APPLICATIONS

Inflection points of a function $f$ are those points on the graph of $y = f(x)$ where the slopes of the tangent lines change from increasing to decreasing or vice versa (Figure 4.1.14). Since the slope of the tangent line at a point on the graph of $y = f(x)$ can be interpreted as the rate of change of $y$ with respect to $x$ at that point, we can interpret inflection points in the following way:

*Inflection points mark the places on the curve $y = f(x)$ where the rate of change of $y$ with respect to $x$ changes from increasing to decreasing, or vice versa.*

This is a subtle idea, since we are dealing with a change in a rate of change. It can help with your understanding of this idea to realize that inflection points may have interpretations in more familiar contexts. For example, consider the statement "Oil prices rose sharply during the first half of the year but have since begun to level off." If the price of oil is plotted as a function of time of year, this statement suggests the existence of an inflection point on the graph near the end of June. (Why?) To give a more visual example, consider the flask shown in Figure 4.1.15. Suppose that water is added to the flask so that the volume increases at a constant rate with respect to the time $t$, and let us examine the rate at which the water level $y$ rises with respect to $t$. Initially, the level $y$ will rise at a slow rate because of the wide base. However, as the diameter of the flask narrows, the rate at which the level $y$ rises will increase until the level is at the narrow point in the neck. From that point on the rate at which the level rises will decrease as the diameter gets wider and wider. Thus, the narrow point in the neck is the point at which the rate of change of $y$ with respect to $t$ changes from increasing to decreasing.

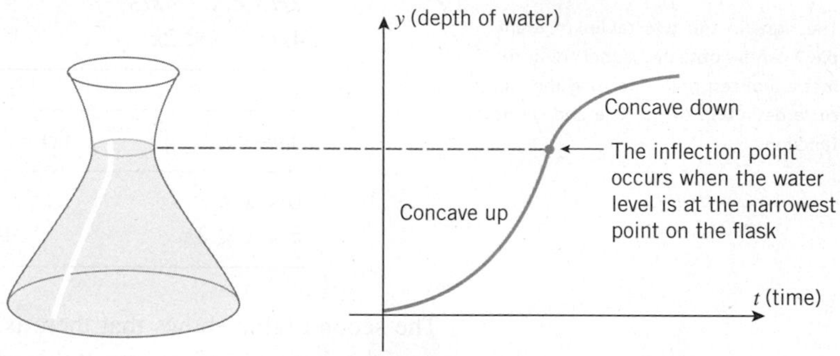

▶ **Figure 4.1.15**

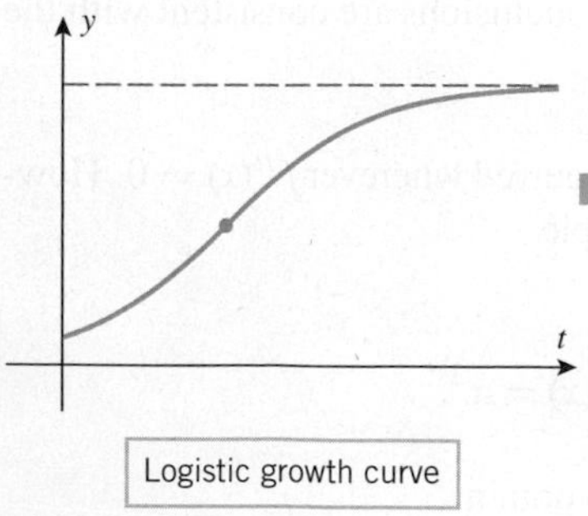

▲ **Figure 4.1.16**

## LOGISTIC CURVES

When a population grows in an environment in which space or food is limited, the graph of population versus time is typically an S-shaped curve of the form shown in Figure 4.1.16. The scenario described by this curve is a population that grows slowly at first and then more and more rapidly as the number of individuals producing offspring increases. However, at a certain point in time (where the inflection point occurs) the environmental factors begin to show their effect, and the growth rate begins a steady decline. Over an extended period of time the population approaches a limiting value that represents the upper limit on the number of individuals that the available space or food can sustain. Population growth curves of this type are called ***logistic growth curves***.

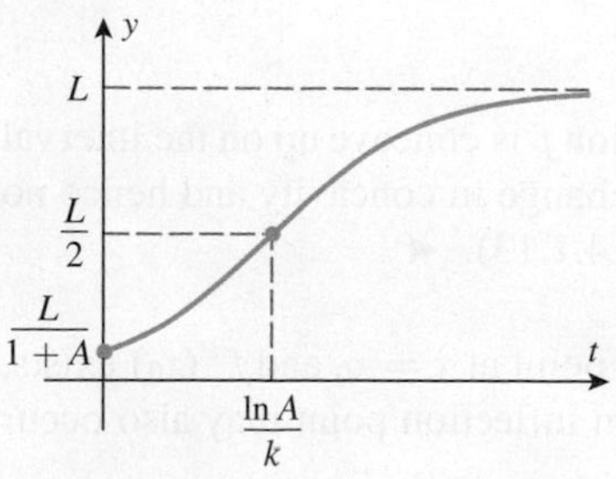

▲ **Figure 4.1.17**

▶ **Example 9** We will see in a later chapter that logistic growth curves arise from equations of the form

$$y = \frac{L}{1 + Ae^{-kt}} \tag{1}$$

where $y$ is the population at time $t$ $(t \geq 0)$ and $A$, $k$, and $L$ are positive constants. Show that Figure 4.1.17 correctly describes the graph of this equation when $A > 1$.

***Solution.*** It follows from (1) that at time $t = 0$ the value of $y$ is

$$y = \frac{L}{1+A}$$

and it follows from (1) and the fact that $0 < e^{-kt} \leq 1$ for $t \geq 0$ that

$$\frac{L}{1+A} \leq y < L \tag{2}$$

(verify). This is consistent with the graph in Figure 4.1.17. The horizontal asymptote at $y = L$ is confirmed by the limit

$$\lim_{t\to+\infty} y = \lim_{t\to+\infty} \frac{L}{1+Ae^{-kt}} = \frac{L}{1+0} = L \tag{3}$$

Physically, Formulas (2) and (3) tell us that $L$ is an upper limit on the population and that the population approaches this limit over time. Again, this is consistent with the graph in Figure 4.1.17.

To investigate intervals of increase and decrease, concavity, and inflection points, we need the first and second derivatives of $y$ with respect to $t$. By multiplying both sides of Equation (1) by $e^{kt}(1+Ae^{-kt})$, we can rewrite (1) as

$$ye^{kt} + Ay = Le^{kt}$$

Using implicit differentiation, we can derive that

$$\frac{dy}{dt} = \frac{k}{L}y(L-y) \tag{4}$$

$$\frac{d^2y}{dt^2} = \frac{k^2}{L^2}y(L-y)(L-2y) \tag{5}$$

(Exercise 70). Since $k > 0$, $y > 0$, and $L - y > 0$, it follows from (4) that $dy/dt > 0$ for all $t$. Thus, $y$ is always increasing, which is consistent with Figure 4.1.17.

Since $y > 0$ and $L - y > 0$, it follows from (5) that

$$\frac{d^2y}{dt^2} > 0 \quad \text{if} \quad L - 2y > 0$$

$$\frac{d^2y}{dt^2} < 0 \quad \text{if} \quad L - 2y < 0$$

Thus, the graph of $y$ versus $t$ is concave up if $y < L/2$, concave down if $y > L/2$, and has an inflection point where $y = L/2$, all of which is consistent with Figure 4.1.17.

Finally, we leave it for you to solve the equation

$$\frac{L}{2} = \frac{L}{1+Ae^{-kt}}$$

for $t$ to show that the inflection point occurs at

$$t = \frac{1}{k}\ln A = \frac{\ln A}{k} \quad ◀ \tag{6}$$

## ✓QUICK CHECK EXERCISES 4.1 *(See page 183 for answers.)*

**1.** (a) A function $f$ is increasing on $(a, b)$ if ______ whenever $a < x_1 < x_2 < b$.
(b) A function $f$ is decreasing on $(a, b)$ if ______ whenever $a < x_1 < x_2 < b$.
(c) A function $f$ is concave up on $(a, b)$ if $f'$ is ______ on $(a, b)$.
(d) If $f''(a)$ exists and $f$ has an inflection point at $x = a$, then $f''(a)$ ______.

**2.** Let $f(x) = 0.1(x^3 - 3x^2 - 9x)$. Then

$$f'(x) = 0.1(3x^2 - 6x - 9) = 0.3(x+1)(x-3)$$
$$f''(x) = 0.6(x-1)$$

(a) Solutions to $f'(x) = 0$ are $x =$ ______.
(b) The function $f$ is increasing on the interval(s) ______.

*(cont.)*

(c) The function $f$ is concave down on the interval(s) ________.

(d) ________ is an inflection point on the graph of $f$.

**3.** Suppose that $f(x)$ has derivative $f'(x) = (x-4)^2 e^{-x/2}$. Then $f''(x) = -\frac{1}{2}(x-4)(x-8)e^{-x/2}$.

(a) The function $f$ is increasing on the interval(s) ________.

(b) The function $f$ is concave up on the interval(s) ________.

(c) The function $f$ is concave down on the interval(s) ________.

**4.** Consider the statement "The rise in the cost of living slowed during the first half of the year." If we graph the cost of living versus time for the first half of the year, how does the graph reflect this statement?

## EXERCISE SET 4.1 Graphing Utility C CAS

**FOCUS ON CONCEPTS**

**1.** In each part, sketch the graph of a function $f$ with the stated properties, and discuss the signs of $f'$ and $f''$.

(a) The function $f$ is concave up and increasing on the interval $(-\infty, +\infty)$.

(b) The function $f$ is concave down and increasing on the interval $(-\infty, +\infty)$.

(c) The function $f$ is concave up and decreasing on the interval $(-\infty, +\infty)$.

(d) The function $f$ is concave down and decreasing on the interval $(-\infty, +\infty)$.

**2.** In each part, sketch the graph of a function $f$ with the stated properties.

(a) $f$ is increasing on $(-\infty, +\infty)$, has an inflection point at the origin, and is concave up on $(0, +\infty)$.

(b) $f$ is increasing on $(-\infty, +\infty)$, has an inflection point at the origin, and is concave down on $(0, +\infty)$.

(c) $f$ is decreasing on $(-\infty, +\infty)$, has an inflection point at the origin, and is concave up on $(0, +\infty)$.

(d) $f$ is decreasing on $(-\infty, +\infty)$, has an inflection point at the origin, and is concave down on $(0, +\infty)$.

**3.** Use the graph of the equation $y = f(x)$ in the accompanying figure to find the signs of $dy/dx$ and $d^2y/dx^2$ at the points $A$, $B$, and $C$.

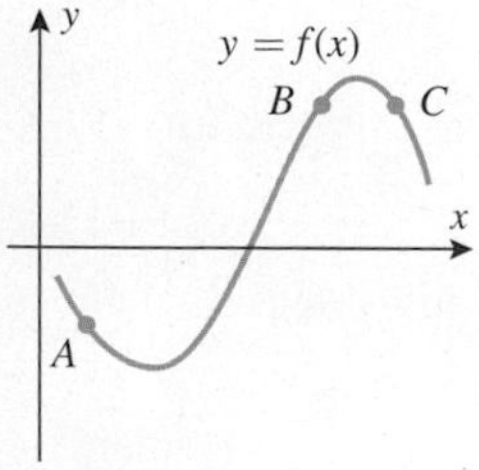


◀ **Figure Ex-3**

**4.** Use the graph of the equation $y = f'(x)$ in the accompanying figure to find the signs of $dy/dx$ and $d^2y/dx^2$ at the points $A$, $B$, and $C$.

**5.** Use the graph of $y = f''(x)$ in the accompanying figure to determine the $x$-coordinates of all inflection points of $f$. Explain your reasoning.

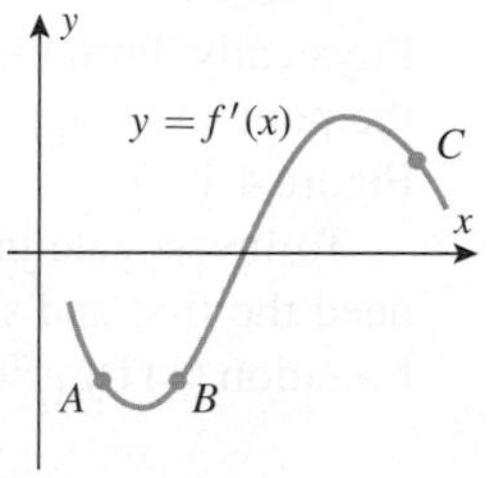


▲ **Figure Ex-4**

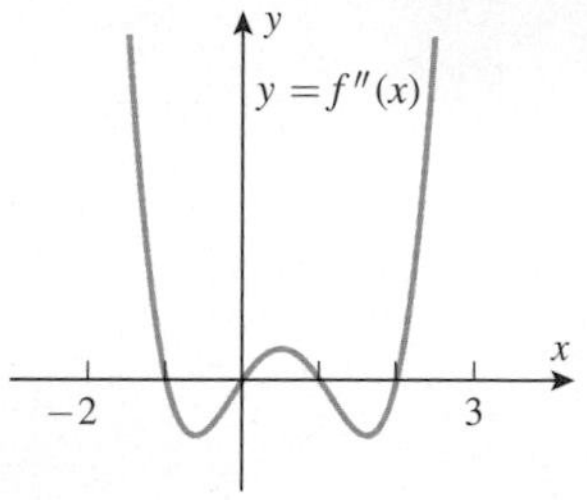


▲ **Figure Ex-5**

**6.** Use the graph of $y = f'(x)$ in the accompanying figure to replace the question mark with <, =, or >, as appropriate. Explain your reasoning.

(a) $f(0)\ ?\ f(1)$ (b) $f(1)\ ?\ f(2)$ (c) $f'(0)\ ?\ 0$

(d) $f'(1)\ ?\ 0$ (e) $f''(0)\ ?\ 0$ (f) $f''(2)\ ?\ 0$

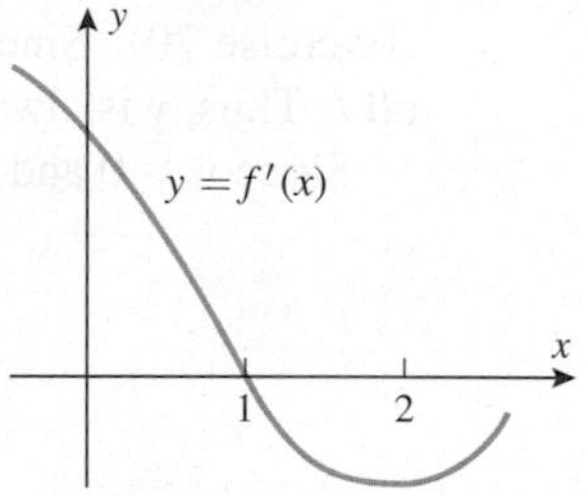


◀ **Figure Ex-6**

**7.** In each part, use the graph of $y = f(x)$ in the accompanying figure to find the requested information.

(a) Find the intervals on which $f$ is increasing.

(b) Find the intervals on which $f$ is decreasing.

(c) Find the open intervals on which $f$ is concave up.

(d) Find the open intervals on which $f$ is concave down.

(e) Find all values of $x$ at which $f$ has an inflection point.

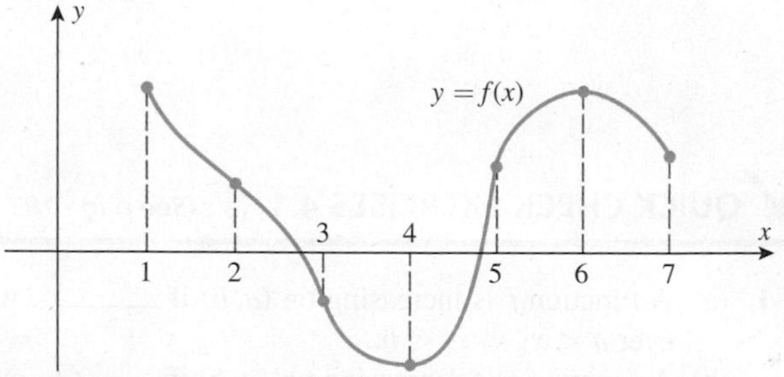


▲ **Figure Ex-7**

**8.** Use the graph in Exercise 7 to make a table that shows the signs of $f'$ and $f''$ over the intervals (1, 2), (2, 3), (3, 4), (4, 5), (5, 6), and (6, 7).

**9–10** A sign chart is presented for the first and second derivatives of a function $f$. Assuming that $f$ is continuous everywhere, find: (a) the intervals on which $f$ is increasing, (b) the intervals on which $f$ is decreasing, (c) the open intervals on which $f$ is concave up, (d) the open intervals on which $f$ is concave down, and (e) the $x$-coordinates of all inflection points. ■

**9.**

| INTERVAL | SIGN OF $f'(x)$ | SIGN OF $f''(x)$ |
|---|---|---|
| $x < 1$ | − | + |
| $1 < x < 2$ | + | + |
| $2 < x < 3$ | + | − |
| $3 < x < 4$ | − | − |
| $4 < x$ | − | + |

**10.**

| INTERVAL | SIGN OF $f'(x)$ | SIGN OF $f''(x)$ |
|---|---|---|
| $x < 1$ | + | + |
| $1 < x < 3$ | + | − |
| $3 < x$ | + | + |

**11–14 True–False** Assume that $f$ is differentiable everywhere. Determine whether the statement is true or false. Explain your answer. ■

**11.** If $f$ is decreasing on $[0, 2]$, then $f(0) > f(1) > f(2)$.

**12.** If $f'(1) > 0$, then $f$ is increasing on $[0, 2]$.

**13.** If $f$ is increasing on $[0, 2]$, then $f'(1) > 0$.

**14.** If $f'$ is increasing on $[0, 1]$ and $f'$ is decreasing on $[1, 2]$, then $f$ has an inflection point at $x = 1$.

**15–32** Find: (a) the intervals on which $f$ is increasing, (b) the intervals on which $f$ is decreasing, (c) the open intervals on which $f$ is concave up, (d) the open intervals on which $f$ is concave down, and (e) the $x$-coordinates of all inflection points. ■

**15.** $f(x) = x^2 - 3x + 8$

**16.** $f(x) = 5 - 4x - x^2$

**17.** $f(x) = (2x + 1)^3$

**18.** $f(x) = 5 + 12x - x^3$

**19.** $f(x) = 3x^4 - 4x^3$

**20.** $f(x) = x^4 - 5x^3 + 9x^2$

**21.** $f(x) = \dfrac{x - 2}{(x^2 - x + 1)^2}$

**22.** $f(x) = \dfrac{x}{x^2 + 2}$

**23.** $f(x) = \sqrt[3]{x^2 + x + 1}$

**24.** $f(x) = x^{4/3} - x^{1/3}$

**25.** $f(x) = (x^{2/3} - 1)^2$

**26.** $f(x) = x^{2/3} - x$

**27.** $f(x) = e^{-x^2/2}$

**28.** $f(x) = xe^{x^2}$

**29.** $f(x) = \ln\sqrt{x^2 + 4}$

**30.** $f(x) = x^3 \ln x$

**31.** $f(x) = \tan^{-1}(x^2 - 1)$

**32.** $f(x) = \sin^{-1} x^{2/3}$

**33–38** Analyze the trigonometric function $f$ over the specified interval, stating where $f$ is increasing, decreasing, concave up, and concave down, and stating the $x$-coordinates of all inflection points. Confirm that your results are consistent with the graph of $f$ generated with a graphing utility. ■

**33.** $f(x) = \sin x - \cos x;\ [-\pi, \pi]$

**34.** $f(x) = \sec x \tan x;\ (-\pi/2, \pi/2)$

**35.** $f(x) = 1 - \tan(x/2);\ (-\pi, \pi)$

**36.** $f(x) = 2x + \cot x;\ (0, \pi)$

**37.** $f(x) = (\sin x + \cos x)^2;\ [-\pi, \pi]$

**38.** $f(x) = \sin^2 2x;\ [0, \pi]$

**FOCUS ON CONCEPTS**

**39.** In parts (a)–(c), sketch a continuous curve $y = f(x)$ with the stated properties.
(a) $f(2) = 4,\ f'(2) = 0,\ f''(x) > 0$ for all $x$
(b) $f(2) = 4,\ f'(2) = 0,\ f''(x) < 0$ for $x < 2$, $f''(x) > 0$ for $x > 2$
(c) $f(2) = 4,\ f''(x) < 0$ for $x \neq 2$ and $\lim_{x\to 2^+} f'(x) = +\infty,\ \lim_{x\to 2^-} f'(x) = -\infty$

**40.** In each part sketch a continuous curve $y = f(x)$ with the stated properties.
(a) $f(2) = 4,\ f'(2) = 0,\ f''(x) < 0$ for all $x$
(b) $f(2) = 4,\ f'(2) = 0,\ f''(x) > 0$ for $x < 2$, $f''(x) < 0$ for $x > 2$
(c) $f(2) = 4,\ f''(x) > 0$ for $x \neq 2$ and $\lim_{x\to 2^+} f'(x) = -\infty,\ \lim_{x\to 2^-} f'(x) = +\infty$

**41–46** If $f$ is increasing on an interval $[0, b)$, then it follows from Definition 4.1.1 that $f(0) < f(x)$ for each $x$ in the interval $(0, b)$. Use this result in these exercises. ■

**41.** Show that $\sqrt[3]{1 + x} < 1 + \frac{1}{3}x$ if $x > 0$, and confirm the inequality with a graphing utility. [*Hint:* Show that the function $f(x) = 1 + \frac{1}{3}x - \sqrt[3]{1 + x}$ is increasing on $[0, +\infty)$.]

**42.** Show that $x < \tan x$ if $0 < x < \pi/2$, and confirm the inequality with a graphing utility. [*Hint:* Show that the function $f(x) = \tan x - x$ is increasing on $[0, \pi/2)$.]

**43.** Use a graphing utility to make a conjecture about the relative sizes of $x$ and $\sin x$ for $x \geq 0$, and prove your conjecture.

**44.** Use a graphing utility to make a conjecture about the relative sizes of $1 - x^2/2$ and $\cos x$ for $x \geq 0$, and prove your conjecture. [*Hint:* Use the result of Exercise 43.]

**45.** (a) Show that $\ln(x + 1) \leq x$ if $x \geq 0$.
(b) Show that $\ln(x + 1) \geq x - \frac{1}{2}x^2$ if $x \geq 0$.
(c) Confirm the inequalities in parts (a) and (b) with a graphing utility.

**46.** (a) Show that $e^x \geq 1 + x$ if $x \geq 0$.
(b) Show that $e^x \geq 1 + x + \frac{1}{2}x^2$ if $x \geq 0$.
(c) Confirm the inequalities in parts (a) and (b) with a graphing utility.

**47–48** Use a graphing utility to generate the graphs of $f'$ and $f''$ over the stated interval; then use those graphs to estimate the $x$-coordinates of the inflection points of $f$, the intervals on which $f$ is concave up or down, and the intervals on which $f$ is increasing or decreasing. Check your estimates by graphing $f$. ■

**47.** $f(x) = x^4 - 24x^2 + 12x,\quad -5 \leq x \leq 5$

**48.** $f(x) = \dfrac{1}{1 + x^2},\quad -5 \leq x \leq 5$

C **49–50** Use a CAS to find $f''$ and to approximate the $x$-coordinates of the inflection points to six decimal places. Confirm that your answer is consistent with the graph of $f$. ■

**49.** $f(x) = \dfrac{10x - 3}{3x^2 - 5x + 8}$  **50.** $f(x) = \dfrac{x^3 - 8x + 7}{\sqrt{x^2 + 1}}$

**51.** Use Definition 4.1.1 to prove that $f(x) = x^2$ is increasing on $[0, +\infty)$.

**52.** Use Definition 4.1.1 to prove that $f(x) = 1/x$ is decreasing on $(0, +\infty)$.

**FOCUS ON CONCEPTS**

**53–54** Determine whether the statements are true or false. If a statement is false, find functions for which the statement fails to hold. ■

**53.** (a) If $f$ and $g$ are increasing on an interval, then so is $f + g$.
(b) If $f$ and $g$ are increasing on an interval, then so is $f \cdot g$.

**54.** (a) If $f$ and $g$ are concave up on an interval, then so is $f + g$.
(b) If $f$ and $g$ are concave up on an interval, then so is $f \cdot g$.

**55.** In each part, find functions $f$ and $g$ that are increasing on $(-\infty, +\infty)$ and for which $f - g$ has the stated property.
(a) $f - g$ is decreasing on $(-\infty, +\infty)$.
(b) $f - g$ is constant on $(-\infty, +\infty)$.
(c) $f - g$ is increasing on $(-\infty, +\infty)$.

**56.** In each part, find functions $f$ and $g$ that are positive and increasing on $(-\infty, +\infty)$ and for which $f/g$ has the stated property.
(a) $f/g$ is decreasing on $(-\infty, +\infty)$.
(b) $f/g$ is constant on $(-\infty, +\infty)$.
(c) $f/g$ is increasing on $(-\infty, +\infty)$.

**57.** (a) Prove that a general cubic polynomial
$$f(x) = ax^3 + bx^2 + cx + d \quad (a \neq 0)$$
has exactly one inflection point.
(b) Prove that if a cubic polynomial has three $x$-intercepts, then the inflection point occurs at the average value of the intercepts.
(c) Use the result in part (b) to find the inflection point of the cubic polynomial $f(x) = x^3 - 3x^2 + 2x$, and check your result by using $f''$ to determine where $f$ is concave up and concave down.

**58.** From Exercise 57, the polynomial $f(x) = x^3 + bx^2 + 1$ has one inflection point. Use a graphing utility to reach a conclusion about the effect of the constant $b$ on the location of the inflection point. Use $f''$ to explain what you have observed graphically.

**59.** Use Definition 4.1.1 to prove:
(a) If $f$ is increasing on the intervals $(a, c]$ and $[c, b)$, then $f$ is increasing on $(a, b)$.
(b) If $f$ is decreasing on the intervals $(a, c]$ and $[c, b)$, then $f$ is decreasing on $(a, b)$.

**60.** Use part (a) of Exercise 59 to show that $f(x) = x + \sin x$ is increasing on the interval $(-\infty, +\infty)$.

**61.** Use part (b) of Exercise 59 to show that $f(x) = \cos x - x$ is decreasing on the interval $(-\infty, +\infty)$.

**62.** Let $y = 1/(1 + x^2)$. Find the values of $x$ for which $y$ is increasing most rapidly or decreasing most rapidly.

**FOCUS ON CONCEPTS**

**63–66** Suppose that water is flowing at a constant rate into the container shown. Make a rough sketch of the graph of the water level $y$ versus the time $t$. Make sure that your sketch conveys where the graph is concave up and concave down, and label the $y$-coordinates of the inflection points. ■

**63.**

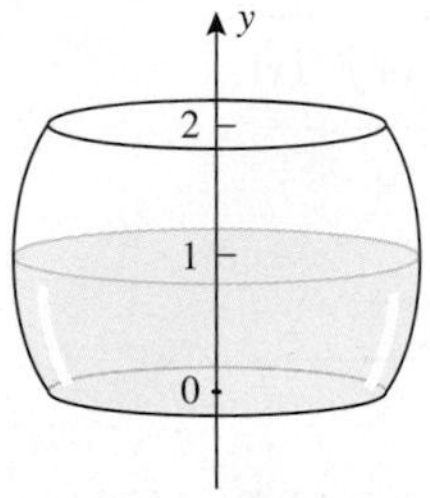


**64.**

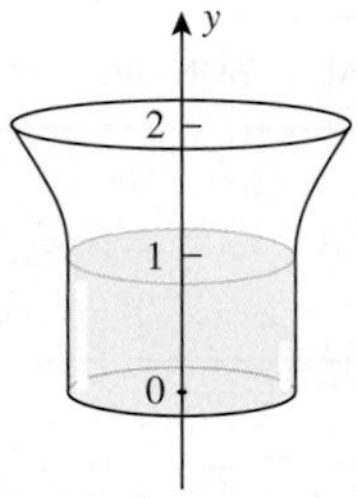


**65.**

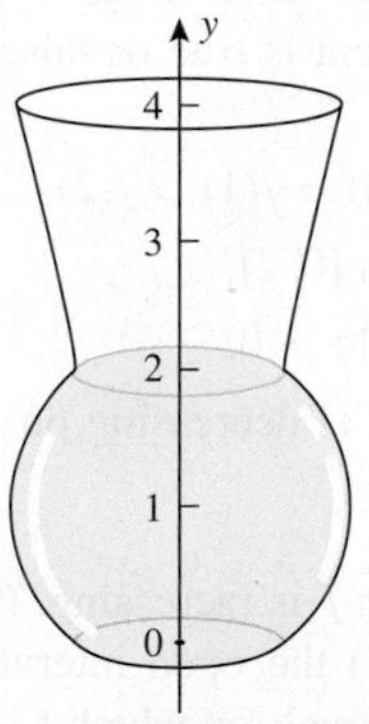


**66.**

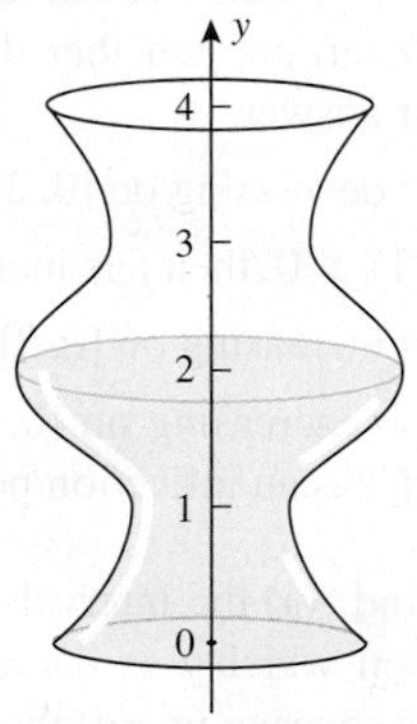


**67.** Suppose that a population $y$ grows according to the logistic model given by Formula (1).
(a) At what rate is $y$ increasing at time $t = 0$?
(b) In words, describe how the rate of growth of $y$ varies with time.
(c) At what time is the population growing most rapidly?

**68.** Suppose that the number of individuals at time $t$ in a certain wildlife population is given by
$$N(t) = \frac{340}{1 + 9(0.77)^t}, \quad t \geq 0$$
where $t$ is in years. Use a graphing utility to estimate the time at which the size of the population is increasing most rapidly.

**69.** Suppose that the spread of a flu virus on a college campus is modeled by the function
$$y(t) = \frac{1000}{1 + 999e^{-0.9t}}$$
where $y(t)$ is the number of infected students at time $t$ (in days, starting with $t = 0$). Use a graphing utility to estimate the day on which the virus is spreading most rapidly.

**70.** The logistic growth model given in Formula (1) is equivalent to
$$ye^{kt} + Ay = Le^{kt}$$
where $y$ is the population at time $t$ ($t \geq 0$) and $A$, $k$, and $L$ are positive constants. Use implicit differentiation to verify that
$$\frac{dy}{dt} = \frac{k}{L}y(L - y)$$
$$\frac{d^2y}{dt^2} = \frac{k^2}{L^2}y(L - y)(L - 2y)$$

**71.** Assuming that $A$, $k$, and $L$ are positive constants, verify that the graph of $y = L/(1 + Ae^{-kt})$ has an inflection point at $\left(\frac{1}{k}\ln A, \frac{1}{2}L\right)$.

**72. Writing** An approaching storm causes the air temperature to fall. Make a statement that indicates there is an inflection point in the graph of temperature versus time. Explain how the existence of an inflection point follows from your statement.

**73. Writing** Explain what the sign analyses of $f'(x)$ and $f''(x)$ tell us about the graph of $y = f(x)$.

---

✓ **QUICK CHECK ANSWERS 4.1** 1. (a) $f(x_1) < f(x_2)$ (b) $f(x_1) > f(x_2)$ (c) increasing (d) $= 0$ 2. (a) $-1, 3$ (b) $(-\infty, -1]$ and $[3, +\infty)$ (c) $(-\infty, 1)$ (d) $(1, -1.1)$ 3. (a) $(-\infty, +\infty)$ (b) $(4, 8)$ (c) $(-\infty, 4), (8, +\infty)$ 4. The graph is increasing and concave down.

---

# 4.2 ANALYSIS OF FUNCTIONS II: RELATIVE EXTREMA; GRAPHING POLYNOMIALS

*In this section we will develop methods for finding the high and low points on the graph of a function and we will discuss procedures for analyzing the graphs of polynomials.*

## RELATIVE MAXIMA AND MINIMA

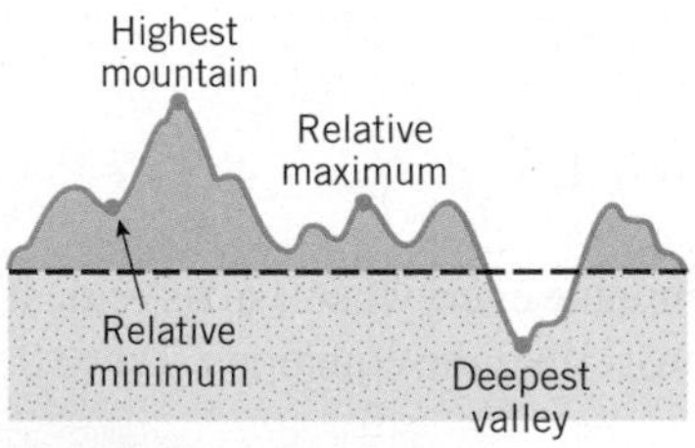

▲ **Figure 4.2.1**

If we imagine the graph of a function $f$ to be a two-dimensional mountain range with hills and valleys, then the tops of the hills are called "relative maxima," and the bottoms of the valleys are called "relative minima" (Figure 4.2.1). The relative maxima are the high points in their *immediate vicinity*, and the relative minima are the low points. A relative maximum need not be the highest point in the entire mountain range, and a relative minimum need not be the lowest point—they are just high and low points *relative* to the nearby terrain. These ideas are captured in the following definition.

> **4.2.1 DEFINITION** A function $f$ is said to have a ***relative maximum*** at $x_0$ if there is an open interval containing $x_0$ on which $f(x_0)$ is the largest value, that is, $f(x_0) \geq f(x)$ for all $x$ in the interval. Similarly, $f$ is said to have a ***relative minimum*** at $x_0$ if there is an open interval containing $x_0$ on which $f(x_0)$ is the smallest value, that is, $f(x_0) \leq f(x)$ for all $x$ in the interval. If $f$ has either a relative maximum or a relative minimum at $x_0$, then $f$ is said to have a ***relative extremum*** at $x_0$.

▶ **Example 1** We can see from Figure 4.2.2 that:

- $f(x) = x^2$ has a relative minimum at $x = 0$ but no relative maxima.
- $f(x) = x^3$ has no relative extrema.
- $f(x) = x^3 - 3x + 3$ has a relative maximum at $x = -1$ and a relative minimum at $x = 1$.
- $f(x) = \frac{1}{2}x^4 - \frac{4}{3}x^3 - x^2 + 4x + 1$ has relative minima at $x = -1$ and $x = 2$ and a relative maximum at $x = 1$.
- $f(x) = \cos x$ has relative maxima at all even multiples of $\pi$ and relative minima at all odd multiples of $\pi$. ◀

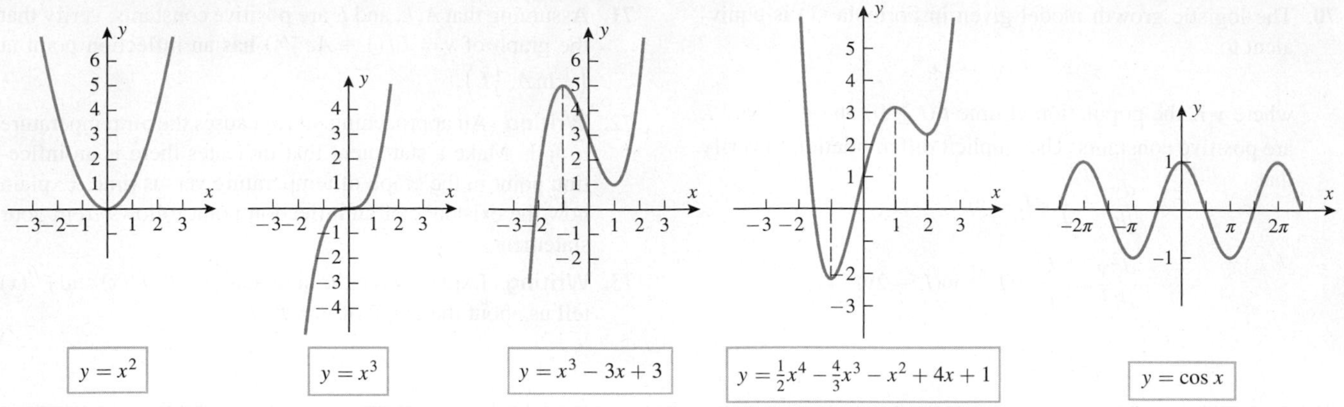


▲ **Figure 4.2.2**

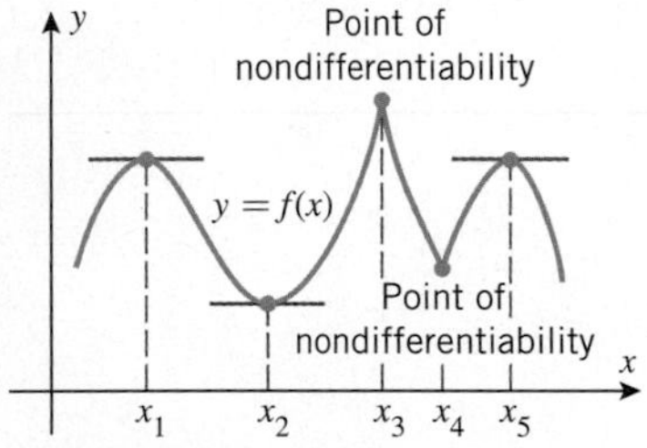


▲ **Figure 4.2.3** The points $x_1, x_2, x_3, x_4$, and $x_5$ are critical points. Of these, $x_1, x_2$, and $x_5$ are stationary points.

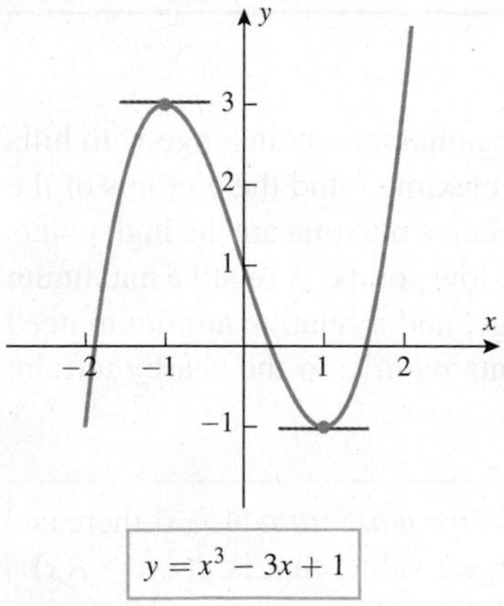


▲ **Figure 4.2.4**

What is the maximum number of critical points that a polynomial of degree $n$ can have? Why?

The relative extrema for the five functions in Example 1 occur at points where the graphs of the functions have horizontal tangent lines. Figure 4.2.3 illustrates that a relative extremum can also occur at a point where a function is not differentiable. In general, we define a ***critical point*** for a function $f$ to be a point in the domain of $f$ at which either the graph of $f$ has a horizontal tangent line or $f$ is not differentiable. To distinguish between the two types of critical points we call $x$ a ***stationary point*** of $f$ if $f'(x) = 0$. The following theorem, which is proved in Web Appendix L, states that the critical points for a function form a complete set of candidates for relative extrema on the interior of the domain of the function.

**4.2.2 THEOREM** *Suppose that $f$ is a function defined on an open interval containing the point $x_0$. If $f$ has a relative extremum at $x = x_0$, then $x = x_0$ is a critical point of $f$; that is, either $f'(x_0) = 0$ or $f$ is not differentiable at $x_0$.*

### ▶ Example 2 Find all critical points of $f(x) = x^3 - 3x + 1$.

***Solution.*** The function $f$, being a polynomial, is differentiable everywhere, so its critical points are all stationary points. To find these points we must solve the equation $f'(x) = 0$. Since

$$f'(x) = 3x^2 - 3 = 3(x + 1)(x - 1)$$

we conclude that the critical points occur at $x = -1$ and $x = 1$. This is consistent with the graph of $f$ in Figure 4.2.4. ◀

### ▶ Example 3 Find all critical points of $f(x) = 3x^{5/3} - 15x^{2/3}$.

***Solution.*** The function $f$ is continuous everywhere and its derivative is

$$f'(x) = 5x^{2/3} - 10x^{-1/3} = 5x^{-1/3}(x - 2) = \frac{5(x - 2)}{x^{1/3}}$$

We see from this that $f'(x) = 0$ if $x = 2$ and $f'(x)$ is undefined if $x = 0$. Thus $x = 0$ and $x = 2$ are critical points and $x = 2$ is a stationary point. This is consistent with the graph of $f$ shown in Figure 4.2.5. ◀

**TECHNOLOGY MASTERY**

Your graphing utility may have trouble producing portions of the graph in Figure 4.2.5 because of the fractional exponents. If this is the case for you, graph the function

$$y = 3(|x|/x)|x|^{5/3} - 15|x|^{2/3}$$

which is equivalent to $f(x)$ for $x \neq 0$. Web Appendix K explores the method suggested here in more detail.

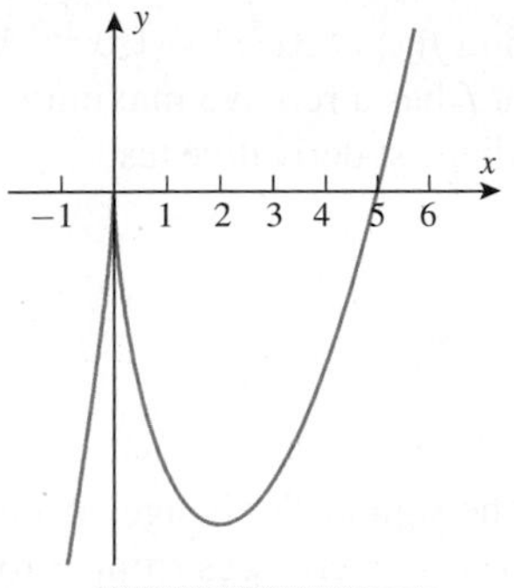


$y = 3x^{5/3} - 15x^{2/3}$

▲ **Figure 4.2.5**

## ■ FIRST DERIVATIVE TEST

Theorem 4.2.2 asserts that the relative extrema must occur at critical points, but it does *not* say that a relative extremum occurs at *every* critical point. For example, for the eight critical points in Figure 4.2.6, relative extrema occur at each $x_0$ in the top row but not at any $x_0$ in the bottom row. Moreover, at the critical points in the first row the derivatives have opposite signs on the two sides of $x_0$, whereas at the critical points in the second row the signs of the derivatives are the same on both sides. This suggests:

*A function $f$ has a relative extremum at those critical points where $f'$ changes sign.*

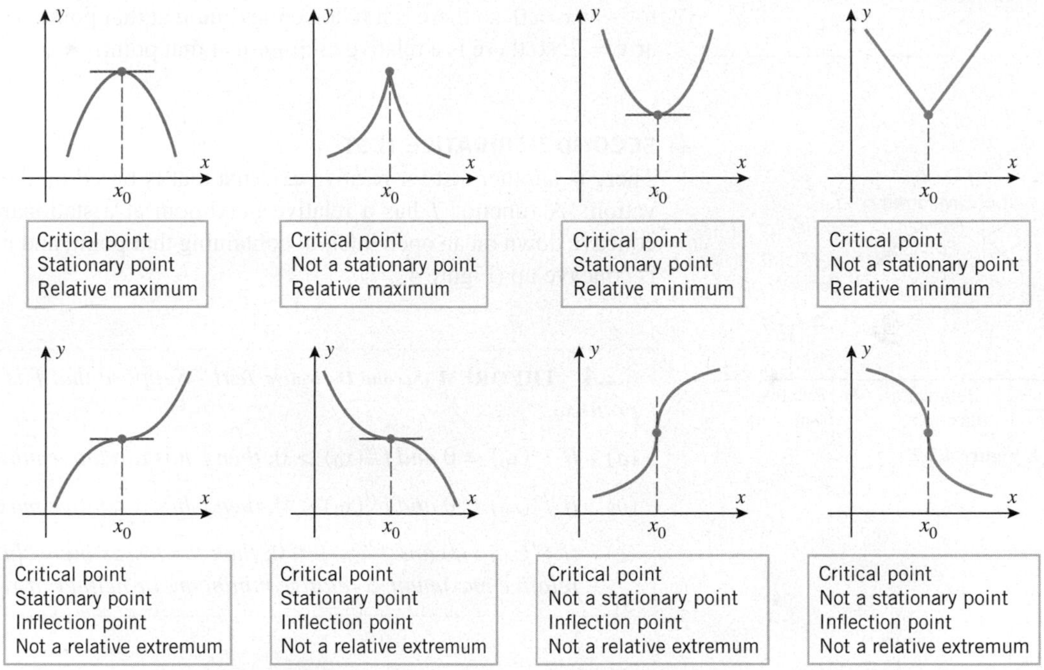


▲ **Figure 4.2.6**

We can actually take this a step further. At the two relative maxima in Figure 4.2.6 the derivative is positive on the left side and negative on the right side, and at the two relative minima the derivative is negative on the left side and positive on the right side. All of this is summarized more precisely in the following theorem.

**4.2.3 THEOREM (*First Derivative Test*)** *Suppose that $f$ is continuous at a critical point $x_0$.*

(*a*) *If $f'(x) > 0$ on an open interval extending left from $x_0$ and $f'(x) < 0$ on an open interval extending right from $x_0$, then $f$ has a relative maximum at $x_0$.*

(*b*) *If $f'(x) < 0$ on an open interval extending left from $x_0$ and $f'(x) > 0$ on an open interval extending right from $x_0$, then $f$ has a relative minimum at $x_0$.*

(*c*) *If $f'(x)$ has the same sign on an open interval extending left from $x_0$ as it does on an open interval extending right from $x_0$, then $f$ does not have a relative extremum at $x_0$.*

Informally stated, parts (*a*) and (*b*) of Theorem 4.2.3 tell us that for a continuous function, relative maxima occur at critical points where the derivative changes from + to − and relative minima where it changes from − to +.

Use the first derivative test to confirm the behavior at $x_0$ of each graph in Figure 4.2.6.

**PROOF** We will prove part (*a*) and leave parts (*b*) and (*c*) as exercises. We are assuming that $f'(x) > 0$ on the interval $(a, x_0)$ and that $f'(x) < 0$ on the interval $(x_0, b)$, and we want to show that

$$f(x_0) \geq f(x)$$

for all $x$ in the interval $(a, b)$. However, the two hypotheses, together with Theorem 4.1.2 and its associated marginal note imply that $f$ is increasing on the interval $(a, x_0]$ and decreasing on the interval $[x_0, b)$. Thus, $f(x_0) \geq f(x)$ for all $x$ in $(a, b)$ with equality only at $x_0$. ■

▶ **Example 4** We showed in Example 3 that the function $f(x) = 3x^{5/3} - 15x^{2/3}$ has critical points at $x = 0$ and $x = 2$. Figure 4.2.5 suggests that $f$ has a relative maximum at $x = 0$ and a relative minimum at $x = 2$. Confirm this using the first derivative test.

***Solution.*** We showed in Example 3 that

$$f'(x) = \frac{5(x-2)}{x^{1/3}}$$

**Table 4.2.1**

| INTERVAL | $5(x-2)/x^{1/3}$ | $f'(x)$ |
|---|---|---|
| $x < 0$ | $(-)/(-)$ | $+$ |
| $0 < x < 2$ | $(-)/(+)$ | $-$ |
| $x > 2$ | $(+)/(+)$ | $+$ |

A sign analysis of this derivative is shown in Table 4.2.1. The sign of $f'$ changes from $+$ to $-$ at $x = 0$, so there is a relative maximum at that point. The sign changes from $-$ to $+$ at $x = 2$, so there is a relative minimum at that point. ◀

## SECOND DERIVATIVE TEST

There is another test for relative extrema that is based on the following geometric observation: A function $f$ has a relative maximum at a stationary point if the graph of $f$ is concave down on an open interval containing that point, and it has a relative minimum if it is concave up (Figure 4.2.7).

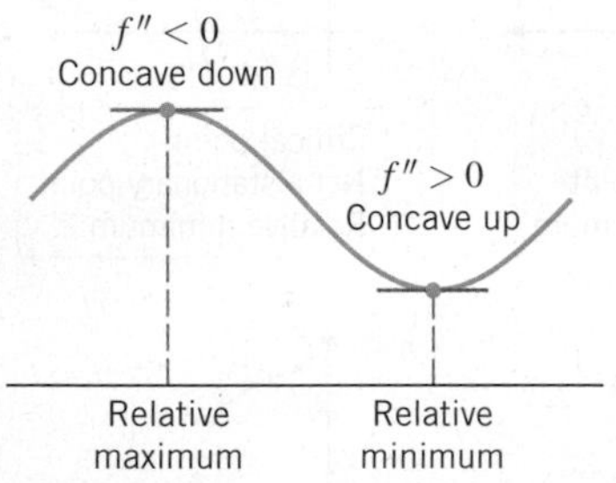


▲ **Figure 4.2.7**

> **4.2.4 THEOREM (*Second Derivative Test*)** *Suppose that $f$ is twice differentiable at the point $x_0$.*
>
> (*a*) *If $f'(x_0) = 0$ and $f''(x_0) > 0$, then $f$ has a relative minimum at $x_0$.*
>
> (*b*) *If $f'(x_0) = 0$ and $f''(x_0) < 0$, then $f$ has a relative maximum at $x_0$.*
>
> (*c*) *If $f'(x_0) = 0$ and $f''(x_0) = 0$, then the test is inconclusive; that is, $f$ may have a relative maximum, a relative minimum, or neither at $x_0$.*

We will prove parts (*a*) and (*c*) and leave part (*b*) as an exercise.

> The second derivative test is often easier to apply than the first derivative test. However, the first derivative test can be used at any critical point of a continuous function, while the second derivative test applies only at stationary points where the second derivative exists.

**PROOF (*a*)** We are given that $f'(x_0) = 0$ and $f''(x_0) > 0$, and we want to show that $f$ has a relative minimum at $x_0$. Expressing $f''(x_0)$ as a limit and using the two given conditions we obtain

$$f''(x_0) = \lim_{x \to x_0} \frac{f'(x) - f'(x_0)}{x - x_0} = \lim_{x \to x_0} \frac{f'(x)}{x - x_0} > 0$$

This implies that for $x$ sufficiently close to but different from $x_0$ we have

$$\frac{f'(x)}{x - x_0} > 0 \tag{1}$$

Thus, there is an open interval extending left from $x_0$ and an open interval extending right from $x_0$ on which (1) holds. On the open interval extending left the denominator in (1) is negative, so $f'(x) < 0$, and on the open interval extending right the denominator is positive, so $f'(x) > 0$. It now follows from part (*b*) of the first derivative test (Theorem 4.2.3) that $f$ has a relative minimum at $x_0$.

**PROOF (*c*)** To prove this part of the theorem we need only provide functions for which $f'(x_0) = 0$ and $f''(x_0) = 0$ at some point $x_0$, but with one having a relative minimum at $x_0$, one having a relative maximum at $x_0$, and one having neither at $x_0$. We leave it as an exercise for you to show that three such functions are $f(x) = x^4$ (relative minimum at $x = 0$), $f(x) = -x^4$ (relative maximum at $x = 0$), and $f(x) = x^3$ (neither a relative maximum nor a relative minimum at $x_0$). ■

**▶ Example 5** Find the relative extrema of $f(x) = 3x^5 - 5x^3$.

***Solution.*** We have

$$f'(x) = 15x^4 - 15x^2 = 15x^2(x^2 - 1) = 15x^2(x + 1)(x - 1)$$
$$f''(x) = 60x^3 - 30x = 30x(2x^2 - 1)$$

Solving $f'(x) = 0$ yields the stationary points $x = 0$, $x = -1$, and $x = 1$. As shown in the following table, we can conclude from the second derivative test that $f$ has a relative maximum at $x = -1$ and a relative minimum at $x = 1$.

| STATIONARY POINT | $30x(2x^2 - 1)$ | $f''(x)$ | SECOND DERIVATIVE TEST |
|---|---|---|---|
| $x = -1$ | $-30$ | $-$ | $f$ has a relative maximum |
| $x = 0$ | $0$ | $0$ | Inconclusive |
| $x = 1$ | $30$ | $+$ | $f$ has a relative minimum |

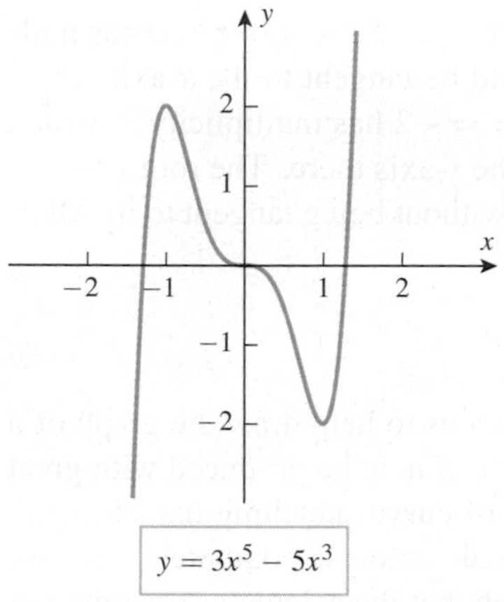


▲ Figure 4.2.8

The test is inconclusive at $x = 0$, so we will try the first derivative test at that point. A sign analysis of $f'$ is given in the following table:

| INTERVAL | $15x^2(x + 1)(x - 1)$ | $f'(x)$ |
|---|---|---|
| $-1 < x < 0$ | $(+)(+)(-)$ | $-$ |
| $0 < x < 1$ | $(+)(+)(-)$ | $-$ |

Since there is no sign change in $f'$ at $x = 0$, there is neither a relative maximum nor a relative minimum at that point. All of this is consistent with the graph of $f$ shown in Figure 4.2.8. ◀

## GEOMETRIC IMPLICATIONS OF MULTIPLICITY

Our final goal in this section is to outline a general procedure that can be used to analyze and graph polynomials. To do so, it will be helpful to understand how the graph of a polynomial behaves in the vicinity of its roots. For example, it would be nice to know what property of the polynomial in Example 5 produced the inflection point and horizontal tangent at the root $x = 0$.

Recall that a root $x = r$ of a polynomial $p(x)$ has ***multiplicity m*** if $(x - r)^m$ divides $p(x)$ but $(x - r)^{m+1}$ does not. A root of multiplicity 1 is called a ***simple root***. Figure 4.2.9 and the following theorem show that the behavior of a polynomial in the vicinity of a real root is determined by the multiplicity of that root (we omit the proof).

**4.2.5 THE GEOMETRIC IMPLICATIONS OF MULTIPLICITY** *Suppose that $p(x)$ is a polynomial with a root of multiplicity $m$ at $x = r$.*

(a) *If $m$ is even, then the graph of $y = p(x)$ is tangent to the x-axis at $x = r$, does not cross the x-axis there, and does not have an inflection point there.*

(b) *If $m$ is odd and greater than 1, then the graph is tangent to the x-axis at $x = r$, crosses the x-axis there, and also has an inflection point there.*

(c) *If $m = 1$ (so that the root is simple), then the graph is not tangent to the x-axis at $x = r$, crosses the x-axis there, and may or may not have an inflection point there.*

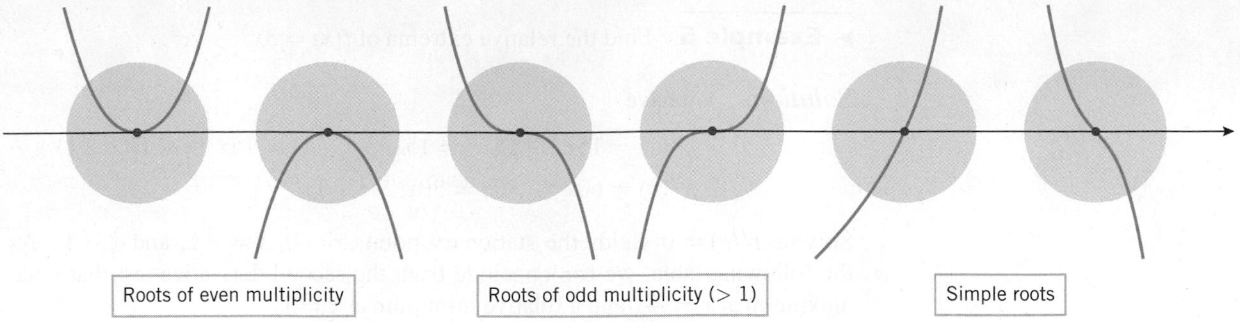


▲ Figure 4.2.9

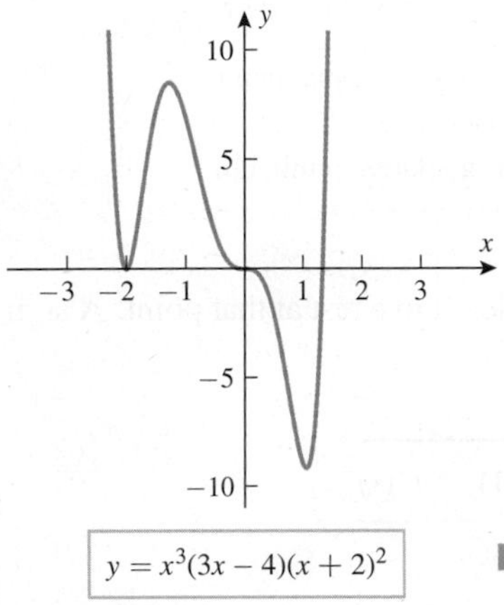


▲ Figure 4.2.10

▶ **Example 6** Make a conjecture about the behavior of the graph of

$$y = x^3(3x - 4)(x + 2)^2$$

in the vicinity of its $x$-intercepts, and test your conjecture by generating the graph.

***Solution.*** The $x$-intercepts occur at $x = 0$, $x = \frac{4}{3}$, and $x = -2$. The root $x = 0$ has multiplicity 3, which is odd, so at that point the graph should be tangent to the $x$-axis, cross the $x$-axis, and have an inflection point there. The root $x = -2$ has multiplicity 2, which is even, so the graph should be tangent to but not cross the $x$-axis there. The root $x = \frac{4}{3}$ is simple, so at that point the curve should cross the $x$-axis without being tangent to it. All of this is consistent with the graph in Figure 4.2.10. ◀

## ANALYSIS OF POLYNOMIALS

Historically, the term "curve sketching" meant using calculus to help draw the graph of a function by hand—the graph was the goal. Since graphs can now be produced with great precision using calculators and computers, the purpose of curve sketching has changed. Today, we typically start with a graph produced by a calculator or computer, then use curve sketching to identify important features of the graph that the calculator or computer might have missed. Thus, the goal of curve sketching is no longer the graph itself, but rather the information it reveals about the function.

Polynomials are among the simplest functions to graph and analyze. Their significant features are symmetry, intercepts, relative extrema, inflection points, and the behavior as $x \to +\infty$ and as $x \to -\infty$. Figure 4.2.11 shows the graphs of four polynomials in $x$. The graphs in Figure 4.2.11 have properties that are common to all polynomials:

- The natural domain of a polynomial is $(-\infty, +\infty)$.
- Polynomials are continuous everywhere.
- Polynomials are differentiable everywhere, so their graphs have no corners or vertical tangent lines.
- The graph of a nonconstant polynomial eventually increases or decreases without bound as $x \to +\infty$ and as $x \to -\infty$. This is because the limit of a nonconstant polynomial as $x \to +\infty$ or as $x \to -\infty$ is $\pm\infty$, depending on the sign of the term of highest degree and whether the polynomial has even or odd degree [see Formulas (13) and (14) of Section 1.3 and the related discussion].

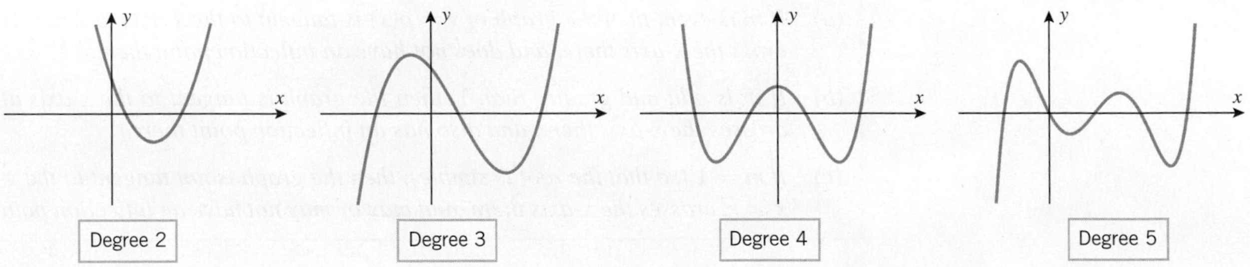


▲ Figure 4.2.11

- The graph of a polynomial of degree $n(>2)$ has at most $n$ $x$-intercepts, at most $n-1$ relative extrema, and at most $n-2$ inflection points. This is because the $x$-intercepts, relative extrema, and inflection points of a polynomial $p(x)$ are among the real solutions of the equations $p(x)=0$, $p'(x)=0$, and $p''(x)=0$, and the polynomials in these equations have degree $n$, $n-1$, and $n-2$, respectively. Thus, for example, the graph of a quadratic polynomial has at most two $x$-intercepts, one relative extremum, and no inflection points; and the graph of a cubic polynomial has at most three $x$-intercepts, two relative extrema, and one inflection point.

For each of the graphs in Figure 4.2.11, count the number of $x$-intercepts, relative extrema, and inflection points, and confirm that your count is consistent with the degree of the polynomial.

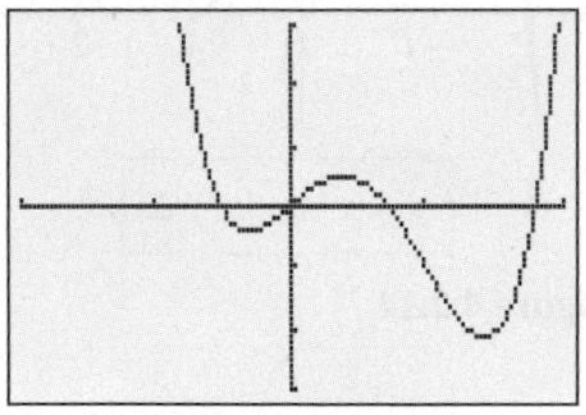
$[-2, 2] \times [-3, 3]$

$y = 3x^4 - 6x^3 + 2x$

▲ Figure 4.2.12

▶ **Example 7** Figure 4.2.12 shows the graph of

$$y = 3x^4 - 6x^3 + 2x$$

produced on a graphing calculator. Confirm that the graph is not missing any significant features.

***Solution.*** We can be confident that the graph shows all significant features of the polynomial because the polynomial has degree 4 and we can account for four roots, three relative extrema, and two inflection points. Moreover, the graph suggests the correct behavior as $x \to +\infty$ and as $x \to -\infty$, since

$$\lim_{x\to+\infty}(3x^4 - 6x^3 + 2x) = \lim_{x\to+\infty} 3x^4 = +\infty$$

$$\lim_{x\to-\infty}(3x^4 - 6x^3 + 2x) = \lim_{x\to-\infty} 3x^4 = +\infty \blacktriangleleft$$

▶ **Example 8** Sketch the graph of the equation

$$y = x^3 - 3x + 2$$

and identify the locations of the intercepts, relative extrema, and inflection points.

***Solution.*** The following analysis will produce the information needed to sketch the graph:

A review of polynomial factoring is given in Web Appendix J.

- *$x$-intercepts:* Factoring the polynomial yields
$$x^3 - 3x + 2 = (x+2)(x-1)^2$$
which tells us that the $x$-intercepts are $x=-2$ and $x=1$.
- *$y$-intercept:* Setting $x=0$ yields $y=2$.
- *End behavior:* We have
$$\lim_{x\to+\infty}(x^3 - 3x + 2) = \lim_{x\to+\infty} x^3 = +\infty$$
$$\lim_{x\to-\infty}(x^3 - 3x + 2) = \lim_{x\to-\infty} x^3 = -\infty$$
so the graph increases without bound as $x \to +\infty$ and decreases without bound as $x \to -\infty$.
- *Derivatives:*
$$\frac{dy}{dx} = 3x^2 - 3 = 3(x-1)(x+1)$$
$$\frac{d^2y}{dx^2} = 6x$$
- *Increase, decrease, relative extrema, inflection points:* Figure 4.2.13 gives a sign analysis of the first and second derivatives and indicates its geometric significance. There are stationary points at $x=-1$ and $x=1$. Since the sign of $dy/dx$ changes from $+$ to $-$ at $x=-1$, there is a relative maximum there, and since it changes from $-$ to $+$ at $x=1$, there is a relative minimum there. The sign of $d^2y/dx^2$ changes from $-$ to $+$ at $x=0$, so there is an inflection point there.
- *Final sketch:* Figure 4.2.14 shows the final sketch with the coordinates of the intercepts, relative extrema, and inflection point labeled. ◀

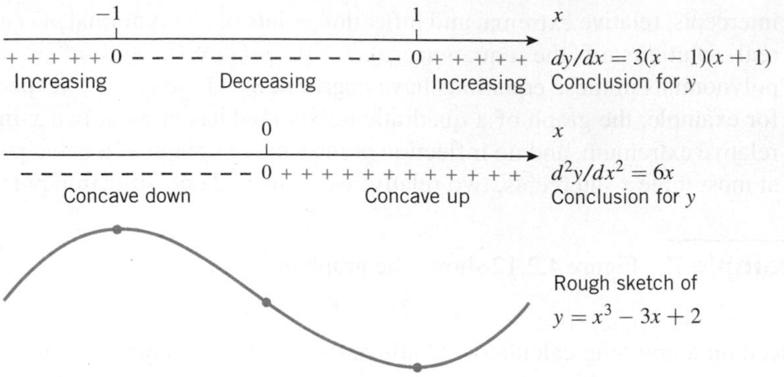


▲ **Figure 4.2.13**

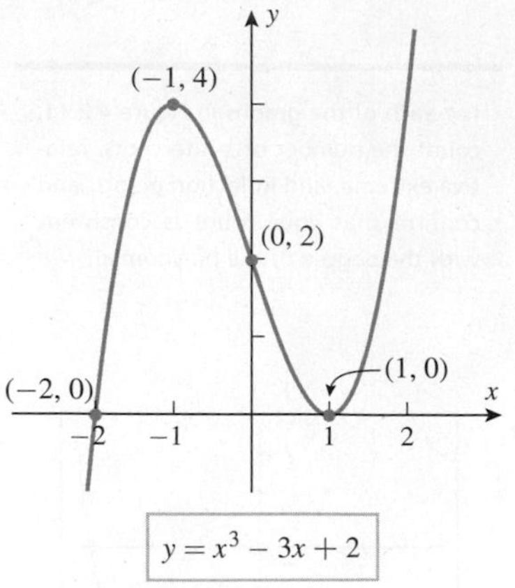


▲ **Figure 4.2.14**

## ✓QUICK CHECK EXERCISES 4.2

*(See page 192 for answers.)*

1. A function $f$ has a relative maximum at $x_0$ if there is an open interval containing $x_0$ on which $f(x)$ is ________ $f(x_0)$ for every $x$ in the interval.

2. Suppose that $f$ is defined everywhere and $x = 2, 3, 5, 7$ are critical points for $f$. If $f'(x)$ is positive on the intervals $(-\infty, 2)$ and $(5, 7)$, and if $f'(x)$ is negative on the intervals $(2, 3)$, $(3, 5)$, and $(7, +\infty)$, then $f$ has relative maxima at $x =$ ________ and $f$ has relative minima at $x =$ ________.

3. Suppose that $f$ is defined everywhere and $x = -2$ and $x = 1$ are critical points for $f$. If $f''(x) = 2x + 1$, then $f$ has a relative ________ at $x = -2$ and $f$ has a relative ________ at $x = 1$.

4. Let $f(x) = (x^2 - 4)^2$. Then $f'(x) = 4x(x^2 - 4)$ and $f''(x) = 4(3x^2 - 4)$. Identify the locations of the (a) relative maxima, (b) relative minima, and (c) inflection points on the graph of $f$.

## EXERCISE SET 4.2 Graphing Utility C CAS

**FOCUS ON CONCEPTS**

1. In each part, sketch the graph of a continuous function $f$ with the stated properties.
   (a) $f$ is concave up on the interval $(-\infty, +\infty)$ and has exactly one relative extremum.
   (b) $f$ is concave up on the interval $(-\infty, +\infty)$ and has no relative extrema.
   (c) The function $f$ has exactly two relative extrema on the interval $(-\infty, +\infty)$, and $f(x) \to +\infty$ as $x \to +\infty$.
   (d) The function $f$ has exactly two relative extrema on the interval $(-\infty, +\infty)$, and $f(x) \to -\infty$ as $x \to +\infty$.

2. In each part, sketch the graph of a continuous function $f$ with the stated properties.
   (a) $f$ has exactly one relative extremum on $(-\infty, +\infty)$, and $f(x) \to 0$ as $x \to +\infty$ and as $x \to -\infty$.
   (b) $f$ has exactly two relative extrema on $(-\infty, +\infty)$, and $f(x) \to 0$ as $x \to +\infty$ and as $x \to -\infty$.
   (c) $f$ has exactly one inflection point and one relative extremum on $(-\infty, +\infty)$.
   (d) $f$ has infinitely many relative extrema, and $f(x) \to 0$ as $x \to +\infty$ and as $x \to -\infty$.

3. (a) Use both the first and second derivative tests to show that $f(x) = 3x^2 - 6x + 1$ has a relative minimum at $x = 1$.
   (b) Use both the first and second derivative tests to show that $f(x) = x^3 - 3x + 3$ has a relative minimum at $x = 1$ and a relative maximum at $x = -1$.

4. (a) Use both the first and second derivative tests to show that $f(x) = \sin^2 x$ has a relative minimum at $x = 0$.
   (b) Use both the first and second derivative tests to show that $g(x) = \tan^2 x$ has a relative minimum at $x = 0$.
   (c) Give an informal verbal argument to explain without calculus why the functions in parts (a) and (b) have relative minima at $x = 0$.

5. (a) Show that both of the functions $f(x) = (x - 1)^4$ and $g(x) = x^3 - 3x^2 + 3x - 2$ have stationary points at $x = 1$.
   (b) What does the second derivative test tell you about the nature of these stationary points?
   (c) What does the first derivative test tell you about the nature of these stationary points?

6. (a) Show that $f(x) = 1 - x^5$ and $g(x) = 3x^4 - 8x^3$ both have stationary points at $x = 0$.
   (b) What does the second derivative test tell you about the nature of these stationary points?
   (c) What does the first derivative test tell you about the nature of these stationary points?

**7–14** Locate the critical points and identify which critical points are stationary points. ■

**7.** $f(x) = 4x^4 - 16x^2 + 17$  **8.** $f(x) = 3x^4 + 12x$

**9.** $f(x) = \dfrac{x+1}{x^2+3}$  **10.** $f(x) = \dfrac{x^2}{x^3+8}$

**11.** $f(x) = \sqrt[3]{x^2 - 25}$  **12.** $f(x) = x^2(x-1)^{2/3}$

**13.** $f(x) = |\sin x|$  **14.** $f(x) = \sin |x|$

**15–18 True–False** Assume that $f$ is continuous everywhere. Determine whether the statement is true or false. Explain your answer. ■

**15.** If $f$ has a relative maximum at $x = 1$, then $f(1) \geq f(2)$.

**16.** If $f$ has a relative maximum at $x = 1$, then $x = 1$ is a critical point for $f$.

**17.** If $f''(x) > 0$, then $f$ has a relative minimum at $x = 1$.

**18.** If $p(x)$ is a polynomial such that $p'(x)$ has a simple root at $x = 1$, then $p$ has a relative extremum at $x = 1$.

**FOCUS ON CONCEPTS**

**19–20** The graph of a function $f(x)$ is given. Sketch graphs of $y = f'(x)$ and $y = f''(x)$. ■

**19.**

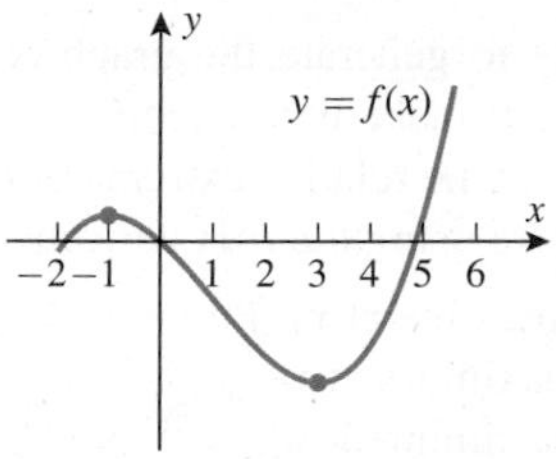


**20.**

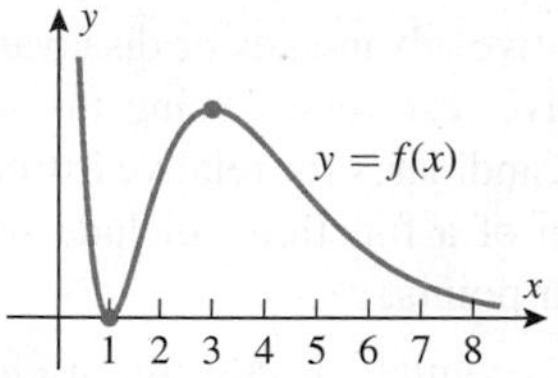


**21–24** Use the graph of $f'$ shown in the figure to estimate all values of $x$ at which $f$ has (a) relative minima, (b) relative maxima, and (c) inflection points. (d) Draw a rough sketch of the graph of a function $f$ with the given derivative. ■

**21.**

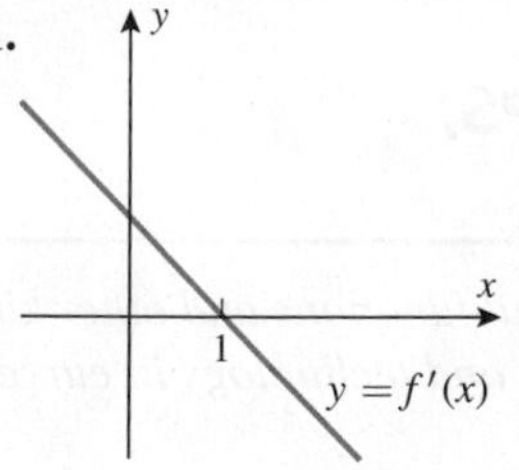


**22.**

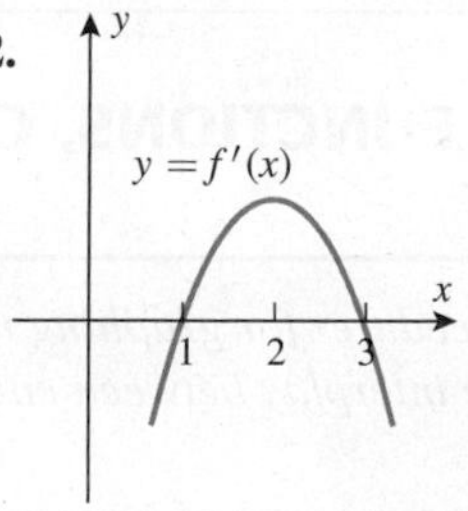


**23.**

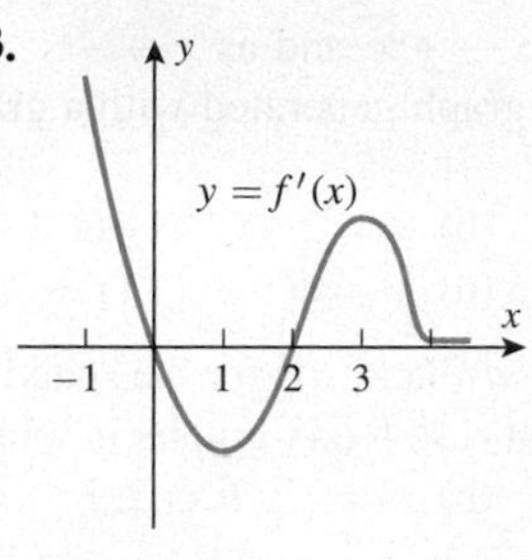


**24.**

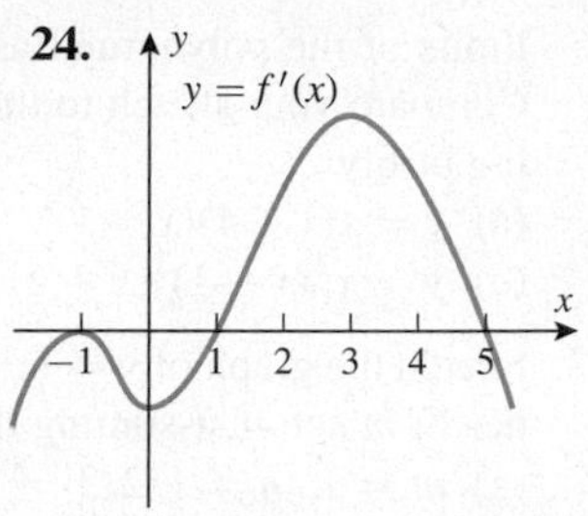


**25–32** Use the given derivative to find all critical points of $f$, and at each critical point determine whether a relative maximum, relative minimum, or neither occurs. Assume in each case that $f$ is continuous everywhere. ■

**25.** $f'(x) = x^2(x^3 - 5)$  **26.** $f'(x) = 4x^3 - 9x$

**27.** $f'(x) = \dfrac{2-3x}{\sqrt[3]{x+2}}$  **28.** $f'(x) = \dfrac{x^2-7}{\sqrt[3]{x^2+4}}$

**29.** $f'(x) = xe^{1-x^2}$  **30.** $f'(x) = x^4(e^x - 3)$

**31.** $f'(x) = \ln\left(\dfrac{2}{1+x^2}\right)$  **32.** $f'(x) = e^{2x} - 5e^x + 6$

**33–36** Find the relative extrema using both first and second derivative tests. ■

**33.** $f(x) = 1 + 8x - 3x^2$  **34.** $f(x) = x^4 - 12x^3$

**35.** $f(x) = \sin 2x, \quad 0 < x < \pi$  **36.** $f(x) = (x-3)e^x$

**37–50** Use any method to find the relative extrema of the function $f$. ■

**37.** $f(x) = x^4 - 4x^3 + 4x^2$  **38.** $f(x) = x(x-4)^3$

**39.** $f(x) = x^3(x+1)^2$  **40.** $f(x) = x^2(x+1)^3$

**41.** $f(x) = 2x + 3x^{2/3}$  **42.** $f(x) = 2x + 3x^{1/3}$

**43.** $f(x) = \dfrac{x+3}{x-2}$  **44.** $f(x) = \dfrac{x^2}{x^4+16}$

**45.** $f(x) = \ln(2 + x^2)$  **46.** $f(x) = \ln|2 + x^3|$

**47.** $f(x) = e^{2x} - e^x$  **48.** $f(x) = (xe^x)^2$

**49.** $f(x) = |3x - x^2|$  **50.** $f(x) = |1 + \sqrt[3]{x}|$

**51–60** Give a graph of the polynomial and label the coordinates of the intercepts, stationary points, and inflection points. Check your work with a graphing utility. ■

**51.** $p(x) = x^2 - 3x - 4$  **52.** $p(x) = 1 + 8x - x^2$

**53.** $p(x) = 2x^3 - 3x^2 - 36x + 5$

**54.** $p(x) = 2 - x + 2x^2 - x^3$

**55.** $p(x) = (x+1)^2(2x - x^2)$

**56.** $p(x) = x^4 - 6x^2 + 5$

**57.** $p(x) = x^4 - 2x^3 + 2x - 1$  **58.** $p(x) = 4x^3 - 9x^4$

**59.** $p(x) = x(x^2 - 1)^2$  **60.** $p(x) = x(x^2 - 1)^3$

**61.** In each part: (i) Make a conjecture about the behavior of the graph in the vicinity of its $x$-intercepts. (ii) Make a rough sketch of the graph based on your conjecture and the

limits of the polynomial as $x \to +\infty$ and as $x \to -\infty$. (iii) Compare your sketch to the graph generated with a graphing utility.
(a) $y = x(x-1)(x+1)$ (b) $y = x^2(x-1)^2(x+1)^2$
(c) $y = x^2(x-1)^2(x+1)^3$ (d) $y = x(x-1)^5(x+1)^4$

**62.** Sketch the graph of $y = (x-a)^m(x-b)^n$ for the stated values of $m$ and $n$, assuming that $a < b$ (six graphs in total).
(a) $m = 1,\ n = 1, 2, 3$ (b) $m = 2,\ n = 2, 3$
(c) $m = 3,\ n = 3$

**63–66** Find the relative extrema in the interval $0 < x < 2\pi$, and confirm that your results are consistent with the graph of $f$ generated with a graphing utility. ■

**63.** $f(x) = |\sin 2x|$ **64.** $f(x) = \sqrt{3}x + 2\sin x$

**65.** $f(x) = \cos^2 x$ **66.** $f(x) = \dfrac{\sin x}{2 - \cos x}$

**67–70** Use a graphing utility to make a conjecture about the relative extrema of $f$, and then check your conjecture using either the first or second derivative test. ■

**67.** $f(x) = x\ln x$ **68.** $f(x) = \dfrac{2}{e^x + e^{-x}}$

**69.** $f(x) = x^2e^{-2x}$ **70.** $f(x) = 10\ln x - x$

**71–72** Use a graphing utility to generate the graphs of $f'$ and $f''$ over the stated interval, and then use those graphs to estimate the $x$-coordinates of the relative extrema of $f$. Check that your estimates are consistent with the graph of $f$. ■

**71.** $f(x) = x^4 - 24x^2 + 12x, \quad -5 \le x \le 5$

**72.** $f(x) = \sin\frac{1}{2}x\cos x, \quad -\pi/2 \le x \le \pi/2$

**C 73–76** Use a CAS to graph $f'$ and $f''$, and then use those graphs to estimate the $x$-coordinates of the relative extrema of $f$. Check that your estimates are consistent with the graph of $f$. ■

**73.** $f(x) = \dfrac{10x^3 - 3}{3x^2 - 5x + 8}$ **74.** $f(x) = \dfrac{\tan^{-1}(x^2 - x)}{x^2 + 4}$

**75.** $f(x) = \sqrt{x^4 + \cos^2 x}$ **76.** $f(x) = x^2(e^{2x} - e^x)$

**77.** In each part, find $k$ so that $f$ has a relative extremum at the point where $x = 3$.
(a) $f(x) = x^2 + \dfrac{k}{x}$ (b) $f(x) = \dfrac{x}{x^2 + k}$

**C 78.** (a) Use a CAS to graph the function
$$f(x) = \frac{x^4 + 1}{x^2 + 1}$$
and use the graph to estimate the $x$-coordinates of the relative extrema.
(b) Find the exact $x$-coordinates by using the CAS to solve the equation $f'(x) = 0$.

**79.** Functions similar to
$$f(x) = \frac{1}{\sqrt{2\pi}}e^{-x^2/2}$$
arise in a wide variety of statistical problems.
(a) Use the first derivative test to show that $f$ has a relative maximum at $x = 0$, and confirm this by using a graphing utility to graph $f$.
(b) Sketch the graph of
$$f(x) = \frac{1}{\sqrt{2\pi}}e^{-(x-\mu)^2/2}$$
where $\mu$ is a constant, and label the coordinates of the relative extrema.

**80.** Functions of the form
$$f(x) = \frac{x^n e^{-x}}{n!}, \quad x > 0$$
where $n$ is a positive integer, arise in the statistical study of traffic flow.
(a) Use a graphing utility to generate the graph of $f$ for $n = 2$, 3, 4, and 5, and make a conjecture about the number and locations of the relative extrema of $f$.
(b) Confirm your conjecture using the first derivative test.

**81.** Let $h$ and $g$ have relative maxima at $x_0$. Prove or disprove:
(a) $h + g$ has a relative maximum at $x_0$
(b) $h - g$ has a relative maximum at $x_0$.

**82.** Sketch some curves that show that the three parts of the first derivative test (Theorem 4.2.3) can be false without the assumption that $f$ is continuous at $x_0$.

**83. Writing** Discuss the relative advantages or disadvantages of using the first derivative test versus using the second derivative test to classify candidates for relative extrema on the interior of the domain of a function. Include specific examples to illustrate your points.

**84. Writing** If $p(x)$ is a polynomial, discuss the usefulness of knowing zeros for $p$, $p'$, and $p''$ when determining information about the graph of $p$.

✓ **QUICK CHECK ANSWERS 4.2** 1. less than or equal to 2. 2, 7; 5 3. maximum; minimum 4. (a) $(0, 16)$ (b) $(-2, 0)$ and $(2, 0)$ (c) $(-2/\sqrt{3}, 64/9)$ and $(2/\sqrt{3}, 64/9)$

## 4.3 ANALYSIS OF FUNCTIONS III: RATIONAL FUNCTIONS, CUSPS, AND VERTICAL TANGENTS

*In this section we will discuss procedures for graphing rational functions and other kinds of curves. We will also discuss the interplay between calculus and technology in curve sketching.*

## PROPERTIES OF GRAPHS

In many problems, the properties of interest in the graph of a function are:

- symmetries
- $x$-intercepts
- relative extrema
- intervals of increase and decrease
- asymptotes
- periodicity
- $y$-intercepts
- concavity
- inflection points
- behavior as $x \to +\infty$ or as $x \to -\infty$

Some of these properties may not be relevant in certain cases; for example, asymptotes are characteristic of rational functions but not of polynomials, and periodicity is characteristic of trigonometric functions but not of polynomial or rational functions. Thus, when analyzing the graph of a function $f$, it helps to know something about the general properties of the family to which it belongs.

In a given problem you will usually have a definite objective for your analysis of a graph. For example, you may be interested in showing all of the important characteristics of the function, you may only be interested in the behavior of the graph as $x \to +\infty$ or as $x \to -\infty$, or you may be interested in some specific feature such as a particular inflection point. Thus, your objectives in the problem will dictate those characteristics on which you want to focus.

## GRAPHING RATIONAL FUNCTIONS

Recall that a rational function is a function of the form $f(x) = P(x)/Q(x)$ in which $P(x)$ and $Q(x)$ are polynomials. Graphs of rational functions are more complicated than those of polynomials because of the possibility of asymptotes and discontinuities. If $P(x)$ and $Q(x)$ have no common factors, then the information obtained in the following steps will usually be sufficient to obtain an accurate sketch of the graph of a rational function.

***Graphing a Rational Function $(fx) = P(x)/Q(x)$ if $P(x)$ and $Q(x)$ Have No Common Factors***

**Step 1. (symmetries).** Determine whether there is symmetry about the $y$-axis or the origin.

**Step 2. ($x$- and $y$-intercepts).** Find the $x$- and $y$-intercepts.

**Step 3. (vertical asymptotes).** Find the values of $x$ for which $Q(x) = 0$. The graph has a vertical asymptote at each such value.

**Step 4. (sign of $f(x)$).** The only places where $f(x)$ can change sign are at the $x$-intercepts or vertical asymptotes. Mark the points on the $x$-axis at which these occur and calculate a sample value of $f(x)$ in each of the open intervals determined by these points. This will tell you whether $f(x)$ is positive or negative over that interval.

**Step 5. (end behavior).** Determine the end behavior of the graph by computing the limits of $f(x)$ as $x \to +\infty$ and as $x \to -\infty$. If either limit has a finite value $L$, then the line $y = L$ is a horizontal asymptote.

**Step 6. (derivatives).** Find $f'(x)$ and $f''(x)$.

**Step 7. (conclusions and graph).** Analyze the sign changes of $f'(x)$ and $f''(x)$ to determine the intervals where $f(x)$ is increasing, decreasing, concave up, and concave down. Determine the locations of all stationary points, relative extrema, and inflection points. Use the sign analysis of $f(x)$ to determine the behavior of the graph in the vicinity of the vertical asymptotes. Sketch a graph of $f$ that exhibits these conclusions.

► **Example 1** Sketch a graph of the equation

$$y = \frac{2x^2 - 8}{x^2 - 16}$$

and identify the locations of the intercepts, relative extrema, inflection points, and asymptotes.

***Solution.*** The numerator and denominator have no common factors, so we will use the procedure just outlined.

- *Symmetries:* Replacing $x$ by $-x$ does not change the equation, so the graph is symmetric about the $y$-axis.
- *$x$- and $y$-intercepts:* Setting $y = 0$ yields the $x$-intercepts $x = -2$ and $x = 2$. Setting $x = 0$ yields the $y$-intercept $y = \frac{1}{2}$.
- *Vertical asymptotes:* We observed above that the numerator and denominator of $y$ have no common factors, so the graph has vertical asymptotes at the points where the denominator of $y$ is zero, namely, at $x = -4$ and $x = 4$.
- *Sign of $y$:* The set of points where $x$-intercepts or vertical asymptotes occur is $\{-4, -2, 2, 4\}$. These points divide the $x$-axis into the open intervals

$$(-\infty, -4), \quad (-4, -2), \quad (-2, 2), \quad (2, 4), \quad (4, +\infty)$$

We can find the sign of $y$ on each interval by choosing an arbitrary test point in the interval and evaluating $y = f(x)$ at the test point (Table 4.3.1). This analysis is summarized on the first line of Figure 4.3.1*a*.

**Table 4.3.1**

SIGN ANALYSIS OF $y = \dfrac{2x^2 - 8}{x^2 - 16}$

| INTERVAL | TEST POINT | VALUE OF $y$ | SIGN OF $y$ |
|---|---|---|---|
| $(-\infty, -4)$ | $-5$ | $14/3$ | $+$ |
| $(-4, -2)$ | $-3$ | $-10/7$ | $-$ |
| $(-2, 2)$ | $0$ | $1/2$ | $+$ |
| $(2, 4)$ | $3$ | $-10/7$ | $-$ |
| $(4, +\infty)$ | $5$ | $14/3$ | $+$ |

- *End behavior:* The limits

$$\lim_{x\to+\infty} \frac{2x^2 - 8}{x^2 - 16} = \lim_{x\to+\infty} \frac{2 - (8/x^2)}{1 - (16/x^2)} = 2$$

$$\lim_{x\to-\infty} \frac{2x^2 - 8}{x^2 - 16} = \lim_{x\to-\infty} \frac{2 - (8/x^2)}{1 - (16/x^2)} = 2$$

yield the horizontal asymptote $y = 2$.

- *Derivatives:*

$$\frac{dy}{dx} = \frac{(x^2 - 16)(4x) - (2x^2 - 8)(2x)}{(x^2 - 16)^2} = -\frac{48x}{(x^2 - 16)^2}$$

$$\frac{d^2y}{dx^2} = \frac{48(16 + 3x^2)}{(x^2 - 16)^3} \quad \text{(verify)}$$

*Conclusions and graph:*

- The sign analysis of $y$ in Figure 4.3.1*a* reveals the behavior of the graph in the vicinity of the vertical asymptotes: The graph increases without bound as $x \to -4^-$ and decreases without bound as $x \to -4^+$; and the graph decreases without bound as $x \to 4^-$ and increases without bound as $x \to 4^+$ (Figure 4.3.1*b*).
- The sign analysis of $dy/dx$ in Figure 4.3.1*a* shows that the graph is increasing to the left of $x = 0$ and is decreasing to the right of $x = 0$. Thus, there is a relative maximum at the stationary point $x = 0$. There are no relative minima.
- The sign analysis of $d^2y/dx^2$ in Figure 4.3.1*a* shows that the graph is concave up to the left of $x = -4$, is concave down between $x = -4$ and $x = 4$, and is concave up to the right of $x = 4$. There are no inflection points.

The graph is shown in Figure 4.3.1*c*. ◄

The procedure we stated for graphing a rational function $P(x)/Q(x)$ applies only if the polynomials $P(x)$ and $Q(x)$ have no common factors. How would you find the graph if those polynomials have common factors?

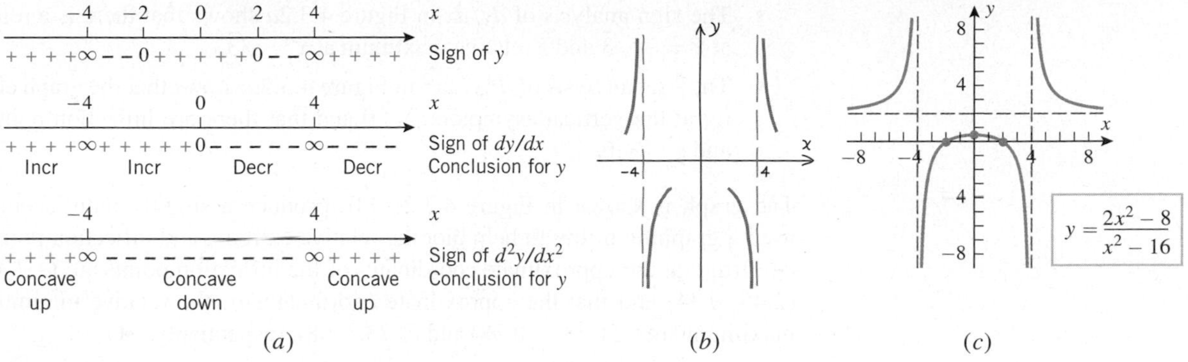


▲ Figure 4.3.1

**▶ Example 2** Sketch a graph of

$$y = \frac{x^2 - 1}{x^3}$$

and identify the locations of all asymptotes, intercepts, relative extrema, and inflection points.

***Solution.*** The numerator and denominator have no common factors, so we will use the procedure outlined previously.

- *Symmetries:* Replacing $x$ by $-x$ and $y$ by $-y$ yields an equation that simplifies to the original equation, so the graph is symmetric about the origin.
- *x- and y-intercepts:* Setting $y = 0$ yields the $x$-intercepts $x = -1$ and $x = 1$. Setting $x = 0$ leads to a division by zero, so there is no $y$-intercept.
- *Vertical asymptotes:* Setting $x^3 = 0$ yields the solution $x = 0$. This is not a root of $x^2 - 1$, so $x = 0$ is a vertical asymptote.
- *Sign of y:* The set of points where $x$-intercepts or vertical asymptotes occur is $\{-1, 0, 1\}$. These points divide the $x$-axis into the open intervals

$$(-\infty, -1), \quad (-1, 0), \quad (0, 1), \quad (1, +\infty)$$

Table 4.3.2 uses the method of test points to produce the sign of $y$ on each of these intervals.

**Table 4.3.2**

SIGN ANALYSIS OF $y = \dfrac{x^2 - 1}{x^3}$

| INTERVAL | TEST POINT | VALUE OF $y$ | SIGN OF $y$ |
|---|---|---|---|
| $(-\infty, -1)$ | $-2$ | $-\frac{3}{8}$ | $-$ |
| $(-1, 0)$ | $-\frac{1}{2}$ | $6$ | $+$ |
| $(0, 1)$ | $\frac{1}{2}$ | $-6$ | $-$ |
| $(1, +\infty)$ | $2$ | $\frac{3}{8}$ | $+$ |

- *End behavior:* The limits

$$\lim_{x \to +\infty} \frac{x^2 - 1}{x^3} = \lim_{x \to +\infty} \left(\frac{1}{x} - \frac{1}{x^3}\right) = 0$$

$$\lim_{x \to -\infty} \frac{x^2 - 1}{x^3} = \lim_{x \to -\infty} \left(\frac{1}{x} - \frac{1}{x^3}\right) = 0$$

yield the horizontal asymptote $y = 0$.

- *Derivatives:*

$$\frac{dy}{dx} = \frac{x^3(2x) - (x^2 - 1)(3x^2)}{(x^3)^2} = \frac{3 - x^2}{x^4} = \frac{(\sqrt{3} + x)(\sqrt{3} - x)}{x^4}$$

$$\frac{d^2y}{dx^2} = \frac{x^4(-2x) - (3 - x^2)(4x^3)}{(x^4)^2} = \frac{2(x^2 - 6)}{x^5} = \frac{2(x - \sqrt{6})(x + \sqrt{6})}{x^5}$$

*Conclusions and graph:*

- The sign analysis of $y$ in Figure 4.3.2*a* reveals the behavior of the graph in the vicinity of the vertical asymptote $x = 0$: The graph increases without bound as $x \to 0^-$ and decreases without bound as $x \to 0^+$ (Figure 4.3.2*b*).

- The sign analysis of $dy/dx$ in Figure 4.3.2$a$ shows that there is a relative minimum at $x = -\sqrt{3}$ and a relative maximum at $x = \sqrt{3}$.
- The sign analysis of $d^2y/dx^2$ in Figure 4.3.2$a$ shows that the graph changes concavity at the vertical asymptote $x = 0$ and that there are inflection points at $x = -\sqrt{6}$ and $x = \sqrt{6}$.

The graph is shown in Figure 4.3.2$c$. To produce a slightly more accurate sketch, we used a graphing utility to help plot the relative extrema and inflection points. You should confirm that the approximate coordinates of the inflection points are $(-2.45, -0.34)$ and $(2.45, 0.34)$ and that the approximate coordinates of the relative minimum and relative maximum are $(-1.73, -0.38)$ and $(1.73, 0.38)$, respectively. ◀

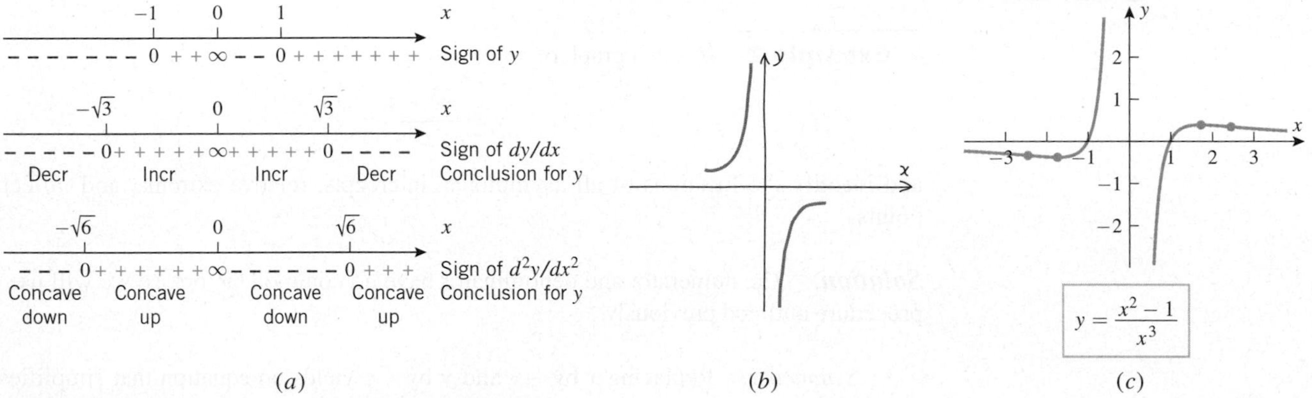


▲ **Figure 4.3.2**

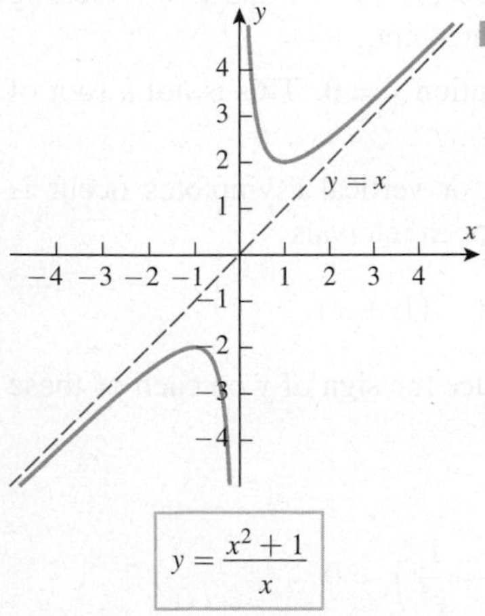


▲ **Figure 4.3.3**

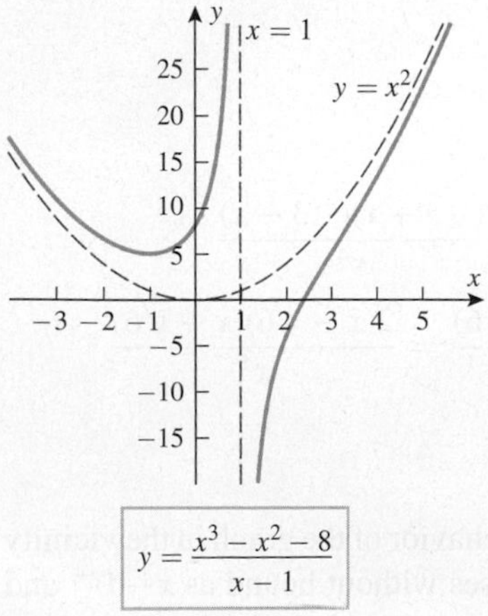


▲ **Figure 4.3.4**

## RATIONAL FUNCTIONS WITH OBLIQUE OR CURVILINEAR ASYMPTOTES

In the rational functions of Examples 1 and 2, the degree of the numerator did not exceed the degree of the denominator, and the asymptotes were either vertical or horizontal. If the numerator of a rational function has greater degree than the denominator, then other kinds of "asymptotes" are possible. For example, consider the rational functions

$$f(x) = \frac{x^2+1}{x} \quad \text{and} \quad g(x) = \frac{x^3-x^2-8}{x-1} \tag{1}$$

By division we can rewrite these as

$$f(x) = x + \frac{1}{x} \quad \text{and} \quad g(x) = x^2 - \frac{8}{x-1}$$

Since the second terms both approach 0 as $x \to +\infty$ or as $x \to -\infty$, it follows that

$$(f(x) - x) \to 0 \quad \text{as } x \to +\infty \text{ or as } x \to -\infty$$
$$(g(x) - x^2) \to 0 \quad \text{as } x \to +\infty \text{ or as } x \to -\infty$$

Geometrically, this means that the graph of $y = f(x)$ eventually gets closer and closer to the line $y = x$ as $x \to +\infty$ or as $x \to -\infty$. The line $y = x$ is called an ***oblique*** or ***slant asymptote*** of $f$. Similarly, the graph of $y = g(x)$ eventually gets closer and closer to the parabola $y = x^2$ as $x \to +\infty$ or as $x \to -\infty$. The parabola is called a ***curvilinear asymptote*** of $g$. The graphs of the functions in (1) are shown in Figures 4.3.3 and 4.3.4.

In general, if $f(x) = P(x)/Q(x)$ is a rational function, then we can find quotient and remainder polynomials $q(x)$ and $r(x)$ such that

$$f(x) = q(x) + \frac{r(x)}{Q(x)}$$

and the degree of $r(x)$ is less than the degree of $Q(x)$. Then $r(x)/Q(x) \to 0$ as $x \to +\infty$ and as $x \to -\infty$, so $y = q(x)$ is an asymptote of $f$. This asymptote will be an oblique line if the degree of $P(x)$ is one greater than the degree of $Q(x)$, and it will be curvilinear if the degree of $P(x)$ exceeds that of $Q(x)$ by two or more. Problems involving these kinds of asymptotes are given in the exercises (Exercises 17 and 18).

## GRAPHS WITH VERTICAL TANGENTS AND CUSPS

Figure 4.3.5 shows four curve elements that are commonly found in graphs of functions that involve radicals or fractional exponents. In all four cases, the function is not differentiable at $x_0$ because the secant line through $(x_0, f(x_0))$ and $(x, f(x))$ approaches a vertical position as $x$ approaches $x_0$ from either side. Thus, in each case, the curve has a vertical tangent line at $(x_0, f(x_0))$. In parts (*a*) and (*b*) of the figure, there is an inflection point at $x_0$ because there is a change in concavity at that point. In parts (*c*) and (*d*), where $f'(x)$ approaches $+\infty$ from one side of $x_0$ and $-\infty$ from the other side, we say that the graph has a ***cusp*** at $x_0$.

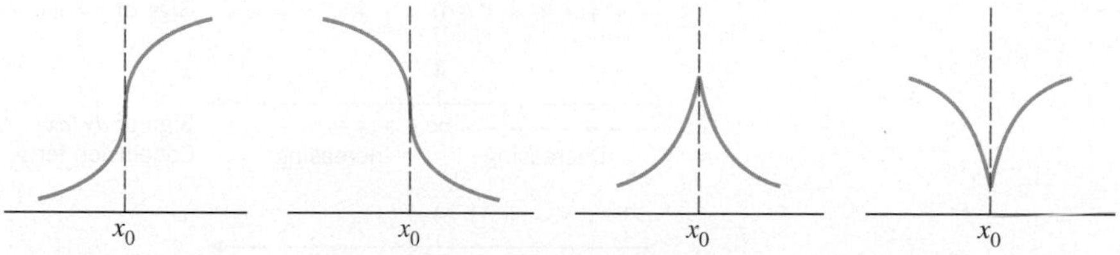


(*a*) $\lim_{x\to x_0^+} f'(x) = +\infty$, $\lim_{x\to x_0^-} f'(x) = +\infty$

(*b*) $\lim_{x\to x_0^+} f'(x) = -\infty$, $\lim_{x\to x_0^-} f'(x) = -\infty$

(*c*) $\lim_{x\to x_0^+} f'(x) = -\infty$, $\lim_{x\to x_0^-} f'(x) = +\infty$

(*d*) $\lim_{x\to x_0^+} f'(x) = +\infty$, $\lim_{x\to x_0^-} f'(x) = -\infty$

▶ **Figure 4.3.5**

The steps that are used to sketch the graph of a rational function can serve as guidelines for sketching graphs of other types of functions. This is illustrated in Examples 3, 4, and 5.

▶ **Example 3** Sketch the graph of $y = (x-4)^{2/3}$.

- *Symmetries:* There are no symmetries about the coordinate axes or the origin (verify). However, the graph of $y = (x-4)^{2/3}$ is symmetric about the line $x = 4$ since it is a translation (4 units to the right) of the graph of $y = x^{2/3}$, which is symmetric about the $y$-axis.
- *$x$- and $y$-intercepts:* Setting $y = 0$ yields the $x$-intercept $x = 4$. Setting $x = 0$ yields the $y$-intercept $y = \sqrt[3]{16} \approx 2.5$.
- *Vertical asymptotes:* None, since $f(x) = (x-4)^{2/3}$ is continuous everywhere.
- *End behavior:* The graph has no horizontal asymptotes since

$$\lim_{x\to+\infty} (x-4)^{2/3} = +\infty \quad \text{and} \quad \lim_{x\to-\infty} (x-4)^{2/3} = +\infty$$

- *Derivatives:*

$$\frac{dy}{dx} = f'(x) = \frac{2}{3}(x-4)^{-1/3} = \frac{2}{3(x-4)^{1/3}}$$

$$\frac{d^2y}{dx^2} = f''(x) = -\frac{2}{9}(x-4)^{-4/3} = -\frac{2}{9(x-4)^{4/3}}$$

- *Vertical tangent lines:* There is a vertical tangent line and cusp at $x = 4$ of the type in Figure 4.3.5*d* since $f(x) = (x-4)^{2/3}$ is continuous at $x = 4$ and

$$\lim_{x\to 4^+} f'(x) = \lim_{x\to 4^+} \frac{2}{3(x-4)^{1/3}} = +\infty$$

$$\lim_{x\to 4^-} f'(x) = \lim_{x\to 4^-} \frac{2}{3(x-4)^{1/3}} = -\infty$$

*Conclusions and graph:*

- The function $f(x) = (x-4)^{2/3} = ((x-4)^{1/3})^2$ is nonnegative for all $x$. There is a zero for $f$ at $x = 4$.

- There is a critical point at $x = 4$ since $f$ is not differentiable there. We saw above that a cusp occurs at this point. The sign analysis of $dy/dx$ in Figure 4.3.6*a* and the first derivative test show that there is a relative minimum at this cusp since $f'(x) < 0$ if $x < 4$ and $f'(x) > 0$ if $x > 4$.
- The sign analysis of $d^2y/dx^2$ in Figure 4.3.6*a* shows that the graph is concave down on both sides of the cusp.

The graph is shown in Figure 4.3.6*b*. ◄

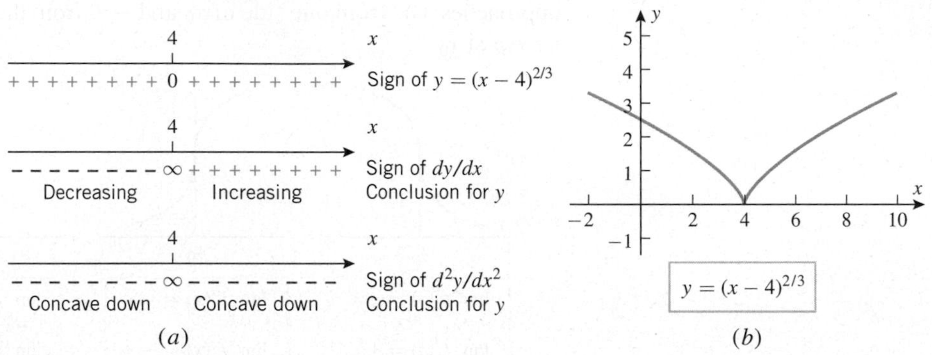


► Figure 4.3.6

**► Example 4** Sketch the graph of $y = 6x^{1/3} + 3x^{4/3}$.

***Solution.*** It will help in our analysis to write

$$f(x) = 6x^{1/3} + 3x^{4/3} = 3x^{1/3}(2 + x)$$

- *Symmetries:* There are no symmetries about the coordinate axes or the origin (verify).
- *x- and y-intercepts:* Setting $y = 3x^{1/3}(2 + x) = 0$ yields the $x$-intercepts $x = 0$ and $x = -2$. Setting $x = 0$ yields the $y$-intercept $y = 0$.
- *Vertical asymptotes:* None, since $f(x) = 6x^{1/3} + 3x^{4/3}$ is continuous everywhere.
- *End behavior:* The graph has no horizontal asymptotes since

$$\lim_{x\to+\infty} (6x^{1/3} + 3x^{4/3}) = \lim_{x\to+\infty} 3x^{1/3}(2 + x) = +\infty$$

$$\lim_{x\to-\infty} (6x^{1/3} + 3x^{4/3}) = \lim_{x\to-\infty} 3x^{1/3}(2 + x) = +\infty$$

- *Derivatives:*

$$\frac{dy}{dx} = f'(x) = 2x^{-2/3} + 4x^{1/3} = 2x^{-2/3}(1 + 2x) = \frac{2(2x + 1)}{x^{2/3}}$$

$$\frac{d^2y}{dx^2} = f''(x) = -\frac{4}{3}x^{-5/3} + \frac{4}{3}x^{-2/3} = \frac{4}{3}x^{-5/3}(-1 + x) = \frac{4(x - 1)}{3x^{5/3}}$$

- *Vertical tangent lines:* There is a vertical tangent line at $x = 0$ since $f$ is continuous there and

$$\lim_{x\to0^+} f'(x) = \lim_{x\to0^+} \frac{2(2x + 1)}{x^{2/3}} = +\infty$$

$$\lim_{x\to0^-} f'(x) = \lim_{x\to0^-} \frac{2(2x + 1)}{x^{2/3}} = +\infty$$

This and the change in concavity at $x = 0$ mean that $(0, 0)$ is an inflection point of the type in Figure 4.3.5*a*.

*Conclusions and graph:*

- From the sign analysis of $y$ in Figure 4.3.7*a*, the graph is below the $x$-axis between the $x$-intercepts $x = -2$ and $x = 0$ and is above the $x$-axis if $x < -2$ or $x > 0$.
- From the formula for $dy/dx$ we see that there is a stationary point at $x = -\frac{1}{2}$ and a critical point at $x = 0$ at which $f$ is not differentiable. We saw above that a vertical tangent line and inflection point are at that critical point.
- The sign analysis of $dy/dx$ in Figure 4.3.7*a* and the first derivative test show that there is a relative minimum at the stationary point at $x = -\frac{1}{2}$ (verify).
- The sign analysis of $d^2y/dx^2$ in Figure 4.3.7*a* shows that in addition to the inflection point at the vertical tangent there is an inflection point at $x = 1$ at which the graph changes from concave down to concave up.

The graph is shown in Figure 4.3.7*b*. ◄

**TECHNOLOGY MASTERY**

The graph in Figure 4.3.7*b* was generated with a graphing utility. However, the inflection point at $x = 1$ is so subtle that it is not evident from this graph. See if you can produce a version of this graph with your graphing utility that makes the inflection point evident.

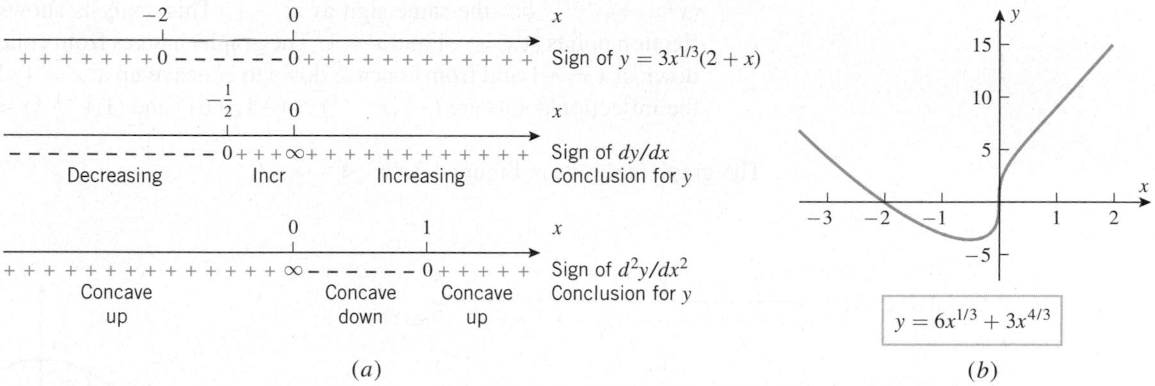


▲ **Figure 4.3.7**

## GRAPHING OTHER KINDS OF FUNCTIONS

We have discussed methods for graphing polynomials, rational functions, and functions with cusps and vertical tangent lines. The same calculus tools that we used to analyze these functions can also be used to analyze and graph trigonometric functions, logarithmic and exponential functions, and an endless variety of other kinds of functions.

► **Example 5** Sketch the graph of $y = e^{-x^2/2}$ and identify the locations of all relative extrema and inflection points.

***Solution.***

- *Symmetries:* Replacing $x$ by $-x$ does not change the equation, so the graph is symmetric about the $y$-axis.
- *$x$- and $y$-intercepts:* Setting $y = 0$ leads to the equation $e^{-x^2/2} = 0$, which has no solutions since all powers of $e$ have positive values. Thus, there are no $x$-intercepts. Setting $x = 0$ yields the $y$-intercept $y = 1$.
- *Vertical asymptotes:* There are no vertical asymptotes since $e^{-x^2/2}$ is continuous on $(-\infty, +\infty)$.
- *End behavior:* The $x$-axis ($y = 0$) is a horizontal asymptote since

$$\lim_{x\to-\infty} e^{-x^2/2} = \lim_{x\to+\infty} e^{-x^2/2} = 0$$

- *Derivatives:*

$$\frac{dy}{dx} = e^{-x^2/2}\frac{d}{dx}\left[-\frac{x^2}{2}\right] = -xe^{-x^2/2}$$

$$\frac{d^2y}{dx^2} = -x\frac{d}{dx}[e^{-x^2/2}] + e^{-x^2/2}\frac{d}{dx}[-x]$$

$$= x^2e^{-x^2/2} - e^{-x^2/2} = (x^2-1)e^{-x^2/2}$$

*Conclusions and graph:*

- The sign analysis of $y$ in Figure 4.3.8$a$ is based on the fact that $e^{-x^2/2} > 0$ for all $x$. This shows that the graph is always above the $x$-axis.
- The sign analysis of $dy/dx$ in Figure 4.3.8$a$ is based on the fact that $dy/dx = -xe^{-x^2/2}$ has the same sign as $-x$. This analysis and the first derivative test show that there is a stationary point at $x = 0$ at which there is a relative maximum. The value of $y$ at the relative maximum is $y = e^0 = 1$.
- The sign analysis of $d^2y/dx^2$ in Figure 4.3.8$a$ is based on the fact that $d^2y/dx^2 = (x^2-1)e^{-x^2/2}$ has the same sign as $x^2 - 1$. This analysis shows that there are inflection points at $x = -1$ and $x = 1$. The graph changes from concave up to concave down at $x = -1$ and from concave down to concave up at $x = 1$. The coordinates of the inflection points are $(-1, e^{-1/2}) \approx (-1, 0.61)$ and $(1, e^{-1/2}) \approx (1, 0.61)$.

The graph is shown in Figure 4.3.8$b$. ◄

▲ Figure 4.3.8

## GRAPHING USING CALCULUS AND TECHNOLOGY TOGETHER

Thus far in this chapter we have used calculus to produce graphs of functions; the graph was the end result. Now we will work in the reverse direction by *starting* with a graph produced by a graphing utility. Our goal will be to use the tools of calculus to determine the exact locations of relative extrema, inflection points, and other features suggested by that graph and to determine whether the graph may be missing some important features that we would like to see.

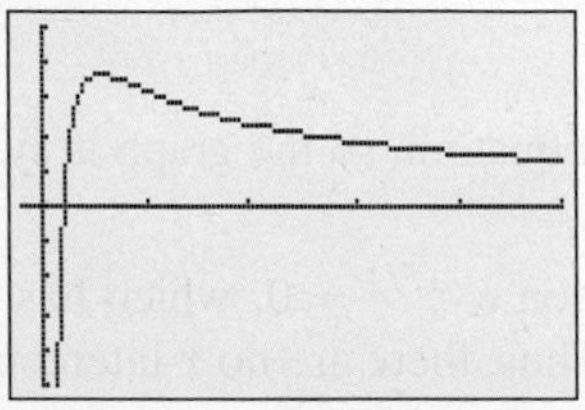

$[-1, 25] \times [-0.5, 0.5]$
$x$Scl = 5, $y$Scl = 0.2

$y = \frac{\ln x}{x}$

▲ Figure 4.3.9

► **Example 6** Use a graphing utility to generate the graph of $f(x) = (\ln x)/x$, and discuss what it tells you about relative extrema, inflection points, asymptotes, and end behavior. Use calculus to find the locations of all key features of the graph.

***Solution.*** Figure 4.3.9 shows a graph of $f$ produced by a graphing utility. The graph suggests that there is an $x$-intercept near $x = 1$, a relative maximum somewhere between $x = 0$ and $x = 5$, an inflection point near $x = 5$, a vertical asymptote at $x = 0$, and possibly a horizontal asymptote $y = 0$. For a more precise analysis of this information we need to consider the derivatives

$$f'(x) = \frac{x\left(\frac{1}{x}\right) - (\ln x)(1)}{x^2} = \frac{1 - \ln x}{x^2}$$

$$f''(x) = \frac{x^2\left(-\frac{1}{x}\right) - (1 - \ln x)(2x)}{x^4} = \frac{2x\ln x - 3x}{x^4} = \frac{2\ln x - 3}{x^3}$$

- *Relative extrema:* Solving $f'(x) = 0$ yields the stationary point $x = e$ (verify). Since

$$f''(e) = \frac{2-3}{e^3} = -\frac{1}{e^3} < 0$$

there is a relative maximum at $x = e \approx 2.7$ by the second derivative test.

- *Inflection points:* Since $f(x) = (\ln x)/x$ is only defined for positive values of $x$, the second derivative $f''(x)$ has the same sign as $2\ln x - 3$. We leave it for you to use the inequalities $(2\ln x - 3) < 0$ and $(2\ln x - 3) > 0$ to show that $f''(x) < 0$ if $x < e^{3/2}$ and $f''(x) > 0$ if $x > e^{3/2}$. Thus, there is an inflection point at $x = e^{3/2} \approx 4.5$.
- *Asymptotes:* Applying L'Hôpital's rule we have

$$\lim_{x\to+\infty} \frac{\ln x}{x} = \lim_{x\to+\infty} \frac{(1/x)}{1} = \lim_{x\to+\infty} \frac{1}{x} = 0$$

so that $y = 0$ is a horizontal asymptote. Also, there is a vertical asymptote at $x = 0$ since

$$\lim_{x\to 0^+} \frac{\ln x}{x} = -\infty$$

(why?).

- *Intercepts:* Setting $f(x) = 0$ yields $(\ln x)/x = 0$. The only real solution of this equation is $x = 1$, so there is an $x$-intercept at this point. ◀

## ✓QUICK CHECK EXERCISES 4.3

(See page 204 for answers.)

**1.** Let $f(x) = \dfrac{3(x+1)(x-3)}{(x+2)(x-4)}$. Given that

$$f'(x) = \frac{-30(x-1)}{(x+2)^2(x-4)^2}, \quad f''(x) = \frac{90(x^2 - 2x + 4)}{(x+2)^3(x-4)^3}$$

determine the following properties of the graph of $f$.

(a) The $x$- and $y$-intercepts are ______.
(b) The vertical asymptotes are ______.
(c) The horizontal asymptote is ______.
(d) The graph is above the $x$-axis on the intervals ______.
(e) The graph is increasing on the intervals ______.
(f) The graph is concave up on the intervals ______.
(g) The relative maximum point on the graph is ______.

**2.** Let $f(x) = \dfrac{x^2 - 4}{x^{8/3}}$. Given that

$$f'(x) = \frac{-2(x^2 - 16)}{3x^{11/3}}, \quad f''(x) = \frac{2(5x^2 - 176)}{9x^{14/3}}$$

determine the following properties of the graph of $f$.

(a) The $x$-intercepts are ______.
(b) The vertical asymptote is ______.
(c) The horizontal asymptote is ______.
(d) The graph is above the $x$-axis on the intervals ______.
(e) The graph is increasing on the intervals ______.
(f) The graph is concave up on the intervals ______.
(g) Inflection points occur at $x =$ ______.

**3.** Let $f(x) = (x-2)^2 e^{x/2}$. Given that

$$f'(x) = \tfrac{1}{2}(x^2 - 4)e^{x/2}, \quad f''(x) = \tfrac{1}{4}(x^2 + 4x - 4)e^{x/2}$$

determine the following properties of the graph of $f$.

(a) The horizontal asymptote is ______.
(b) The graph is above the $x$-axis on the intervals ______.
(c) The graph is increasing on the intervals ______.
(d) The graph is concave up on the intervals ______.
(e) The relative minimum point on the graph is ______.
(f) The relative maximum point on the graph is ______.
(g) Inflection points occur at $x =$ ______.

## EXERCISE SET 4.3 Graphing Utility

**1–14** Give a graph of the rational function and label the coordinates of the stationary points and inflection points. Show the horizontal and vertical asymptotes and label them with their equations. Label point(s), if any, where the graph crosses a horizontal asymptote. Check your work with a graphing utility. ■

1. $\dfrac{2x-6}{4-x}$ 2. $\dfrac{8}{x^2-4}$ 3. $\dfrac{x}{x^2-4}$

4. $\dfrac{x^2}{x^2-4}$ 5. $\dfrac{x^2}{x^2+4}$ 6. $\dfrac{(x^2-1)^2}{x^4+1}$

7. $\dfrac{x^3+1}{x^3-1}$ 8. $2-\dfrac{1}{3x^2+x^3}$

9. $\dfrac{4}{x^2}-\dfrac{2}{x}+3$ 10. $\dfrac{3(x+1)^2}{(x-1)^2}$

11. $\dfrac{(3x+1)^2}{(x-1)^2}$ 12. $3+\dfrac{x+1}{(x-1)^4}$

13. $\dfrac{x^2+x}{1-x^2}$ 14. $\dfrac{x^2}{1-x^3}$

**15–16** In each part, make a rough sketch of the graph using asymptotes and appropriate limits but no derivatives. Compare your graph to that generated with a graphing utility. ■

15. (a) $y=\dfrac{3x^2-8}{x^2-4}$ (b) $y=\dfrac{x^2+2x}{x^2-1}$

16. (a) $y=\dfrac{2x-x^2}{x^2+x-2}$ (b) $y=\dfrac{x^2}{x^2-x-2}$

17. Show that $y=x+3$ is an oblique asymptote of the graph of $f(x)=x^2/(x-3)$. Sketch the graph of $y=f(x)$ showing this asymptotic behavior.

18. Show that $y=3-x^2$ is a curvilinear asymptote of the graph of $f(x)=(2+3x-x^3)/x$. Sketch the graph of $y=f(x)$ showing this asymptotic behavior.

**19–24** Sketch a graph of the rational function and label the coordinates of the stationary points and inflection points. Show the horizontal, vertical, oblique, and curvilinear asymptotes and label them with their equations. Label point(s), if any, where the graph crosses an asymptote. Check your work with a graphing utility. ■

19. $x^2-\dfrac{1}{x}$ 20. $\dfrac{x^2-2}{x}$

21. $\dfrac{(x-2)^3}{x^2}$ 22. $x-\dfrac{1}{x}-\dfrac{1}{x^2}$

23. $\dfrac{x^3-4x-8}{x+2}$ 24. $\dfrac{x^5}{x^2+1}$

**FOCUS ON CONCEPTS**

25. In each part, match the function with graphs I–VI.
(a) $x^{1/3}$ (b) $x^{1/4}$ (c) $x^{1/5}$
(d) $x^{2/5}$ (e) $x^{4/3}$ (f) $x^{-1/3}$

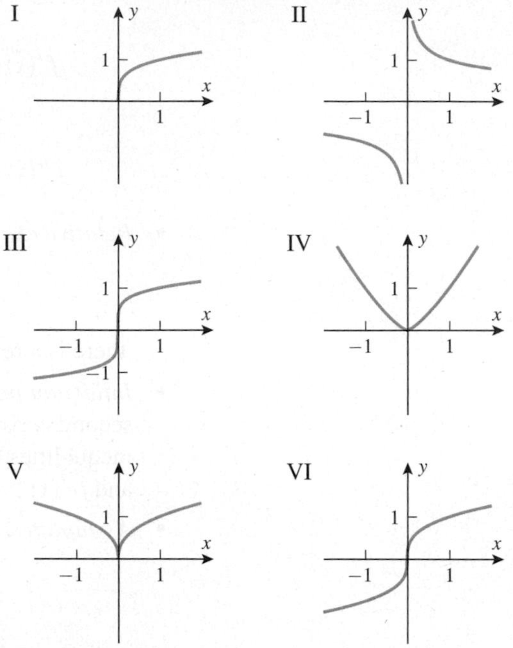


▲ Figure Ex-25

26. Sketch the general shape of the graph of $y=x^{1/n}$, and then explain in words what happens to the shape of the graph as $n$ increases if
(a) $n$ is a positive even integer
(b) $n$ is a positive odd integer.

**27–30 True–False** Determine whether the statement is true or false. Explain your answer. ■

27. Suppose that $f(x)=P(x)/Q(x)$, where $P$ and $Q$ are polynomials with no common factors. If $y=5$ is a horizontal asymptote for the graph of $f$, then $P$ and $Q$ have the same degree.

28. If the graph of $f$ has a vertical asymptote at $x=1$, then $f$ cannot be continuous at $x=1$.

29. If the graph of $f'$ has a vertical asymptote at $x=1$, then $f$ cannot be continuous at $x=1$.

30. If the graph of $f$ has a cusp at $x=1$, then $f$ cannot have an inflection point at $x=1$.

**31–38** Give a graph of the function and identify the locations of all critical points and inflection points. Check your work with a graphing utility. ■

31. $\sqrt{4x^2-1}$ 32. $\sqrt[3]{x^2-4}$

33. $2x+3x^{2/3}$ 34. $2x^2-3x^{4/3}$

35. $4x^{1/3}-x^{4/3}$ 36. $5x^{2/3}+x^{5/3}$

37. $\dfrac{8+x}{2+\sqrt[3]{x}}$ 38. $\dfrac{8(\sqrt{x}-1)}{x}$

**39–44** Give a graph of the function and identify the locations of all relative extrema and inflection points. Check your work with a graphing utility. ■

**39.** $x + \sin x$

**40.** $x - \tan x$

**41.** $\sqrt{3}\cos x + \sin x$

**42.** $\sin x + \cos x$

**43.** $\sin^2 x - \cos x, \quad -\pi \le x \le 3\pi$

**44.** $\sqrt{\tan x}, \quad 0 \le x < \pi/2$

**45–54** Using L'Hôpital's rule (Section 3.6) one can verify that

$$\lim_{x\to+\infty} \frac{e^x}{x} = +\infty, \quad \lim_{x\to+\infty} \frac{x}{e^x} = 0, \quad \lim_{x\to-\infty} xe^x = 0$$

In these exercises: (a) Use these results, as necessary, to find the limits of $f(x)$ as $x\to+\infty$ and as $x\to-\infty$. (b) Sketch a graph of $f(x)$ and identify all relative extrema, inflection points, and asymptotes (as appropriate). Check your work with a graphing utility. ■

**45.** $f(x) = xe^x$

**46.** $f(x) = xe^{-x}$

**47.** $f(x) = x^2e^{-2x}$

**48.** $f(x) = x^2e^{2x}$

**49.** $f(x) = x^2e^{-x^2}$

**50.** $f(x) = e^{-1/x^2}$

**51.** $f(x) = \dfrac{e^x}{1-x}$

**52.** $f(x) = x^{2/3}e^x$

**53.** $f(x) = x^2e^{1-x}$

**54.** $f(x) = x^3e^{x-1}$

**55–60** Using L'Hôpital's rule (Section 3.6) one can verify that

$$\lim_{x\to+\infty} \frac{\ln x}{x^r} = 0, \quad \lim_{x\to+\infty} \frac{x^r}{\ln x} = +\infty, \quad \lim_{x\to 0^+} x^r \ln x = 0$$

for any positive real number $r$. In these exercises: (a) Use these results, as necessary, to find the limits of $f(x)$ as $x\to+\infty$ and as $x\to 0^+$. (b) Sketch a graph of $f(x)$ and identify all relative extrema, inflection points, and asymptotes (as appropriate). Check your work with a graphing utility. ■

**55.** $f(x) = x\ln x$

**56.** $f(x) = x^2 \ln x$

**57.** $f(x) = x^2 \ln(2x)$

**58.** $f(x) = \ln(x^2+1)$

**59.** $f(x) = x^{2/3}\ln x$

**60.** $f(x) = x^{-1/3}\ln x$

**FOCUS ON CONCEPTS**

**61.** Consider the family of curves $y = xe^{-bx}$ $(b > 0)$.
(a) Use a graphing utility to generate some members of this family.
(b) Discuss the effect of varying $b$ on the shape of the graph, and discuss the locations of the relative extrema and inflection points.

**62.** Consider the family of curves $y = e^{-bx^2}$ $(b > 0)$.
(a) Use a graphing utility to generate some members of this family.
(b) Discuss the effect of varying $b$ on the shape of the graph, and discuss the locations of the relative extrema and inflection points.

**63.** (a) Determine whether the following limits exist, and if so, find them:

$$\lim_{x\to+\infty} e^x \cos x, \quad \lim_{x\to-\infty} e^x \cos x$$

(b) Sketch the graphs of the equations $y = e^x$, $y = -e^x$, and $y = e^x \cos x$ in the same coordinate system, and label any points of intersection.
(c) Use a graphing utility to generate some members of the family $y = e^{ax}\cos bx$ $(a > 0$ and $b > 0)$, and discuss the effect of varying $a$ and $b$ on the shape of the curve.

**64.** Consider the family of curves $y = x^n e^{-x^2/n}$, where $n$ is a positive integer.
(a) Use a graphing utility to generate some members of this family.
(b) Discuss the effect of varying $n$ on the shape of the graph, and discuss the locations of the relative extrema and inflection points.

**65.** The accompanying figure shows the graph of the *derivative* of a function $h$ that is defined and continuous on the interval $(-\infty, +\infty)$. Assume that the graph of $h'$ has a vertical asymptote at $x = 3$ and that

$$h'(x)\to 0^+ \text{ as } x\to-\infty$$
$$h'(x)\to -\infty \text{ as } x\to+\infty$$

(a) What are the critical points for $h(x)$?
(b) Identify the intervals on which $h(x)$ is increasing.
(c) Identify the $x$-coordinates of relative extrema for $h(x)$ and classify each as a relative maximum or relative minimum.
(d) Estimate the $x$-coordinates of inflection points for $h(x)$.

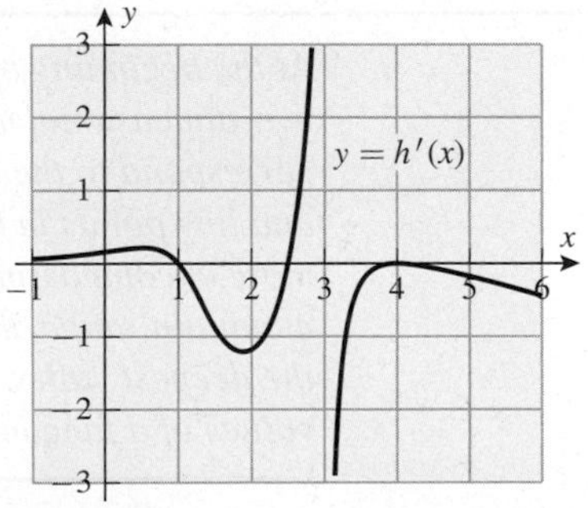


◀ **Figure Ex-65**

**66.** Let $f(x) = (1 - 2x)h(x)$, where $h(x)$ is as given in Exercise 65. Suppose that $x = 5$ is a critical point for $f(x)$.
(a) Estimate $h(5)$.
(b) Use the second derivative test to determine whether $f(x)$ has a relative maximum or a relative minimum at $x = 5$.

**67.** A rectangular plot of land is to be fenced off so that the area enclosed will be 400 ft$^2$. Let $L$ be the length of fencing needed and $x$ the length of one side of the rectangle. Show that $L = 2x + 800/x$ for $x > 0$, and sketch the graph of $L$ versus $x$ for $x > 0$.

**68.** A box with a square base and open top is to be made from sheet metal so that its volume is 500 in$^3$. Let $S$ be the area of the surface of the box and $x$ the length of a side of the square base. Show that $S = x^2 + 2000/x$ for $x > 0$, and sketch the graph of $S$ versus $x$ for $x > 0$.

**69.** The accompanying figure shows a computer-generated graph of the polynomial $y = 0.1x^5(x - 1)$ using a viewing window of $[-2, 2.5] \times [-1, 5]$. Show that the choice of the vertical scale caused the computer to miss important features of the graph. Find the features that were missed and make your own sketch of the graph that shows the missing features.

**70.** The accompanying figure shows a computer-generated graph of the polynomial $y = 0.1x^5(x + 1)^2$ using a viewing window of $[-2, 1.5] \times [-0.2, 0.2]$. Show that the choice of the vertical scale caused the computer to miss important features of the graph. Find the features that were missed and make your own sketch of the graph that shows the missing features.

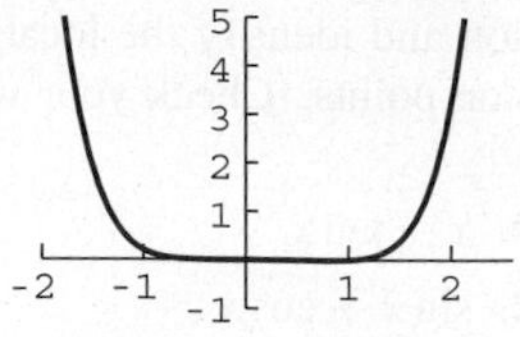

*Generated by Mathematica*

▲ **Figure Ex-69**

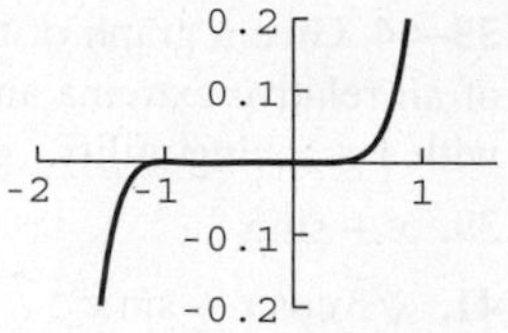

*Generated by Mathematica*

▲ **Figure Ex-70**

**71. Writing** Suppose that $x = x_0$ is a point at which a function $f$ is continuous but not differentiable and that $f'(x)$ approaches different finite limits as $x$ approaches $x_0$ from either side. Invent your own term to describe the graph of $f$ at such a point and discuss the appropriateness of your term.

**72. Writing** Suppose that the graph of a function $f$ is obtained using a graphing utility. Discuss the information that calculus techniques can provide about $f$ to add to what can already be inferred about $f$ from the graph as shown on your utility's display.

✓ **QUICK CHECK ANSWERS 4.3** **1.** (a) $(-1, 0), (3, 0), (0, \frac{9}{8})$ (b) $x = -2$ and $x = 4$ (c) $y = 3$ (d) $(-\infty, -2), (-1, 3)$, and $(4, +\infty)$ (e) $(-\infty, -2)$ and $(-2, 1]$ (f) $(-\infty, -2)$ and $(4, +\infty)$ (g) $(1, \frac{4}{3})$ **2.** (a) $(-2, 0), (2, 0)$ (b) $x = 0$ (c) $y = 0$ (d) $(-\infty, -2)$ and $(2, +\infty)$ (e) $(-\infty, -4]$ and $(0, 4]$ (f) $(-\infty, -4\sqrt{11/5})$ and $(4\sqrt{11/5}, +\infty)$ (g) $\pm 4\sqrt{11/5} \approx \pm 5.93$ **3.** (a) $y = 0$ (as $x \to -\infty$) (b) $(-\infty, 2)$ and $(2, +\infty)$ (c) $(-\infty, -2]$ and $[2, +\infty)$ (d) $(-\infty, -2 - 2\sqrt{2})$ and $(-2 + 2\sqrt{2}, +\infty)$ (e) $(2, 0)$ (f) $(-2, 16e^{-1}) \approx (-2, 5.89)$ (g) $-2 \pm 2\sqrt{2}$

## 4.4 ABSOLUTE MAXIMA AND MINIMA

*At the beginning of Section 4.2 we observed that if the graph of a function f is viewed as a two-dimensional mountain range (Figure 4.2.1), then the relative maxima and minima correspond to the tops of the hills and the bottoms of the valleys; that is, they are the high and low points in their immediate vicinity. In this section we will be concerned with the more encompassing problem of finding the highest and lowest points over the entire mountain range, that is, we will be looking for the top of the highest hill and the bottom of the deepest valley. In mathematical terms, we will be looking for the largest and smallest values of a function over an interval.*

### ABSOLUTE EXTREMA

We will begin with some terminology for describing the largest and smallest values of a function on an interval.

**4.4.1 DEFINITION** Consider an interval in the domain of a function $f$ and a point $x_0$ in that interval. We say that $f$ has an ***absolute maximum*** at $x_0$ if $f(x) \le f(x_0)$ for all $x$ in the interval, and we say that $f$ has an ***absolute minimum*** at $x_0$ if $f(x_0) \le f(x)$ for all $x$ in the interval. We say that $f$ has an ***absolute extremum*** at $x_0$ if it has either an absolute maximum or an absolute minimum at that point.

If $f$ has an absolute maximum at the point $x_0$ on an interval, then $f(x_0)$ is the largest value of $f$ on the interval, and if $f$ has an absolute minimum at $x_0$, then $f(x_0)$ is the smallest value of $f$ on the interval. In general, there is no guarantee that a function will actually have an absolute maximum or minimum on a given interval (Figure 4.4.1).

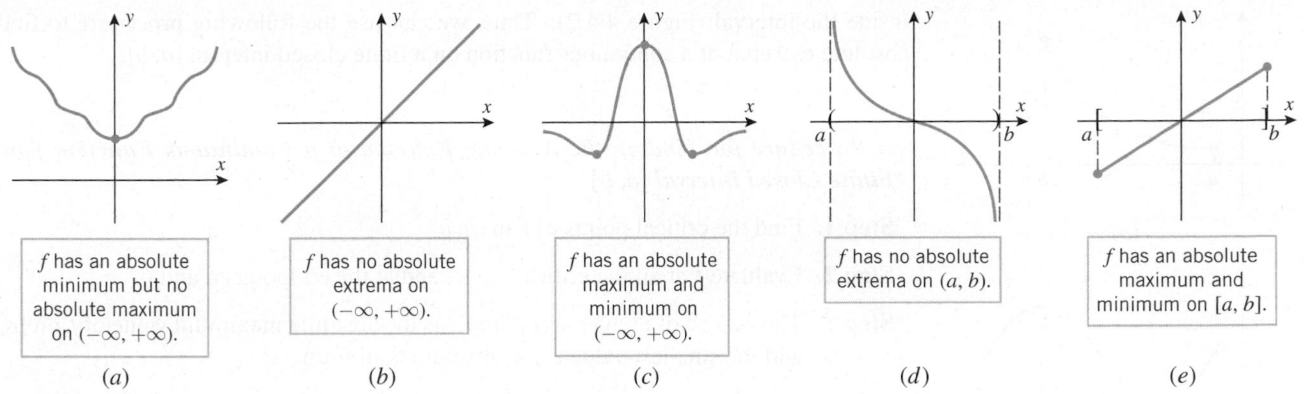


▲ **Figure 4.4.1**

## THE EXTREME VALUE THEOREM

Parts (*a*)–(*d*) of Figure 4.4.1 show that a continuous function may or may not have absolute maxima or minima on an infinite interval or on a finite open interval. However, the following theorem shows that a continuous function must have both an absolute maximum and an absolute minimum on every *finite closed* interval [see part (*e*) of Figure 4.4.1].

The hypotheses in the Extreme-Value Theorem are essential. That is, if either the interval is not closed or *f* is not continuous on the interval, then *f* need not have absolute extrema on the interval (Exercises 4–6).

**4.4.2 THEOREM (*Extreme-Value Theorem*)** *If a function f is continuous on a finite closed interval* $[a, b]$, *then f has both an absolute maximum and an absolute minimum on* $[a, b]$.

**REMARK** Although the proof of this theorem is too difficult to include here, you should be able to convince yourself of its validity with a little experimentation—try graphing various continuous functions over the interval $[0, 1]$, and convince yourself that there is no way to avoid having a highest and lowest point on a graph. As a physical analogy, if you imagine the graph to be a roller-coaster track starting at $x = 0$ and ending at $x = 1$, the roller coaster will have to pass through a highest point and a lowest point during the trip.

The Extreme-Value Theorem is an example of what mathematicians call an ***existence theorem***. Such theorems state conditions under which certain objects exist, in this case absolute extrema. However, knowing that an object exists and finding it are two separate things. We will now address methods for determining the locations of absolute extrema under the conditions of the Extreme-Value Theorem.

If *f* is continuous on the finite closed interval $[a, b]$, then the absolute extrema of *f* occur either at the endpoints of the interval or inside the open interval $(a, b)$. If the absolute extrema happen to fall inside, then the following theorem tells us that they must occur at critical points of *f*.

Theorem 4.4.3 is also valid on infinite open intervals, that is, intervals of the form $(-\infty, +\infty)$, $(a, +\infty)$, and $(-\infty, b)$.

**4.4.3 THEOREM** *If f has an absolute extremum on an open interval* $(a, b)$, *then it must occur at a critical point of f.*

**PROOF** If *f* has an absolute maximum on $(a, b)$ at $x_0$, then $f(x_0)$ is also a relative maximum for *f*; for if $f(x_0)$ is the largest value of *f* on all $(a, b)$, then $f(x_0)$ is certainly the largest value for *f* in the immediate vicinity of $x_0$. Thus, $x_0$ is a critical point of *f* by Theorem 4.2.2. The proof for absolute minima is similar. ■

It follows from this theorem that if *f* is continuous on the finite closed interval $[a, b]$, then the absolute extrema occur either at the endpoints of the interval or at critical points

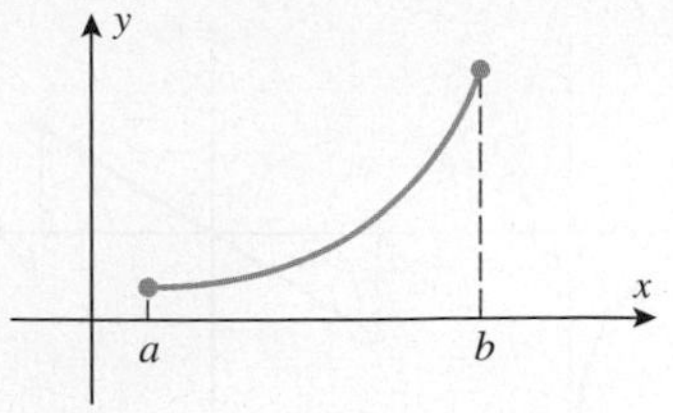


(a)

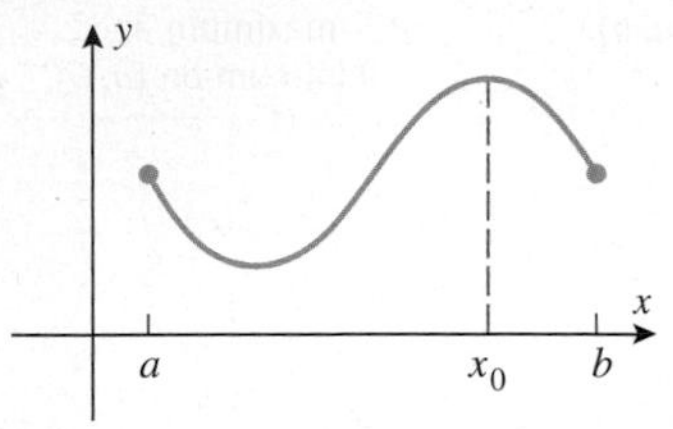


(b)

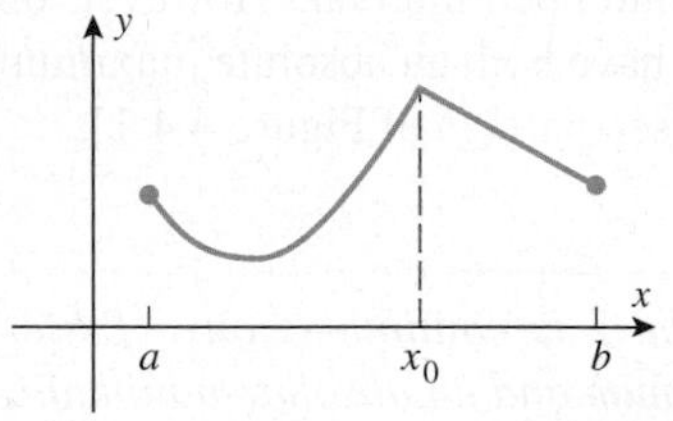


(c)

▲ **Figure 4.4.2** In part (a) the absolute maximum occurs at an endpoint of $[a, b]$, in part (b) it occurs at a stationary point in $(a, b)$, and in part (c) it occurs at a critical point in $(a, b)$ where $f$ is not differentiable.

inside the interval (Figure 4.4.2). Thus, we can use the following procedure to find the absolute extrema of a continuous function on a finite closed interval $[a, b]$.

***A Procedure for Finding the Absolute Extrema of a Continuous Function f on a Finite Closed Interval [a, b]***

**Step 1.** Find the critical points of $f$ in $(a, b)$.

**Step 2.** Evaluate $f$ at all the critical points and at the endpoints $a$ and $b$.

**Step 3.** The largest of the values in Step 2 is the absolute maximum value of $f$ on $[a, b]$ and the smallest value is the absolute minimum.

▶ **Example 1** Find the absolute maximum and minimum values of the function $f(x) = 2x^3 - 15x^2 + 36x$ on the interval $[1, 5]$, and determine where these values occur.

***Solution.*** Since $f$ is continuous and differentiable everywhere, the absolute extrema must occur either at endpoints of the interval or at solutions to the equation $f'(x) = 0$ in the open interval $(1, 5)$. The equation $f'(x) = 0$ can be written as

$$6x^2 - 30x + 36 = 6(x^2 - 5x + 6) = 6(x - 2)(x - 3) = 0$$

Thus, there are stationary points at $x = 2$ and at $x = 3$. Evaluating $f$ at the endpoints, at $x = 2$, and at $x = 3$ yields

$$f(1) = 2(1)^3 - 15(1)^2 + 36(1) = 23$$
$$f(2) = 2(2)^3 - 15(2)^2 + 36(2) = 28$$
$$f(3) = 2(3)^3 - 15(3)^2 + 36(3) = 27$$
$$f(5) = 2(5)^3 - 15(5)^2 + 36(5) = 55$$

from which we conclude that the absolute minimum of $f$ on $[1, 5]$ is 23, occurring at $x = 1$, and the absolute maximum of $f$ on $[1, 5]$ is 55, occurring at $x = 5$. This is consistent with the graph of $f$ in Figure 4.4.3. ◀

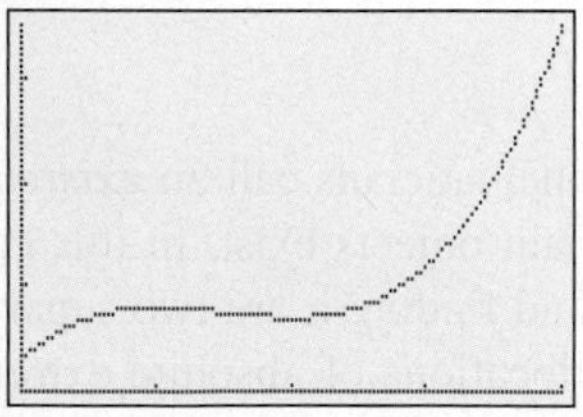

$[1, 5] \times [20, 55]$
$x\text{Scl} = 1, y\text{Scl} = 10$

$y = 2x^3 - 15x^2 + 36x$

▲ **Figure 4.4.3**

▶ **Example 2** Find the absolute extrema of $f(x) = 6x^{4/3} - 3x^{1/3}$ on the interval $[-1, 1]$, and determine where these values occur.

***Solution.*** Note that $f$ is continuous everywhere and therefore the Extreme-Value Theorem guarantees that $f$ has a maximum and a minimum value in the interval $[-1, 1]$. Differentiating, we obtain

$$f'(x) = 8x^{1/3} - x^{-2/3} = x^{-2/3}(8x - 1) = \frac{8x - 1}{x^{2/3}}$$

Thus, $f'(x) = 0$ at $x = \frac{1}{8}$, and $f'(x)$ is undefined at $x = 0$. Evaluating $f$ at these critical points and endpoints yields Table 4.4.1, from which we conclude that an absolute minimum value of $-\frac{9}{8}$ occurs at $x = \frac{1}{8}$, and an absolute maximum value of 9 occurs at $x = -1$. ◀

**Table 4.4.1**

| | | | | |
|---|---|---|---|---|
| $x$ | $-1$ | 0 | $\frac{1}{8}$ | 1 |
| $f(x)$ | 9 | 0 | $-\frac{9}{8}$ | 3 |

## ABSOLUTE EXTREMA ON INFINITE INTERVALS

We observed earlier that a continuous function may or may not have absolute extrema on an infinite interval (see Figure 4.4.1). However, certain conclusions about the existence of absolute extrema of a continuous function $f$ on $(-\infty, +\infty)$ can be drawn from the behavior of $f(x)$ as $x \to -\infty$ and as $x \to +\infty$ (Table 4.4.2).

**Table 4.4.2**
ABSOLUTE EXTREMA ON INFINITE INTERVALS

| | | | | |
|---|---|---|---|---|
| **LIMITS** | $\lim_{x\to-\infty} f(x) = +\infty$ <br> $\lim_{x\to+\infty} f(x) = +\infty$ | $\lim_{x\to-\infty} f(x) = -\infty$ <br> $\lim_{x\to+\infty} f(x) = -\infty$ | $\lim_{x\to-\infty} f(x) = -\infty$ <br> $\lim_{x\to+\infty} f(x) = +\infty$ | $\lim_{x\to-\infty} f(x) = +\infty$ <br> $\lim_{x\to+\infty} f(x) = -\infty$ |
| **CONCLUSION IF $f$ IS CONTINUOUS EVERYWHERE** | $f$ has an absolute minimum but no absolute maximum on $(-\infty, +\infty)$. | $f$ has an absolute maximum but no absolute minimum on $(-\infty, +\infty)$. | $f$ has neither an absolute maximum nor an absolute minimum on $(-\infty, +\infty)$. | $f$ has neither an absolute maximum nor an absolute minimum on $(-\infty, +\infty)$. |
| **GRAPH** | 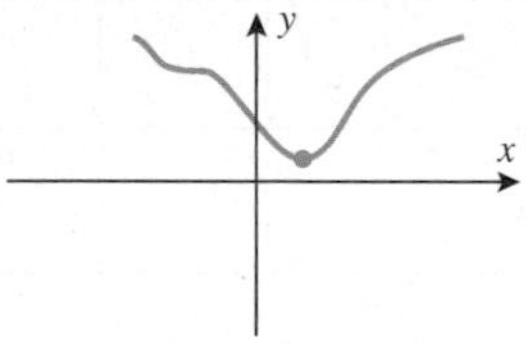  | 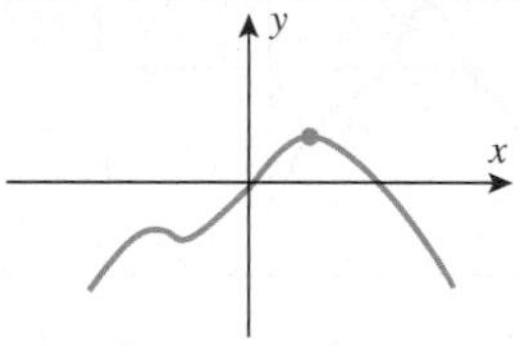  | 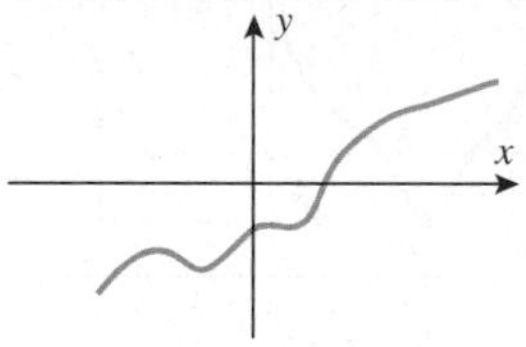  | 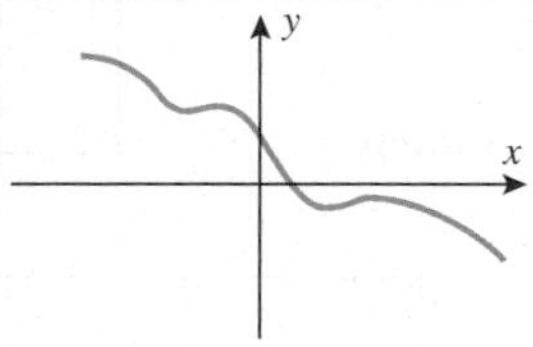  |

▶ **Example 3** What can you say about the existence of absolute extrema on $(-\infty, +\infty)$ for polynomials?

***Solution.*** If $p(x)$ is a polynomial of odd degree, then

$$\lim_{x\to+\infty} p(x) \quad \text{and} \quad \lim_{x\to-\infty} p(x) \tag{1}$$

have opposite signs (one is $+\infty$ and the other is $-\infty$), so there are no absolute extrema. On the other hand, if $p(x)$ has even degree, then the limits in (1) have the same sign (both $+\infty$ or both $-\infty$). If the leading coefficient is positive, then both limits are $+\infty$, and there is an absolute minimum but no absolute maximum; if the leading coefficient is negative, then both limits are $-\infty$, and there is an absolute maximum but no absolute minimum. ◀

▶ **Example 4** Determine by inspection whether $p(x) = 3x^4 + 4x^3$ has any absolute extrema. If so, find them and state where they occur.

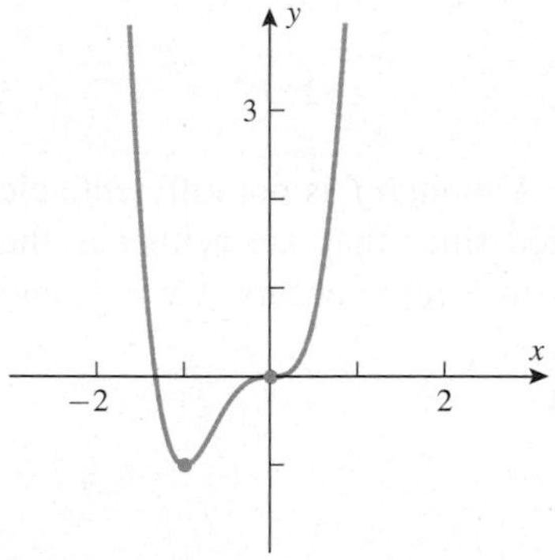

$p(x) = 3x^4 + 4x^3$

▲ **Figure 4.4.4**

***Solution.*** Since $p(x)$ has even degree and the leading coefficient is positive, $p(x)\to+\infty$ as $x\to\pm\infty$. Thus, there is an absolute minimum but no absolute maximum. From Theorem 4.4.3 [applied to the interval $(-\infty, +\infty)$], the absolute minimum must occur at a critical point of $p$. Since $p$ is differentiable everywhere, we can find all critical points by solving the equation $p'(x) = 0$. This equation is

$$12x^3 + 12x^2 = 12x^2(x+1) = 0$$

from which we conclude that the critical points are $x = 0$ and $x = -1$. Evaluating $p$ at these critical points yields

$$p(0) = 0 \quad \text{and} \quad p(-1) = -1$$

Therefore, $p$ has an absolute minimum of $-1$ at $x = -1$ (Figure 4.4.4). ◀

## ABSOLUTE EXTREMA ON OPEN INTERVALS

We know that a continuous function may or may not have absolute extrema on an open interval. However, certain conclusions about the existence of absolute extrema of a continuous function $f$ on a finite open interval $(a, b)$ can be drawn from the behavior of $f(x)$ as $x\to a^+$ and as $x\to b^-$ (Table 4.4.3). Similar conclusions can be drawn for intervals of the form $(-\infty, b)$ or $(a, +\infty)$.

**Table 4.4.3**
ABSOLUTE EXTREMA ON OPEN INTERVALS

| | | | | |
|---|---|---|---|---|
| LIMITS | $\lim_{x\to a^+} f(x) = +\infty$<br>$\lim_{x\to b^-} f(x) = +\infty$ | $\lim_{x\to a^+} f(x) = -\infty$<br>$\lim_{x\to b^-} f(x) = -\infty$ | $\lim_{x\to a^+} f(x) = -\infty$<br>$\lim_{x\to b^-} f(x) = +\infty$ | $\lim_{x\to a^+} f(x) = +\infty$<br>$\lim_{x\to b^-} f(x) = -\infty$ |
| CONCLUSION IF $f$ IS CONTINUOUS ON $(a, b)$ | $f$ has an absolute minimum but no absolute maximum on $(a, b)$. | $f$ has an absolute maximum but no absolute minimum on $(a, b)$. | $f$ has neither an absolute maximum nor an absolute minimum on $(a, b)$. | $f$ has neither an absolute maximum nor an absolute minimum on $(a, b)$. |
| GRAPH | 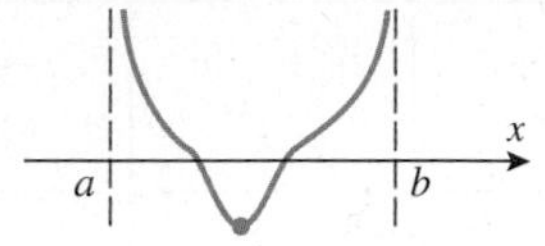 | 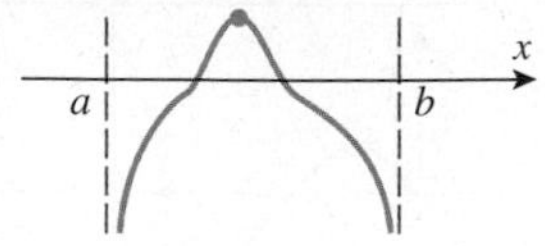 | 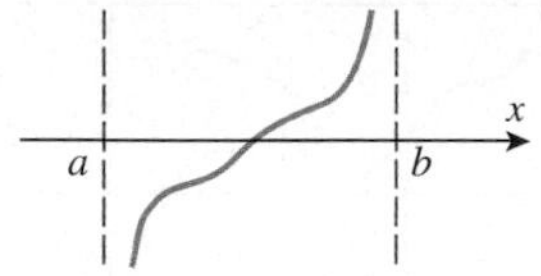 | 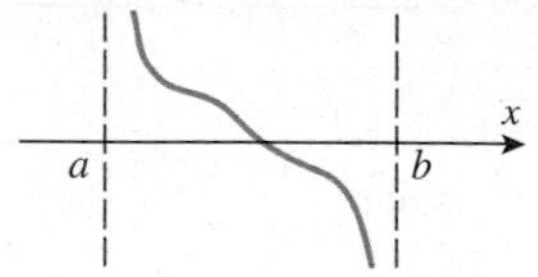 |

▶ **Example 5** Determine whether the function

$$f(x) = \frac{1}{x^2 - x}$$

has any absolute extrema on the interval (0, 1). If so, find them and state where they occur.

***Solution.*** Since $f$ is continuous on the interval (0, 1) and

$$\lim_{x\to 0^+} f(x) = \lim_{x\to 0^+} \frac{1}{x^2 - x} = \lim_{x\to 0^+} \frac{1}{x(x-1)} = -\infty$$

$$\lim_{x\to 1^-} f(x) = \lim_{x\to 1^-} \frac{1}{x^2 - x} = \lim_{x\to 1^-} \frac{1}{x(x-1)} = -\infty$$

the function $f$ has an absolute maximum but no absolute minimum on the interval (0, 1). By Theorem 4.4.3 the absolute maximum must occur at a critical point of $f$ in the interval (0, 1). We have

$$f'(x) = -\frac{2x - 1}{(x^2 - x)^2}$$

so the only solution of the equation $f'(x) = 0$ is $x = \frac{1}{2}$. Although $f$ is not differentiable at $x = 0$ or at $x = 1$, these values are doubly disqualified since they are neither in the domain of $f$ nor in the interval (0, 1). Thus, the absolute maximum occurs at $x = \frac{1}{2}$, and this absolute maximum is

$$f\left(\tfrac{1}{2}\right) = \frac{1}{\left(\frac{1}{2}\right)^2 - \frac{1}{2}} = -4$$

(Figure 4.4.5). ◀

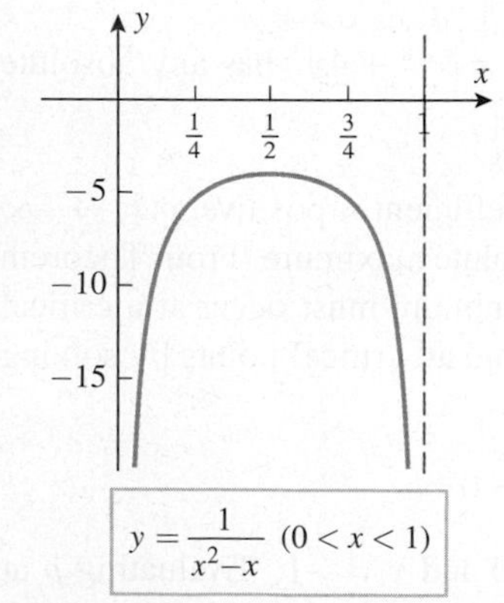

▲ **Figure 4.4.5**

## ■ ABSOLUTE EXTREMA OF FUNCTIONS WITH ONE RELATIVE EXTREMUM

If a continuous function has only one relative extremum on a finite or infinite interval, then that relative extremum must of necessity also be an absolute extremum. To understand why this is so, suppose that $f$ has a relative maximum at $x_0$ in an interval, and there are no other relative extrema of $f$ on the interval. If $f(x_0)$ is *not* the absolute maximum of $f$ on the interval, then the graph of $f$ has to make an upward turn somewhere on the interval to rise above $f(x_0)$. However, this cannot happen because in the process of making an upward turn it would produce a second relative extremum (Figure 4.4.6). Thus, $f(x_0)$ must be the absolute maximum as well as a relative maximum. This idea is captured in the following theorem, which we state without proof.

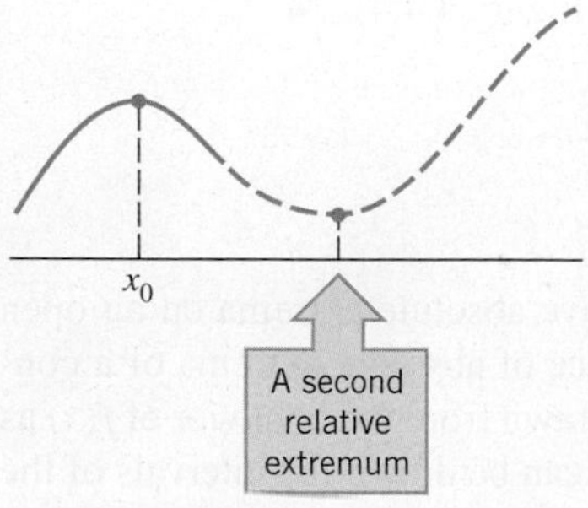

▲ **Figure 4.4.6**

**4.4.4 THEOREM** *Suppose that $f$ is continuous and has exactly one relative extremum on an interval, say at $x_0$.*

(a) *If $f$ has a relative minimum at $x_0$, then $f(x_0)$ is the absolute minimum of $f$ on the interval.*

(b) *If $f$ has a relative maximum at $x_0$, then $f(x_0)$ is the absolute maximum of $f$ on the interval.*

This theorem is often helpful in situations where other methods are difficult or tedious to apply.

▶ **Example 6** Find the absolute extrema, if any, of the function $f(x) = e^{(x^3-3x^2)}$ on the interval $(0, +\infty)$.

***Solution.*** We have

$$\lim_{x\to+\infty} f(x) = +\infty$$

(verify), so $f$ does not have an absolute maximum on the interval $(0, +\infty)$. However, the continuity of $f$ together with the fact that

$$\lim_{x\to0^+} f(x) = e^0 = 1$$

is finite allow for the possibility that $f$ has an absolute minimum on $(0, +\infty)$. If so, it would have to occur at a critical point of $f$, so we consider

$$f'(x) = e^{(x^3-3x^2)}(3x^2 - 6x) = 3x(x-2)e^{(x^3-3x^2)}$$

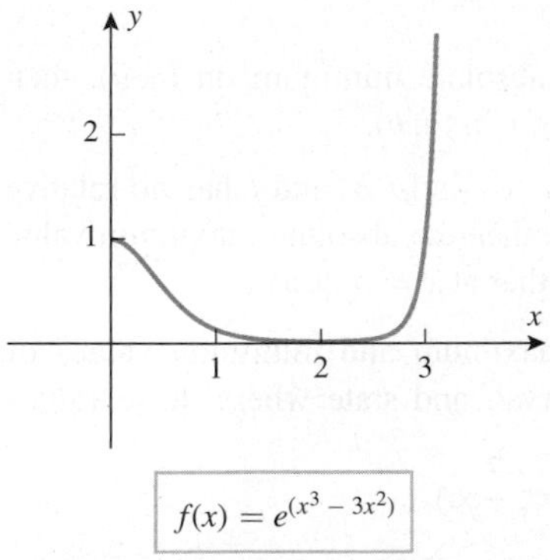


▲ **Figure 4.4.7**

Since $e^{(x^3-3x^2)} > 0$ for all values of $x$, we see that $x = 0$ and $x = 2$ are the only critical points of $f$. Of these, only $x = 2$ is in the interval $(0, +\infty)$, so this is the point at which an absolute minimum could occur. To see whether an absolute minimum actually does occur at this point, we can apply part (*a*) of Theorem 4.4.4. Since

$$f''(x) = e^{(x^3-3x^2)}(3x^2 - 6x)^2 + e^{(x^3-3x^2)}(6x - 6)$$
$$= [(3x^2 - 6x)^2 + (6x - 6)]e^{(x^3-3x^2)}$$

we have

$$f''(2) = (0 + 6)e^{-4} = 6e^{-4} > 0$$

so a relative minimum occurs at $x = 2$ by the second derivative test. Thus, $f(x)$ has an absolute minimum at $x = 2$, and this absolute minimum is $f(2) = e^{-4} \approx 0.0183$ (Figure 4.4.7). ◀

Does the function in Example 6 have an absolute minimum on the interval $(-\infty, +\infty)$?

## ✓ QUICK CHECK EXERCISES 4.4 *(See page 212 for answers.)*

1. Use the accompanying graph to find the $x$-coordinates of the relative extrema and absolute extrema of $f$ on $[0, 6]$.

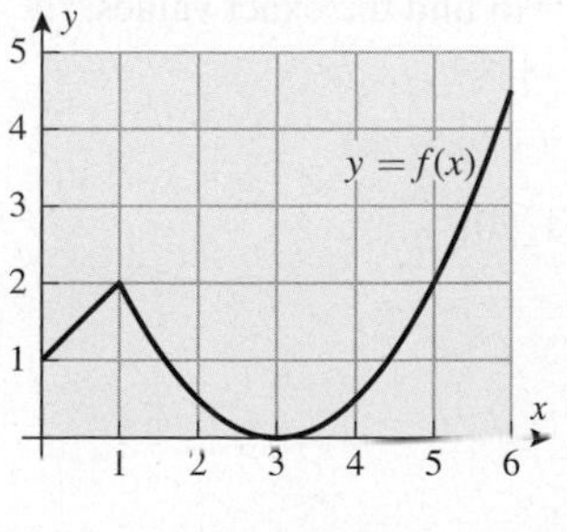


◀ **Figure Ex-1**

2. Suppose that a function $f$ is continuous on $[-4, 4]$ and has critical points at $x = -3, 0, 2$. Use the accompanying table to determine the absolute maximum and absolute minimum values, if any, for $f$ on the indicated intervals.
(a) $[1, 4]$ (b) $[-2, 2]$ (c) $[-4, 4]$ (d) $(-4, 4)$

| $x$ | −4 | −3 | −2 | −1 | 0 | 1 | 2 | 3 | 4 |
|---|---|---|---|---|---|---|---|---|---|
| $f(x)$ | 2224 | 1333 | 0 | 1603 | 2096 | 2293 | 2400 | 2717 | 6064 |

**3.** Let $f(x) = x^3 - 3x^2 - 9x + 25$. Use the derivative $f'(x) = 3(x + 1)(x - 3)$ to determine the absolute maximum and absolute minimum values, if any, for $f$ on each of the given intervals.

(a) $[0, 4]$ (b) $[-2, 4]$ (c) $[-4, 2]$
(d) $[-5, 10]$ (e) $(-5, 4)$

## EXERCISE SET 4.4 Graphing Utility C CAS

**FOCUS ON CONCEPTS**

**1–2** Use the graph to find $x$-coordinates of the relative extrema and absolute extrema of $f$ on $[0, 7]$. ■

**1.**

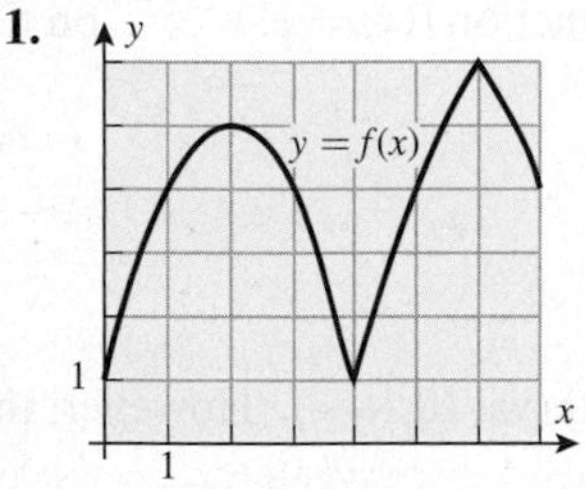


**2.**

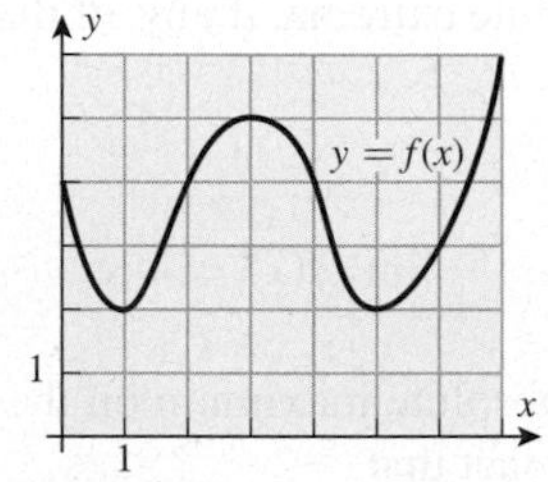


**3.** In each part, sketch the graph of a continuous function $f$ with the stated properties on the interval $[0, 10]$.
(a) $f$ has an absolute minimum at $x = 0$ and an absolute maximum at $x = 10$.
(b) $f$ has an absolute minimum at $x = 2$ and an absolute maximum at $x = 7$.
(c) $f$ has relative minima at $x = 1$ and $x = 8$, has relative maxima at $x = 3$ and $x = 7$, has an absolute minimum at $x = 5$, and has an absolute maximum at $x = 10$.

**4.** In each part, sketch the graph of a continuous function $f$ with the stated properties on the interval $(-\infty, +\infty)$.
(a) $f$ has no relative extrema or absolute extrema.
(b) $f$ has an absolute minimum at $x = 0$ but no absolute maximum.
(c) $f$ has an absolute maximum at $x = -5$ and an absolute minimum at $x = 5$.

**5.** Let
$$f(x) = \begin{cases} \dfrac{1}{1-x}, & 0 \le x < 1 \\ 0, & x = 1 \end{cases}$$
Explain why $f$ has a minimum value but no maximum value on the closed interval $[0, 1]$.

**6.** Let
$$f(x) = \begin{cases} x, & 0 < x < 1 \\ \frac{1}{2}, & x = 0, 1 \end{cases}$$
Explain why $f$ has neither a minimum value nor a maximum value on the closed interval $[0, 1]$.

**7–16** Find the absolute maximum and minimum values of $f$ on the given closed interval, and state where those values occur. ■

**7.** $f(x) = 4x^2 - 12x + 10$; $[1, 2]$

**8.** $f(x) = 8x - x^2$; $[0, 6]$

**9.** $f(x) = (x - 2)^3$; $[1, 4]$

**10.** $f(x) = 2x^3 + 3x^2 - 12x$; $[-3, 2]$

**11.** $f(x) = \dfrac{3x}{\sqrt{4x^2 + 1}}$; $[-1, 1]$

**12.** $f(x) = (x^2 + x)^{2/3}$; $[-2, 3]$

**13.** $f(x) = x - 2\sin x$; $[-\pi/4, \pi/2]$

**14.** $f(x) = \sin x - \cos x$; $[0, \pi]$

**15.** $f(x) = 1 + |9 - x^2|$; $[-5, 1]$

**16.** $f(x) = |6 - 4x|$; $[-3, 3]$

**17–20 True–False** Determine whether the statement is true or false. Explain your answer. ■

**17.** If a function $f$ is continuous on $[a, b]$, then $f$ has an absolute maximum on $[a, b]$.

**18.** If a function $f$ is continuous on $(a, b)$, then $f$ has an absolute minimum on $(a, b)$.

**19.** If a function $f$ has an absolute minimum on $(a, b)$, then there is a critical point of $f$ in $(a, b)$.

**20.** If a function $f$ is continuous on $[a, b]$ and $f$ has no relative extreme values in $(a, b)$, then the absolute maximum value of $f$ exists and occurs either at $x = a$ or at $x = b$.

**21–28** Find the absolute maximum and minimum values of $f$, if any, on the given interval, and state where those values occur. ■

**21.** $f(x) = x^2 - x - 2$; $(-\infty, +\infty)$

**22.** $f(x) = 3 - 4x - 2x^2$; $(-\infty, +\infty)$

**23.** $f(x) = 4x^3 - 3x^4$; $(-\infty, +\infty)$

**24.** $f(x) = x^4 + 4x$; $(-\infty, +\infty)$

**25.** $f(x) = 2x^3 - 6x + 2$; $(-\infty, +\infty)$

**26.** $f(x) = x^3 - 9x + 1$; $(-\infty, +\infty)$

**27.** $f(x) = \dfrac{x^2 + 1}{x + 1}$; $(-5, -1)$

**28.** $f(x) = \dfrac{x - 2}{x + 1}$; $(-1, 5]$

**29–42** Use a graphing utility to estimate the absolute maximum and minimum values of $f$, if any, on the stated interval, and then use calculus methods to find the exact values. ■

**29.** $f(x) = (x^2 - 2x)^2$; $(-\infty, +\infty)$

**30.** $f(x) = (x - 1)^2(x + 2)^2$; $(-\infty, +\infty)$

**31.** $f(x) = x^{2/3}(20 - x)$; $[-1, 20]$

**32.** $f(x) = \dfrac{x}{x^2 + 2}$; $[-1, 4]$

**33.** $f(x) = 1 + \dfrac{1}{x}$; $(0, +\infty)$

**34.** $f(x) = \dfrac{2x^2 - 3x + 3}{x^2 - 2x + 2}$; $[1, +\infty)$

**35.** $f(x) = \dfrac{2 - \cos x}{\sin x}$; $[\pi/4, 3\pi/4]$

**36.** $f(x) = \sin^2 x + \cos x$; $[-\pi, \pi]$

**37.** $f(x) = x^3 e^{-2x}$; $[1, 4]$

**38.** $f(x) = \dfrac{\ln(2x)}{x}$; $[1, e]$

**39.** $f(x) = 5\ln(x^2 + 1) - 3x$; $[0, 4]$

**40.** $f(x) = (x^2 - 1)e^x$; $[-2, 2]$

**41.** $f(x) = \sin(\cos x)$; $[0, 2\pi]$

**42.** $f(x) = \cos(\sin x)$; $[0, \pi]$

**43.** Find the absolute maximum and minimum values of

$$f(x) = \begin{cases} 4x - 2, & x < 1 \\ (x-2)(x-3), & x \geq 1 \end{cases}$$

on $\left[\frac{1}{2}, \frac{7}{2}\right]$.

**44.** Let $f(x) = x^2 + px + q$. Find the values of $p$ and $q$ such that $f(1) = 3$ is an extreme value of $f$ on $[0, 2]$. Is this value a maximum or minimum?

**45–46** If $f$ is a periodic function, then the locations of all absolute extrema on the interval $(-\infty, +\infty)$ can be obtained by finding the locations of the absolute extrema for one period and using the periodicity to locate the rest. Use this idea in these exercises to find the absolute maximum and minimum values of the function, and state the $x$-values at which they occur. ■

**45.** $f(x) = 2\cos x + \cos 2x$ **46.** $f(x) = 3\cos\dfrac{x}{3} + 2\cos\dfrac{x}{2}$

**47–48** One way of proving that $f(x) \leq g(x)$ for all $x$ in a given interval is to show that $0 \leq g(x) - f(x)$ for all $x$ in the interval; and one way of proving the latter inequality is to show that the absolute minimum value of $g(x) - f(x)$ on the interval is nonnegative. Use this idea to prove the inequalities in these exercises. ■

**47.** Prove that $\sin x \leq x$ for all $x$ in the interval $[0, 2\pi]$.

**48.** Prove that $\cos x \geq 1 - (x^2/2)$ for all $x$ in the interval $[0, 2\pi]$.

**49.** What is the smallest possible slope for a tangent to the graph of the equation $y = x^3 - 3x^2 + 5x$?

**50.** (a) Show that $f(x) = \sec x + \csc x$ has a minimum value but no maximum value on the interval $(0, \pi/2)$.
(b) Find the minimum value in part (a).

C **51.** Show that the absolute minimum value of

$$f(x) = x^2 + \frac{x^2}{(8-x)^2}, \quad x > 8$$

occurs at $x = 10$ by using a CAS to find $f'(x)$ and to solve the equation $f'(x) = 0$.

**52.** The concentration $C(t)$ of a drug in the bloodstream $t$ hours after it has been injected is commonly modeled by an equation of the form

$$C(t) = \frac{K(e^{-bt} - e^{-at})}{a - b}$$

where $K > 0$ and $a > b > 0$.

(a) At what time does the maximum concentration occur?
(b) Let $K = 1$ for simplicity, and use a graphing utility to check your result in part (a) by graphing $C(t)$ for various values of $a$ and $b$.

**53.** A rectangular poster has one side of length $x$ inches and total area 700 square inches. The poster must have margins so that the region available for printing has area

$$A(x) = 728 - 7x - \frac{2800}{x} \text{ square inches}$$

What are the dimensions of the poster with the greatest printing area?

**54.** A small soft drink can is designed to have volume 222 cubic centimeters. The top of the can is thicker than the sides or bottom, so that if it has radius $x$ centimeters, then the cost of materials for the can is proportional to $C = \pi x^2 + 111/x$. What are the dimensions of the can that yield the least cost of materials?

**55.** At a construction site, a worker raises an 8-foot sheet of plywood to a platform by sliding the sheet up over the edge of the platform in such a way that the horizontal distance between the bottom of the plywood and the platform edge is kept at 1 foot. If the distance along the plywood from its bottom to the platform edge measures $x$ feet, then the top of the plywood will be

$$y = \left(\frac{8}{x} - 1\right)\sqrt{x^2 - 1} \text{ feet}$$

above the platform $(1 \leq x \leq 8)$. What is the greatest distance above the platform that the top of the plywood reaches?

**56.** In the context of Exercise 55, suppose that $0 < A < B$ and the plywood sheet is $B$ feet tall, while the sheet is raised so that the horizontal distance between the bottom of the plywood and the platform edge is kept at $A$ feet. If the distance along the plywood from its bottom to the platform edge measures $x$ feet, then the top of the plywood will be

$$y = \left(\frac{B}{x} - 1\right)\sqrt{x^2 - A^2} \text{ feet}$$

above the platform $(A \leq x \leq B)$. What is the greatest distance above the platform that the top of the plywood reaches?

**57.** Suppose that the equations of motion of a paper airplane during the first 12 seconds of flight are

$$x = t - 2\sin t, \quad y = 2 - 2\cos t \qquad (0 \leq t \leq 12)$$

What are the highest and lowest points in the trajectory, and when is the airplane at those points?

**58.** The accompanying figure on the next page shows the path of a fly whose equations of motion are

$$x = \frac{\cos t}{2 + \sin t}, \quad y = 3 + \sin(2t) - 2\sin^2 t \qquad (0 \leq t \leq 2\pi)$$

(a) How high and low does it fly?
(b) How far left and right of the origin does it fly?

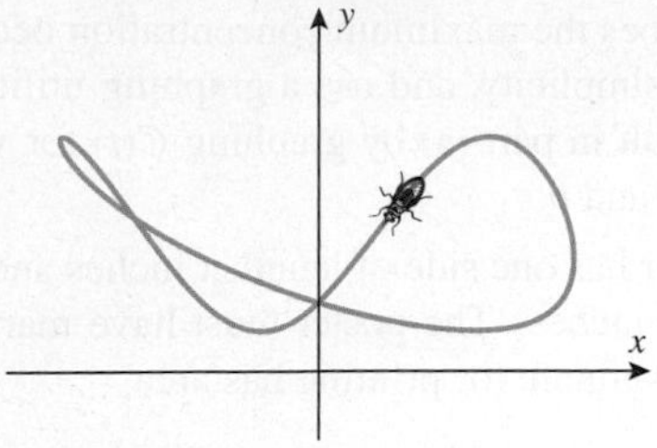


◀ Figure Ex-58

**59.** Let $f(x) = ax^2 + bx + c$, where $a > 0$. Prove that $f(x) \geq 0$ for all $x$ if and only if $b^2 - 4ac \leq 0$. [*Hint:* Find the minimum of $f(x)$.]

**60.** Prove Theorem 4.4.3 in the case where the extreme value is a minimum.

**61. Writing** Suppose that $f$ is continuous and positive-valued everywhere and that the $x$-axis is an asymptote for the graph of $f$, both as $x \to -\infty$ and as $x \to +\infty$. Explain why $f$ cannot have an absolute minimum but may have a relative minimum.

**62. Writing** Explain the difference between a relative maximum and an absolute maximum. Sketch a graph that illustrates a function with a relative maximum that is not an absolute maximum, and sketch another graph illustrating an absolute maximum that is not a relative maximum. Explain how these graphs satisfy the given conditions.

✓ **QUICK CHECK ANSWERS 4.4** **1.** There is a relative minimum at $x = 3$, a relative maximum at $x = 1$, an absolute minimum at $x = 3$, and an absolute maximum at $x = 6$. **2.** (a) max, 6064; min, 2293 (b) max, 2400; min, 0 (c) max, 6064; min, $-1333$ (d) no max; min, $-1333$ **3.** (a) max, $f(0) = 25$; min, $f(3) = -2$ (b) max, $f(-1) = 30$; min, $f(3) = -2$ (c) max, $f(-1) = 30$; min, $f(-4) = -51$ (d) max, $f(10) = 635$; min, $f(-5) = -130$ (e) max, $f(-1) = 30$; no min

# 4.5 APPLIED MAXIMUM AND MIMIMUM PROBLEMS

*In this section we will show how the methods discussed in the last section can be used to solve various applied optimization problems.*

## CLASSIFICATION OF OPTIMIZATION PROBLEMS

The applied optimization problems that we will consider in this section fall into the following two categories:

- Problems that reduce to maximizing or minimizing a continuous function over a finite closed interval.
- Problems that reduce to maximizing or minimizing a continuous function over an infinite interval or a finite interval that is not closed.

For problems of the first type the Extreme-Value Theorem (4.4.2) guarantees that the problem has a solution, and we know that the solution can be obtained by examining the values of the function at the critical points and at the endpoints. However, for problems of the second type there may or may not be a solution. If the function is continuous and has exactly one relative extremum of the appropriate type on the interval, then Theorem 4.4.4 guarantees the existence of a solution and provides a method for finding it. In cases where this theorem is not applicable some ingenuity may be required to solve the problem.

## PROBLEMS INVOLVING FINITE CLOSED INTERVALS

In his *On a Method for the Evaluation of Maxima and Minima*, the seventeenth century French mathematician Pierre de Fermat solved an optimization problem very similar to the one posed in our first example. Fermat's work on such optimization problems prompted the French mathematician Laplace to proclaim Fermat the "true inventor of the differential calculus." Although this honor must still reside with Newton and Leibniz, it is the case that Fermat developed procedures that anticipated parts of differential calculus.

► **Example 1** A garden is to be laid out in a rectangular area and protected by a chicken wire fence. What is the largest possible area of the garden if only 100 running feet of chicken wire is available for the fence?

***Solution.*** Let

$$x = \text{length of the rectangle (ft)}$$
$$y = \text{width of the rectangle (ft)}$$
$$A = \text{area of the rectangle (ft}^2\text{)}$$

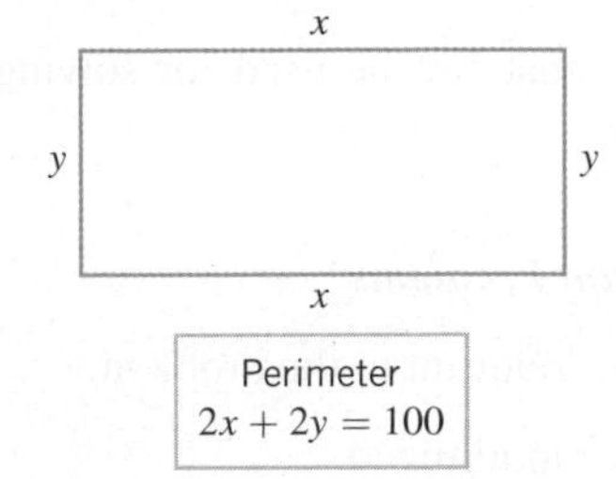


▲ **Figure 4.5.1**

Then

$$A = xy \tag{1}$$

Since the perimeter of the rectangle is 100 ft, the variables $x$ and $y$ are related by the equation

$$2x + 2y = 100 \quad \text{or} \quad y = 50 - x \tag{2}$$

(See Figure 4.5.1.) Substituting (2) in (1) yields

$$A = x(50 - x) = 50x - x^2 \tag{3}$$

Because $x$ represents a length, it cannot be negative, and because the two sides of length $x$ cannot have a combined length exceeding the total perimeter of 100 ft, the variable $x$ must satisfy

$$0 \le x \le 50 \tag{4}$$

**Table 4.5.1**

| $x$ | 0 | 25 | 50 |
|---|---|---|---|
| $A$ | 0 | 625 | 0 |

Thus, we have reduced the problem to that of finding the value (or values) of $x$ in $[0, 50]$, for which $A$ is maximum. Since $A$ is a polynomial in $x$, it is continuous on $[0, 50]$, and so the maximum must occur at an endpoint of this interval or at a critical point.

From (3) we obtain

$$\frac{dA}{dx} = 50 - 2x$$

Setting $dA/dx = 0$ we obtain

$$50 - 2x = 0$$

or $x = 25$. Thus, the maximum occurs at one of the values

$$x = 0, \quad x = 25, \quad x = 50$$

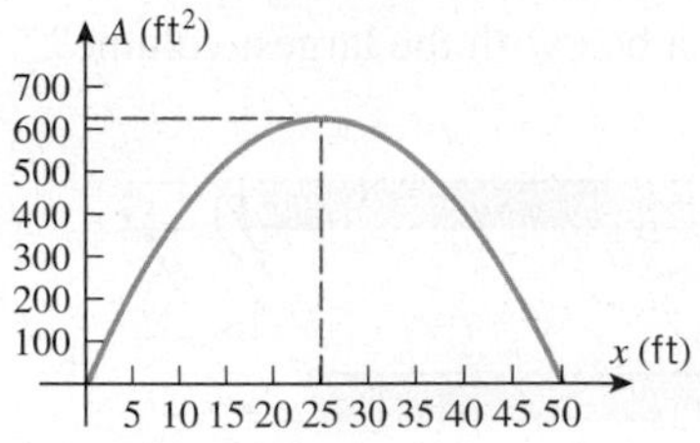


▲ **Figure 4.5.2**

Substituting these values in (3) yields Table 4.5.1, which tells us that the maximum area of 625 ft$^2$ occurs at $x = 25$, which is consistent with the graph of (3) in Figure 4.5.2. From

**Pierre de Fermat (1601–1665)** Fermat, the son of a successful French leather merchant, was a lawyer who practiced mathematics as a hobby. He received a Bachelor of Civil Laws degree from the University of Orleans in 1631 and subsequently held various government positions, including a post as councillor to the Toulouse parliament. Although he was apparently financially successful, confidential documents of that time suggest that his performance in office and as a lawyer was poor, perhaps because he devoted so much time to mathematics. Throughout his life, Fermat fought all efforts to have his mathematical results published. He had the unfortunate habit of scribbling his work in the margins of books and often sent his results to friends without keeping copies for himself. As a result, he never received credit for many major achievements until his name was raised from obscurity in the mid-nineteenth century. It is now known that Fermat, simultaneously and independently of Descartes, developed analytic geometry. Unfortunately, Descartes and Fermat argued bitterly over various problems so that there was never any real cooperation between these two great geniuses.

Fermat solved many fundamental calculus problems. He obtained the first procedure for differentiating polynomials, and solved many important maximization, minimization, area, and tangent problems. His work served to inspire Isaac Newton. Fermat is best known for his work in number theory, the study of properties of and relationships between whole numbers. He was the first mathematician to make substantial contributions to this field after the ancient Greek mathematician Diophantus. Unfortunately, none of Fermat's contemporaries appreciated his work in this area, a fact that eventually pushed Fermat into isolation and obscurity in later life. In addition to his work in calculus and number theory, Fermat was one of the founders of probability theory and made major contributions to the theory of optics. Outside mathematics, Fermat was a classical scholar of some note, was fluent in French, Italian, Spanish, Latin, and Greek, and he composed a considerable amount of Latin poetry.

One of the great mysteries of mathematics is shrouded in Fermat's work in number theory. In the margin of a book by Diophantus, Fermat scribbled that for integer values of $n$ greater than 2, the equation $x^n + y^n = z^n$ has no nonzero integer solutions for $x$, $y$, and $z$. He stated, "I have discovered a truly marvelous proof of this, which however the margin is not large enough to contain." This result, which became known as "Fermat's last theorem," appeared to be true, but its proof evaded the greatest mathematical geniuses for 300 years until Professor Andrew Wiles of Princeton University presented a proof in June 1993 in a dramatic series of three lectures that drew international media attention (see *New York Times*, June 27, 1993). As it turned out, that proof had a serious gap that Wiles and Richard Taylor fixed and published in 1995. A prize of 100,000 German marks was offered in 1908 for the solution, but it is worthless today because of inflation.

[*Image: marzolino/Depositphotos*]

(2) the corresponding value of $y$ is 25, so the rectangle of perimeter 100 ft with greatest area is a square with sides of length 25 ft. ◀

In Example 1 we included $x = 0$ and $x = 50$ as possible values of $x$, even though these correspond to rectangles with two sides of length zero. If we view this as a purely mathematical problem, then there is nothing wrong with this. However, if we view this as an applied problem in which the rectangle will be formed from physical material, then it would make sense to exclude these values.

Example 1 illustrates the following five-step procedure that can be used for solving many applied maximum and minimum problems.

***A Procedure for Solving Applied Maximum and Minimum Problems***

**Step 1.** Draw an appropriate figure and label the quantities relevant to the problem.

**Step 2.** Find a formula for the quantity to be maximized or minimized.

**Step 3.** Using the conditions stated in the problem to eliminate variables, express the quantity to be maximized or minimized as a function of one variable.

**Step 4.** Find the interval of possible values for this variable from the physical restrictions in the problem.

**Step 5.** If applicable, use the techniques of the preceding section to obtain the maximum or minimum.

▶ **Example 2** An open box is to be made from a 16-inch by 30-inch piece of cardboard by cutting out squares of equal size from the four corners and bending up the sides (Figure 4.5.3). What size should the squares be to obtain a box with the largest volume?

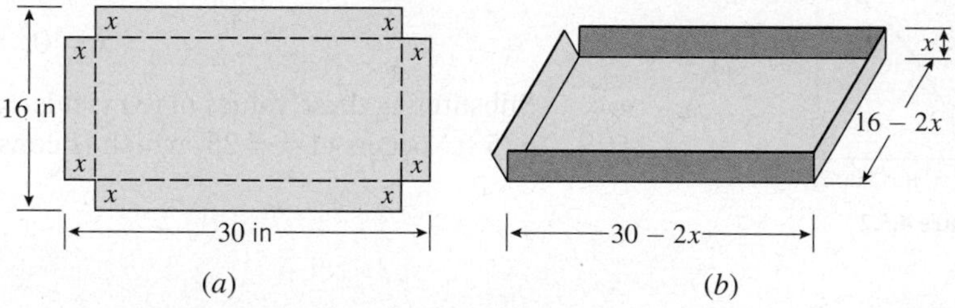


▶ **Figure 4.5.3**

***Solution.*** For emphasis, we explicitly list the steps of the five-step problem-solving procedure given above as an outline for the solution of this problem. (In later examples we will follow these guidelines without listing the steps.)

- *Step 1:* Figure 4.5.3*a* illustrates the cardboard piece with squares removed from its corners. Let

$$x = \text{length (in inches) of the sides of the squares to be cut out}$$
$$V = \text{volume (in cubic inches) of the resulting box}$$

- *Step 2:* Because we are removing a square of side $x$ from each corner, the resulting box will have dimensions $16 - 2x$ by $30 - 2x$ by $x$ (Figure 4.5.3*b*). Since the volume of a box is the product of its dimensions, we have

$$V = (16 - 2x)(30 - 2x)x = 480x - 92x^2 + 4x^3 \tag{5}$$

- *Step 3:* Note that our volume expression is already in terms of the single variable $x$.
- *Step 4:* The variable $x$ in (5) is subject to certain restrictions. Because $x$ represents a length, it cannot be negative, and because the width of the cardboard is 16 inches, we cannot cut out squares whose sides are more than 8 inches long. Thus, the variable $x$ in (5) must satisfy

$$0 \le x \le 8$$

and hence we have reduced our problem to finding the value (or values) of $x$ in the interval $[0, 8]$ for which (5) is a maximum.

**Table 4.5.2**

| | | | |
|---|---|---|---|
| $x$ | 0 | $\frac{10}{3}$ | 8 |
| $V$ | 0 | $\frac{19{,}600}{27} \approx 726$ | 0 |

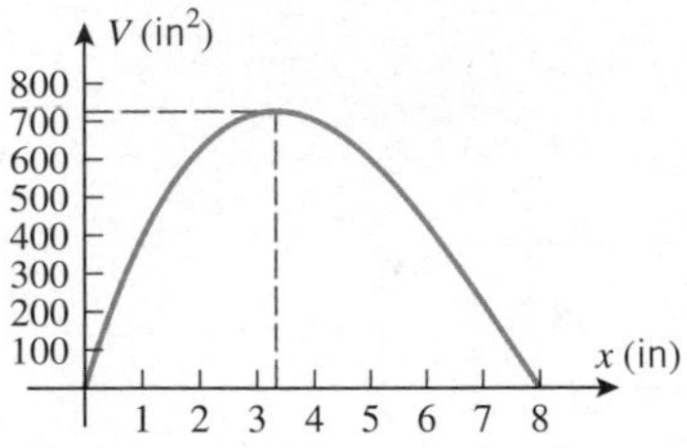


▲ **Figure 4.5.4**

- *Step 5:* From (5) we obtain

$$\frac{dV}{dx} = 480 - 184x + 12x^2 = 4(120 - 46x + 3x^2)$$
$$= 4(x - 12)(3x - 10)$$

Setting $dV/dx = 0$ yields

$$x = \tfrac{10}{3} \quad \text{and} \quad x = 12$$

Since $x = 12$ falls outside the interval $[0, 8]$, the maximum value of $V$ occurs either at the critical point $x = \frac{10}{3}$ or at the endpoints $x = 0$, $x = 8$. Substituting these values into (5) yields Table 4.5.2, which tells us that the greatest possible volume $V = \frac{19{,}600}{27}\text{ in}^3 \approx 726\text{ in}^3$ occurs when we cut out squares whose sides have length $\frac{10}{3}$ inches. This is consistent with the graph of (5) shown in Figure 4.5.4. ◀

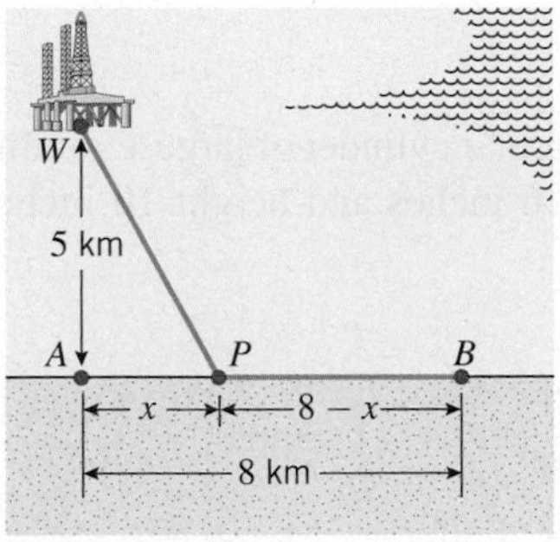


▲ **Figure 4.5.5**

▶ **Example 3** Figure 4.5.5 shows an offshore oil well located at a point $W$ that is 5 km from the closest point $A$ on a straight shoreline. Oil is to be piped from $W$ to a shore point $B$ that is 8 km from $A$ by piping it on a straight line under water from $W$ to some shore point $P$ between $A$ and $B$ and then on to $B$ via pipe along the shoreline. If the cost of laying pipe is \$1,000,000/km under water and \$500,000/km over land, where should the point $P$ be located to minimize the cost of laying the pipe?

***Solution.*** Let

$$x = \text{distance (in kilometers) between } A \text{ and } P$$
$$c = \text{cost (in millions of dollars) for the entire pipeline}$$

From Figure 4.5.5 the length of pipe under water is the distance between $W$ and $P$. By the Theorem of Pythagoras that length is

$$\sqrt{x^2 + 25} \tag{6}$$

Also from Figure 4.5.5, the length of pipe over land is the distance between $P$ and $B$, which is

$$8 - x \tag{7}$$

From (6) and (7) it follows that the total cost $c$ (in millions of dollars) for the pipeline is

$$c = 1(\sqrt{x^2 + 25}) + \tfrac{1}{2}(8 - x) = \sqrt{x^2 + 25} + \tfrac{1}{2}(8 - x) \tag{8}$$

Because the distance between $A$ and $B$ is 8 km, the distance $x$ between $A$ and $P$ must satisfy

$$0 \le x \le 8$$

We have thus reduced our problem to finding the value (or values) of $x$ in the interval $[0, 8]$ for which $c$ is a minimum. Since $c$ is a continuous function of $x$ on the closed interval $[0, 8]$, we can use the methods developed in the preceding section to find the minimum.

From (8) we obtain

$$\frac{dc}{dx} = \frac{x}{\sqrt{x^2 + 25}} - \frac{1}{2}$$

Setting $dc/dx = 0$ and solving for $x$ yields

$$\frac{x}{\sqrt{x^2 + 25}} = \frac{1}{2} \tag{9}$$

$$x^2 = \frac{1}{4}(x^2 + 25)$$

$$x = \pm\frac{5}{\sqrt{3}}$$

**TECHNOLOGY MASTERY**

If you have a CAS, use it to check all of the computations in Example 3. Specifically, differentiate $c$ with respect to $x$, solve the equation $dc/dx = 0$, and perform all of the numerical calculations.

The number $-5/\sqrt{3}$ is not a solution of (9) and must be discarded, leaving $x = 5/\sqrt{3}$ as the only critical point. Since this point lies in the interval [0, 8], the minimum must occur at one of the values

$$x = 0, \quad x = 5/\sqrt{3}, \quad x = 8$$

Substituting these values into (8) yields Table 4.5.3, which tells us that the least possible cost of the pipeline (to the nearest dollar) is $c = \$8{,}330{,}127$, and this occurs when the point $P$ is located at a distance of $5/\sqrt{3} \approx 2.89$ km from $A$. ◄

**Table 4.5.3**

| $x$ | 0 | $\frac{5}{\sqrt{3}}$ | 8 |
|---|---|---|---|
| $c$ | 9 | $\frac{10}{\sqrt{3}} + \left(4 - \frac{5}{2\sqrt{3}}\right) \approx 8.330127$ | $\sqrt{89} \approx 9.433981$ |

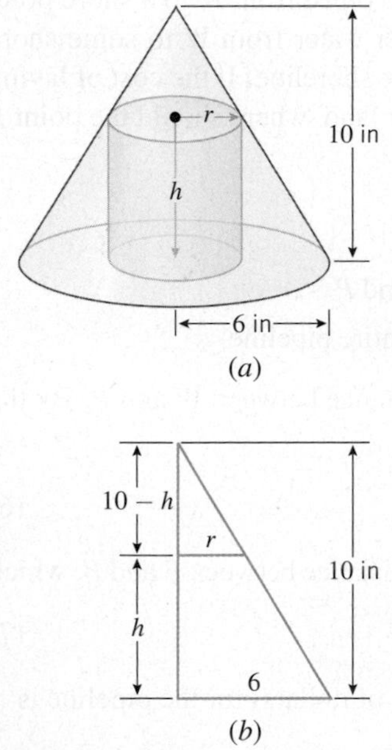


▲ Figure 4.5.6

► **Example 4** Find the radius and height of the right circular cylinder of largest volume that can be inscribed in a right circular cone with radius 6 inches and height 10 inches (Figure 4.5.6*a*).

***Solution.*** Let

$r$ = radius (in inches) of the cylinder
$h$ = height (in inches) of the cylinder
$V$ = volume (in cubic inches) of the cylinder

The formula for the volume of the inscribed cylinder is

$$V = \pi r^2 h \tag{10}$$

To eliminate one of the variables in (10) we need a relationship between $r$ and $h$. Using similar triangles (Figure 4.5.6*b*) we obtain

$$\frac{10-h}{r} = \frac{10}{6} \quad \text{or} \quad h = 10 - \frac{5}{3}r \tag{11}$$

Substituting (11) into (10) we obtain

$$V = \pi r^2\left(10 - \frac{5}{3}r\right) = 10\pi r^2 - \frac{5}{3}\pi r^3 \tag{12}$$

which expresses $V$ in terms of $r$ alone. Because $r$ represents a radius, it cannot be negative, and because the radius of the inscribed cylinder cannot exceed the radius of the cone, the variable $r$ must satisfy

$$0 \le r \le 6$$

Thus, we have reduced the problem to that of finding the value (or values) of $r$ in [0, 6] for which (12) is a maximum. Since $V$ is a continuous function of $r$ on [0, 6], the methods developed in the preceding section apply.

From (12) we obtain

$$\frac{dV}{dr} = 20\pi r - 5\pi r^2 = 5\pi r(4 - r)$$

Setting $dV/dr = 0$ gives

$$5\pi r(4 - r) = 0$$

so $r = 0$ and $r = 4$ are critical points. Since these lie in the interval [0, 6], the maximum must occur at one of the values

$$r = 0, \quad r = 4, \quad r = 6$$

Table 4.5.4

| $r$ | 0 | 4 | 6 |
|---|---|---|---|
| $V$ | 0 | $\frac{160}{3}\pi$ | 0 |

Substituting these values into (12) yields Table 4.5.4, which tells us that the maximum volume $V = \frac{160}{3}\pi \approx 168$ in$^3$ occurs when the inscribed cylinder has radius 4 in. When $r = 4$ it follows from (11) that $h = \frac{10}{3}$. Thus, the inscribed cylinder of largest volume has radius $r = 4$ in and height $h = \frac{10}{3}$ in. ◀

## PROBLEMS INVOLVING INTERVALS THAT ARE NOT BOTH FINITE AND CLOSED

▶ **Example 5** A closed cylindrical can is to hold 1 liter (1000 cm$^3$) of liquid. How should we choose the height and radius to minimize the amount of material needed to manufacture the can?

***Solution.*** Let

$$h = \text{height (in cm) of the can}$$
$$r = \text{radius (in cm) of the can}$$
$$S = \text{surface area (in cm}^2\text{) of the can}$$

Assuming there is no waste or overlap, the amount of material needed for manufacture will be the same as the surface area of the can. Since the can consists of two circular disks of radius $r$ and a rectangular sheet with dimensions $h$ by $2\pi r$ (Figure 4.5.7), the surface area will be

$$S = 2\pi r^2 + 2\pi rh \tag{13}$$

Since $S$ depends on two variables, $r$ and $h$, we will look for some condition in the problem that will allow us to express one of these variables in terms of the other. For this purpose, observe that the volume of the can is 1000 cm$^3$, so it follows from the formula $V = \pi r^2 h$ for the volume of a cylinder that

$$1000 = \pi r^2 h \quad \text{or} \quad h = \frac{1000}{\pi r^2} \tag{14–15}$$

Substituting (15) in (13) yields

$$S = 2\pi r^2 + \frac{2000}{r} \tag{16}$$

Thus, we have reduced the problem to finding a value of $r$ in the interval $(0, +\infty)$ for which $S$ is minimum. Since $S$ is a continuous function of $r$ on the interval $(0, +\infty)$ and

$$\lim_{r \to 0^+} \left(2\pi r^2 + \frac{2000}{r}\right) = +\infty \quad \text{and} \quad \lim_{r \to +\infty} \left(2\pi r^2 + \frac{2000}{r}\right) = +\infty$$

the analysis in Table 4.4.3 implies that $S$ does have a minimum on the interval $(0, +\infty)$. Since this minimum must occur at a critical point, we calculate

$$\frac{dS}{dr} = 4\pi r - \frac{2000}{r^2} \tag{17}$$

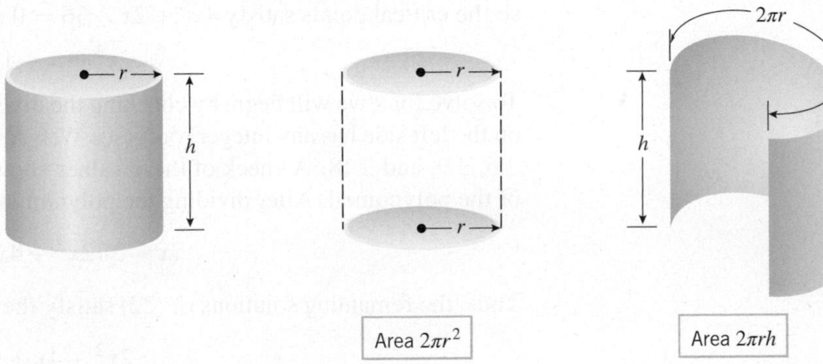


▲ Figure 4.5.7

Setting $dS/dr = 0$ gives

$$r = \frac{10}{\sqrt[3]{2\pi}} \approx 5.4 \tag{18}$$

Since (18) is the only critical point in the interval $(0, +\infty)$, this value of $r$ yields the minimum value of $S$. From (15) the value of $h$ corresponding to this $r$ is

$$h = \frac{1000}{\pi(10/\sqrt[3]{2\pi})^2} = \frac{20}{\sqrt[3]{2\pi}} = 2r$$

It is not an accident here that the minimum occurs when the height of the can is equal to the diameter of its base (Exercise 29).

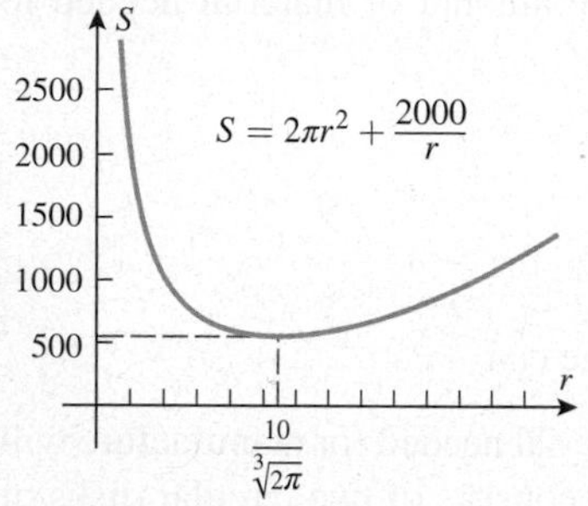

▲ **Figure 4.5.8**

***Second Solution.*** The conclusion that a minimum occurs at the value of $r$ in (18) can be deduced from Theorem 4.4.4 and the second derivative test by noting that

$$\frac{d^2S}{dr^2} = 4\pi + \frac{4000}{r^3}$$

is positive if $r > 0$ and hence is positive if $r = 10/\sqrt[3]{2\pi}$. This implies that a relative minimum, and therefore a minimum, occurs at the critical point $r = 10/\sqrt[3]{2\pi}$.

***Third Solution.*** An alternative justification that the critical point $r = 10/\sqrt[3]{2\pi}$ corresponds to a minimum for $S$ is to view the graph of $S$ versus $r$ (Figure 4.5.8). ◄

In Example 5, the surface area $S$ has no absolute maximum, since $S$ increases without bound as the radius $r$ approaches 0 (Figure 4.5.8). Thus, had we asked for the dimensions of the can requiring the *maximum* amount of material for its manufacture, there would have been no solution to the problem. Optimization problems with no solution are sometimes called *ill posed.*

▶ **Example 6** Find a point on the curve $y = x^2$ that is closest to the point $(18, 0)$.

***Solution.*** The distance $L$ between $(18, 0)$ and an arbitrary point $(x, y)$ on the curve $y = x^2$ (Figure 4.5.9) is given by

$$L = \sqrt{(x-18)^2 + (y-0)^2}$$

Since $(x, y)$ lies on the curve, $x$ and $y$ satisfy $y = x^2$; thus,

$$L = \sqrt{(x-18)^2 + x^4} \tag{19}$$

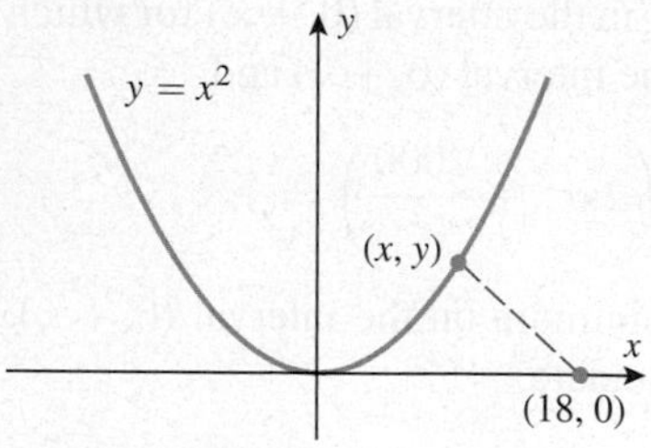

▲ **Figure 4.5.9**

Because there are no restrictions on $x$, the problem reduces to finding a value of $x$ in $(-\infty, +\infty)$ for which (19) is a minimum. The distance $L$ and the square of the distance $L^2$ are minimized at the same value (see Exercise 68). Thus, the minimum value of $L$ in (19) and the minimum value of

$$S = L^2 = (x-18)^2 + x^4 \tag{20}$$

occur at the same $x$-value.

From (20),

$$\frac{dS}{dx} = 2(x-18) + 4x^3 = 4x^3 + 2x - 36 \tag{21}$$

so the critical points satisfy $4x^3 + 2x - 36 = 0$ or, equivalently,

$$2x^3 + x - 18 = 0 \tag{22}$$

To solve for $x$ we will begin by checking the divisors of $-18$ to see whether the polynomial on the left side has any integer roots (see Web Appendix J). These divisors are $\pm1$, $\pm2$, $\pm3$, $\pm6$, $\pm9$, and $\pm18$. A check of these values shows that $x = 2$ is a root, so $x - 2$ is a factor of the polynomial. After dividing the polynomial by this factor we can rewrite (22) as

$$(x-2)(2x^2 + 4x + 9) = 0$$

Thus, the remaining solutions of (22) satisfy the quadratic equation

$$2x^2 + 4x + 9 = 0$$

But this equation has no real solutions (using the quadratic formula), so $x = 2$ is the only critical point of $S$. To determine the nature of this critical point we will use the second derivative test. From (21),

$$\frac{d^2S}{dx^2} = 12x^2 + 2, \quad \text{so} \quad \left.\frac{d^2S}{dx^2}\right|_{x=2} = 50 > 0$$

which shows that a relative minimum occurs at $x = 2$. Since $x = 2$ yields the only relative extremum for $L$, it follows from Theorem 4.4.4 that an absolute minimum value of $L$ also occurs at $x = 2$. Thus, the point on the curve $y = x^2$ closest to (18, 0) is

$$(x, y) = (x, x^2) = (2, 4) \blacktriangleleft$$

## AN APPLICATION TO ECONOMICS

Three functions of importance to an economist or a manufacturer are

$C(x)$ = total cost of producing $x$ units of a product during some time period
$R(x)$ = total revenue from selling $x$ units of the product during the time period
$P(x)$ = total profit obtained by selling $x$ units of the product during the time period

These are called, respectively, the ***cost function***, ***revenue function***, and ***profit function***. If all units produced are sold, then these are related by

$$P(x) = R(x) - C(x) \qquad (23)$$
$$\text{[profit]} = \text{[revenue]} - \text{[cost]}$$

The total cost $C(x)$ of producing $x$ units can be expressed as a sum

$$C(x) = a + M(x) \qquad (24)$$

where $a$ is a constant, called ***overhead***, and $M(x)$ is a function representing ***manufacturing cost***. The overhead, which includes such fixed costs as rent and insurance, does not depend on $x$; it must be paid even if nothing is produced. On the other hand, the manufacturing cost $M(x)$, which includes such items as cost of materials and labor, depends on the number of items manufactured. It is shown in economics that with suitable simplifying assumptions, $M(x)$ can be expressed in the form

$$M(x) = bx + cx^2$$

where $b$ and $c$ are constants. Substituting this in (24) yields

$$C(x) = a + bx + cx^2 \qquad (25)$$

If a manufacturing firm can sell all the items it produces for $p$ dollars apiece, then its total revenue $R(x)$ (in dollars) will be

$$R(x) = px \qquad (26)$$

and its total profit $P(x)$ (in dollars) will be

$$P(x) = \text{[total revenue]} - \text{[total cost]} = R(x) - C(x) = px - C(x)$$

Thus, if the cost function is given by (25),

$$P(x) = px - (a + bx + cx^2) \qquad (27)$$

Depending on such factors as number of employees, amount of machinery available, economic conditions, and competition, there will be some upper limit $l$ on the number of items a manufacturer is capable of producing and selling. Thus, during a fixed time period the variable $x$ in (27) will satisfy

$$0 \le x \le l$$

By determining the value or values of $x$ in $[0, l]$ that maximize (27), the firm can determine how many units of its product must be manufactured and sold to yield the greatest profit. This is illustrated in the following numerical example.

Nickondr/Depositphotos

*A pharmaceutical firm's profit is a function of the number of units produced.*

▶ **Example 7** A liquid form of antibiotic manufactured by a pharmaceutical firm is sold in bulk at a price of \$200 per unit. If the total production cost (in dollars) for $x$ units is

$$C(x) = 500{,}000 + 80x + 0.003x^2$$

and if the production capacity of the firm is at most 30,000 units in a specified time, how many units of antibiotic must be manufactured and sold in that time to maximize the profit?

***Solution.*** Since the total revenue for selling $x$ units is $R(x) = 200x$, the profit $P(x)$ on $x$ units will be

$$P(x) = R(x) - C(x) = 200x - (500{,}000 + 80x + 0.003x^2) \tag{28}$$

Since the production capacity is at most 30,000 units, $x$ must lie in the interval [0, 30,000]. From (28)

$$\frac{dP}{dx} = 200 - (80 + 0.006x) = 120 - 0.006x$$

Setting $dP/dx = 0$ gives

$$120 - 0.006x = 0 \quad \text{or} \quad x = 20{,}000$$

Since this critical point lies in the interval [0, 30,000], the maximum profit must occur at one of the values

$$x = 0, \quad x = 20{,}000, \quad \text{or} \quad x = 30{,}000$$

Substituting these values in (28) yields Table 4.5.5, which tells us that the maximum profit $P = \$700{,}000$ occurs when $x = 20{,}000$ units are manufactured and sold in the specified time. ◀

**Table 4.5.5**

| $x$ | 0 | 20,000 | 30,000 |
|---|---|---|---|
| $P(x)$ | −500,000 | 700,000 | 400,000 |

## MARGINAL ANALYSIS

Economists call $P'(x)$, $R'(x)$, and $C'(x)$ the ***marginal profit***, ***marginal revenue***, and ***marginal cost***, respectively; and they interpret these quantities as the *additional* profit, revenue, and cost that result from producing and selling one additional unit of the product when the production and sales levels are at $x$ units. These interpretations follow from the local linear approximations of the profit, revenue, and cost functions. For example, it follows from Formula (2) of Section 3.5 that when the production and sales levels are at $x$ units the local linear approximation of the profit function is

$$P(x + \Delta x) \approx P(x) + P'(x)\Delta x$$

Thus, if $\Delta x = 1$ (one additional unit produced and sold), this formula implies

$$P(x + 1) \approx P(x) + P'(x)$$

and hence the *additional* profit that results from producing and selling one additional unit can be approximated as

$$P(x + 1) - P(x) \approx P'(x)$$

Similarly, $R(x + 1) - R(x) \approx R'(x)$ and $C(x + 1) - C(x) \approx C'(x)$.

## A BASIC PRINCIPLE OF ECONOMICS

It follows from (23) that $P'(x) = 0$ has the same solution as $C'(x) = R'(x)$, and this implies that the maximum profit must occur at a point where the marginal revenue is equal to the marginal cost; that is:

*If profit is maximum, then the cost of manufacturing and selling an additional unit of a product is approximately equal to the revenue generated by the additional unit.*

In Example 7, the maximum profit occurs when $x = 20{,}000$ units. Note that

$$C(20{,}001) - C(20{,}000) = \$200.003 \quad \text{and} \quad R(20{,}001) - R(20{,}000) = \$200$$

which is consistent with this basic economic principle.

## ✓QUICK CHECK EXERCISES 4.5 (See page 225 for answers.)

**1.** A positive number $x$ and its reciprocal are added together. The smallest possible value of this sum is obtained by minimizing $f(x) =$ ______ for $x$ in the interval ______.

**2.** Two nonnegative numbers, $x$ and $y$, have a sum equal to 10. The largest possible product of the two numbers is obtained by maximizing $f(x) =$ ______ for $x$ in the interval ______.

**3.** A rectangle in the $xy$-plane has one corner at the origin, an adjacent corner at the point $(x, 0)$, and a third corner at a point on the line segment from $(0, 4)$ to $(3, 0)$. The largest possible area of the rectangle is obtained by maximizing $A(x) =$ ______ for $x$ in the interval ______.

**4.** An open box is to be made from a 20-inch by 32-inch piece of cardboard by cutting out $x$-inch by $x$-inch squares from the four corners and bending up the sides. The largest possible volume of the box is obtained by maximizing $V(x) =$ ______ for $x$ in the interval ______.

## EXERCISE SET 4.5

**1.** Find a number in the closed interval $\left[\frac{1}{2}, \frac{3}{2}\right]$ such that the sum of the number and its reciprocal is
(a) as small as possible
(b) as large as possible.

**2.** How should two nonnegative numbers be chosen so that their sum is 1 and the sum of their squares is
(a) as large as possible
(b) as small as possible?

**3.** A rectangular field is to be bounded by a fence on three sides and by a straight stream on the fourth side. Find the dimensions of the field with maximum area that can be enclosed using 1000 ft of fence.

**4.** The boundary of a field is a right triangle with a straight stream along its hypotenuse and with fences along its other two sides. Find the dimensions of the field with maximum area that can be enclosed using 1000 ft of fence.

**5.** A rectangular plot of land is to be fenced in using two kinds of fencing. Two opposite sides will use heavy-duty fencing selling for \$3 a foot, while the remaining two sides will use standard fencing selling for \$2 a foot. What are the dimensions of the rectangular plot of greatest area that can be fenced in at a cost of \$6000?

**6.** A rectangle is to be inscribed in a right triangle having sides of length 6 in, 8 in, and 10 in. Find the dimensions of the rectangle with greatest area assuming the rectangle is positioned as in Figure Ex-6.

**7.** Solve the problem in Exercise 6 assuming the rectangle is positioned as in Figure Ex-7.

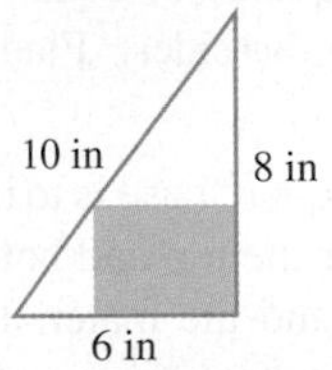

▲ **Figure Ex-6**

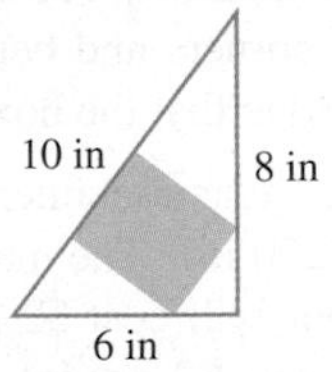

▲ **Figure Ex-7**

**8.** A rectangle has its two lower corners on the $x$-axis and its two upper corners on the curve $y = 16 - x^2$. For all such rectangles, what are the dimensions of the one with largest area?

**9.** Find the dimensions of the rectangle with maximum area that can be inscribed in a circle of radius 10.

**10.** Find the point $P$ in the first quadrant on the curve $y = x^{-2}$ such that a rectangle with sides on the coordinate axes and a vertex at $P$ has the smallest possible perimeter.

**11.** A rectangular area of 3200 $\text{ft}^2$ is to be fenced off. Two opposite sides will use fencing costing \$1 per foot and the remaining sides will use fencing costing \$2 per foot. Find the dimensions of the rectangle of least cost.

**12.** Show that among all rectangles with perimeter $p$, the square has the maximum area.

**13.** Show that among all rectangles with area $A$, the square has the minimum perimeter.

**14.** A wire of length 12 in can be bent into a circle, bent into a square, or cut into two pieces to make both a circle and a square. How much wire should be used for the circle if the total area enclosed by the figure(s) is to be
(a) a maximum (b) a minimum?

**15.** A rectangle $R$ in the plane has corners at $(\pm 8, \pm 12)$, and a 100 by 100 square $S$ is positioned in the plane so that its sides are parallel to the coordinate axes and the lower left corner of $S$ is on the line $y = -3x$. What is the largest possible area of a region in the plane that is contained in both $R$ and $S$?

**16.** Solve the problem in Exercise 15 if $S$ is a 16 by 16 square.

**17.** Solve the problem in Exercise 15 if $S$ is positioned with its lower left corner on the line $y = -6x$.

**18.** A rectangular page is to contain 42 square inches of printable area. The margins at the top and bottom of the page are each 1 inch, one side margin is 1 inch, and the other side margin is 2 inches. What should the dimensions of the page be so that the least amount of paper is used?

**19.** A box with a square base is taller than it is wide. In order to send the box through the U.S. mail, the height of the box and the perimeter of the base can sum to no more than 108 in. What is the maximum volume for such a box?

**20.** A box with a square base is wider than it is tall. In order to send the box through the U.S. mail, the width of the box and the perimeter of one of the (nonsquare) sides of the box can sum to no more than 108 in. What is the maximum volume for such a box?

**21.** An open box is to be made from a 3 ft by 8 ft rectangular piece of sheet metal by cutting out squares of equal size from the four corners and bending up the sides. Find the maximum volume that the box can have.

**22.** A closed rectangular container with a square base is to have a volume of 2250 $in^3$. The material for the top and bottom of the container will cost \$2 per $in^2$, and the material for the sides will cost \$3 per $in^2$. Find the dimensions of the container of least cost.

**23.** A closed rectangular container with a square base is to have a volume of 2000 $cm^3$. It costs twice as much per square centimeter for the top and bottom as it does for the sides. Find the dimensions of the container of least cost.

**24.** A container with square base, vertical sides, and open top is to be made from 1000 $ft^2$ of material. Find the dimensions of the container with greatest volume.

**25.** A rectangular container with two square sides and an open top is to have a volume of $V$ cubic units. Find the dimensions of the container with minimum surface area.

**26.** A church window consisting of a rectangle topped by a semicircle is to have a perimeter $p$. Find the radius of the semicircle if the area of the window is to be maximum.

**27.** Find the dimensions of the right circular cylinder of largest volume that can be inscribed in a sphere of radius $R$.

**28.** Find the dimensions of the right circular cylinder of greatest surface area that can be inscribed in a sphere of radius $R$.

**29.** A closed, cylindrical can is to have a volume of $V$ cubic units. Show that the can of minimum surface area is achieved when the height is equal to the diameter of the base.

**30.** A closed cylindrical can is to have a surface area of $S$ square units. Show that the can of maximum volume is achieved when the height is equal to the diameter of the base.

**31.** A cylindrical can, open at the top, is to hold 500 $cm^3$ of liquid. Find the height and radius that minimize the amount of material needed to manufacture the can.

**32.** A soup can in the shape of a right circular cylinder of radius $r$ and height $h$ is to have a prescribed volume $V$. The top and bottom are cut from squares as shown in Figure Ex-32. If the shaded corners are wasted, but there is no other waste, find the ratio $r/h$ for the can requiring the least material (including waste).

**33.** A box-shaped wire frame consists of two identical wire squares whose vertices are connected by four straight wires of equal length (Figure Ex-33). If the frame is to be made from a wire of length $L$, what should the dimensions be to obtain a box of greatest volume?

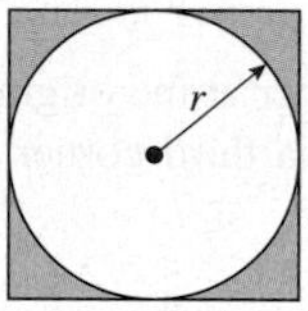

▲ Figure Ex-32

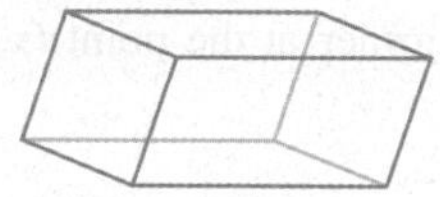
▲ Figure Ex-33

**34.** Suppose that the sum of the surface areas of a sphere and a cube is a constant.
(a) Show that the sum of their volumes is smallest when the diameter of the sphere is equal to the length of an edge of the cube.
(b) When will the sum of their volumes be greatest?

**35.** Find the height and radius of the cone of slant height $L$ whose volume is as large as possible.

**36.** A cone is made from a circular sheet of radius $R$ by cutting out a sector and gluing the cut edges of the remaining piece together (Figure Ex-36). What is the maximum volume attainable for the cone?

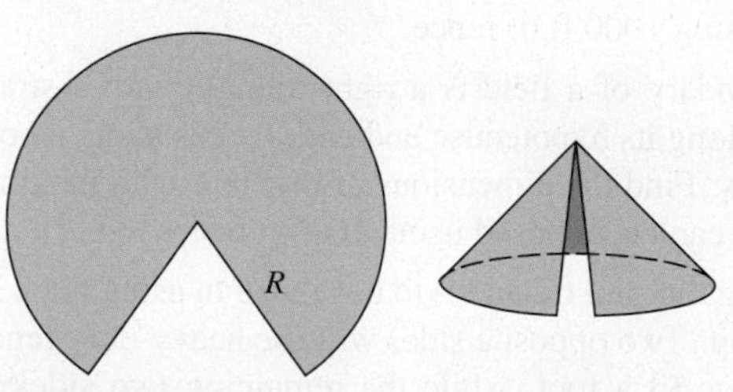

▲ Figure Ex-36

**37.** A cone-shaped paper drinking cup is to hold 100 $cm^3$ of water. Find the height and radius of the cup that will require the least amount of paper.

**38.** Find the dimensions of the isosceles triangle of least area that can be circumscribed about a circle of radius $R$.

**39.** Find the height and radius of the right circular cone with least volume that can be circumscribed about a sphere of radius $R$.

**40.** A commercial cattle ranch currently allows 20 steers per acre of grazing land; on the average its steers weigh 2000 lb at market. Estimates by the Agriculture Department indicate that the average market weight per steer will be reduced by 50 lb for each additional steer added per acre of grazing land. How many steers per acre should be allowed in order for the ranch to get the largest possible total market weight for its cattle?

**41.** A company mines low-grade nickel ore. If the company mines $x$ tons of ore, it can sell the ore for $p = 225 - 0.25x$ dollars per ton. Find the revenue and marginal revenue functions. At what level of production would the company obtain the maximum revenue?

**42.** A fertilizer producer finds that it can sell its product at a price of $p = 300 - 0.1x$ dollars per unit when it produces $x$ units of fertilizer. The total production cost (in dollars) for $x$ units is

$$C(x) = 15{,}000 + 125x + 0.025x^2$$

If the production capacity of the firm is at most 1000 units of fertilizer in a specified time, how many units must be manufactured and sold in that time to maximize the profit?

**43.** (a) A chemical manufacturer sells sulfuric acid in bulk at a price of \$100 per unit. If the daily total production cost in dollars for $x$ units is

$$C(x) = 100{,}000 + 50x + 0.0025x^2$$

and if the daily production capacity is at most 7000 units, how many units of sulfuric acid must be manufactured and sold daily to maximize the profit?

(b) Would it benefit the manufacturer to expand the daily production capacity?

(c) Use marginal analysis to approximate the effect on profit if daily production could be increased from 7000 to 7001 units.

**44.** A firm determines that $x$ units of its product can be sold daily at $p$ dollars per unit, where

$$x = 1000 - p$$

The cost of producing $x$ units per day is

$$C(x) = 3000 + 20x$$

(a) Find the revenue function $R(x)$.

(b) Find the profit function $P(x)$.

(c) Assuming that the production capacity is at most 500 units per day, determine how many units the company must produce and sell each day to maximize the profit.

(d) Find the maximum profit.

(e) What price per unit must be charged to obtain the maximum profit?

**45.** In a certain chemical manufacturing process, the daily weight $y$ of defective chemical output depends on the total weight $x$ of all output according to the empirical formula

$$y = 0.01x + 0.00003x^2$$

where $x$ and $y$ are in pounds. If the profit is \$100 per pound of nondefective chemical produced and the loss is \$20 per pound of defective chemical produced, how many pounds of chemical should be produced daily to maximize the total daily profit?

**46.** An independent truck driver charges a client \$15 for each hour of driving, plus the cost of fuel. At highway speeds of $v$ miles per hour, the trucker's rig gets $10 - 0.07v$ miles per gallon of diesel fuel. If diesel fuel costs \$2.50 per gallon, what speed $v$ will minimize the cost to the client?

**47.** A trapezoid is inscribed in a semicircle of radius 2 so that one side is along the diameter (Figure Ex-47). Find the maximum possible area for the trapezoid. [*Hint:* Express the area of the trapezoid in terms of $\theta$.]

**48.** A drainage channel is to be made so that its cross section is a trapezoid with equally sloping sides (Figure Ex-48). If the sides and bottom all have a length of 5 ft, how should the angle $\theta$ $(0 \leq \theta \leq \pi/2)$ be chosen to yield the greatest cross-sectional area of the channel?

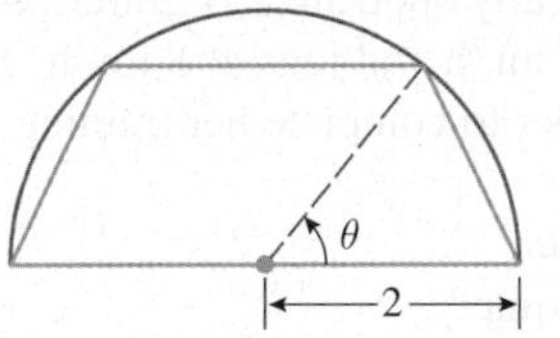


▲ **Figure Ex-47**

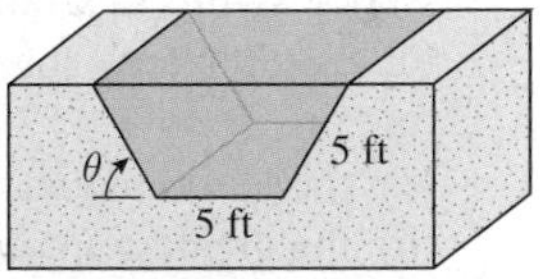


▲ **Figure Ex-48**

**49.** A lamp is suspended above the center of a round table of radius $r$. How high above the table should the lamp be placed to achieve maximum illumination at the edge of the table? [Assume that the illumination $I$ is directly proportional to the cosine of the angle of incidence $\phi$ of the light rays and inversely proportional to the square of the distance $l$ from the light source (Figure Ex-49).]

**50.** A plank is used to reach over a fence 8 ft high to support a wall that is 1 ft behind the fence (Figure Ex-50). What is the length of the shortest plank that can be used? [*Hint:* Express the length of the plank in terms of the angle $\theta$ shown in the figure.]

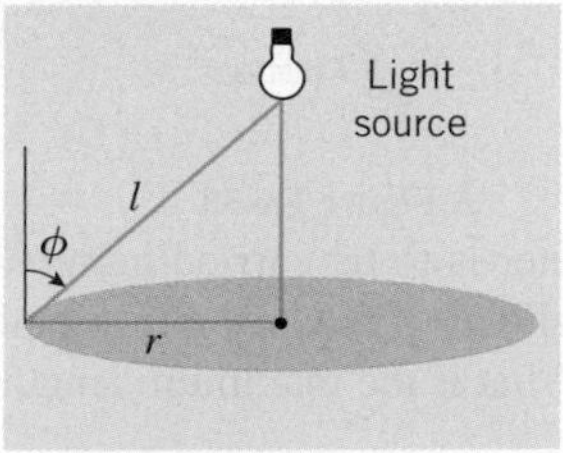


▲ **Figure Ex-49**

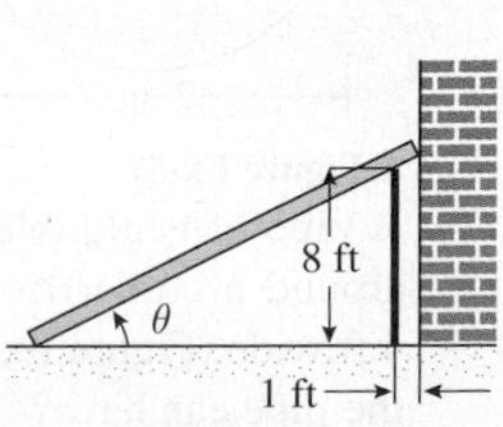


▲ **Figure Ex-50**

**51.** Two particles, $A$ and $B$, are in motion in the $xy$-plane. Their coordinates at each instant of time $t$ $(t \geq 0)$ are given by $x_A = t$, $y_A = 2t$, $x_B = 1 - t$, and $y_B = t$. Find the minimum distance between $A$ and $B$.

**52.** Follow the directions of Exercise 51, with $x_A = t, y_A = t^2$, $x_B = 2t$, and $y_B = 2$.

**53.** Find the coordinates of the point $P$ on the curve
$$y = \frac{1}{x^2} \quad (x > 0)$$
where the segment of the tangent line at $P$ that is cut off by the coordinate axes has its shortest length.

**54.** Find the $x$-coordinate of the point $P$ on the parabola
$$y = 1 - x^2 \quad (0 < x \le 1)$$
where the triangle that is enclosed by the tangent line at $P$ and the coordinate axes has the smallest area.

**55.** Where on the curve $y = \left(1 + x^2\right)^{-1}$ does the tangent line have the greatest slope?

**56.** Suppose that the number of bacteria in a culture at time $t$ is given by $N = 5000(25 + te^{-t/20})$.
(a) Find the largest and smallest number of bacteria in the culture during the time interval $0 \le t \le 100$.
(b) At what time during the time interval in part (a) is the number of bacteria decreasing most rapidly?

**57.** The shoreline of Circle Lake is a circle with diameter 2 mi. Nancy's training routine begins at point $E$ on the eastern shore of the lake. She jogs along the north shore to a point $P$ and then swims the straight line distance, if any, from $P$ to point $W$ diametrically opposite $E$ (Figure Ex-57). Nancy swims at a rate of 2 mi/h and jogs at 8 mi/h. How far should Nancy jog in order to complete her training routine in
(a) the least amount of time
(b) the greatest amount of time?

**58.** A man is floating in a rowboat 1 mile from the (straight) shoreline of a large lake. A town is located on the shoreline 1 mile from the point on the shoreline closest to the man. As suggested in Figure Ex-58, he intends to row in a straight line to some point $P$ on the shoreline and then walk the remaining distance to the town. To what point should he row in order to reach his destination in the least time if
(a) he can walk 5 mi/h and row 3 mi/h
(b) he can walk 5 mi/h and row 4 mi/h?

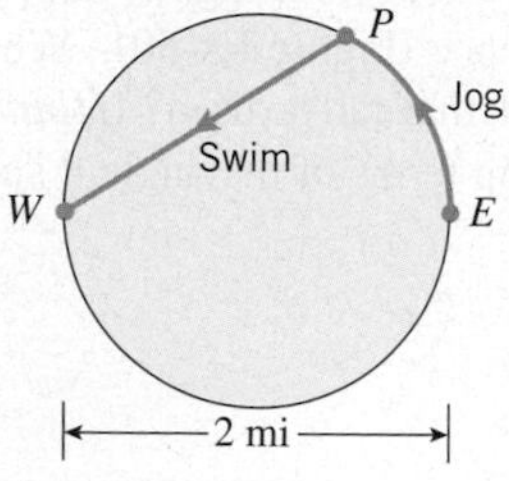

▲ Figure Ex-57

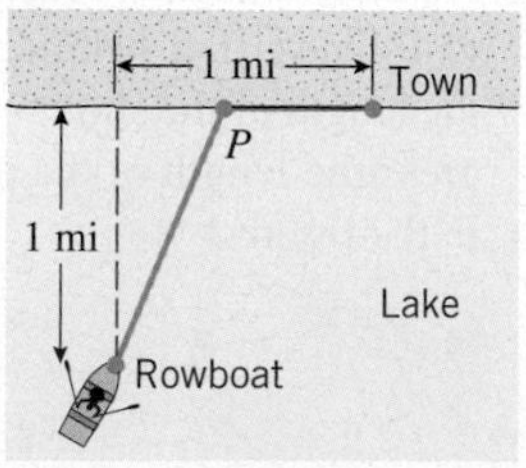

▲ Figure Ex-58

**59.** A pipe of negligible diameter is to be carried horizontally around a corner from a hallway 8 ft wide into a hallway 4 ft wide (Figure Ex-59). What is the maximum length that the pipe can have?

**Source:** An interesting discussion of this problem in the case where the diameter of the pipe is not neglected is given by Norman Miller in the *American Mathematical Monthly*, Vol. 56, 1949, pp. 177–179.

**60.** A concrete barrier whose cross section is an isosceles triangle runs parallel to a wall. The height of the barrier is 3 ft, the width of the base of a cross section is 8 ft, and the barrier is positioned on level ground with its base 1 ft from the wall. A straight, stiff metal rod of negligible diameter has one end on the ground, the other end against the wall, and touches the top of the barrier (Figure Ex-60). What is the minimum length the rod can have?

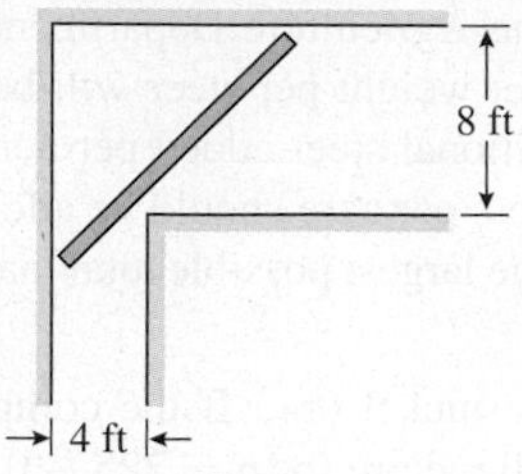

▲ Figure Ex-59

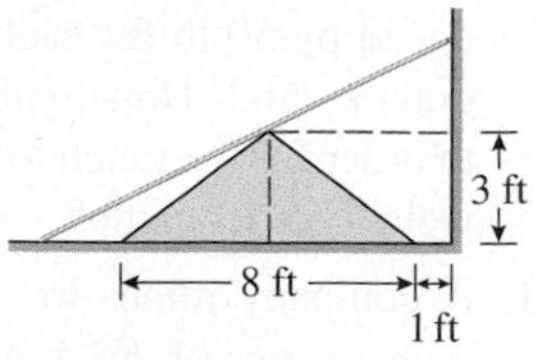

▲ Figure Ex-60

**61.** Suppose that the intensity of a point light source is directly proportional to the strength of the source and inversely proportional to the square of the distance from the source. Two point light sources with strengths of $S$ and $8S$ are separated by a distance of 90 cm. Where on the line segment between the two sources is the total intensity a minimum?

**62.** Given points $A(2, 1)$ and $B(5, 4)$, find the point $P$ in the interval $[2, 5]$ on the $x$-axis that maximizes angle $APB$.

**63.** The lower edge of a painting, 10 ft in height, is 2 ft above an observer's eye level. Assuming that the best view is obtained when the angle subtended at the observer's eye by the painting is maximum, how far from the wall should the observer stand?

**FOCUS ON CONCEPTS**

**64.** ***Fermat's principle*** (biography on p. 213) in optics states that light traveling from one point to another follows that path for which the total travel time is minimum. In a uniform medium, the paths of "minimum time" and "shortest distance" turn out to be the same, so that light, if unobstructed, travels along a straight line. Assume that we have a light source, a flat mirror, and an observer in a uniform medium. If a light ray leaves the source, bounces off the mirror, and travels on to the observer, then its path will consist of two line segments, as shown in Figure Ex-64. According to Fermat's principle, the path will be such that the total travel time $t$ is minimum or, since the medium is uniform, the path will be such that the total distance traveled from $A$ to $P$ to $B$ is as small as possible. Assuming the minimum occurs when $dt/dx = 0$, show that the light ray will strike the mirror at the point $P$ where the "angle of incidence" $\theta_1$ equals the "angle of reflection" $\theta_2$.

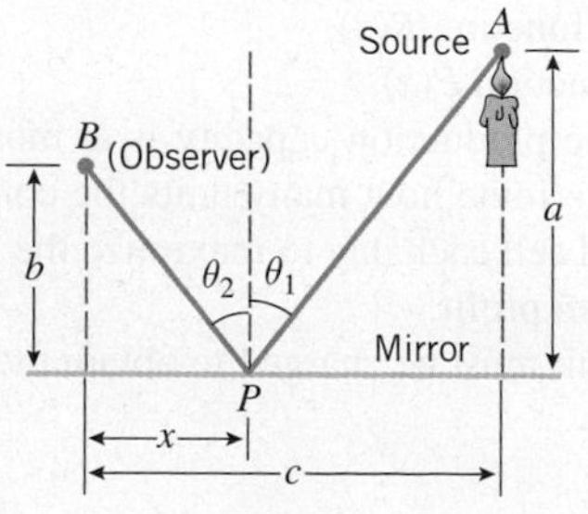

◀ Figure Ex-64

**65.** Fermat's principle (Exercise 64) also explains why light rays traveling between air and water undergo bending (refraction). Imagine that we have two uniform media (such as air and water) and a light ray traveling from a source $A$ in one medium to an observer $B$ in the other medium (Figure Ex-65). It is known that light travels at a constant speed in a uniform medium, but more slowly in a dense medium (such as water) than in a thin medium (such as air). Consequently, the path of shortest time from $A$ to $B$ is not necessarily a straight line, but rather some broken line path $A$ to $P$ to $B$ allowing the light to take greatest advantage of its higher speed through the thin medium. ***Snell's law of refraction*** (biography on p. 226) states that the path of the light ray will be such that

$$\frac{\sin\theta_1}{v_1} = \frac{\sin\theta_2}{v_2}$$

where $v_1$ is the speed of light in the first medium, $v_2$ is the speed of light in the second medium, and $\theta_1$ and $\theta_2$ are the angles shown in Figure Ex-65. Show that this follows from the assumption that the path of minimum time occurs when $dt/dx = 0$.

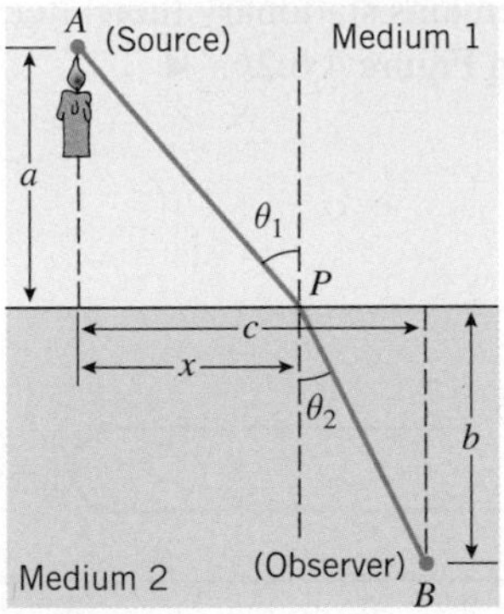


▲ **Figure Ex-65**

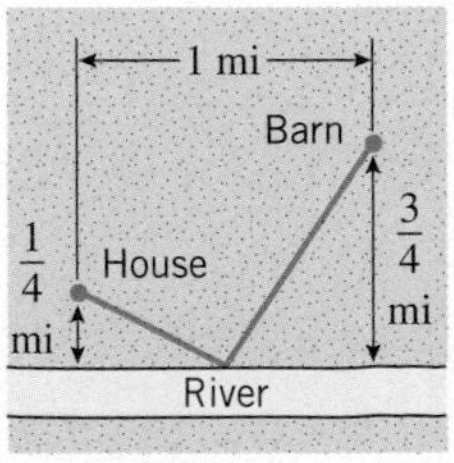


▲ **Figure Ex-66**

**66.** A farmer wants to walk at a constant rate from her barn to a straight river, fill her pail, and carry it to her house in the least time.

(a) Explain how this problem relates to Fermat's principle and the light-reflection problem in Exercise 64.

(b) Use the result of Exercise 64 to describe geometrically the best path for the farmer to take.

(c) Use part (b) to determine where the farmer should fill her pail if her house and barn are located as in Figure Ex-66.

**67.** If an unknown physical quantity $x$ is measured $n$ times, the measurements $x_1, x_2, \ldots, x_n$ often vary because of uncontrollable factors such as temperature, atmospheric pressure, and so forth. Thus, a scientist is often faced with the problem of using $n$ different observed measurements to obtain an estimate $\bar{x}$ of an unknown quantity $x$. One method for making such an estimate is based on the ***least squares principle***, which states that the estimate $\bar{x}$ should be chosen to minimize

$$s = (x_1 - \bar{x})^2 + (x_2 - \bar{x})^2 + \cdots + (x_n - \bar{x})^2$$

which is the sum of the squares of the deviations between the estimate $\bar{x}$ and the measured values. Show that the estimate resulting from the least squares principle is

$$\bar{x} = \frac{1}{n}(x_1 + x_2 + \cdots + x_n)$$

that is, $\bar{x}$ is the arithmetic average of the observed values.

**68.** Prove: If $f(x) \geq 0$ on an interval and if $f(x)$ has a maximum value on that interval at $x_0$, then $\sqrt{f(x)}$ also has a maximum value at $x_0$. Similarly for minimum values. [*Hint:* Use the fact that $\sqrt{x}$ is an increasing function on the interval $[0, +\infty)$.]

**69. Writing** Discuss the importance of finding intervals of possible values imposed by physical restrictions on variables in an applied maximum or minimum problem.

✓ **QUICK CHECK ANSWERS 4.5** 1. $x + \frac{1}{x}$; $(0, +\infty)$ 2. $x(10 - x)$; $[0, 10]$ 3. $x\left(-\frac{4}{3}x + 4\right) = -\frac{4}{3}x^2 + 4x$; $[0, 3]$ 4. $x(20 - 2x)(32 - 2x) = 4x^3 - 104x^2 + 640x$; $[0, 10]$

## 4.6 RECTILINEAR MOTION

*In this section we will continue the study of rectilinear motion that we began in Section 2.1. We will define the notion of "acceleration" mathematically, and we will show how the tools of calculus developed earlier in this chapter can be used to analyze rectilinear motion in more depth.*

## REVIEW OF TERMINOLOGY

Recall from Section 2.1 that a particle that can move in either direction along a coordinate line is said to be in ***rectilinear motion***. The line might be an $x$-axis, a $y$-axis, or a coordinate line inclined at some angle. In general discussions we will designate the coordinate line as the $s$-axis. We will assume that units are chosen for measuring distance and time and that we begin observing the motion of the particle at time $t = 0$. As the particle moves along the $s$-axis, its coordinate $s$ will be some function of time, say $s = s(t)$. We call $s(t)$ the ***position function*** of the particle,* and we call the graph of $s$ versus $t$ the ***position versus time curve***. If the coordinate of a particle at time $t_1$ is $s(t_1)$ and the coordinate at a later time $t_2$ is $s(t_2)$, then $s(t_2) - s(t_1)$ is called the ***displacement*** of the particle over the time interval $[t_1, t_2]$. The displacement describes the change in position of the particle.

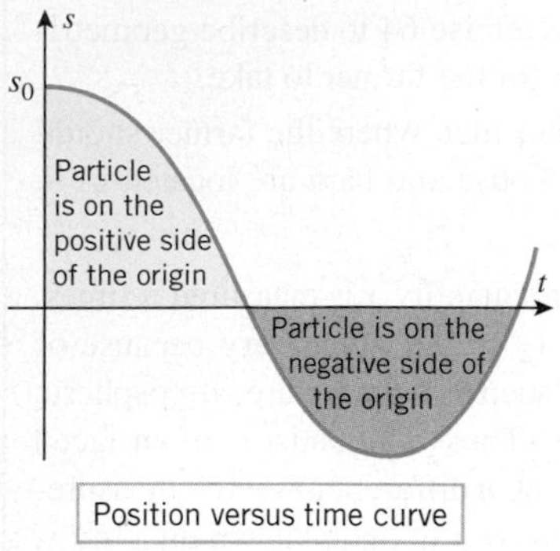


▲ **Figure 4.6.1**

Figure 4.6.1 shows a typical position versus time curve for a particle in rectilinear motion. We can tell from that graph that the coordinate of the particle at time $t = 0$ is $s_0$, and we can tell from the sign of $s$ when the particle is on the negative or the positive side of the origin as it moves along the coordinate line.

▶ **Example 1** Figure 4.6.2*a* shows the position versus time curve for a particle moving along an $s$-axis. In words, describe how the position of the particle changes with time.

***Solution.*** The particle is at $s = -3$ at time $t = 0$. It moves in the positive direction until time $t = 4$, since $s$ is increasing. At time $t = 4$ the particle is at position $s = 3$. At that time it turns around and travels in the negative direction until time $t = 7$, since $s$ is decreasing. At time $t = 7$ the particle is at position $s = -1$, and it remains stationary thereafter, since $s$ is constant for $t > 7$. This is illustrated schematically in Figure 4.6.2*b*. ◀

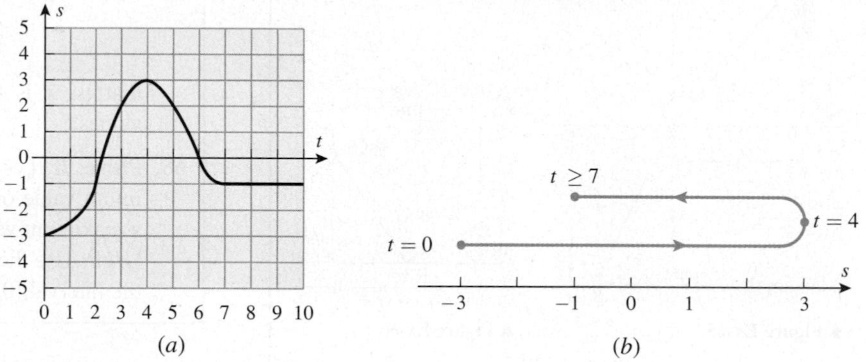


▲ **Figure 4.6.2**

## VELOCITY AND SPEED

Recall from Formula (5) of Section 2.1 and Formula (4) of Section 2.2 that the instantaneous velocity of a particle in rectilinear motion is the derivative of the position function. Thus, if a particle in rectilinear motion has position function $s(t)$, then we define its ***velocity function*** $v(t)$ to be

$$v(t) = s'(t) = \frac{ds}{dt} \qquad (1)$$

We should more properly call $v(t)$ the ***instantaneous velocity function*** to distinguish instantaneous velocity from average velocity. However, we will follow the standard practice of referring to it as the "velocity function," leaving it understood that it describes instantaneous velocity.

* In writing $s = s(t)$, rather than the more familiar $s = f(t)$, we are using the letter $s$ both as the dependent variable and the name of the function. This is common practice in engineering and physics.

**Willebrord van Roijen Snell (1591–1626)** Dutch mathematician. Snell, who succeeded his father to the post of Professor of Mathematics at the University of Leiden in 1613, is most famous for the result of light refraction that bears his name. Although this phenomenon was studied as far back as the ancient Greek astronomer Ptolemy, until Snell's work the relationship was incorrectly thought to be $\theta_1/v_1 = \theta_2/v_2$. Snell's law was published by Descartes in 1638 without giving proper credit to Snell. Snell also discovered a method for determining distances by triangulation that founded the modern technique of mapmaking.

The sign of the velocity tells which way the particle is moving—a positive value for $v(t)$ means that $s$ is increasing with time, so the particle is moving in the positive direction, and a negative value for $v(t)$ means that $s$ is decreasing with time, so the particle is moving in the negative direction. If $v(t) = 0$, then the particle has momentarily stopped.

For a particle in rectilinear motion it is important to distinguish between its ***velocity***, which describes how fast and in what direction the particle is moving, and its ***speed***, which describes only how fast the particle is moving. We make this distinction by defining speed to be the absolute value of velocity. Thus a particle with a velocity of 2 m/s has a speed of 2 m/s and is moving in the positive direction, while a particle with a velocity of −2 m/s also has a speed of 2 m/s but is moving in the negative direction.

Since the instantaneous speed of a particle is the absolute value of its instantaneous velocity, we define its ***speed function*** to be

$$|v(t)| = |s'(t)| = \left|\frac{ds}{dt}\right| \tag{2}$$

The speed function, which is always nonnegative, tells us how fast the particle is moving but not its direction of motion.

► **Example 2** Let $s(t) = t^3 - 6t^2$ be the position function of a particle moving along an $s$-axis, where $s$ is in meters and $t$ is in seconds. Find the velocity and speed functions, and show the graphs of position, velocity, and speed versus time.

***Solution.*** From (1) and (2), the velocity and speed functions are given by

$$v(t) = \frac{ds}{dt} = 3t^2 - 12t \quad \text{and} \quad |v(t)| = |3t^2 - 12t|$$

The graphs of position, velocity, and speed versus time are shown in Figure 4.6.3. Observe that velocity and speed both have units of meters per second (m/s), since $s$ is in meters (m) and time is in seconds (s). ◄

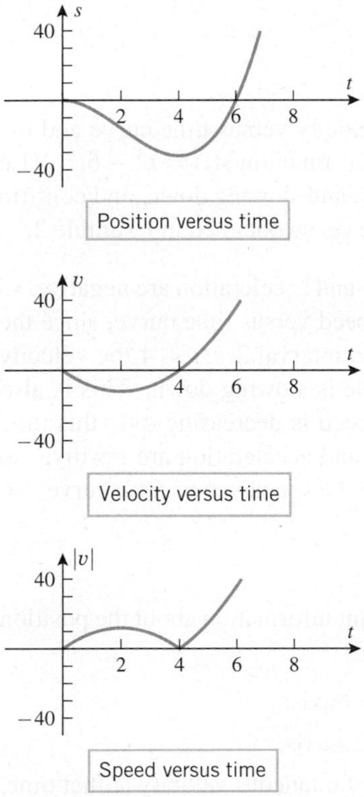

▲ **Figure 4.6.3**

The graphs in Figure 4.6.3 provide a wealth of visual information about the motion of the particle. For example, the position versus time curve tells us that the particle is on the negative side of the origin for $0 < t < 6$, is on the positive side of the origin for $t > 6$, and is at the origin at times $t = 0$ and $t = 6$. The velocity versus time curve tells us that the particle is moving in the negative direction if $0 < t < 4$, is moving in the positive direction if $t > 4$, and is momentarily stopped at times $t = 0$ and $t = 4$ (the velocity is zero at those times). The speed versus time curve tells us that the speed of the particle is increasing for $0 < t < 2$, decreasing for $2 < t < 4$, and increasing again for $t > 4$.

## ACCELERATION

In rectilinear motion, the rate at which the instantaneous velocity of a particle changes with time is called its ***instantaneous acceleration***. Thus, if a particle in rectilinear motion has velocity function $v(t)$, then we define its ***acceleration function*** to be

$$a(t) = v'(t) = \frac{dv}{dt} \tag{3}$$

Alternatively, we can use the fact that $v(t) = s'(t)$ to express the acceleration function in terms of the position function as

$$a(t) = s''(t) = \frac{d^2s}{dt^2} \tag{4}$$

► **Example 3** Let $s(t) = t^3 - 6t^2$ be the position function of a particle moving along an $s$-axis, where $s$ is in meters and $t$ is in seconds. Find the acceleration function $a(t)$, and show the graph of acceleration versus time.

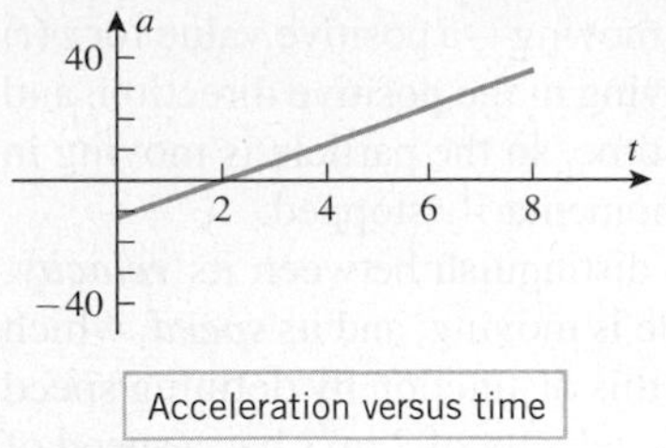


▲ Figure 4.6.4

***Solution.*** From Example 2, the velocity function of the particle is $v(t) = 3t^2 - 12t$, so the acceleration function is

$$a(t) = \frac{dv}{dt} = 6t - 12$$

and the acceleration versus time curve is the line shown in Figure 4.6.4. Note that in this example the acceleration has units of $\mathrm{m/s^2}$, since $v$ is in meters per second (m/s) and time is in seconds (s). ◀

## SPEEDING UP AND SLOWING DOWN

We will say that a particle in rectilinear motion is ***speeding up*** when its speed is increasing and is ***slowing down*** when its speed is decreasing. In everyday language an object that is speeding up is said to be "accelerating" and an object that is slowing down is said to be "decelerating"; thus, one might expect that a particle in rectilinear motion will be speeding up when its acceleration is positive and slowing down when it is negative. Although this is true for a particle moving in the positive direction, it is *not* true for a particle moving in the negative direction—a particle with negative velocity is speeding up when its acceleration is negative and slowing down when its acceleration is positive. This is because a positive acceleration implies an increasing velocity, and increasing a negative velocity decreases its absolute value; similarly, a negative acceleration implies a decreasing velocity, and decreasing a negative velocity increases its absolute value.

The preceding informal discussion can be summarized as follows (Exercise 41):

If $a(t) = 0$ over a certain time interval, what does this tell you about the motion of the particle during that time?

**INTERPRETING THE SIGN OF ACCELERATION** *A particle in rectilinear motion is speeding up when its velocity and acceleration have the same sign and slowing down when they have opposite signs.*

▶ **Example 4** In Examples 2 and 3 we found the velocity versus time curve and the acceleration versus time curve for a particle with position function $s(t) = t^3 - 6t^2$. Use those curves to determine when the particle is speeding up and slowing down, and confirm that your results are consistent with the speed versus time curve obtained in Example 2.

***Solution.*** Over the time interval $0 < t < 2$ the velocity and acceleration are negative, so the particle is speeding up. This is consistent with the speed versus time curve, since the speed is increasing over this time interval. Over the time interval $2 < t < 4$ the velocity is negative and the acceleration is positive, so the particle is slowing down. This is also consistent with the speed versus time curve, since the speed is decreasing over this time interval. Finally, on the time interval $t > 4$ the velocity and acceleration are positive, so the particle is speeding up, which again is consistent with the speed versus time curve. ◀

## ANALYZING THE POSITION VERSUS TIME CURVE

The position versus time curve contains all of the significant information about the position and velocity of a particle in rectilinear motion:

- If $s(t) > 0$, the particle is on the positive side of the $s$-axis.
- If $s(t) < 0$, the particle is on the negative side of the $s$-axis.
- The slope of the curve at any time is equal to the instantaneous velocity at that time.
- Where the curve has positive slope, the velocity is positive and the particle is moving in the positive direction.
- Where the curve has negative slope, the velocity is negative and the particle is moving in the negative direction.
- Where the slope of the curve is zero, the velocity is zero, and the particle is momentarily stopped.

Information about the acceleration of a particle in rectilinear motion can also be deduced from the position versus time curve by examining its concavity. For example, we know that the position versus time curve will be concave up on intervals where $s''(t) > 0$ and will be concave down on intervals where $s''(t) < 0$. But we know from (4) that $s''(t)$ is the acceleration, so that on intervals where the position versus time curve is concave up the particle has a positive acceleration, and on intervals where it is concave down the particle has a negative acceleration.

Table 4.6.1 summarizes our observations about the position versus time curve.

**Table 4.6.1**
ANALYSIS OF PARTICLE MOTION

| POSITION VERSUS TIME CURVE | CHARACTERISTICS OF THE CURVE AT $t = t_0$ | BEHAVIOR OF THE PARTICLE AT TIME $t = t_0$ |
|---|---|---|
| 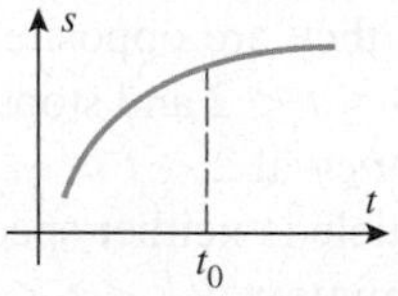 | • $s(t_0) > 0$<br>• Curve has positive slope.<br>• Curve is concave down. | • Particle is on the positive side of the origin.<br>• Particle is moving in the positive direction.<br>• Velocity is decreasing.<br>• Particle is slowing down. |
| 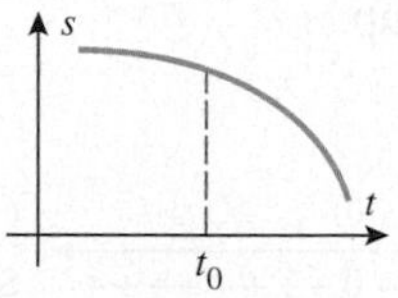 | • $s(t_0) > 0$<br>• Curve has negative slope.<br>• Curve is concave down. | • Particle is on the positive side of the origin.<br>• Particle is moving in the negative direction.<br>• Velocity is decreasing.<br>• Particle is speeding up. |
| 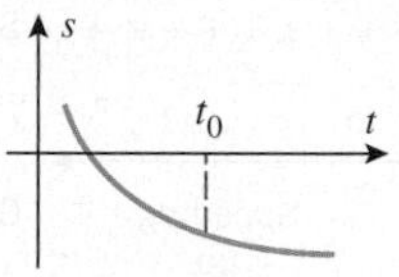 | • $s(t_0) < 0$<br>• Curve has negative slope.<br>• Curve is concave up. | • Particle is on the negative side of the origin.<br>• Particle is moving in the negative direction.<br>• Velocity is increasing.<br>• Particle is slowing down. |
| 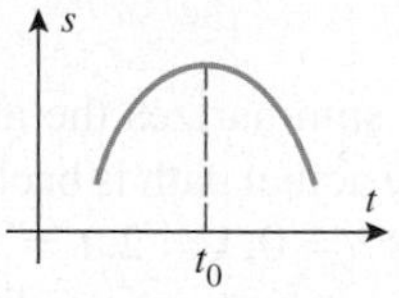 | • $s(t_0) > 0$<br>• Curve has zero slope.<br>• Curve is concave down. | • Particle is on the positive side of the origin.<br>• Particle is momentarily stopped.<br>• Velocity is decreasing. |

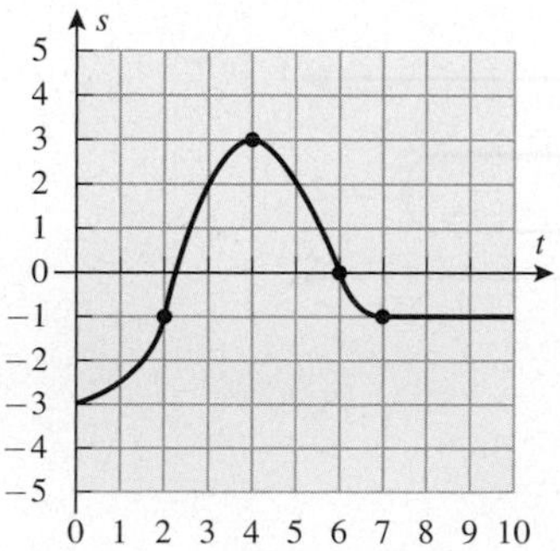

▲ **Figure 4.6.5**

▶ **Example 5** Use the position versus time curve in Figure 4.6.5 to determine when the particle in Example 1 is speeding up and slowing down.

***Solution.*** From $t = 0$ to $t = 2$, the acceleration and velocity are positive, so the particle is speeding up. From $t = 2$ to $t = 4$, the acceleration is negative and the velocity is positive, so the particle is slowing down. At $t = 4$, the velocity is zero, so the particle has momentarily stopped. From $t = 4$ to $t = 6$, the acceleration is negative and the velocity is negative, so the particle is speeding up. From $t = 6$ to $t = 7$, the acceleration is positive and the velocity is negative, so the particle is slowing down. Thereafter, the velocity is zero, so the particle has stopped. ◀

▶ **Example 6** Suppose that the position function of a particle moving on a coordinate line is given by $s(t) = 2t^3 - 21t^2 + 60t + 3$. Analyze the motion of the particle for $t \geq 0$.

***Solution.*** The velocity and acceleration functions are

$$v(t) = s'(t) = 6t^2 - 42t + 60 = 6(t-2)(t-5)$$
$$a(t) = v'(t) = 12t - 42 = 12\left(t - \tfrac{7}{2}\right)$$

- *Direction of motion:* The sign analysis of the velocity function in Figure 4.6.6 shows that the particle is moving in the positive direction over the time interval $0 \le t < 2$, stops momentarily at time $t = 2$, moves in the negative direction over the time interval $2 < t < 5$, stops momentarily at time $t = 5$, and then moves in the positive direction thereafter.

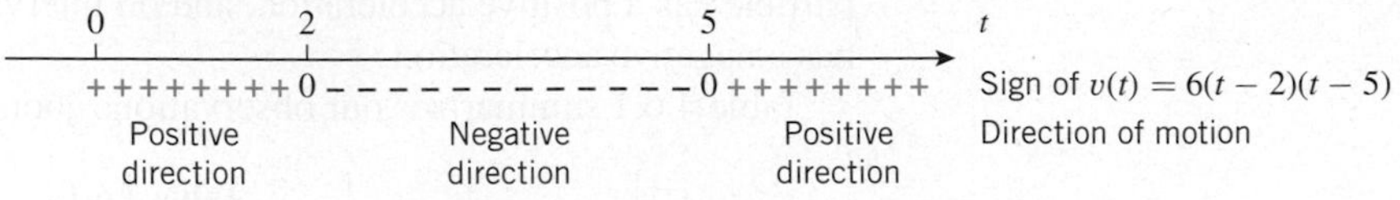


▲ **Figure 4.6.6**

- *Change in speed:* A comparison of the signs of the velocity and acceleration functions is shown in Figure 4.6.7. Since the particle is speeding up when the signs are the same and is slowing down when they are opposite, we see that the particle is slowing down over the time interval $0 \le t < 2$ and stops momentarily at time $t = 2$. It is then speeding up over the time interval $2 < t < \frac{7}{2}$. At time $t = \frac{7}{2}$ the instantaneous acceleration is zero, so the particle is neither speeding up nor slowing down. It is then slowing down over the time interval $\frac{7}{2} < t < 5$ and stops momentarily at time $t = 5$. Thereafter, it is speeding up.

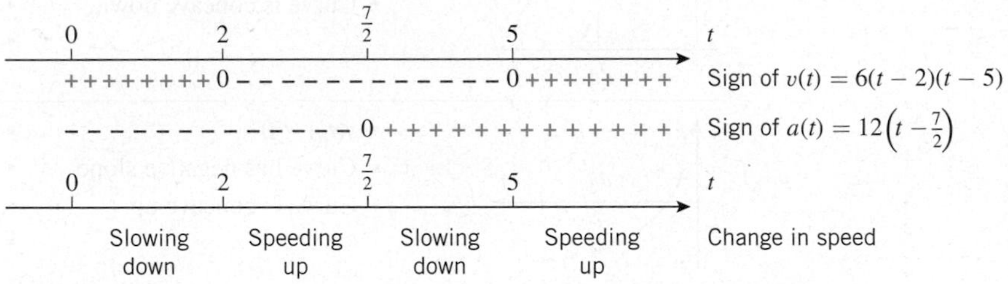


▲ **Figure 4.6.7**

*Conclusions:* The diagram in Figure 4.6.8 summarizes the above information schematically. The curved line is descriptive only; the actual path is back and forth on the coordinate line. The coordinates of the particle at times $t = 0$, $t = 2$, $t = \frac{7}{2}$, and $t = 5$ were computed from $s(t)$. Segments in red indicate that the particle is speeding up and segments in blue indicate that it is slowing down. ◄

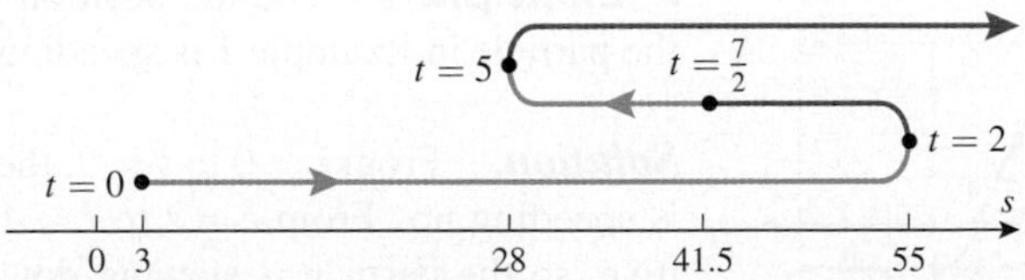


► **Figure 4.6.8**

## ✓ QUICK CHECK EXERCISES 4.6 (See page 233 for answers.)

1. For a particle in rectilinear motion, the velocity and position functions $v(t)$ and $s(t)$ are related by the equation ________, and the acceleration and velocity functions $a(t)$ and $v(t)$ are related by the equation ________.

2. Suppose that a particle moving along the $s$-axis has position function $s(t) = 7t - 2t^2$. At time $t = 3$, the particle's position is ________, its velocity is ________, its speed is ________, and its acceleration is ________.

3. A particle in rectilinear motion is speeding up if the signs of its velocity and acceleration are ________, and it is slowing down if these signs are ________.

4. Suppose that a particle moving along the $s$-axis has position function $s(t) = t^4 - 24t^2$ over the time interval $t \ge 0$. The particle slows down over the time interval(s) ________.

## EXERCISE SET 4.6 Graphing Utility

### FOCUS ON CONCEPTS

**1.** The graphs of three position functions are shown in the accompanying figure. In each case determine the signs of the velocity and acceleration, and then determine whether the particle is speeding up or slowing down.

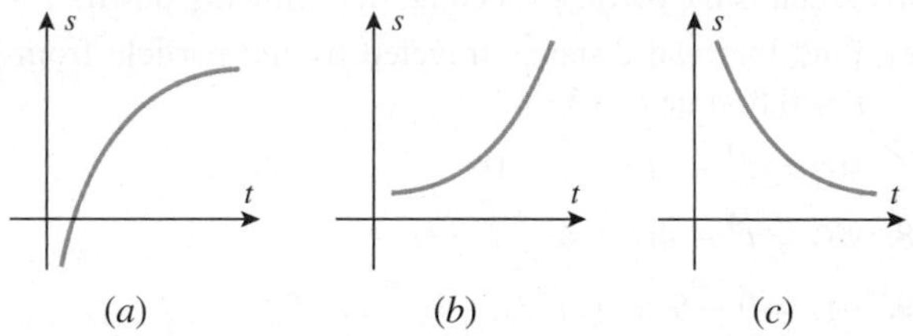


▲ **Figure Ex-1**

**2.** The graphs of three velocity functions are shown in the accompanying figure. In each case determine the sign of the acceleration, and then determine whether the particle is speeding up or slowing down.

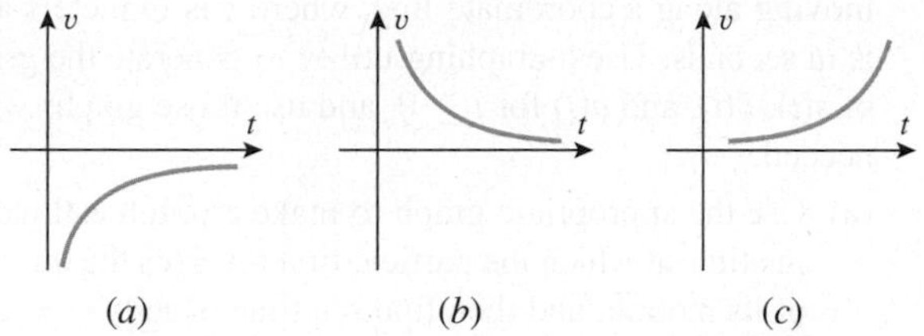


▲ **Figure Ex-2**

**3.** The graph of the position function of a particle moving on a horizontal line is shown in the accompanying figure.

(a) Is the particle moving left or right at time $t_0$?

(b) Is the acceleration positive or negative at time $t_0$?

(c) Is the particle speeding up or slowing down at time $t_0$?

(d) Is the particle speeding up or slowing down at time $t_1$?

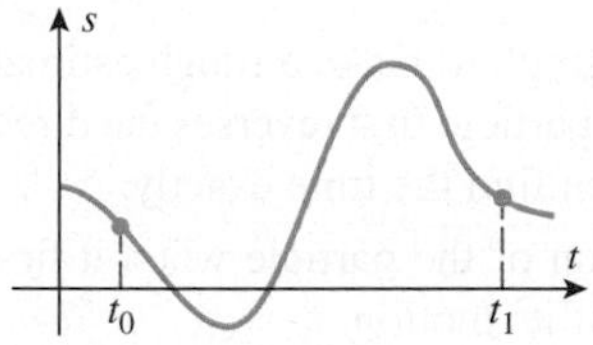


◀ **Figure Ex-3**

**4.** For the graphs in the accompanying figure, match the position functions (*a*)–(*c*) with their corresponding velocity functions (I)–(III).

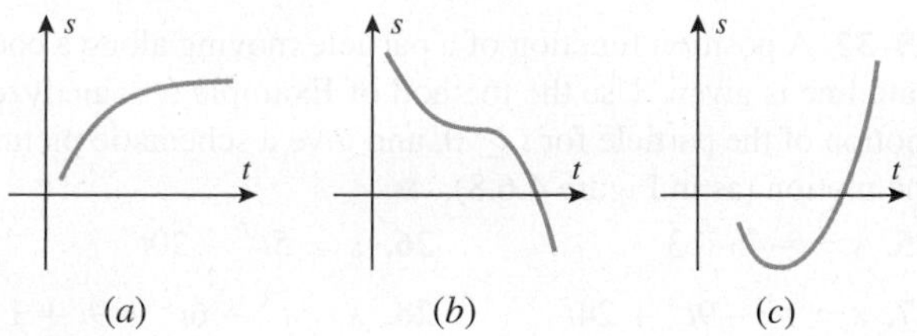


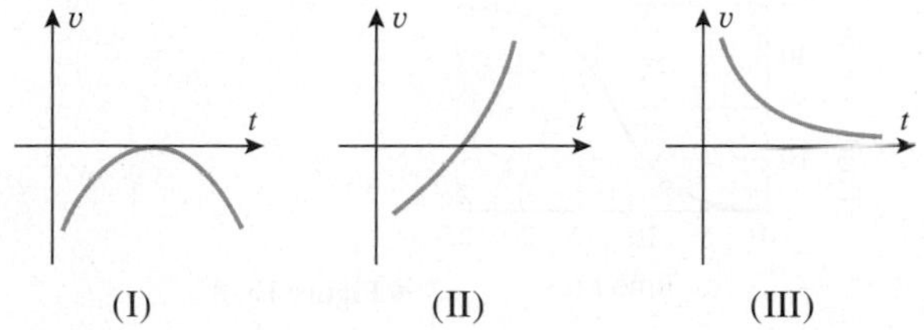


▲ **Figure Ex-4**

**5.** Sketch a reasonable graph of $s$ versus $t$ for a mouse that is trapped in a narrow corridor (an $s$-axis with the positive direction to the right) and scurries back and forth as follows. It runs right with a constant speed of 1.2 m/s for a while, then gradually slows down to 0.6 m/s, then quickly speeds up to 2.0 m/s, then gradually slows to a stop but immediately reverses direction and quickly speeds up to 1.2 m/s.

**6.** The accompanying figure shows the position versus time curve for an ant that moves along a narrow vertical pipe, where $t$ is measured in seconds and the $s$-axis is along the pipe with the positive direction up.

(a) When, if ever, is the ant above the origin?

(b) When, if ever, does the ant have velocity zero?

(c) When, if ever, is the ant moving down the pipe?

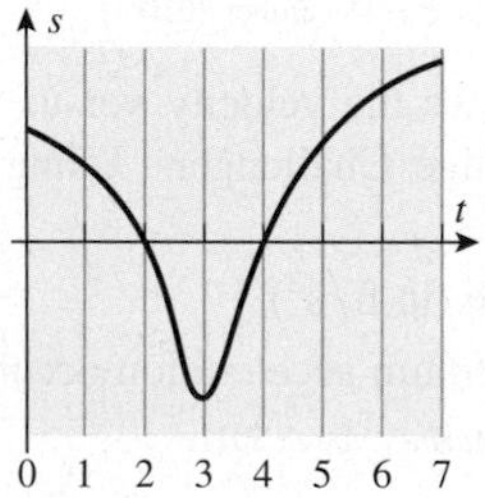


◀ **Figure Ex-6**

**7.** The accompanying figure shows the graph of velocity versus time for a particle moving along a coordinate line. Make a rough sketch of the graphs of speed versus time and acceleration versus time.

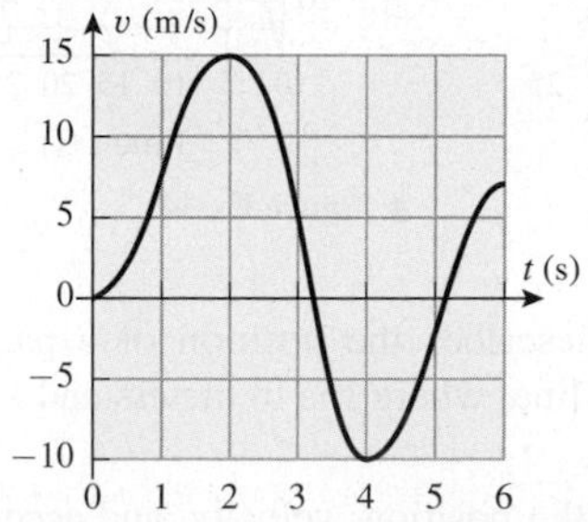


◀ **Figure Ex-7**

**8.** The accompanying figure (on the next page) shows the position versus time graph for an elevator that ascends 40 m from one stop to the next.

(a) Estimate the velocity when the elevator is halfway up to the top. *(cont.)*

(b) Sketch rough graphs of the velocity versus time curve and the acceleration versus time curve.

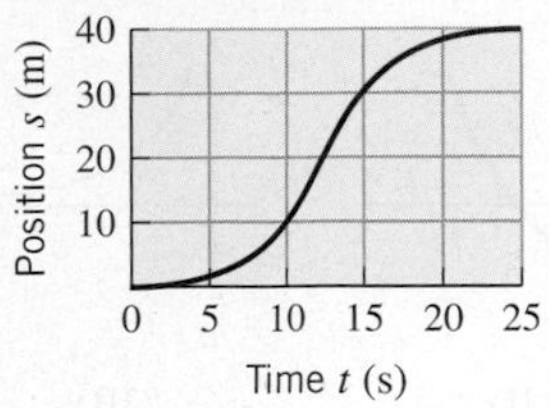


◀ **Figure Ex-8**

**9–12 True–False** Determine whether the statement is true or false. Explain your answer. ■

**9.** A particle is speeding up when its position versus time graph is increasing.

**10.** Velocity is the derivative of position with respect to time.

**11.** Acceleration is the absolute value of velocity.

**12.** If the position versus time curve is increasing and concave down, then the particle is slowing down.

**13.** The accompanying figure shows the velocity versus time graph for a test run on a Chevrolet Volt. Using this graph, estimate

(a) the acceleration at 60 mi/h (in ft/s$^2$)

(b) the time at which the maximum acceleration occurs.

***Source:*** Data from *Car and Driver Magazine*, December 2010.

**14.** The accompanying figure shows the velocity versus time graph for a test run on a Dodge Challenger. Using this graph, estimate

(a) the acceleration at 60 mi/h (in ft/s$^2$)

(b) the time at which the maximum acceleration occurs.

***Source:*** Data from *Car and Driver Magazine*, March 2011.

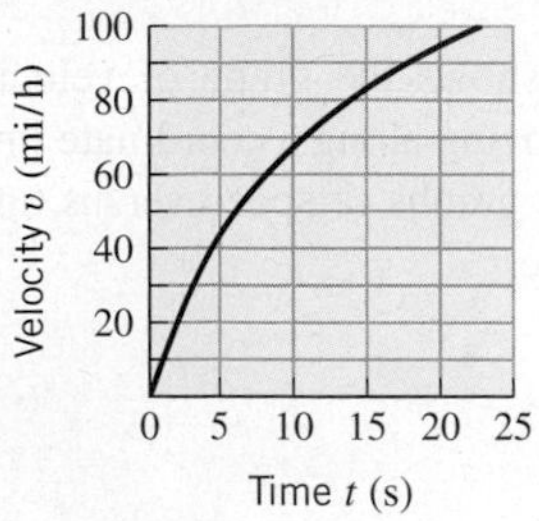


▲ **Figure Ex-13**

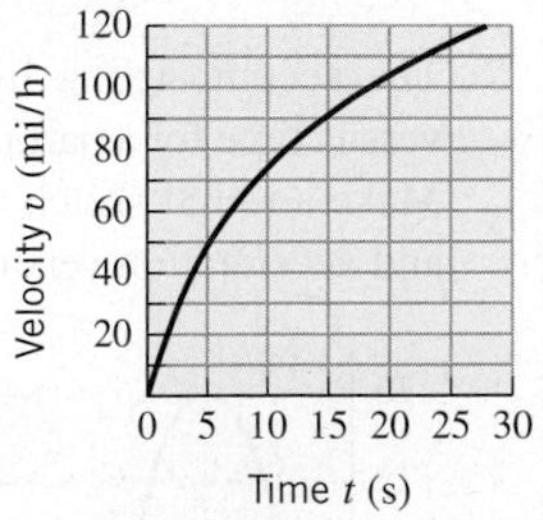


▲ **Figure Ex-14**

**15–16** The function $s(t)$ describes the position of a particle moving along a coordinate line, where $s$ is in meters and $t$ is in seconds.

(a) Make a table showing the position, velocity, and acceleration to two decimal places at times $t = 1, 2, 3, 4, 5$.

(b) At each of the times in part (a), determine whether the particle is stopped; if it is not, state its direction of motion.

(c) At each of the times in part (a), determine whether the particle is speeding up, slowing down, or neither. ■

**15.** $s(t) = \sin \dfrac{\pi t}{4}$  **16.** $s(t) = t^4 e^{-t}, \quad t \geq 0$

**17–22** The function $s(t)$ describes the position of a particle moving along a coordinate line, where $s$ is in feet and $t$ is in seconds.

(a) Find the velocity and acceleration functions.

(b) Find the position, velocity, speed, and acceleration at time $t = 1$.

(c) At what times is the particle stopped?

(d) When is the particle speeding up? Slowing down?

(e) Find the total distance traveled by the particle from time $t = 0$ to time $t = 5$. ■

**17.** $s(t) = t^3 - 3t^2, \quad t \geq 0$

**18.** $s(t) = t^4 - 4t^2 + 4, \quad t \geq 0$

**19.** $s(t) = 9 - 9\cos(\pi t/3), \quad 0 \leq t \leq 5$

**20.** $s(t) = \dfrac{t}{t^2 + 4}, \quad t \geq 0$

**21.** $s(t) = (t^2 + 8)e^{-t/3}, \quad t \geq 0$

**22.** $s(t) = \frac{1}{4}t^2 - \ln(t + 1), \quad t \geq 0$

**23.** Let $s(t) = t/(t^2 + 5)$ be the position function of a particle moving along a coordinate line, where $s$ is in meters and $t$ is in seconds. Use a graphing utility to generate the graphs of $s(t)$, $v(t)$, and $a(t)$ for $t \geq 0$, and use those graphs where needed.

(a) Use the appropriate graph to make a rough estimate of the time at which the particle first reverses the direction of its motion; and then find the time exactly.

(b) Find the exact position of the particle when it first reverses the direction of its motion.

(c) Use the appropriate graphs to make a rough estimate of the time intervals on which the particle is speeding up and on which it is slowing down; and then find those time intervals exactly.

**24.** Let $s(t) = t/e^t$ be the position function of a particle moving along a coordinate line, where $s$ is in meters and $t$ is in seconds. Use a graphing utility to generate the graphs of $s(t)$, $v(t)$, and $a(t)$ for $t \geq 0$, and use those graphs where needed.

(a) Use the appropriate graph to make a rough estimate of the time at which the particle first reverses the direction of its motion; and then find the time exactly.

(b) Find the exact position of the particle when it first reverses the direction of its motion.

(c) Use the appropriate graphs to make a rough estimate of the time intervals on which the particle is speeding up and on which it is slowing down; and then find those time intervals exactly.

**25–32** A position function of a particle moving along a coordinate line is given. Use the method of Example 6 to analyze the motion of the particle for $t \geq 0$, and give a schematic picture of the motion (as in Figure 4.6.8). ■

**25.** $s = -4t + 3$  **26.** $s = 5t^2 - 20t$

**27.** $s = t^3 - 9t^2 + 24t$  **28.** $s = t^3 - 6t^2 + 9t + 1$

**29.** $s = 16te^{-(t^2/8)}$ **30.** $s = t + \dfrac{25}{t+2}$

**31.** $s = \begin{cases} \cos t, & 0 \le t < 2\pi \\ 1, & t \ge 2\pi \end{cases}$

**32.** $s = \begin{cases} 2t(t-2)^2, & 0 \le t < 3 \\ 13 - 7(t-4)^2, & t \ge 3 \end{cases}$

**33.** Let $s(t) = 5t^2 - 22t$ be the position function of a particle moving along a coordinate line, where $s$ is in feet and $t$ is in seconds.

(a) Find the maximum speed of the particle during the time interval $1 \le t \le 3$.

(b) When, during the time interval $1 \le t \le 3$, is the particle farthest from the origin? What is its position at that instant?

**34.** Let $s = 100/(t^2 + 12)$ be the position function of a particle moving along a coordinate line, where $s$ is in feet and $t$ is in seconds. Find the maximum speed of the particle for $t \ge 0$, and find the direction of motion of the particle when it has its maximum speed.

**35–36** A position function of a particle moving along a coordinate line is provided. (a) Evaluate $s$ and $v$ when $a = 0$. (b) Evaluate $s$ and $a$ when $v = 0$. ■

**35.** $s = \ln(3t^2 - 12t + 13)$ **36.** $s = t^3 - 6t^2 + 1$

**37.** Let $s = \sqrt{2t^2 + 1}$ be the position function of a particle moving along a coordinate line.

(a) Use a graphing utility to generate the graph of $v$ versus $t$, and make a conjecture about the velocity of the particle as $t \to +\infty$.

(b) Check your conjecture by finding $\lim_{t \to +\infty} v$.

**38.** (a) Use the chain rule to show that for a particle in rectilinear motion $a = v(dv/ds)$.

(b) Let $s = \sqrt{3t + 7}, t \ge 0$. Find a formula for $v$ in terms of $s$ and use the equation in part (a) to find the acceleration when $s = 5$.

**39.** Suppose that the position functions of two particles, $P_1$ and $P_2$, in motion along the same line are

$$s_1 = \tfrac{1}{2}t^2 - t + 3 \quad \text{and} \quad s_2 = -\tfrac{1}{4}t^2 + t + 1$$

respectively, for $t \ge 0$.

(a) Prove that $P_1$ and $P_2$ do not collide.

(b) How close do $P_1$ and $P_2$ get to each other?

(c) During what intervals of time are they moving in opposite directions?

**40.** Let $s_A = 15t^2 + 10t + 20$ and $s_B = 5t^2 + 40t, t \ge 0$, be the position functions of cars $A$ and $B$ that are moving along parallel straight lanes of a highway.

(a) How far is car $A$ ahead of car $B$ when $t = 0$?

(b) At what instants of time are the cars next to each other?

(c) At what instant of time do they have the same velocity? Which car is ahead at this instant?

**41.** Prove that a particle is speeding up if the velocity and acceleration have the same sign, and slowing down if they have opposite signs. [*Hint:* Let $r(t) = |v(t)|$ and find $r'(t)$ using the chain rule.]

**42. Writing** A speedometer on a bicycle calculates the bicycle's speed by measuring the time per rotation for one of the bicycle's wheels. Explain how this measurement can be used to calculate an average velocity for the bicycle, and discuss how well it approximates the instantaneous velocity for the bicycle.

**43. Writing** A toy rocket is launched into the air and falls to the ground after its fuel runs out. Describe the rocket's acceleration and when the rocket is speeding up or slowing down during its flight. Accompany your description with a sketch of a graph of the rocket's acceleration versus time.

---

✓ **QUICK CHECK ANSWERS 4.6** 1. $v(t) = s'(t)$; $a(t) = v'(t)$ 2. 3; −5; 5; −4 3. the same; opposite 4. $2 < t < 2\sqrt{3}$

---

## 4.7 NEWTON'S METHOD

*In Section 1.5 we showed how to approximate the roots of an equation $f(x) = 0$ using the Intermediate-Value Theorem. In this section we will study a technique, called "Newton's Method," that is usually more efficient than that method. Newton's Method is the technique used by many commercial and scientific computer programs for finding roots.*

### NEWTON'S METHOD

In beginning algebra one learns that the solution of a first-degree equation $ax + b = 0$ is given by the formula $x = -b/a$, and the solutions of a second-degree equation

$$ax^2 + bx + c = 0$$

are given by the quadratic formula. Formulas also exist for the solutions of all third- and fourth-degree equations, although they are too complicated to be of practical use. In 1826 it was shown by the Norwegian mathematician Niels Henrik Abel that it is impossible to construct a similar formula for the solutions of a *general* fifth-degree equation or higher. Thus, for a *specific* fifth-degree polynomial equation such as

$$x^5 - 9x^4 + 2x^3 - 5x^2 + 17x - 8 = 0$$

it may be difficult or impossible to find exact values for all of the solutions. Similar difficulties occur for nonpolynomial equations such as

$$x - \cos x = 0$$

For such equations the solutions are generally approximated in some way, often by the method we will now discuss.

Suppose that we are trying to find a root $r$ of the equation $f(x) = 0$, and suppose that by some method we are able to obtain an initial rough estimate, $x_1$, of $r$, say by generating the graph of $y = f(x)$ with a graphing utility and examining the $x$-intercept. If $f(x_1) = 0$, then $r = x_1$. If $f(x_1) \neq 0$, then we consider an easier problem, that of finding a root to a linear equation. The best linear approximation to $y = f(x)$ near $x = x_1$ is given by the tangent line to the graph of $f$ at $x_1$, so it might be reasonable to expect that the $x$-intercept to this tangent line provides an improved approximation to $r$. Call this intercept $x_2$ (Figure 4.7.1). We can now treat $x_2$ in the same way we did $x_1$. If $f(x_2) = 0$, then $r = x_2$. If $f(x_2) \neq 0$, then construct the tangent line to the graph of $f$ at $x_2$, and take $x_3$ to be the $x$-intercept of this tangent line. Continuing in this way we can generate a succession of values $x_1, x_2, x_3, x_4, \ldots$ that will usually approach $r$. This procedure for approximating $r$ is called ***Newton's Method***.

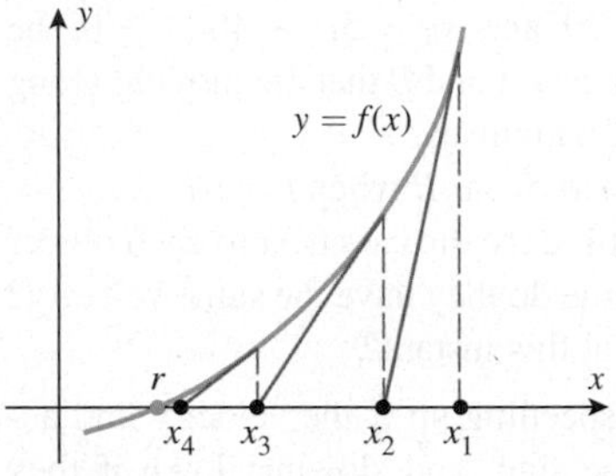

▲ **Figure 4.7.1**

To implement Newton's Method analytically, we must derive a formula that will tell us how to calculate each improved approximation from the preceding approximation. For this purpose, we note that the point-slope form of the tangent line to $y = f(x)$ at the initial approximation $x_1$ is

$$y - f(x_1) = f'(x_1)(x - x_1) \tag{1}$$

If $f'(x_1) \neq 0$, then this line is not parallel to the $x$-axis and consequently it crosses the $x$-axis at some point $(x_2, 0)$. Substituting the coordinates of this point in (1) yields

$$-f(x_1) = f'(x_1)(x_2 - x_1)$$

**Niels Henrik Abel (1802–1829)** Norwegian mathematician. Abel was the son of a poor Lutheran minister and a remarkably beautiful mother from whom he inherited strikingly good looks. In his brief life of 26 years Abel lived in virtual poverty and suffered a succession of adversities, yet he managed to prove major results that altered the mathematical landscape forever. At the age of thirteen he was sent away from home to a school whose better days had long passed. By a stroke of luck the school had just hired a teacher named Bernt Michael Holmboe, who quickly discovered that Abel had extraordinary mathematical ability. Together, they studied the calculus texts of Euler and works of Newton and the later French mathematicians. By the time he graduated, Abel was familar with most of the great mathematical literature. In 1820 his father died, leaving the family in dire financial straits. Abel was able to enter the University of Christiania in Oslo only because he was granted a free room and several professors supported him directly from their salaries. The University had no advanced courses in mathematics, so Abel took a preliminary degree in 1822 and then continued to study mathematics on his own. In 1824 he published at his own expense the proof that it is impossible to solve the general fifth-degree polynomial equation algebraically. With the hope that this landmark paper would lead to his recognition and acceptance by the European mathematical community, Abel sent the paper to the great German mathematician Gauss, who casually declared it to be a "monstrosity" and tossed it aside. However, in 1826 Abel's paper on the fifth-degree equation and other work was published in the first issue of a new journal, founded by his friend, Leopold Crelle. In the summer of 1826 he completed a landmark work on transcendental functions, which he submitted to the French Academy of Sciences. He hoped to establish himself as a major mathematician, for many young mathematicians had gained quick distinction by having their work accepted by the Academy. However, Abel waited in vain because the paper was either ignored or misplaced by one of the referees, and it did not surface again until two years after his death. That paper was later described by one major mathematician as "...the most important mathematical discovery that has been made in our century...." After submitting his paper, Abel returned to Norway, ill with tuberculosis and in heavy debt. While eking out a meager living as a tutor, he continued to produce great work and his fame spread. Soon great efforts were being made to secure a suitable mathematical position for him. Fearing that his great work had been lost by the Academy, he mailed a proof of the main results to Crelle in January of 1829. In April he suffered a violent hemorrhage and died. Two days later Crelle wrote to inform him that an appointment had been secured for him in Berlin and his days of poverty were over! Abel's great paper was finally published by the Academy twelve years after his death.

*[Image: Etching after Johan Gørbitz in C. A. Bjerknes, Niels-Henrik Abel: Tableau de sa vie et de son action scientifique (1885)]*

Solving for $x_2$ we obtain

$$x_2 = x_1 - \frac{f(x_1)}{f'(x_1)} \tag{2}$$

The next approximation can be obtained more easily. If we view $x_2$ as the starting approximation and $x_3$ the new approximation, we can simply apply (2) with $x_2$ in place of $x_1$ and $x_3$ in place of $x_2$. This yields

$$x_3 = x_2 - \frac{f(x_2)}{f'(x_2)} \tag{3}$$

provided $f'(x_2) \neq 0$. In general, if $x_n$ is the $n$th approximation, then it is evident from the pattern in (2) and (3) that the improved approximation $x_{n+1}$ is given by

***Newton's Method***

$$x_{n+1} = x_n - \frac{f(x_n)}{f'(x_n)}, \quad n = 1, 2, 3, \ldots \tag{4}$$

▶ **Example 1** Use Newton's Method to approximate the real solutions of

$$x^3 - x - 1 = 0$$

***Solution.*** Let $f(x) = x^3 - x - 1$, so $f'(x) = 3x^2 - 1$ and (4) becomes

$$x_{n+1} = x_n - \frac{x_n^3 - x_n - 1}{3x_n^2 - 1} \tag{5}$$

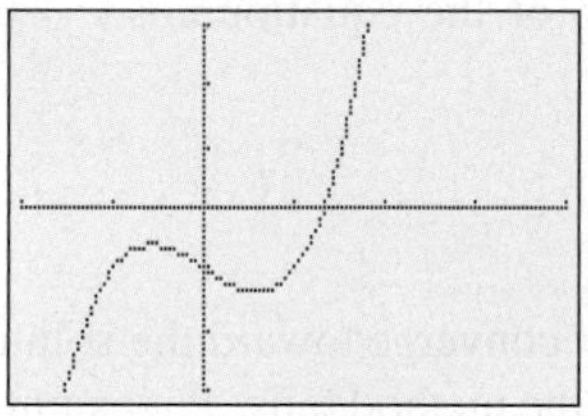

$[-2, 4] \times [-3, 3]$
$x\text{Scl} = 1, y\text{Scl} = 1$

$y = x^3 - x - 1$

▲ **Figure 4.7.2**

**TECHNOLOGY MASTERY**

Many calculators and computer programs calculate internally with more digits than they display. Where possible, you should use stored calculated values rather than values displayed from earlier calculations. Thus, in Example 1 the value of $x_2$ used in (7) should be the stored value, not the value in (6).

From the graph of $f$ in Figure 4.7.2, we see that the given equation has only one real solution. This solution lies between 1 and 2 because $f(1) = -1 < 0$ and $f(2) = 5 > 0$. We will use $x_1 = 1.5$ as our first approximation ($x_1 = 1$ or $x_1 = 2$ would also be reasonable choices).

Letting $n = 1$ in (5) and substituting $x_1 = 1.5$ yields

$$x_2 = 1.5 - \frac{(1.5)^3 - 1.5 - 1}{3(1.5)^2 - 1} \approx 1.34782609 \tag{6}$$

(We used a calculator that displays nine digits.) Next, we let $n = 2$ in (5) and substitute $x_2$ to obtain

$$x_3 = x_2 - \frac{x_2^3 - x_2 - 1}{3x_2^2 - 1} \approx 1.32520040 \tag{7}$$

If we continue this process until two identical approximations are generated in succession, we obtain

$$\begin{aligned} x_1 &= 1.5 \\ x_2 &\approx 1.34782609 \\ x_3 &\approx 1.32520040 \\ x_4 &\approx 1.32471817 \\ x_5 &\approx 1.32471796 \\ x_6 &\approx 1.32471796 \end{aligned}$$

At this stage there is no need to continue further because we have reached the display accuracy limit of our calculator, and all subsequent approximations that the calculator generates will likely be the same. Thus, the solution is approximately $x \approx 1.32471796$. ◀

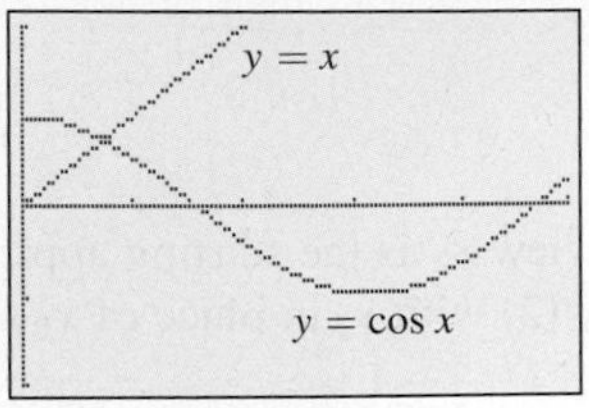


[0, 5] × [−2, 2]
xScl = 1, yScl = 1

▲ Figure 4.7.3

▶ **Example 2** It is evident from Figure 4.7.3 that if $x$ is in radians, then the equation

$$\cos x = x$$

has a solution between 0 and 1. Use Newton's Method to approximate it.

***Solution.*** Rewrite the equation as

$$x - \cos x = 0$$

and apply (4) with $f(x) = x - \cos x$. Since $f'(x) = 1 + \sin x$, (4) becomes

$$x_{n+1} = x_n - \frac{x_n - \cos x_n}{1 + \sin x_n} \tag{8}$$

From Figure 4.7.3, the solution seems closer to $x = 1$ than $x = 0$, so we will use $x_1 = 1$ (radian) as our initial approximation. Letting $n = 1$ in (8) and substituting $x_1 = 1$ yields

$$x_2 = 1 - \frac{1 - \cos 1}{1 + \sin 1} \approx 0.750363868$$

Next, letting $n = 2$ in (8) and substituting this value of $x_2$ yields

$$x_3 = x_2 - \frac{x_2 - \cos x_2}{1 + \sin x_2} \approx 0.739112891$$

If we continue this process until two identical approximations are generated in succession, we obtain

$$\begin{aligned} x_1 &= 1 \\ x_2 &\approx 0.750363868 \\ x_3 &\approx 0.739112891 \\ x_4 &\approx 0.739085133 \\ x_5 &\approx 0.739085133 \end{aligned}$$

Thus, to the accuracy limit of our calculator, the solution of the equation $\cos x = x$ is $x \approx 0.739085133$. ◀

## SOME DIFFICULTIES WITH NEWTON'S METHOD

When Newton's Method works, the approximations usually converge toward the solution with dramatic speed. However, there are situations in which the method fails. For example, if $f'(x_n) = 0$ for some $n$, then (4) involves a division by zero, making it impossible to generate $x_{n+1}$. However, this is to be expected because the tangent line to $y = f(x)$ is parallel to the $x$-axis where $f'(x_n) = 0$, and hence this tangent line does not cross the $x$-axis to generate the next approximation (Figure 4.7.4).

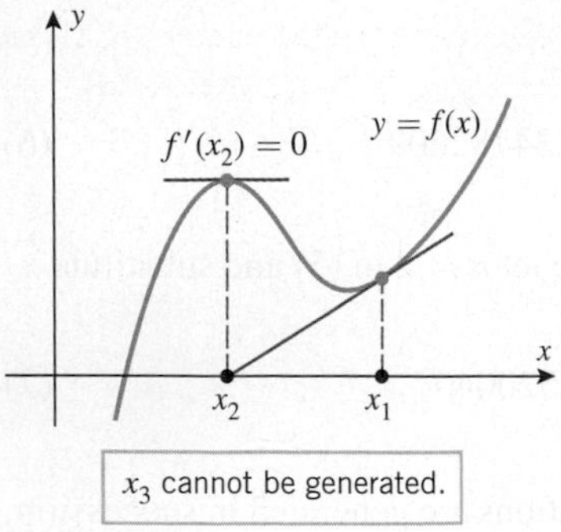


▲ Figure 4.7.4

Newton's Method can fail for other reasons as well; sometimes it may overlook the root you are trying to find and converge to a different root, and sometimes it may fail to converge altogether. For example, consider the equation

$$x^{1/3} = 0$$

which has $x = 0$ as its only solution, and try to approximate this solution by Newton's Method with a starting value of $x_0 = 1$. Letting $f(x) = x^{1/3}$, Formula (4) becomes

$$x_{n+1} = x_n - \frac{(x_n)^{1/3}}{\frac{1}{3}(x_n)^{-2/3}} = x_n - 3x_n = -2x_n$$

Beginning with $x_1 = 1$, the successive values generated by this formula are

$$x_1 = 1, \quad x_2 = -2, \quad x_3 = 4, \quad x_4 = -8, \ldots$$

which obviously do not converge to $x = 0$. Figure 4.7.5 illustrates what is happening geometrically in this situation.

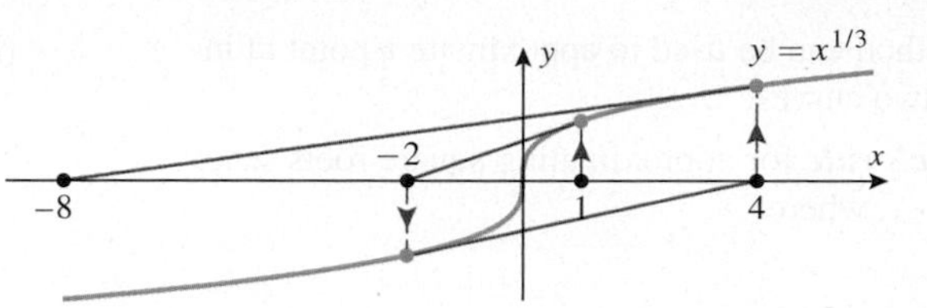


▶ **Figure 4.7.5**

To learn more about the conditions under which Newton's Method converges and for a discussion of error questions, you should consult a book on numerical analysis. For a more in-depth discussion of Newton's Method and its relationship to contemporary studies of chaos and fractals, you may want to read the article, "Newton's Method and Fractal Patterns," by Philip Straffin, which appears in *Applications of Calculus*, MAA Notes, Vol. 3, No. 29, 1993, published by the Mathematical Association of America.

## ✓ QUICK CHECK EXERCISES 4.7 *(See page 239 for answers.)*

1. Use the accompanying graph to estimate $x_2$ and $x_3$ if Newton's Method is applied to the equation $y = f(x)$ with $x_1 = 8$.
2. Suppose that $f(1) = 2$ and $f'(1) = 4$. If Newton's Method is applied to $y = f(x)$ with $x_1 = 1$, then $x_2 =$ ______.
3. Suppose we are given that $f(0) = 3$ and that $x_2 = 3$ when Newton's Method is applied to $y = f(x)$ with $x_1 = 0$. Then $f'(0) =$ ______.
4. If Newton's Method is applied to $y = e^x - 1$ with $x_1 = \ln 2$, then $x_2 =$ ______.

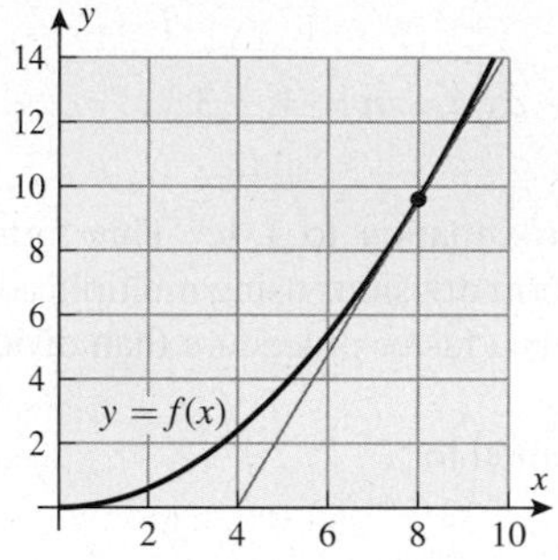


◀ **Figure Ex-1**

## EXERCISE SET 4.7 Graphing Utility

In this exercise set, express your answers with as many decimal digits as your calculating utility can display, but use the procedure in the Technology Mastery on p. 235. ■

1. Approximate $\sqrt{2}$ by applying Newton's Method to the equation $x^2 - 2 = 0$.
2. Approximate $\sqrt{5}$ by applying Newton's Method to the equation $x^2 - 5 = 0$.
3. Approximate $\sqrt[3]{6}$ by applying Newton's Method to the equation $x^3 - 6 = 0$.
4. To what equation would you apply Newton's Method to approximate the $n$th root of $a$?

**5–8** The given equation has one real solution. Approximate it by Newton's Method. ■

5. $x^3 - 2x - 2 = 0$
6. $x^3 + x - 1 = 0$
7. $x^5 + x^4 - 5 = 0$
8. $x^5 - 3x + 3 = 0$

**9–14** Use a graphing utility to determine how many solutions the equation has, and then use Newton's Method to approximate the solution that satisfies the stated condition. ■

9. $x^4 + x^2 - 4 = 0;\ x < 0$
10. $x^5 - 5x^3 - 2 = 0;\ x > 0$
11. $2\cos x = x;\ x > 0$
12. $\sin x = x^2;\ x > 0$
13. $x - \tan x = 0;\ \pi/2 < x < 3\pi/2$
14. $1 + e^x \sin x = 0;\ \pi/2 < x < 3\pi/2$

**15–20** Use a graphing utility to determine the number of times the curves intersect; and then apply Newton's Method, where needed, to approximate the $x$-coordinates of all intersections. ■

15. $y = x^3$ and $y = 1 - x$
16. $y = \sin x$ and $y = x^3 - 2x^2 + 1$
17. $y = x^2$ and $y = \sqrt{2x + 1}$
18. $y = \frac{1}{8}x^3 - 1$ and $y = \cos x - 2$
19. $y = 1$ and $y = e^x \sin x;\ 0 < x < \pi$
20. $y = e^{-x}$ and $y = \ln x$

**21–24 True–False** Determine whether the statement is true or false. Explain your answer. ■

21. Newton's Method uses the tangent line to $y = f(x)$ at $x = x_n$ to compute $x_{n+1}$.
22. Newton's Method is a process to find exact solutions to $f(x) = 0$.
23. If $f(x) = 0$ has a root, then Newton's Method starting at $x = x_1$ will approximate the root nearest $x_1$.

**24.** Newton's Method can be used to appoximate a point of intersection of two curves.

**25.** The ***mechanic's rule*** for approximating square roots states that $\sqrt{a} \approx x_{n+1}$, where

$$x_{n+1} = \frac{1}{2}\left(x_n + \frac{a}{x_n}\right), \quad n = 1, 2, 3, \ldots$$

and $x_1$ is any positive approximation to $\sqrt{a}$.
(a) Apply Newton's Method to

$$f(x) = x^2 - a$$

to derive the mechanic's rule.
(b) Use the mechanic's rule to approximate $\sqrt{10}$.

**26.** Many calculators compute reciprocals using the approximation $1/a \approx x_{n+1}$, where

$$x_{n+1} = x_n(2 - ax_n), \quad n = 1, 2, 3, \ldots$$

and $x_1$ is an initial approximation to $1/a$. This formula makes it possible to perform divisions using multiplications and subtractions, which is a faster procedure than dividing directly.
(a) Apply Newton's Method to

$$f(x) = \frac{1}{x} - a$$

to derive this approximation.
(b) Use the formula to approximate $\frac{1}{17}$.

**27.** Use Newton's Method to approximate the absolute minimum of $f(x) = \frac{1}{4}x^4 + x^2 - 5x$.

**28.** Use Newton's Method to approximate the absolute maximum of $f(x) = x \sin x$ on the interval $[0, \pi]$.

**29.** For the function

$$f(x) = \frac{e^{-x}}{1 + x^2}$$

use Newton's Method to approximate the $x$-coordinates of the inflection points to two decimal places.

**30.** Use Newton's Method to approximate the absolute maximum of $f(x) = (1 - 2x)\tan^{-1} x$.

**31.** Use Newton's Method to approximate the coordinates of the point on the parabola $y = x^2$ that is closest to the point $(1, 0)$.

**32.** Use Newton's Method to approximate the dimensions of the rectangle of largest area that can be inscribed under the curve $y = \cos x$ for $0 \le x \le \pi/2$ (Figure Ex-32).

**33.** (a) Show that on a circle of radius $r$, the central angle $\theta$ that subtends an arc whose length is 1.5 times the length $L$ of its chord satisfies the equation $\theta = 3\sin(\theta/2)$ (Figure Ex-33).
(b) Use Newton's Method to approximate $\theta$.

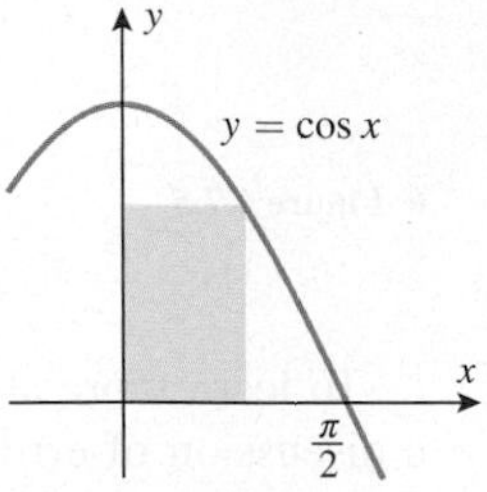


▲ Figure Ex-32

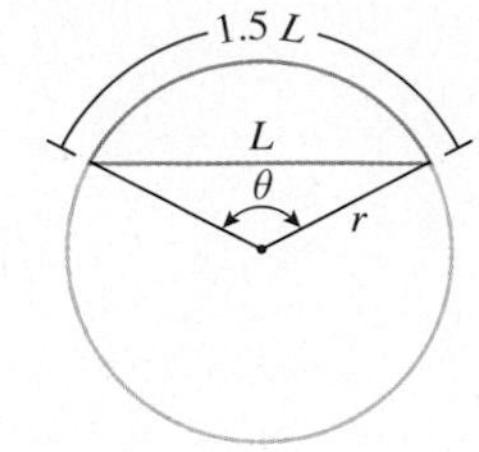


▲ Figure Ex-33

**34.** A ***segment*** of a circle is the region enclosed by an arc and its chord (Figure Ex-34). If $r$ is the radius of the circle and $\theta$ the angle subtended at the center of the circle, then it can be shown that the area $A$ of the segment is $A = \frac{1}{2}r^2(\theta - \sin\theta)$, where $\theta$ is in radians. Find the value of $\theta$ for which the area of the segment is one-fourth the area of the circle. Give $\theta$ to the nearest degree.

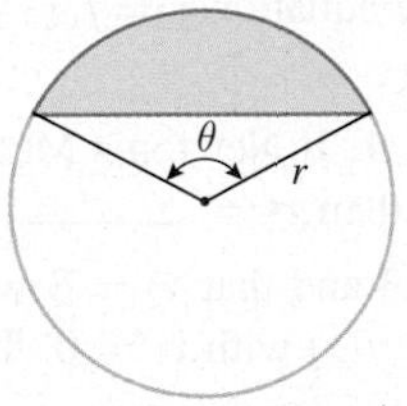


◀ Figure Ex-34

**35.** A walker exercises on an elliptical track given by the equation $4x^2 + 9y^2 = 36$, where $x$ and $y$ are measured in units of 100 meters. Use Newton's Method to approximate the point on the track at which the walker is nearest to a flag pole located at the point $(2, 1)$. What is the distance between the walker and the flag pole for this approximation?

**36.** A 6-inch tall plastic "bubble" sits on a flat surface. Any vertical cross section taken through the center of the bubble is given by the curve $y = 6\cos x$ for $-\pi/2 \le x \le \pi/2$. A can in the shape of a right circular cylinder sits on the surface inside the bubble. Use Newton's Method to approximate the radius of the can with largest possible volume. What is the volume of the can with this approximate radius?

**37–38** Use Newton's Method to approximate all real values of $y$ satisfying the given equation for the indicated value of $x$. ■

**37.** $xy^4 + x^3y = 1;\ x = 1$

**38.** $xy - \cos\left(\frac{1}{2}xy\right) = 0;\ x = 2$

**39.** An ***annuity*** is a sequence of equal payments that are paid or received at regular time intervals. For example, you may want to deposit equal amounts at the end of each year into an interest-bearing account for the purpose of accumulating a lump sum at some future time. If, at the end of each year, interest of $i \times 100\%$ on the account balance for that year is added to the account, then the account is said to pay $i \times 100\%$ interest, ***compounded annually***. It can be shown that if payments of $Q$ dollars are deposited at the end of each year into an account that pays $i \times 100\%$ compounded annually, then at the time when the $n$th payment and the accrued interest for the past year are deposited, the amount $S(n)$ in the account is given by the formula

$$S(n) = \frac{Q}{i}[(1+i)^n - 1]$$

Suppose that you can invest $5000 in an interest-bearing account at the end of each year, and your objective is to have $250,000 on the 25th payment. Approximately what annual compound interest rate must the account pay for you to achieve your goal? [*Hint:* Show that the interest rate $i$ satisfies the equation $50i = (1+i)^{25} - 1$, and solve it using Newton's Method.]

**FOCUS ON CONCEPTS**

**40.** (a) Use a graphing utility to generate the graph of

$$f(x) = \frac{x}{x^2+1}$$

and use it to explain what happens if you apply Newton's Method with a starting value of $x_1 = 2$. Check your conclusion by computing $x_2$, $x_3$, $x_4$, and $x_5$.

(b) Use the graph generated in part (a) to explain what happens if you apply Newton's Method with a starting value of $x_1 = 0.5$. Check your conclusion by computing $x_2, x_3, x_4$, and $x_5$.

**41.** (a) Apply Newton's Method to $f(x) = x^2 + 1$ with a starting value of $x_1 = 0.5$, and determine if the values of $x_2, \ldots, x_{10}$ appear to converge.

(b) Explain what is happening.

**42.** In each part, explain what happens if you apply Newton's Method to a function $f$ when the given condition is satisfied for some value of $n$.

(a) $f(x_n) = 0$ (b) $x_{n+1} = x_n$

(c) $x_{n+2} = x_n \neq x_{n+1}$

**43. Writing** Compare Newton's Method and the Intermediate-Value Theorem (1.5.7; see Example 5 in Section 1.5) as methods to locate solutions to $f(x) = 0$.

**44. Writing** Newton's Method uses a local linear approximation to $y = f(x)$ at $x = x_n$ to find an "improved" approximation $x_{n+1}$ to a zero of $f$. Your friend proposes a process that uses a local quadratic approximation to $y = f(x)$ at $x = x_n$ (that is, matching values for the function and its first two derivatives) to obtain $x_{n+1}$. Discuss the pros and cons of this proposal. Support your statements with some examples.

✓ **QUICK CHECK ANSWERS 4.7** 1. $x_2 \approx 4$, $x_3 \approx 2$ 2. $\frac{1}{2}$ 3. $-1$ 4. $\ln 2 - \frac{1}{2} \approx 0.193147$

## 4.8 ROLLE'S THEOREM; MEAN-VALUE THEOREM

*In this section we will discuss a result called the Mean-Value Theorem. This theorem has so many important consequences that it is regarded as one of the major principles in calculus.*

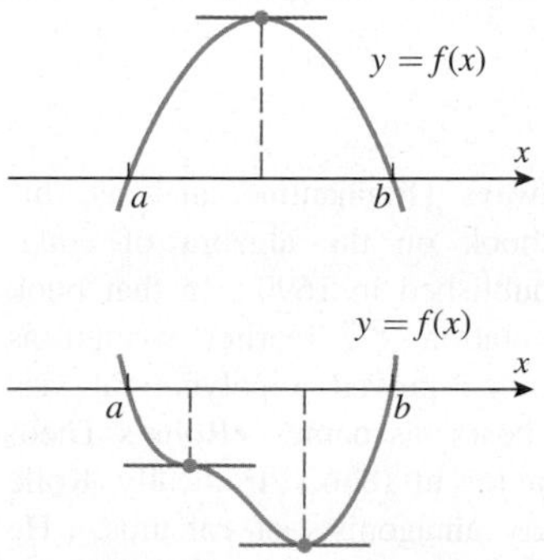

▲ **Figure 4.8.1**

### ROLLE'S THEOREM

We will begin with a special case of the Mean-Value Theorem, called Rolle's Theorem, in honor of the mathematician Michel Rolle. This theorem states the geometrically obvious fact that if the graph of a differentiable function intersects the $x$-axis at two places, $a$ and $b$, then somewhere between $a$ and $b$ there must be at least one place where the tangent line is horizontal (Figure 4.8.1). The precise statement of the theorem is as follows.

**4.8.1 THEOREM** (*Rolle's Theorem*) *Let $f$ be continuous on the closed interval $[a, b]$ and differentiable on the open interval $(a, b)$. If*

$$f(a) = 0 \quad \textit{and} \quad f(b) = 0$$

*then there is at least one point $c$ in the interval $(a, b)$ such that $f'(c) = 0$.*

PROOF We will divide the proof into three cases: the case where $f(x) = 0$ for all $x$ in $(a, b)$, the case where $f(x) > 0$ at some point in $(a, b)$, and the case where $f(x) < 0$ at some point in $(a, b)$.

CASE 1 If $f(x) = 0$ for all $x$ in $(a, b)$, then $f'(c) = 0$ at every point $c$ in $(a, b)$ because $f$ is a constant function on that interval.

CASE 2 Assume that $f(x) > 0$ at some point in $(a, b)$. Since $f$ is continuous on $[a, b]$, it follows from the Extreme-Value Theorem (4.4.2) that $f$ has an absolute maximum on $[a, b]$. The absolute maximum value cannot occur at an endpoint of $[a, b]$ because we have assumed that $f(a) = f(b) = 0$, and that $f(x) > 0$ at some point in $(a, b)$. Thus, the absolute maximum must occur at some point $c$ in $(a, b)$. It follows from Theorem 4.4.3 that $c$ is a critical point of $f$, and since $f$ is differentiable on $(a, b)$, this critical point must be a stationary point; that is, $f'(c) = 0$.

CASE 3 Assume that $f(x) < 0$ at some point in $(a, b)$. The proof of this case is similar to Case 2 and will be omitted. ■

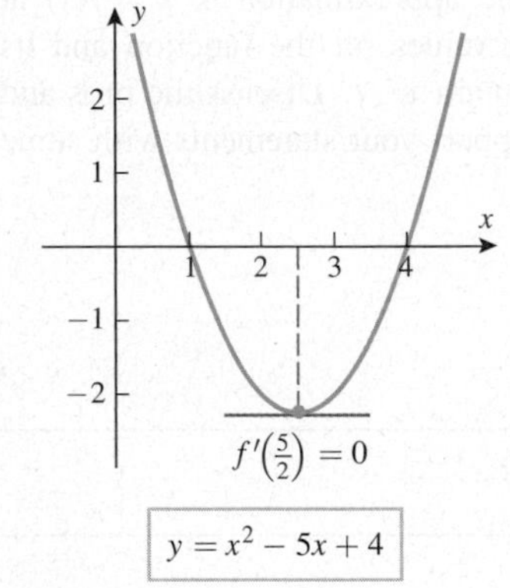


▲ Figure 4.8.2

► **Example 1** Find the two $x$-intercepts of the function $f(x) = x^2 - 5x + 4$ and confirm that $f'(c) = 0$ at some point $c$ between those intercepts.

***Solution.*** The function $f$ can be factored as

$$x^2 - 5x + 4 = (x - 1)(x - 4)$$

so the $x$-intercepts are $x = 1$ and $x = 4$. Since the polynomial $f$ is continuous and differentiable everywhere, the hypotheses of Rolle's Theorem are satisfied on the interval $[1, 4]$. Thus, we are guaranteed the existence of at least one point $c$ in the interval $(1, 4)$ such that $f'(c) = 0$. Differentiating $f$ yields

$$f'(x) = 2x - 5$$

Solving the equation $f'(x) = 0$ yields $x = \frac{5}{2}$, so $c = \frac{5}{2}$ is a point in the interval $(1, 4)$ at which $f'(c) = 0$ (Figure 4.8.2). ◄

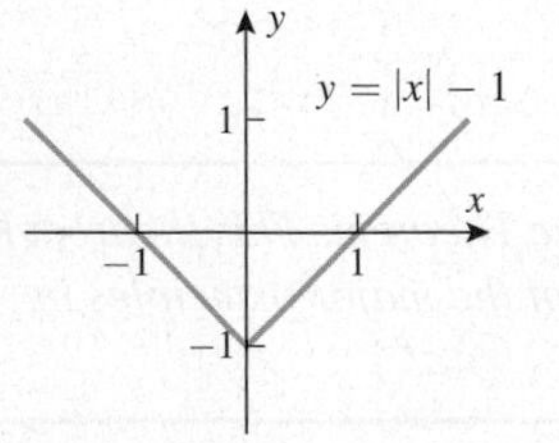


▲ Figure 4.8.3

► **Example 2** The differentiability requirement in Rolle's Theorem is critical. If $f$ fails to be differentiable at even one place in the interval $(a, b)$, then the conclusion of the theorem may not hold. For example, the function $f(x) = |x| - 1$ graphed in Figure 4.8.3 has roots at $x = -1$ and $x = 1$, yet there is no horizontal tangent to the graph of $f$ over the interval $(-1, 1)$. ◄

**Michel Rolle (1652–1719)** French mathematician. Rolle, the son of a shopkeeper, received only an elementary education. He married early and as a young man struggled hard to support his family on the meager wages of a transcriber for notaries and attorneys. In spite of his financial problems and minimal education, Rolle studied algebra and Diophantine analysis (a branch of number theory) on his own. Rolle's fortune changed dramatically in 1682 when he published an elegant solution of a difficult, unsolved problem in Diophantine analysis. The public recognition of his achievement led to a patronage under minister Louvois, a job as an elementary mathematics teacher, and eventually to a short-term administrative post in the Ministry of War. In 1685 he joined the Académie des Sciences in a low-level position for which he received no regular salary until 1699. He stayed at the Académie until he died of apoplexy in 1719.

While Rolle's forte was always Diophantine analysis, his most important work was a book on the algebra of equations, called *Traité d'algèbre*, published in 1690. In that book Rolle firmly established the notation $\sqrt[n]{a}$ [earlier written as $\sqrt{ⓝ\ a}$] for the $n$th root of $a$, and proved a polynomial version of the theorem that today bears his name. (Rolle's Theorem was named by Giusto Bellavitis in 1846.) Ironically, Rolle was one of the most vocal early antagonists of calculus. He strove intently to demonstrate that it gave erroneous results and was based on unsound reasoning. He quarreled so vigorously on the subject that the Académie des Sciences was forced to intervene on several occasions. Among his several achievements, Rolle helped advance the currently accepted size order for negative numbers. Descartes, for example, viewed −2 as smaller than −5. Rolle preceded most of his contemporaries by adopting the current convention in 1691.

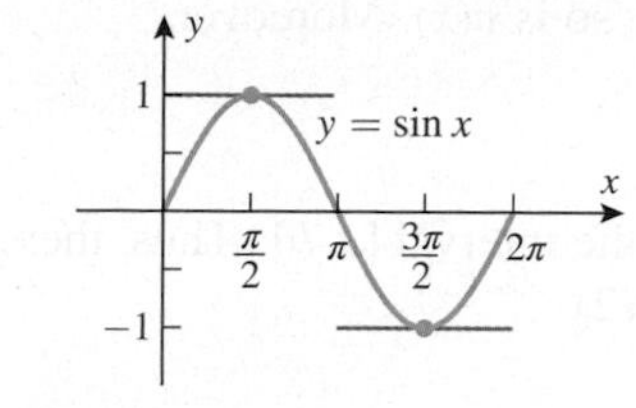


▲ Figure 4.8.4

▶ **Example 3** If $f$ satisfies the conditions of Rolle's Theorem on $[a, b]$, then the theorem guarantees the existence of *at least* one point $c$ in $(a, b)$ at which $f'(c) = 0$. There may, however, be more than one such $c$. For example, the function $f(x) = \sin x$ is continuous and differentiable everywhere, so the hypotheses of Rolle's Theorem are satisfied on the interval $[0, 2\pi]$ whose endpoints are roots of $f$. As indicated in Figure 4.8.4, there are two points in the interval $[0, 2\pi]$ at which the graph of $f$ has a horizontal tangent, $c_1 = \pi/2$ and $c_2 = 3\pi/2$. ◀

## THE MEAN-VALUE THEOREM

Rolle's Theorem is a special case of a more general result, called the ***Mean-Value Theorem***. Geometrically, this theorem states that between any two points $A(a, f(a))$ and $B(b, f(b))$ on the graph of a differentiable function $f$, there is at least one place where the tangent line to the graph is parallel to the secant line joining $A$ and $B$ (Figure 4.8.5).

In Examples 1 and 3 we were able to find exact values of $c$ because the equation $f'(x) = 0$ was easy to solve. However, in the applications of Rolle's Theorem it is usually the *existence* of $c$ that is important and not its actual value.

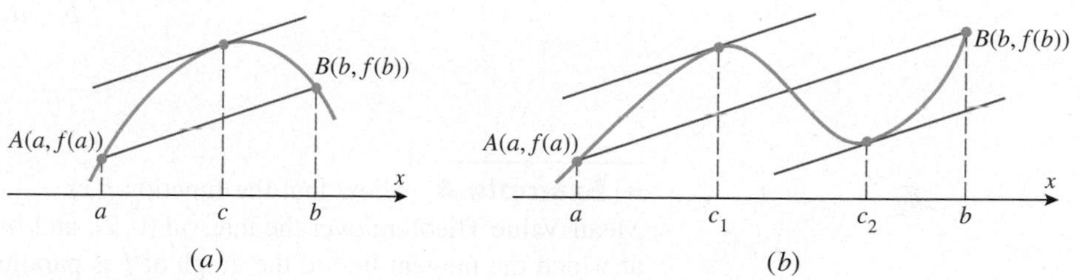


▲ Figure 4.8.5

Note that the slope of the secant line joining $A(a, f(a))$ and $B(b, f(b))$ is

$$\frac{f(b) - f(a)}{b - a}$$

and that the slope of the tangent line at $c$ in Figure 4.8.5*a* is $f'(c)$. Similarly, in Figure 4.8.5*b* the slopes of the tangent lines at $c_1$ and $c_2$ are $f'(c_1)$ and $f'(c_2)$, respectively. Since nonvertical parallel lines have the same slope, the Mean-Value Theorem can be stated precisely as follows.

**4.8.2 THEOREM (*Mean-Value Theorem*)** *Let $f$ be continuous on the closed interval $[a, b]$ and differentiable on the open interval $(a, b)$. Then there is at least one point $c$ in $(a, b)$ such that*

$$f'(c) = \frac{f(b) - f(a)}{b - a} \tag{1}$$

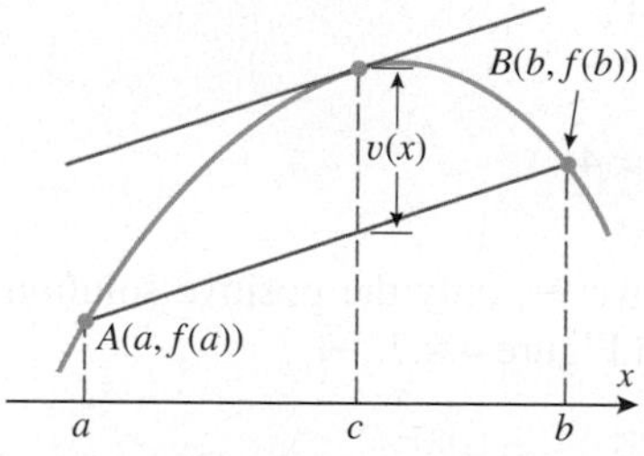


The tangent line is parallel to the secant line where the vertical distance $v(x)$ between the secant line and the graph of $f$ is maximum.

▲ Figure 4.8.6

**MOTIVATION FOR THE PROOF OF THEOREM 4.8.2** Figure 4.8.6 suggests that (1) will hold (i.e., the tangent line will be parallel to the secant line) at a point $c$ where the vertical distance between the curve and the secant line is maximum. Thus, to prove the Mean-Value Theorem it is natural to begin by looking for a formula for the vertical distance $v(x)$ between the curve $y = f(x)$ and the secant line joining $(a, f(a))$ and $(b, f(b))$.

**PROOF OF THEOREM 4.8.2** Since the two-point form of the equation of the secant line joining $(a, f(a))$ and $(b, f(b))$ is

$$y - f(a) = \frac{f(b) - f(a)}{b - a}(x - a)$$

or, equivalently,

$$y = \frac{f(b) - f(a)}{b - a}(x - a) + f(a)$$

the difference $v(x)$ between the height of the graph of $f$ and the height of the secant line is

$$v(x) = f(x) - \left[\frac{f(b) - f(a)}{b - a}(x - a) + f(a)\right] \tag{2}$$

Since $f(x)$ is continuous on $[a, b]$ and differentiable on $(a, b)$, so is $v(x)$. Moreover,

$$v(a) = 0 \quad \text{and} \quad v(b) = 0$$

so that $v(x)$ satisfies the hypotheses of Rolle's Theorem on the interval $[a, b]$. Thus, there is a point $c$ in $(a, b)$ such that $v'(c) = 0$. But from Equation (2)

$$v'(x) = f'(x) - \frac{f(b) - f(a)}{b - a}$$

so

$$v'(c) = f'(c) - \frac{f(b) - f(a)}{b - a}$$

Since $v'(c) = 0$, we have

$$f'(c) = \frac{f(b) - f(a)}{b - a} \quad \blacksquare$$

▶ **Example 4** Show that the function $f(x) = \frac{1}{4}x^3 + 1$ satisfies the hypotheses of the Mean-Value Theorem over the interval $[0, 2]$, and find all values of $c$ in the interval $(0, 2)$ at which the tangent line to the graph of $f$ is parallel to the secant line joining the points $(0, f(0))$ and $(2, f(2))$.

***Solution.*** The function $f$ is continuous and differentiable everywhere because it is a polynomial. In particular, $f$ is continuous on $[0, 2]$ and differentiable on $(0, 2)$, so the hypotheses of the Mean-Value Theorem are satisfied with $a = 0$ and $b = 2$. But

$$f(a) = f(0) = 1, \quad f(b) = f(2) = 3$$

$$f'(x) = \frac{3x^2}{4}, \quad f'(c) = \frac{3c^2}{4}$$

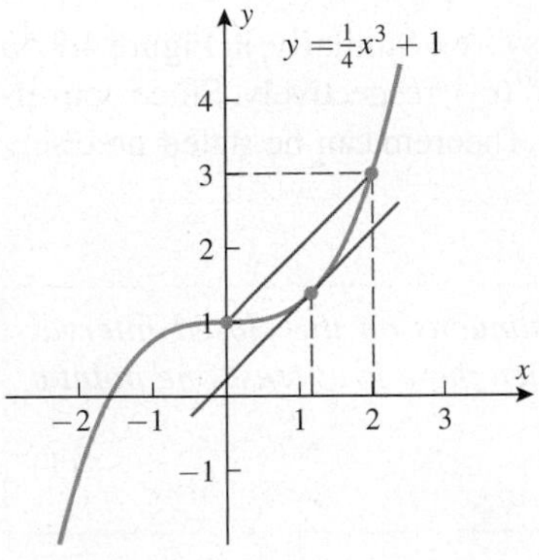


▲ Figure 4.8.7

so in this case Equation (1) becomes

$$\frac{3c^2}{4} = \frac{3 - 1}{2 - 0} \quad \text{or} \quad 3c^2 = 4$$

which has the two solutions $c = \pm 2/\sqrt{3} \approx \pm 1.15$. However, only the positive solution lies in the interval $(0, 2)$; this value of $c$ is consistent with Figure 4.8.7. ◀

## VELOCITY INTERPRETATION OF THE MEAN-VALUE THEOREM

There is a nice interpretation of the Mean-Value Theorem in the situation where $x = f(t)$ is the position versus time curve for a car moving along a straight road. In this case, the right side of (1) is the average velocity of the car over the time interval from $a \le t \le b$, and the left side is the instantaneous velocity at time $t = c$. Thus, the Mean-Value Theorem implies that at least once during the time interval the instantaneous velocity must equal the average velocity. This agrees with our real-world experience—if the average velocity for a trip is 40 mi/h, then sometime during the trip the speedometer has to read 40 mi/h.

▶ **Example 5** You are driving on a straight highway on which the speed limit is 55 mi/h. At 8:05 A.M. a police car clocks your velocity at 50 mi/h and at 8:10 A.M. a second police car posted 5 mi down the road clocks your velocity at 55 mi/h. Explain why the police have a right to charge you with a speeding violation.

***Solution.*** You traveled 5 mi in 5 min $\left(=\frac{1}{12}\text{ h}\right)$, so your average velocity was 60 mi/h. Therefore, the Mean-Value Theorem guarantees the police that your instantaneous velocity was 60 mi/h at least once over the 5 mi section of highway. ◄

## CONSEQUENCES OF THE MEAN-VALUE THEOREM

We stated at the beginning of this section that the Mean-Value Theorem is the starting point for many important results in calculus. As an example of this, we will use it to prove Theorem 4.1.2, which was one of our fundamental tools for analyzing graphs of functions.

> **4.1.2 THEOREM (*Revisited*)** *Let $f$ be a function that is continuous on a closed interval $[a, b]$ and differentiable on the open interval $(a, b)$.*
>
> (*a*) *If $f'(x) > 0$ for every value of $x$ in $(a, b)$, then $f$ is increasing on $[a, b]$.*
>
> (*b*) *If $f'(x) < 0$ for every value of $x$ in $(a, b)$, then $f$ is decreasing on $[a, b]$.*
>
> (*c*) *If $f'(x) = 0$ for every value of $x$ in $(a, b)$, then $f$ is constant on $[a, b]$.*

**PROOF (*a*)** Suppose that $x_1$ and $x_2$ are points in $[a, b]$ such that $x_1 < x_2$. We must show that $f(x_1) < f(x_2)$. Because the hypotheses of the Mean-Value Theorem are satisfied on the entire interval $[a, b]$, they are satisfied on the subinterval $[x_1, x_2]$. Thus, there is some point $c$ in the open interval $(x_1, x_2)$ such that

$$f'(c) = \frac{f(x_2) - f(x_1)}{x_2 - x_1}$$

or, equivalently,

$$f(x_2) - f(x_1) = f'(c)(x_2 - x_1) \tag{3}$$

Since $c$ is in the open interval $(x_1, x_2)$, it follows that $a < c < b$; thus, $f'(c) > 0$. However, $x_2 - x_1 > 0$ since we assumed that $x_1 < x_2$. It follows from (3) that $f(x_2) - f(x_1) > 0$ or, equivalently, $f(x_1) < f(x_2)$, which is what we were to prove. The proofs of parts (*b*) and (*c*) are similar and are left as exercises. ■

## THE CONSTANT DIFFERENCE THEOREM

We know from our earliest study of derivatives that the derivative of a constant is zero. Part (*c*) of Theorem 4.1.2 is the converse of that result; that is, a function whose derivative is zero on an interval must be constant on that interval. If we apply this to the difference of two functions, we obtain the following useful theorem.

> **4.8.3 THEOREM (*Constant Difference Theorem*)** *If $f$ and $g$ are differentiable on an interval, and if $f'(x) = g'(x)$ for all $x$ in that interval, then $f - g$ is constant on the interval; that is, there is a constant $k$ such that $f(x) - g(x) = k$ or, equivalently,*
>
> $$f(x) = g(x) + k$$
>
> *for all $x$ in the interval.*

**PROOF** Let $x_1$ and $x_2$ be any points in the interval such that $x_1 < x_2$. Since the functions $f$ and $g$ are differentiable on the interval, they are continuous on the interval. Since $[x_1, x_2]$ is a subinterval, it follows that $f$ and $g$ are continuous on $[x_1, x_2]$ and differentiable on $(x_1, x_2)$. Moreover, it follows from the basic properties of derivatives and continuity that the same is true of the function

$$F(x) = f(x) - g(x)$$

Since

$$f'(x) = f'(x) - g'(x) = 0$$

it follows from part (c) of Theorem 4.1.2 that $F(x) = f(x) - g(x)$ is constant on the interval $[x_1, x_2]$. This means that $f(x) - g(x)$ has the same value at any two points $x_1$ and $x_2$ in the interval, and this implies that $f - g$ is constant on the interval. ■

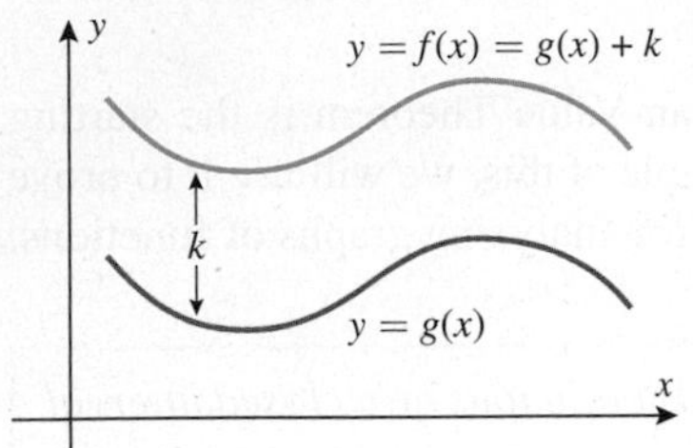


If $f'(x) = g'(x)$ on an interval, then the graphs of $f$ and $g$ are vertical translations of each other.

▲ **Figure 4.8.8**

Geometrically, the Constant Difference Theorem tells us that if $f$ and $g$ have the same derivative on an interval, then the graphs of $f$ and $g$ are vertical translations of each other over that interval (Figure 4.8.8).

▶ **Example 6** Part (c) of Theorem 4.1.2 is sometimes useful for establishing identities. For example, although we do not need calculus to prove the identity

$$\sin^{-1} x + \cos^{-1} x = \frac{\pi}{2} \qquad (-1 \le x \le 1) \tag{4}$$

it can be done by letting $f(x) = \sin^{-1} x + \cos^{-1} x$. It follows from Formulas (9) and (10) of Section 3.3 that

$$f'(x) = \frac{d}{dx}[\sin^{-1} x] + \frac{d}{dx}[\cos^{-1} x] = \frac{1}{\sqrt{1-x^2}} - \frac{1}{\sqrt{1-x^2}} = 0$$

so $f(x) = \sin^{-1} x + \cos^{-1} x$ is constant on the interval $[-1, 1]$. We can find this constant by evaluating $f$ at any convenient point in this interval. For example, using $x = 0$ we obtain

$$f(0) = \sin^{-1} 0 + \cos^{-1} 0 = 0 + \frac{\pi}{2} = \frac{\pi}{2}$$

which proves (4). ◀

## ✓ QUICK CHECK EXERCISES 4.8 (See page 247 for answers.)

**1.** Let $f(x) = x^2 - x$.

(a) An interval on which $f$ satisfies the hypotheses of Rolle's Theorem is ______.

(b) Find all values of $c$ that satisfy the conclusion of Rolle's Theorem for the function $f$ on the interval in part (a).

**2.** Use the accompanying graph of $f$ to find an interval $[a, b]$ on which Rolle's Theorem applies, and find all values of $c$ in that interval that satisfy the conclusion of the theorem.

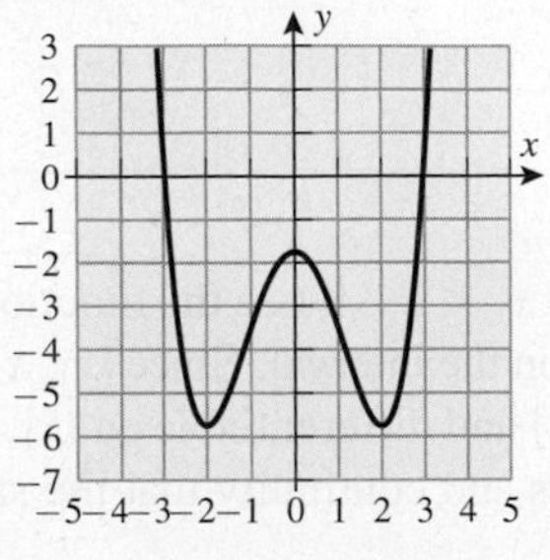


◀ **Figure Ex-2**

**3.** Let $f(x) = x^2 - x$.

(a) Find a point $b$ such that the slope of the secant line through $(0, 0)$ and $(b, f(b))$ is 1.

(b) Find all values of $c$ that satisfy the conclusion of the Mean-Value Theorem for the function $f$ on the interval $[0, b]$, where $b$ is the point found in part (a).

**4.** Use the graph of $f$ in the accompanying figure to estimate all values of $c$ that satisfy the conclusion of the Mean-Value Theorem on the interval

(a) $[0, 8]$ (b) $[0, 4]$.

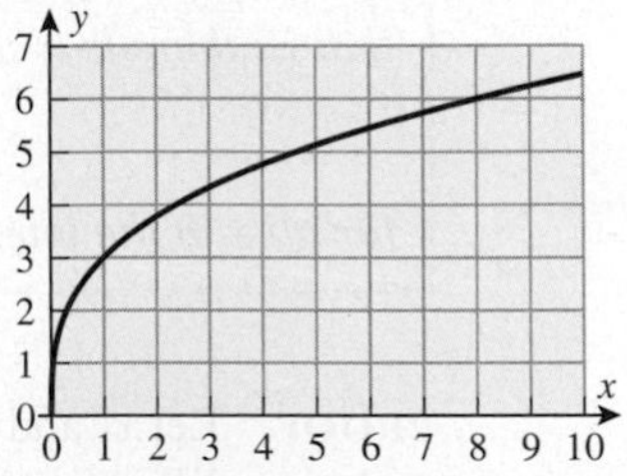


◀ **Figure Ex-4**

**5.** Find a function $f$ such that the graph of $f$ contains the point $(1, 5)$ and such that for every value of $x_0$ the tangent line to the graph of $f$ at $x_0$ is parallel to the tangent line to the graph of $y = x^2$ at $x_0$.

## EXERCISE SET 4.8 Graphing Utility

**1–4** Verify that the hypotheses of Rolle's Theorem are satisfied on the given interval, and find all values of $c$ in that interval that satisfy the conclusion of the theorem. ■

**1.** $f(x) = x^2 - 8x + 15;\ [3, 5]$

**2.** $f(x) = \frac{1}{2}x - \sqrt{x};\ [0, 4]$

**3.** $f(x) = \cos x;\ [\pi/2, 3\pi/2]$

**4.** $f(x) = \ln(4 + 2x - x^2);\ [-1, 3]$

**5–8** Verify that the hypotheses of the Mean-Value Theorem are satisfied on the given interval, and find all values of $c$ in that interval that satisfy the conclusion of the theorem. ■

**5.** $f(x) = x^2 - x;\ [-3, 5]$

**6.** $f(x) = x^3 + x - 4;\ [-1, 2]$

**7.** $f(x) = \sqrt{25 - x^2};\ [-5, 3]$

**8.** $f(x) = x - \dfrac{1}{x};\ [3, 4]$

**9.** (a) Find an interval $[a, b]$ on which

$$f(x) = x^4 + x^3 - x^2 + x - 2$$

satisfies the hypotheses of Rolle's Theorem.

(b) Generate the graph of $f'(x)$, and use it to make rough estimates of all values of $c$ in the interval obtained in part (a) that satisfy the conclusion of Rolle's Theorem.

(c) Use Newton's Method to improve on the rough estimates obtained in part (b).

**10.** Let $f(x) = x^3 - 4x$.

(a) Find the equation of the secant line through the points $(-2, f(-2))$ and $(1, f(1))$.

(b) Show that there is only one point $c$ in the interval $(-2, 1)$ that satisfies the conclusion of the Mean-Value Theorem for the secant line in part (a).

(c) Find the equation of the tangent line to the graph of $f$ at the point $(c, f(c))$.

(d) Use a graphing utility to generate the secant line in part (a) and the tangent line in part (c) in the same coordinate system, and confirm visually that the two lines seem parallel.

**11–14 True–False** Determine whether the statement is true or false. Explain your answer. ■

**11.** Rolle's Theorem says that if $f$ is a continuous function on $[a, b]$ and $f(a) = f(b)$, then there is a point between $a$ and $b$ at which the curve $y = f(x)$ has a horizontal tangent line.

**12.** If $f$ is continuous on a closed interval $[a, b]$ and differentiable on $(a, b)$, then there is a point between $a$ and $b$ at which the instantaneous rate of change of $f$ matches the average rate of change of $f$ over $[a, b]$.

**13.** The Constant Difference Theorem says that if two functions have derivatives that differ by a constant on an interval, then the functions are equal on the interval.

**14.** One application of the Mean-Value Theorem is to prove that a function with positive derivative on an interval must be increasing on that interval.

**FOCUS ON CONCEPTS**

**15.** Let $f(x) = \tan x$.

(a) Show that there is no point $c$ in the interval $(0, \pi)$ such that $f'(c) = 0$, even though $f(0) = f(\pi) = 0$.

(b) Explain why the result in part (a) does not contradict Rolle's Theorem.

**16.** Let $f(x) = x^{2/3}$, $a = -1$, and $b = 8$.

(a) Show that there is no point $c$ in $(a, b)$ such that

$$f'(c) = \frac{f(b) - f(a)}{b - a}$$

(b) Explain why the result in part (a) does not contradict the Mean-Value Theorem.

**17.** (a) Show that if $f$ is differentiable on $(-\infty, +\infty)$, and if $y = f(x)$ and $y = f'(x)$ are graphed in the same coordinate system, then between any two $x$-intercepts of $f$ there is at least one $x$-intercept of $f'$.

(b) Give some examples that illustrate this.

**18.** Review Formulas (6) and (7) in Section 2.1 and use the Mean-Value Theorem to show that if $f$ is differentiable on $(-\infty, +\infty)$, then for any interval $[x_0, x_1]$ there is at least one point in $(x_0, x_1)$ where the instantaneous rate of change of $y$ with respect to $x$ is equal to the average rate of change over the interval.

**19–21** Use the result of Exercise 18 in these exercises. ■

**19.** An automobile travels 4 mi along a straight road in 5 min. Show that the speedometer reads exactly 48 mi/h at least once during the trip.

**20.** At 11 A.M. on a certain morning the outside temperature was 76° F. At 11 P.M. that evening it had dropped to 52° F.

(a) Show that at some instant during this period the temperature was decreasing at the rate of 2° F/h.

(b) Suppose that you know the temperature reached a high of 88° F sometime between 11 A.M. and 11 P.M. Show that at some instant during this period the temperature was decreasing at a rate greater than 3° F/h.

**21.** Suppose that two runners in a 100 m dash finish in a tie. Show that they had the same velocity at least once during the race.

**22.** Use the fact that

$$\frac{d}{dx}[x \ln(2 - x)] = \ln(2 - x) - \frac{x}{2 - x}$$

to show that the equation $x = (2 - x)\ln(2 - x)$ has at least one solution in the interval $(0, 1)$.

**23.** (a) Use the Constant Difference Theorem (4.8.3) to show that if $f'(x) = g'(x)$ for all $x$ in the interval $(-\infty, +\infty)$, and if $f$ and $g$ have the same value at some point $x_0$, then $f(x) = g(x)$ for all $x$ in $(-\infty, +\infty)$.
(b) Use the result in part (a) to confirm the trigonometric identity $\sin^2 x + \cos^2 x = 1$.

**24.** (a) Use the Constant Difference Theorem (4.8.3) to show that if $f'(x) = g'(x)$ for all $x$ in $(-\infty, +\infty)$, and if $f(x_0) - g(x_0) = c$ at some point $x_0$, then

$$f(x) - g(x) = c$$

for all $x$ in $(-\infty, +\infty)$.
(b) Use the result in part (a) to show that the function

$$h(x) = (x-1)^3 - (x^2+3)(x-3)$$

is constant for all $x$ in $(-\infty, +\infty)$, and find the constant.
(c) Check the result in part (b) by multiplying out and simplifying the formula for $h(x)$.

**25.** Let $g(x) = xe^x - e^x$. Find $f(x)$ so that $f'(x) = g'(x)$ and $f(1) = 2$.

**26.** Let $g(x) = \tan^{-1} x$. Find $f(x)$ so that $f'(x) = g'(x)$ and $f(1) = 2$.

**FOCUS ON CONCEPTS**

**27.** (a) Use the Mean-Value Theorem to show that if $f$ is differentiable on an interval, and if $|f'(x)| \le M$ for all values of $x$ in the interval, then

$$|f(x) - f(y)| \le M|x - y|$$

for all values of $x$ and $y$ in the interval.
(b) Use the result in part (a) to show that

$$|\sin x - \sin y| \le |x - y|$$

for all real values of $x$ and $y$.

**28.** (a) Use the Mean-Value Theorem to show that if $f$ is differentiable on an open interval, and if $|f'(x)| \ge M$ for all values of $x$ in the interval, then

$$|f(x) - f(y)| \ge M|x - y|$$

for all values of $x$ and $y$ in the interval.
(b) Use the result in part (a) to show that

$$|\tan x - \tan y| \ge |x - y|$$

for all values of $x$ and $y$ in the interval $(-\pi/2, \pi/2)$.
(c) Use the result in part (b) to show that

$$|\tan x + \tan y| \ge |x + y|$$

for all values of $x$ and $y$ in the interval $(-\pi/2, \pi/2)$.

**29.** (a) Use the Mean-Value Theorem to show that

$$\sqrt{y} - \sqrt{x} < \frac{y - x}{2\sqrt{x}}$$

if $0 < x < y$.
(b) Use the result in part (a) to show that if $0 < x < y$, then $\sqrt{xy} < \frac{1}{2}(x + y)$.

**30.** Show that if $f$ is differentiable on an open interval and $f'(x) \ne 0$ on the interval, the equation $f(x) = 0$ can have at most one real root in the interval.

**31.** Use the result in Exercise 30 to show the following:
(a) The equation $x^3 + 4x - 1 = 0$ has exactly one real root.
(b) If $b^2 - 3ac < 0$ and if $a \ne 0$, then the equation

$$ax^3 + bx^2 + cx + d = 0$$

has exactly one real root.

**32.** Use the inequality $\sqrt{3} < 1.8$ to prove that

$$1.7 < \sqrt{3} < 1.75$$

[*Hint:* Let $f(x) = \sqrt{x}$, $a = 3$, and $b = 4$ in the Mean-Value Theorem.]

**33.** Use the Mean-Value Theorem to prove that

$$\frac{x}{1+x^2} < \tan^{-1} x < x \quad (x > 0)$$

**34.** (a) Show that if $f$ and $g$ are functions for which

$$f'(x) = g(x) \quad \text{and} \quad g'(x) = f(x)$$

for all $x$, then $f^2(x) - g^2(x)$ is a constant.
(b) Show that the function $f(x) = \frac{1}{2}(e^x + e^{-x})$ and the function $g(x) = \frac{1}{2}(e^x - e^{-x})$ have this property.

**35.** (a) Show that if $f$ and $g$ are functions for which

$$f'(x) = g(x) \quad \text{and} \quad g'(x) = -f(x)$$

for all $x$, then $f^2(x) + g^2(x)$ is a constant.
(b) Give an example of functions $f$ and $g$ with this property.

**FOCUS ON CONCEPTS**

**36.** Let $f$ and $g$ be continuous on $[a, b]$ and differentiable on $(a, b)$. Prove: If $f(a) = g(a)$ and $f(b) = g(b)$, then there is a point $c$ in $(a, b)$ such that $f'(c) = g'(c)$.

**37.** Illustrate the result in Exercise 36 by drawing an appropriate picture.

**38.** (a) Prove that if $f''(x) > 0$ for all $x$ in $(a, b)$, then $f'(x) = 0$ at most once in $(a, b)$.
(b) Give a geometric interpretation of the result in (a).

**39.** (a) Prove part (*b*) of Theorem 4.1.2.
(b) Prove part (*c*) of Theorem 4.1.2.

**40.** Use the Mean-Value Theorem to prove the following result: Let $f$ be continuous at $x_0$ and suppose that $\lim_{x \to x_0} f'(x)$ exists. Then $f$ is differentiable at $x_0$, and

$$f'(x_0) = \lim_{x \to x_0} f'(x)$$

[*Hint:* The derivative $f'(x_0)$ is given by

$$f'(x_0) = \lim_{x \to x_0} \frac{f(x) - f(x_0)}{x - x_0}$$

provided this limit exists.]

**FOCUS ON CONCEPTS**

**41.** Let
$$f(x) = \begin{cases} 3x^2, & x \le 1 \\ ax + b, & x > 1 \end{cases}$$
Find the values of $a$ and $b$ so that $f$ will be differentiable at $x = 1$.

**42.** (a) Let
$$f(x) = \begin{cases} x^2, & x \le 0 \\ x^2 + 1, & x > 0 \end{cases}$$
Show that
$$\lim_{x\to 0^-} f'(x) = \lim_{x\to 0^+} f'(x)$$
but that $f'(0)$ does not exist.

(b) Let
$$f(x) = \begin{cases} x^2, & x \le 0 \\ x^3, & x > 0 \end{cases}$$
Show that $f'(0)$ exists but $f''(0)$ does not.

**43.** Use the Mean-Value Theorem to prove the following result: The graph of a function $f$ has a point of vertical tangency at $(x_0, f(x_0))$ if $f$ is continuous at $x_0$ and $f'(x)$ approaches either $+\infty$ or $-\infty$ as $x \to x_0^+$ and as $x \to x_0^-$.

**44. Writing** Suppose that $p(x)$ is a nonconstant polynomial with zeros at $x = a$ and $x = b$. Explain how both the Extreme-Value Theorem (4.4.2) and Rolle's Theorem can be used to show that $p$ has a critical point between $a$ and $b$.

**45. Writing** Find and describe a physical situation that illustrates the Mean-Value Theorem.

**✓ QUICK CHECK ANSWERS 4.8** 1. (a) $[0, 1]$ (b) $c = \frac{1}{2}$ 2. $[-3, 3]$; $c = -2, 0, 2$ 3. (a) $b = 2$ (b) $c = 1$ 4. (a) 1.5 (b) 0.8 5. $f(x) = x^2 + 4$

## CHAPTER 4 REVIEW EXERCISES

Graphing Utility   C CAS

**1.** (a) If $x_1 < x_2$, what relationship must hold between $f(x_1)$ and $f(x_2)$ if $f$ is increasing on an interval containing $x_1$ and $x_2$? Decreasing? Constant?
(b) What condition on $f'$ ensures that $f$ is increasing on an interval $[a, b]$? Decreasing? Constant?

**2.** (a) What condition on $f'$ ensures that $f$ is concave up on an open interval? Concave down?
(b) What condition on $f''$ ensures that $f$ is concave up on an open interval? Concave down?
(c) In words, what is an inflection point of $f$?

**3–10** Find: (a) the intervals on which $f$ is increasing, (b) the intervals on which $f$ is decreasing, (c) the open intervals on which $f$ is concave up, (d) the open intervals on which $f$ is concave down, and (e) the $x$-coordinates of all inflection points. ■

**3.** $f(x) = x^2 - 5x + 6$ **4.** $f(x) = x^4 - 8x^2 + 16$

**5.** $f(x) = \dfrac{x^2}{x^2 + 2}$ **6.** $f(x) = \sqrt[3]{x + 2}$

**7.** $f(x) = x^{1/3}(x + 4)$ **8.** $f(x) = x^{4/3} - x^{1/3}$

**9.** $f(x) = 1/e^{x^2}$ **10.** $f(x) = \tan^{-1} x^2$

**11–14** Analyze the trigonometric function $f$ over the specified interval, stating where $f$ is increasing, decreasing, concave up, and concave down, and stating the $x$-coordinates of all inflection points. Confirm that your results are consistent with the graph of $f$ generated with a graphing utility. ■

**11.** $f(x) = \cos x$; $[0, 2\pi]$

**12.** $f(x) = \tan x$; $(-\pi/2, \pi/2)$

**13.** $f(x) = \sin x \cos x$; $[0, \pi]$

**14.** $f(x) = \cos^2 x - 2 \sin x$; $[0, 2\pi]$

**15.** In each part, sketch a continuous curve $y = f(x)$ with the stated properties.
(a) $f(2) = 4$, $f'(2) = 1$, $f''(x) < 0$ for $x < 2$, $f''(x) > 0$ for $x > 2$
(b) $f(2) = 4$, $f''(x) > 0$ for $x < 2$, $f''(x) < 0$ for $x > 2$, $\lim_{x\to 2^-} f'(x) = +\infty$, $\lim_{x\to 2^+} f'(x) = +\infty$
(c) $f(2) = 4$, $f''(x) < 0$ for $x \ne 2$, $\lim_{x\to 2^-} f'(x) = 1$, $\lim_{x\to 2^+} f'(x) = -1$

**16.** In parts (a)–(d), the graph of a polynomial with degree at most 6 is given. Find equations for polynomials that produce graphs with these shapes, and check your answers with a graphing utility.

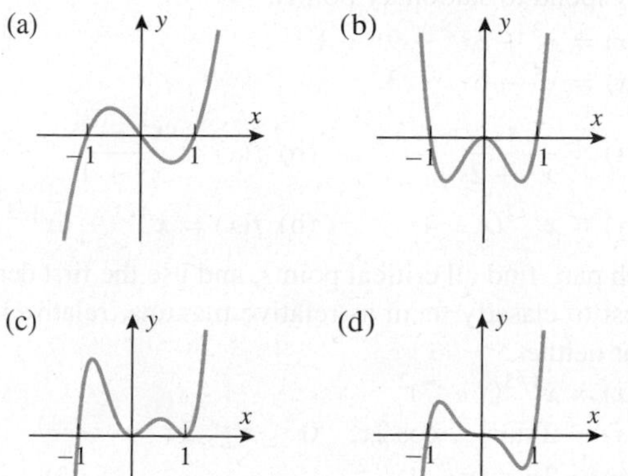

**17.** For a general quadratic polynomial

$$f(x) = ax^2 + bx + c \quad (a \neq 0)$$

find conditions on $a$, $b$, and $c$ to ensure that $f$ is always increasing or always decreasing on $[0, +\infty)$.

**18.** For the general cubic polynomial

$$f(x) = ax^3 + bx^2 + cx + d \quad (a \neq 0)$$

find conditions on $a$, $b$, $c$, and $d$ to ensure that $f$ is always increasing or always decreasing on $(-\infty, +\infty)$.

**19.** Use a graphing utility to estimate the value of $x$ at which

$$f(x) = \frac{2^x}{1 + 2^{x+1}}$$

is increasing most rapidly.

**20.** Prove that for any positive constants $a$ and $k$, the graph of

$$y = \frac{a^x}{1 + a^{x+k}}$$

has an inflection point at $x = -k$.

**21.** (a) Where on the graph of $y = f(x)$ would you expect $y$ to be increasing or decreasing most rapidly with respect to $x$?
(b) In words, what is a relative extremum?
(c) State a procedure for determining where the relative extrema of $f$ occur.

**22.** Determine whether the statement is true or false. If it is false, give an example for which the statement fails.
(a) If $f$ has a relative maximum at $x_0$, then $f(x_0)$ is the largest value that $f(x)$ can have.
(b) If the largest value for $f$ on the interval $(a, b)$ is at $x_0$, then $f$ has a relative maximum at $x_0$.
(c) A function $f$ has a relative extremum at each of its critical points.

**23.** (a) According to the first derivative test, what conditions ensure that $f$ has a relative maximum at $x_0$? A relative minimum?
(b) According to the second derivative test, what conditions ensure that $f$ has a relative maximum at $x_0$? A relative minimum?

**24–26** Locate the critical points and identify which critical points correspond to stationary points. ■

**24.** (a) $f(x) = x^3 + 3x^2 - 9x + 1$
(b) $f(x) = x^4 - 6x^2 - 3$

**25.** (a) $f(x) = \dfrac{x}{x^2 + 2}$ (b) $f(x) = \dfrac{x^2 - 3}{x^2 + 1}$

**26.** (a) $f(x) = x^{1/3}(x - 4)$ (b) $f(x) = x^{4/3} - 6x^{1/3}$

**27.** In each part, find all critical points, and use the first derivative test to classify them as relative maxima, relative minima, or neither.
(a) $f(x) = x^{1/3}(x - 7)^2$
(b) $f(x) = 2\sin x - \cos 2x, \quad 0 \leq x \leq 2\pi$
(c) $f(x) = 3x - (x - 1)^{3/2}$

**28.** In each part, find all critical points, and use the second derivative test (where possible) to classify them as relative maxima, relative minima, or neither.
(a) $f(x) = x^{-1/2} + \frac{1}{9}x^{1/2}$
(b) $f(x) = x^2 + 8/x$
(c) $f(x) = \sin^2 x - \cos x, \quad 0 \leq x \leq 2\pi$

**29–36** Give a graph of the function $f$, and identify the limits as $x \to \pm\infty$, as well as locations of all relative extrema, inflection points, and asymptotes (as appropriate). ■

**29.** $f(x) = x^4 - 3x^3 + 3x^2 + 1$

**30.** $f(x) = x^5 - 4x^4 + 4x^3$

**31.** $f(x) = \tan(x^2 + 1)$ **32.** $f(x) = x - \cos x$

**33.** $f(x) = \dfrac{x^2}{x^2 + 2x + 5}$ **34.** $f(x) = \dfrac{25 - 9x^2}{x^3}$

**35.** $f(x) = \begin{cases} \frac{1}{2}x^2, & x \leq 0 \\ -x^2, & x > 0 \end{cases}$

**36.** $f(x) = (1 + x)^{2/3}(3 - x)^{1/3}$

**37–44** Use any method to find the relative extrema of the function $f$. ■

**37.** $f(x) = x^3 + 5x - 2$ **38.** $f(x) = x^4 - 2x^2 + 7$

**39.** $f(x) = x^{4/5}$ **40.** $f(x) = 2x + x^{2/3}$

**41.** $f(x) = \dfrac{x^2}{x^2 + 1}$ **42.** $f(x) = \dfrac{x}{x + 2}$

**43.** $f(x) = \ln(1 + x^2)$ **44.** $f(x) = x^2 e^x$

**45–46** When using a graphing utility, important features of a graph may be missed if the viewing window is not chosen appropriately. This is illustrated in Exercises 45 and 46. ■

**45.** (a) Generate the graph of $f(x) = \frac{1}{3}x^3 - \frac{1}{400}x$ over the interval $[-5, 5]$, and make a conjecture about the locations and nature of all critical points.
(b) Find the exact locations of all the critical points, and classify them as relative maxima, relative minima, or neither.
(c) Confirm the results in part (b) by graphing $f$ over an appropriate interval.

**46.** (a) Generate the graph of

$$f(x) = \tfrac{1}{5}x^5 - \tfrac{7}{8}x^4 + \tfrac{1}{3}x^3 + \tfrac{7}{2}x^2 - 6x$$

over the interval $[-5, 5]$, and make a conjecture about the locations and nature of all critical points.
(b) Find the exact locations of all the critical points, and classify them as relative maxima, relative minima, or neither.
(c) Confirm the results in part (b) by graphing portions of $f$ over appropriate intervals. [*Note:* It will not be possible to find a single window in which all of the critical points are discernible.]

**47.** (a) Use a graphing utility to generate the graphs of $y = x$ and $y = (x^3 - 8)/(x^2 + 1)$ together over the interval $[-5, 5]$, and make a conjecture about the relationship between the two graphs.
(b) Confirm your conjecture in part (a).

**48.** Use implicit differentiation to show that a function defined implicitly by $\sin x + \cos y = 2y$ has a critical point whenever $\cos x = 0$. Then use either the first or second derivative test to classify these critical points as relative maxima or minima.

**49.** Let

$$f(x) = \frac{2x^3 + x^2 - 15x + 7}{(2x - 1)(3x^2 + x - 1)}$$

Graph $y = f(x)$, and find the equations of all horizontal and vertical asymptotes. Explain why there is no vertical asymptote at $x = \frac{1}{2}$, even though the denominator of $f$ is zero at that point.

**50.** Let

$$f(x) = \frac{x^5 - x^4 - 3x^3 + 2x + 4}{x^7 - 2x^6 - 3x^5 + 6x^4 + 4x - 8}$$

(a) Use a CAS to factor the numerator and denominator of $f$, and use the results to determine the locations of all vertical asymptotes.
(b) Confirm that your answer is consistent with the graph of $f$.

**51.** (a) What inequality must $f(x)$ satisfy for the function $f$ to have an absolute maximum on an interval $I$ at $x_0$?
(b) What inequality must $f(x)$ satisfy for $f$ to have an absolute minimum on an interval $I$ at $x_0$?
(c) What is the difference between an absolute extremum and a relative extremum?

**52.** According to the Extreme-Value Theorem, what conditions on a function $f$ and a given interval guarantee that $f$ will have both an absolute maximum and an absolute minimum on the interval?

**53.** In each part, determine whether the statement is true or false, and justify your answer.
(a) If $f$ is differentiable on the open interval $(a, b)$, and if $f$ has an absolute extremum on that interval, then it must occur at a stationary point of $f$.
(b) If $f$ is continuous on the open interval $(a, b)$, and if $f$ has an absolute extremum on that interval, then it must occur at a stationary point of $f$.

**54–56** In each part, find the absolute minimum $m$ and the absolute maximum $M$ of $f$ on the given interval (if they exist), and state where the absolute extrema occur. ■

**54.** (a) $f(x) = 1/x$; $[-2, -1]$
(b) $f(x) = x^3 - x^4$; $\left[-1, \frac{3}{2}\right]$
(c) $f(x) = x - \tan x$; $[-\pi/4, \pi/4]$
(d) $f(x) = -|x^2 - 2x|$; $[1, 3]$

**55.** (a) $f(x) = x^2 - 3x - 1$; $(-\infty, +\infty)$
(b) $f(x) = x^3 - 3x - 2$; $(-\infty, +\infty)$
(c) $f(x) = e^x/x^2$; $(0, +\infty)$
(d) $f(x) = x^x$; $(0, +\infty)$

**56.** (a) $f(x) = 2x^5 - 5x^4 + 7$; $(-1, 3)$
(b) $f(x) = (3 - x)/(2 - x)$; $(0, 2)$
(c) $f(x) = 2x/(x^2 + 3)$; $(0, 2]$
(d) $f(x) = x^2(x - 2)^{1/3}$; $(0, 3]$

**57.** In each part, use a graphing utility to estimate the absolute maximum and minimum values of $f$, if any, on the stated interval, and then use calculus methods to find the exact values.
(a) $f(x) = (x^2 - 1)^2$; $(-\infty, +\infty)$
(b) $f(x) = x/(x^2 + 1)$; $[0, +\infty)$
(c) $f(x) = 2\sec x - \tan x$; $[0, \pi/4]$
(d) $f(x) = x/2 + \ln(x^2 + 1)$; $[-4, 0]$

**58.** Prove that $x \le \sin^{-1} x$ for all $x$ in $[0, 1]$.

**59.** Let

$$f(x) = \frac{x^3 + 2}{x^4 + 1}$$

(a) Generate the graph of $y = f(x)$, and use the graph to make rough estimates of the coordinates of the absolute extrema.
(b) Use a CAS to solve the equation $f'(x) = 0$ and then use it to make more accurate approximations of the coordinates in part (a).

**60.** A church window consists of a blue semicircular section surmounting a clear rectangular section as shown in the accompanying figure. The blue glass lets through half as much light per unit area as the clear glass. Find the radius $r$ of the window that admits the most light if the perimeter of the entire window is to be $P$ feet.

**61.** Find the dimensions of the rectangle of maximum area that can be inscribed inside the ellipse $(x/4)^2 + (y/3)^2 = 1$ (see the accompanying figure).

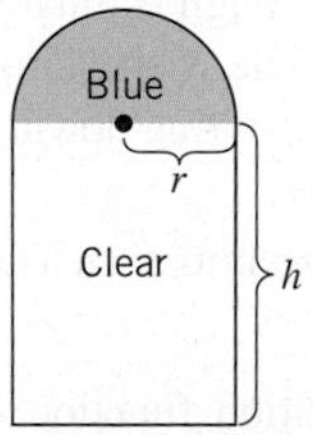


▲ **Figure Ex-60**

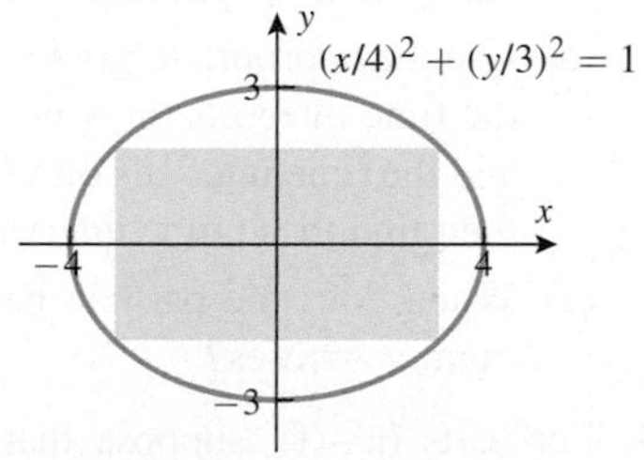


▲ **Figure Ex-61**

**62.** As shown in the accompanying figure on the next page, suppose that a boat enters the river at the point $(1, 0)$ and maintains a heading toward the origin. As a result of the strong current, the boat follows the path

$$y = \frac{x^{10/3} - 1}{2x^{2/3}}$$

where $x$ and $y$ are in miles.
(a) Graph the path taken by the boat.
(b) Can the boat reach the origin? If not, discuss its fate and find how close it comes to the origin.

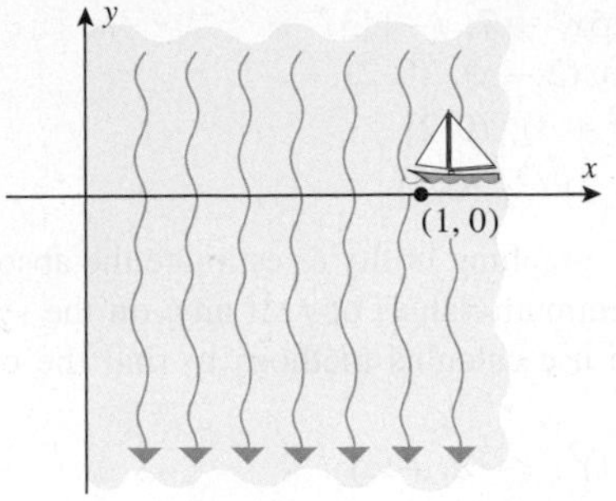


◀ Figure Ex-62

**63.** A sheet of cardboard 12 in square is used to make an open box by cutting squares of equal size from the four corners and folding up the sides. What size squares should be cut to obtain a box with largest possible volume?

**64.** Is it true or false that a particle in rectilinear motion is speeding up when its velocity is increasing and slowing down when its velocity is decreasing? Justify your answer.

**65.** (a) Can an object in rectilinear motion reverse direction if its acceleration is constant? Justify your answer using a velocity versus time curve.

(b) Can an object in rectilinear motion have increasing speed and decreasing acceleration? Justify your answer using a velocity versus time curve.

**66.** Suppose that the position function of a particle in rectilinear motion is given by the formula $s(t) = t/(2t^2 + 8)$ for $t \geq 0$.

(a) Use a graphing utility to generate the position, velocity, and acceleration versus time curves.

(b) Use the appropriate graph to make a rough estimate of the time when the particle reverses direction, and then find that time exactly.

(c) Find the position, velocity, and acceleration at the instant when the particle reverses direction.

(d) Use the appropriate graphs to make rough estimates of the time intervals on which the particle is speeding up and the time intervals on which it is slowing down, and then find those time intervals exactly.

(e) When does the particle have its maximum and minimum velocities?

**67.** For parts (a)–(f), suppose that the position function of a particle in rectilinear motion is given by the formula

$$s(t) = \frac{t^2 + 1}{t^4 + 1}, \quad t \geq 0$$

(a) Use a CAS to find simplified formulas for the velocity function $v(t)$ and the acceleration function $a(t)$.

(b) Graph the position, velocity, and acceleration versus time curves.

(c) Use the appropriate graph to make a rough estimate of the time at which the particle is farthest from the origin and its distance from the origin at that time.

(d) Use the appropriate graph to make a rough estimate of the time interval during which the particle is moving in the positive direction.

(e) Use the appropriate graphs to make rough estimates of the time intervals during which the particle is speeding up and the time intervals during which it is slowing down.

(f) Use the appropriate graph to make a rough estimate of the maximum speed of the particle and the time at which the maximum speed occurs.

**68.** Draw an appropriate picture, and describe the basic idea of Newton's Method without using any formulas.

**69.** Use Newton's Method to approximate all three solutions of $x^3 - 4x + 1 = 0$.

**70.** Use Newton's Method to approximate the smallest positive solution of $\sin x + \cos x = 0$.

**71.** Use a graphing utility to determine the number of times the curve $y = x^3$ intersects the curve $y = (x/2) - 1$. Then apply Newton's Method to approximate the $x$-coordinates of all intersections.

**72.** According to ***Kepler's law***, the planets in our solar system move in elliptical orbits around the Sun. If a planet's closest approach to the Sun occurs at time $t = 0$, then the distance $r$ from the center of the planet to the center of the Sun at some later time $t$ can be determined from the equation

$$r = a(1 - e\cos\phi)$$

where $a$ is the average distance between centers, $e$ is a positive constant that measures the "flatness" of the elliptical orbit, and $\phi$ is the solution of *Kepler's equation*

$$\frac{2\pi t}{T} = \phi - e\sin\phi$$

in which $T$ is the time it takes for one complete orbit of the planet. Estimate the distance from the Earth to the Sun when $t = 90$ days. [First find $\phi$ from Kepler's equation, and then use this value of $\phi$ to find the distance. Use $a = 150 \times 10^6$ km, $e = 0.0167$, and $T = 365$ days.]

**73.** Using the formulas in Exercise 72, find the distance from the planet Mars to the Sun when $t = 1$ year. For Mars use $a = 228 \times 10^6$ km, $e = 0.0934$, and $T = 1.88$ years.

**74.** Suppose that $f$ is continuous on the closed interval $[a, b]$ and differentiable on the open interval $(a, b)$, and suppose that $f(a) = f(b)$. Is it true or false that $f$ must have at least one stationary point in $(a, b)$? Justify your answer.

**75.** In each part, determine whether all of the hypotheses of Rolle's Theorem are satisfied on the stated interval. If not, state which hypotheses fail; if so, find all values of $c$ guaranteed in the conclusion of the theorem.

(a) $f(x) = \sqrt{4 - x^2}$ on $[-2, 2]$

(b) $f(x) = x^{2/3} - 1$ on $[-1, 1]$

(c) $f(x) = \sin(x^2)$ on $[0, \sqrt{\pi}]$

**76.** In each part, determine whether all of the hypotheses of the Mean-Value Theorem are satisfied on the stated interval. If not, state which hypotheses fail; if so, find all values of $c$ guaranteed in the conclusion of the theorem.

(a) $f(x) = |x - 1|$ on $[-2, 2]$

*(cont.)*

(b) $f(x) = \dfrac{x+1}{x-1}$ on $[2, 3]$

(c) $f(x) = \begin{cases} 3 - x^2 & \text{if } x \le 1 \\ 2/x & \text{if } x > 1 \end{cases}$ on $[0, 2]$

**77.** Use the fact that

$$\frac{d}{dx}(x^6 - 2x^2 + x) = 6x^5 - 4x + 1$$

to show that the equation $6x^5 - 4x + 1 = 0$ has at least one solution in the interval $(0, 1)$.

**78.** Let $g(x) = x^3 - 4x + 6$. Find $f(x)$ so that $f'(x) = g'(x)$ and $f(1) = 2$.

## CHAPTER 4 MAKING CONNECTIONS

**1.** Suppose that $g(x)$ is a function that is defined and differentiable for all real numbers $x$ and that $g(x)$ has the following properties:

(i) $g(0) = 2$ and $g'(0) = -\frac{2}{3}$.

(ii) $g(4) = 3$ and $g'(4) = 3$.

(iii) $g(x)$ is concave up for $x < 4$ and concave down for $x > 4$.

(iv) $g(x) \ge -10$ for all $x$.

Use these properties to answer the following questions.

(a) How many zeros does $g$ have?

(b) How many zeros does $g'$ have?

(c) Exactly one of the following limits is possible:

$$\lim_{x\to+\infty} g'(x) = -5, \quad \lim_{x\to+\infty} g'(x) = 0, \quad \lim_{x\to+\infty} g'(x) = 5$$

Identify which of these results is possible and draw a rough sketch of the graph of such a function $g(x)$. Explain why the other two results are impossible.

**2.** The two graphs in the accompanying figure depict a function $r(x)$ and its derivative $r'(x)$.

(a) Approximate the coordinates of each inflection point on the graph of $y = r(x)$.

(b) Suppose that $f(x)$ is a function that is continuous everywhere and whose *derivative* satisfies

$$f'(x) = (x^2 - 4) \cdot r(x)$$

What are the critical points for $f(x)$? At each critical point, identify whether $f(x)$ has a (relative) maximum, minimum, or neither a maximum or minimum. Approximate $f''(1)$.

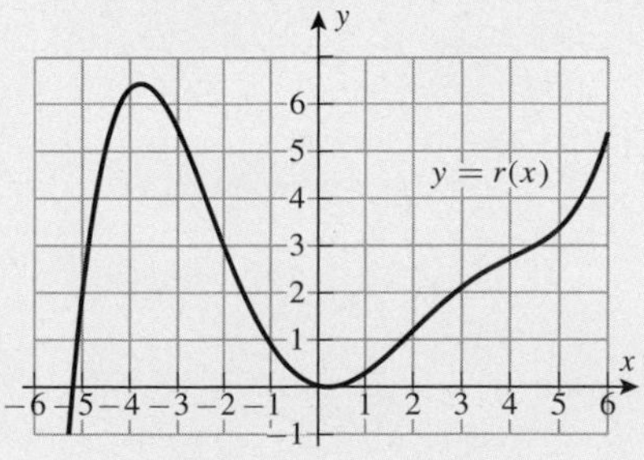


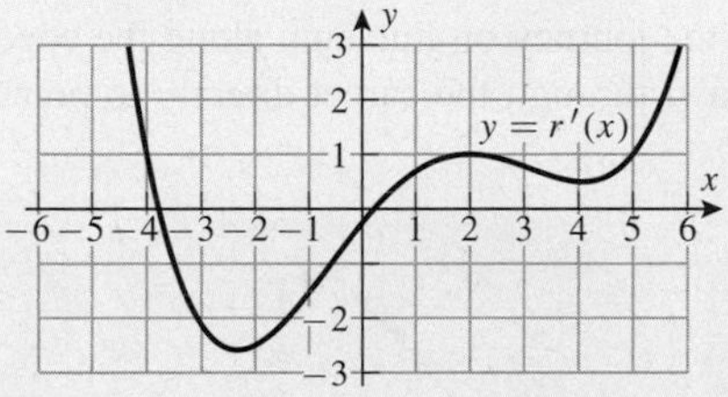


◀ **Figure Ex-2**

**3.** With the function $r(x)$ as provided in Exercise 2, let $g(x)$ be a function that is continuous everywhere such that $g'(x) = x - r(x)$. For which values of $x$ does $g(x)$ have an inflection point?

**4.** Suppose that $f$ is a function whose derivative is continuous everywhere. Assume that there exists a real number $c$ such that when Newton's Method is applied to $f$, the inequality

$$|x_n - c| < \frac{1}{n}$$

is satisfied for all values of $n = 1, 2, 3, \ldots$.

(a) Explain why

$$|x_{n+1} - x_n| < \frac{2}{n}$$

for all values of $n = 1, 2, 3, \ldots$.

(b) Show that there exists a positive constant $M$ such that

$$|f(x_n)| \le M|x_{n+1} - x_n| < \frac{2M}{n}$$

for all values of $n = 1, 2, 3, \ldots$.

(c) Prove that if $f(c) \ne 0$, then there exists a positive integer $N$ such that

$$\frac{|f(c)|}{2} < |f(x_n)|$$

if $n > N$. [*Hint:* Argue that $f(x) \to f(c)$ as $x \to c$ and then apply Definition 1.4.1 with $\epsilon = \frac{1}{2}|f(c)|$.]

(d) What can you conclude from parts (b) and (c)?

**5.** What are the important elements in the argument suggested by Exercise 4? Can you extend this argument to a wider collection of functions?

**6.** A bug crawling on a linoleum floor along the edge of a plush carpet encounters an irregularity in the form of a 2 in by 3 in rectangular section of carpet that juts out into the linoleum as illustrated in Figure Ex-6a on the next page.

◀ Figure Ex-6a

The bug crawls at 0.7 in/s on the linoleum, but only at 0.3 in/s through the carpet, and its goal is to travel from point $A$ to point $B$. Four possible routes from $A$ to $B$ are as follows: (i) crawl on linoleum along the edge of the carpet; (ii) crawl through the carpet to a point on the wider side of the rectangle, and finish the journey on linoleum along the edge of the carpet; (iii) crawl through the carpet to a point on the shorter side of the rectangle, and finish the journey on linoleum along the edge of the carpet; or (iv) crawl through the carpet directly to point $B$. (See Figure Ex-6b.)

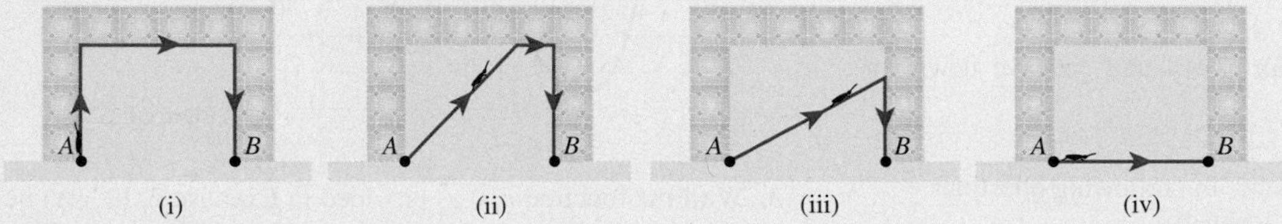

▲ Figure Ex-6b

(a) Calculate the times it would take the bug to crawl from $A$ to $B$ via routes (i) and (iv).

(b) Suppose the bug follows route (ii) and use $x$ to represent the total distance the bug crawls on linoleum. Identify the appropriate interval for $x$ in this case, and determine the shortest time for the bug to complete the journey using route (ii).

(c) Suppose the bug follows route (iii) and again use $x$ to represent the total distance the bug crawls on linoleum. Identify the appropriate interval for $x$ in this case, and determine the shortest time for the bug to complete the journey using route (iii).

(d) Which of routes (i), (ii), (iii), or (iv) is quickest? What is the shortest time for the bug to complete the journey?

# 5

# INTEGRATION

HelleM/Shutterstock

*If a dragster moves with varying velocity over a certain time interval, it is possible to find the distance it travels during that time interval using techniques of calculus.*

In this chapter we will introduce "integration," a process motivated by the problem of computing the area of plane regions. After an informal overview of the problem, we will discuss a surprising relationship between integration and differentiation that is known as the Fundamental Theorem of Calculus. We will then apply integration to continue our study of rectilinear motion and to define the "average value" of a function. We conclude the chapter by studying functions that can be defined using integration, with a focus on the natural logarithm function.

## 5.1 AN OVERVIEW OF THE AREA PROBLEM

*In this introductory section we will consider the problem of calculating areas of plane regions with curvilinear boundaries. All of the results in this section will be reexamined in more detail later in this chapter. Our purpose here is simply to introduce and motivate the fundamental concepts.*

### THE AREA PROBLEM

Formulas for the areas of polygons, such as squares, rectangles, triangles, and trapezoids, were well known in many early civilizations. However, the problem of finding formulas for regions with curved boundaries (a circle being the simplest example) caused difficulties for early mathematicians.

The first real progress in dealing with the general area problem was made by the Greek mathematician Archimedes, who obtained areas of regions bounded by circular arcs, parabolas, spirals, and various other curves using an ingenious procedure that was later called the *method of exhaustion*. The method, when applied to a circle, consists of inscribing a succession of regular polygons in the circle and allowing the number of sides to increase indefinitely (Figure 5.1.1). As the number of sides increases, the polygons tend to "exhaust" the region inside the circle, and the areas of the polygons become better and better approximations of the exact area of the circle.

To see how this works numerically, let $A(n)$ denote the area of a regular $n$-sided polygon inscribed in a circle of radius 1. Table 5.1.1 shows the values of $A(n)$ for various choices of $n$. Note that for large values of $n$ the area $A(n)$ appears to be close to $\pi$ (square units), as one would expect. This suggests that for a circle of radius 1, the method of exhaustion is equivalent to an equation of the form

$$\lim_{n\to\infty} A(n) = \pi$$

Since Greek mathematicians were suspicious of the concept of "infinity," they avoided its use in mathematical arguments. As a result, computation of area using the method of exhaustion was a very cumbersome procedure. It remained for Newton and Leibniz to obtain a general method for finding areas that explicitly used the notion of a limit. We will discuss their method in the context of the following problem.

**Table 5.1.1**

| $n$ | $A(n)$ |
|---|---|
| 100 | 3.13952597647 |
| 200 | 3.14107590781 |
| 300 | 3.14136298250 |
| 400 | 3.14146346236 |
| 500 | 3.14150997084 |
| 1000 | 3.14157198278 |
| 2000 | 3.14158748588 |
| 3000 | 3.14159035683 |
| 4000 | 3.14159136166 |
| 5000 | 3.14159182676 |
| 10,000 | 3.14159244688 |

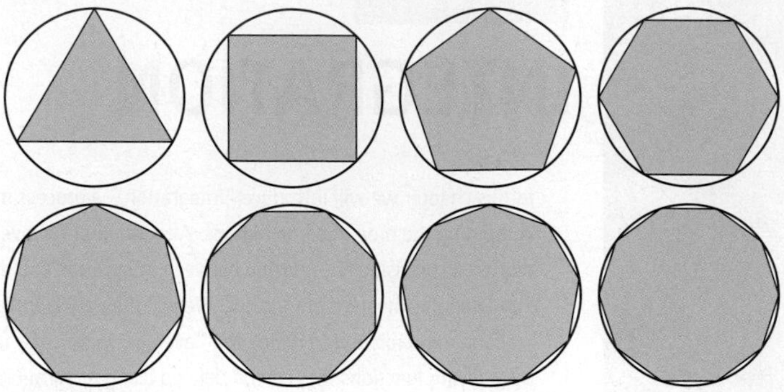

▲ **Figure 5.1.1**

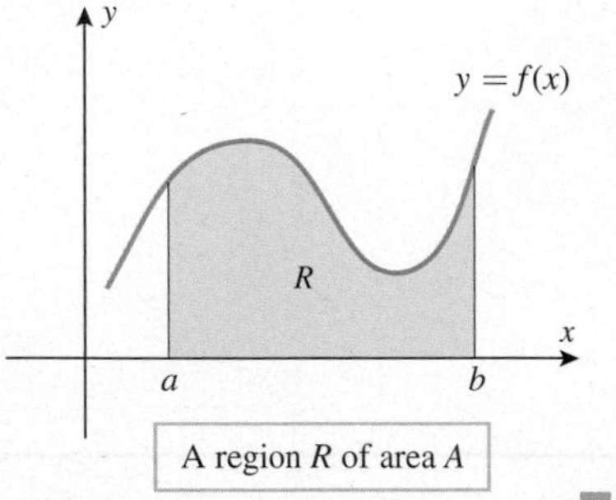


▲ **Figure 5.1.2**

**5.1.1 THE AREA PROBLEM** Given a function $f$ that is continuous and nonnegative on an interval $[a, b]$, find the area $A$ of the region $R$ that lies between the graph of $f$ and the interval $[a, b]$ on the $x$-axis (Figure 5.1.2).

## THE RECTANGLE METHOD FOR FINDING AREAS

One approach to the area problem is to use Archimedes' method of exhaustion in the following way:

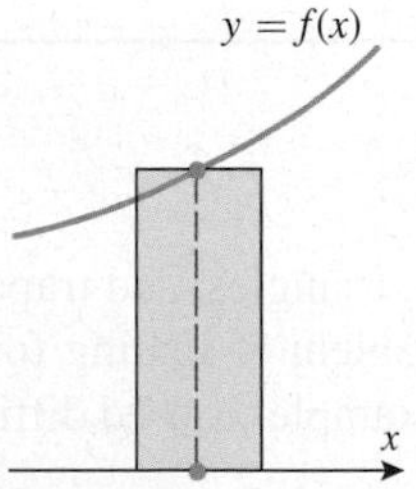


▲ **Figure 5.1.3**

- Divide the interval $[a, b]$ into $n$ equal subintervals, and over each subinterval construct a rectangle that extends from the $x$-axis to any point on the curve $y = f(x)$ that is above the subinterval. In Figure 5.1.3 this point is above the center of the subinterval.
- For each $n$, the total area $A(n)$ of the rectangles can be viewed as an *approximation* to the area $A$. As $n$ increases, these approximations will get better and better and will approach $A$ as a limit

$$A = \lim_{n \to +\infty} A_n$$

(Figure 5.1.4). We will call this the ***rectangle method*** for computing $A$.

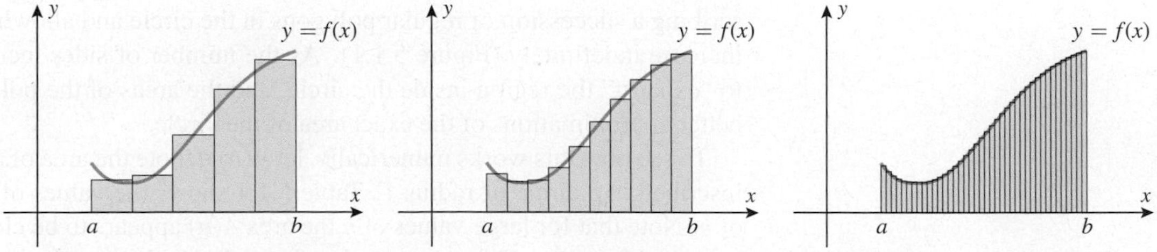


▲ **Figure 5.1.4**

Logically speaking, we cannot really talk about computing areas without a precise mathematical definition of the term "area." Later in this chapter we will give such a definition, but for now we will treat the concept intuitively.

To illustrate this idea, we will use the rectangle method to approximate the area under the curve $y = x^2$ over the interval $[0, 1]$ (Figure 5.1.5). We will begin by dividing the interval $[0, 1]$ into $n$ equal subintervals of length $1/n$; the endpoints of the subintervals occur at

$$0, \ \frac{1}{n}, \ \frac{2}{n}, \ \frac{3}{n}, \ldots, \ \frac{n-1}{n}, \ 1$$

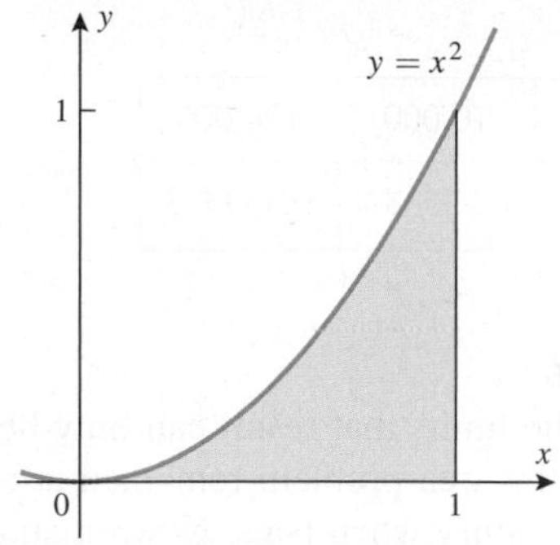


▲ Figure 5.1.5

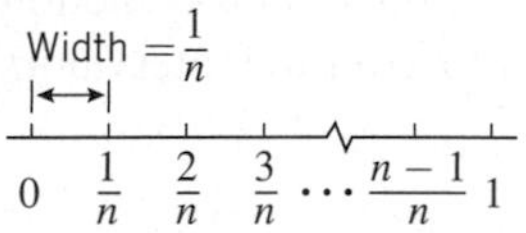


Subdivision of [0, 1] into $n$ subintervals of equal length

▲ Figure 5.1.6

(Figure 5.1.6). We will construct a rectangle over each of these subintervals whose height is the value of the function $f(x) = x^2$ at the right endpoint in the subinterval. The heights of our rectangles will be

$$\left(\frac{1}{n}\right)^2, \left(\frac{2}{n}\right)^2, \left(\frac{3}{n}\right)^2, \ldots, 1^2$$

and since each rectangle has a base of width $1/n$, the total area $A_n$ of the $n$ rectangles will be

$$A_n = \left[\left(\frac{1}{n}\right)^2 + \left(\frac{2}{n}\right)^2 + \left(\frac{3}{n}\right)^2 + \cdots + 1^2\right]\left(\frac{1}{n}\right) \tag{1}$$

For example, if $n = 4$, then the total area of the four approximating rectangles would be

$$A_4 = \left[\left(\tfrac{1}{4}\right)^2 + \left(\tfrac{2}{4}\right)^2 + \left(\tfrac{3}{4}\right)^2 + 1^2\right]\left(\tfrac{1}{4}\right) = \tfrac{15}{32} = 0.46875$$

Table 5.1.2 shows the result of evaluating (1) on a computer for some increasingly large values of $n$. These computations suggest that the exact area is close to $\frac{1}{3}$. Later in this chapter we will prove that this area is exactly $\frac{1}{3}$ by showing that

$$\lim_{n\to\infty} A_n = \tfrac{1}{3}$$

**Archimedes (287 B.C.–212 B.C.)** Greek mathematician and scientist. Born in Syracuse, Sicily, Archimedes was the son of the astronomer Pheidias and possibly related to Heiron II, king of Syracuse. Most of the facts about his life come from the Roman biographer, Plutarch, who inserted a few tantalizing pages about him in the massive biography of the Roman soldier, Marcellus. In the words of one writer, "the account of Archimedes is slipped like a tissue-thin shaving of ham in a bull-choking sandwich."

Archimedes ranks with Newton and Gauss as one of the three greatest mathematicians who ever lived, and he is certainly the greatest mathematician of antiquity. His mathematical work is so modern in spirit and technique that it is barely distinguishable from that of a seventeenth-century mathematician, yet it was all done without benefit of algebra or a convenient number system. Among his mathematical achievements, Archimedes developed a general method (exhaustion) for finding areas and volumes, and he used the method to find areas bounded by parabolas and spirals and to find volumes of cylinders, paraboloids, and segments of spheres. He gave a procedure for approximating $\pi$ and bounded its value between $3\frac{10}{71}$ and $3\frac{1}{7}$. In spite of the limitations of the Greek numbering system, he devised methods for finding square roots and invented a method based on the Greek myriad (10,000) for representing numbers as large as 1 followed by 80 million billion zeros.

Of all his mathematical work, Archimedes was most proud of his discovery of a method for finding the volume of a sphere—he showed that the volume of a sphere is two-thirds the volume of the smallest cylinder that can contain it. At his request, the figure of a sphere and cylinder was engraved on his tombstone.

In addition to mathematics, Archimedes worked extensively in mechanics and hydrostatics. Nearly every schoolchild knows Archimedes as the absent-minded scientist who, on realizing that a floating object displaces its weight of liquid, leaped from his bath and ran naked through the streets of Syracuse shouting, "Eureka, Eureka!"—(meaning, "I have found it!"). Archimedes actually created the discipline of hydrostatics and used it to find equilibrium positions for various floating bodies. He laid down the fundamental postulates of mechanics, discovered the laws of levers, and calculated centers of gravity for various flat surfaces and solids. In the excitement of discovering the mathematical laws of the lever, he is said to have declared, "Give me a place to stand and I will move the earth."

Although Archimedes was apparently more interested in pure mathematics than its applications, he was an engineering genius. During the second Punic war, when Syracuse was attacked by the Roman fleet under the command of Marcellus, it was reported by Plutarch that Archimedes' military inventions held the fleet at bay for three years. He invented super catapults that showered the Romans with rocks weighing a quarter ton or more, and fearsome mechanical devices with iron "beaks and claws" that reached over the city walls, grasped the ships, and spun them against the rocks. After the first repulse, Marcellus called Archimedes a "geometrical Briareus (a hundred-armed mythological monster) who uses our ships like cups to ladle water from the sea."

Eventually the Roman army was victorious and contrary to Marcellus' specific orders the 75-year-old Archimedes was killed by a Roman soldier. According to one report of the incident, the soldier cast a shadow across the sand in which Archimedes was working on a mathematical problem. When the annoyed Archimedes yelled, "Don't disturb my circles," the soldier flew into a rage and cut the old man down.

Although there is no known likeness or statue of this great man, nine works of Archimedes have survived to the present day. Especially important is his treatise, *The Method of Mechanical Theorems*, which was part of a palimpsest found in Constantinople in 1906. In this treatise Archimedes explains how he made some of his discoveries, using reasoning that anticipated ideas of the integral calculus. Thought to be lost, the Archimedes palimpsest later resurfaced in 1998, when it was purchased by an anonymous private collector for two million dollars.

[*Image: Archimedes Siracus. Line engraving by Remondini/Wellcome Library, London*]

**TECHNOLOGY MASTERY**

Use a calculating utility to compute the value of $A_{10}$ in Table 5.1.2. Some calculating utilities have special commands for computing sums such as that in (1) for any specified value of $n$. If your utility has this feature, use it to compute $A_{100}$ as well.

**Table 5.1.2**

| $n$ | 4 | 10 | 100 | 1000 | 10,000 | 100,000 |
|---|---|---|---|---|---|---|
| $A_n$ | 0.468750 | 0.385000 | 0.338350 | 0.333834 | 0.333383 | 0.333338 |

## THE ANTIDERIVATIVE METHOD FOR FINDING AREAS

Although the rectangle method is appealing intuitively, the limits that result can only be evaluated in certain cases. For this reason, progress on the area problem remained at a rudimentary level until the latter part of the seventeenth century when Isaac Newton and Gottfried Leibniz independently discovered a fundamental relationship between areas and derivatives. Briefly stated, they showed that if $f$ is a nonnegative continuous function on the interval $[a, b]$, and if $A(x)$ denotes the area under the graph of $f$ over the interval $[a, x]$, where $x$ is any point in the interval $[a, b]$ (Figure 5.1.7), then

$$A'(x) = f(x) \tag{2}$$

The following example confirms Formula (2) in a simple case.

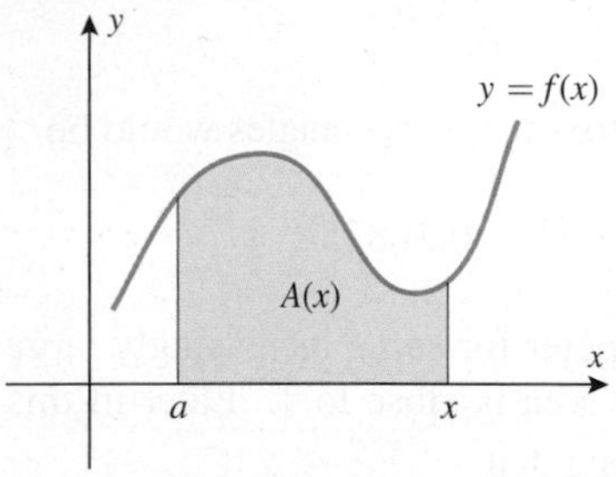


▲ **Figure 5.1.7**

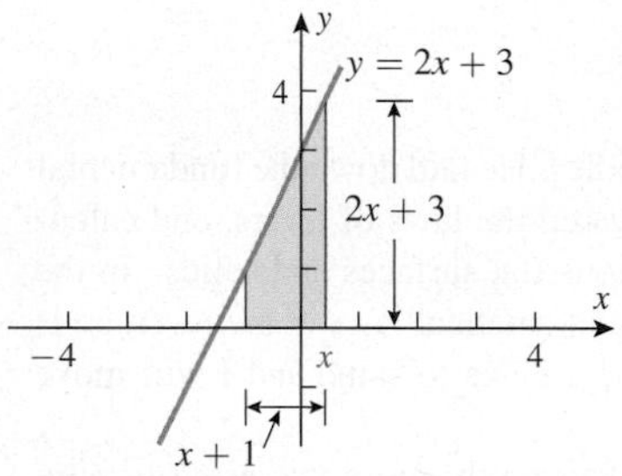


▲ **Figure 5.1.8**

▶ **Example 1** Find the area $A(x)$ between the graph of $f(x) = 2x + 3$ and the interval $[a, x] = [-1, x]$, and find the derivative $A'(x)$ of this area function.

***Solution.*** Recall that the formula for the area of a trapezoid is $A = \frac{1}{2}(b + b')h$, where $b$ and $b'$ denote the lengths of the parallel sides of the trapezoid, and the altitude $h$ denotes the distance between the parallel sides. From Figure 5.1.8 we see that

$$A(x) = \tfrac{1}{2}((2x + 3) + 1)(x - (-1)) = x^2 + 3x + 2$$

is the area of a trapezoid with parallel sides of lengths 1 and $2x + 3$ and with altitude $x - (-1) = x + 1$. For this area function,

$$A'(x) = 2x + 3 = f(x) \blacktriangleleft$$

Formula (2) is important because it relates the area function $A$ and the region-bounding function $f$. Although a formula for $A(x)$ may be difficult to obtain directly, its derivative, $f(x)$, is given. If a formula for $A(x)$ can be recovered from the given formula for $A'(x)$, then the area under the graph of $f$ over the interval $[a, b]$ can be obtained by computing $A(b)$.

The process of finding a function from its derivative is called ***antidifferentiation***, and a procedure for finding areas via antidifferentiation is called the ***antiderivative method***. To illustrate this method, let us revisit the problem of finding the area in Figure 5.1.5.

▶ **Example 2** Use the antiderivative method to find the area under the graph of $y = x^2$ over the interval $[0, 1]$.

How does the solution to Example 2 change if the interval $[0, 1]$ is replaced by the interval $[-1, 1]$?

***Solution.*** Let $x$ be any point in the interval $[0, 1]$, and let $A(x)$ denote the area under the graph of $f(x) = x^2$ over the interval $[0, x]$. It follows from (2) that

$$A'(x) = x^2 \tag{3}$$

To find $A(x)$ we must look for a function whose derivative is $x^2$. By guessing, we see that one such function is $\frac{1}{3}x^3$, so by Theorem 4.8.3

$$A(x) = \tfrac{1}{3}x^3 + C \tag{4}$$

for some real constant $C$. We can determine the specific value for $C$ by considering the case where $x = 0$. In this case (4) implies that

$$A(0) = C \tag{5}$$

But if $x = 0$, then the interval $[0, x]$ reduces to a single point. If we agree that the area above a single point should be taken as zero, then $A(0) = 0$ and (5) implies that $C = 0$. Thus, it follows from (4) that

$$A(x) = \tfrac{1}{3}x^3$$

is the area function we are seeking. This implies that the area under the graph of $y = x^2$ over the interval [0, 1] is

$$A(1) = \tfrac{1}{3}(1^3) = \tfrac{1}{3}$$

This is consistent with the result that we previously obtained numerically. ◀

As Example 2 illustrates, antidifferentiation is a process in which one tries to "undo" a differentiation. One of the objectives in this chapter is to develop efficient antidifferentiation procedures.

## THE RECTANGLE METHOD AND THE ANTIDERIVATIVE METHOD COMPARED

The rectangle method and the antiderivative method provide two very different approaches to the area problem, each of which is important. The antiderivative method is usually the more efficient way to *compute* areas, but it is the rectangle method that is used to formally *define* the notion of area, thereby allowing us to prove mathematical results about areas. The underlying idea of the rectangle approach is also important because it can be adapted readily to such diverse problems as finding the volume of a solid, the length of a curve, the mass of an object, and the work done in pumping water out of a tank, to name a few.

## ✓ QUICK CHECK EXERCISES 5.1 (See page 258 for answers.)

1. Let $R$ denote the region below the graph of $f(x) = \sqrt{1 - x^2}$ and above the interval $[-1, 1]$.
   (a) Use a geometric argument to find the area of $R$.
   (b) What estimate results if the area of $R$ is approximated by the total area within the rectangles of the accompanying figure?

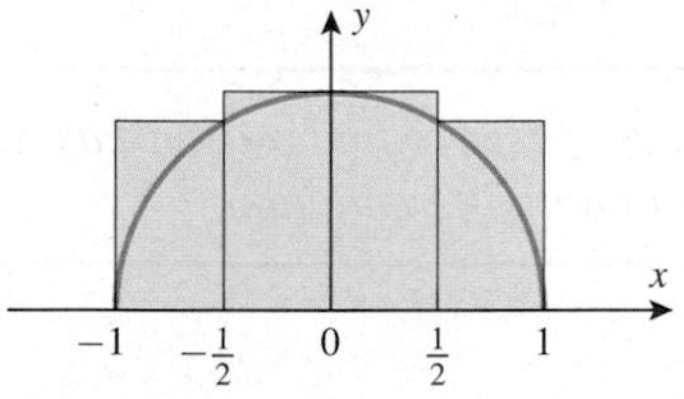


◀ **Figure Ex-1**

2. Suppose that when the area $A$ between the graph of a function $y = f(x)$ and an interval $[a, b]$ is approximated by the areas of $n$ rectangles, the total area of the rectangles is $A_n = 2 + (2/n)$, $n = 1, 2, \ldots$. Then, $A =$ ______.
3. The area under the graph of $y = x^2$ over the interval [0, 3] is ______.
4. Find a formula for the area $A(x)$ between the graph of the function $f(x) = x$ and the interval $[0, x]$, and verify that $A'(x) = f(x)$.
5. The area under the graph of $y = f(x)$ over the interval $[0, x]$ is $A(x) = x + e^x - 1$. It follows that $f(x) =$ ______.

## EXERCISE SET 5.1

**1–12** Estimate the area between the graph of the function $f$ and the interval $[a, b]$. Use an approximation scheme with $n$ rectangles similar to our treatment of $f(x) = x^2$ in this section. If your calculating utility will perform automatic summations, estimate the specified area using $n = 10, 50$, and 100 rectangles. Otherwise, estimate this area using $n = 2, 5$, and 10 rectangles. ■

1. $f(x) = \sqrt{x}$; $[a, b] = [0, 1]$
2. $f(x) = \dfrac{1}{x+1}$; $[a, b] = [0, 1]$
3. $f(x) = \sin x$; $[a, b] = [0, \pi]$
4. $f(x) = \cos x$; $[a, b] = [0, \pi/2]$
5. $f(x) = \dfrac{1}{x}$; $[a, b] = [1, 2]$
6. $f(x) = \cos x$; $[a, b] = [-\pi/2, \pi/2]$
7. $f(x) = \sqrt{1 - x^2}$; $[a, b] = [0, 1]$
8. $f(x) = \sqrt{1 - x^2}$; $[a, b] = [-1, 1]$
9. $f(x) = e^x$; $[a, b] = [-1, 1]$
10. $f(x) = \ln x$; $[a, b] = [1, 2]$
11. $f(x) = \sin^{-1} x$; $[a, b] = [0, 1]$
12. $f(x) = \tan^{-1} x$; $[a, b] = [0, 1]$

**13–18** Graph each function over the specified interval. Then use simple area formulas from geometry to find the area function $A(x)$ that gives the area between the graph of the specified function $f$ and the interval $[a, x]$. Confirm that $A'(x) = f(x)$ in every case. ■

**13.** $f(x) = 3$; $[a, x] = [1, x]$

**14.** $f(x) = 5$; $[a, x] = [2, x]$

**15.** $f(x) = 2x + 2$; $[a, x] = [0, x]$

**16.** $f(x) = 3x - 3$; $[a, x] = [1, x]$

**17.** $f(x) = 2x + 2$; $[a, x] = [1, x]$

**18.** $f(x) = 3x - 3$; $[a, x] = [2, x]$

**19–22 True–False** Determine whether the statement is true or false. Explain your answer. ■

**19.** If $A(n)$ denotes the area of a regular $n$-sided polygon inscribed in a circle of radius 2, then $\lim_{n\to+\infty} A(n) = 2\pi$.

**20.** If the area under the curve $y = x^2$ over an interval is approximated by the total area of a collection of rectangles, the approximation will be too large.

**21.** If $A(x)$ is the area under the graph of a nonnegative continuous function $f$ over an interval $[a, x]$, then $A'(x) = f(x)$.

**22.** If $A(x)$ is the area under the graph of a nonnegative continuous function $f$ over an interval $[a, x]$, then $A(x)$ will be a continuous function.

**FOCUS ON CONCEPTS**

**23.** Explain how to use the formula for $A(x)$ found in the solution to Example 2 to determine the area between the graph of $y = x^2$ and the interval $[3, 6]$.

**24.** Repeat Exercise 23 for the interval $[-3, 9]$.

**25.** Let $A$ denote the area between the graph of $f(x) = \sqrt{x}$ and the interval $[0, 1]$, and let $B$ denote the area between the graph of $f(x) = x^2$ and the interval $[0, 1]$. Explain geometrically why $A + B = 1$.

**26.** Let $A$ denote the area between the graph of $f(x) = 1/x$ and the interval $[1, 2]$, and let $B$ denote the area between the graph of $f$ and the interval $\left[\frac{1}{2}, 1\right]$. Explain geometrically why $A = B$.

**27–28** The area $A(x)$ under the graph of $f$ and over the interval $[a, x]$ is given. Find the function $f$ and the value of $a$. ■

**27.** $A(x) = x^2 - 4$

**28.** $A(x) = x^2 - x$

**29. Writing** Compare and contrast the rectangle method and the antiderivative method.

**30. Writing** Suppose that $f$ is a nonnegative continuous function on an interval $[a, b]$ and that $g(x) = f(x) + C$, where $C$ is a positive constant. What will be the area of the region *between* the graphs of $f$ and $g$?

✓ **QUICK CHECK ANSWERS 5.1** 1. (a) $\frac{\pi}{2}$ (b) $1 + \frac{\sqrt{3}}{2}$ 2. 2 3. 9 4. $A(x) = \frac{x^2}{2}$; $A'(x) = \frac{2x}{2} = x = f(x)$ 5. $e^x + 1$

## 5.2 THE INDEFINITE INTEGRAL

*In the last section we saw how antidifferentiation could be used to find exact areas. In this section we will develop some fundamental results about antidifferentiation.*

### ANTIDERIVATIVES

> **5.2.1 DEFINITION** A function $F$ is called an ***antiderivative*** of a function $f$ on a given open interval if $F'(x) = f(x)$ for all $x$ in the interval.

For example, the function $F(x) = \frac{1}{3}x^3$ is an antiderivative of $f(x) = x^2$ on the interval $(-\infty, +\infty)$ because for each $x$ in this interval

$$F'(x) = \frac{d}{dx}\left[\tfrac{1}{3}x^3\right] = x^2 = f(x)$$

However, $F(x) = \frac{1}{3}x^3$ is not the only antiderivative of $f$ on this interval. If we add any constant $C$ to $\frac{1}{3}x^3$, then the function $G(x) = \frac{1}{3}x^3 + C$ is also an antiderivative of $f$ on $(-\infty, +\infty)$, since

$$G'(x) = \frac{d}{dx}\left[\tfrac{1}{3}x^3 + C\right] = x^2 + 0 = f(x)$$

In general, once any single antiderivative is known, other antiderivatives can be obtained by adding constants to the known antiderivative. Thus,

$$\tfrac{1}{3}x^3, \quad \tfrac{1}{3}x^3 + 2, \quad \tfrac{1}{3}x^3 - 5, \quad \tfrac{1}{3}x^3 + \sqrt{2}$$

are all antiderivatives of $f(x) = x^2$.

It is reasonable to ask if there are antiderivatives of a function $f$ that cannot be obtained by adding some constant to a known antiderivative $F$. The answer is *no* since Theorem 4.8.3 tells us that if two functions have the same derivative on an open interval, then the functions differ by a constant on the interval. The following theorem summarizes these observations.

**5.2.2 THEOREM** *If $F(x)$ is any antiderivative of $f(x)$ on an open interval, then for any constant $C$ the function $F(x) + C$ is also an antiderivative on that interval. Moreover, each antiderivative of $f(x)$ on the interval can be expressed in the form $F(x) + C$ by choosing the constant $C$ appropriately.*

## THE INDEFINITE INTEGRAL

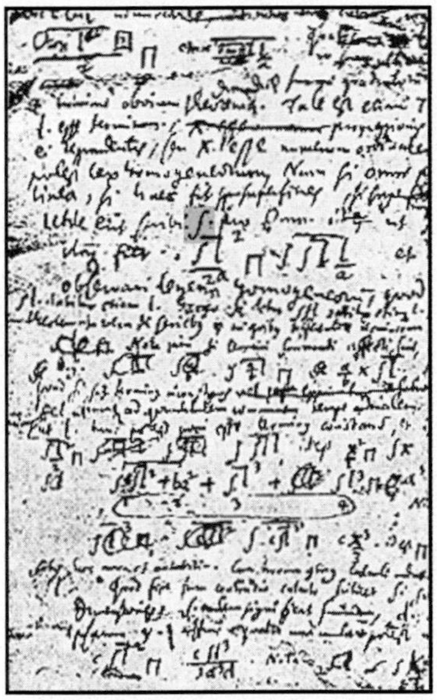

Reproduced from C. I. Gerhardt's "Briefwechsel von G. W. Leibniz mit Mathematikern (1899)".

*Extract from the manuscript of Leibniz dated October 29, 1675 in which the integral sign first appeared (see yellow highlight).*

The process of finding antiderivatives is called ***antidifferentiation*** or ***integration***. Thus, if

$$\frac{d}{dx}[F(x)] = f(x) \tag{1}$$

then ***integrating*** (or ***antidifferentiating***) the function $f(x)$ produces an antiderivative of the form $F(x) + C$. To emphasize this process, Equation (1) is recast using ***integral notation***,

$$\int f(x)\,dx = F(x) + C \tag{2}$$

where $C$ is understood to represent an arbitrary constant. It is important to note that (1) and (2) are just different notations to express the same fact. For example,

$$\int x^2\,dx = \tfrac{1}{3}x^3 + C \quad \text{is equivalent to} \quad \frac{d}{dx}\left[\tfrac{1}{3}x^3\right] = x^2$$

Note that if we differentiate an antiderivative of $f(x)$, we obtain $f(x)$ back again. Thus,

$$\frac{d}{dx}\left[\int f(x)\,dx\right] = f(x) \tag{3}$$

The expression $\int f(x)\,dx$ is called an ***indefinite integral***. The adjective "indefinite" emphasizes that the result of antidifferentiation is a "generic" function, described only up to a constant term. The "elongated s" that appears on the left side of (2) is called an ***integral sign***,* the function $f(x)$ is called the ***integrand***, and the constant $C$ is called the ***constant of integration***. Equation (2) should be read as:

*The integral of $f(x)$ with respect to $x$ is equal to $F(x)$ plus a constant.*

The differential symbol, $dx$, in the differentiation and antidifferentiation operations

$$\frac{d}{dx}[\ ] \quad \text{and} \quad \int [\ ]\,dx$$

* This notation was devised by Leibniz. In his early papers Leibniz used the notation "omn." (an abbreviation for the Latin word "omnes") to denote integration. Then on October 29, 1675 he wrote, "It will be useful to write $\int$ for omn., thus $\int l$ for omn. $l$. . . ." Two or three weeks later he refined the notation further and wrote $\int [\ ]\,dx$ rather than $\int$ alone. This notation is so useful and so powerful that its development by Leibniz must be regarded as a major milestone in the history of mathematics and science.

serves to identify the independent variable. If an independent variable other than $x$ is used, say $t$, then the notation must be adjusted appropriately. Thus,

$$\frac{d}{dt}[F(t)] = f(t) \quad \text{and} \quad \int f(t)\,dt = F(t) + C$$

are equivalent statements. For simplicity, the $dx$ is sometimes absorbed into the integrand. For example,

$$\int 1\,dx \quad \text{can be written as} \quad \int dx$$

$$\int \frac{1}{x^2}\,dx \quad \text{can be written as} \quad \int \frac{dx}{x^2}$$

## INTEGRATION FORMULAS

Integration is essentially educated guesswork—given the derivative $f$ of a function $F$, one tries to guess what the function $F$ is. However, many basic integration formulas can be obtained directly from their companion differentiation formulas. Some of the most important are given in Table 5.2.1.

**Table 5.2.1**
INTEGRATION FORMULAS

| DIFFERENTIATION FORMULA | INTEGRATION FORMULA | DIFFERENTIATION FORMULA | INTEGRATION FORMULA |
|---|---|---|---|
| 1. $\frac{d}{dx}[x] = 1$ | $\int dx = x + C$ | 8. $\frac{d}{dx}[-\csc x] = \csc x \cot x$ | $\int \csc x \cot x\,dx = -\csc x + C$ |
| 2. $\frac{d}{dx}\left[\frac{x^{r+1}}{r+1}\right] = x^r \ (r \neq -1)$ | $\int x^r\,dx = \frac{x^{r+1}}{r+1} + C \ (r \neq -1)$ | 9. $\frac{d}{dx}[e^x] = e^x$ | $\int e^x\,dx = e^x + C$ |
| 3. $\frac{d}{dx}[\sin x] = \cos x$ | $\int \cos x\,dx = \sin x + C$ | 10. $\frac{d}{dx}\left[\frac{b^x}{\ln b}\right] = b^x \ (0 < b, b \neq 1)$ | $\int b^x\,dx = \frac{b^x}{\ln b} + C \ (0 < b, b \neq 1)$ |
| 4. $\frac{d}{dx}[-\cos x] = \sin x$ | $\int \sin x\,dx = -\cos x + C$ | 11. $\frac{d}{dx}[\ln\lvert x\rvert] = \frac{1}{x}$ | $\int \frac{1}{x}\,dx = \ln\lvert x\rvert + C$ |
| 5. $\frac{d}{dx}[\tan x] = \sec^2 x$ | $\int \sec^2 x\,dx = \tan x + C$ | 12. $\frac{d}{dx}[\tan^{-1} x] = \frac{1}{1+x^2}$ | $\int \frac{1}{1+x^2}\,dx = \tan^{-1} x + C$ |
| 6. $\frac{d}{dx}[-\cot x] = \csc^2 x$ | $\int \csc^2 x\,dx = -\cot x + C$ | 13. $\frac{d}{dx}[\sin^{-1} x] = \frac{1}{\sqrt{1-x^2}}$ | $\int \frac{1}{\sqrt{1-x^2}}\,dx = \sin^{-1} x + C$ |
| 7. $\frac{d}{dx}[\sec x] = \sec x \tan x$ | $\int \sec x \tan x\,dx = \sec x + C$ | 14. $\frac{d}{dx}[\sec^{-1}\lvert x\rvert] = \frac{1}{x\sqrt{x^2-1}}$ | $\int \frac{1}{x\sqrt{x^2-1}}\,dx = \sec^{-1}\lvert x\rvert + C$ |

See Exercise 70 for a justification of Formula 14 in Table 5.2.1.

▶ **Example 1** The second integration formula in Table 5.2.1 will be easier to remember if you express it in words:

*To integrate a power of x (other than −1), add 1 to the exponent and divide by the new exponent.*

Although Formula 2 in Table 5.2.1 is not applicable to integrating $x^{-1}$, this function can be integrated by rewriting the integral in Formula 11 as

$$\int \frac{1}{x}\,dx = \int x^{-1}\,dx = \ln|x| + C$$

Here are some examples:

$$\int x^2\,dx = \frac{x^3}{3} + C \qquad \boxed{r = 2}$$

$$\int x^3\,dx = \frac{x^4}{4} + C \qquad \boxed{r = 3}$$

$$\int \frac{1}{x^5}\,dx = \int x^{-5}\,dx = \frac{x^{-5+1}}{-5+1} + C = -\frac{1}{4x^4} + C \qquad \boxed{r = -5}$$

$$\int \sqrt{x}\,dx = \int x^{\frac{1}{2}}\,dx = \frac{x^{\frac{1}{2}+1}}{\frac{1}{2}+1} + C = \tfrac{2}{3}x^{\frac{3}{2}} + C = \tfrac{2}{3}(\sqrt{x})^3 + C \qquad \boxed{r = \tfrac{1}{2}}$$ ◀

## PROPERTIES OF THE INDEFINITE INTEGRAL

Our first properties of antiderivatives follow directly from the simple constant factor, sum, and difference rules for derivatives.

**5.2.3 THEOREM** *Suppose that $F(x)$ and $G(x)$ are antiderivatives of $f(x)$ and $g(x)$, respectively, and that $c$ is a constant. Then:*

(*a*) *A constant factor can be moved through an integral sign; that is,*

$$\int cf(x)\,dx = cF(x) + C$$

(*b*) *An antiderivative of a sum is the sum of the antiderivatives; that is,*

$$\int [f(x) + g(x)]\,dx = F(x) + G(x) + C$$

(*c*) *An antiderivative of a difference is the difference of the antiderivatives; that is,*

$$\int [f(x) - g(x)]\,dx = F(x) - G(x) + C$$

**PROOF** In general, to establish the validity of an equation of the form

$$\int h(x)\,dx = H(x) + C$$

one must show that

$$\frac{d}{dx}[H(x)] = h(x)$$

We are given that $F(x)$ and $G(x)$ are antiderivatives of $f(x)$ and $g(x)$, respectively, so we know that

$$\frac{d}{dx}[F(x)] = f(x) \quad \text{and} \quad \frac{d}{dx}[G(x)] = g(x)$$

Thus,

$$\frac{d}{dx}[cF(x)] = c\frac{d}{dx}[F(x)] = cf(x)$$

$$\frac{d}{dx}[F(x) + G(x)] = \frac{d}{dx}[F(x)] + \frac{d}{dx}[G(x)] = f(x) + g(x)$$

$$\frac{d}{dx}[F(x) - G(x)] = \frac{d}{dx}[F(x)] - \frac{d}{dx}[G(x)] = f(x) - g(x)$$

which proves the three statements of the theorem. ■

The statements in Theorem 5.2.3 can be summarized by the following formulas:

$$\int cf(x)\,dx = c\int f(x)\,dx \tag{4}$$

$$\int [f(x) + g(x)]\,dx = \int f(x)\,dx + \int g(x)\,dx \tag{5}$$

$$\int [f(x) - g(x)]\,dx = \int f(x)\,dx - \int g(x)\,dx \tag{6}$$

However, these equations must be applied carefully to avoid errors and unnecessary complexities arising from the constants of integration. For example, if you use (4) to integrate $2x$ by writing

$$\int 2x\,dx = 2\int x\,dx = 2\left(\frac{x^2}{2} + C\right) = x^2 + 2C$$

then you will have an unnecessarily complicated form of the arbitrary constant. This kind of problem can be avoided by inserting the constant of integration in the final result rather than in intermediate calculations.

**▶ Example 2** Evaluate

$$\text{(a)}\ \int 4\cos x\,dx \qquad \text{(b)}\ \int (x + x^2)\,dx$$

***Solution (a).*** Since $F(x) = \sin x$ is an antiderivative for $f(x) = \cos x$ (Table 5.2.1), we obtain

$$\int 4\cos x\,dx \underset{(4)}{=} 4\int \cos x\,dx = 4\sin x + C$$

***Solution (b).*** From Table 5.2.1 we obtain

$$\int (x + x^2)\,dx \underset{(5)}{=} \int x\,dx + \int x^2\,dx = \frac{x^2}{2} + \frac{x^3}{3} + C \ ◀$$

Parts (*b*) and (*c*) of Theorem 5.2.3 can be extended to more than two functions, which in combination with part (*a*) results in the following general formula:

$$\begin{aligned}&\int [c_1 f_1(x) + c_2 f_2(x) + \cdots + c_n f_n(x)]\,dx\\&\qquad = c_1\int f_1(x)\,dx + c_2\int f_2(x)\,dx + \cdots + c_n\int f_n(x)\,dx\end{aligned} \tag{7}$$

**▶ Example 3**

$$\begin{aligned}\int (3x^6 - 2x^2 + 7x + 1)\,dx &= 3\int x^6\,dx - 2\int x^2\,dx + 7\int x\,dx + \int 1\,dx\\&= \frac{3x^7}{7} - \frac{2x^3}{3} + \frac{7x^2}{2} + x + C \ ◀\end{aligned}$$

Sometimes it is useful to rewrite an integrand in a different form before performing the integration. This is illustrated in the following example.

**▶ Example 4** Evaluate

$$\text{(a)}\ \int \frac{\cos x}{\sin^2 x}\,dx \qquad \text{(b)}\ \int \frac{t^2 - 2t^4}{t^4}\,dt \qquad \text{(c)}\ \int \frac{x^2}{x^2+1}\,dx$$

***Solution (a).***

$$\int \frac{\cos x}{\sin^2 x}\,dx = \int \frac{1}{\sin x}\,\frac{\cos x}{\sin x}\,dx = \int \csc x\cot x\,dx \underset{\text{Formula 8 in Table 5.2.1}}{=} -\csc x + C$$

***Solution (b).***

$$\begin{aligned}\int \frac{t^2 - 2t^4}{t^4}\,dt &= \int \left(\frac{1}{t^2} - 2\right)dt = \int (t^{-2} - 2)\,dt\\&= \frac{t^{-1}}{-1} - 2t + C = -\frac{1}{t} - 2t + C\end{aligned}$$

Perform the integration in part (c) by first performing a long division on the integrand.

***Solution (c).*** By adding and subtracting 1 from the numerator of the integrand, we can rewrite the integral in a form in which Formulas 1 and 12 of Table 5.2.1 can be applied:

$$\int \frac{x^2}{x^2+1}\,dx = \int \left(\frac{x^2+1}{x^2+1} - \frac{1}{x^2+1}\right) dx$$
$$= \int \left(1 - \frac{1}{x^2+1}\right) dx = x - \tan^{-1} x + C \blacktriangleleft$$

## INTEGRAL CURVES

Graphs of antiderivatives of a function $f$ are called ***integral curves*** of $f$. We know from Theorem 5.2.2 that if $y = F(x)$ is any integral curve of $f(x)$, then all other integral curves are vertical translations of this curve, since they have equations of the form $y = F(x) + C$. For example, $y = \frac{1}{3}x^3$ is one integral curve for $f(x) = x^2$, so all the other integral curves have equations of the form $y = \frac{1}{3}x^3 + C$; conversely, the graph of any equation of this form is an integral curve (Figure 5.2.1).

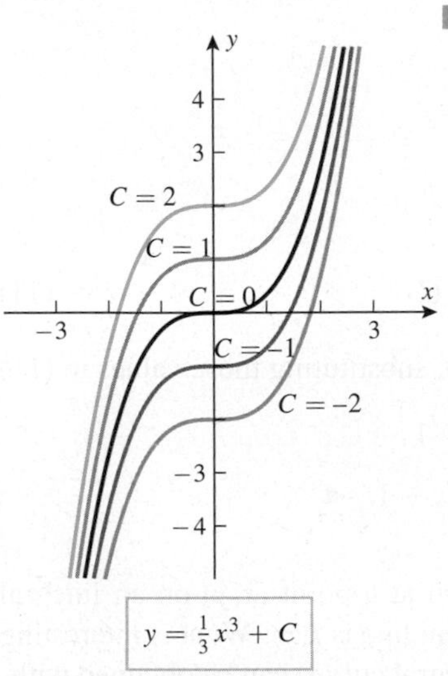

▲ **Figure 5.2.1**

In many problems one is interested in finding a function whose derivative satisfies specified conditions. The following example illustrates a geometric problem of this type.

▶ **Example 5** Suppose that a curve $y = f(x)$ in the $xy$-plane has the property that at each point $(x, y)$ on the curve, the tangent line has slope $x^2$. Find an equation for the curve given that it passes through the point (2, 1).

***Solution.*** Since the slope of the line tangent to $y = f(x)$ is $dy/dx$, we have $dy/dx = x^2$, and

$$y = \int x^2\,dx = \tfrac{1}{3}x^3 + C$$

Since the curve passes through (2, 1), a specific value for $C$ can be found by using the fact that $y = 1$ if $x = 2$. Substituting these values in the above equation yields

$$1 = \tfrac{1}{3}(2^3) + C \quad \text{or} \quad C = -\tfrac{5}{3}$$

so an equation of the curve is

$$y = \tfrac{1}{3}x^3 - \tfrac{5}{3}$$

(Figure 5.2.2). ◀

In Example 5, the requirement that the graph of $f$ pass through the point (2, 1) selects the single integral curve $y = \frac{1}{3}x^3 - \frac{5}{3}$ from the family of curves $y = \frac{1}{3}x^3 + C$ (Figure 5.2.2).

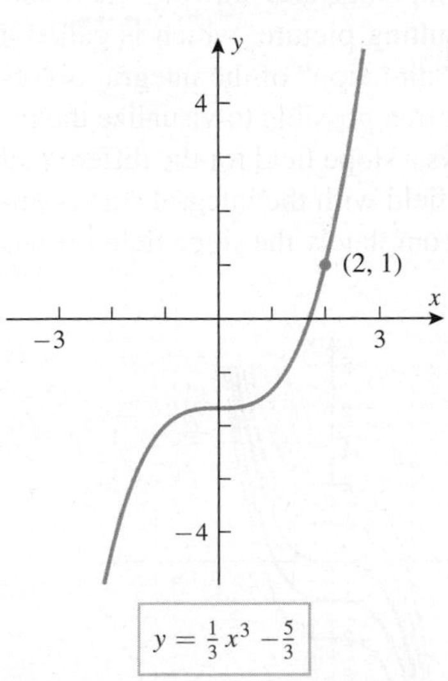

▲ **Figure 5.2.2**

## INTEGRATION FROM THE VIEWPOINT OF DIFFERENTIAL EQUATIONS

We will now consider another way of looking at integration that will be useful in our later work. Suppose that $f(x)$ is a known function and we are interested in finding a function $F(x)$ such that $y = F(x)$ satisfies the equation

$$\frac{dy}{dx} = f(x) \tag{8}$$

The solutions of this equation are the antiderivatives of $f(x)$, and we know that these can be obtained by integrating $f(x)$. For example, the solutions of the equation

$$\frac{dy}{dx} = x^2 \tag{9}$$

are

$$y = \int x^2\,dx = \frac{x^3}{3} + C$$

Equation (8) is called a ***differential equation*** because it involves a derivative of an unknown function. Differential equations are different from the kinds of equations we have encountered so far in that the unknown is a *function* and not a *number* as in an equation such as $x^2 + 5x - 6 = 0$.

Sometimes we will not be interested in finding all of the solutions of (8), but rather we will want only the solution whose graph passes through a specified point $(x_0, y_0)$. For example, in Example 5 we solved (9) for the integral curve that passed through the point (2, 1).

For simplicity, it is common in the study of differential equations to denote a solution of $dy/dx = f(x)$ as $y(x)$ rather than $F(x)$, as earlier. With this notation, the problem of finding a function $y(x)$ whose derivative is $f(x)$ and whose graph passes through the point $(x_0, y_0)$ is expressed as

$$\frac{dy}{dx} = f(x), \quad y(x_0) = y_0 \tag{10}$$

This is called an ***initial-value problem***, and the requirement that $y(x_0) = y_0$ is called the ***initial condition*** for the problem.

▶ **Example 6** Solve the initial-value problem

$$\frac{dy}{dx} = \cos x, \quad y(0) = 1$$

***Solution.*** The solution of the differential equation is

$$y = \int \cos x\, dx = \sin x + C \tag{11}$$

The initial condition $y(0) = 1$ implies that $y = 1$ if $x = 0$; substituting these values in (11) yields

$$1 = \sin(0) + C \quad \text{or} \quad C = 1$$

Thus, the solution of the initial-value problem is $y = \sin x + 1$. ◀

## SLOPE FIELDS

If we interpret $dy/dx$ as the slope of a tangent line, then at a point $(x, y)$ on an integral curve of the equation $dy/dx = f(x)$, the slope of the tangent line is $f(x)$. What is interesting about this is that the slopes of the tangent lines to the integral curves can be obtained without actually solving the differential equation. For example, if

$$\frac{dy}{dx} = \sqrt{x^2 + 1}$$

then we know without solving the equation that at the point where $x = 1$ the tangent line to an integral curve has slope $\sqrt{1^2 + 1} = \sqrt{2}$; and more generally, at a point where $x = a$, the tangent line to an integral curve has slope $\sqrt{a^2 + 1}$.

A geometric description of the integral curves of a differential equation $dy/dx = f(x)$ can be obtained by choosing a rectangular grid of points in the $xy$-plane, calculating the slopes of the tangent lines to the integral curves at the gridpoints, and drawing small portions of the tangent lines through those points. The resulting picture, which is called a ***slope field*** or ***direction field*** for the equation, shows the "direction" of the integral curves at the gridpoints. With sufficiently many gridpoints it is often possible to visualize the integral curves themselves; for example, Figure 5.2.3*a* shows a slope field for the differential equation $dy/dx = x^2$, and Figure 5.2.3*b* shows that same field with the integral curves imposed on it—the more gridpoints that are used, the more completely the slope field reveals

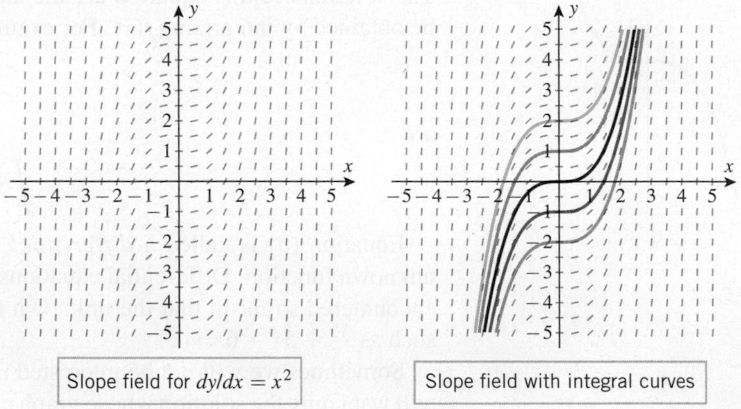


▶ **Figure 5.2.3** (*a*) (*b*)

the shape of the integral curves. However, the amount of computation can be considerable, so computers are usually used when slope fields with many gridpoints are needed.

Slope fields will be studied in more detail later in the text.

## ✓ QUICK CHECK EXERCISES 5.2 *(See page 267 for answers.)*

1. A function $F$ is an antiderivative of a function $f$ on an interval if ______ for all $x$ in the interval.
2. Write an equivalent integration formula for each given derivative formula.
   (a) $\frac{d}{dx}[\sqrt{x}] = \frac{1}{2\sqrt{x}}$ (b) $\frac{d}{dx}[e^{4x}] = 4e^{4x}$
3. Evaluate the integrals.
   (a) $\int [x^3 + x + 5]\, dx$ (b) $\int [\sec^2 x - \csc x \cot x]\, dx$
4. The graph of $y = x^2 + x$ is an integral curve for the function $f(x) =$ ______. If $G$ is a function whose graph is also an integral curve for $f$, and if $G(1) = 5$, then $G(x) =$ ______.
5. A slope field for the differential equation
$$\frac{dy}{dx} = \frac{2x}{x^2 - 4}$$
has a line segment with slope ______ through the point $(0, 5)$ and has a line segment with slope ______ through the point $(-4, 1)$.

## EXERCISE SET 5.2 [Graphing Utility] [C] CAS

1. In each part, confirm that the formula is correct, and state a corresponding integration formula.
   (a) $\frac{d}{dx}[\sqrt{1+x^2}] = \frac{x}{\sqrt{1+x^2}}$
   (b) $\frac{d}{dx}[xe^x] = (x+1)e^x$
2. In each part, confirm that the stated formula is correct by differentiating.
   (a) $\int x \sin x\, dx = \sin x - x \cos x + C$
   (b) $\int \frac{dx}{(1-x^2)^{3/2}} = \frac{x}{\sqrt{1-x^2}} + C$

**FOCUS ON CONCEPTS**

3. What is a *constant of integration*? Why does an answer to an integration problem involve a constant of integration?
4. What is an *integral curve* of a function $f$? How are two integral curves of a function $f$ related?

**5–8** Find the derivative and state a corresponding integration formula. ■

5. $\frac{d}{dx}[\sqrt{x^3+5}]$
6. $\frac{d}{dx}\left[\frac{x}{x^2+3}\right]$
7. $\frac{d}{dx}[\sin(2\sqrt{x})]$
8. $\frac{d}{dx}[\sin x - x \cos x]$

**9–10** Evaluate the integral by rewriting the integrand appropriately, if required, and applying the power rule (Formula 2 in Table 5.2.1). ■

9. (a) $\int x^8\, dx$ (b) $\int x^{5/7}\, dx$ (c) $\int x^3 \sqrt{x}\, dx$
10. (a) $\int \sqrt[3]{x^2}\, dx$ (b) $\int \frac{1}{x^6}\, dx$ (c) $\int x^{-7/8}\, dx$

**11–14** Evaluate each integral by applying Theorem 5.2.3 and Formula 2 in Table 5.2.1 appropriately. ■

11. $\int \left[5x + \frac{2}{3x^5}\right] dx$
12. $\int [x^{-1/2} - 3x^{7/5} + \frac{1}{9}]\, dx$
13. $\int [x^{-3} - 3x^{1/4} + 8x^2]\, dx$
14. $\int \left[\frac{10}{y^{3/4}} - \sqrt[3]{y} + \frac{4}{\sqrt{y}}\right] dy$

**15–34** Evaluate the integral and check your answer by differentiating. ■

15. $\int x(1+x^3)\, dx$
16. $\int (2+y^2)^2\, dy$
17. $\int x^{1/3}(2-x)^2\, dx$
18. $\int (1+x^2)(2-x)\, dx$
19. $\int \frac{x^5 + 2x^2 - 1}{x^4}\, dx$
20. $\int \frac{1-2t^3}{t^3}\, dt$
21. $\int \left[\frac{2}{x} + 3e^x\right] dx$
22. $\int \left[\frac{1}{2t} - \sqrt{2}e^t\right] dt$
23. $\int [3 \sin x - 2 \sec^2 x]\, dx$
24. $\int [\csc^2 t - \sec t \tan t]\, dt$
25. $\int \sec x(\sec x + \tan x)\, dx$
26. $\int \csc x(\sin x + \cot x)\, dx$
27. $\int \frac{\sec\theta}{\cos\theta}\, d\theta$
28. $\int \frac{dy}{\csc y}$
29. $\int \frac{\sin x}{\cos^2 x}\, dx$
30. $\int \left[\phi + \frac{2}{\sin^2 \phi}\right] d\phi$

**31.** $\int [1 + \sin^2\theta \csc\theta]\, d\theta$ **32.** $\int \frac{\sec x + \cos x}{2\cos x}\, dx$

**33.** $\int \left[\frac{1}{2\sqrt{1-x^2}} - \frac{3}{1+x^2}\right] dx$

**34.** $\int \left[\frac{4}{x\sqrt{x^2-1}} + \frac{1+x+x^3}{1+x^2}\right] dx$

**35.** Evaluate the integral

$$\int \frac{1}{1+\sin x}\, dx$$

by multiplying the numerator and denominator by an appropriate expression.

**36.** Use the double-angle formula $\cos 2x = 2\cos^2 x - 1$ to evaluate the integral

$$\int \frac{1}{1+\cos 2x}\, dx$$

**37–40 True–False** Determine whether the statement is true or false. Explain your answer. ■

**37.** If $F(x)$ is an antiderivative of $f(x)$, then

$$\int f(x)\, dx = F(x) + C$$

**38.** If $C$ denotes a constant of integration, the two formulas

$$\int \cos x\, dx = \sin x + C$$

$$\int \cos x\, dx = (\sin x + \pi) + C$$

are both correct equations.

**39.** The function $f(x) = e^{-x} + 1$ is a solution to the initial-value problem

$$\frac{dy}{dx} = -\frac{1}{e^x}, \quad y(0) = 1$$

**40.** Every integral curve of the slope field

$$\frac{dy}{dx} = \frac{1}{\sqrt{x^2+1}}$$

is the graph of an increasing function of $x$.

**41.** Use a graphing utility to generate some representative integral curves of the function $f(x) = 5x^4 - \sec^2 x$ over the interval $(-\pi/2, \pi/2)$.

**42.** Use a graphing utility to generate some representative integral curves of the function $f(x) = (x-1)/x$ over the interval $(0, 5)$.

**43–46** Solve the initial-value problems. ■

**43.** (a) $\frac{dy}{dx} = \sqrt[3]{x},\ y(1) = 2$

(b) $\frac{dy}{dt} = \sin t + 1,\ y\left(\frac{\pi}{3}\right) = \frac{1}{2}$

(c) $\frac{dy}{dx} = \frac{x+1}{\sqrt{x}},\ y(1) = 0$

**44.** (a) $\frac{dy}{dx} = \frac{1}{(2x)^3},\ y(1) = 0$

(b) $\frac{dy}{dt} = \sec^2 t - \sin t,\ y\left(\frac{\pi}{4}\right) = 1$

(c) $\frac{dy}{dx} = x^2\sqrt{x^3},\ y(0) = 0$

**45.** (a) $\frac{dy}{dx} = 4e^x,\ y(0) = 1$ (b) $\frac{dy}{dt} = \frac{1}{t},\ y(-1) = 5$

**46.** (a) $\frac{dy}{dt} = \frac{3}{\sqrt{1-t^2}},\ y\left(\frac{\sqrt{3}}{2}\right) = 0$

(b) $\frac{dy}{dx} = \frac{x^2-1}{x^2+1},\ y(1) = \frac{\pi}{2}$

**47–50** A particle moves along an $s$-axis with position function $s = s(t)$ and velocity function $v(t) = s'(t)$. Use the given information to find $s(t)$. ■

**47.** $v(t) = 32t;\ s(0) = 20$ **48.** $v(t) = \cos t;\ s(0) = 2$

**49.** $v(t) = 3\sqrt{t};\ s(4) = 1$ **50.** $v(t) = 3e^t;\ s(1) = 0$

**51.** Find the general form of a function whose second derivative is $\sqrt{x}$. [*Hint:* Solve the equation $f''(x) = \sqrt{x}$ for $f(x)$ by integrating both sides twice.]

**52.** Find a function $f$ such that $f''(x) = x + \cos x$ and such that $f(0) = 1$ and $f'(0) = 2$. [*Hint:* Integrate both sides of the equation twice.]

**53–57** Find an equation of the curve that satisfies the given conditions. ■

**53.** At each point $(x, y)$ on the curve the slope is $2x + 1$; the curve passes through the point $(-3, 0)$.

**54.** At each point $(x, y)$ on the curve the slope is $(x+1)^2$; the curve passes through the point $(-2, 8)$.

**55.** At each point $(x, y)$ on the curve the slope is $-\sin x$; the curve passes through the point $(0, 2)$.

**56.** At each point $(x, y)$ on the curve the slope equals the square of the distance between the point and the $y$-axis; the point $(-1, 2)$ is on the curve.

**57.** At each point $(x, y)$ on the curve, $y$ satisfies the condition $d^2y/dx^2 = 6x$; the line $y = 5 - 3x$ is tangent to the curve at the point where $x = 1$.

C **58.** In each part, use a CAS to solve the initial-value problem.

(a) $\frac{dy}{dx} = x^2\cos 3x,\ y(\pi/2) = -1$

(b) $\frac{dy}{dx} = \frac{x^3}{(4+x^2)^{3/2}},\ y(0) = -2$

**59.** (a) Use a graphing utility to generate a slope field for the differential equation $dy/dx = x$ in the region $-5 \le x \le 5$ and $-5 \le y \le 5$.

(b) Graph some representative integral curves of the function $f(x) = x$.

(c) Find an equation for the integral curve that passes through the point $(2, 1)$.

**60.** (a) Use a graphing utility to generate a slope field for the differential equation $dy/dx = e^x/2$ in the region $-1 \le x \le 4$ and $-1 \le y \le 4$.

(b) Graph some representative integral curves of the function $f(x) = e^x/2$.

(c) Find an equation for the integral curve that passes through the point $(0, 1)$.

**61–64** The given slope field figure corresponds to one of the differential equations below. Identify the differential equation that matches the figure, and sketch solution curves through the highlighted points.

(a) $\dfrac{dy}{dx} = 2$ (b) $\dfrac{dy}{dx} = -x$

(c) $\dfrac{dy}{dx} = x^2 - 4$ (d) $\dfrac{dy}{dx} = e^{x/3}$ ■

**61.**

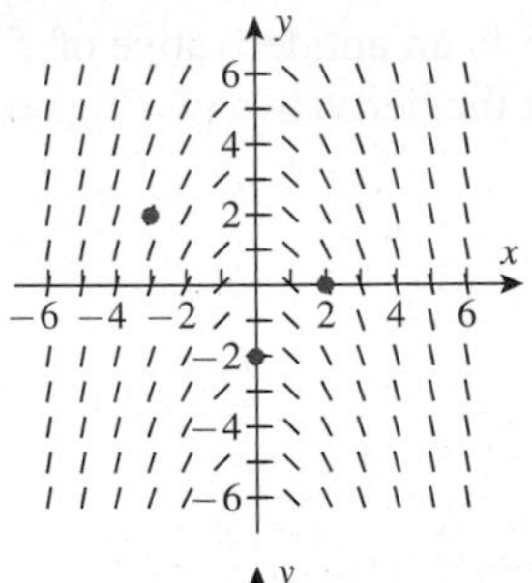

**62.**

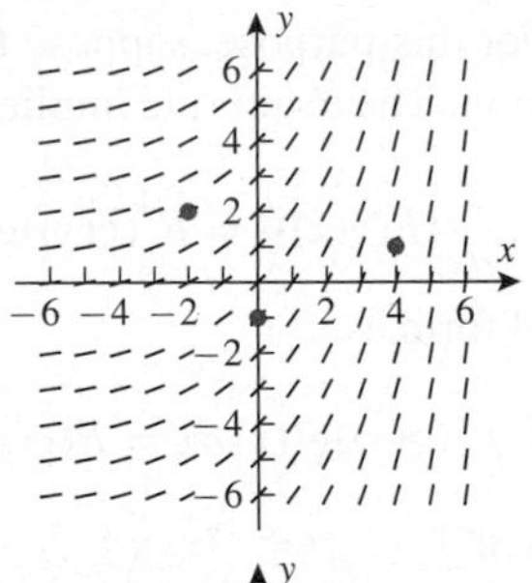

**63.**

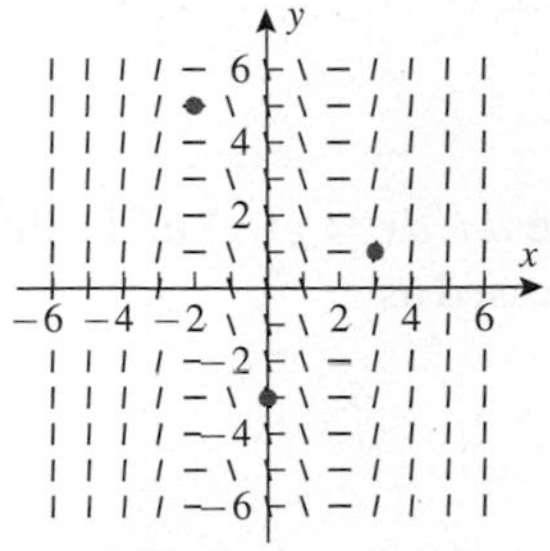

**64.**

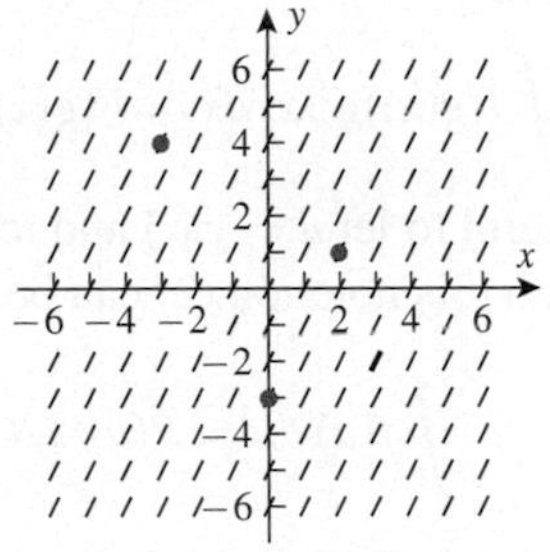

**FOCUS ON CONCEPTS**

**65.** (a) Show that

$$F(x) = \tan^{-1} x \quad \text{and} \quad G(x) = -\tan^{-1}(1/x)$$

differ by a constant on the interval $(0, +\infty)$ by showing that they are antiderivatives of the same function.

(b) Find the constant $C$ such that $F(x) - G(x) = C$ by evaluating the functions $F(x)$ and $G(x)$ at a particular value of $x$.

(c) Check your answer to part (b) by using trigonometric identities.

**66.** Let $F$ and $G$ be the functions defined by

$$F(x) = \frac{x^2 + 3x}{x} \quad \text{and} \quad G(x) = \begin{cases} x + 3, & x > 0 \\ x, & x < 0 \end{cases}$$

(a) Show that $F$ and $G$ have the same derivative.

(b) Show that $G(x) \neq F(x) + C$ for any constant $C$.

(c) Do parts (a) and (b) contradict Theorem 5.2.2? Explain.

**67–68** Use a trigonometric identity to evaluate the integral. ■

**67.** $\displaystyle\int \tan^2 x\, dx$ **68.** $\displaystyle\int \cot^2 x\, dx$

**69.** Use the identities $\cos 2\theta = 1 - 2\sin^2\theta = 2\cos^2\theta - 1$ to help evaluate the integrals

(a) $\displaystyle\int \sin^2(x/2)\, dx$ (b) $\displaystyle\int \cos^2(x/2)\, dx$

**70.** Recall that

$$\frac{d}{dx}[\sec^{-1} x] = \frac{1}{|x|\sqrt{x^2 - 1}}$$

Use this to verify Formula 14 in Table 5.2.1.

**71.** The speed of sound in air at 0°C (or 273 K on the Kelvin scale) is 1087 ft/s, but the speed $v$ increases as the temperature $T$ rises. Experimentation has shown that the rate of change of $v$ with respect to $T$ is

$$\frac{dv}{dT} = \frac{1087}{2\sqrt{273}} T^{-1/2}$$

where $v$ is in feet per second and $T$ is in kelvins (K). Find a formula that expresses $v$ as a function of $T$.

**72.** The time $t$ between tosses of a juggling ball is a function of the height $h$ of the toss. Suppose that a ball tossed 4 feet high spends 1 second in the air and that the rate of change of $t$ with respect to $h$ is

$$\frac{dt}{dh} = \frac{1}{4\sqrt{h}}$$

Find a formula that expresses $t$ as a function of $h$.

**73.** Suppose that a uniform metal rod 50 cm long is insulated laterally, and the temperatures at the exposed ends are maintained at 25°C and 85°C, respectively. Assume that an $x$-axis is chosen as in the accompanying figure and that the temperature $T(x)$ satisfies the equation

$$\frac{d^2T}{dx^2} = 0$$

Find $T(x)$ for $0 \le x \le 50$.

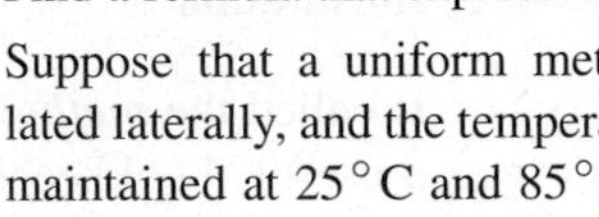


◀ **Figure Ex-73**

**74. Writing** What is an *initial-value problem*? Describe the sequence of steps for solving an initial-value problem.

**75. Writing** What is a *slope field*? How are slope fields and integral curves related?

✓ **QUICK CHECK ANSWERS 5.2** 1. $F'(x) = f(x)$ 2. (a) $\displaystyle\int \frac{1}{2\sqrt{x}}\, dx = \sqrt{x} + C$ (b) $\displaystyle\int 4e^{4x}\, dx = e^{4x} + C$
3. (a) $\frac{1}{4}x^4 + \frac{1}{2}x^2 + 5x + C$ (b) $\tan x + \csc x + C$ 4. $2x + 1$; $x^2 + x + 3$ 5. 0; $-\frac{2}{3}$

## 5.3 INTEGRATION BY SUBSTITUTION

*In this section we will study a technique, called **substitution**, that can often be used to transform complicated integration problems into simpler ones.*

### u-SUBSTITUTION

The method of substitution can be motivated by examining the chain rule from the viewpoint of antidifferentiation. For this purpose, suppose that $F$ is an antiderivative of $f$ and that $g$ is a differentiable function. The chain rule implies that the derivative of $F(g(x))$ can be expressed as

$$\frac{d}{dx}[F(g(x))] = F'(g(x))g'(x)$$

which we can write in integral form as

$$\int F'(g(x))g'(x)\,dx = F(g(x)) + C \tag{1}$$

or since $F$ is an antiderivative of $f$,

$$\int f(g(x))g'(x)\,dx = F(g(x)) + C \tag{2}$$

For our purposes it will be useful to let $u = g(x)$ and to write $du/dx = g'(x)$ in the differential form $du = g'(x)\,dx$. With this notation (2) can be expressed as

$$\int f(u)\,du = F(u) + C \tag{3}$$

The process of evaluating an integral of form (2) by converting it into form (3) with the substitution

$$u = g(x) \quad \text{and} \quad du = g'(x)\,dx$$

is called the ***method of u-substitution***. Here the differential notation serves primarily as a useful "bookkeeping" device for the method of $u$-substitution. The following example illustrates how the method works.

▶ **Example 1** Evaluate $\int (x^2 + 1)^{50} \cdot 2x\,dx$.

***Solution.*** If we let $u = x^2 + 1$, then $du/dx = 2x$, which implies that $du = 2x\,dx$. Thus, the given integral can be written as

$$\int (x^2 + 1)^{50} \cdot 2x\,dx = \int u^{50}\,du = \frac{u^{51}}{51} + C = \frac{(x^2 + 1)^{51}}{51} + C \; ◀$$

It is important to realize that in the method of $u$-substitution you have control over the choice of $u$, but once you make that choice the value of $du$ is *computed*. The method of $u$-substitution will fail if the chosen $u$ and the computed $du$ cannot be used to produce an integrand in which no expressions involving $x$ remain, or if you cannot evaluate the resulting integral. Thus, for example, the substitution $u = x^2$, $du = 2x\,dx$ will not work for the integral

$$\int 2x \sin x^4\,dx$$

because this substitution results in the integral

$$\int \sin u^2\,du$$

which still cannot be evaluated in terms of familiar functions.

There are no hard and fast rules for choosing $u$, and in some problems no choice of $u$ will work. In such cases other methods need to be used, some of which will be discussed later. Making appropriate choices for $u$ will come with experience, but you may find the following guidelines, combined with a mastery of the basic integrals in Table 5.2.1, helpful.

> ***Guidelines for u-Substitution***
>
> **Step 1.** Look for some composition $f(g(x))$ within the integrand for which the substitution
> $$u = g(x), \quad du = g'(x)\,dx$$
> produces an integral that is expressed entirely in terms of $u$ and its differential $du$. This may or may not be possible.
>
> **Step 2.** If you are successful in Step 1, then try to evaluate the resulting integral in terms of $u$. Again, this may or may not be possible.
>
> **Step 3.** If you are successful in Step 2, then replace $u$ by $g(x)$ to express your final answer in terms of $x$.

## EASY TO RECOGNIZE SUBSTITUTIONS

The easiest substitutions occur when the integrand is the derivative of a known function, except for a constant added to or subtracted from the independent variable.

### ▶ Example 2

$$\int \sin(x+9)\,dx = \int \sin u\,du = -\cos u + C = -\cos(x+9) + C$$

$$\boxed{\begin{array}{c} u = x+9 \\ du = 1 \cdot dx = dx \end{array}}$$

$$\int (x-8)^{23}\,dx = \int u^{23}\,du = \frac{u^{24}}{24} + C = \frac{(x-8)^{24}}{24} + C \quad \blacktriangleleft$$

$$\boxed{\begin{array}{c} u = x-8 \\ du = 1 \cdot dx = dx \end{array}}$$

Another easy $u$-substitution occurs when the integrand is the derivative of a known function, except for a constant that multiplies or divides the independent variable. The following example illustrates two ways to evaluate such integrals.

### ▶ Example 3 Evaluate $\int \cos 5x\,dx$.

***Solution.***

$$\int \cos 5x\,dx = \int (\cos u) \cdot \frac{1}{5}\,du = \frac{1}{5}\int \cos u\,du = \frac{1}{5}\sin u + C = \frac{1}{5}\sin 5x + C$$

$$\boxed{\begin{array}{c} u = 5x \\ du = 5\,dx \text{ or } dx = \frac{1}{5}\,du \end{array}}$$

***Alternative Solution.*** There is a variation of the preceding method that some people prefer. The substitution $u = 5x$ requires $du = 5\,dx$. If there were a factor of 5 in the integrand, then we could group the 5 and $dx$ together to form the $du$ required by the substitution. Since there is no factor of 5, we will insert one and compensate by putting a factor of $\frac{1}{5}$ in front of the integral. The computations are as follows:

$$\int \cos 5x\,dx = \frac{1}{5}\int \cos 5x \cdot 5\,dx = \frac{1}{5}\int \cos u\,du = \frac{1}{5}\sin u + C = \frac{1}{5}\sin 5x + C \quad \blacktriangleleft$$

$$\boxed{\begin{array}{c} u = 5x \\ du = 5\,dx \end{array}}$$

More generally, if the integrand is a composition of the form $f(ax+b)$, where $f(x)$ is an easy to integrate function, then the substitution $u = ax + b$, $du = a\,dx$ will work.

**▶ Example 4**

$$\int \frac{dx}{\left(\frac{1}{3}x-8\right)^5} = \int \frac{3\,du}{u^5} = 3\int u^{-5}\,du = -\frac{3}{4}u^{-4} + C = -\frac{3}{4}\left(\frac{1}{3}x-8\right)^{-4} + C \blacktriangleleft$$

$u = \frac{1}{3}x - 8$
$du = \frac{1}{3}\,dx$ or $dx = 3\,du$

**▶ Example 5** Evaluate $\displaystyle\int \frac{dx}{1+3x^2}$.

***Solution.*** Substituting

$$u = \sqrt{3}x, \quad du = \sqrt{3}\,dx$$

yields

$$\int \frac{dx}{1+3x^2} = \frac{1}{\sqrt{3}}\int \frac{du}{1+u^2} = \frac{1}{\sqrt{3}}\tan^{-1} u + C = \frac{1}{\sqrt{3}}\tan^{-1}(\sqrt{3}x) + C \blacktriangleleft$$

With the help of Theorem 5.2.3, a complicated integral can sometimes be computed by expressing it as a sum of simpler integrals.

**▶ Example 6**

$$\begin{aligned}\int \left(\frac{1}{x} + \sec^2 \pi x\right) dx &= \int \frac{dx}{x} + \int \sec^2 \pi x\,dx \\ &= \ln|x| + \int \sec^2 \pi x\,dx \\ &= \ln|x| + \frac{1}{\pi}\int \sec^2 u\,du \\ &= \ln|x| + \frac{1}{\pi}\tan u + C = \ln|x| + \frac{1}{\pi}\tan \pi x + C \blacktriangleleft\end{aligned}$$

$u = \pi x$
$du = \pi\,dx$ or $dx = \frac{1}{\pi}\,du$

The next four examples illustrate a substitution $u = g(x)$ where $g(x)$ is a nonlinear function.

**▶ Example 7** Evaluate $\displaystyle\int \sin^2 x \cos x\,dx$.

***Solution.*** If we let $u = \sin x$, then

$$\frac{du}{dx} = \cos x, \quad \text{so} \quad du = \cos x\,dx$$

Thus,

$$\int \sin^2 x \cos x\,dx = \int u^2\,du = \frac{u^3}{3} + C = \frac{\sin^3 x}{3} + C \blacktriangleleft$$

**▶ Example 8** Evaluate $\displaystyle\int \frac{e^{\sqrt{x}}}{\sqrt{x}}\,dx$.

***Solution.*** If we let $u = \sqrt{x}$, then

$$\frac{du}{dx} = \frac{1}{2\sqrt{x}}, \quad \text{so} \quad du = \frac{1}{2\sqrt{x}}\,dx \quad \text{or} \quad 2\,du = \frac{1}{\sqrt{x}}\,dx$$

Thus,

$$\int \frac{e^{\sqrt{x}}}{\sqrt{x}}\,dx = \int 2e^u\,du = 2\int e^u\,du = 2e^u + C = 2e^{\sqrt{x}} + C \blacktriangleleft$$

▶ **Example 9** Evaluate $\int t^4 \sqrt[3]{3-5t^5}\, dt$.

***Solution.***

$$\int t^4 \sqrt[3]{3-5t^5}\, dt = -\frac{1}{25}\int \sqrt[3]{u}\, du = -\frac{1}{25}\int u^{1/3}\, du$$

$u = 3 - 5t^5$
$du = -25t^4\, dt$ or $-\frac{1}{25}\, du = t^4\, dt$

$$= -\frac{1}{25}\frac{u^{4/3}}{4/3} + C = -\frac{3}{100}(3-5t^5)^{4/3} + C \blacktriangleleft$$

▶ **Example 10** Evaluate $\int \frac{e^x}{\sqrt{1-e^{2x}}}\, dx$.

***Solution.*** Substituting

$$u = e^x, \quad du = e^x\, dx$$

yields

$$\int \frac{e^x}{\sqrt{1-e^{2x}}}\, dx = \int \frac{du}{\sqrt{1-u^2}} = \sin^{-1} u + C = \sin^{-1}(e^x) + C \blacktriangleleft$$

## LESS APPARENT SUBSTITUTIONS

The method of substitution is relatively straightforward, provided the integrand contains an easily recognized composition $f(g(x))$ and the remainder of the integrand is a constant multiple of $g'(x)$. If this is not the case, the method may still apply but may require more computation.

▶ **Example 11** Evaluate $\int x^2\sqrt{x-1}\, dx$.

***Solution.*** The composition $\sqrt{x-1}$ suggests the substitution

$$u = x - 1 \quad \text{so that} \quad du = dx \tag{4}$$

From the first equality in (4)

$$x^2 = (u+1)^2 = u^2 + 2u + 1$$

so that

$$\int x^2\sqrt{x-1}\, dx = \int (u^2+2u+1)\sqrt{u}\, du = \int (u^{5/2} + 2u^{3/2} + u^{1/2})\, du$$

$$= \tfrac{2}{7}u^{7/2} + \tfrac{4}{5}u^{5/2} + \tfrac{2}{3}u^{3/2} + C$$

$$= \tfrac{2}{7}(x-1)^{7/2} + \tfrac{4}{5}(x-1)^{5/2} + \tfrac{2}{3}(x-1)^{3/2} + C \blacktriangleleft$$

▶ **Example 12** Evaluate $\int \cos^3 x\, dx$.

***Solution.*** The only compositions in the integrand that suggest themselves are

$$\cos^3 x = (\cos x)^3 \quad \text{and} \quad \cos^2 x = (\cos x)^2$$

However, neither the substitution $u = \cos x$ nor the substitution $u = \cos^2 x$ works (verify). In this case, an appropriate substitution is not suggested by the composition contained in the integrand. On the other hand, note from Equation (2) that the derivative $g'(x)$ appears as a factor in the integrand. This suggests that we write

$$\int \cos^3 x\, dx = \int \cos^2 x \cos x\, dx$$

and solve the equation $du = \cos x\,dx$ for $u = \sin x$. Since $\sin^2 x + \cos^2 x = 1$, we then have

$$\int \cos^3 x\,dx = \int \cos^2 x \cos x\,dx = \int (1 - \sin^2 x)\cos x\,dx = \int (1 - u^2)\,du$$

$$= u - \frac{u^3}{3} + C = \sin x - \frac{1}{3}\sin^3 x + C \blacktriangleleft$$

**▶ Example 13** Evaluate $\displaystyle\int \frac{dx}{a^2 + x^2}\,dx$, where $a \neq 0$ is a constant.

***Solution.*** Some simple algebra and an appropriate $u$-substitution will allow us to use Formula 12 in Table 5.2.1.

$$\int \frac{dx}{a^2 + x^2} = \int \frac{a(dx/a)}{a^2(1 + (x/a)^2)} = \frac{1}{a}\int \frac{dx/a}{1 + (x/a)^2} \qquad \boxed{\begin{array}{c} u = x/a \\ du = dx/a \end{array}}$$

$$= \frac{1}{a}\int \frac{du}{1 + u^2} = \frac{1}{a}\tan^{-1} u + C = \frac{1}{a}\tan^{-1}\frac{x}{a} + C \blacktriangleleft$$

The method of Example 13 leads to the following generalizations of Formulas 12, 13, and 14 in Table 5.2.1 for $a > 0$:

$$\int \frac{du}{a^2 + u^2} = \frac{1}{a}\tan^{-1}\frac{u}{a} + C \tag{5}$$

$$\int \frac{du}{\sqrt{a^2 - u^2}} = \sin^{-1}\frac{u}{a} + C \tag{6}$$

$$\int \frac{du}{u\sqrt{u^2 - a^2}} = \frac{1}{a}\sec^{-1}\left|\frac{u}{a}\right| + C \tag{7}$$

**▶ Example 14** Evaluate $\displaystyle\int \frac{dx}{\sqrt{2 - x^2}}$.

***Solution.*** Applying (6) with $u = x$ and $a = \sqrt{2}$ yields

$$\int \frac{dx}{\sqrt{2 - x^2}} = \sin^{-1}\frac{x}{\sqrt{2}} + C \blacktriangleleft$$

## INTEGRATION USING COMPUTER ALGEBRA SYSTEMS

The advent of computer algebra systems has made it possible to evaluate many kinds of integrals that would be laborious to evaluate by hand. For example, a handheld calculator evaluated the integral

$$\int \frac{5x^2}{(1 + x)^{1/3}}\,dx = \frac{3(x + 1)^{2/3}(5x^2 - 6x + 9)}{8} + C$$

in about a second. The computer algebra system *Mathematica*, running on a personal computer, required even less time to evaluate this same integral. However, just as one would not want to rely on a calculator to compute $2 + 2$, so one would not want to use a CAS to integrate a simple function such as $f(x) = x^2$. Thus, even if you have a CAS, you will want to develop a reasonable level of competence in evaluating basic integrals. Moreover, the mathematical techniques that we will introduce for evaluating basic integrals are precisely the techniques that computer algebra systems use to evaluate more complicated integrals.

**TECHNOLOGY MASTERY**

If you have a CAS, use it to calculate the integrals in the examples in this section. If your CAS produces an answer that is different from the one in the text, then confirm algebraically that the two answers agree. Also, explore the effect of using the CAS to simplify the expressions it produces for the integrals.

## ✓ QUICK CHECK EXERCISES 5.3 (See page 275 for answers.)

1. Indicate the $u$-substitution.
(a) $\int 3x^2(1+x^3)^{25}\,dx = \int u^{25}\,du$ if $u =$ ______ and $du =$ ______.
(b) $\int 2x\sin x^2\,dx = \int \sin u\,du$ if $u =$ ______ and $du =$ ______.
(c) $\int \frac{18x}{1+9x^2}\,dx = \int \frac{1}{u}\,du$ if $u =$ ______ and $du =$ ______.
(d) $\int \frac{3}{1+9x^2}\,dx = \int \frac{1}{1+u^2}\,du$ if $u =$ ______ and $du =$ ______.

2. Supply the missing integrand corresponding to the indicated $u$-substitution.
(a) $\int 5(5x-3)^{-1/3}\,dx = \int$ ______ $du$; $u = 5x-3$
(b) $\int (3-\tan x)\sec^2 x\,dx = \int$ ______ $du$; $u = 3-\tan x$
(c) $\int \frac{\sqrt[3]{8+\sqrt{x}}}{\sqrt{x}}\,dx = \int$ ______ $du$; $u = 8+\sqrt{x}$
(d) $\int e^{3x}\,dx = \int$ ______ $du$; $u = 3x$

## EXERCISE SET 5.3 Graphing Utility C CAS

**1–12** Evaluate the integrals using the indicated substitutions.

1. (a) $\int 2x(x^2+1)^{23}\,dx$; $u = x^2+1$
(b) $\int \cos^3 x\sin x\,dx$; $u = \cos x$

2. (a) $\int \frac{1}{\sqrt{x}}\sin\sqrt{x}\,dx$; $u = \sqrt{x}$
(b) $\int \frac{3x\,dx}{\sqrt{4x^2+5}}$; $u = 4x^2+5$

3. (a) $\int \sec^2(4x+1)\,dx$; $u = 4x+1$
(b) $\int y\sqrt{1+2y^2}\,dy$; $u = 1+2y^2$

4. (a) $\int \sqrt{\sin\pi\theta}\cos\pi\theta\,d\theta$; $u = \sin\pi\theta$
(b) $\int (2x+7)(x^2+7x+3)^{4/5}\,dx$; $u = x^2+7x+3$

5. (a) $\int \cot x\csc^2 x\,dx$; $u = \cot x$
(b) $\int (1+\sin t)^9\cos t\,dt$; $u = 1+\sin t$

6. (a) $\int \cos 2x\,dx$; $u = 2x$ (b) $\int x\sec^2 x^2\,dx$; $u = x^2$

7. (a) $\int x^2\sqrt{1+x}\,dx$; $u = 1+x$
(b) $\int [\csc(\sin x)]^2\cos x\,dx$; $u = \sin x$

8. (a) $\int \sin(x-\pi)\,dx$; $u = x-\pi$
(b) $\int \frac{5x^4}{(x^5+1)^2}\,dx$; $u = x^5+1$

9. (a) $\int \frac{dx}{x\ln x}$; $u = \ln x$
(b) $\int e^{-5x}\,dx$; $u = -5x$

10. (a) $\int \frac{\sin 3\theta}{1+\cos 3\theta}\,d\theta$; $u = 1+\cos 3\theta$
(b) $\int \frac{e^x}{1+e^x}\,dx$; $u = 1+e^x$

11. (a) $\int \frac{x^2\,dx}{1+x^6}$; $u = x^3$
(b) $\int \frac{dx}{x\sqrt{1-(\ln x)^2}}$; $u = \ln x$

12. (a) $\int \frac{dx}{x\sqrt{9x^2-1}}$; $u = 3x$
(b) $\int \frac{dx}{\sqrt{x}(1+x)}$; $u = \sqrt{x}$

**FOCUS ON CONCEPTS**

13. Explain the connection between the chain rule for differentiation and the method of $u$-substitution for integration.

14. Explain how the substitution $u = ax+b$ helps to perform an integration in which the integrand is $f(ax+b)$, where $f(x)$ is an easy to integrate function.

**15–56** Evaluate the integrals using appropriate substitutions.

15. $\int (4x-3)^9\,dx$

16. $\int x^3\sqrt{5+x^4}\,dx$

17. $\int \sin 7x\,dx$

18. $\int \cos\frac{x}{3}\,dx$

19. $\int \sec 4x\tan 4x\,dx$

20. $\int \sec^2 5x\,dx$

21. $\int e^{2x}\,dx$

22. $\int \frac{dx}{2x}$

**23.** $\int \frac{dx}{\sqrt{1-4x^2}}$ **24.** $\int \frac{dx}{1+16x^2}$

**25.** $\int t\sqrt{7t^2+12}\,dt$ **26.** $\int \frac{x}{\sqrt{4-5x^2}}\,dx$

**27.** $\int \frac{6}{(1-2x)^3}\,dx$ **28.** $\int \frac{x^2+1}{\sqrt{x^3+3x}}\,dx$

**29.** $\int \frac{x^3}{(5x^4+2)^3}\,dx$ **30.** $\int \frac{\sin(1/x)}{3x^2}\,dx$

**31.** $\int e^{\sin x}\cos x\,dx$ **32.** $\int x^3 e^{x^4}\,dx$

**33.** $\int x^2 e^{-2x^3}\,dx$ **34.** $\int \frac{e^x+e^{-x}}{e^x-e^{-x}}\,dx$

**35.** $\int \frac{e^x}{1+e^{2x}}\,dx$ **36.** $\int \frac{t}{t^4+1}\,dt$

**37.** $\int \frac{\sin(5/x)}{x^2}\,dx$ **38.** $\int \frac{\sec^2(\sqrt{x})}{\sqrt{x}}\,dx$

**39.** $\int \cos^4 3t\sin 3t\,dt$ **40.** $\int \cos 2t\sin^5 2t\,dt$

**41.** $\int x\sec^2(x^2)\,dx$ **42.** $\int \frac{\cos 4\theta}{(1+2\sin 4\theta)^4}\,d\theta$

**43.** $\int \cos 4\theta\sqrt{2-\sin 4\theta}\,d\theta$ **44.** $\int \tan^3 5x\sec^2 5x\,dx$

**45.** $\int \frac{\sec^2 x\,dx}{\sqrt{1-\tan^2 x}}$ **46.** $\int \frac{\sin\theta}{\cos^2\theta+1}\,d\theta$

**47.** $\int \sec^3 2x\tan 2x\,dx$ **48.** $\int [\sin(\sin\theta)]\cos\theta\,d\theta$

**49.** $\int \frac{dx}{e^x}$ **50.** $\int \sqrt{e^x}\,dx$

**51.** $\int \frac{dx}{\sqrt{x}\,e^{(2\sqrt{x})}}$ **52.** $\int \frac{e^{\sqrt{2y+1}}}{\sqrt{2y+1}}\,dy$

**53.** $\int \frac{y}{\sqrt{2y+1}}\,dy$ **54.** $\int x\sqrt{4-x}\,dx$

**55.** $\int \sin^3 2\theta\,d\theta$

**56.** $\int \sec^4 3\theta\,d\theta$ [*Hint:* Apply a trigonometric identity.]

**57–60** Evaluate each integral by first modifying the form of the integrand and then making an appropriate substitution, if needed. ■

**57.** $\int \frac{t+1}{t}\,dt$ **58.** $\int e^{2\ln x}\,dx$

**59.** $\int [\ln(e^x)+\ln(e^{-x})]\,dx$ **60.** $\int \cot x\,dx$

**61–62** Evaluate the integrals with the aid of Formulas (5), (6), and (7). ■

**61.** (a) $\int \frac{dx}{\sqrt{9-x^2}}$ (b) $\int \frac{dx}{5+x^2}$ (c) $\int \frac{dx}{x\sqrt{x^2-\pi}}$

**62.** (a) $\int \frac{e^x}{4+e^{2x}}\,dx$ (b) $\int \frac{dx}{\sqrt{9-4x^2}}$ (c) $\int \frac{dy}{y\sqrt{5y^2-3}}$

**63–65** Evaluate the integrals assuming that $n$ is a positive integer and $b \neq 0$. ■

**63.** $\int (a+bx)^n\,dx$ **64.** $\int \sqrt[n]{a+bx}\,dx$

**65.** $\int \sin^n(a+bx)\cos(a+bx)\,dx$

C **66.** Use a CAS to check the answers you obtained in Exercises 63–65. If the answer produced by the CAS does not match yours, show that the two answers are equivalent. [*Suggestion: Mathematica* users may find it helpful to apply the Simplify command to the answer.]

**FOCUS ON CONCEPTS**

**67.** (a) Evaluate the integral $\int \sin x\cos x\,dx$ by two methods: first by letting $u = \sin x$, and then by letting $u = \cos x$.
(b) Explain why the two apparently different answers obtained in part (a) are really equivalent.

**68.** (a) Evaluate the integral $\int (5x-1)^2\,dx$ by two methods: first square and integrate, then let $u = 5x-1$.
(b) Explain why the two apparently different answers obtained in part (a) are really equivalent.

**69–72** Solve the initial-value problems. ■

**69.** $\frac{dy}{dx} = \sqrt{5x+1},\ y(3) = -2$

**70.** $\frac{dy}{dx} = 2+\sin 3x,\ y(\pi/3) = 0$

**71.** $\frac{dy}{dt} = -e^{2t},\ y(0) = 6$

**72.** $\frac{dy}{dt} = \frac{1}{25+9t^2},\ y\left(-\frac{5}{3}\right) = \frac{\pi}{30}$

**73.** (a) Evaluate $\int [x/\sqrt{x^2+1}]\,dx$.
(b) Use a graphing utility to generate some typical integral curves of $f(x) = x/\sqrt{x^2+1}$ over the interval $(-5, 5)$.

**74.** (a) Evaluate $\int [x/(x^2+1)]\,dx$.
(b) Use a graphing utility to generate some typical integral curves of $f(x) = x/(x^2+1)$ over the interval $(-5, 5)$.

**75.** Find a function $f$ such that the slope of the tangent line at a point $(x, y)$ on the curve $y = f(x)$ is $\sqrt{3x+1}$ and the curve passes through the point $(0, 1)$.

**76.** A population of minnows in a lake is estimated to be 100,000 at the beginning of the year 2015. Suppose that $t$ years after the beginning of 2015 the rate of growth of the population $p(t)$ (in thousands) is given by $p'(t) = (3+0.12t)^{3/2}$. Estimate the projected population at the beginning of the year 2020.

**77.** Let $y(t)$ denote the number of *E. coli* cells in a container of nutrient solution $t$ minutes after the start of an experiment. Assume that $y(t)$ is modeled by the initial-value problem

$$\frac{dy}{dt} = (\ln 2)2^{t/20}, \qquad y(0) = 20$$

Use this model to estimate the number of *E. coli* cells in the container 2 hours after the start of the experiment.

**78.** Derive integration Formula (6).

**79.** Derive integration Formula (7).

**80. Writing** If you want to evaluate an integral by $u$-substitution, how do you decide what part of the integrand to choose for $u$?

**81. Writing** The evaluation of an integral can sometimes result in apparently different answers (Exercises 67 and 68). Explain why this occurs and give an example. How might you show that two apparently different answers are actually equivalent?

**✓ QUICK CHECK ANSWERS 5.3** 1. (a) $1+x^3$; $3x^2\,dx$ (b) $x^2$; $2x\,dx$ (c) $1+9x^2$; $18x\,dx$ (d) $3x$; $3\,dx$ 2. (a) $u^{-1/3}$ (b) $-u$ (c) $2\sqrt[3]{u}$ (d) $\frac{1}{3}e^u$

## 5.4 THE DEFINITION OF AREA AS A LIMIT; SIGMA NOTATION

*Our main goal in this section is to use the rectangle method to give a precise mathematical definition of the "area under a curve."*

### SIGMA NOTATION

We begin by discussing a useful notation for expressing lengthy sums in a compact form. This notation is called ***sigma notation*** or ***summation notation*** because it uses the uppercase Greek letter $\Sigma$ to denote various kinds of sums. If $f(k)$ is a function of $k$, and if $m \le n$ are integers, then

$$\sum_{k=m}^{n} f(k)$$

is read "the summation of $f(k)$, where $k$ runs from $m$ to $n$" and denotes the sum

$$\sum_{k=m}^{n} f(k) = f(m) + f(m+1) + \cdots + f(n-1) + f(n) \tag{1}$$

(Figure 5.4.1).

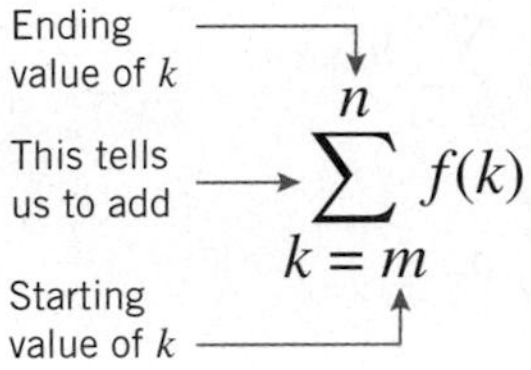


▲ **Figure 5.4.1**

**▶ Example 1**

$$\sum_{k=1}^{5} 2k = 2\cdot 1 + 2\cdot 2 + 2\cdot 3 + 2\cdot 4 + 2\cdot 5 = 2 + 4 + 6 + 8 + 10$$

$$\sum_{k=4}^{8} k^3 = 4^3 + 5^3 + 6^3 + 7^3 + 8^3$$

$$\sum_{k=0}^{5} (-1)^k(2k+1) = 1 - 3 + 5 - 7 + 9 - 11$$

$$\sum_{k=-3}^{1} k^3 = (-3)^3 + (-2)^3 + (-1)^3 + 0^3 + 1^3 = -27 - 8 - 1 + 0 + 1 \blacktriangleleft$$

The numbers $m$ and $n$ in (1) are called, respectively, the ***lower*** and ***upper limits of summation***; and the letter $k$ is called the ***index of summation***. It is not essential to use $k$ as the index of summation; any letter not reserved for another purpose will do. For example,

$$\sum_{i=1}^{6} \frac{1}{i}, \quad \sum_{j=1}^{6} \frac{1}{j}, \quad \text{and} \quad \sum_{n=1}^{6} \frac{1}{n}$$

all denote the sum

$$1 + \frac{1}{2} + \frac{1}{3} + \frac{1}{4} + \frac{1}{5} + \frac{1}{6}$$

If the upper and lower limits of summation are the same, then the "sum" in (1) reduces to a single term. For example,

$$\sum_{k=2}^{2} k^3 = 2^3 \quad \text{and} \quad \sum_{i=1}^{1} \frac{1}{i+2} = \frac{1}{1+2} = \frac{1}{3}$$

In the sums

$$\sum_{i=1}^{5} 2 \quad \text{and} \quad \sum_{j=0}^{2} x^3$$

the expression to the right of the $\Sigma$ sign does not involve the index of summation. In such cases, we take all the terms in the sum to be the same, with one term for each allowable value of the summation index. Thus,

$$\sum_{i=1}^{5} 2 = 2+2+2+2+2 \quad \text{and} \quad \sum_{j=0}^{2} x^3 = x^3+x^3+x^3$$

## CHANGING THE LIMITS OF SUMMATION

A sum can be written in more than one way using sigma notation with different limits of summation and correspondingly different summands. For example,

$$\sum_{i=1}^{5} 2i = 2+4+6+8+10 = \sum_{j=0}^{4}(2j+2) = \sum_{k=3}^{7}(2k-4)$$

## PROPERTIES OF SUMS

When stating general properties of sums it is often convenient to use a subscripted letter such as $a_k$ in place of the function notation $f(k)$. For example,

$$\sum_{k=1}^{5} a_k = a_1+a_2+a_3+a_4+a_5 = \sum_{j=1}^{5} a_j = \sum_{k=-1}^{3} a_{k+2}$$

$$\sum_{k=1}^{n} a_k = a_1+a_2+\cdots+a_n = \sum_{j=1}^{n} a_j = \sum_{k=-1}^{n-2} a_{k+2}$$

Our first properties provide some basic rules for manipulating sums.

**5.4.1 THEOREM**

(*a*) $\displaystyle\sum_{k=1}^{n} ca_k = c\sum_{k=1}^{n} a_k$ (*if c does not depend on k*)

(*b*) $\displaystyle\sum_{k=1}^{n}(a_k+b_k) = \sum_{k=1}^{n} a_k + \sum_{k=1}^{n} b_k$

(*c*) $\displaystyle\sum_{k=1}^{n}(a_k-b_k) = \sum_{k=1}^{n} a_k - \sum_{k=1}^{n} b_k$

We will prove part (*b*) and leave parts (*a*) and (*c*) as exercises.

**PROOF (*b*)**

$$\sum_{k=1}^{n}(a_k+b_k) = (a_1+b_1)+(a_2+b_2)+\cdots+(a_n+b_n)$$

$$= (a_1+a_2+\cdots+a_n)+(b_1+b_2+\cdots+b_n) = \sum_{k=1}^{n} a_k + \sum_{k=1}^{n} b_k \quad \blacksquare$$

Restating Theorem 5.4.1 in words:

(*a*) *A constant factor can be moved through a sigma sign.*

(*b*) *Sigma distributes across sums.*

(*c*) *Sigma distributes across differences.*

## SUMMATION FORMULAS

The following theorem lists some useful formulas for sums of powers of integers. The derivations of these formulas are given in Web Appendix L.

**5.4.2 THEOREM**

(a) $\sum_{k=1}^{n} k = 1 + 2 + \cdots + n = \frac{n(n+1)}{2}$

(b) $\sum_{k=1}^{n} k^2 = 1^2 + 2^2 + \cdots + n^2 = \frac{n(n+1)(2n+1)}{6}$

(c) $\sum_{k=1}^{n} k^3 = 1^3 + 2^3 + \cdots + n^3 = \left[\frac{n(n+1)}{2}\right]^2$

**TECHNOLOGY MASTERY**

Many calculating utilities provide some way of evaluating sums expressed in sigma notation. If your utility has this capability, use it to confirm that the result in Example 2 is correct.

▶ **Example 2** Evaluate $\sum_{k=1}^{30} k(k+1)$.

***Solution.***

$$\sum_{k=1}^{30} k(k+1) = \sum_{k=1}^{30} (k^2 + k) = \sum_{k=1}^{30} k^2 + \sum_{k=1}^{30} k$$

$$= \frac{30(31)(61)}{6} + \frac{30(31)}{2} = 9920 \qquad \text{Theorem 5.4.2(a), (b)} \quad ◀$$

In formulas such as

$$\sum_{k=1}^{n} k = \frac{n(n+1)}{2} \quad \text{or} \quad 1 + 2 + \cdots + n = \frac{n(n+1)}{2}$$

the left side of the equality is said to express the sum in ***open form*** and the right side is said to express it in ***closed form***. The open form indicates the summands and the closed form is an explicit formula for the sum.

**TECHNOLOGY MASTERY**

If you have access to a CAS, it will provide a method for finding closed forms such as those in Theorem 5.4.2. Use your CAS to confirm the formulas in that theorem, and then find closed forms for

$$\sum_{k=1}^{n} k^4 \quad \text{and} \quad \sum_{k=1}^{n} k^5$$

▶ **Example 3** Express $\sum_{k=1}^{n} (3+k)^2$ in closed form.

***Solution.***

$$\sum_{k=1}^{n} (3+k)^2 = 4^2 + 5^2 + \cdots + (3+n)^2$$

$$= [1^2 + 2^2 + 3^2 + 4^2 + 5^2 + \cdots + (3+n)^2] - [1^2 + 2^2 + 3^2]$$

$$= \left(\sum_{k=1}^{3+n} k^2\right) - 14$$

$$= \frac{(3+n)(4+n)(7+2n)}{6} - 14 = \frac{1}{6}(73n + 21n^2 + 2n^3) \quad ◀$$

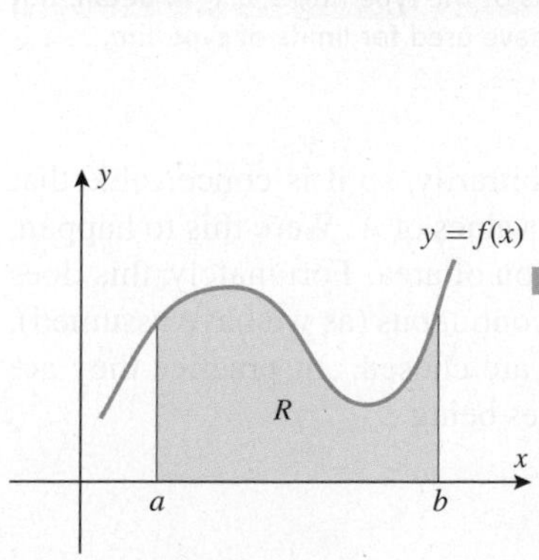

▲ Figure 5.4.2

## A DEFINITION OF AREA

We now turn to the problem of giving a precise definition of what is meant by the "area under a curve." Specifically, suppose that the function $f$ is continuous and nonnegative on the interval $[a, b]$, and let $R$ denote the region bounded below by the $x$-axis, bounded on the sides by the vertical lines $x = a$ and $x = b$, and bounded above by the curve $y = f(x)$ (Figure 5.4.2). Using the rectangle method of Section 5.1, we can motivate a definition for the area of $R$ as follows:

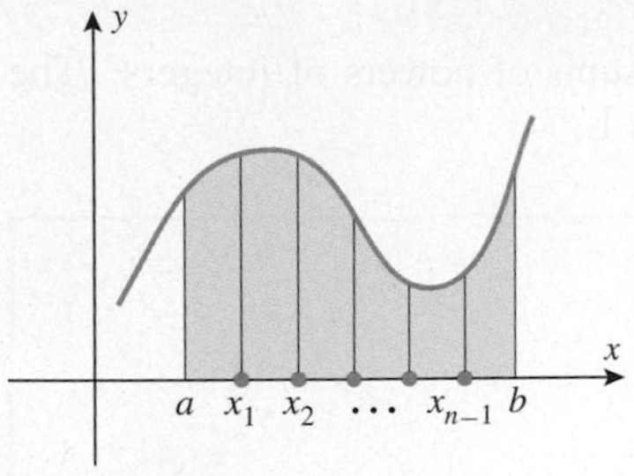


▲ Figure 5.4.3

- Divide the interval $[a, b]$ into $n$ equal subintervals of width

$$\Delta x = \frac{b-a}{n}$$

by inserting $n-1$ equally spaced points $x_1, x_2, \ldots, x_{n-1}$ (Figure 5.4.3).

- Over each subinterval construct a rectangle whose height is the value of $f$ at a selected point in the subinterval. Thus if $x_1^*, x_2^*, \ldots, x_n^*$ denote the $n$ selected points, then the rectangles will have heights $f(x_1^*), f(x_2^*), \ldots, f(x_n^*)$ and areas

$$f(x_1^*)\Delta x, \quad f(x_2^*)\Delta x, \ldots, \quad f(x_n^*)\Delta x$$

(Figure 5.4.4).

- The union of the rectangles forms a region $R_n$ whose area can be regarded as an approximation to the area $A$ of $R$; that is,

$$A = \text{area}(R) \approx \text{area}(R_n) = f(x_1^*)\Delta x + f(x_2^*)\Delta x + \cdots + f(x_n^*)\Delta x = \sum_{k=1}^{n} f(x_k^*)\Delta x$$

(Figure 5.4.5).

- Repeat the process using more and more subdivisions, and define the area of $R$ to be the "limit"

$$A = \lim_{n \to +\infty} \sum_{k=1}^{n} f(x_k^*)\Delta x$$

of the areas of approximating regions $R_n$ as $n$ increases without bound.

In summary, we make the following definition.

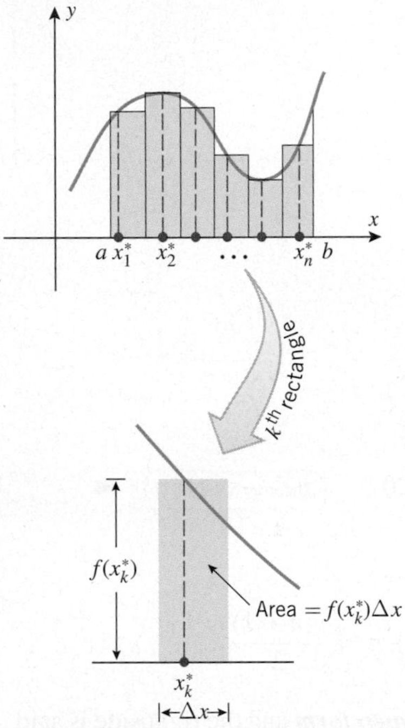


▲ Figure 5.4.4

The limit in (2) is interpreted to mean that given any number $\epsilon > 0$ the inequality

$$\left| A - \sum_{k=1}^{n} f(x_k^*)\Delta x \right| < \epsilon$$

holds when $n$ is sufficiently large, no matter how the points $x_k^*$ are selected.

**5.4.3 DEFINITION** ***(Area Under a Curve)*** If the function $f$ is continuous on $[a, b]$ and if $f(x) \geq 0$ for all $x$ in $[a, b]$, then the ***area*** $A$ under the curve $y = f(x)$ over the interval $[a, b]$ is defined by

$$A = \lim_{n \to +\infty} \sum_{k=1}^{n} f(x_k^*)\Delta x \tag{2}$$

**REMARK** There is a difference in interpretation between $\lim_{n\to+\infty}$ and $\lim_{x\to+\infty}$, where $n$ represents a positive integer and $x$ represents a real number. Later we will study limits of the type $\lim_{n\to+\infty}$ in detail, but for now suffice it to say that the computational techniques we have used for limits of type $\lim_{x\to+\infty}$ will also work for $\lim_{n\to+\infty}$.

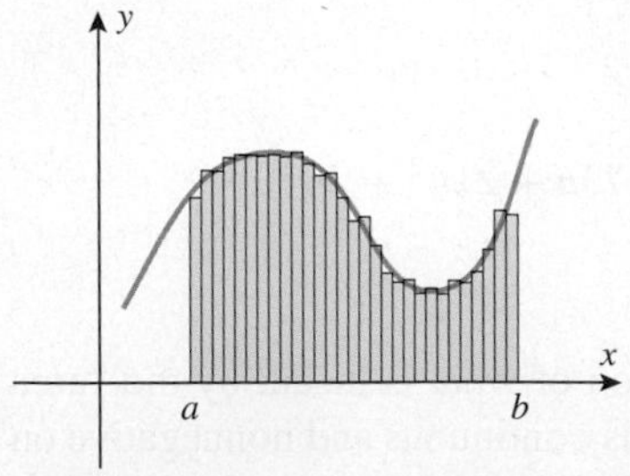


▲ Figure 5.4.5 area $(R_n) \approx$ area $(R)$

The values of $x_1^*, x_2^*, \ldots, x_n^*$ in (2) can be chosen arbitrarily, so it is conceivable that different choices of these values might produce different values of $A$. Were this to happen, then Definition 5.4.3 would not be an acceptable definition of area. Fortunately, this does not happen; it is proved in advanced courses that if $f$ is continuous (as we have assumed), then the same value of $A$ results no matter how the $x_k^*$ are chosen. In practice they are chosen in some systematic fashion, some common choices being

- the left endpoint of each subinterval
- the right endpoint of each subinterval
- the midpoint of each subinterval

To be more specific, suppose that the interval $[a, b]$ is divided into $n$ equal parts of length $\Delta x = (b - a)/n$ by the points $x_1, x_2, \ldots, x_{n-1}$, and let $x_0 = a$ and $x_n = b$ (Figure 5.4.6). Then,

$$x_k = a + k\Delta x \quad \text{for } k = 0, 1, 2, \ldots, n$$

Thus, the left endpoint, right endpoint, and midpoint choices for $x_1^*, x_2^*, \ldots, x_n^*$ are given by

$$x_k^* = x_{k-1} = a + (k-1)\Delta x \quad \boxed{\text{Left endpoint}} \tag{3}$$

$$x_k^* = x_k = a + k\Delta x \quad \boxed{\text{Right endpoint}} \tag{4}$$

$$x_k^* = \tfrac{1}{2}(x_{k-1} + x_k) = a + \left(k - \tfrac{1}{2}\right)\Delta x \quad \boxed{\text{Midpoint}} \tag{5}$$

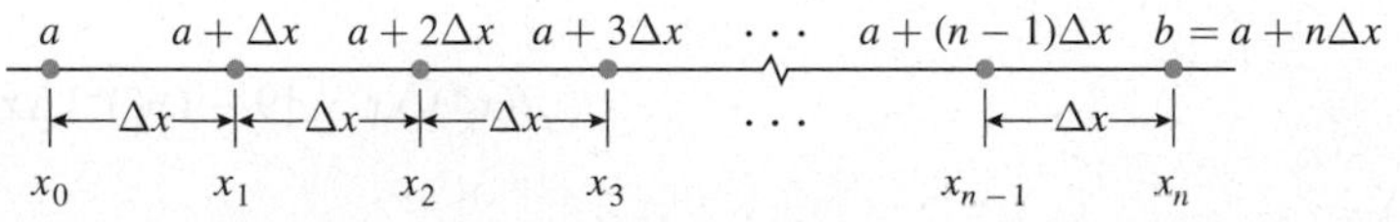


▶ **Figure 5.4.6**

When applicable, the antiderivative method will be the method of choice for finding exact areas. However, the following examples will help to reinforce the ideas that we have just discussed.

▶ **Example 4** Use Definition 5.4.3 with $x_k^*$ as the right endpoint of each subinterval to find the area between the graph of $f(x) = x^2$ and the interval $[0, 1]$.

***Solution.*** The length of each subinterval is

$$\Delta x = \frac{b-a}{n} = \frac{1-0}{n} = \frac{1}{n}$$

so it follows from (4) that

$$x_k^* = a + k\Delta x = \frac{k}{n}$$

Thus,

$$\sum_{k=1}^{n} f(x_k^*)\Delta x = \sum_{k=1}^{n} (x_k^*)^2 \Delta x = \sum_{k=1}^{n} \left(\frac{k}{n}\right)^2 \frac{1}{n} = \frac{1}{n^3} \sum_{k=1}^{n} k^2$$

$$= \frac{1}{n^3}\left[\frac{n(n+1)(2n+1)}{6}\right] \quad \boxed{\text{Part } (b) \text{ of Theorem 5.4.2}}$$

$$= \frac{1}{6}\left(\frac{n}{n} \cdot \frac{n+1}{n} \cdot \frac{2n+1}{n}\right) = \frac{1}{6}\left(1 + \frac{1}{n}\right)\left(2 + \frac{1}{n}\right)$$

from which it follows that

$$A = \lim_{n \to +\infty} \sum_{k=1}^{n} f(x_k^*)\Delta x = \lim_{n \to +\infty} \left[\frac{1}{6}\left(1 + \frac{1}{n}\right)\left(2 + \frac{1}{n}\right)\right] = \frac{1}{3}$$

Observe that this is consistent with the results in Table 5.1.2 and the related discussion in Section 5.1. ◀

In the solution to Example 4 we made use of one of the "closed form" summation formulas from Theorem 5.4.2. The next result collects some consequences of Theorem 5.4.2 that can facilitate computations of area using Definition 5.4.3.

What pattern is revealed by parts (*b*)–(*d*) of Theorem 5.4.4? Does part (*a*) also fit this pattern? What would you conjecture to be the value of

$$\lim_{n \to +\infty} \frac{1}{n^m} \sum_{k=1}^{n} k^{m-1}?$$

**5.4.4 THEOREM**

(*a*) $\displaystyle \lim_{n \to +\infty} \frac{1}{n} \sum_{k=1}^{n} 1 = 1$ (*b*) $\displaystyle \lim_{n \to +\infty} \frac{1}{n^2} \sum_{k=1}^{n} k = \frac{1}{2}$

(*c*) $\displaystyle \lim_{n \to +\infty} \frac{1}{n^3} \sum_{k=1}^{n} k^2 = \frac{1}{3}$ (*d*) $\displaystyle \lim_{n \to +\infty} \frac{1}{n^4} \sum_{k=1}^{n} k^3 = \frac{1}{4}$

The proof of Theorem 5.4.4 is left as an exercise for the reader.

► **Example 5** Use Definition 5.4.3 with $x_k^*$ as the midpoint of each subinterval to find the area under the parabola $y = f(x) = 9 - x^2$ and over the interval $[0, 3]$.

***Solution.*** Each subinterval has length

$$\Delta x = \frac{b-a}{n} = \frac{3-0}{n} = \frac{3}{n}$$

so it follows from (5) that

$$x_k^* = a + \left(k - \frac{1}{2}\right)\Delta x = \left(k - \frac{1}{2}\right)\left(\frac{3}{n}\right)$$

Thus,

$$\begin{aligned} f(x_k^*)\Delta x = [9 - (x_k^*)^2]\Delta x &= \left[9 - \left(k - \frac{1}{2}\right)^2\left(\frac{3}{n}\right)^2\right]\left(\frac{3}{n}\right) \\ &= \left[9 - \left(k^2 - k + \frac{1}{4}\right)\left(\frac{9}{n^2}\right)\right]\left(\frac{3}{n}\right) \\ &= \frac{27}{n} - \frac{27}{n^3}k^2 + \frac{27}{n^3}k - \frac{27}{4n^3} \end{aligned}$$

from which it follows that

$$\begin{aligned} A &= \lim_{n\to+\infty} \sum_{k=1}^{n} f(x_k^*)\Delta x \\ &= \lim_{n\to+\infty} \sum_{k=1}^{n} \left(\frac{27}{n} - \frac{27}{n^3}k^2 + \frac{27}{n^3}k - \frac{27}{4n^3}\right) \\ &= \lim_{n\to+\infty} 27\left[\frac{1}{n}\sum_{k=1}^{n} 1 - \frac{1}{n^3}\sum_{k=1}^{n} k^2 + \frac{1}{n}\left(\frac{1}{n^2}\sum_{k=1}^{n} k\right) - \frac{1}{4n^2}\left(\frac{1}{n}\sum_{k=1}^{n} 1\right)\right] \\ &= 27\left[1 - \frac{1}{3} + 0 \cdot \frac{1}{2} - 0 \cdot 1\right] = 18 \qquad \boxed{\text{Theorem 5.4.4}} \end{aligned}$$

◄

## NUMERICAL APPROXIMATIONS OF AREA

It follows from Definition 5.4.3 that if $n$ is large, then

$$\sum_{k=1}^{n} f(x_k^*)\Delta x = \Delta x \sum_{k=1}^{n} f(x_k^*) = \Delta x[f(x_1^*) + f(x_2^*) + \cdots + f(x_n^*)] \tag{6}$$

will be a good approximation to the area $A$. If one of Formulas (3), (4), or (5) is used to choose the $x_k^*$ in (6), then the result is called the ***left endpoint approximation***, the ***right endpoint approximation***, or the ***midpoint approximation***, respectively (Figure 5.4.7).

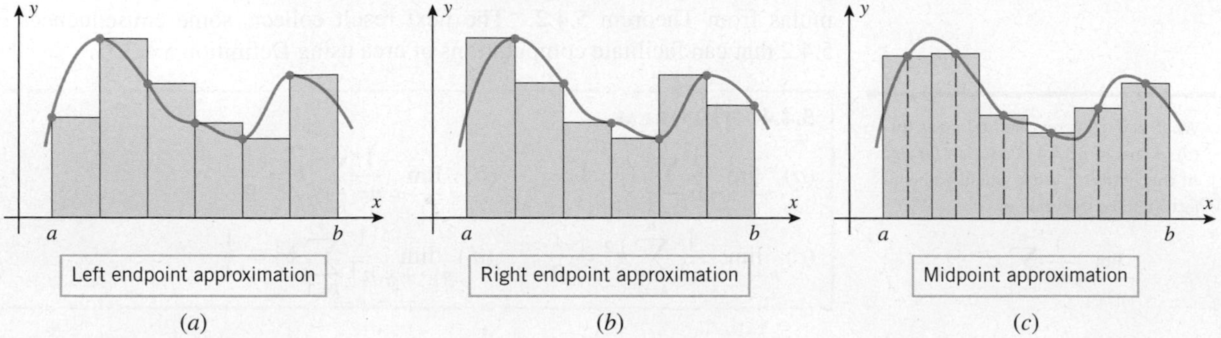


▲ **Figure 5.4.7**

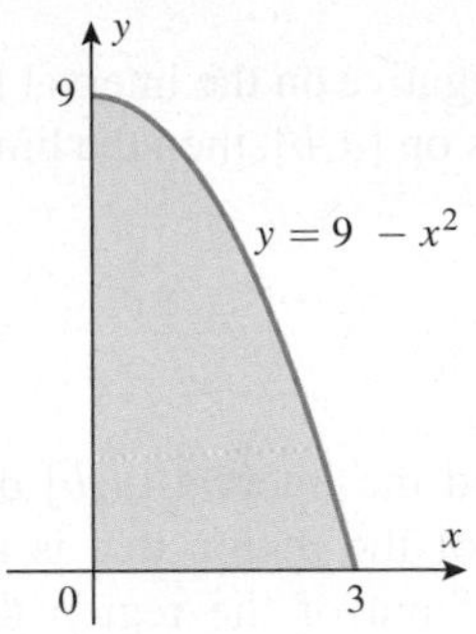

▲ Figure 5.4.8

▶ **Example 6** Find the left endpoint, right endpoint, and midpoint approximations of the area under the curve $y = 9 - x^2$ over the interval $[0, 3]$ with $n = 10, n = 20$, and $n = 50$ (Figure 5.4.8). Compare the accuracies of these three methods.

***Solution.*** Details of the computations for the case $n = 10$ are shown to six decimal places in Table 5.4.1 and the results of all the computations are given in Table 5.4.2. We showed in Example 5 that the exact area is 18 (i.e., 18 square units), so in this case the midpoint approximation is more accurate than the endpoint approximations. This is also evident geometrically from Figure 5.4.9. You can also see from the figure that in this case the left endpoint approximation overestimates the area and the right endpoint approximation underestimates it. Later in the text we will investigate the error that results when an area is approximated by the midpoint approximation. ◀

**Table 5.4.1**

$n = 10, \Delta x = (b - a)/n = (3 - 0)/10 = 0.3$

| | LEFT ENDPOINT APPROXIMATION | | RIGHT ENDPOINT APPROXIMATION | | MIDPOINT APPROXIMATION | |
|---|---|---|---|---|---|---|
| $k$ | $x_k^*$ | $9 - (x_k^*)^2$ | $x_k^*$ | $9 - (x_k^*)^2$ | $x_k^*$ | $9 - (x_k^*)^2$ |
| 1 | 0.0 | 9.000000 | 0.3 | 8.910000 | 0.15 | 8.977500 |
| 2 | 0.3 | 8.910000 | 0.6 | 8.640000 | 0.45 | 8.797500 |
| 3 | 0.6 | 8.640000 | 0.9 | 8.190000 | 0.75 | 8.437500 |
| 4 | 0.9 | 8.190000 | 1.2 | 7.560000 | 1.05 | 7.897500 |
| 5 | 1.2 | 7.560000 | 1.5 | 6.750000 | 1.35 | 7.177500 |
| 6 | 1.5 | 6.750000 | 1.8 | 5.760000 | 1.65 | 6.277500 |
| 7 | 1.8 | 5.760000 | 2.1 | 4.590000 | 1.95 | 5.197500 |
| 8 | 2.1 | 4.590000 | 2.4 | 3.240000 | 2.25 | 3.937500 |
| 9 | 2.4 | 3.240000 | 2.7 | 1.710000 | 2.55 | 2.497500 |
| 10 | 2.7 | 1.710000 | 3.0 | 0.000000 | 2.85 | 0.877500 |
| | | 64.350000 | | 55.350000 | | 60.075000 |
| $\Delta x \sum_{k=1}^{n} f(x_k^*)$ | | (0.3)(64.350000) = 19.305000 | | (0.3)(55.350000) = 16.605000 | | (0.3)(60.075000) = 18.022500 |

**Table 5.4.2**

| $n$ | LEFT ENDPOINT APPROXIMATION | RIGHT ENDPOINT APPROXIMATION | MIDPOINT APPROXIMATION |
|---|---|---|---|
| 10 | 19.305000 | 16.605000 | 18.022500 |
| 20 | 18.663750 | 17.313750 | 18.005625 |
| 50 | 18.268200 | 17.728200 | 18.000900 |

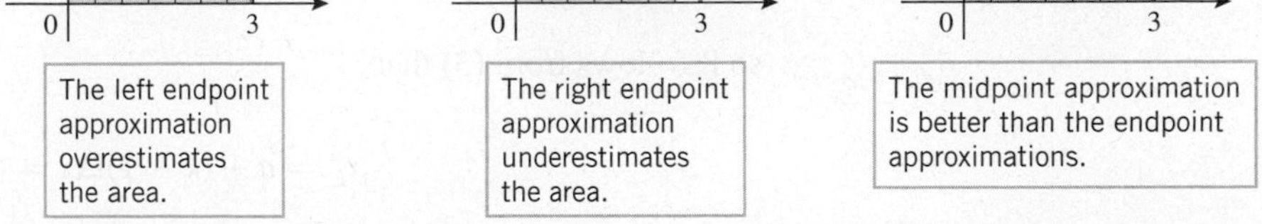

▲ Figure 5.4.9

## NET SIGNED AREA

In Definition 5.4.3 we assumed that $f$ is continuous and nonnegative on the interval $[a, b]$. If $f$ is continuous and attains both positive and negative values on $[a, b]$, then the limit

$$\lim_{n\to+\infty}\sum_{k=1}^{n} f(x_k^*)\Delta x \tag{7}$$

no longer represents the area between the curve $y = f(x)$ and the interval $[a, b]$ on the $x$-axis; rather, it represents a difference of areas—the area of the region that is above the interval $[a, b]$ and below the curve $y = f(x)$ minus the area of the region that is below the interval $[a, b]$ and above the curve $y = f(x)$. We call this the ***net signed area*** between the graph of $y = f(x)$ and the interval $[a, b]$. For example, in Figure 5.4.10*a*, the net signed area between the curve $y = f(x)$ and the interval $[a, b]$ is

$$(A_I + A_{III}) - A_{II} = [\text{area above } [a, b]] - [\text{area below } [a, b]]$$

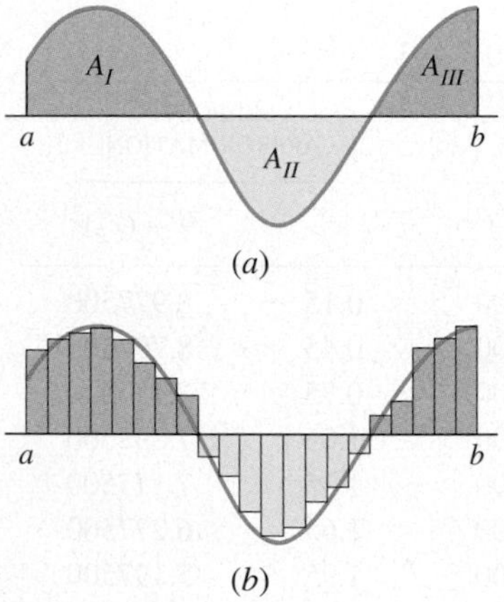


▲ **Figure 5.4.10**

To explain why the limit in (7) represents this net signed area, let us subdivide the interval $[a, b]$ in Figure 5.4.10*a* into $n$ equal subintervals and examine the terms in the sum

$$\sum_{k=1}^{n} f(x_k^*)\Delta x \tag{8}$$

If $f(x_k^*)$ is positive, then the product $f(x_k^*)\Delta x$ represents the area of the rectangle with height $f(x_k^*)$ and base $\Delta x$ (the pink rectangles in Figure 5.4.10*b*). However, if $f(x_k^*)$ is negative, then the product $f(x_k^*)\Delta x$ is the *negative* of the area of the rectangle with height $|f(x_k^*)|$ and base $\Delta x$ (the green rectangles in Figure 5.4.10*b*). Thus, (8) represents the total area of the pink rectangles minus the total area of the green rectangles. As $n$ increases, the pink rectangles fill out the regions with areas $A_I$ and $A_{III}$ and the green rectangles fill out the region with area $A_{II}$, which explains why the limit in (7) represents the signed area between $y = f(x)$ and the interval $[a, b]$. We formalize this in the following definition.

As with Definition 5.4.3, it can be proved that the limit in (9) always exists and that the same value of $A$ results no matter how the points in the subintervals are chosen.

**5.4.5 DEFINITION** (***Net Signed Area***) If the function $f$ is continuous on $[a, b]$, then the ***net signed area*** $A$ between $y = f(x)$ and the interval $[a, b]$ is defined by

$$A = \lim_{n\to+\infty}\sum_{k=1}^{n} f(x_k^*)\Delta x \tag{9}$$

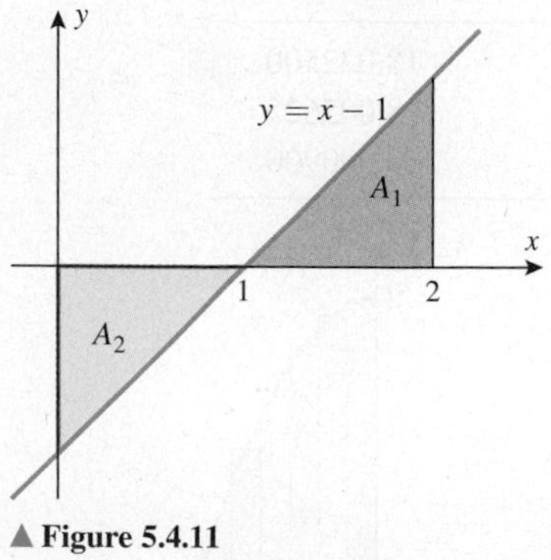


▲ **Figure 5.4.11**

Figure 5.4.11 shows the graph of $f(x) = x - 1$ over the interval $[0, 2]$. It is geometrically evident that the areas $A_1$ and $A_2$ in that figure are equal, so we expect the net signed area between the graph of $f$ and the interval $[0, 2]$ to be zero.

► **Example 7** Confirm that the net signed area between the graph of $f(x) = x - 1$ and the interval $[0, 2]$ is zero by using Definition 5.4.5 with $x_k^*$ chosen to be the left endpoint of each subinterval.

***Solution.*** Each subinterval has length

$$\Delta x = \frac{b-a}{n} = \frac{2-0}{n} = \frac{2}{n}$$

so it follows from (3) that

$$x_k^* = a + (k-1)\Delta x = (k-1)\left(\frac{2}{n}\right)$$

Thus,

$$\sum_{k=1}^{n} f(x_k^*)\Delta x = \sum_{k=1}^{n}(x_k^* - 1)\Delta x = \sum_{k=1}^{n}\left[(k-1)\left(\frac{2}{n}\right) - 1\right]\left(\frac{2}{n}\right)$$

$$= \sum_{k=1}^{n}\left[\left(\frac{4}{n^2}\right)k - \frac{4}{n^2} - \frac{2}{n}\right]$$

from which it follows that

$$A = \lim_{n\to+\infty}\sum_{k=1}^{n} f(x_k^*)\Delta x = \lim_{n\to+\infty}\left[4\left(\frac{1}{n^2}\sum_{k=1}^{n} k\right) - \frac{4}{n}\left(\frac{1}{n}\sum_{k=1}^{n} 1\right) - 2\left(\frac{1}{n}\sum_{k=1}^{n} 1\right)\right]$$

$$= 4\left(\frac{1}{2}\right) - 0\cdot 1 - 2\cdot 1 = 0 \qquad \boxed{\text{Theorem 5.4.4}}$$

This confirms that the net signed area is zero. ◀

## ✓QUICK CHECK EXERCISES 5.4 *(See page 285 for answers.)*

1. (a) Write the sum in two ways:

$$\frac{1}{2}+\frac{1}{4}+\frac{1}{6}+\frac{1}{8} = \sum_{k=1}^{4}\_\_\_\_ = \sum_{j=0}^{3}\_\_\_\_$$

(b) Express the sum $10 + 10^2 + 10^3 + 10^4 + 10^5$ using sigma notation.

2. Express the sums in closed form.

(a) $\sum_{k=1}^{n} k$ (b) $\sum_{k=1}^{n}(6k+1)$ (c) $\sum_{k=1}^{n} k^2$

3. Divide the interval $[1, 3]$ into $n = 4$ subintervals of equal length.

(a) Each subinterval has width ________.

(b) The left endpoints of the subintervals are ________.

(c) The midpoints of the subintervals are ________.

(d) The right endpoints of the subintervals are ________.

4. Find the left endpoint approximation for the area between the curve $y = x^2$ and the interval $[1, 3]$ using $n = 4$ equal subdivisions of the interval.

5. The right endpoint approximation for the net signed area between $y = f(x)$ and an interval $[a, b]$ is given by

$$\sum_{k=1}^{n}\frac{6k+1}{n^2}$$

Find the exact value of this net signed area.

## EXERCISE SET 5.4 C CAS

1. Evaluate.

(a) $\sum_{k=1}^{3} k^3$ (b) $\sum_{j=2}^{6}(3j-1)$ (c) $\sum_{i=-4}^{1}(i^2 - i)$

(d) $\sum_{n=0}^{5} 1$ (e) $\sum_{k=0}^{4}(-2)^k$ (f) $\sum_{n=1}^{6}\sin n\pi$

2. Evaluate.

(a) $\sum_{k=1}^{4} k\sin\frac{k\pi}{2}$ (b) $\sum_{j=0}^{5}(-1)^j$ (c) $\sum_{i=7}^{20}\pi^2$

(d) $\sum_{m=3}^{5} 2^{m+1}$ (e) $\sum_{n=1}^{6}\sqrt{n}$ (f) $\sum_{k=0}^{10}\cos k\pi$

**3–8** Write each expression in sigma notation but do not evaluate. ■

3. $1 + 2 + 3 + \cdots + 10$

4. $3\cdot 1 + 3\cdot 2 + 3\cdot 3 + \cdots + 3\cdot 20$

5. $2 + 4 + 6 + 8 + \cdots + 20$

6. $1 + 3 + 5 + 7 + \cdots + 15$

7. $1 - 3 + 5 - 7 + 9 - 11$

8. $1 - \frac{1}{2} + \frac{1}{3} - \frac{1}{4} + \frac{1}{5}$

9. (a) Express the sum of the even integers from 2 to 100 in sigma notation.

(b) Express the sum of the odd integers from 1 to 99 in sigma notation.

10. Express in sigma notation.

(a) $a_1 - a_2 + a_3 - a_4 + a_5$

(b) $-b_0 + b_1 - b_2 + b_3 - b_4 + b_5$

(c) $a_0 + a_1x + a_2x^2 + \cdots + a_nx^n$

(d) $a^5 + a^4b + a^3b^2 + a^2b^3 + ab^4 + b^5$

**11–16** Use Theorem 5.4.2 to evaluate the sums. Check your answers using the summation feature of a calculating utility. ■

11. $\sum_{k=1}^{100} k$

12. $\sum_{k=1}^{100}(7k+1)$

13. $\sum_{k=1}^{20} k^2$

14. $\sum_{k=4}^{20} k^2$

15. $\sum_{k=1}^{30} k(k-2)(k+2)$

16. $\sum_{k=1}^{6}(k - k^3)$

**17–20** Express the sums in closed form. ■

**17.** $\sum_{k=1}^{n} \frac{3k}{n}$ **18.** $\sum_{k=1}^{n-1} \frac{k^2}{n}$ **19.** $\sum_{k=1}^{n-1} \frac{k^3}{n^2}$

**20.** $\sum_{k=1}^{n} \left(\frac{5}{n} - \frac{2k}{n}\right)$

**21–24 True–False** Determine whether the statement is true or false. Explain your answer. ■

**21.** For all positive integers $n$

$$1^3 + 2^3 + \cdots + n^3 = (1 + 2 + \cdots + n)^2$$

**22.** The midpoint approximation is the average of the left endpoint approximation and the right endpoint approximation.

**23.** Every right endpoint approximation for the area under the graph of $y = x^2$ over an interval $[a, b]$ will be an overestimate.

**24.** For any continuous function $f$, the area between the graph of $f$ and an interval $[a, b]$ (on which $f$ is defined) is equal to the absolute value of the net signed area between the graph of $f$ and the interval $[a, b]$.

**FOCUS ON CONCEPTS**

**25.** (a) Write the first three and final two summands in the sum

$$\sum_{k=1}^{n} \left(2 + k \cdot \frac{3}{n}\right)^4 \frac{3}{n}$$

Explain why this sum gives the right endpoint approximation for the area under the curve $y = x^4$ over the interval $[2, 5]$.

(b) Show that a change in the index range of the sum in part (a) can produce the left endpoint approximation for the area under the curve $y = x^4$ over the interval $[2, 5]$.

**26.** For a function $f$ that is continuous on $[a, b]$, Definition 5.4.5 says that the net signed area $A$ between $y = f(x)$ and the interval $[a, b]$ is

$$A = \lim_{n \to +\infty} \sum_{k=1}^{n} f(x_k^*)\Delta x$$

Give geometric interpretations for the symbols $n$, $x_k^*$, and $\Delta x$. Explain how to interpret the limit in this definition.

**27–30** Divide the specified interval into $n = 4$ subintervals of equal length and then compute

$$\sum_{k=1}^{4} f(x_k^*)\Delta x$$

with $x_k^*$ as (a) the left endpoint of each subinterval, (b) the midpoint of each subinterval, and (c) the right endpoint of each subinterval. Illustrate each part with a graph of $f$ that includes the rectangles whose areas are represented in the sum. ■

**27.** $f(x) = 3x + 1$; $[2, 6]$ **28.** $f(x) = 1/x$; $[1, 9]$

**29.** $f(x) = \cos x$; $[0, \pi]$ **30.** $f(x) = 2x - x^2$; $[-1, 3]$

C **31–34** Use a calculating utility with summation capabilities or a CAS to obtain an approximate value for the area between the curve $y = f(x)$ and the specified interval with $n = 10$, 20, and 50 subintervals using the (a) left endpoint, (b) midpoint, and (c) right endpoint approximations. ■

**31.** $f(x) = 1/x$; $[1, 2]$ **32.** $f(x) = 1/x^2$; $[1, 3]$

**33.** $f(x) = \sqrt{x}$; $[0, 4]$ **34.** $f(x) = \sin x$; $[0, \pi/2]$

**35–40** Use Definition 5.4.3 with $x_k^*$ as the *right* endpoint of each subinterval to find the area under the curve $y = f(x)$ over the specified interval. ■

**35.** $f(x) = x/2$; $[1, 4]$ **36.** $f(x) = 5 - x$; $[0, 5]$

**37.** $f(x) = 9 - x^2$; $[0, 3]$ **38.** $f(x) = 4 - \frac{1}{4}x^2$; $[0, 3]$

**39.** $f(x) = x^3$; $[2, 6]$ **40.** $f(x) = 1 - x^3$; $[-3, -1]$

**41–44** Use Definition 5.4.3 with $x_k^*$ as the *left* endpoint of each subinterval to find the area under the curve $y = f(x)$ over the specified interval. ■

**41.** $f(x) = x/2$; $[1, 4]$ **42.** $f(x) = 5 - x$; $[0, 5]$

**43.** $f(x) = 9 - x^2$; $[0, 3]$ **44.** $f(x) = 4 - \frac{1}{4}x^2$; $[0, 3]$

**45–48** Use Definition 5.4.3 with $x_k^*$ as the *midpoint* of each subinterval to find the area under the curve $y = f(x)$ over the specified interval. ■

**45.** $f(x) = 2x$; $[0, 4]$ **46.** $f(x) = 6 - x$; $[1, 5]$

**47.** $f(x) = x^2$; $[0, 1]$ **48.** $f(x) = x^2$; $[-1, 1]$

**49–52** Use Definition 5.4.5 with $x_k^*$ as the *right* endpoint of each subinterval to find the net signed area between the curve $y = f(x)$ and the specified interval. ■

**49.** $f(x) = x$; $[-1, 1]$. Verify your answer with a simple geometric argument.

**50.** $f(x) = x$; $[-1, 2]$. Verify your answer with a simple geometric argument.

**51.** $f(x) = x^2 - 1$; $[0, 2]$ **52.** $f(x) = x^3$; $[-1, 1]$

**53.** (a) Show that the area under the graph of $y = x^3$ and over the interval $[0, b]$ is $b^4/4$.

(b) Find a formula for the area under $y = x^3$ over the interval $[a, b]$, where $a \geq 0$.

**54.** Find the area between the graph of $y = \sqrt{x}$ and the interval $[0, 1]$. [*Hint:* Use the result of Exercise 25 of Section 5.1.]

**55.** An artist wants to create a rough triangular design using uniform square tiles glued edge to edge. She places $n$ tiles in a row to form the base of the triangle and then makes each successive row two tiles shorter than the preceding row. Find a formula for the number of tiles used in the design. [*Hint:* Your answer will depend on whether $n$ is even or odd.]

**56.** An artist wants to create a sculpture by gluing together uniform spheres. She creates a rough rectangular base that has 50 spheres along one edge and 30 spheres along the other. She then creates successive layers by gluing spheres in the grooves of the preceding layer. How many spheres will there be in the sculpture?

**57–60** Consider the sum

$$\begin{aligned}\sum_{k=1}^{4}[(k+1)^3-k^3] &= [5^3-4^3]+[4^3-3^3]\\ &\quad +[3^3-2^3]+[2^3-1^3]\\ &= 5^3-1^3=124\end{aligned}$$

For convenience, the terms are listed in reverse order. Note how cancellation allows the entire sum to collapse like a telescope. A sum is said to ***telescope*** when part of each term cancels part of an adjacent term, leaving only portions of the first and last terms uncanceled. Evaluate the telescoping sums in these exercises.

**57.** $\sum_{k=5}^{17}(3^k-3^{k-1})$ **58.** $\sum_{k=1}^{50}\left(\frac{1}{k}-\frac{1}{k+1}\right)$

**59.** $\sum_{k=2}^{20}\left(\frac{1}{k^2}-\frac{1}{(k-1)^2}\right)$ **60.** $\sum_{k=1}^{100}(2^{k+1}-2^k)$

**61.** (a) Show that

$$\frac{1}{1\cdot 3}+\frac{1}{3\cdot 5}+\cdots+\frac{1}{(2n-1)(2n+1)}=\frac{n}{2n+1}$$

$$\left[\textit{Hint: }\frac{1}{(2n-1)(2n+1)}=\frac{1}{2}\left(\frac{1}{2n-1}-\frac{1}{2n+1}\right)\right]$$

(b) Use the result in part (a) to find

$$\lim_{n\to+\infty}\sum_{k=1}^{n}\frac{1}{(2k-1)(2k+1)}$$

**62.** (a) Show that

$$\frac{1}{1\cdot 2}+\frac{1}{2\cdot 3}+\frac{1}{3\cdot 4}+\cdots+\frac{1}{n(n+1)}=\frac{n}{n+1}$$

$$\left[\textit{Hint: }\frac{1}{n(n+1)}=\frac{1}{n}-\frac{1}{n+1}\right]$$

(b) Use the result in part (a) to find

$$\lim_{n\to+\infty}\sum_{k=1}^{n}\frac{1}{k(k+1)}$$

**63.** Let $\bar{x}$ denote the arithmetic average of the $n$ numbers $x_1, x_2, \ldots, x_n$. Use Theorem 5.4.1 to prove that

$$\sum_{i=1}^{n}(x_i-\bar{x})=0$$

**64.** Let

$$S=\sum_{k=0}^{n}ar^k$$

Show that $S-rS=a-ar^{n+1}$ and hence that

$$\sum_{k=0}^{n}ar^k=\frac{a-ar^{n+1}}{1-r}\quad (r\neq 1)$$

(A sum of this form is called a ***geometric sum***.)

**65.** By writing out the sums, determine whether the following are valid identities.

(a) $\int\left[\sum_{i=1}^{n}f_i(x)\right]dx=\sum_{i=1}^{n}\left[\int f_i(x)\,dx\right]$

(b) $\frac{d}{dx}\left[\sum_{i=1}^{n}f_i(x)\right]=\sum_{i=1}^{n}\left[\frac{d}{dx}[f_i(x)]\right]$

**66.** Which of the following are valid identities?

(a) $\sum_{i=1}^{n}a_ib_i=\sum_{i=1}^{n}a_i\sum_{i=1}^{n}b_i$ (b) $\sum_{i=1}^{n}a_i^2=\left(\sum_{i=1}^{n}a_i\right)^2$

(c) $\sum_{i=1}^{n}\frac{a_i}{b_i}=\frac{\sum_{i=1}^{n}a_i}{\sum_{i=1}^{n}b_i}$ (d) $\sum_{i=1}^{n}a_i=\sum_{j=0}^{n-1}a_{j+1}$

**67.** Prove parts (*a*) and (*c*) of Theorem 5.4.1.

**68.** Prove Theorem 5.4.4.

**69. Writing** What is *net signed area*? How does this concept expand our application of the rectangle method?

**70. Writing** Based on Example 6, one might conjecture that the midpoint approximation always provides a better approximation than either endpoint approximation. Discuss the merits of this conjecture.

✔ **QUICK CHECK ANSWERS 5.4** 1. (a) $\frac{1}{2k};\ \frac{1}{2(j+1)}$ (b) $\sum_{k=1}^{5}10^k$ 2. (a) $\frac{n(n+1)}{2}$ (b) $3n(n+1)+n$ (c) $\frac{n(n+1)(2n+1)}{6}$ 3. (a) 0.5 (b) 1, 1.5, 2, 2.5 (c) 1.25, 1.75, 2.25, 2.75 (d) 1.5, 2, 2.5, 3 4. 6.75 5. $\lim_{n\to+\infty}\frac{3n^2+4n}{n^2}=3$

## 5.5 THE DEFINITE INTEGRAL

*In this section we will introduce the concept of a "definite integral," which will link the concept of area to other important concepts such as length, volume, density, probability, and work.*

### ■ RIEMANN SUMS AND THE DEFINITE INTEGRAL

In our definition of net signed area (Definition 5.4.5), we assumed that for each positive number $n$, the interval $[a, b]$ was subdivided into $n$ subintervals of equal length to create bases for the approximating rectangles. For some functions it may be more convenient to use rectangles with different widths (see Making Connections Exercises 2 and 3); however, if we are to "exhaust" an area with rectangles of different widths, then it is important that

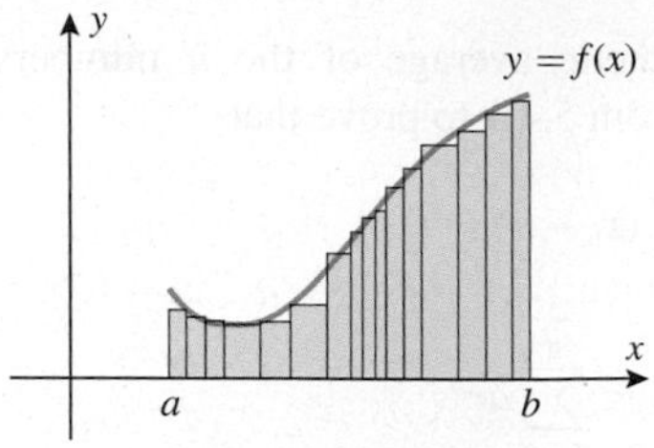


▲ Figure 5.5.1

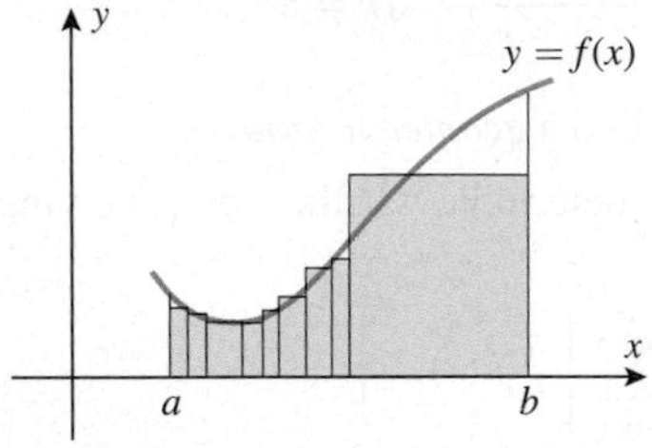


▲ Figure 5.5.2

successive subdivisions be constructed in such a way that the widths of all the rectangles approach zero as $n$ increases (Figure 5.5.1). Thus, we must preclude the kind of situation that occurs in Figure 5.5.2 in which the right half of the interval is never subdivided. If this kind of subdivision were allowed, the error in the approximation would not approach zero as $n$ increased.

A ***partition*** of the interval $[a, b]$ is a collection of points

$$a = x_0 < x_1 < x_2 < \cdots < x_{n-1} < x_n = b$$

that divides $[a, b]$ into $n$ subintervals of lengths

$$\Delta x_1 = x_1 - x_0, \quad \Delta x_2 = x_2 - x_1, \quad \Delta x_3 = x_3 - x_2, \ldots, \quad \Delta x_n = x_n - x_{n-1}$$

The partition is said to be ***regular*** provided the subintervals all have the same length

$$\Delta x_k = \Delta x = \frac{b-a}{n}$$

For a regular partition, the widths of the approximating rectangles approach zero as $n$ is made large. Since this need not be the case for a general partition, we need some way to measure the "size" of these widths. One approach is to let $\max \Delta x_k$ denote the largest of the subinterval widths. The magnitude $\max \Delta x_k$ is called the ***mesh size*** of the partition. For example, Figure 5.5.3 shows a partition of the interval $[0, 6]$ into four subintervals with a mesh size of 2.

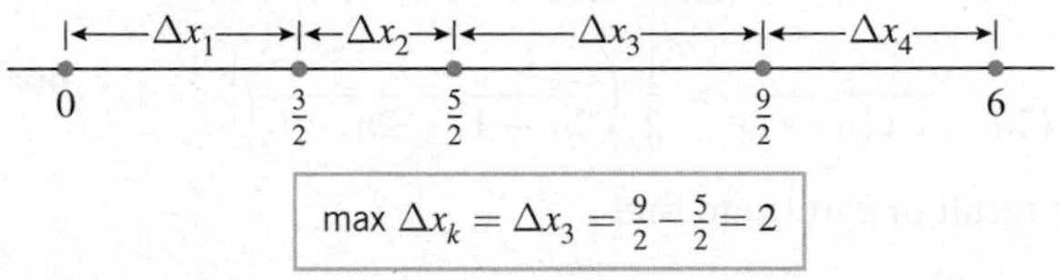


► Figure 5.5.3

If we are to generalize Definition 5.4.5 so that it allows for unequal subinterval widths, we must replace the constant length $\Delta x$ by the variable length $\Delta x_k$. When this is done the sum

$$\sum_{k=1}^{n} f(x_k^*)\Delta x \quad \text{is replaced by} \quad \sum_{k=1}^{n} f(x_k^*)\Delta x_k$$

> Some writers use the symbol $\|\Delta\|$ rather than $\max \Delta x_k$ for the mesh size of the partition, in which case $\max \Delta x_k \to 0$ would be replaced by $\|\Delta\| \to 0$.

We also need to replace the expression $n \to +\infty$ by an expression that guarantees us that the lengths of all subintervals approach zero. We will use the expression $\max \Delta x_k \to 0$ for this purpose. Based on our intuitive concept of area, we would then expect the net signed area $A$ between the graph of $f$ and the interval $[a, b]$ to satisfy the equation

$$A = \lim_{\max \Delta x_k \to 0} \sum_{k=1}^{n} f(x_k^*)\Delta x_k$$

(We will see in a moment that this is the case.) The limit that appears in this expression is one of the fundamental concepts of integral calculus and forms the basis for the following definition.

**5.5.1 DEFINITION** A function $f$ is said to be ***integrable*** on a finite closed interval $[a, b]$ if the limit

$$\lim_{\max \Delta x_k \to 0} \sum_{k=1}^{n} f(x_k^*)\Delta x_k$$

exists and does not depend on the choice of partitions or on the choice of the points $x_k^*$ in the subintervals. When this is the case we denote the limit by the symbol

$$\int_a^b f(x)\,dx = \lim_{\max \Delta x_k \to 0} \sum_{k=1}^{n} f(x_k^*)\Delta x_k$$

which is called the ***definite integral*** of $f$ from $a$ to $b$. The numbers $a$ and $b$ are called the ***lower limit of integration*** and the ***upper limit of integration***, respectively, and $f(x)$ is called the ***integrand***.

The notation used for the definite integral deserves some comment. Historically, the expression "$f(x)\,dx$" was interpreted to be the "infinitesimal area" of a rectangle with height $f(x)$ and "infinitesimal" width $dx$. By "summing" these infinitesimal areas, the entire area under the curve was obtained. The integral symbol "$\int$" is an "elongated s" that was used to indicate this summation. For us, the integral symbol "$\int$" and the symbol "$dx$" can serve as reminders that the definite integral is actually a limit of a *summation* as $\Delta x_k \to 0$. The sum that appears in Definition 5.5.1 is called a ***Riemann sum***, and the definite integral is sometimes called the ***Riemann integral*** in honor of the German mathematician Bernhard Riemann who formulated many of the basic concepts of integral calculus. (The reason for the similarity in notation between the definite integral and the indefinite integral will become clear in the next section, where we will establish a link between the two types of "integration.")

The limit that appears in Definition 5.5.1 is somewhat different from the kinds of limits discussed in Chapter 1. Loosely phrased, the expression

$$\lim_{\max \Delta x_k \to 0} \sum_{k=1}^{n} f(x_k^*)\Delta x_k = L$$

is intended to convey the idea that we can force the Riemann sums to be as close as we please to $L$, regardless of how the values of $x_k^*$ are chosen, by making the mesh size of the partition sufficiently small. While it is possible to give a more formal definition of this limit, we will simply rely on intuitive arguments when applying Definition 5.5.1.

Although a function need not be continuous on an interval to be integrable on that interval (Exercise 42), we will be interested primarily in definite integrals of continuous functions. The following theorem, which we will state without proof, says that if a function is continuous on a finite closed interval, then it is integrable on that interval, and its definite integral is the net signed area between the graph of the function and the interval.

**5.5.2 THEOREM** *If a function $f$ is continuous on an interval $[a, b]$, then $f$ is integrable on $[a, b]$, and the net signed area $A$ between the graph of $f$ and the interval $[a, b]$ is*

$$A = \int_a^b f(x)\,dx \tag{1}$$

**REMARK** Formula (1) follows from the integrability of $f$, since the integrability allows us to use any partitions to evaluate the integral. In particular, if we use *regular* partitions of $[a, b]$, then

$$\Delta x_k = \Delta x = \frac{b-a}{n}$$

for all values of $k$. This implies that $\max\Delta x_k = (b-a)/n$, from which it follows that $\max\Delta x_k \to 0$ if and only if $n \to +\infty$. Thus,

$$\int_a^b f(x)\,dx = \lim_{\max\Delta x_k \to 0} \sum_{k=1}^{n} f(x_k^*)\Delta x_k = \lim_{n\to+\infty} \sum_{k=1}^{n} f(x_k^*)\Delta x = A$$

**Georg Friedrich Bernhard Riemann (1826–1866)** German mathematician. Bernhard Riemann, as he is commonly known, was the son of a Protestant minister. He received his elementary education from his father and showed brilliance in arithmetic at an early age. In 1846 he enrolled at Göttingen University to study theology and philology, but he soon transferred to mathematics. He studied physics under W. E. Weber and mathematics under Carl Friedrich Gauss, whom some people consider to be the greatest mathematician who ever lived. In 1851 Riemann received his Ph.D. under Gauss, after which he remained at Göttingen to teach. In 1862, one month after his marriage, Riemann suffered an attack of pleuritis, and for the remainder of his life was an extremely sick man. He finally succumbed to tuberculosis in 1866 at age 39.

An interesting story surrounds Riemann's work in geometry. For his introductory lecture prior to becoming an associate professor, Riemann submitted three possible topics to Gauss. Gauss surprised Riemann by choosing the topic Riemann liked the least, the foundations of geometry. The lecture was like a scene from a movie. The old and failing Gauss, a giant in his day, watching intently as his brilliant and youthful protégé skillfully pieced together portions of the old man's own work into a complete and beautiful system. Gauss is said to have gasped with delight as the lecture neared its end, and on the way home he marveled at his student's brilliance. Gauss died shortly thereafter. The results presented by Riemann that day eventually evolved into a fundamental tool that Einstein used some 50 years later to develop relativity theory.

In addition to his work in geometry, Riemann made major contributions to the theory of complex functions and mathematical physics. The notion of the definite integral, as it is presented in most basic calculus courses, is due to him. Riemann's early death was a great loss to mathematics, for his mathematical work was brilliant and of fundamental importance.

*[Image: Library of Congress Prints and Photographs Division; LC-USZ62-120354]*

In the simplest cases, definite integrals of continuous functions can be calculated using formulas from plane geometry to compute signed areas.

In Example 1, it is understood that the units of area are the squared units of length, even though we have not stated the units of length explicitly.

**▶ Example 1** Sketch the region whose area is represented by the definite integral, and evaluate the integral using an appropriate formula from geometry.

$$\text{(a)} \int_1^4 2\,dx \qquad \text{(b)} \int_{-1}^2 (x+2)\,dx \qquad \text{(c)} \int_0^1 \sqrt{1-x^2}\,dx$$

***Solution (a).*** The graph of the integrand is the horizontal line $y = 2$, so the region is a rectangle of height 2 extending over the interval from 1 to 4 (Figure 5.5.4*a*). Thus,

$$\int_1^4 2\,dx = (\text{area of rectangle}) = 2(3) = 6$$

***Solution (b).*** The graph of the integrand is the line $y = x + 2$, so the region is a trapezoid whose base extends from $x = -1$ to $x = 2$ (Figure 5.5.4*b*). Thus,

$$\int_{-1}^2 (x+2)\,dx = (\text{area of trapezoid}) = \frac{1}{2}(1+4)(3) = \frac{15}{2}$$

***Solution (c).*** The graph of $y = \sqrt{1-x^2}$ is the upper semicircle of radius 1, centered at the origin, so the region is the right quarter-circle extending from $x = 0$ to $x = 1$ (Figure 5.5.4*c*). Thus,

$$\int_0^1 \sqrt{1-x^2}\,dx = (\text{area of quarter-circle}) = \frac{1}{4}\pi(1^2) = \frac{\pi}{4} \blacktriangleleft$$

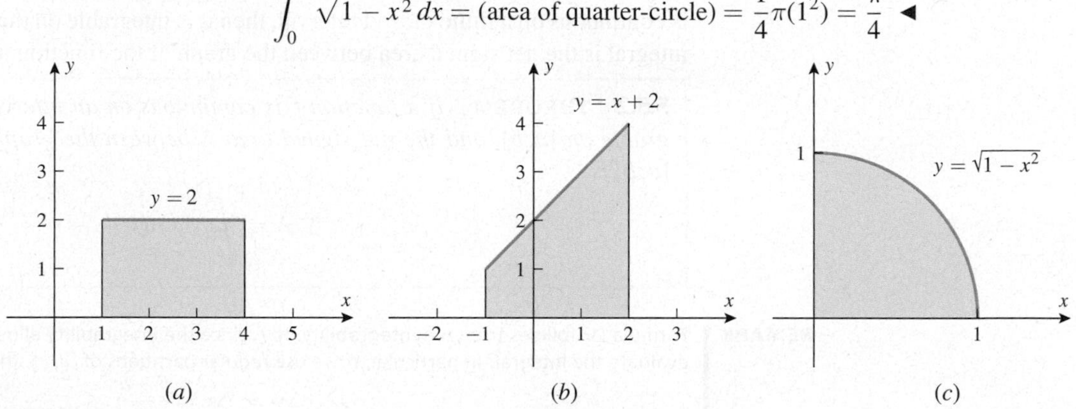


▲ **Figure 5.5.4**

**▶ Example 2** Evaluate

$$\text{(a)} \int_0^2 (x-1)\,dx \qquad \text{(b)} \int_0^1 (x-1)\,dx$$

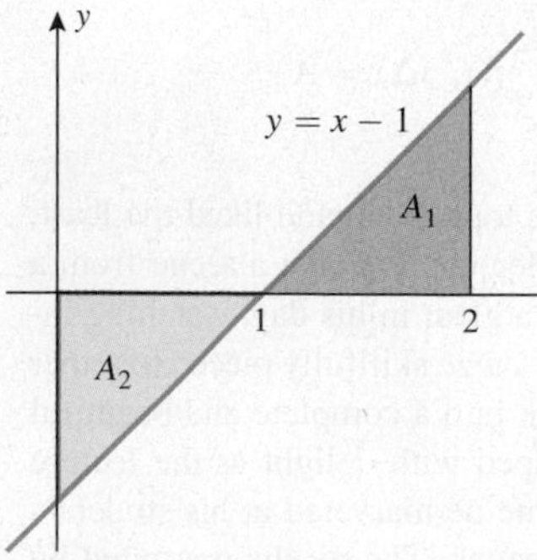


▲ **Figure 5.5.5**

***Solution.*** The graph of $y = x - 1$ is shown in Figure 5.5.5, and we leave it for you to verify that the shaded triangular regions both have area $\frac{1}{2}$. Over the interval $[0, 2]$ the net signed area is $A_1 - A_2 = \frac{1}{2} - \frac{1}{2} = 0$, and over the interval $[0, 1]$ the net signed area is $-A_2 = -\frac{1}{2}$. Thus,

$$\int_0^2 (x-1)\,dx = 0 \quad \text{and} \quad \int_0^1 (x-1)\,dx = -\tfrac{1}{2}$$

(Recall that in Example 7 of Section 5.4, we used Definition 5.4.5 to show that the net signed area between the graph of $y = x - 1$ and the interval $[0, 2]$ is zero.) ◀

## PROPERTIES OF THE DEFINITE INTEGRAL

It is assumed in Definition 5.5.1 that $[a, b]$ is a finite closed interval with $a < b$, and hence the upper limit of integration in the definite integral is greater than the lower limit of integration. However, it will be convenient to extend this definition to allow for cases in which the upper and lower limits of integration are equal or the lower limit of integration is greater than the upper limit of integration. For this purpose we make the following special definitions.

**5.5.3 DEFINITION**

(a) If $a$ is in the domain of $f$, we define

$$\int_a^a f(x)\,dx = 0$$

(b) If $f$ is integrable on $[a, b]$, then we define

$$\int_b^a f(x)\,dx = -\int_a^b f(x)\,dx$$

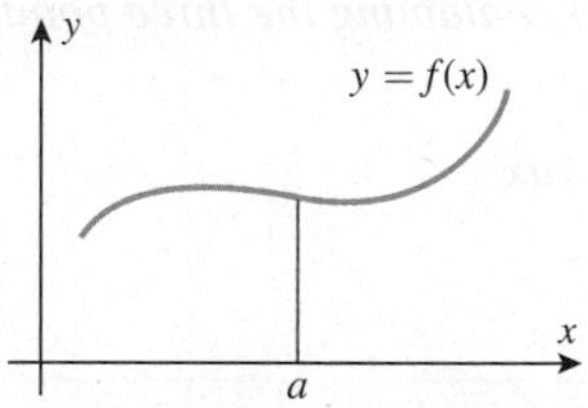


▲ Figure 5.5.6

Part (a) of this definition is consistent with the intuitive idea that the area between a point on the $x$-axis and a curve $y = f(x)$ should be zero (Figure 5.5.6). Part (b) of the definition is simply a useful convention; it states that interchanging the limits of integration reverses the sign of the integral.

### ▶ Example 3

(a) $\displaystyle\int_1^1 x^2\,dx = 0$

(b) $\displaystyle\int_1^0 \sqrt{1-x^2}\,dx = -\int_0^1 \sqrt{1-x^2}\,dx = -\frac{\pi}{4}$ ◀ (Example 1(c))

Because definite integrals are defined as limits, they inherit many of the properties of limits. For example, we know that constants can be moved through limit signs and that the limit of a sum or difference is the sum or difference of the limits. Thus, you should not be surprised by the following theorem, which we state without formal proof.

**5.5.4 THEOREM** *If $f$ and $g$ are integrable on $[a, b]$ and if $c$ is a constant, then $cf$, $f+g$, and $f-g$ are integrable on $[a, b]$ and*

(a) $\displaystyle\int_a^b cf(x)\,dx = c\int_a^b f(x)\,dx$

(b) $\displaystyle\int_a^b [f(x)+g(x)]\,dx = \int_a^b f(x)\,dx + \int_a^b g(x)\,dx$

(c) $\displaystyle\int_a^b [f(x)-g(x)]\,dx = \int_a^b f(x)\,dx - \int_a^b g(x)\,dx$

Part (*b*) of this theorem can be extended to more than two functions. More precisely,

$$\int_a^b [f_1(x)+f_2(x)+\cdots+f_n(x)]\,dx = \int_a^b f_1(x)\,dx + \int_a^b f_2(x)\,dx + \cdots + \int_a^b f_n(x)\,dx$$

Some properties of definite integrals can be motivated by interpreting the integral as an area. For example, if $f$ is continuous and nonnegative on the interval $[a, b]$, and if $c$ is a point between $a$ and $b$, then the area under $y = f(x)$ over the interval $[a, b]$ can be split into two parts and expressed as the area under the graph from $a$ to $c$ plus the area under the graph from $c$ to $b$ (Figure 5.5.7), that is,

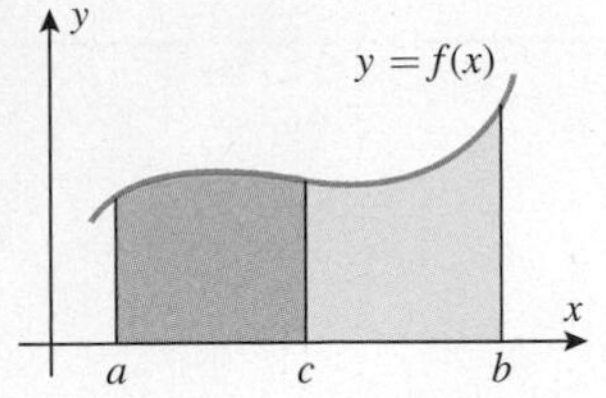


▲ **Figure 5.5.7**

$$\int_a^b f(x)\,dx = \int_a^c f(x)\,dx + \int_c^b f(x)\,dx$$

This is a special case of the following theorem about definite integrals, which we state without proof.

**5.5.5 THEOREM** *If $f$ is integrable on a closed interval containing the three points $a$, $b$, and $c$, then*

$$\int_a^b f(x)\,dx = \int_a^c f(x)\,dx + \int_c^b f(x)\,dx$$

*no matter how the points are ordered.*

The following theorem, which we state without formal proof, can also be motivated by interpreting definite integrals as areas.

**5.5.6 THEOREM**

(*a*) *If $f$ is integrable on $[a, b]$ and $f(x) \geq 0$ for all $x$ in $[a, b]$, then*

$$\int_a^b f(x)\,dx \geq 0$$

(*b*) *If $f$ and $g$ are integrable on $[a, b]$ and $f(x) \geq g(x)$ for all $x$ in $[a, b]$, then*

$$\int_a^b f(x)\,dx \geq \int_a^b g(x)\,dx$$

Part (*b*) of Theorem 5.5.6 states that the direction (sometimes called the *sense*) of the inequality $f(x) \geq g(x)$ is unchanged if one integrates both sides. Moreover, if $b > a$, then both parts of the theorem remain true if $\geq$ is replaced by $\leq$, $>$, or $<$ throughout.

Geometrically, part (*a*) of this theorem states the obvious fact that if $f$ is nonnegative on $[a, b]$, then the net signed area between the graph of $f$ and the interval $[a, b]$ is also nonnegative (Figure 5.5.8). Part (*b*) has its simplest interpretation when $f$ and $g$ are nonnegative on $[a, b]$, in which case the theorem states that if the graph of $f$ does not go below the graph of $g$, then the area under the graph of $f$ is at least as large as the area under the graph of $g$ (Figure 5.5.9).

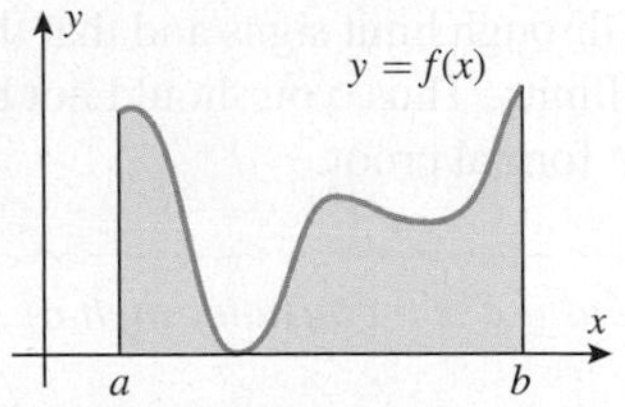


▲ **Figure 5.5.8**

► **Example 4** Evaluate

$$\int_0^1 (5 - 3\sqrt{1 - x^2})\,dx$$

***Solution.*** From parts (*a*) and (*c*) of Theorem 5.5.4 we can write

$$\int_0^1 (5 - 3\sqrt{1 - x^2})\,dx = \int_0^1 5\,dx - \int_0^1 3\sqrt{1 - x^2}\,dx = \int_0^1 5\,dx - 3\int_0^1 \sqrt{1 - x^2}\,dx$$

The first integral in this difference can be interpreted as the area of a rectangle of height 5 and base 1, so its value is 5, and from Example 1 the value of the second integral is $\pi/4$. Thus,

$$\int_0^1 (5 - 3\sqrt{1 - x^2})\,dx = 5 - 3\left(\frac{\pi}{4}\right) = 5 - \frac{3\pi}{4} \blacktriangleleft$$

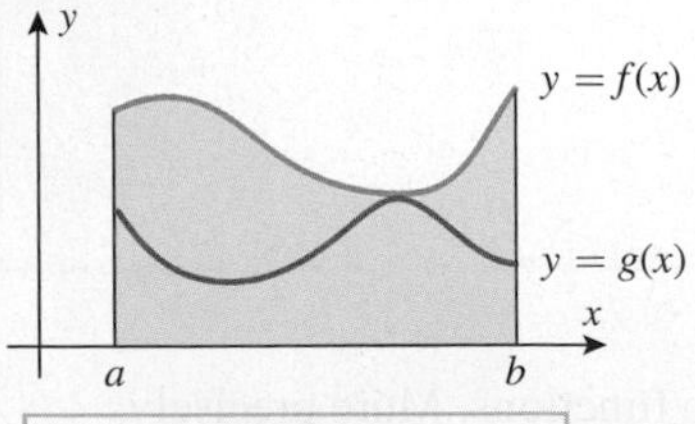


▲ **Figure 5.5.9**

## DISCONTINUITIES AND INTEGRABILITY

In the late nineteenth and early twentieth centuries, mathematicians began to investigate conditions under which the limit that defines an integral fails to exist, that is, conditions under which a function fails to be integrable. The matter is quite complex and beyond the scope of this text. However, there are a few basic results about integrability that are important to know; we begin with a definition.

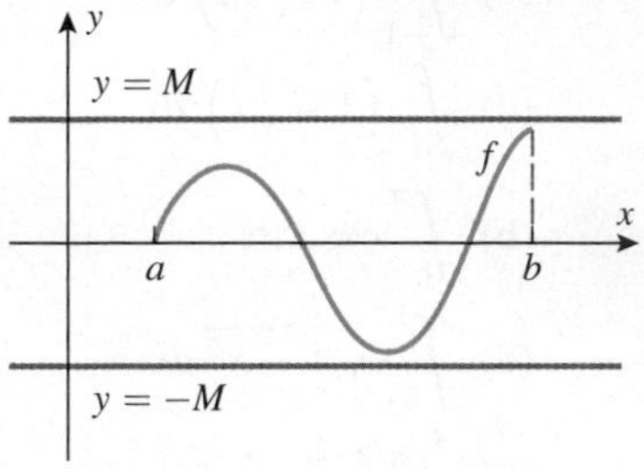


$f$ is bounded on $[a, b]$.

▲ **Figure 5.5.10**

**5.5.7 DEFINITION** A function $f$ that is defined on an interval is said to be ***bounded*** on the interval if there is a positive number $M$ such that

$$-M \leq f(x) \leq M$$

for all $x$ in the interval. Geometrically, this means that the graph of $f$ over the interval lies between the lines $y = -M$ and $y = M$.

For example, a continuous function $f$ is bounded on *every* finite closed interval because the Extreme-Value Theorem (4.4.2) implies that $f$ has an absolute maximum and an absolute minimum on the interval; hence, its graph will lie between the lines $y = -M$ and $y = M$, provided we make $M$ large enough (Figure 5.5.10). In contrast, a function that has a vertical asymptote inside of an interval is not bounded on that interval because its graph over the interval cannot be made to lie between the lines $y = -M$ and $y = M$, no matter how large we make the value of $M$ (Figure 5.5.11).

The following theorem, which we state without proof, provides some facts about integrability for functions with discontinuities. In the exercises we have included some problems that are concerned with this theorem (Exercises 42, 43, and 44).

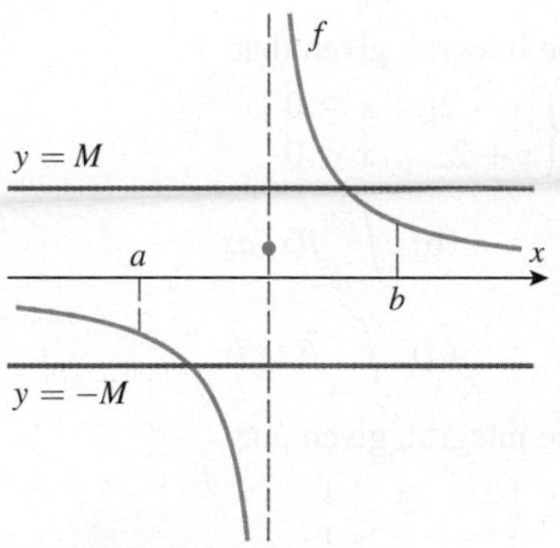


$f$ is not bounded on $[a, b]$.

▲ **Figure 5.5.11**

**5.5.8 THEOREM** *Let $f$ be a function that is defined on the finite closed interval $[a, b]$.*

(a) *If $f$ has finitely many discontinuities in $[a, b]$ but is bounded on $[a, b]$, then $f$ is integrable on $[a, b]$.*

(b) *If $f$ is not bounded on $[a, b]$, then $f$ is not integrable on $[a, b]$.*

## ✓QUICK CHECK EXERCISES 5.5 *(See page 294 for answers.)*

**1.** In each part, use the partition of $[2, 7]$ in the accompanying figure.

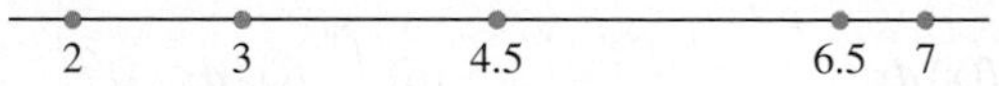


▲ **Figure Ex-1**

(a) What is $n$, the number of subintervals in this partition?

(b) $x_0 =$ ______; $x_1 =$ ______; $x_2 =$ ______;
$x_3 =$ ______; $x_4 =$ ______

(c) $\Delta x_1 =$ ______; $\Delta x_2 =$ ______; $\Delta x_3 =$ ______; $\Delta x_4 =$ ______

(d) The mesh of this partition is ______.

**2.** Let $f(x) = 2x - 8$. Use the partition of $[2, 7]$ in Quick Check Exercise 1 and the choices $x_1^* = 2$, $x_2^* = 4$, $x_3^* = 5$, and $x_4^* = 7$ to evaluate the Riemann sum

$$\sum_{k=1}^{4} f(x_k^*)\Delta x_k$$

**3.** Use the accompanying figure to evaluate

$$\int_2^7 (2x - 8)\, dx$$

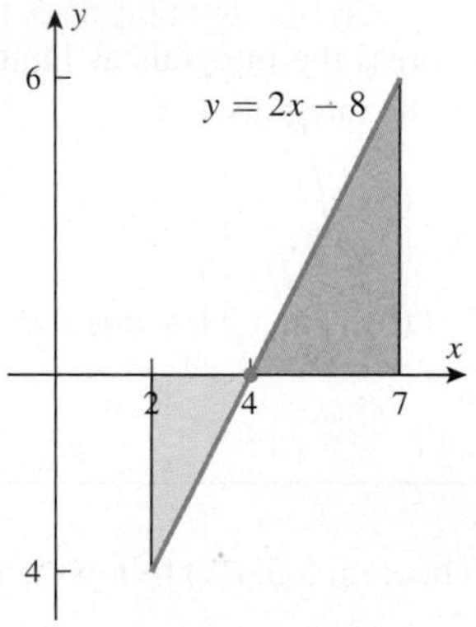


◀ **Figure Ex-3**

**4.** Suppose that $g(x)$ is a function for which

$$\int_{-2}^{1} g(x)\, dx = 5 \quad \text{and} \quad \int_1^2 g(x)\, dx = -2$$

Use this information to evaluate the definite integrals.

(a) $\displaystyle\int_1^2 5g(x)\, dx$  (b) $\displaystyle\int_{-2}^{2} g(x)\, dx$

(c) $\displaystyle\int_1^1 [g(x)]^2\, dx$  (d) $\displaystyle\int_2^{-2} 4g(x)\, dx$

## EXERCISE SET 5.5

**1–4** Find the value of

(a) $\sum_{k=1}^{n} f(x_k^*)\,\Delta x_k$ (b) $\max \Delta x_k$. ■

**1.** $f(x) = x + 1;\ a = 0, b = 4;\ n = 3;$
$\Delta x_1 = 1, \Delta x_2 = 1, \Delta x_3 = 2;$
$x_1^* = \frac{1}{3}, x_2^* = \frac{3}{2}, x_3^* = 3$

**2.** $f(x) = \cos x;\ a = 0, b = 2\pi;\ n = 4;$
$\Delta x_1 = \pi/2, \Delta x_2 = 3\pi/4, \Delta x_3 = \pi/2, \Delta x_4 = \pi/4;$
$x_1^* = \pi/4, x_2^* = \pi, x_3^* = 3\pi/2, x_4^* = 7\pi/4$

**3.** $f(x) = 4 - x^2;\ a = -3, b = 4;\ n = 4;$
$\Delta x_1 = 1, \Delta x_2 = 2, \Delta x_3 = 1, \Delta x_4 = 3;$
$x_1^* = -\frac{5}{2}, x_2^* = -1, x_3^* = \frac{1}{4}, x_4^* = 3$

**4.** $f(x) = x^3;\ a = -3, b = 3;\ n = 4;$
$\Delta x_1 = 2, \Delta x_2 = 1, \Delta x_3 = 1, \Delta x_4 = 2;$
$x_1^* = -2, x_2^* = 0, x_3^* = 0, x_4^* = 2$

**5–8** Use the given values of $a$ and $b$ to express the following limits as integrals. (Do not evaluate the integrals.) ■

**5.** $\lim_{\max \Delta x_k \to 0} \sum_{k=1}^{n} (x_k^*)^2 \Delta x_k;\ a = -1, b = 2$

**6.** $\lim_{\max \Delta x_k \to 0} \sum_{k=1}^{n} (x_k^*)^3 \Delta x_k;\ a = 1, b = 2$

**7.** $\lim_{\max \Delta x_k \to 0} \sum_{k=1}^{n} 4x_k^*(1 - 3x_k^*)\Delta x_k;\ a = -3, b = 3$

**8.** $\lim_{\max \Delta x_k \to 0} \sum_{k=1}^{n} (\sin^2 x_k^*)\Delta x_k;\ a = 0, b = \pi/2$

**9–10** Use Definition 5.5.1 to express the integrals as limits of Riemann sums. (Do not evaluate the integrals.) ■

**9.** (a) $\int_1^2 2x\,dx$ (b) $\int_0^1 \frac{x}{x+1}\,dx$

**10.** (a) $\int_1^2 \sqrt{x}\,dx$ (b) $\int_{-\pi/2}^{\pi/2} (1 + \cos x)\,dx$

**FOCUS ON CONCEPTS**

**11.** Explain informally why Theorem 5.5.4(*a*) follows from Definition 5.5.1.

**12.** Explain informally why Theorem 5.5.6(*a*) follows from Definition 5.5.1.

**13–16** Sketch the region whose signed area is represented by the definite integral, and evaluate the integral using an appropriate formula from geometry, where needed. ■

**13.** (a) $\int_0^3 x\,dx$ (b) $\int_{-2}^{-1} x\,dx$
(c) $\int_{-1}^{4} x\,dx$ (d) $\int_{-5}^{5} x\,dx$

**14.** (a) $\int_0^2 \left(1 - \frac{1}{2}x\right) dx$ (b) $\int_{-1}^{1} \left(1 - \frac{1}{2}x\right) dx$
(c) $\int_2^3 \left(1 - \frac{1}{2}x\right) dx$ (d) $\int_0^3 \left(1 - \frac{1}{2}x\right) dx$

**15.** (a) $\int_0^5 2\,dx$ (b) $\int_0^{\pi} \cos x\,dx$
(c) $\int_{-1}^{2} |2x - 3|\,dx$ (d) $\int_{-1}^{1} \sqrt{1 - x^2}\,dx$

**16.** (a) $\int_{-10}^{-5} 6\,dx$ (b) $\int_{-\pi/3}^{\pi/3} \sin x\,dx$
(c) $\int_0^3 |x - 2|\,dx$ (d) $\int_0^2 \sqrt{4 - x^2}\,dx$

**17.** In each part, evaluate the integral, given that

$$f(x) = \begin{cases} |x - 2|, & x \geq 0 \\ x + 2, & x < 0 \end{cases}$$

(a) $\int_{-2}^{0} f(x)\,dx$ (b) $\int_{-2}^{2} f(x)\,dx$
(c) $\int_0^6 f(x)\,dx$ (d) $\int_{-4}^{6} f(x)\,dx$

**18.** In each part, evaluate the integral, given that

$$f(x) = \begin{cases} 2x, & x \leq 1 \\ 2, & x > 1 \end{cases}$$

(a) $\int_0^1 f(x)\,dx$ (b) $\int_{-1}^{1} f(x)\,dx$
(c) $\int_1^{10} f(x)\,dx$ (d) $\int_{1/2}^{5} f(x)\,dx$

**FOCUS ON CONCEPTS**

**19–20** Use the areas shown in the figure to find

(a) $\int_a^b f(x)\,dx$ (b) $\int_b^c f(x)\,dx$
(c) $\int_a^c f(x)\,dx$ (d) $\int_a^d f(x)\,dx$. ■

**19.**

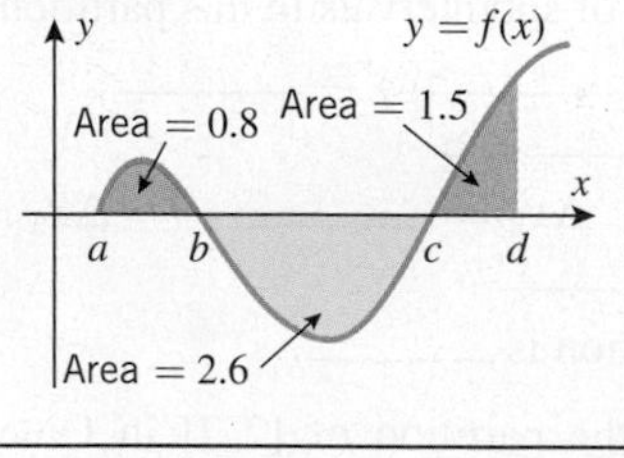


**20.**

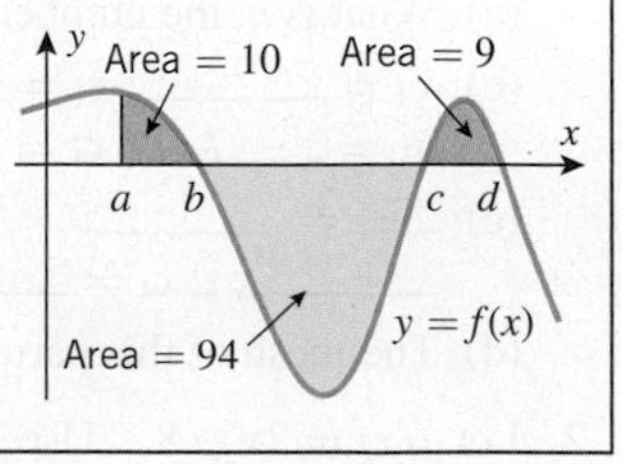


**21.** Find $\int_{-1}^{2} [f(x) + 2g(x)]\,dx$ if

$$\int_{-1}^{2} f(x)\,dx = 5 \quad \text{and} \quad \int_{-1}^{2} g(x)\,dx = -3$$

**22.** Find $\int_1^4 [3f(x) - g(x)]\,dx$ if

$$\int_1^4 f(x)\,dx = 2 \quad \text{and} \quad \int_1^4 g(x)\,dx = 10$$

**23.** Find $\int_1^5 f(x)\,dx$ if

$$\int_0^1 f(x)\,dx = -2 \quad \text{and} \quad \int_0^5 f(x)\,dx = 1$$

**24.** Find $\int_3^{-2} f(x)\,dx$ if

$$\int_{-2}^1 f(x)\,dx = 2 \quad \text{and} \quad \int_1^3 f(x)\,dx = -6$$

**25–28** Use Theorem 5.5.4 and appropriate formulas from geometry to evaluate the integrals. ■

**25.** $\int_{-1}^{3} (4 - 5x)\,dx$ **26.** $\int_{-2}^{2} (1 - 3|x|)\,dx$

**27.** $\int_0^1 (x + 2\sqrt{1 - x^2})\,dx$ **28.** $\int_{-3}^{0} (2 + \sqrt{9 - x^2})\,dx$

**29–32 True–False** Determine whether the statement is true or false. Explain your answer. ■

**29.** If $f(x)$ is integrable on $[a, b]$, then $f(x)$ is continuous on $[a, b]$.

**30.** It is the case that

$$0 < \int_{-1}^{1} \frac{\cos x}{\sqrt{1 + x^2}}\,dx$$

**31.** If the integral of $f(x)$ over the interval $[a, b]$ is negative, then $f(x) \le 0$ for $a \le x \le b$.

**32.** The function

$$f(x) = \begin{cases} 0, & x \le 0 \\ x^2, & x > 0 \end{cases}$$

is integrable over every closed interval $[a, b]$.

**33–34** Use Theorem 5.5.6 to determine whether the value of the integral is positive or negative. ■

**33.** (a) $\int_2^3 \frac{\sqrt{x}}{1 - x}\,dx$ (b) $\int_0^4 \frac{x^2}{3 - \cos x}\,dx$

**34.** (a) $\int_{-3}^{-1} \frac{x^4}{\sqrt{3 - x}}\,dx$ (b) $\int_{-2}^{2} \frac{x^3 - 9}{|x| + 1}\,dx$

**35.** Prove that if $f$ is continuous and if $m \le f(x) \le M$ on $[a, b]$, then

$$m(b - a) \le \int_a^b f(x)\,dx \le M(b - a)$$

**36.** Find the maximum and minimum values of $\sqrt{x^3 + 2}$ for $0 \le x \le 3$. Use these values, and the inequalities in Exercise 35, to find bounds on the value of the integral

$$\int_0^3 \sqrt{x^3 + 2}\,dx$$

**37–38** Evaluate the integrals by completing the square and applying appropriate formulas from geometry. ■

**37.** $\int_0^{10} \sqrt{10x - x^2}\,dx$ **38.** $\int_0^3 \sqrt{6x - x^2}\,dx$

**39–40** Evaluate the limit by expressing it as a definite integral over the interval $[a, b]$ and applying appropriate formulas from geometry. ■

**39.** $\lim_{\max \Delta x_k \to 0} \sum_{k=1}^{n} (3x_k^* + 1)\Delta x_k;\ a = 0, b = 1$

**40.** $\lim_{\max \Delta x_k \to 0} \sum_{k=1}^{n} \sqrt{4 - (x_k^*)^2}\,\Delta x_k;\ a = -2, b = 2$

**FOCUS ON CONCEPTS**

**41.** Let $f(x) = C$ be a constant function.
(a) Use a formula from geometry to show that

$$\int_a^b f(x)\,dx = C(b - a)$$

(b) Show that any Riemann sum for $f(x)$ over $[a, b]$ evaluates to $C(b - a)$. Use Definition 5.5.1 to show that

$$\int_a^b f(x)\,dx = C(b - a)$$

**42.** Define a function $f$ on $[0, 1]$ by

$$f(x) = \begin{cases} 1, & 0 < x \le 1 \\ 0, & x = 0 \end{cases}$$

Use Definition 5.5.1 to show that

$$\int_0^1 f(x)\,dx = 1$$

**43.** It can be shown that every interval contains both rational and irrational numbers. Accepting this to be so, do you believe that the function

$$f(x) = \begin{cases} 1 & \text{if } x \text{ is rational} \\ 0 & \text{if } x \text{ is irrational} \end{cases}$$

is integrable on a closed interval $[a, b]$? Explain your reasoning.

**44.** Define the function $f$ by

$$f(x) = \begin{cases} \dfrac{1}{x}, & x \ne 0 \\ 0, & x = 0 \end{cases}$$

It follows from Theorem 5.5.8(*b*) that $f$ is not integrable on the interval $[0, 1]$. Prove this to be the case by applying Definition 5.5.1. [*Hint:* Argue that no matter how small the mesh size is for a partition of $[0, 1]$, there will always be a choice of $x_1^*$ that will make the Riemann sum in Definition 5.5.1 as large as we like.]

**45.** In each part, use Theorems 5.5.2 and 5.5.8 to determine whether the function $f$ is integrable on the interval $[-1, 1]$.
(a) $f(x) = \cos x$
(b) $f(x) = \begin{cases} x/|x|, & x \ne 0 \\ 0, & x = 0 \end{cases}$
(c) $f(x) = \begin{cases} 1/x^2, & x \ne 0 \\ 0, & x = 0 \end{cases}$
(d) $f(x) = \begin{cases} \sin 1/x, & x \ne 0 \\ 0, & x = 0 \end{cases}$

**46. Writing** Write a short paragraph that discusses the similarities and differences between indefinite integrals and definite integrals.

**47. Writing** Write a paragraph that explains informally what it means for a function to be "integrable."

✓ **QUICK CHECK ANSWERS 5.5** 1. (a) $n = 4$ (b) 2, 3, 4.5, 6.5, 7 (c) 1, 1.5, 2, 0.5 (d) 2 2. 3 3. 5
4. (a) −10 (b) 3 (c) 0 (d) −12

# 5.6 THE FUNDAMENTAL THEOREM OF CALCULUS

*In this section we will establish two basic relationships between definite and indefinite integrals that together constitute a result called the "Fundamental Theorem of Calculus." One part of this theorem will relate the rectangle and antiderivative methods for calculating areas, and the second part will provide a powerful method for evaluating definite integrals using antiderivatives.*

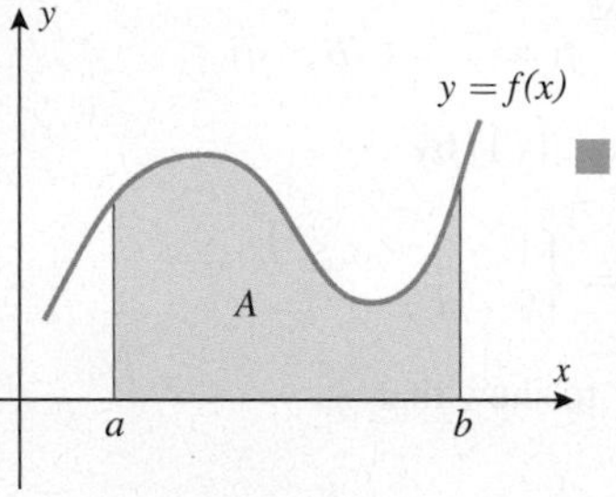


▲ **Figure 5.6.1**

## THE FUNDAMENTAL THEOREM OF CALCULUS

As in earlier sections, let us begin by assuming that $f$ is nonnegative and continuous on an interval $[a, b]$, in which case the area $A$ under the graph of $f$ over the interval $[a, b]$ is represented by the definite integral

$$A = \int_a^b f(x)\,dx \tag{1}$$

(Figure 5.6.1).

Recall that our discussion of the antiderivative method in Section 5.1 suggested that if $A(x)$ is the area under the graph of $f$ from $a$ to $x$ (Figure 5.6.2), then

- $A'(x) = f(x)$
- $A(a) = 0$ — The area under the curve from $a$ to $a$ is the area above the single point $a$, and hence is zero.
- $A(b) = A$ — The area under the curve from $a$ to $b$ is $A$.

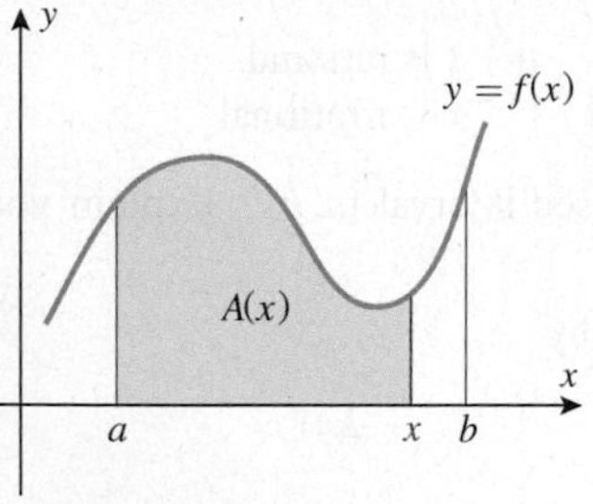


▲ **Figure 5.6.2**

The formula $A'(x) = f(x)$ states that $A(x)$ is an antiderivative of $f(x)$, which implies that every other antiderivative of $f(x)$ on $[a, b]$ can be obtained by adding a constant to $A(x)$. Accordingly, let

$$F(x) = A(x) + C$$

be any antiderivative of $f(x)$, and consider what happens when we subtract $F(a)$ from $F(b)$:

$$F(b) - F(a) = [A(b) + C] - [A(a) + C] = A(b) - A(a) = A - 0 = A$$

Hence (1) can be expressed as

$$\int_a^b f(x)\,dx = F(b) - F(a)$$

In words, this equation states:

*The definite integral can be evaluated by finding any antiderivative of the integrand and then subtracting the value of this antiderivative at the lower limit of integration from its value at the upper limit of integration.*

Although our evidence for this result assumed that $f$ is nonnegative on $[a, b]$, this assumption is not essential.

**5.6.1 THEOREM** ***(The Fundamental Theorem of Calculus, Part 1)*** *If $f$ is continuous on $[a, b]$ and $F$ is any antiderivative of $f$ on $[a, b]$, then*

$$\int_a^b f(x)\,dx = F(b) - F(a) \tag{2}$$

**PROOF** Let $x_1, x_2, \ldots, x_{n-1}$ be any points in $[a, b]$ such that

$$a < x_1 < x_2 < \cdots < x_{n-1} < b$$

These values divide $[a, b]$ into $n$ subintervals

$$[a, x_1], [x_1, x_2], \ldots, [x_{n-1}, b] \tag{3}$$

whose lengths, as usual, we denote by

$$\Delta x_1, \Delta x_2, \ldots, \Delta x_n$$

(see Figure 5.6.3). By hypothesis, $F'(x) = f(x)$ for all $x$ in $[a, b]$, so $F$ satisfies the hypotheses of the Mean-Value Theorem (4.8.2) on each subinterval in (3). Hence, we can find points $x_1^*, x_2^*, \ldots, x_n^*$ in the respective subintervals in (3) such that

$$\begin{aligned}
F(x_1) - F(a) &= F'(x_1^*)(x_1 - a) = f(x_1^*)\Delta x_1\\
F(x_2) - F(x_1) &= F'(x_2^*)(x_2 - x_1) = f(x_2^*)\Delta x_2\\
F(x_3) - F(x_2) &= F'(x_3^*)(x_3 - x_2) = f(x_3^*)\Delta x_3\\
&\vdots\\
F(b) - F(x_{n-1}) &= F'(x_n^*)(b - x_{n-1}) = f(x_n^*)\Delta x_n
\end{aligned}$$

Adding the preceding equations yields

$$F(b) - F(a) = \sum_{k=1}^{n} f(x_k^*)\Delta x_k \tag{4}$$

Let us now increase $n$ in such a way that $\max \Delta x_k \to 0$. Since $f$ is assumed to be continuous, the right side of (4) approaches $\int_a^b f(x)\,dx$ by Theorem 5.5.2 and Definition 5.5.1. However, the left side of (4) is independent of $n$; that is, the left side of (4) remains constant as $n$ increases. Thus,

$$F(b) - F(a) = \lim_{\max \Delta x_k \to 0} \sum_{k=1}^{n} f(x_k^*)\Delta x_k = \int_a^b f(x)\,dx \quad \blacksquare$$

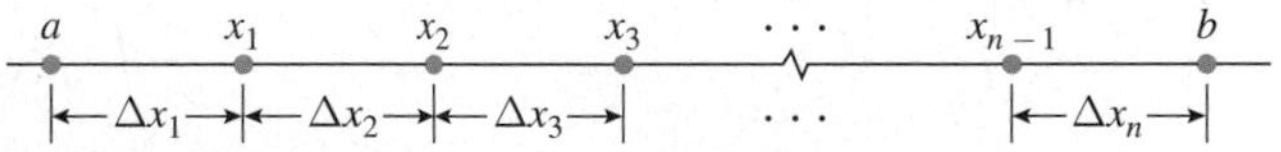


▶ **Figure 5.6.3**

It is standard to denote the difference $F(b) - F(a)$ as

$$F(x)\Big]_a^b = F(b) - F(a) \quad \text{or} \quad \big[F(x)\big]_a^b = F(b) - F(a)$$

For example, using the first of these notations we can express (2) as

$$\int_a^b f(x)\,dx = F(x)\Big]_a^b \tag{5}$$

We will sometimes write

$$F(x)\Big]_{x=a}^b = F(b) - F(a)$$

when it is important to emphasize that $a$ and $b$ are values for the variable $x$.

▶ **Example 1** Evaluate $\displaystyle\int_1^2 x\,dx$.

The integral in Example 1 represents the area of a certain trapezoid. Sketch the trapezoid, and find its area using geometry.

***Solution.*** The function $F(x) = \frac{1}{2}x^2$ is an antiderivative of $f(x) = x$; thus, from (2)

$$\int_1^2 x\,dx = \frac{1}{2}x^2\Big]_1^2 = \frac{1}{2}(2)^2 - \frac{1}{2}(1)^2 = 2 - \frac{1}{2} = \frac{3}{2} \quad ◀$$

▶ **Example 2** In Example 5 of Section 5.4 we used the definition of area to show that the area under the graph of $y = 9 - x^2$ over the interval $[0, 3]$ is 18 (square units). We can now solve that problem much more easily using the Fundamental Theorem of Calculus:

$$A = \int_0^3 (9 - x^2)\,dx = \left[9x - \frac{x^3}{3}\right]_0^3 = \left(27 - \frac{27}{3}\right) - 0 = 18 \quad ◀$$

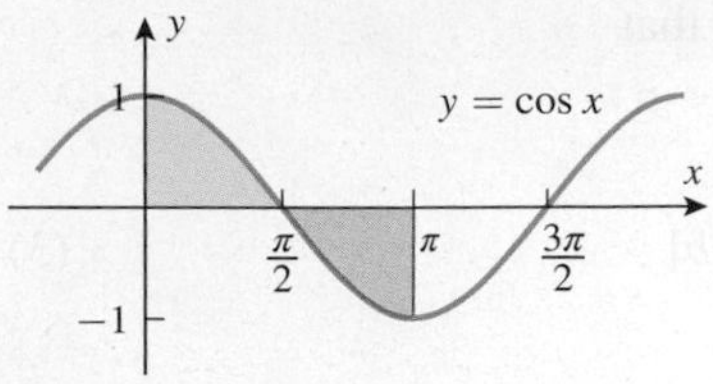


▲ Figure 5.6.4

► **Example 3**

(a) Find the area under the curve $y = \cos x$ over the interval $[0, \pi/2]$ (Figure 5.6.4).
(b) Make a conjecture about the value of the integral

$$\int_0^{\pi} \cos x\, dx$$

and confirm your conjecture using the Fundamental Theorem of Calculus.

***Solution (a).*** Since $\cos x \geq 0$ over the interval $[0, \pi/2]$, the area $A$ under the curve is

$$A = \int_0^{\pi/2} \cos x\, dx = \sin x\Big]_0^{\pi/2} = \sin\frac{\pi}{2} - \sin 0 = 1$$

***Solution (b).*** The given integral can be interpreted as the signed area between the graph of $y = \cos x$ and the interval $[0, \pi]$. The graph in Figure 5.6.4 suggests that over the interval $[0, \pi]$ the portion of area above the $x$-axis is the same as the portion of area below the $x$-axis, so we conjecture that the signed area is zero; this implies that the value of the integral is zero. This is confirmed by the computations

$$\int_0^{\pi} \cos x\, dx = \sin x\Big]_0^{\pi} = \sin\pi - \sin 0 = 0 \blacktriangleleft$$

## THE RELATIONSHIP BETWEEN DEFINITE AND INDEFINITE INTEGRALS

Let $F$ be any antiderivative of $f$ on $[a, b]$ and let $C$ denote an arbitrary constant. Then

$$\int f(x)\, dx\Big]_a^b = (F(x) + C)\Big]_a^b = (F(b) + C) - (F(a) + C) = F(b) - F(a) = \int_a^b f(x)\, dx$$

by Theorem 5.6.1. Hence

$$\int_a^b f(x)\, dx = \int f(x)\, dx\Big]_a^b \qquad (6)$$

which relates the definite and indefinite integrals.

► **Example 4** Table 5.2.1 will be helpful for the following computations.

$$\int_1^9 \sqrt{x}\, dx = \int x^{1/2}\, dx\Big]_1^9 = \frac{2}{3}x^{3/2}\Big]_1^9 = \frac{2}{3}(27 - 1) = \frac{52}{3}$$

$$\int_4^9 x^2\sqrt{x}\, dx = \int_4^9 x^{5/2}\, dx = \frac{2}{7}x^{7/2}\Big]_4^9 = \frac{2}{7}(2187 - 128) = \frac{4118}{7} = 588\frac{2}{7}$$

$$\int_0^{\pi/2} \frac{\sin x}{5}\, dx = -\frac{1}{5}\cos x\Big]_0^{\pi/2} = -\frac{1}{5}\left[\cos\left(\frac{\pi}{2}\right) - \cos 0\right] = -\frac{1}{5}[0 - 1] = \frac{1}{5}$$

$$\int_0^{\pi/3} \sec^2 x\, dx = \tan x\Big]_0^{\pi/3} = \tan\left(\frac{\pi}{3}\right) - \tan 0 = \sqrt{3} - 0 = \sqrt{3}$$

$$\int_0^{\ln 3} 5e^x\, dx = 5e^x\Big]_0^{\ln 3} = 5[e^{\ln 3} - e^0] = 5[3 - 1] = 10$$

$$\int_{-e}^{-1} \frac{1}{x}\, dx = \ln|x|\Big]_{-e}^{-1} = \ln|-1| - \ln|-e| = 0 - 1 = -1$$

$$\int_{-1/2}^{1/2} \frac{1}{\sqrt{1 - x^2}}\, dx = \sin^{-1} x\Big]_{-1/2}^{1/2} = \sin^{-1}\left(\frac{1}{2}\right) - \sin^{-1}\left(-\frac{1}{2}\right) = \frac{\pi}{6} - \left(-\frac{\pi}{6}\right) = \frac{\pi}{3} \blacktriangleleft$$

**TECHNOLOGY MASTERY**

If you have a CAS, read the documentation on evaluating definite integrals and then check the results in Example 4.

**WARNING** The requirements in the Fundamental Theorem of Calculus that $f$ be continuous on $[a, b]$ and that $F$ be an antiderivative for $f$ over the entire interval $[a, b]$ are important to keep in mind. Disregarding these assumptions will likely lead to incorrect results. For example, the function $f(x) = 1/x^2$ fails on two counts to be continuous at $x = 0$: $f(x)$ is not defined at $x = 0$ and $\lim_{x\to 0} f(x)$ does not exist. Thus, the Fundamental Theorem of Calculus should not be used to integrate $f$ on any interval that contains $x = 0$. However, if we ignore this and mistakenly apply Formula (2) over the interval $[-1, 1]$, we might *incorrectly* compute $\int_{-1}^{1} (1/x^2)\,dx$ by evaluating an antiderivative, $-1/x$, at the endpoints, arriving at the answer

$$-\frac{1}{x}\bigg]_{-1}^{1} = -[1 - (-1)] = -2$$

But $f(x) = 1/x^2$ is a nonnegative function, so clearly a negative value for the definite integral is impossible.

The Fundamental Theorem of Calculus can be applied without modification to definite integrals in which the lower limit of integration is greater than or equal to the upper limit of integration.

**▶ Example 5**

$$\int_1^1 x^2\,dx = \frac{x^3}{3}\bigg]_1^1 = \frac{1}{3} - \frac{1}{3} = 0$$

$$\int_4^0 x\,dx = \frac{x^2}{2}\bigg]_4^0 = \frac{0}{2} - \frac{16}{2} = -8$$

The latter result is consistent with the result that would be obtained by first reversing the limits of integration in accordance with Definition 5.5.3(b):

$$\int_4^0 x\,dx = -\int_0^4 x\,dx = -\frac{x^2}{2}\bigg]_0^4 = -\left[\frac{16}{2} - \frac{0}{2}\right] = -8 \blacktriangleleft$$

To integrate a continuous function that is defined piecewise on an interval $[a, b]$, split this interval into subintervals at the breakpoints of the function, and integrate separately over each subinterval in accordance with Theorem 5.5.5.

**▶ Example 6** Evaluate $\int_0^3 f(x)\,dx$ if

$$f(x) = \begin{cases} x^2, & x < 2 \\ 3x - 2, & x \geq 2 \end{cases}$$

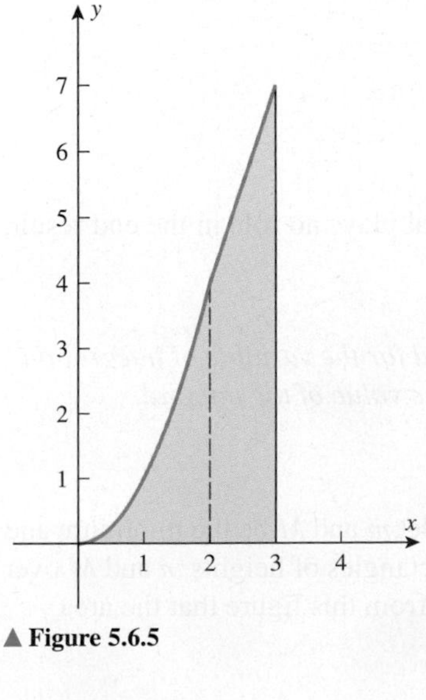

▲ Figure 5.6.5

***Solution.*** See Figure 5.6.5. From Theorem 5.5.5 we can integrate from 0 to 2 and from 2 to 3 separately and add the results. This yields

$$\int_0^3 f(x)\,dx = \int_0^2 f(x)\,dx + \int_2^3 f(x)\,dx = \int_0^2 x^2\,dx + \int_2^3 (3x - 2)\,dx$$

$$= \frac{x^3}{3}\bigg]_0^2 + \left[\frac{3x^2}{2} - 2x\right]_2^3 = \left(\frac{8}{3} - 0\right) + \left(\frac{15}{2} - 2\right) = \frac{49}{6} \blacktriangleleft$$

If $f$ is a continuous function on the interval $[a, b]$, then we define the ***total area*** between the curve $y = f(x)$ and the interval $[a, b]$ to be

$$\text{total area} = \int_a^b |f(x)|\,dx \tag{7}$$

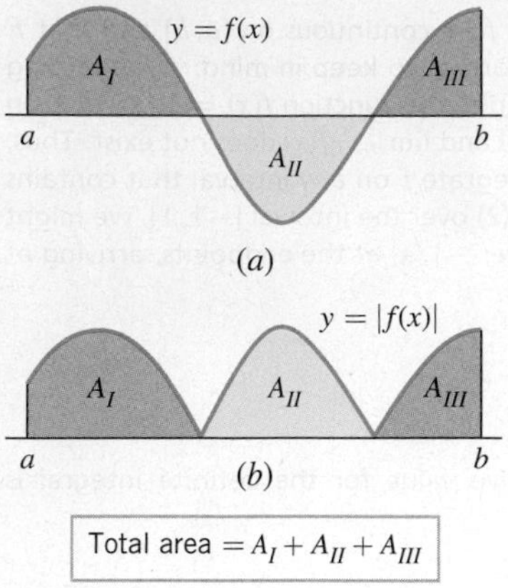


▲ Figure 5.6.6

(Figure 5.6.6). To compute total area using Formula (7), begin by dividing the interval of integration into subintervals on which $f(x)$ does not change sign. On the subintervals for which $0 \leq f(x)$ replace $|f(x)|$ by $f(x)$, and on the subintervals for which $f(x) \leq 0$ replace $|f(x)|$ by $-f(x)$. Adding the resulting integrals then yields the total area.

▶ **Example 7** Find the total area between the curve $y = 1 - x^2$ and the $x$-axis over the interval $[0, 2]$ (Figure 5.6.7).

***Solution.*** The area $A$ is given by

$$A = \int_0^2 |1 - x^2|\,dx = \int_0^1 (1 - x^2)\,dx + \int_1^2 -(1 - x^2)\,dx$$

$$= \left[x - \frac{x^3}{3}\right]_0^1 - \left[x - \frac{x^3}{3}\right]_1^2$$

$$= \frac{2}{3} - \left(-\frac{4}{3}\right) = 2 \blacktriangleleft$$

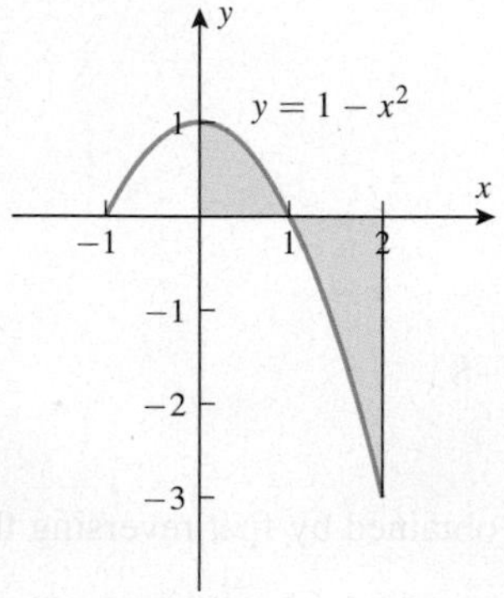


▲ Figure 5.6.7

## DUMMY VARIABLES

Integrating a function of $x$ over an interval and integrating the same function of $t$ over the same interval of integration produce the same value for the integral. For example,

$$\int_1^3 x^2\,dx = \left.\frac{x^3}{3}\right]_{x=1}^3 = \frac{27}{3} - \frac{1}{3} = \frac{26}{3} \quad \text{and} \quad \int_1^3 t^2\,dt = \left.\frac{t^3}{3}\right]_{t=1}^3 = \frac{27}{3} - \frac{1}{3} = \frac{26}{3}$$

However, this result should not be surprising, since the area under the graph of the curve $y = f(x)$ over an interval $[a, b]$ on the $x$-axis is the same as the area under the graph of the curve $y = f(t)$ over the interval $[a, b]$ on the $t$-axis (Figure 5.6.8).

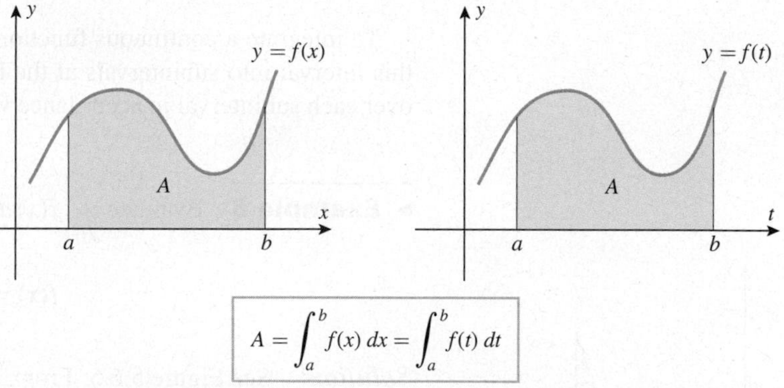


▶ Figure 5.6.8

Because the variable of integration in a definite integral plays no role in the end result, it is often referred to as a ***dummy variable***. In summary:

*Whenever you find it convenient to change the letter used for the variable of integration in a definite integral, you can do so without changing the value of the integral.*

## THE MEAN-VALUE THEOREM FOR INTEGRALS

Let $f$ be a continuous nonnegative function on $[a, b]$, and let $m$ and $M$ be the minimum and maximum values of $f(x)$ on this interval. Consider the rectangles of heights $m$ and $M$ over the interval $[a, b]$ (Figure 5.6.9). It is clear geometrically from this figure that the area

$$A = \int_a^b f(x)\,dx$$

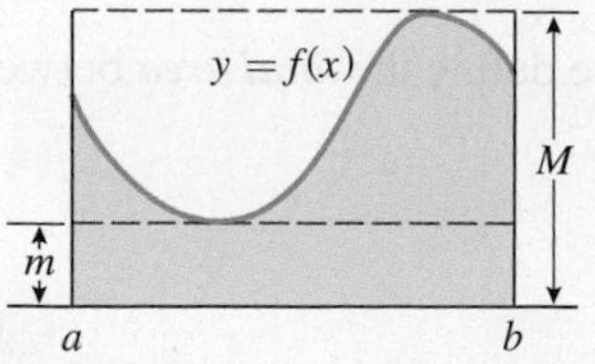


▲ Figure 5.6.9

under $y = f(x)$ is at least as large as the area of the rectangle of height $m$ and no larger than the area of the rectangle of height $M$. It seems reasonable, therefore, that there is a rectangle over the interval $[a, b]$ of some appropriate height $f(x^*)$ between $m$ and $M$ whose area is precisely $A$; that is,

$$\int_a^b f(x)\,dx = f(x^*)(b-a)$$

(Figure 5.6.10). This is a special case of the following result.

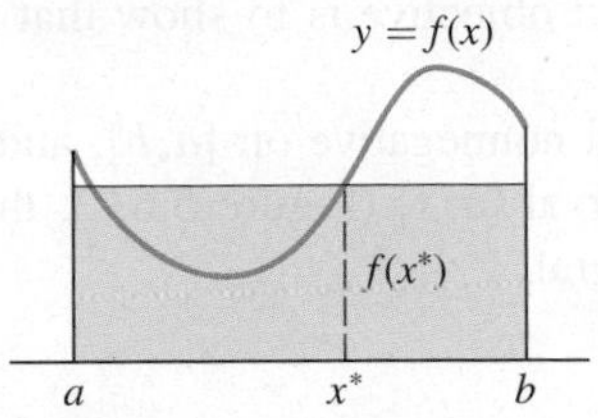


The area of the shaded rectangle is equal to the area of the shaded region in Figure 5.6.9.

▲ **Figure 5.6.10**

**5.6.2 THEOREM (The Mean-Value Theorem for Integrals)** *If $f$ is continuous on a closed interval $[a, b]$, then there is at least one point $x^*$ in $[a, b]$ such that*

$$\int_a^b f(x)\,dx = f(x^*)(b-a) \tag{8}$$

**PROOF** By the Extreme-Value Theorem (4.4.2), $f$ assumes a maximum value $M$ and a minimum value $m$ on $[a, b]$. Thus, for all $x$ in $[a, b]$,

$$m \le f(x) \le M$$

and from Theorem 5.5.6(*b*)

$$\int_a^b m\,dx \le \int_a^b f(x)\,dx \le \int_a^b M\,dx$$

or

$$m(b-a) \le \int_a^b f(x)\,dx \le M(b-a) \tag{9}$$

or

$$m \le \frac{1}{b-a}\int_a^b f(x)\,dx \le M$$

This implies that

$$\frac{1}{b-a}\int_a^b f(x)\,dx \tag{10}$$

is a number between $m$ and $M$, and since $f(x)$ assumes the values $m$ and $M$ on $[a, b]$, it follows from the Intermediate-Value Theorem (1.5.7) that $f(x)$ must assume the value (10) at some $x^*$ in $[a, b]$; that is,

$$\frac{1}{b-a}\int_a^b f(x)\,dx = f(x^*) \quad \text{or} \quad \int_a^b f(x)\,dx = f(x^*)(b-a) \;\blacksquare$$

---

▶ **Example 8** Since $f(x) = x^2$ is continuous on the interval $[1, 4]$, the Mean-Value Theorem for Integrals guarantees that there is a point $x^*$ in $[1, 4]$ such that

$$\int_1^4 x^2\,dx = f(x^*)(4-1) = (x^*)^2(4-1) = 3(x^*)^2$$

But

$$\int_1^4 x^2\,dx = \left.\frac{x^3}{3}\right]_1^4 = 21$$

so that

$$3(x^*)^2 = 21 \quad \text{or} \quad (x^*)^2 = 7 \quad \text{or} \quad x^* = \pm\sqrt{7}$$

Thus, $x^* = \sqrt{7} \approx 2.65$ is the point in the interval $[1, 4]$ whose existence is guaranteed by the Mean-Value Theorem for Integrals. ◀

## PART 2 OF THE FUNDAMENTAL THEOREM OF CALCULUS

To evaluate a definite integral using the Fundamental Theorem of Calculus, one needs to be able to find an antiderivative of the integrand. Our next objective is to show that all continuous functions have antiderivatives.

In Section 5.1 we suggested that if $f$ is continuous and nonnegative on $[a, b]$, and if $A(x)$ is the area under the graph of $y = f(x)$ over the interval $[a, x]$ (Figure 5.6.2), then $A'(x) = f(x)$. But $A(x)$ can be expressed as the definite integral

$$A(x) = \int_a^x f(t)\,dt$$

(where we have used $t$ rather than $x$ as the variable of integration to avoid confusion with the $x$ that appears as the upper limit of integration). Thus, the relationship $A'(x) = f(x)$ can be expressed as

$$\frac{d}{dx}\left[\int_a^x f(t)\,dt\right] = f(x)$$

This is a special case of the following more general result, which applies even if $f$ has negative values.

**5.6.3 THEOREM** (*The Fundamental Theorem of Calculus, Part 2*) *If $f$ is continuous on an interval, then $f$ has an antiderivative on that interval. In particular, if $a$ is any point in the interval, then the function $F$ defined by*

$$F(x) = \int_a^x f(t)\,dt$$

*is an antiderivative of $f$; that is, $F'(x) = f(x)$ for each $x$ in the interval, or in an alternative notation*

$$\frac{d}{dx}\left[\int_a^x f(t)\,dt\right] = f(x) \tag{11}$$

**PROOF** We will show first that $F(x)$ is defined at each $x$ in the interval. If $x > a$ and $x$ is in the interval, then Theorem 5.5.2 applied to the interval $[a, x]$ and the continuity of $f$ ensure that $F(x)$ is defined; and if $x$ is in the interval and $x \leq a$, then Definition 5.5.3 combined with Theorem 5.5.2 ensures that $F(x)$ is defined. Thus, $F(x)$ is defined for all $x$ in the interval.

Next we will show that $F'(x) = f(x)$ for each $x$ in the interval. If $x$ is not an endpoint, then it follows from the definition of a derivative that

$$\begin{aligned} F'(x) &= \lim_{h\to 0} \frac{F(x+h) - F(x)}{h} \\ &= \lim_{h\to 0} \frac{1}{h}\left[\int_a^{x+h} f(t)\,dt - \int_a^x f(t)\,dt\right] \\ &= \lim_{h\to 0} \frac{1}{h}\left[\int_a^{x+h} f(t)\,dt + \int_x^a f(t)\,dt\right] \\ &= \lim_{h\to 0} \frac{1}{h}\int_x^{x+h} f(t)\,dt \qquad \text{Theorem 5.5.5} \end{aligned} \tag{12}$$

Applying the Mean-Value Theorem for Integrals (5.6.2) to the integral in (12) we obtain

$$\frac{1}{h}\int_x^{x+h} f(t)\,dt = \frac{1}{h}[f(t^*)\cdot h] = f(t^*) \tag{13}$$

where $t^*$ is some number between $x$ and $x + h$. Because $t^*$ is trapped between $x$ and $x + h$, it follows that $t^* \to x$ as $h \to 0$. Thus, the continuity of $f$ at $x$ implies that $f(t^*) \to f(x)$ as $h \to 0$. Therefore, it follows from (12) and (13) that

$$F'(x) = \lim_{h\to 0}\left(\frac{1}{h}\int_x^{x+h} f(t)\,dt\right) = \lim_{h\to 0} f(t^*) = f(x)$$

If $x$ is an endpoint of the interval, then the two-sided limits in the proof must be replaced by the appropriate one-sided limits, but otherwise the arguments are identical. ■

In words, Formula (11) states:

*If a definite integral has a variable upper limit of integration, a constant lower limit of integration, and a continuous integrand, then the derivative of the integral with respect to its upper limit is equal to the integrand evaluated at the upper limit.*

▶ **Example 9** Find

$$\frac{d}{dx}\left[\int_1^x t^3\,dt\right]$$

by applying Part 2 of the Fundamental Theorem of Calculus, and then confirm the result by performing the integration and then differentiating.

***Solution.*** The integrand is a continuous function, so from (11)

$$\frac{d}{dx}\left[\int_1^x t^3\,dt\right] = x^3$$

Alternatively, evaluating the integral and then differentiating yields

$$\int_1^x t^3\,dt = \frac{t^4}{4}\bigg]_{t=1}^x = \frac{x^4}{4} - \frac{1}{4}, \quad \frac{d}{dx}\left[\frac{x^4}{4} - \frac{1}{4}\right] = x^3$$

so the two methods for differentiating the integral agree. ◀

▶ **Example 10** Since

$$f(x) = \frac{\sin x}{x}$$

is continuous on any interval that does not contain the origin, it follows from (11) that on the interval $(0, +\infty)$ we have

$$\frac{d}{dx}\left[\int_1^x \frac{\sin t}{t}\,dt\right] = \frac{\sin x}{x}$$

Unlike the preceding example, there is no way to evaluate the integral in terms of familiar functions, so Formula (11) provides the only simple method for finding the derivative. ◀

## DIFFERENTIATION AND INTEGRATION ARE INVERSE PROCESSES

The two parts of the Fundamental Theorem of Calculus, when taken together, tell us that differentiation and integration are inverse processes in the sense that each undoes the effect of the other. To see why this is so, note that Part 1 of the Fundamental Theorem of Calculus (5.6.1) implies that

$$\int_a^x f'(t)\,dt = f(x) - f(a)$$

which tells us that if the value of $f(a)$ is known, then the function $f$ can be recovered from its derivative $f'$ by integrating. Conversely, Part 2 of the Fundamental Theorem of Calculus (5.6.3) states that

$$\frac{d}{dx}\left[\int_a^x f(t)\,dt\right] = f(x)$$

which tells us that the function $f$ can be recovered from its integral by differentiating. Thus, differentiation and integration can be viewed as inverse processes.

It is common to treat parts 1 and 2 of the Fundamental Theorem of Calculus as a single theorem and refer to it simply as the *Fundamental Theorem of Calculus*. This theorem ranks as one of the greatest discoveries in the history of science, and its formulation by Newton and Leibniz is generally regarded to be the "discovery of calculus."

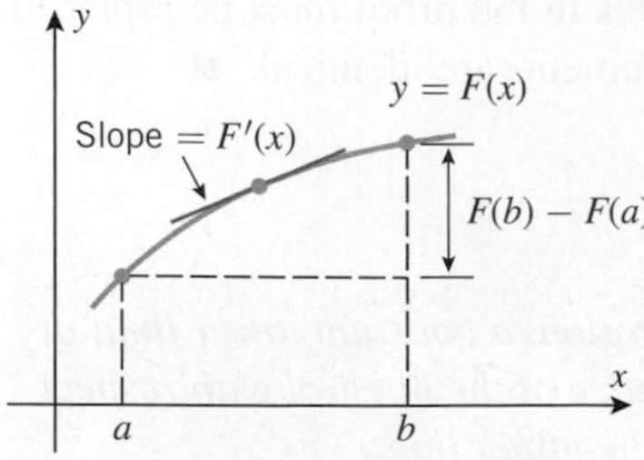


Integrating the slope of $y = F(x)$ over the interval $[a, b]$ produces the change $F(b) - F(a)$ in the value of $F(x)$.

▲ **Figure 5.6.11**

## INTEGRATING RATES OF CHANGE

The Fundamental Theorem of Calculus

$$\int_a^b f(x)\,dx = F(b) - F(a) \tag{14}$$

has a useful interpretation that can be seen by rewriting it in a slightly different form. Since $F$ is an antiderivative of $f$ on the interval $[a, b]$, we can use the relationship $F'(x) = f(x)$ to rewrite (14) as

$$\int_a^b F'(x)\,dx = F(b) - F(a) \tag{15}$$

In this formula we can view $F'(x)$ as the rate of change of $F(x)$ with respect to $x$, and we can view $F(b) - F(a)$ as the *change* in the value of $F(x)$ as $x$ increases from $a$ to $b$ (Figure 5.6.11). Thus, we have the following useful principle.

> **5.6.4 INTEGRATING A RATE OF CHANGE** Integrating the rate of change of $F(x)$ with respect to $x$ over an interval $[a, b]$ produces the change in the value of $F(x)$ that occurs as $x$ increases from $a$ to $b$.

Here are some examples of this idea:

- If $s(t)$ is the position of a particle in rectilinear motion, then $s'(t)$ is the instantaneous velocity of the particle at time $t$, and
$$\int_{t_1}^{t_2} s'(t)\,dt = s(t_2) - s(t_1)$$
is the displacement (or the change in the position) of the particle between the times $t_1$ and $t_2$.
- If $P(t)$ is a population (e.g., plants, animals, or people) at time $t$, then $P'(t)$ is the rate at which the population is changing at time $t$, and
$$\int_{t_1}^{t_2} P'(t)\,dt = P(t_2) - P(t_1)$$
is the change in the population between times $t_1$ and $t_2$.

matthi/Shutterstock

*Mathematical analysis plays an important role in understanding human population growth.*

- If $A(t)$ is the area of an oil spill at time $t$, then $A'(t)$ is the rate at which the area of the spill is changing at time $t$, and
$$\int_{t_1}^{t_2} A'(t)\,dt = A(t_2) - A(t_1)$$
is the change in the area of the spill between times $t_1$ and $t_2$.
- If $P'(x)$ is the marginal profit that results from producing and selling $x$ units of a product (see Section 4.5), then
$$\int_{x_1}^{x_2} P'(x)\,dx = P(x_2) - P(x_1)$$
is the change in the profit that results when the production level increases from $x_1$ units to $x_2$ units.

## ✓ QUICK CHECK EXERCISES 5.6 

*(See page 305 for answers.)*

**1.** (a) If $F(x)$ is an antiderivative for $f(x)$, then
$$\int_a^b f(x)\,dx = \_\_\_\_\_\_$$
(b) $\int_a^b F'(x)\,dx = \_\_\_\_\_\_$

(c) $\frac{d}{dx}\left[\int_a^x f(t)\,dt\right] = \_\_\_\_\_\_$

**2.** (a) $\int_0^2 (3x^2 - 2x)\,dx = \_\_\_\_\_\_$

(b) $\int_{-\pi}^{\pi} \cos x\,dx = \_\_\_\_\_\_$

*(cont.)*

(c) $\displaystyle\int_0^{\frac{1}{2}\ln 5} e^x\,dx =$ ______

(d) $\displaystyle\int_{-1/2}^{1/2} \frac{1}{\sqrt{1-x^2}}\,dx =$ ______

3. For the function $f(x) = 3x^2 - 2x$ and an interval $[a, b]$, the point $x^*$ guaranteed by the Mean-Value Theorem for Integrals is $x^* = \frac{2}{3}$. It follows that

$$\int_a^b (3x^2 - 2x)\,dx = \text{\_\_\_\_\_\_}$$

4. The area of an oil spill is increasing at a rate of $25t$ ft$^2$/s $t$ seconds after the spill. Between times $t = 2$ and $t = 4$ the area of the spill increases by ______ ft$^2$.

## EXERCISE SET 5.6 ☐ Graphing Utility ☐ CAS

1. In each part, use a definite integral to find the area of the region, and check your answer using an appropriate formula from geometry.

(a) (b) (c)

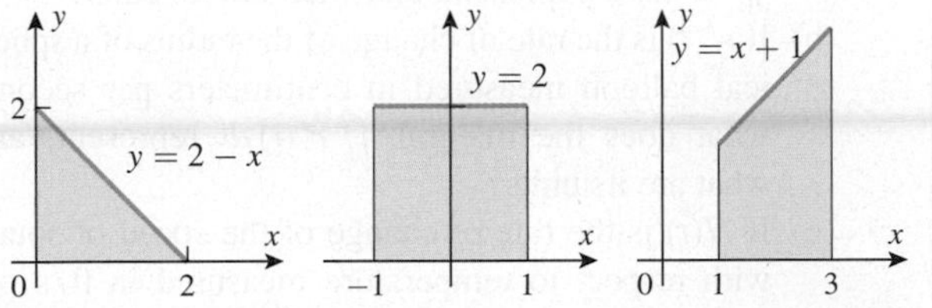


2. In each part, use a definite integral to find the area under the curve $y = f(x)$ over the stated interval, and check your answer using an appropriate formula from geometry.
(a) $f(x) = x$; $[0, 5]$
(b) $f(x) = 5$; $[3, 9]$
(c) $f(x) = x + 3$; $[-1, 2]$

3. In each part, sketch the analogue of Figure 5.6.10 for the specified region. [Let $y = f(x)$ denote the upper boundary of the region. If $x^*$ is unique, label both it and $f(x^*)$ on your sketch. Otherwise, label $f(x^*)$ on your sketch, and determine all values of $x^*$ that satisfy Equation (8).]
(a) The region in part (a) of Exercise 1.
(b) The region in part (b) of Exercise 1.
(c) The region in part (c) of Exercise 1.

4. In each part, sketch the analogue of Figure 5.6.10 for the function and interval specified. [If $x^*$ is unique, label both it and $f(x^*)$ on your sketch. Otherwise, label $f(x^*)$ on your sketch, and determine all values of $x^*$ that satisfy Equation (8).]
(a) The function and interval in part (a) of Exercise 2.
(b) The function and interval in part (b) of Exercise 2.
(c) The function and interval in part (c) of Exercise 2.

**5–10** Find the area under the curve $y = f(x)$ over the stated interval. ■

5. $f(x) = x^3$; $[2, 3]$
6. $f(x) = x^4$; $[-1, 1]$
7. $f(x) = 3\sqrt{x}$; $[1, 4]$
8. $f(x) = x^{-2/3}$; $[1, 27]$
9. $f(x) = e^{2x}$; $[0, \ln 2]$
10. $f(x) = \dfrac{1}{x}$; $[1, 5]$

**11–12** Find all values of $x^*$ in the stated interval that satisfy Equation (8) in the Mean-Value Theorem for Integrals (5.6.2), and explain what these numbers represent. ■

11. (a) $f(x) = \sqrt{x}$; $[0, 3]$
(b) $f(x) = x^2 + x$; $[-12, 0]$

12. (a) $f(x) = \sin x$; $[-\pi, \pi]$ (b) $f(x) = 1/x^2$; $[1, 3]$

**13–30** Evaluate the integrals using Part 1 of the Fundamental Theorem of Calculus. ■

13. $\displaystyle\int_{-2}^{1} (x^2 - 6x + 12)\,dx$
14. $\displaystyle\int_{-1}^{2} 4x(1 - x^2)\,dx$
15. $\displaystyle\int_1^4 \frac{4}{x^2}\,dx$
16. $\displaystyle\int_1^2 \frac{1}{x^6}\,dx$
17. $\displaystyle\int_4^9 2x\sqrt{x}\,dx$
18. $\displaystyle\int_1^4 \frac{1}{x\sqrt{x}}\,dx$
19. $\displaystyle\int_{-\pi/2}^{\pi/2} \sin\theta\,d\theta$
20. $\displaystyle\int_0^{\pi/4} \sec^2\theta\,d\theta$
21. $\displaystyle\int_{-\pi/4}^{\pi/4} \cos x\,dx$
22. $\displaystyle\int_0^{\pi/3} (2x - \sec x\tan x)\,dx$
23. $\displaystyle\int_{\ln 2}^{3} 5e^x\,dx$
24. $\displaystyle\int_{1/2}^{1} \frac{1}{2x}\,dx$
25. $\displaystyle\int_0^{1/\sqrt{2}} \frac{dx}{\sqrt{1-x^2}}$
26. $\displaystyle\int_{-1}^{1} \frac{dx}{1+x^2}$
27. $\displaystyle\int_{\sqrt{2}}^{2} \frac{dx}{x\sqrt{x^2-1}}$
28. $\displaystyle\int_{-\sqrt{2}}^{-2/\sqrt{3}} \frac{dx}{x\sqrt{x^2-1}}$
29. $\displaystyle\int_1^4 \left(\frac{1}{\sqrt{t}} - 3\sqrt{t}\right) dt$
30. $\displaystyle\int_{\pi/6}^{\pi/2} \left(x + \frac{2}{\sin^2 x}\right) dx$

**31–34** Use Theorem 5.5.5 to evaluate the given integrals. ■

31. (a) $\displaystyle\int_{-1}^{1} |2x - 1|\,dx$ (b) $\displaystyle\int_0^{3\pi/4} |\cos x|\,dx$

32. (a) $\displaystyle\int_{-1}^{2} \sqrt{2 + |x|}\,dx$ (b) $\displaystyle\int_0^{\pi/2} \left|\tfrac{1}{2} - \cos x\right| dx$

33. (a) $\displaystyle\int_{-1}^{1} |e^x - 1|\,dx$ (b) $\displaystyle\int_1^4 \frac{|2 - x|}{x}\,dx$

34. (a) $\displaystyle\int_{-3}^{3} \left|x^2 - 1 - \frac{15}{x^2 + 1}\right| dx$

(b) $\displaystyle\int_0^{\sqrt{3}/2} \left|\frac{1}{\sqrt{1-x^2}} - \sqrt{2}\right| dx$

**35–36** A function $f(x)$ is defined piecewise on an interval. In these exercises: (a) Use Theorem 5.5.5 to find the integral of $f(x)$ over the interval. (b) Find an antiderivative of $f(x)$ on the interval. (c) Use parts (a) and (b) to verify Part 1 of the Fundamental Theorem of Calculus. ■

**35.** $f(x) = \begin{cases} x, & 0 \le x \le 1 \\ x^2, & 1 < x \le 2 \end{cases}$

**36.** $f(x) = \begin{cases} \sqrt{x}, & 0 \le x < 1 \\ 1/x^2, & 1 \le x \le 4 \end{cases}$

**37–40 True–False** Determine whether the statement is true or false. Explain your answer. ■

**37.** There does not exist a differentiable function $F(x)$ such that $F'(x) = |x|$.

**38.** If $f(x)$ is continuous on the interval $[a, b]$, and if the definite integral of $f(x)$ over this interval has value 0, then the equation $f(x) = 0$ has at least one solution in the interval $[a, b]$.

**39.** If $F(x)$ is an antiderivative of $f(x)$ and $G(x)$ is an antiderivative of $g(x)$, then

$$\int_a^b f(x)\,dx = \int_a^b g(x)\,dx$$

if and only if

$$G(a) + F(b) = F(a) + G(b)$$

**40.** If $f(x)$ is continuous everywhere and

$$F(x) = \int_0^x f(t)\,dt$$

then the equation $F(x) = 0$ has at least one solution.

**41–44** Use a calculating utility to find the midpoint approximation of the integral using $n = 20$ subintervals, and then find the exact value of the integral using Part 1 of the Fundamental Theorem of Calculus. ■

**41.** $\displaystyle\int_1^3 \frac{1}{x^2}\,dx$ **42.** $\displaystyle\int_0^{\pi/2} \sin x\,dx$

**43.** $\displaystyle\int_{-1}^1 \sec^2 x\,dx$ **44.** $\displaystyle\int_1^3 \frac{1}{x}\,dx$

**45–48** Sketch the region described and find its area. ■

**45.** The region under the curve $y = x^2 + 1$ and over the interval $[0, 3]$.

**46.** The region below the curve $y = x - x^2$ and above the $x$-axis.

**47.** The region under the curve $y = 3\sin x$ and over the interval $[0, 2\pi/3]$.

**48.** The region below the interval $[-2, -1]$ and above the curve $y = x^3$.

**49–52** Sketch the curve and find the total area between the curve and the given interval on the $x$-axis. ■

**49.** $y = x^2 - x;\ [0, 2]$ **50.** $y = \sin x;\ [0, 3\pi/2]$

**51.** $y = e^x - 1;\ [-1, 1]$ **52.** $y = \dfrac{x^2 - 1}{x^2};\ \left[\frac{1}{2}, 2\right]$

**53.** A student wants to find the area enclosed by the graphs of $y = 1/\sqrt{1 - x^2}$, $y = 0$, $x = 0$, and $x = 0.8$.
(a) Show that the exact area is $\sin^{-1} 0.8$.
(b) The student uses a calculator to approximate the result in part (a) to two decimal places and obtains an incorrect answer of 53.13. What was the student's error? Find the correct approximation.

**FOCUS ON CONCEPTS**

**54.** Explain why the Fundamental Theorem of Calculus may be applied without modification to definite integrals in which the lower limit of integration is greater than or equal to the upper limit of integration.

**55.** (a) If $h'(t)$ is the rate of change of a child's height measured in inches per year, what does the integral $\int_0^{10} h'(t)\,dt$ represent, and what are its units?
(b) If $r'(t)$ is the rate of change of the radius of a spherical balloon measured in centimeters per second, what does the integral $\int_1^2 r'(t)\,dt$ represent, and what are its units?
(c) If $H(t)$ is the rate of change of the speed of sound with respect to temperature measured in ft/s per °F, what does the integral $\int_{32}^{100} H(t)\,dt$ represent, and what are its units?
(d) If $v(t)$ is the velocity of a particle in rectilinear motion, measured in cm/h, what does the integral $\int_{t_1}^{t_2} v(t)\,dt$ represent, and what are its units?

**56.** (a) Use a graphing utility to generate the graph of

$$f(x) = \frac{1}{100}(x + 2)(x + 1)(x - 3)(x - 5)$$

and use the graph to make a conjecture about the sign of the integral

$$\int_{-2}^{5} f(x)\,dx$$

(b) Check your conjecture by evaluating the integral.

**57.** Define $F(x)$ by

$$F(x) = \int_1^x (3t^2 - 3)\,dt$$

(a) Use Part 2 of the Fundamental Theorem of Calculus to find $F'(x)$.
(b) Check the result in part (a) by first integrating and then differentiating.

**58.** Define $F(x)$ by

$$F(x) = \int_{\pi/4}^x \cos 2t\,dt$$

(a) Use Part 2 of the Fundamental Theorem of Calculus to find $F'(x)$.
(b) Check the result in part (a) by first integrating and then differentiating.

**59–62** Use Part 2 of the Fundamental Theorem of Calculus to find the derivatives. ■

**59.** (a) $\displaystyle\frac{d}{dx}\int_1^x \sin(t^2)\,dt$ (b) $\displaystyle\frac{d}{dx}\int_0^x e^{\sqrt{t}}\,dt$

**60.** (a) $\displaystyle\frac{d}{dx}\int_0^x \frac{dt}{1 + \sqrt{t}}$ (b) $\displaystyle\frac{d}{dx}\int_1^x \ln t\,dt$

**61.** $\dfrac{d}{dx}\displaystyle\int_x^0 t\sec t\,dt$ [*Hint:* Use Definition 5.5.3(b).]

**62.** $\dfrac{d}{du}\displaystyle\int_0^u |x|\,dx$

**63.** Let $F(x) = \displaystyle\int_4^x \sqrt{t^2+9}\,dt$. Find
(a) $F(4)$ (b) $F'(4)$ (c) $F''(4)$.

**64.** Let $F(x) = \displaystyle\int_{\sqrt{3}}^x \tan^{-1} t\,dt$. Find
(a) $F(\sqrt{3})$ (b) $F'(\sqrt{3})$ (c) $F''(\sqrt{3})$.

**65.** Let $F(x) = \displaystyle\int_0^x \frac{t-3}{t^2+7}\,dt$ for $-\infty < x < +\infty$.
(a) Find the value of $x$ where $F$ attains its minimum value.
(b) Find intervals over which $F$ is only increasing or only decreasing.
(c) Find open intervals over which $F$ is only concave up or only concave down.

C **66.** Use the plotting and numerical integration commands of a CAS to generate the graph of the function $F$ in Exercise 65 over the interval $-20 \le x \le 20$, and confirm that the graph is consistent with the results obtained in that exercise.

**67.** (a) Over what open interval does the formula

$$F(x) = \int_0^x \sec t\,dt$$

represent an antiderivative of $f(x) = \sec x$?
(b) Find a point where the graph of $F$ crosses the $x$-axis.

**68.** (a) Over what open interval does the formula

$$F(x) = \int_1^x \frac{1}{t^2-9}\,dt$$

represent an antiderivative of

$$f(x) = \frac{1}{x^2-9}?$$

(b) Find a point where the graph of $F$ crosses the $x$-axis.

**69.** (a) Suppose that a reservoir supplies water to an industrial park at a constant rate of $r = 4$ gallons per minute (gal/min) between 8:30 A.M. and 9:00 A.M. How much water does the reservoir supply during that time period?
(b) Suppose that one of the industrial plants increases its water consumption between 9:00 A.M. and 10:00 A.M. and that the rate at which the reservoir supplies water increases linearly, as shown in the accompanying figure. How much water does the reservoir supply during that 1-hour time period?
(c) Suppose that from 10:00 A.M. to 12 noon the rate at which the reservoir supplies water is given by the formula $r(t) = 10 + \sqrt{t}$ gal/min, where $t$ is the time (in minutes) since 10:00 A.M. How much water does the reservoir supply during that 2-hour time period?

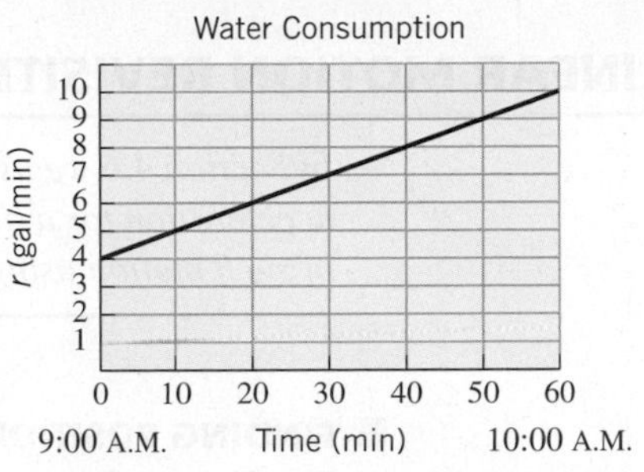

◀ **Figure Ex-69**

**70.** A traffic engineer monitors the rate at which cars enter the main highway during the afternoon rush hour. From her data she estimates that between 4:30 P.M. and 5:30 P.M. the rate $R(t)$ at which cars enter the highway is given by the formula $R(t) = 100(1 - 0.0001t^2)$ cars per minute, where $t$ is the time (in minutes) since 4:30 P.M.
(a) When does the peak traffic flow into the highway occur?
(b) Estimate the number of cars that enter the highway during the rush hour.

**71.** Suppose that $t$ days after a diagnosed outbreak of flu in a high school the disease is spreading amongst the students at a rate of $r(t) = 2.7 + 0.4t$ students per day. Based upon this model, how many additional students will have contracted the disease four days after the diagnosis?

**72.** Suppose that $t$ hours after a pitcher of iced tea is removed from a refrigerator its temperature is rising at a rate of $r(t) = 15e^{-t/2}$ (°F/hour). To the nearest degree, what will be the change in the temperature of the tea two hours after its removal from the refrigerator?

**73–74** Evaluate each limit by interpreting it as a Riemann sum in which the given interval is divided into $n$ subintervals of equal width. ■

**73.** $\displaystyle\lim_{n\to+\infty}\sum_{k=1}^{n}\frac{\pi}{4n}\sec^2\left(\frac{\pi k}{4n}\right);\ \left[0, \frac{\pi}{4}\right]$

**74.** $\displaystyle\lim_{n\to+\infty}\sum_{k=1}^{n}\frac{n}{n^2+k^2};\ [0, 1]$

**75.** Prove the Mean-Value Theorem for Integrals (Theorem 5.6.2) by applying the Mean-Value Theorem (4.8.2) to an antiderivative $F$ for $f$.

**76. Writing** Write a short paragraph that describes the various ways in which integration and differentiation may be viewed as inverse processes. (Be sure to discuss both definite and indefinite integrals.)

**77. Writing** Let $f$ denote a function that is continuous on an interval $[a, b]$, and let $x^*$ denote the point guaranteed by the Mean-Value Theorem for Integrals. Explain geometrically why $f(x^*)$ may be interpreted as a "mean" or average value of $f(x)$ over $[a, b]$. (In Section 5.8 we will discuss the concept of "average value" in more detail.)

✓ **QUICK CHECK ANSWERS 5.6** 1. (a) $F(b) - F(a)$ (b) $F(b) - F(a)$ (c) $f(x)$ 2. (a) 4 (b) 0 (c) $\sqrt{5} - 1$ (d) $\pi/3$ 3. 0 4. 150 ft²

# 5.7 RECTILINEAR MOTION REVISITED USING INTEGRATION

*In Section 4.6 we used the derivative to define the notions of instantaneous velocity and acceleration for a particle in rectilinear motion. In this section we will resume the study of such motion using the tools of integration.*

## FINDING POSITION AND VELOCITY BY INTEGRATION

Recall from Formulas (1) and (3) of Section 4.6 that if a particle in rectilinear motion has position function $s(t)$, then its instantaneous velocity and acceleration are given by the formulas

$$v(t) = s'(t) \quad \text{and} \quad a(t) = v'(t)$$

It follows from these formulas that $s(t)$ is an antiderivative of $v(t)$ and $v(t)$ is an antiderivative of $a(t)$; that is,

$$s(t) = \int v(t)\,dt \quad \text{and} \quad v(t) = \int a(t)\,dt \tag{1–2}$$

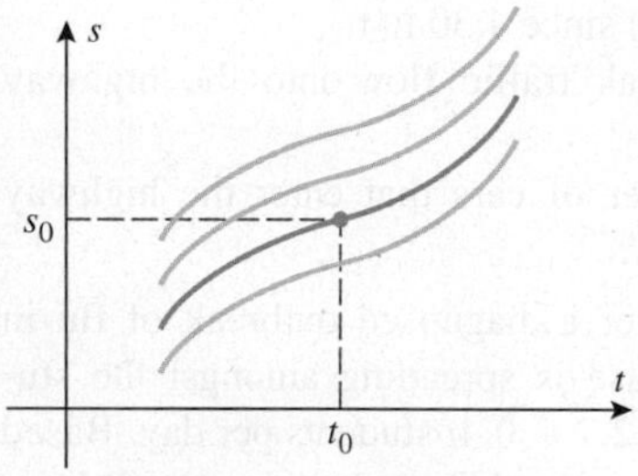


There is a unique position function such that $s(t_0) = s_0$.

▲ Figure 5.7.1

By Formula (1), if we know the velocity function $v(t)$ of a particle in rectilinear motion, then by integrating $v(t)$ we can produce a family of position functions with that velocity function. If, in addition, we know the position $s_0$ of the particle at any time $t_0$, then we have sufficient information to find the constant of integration and determine a unique position function (Figure 5.7.1). Similarly, if we know the acceleration function $a(t)$ of the particle, then by integrating $a(t)$ we can produce a family of velocity functions with that acceleration function. If, in addition, we know the velocity $v_0$ of the particle at any time $t_0$, then we have sufficient information to find the constant of integration and determine a unique velocity function (Figure 5.7.2).

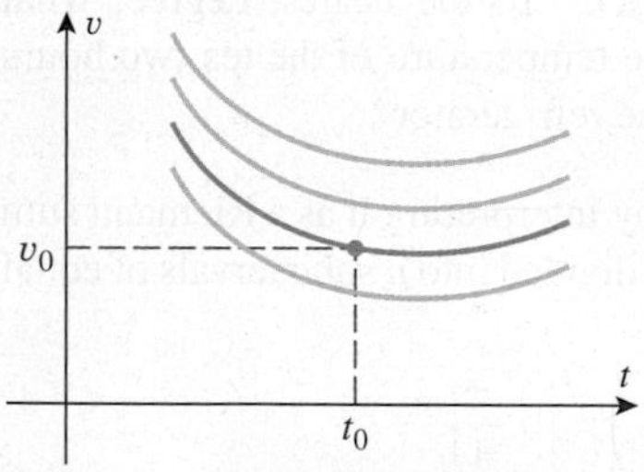


There is a unique velocity function such that $v(t_0) = v_0$.

▲ Figure 5.7.2

► **Example 1** Suppose that a particle moves with velocity $v(t) = \cos \pi t$ along a coordinate line. Assuming that the particle has coordinate $s = 4$ at time $t = 0$, find its position function.

***Solution.*** The position function is

$$s(t) = \int v(t)\,dt = \int \cos \pi t\,dt = \frac{1}{\pi}\sin \pi t + C$$

Since $s = 4$ when $t = 0$, it follows that

$$4 = s(0) = \frac{1}{\pi}\sin 0 + C = C$$

Thus,

$$s(t) = \frac{1}{\pi}\sin \pi t + 4 \quad ◄$$

## COMPUTING DISPLACEMENT AND DISTANCE TRAVELED BY INTEGRATION

Recall that the displacement over a time interval of a particle in rectilinear motion is its final coordinate minus its initial coordinate. Thus, if the position function of the particle is $s(t)$, then its displacement (or change in position) over the time interval $[t_0, t_1]$ is $s(t_1) - s(t_0)$. This can be written in integral form as

Recall that Formula (3) is a special case of the formula

$$\int_a^b F'(x)\,dx = F(b) - F(a)$$

for integrating a rate of change.

$$\begin{bmatrix}\text{displacement}\\ \text{over the time}\\ \text{interval } [t_0, t_1]\end{bmatrix} = \int_{t_0}^{t_1} v(t)\,dt = \int_{t_0}^{t_1} s'(t)\,dt = s(t_1) - s(t_0) \tag{3}$$

In contrast, to find the distance traveled by the particle over the time interval $[t_0, t_1]$ (distance traveled in the positive direction plus the distance traveled in the negative direction), we must integrate the absolute value of the velocity function; that is,

$$\begin{bmatrix}\text{distance traveled}\\ \text{during time}\\ \text{interval } [t_0, t_1]\end{bmatrix} = \int_{t_0}^{t_1} |v(t)|\, dt \tag{4}$$

Since the absolute value of velocity is speed, Formulas (3) and (4) can be summarized informally as follows:

*Integrating velocity over a time interval produces displacement, and integrating speed over a time interval produces distance traveled.*

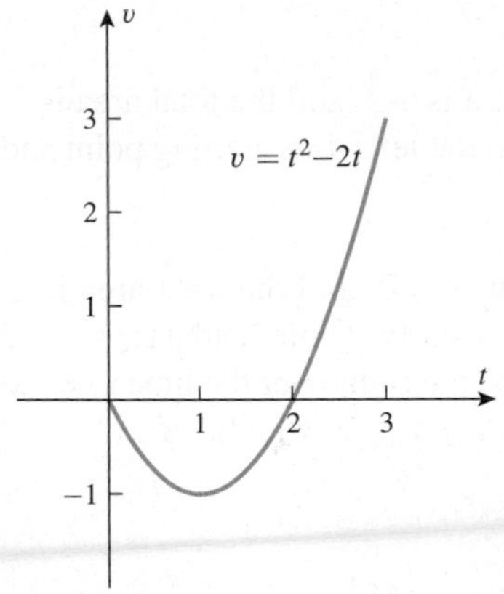


▲ Figure 5.7.3

**▶ Example 2** Suppose that a particle moves on a coordinate line so that its velocity at time $t$ is $v(t) = t^2 - 2t$ m/s (Figure 5.7.3).

(a) Find the displacement of the particle during the time interval $0 \le t \le 3$.

(b) Find the distance traveled by the particle during the time interval $0 \le t \le 3$.

***Solution (a).*** From (3) the displacement is

$$\int_0^3 v(t)\, dt = \int_0^3 (t^2 - 2t)\, dt = \left[\frac{t^3}{3} - t^2\right]_0^3 = 0$$

Thus, the particle is at the same position at time $t = 3$ as at $t = 0$.

***Solution (b).*** The velocity can be written as $v(t) = t^2 - 2t = t(t-2)$, from which we see that $v(t) \le 0$ for $0 \le t \le 2$ and $v(t) \ge 0$ for $2 \le t \le 3$. Thus, it follows from (4) that the distance traveled is

$$\begin{aligned}\int_0^3 |v(t)|\, dt &= \int_0^2 -v(t)\, dt + \int_2^3 v(t)\, dt\\ &= \int_0^2 -(t^2 - 2t)\, dt + \int_2^3 (t^2 - 2t)\, dt\\ &= -\left[\frac{t^3}{3} - t^2\right]_0^2 + \left[\frac{t^3}{3} - t^2\right]_2^3 = \frac{4}{3} + \frac{4}{3} = \frac{8}{3} \text{ m} \blacktriangleleft\end{aligned}$$

In physical problems it is important to associate correct units with definite integrals. In general, the units for

$$\int_a^b f(x)\, dx$$

are units of $f(x)$ times units of $x$, since the integral is the limit of Riemann sums, each of whose terms has these units. For example, if $v(t)$ is in meters per second (m/s) and $t$ is in seconds (s), then

$$\int_a^b v(t)\, dt$$

is in meters since

$$(\text{m/s}) \times \text{s} = \text{m}$$

## ■ ANALYZING THE VELOCITY VERSUS TIME CURVE

In Section 4.6 we showed how to use the position versus time curve to obtain information about the behavior of a particle in rectilinear motion (Table 4.6.1). Similarly, there is valuable information that can be obtained from the velocity versus time curve. For example, the integral in (3) can be interpreted geometrically as the *net signed area* between the graph of $v(t)$ and the interval $[t_0, t_1]$, and the integral in (4) can be interpreted as the *total area* between the graph of $v(t)$ and the interval $[t_0, t_1]$. Thus we have the following result.

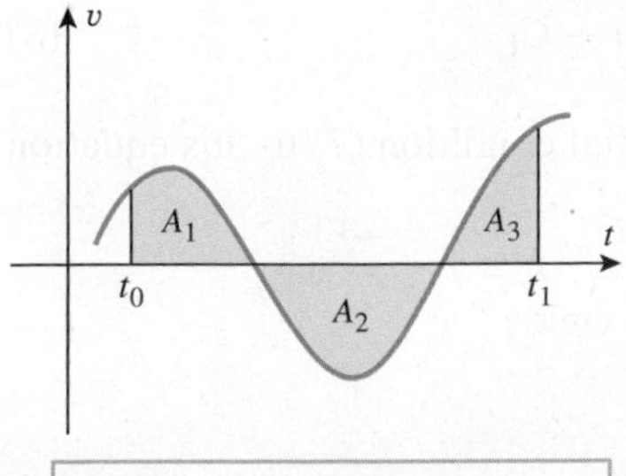


$A_1 - A_2 + A_3$ = displacement
$A_1 + A_2 + A_3$ = distance traveled

▲ Figure 5.7.4

**5.7.1 FINDING DISPLACEMENT AND DISTANCE TRAVELED FROM THE VELOCITY VERSUS TIME CURVE** For a particle in rectilinear motion, the net signed area between the velocity versus time curve and the interval $[t_0, t_1]$ on the $t$-axis represents the displacement of the particle over that time interval, and the total area between the velocity versus time curve and the interval $[t_0, t_1]$ on the $t$-axis represents the distance traveled by the particle over that time interval (Figure 5.7.4).

▶ **Example 3** Figure 5.7.5 shows three velocity versus time curves for a particle in rectilinear motion along a horizontal line with the positive direction to the right. In each case find the displacement and the distance traveled over the time interval $0 \le t \le 4$, and explain what that information tells you about the motion of the particle.

***Solution (a).*** In part (*a*) of the figure the area and the net signed area over the interval are both 2. Thus, at the end of the time period the particle is 2 units to the right of its starting point and has traveled a distance of 2 units.

***Solution (b).*** In part (*b*) of the figure the net signed area is $-2$, and the total area is 2. Thus, at the end of the time period the particle is 2 units to the left of its starting point and has traveled a distance of 2 units.

***Solution (c).*** In part (*c*) of the figure the net signed area is 0, and the total area is 2. Thus, at the end of the time period the particle is back at its starting point and has traveled a distance of 2 units. More specifically, it traveled 1 unit to the right over the time interval $0 \le t \le 1$ and then 1 unit to the left over the time interval $1 \le t \le 2$ (why?). ◀

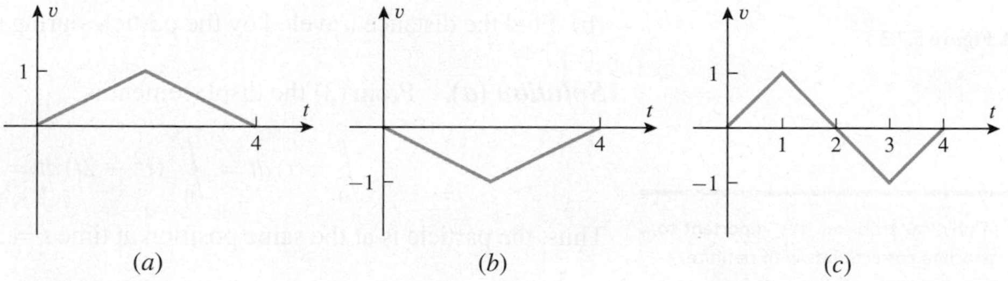


▲ **Figure 5.7.5**

## CONSTANT ACCELERATION

One of the most important cases of rectilinear motion occurs when a particle has ***constant acceleration***. Suppose that the particle has constant acceleration

$$a(t) = a \tag{5}$$

and

$$s = s_0 \quad \text{when} \quad t = 0 \tag{6}$$

$$v = v_0 \quad \text{when} \quad t = 0 \tag{7}$$

where $s_0$ and $v_0$ are known. We call (6) and (7) the ***initial conditions***.

With (5) as a starting point, we can integrate $a(t)$ to obtain $v(t)$, and we can integrate $v(t)$ to obtain $s(t)$, using an initial condition in each case to determine the constant of integration. The computations are as follows:

$$v(t) = \int a(t)\,dt = \int a\,dt = at + C_1 \tag{8}$$

To determine the constant of integration $C_1$ we apply initial condition (7) to this equation to obtain

$$v_0 = v(0) = a \cdot 0 + C_1 = C_1$$

Substituting this in (8) and putting the constant term first yields

$$v(t) = v_0 + at$$

Since $v_0$ is constant, it follows that

$$s(t) = \int v(t)\,dt = \int (v_0 + at)\,dt = v_0 t + \tfrac{1}{2}at^2 + C_2 \tag{9}$$

To determine the constant $C_2$ we apply initial condition (6) to this equation to obtain

$$s_0 = s(0) = v_0 \cdot 0 + \tfrac{1}{2}a \cdot 0 + C_2 = C_2$$

Substituting this in (9) and putting the constant term first yields

$$s(t) = s_0 + v_0 t + \tfrac{1}{2}at^2$$

In summary, we have the following result.

**5.7.2 CONSTANT ACCELERATION** If a particle moves with constant acceleration $a$ along an $s$-axis, and if the position and velocity at time $t = 0$ are $s_0$ and $v_0$, respectively, then the position and velocity functions of the particle are

$$s(t) = s_0 + v_0 t + \tfrac{1}{2}at^2 \tag{10}$$

$$v(t) = v_0 + at \tag{11}$$

How can you tell from the graph of the velocity versus time curve whether a particle moving along a line has constant acceleration?

▶ **Example 4** Suppose that an intergalactic spacecraft uses a sail and the "solar wind" to produce a constant acceleration of 0.032 m/s$^2$. Assuming that the spacecraft has a velocity of 10,000 m/s when the sail is first raised, how far will the spacecraft travel in 1 hour, and what will its velocity be at the end of this hour?

***Solution.*** In this problem the choice of a coordinate axis is at our discretion, so we will choose it to make the computations as simple as possible. Accordingly, let us introduce an $s$-axis whose positive direction is in the direction of motion, and let us take the origin to coincide with the position of the spacecraft at the time $t = 0$ when the sail is raised. Thus, Formulas (10) and (11) apply with

$$s_0 = s(0) = 0, \quad v_0 = v(0) = 10{,}000, \quad \text{and} \quad a = 0.032$$

Since 1 hour corresponds to $t = 3600$ s, it follows from (10) that in 1 hour the spacecraft travels a distance of

$$s(3600) = 10{,}000(3600) + \tfrac{1}{2}(0.032)(3600)^2 \approx 36{,}200{,}000 \text{ m}$$

and it follows from (11) that after 1 hour its velocity is

$$v(3600) = 10{,}000 + (0.032)(3600) \approx 10{,}100 \text{ m/s} \blacktriangleleft$$

▶ **Example 5** A bus has stopped to pick up riders, and a woman is running at a constant velocity of 5 m/s to catch it. When she is 11 m behind the front door the bus pulls away with a constant acceleration of 1 m/s$^2$. From that point in time, how long will it take for the woman to reach the front door of the bus if she keeps running with a velocity of 5 m/s?

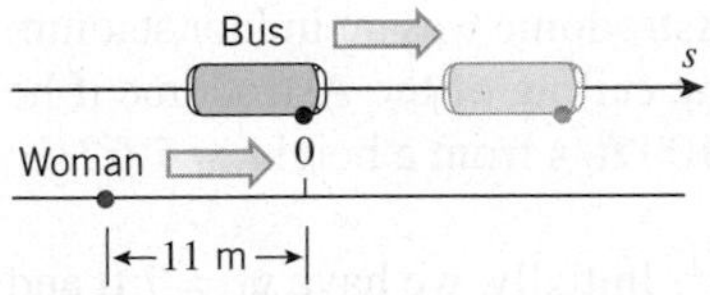

▲ **Figure 5.7.6**

***Solution.*** As shown in Figure 5.7.6, choose the $s$-axis so that the bus and the woman are moving in the positive direction, and the front door of the bus is at the origin at the time $t = 0$ when the bus begins to pull away. To catch the bus at some later time $t$, the woman will have to cover a distance $s_w(t)$ that is equal to 11 m plus the distance $s_b(t)$ traveled by the bus; that is, the woman will catch the bus when

$$s_w(t) = s_b(t) + 11 \tag{12}$$

Since the woman has a constant velocity of 5 m/s, the distance she travels in $t$ seconds is $s_w(t) = 5t$. Thus, (12) can be written as

$$s_b(t) = 5t - 11 \tag{13}$$

Since the bus has a constant acceleration of $a = 1\ \text{m/s}^2$, and since $s_0 = v_0 = 0$ at time $t = 0$ (why?), it follows from (10) that

$$s_b(t) = \tfrac{1}{2}t^2$$

Substituting this equation into (13) and reorganizing the terms yields the quadratic equation

$$\tfrac{1}{2}t^2 - 5t + 11 = 0 \quad \text{or} \quad t^2 - 10t + 22 = 0$$

Solving this equation for $t$ using the quadratic formula yields two solutions:

$$t = 5 - \sqrt{3} \approx 3.3 \quad \text{and} \quad t = 5 + \sqrt{3} \approx 6.7$$

(verify). Thus, the woman can reach the door at two different times, $t = 3.3$ s and $t = 6.7$ s. The reason that there are two solutions can be explained as follows: When the woman first reaches the door, she is running faster than the bus and can run past it if the driver does not see her. However, as the bus speeds up, it eventually catches up to her, and she has another chance to flag it down. ◀

## FREE-FALL MODEL

Motion that occurs when an object near the Earth is imparted some initial velocity (up or down) and thereafter moves along a vertical line is called ***free-fall motion***. In modeling free-fall motion we assume that the only force acting on the object is the Earth's gravity and that the object stays sufficiently close to the Earth that the gravitational force is constant. In particular, air resistance and the gravitational pull of other celestial bodies are neglected.

In our model we will ignore the physical size of the object by treating it as a particle, and we will assume that it moves along an $s$-axis whose origin is at the surface of the Earth and whose positive direction is up. With this convention, the $s$-coordinate of the particle is the height of the particle above the surface of the Earth (Figure 5.7.7).

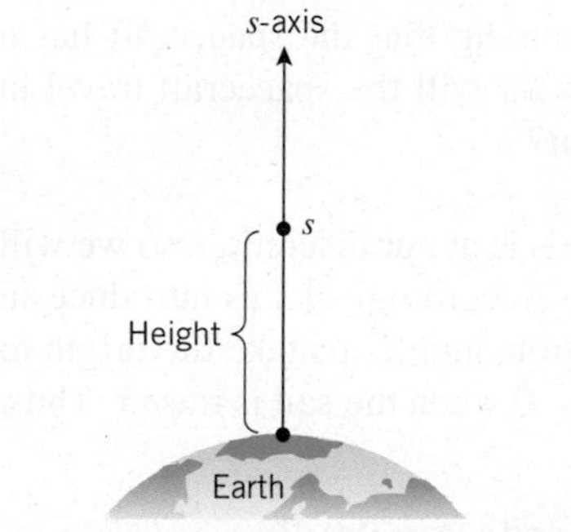

▲ **Figure 5.7.7**

It is a fact of physics that a particle with free-fall motion has constant acceleration. The magnitude of this constant, denoted by the letter $g$, is called the ***acceleration due to gravity*** and is approximately $9.8\ \text{m/s}^2$ or $32\ \text{ft/s}^2$, depending on whether distance is measured in meters or feet.* Because we have chosen the positive direction to be up, the acceleration of a particle in free fall is

$$a(t) = -g \tag{14}$$

for all values of $t$. It now follows from this and Formulas (10) and (11) that the position and velocity functions for a particle in free-fall motion are

$$s(t) = s_0 + v_0 t - \tfrac{1}{2}gt^2 \tag{15}$$

$$v(t) = v_0 - gt \tag{16}$$

How would Formulas (14), (15), and (16) change if we choose the direction of the positive $s$-axis to be down?

▶ **Example 6** Nolan Ryan, a member of the Baseball Hall of Fame and one of the fastest baseball pitchers of all time, was able to throw a baseball 150 ft/s (over 102 mi/h). During his career, he had the opportunity to pitch in the Houston Astrodome, home to the Houston Astros Baseball Team from 1965 to 1999. The Astrodome was an indoor stadium with a ceiling 208 ft high. Could Nolan Ryan have hit the ceiling of the Astrodome if he were capable of giving a baseball an upward velocity of 100 ft/s from a height of 7 ft?

Bettmann/Corbis Images

*Nolan Ryan as a rookie.*

***Solution.*** Since distance is in feet, we take $g = 32\ \text{ft/s}^2$. Initially, we have $s_0 = 7$ ft and $v_0 = 100$ ft/s, so from (15) and (16) we have

$$s(t) = 7 + 100t - 16t^2$$
$$v(t) = 100 - 32t$$

* Strictly speaking, the constant $g$ varies with the latitude and the distance from the Earth's center. However, for motion at a fixed latitude and near the surface of the Earth, the assumption of a constant $g$ is satisfactory for many applications.

In Example 6 the ball is moving up when the velocity is positive and is moving down when the velocity is negative, so it makes sense physically that the velocity is zero when the ball reaches its peak.

The ball will rise until $v(t) = 0$, that is, until $100 - 32t = 0$. Solving this equation we see that the ball is at its maximum height at time $t = \frac{25}{8}$. To find the height of the ball at this instant we substitute this value of $t$ into the position function to obtain

$$s\left(\tfrac{25}{8}\right) = 7 + 100\left(\tfrac{25}{8}\right) - 16\left(\tfrac{25}{8}\right)^2 = 163.25 \text{ ft}$$

which is roughly 45 ft short of hitting the ceiling. ◀

▶ **Example 7** A penny is released from rest near the top of the Empire State Building at a point that is 1250 ft above the ground (Figure 5.7.8). Assuming that the free-fall model applies, how long does it take for the penny to hit the ground, and what is its speed at the time of impact?

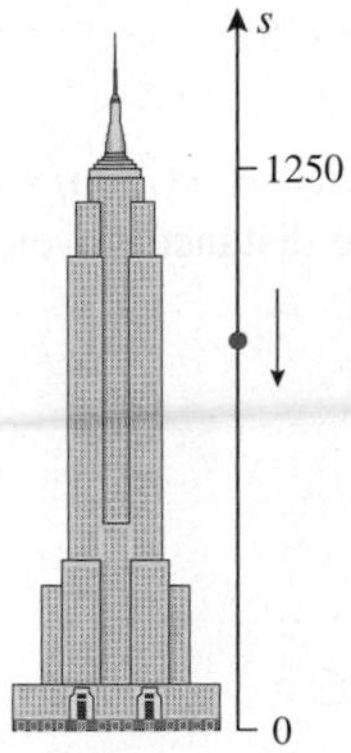


▲ Figure 5.7.8

***Solution.*** Since distance is in feet, we take $g = 32 \text{ ft/s}^2$. Initially, we have $s_0 = 1250$ and $v_0 = 0$, so from (15)

$$s(t) = 1250 - 16t^2 \tag{17}$$

Impact occurs when $s(t) = 0$. Solving this equation for $t$, we obtain

$$1250 - 16t^2 = 0$$

$$t^2 = \frac{1250}{16} = \frac{625}{8}$$

$$t = \pm\frac{25}{\sqrt{8}} \approx \pm 8.8 \text{ s}$$

Since $t \geq 0$, we can discard the negative solution and conclude that it takes $25/\sqrt{8} \approx 8.8$ s for the penny to hit the ground. To obtain the velocity at the time of impact, we substitute $t = 25/\sqrt{8}$, $v_0 = 0$, and $g = 32$ in (16) to obtain

$$v\left(\frac{25}{\sqrt{8}}\right) = 0 - 32\left(\frac{25}{\sqrt{8}}\right) = -200\sqrt{2} \approx -282.8 \text{ ft/s}$$

Thus, the speed at the time of impact is

$$\left|v\left(\frac{25}{\sqrt{8}}\right)\right| = 200\sqrt{2} \approx 282.8 \text{ ft/s}$$

which is more than 192 mi/h. ◀

## ✓ QUICK CHECK EXERCISES 5.7 (See page 314 for answers.)

1. Suppose that a particle is moving along an $s$-axis with velocity $v(t) = 2t + 1$. If at time $t = 0$ the particle is at position $s = 2$, the position function of the particle is $s(t) =$ ________.

2. Let $v(t)$ denote the velocity function of a particle that is moving along an $s$-axis with constant acceleration $a = -2$. If $v(1) = 4$, then $v(t) =$ ________.

3. Let $v(t)$ denote the velocity function of a particle in rectilinear motion. Suppose that $v(0) = -1$, $v(3) = 2$, and the velocity versus time curve is a straight line. The displacement of the particle between times $t = 0$ and $t = 3$ is ________, and the distance traveled by the particle over this period of time is ________.

4. Based on the free-fall model, from what height must a coin be dropped so that it strikes the ground with speed 48 ft/s?

## EXERCISE SET 5.7 Graphing Utility C CAS

**FOCUS ON CONCEPTS**

**1.** In each part, the velocity versus time curve is given for a particle moving along a line. Use the curve to find the displacement and the distance traveled by the particle over the time interval $0 \le t \le 3$.

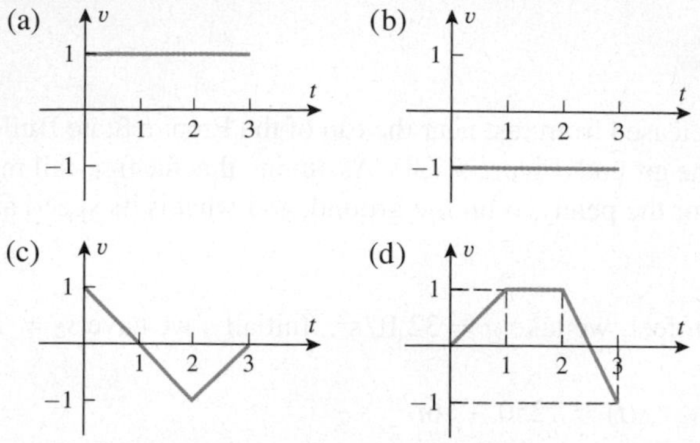


**2.** Given a push, a ball rolls up an inclined plane and returns to its original position after 4 s. If the total distance traveled by the ball is 16 ft, sketch a velocity versus time curve for the ball.

**3.** The accompanying figure shows the acceleration versus time curve for a particle moving along a coordinate line. If the initial velocity of the particle is 20 m/s, estimate
(a) the velocity at time $t = 4$ s
(b) the velocity at time $t = 6$ s.

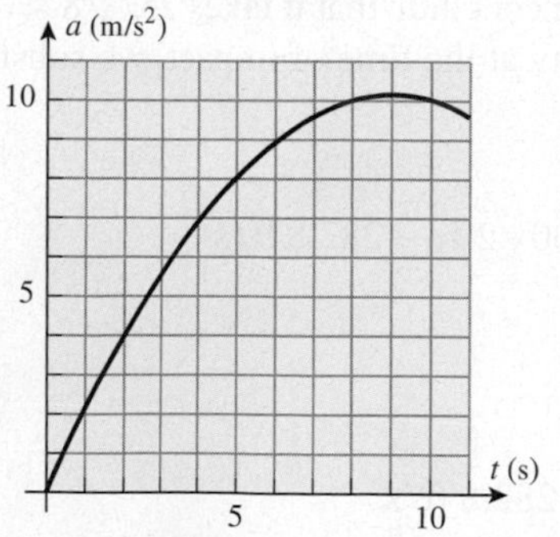


**Figure Ex-3**

**4.** The accompanying figure shows the velocity versus time curve over the time interval $1 \le t \le 5$ for a particle moving along a horizontal coordinate line.
(a) What can you say about the sign of the acceleration over the time interval?
(b) When is the particle speeding up? Slowing down?
(c) What can you say about the location of the particle at time $t = 5$ relative to its location at time $t = 1$? Explain your reasoning.

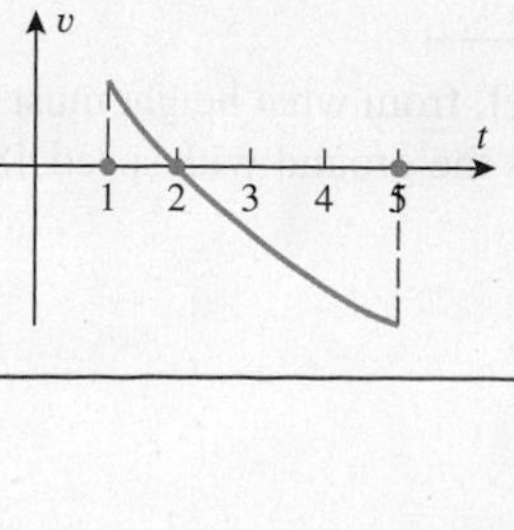


**Figure Ex-4**

**5–8** A particle moves along an $s$-axis. Use the given information to find the position function of the particle. ■

**5.** (a) $v(t) = 3t^2 - 2t;\ s(0) = 1$
(b) $a(t) = 3\sin 3t;\ v(0) = 3;\ s(0) = 3$

**6.** (a) $v(t) = 1 + \sin t;\ s(0) = -3$
(b) $a(t) = t^2 - 3t + 1;\ v(0) = 0;\ s(0) = 0$

**7.** (a) $v(t) = 3t + 1;\ s(2) = 4$
(b) $a(t) = t^{-2};\ v(1) = 0;\ s(1) = 2$

**8.** (a) $v(t) = t^{2/3};\ s(8) = 0$
(b) $a(t) = \sqrt{t};\ v(4) = 1;\ s(4) = -5$

**9–12** A particle moves with a velocity of $v(t)$ m/s along an $s$-axis. Find the displacement and the distance traveled by the particle during the given time interval. ■

**9.** (a) $v(t) = \sin t;\ 0 \le t \le \pi/2$
(b) $v(t) = \cos t;\ \pi/2 \le t \le 2\pi$

**10.** (a) $v(t) = 3t - 2;\ 0 \le t \le 2$
(b) $v(t) = |1 - 2t|;\ 0 \le t \le 2$

**11.** (a) $v(t) = t^3 - 3t^2 + 2t;\ 0 \le t \le 3$
(b) $v(t) = \sqrt{t} - 2;\ 0 \le t \le 3$

**12.** (a) $v(t) = t - \sqrt{t};\ 0 \le t \le 4$
(b) $v(t) = \dfrac{1}{\sqrt{t+1}};\ 0 \le t \le 3$

**13–16** A particle moves with acceleration $a(t)$ m/s$^2$ along an $s$-axis and has velocity $v_0$ m/s at time $t = 0$. Find the displacement and the distance traveled by the particle during the given time interval. ■

**13.** $a(t) = 3;\ v_0 = -1;\ 0 \le t \le 2$

**14.** $a(t) = t - 2;\ v_0 = 0;\ 1 \le t \le 5$

**15.** $a(t) = 1/\sqrt{3t+1};\ v_0 = \frac{4}{3};\ 1 \le t \le 5$

**16.** $a(t) = \sin t;\ v_0 = 1;\ \pi/4 \le t \le \pi/2$

**17.** In each part, use the given information to find the position, velocity, speed, and acceleration at time $t = 1$.
(a) $v = \sin \frac{1}{2}\pi t;\ s = 0$ when $t = 0$
(b) $a = -3t;\ s = 1$ and $v = 0$ when $t = 0$

**18.** In each part, use the given information to find the position, velocity, speed, and acceleration at time $t = 1$.
(a) $v = \cos \frac{1}{3}\pi t;\ s = 0$ when $t = \frac{3}{2}$
(b) $a = 4e^{2t-2};\ s = 1/e^2$ and $v = (2/e^2) - 3$ when $t = 0$

**19.** The velocity of an ant running along the edge of a shelf is modeled by the function

$$v(t) = \begin{cases} 5t, & 0 \le t < 1 \\ 6\sqrt{t} - \dfrac{1}{t}, & 1 \le t \le 2 \end{cases}$$

where $t$ is in seconds and $v$ is in centimeters per second. Estimate the time at which the ant is 4 cm from its starting position.

**20.** The velocity of a mouse running alongside the baseboard of a room is modeled by the function

$$v(t) = \frac{3}{t^2+1} - 0.5t, \quad 0 \le t \le 6$$

where $t$ is in seconds and $v$ is in meters per second. (Assume that positive values of $v$ indicate motion to the right.) Estimate the time(s) at which the mouse is 2 m from its starting position.

**21.** Suppose that the velocity function of a particle moving along an $s$-axis is $v(t) = 20t^2 - 110t + 120$ ft/s and that the particle is at the origin at time $t = 0$. Use a graphing utility to generate the graphs of $s(t)$, $v(t)$, and $a(t)$ for the first 6 s of motion.

**22.** Suppose that the acceleration function of a particle moving along an $s$-axis is $a(t) = 4t - 30$ m/s$^2$ and that the position and velocity at time $t = 0$ are $s_0 = -5$ m and $v_0 = 3$ m/s. Use a graphing utility to generate the graphs of $s(t)$, $v(t)$, and $a(t)$ for the first 25 s of motion.

**23–26 True–False** Determine whether the statement is true or false. Explain your answer. Each question refers to a particle in rectilinear motion. ■

**23.** If the particle has constant acceleration, the velocity versus time graph will be a straight line.

**24.** If the particle has constant nonzero acceleration, its position versus time curve will be a parabola.

**25.** If the total area between the velocity versus time curve and a time interval $[a, b]$ is positive, then the displacement of the particle over this time interval will be nonzero.

**26.** If $D(t)$ denotes the distance traveled by the particle over the time interval $[0, t]$, then $D(t)$ is an antiderivative for the speed of the particle.

**27–30** For the given velocity function $v(t)$:
(a) Generate the velocity versus time curve, and use it to make a conjecture about the sign of the displacement over the given time interval.
(b) Use a CAS to find the displacement. ■

**27.** $v(t) = 0.5 - t \sin t;\ 0 \le t \le 5$

**28.** $v(t) = 0.5 - t \cos \pi t;\ 0 \le t \le 1$

**29.** $v(t) = 0.5 - te^{-t};\ 0 \le t \le 5$

**30.** $v(t) = t \ln(t + 0.1);\ 0 \le t \le 1$

**31.** Suppose that at time $t = 0$ a particle is at the origin of an $x$-axis and has a velocity of $v_0 = 25$ cm/s. For the first 4 s thereafter it has no acceleration, and then it is acted on by a retarding force that produces a constant negative acceleration of $a = -10$ cm/s$^2$.
(a) Sketch the acceleration versus time curve over the interval $0 \le t \le 12$.
(b) Sketch the velocity versus time curve over the time interval $0 \le t \le 12$.
(c) Find the $x$-coordinate of the particle at times $t = 8$ s and $t = 12$ s.
(d) What is the maximum $x$-coordinate of the particle over the time interval $0 \le t \le 12$?

**32–38** In these exercises assume that the object is moving with constant acceleration in the positive direction of a coordinate line, and apply Formulas (10) and (11) as appropriate. In some of these problems you will need the fact that 88 ft/s = 60 mi/h. ■

**32.** A car traveling 60 mi/h along a straight road decelerates at a constant rate of 11 ft/s$^2$.
(a) How long will it take until the speed is 45 mi/h?
(b) How far will the car travel before coming to a stop?

**33.** Spotting a police car, you hit the brakes on your new Porsche to reduce your speed from 90 mi/h to 60 mi/h at a constant rate over a distance of 200 ft.
(a) Find the acceleration in ft/s$^2$.
(b) How long does it take for you to reduce your speed to 55 mi/h?
(c) At the acceleration obtained in part (a), how long would it take for you to bring your Porsche to a complete stop from 90 mi/h?

**34.** A particle moving along a straight line is accelerating at a constant rate of 5 m/s$^2$. Find the initial velocity if the particle moves 60 m in the first 4 s.

**35.** A motorcycle, starting from rest, speeds up with a constant acceleration of 2.6 m/s$^2$. After it has traveled 120 m, it slows down with a constant acceleration of $-1.5$ m/s$^2$ until it attains a speed of 12 m/s. What is the distance traveled by the motorcycle at that point?

**36.** A sprinter in a 100 m race explodes out of the starting block with an acceleration of 4.0 m/s$^2$, which she sustains for 2.0 s. Her acceleration then drops to zero for the rest of the race.
(a) What is her time for the race?
(b) Make a graph of her distance from the starting block versus time.

**37.** A car that has stopped at a toll booth leaves the booth with a constant acceleration of 4 ft/s$^2$. At the time the car leaves the booth it is 2500 ft behind a truck traveling with a constant velocity of 50 ft/s. How long will it take for the car to catch the truck, and how far will the car be from the toll booth at that time?

**38.** In the final sprint of a rowing race the challenger is rowing at a constant speed of 12 m/s. At the point where the leader is 100 m from the finish line and the challenger is 15 m behind, the leader is rowing at 8 m/s but starts accelerating at a constant 0.5 m/s$^2$. Who wins?

**39–45** Assume that a free-fall model applies. Solve these exercises by applying Formulas (15) and (16). In these exercises take $g = 32$ ft/s$^2$ or $g = 9.8$ m/s$^2$, depending on the units. ■

**39.** A projectile is launched vertically upward from ground level with an initial velocity of 112 ft/s.
(a) Find the velocity at $t = 3$ s and $t = 5$ s.
(b) How high will the projectile rise?
(c) Find the speed of the projectile when it hits the ground.

**40.** A rock tossed downward from a height of 112 ft reaches the ground in 2 s. What is its initial velocity?

41. A projectile is fired vertically upward from ground level with an initial velocity of 16 ft/s.
(a) How long will it take for the projectile to hit the ground?
(b) How long will the projectile be moving upward?

42. In 1939, Joe Sprinz of the San Francisco Seals Baseball Club attempted to catch a ball dropped from a blimp at a height of 800 ft (for the purpose of breaking the record for catching a ball dropped from the greatest height set the preceding year by members of the Cleveland Indians).
(a) How long does it take for a ball to drop 800 ft?
(b) What is the velocity of a ball in miles per hour after an 800 ft drop (88 ft/s = 60 mi/h)?
[*Note:* As a practical matter, it is unrealistic to ignore wind resistance in this problem; however, even with the slowing effect of wind resistance, the impact of the ball slammed Sprinz's glove hand into his face, fractured his upper jaw in 12 places, broke five teeth, and knocked him unconscious. He dropped the ball!]

43. A model rocket is launched upward from ground level with an initial speed of 60 m/s.
(a) How long does it take for the rocket to reach its highest point?
(b) How high does the rocket go?
(c) How long does it take for the rocket to drop back to the ground from its highest point?
(d) What is the speed of the rocket when it hits the ground?

44. (a) Use the results in Exercise 43 to make a conjecture about the relationship between the initial and final speeds of a projectile that is launched upward from ground level and returns to ground level.
(b) Prove your conjecture.

45. A model rocket is fired vertically upward with an initial velocity of 49 m/s from a tower 150 m high.
(a) How long will it take for the rocket to reach its maximum height?
(b) What is the maximum height?
(c) How long will it take for the rocket to pass its starting point on the way down?
(d) What is the velocity when it passes the starting point on the way down?
(e) How long will it take for the rocket to hit the ground?
(f) What will be its speed at impact?

46. **Writing** Make a list of important features of a velocity versus time curve, and interpret each feature in terms of the motion.

47. **Writing** Use Riemann sums to argue informally that integrating speed over a time interval produces the distance traveled.

✓ **QUICK CHECK ANSWERS 5.7** 1. $t^2+t+2$ 2. $6-2t$ 3. $\frac{3}{2}$; $\frac{5}{2}$ 4. 36 ft

## 5.8 AVERAGE VALUE OF A FUNCTION AND ITS APPLICATIONS

*In this section we will define the notion of the "average value" of a function, and we will give various applications of this idea.*

### AVERAGE VELOCITY REVISITED

Let $s = s(t)$ denote the position function of a particle in rectilinear motion. In Section 2.1 we defined the average velocity $v_{\text{ave}}$ of the particle over the time interval $[t_0, t_1]$ to be

$$v_{\text{ave}} = \frac{s(t_1) - s(t_0)}{t_1 - t_0}$$

Let $v(t) = s'(t)$ denote the velocity function of the particle. We saw in Section 5.7 that integrating $s'(t)$ over a time interval gives the displacement of the particle over that interval. Thus,

$$\int_{t_0}^{t_1} v(t)\,dt = \int_{t_0}^{t_1} s'(t)\,dt = s(t_1) - s(t_0)$$

It follows that

$$v_{\text{ave}} = \frac{s(t_1) - s(t_0)}{t_1 - t_0} = \frac{1}{t_1 - t_0}\int_{t_0}^{t_1} v(t)\,dt \qquad (1)$$

▶ **Example 1** Suppose that a particle moves along a coordinate line so that its velocity at time $t$ is $v(t) = 2 + \cos t$. Find the average velocity of the particle during the time interval $0 \le t \le \pi$.

***Solution.*** From (1) the average velocity is

$$\frac{1}{\pi - 0}\int_0^{\pi}(2+\cos t)\,dt = \frac{1}{\pi}\left[2t + \sin t\right]_0^{\pi} = \frac{1}{\pi}(2\pi) = 2 \blacktriangleleft$$

We will see that Formula (1) is a special case of a formula for what we will call the *average value* of a continuous function over a given interval.

## AVERAGE VALUE OF A CONTINUOUS FUNCTION

In scientific work, numerical information is often summarized by an *average value* or *mean value* of the observed data. There are various kinds of averages, but the most common is the ***arithmetic mean*** or ***arithmetic average***, which is formed by adding the data and dividing by the number of data points. Thus, the arithmetic average $\overline{a}$ of $n$ numbers $a_1, a_2, \ldots, a_n$ is

$$\overline{a} = \frac{1}{n}(a_1 + a_2 + \cdots + a_n) = \frac{1}{n}\sum_{k=1}^{n} a_k$$

In the case where the $a_k$'s are values of a function $f$, say,

$$a_1 = f(x_1), a_2 = f(x_2), \ldots, a_n = f(x_n)$$

then the arithmetic average $\overline{a}$ of these function values is

$$\overline{a} = \frac{1}{n}\sum_{k=1}^{n} f(x_k)$$

We will now show how to extend this concept so that we can compute not only the arithmetic average of finitely many function values but an average of *all* values of $f(x)$ as $x$ varies over a closed interval $[a, b]$. For this purpose recall the Mean-Value Theorem for Integrals (5.6.2), which states that if $f$ is continuous on the interval $[a, b]$, then there is at least one point $x^*$ in this interval such that

$$\int_a^b f(x)\,dx = f(x^*)(b-a)$$

The quantity

$$f(x^*) = \frac{1}{b-a}\int_a^b f(x)\,dx$$

will be our candidate for the average value of $f$ over the interval $[a, b]$. To explain what motivates this, divide the interval $[a, b]$ into $n$ subintervals of equal length

$$\Delta x = \frac{b-a}{n} \tag{2}$$

and choose arbitrary points $x_1^*, x_2^*, \ldots, x_n^*$ in successive subintervals. Then the arithmetic average of the values $f(x_1^*), f(x_2^*), \ldots, f(x_n^*)$ is

$$\text{ave} = \frac{1}{n}[f(x_1^*) + f(x_2^*) + \cdots + f(x_n^*)]$$

or from (2)

$$\text{ave} = \frac{1}{b-a}[f(x_1^*)\Delta x + f(x_2^*)\Delta x + \cdots + f(x_n^*)\Delta x] = \frac{1}{b-a}\sum_{k=1}^{n} f(x_k^*)\Delta x$$

Taking the limit as $n \to +\infty$ yields

$$\lim_{n\to+\infty}\frac{1}{b-a}\sum_{k=1}^{n} f(x_k^*)\Delta x = \frac{1}{b-a}\int_a^b f(x)\,dx$$

Since this equation describes what happens when we compute the average of "more and more" values of $f(x)$, we are led to the following definition.

> **5.8.1 DEFINITION** If $f$ is continuous on $[a, b]$, then the ***average value*** (or ***mean value***) of $f$ on $[a, b]$ is defined to be
>
> $$f_{\text{ave}} = \frac{1}{b-a}\int_a^b f(x)\,dx \tag{3}$$

Note that the Mean-Value Theorem for Integrals, when expressed in form (3), ensures that there is always at least one point $x^*$ in $[a, b]$ at which the value of $f$ is equal to the average value of $f$ over the interval.

**REMARK** When $f$ is nonnegative on $[a, b]$, the quantity $f_{\text{ave}}$ has a simple geometric interpretation, which can be seen by writing (3) as

$$f_{\text{ave}} \cdot (b-a) = \int_a^b f(x)\,dx$$

The left side of this equation is the area of a rectangle with a height of $f_{\text{ave}}$ and base of length $b - a$, and the right side is the area under $y = f(x)$ over $[a, b]$. Thus, $f_{\text{ave}}$ is the height of a rectangle constructed over the interval $[a, b]$, whose area is the same as the area under the graph of $f$ over that interval (Figure 5.8.1).

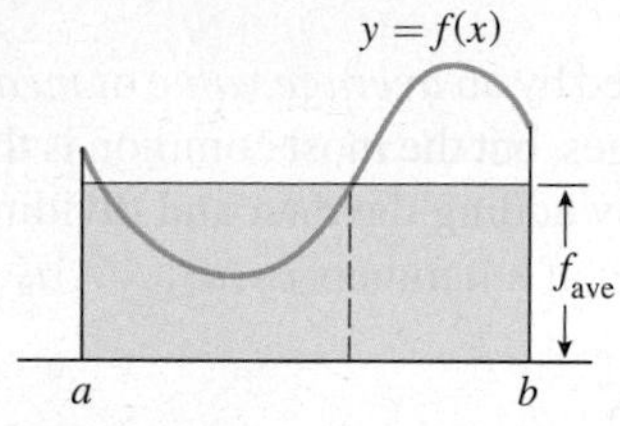

▲ **Figure 5.8.1**

▶ **Example 2** Find the average value of the function $f(x) = \sqrt{x}$ over the interval $[1, 4]$, and find all points in the interval at which the value of $f$ is the same as the average.

***Solution.***

$$f_{\text{ave}} = \frac{1}{b-a}\int_a^b f(x)\,dx = \frac{1}{4-1}\int_1^4 \sqrt{x}\,dx = \frac{1}{3}\left[\frac{2x^{3/2}}{3}\right]_1^4$$

$$= \frac{1}{3}\left[\frac{16}{3} - \frac{2}{3}\right] = \frac{14}{9} \approx 1.6$$

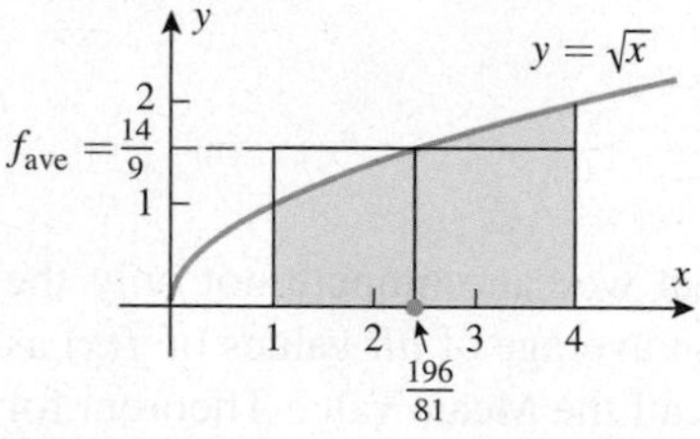

▲ **Figure 5.8.2**

The $x$-values at which $f(x) = \sqrt{x}$ is the same as this average satisfy $\sqrt{x} = 14/9$, from which we obtain $x = 196/81 \approx 2.4$ (Figure 5.8.2). ◀

▶ **Example 3** A glass of lemonade with a temperature of 40°F is left to sit in a room whose temperature is a constant 70°F. Using a principle of physics called ***Newton's Law of Cooling***, one can show that if the temperature of the lemonade reaches 52°F in 1 hour, then the temperature $T$ of the lemonade as a function of the elapsed time $t$ is modeled by the equation

$$T = 70 - 30e^{-0.5t}$$

where $T$ is in degrees Fahrenheit and $t$ is in hours. The graph of this equation, shown in Figure 5.8.3, conforms to our everyday experience that the temperature of the lemonade gradually approaches the temperature of the room. Find the average temperature $T_{\text{ave}}$ of the lemonade over the first 5 hours.

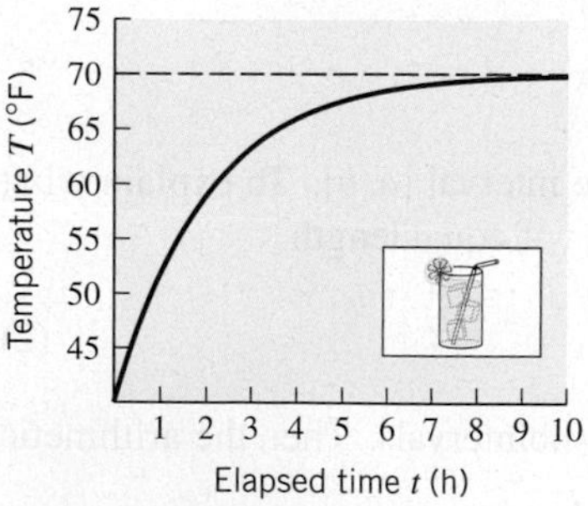

▲ **Figure 5.8.3**

***Solution.*** From Definition 5.8.1 the average value of $T$ over the time interval $[0, 5]$ is

$$T_{\text{ave}} = \frac{1}{5}\int_0^5 (70 - 30e^{-0.5t})\,dt \tag{4}$$

To evaluate the definite integral, we first find the indefinite integral

$$\int (70 - 30e^{-0.5t})\,dt$$

by making the substitution

$$u = -0.5t \quad \text{so that} \quad du = -0.5\,dt \quad (\text{or } dt = -2\,du)$$

Thus,

$$\int (70 - 30e^{-0.5t})\,dt = \int (70 - 30e^{u})(-2)\,du = -2(70u - 30e^{u}) + C$$

$$= -2[70(-0.5t) - 30e^{-0.5t}] + C = 70t + 60e^{-0.5t} + C$$

In Example 3, the temperature $T$ of the lemonade rises from an initial temperature of 40°F toward the room temperature of 70°F. Explain why the formula

$$T = 70 - 30e^{-0.5t}$$

is a good model for this situation.

and (4) can be expressed as

$$T_{\text{ave}} = \frac{1}{5}\left[70t + 60e^{-0.5t}\right]_0^5 = \frac{1}{5}\left[(350 + 60e^{-2.5}) - 60\right]$$

$$= 58 + 12e^{-2.5} \approx 59°\text{F} ◀$$

## AVERAGE VALUE AND AVERAGE VELOCITY

We now have two ways to calculate the average velocity of a particle in rectilinear motion, since

$$\frac{s(t_1) - s(t_0)}{t_1 - t_0} = \frac{1}{t_1 - t_0}\int_{t_0}^{t_1} v(t)\,dt \tag{5}$$

and both of these expressions are equal to the average velocity. The left side of (5) gives the average rate of change of $s$ over $[t_0, t_1]$, while the right side gives the average value of $v = s'$ over the interval $[t_0, t_1]$. That is, *the average velocity of the particle over the time interval* $[t_0, t_1]$ *is the same as the average value of the velocity function over that interval.*

Since velocity functions are generally continuous, it follows from the marginal note associated with Definition 5.8.1 that a particle's average velocity over a time interval matches the particle's velocity at some time in the interval.

▶ **Example 4** Show that if a body released from rest (initial velocity zero) is in free fall, then its average velocity over a time interval $[0, T]$ during its fall is its velocity at time $t = T/2$.

***Solution.*** It follows from Formula (16) of Section 5.7 with $v_0 = 0$ that the velocity function of the body is $v(t) = -gt$. Thus, its average velocity over a time interval $[0, T]$ is

$$v_{\text{ave}} = \frac{1}{T-0}\int_0^T v(t)\,dt$$

$$= \frac{1}{T}\int_0^T -gt\,dt$$

$$= -\frac{g}{T}\left[\frac{1}{2}t^2\right]_0^T = -g\cdot\frac{T}{2} = v\left(\frac{T}{2}\right) ◀$$

The result of Example 4 can be generalized to show that the average velocity of a particle with constant acceleration during a time interval $[a, b]$ is the velocity at time $t = (a+b)/2$. (See Exercise 18.)

## ✓QUICK CHECK EXERCISES 5.8 (See page 319 for answers.)

1. The arithmetic average of $n$ numbers, $a_1, a_2, \ldots, a_n$ is ______.
2. If $f$ is continuous on $[a, b]$, then the average value of $f$ on $[a, b]$ is ______.
3. If $f$ is continuous on $[a, b]$, then the Mean-Value Theorem for Integrals guarantees that for at least one point $x^*$ in $[a, b]$ ______ equals the average value of $f$ on $[a, b]$.
4. The average value of $f(x) = 4x^3$ on $[1, 3]$ is ______.

## EXERCISE SET 5.8

1. (a) Find $f_{\text{ave}}$ of $f(x) = 2x$ over $[0, 4]$.
   (b) Find a point $x^*$ in $[0, 4]$ such that $f(x^*) = f_{\text{ave}}$.
   (c) Sketch a graph of $f(x) = 2x$ over $[0, 4]$, and construct a rectangle over the interval whose area is the same as the area under the graph of $f$ over the interval.
2. (a) Find $f_{\text{ave}}$ of $f(x) = x^2$ over $[0, 2]$.
   (b) Find a point $x^*$ in $[0, 2]$ such that $f(x^*) = f_{\text{ave}}$.
   (c) Sketch a graph of $f(x) = x^2$ over $[0, 2]$, and construct a rectangle over the interval whose area is the same as the area under the graph of $f$ over the interval.

**3–12** Find the average value of the function over the given interval. ■

3. $f(x) = 3x;\ [1, 3]$
4. $f(x) = \sqrt[3]{x};\ [-1, 8]$
5. $f(x) = \sin x;\ [0, \pi]$
6. $f(x) = \sec x \tan x;\ [0, \pi/3]$
7. $f(x) = 1/x;\ [1, e]$
8. $f(x) = e^x;\ [-1, \ln 5]$
9. $f(x) = \dfrac{1}{1+x^2};\ [1, \sqrt{3}]$
10. $f(x) = \dfrac{1}{\sqrt{1-x^2}};\ \left[-\frac{1}{2}, 0\right]$
11. $f(x) = e^{-2x};\ [0, 4]$
12. $f(x) = \sec^2 x;\ [-\pi/4, \pi/4]$

**FOCUS ON CONCEPTS**

**13.** Let $f(x) = 3x^2$.
(a) Find the arithmetic average of the values $f(0.4)$, $f(0.8), f(1.2), f(1.6)$, and $f(2.0)$.
(b) Find the arithmetic average of the values $f(0.1)$, $f(0.2), f(0.3), \ldots, f(2.0)$.
(c) Find the average value of $f$ on $[0, 2]$.
(d) Explain why the answer to part (c) is less than the answers to parts (a) and (b).

**14.** In parts (a)–(d), let $f(x) = 1 + (1/x)$.
(a) Find the arithmetic average of the values $f\left(\frac{6}{5}\right)$, $f\left(\frac{7}{5}\right), f\left(\frac{8}{5}\right), f\left(\frac{9}{5}\right)$, and $f(2)$.
(b) Find the arithmetic average of the values $f(1.1)$, $f(1.2), f(1.3), \ldots, f(2)$.
(c) Find the average value of $f$ on $[1, 2]$.
(d) Explain why the answer to part (c) is greater than the answers to parts (a) and (b).

**15.** In each part, the velocity versus time curve is given for a particle moving along a line. Use the curve to find the average velocity of the particle over the time interval $0 \le t \le 3$.

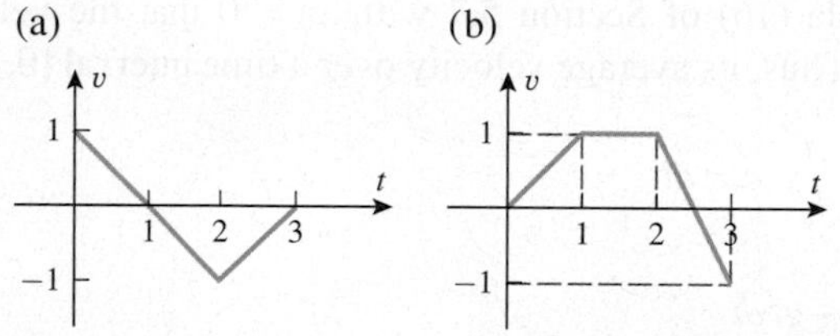


**16.** Suppose that a particle moving along a line starts from rest and has an average velocity of 2 ft/s over the time interval $0 \le t \le 5$. Sketch a velocity versus time curve for the particle assuming that the particle is also at rest at time $t = 5$. Explain how your curve satisfies the required properties.

**17.** Suppose that $f$ is a linear function. Using the graph of $f$, explain why the average value of $f$ on $[a, b]$ is

$$f\left(\frac{a+b}{2}\right)$$

**18.** Suppose that a particle moves along a coordinate line with constant acceleration. Show that the average velocity of the particle during a time interval $[a, b]$ matches the velocity of the particle at the midpoint of the interval.

**19–22 True–False** Determine whether the statement is true or false. Explain your answer. (Assume that $f$ and $g$ denote continuous functions on an interval $[a, b]$ and that $f_{\text{ave}}$ and $g_{\text{ave}}$ denote the respective average values of $f$ and $g$ on $[a, b]$.) ■

**19.** If $g_{\text{ave}} < f_{\text{ave}}$, then $g(x) \le f(x)$ on $[a, b]$.

**20.** The average value of a constant multiple of $f$ is the same multiple of $f_{\text{ave}}$; that is, if $c$ is any constant,

$$(c \cdot f)_{\text{ave}} = c \cdot f_{\text{ave}}$$

**21.** The average of the sum of two functions on an interval is the sum of the average values of the two functions on the interval; that is,

$$(f + g)_{\text{ave}} = f_{\text{ave}} + g_{\text{ave}}$$

**22.** The average of the product of two functions on an interval is the product of the average values of the two functions on the interval; that is,

$$(f \cdot g)_{\text{ave}} = f_{\text{ave}} \cdot g_{\text{ave}}$$

**23.** (a) Suppose that the velocity function of a particle moving along a coordinate line is $v(t) = 3t^3 + 2$. Find the average velocity of the particle over the time interval $1 \le t \le 4$ by integrating.
(b) Suppose that the position function of a particle moving along a coordinate line is $s(t) = 6t^2 + t$. Find the average velocity of the particle over the time interval $1 \le t \le 4$ algebraically.

**24.** (a) Suppose that the acceleration function of a particle moving along a coordinate line is $a(t) = t + 1$. Find the average acceleration of the particle over the time interval $0 \le t \le 5$ by integrating.
(b) Suppose that the velocity function of a particle moving along a coordinate line is $v(t) = \cos t$. Find the average acceleration of the particle over the time interval $0 \le t \le \pi/4$ algebraically.

**25.** Water is run at a constant rate of 1 $\text{ft}^3/\text{min}$ to fill a cylindrical tank of radius 3 ft and height 5 ft. Assuming that the tank is initially empty, make a conjecture about the average weight of the water in the tank over the time period required to fill it, and then check your conjecture by integrating. [Take the weight density of water to be 62.4 $\text{lb}/\text{ft}^3$.]

**26.** (a) The temperature of a 10 m long metal bar is 15°C at one end and 30°C at the other end. Assuming that the temperature increases linearly from the cooler end to the hotter end, what is the average temperature of the bar?
(b) Explain why there must be a point on the bar where the temperature is the same as the average, and find it.

**27.** A traffic engineer monitors the rate at which cars enter the main highway during the afternoon rush hour. From her data she estimates that between 4:30 P.M. and 5:30 P.M. the rate $R(t)$ at which cars enter the highway is given by the formula $R(t) = 100(1 - 0.0001t^2)$ cars per minute, where $t$ is the time (in minutes) since 4:30 P.M. Find the average rate, in cars per minute, at which cars enter the highway during the first half hour of rush hour.

**28.** Suppose that the value of a yacht in dollars after $t$ years of use is $V(t) = 275{,}000e^{-0.17t}$. What is the average value of the yacht over its first 10 years of use?

**29.** A large juice glass containing 60 ml of orange juice is replenished by a server. The accompanying figure shows the rate at which orange juice is poured into the glass in milliliters per second (ml/s). Show that the average rate of change of the volume of juice in the glass during these 5 s is equal to the average value of the rate of flow of juice into the glass.

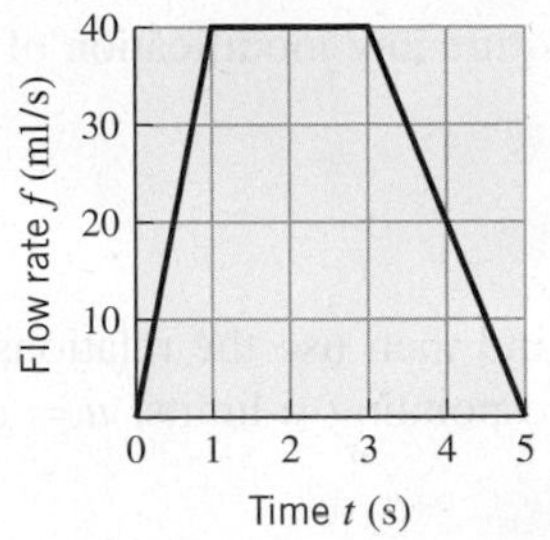


◀ **Figure Ex-29**

**30.** For the years 1990–1999, the number $P$ of gray wolves in Wisconsin can be modeled by the population function

$$P = P(t) = 28.3e^{0.217(t-1990)} \quad (1990 \le t \le 1999)$$

Based upon this model, what was the average gray wolf population in Wisconsin over the period 1990–1999?

**31.** For the years 2000–2011, the number $P$ of gray wolves in Wisconsin can be modeled by the population function

$$P = P(t) = 248e^{0.105(t-2000)} \quad (2000 \le t \le 2011)$$

Based upon this model, what was the average gray wolf population in Wisconsin over the period 2000–2011?

**32.** Suppose that a tumor grows at the rate of $r(t) = kt$ grams per week for some positive constant $k$, where $t$ is the number of weeks since the tumor appeared. When, during the second 26 weeks of growth, is the mass of the tumor the same as its average mass during that period?

**33. Writing** Consider the following statement: *The average value of the rate of change of a function over an interval is equal to the average rate of change of the function over that interval.* Write a short paragraph that explains why this statement may be interpreted as a rewording of Part 1 of the Fundamental Theorem of Calculus.

**34. Writing** If an automobile gets an average of 25 miles per gallon of gasoline, then it is also the case that on average the automobile expends $1/25$ gallon of gasoline per mile. Interpret this statement using the concept of the average value of a function over an interval.

✓ **QUICK CHECK ANSWERS 5.8** 1. $\frac{1}{n}\sum_{k=1}^{n} a_k$ 2. $\frac{1}{b-a}\int_a^b f(x)\,dx$ 3. $f(x^*)$ 4. 40

## 5.9 EVALUATING DEFINITE INTEGRALS BY SUBSTITUTION

*In this section we will discuss two methods for evaluating definite integrals in which a substitution is required.*

### TWO METHODS FOR MAKING SUBSTITUTIONS IN DEFINITE INTEGRALS

Recall from Section 5.3 that indefinite integrals of the form

$$\int f(g(x))g'(x)\,dx$$

can sometimes be evaluated by making the $u$-substitution

$$u = g(x), \quad du = g'(x)\,dx \tag{1}$$

which converts the integral to the form

$$\int f(u)\,du$$

To apply this method to a definite integral of the form

$$\int_a^b f(g(x))g'(x)\,dx$$

we need to account for the effect that the substitution has on the $x$-limits of integration. There are two ways of doing this.

**Method 1.**

First evaluate the indefinite integral

$$\int f(g(x))g'(x)\,dx$$

by substitution, and then use the relationship

$$\int_a^b f(g(x))g'(x)\,dx = \left[\int f(g(x))g'(x)\,dx\right]_a^b$$

to evaluate the definite integral. This procedure does not require any modification of the $x$-limits of integration.

**Method 2.**

Make the substitution (1) directly in the definite integral, and then use the relationship $u = g(x)$ to replace the $x$-limits, $x = a$ and $x = b$, by corresponding $u$-limits, $u = g(a)$ and $u = g(b)$. This produces a new definite integral

$$\int_{g(a)}^{g(b)} f(u)\,du$$

that is expressed entirely in terms of $u$.

**▶ Example 1** Use the two methods above to evaluate $\int_0^2 x(x^2+1)^3\,dx$.

***Solution by Method 1.*** If we let

$$u = x^2 + 1 \quad \text{so that} \quad du = 2x\,dx \tag{2}$$

then we obtain

$$\int x(x^2+1)^3\,dx = \frac{1}{2}\int u^3\,du = \frac{u^4}{8} + C = \frac{(x^2+1)^4}{8} + C$$

Thus,

$$\int_0^2 x(x^2+1)^3\,dx = \left[\int x(x^2+1)^3\,dx\right]_{x=0}^{2}$$

$$= \frac{(x^2+1)^4}{8}\bigg]_{x=0}^{2} = \frac{625}{8} - \frac{1}{8} = 78$$

***Solution by Method 2.*** If we make the substitution $u = x^2 + 1$ in (2), then

$$\text{if} \quad x = 0, \quad u = 1$$

$$\text{if} \quad x = 2, \quad u = 5$$

Thus,

$$\int_0^2 x(x^2+1)^3\,dx = \frac{1}{2}\int_1^5 u^3\,du$$

$$= \frac{u^4}{8}\bigg]_{u=1}^{5} = \frac{625}{8} - \frac{1}{8} = 78$$

which agrees with the result obtained by Method 1. ◀

The following theorem states precise conditions under which Method 2 can be used.

**5.9.1 THEOREM** *If $g'$ is continuous on $[a, b]$ and $f$ is continuous on an interval containing the values of $g(x)$ for $a \le x \le b$, then*

$$\int_a^b f(g(x))g'(x)\,dx = \int_{g(a)}^{g(b)} f(u)\,du$$

**PROOF** Since $f$ is continuous on an interval containing the values of $g(x)$ for $a \le x \le b$, it follows that $f$ has an antiderivative $F$ on that interval. If we let $u = g(x)$, then the chain rule implies that

$$\frac{d}{dx}F(g(x)) = \frac{d}{dx}F(u) = \frac{dF}{du}\frac{du}{dx} = f(u)\frac{du}{dx} = f(g(x))g'(x)$$

for each $x$ in $[a, b]$. Thus, $F(g(x))$ is an antiderivative of $f(g(x))g'(x)$ on $[a, b]$. Therefore, by Part 1 of the Fundamental Theorem of Calculus (5.6.1)

$$\int_a^b f(g(x))g'(x)\,dx = F(g(x))\Big]_a^b = F(g(b)) - F(g(a)) = \int_{g(a)}^{g(b)} f(u)\,du \quad \blacksquare$$

The choice of methods for evaluating definite integrals by substitution is generally a matter of taste, but in the following examples we will use the second method, since the idea is new.

► **Example 2** Evaluate

$$\text{(a)} \int_0^{\pi/8} \sin^5 2x \cos 2x\,dx \qquad \text{(b)} \int_2^5 (2x-5)(x-3)^9\,dx$$

***Solution (a).*** Let

$$u = \sin 2x \quad \text{so that} \quad du = 2\cos 2x\,dx \quad \left(\text{or } \tfrac{1}{2}\,du = \cos 2x\,dx\right)$$

With this substitution,

$$\begin{aligned} &\text{if} \quad x = 0, \quad u = \sin(0) = 0 \\ &\text{if} \quad x = \pi/8, \quad u = \sin(\pi/4) = 1/\sqrt{2} \end{aligned}$$

so

$$\begin{aligned} \int_0^{\pi/8} \sin^5 2x \cos 2x\,dx &= \frac{1}{2}\int_0^{1/\sqrt{2}} u^5\,du \\ &= \frac{1}{2}\cdot\frac{u^6}{6}\Big]_{u=0}^{1/\sqrt{2}} = \frac{1}{2}\left[\frac{1}{6(\sqrt{2})^6} - 0\right] = \frac{1}{96} \end{aligned}$$

***Solution (b).*** Let

$$u = x - 3 \quad \text{so that} \quad du = dx$$

This leaves a factor of $2x - 5$ unresolved in the integrand. However,

$$x = u + 3, \quad \text{so} \quad 2x - 5 = 2(u+3) - 5 = 2u + 1$$

With this substitution,

$$\begin{aligned} &\text{if} \quad x = 2, \quad u = 2 - 3 = -1 \\ &\text{if} \quad x = 5, \quad u = 5 - 3 = 2 \end{aligned}$$

so

$$\begin{aligned} \int_2^5 (2x-5)(x-3)^9\,dx &= \int_{-1}^2 (2u+1)u^9\,du = \int_{-1}^2 (2u^{10} + u^9)\,du \\ &= \left[\frac{2u^{11}}{11} + \frac{u^{10}}{10}\right]_{u=-1}^2 = \left(\frac{2^{12}}{11} + \frac{2^{10}}{10}\right) - \left(-\frac{2}{11} + \frac{1}{10}\right) \\ &= \frac{52{,}233}{110} \approx 474.8 \end{aligned}$$ ◄

▶ **Example 3** Evaluate

$$\text{(a)} \int_0^{3/4} \frac{dx}{1-x} \qquad \text{(b)} \int_0^{\ln 3} e^x(1+e^x)^{1/2}\,dx$$

***Solution (a).*** Let

$$u = 1 - x \quad \text{so that} \quad du = -dx$$

With this substitution,

$$\text{if } x = 0, \quad u = 1$$
$$\text{if } x = \tfrac{3}{4}, \quad u = \tfrac{1}{4}$$

$$\int_0^{3/4} \frac{dx}{1-x} = -\int_1^{1/4} \frac{du}{u}$$

$$= -\ln|u|\Big]_{u=1}^{1/4} = -\left[\ln\left(\frac{1}{4}\right) - \ln(1)\right] = \ln 4$$

***Solution (b).*** Make the $u$-substitution

$$u = 1 + e^x, \quad du = e^x\,dx$$

and change the $x$-limits of integration ($x = 0, x = \ln 3$) to the $u$-limits

$$u = 1 + e^0 = 2, \quad u = 1 + e^{\ln 3} = 1 + 3 = 4$$

This yields

$$\int_0^{\ln 3} e^x(1+e^x)^{1/2}\,dx = \int_2^4 u^{1/2}\,du$$

$$= \frac{2}{3}u^{3/2}\Big]_{u=2}^{4} = \frac{2}{3}[4^{3/2} - 2^{3/2}] = \frac{16 - 4\sqrt{2}}{3} \blacktriangleleft$$

The $u$-substitution in Example 3(a) produces an integral in which the upper $u$-limit is smaller than the lower $u$-limit. Use Definition 5.5.3(b) to convert this integral to one whose lower limit is smaller than the upper limit and verify that it produces an integral with the same value as that in the example.

## ✓ QUICK CHECK EXERCISES 5.9 *(See page 325 for answers.)*

1. Assume that $g'$ is continuous on $[a, b]$ and that $f$ is continuous on an interval containing the values of $g(x)$ for $a \le x \le b$. If $F$ is an antiderivative for $f$, then

$$\int_a^b f(g(x))g'(x)\,dx = \underline{\qquad}$$

2. In each part, use the substitution to replace the given integral with an integral involving the variable $u$. (Do not evaluate the integral.)
   (a) $\int_0^2 3x^2(1+x^3)^3\,dx;\ u = 1 + x^3$
   (b) $\int_0^2 \frac{x}{\sqrt{5-x^2}}\,dx;\ u = 5 - x^2$
   (c) $\int_0^1 \frac{e^{\sqrt{x}}}{\sqrt{x}}\,dx;\ u = \sqrt{x}$

3. Evaluate the integral by making an appropriate substitution.
   (a) $\int_{-\pi}^0 \sin(3x - \pi)\,dx = \underline{\qquad}$
   (b) $\int_2^3 \frac{x}{x^2-2}\,dx = \underline{\qquad}$
   (c) $\int_0^{\pi/2} \sqrt[3]{\sin x}\cos x\,dx = \underline{\qquad}$

## EXERCISE SET 5.9 Graphing Utility C CAS

**1–4** Express the integral in terms of the variable $u$, but do not evaluate it. ■

1. (a) $\int_1^3 (2x-1)^3\,dx;\ u = 2x - 1$
   (b) $\int_0^4 3x\sqrt{25-x^2}\,dx;\ u = 25 - x^2$
   (c) $\int_{-1/2}^{1/2} \cos(\pi\theta)\,d\theta;\ u = \pi\theta$
   (d) $\int_0^1 (x+2)(x+1)^5\,dx;\ u = x + 1$

2. (a) $\int_{-1}^4 (5-2x)^8\,dx;\ u = 5 - 2x$
   (b) $\int_{-\pi/3}^{2\pi/3} \frac{\sin x}{\sqrt{2+\cos x}}\,dx;\ u = 2 + \cos x$
   (c) $\int_0^{\pi/4} \tan^2 x\sec^2 x\,dx;\ u = \tan x$
   (d) $\int_0^1 x^3\sqrt{x^2+3}\,dx;\ u = x^2 + 3$

**3.** (a) $\int_0^1 e^{2x-1}\,dx;\ u = 2x - 1$

(b) $\int_e^{e^2} \frac{\ln x}{x}\,dx;\ u = \ln x$

**4.** (a) $\int_1^{\sqrt{3}} \frac{\sqrt{\tan^{-1} x}}{1+x^2}\,dx;\ u = \tan^{-1} x$

(b) $\int_1^{\sqrt{e}} \frac{dx}{x\sqrt{1-(\ln x)^2}};\ u = \ln x$

**5–18** Evaluate the definite integral two ways: first by a $u$-substitution in the definite integral and then by a $u$-substitution in the corresponding indefinite integral. ■

**5.** $\int_0^1 (2x+1)^3\,dx$ **6.** $\int_1^2 (4x-2)^3\,dx$

**7.** $\int_0^1 (2x-1)^3\,dx$ **8.** $\int_1^2 (4-3x)^8\,dx$

**9.** $\int_0^8 x\sqrt{1+x}\,dx$ **10.** $\int_{-3}^0 x\sqrt{1-x}\,dx$

**11.** $\int_0^{\pi/2} 4\sin(x/2)\,dx$ **12.** $\int_0^{\pi/6} 2\cos 3x\,dx$

**13.** $\int_{-2}^{-1} \frac{x}{(x^2+2)^3}\,dx$ **14.** $\int_{1-\pi}^{1+\pi} \sec^2\left(\frac{1}{4}x - \frac{1}{4}\right)dx$

**15.** $\int_{-\ln 3}^{\ln 3} \frac{e^x}{e^x+4}\,dx$ **16.** $\int_0^{\ln 5} e^x(3-4e^x)\,dx$

**17.** $\int_1^3 \frac{dx}{\sqrt{x}(x+1)}$ **18.** $\int_{\ln 2}^{\ln(2/\sqrt{3})} \frac{e^{-x}\,dx}{\sqrt{1-e^{-2x}}}$

**19–22** Evaluate the definite integral by expressing it in terms of $u$ and evaluating the resulting integral using a formula from geometry. ■

**19.** $\int_{-5/3}^{5/3} \sqrt{25-9x^2}\,dx;\ u = 3x$

**20.** $\int_0^2 x\sqrt{16-x^4}\,dx;\ u = x^2$

**21.** $\int_{\pi/3}^{\pi/2} \sin\theta\sqrt{1-4\cos^2\theta}\,d\theta;\ u = 2\cos\theta$

**22.** $\int_{e^{-3}}^{e^3} \frac{\sqrt{9-(\ln x)^2}}{x}\,dx;\ u = \ln x$

**23.** A particle moves with a velocity of $v(t) = \sin \pi t$ m/s along an $s$-axis. Find the distance traveled by the particle over the time interval $0 \le t \le 1$.

**24.** A particle moves with a velocity of $v(t) = 3\cos 2t$ m/s along an $s$-axis. Find the distance traveled by the particle over the time interval $0 \le t \le \pi/8$.

**25.** Find the area under the curve $y = 9/(x+2)^2$ over the interval $[-1, 1]$.

**26.** Find the area under the curve $y = 1/(3x+1)^2$ over the interval $[0, 1]$.

**27.** Find the area of the region enclosed by the graphs of $y = 1/\sqrt{1-9x^2}$, $y = 0$, $x = 0$, and $x = \frac{1}{6}$.

**28.** Find the area of the region enclosed by the graphs of $y = \sin^{-1} x$, $x = 0$, and $y = \pi/2$.

**29.** Find the average value of $f(x) = x/(5x^2+1)^2$ over the interval $[0, 2]$.

**30.** Find the average value of $f(x) = e^{3x}/(1+e^{6x})$ over the interval $[-(\ln 3)/6, 0]$.

**31–50** Evaluate the integrals by any method. ■

**31.** $\int_1^5 \frac{dx}{\sqrt{2x-1}}$ **32.** $\int_1^2 \sqrt{5x-1}\,dx$

**33.** $\int_{-1}^1 \frac{x^2\,dx}{\sqrt{x^3+9}}$ **34.** $\int_{\pi/2}^{\pi} 6\sin x(\cos x+1)^5\,dx$

**35.** $\int_1^3 \frac{x+2}{\sqrt{x^2+4x+7}}\,dx$ **36.** $\int_1^2 \frac{dx}{x^2-6x+9}$

**37.** $\int_0^{\pi/4} 4\sin x\cos x\,dx$ **38.** $\int_0^{\pi/4} \sqrt{\tan x}\sec^2 x\,dx$

**39.** $\int_0^{\sqrt{\pi}} 5x\cos(x^2)\,dx$ **40.** $\int_{\pi^2}^{4\pi^2} \frac{1}{\sqrt{x}}\sin\sqrt{x}\,dx$

**41.** $\int_{\pi/12}^{\pi/9} \sec^2 3\theta\,d\theta$ **42.** $\int_0^{\pi/6} \tan 2\theta\,d\theta$

**43.** $\int_0^1 \frac{y^2\,dy}{\sqrt{4-3y}}$ **44.** $\int_{-1}^4 \frac{x\,dx}{\sqrt{5+x}}$

**45.** $\int_0^e \frac{dx}{2x+e}$ **46.** $\int_1^{\sqrt{2}} xe^{-x^2}\,dx$

**47.** $\int_0^1 \frac{x}{\sqrt{4-3x^4}}\,dx$ **48.** $\int_1^2 \frac{1}{\sqrt{x}\sqrt{4-x}}\,dx$

**49.** $\int_0^{1/\sqrt{3}} \frac{1}{1+9x^2}\,dx$ **50.** $\int_1^{\sqrt{2}} \frac{x}{3+x^4}\,dx$

C **51.** (a) Use a CAS to find the exact value of the integral

$$\int_0^{\pi/6} \sin^4 x\cos^3 x\,dx$$

(b) Confirm the exact value by hand calculation. [*Hint:* Use the identity $\cos^2 x = 1 - \sin^2 x$.]

C **52.** (a) Use a CAS to find the exact value of the integral

$$\int_{-\pi/4}^{\pi/4} \tan^4 x\,dx$$

(b) Confirm the exact value by hand calculation. [*Hint:* Use the identity $1 + \tan^2 x = \sec^2 x$.]

**53.** (a) Find $\int_0^1 f(3x+1)\,dx$ if $\int_1^4 f(x)\,dx = 5$.

(b) Find $\int_0^3 f(3x)\,dx$ if $\int_0^9 f(x)\,dx = 5$.

(c) Find $\int_{-2}^0 xf(x^2)\,dx$ if $\int_0^4 f(x)\,dx = 1$.

**54.** Given that $m$ and $n$ are positive integers, show that

$$\int_0^1 x^m(1-x)^n\,dx = \int_0^1 x^n(1-x)^m\,dx$$

by making a substitution. Do not attempt to evaluate the integrals.

**55.** Given that $n$ is a positive integer, show that

$$\int_0^{\pi/2} \sin^n x\,dx = \int_0^{\pi/2} \cos^n x\,dx$$

by using a trigonometric identity and making a substitution. Do not attempt to evaluate the integrals.

**56.** Given that $n$ is a positive integer, evaluate the integral

$$\int_0^1 x(1-x)^n\,dx$$

**57–60** Medication can be administered to a patient in different ways. For a given method, let $c(t)$ denote the concentration of medication in the patient's bloodstream (measured in mg/L) $t$ hours after the dose is given. Over the time interval $0 \le t \le b$, the area between the graph of $c = c(t)$ and the interval $[0, b]$ indicates the "availability" of the medication for the patient's body over that time period. Determine which method provides the greater availability over the given interval. ■

**57.** Method 1: $c(t) = 5(e^{-0.2t} - e^{-t})$,
Method 2: $c(t) = 4(e^{-0.2t} - e^{-3t})$; $[0, 4]$

**58.** Method 1: $c(t) = 5(e^{-0.2t} - e^{-t})$,
Method 2: $c(t) = 4(e^{-0.2t} - e^{-3t})$; $[0, 24]$

**59.** Method 1: $c(t) = 5.78(e^{-0.4t} - e^{-1.3t})$,
Method 2: $c(t) = 4.15(e^{-0.4t} - e^{-3t})$; $[0, 4]$

**60.** Method 1: $c(t) = 5.78(e^{-0.4t} - e^{-1.3t})$,
Method 2: $c(t) = 4.15(e^{-0.4t} - e^{-3t})$; $[0, 24]$

**61.** Suppose that at time $t = 0$ there are 750 bacteria in a growth medium and the bacteria population $y(t)$ grows at the rate $y'(t) = 802.137e^{1.528t}$ bacteria per hour. How many bacteria will there be in 12 hours?

**62.** Suppose that a particle moving along a coordinate line has velocity $v(t) = 25 + 10e^{-0.05t}$ ft/s.
(a) What is the distance traveled by the particle from time $t = 0$ to time $t = 10$?
(b) Does the term $10e^{-0.05t}$ have much effect on the distance traveled by the particle over that time interval? Explain your reasoning.

**63.** (a) The accompanying table shows the fraction of the Moon that is illuminated (as seen from Earth) at midnight (Eastern Standard Time) for the first week of 2005. Find the average fraction of the Moon illuminated during the first week of 2005.

***Source:*** Data from the U.S Naval Observatory Astronomical Applications Department.

(b) The function $f(x) = 0.5 + 0.5\sin(0.213x + 2.481)$ models data for illumination of the Moon for the first 60 days of 2005. Find the average value of this illumination function over the interval $[0, 7]$.

| DAY | 1 | 2 | 3 | 4 | 5 | 6 | 7 |
|---|---|---|---|---|---|---|---|
| ILLUMINATION | 0.74 | 0.65 | 0.56 | 0.45 | 0.35 | 0.25 | 0.16 |

▲ Table Ex-63

**64.** Electricity is supplied to homes in the form of ***alternating current***, which means that the voltage has a sinusoidal waveform described by an equation of the form

$$V = V_p \sin(2\pi f t)$$

(see the accompanying figure). In this equation, $V_p$ is called the ***peak voltage*** or ***amplitude*** of the current, $f$ is called its ***frequency***, and $1/f$ is called its ***period***. The voltages $V$ and $V_p$ are measured in volts (V), the time $t$ is measured in seconds (s), and the frequency is measured in hertz (Hz). (1 Hz = 1 cycle per second; a ***cycle*** is the electrical term for one period of the waveform.) Most alternating-current voltmeters read what is called the ***rms*** or ***root-mean-square*** value of $V$. By definition, this is the square root of the average value of $V^2$ over one period.
(a) Show that

$$V_{\text{rms}} = \frac{V_p}{\sqrt{2}}$$

[*Hint:* Compute the average over the cycle from $t = 0$ to $t = 1/f$, and use the identity $\sin^2\theta = \frac{1}{2}(1 - \cos 2\theta)$ to help evaluate the integral.]
(b) In the United States, electrical outlets supply alternating current with an rms voltage of 120 V at a frequency of 60 Hz. What is the peak voltage at such an outlet?

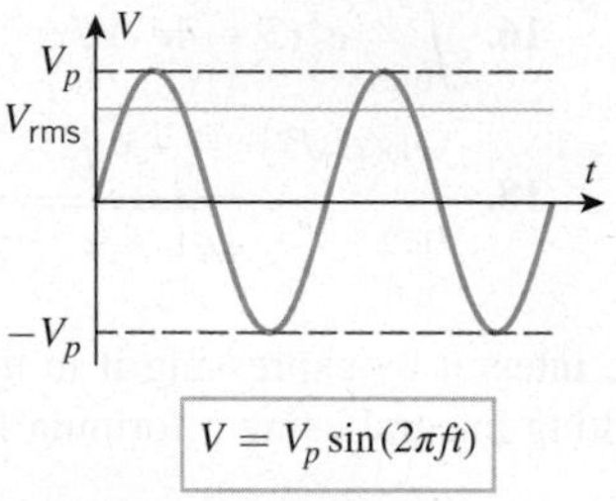


◀ **Figure Ex-64**

**65.** Find a positive value of $k$ such that the area under the graph of $y = e^{2x}$ over the interval $[0, k]$ is 3 square units.

**66.** Use a graphing utility to estimate the value of $k$ ($k > 0$) so that the region enclosed by $y = 1/(1 + kx^2)$, $y = 0$, $x = 0$, and $x = 2$ has an area of 0.6 square unit.

C **67.** (a) Find the limit

$$\lim_{n\to+\infty} \sum_{k=1}^{n} \frac{\sin(k\pi/n)}{n}$$

by evaluating an appropriate definite integral over the interval $[0, 1]$.
(b) Check your answer to part (a) by evaluating the limit directly with a CAS.

**FOCUS ON CONCEPTS**

**68.** Let

$$I = \int_{-1}^{1} \frac{1}{1+x^2}\,dx$$

(a) Explain why $I > 0$.
(b) Show that the substitution $x = 1/u$ results in

$$I = -\int_{-1}^{1} \frac{1}{1+x^2}\,dx = -I$$

*(cont.)*

Thus, $2I = 0$, which implies that $I = 0$. But this contradicts part (a). What is the error?

**69.** (a) Prove that if $f$ is an odd function, then

$$\int_{-a}^{a} f(x)\,dx = 0$$

and give a geometric explanation of this result. [*Hint:* One way to prove that a quantity $q$ is zero is to show that $q = -q$.]

(b) Prove that if $f$ is an even function, then

$$\int_{-a}^{a} f(x)\,dx = 2\int_{0}^{a} f(x)\,dx$$

and give a geometric explanation of this result. [*Hint:* Split the interval of integration from $-a$ to $a$ into two parts at 0.]

**70.** Show that if $f$ and $g$ are continuous functions, then

$$\int_0^t f(t-x)g(x)\,dx = \int_0^t f(x)g(t-x)\,dx$$

**71.** (a) Let

$$I = \int_0^a \frac{f(x)}{f(x) + f(a-x)}\,dx$$

Show that $I = a/2$.

[*Hint:* Let $u = a - x$, and then note the difference between the resulting integrand and 1.]

(b) Use the result of part (a) to find

$$\int_0^3 \frac{\sqrt{x}}{\sqrt{x} + \sqrt{3-x}}\,dx$$

(c) Use the result of part (a) to find

$$\int_0^{\pi/2} \frac{\sin x}{\sin x + \cos x}\,dx$$

**72.** Evaluate

(a) $\displaystyle\int_{-1}^{1} x\sqrt{\cos(x^2)}\,dx$

(b) $\displaystyle\int_{0}^{\pi} \sin^8 x \cos^5 x\,dx.$

[*Hint:* Use the substitution $u = x - (\pi/2)$.]

**73. Writing** The two substitution methods discussed in this section yield the same result when used to evaluate a definite integral. Write a short paragraph that carefully explains why this is the case.

**74. Writing** In some cases, the second method for the evaluation of definite integrals has distinct advantages over the first. Provide some illustrations, and write a short paragraph that discusses the advantages of the second method in each case. [*Hint:* To get started, consider the results in Exercises 54–56, 69, and 71.]

✓ **QUICK CHECK ANSWERS 5.9** 1. $F(g(b)) - F(g(a))$ 2. (a) $\displaystyle\int_1^9 u^3\,du$ (b) $\displaystyle\int_1^5 \frac{1}{2\sqrt{u}}\,du$ (c) $\displaystyle\int_0^1 2e^u\,du$ 3. (a) $\frac{2}{3}$ (b) $\frac{1}{2}\ln\left(\frac{7}{2}\right)$ (c) $\frac{3}{4}$

# 5.10 LOGARITHMIC AND OTHER FUNCTIONS DEFINED BY INTEGRALS

*In Section 1.8 we defined the natural logarithm function* $\ln x$ *to be the inverse of* $e^x$*. Although this was convenient and enabled us to deduce many properties of* $\ln x$*, the mathematical foundation was shaky in that we accepted the continuity of* $e^x$ *and of all exponential functions without proof. In this section we will show that* $\ln x$ *can be defined as a certain integral, and we will use this new definition to prove that exponential functions are continuous. This integral definition is also important in applications because it provides a way of recognizing when integrals that appear in solutions of problems can be expressed as natural logarithms.*

## THE CONNECTION BETWEEN NATURAL LOGARITHMS AND INTEGRALS

The connection between natural logarithms and integrals was made in the middle of the seventeenth century in the course of investigating areas under the curve $y = 1/t$. The problem being considered was to find values of $t_1, t_2, t_3, \ldots, t_n, \ldots$ for which the areas $A_1, A_2, A_3, \ldots, A_n, \ldots$ in Figure 5.10.1*a* would be equal. Through the combined work of Isaac Newton, the Belgian Jesuit priest Gregory of St. Vincent (1584–1667), and Gregory's student Alfons A. de Sarasa (1618–1667), it was shown that by taking the points to be

$$t_1 = e, \quad t_2 = e^2, \quad t_3 = e^3, \ldots, \quad t_n = e^n, \ldots$$

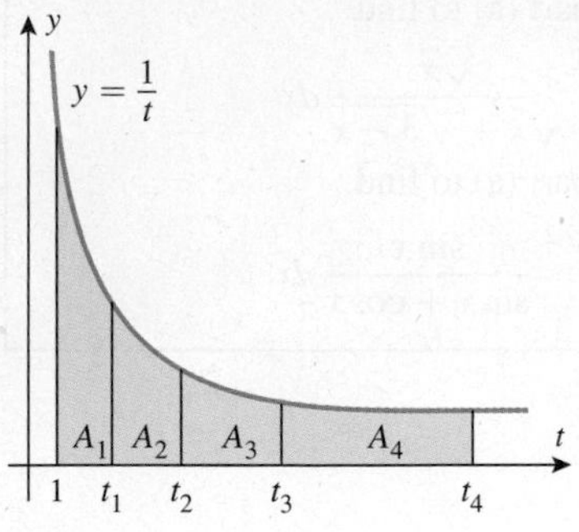

(a)

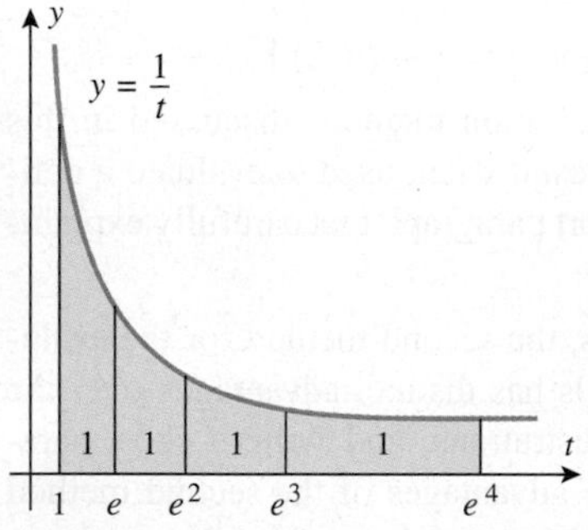

(b)

*Not drawn to scale*

▲ **Figure 5.10.1**

each of the areas would be 1 (Figure 5.10.1*b*). Thus, in modern integral notation

$$\int_1^{e^n} \frac{1}{t}\,dt = n$$

which can be expressed as

$$\int_1^{e^n} \frac{1}{t}\,dt = \ln(e^n)$$

By comparing the upper limit of the integral and the expression inside the logarithm, it is a natural leap to the more general result

$$\int_1^{x} \frac{1}{t}\,dt = \ln x$$

which today we take as the formal definition of the natural logarithm.

**5.10.1 DEFINITION** The ***natural logarithm*** of $x$ is denoted by $\ln x$ and is defined by the integral

$$\ln x = \int_1^{x} \frac{1}{t}\,dt, \quad x > 0 \tag{1}$$

Our strategy for putting the study of logarithmic and exponential functions on a sound mathematical footing is to use (1) as a starting point and then define $e^x$ as the inverse of $\ln x$. This is the exact opposite of our previous approach in which we defined $\ln x$ to be the inverse of $e^x$. However, whereas previously we had to *assume* that $e^x$ is continuous, the continuity of $e^x$ will now follow from our definitions as a *theorem*. Our first challenge is to demonstrate that the properties of $\ln x$ resulting from Definition 5.10.1 are consistent with those obtained earlier. To start, observe that Part 2 of the Fundamental Theorem of Calculus (5.6.3) implies that $\ln x$ is differentiable and

Review Theorem 5.5.8 and then explain why $x$ is required to be positive in Definition 5.10.1.

$$\frac{d}{dx}[\ln x] = \frac{d}{dx}\left[\int_1^{x} \frac{1}{t}\,dt\right] = \frac{1}{x} \quad (x > 0) \tag{2}$$

None of the properties of $\ln x$ obtained in this section should be new, but now, for the first time, we give them a sound mathematical footing.

This is consistent with the derivative formula for $\ln x$ that we obtained previously. Moreover, because differentiability implies continuity, it follows that $\ln x$ is a continuous function on the interval $(0, +\infty)$.

Other properties of $\ln x$ can be obtained by interpreting the integral in (1) geometrically: In the case where $x > 1$, this integral represents the area under the curve $y = 1/t$ from $t = 1$ to $t = x$ (Figure 5.10.2*a*); in the case where $0 < x < 1$, the integral represents the negative of the area under the curve $y = 1/t$ from $t = x$ to $t = 1$ (Figure 5.10.2*b*); and

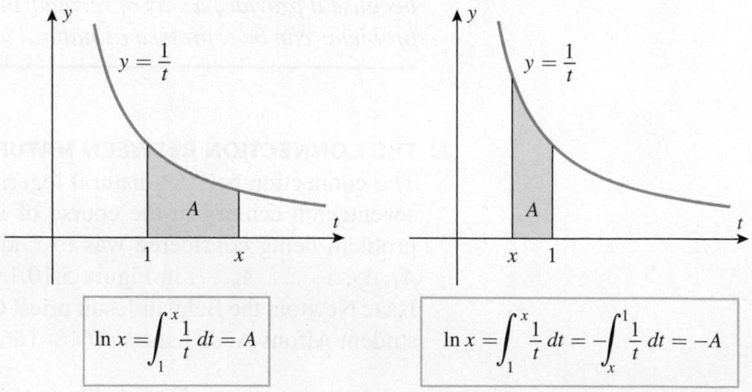

▶ **Figure 5.10.2** (a) (b)

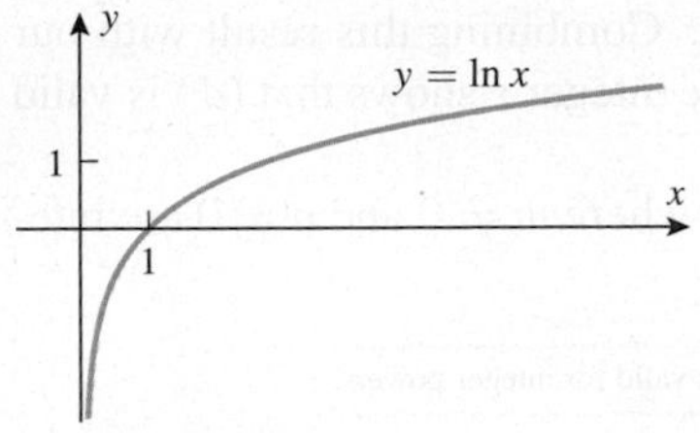


▲ **Figure 5.10.3**

in the case where $x = 1$, the integral has value 0 because its upper and lower limits of integration are the same. These geometric observations imply that

$$\begin{aligned} \ln x > 0 &\quad \text{if} \quad x > 1 \\ \ln x < 0 &\quad \text{if} \quad 0 < x < 1 \\ \ln x = 0 &\quad \text{if} \quad x = 1 \end{aligned}$$

Also, since $1/x$ is positive for $x > 0$, it follows from (2) that $\ln x$ is an increasing function on the interval $(0, +\infty)$. This is all consistent with the graph of $\ln x$ in Figure 5.10.3.

## ALGEBRAIC PROPERTIES OF ln x

We can use (2) to show that Definition 5.10.1 produces the standard algebraic properties of logarithms.

> **5.10.2 THEOREM** *For any positive numbers a and c and any rational number r:*
>
> (*a*) $\ln ac = \ln a + \ln c$ (*b*) $\ln \dfrac{1}{c} = -\ln c$
>
> (*c*) $\ln \dfrac{a}{c} = \ln a - \ln c$ (*d*) $\ln a^r = r \ln a$

**PROOF (*a*)** Treating $a$ as a constant, consider the function $f(x) = \ln(ax)$. Then

$$f'(x) = \frac{1}{ax} \cdot \frac{d}{dx}(ax) = \frac{1}{ax} \cdot a = \frac{1}{x}$$

Thus, $\ln ax$ and $\ln x$ have the same derivative on $(0, +\infty)$, so these functions must differ by a constant on this interval. That is, there is a constant $k$ such that

$$\ln ax - \ln x = k \tag{3}$$

on $(0, +\infty)$. Substituting $x = 1$ into this equation we conclude that $\ln a = k$ (verify). Thus, (3) can be written as

$$\ln ax - \ln x = \ln a$$

Setting $x = c$ establishes that

$$\ln ac - \ln c = \ln a \quad \text{or} \quad \ln ac = \ln a + \ln c$$

**PROOFS (*b*) AND (*c*)** Part (*b*) follows immediately from part (*a*) by substituting $1/c$ for $a$ (verify). Then

$$\ln \frac{a}{c} = \ln \left( a \cdot \frac{1}{c} \right) = \ln a + \ln \frac{1}{c} = \ln a - \ln c$$

**PROOF (*d*)** First, we will argue that part (*d*) is satisfied if $r$ is any nonnegative integer. If $r = 1$, then (*d*) is clearly satisfied; if $r = 0$, then (*d*) follows from the fact that $\ln 1 = 0$. Suppose that we know (*d*) is satisfied for $r$ equal to some integer $n$. It then follows from part (*a*) that

$$\ln a^{n+1} = \ln[a \cdot a^n] = \ln a + \ln a^n = \ln a + n \ln a = (n+1) \ln a$$

That is, if (*d*) is valid for $r$ equal to some integer $n$, then it is also valid for $r = n + 1$. However, since we know (*d*) is satisfied if $r = 1$, it follows that (*d*) is valid for $r = 2$. But this implies that (*d*) is satisfied for $r = 3$, which in turn implies that (*d*) is valid for $r = 4$, and so forth. We conclude that (*d*) is satisfied if $r$ is any nonnegative integer.

Next, suppose that $r = -m$ is a negative integer. Then

$$\begin{aligned} \ln a^r = \ln a^{-m} = \ln \frac{1}{a^m} &= -\ln a^m && \text{By part (b)} \\ &= -m \ln a && \text{Part (d) is valid for positive powers.} \\ &= r \ln a \end{aligned}$$

> How is the proof of Theorem 5.10.2(*d*) for the case where *r* is a nonnegative integer analogous to a row of falling dominos? (This "domino" argument uses an informal version of a property of the integers known as the *principle of mathematical induction*.)

which shows that $(d)$ is valid for any negative integer $r$. Combining this result with our previous conclusion that $(d)$ is satisfied for a nonnegative integer $r$ shows that $(d)$ is valid if $r$ is *any* integer.

Finally, suppose that $r = m/n$ is any rational number, where $m \neq 0$ and $n \neq 0$ are integers. Then

$$\begin{aligned}
\ln a^r = \frac{n \ln a^r}{n} &= \frac{\ln[(a^r)^n]}{n} && \text{Part } (d) \text{ is valid for integer powers.} \\
&= \frac{\ln a^{rn}}{n} && \text{Property of exponents} \\
&= \frac{\ln a^m}{n} && \text{Definition of } r \\
&= \frac{m \ln a}{n} && \text{Part } (d) \text{ is valid for integer powers.} \\
&= \frac{m}{n} \ln a = r \ln a
\end{aligned}$$

which shows that $(d)$ is valid for any rational number $r$. ■

## APPROXIMATING ln *x* NUMERICALLY

For specific values of $x$, the value of $\ln x$ can be approximated numerically by approximating the definite integral in (1), say by using the midpoint approximation that was discussed in Section 5.4.

**Table 5.10.1**

$n = 10$
$\Delta t = (b-a)/n = (2-1)/10 = 0.1$

| $k$ | $t_k^*$ | $1/t_k^*$ |
|---|---|---|
| 1 | 1.05 | 0.952381 |
| 2 | 1.15 | 0.869565 |
| 3 | 1.25 | 0.800000 |
| 4 | 1.35 | 0.740741 |
| 5 | 1.45 | 0.689655 |
| 6 | 1.55 | 0.645161 |
| 7 | 1.65 | 0.606061 |
| 8 | 1.75 | 0.571429 |
| 9 | 1.85 | 0.540541 |
| 10 | 1.95 | 0.512821 |
| | | 6.928355 |

$$\Delta t \sum_{k=1}^{n} f(t_k^*) \approx (0.1)(6.928355) \approx 0.692836$$

▶ **Example 1** Approximate $\ln 2$ using the midpoint approximation with $n = 10$.

***Solution.*** From (1), the exact value of $\ln 2$ is represented by the integral

$$\ln 2 = \int_1^2 \frac{1}{t}\, dt$$

The midpoint rule is given in Formulas (5) and (6) of Section 5.4. Expressed in terms of $t$, the latter formula is

$$\int_a^b f(t)\, dt \approx \Delta t \sum_{k=1}^{n} f(t_k^*)$$

where $\Delta t$ is the common width of the subintervals and $t_1^*, t_2^*, \ldots, t_n^*$ are the midpoints. In this case we have 10 subintervals, so $\Delta t = (2-1)/10 = 0.1$. The computations to six decimal places are shown in Table 5.10.1. By comparison, a calculator set to display six decimal places gives $\ln 2 \approx 0.693147$, so the magnitude of the error in the midpoint approximation is about 0.000311. Greater accuracy in the midpoint approximation can be obtained by increasing $n$. For example, the midpoint approximation with $n = 100$ yields $\ln 2 \approx 0.693144$, which is correct to five decimal places. ◀

## DOMAIN, RANGE, AND END BEHAVIOR OF ln *x*

**5.10.3 THEOREM**

(a) *The domain of* $\ln x$ *is* $(0, +\infty)$.

(b) $\lim_{x \to 0^+} \ln x = -\infty$ *and* $\lim_{x \to +\infty} \ln x = +\infty$

(c) *The range of* $\ln x$ *is* $(-\infty, +\infty)$.

**PROOFS (*a*) AND (*b*)** We have already shown that $\ln x$ is defined and increasing on the interval $(0, +\infty)$. To prove that $\ln x \to +\infty$ as $x \to +\infty$, we must show that given any number $M > 0$, the value of $\ln x$ exceeds $M$ for sufficiently large values of $x$. To do this, let $N$ be any integer. If $x > 2^N$, then

$$\ln x > \ln 2^N = N \ln 2 \tag{4}$$

by Theorem 5.10.2(*d*). Since

$$\ln 2 = \int_1^2 \frac{1}{t}\, dt > 0$$

it follows that $N \ln 2$ can be made arbitrarily large by choosing $N$ sufficiently large. In particular, we can choose $N$ so that $N \ln 2 > M$. It now follows from (4) that if $x > 2^N$, then $\ln x > M$, and this proves that

$$\lim_{x \to +\infty} \ln x = +\infty$$

Furthermore, by observing that $v = 1/x \to +\infty$ as $x \to 0^+$, we can use the preceding limit and Theorem 5.10.2(*b*) to conclude that

$$\lim_{x \to 0^+} \ln x = \lim_{v \to +\infty} \ln \frac{1}{v} = \lim_{v \to +\infty} (-\ln v) = -\infty$$

**PROOF (*c*)** It follows from part (*a*), the continuity of $\ln x$, and the Intermediate-Value Theorem (1.5.7) that $\ln x$ assumes every real value as $x$ varies over the interval $(0, +\infty)$ (why?). ■

## DEFINITION OF $e^x$

In Chapter 1 we defined $\ln x$ to be the inverse of the natural exponential function $e^x$. Now that we have a formal definition of $\ln x$ in terms of an integral, we will define the natural exponential function to be the inverse of $\ln x$.

Since $\ln x$ is increasing and continuous on $(0, +\infty)$ with range $(-\infty, +\infty)$, there is exactly one (positive) solution to the equation $\ln x = 1$. We *define* $e$ to be the unique solution to $\ln x = 1$, so

$$\ln e = 1 \tag{5}$$

Furthermore, if $x$ is any real number, there is a unique positive solution $y$ to $\ln y = x$, so for irrational values of $x$ we *define* $e^x$ to be this solution. That is, when $x$ is irrational, $e^x$ is defined by

$$\ln e^x = x \tag{6}$$

Note that for rational values of $x$, we also have $\ln e^x = x \ln e = x$ from Theorem 5.10.2(*d*). Moreover, it follows immediately that $e^{\ln x} = x$ for any $x > 0$. Thus, (6) defines the exponential function for all real values of $x$ as the inverse of the natural logarithm function.

**5.10.4 DEFINITION** The inverse of the natural logarithm function $\ln x$ is denoted by $e^x$ and is called the ***natural exponential function***.

We can now establish the differentiability of $e^x$ and confirm that

$$\frac{d}{dx}[e^x] = e^x$$

**5.10.5 THEOREM** *The natural exponential function $e^x$ is differentiable, and hence continuous, on $(-\infty, +\infty)$, and its derivative is*

$$\frac{d}{dx}[e^x] = e^x$$

**PROOF** Because $\ln x$ is differentiable and

$$\frac{d}{dx}[\ln x] = \frac{1}{x} > 0$$

for all $x$ in $(0, +\infty)$, it follows from Theorem 3.3.1, with $f(x) = \ln x$ and $f^{-1}(x) = e^x$, that $e^x$ is differentiable on $(-\infty, +\infty)$ and its derivative is

$$\frac{d}{dx}\underbrace{[e^x]}_{f^{-1}(x)} = \underbrace{\frac{1}{1/e^x}}_{f'(f^{-1}(x))} = e^x \quad \blacksquare$$

## IRRATIONAL EXPONENTS

Recall from Theorem 5.10.2(*d*) that if $a > 0$ and $r$ is a rational number, then $\ln a^r = r \ln a$. Then $a^r = e^{\ln a^r} = e^{r \ln a}$ for any positive value of $a$ and any rational number $r$. But the expression $e^{r \ln a}$ makes sense for *any* real number $r$, whether rational or irrational, so it is a good candidate to give meaning to $a^r$ for any real number $r$.

Use Definition 5.10.6 to prove that if $a > 0$ and $r$ is a real number, then $\ln a^r = r \ln a$.

**5.10.6 DEFINITION** If $a > 0$ and $r$ is a real number, $a^r$ is defined by

$$a^r = e^{r \ln a} \tag{7}$$

With this definition it can be shown that the standard algebraic properties of exponents, such as

$$a^p a^q = a^{p+q}, \quad \frac{a^p}{a^q} = a^{p-q}, \quad (a^p)^q = a^{pq}, \quad (a^p)(b^p) = (ab)^p$$

hold for any real values of $a, b, p$, and $q$, where $a$ and $b$ are positive. In addition, using (7) for a real exponent $r$, we can define the power function $x^r$ whose domain consists of all positive real numbers, and for a positive base $b$ we can define the ***base b exponential function*** $b^x$ whose domain consists of all real numbers.

**5.10.7 THEOREM**

(*a*) *For any real number $r$, the power function $x^r$ is differentiable on $(0, +\infty)$ and its derivative is*

$$\frac{d}{dx}[x^r] = rx^{r-1}$$

(*b*) *For $b > 0$ and $b \neq 1$, the base $b$ exponential function $b^x$ is differentiable on $(-\infty, +\infty)$ and its derivative is*

$$\frac{d}{dx}[b^x] = b^x \ln b$$

**PROOF** The differentiability of $x^r = e^{r \ln x}$ and $b^x = e^{x \ln b}$ on their domains follows from the differentiability of $\ln x$ on $(0, +\infty)$ and of $e^x$ on $(-\infty, +\infty)$:

$$\frac{d}{dx}[x^r] = \frac{d}{dx}[e^{r \ln x}] = e^{r \ln x} \cdot \frac{d}{dx}[r \ln x] = x^r \cdot \frac{r}{x} = rx^{r-1}$$

$$\frac{d}{dx}[b^x] = \frac{d}{dx}[e^{x \ln b}] = e^{x \ln b} \cdot \frac{d}{dx}[x \ln b] = b^x \ln b \quad \blacksquare$$

We expressed $e$ as the value of a limit in Formulas (7) and (8) of Section 1.3 and in Formula (1) of Section 3.2. We now have the mathematical tools necessary to prove the existence of these limits.

**5.10.8 THEOREM**

(*a*) $\lim_{x \to 0} (1 + x)^{1/x} = e$ (*b*) $\lim_{x \to +\infty} \left(1 + \frac{1}{x}\right)^x = e$ (*c*) $\lim_{x \to -\infty} \left(1 + \frac{1}{x}\right)^x = e$

**PROOF** We will prove part (*a*); the proofs of parts (*b*) and (*c*) follow from this limit and are left as exercises. We first observe that

$$\frac{d}{dx}[\ln(x+1)]\bigg|_{x=0} = \frac{1}{x+1}\cdot 1\bigg|_{x=0} = 1$$

However, using the definition of the derivative, we obtain

$$\begin{aligned} 1 = \frac{d}{dx}[\ln(x+1)]\bigg|_{x=0} &= \lim_{h\to 0}\frac{\ln(0+h+1)-\ln(0+1)}{h} \\ &= \lim_{h\to 0}\left[\frac{1}{h}\cdot\ln(1+h)\right] \end{aligned}$$

or, equivalently,

$$\lim_{x\to 0}\frac{1}{x}\cdot\ln(1+x) = 1 \tag{8}$$

Now

$$\begin{aligned} \lim_{x\to 0}(1+x)^{1/x} &= \lim_{x\to 0} e^{(\ln(1+x))/x} && \text{Definition 5.10.6} \\ &= e^{\lim_{x\to 0}[(\ln(1+x))/x]} && \text{Theorem 1.5.5} \\ &= e^1 && \text{Equation (8)} \\ &= e \quad \blacksquare \end{aligned}$$

## GENERAL LOGARITHMS

We note that for $b > 0$ and $b \neq 1$, the function $b^x$ is one-to-one and so has an inverse function. Using the definition of $b^x$, we can solve $y = b^x$ for $x$ as a function of $y$:

$$\begin{aligned} &y = b^x = e^{x\ln b} \\ &\ln y = \ln(e^{x\ln b}) = x\ln b \\ &\frac{\ln y}{\ln b} = x \end{aligned}$$

Thus, the inverse function for $b^x$ is $(\ln x)/(\ln b)$.

**5.10.9 DEFINITION** For $b > 0$ and $b \neq 1$, the ***base b logarithm*** function, denoted $\log_b x$, is defined by

$$\log_b x = \frac{\ln x}{\ln b} \tag{9}$$

It follows immediately from this definition that $\log_b x$ is the inverse function for $b^x$ and satisfies the properties in Table 1.8.3. Furthermore, $\log_b x$ is differentiable, and hence continuous, on $(0, +\infty)$, and its derivative is

$$\frac{d}{dx}[\log_b x] = \frac{1}{x\ln b}$$

As a final note of consistency, we observe that $\log_e x = \ln x$.

## FUNCTIONS DEFINED BY INTEGRALS

The functions we have dealt with thus far in this text are called ***elementary functions***; they include polynomial, rational, power, exponential, logarithmic, trigonometric, and inverse trigonometric functions, and all other functions that can be obtained from these by addition, subtraction, multiplication, division, root extraction, and composition.

However, there are many important functions that do not fall into this category. Such functions occur in many ways, but they commonly arise in the course of solving initial-value problems of the form

$$\frac{dy}{dx} = f(x), \quad y(x_0) = y_0 \tag{10}$$

Recall from Example 6 of Section 5.2 and the discussion preceding it that the basic method for solving (10) is to integrate $f(x)$, and then use the initial condition to determine the constant of integration. It can be proved that if $f$ is continuous, then (10) has a unique solution and that this procedure produces it. However, there is another approach: Instead of solving each initial-value problem individually, we can find a general formula for the solution of (10), and then apply that formula to solve specific problems. We will now show that

$$y(x) = y_0 + \int_{x_0}^{x} f(t)\,dt \tag{11}$$

is a formula for the solution of (10). To confirm this we must show that $dy/dx = f(x)$ and that $y(x_0) = y_0$. The computations are as follows:

$$\frac{dy}{dx} = \frac{d}{dx}\left[y_0 + \int_{x_0}^{x} f(t)\,dt\right] = 0 + f(x) = f(x)$$

$$y(x_0) = y_0 + \int_{x_0}^{x_0} f(t)\,dt = y_0 + 0 = y_0$$

▶ **Example 2** In Example 6 of Section 5.2 we showed that the solution of the initial-value problem

$$\frac{dy}{dx} = \cos x, \quad y(0) = 1$$

is $y(x) = 1 + \sin x$. This initial-value problem can also be solved by applying Formula (11) with $f(x) = \cos x$, $x_0 = 0$, and $y_0 = 1$. This yields

$$y(x) = 1 + \int_0^x \cos t\,dt = 1 + [\sin t]_{t=0}^{x} = 1 + \sin x \blacktriangleleft$$

In the last example we were able to perform the integration in Formula (11) and express the solution of the initial-value problem as an elementary function. However, sometimes this will not be possible, in which case the solution of the initial-value problem must be left in terms of an "unevaluated" integral. For example, from (11), the solution of the initial-value problem

$$\frac{dy}{dx} = e^{-x^2}, \quad y(0) = 1$$

is

$$y(x) = 1 + \int_0^x e^{-t^2}\,dt$$

However, it can be shown that there is no way to express the integral in this solution as an elementary function. Thus, we have encountered a *new* function, which we regard to be *defined* by the integral. A close relative of this function, known as the ***error function***, plays an important role in probability and statistics; it is denoted by $\operatorname{erf}(x)$ and is defined as

$$\operatorname{erf}(x) = \frac{2}{\sqrt{\pi}} \int_0^x e^{-t^2}\,dt \tag{12}$$

Indeed, many of the most important functions in science and engineering are defined as integrals that have special names and notations associated with them. For example, the functions defined by

$$S(x) = \int_0^x \sin\left(\frac{\pi t^2}{2}\right) dt \quad \text{and} \quad C(x) = \int_0^x \cos\left(\frac{\pi t^2}{2}\right) dt \tag{13–14}$$

are called the ***Fresnel sine and cosine functions***, respectively, in honor of the French physicist Augustin Fresnel (1788–1827), who first encountered them in his study of diffraction of light waves.

## EVALUATING AND GRAPHING FUNCTIONS DEFINED BY INTEGRALS

The following values of $S(1)$ and $C(1)$ were produced by a CAS that has a built-in algorithm for approximating definite integrals:

$$S(1) = \int_0^1 \sin\left(\frac{\pi t^2}{2}\right) dt \approx 0.438259, \qquad C(1) = \int_0^1 \cos\left(\frac{\pi t^2}{2}\right) dt \approx 0.779893$$

To generate graphs of functions defined by integrals, computer programs choose a set of $x$-values in the domain, approximate the integral for each of those values, and then plot the resulting points. Thus, there is a lot of computation involved in generating such graphs, since each plotted point requires the approximation of an integral. The graphs of the Fresnel functions in Figure 5.10.4 were generated in this way using a CAS.

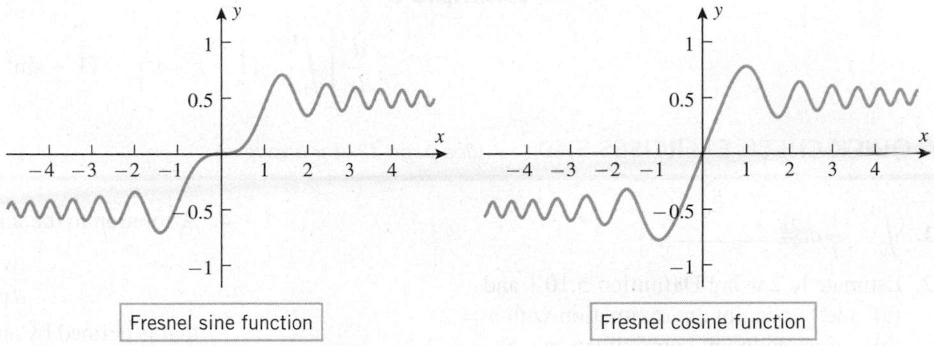


▶ **Figure 5.10.4**

**REMARK** Although it required a considerable amount of computation to generate the graphs of the Fresnel functions, the derivatives of $S(x)$ and $C(x)$ are easy to obtain using Part 2 of the Fundamental Theorem of Calculus (5.6.3); they are

$$S'(x) = \sin\left(\frac{\pi x^2}{2}\right) \quad \text{and} \quad C'(x) = \cos\left(\frac{\pi x^2}{2}\right) \tag{15–16}$$

These derivatives can be used to determine the locations of the relative extrema and inflection points and to investigate other properties of $S(x)$ and $C(x)$.

## INTEGRALS WITH FUNCTIONS AS LIMITS OF INTEGRATION

Various applications can lead to integrals in which at least one of the limits of integration is a function of $x$. Some examples are

$$\int_x^1 \sqrt{\sin t}\, dt, \qquad \int_{x^2}^{\sin x} \sqrt{t^3+1}\, dt, \qquad \int_{\ln x}^{\pi} \frac{dt}{t^7 - 8}$$

We will complete this section by showing how to differentiate integrals of the form

$$\int_a^{g(x)} f(t)\, dt \tag{17}$$

where $a$ is constant. Derivatives of other kinds of integrals with functions as limits of integration will be discussed in the exercises.

To differentiate (17) we can view the integral as a composition $F(g(x))$, where

$$F(x) = \int_a^x f(t)\, dt$$

If we now apply the chain rule, we obtain

$$\frac{d}{dx}\left[\int_a^{g(x)} f(t)\, dt\right] = \frac{d}{dx}[F(g(x))] = F'(g(x))g'(x) = f(g(x))g'(x)$$

Theorem 5.6.3

Thus,

$$\frac{d}{dx}\left[\int_a^{g(x)} f(t)\,dt\right] = f(g(x))g'(x) \tag{18}$$

In words:

*To differentiate an integral with a constant lower limit and a function as the upper limit, substitute the upper limit into the integrand, and multiply by the derivative of the upper limit.*

**▶ Example 3**

$$\frac{d}{dx}\left[\int_1^{\sin x} (1-t^2)\,dt\right] = (1-\sin^2 x)\cos x = \cos^3 x \blacktriangleleft$$

## ✓QUICK CHECK EXERCISES 5.10 (See page 337 for answers.)

1. $\int_1^{1/e} \frac{1}{t}\,dt =$ ______
2. Estimate ln 2 using Definition 5.10.1 and
   (a) a left endpoint approximation with $n = 2$
   (b) a right endpoint approximation with $n = 2$.
3. $\pi^{1/(\ln \pi)} =$ ______
4. A solution to the initial-value problem
   $$\frac{dy}{dx} = \cos x^3, \quad y(0) = 2$$
   that is defined by an integral is $y =$ ______.
5. $\frac{d}{dx}\left[\int_0^{e^{-x}} \frac{1}{1+t^4}\,dt\right] =$ ______

## EXERCISE SET 5.10 Graphing Utility C CAS

1. Sketch the curve $y = 1/t$, and shade a region under the curve whose area is
   (a) ln 2 (b) −ln 0.5 (c) 2.
2. Sketch the curve $y = 1/t$, and shade two different regions under the curve whose areas are ln 1.5.
3. Given that $\ln a = 2$ and $\ln c = 5$, find
   (a) $\int_1^{ac} \frac{1}{t}\,dt$ (b) $\int_1^{1/c} \frac{1}{t}\,dt$
   (c) $\int_1^{a/c} \frac{1}{t}\,dt$ (d) $\int_1^{a^3} \frac{1}{t}\,dt$.
4. Given that $\ln a = 9$, find
   (a) $\int_1^{\sqrt{a}} \frac{1}{t}\,dt$ (b) $\int_1^{2a} \frac{1}{t}\,dt$
   (c) $\int_1^{2/a} \frac{1}{t}\,dt$ (d) $\int_2^{a} \frac{1}{t}\,dt$.
5. Approximate ln 5 using the midpoint approximation with $n = 10$, and estimate the magnitude of the error by comparing your answer to that produced directly by a calculating utility.
6. Approximate ln 3 using the midpoint approximation with $n = 20$, and estimate the magnitude of the error by comparing your answer to that produced directly by a calculating utility.
7. Simplify the expression and state the values of $x$ for which your simplification is valid.
   (a) $e^{-\ln x}$ (b) $e^{\ln x^2}$
   (c) $\ln\left(e^{-x^2}\right)$ (d) $\ln(1/e^x)$
   (e) $\exp(3\ln x)$ (f) $\ln(xe^x)$
   (g) $\ln\left(e^{x-\sqrt[3]{x}}\right)$ (h) $e^{x-\ln x}$
8. (a) Let $f(x) = e^{-2x}$. Find the simplest exact value of the function $f(\ln 3)$.
   (b) Let $f(x) = e^x + 3e^{-x}$. Find the simplest exact value of the function $f(\ln 2)$.

**9–10** Express the given quantity as a power of $e$. ■

9. (a) $3^\pi$ (b) $2^{\sqrt{2}}$
10. (a) $\pi^{-x}$ (b) $x^{2x}$, $x > 0$

**11–12** Find the limits by making appropriate substitutions in the limits given in Theorem 5.10.8. ■

11. (a) $\lim_{x\to+\infty}\left(1+\frac{1}{2x}\right)^x$ (b) $\lim_{x\to 0}(1+2x)^{1/x}$
12. (a) $\lim_{x\to+\infty}\left(1+\frac{3}{x}\right)^x$ (b) $\lim_{x\to 0}(1+x)^{1/(3x)}$

**13–14** Find $g'(x)$ using Part 2 of the Fundamental Theorem of Calculus, and check your answer by evaluating the integral and then differentiating. ■

13. $g(x) = \int_1^x (t^2 - t)\,dt$
14. $g(x) = \int_\pi^x (1 - \cos t)\,dt$

**15–16** Find the derivative using Formula (18), and check your answer by evaluating the integral and then differentiating the result. ■

**15.** (a) $\dfrac{d}{dx}\displaystyle\int_1^{x^3}\frac{1}{t}\,dt$ (b) $\dfrac{d}{dx}\displaystyle\int_1^{\ln x} e^t\,dt$

**16.** (a) $\dfrac{d}{dx}\displaystyle\int_{-1}^{x^2}\sqrt{t+1}\,dt$ (b) $\dfrac{d}{dx}\displaystyle\int_{\pi}^{1/x}\sin t\,dt$

**17.** Let $F(x)=\displaystyle\int_0^x \frac{\sin t}{t^2+1}\,dt$. Find
(a) $F(0)$ (b) $F'(0)$ (c) $F''(0)$.

**18.** Let $F(x)=\displaystyle\int_2^x \sqrt{3t^2+1}\,dt$. Find
(a) $F(2)$ (b) $F'(2)$ (c) $F''(2)$.

**19–22 True–False** Determine whether the equation is true or false. Explain your answer. ■

**19.** $\displaystyle\int_1^{1/a}\frac{1}{t}\,dt=-\int_1^a\frac{1}{t}\,dt$, for $0<a$

**20.** $\displaystyle\int_1^{\sqrt{a}}\frac{1}{t}\,dt=\frac{1}{2}\int_1^a\frac{1}{t}\,dt$, for $0<a$

**21.** $\displaystyle\int_{-1}^{e}\frac{1}{t}\,dt=1$

**22.** $\displaystyle\int\frac{2x}{1+x^2}\,dx=\int_1^{1+x^2}\frac{1}{t}\,dt+C$

C **23.** (a) Use Formula (18) to find

$$\frac{d}{dx}\int_1^{x^2} t\sqrt{1+t}\,dt$$

(b) Use a CAS to evaluate the integral and differentiate the resulting function.
(c) Use the simplification command of the CAS, if necessary, to confirm that the answers in parts (a) and (b) are the same.

**24.** Show that
(a) $\dfrac{d}{dx}\left[\displaystyle\int_x^a f(t)\,dt\right]=-f(x)$
(b) $\dfrac{d}{dx}\left[\displaystyle\int_{g(x)}^a f(t)\,dt\right]=-f(g(x))g'(x)$.

**25–26** Use the results in Exercise 24 to find the derivative. ■

**25.** (a) $\dfrac{d}{dx}\displaystyle\int_x^{\pi}\cos(t^3)\,dt$ (b) $\dfrac{d}{dx}\displaystyle\int_{\tan x}^{3}\frac{t^2}{1+t^2}\,dt$

**26.** (a) $\dfrac{d}{dx}\displaystyle\int_x^0\frac{1}{(t^2+1)^2}\,dt$ (b) $\dfrac{d}{dx}\displaystyle\int_{1/x}^{\pi}\cos^3 t\,dt$

**27.** Find

$$\frac{d}{dx}\left[\int_{3x}^{x^2}\frac{t-1}{t^2+1}\,dt\right]$$

by writing

$$\int_{3x}^{x^2}\frac{t-1}{t^2+1}\,dt=\int_{3x}^{0}\frac{t-1}{t^2+1}\,dt+\int_0^{x^2}\frac{t-1}{t^2+1}\,dt$$

**28.** Use Exercise 24(b) and the idea in Exercise 27 to show that

$$\frac{d}{dx}\int_{h(x)}^{g(x)} f(t)\,dt=f(g(x))g'(x)-f(h(x))h'(x)$$

**29.** Use the result obtained in Exercise 28 to perform the following differentiations:
(a) $\dfrac{d}{dx}\displaystyle\int_{x^2}^{x^3}\sin^2 t\,dt$ (b) $\dfrac{d}{dx}\displaystyle\int_{-x}^{x}\frac{1}{1+t}\,dt$.

**30.** Prove that the function

$$F(x)=\int_x^{5x}\frac{1}{t}\,dt$$

is constant on the interval $(0,+\infty)$ by using Exercise 28 to find $F'(x)$. What is that constant?

**FOCUS ON CONCEPTS**

**31.** Let $F(x)=\int_0^x f(t)\,dt$, where $f$ is the function whose graph is shown in the accompanying figure.
(a) Find $F(0)$, $F(3)$, $F(5)$, $F(7)$, and $F(10)$.
(b) On what subintervals of the interval $[0,10]$ is $F$ increasing? Decreasing?
(c) Where does $F$ have its maximum value? Its minimum value?
(d) Sketch the graph of $F$.

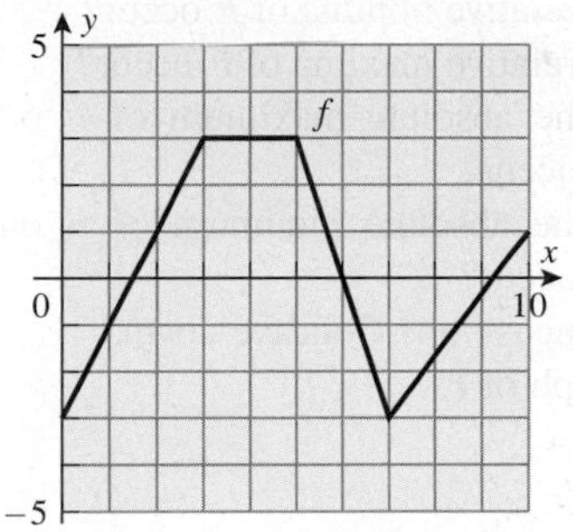


◀ **Figure Ex-31**

**32.** Determine the inflection point(s) for the graph of $F$ in Exercise 31.

**33–34** Express $F(x)$ in a piecewise form that does not involve an integral. ■

**33.** $F(x)=\displaystyle\int_{-1}^{x}|t|\,dt$

**34.** $F(x)=\displaystyle\int_0^x f(t)\,dt$, where $f(x)=\begin{cases}x, & 0\le x\le 2\\ 2, & x>2\end{cases}$

**35–38** Use Formula (11) to solve the initial-value problem. ■

**35.** $\dfrac{dy}{dx}=\dfrac{2x^2+1}{x}$, $y(1)=2$ **36.** $\dfrac{dy}{dx}=\dfrac{x+1}{\sqrt{x}}$, $y(1)=0$

**37.** $\dfrac{dy}{dx}=\sec^2 x-\sin x$, $y(\pi/4)=1$

**38.** $\dfrac{dy}{dx}=\dfrac{1}{x\ln x}$, $y(e)=1$

**39.** Suppose that at time $t=0$ there are $P_0$ individuals who have disease X, and suppose that a certain model for the spread of the disease predicts that the disease will spread at the rate of $r(t)$ individuals per day. Write a formula for the number of individuals who will have disease X after $x$ days.

**40.** Suppose that $v(t)$ is the velocity function of a particle moving along an $s$-axis. Write a formula for the coordinate of the particle at time $T$ if the particle is at $s_1$ at time $t=1$.

**FOCUS ON CONCEPTS**

**41.** The accompanying figure shows the graphs of $y = f(x)$ and $y = \int_0^x f(t)\,dt$. Determine which graph is which, and explain your reasoning.

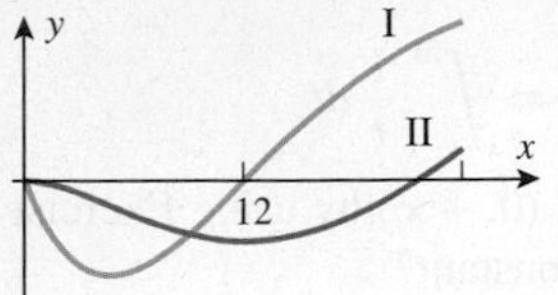


Figure Ex-41

**42.** (a) Make a conjecture about the value of the limit

$$\lim_{k\to 0} \int_1^b t^{k-1}\,dt \quad (b > 0)$$

(b) Check your conjecture by evaluating the integral and finding the limit. [*Hint:* Interpret the limit as the definition of the derivative of an exponential function.]

**43.** Let $F(x) = \int_0^x f(t)\,dt$, where $f$ is the function graphed in the accompanying figure.

(a) Where do the relative minima of $F$ occur?

(b) Where do the relative maxima of $F$ occur?

(c) Where does the absolute maximum of $F$ on the interval $[0, 5]$ occur?

(d) Where does the absolute minimum of $F$ on the interval $[0, 5]$ occur?

(e) Where is $F$ concave up? Concave down?

(f) Sketch the graph of $F$.

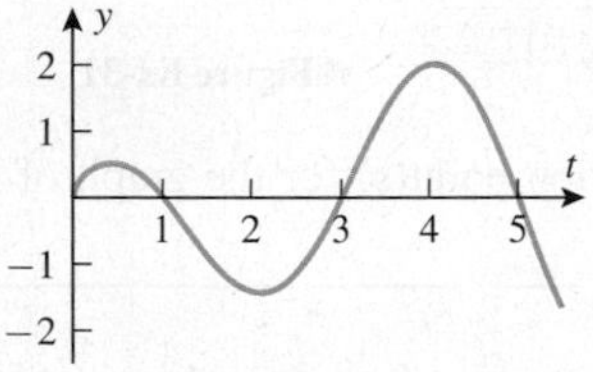


Figure Ex-43

C **44.** CAS programs have commands for working with most of the important nonelementary functions. Check your CAS documentation for information about the error function erf($x$) [see Formula (12)], and then complete the following.

(a) Generate the graph of erf($x$).

(b) Use the graph to make a conjecture about the existence and location of any relative maxima and minima of erf($x$).

(c) Check your conjecture in part (b) using the derivative of erf($x$).

(d) Use the graph to make a conjecture about the existence and location of any inflection points of erf($x$).

(e) Check your conjecture in part (d) using the second derivative of erf($x$).

(f) Use the graph to make a conjecture about the existence of horizontal asymptotes of erf($x$).

(g) Check your conjecture in part (f) by using the CAS to find the limits of erf($x$) as $x\to\pm\infty$.

**45.** The Fresnel sine and cosine functions $S(x)$ and $C(x)$ were defined in Formulas (13) and (14) and graphed in Figure 5.10.4. Their derivatives were given in Formulas (15) and (16).

(a) At what points does $C(x)$ have relative minima? Relative maxima?

(b) Where do the inflection points of $C(x)$ occur?

(c) Confirm that your answers in parts (a) and (b) are consistent with the graph of $C(x)$.

**46.** Find the limit

$$\lim_{h\to 0} \frac{1}{h} \int_x^{x+h} \ln t\,dt$$

**47.** Find a function $f$ and a number $a$ such that

$$4 + \int_a^x f(t)\,dt = e^{2x}$$

**48.** (a) Give a geometric argument to show that

$$\frac{1}{x+1} < \int_x^{x+1} \frac{1}{t}\,dt < \frac{1}{x}, \quad x > 0$$

(b) Use the result in part (a) to prove that

$$\frac{1}{x+1} < \ln\left(1 + \frac{1}{x}\right) < \frac{1}{x}, \quad x > 0$$

(c) Use the result in part (b) to prove that

$$e^{x/(x+1)} < \left(1 + \frac{1}{x}\right)^x < e, \quad x > 0$$

and hence that

$$\lim_{x\to +\infty} \left(1 + \frac{1}{x}\right)^x = e$$

(d) Use the result in part (b) to prove that

$$\left(1 + \frac{1}{x}\right)^x < e < \left(1 + \frac{1}{x}\right)^{x+1}, \quad x > 0$$

**49.** Use a graphing utility to generate the graph of

$$y = \left(1 + \frac{1}{x}\right)^{x+1} - \left(1 + \frac{1}{x}\right)^x$$

in the window $[0, 100] \times [0, 0.2]$, and use that graph and part (d) of Exercise 48 to make a rough estimate of the error in the approximation

$$e \approx \left(1 + \frac{1}{50}\right)^{50}$$

**50.** Prove: If $f$ is continuous on an open interval and $a$ is any point in that interval, then

$$F(x) = \int_a^x f(t)\,dt$$

is continuous on the interval.

**51. Writing** A student objects that it is circular reasoning to make the definition

$$\ln x = \int_1^x \frac{1}{t}\,dt$$

since to evaluate the integral we need to know the value of $\ln x$. Write a short paragraph that answers this student's objection.

**52. Writing** Write a short paragraph that compares Definition 5.10.1 with the definition of the natural logarithm function given in Chapter 1. Be sure to discuss the issues surrounding continuity and differentiability.

✓ **QUICK CHECK ANSWERS 5.10** 1. $-1$ 2. (a) $\frac{5}{6}$ (b) $\frac{7}{12}$ 3. $e$ 4. $y = 2 + \int_0^x \cos t^3\,dt$ 5. $-\dfrac{e^{-x}}{1+e^{-4x}}$

## CHAPTER 5 REVIEW EXERCISES

Graphing Utility   C CAS

**1–8** Evaluate the integrals. ■

**1.** $\displaystyle\int \left[\frac{1}{2x^3} + 4\sqrt{x}\right] dx$  **2.** $\displaystyle\int [u^3 - 2u + 7]\,du$

**3.** $\displaystyle\int [4\sin x + 2\cos x]\,dx$  **4.** $\displaystyle\int \sec x(\tan x + \cos x)\,dx$

**5.** $\displaystyle\int [x^{-2/3} - 5e^x]\,dx$  **6.** $\displaystyle\int \left[\frac{3}{4x} - \sec^2 x\right] dx$

**7.** $\displaystyle\int \left[\frac{1}{1+x^2} + \frac{2}{\sqrt{1-x^2}}\right] dx$

**8.** $\displaystyle\int \left[\frac{12}{x\sqrt{x^2-1}} + \frac{1-x^4}{1+x^2}\right] dx$

**9.** Solve the initial-value problems.

(a) $\dfrac{dy}{dx} = \dfrac{1-x}{\sqrt{x}},\ y(1) = 0$

(b) $\dfrac{dy}{dx} = \cos x - 5e^x,\ y(0) = 0$

(c) $\dfrac{dy}{dx} = \sqrt[3]{x},\ y(1) = 2$  (d) $\dfrac{dy}{dx} = xe^{x^2},\ y(0) = 0$

**10.** The accompanying figure shows the slope field for a differential equation $dy/dx = f(x)$. Which of the following functions is most likely to be $f(x)$?

$$\sqrt{x},\quad \sin x,\quad x^4,\quad x$$

Explain your reasoning.

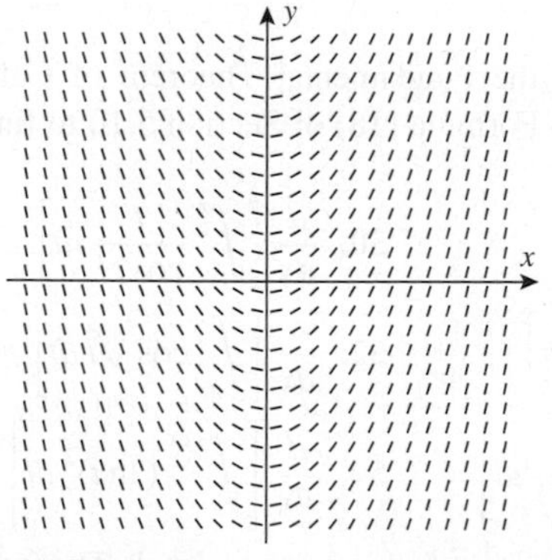


◀ **Figure Ex-10**

**11.** (a) Show that the substitutions $u = \sec x$ and $u = \tan x$ produce different values for the integral

$$\int \sec^2 x \tan x\,dx$$

(b) Explain why both are correct.

**12.** Use the two substitutions in Exercise 11 to evaluate the definite integral

$$\int_0^{\pi/4} \sec^2 x \tan x\,dx$$

and confirm that they produce the same result.

**13.** Evaluate the integral

$$\int \frac{x}{(x^2-1)\sqrt{x^4-2x^2}}\,dx$$

by making the substitution $u = x^2 - 1$.

**14.** Evaluate the integral

$$\int \sqrt{1 + x^{-2/3}}\,dx$$

by making the substitution $u = 1 + x^{2/3}$.

C **15–18** Evaluate the integrals by hand, and check your answers with a CAS if you have one. ■

**15.** $\displaystyle\int \frac{\cos 3x}{\sqrt{5+2\sin 3x}}\,dx$  **16.** $\displaystyle\int \frac{\sqrt{3+\sqrt{x}}}{\sqrt{x}}\,dx$

**17.** $\displaystyle\int \frac{x^2}{(ax^3+b)^2}\,dx$  **18.** $\displaystyle\int x\sec^2(ax^2)\,dx$

**19.** Express

$$\sum_{k=4}^{18} k(k-3)$$

in sigma notation with
(a) $k = 0$ as the lower limit of summation
(b) $k = 5$ as the lower limit of summation.

**20.** (a) Fill in the blank:

$$1 + 3 + 5 + \cdots + (2n-1) = \sum_{k=1}^{n} \underline{\qquad\qquad}$$

(b) Use part (a) to prove that the sum of the first $n$ consecutive odd integers is a perfect square.

**21.** Find the area under the graph of $f(x) = 4x - x^2$ over the interval $[0, 4]$ using Definition 5.4.3 with $x_k^*$ as the *right* endpoint of each subinterval.

**22.** Find the area under the graph of $f(x) = 5x - x^2$ over the interval $[0, 5]$ using Definition 5.4.3 with $x_k^*$ as the *left* endpoint of each subinterval.

**23–24** Use a calculating utility to find the left endpoint, right endpoint, and midpoint approximations to the area under the curve $y = f(x)$ over the stated interval using $n = 10$ subintervals. ■

**23.** $y = \ln x;\ [1, 2]$  **24.** $y = e^x;\ [0, 1]$

**25.** The *definite integral* of $f$ over the interval $[a, b]$ is defined as the limit

$$\int_a^b f(x)\,dx = \lim_{\max \Delta x_k \to 0} \sum_{k=1}^{n} f(x_k^*)\Delta x_k$$

Explain what the various symbols on the right side of this equation mean.

**26.** Use a geometric argument to evaluate

$$\int_0^1 |2x-1|\,dx$$

**27.** Suppose that

$$\int_0^1 f(x)\,dx = \tfrac{1}{2}, \quad \int_1^2 f(x)\,dx = \tfrac{1}{4},$$

$$\int_0^3 f(x)\,dx = -1, \quad \int_0^1 g(x)\,dx = 2$$

In each part, use this information to evaluate the given integral, if possible. If there is not enough information to evaluate the integral, then say so.

(a) $\int_0^2 f(x)\,dx$ (b) $\int_1^3 f(x)\,dx$ (c) $\int_2^3 5f(x)\,dx$

(d) $\int_1^0 g(x)\,dx$ (e) $\int_0^1 g(2x)\,dx$ (f) $\int_0^1 [g(x)]^2\,dx$

**28.** In parts (a)–(d), use the information in Exercise 27 to evaluate the given integral. If there is not enough information to evaluate the integral, then say so.

(a) $\int_0^1 [f(x)+g(x)]\,dx$ (b) $\int_0^1 f(x)g(x)\,dx$

(c) $\int_0^1 \frac{f(x)}{g(x)}\,dx$ (d) $\int_0^1 [4g(x)-3f(x)]\,dx$

**29.** In each part, evaluate the integral. Where appropriate, you may use a geometric formula.

(a) $\int_{-1}^1 (1+\sqrt{1-x^2})\,dx$

(b) $\int_0^3 (x\sqrt{x^2+1}-\sqrt{9-x^2})\,dx$

(c) $\int_0^1 x\sqrt{1-x^4}\,dx$

**30.** In each part, find the limit by interpreting it as a limit of Riemann sums in which the interval [0, 1] is divided into $n$ subintervals of equal length.

(a) $\lim_{n\to+\infty} \frac{\sqrt{1}+\sqrt{2}+\sqrt{3}+\cdots+\sqrt{n}}{n^{3/2}}$

(b) $\lim_{n\to+\infty} \frac{1^4+2^4+3^4+\cdots+n^4}{n^5}$

(c) $\lim_{n\to+\infty} \frac{e^{1/n}+e^{2/n}+e^{3/n}+\cdots+e^{n/n}}{n}$

**31–38** Evaluate the integrals using the Fundamental Theorem of Calculus and (if necessary) properties of the definite integral. ■

**31.** $\int_{-3}^0 (x^2-4x+7)\,dx$ **32.** $\int_{-1}^2 x(1+x^3)\,dx$

**33.** $\int_1^3 \frac{1}{x^2}\,dx$ **34.** $\int_1^8 (5x^{2/3}-4x^{-2})\,dx$

**35.** $\int_0^1 (x-\sec x\tan x)\,dx$

**36.** $\int_1^4 \left(\frac{3}{\sqrt{t}}-5\sqrt{t}-t^{-3/2}\right)dt$

**37.** $\int_0^2 |2x-3|\,dx$ **38.** $\int_0^{\pi/2} \left|\tfrac{1}{2}-\sin x\right|\,dx$

**39–42** Find the area under the curve $y=f(x)$ over the stated interval. ■

**39.** $f(x)=\sqrt{x}$; $[1,9]$ **40.** $f(x)=x^{-3/5}$; $[1,4]$

**41.** $f(x)=e^x$; $[1,3]$ **42.** $f(x)=\frac{1}{x}$; $[1,e^3]$

**43.** Find the area that is above the $x$-axis but below the curve $y=(1-x)(x-2)$. Make a sketch of the region.

C **44.** Use a CAS to find the area of the region in the first quadrant that lies below the curve $y=x+x^2-x^3$ and above the $x$-axis.

**45–46** Sketch the curve and find the total area between the curve and the given interval on the $x$-axis. ■

**45.** $y=x^2-1$; $[0,3]$ **46.** $y=\sqrt{x+1}-1$; $[-1,1]$

**47.** Define $F(x)$ by

$$F(x)=\int_1^x (t^3+1)\,dt$$

(a) Use Part 2 of the Fundamental Theorem of Calculus to find $F'(x)$.

(b) Check the result in part (a) by first integrating and then differentiating.

**48.** Define $F(x)$ by

$$F(x)=\int_4^x \frac{1}{\sqrt{t}}\,dt$$

(a) Use Part 2 of the Fundamental Theorem of Calculus to find $F'(x)$.

(b) Check the result in part (a) by first integrating and then differentiating.

**49–54** Use Part 2 of the Fundamental Theorem of Calculus and (where necessary) Formula (18) of Section 5.10 to find the derivatives. ■

**49.** $\frac{d}{dx}\left[\int_0^x e^{t^2}\,dt\right]$ **50.** $\frac{d}{dx}\left[\int_0^x \frac{t}{\cos t^2}\,dt\right]$

**51.** $\frac{d}{dx}\left[\int_0^x |t-1|\,dt\right]$ **52.** $\frac{d}{dx}\left[\int_\pi^x \cos\sqrt{t}\,dt\right]$

**53.** $\frac{d}{dx}\left[\int_2^{\sin x} \frac{1}{1+t^3}\,dt\right]$ **54.** $\frac{d}{dx}\left[\int_e^{\sqrt{x}} (\ln t)^2\,dt\right]$

**55.** State the two parts of the Fundamental Theorem of Calculus, and explain what is meant by the statement "Differentiation and integration are inverse processes."

C **56.** Let $F(x)=\int_0^x \frac{t^2-3}{t^4+7}\,dt$.

(a) Find the intervals on which $F$ is increasing and those on which $F$ is decreasing.

(b) Find the open intervals on which $F$ is concave up and those on which $F$ is concave down.

(c) Find the $x$-values, if any, at which the function $F$ has absolute extrema.

(d) Use a CAS to graph $F$, and confirm that the results in parts (a), (b), and (c) are consistent with the graph.

**57.** (a) Use differentiation to prove that the function

$$F(x) = \int_0^x \frac{1}{1+t^2}\,dt + \int_0^{1/x} \frac{1}{1+t^2}\,dt$$

is constant on the interval $(0, +\infty)$.

(b) Determine the constant value of the function in part (a) and then interpret (a) as an identity involving the inverse tangent function.

**58.** What is the natural domain of the function

$$F(x) = \int_1^x \frac{1}{t^2-9}\,dt?$$

Explain your reasoning.

**59.** In each part, determine the values of $x$ for which $F(x)$ is positive, negative, or zero without performing the integration; explain your reasoning.

(a) $F(x) = \displaystyle\int_1^x \frac{t^4}{t^2+3}\,dt$ (b) $F(x) = \displaystyle\int_{-1}^x \sqrt{4-t^2}\,dt$

C **60.** Use a CAS to approximate the largest and smallest values of the integral

$$\int_{-1}^x \frac{t}{\sqrt{2+t^3}}\,dt$$

for $1 \le x \le 3$.

**61.** Find all values of $x^*$ in the stated interval that are guaranteed to exist by the Mean-Value Theorem for Integrals, and explain what these numbers represent.

(a) $f(x) = \sqrt{x}$; $[0, 3]$ (b) $f(x) = 1/x$; $[1, e]$

**62.** A 10-gram tumor is discovered in a laboratory rat on March 1. The tumor is growing at a rate of $r(t) = t/7$ grams per week, where $t$ denotes the number of weeks since March 1. What will be the mass of the tumor on June 7?

**63.** Use the graph of $f$ shown in the accompanying figure to find the average value of $f$ on the interval $[0, 10]$.

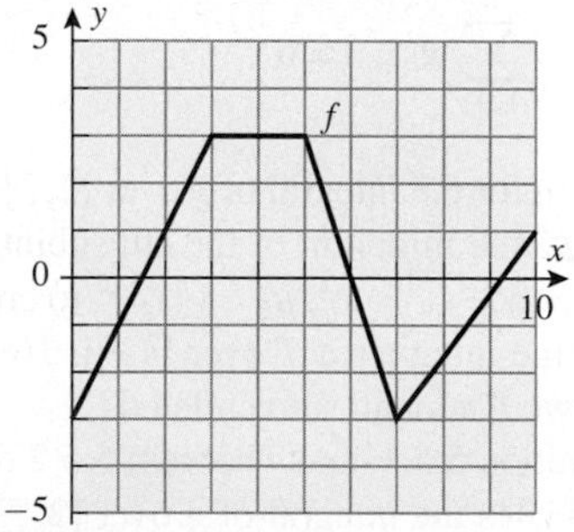


◀ **Figure Ex-63**

**64.** Find the average value of $f(x) = e^x + e^{-x}$ over the interval $\left[\ln \frac{1}{2}, \ln 2\right]$.

**65.** Derive the formulas for the position and velocity functions of a particle that moves with constant acceleration along a coordinate line.

**66.** The velocity of a particle moving along an $s$-axis is measured at 5 s intervals for 40 s, and the velocity function is modeled by a smooth curve. (The curve and the data points are shown in the accompanying figure.) Use this model in each part.

(a) Does the particle have constant acceleration? Explain your reasoning.

(b) Is there any 15 s time interval during which the acceleration is constant? Explain your reasoning.

(c) Estimate the distance traveled by the particle from time $t = 0$ to time $t = 40$.

(d) Estimate the average velocity of the particle over the 40 s time period.

(e) Is the particle ever slowing down during the 40 s time period? Explain your reasoning.

(f) Is there sufficient information for you to determine the $s$-coordinate of the particle at time $t = 10$? If so, find it. If not, explain what additional information you need.

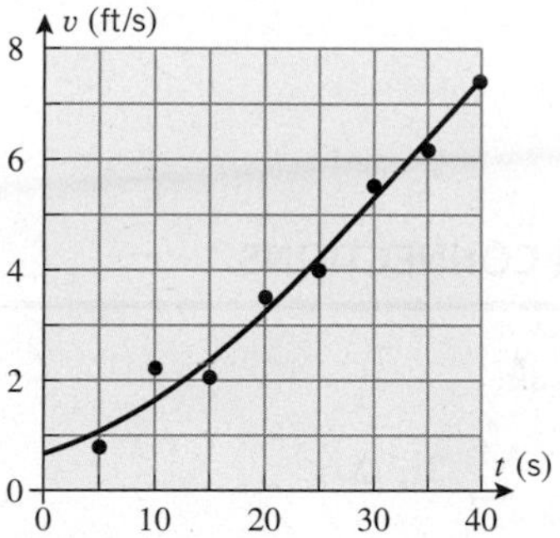


◀ **Figure Ex-66**

**67–70** A particle moves along an $s$-axis. Use the given information to find the position function of the particle. ■

**67.** $v(t) = t^3 - 2t^2 + 1$; $s(0) = 1$

**68.** $a(t) = 4\cos 2t$; $v(0) = -1, s(0) = -3$

**69.** $v(t) = 2t - 3$; $s(1) = 5$

**70.** $a(t) = \cos t - 2t$; $v(0) = 0, s(0) = 0$

**71–74** A particle moves with a velocity of $v(t)$ m/s along an $s$-axis. Find the displacement and the distance traveled by the particle during the given time interval. ■

**71.** $v(t) = 2t - 4$; $0 \le t \le 6$

**72.** $v(t) = |t - 3|$; $0 \le t \le 5$

**73.** $v(t) = \dfrac{1}{2} - \dfrac{1}{t^2}$; $1 \le t \le 3$

**74.** $v(t) = \dfrac{3}{\sqrt{t}}$; $4 \le t \le 9$

**75–76** A particle moves with acceleration $a(t)$ m/s$^2$ along an $s$-axis and has velocity $v_0$ m/s at time $t = 0$. Find the displacement and the distance traveled by the particle during the given time interval. ■

**75.** $a(t) = -2$; $v_0 = 3$; $1 \le t \le 4$

**76.** $a(t) = \dfrac{1}{\sqrt{5t+1}}$; $v_0 = 2$; $0 \le t \le 3$

**77.** A car traveling 60 mi/h (= 88 ft/s) along a straight road decelerates at a constant rate of 10 ft/s$^2$.

(a) How long will it take until the speed is 45 mi/h?

(b) How far will the car travel before coming to a stop?

**78.** Suppose that the velocity function of a particle moving along an $s$-axis is $v(t) = 20t^2 - 100t + 50$ ft/s and that the particle is at the origin at time $t = 0$. Use a graphing utility to generate the graphs of $s(t)$, $v(t)$, and $a(t)$ for the first 6 s of motion.

**79.** A ball is thrown vertically upward from a height of $s_0$ ft with an initial velocity of $v_0$ ft/s. If the ball is caught at height $s_0$, determine its average speed through the air using the free-fall model.

**80.** A rock, dropped from an unknown height, strikes the ground with a speed of 24 m/s. Find the height from which the rock was dropped.

**81–88** Evaluate the integrals by making an appropriate substitution. ■

**81.** $\int_0^1 (2x+1)^4\,dx$ **82.** $\int_{-5}^0 x\sqrt{4-x}\,dx$

**83.** $\int_0^1 \frac{dx}{\sqrt{3x+1}}$ **84.** $\int_0^{\sqrt{\pi}} x\sin x^2\,dx$

**85.** $\int_0^1 \sin^2(\pi x)\cos(\pi x)\,dx$ **86.** $\int_e^{e^2} \frac{dx}{x\ln x}$

**87.** $\int_0^1 \frac{dx}{\sqrt{e^x}}$ **88.** $\int_0^{2/\sqrt{3}} \frac{1}{4+9x^2}\,dx$

**89.** Evaluate the limits.

(a) $\lim_{x\to+\infty}\left(1+\frac{1}{x}\right)^{2x}$ (b) $\lim_{x\to+\infty}\left(1+\frac{1}{3x}\right)^{x}$

**90.** Find a function $f$ and a number $a$ such that

$$2 + \int_a^x f(t)\,dt = e^{3x}$$

## CHAPTER 5 MAKING CONNECTIONS

**1.** Consider a Riemann sum

$$\sum_{k=1}^{n} 2x_k^*\Delta x_k$$

for the integral of $f(x) = 2x$ over an interval $[a, b]$.

(a) Show that if $x_k^*$ is the midpoint of the $k$th subinterval, the Riemann sum is a telescoping sum. (See Exercises 57–60 of Section 5.4 for other examples of telescoping sums.)

(b) Use part (a), Definition 5.5.1, and Theorem 5.5.2 to evaluate the definite integral of $f(x) = 2x$ over $[a, b]$.

**2.** The function $f(x) = \sqrt{x}$ is continuous on $[0, 4]$ and therefore integrable on this interval. Evaluate

$$\int_0^4 \sqrt{x}\,dx$$

by using Definition 5.5.1. Use subintervals of unequal length given by the partition

$$0 < 4(1)^2/n^2 < 4(2)^2/n^2 < \cdots < 4(n-1)^2/n^2 < 4$$

and let $x_k^*$ be the right endpoint of the $k$th subinterval.

**3.** Make appropriate modifications and repeat Exercise 2 for

$$\int_0^8 \sqrt[3]{x}\,dx$$

**4.** Given a continuous function $f$ and a positive real number $m$, let $g$ denote the function defined by the composition $g(x) = f(mx)$.

(a) Suppose that

$$\sum_{k=1}^{n} g(x_k^*)\Delta x_k$$

is any Riemann sum for the integral of $g$ over $[0, 1]$. Use the correspondence $u_k = mx_k$, $u_k^* = mx_k^*$ to create a Riemann sum for the integral of $f$ over $[0, m]$. How are the values of the two Riemann sums related?

(b) Use part (a), Definition 5.5.1, and Theorem 5.5.2 to find an equation that relates the integral of $g$ over $[0, 1]$ with the integral of $f$ over $[0, m]$.

(c) How is your answer to part (b) related to Theorem 5.9.1?

**5.** Given a continuous function $f$, let $g$ denote the function defined by $g(x) = 2xf(x^2)$.

(a) Suppose that

$$\sum_{k=1}^{n} g(x_k^*)\Delta x_k$$

is any Riemann sum for the integral of $g$ over $[2, 3]$, with $x_k^* = (x_k + x_{k-1})/2$ the midpoint of the $k$th subinterval. Use the correspondence $u_k = x_k^2$, $u_k^* = (x_k^*)^2$ to create a Riemann sum for the integral of $f$ over $[4, 9]$. How are the values of the two Riemann sums related?

(b) Use part (a), Definition 5.5.1, and Theorem 5.5.2 to find an equation that relates the integral of $g$ over $[2, 3]$ with the integral of $f$ over $[4, 9]$.

(c) How is your answer to part (b) related to Theorem 5.9.1?

# 6

Courtesy NASA; photograph by Neil Armstrong

*Calculus is essential for the computations required to land an astronaut on the Moon.*

# APPLICATIONS OF THE DEFINITE INTEGRAL IN GEOMETRY, SCIENCE, AND ENGINEERING

In the last chapter we introduced the definite integral as the limit of Riemann sums in the context of finding areas. However, Riemann sums and definite integrals have applications that extend far beyond the area problem. In this chapter we will show how Riemann sums and definite integrals arise in such problems as finding the volume and surface area of a solid, finding the length of a plane curve, calculating the work done by a force, finding the center of gravity of a planar region, finding the pressure and force exerted by a fluid on a submerged object, and finding properties of suspended cables.

Although these problems are diverse, the required calculations can all be approached by the same procedure that we used to find areas—breaking the required calculation into "small parts," making an approximation for each part, adding the approximations from the parts to produce a Riemann sum that approximates the entire quantity to be calculated, and then taking the limit of the Riemann sums to produce an exact result.

## 6.1 AREA BETWEEN TWO CURVES

*In the last chapter we showed how to find the area between a curve $y = f(x)$ and an interval on the x-axis. Here we will show how to find the area between two curves.*

### A REVIEW OF RIEMANN SUMS

Before we consider the problem of finding the area between two curves it will be helpful to review the basic principle that underlies the calculation of area as a definite integral. Recall that if $f$ is continuous and nonnegative on $[a, b]$, then the definite integral for the area $A$ under $y = f(x)$ over the interval $[a, b]$ is obtained in four steps (Figure 6.1.1):

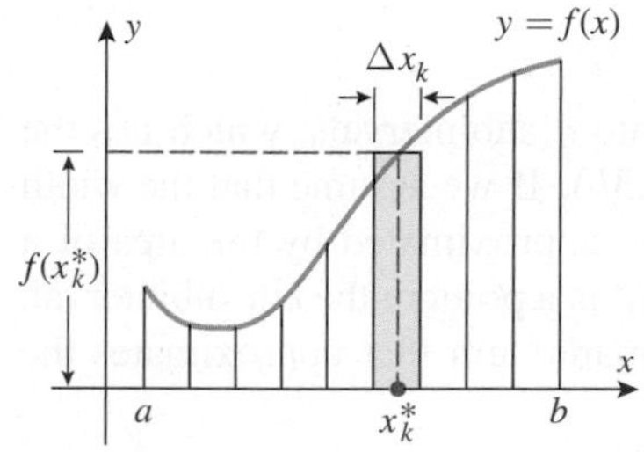


▲ **Figure 6.1.1**

- Divide the interval $[a, b]$ into $n$ subintervals, and use those subintervals to divide the region under the curve $y = f(x)$ into $n$ strips.
- Assuming that the width of the $k$th strip is $\Delta x_k$, approximate the area of that strip by the area $f(x_k^*)\Delta x_k$ of a rectangle of width $\Delta x_k$ and height $f(x_k^*)$, where $x_k^*$ is a point in the $k$th subinterval.
- Add the approximate areas of the strips to approximate the entire area $A$ by the Riemann sum:

$$A \approx \sum_{k=1}^{n} f(x_k^*)\Delta x_k$$

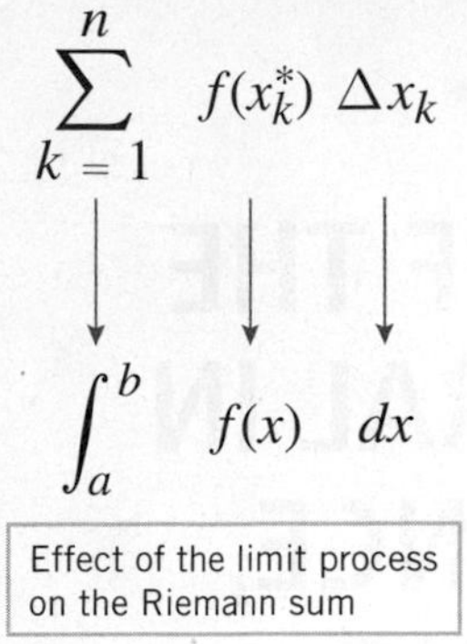


▲ **Figure 6.1.2**

- Take the limit of the Riemann sums as the number of subintervals increases and all their widths approach zero. This causes the error in the approximations to approach zero and produces the following definite integral for the exact area $A$:

$$A = \lim_{\max \Delta x_k \to 0} \sum_{k=1}^{n} f(x_k^*)\Delta x_k = \int_a^b f(x)\,dx$$

Figure 6.1.2 illustrates the effect that the limit process has on the various parts of the Riemann sum:

- The quantity $x_k^*$ in the Riemann sum becomes the variable $x$ in the definite integral.
- The interval width $\Delta x_k$ in the Riemann sum becomes the $dx$ in the definite integral.
- The interval $[a, b]$, which is the union of the subintervals with widths $\Delta x_1$, $\Delta x_2, \ldots, \Delta x_n$, does not appear explicitly in the Riemann sum but is represented by the upper and lower limits of integration in the definite integral.

## AREA BETWEEN $y = f(x)$ AND $y = g(x)$

We will now consider the following extension of the area problem.

> **6.1.1 FIRST AREA PROBLEM** Suppose that $f$ and $g$ are continuous functions on an interval $[a, b]$ and
>
> $$f(x) \geq g(x) \quad \text{for} \quad a \leq x \leq b$$
>
> [This means that the curve $y = f(x)$ lies above the curve $y = g(x)$ and that the two can touch but not cross.] Find the area $A$ of the region bounded above by $y = f(x)$, below by $y = g(x)$, and on the sides by the lines $x = a$ and $x = b$ (Figure 6.1.3*a*).

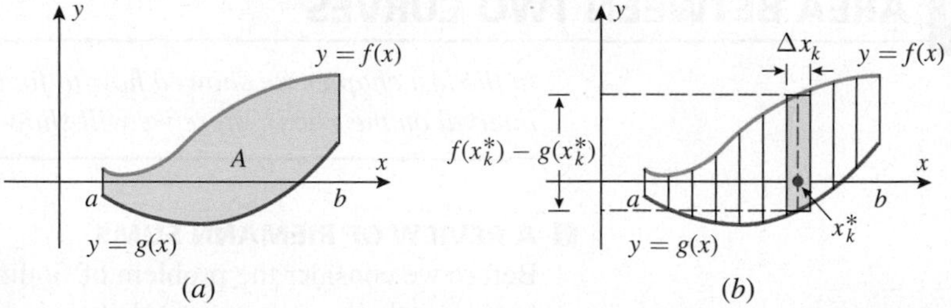


▶ **Figure 6.1.3**

To solve this problem we divide the interval $[a, b]$ into $n$ subintervals, which has the effect of subdividing the region into $n$ strips (Figure 6.1.3*b*). If we assume that the width of the $k$th strip is $\Delta x_k$, then the area of the strip can be approximated by the area of a rectangle of width $\Delta x_k$ and height $f(x_k^*) - g(x_k^*)$, where $x_k^*$ is a point in the $k$th subinterval. Adding these approximations yields the following Riemann sum that approximates the area $A$:

$$A \approx \sum_{k=1}^{n} [f(x_k^*) - g(x_k^*)]\Delta x_k$$

Taking the limit as $n$ increases and the widths of all the subintervals approach zero yields the following definite integral for the area $A$ between the curves:

$$A = \lim_{\max \Delta x_k \to 0} \sum_{k=1}^{n} [f(x_k^*) - g(x_k^*)]\Delta x_k = \int_a^b [f(x) - g(x)]\,dx$$

In summary, we have the following result.

**6.1.2 AREA FORMULA** If $f$ and $g$ are continuous functions on the interval $[a, b]$, and if $f(x) \geq g(x)$ for all $x$ in $[a, b]$, then the area of the region bounded above by $y = f(x)$, below by $y = g(x)$, on the left by the line $x = a$, and on the right by the line $x = b$ is

$$A = \int_a^b [f(x) - g(x)]\, dx \tag{1}$$

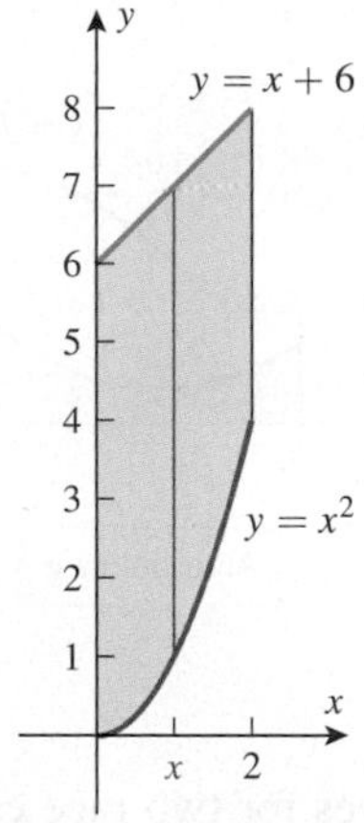

▲ Figure 6.1.4

**▶ Example 1** Find the area of the region bounded above by $y = x + 6$, bounded below by $y = x^2$, and bounded on the sides by the lines $x = 0$ and $x = 2$.

***Solution.*** The region and a cross section are shown in Figure 6.1.4. The cross section extends from $g(x) = x^2$ on the bottom to $f(x) = x + 6$ on the top. If the cross section is moved through the region, then its leftmost position will be $x = 0$ and its rightmost position will be $x = 2$. Thus, from (1)

$$A = \int_0^2 [(x + 6) - x^2]\, dx = \left[\frac{x^2}{2} + 6x - \frac{x^3}{3}\right]_0^2 = \frac{34}{3} - 0 = \frac{34}{3} \blacktriangleleft$$

What does the integral in (1) represent if the graphs of $f$ and $g$ cross each other over the interval $[a, b]$? How would you find the area between the curves in this case?

It is possible that the upper and lower boundaries of a region may intersect at one or both endpoints, in which case the sides of the region will be points, rather than vertical line segments (Figure 6.1.5). When that occurs you will have to determine the points of intersection to obtain the limits of integration.

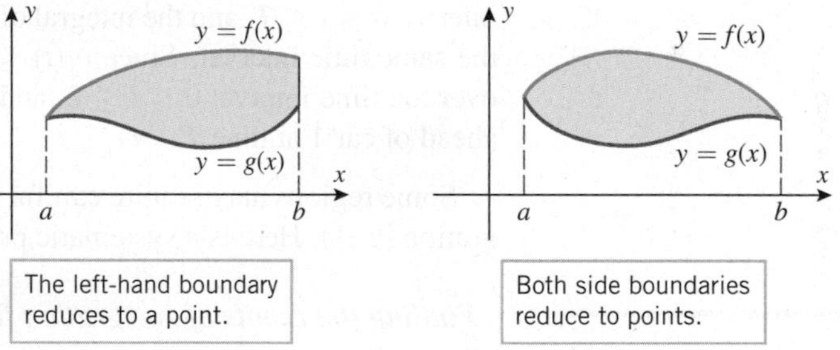

▶ Figure 6.1.5

**▶ Example 2** Find the area of the region that is enclosed between the curves $y = x^2$ and $y = x + 6$.

***Solution.*** A sketch of the region (Figure 6.1.6) shows that the lower boundary is $y = x^2$ and the upper boundary is $y = x + 6$. At the endpoints of the region, the upper and lower boundaries have the same $y$-coordinates; thus, to find the endpoints we equate

$$y = x^2 \quad \text{and} \quad y = x + 6 \tag{2}$$

This yields

$$x^2 = x + 6 \quad \text{or} \quad x^2 - x - 6 = 0 \quad \text{or} \quad (x + 2)(x - 3) = 0$$

from which we obtain

$$x = -2 \quad \text{and} \quad x = 3$$

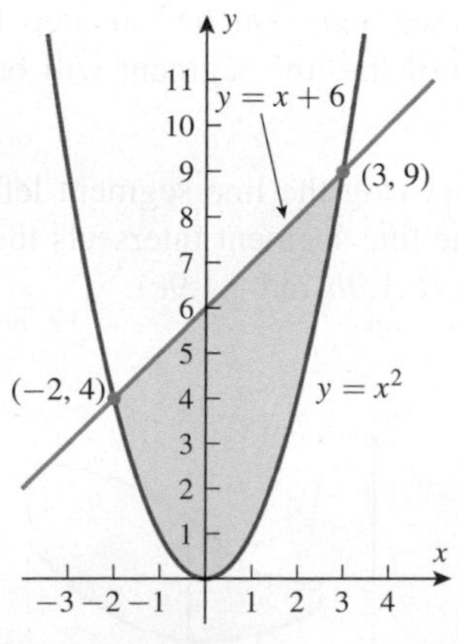

▲ Figure 6.1.6

Although the $y$-coordinates of the endpoints are not essential to our solution, they may be obtained from (2) by substituting $x = -2$ and $x = 3$ in either equation. This yields $y = 4$ and $y = 9$, so the upper and lower boundaries intersect at $(-2, 4)$ and $(3, 9)$.

From (1) with $f(x) = x + 6$, $g(x) = x^2$, $a = -2$, and $b = 3$, we obtain the area

$$A = \int_{-2}^3 [(x + 6) - x^2]\, dx = \left[\frac{x^2}{2} + 6x - \frac{x^3}{3}\right]_{-2}^3 = \frac{27}{2} - \left(-\frac{22}{3}\right) = \frac{125}{6} \blacktriangleleft$$

In the case where $f$ and $g$ are *nonnegative* on the interval $[a, b]$, the formula

$$A = \int_a^b [f(x) - g(x)]\,dx = \int_a^b f(x)\,dx - \int_a^b g(x)\,dx$$

states that the area $A$ between the curves can be obtained by subtracting the area under $y = g(x)$ from the area under $y = f(x)$ (Figure 6.1.7).

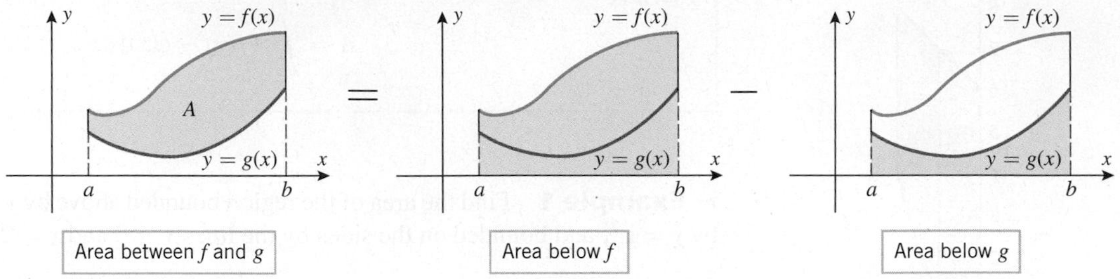


▲ Figure 6.1.7

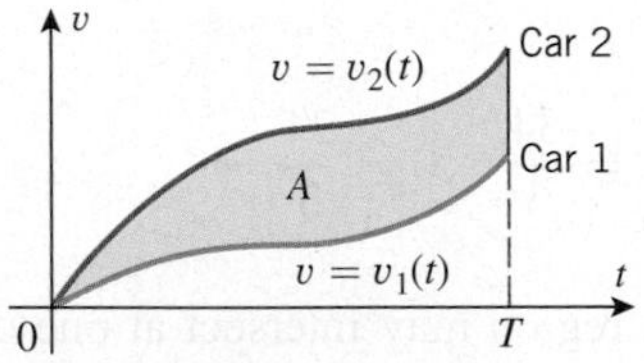


▲ Figure 6.1.8

▶ **Example 3** Figure 6.1.8 shows velocity versus time curves for two race cars that move along a straight track, starting from rest at the same time. Give a physical interpretation of the area $A$ between the curves over the interval $0 \le t \le T$.

***Solution.*** From (1)

$$A = \int_0^T [v_2(t) - v_1(t)]\,dt = \int_0^T v_2(t)\,dt - \int_0^T v_1(t)\,dt$$

Since $v_1$ and $v_2$ are nonnegative functions on $[0, T]$, it follows from Formula (4) of Section 5.7 that the integral of $v_1$ over $[0, T]$ is the distance traveled by car 1 during the time interval $0 \le t \le T$, and the integral of $v_2$ over $[0, T]$ is the distance traveled by car 2 during the same time interval. Since $v_1(t) \le v_2(t)$ on $[0, T]$, car 2 travels farther than car 1 does over the time interval $0 \le t \le T$, and the area $A$ represents the distance by which car 2 is ahead of car 1 at time $T$. ◀

Some regions may require careful thought to determine the integrand and limits of integration in (1). Here is a systematic procedure that you can follow to set up this formula.

It is not necessary to make an extremely accurate sketch in Step 1; the only purpose of the sketch is to determine which curve is the upper boundary and which is the lower boundary.

***Finding the Limits of Integration for the Area Between Two Curves***

**Step 1.** Sketch the region and then draw a vertical line segment through the region at an arbitrary point $x$ on the $x$-axis, connecting the top and bottom boundaries (Figure 6.1.9*a*).

**Step 2.** The $y$-coordinate of the top endpoint of the line segment sketched in Step 1 will be $f(x)$, the bottom one $g(x)$, and the length of the line segment will be $f(x) - g(x)$. This is the integrand in (1).

**Step 3.** To determine the limits of integration, imagine moving the line segment left and then right. The leftmost position at which the line segment intersects the region is $x = a$ and the rightmost is $x = b$ (Figures 6.1.9*b* and 6.1.9*c*).

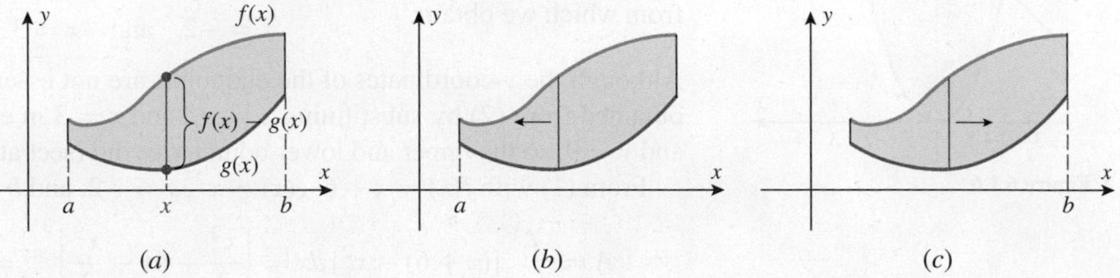


▲ Figure 6.1.9

There is a useful way of thinking about this procedure:

*If you view the vertical line segment as the "cross section" of the region at the point x, then Formula (1) states that the area between the curves is obtained by integrating the length of the cross section over the interval [a, b].*

It is possible for the upper or lower boundary of a region to consist of two or more different curves, in which case it will be convenient to subdivide the region into smaller pieces in order to apply Formula (1). This is illustrated in the next example.

▶ **Example 4** Find the area of the region enclosed by $x = y^2$ and $y = x - 2$.

***Solution.*** To determine the appropriate boundaries of the region, we need to know where the curves $x = y^2$ and $y = x - 2$ intersect. In Example 2 we found intersections by equating the expressions for $y$. Here it is easier to rewrite the latter equation as $x = y + 2$ and equate the expressions for $x$, namely,

$$x = y^2 \quad \text{and} \quad x = y + 2 \tag{3}$$

This yields

$$y^2 = y + 2 \quad \text{or} \quad y^2 - y - 2 = 0 \quad \text{or} \quad (y+1)(y-2) = 0$$

from which we obtain $y = -1$, $y = 2$. Substituting these values in either equation in (3) we see that the corresponding $x$-values are $x = 1$ and $x = 4$, respectively, so the points of intersection are $(1, -1)$ and $(4, 2)$ (Figure 6.1.10*a*).

To apply Formula (1), the equations of the boundaries must be written so that $y$ is expressed explicitly as a function of $x$. The upper boundary can be written as $y = \sqrt{x}$ (rewrite $x = y^2$ as $y = \pm\sqrt{x}$ and choose the + for the upper portion of the curve). The lower boundary consists of two parts:

$$y = -\sqrt{x} \quad \text{for} \quad 0 \le x \le 1 \qquad \text{and} \qquad y = x - 2 \quad \text{for} \quad 1 \le x \le 4$$

(Figure 6.1.10*b*). Because of this change in the formula for the lower boundary, it is necessary to divide the region into two parts and find the area of each part separately.

From (1) with $f(x) = \sqrt{x}$, $g(x) = -\sqrt{x}$, $a = 0$, and $b = 1$, we obtain

$$A_1 = \int_0^1 [\sqrt{x} - (-\sqrt{x})]\,dx = 2\int_0^1 \sqrt{x}\,dx = 2\left[\frac{2}{3}x^{3/2}\right]_0^1 = \frac{4}{3} - 0 = \frac{4}{3}$$

From (1) with $f(x) = \sqrt{x}$, $g(x) = x - 2$, $a = 1$, and $b = 4$, we obtain

$$A_2 = \int_1^4 [\sqrt{x} - (x-2)]\,dx = \int_1^4 (\sqrt{x} - x + 2)\,dx$$

$$= \left[\frac{2}{3}x^{3/2} - \frac{1}{2}x^2 + 2x\right]_1^4 = \left(\frac{16}{3} - 8 + 8\right) - \left(\frac{2}{3} - \frac{1}{2} + 2\right) = \frac{19}{6}$$

Thus, the area of the entire region is

$$A = A_1 + A_2 = \frac{4}{3} + \frac{19}{6} = \frac{9}{2} \quad ◀$$

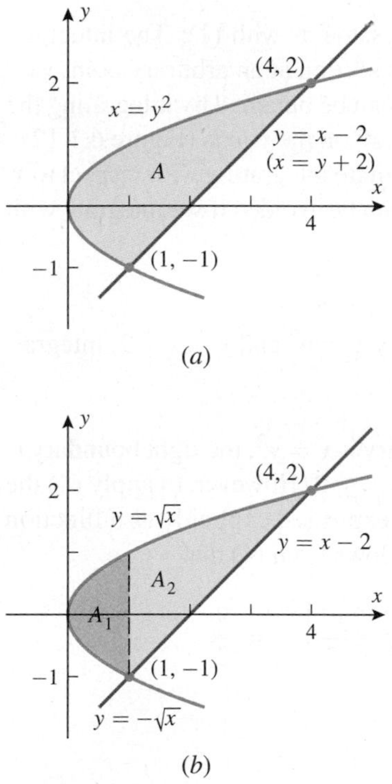

▲ **Figure 6.1.10**

## ■ REVERSING THE ROLES OF x AND y

Sometimes it is much easier to find the area of a region by integrating with respect to $y$ rather than $x$. We will now show how this can be done.

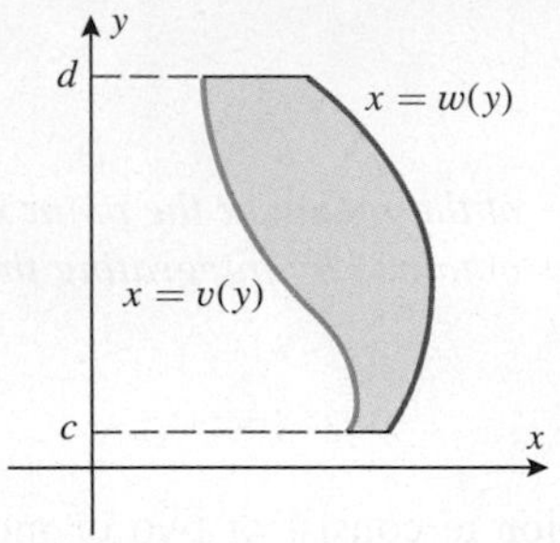


▲ Figure 6.1.11

**6.1.3 SECOND AREA PROBLEM** Suppose that $w$ and $v$ are continuous functions of $y$ on an interval $[c, d]$ and that

$$w(y) \geq v(y) \quad \text{for} \quad c \leq y \leq d$$

[This means that the curve $x = w(y)$ lies to the right of the curve $x = v(y)$ and that the two can touch but not cross.] Find the area $A$ of the region bounded on the left by $x = v(y)$, on the right by $x = w(y)$, and above and below by the lines $y = d$ and $y = c$ (Figure 6.1.11).

Proceeding as in the derivation of (1), but with the roles of $x$ and $y$ reversed, leads to the following analog of 6.1.2.

**6.1.4 AREA FORMULA** If $w$ and $v$ are continuous functions and if $w(y) \geq v(y)$ for all $y$ in $[c, d]$, then the area of the region bounded on the left by $x = v(y)$, on the right by $x = w(y)$, below by $y = c$, and above by $y = d$ is

$$A = \int_c^d [w(y) - v(y)]\, dy \tag{4}$$

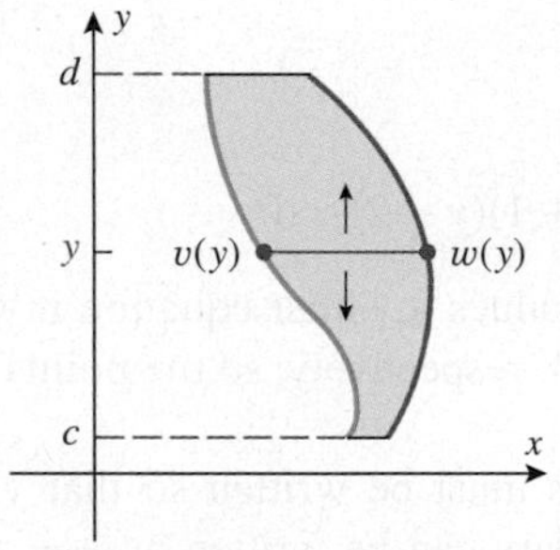


▲ Figure 6.1.12

The guiding principle in applying this formula is the same as with (1): The integrand in (4) can be viewed as the length of the horizontal cross section at an arbitrary point $y$ on the $y$-axis, in which case Formula (4) states that the area can be obtained by integrating the length of the horizontal cross section over the interval $[c, d]$ on the $y$-axis (Figure 6.1.12).

In Example 4, we split the region into two parts to facilitate integrating with respect to $x$. In the next example we will see that splitting this region can be avoided if we integrate with respect to $y$.

▶ **Example 5** Find the area of the region enclosed by $x = y^2$ and $y = x - 2$, integrating with respect to $y$.

The choice between Formulas (1) and (4) is usually dictated by the shape of the region and which formula requires the least amount of splitting. However, sometimes one might choose the formula that requires more splitting because it is easier to evaluate the resulting integrals.

***Solution.*** As indicated in Figure 6.1.10 the left boundary is $x = y^2$, the right boundary is $y = x - 2$, and the region extends over the interval $-1 \leq y \leq 2$. However, to apply (4) the equations for the boundaries must be written so that $x$ is expressed explicitly as a function of $y$. Thus, we rewrite $y = x - 2$ as $x = y + 2$. It now follows from (4) that

$$A = \int_{-1}^{2} [(y+2) - y^2]\, dy = \left[\frac{y^2}{2} + 2y - \frac{y^3}{3}\right]_{-1}^{2} = \frac{9}{2}$$

which agrees with the result obtained in Example 4. ◀

## ✓ QUICK CHECK EXERCISES 6.1 *(See page 348 for answers.)*

1. An integral expression for the area of the region between the curves $y = 20 - 3x^2$ and $y = e^x$ and bounded on the sides by $x = 0$ and $x = 2$ is ______.
2. An integral expression for the area of the parallelogram bounded by $y = 2x + 8$, $y = 2x - 3$, $x = -1$, and $x = 5$ is ______. The value of this integral is ______.
3. (a) The points of intersection for the circle $x^2 + y^2 = 4$ and the line $y = x + 2$ are ______ and ______.
   (b) Expressed as a definite integral with respect to $x$, ______ gives the area of the region inside the circle $x^2 + y^2 = 4$ and above the line $y = x + 2$.
   (c) Expressed as a definite integral with respect to $y$, ______ gives the area of the region described in part (b).
4. The area of the region enclosed by the curves $y = x^2$ and $y = \sqrt[3]{x}$ is ______.

## EXERCISE SET 6.1 Graphing Utility C CAS

**1–4** Find the area of the shaded region. ■

**1.**
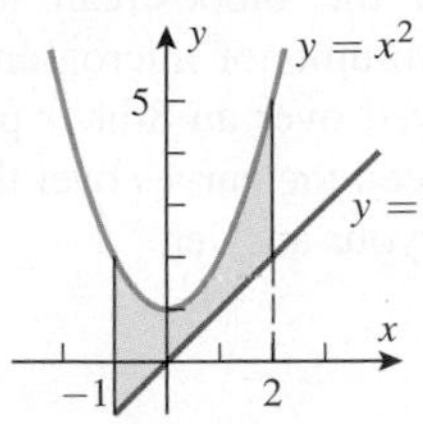


**2.**
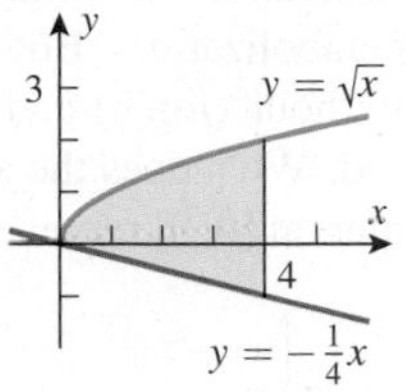


**3.**
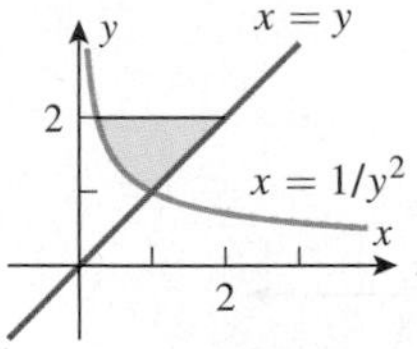


**4.**
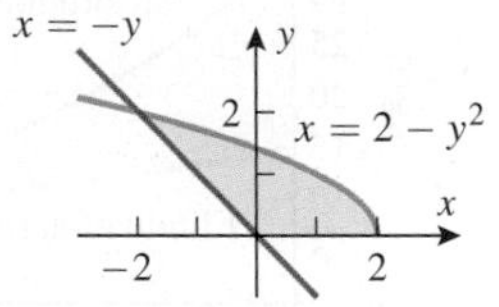


**5–6** Find the area of the shaded region by (a) integrating with respect to $x$ and (b) integrating with respect to $y$. ■

**5.**
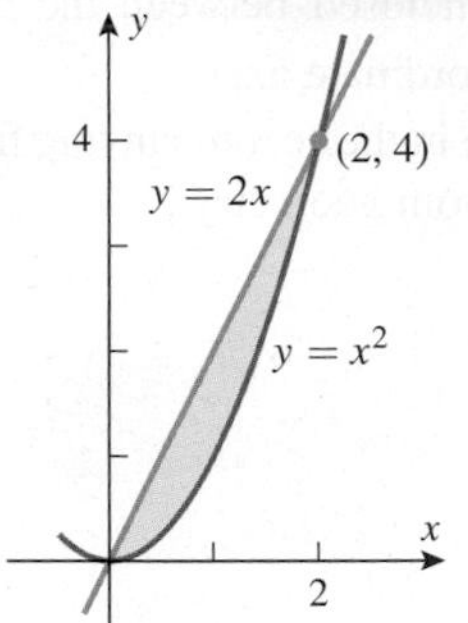


**6.**
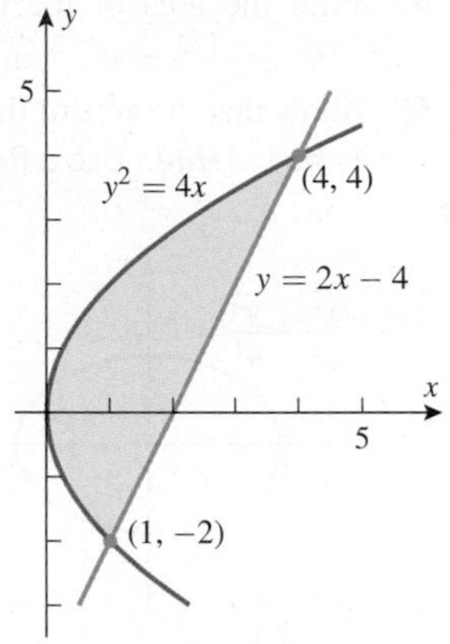


**7–18** Sketch the region enclosed by the curves and find its area. ■

**7.** $y = x^2,\ y = \sqrt{x},\ x = \frac{1}{4},\ x = 1$

**8.** $y = x^3 - 4x,\ y = 0,\ x = 0,\ x = 2$

**9.** $y = \cos 2x,\ y = 0,\ x = \pi/4,\ x = \pi/2$

**10.** $y = \sec^2 x,\ y = 2,\ x = -\pi/4,\ x = \pi/4$

**11.** $x = \sin y,\ x = 0,\ y = \pi/4,\ y = 3\pi/4$

**12.** $x^2 = y,\ x = y - 2$

**13.** $y = e^x,\ y = e^{2x},\ x = 0,\ x = \ln 2$

**14.** $x = 1/y,\ x = 0,\ y = 1,\ y = e$

**15.** $y = \dfrac{2}{1+x^2},\ y = |x|$

**16.** $y = \dfrac{1}{\sqrt{1-x^2}},\ y = 2$

**17.** $y = 2 + |x - 1|,\ y = -\frac{1}{5}x + 7$

**18.** $y = x,\ y = 4x,\ y = -x + 2$

**19–26** Use a graphing utility, where helpful, to find the area of the region enclosed by the curves. ■

**19.** $y = x^3 - 4x^2 + 3x,\ y = 0$

**20.** $y = x^3 - 2x^2,\ y = 2x^2 - 3x$

**21.** $y = \sin x,\ y = \cos x,\ x = 0,\ x = 2\pi$

**22.** $y = x^3 - 4x,\ y = 0$

**23.** $x = y^3 - y,\ x = 0$

**24.** $x = y^3 - 4y^2 + 3y,\ x = y^2 - y$

**25.** $y = xe^{x^2},\ y = 2|x|$

**26.** $y = \dfrac{1}{x\sqrt{1-(\ln x)^2}},\ y = \dfrac{3}{x}$

**27–30 True–False** Determine whether the statement is true or false. Explain your answer. [In each exercise, assume that $f$ and $g$ are distinct continuous functions on $[a, b]$ and that $A$ denotes the area of the region bounded by the graphs of $y = f(x)$, $y = g(x)$, $x = a$, and $x = b$.] ■

**27.** If $f$ and $g$ differ by a positive constant $c$, then $A = c(b - a)$.

**28.** If
$$\int_a^b [f(x) - g(x)]\,dx = -3$$
then $A = 3$.

**29.** If
$$\int_a^b [f(x) - g(x)]\,dx = 0$$
then the graphs of $y = f(x)$ and $y = g(x)$ cross at least once on $[a, b]$.

**30.** If
$$A = \left|\int_a^b [f(x) - g(x)]\,dx\right|$$
then the graphs of $y = f(x)$ and $y = g(x)$ don't cross on $[a, b]$.

**31.** Estimate the value of $k\ (0 < k < 1)$ so that the region enclosed by $y = 1/\sqrt{1-x^2}$, $y = x$, $x = 0$, and $x = k$ has an area of 1 square unit.

**32.** Estimate the area of the region in the first quadrant enclosed by $y = \sin 2x$ and $y = \sin^{-1} x$.

C **33.** Use a CAS to find the area enclosed by $y = 3 - 2x$ and $y = x^6 + 2x^5 - 3x^4 + x^2$.

C **34.** Use a CAS to find the exact area enclosed by the curves $y = x^5 - 2x^3 - 3x$ and $y = x^3$.

**35.** Find a horizontal line $y = k$ that divides the area between $y = x^2$ and $y = 9$ into two equal parts.

**36.** Find a vertical line $x = k$ that divides the area enclosed by $x = \sqrt{y}$, $x = 2$, and $y = 0$ into two equal parts.

**37.** (a) Find the area of the region enclosed by the parabola $y = 2x - x^2$ and the $x$-axis.

(b) Find the value of $m$ so that the line $y = mx$ divides the region in part (a) into two regions of equal area.

**38.** Find the area between the curve $y = \sin x$ and the line segment joining the points $(0, 0)$ and $(5\pi/6, 1/2)$ on the curve.

**39–42** Use Newton's Method (Section 4.7), where needed, to approximate the $x$-coordinates of the intersections of the curves to at least four decimal places, and then use those approximations to approximate the area of the region. ■

**39.** The region that lies below the curve $y = \sin x$ and above the line $y = 0.2x$, where $x \geq 0$.

**40.** The region enclosed by the graphs of $y = x^2$ and $y = \cos x$.

**41.** The region enclosed by the graphs of $y = (\ln x)/x$ and $y = x - 2$.

**42.** The region enclosed by the graphs of $y = 3 - 2\cos x$ and $y = 2/(1 + x^2)$.

**43.** Find the area of the region that is enclosed by the curves $y = x^2 - 1$ and $y = 2\sin x$.

C **44.** Referring to the accompanying figure, use a CAS to estimate the value of $k$ so that the areas of the shaded regions are equal.

***Source:*** This exercise is based on Problem A1 that was posed in the Fifty-Fourth Annual William Lowell Putnam Mathematical Competition.

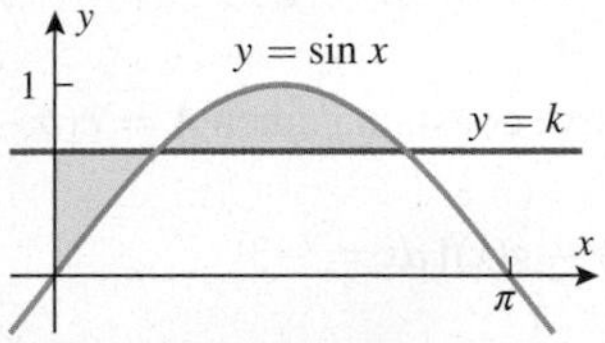


◀ **Figure Ex-44**

**FOCUS ON CONCEPTS**

**45.** Two racers in adjacent lanes move with velocity functions $v_1(t)$ m/s and $v_2(t)$ m/s, respectively. Suppose that the racers are even at time $t = 60$ s. Interpret the value of the integral

$$\int_0^{60} [v_2(t) - v_1(t)]\, dt$$

in this context.

**46.** The accompanying figure shows acceleration versus time curves for two cars that move along a straight track, accelerating from rest at the starting line. What does the area $A$ between the curves over the interval $0 \le t \le T$ represent? Justify your answer.

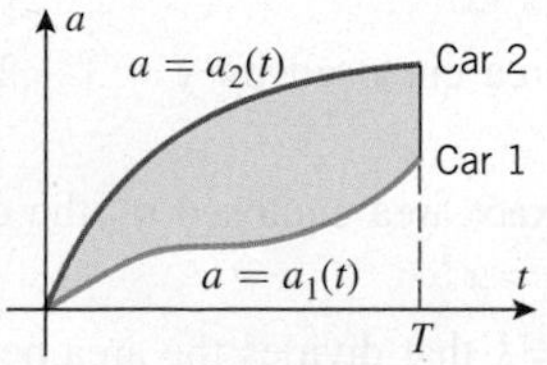


◀ **Figure Ex-46**

**47.** The curves in the accompanying figure model the birth rates and death rates (in millions of people per year) for a country over a 50-year period. What does the area $A$ between the curves over the interval [1960, 2010] represent? Justify your answer.

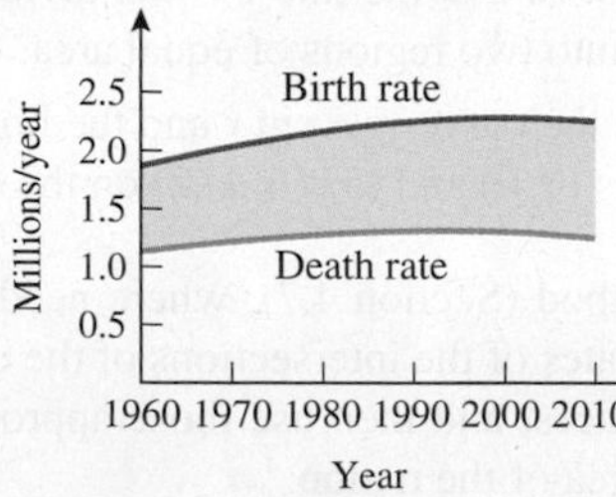


◀ **Figure Ex-47**

**48.** The accompanying figure shows the rate at which transdermal medication is absorbed into the bloodstream of an individual, as well as the rate at which the medication is eliminated from the bloodstream by metabolization. Both rates are in units of micrograms per hour ($\mu$g/h) and are displayed over an 8-hour period. What does the area $A$ between the curves over the interval [0, 8] represent? Justify your answer.

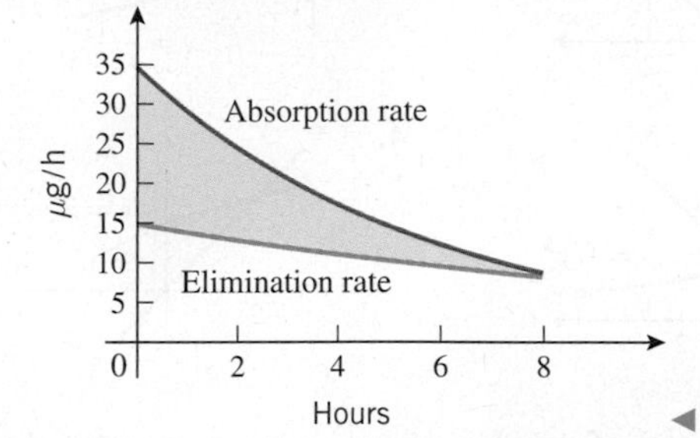


◀ **Figure Ex-48**

**49.** Find the area of the region enclosed between the curve $x^{1/2} + y^{1/2} = a^{1/2}$ and the coordinate axes.

**50.** Show that the area of the ellipse in the accompanying figure is $\pi ab$. [*Hint:* Use a formula from geometry.]

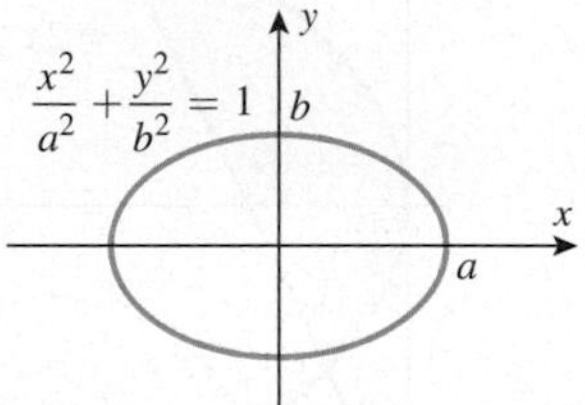


◀ **Figure Ex-50**

**51. Writing** Suppose that $f$ and $g$ are continuous on $[a, b]$ but that the graphs of $y = f(x)$ and $y = g(x)$ cross several times. Describe a step-by-step procedure for determining the area bounded by the graphs of $y = f(x)$, $y = g(x)$, $x = a$, and $x = b$.

**52. Writing** Suppose that $R$ and $S$ are two regions in the $xy$-plane that lie between a pair of lines $L_1$ and $L_2$ that are parallel to the $y$-axis. Assume that each line between $L_1$ and $L_2$ that is parallel to the $y$-axis intersects $R$ and $S$ in line segments of equal length. Give an informal argument that the area of $R$ is equal to the area of $S$. (Make reasonable assumptions about the boundaries of $R$ and $S$.)

✓ **QUICK CHECK ANSWERS 6.1** 1. $\int_0^2 [(20 - 3x^2) - e^x]\, dx$ 2. $\int_{-1}^5 [(2x + 8) - (2x - 3)]\, dx$; 66
3. (a) $(-2, 0)$; $(0, 2)$ (b) $\int_{-2}^0 [\sqrt{4 - x^2} - (x + 2)]\, dx$ (c) $\int_0^2 [(y - 2) + \sqrt{4 - y^2}]\, dy$ 4. $\frac{5}{12}$

# 6.2 VOLUMES BY SLICING; DISKS AND WASHERS

*In the last section we showed that the area of a plane region bounded by two curves can be obtained by integrating the length of a general cross section over an appropriate interval. In this section we will see that the same basic principle can be used to find volumes of certain three-dimensional solids.*

## VOLUMES BY SLICING

Recall that the underlying principle for finding the area of a plane region is to divide the region into thin strips, approximate the area of each strip by the area of a rectangle, add the approximations to form a Riemann sum, and take the limit of the Riemann sums to produce an integral for the area. Under appropriate conditions, the same strategy can be used to find the volume of a solid. The idea is to divide the solid into thin slabs, approximate the volume of each slab, add the approximations to form a Riemann sum, and take the limit of the Riemann sums to produce an integral for the volume (Figure 6.2.1).

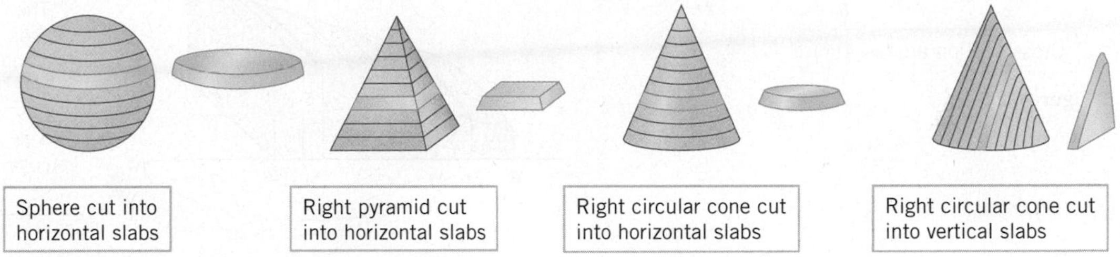


▲ **Figure 6.2.1**

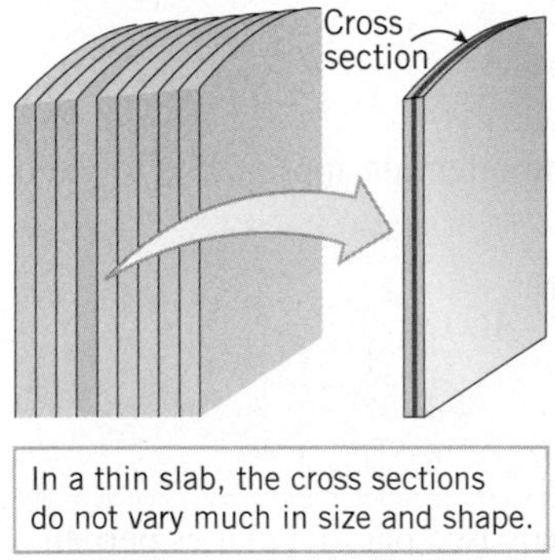


▲ **Figure 6.2.2**

What makes this method work is the fact that a *thin* slab has a cross section that does not vary much in size or shape, which, as we will see, makes its volume easy to approximate (Figure 6.2.2). Moreover, the thinner the slab, the less variation in its cross sections and the better the approximation. Thus, once we approximate the volumes of the slabs, we can set up a Riemann sum whose limit is the volume of the entire solid. We will give the details shortly, but first we need to discuss how to find the volume of a solid whose cross sections do not vary in size and shape (i.e., are congruent).

One of the simplest examples of a solid with congruent cross sections is a right circular cylinder of radius $r$, since all cross sections taken perpendicular to the central axis are circular regions of radius $r$. The volume $V$ of a right circular cylinder of radius $r$ and height $h$ can be expressed in terms of the height and the area of a cross section as

$$V = \pi r^2 h = [\text{area of a cross section}] \times [\text{height}] \qquad (1)$$

This is a special case of a more general volume formula that applies to solids called right cylinders. A ***right cylinder*** is a solid that is generated when a plane region is translated along a line or ***axis*** that is perpendicular to the region (Figure 6.2.3).

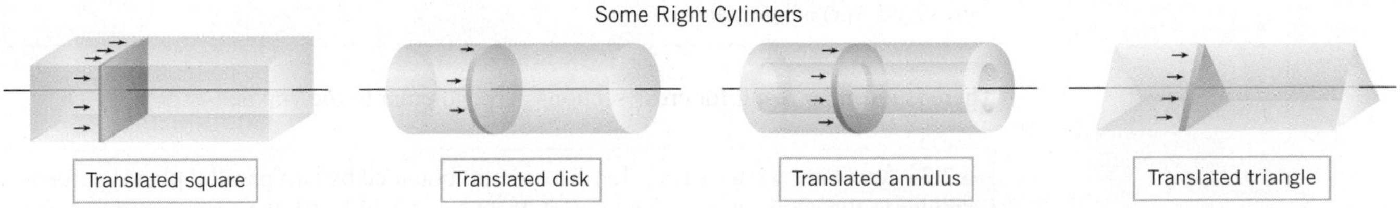


▲ **Figure 6.2.3**

If a right cylinder is generated by translating a region of area $A$ through a distance $h$, then $h$ is called the ***height*** (or sometimes the ***width***) of the cylinder, and the volume $V$ of the cylinder is defined to be

$$V = A \cdot h = [\text{area of a cross section}] \times [\text{height}] \qquad (2)$$

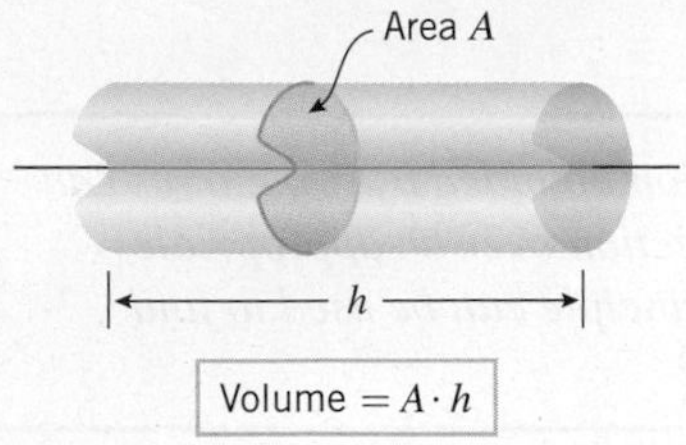


▲ **Figure 6.2.4**

(Figure 6.2.4). Note that this is consistent with Formula (1) for the volume of a right *circular* cylinder.

We now have all of the tools required to solve the following problem.

**6.2.1 PROBLEM** Let $S$ be a solid that extends along the $x$-axis and is bounded on the left and right, respectively, by the planes that are perpendicular to the $x$-axis at $x = a$ and $x = b$ (Figure 6.2.5). Find the volume $V$ of the solid, assuming that its cross-sectional area $A(x)$ is known at each $x$ in the interval $[a, b]$.

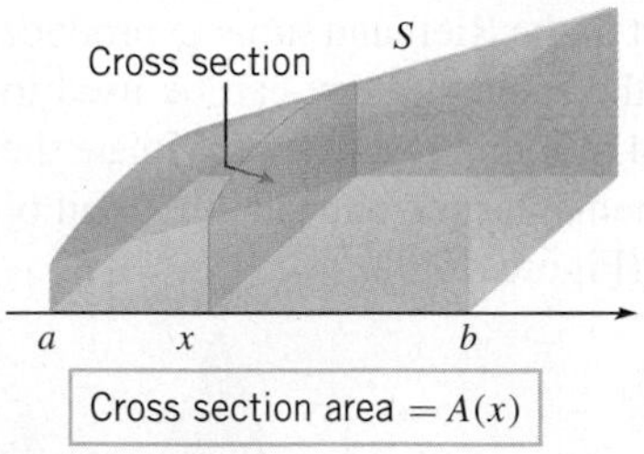


▲ **Figure 6.2.5**

To solve this problem we begin by dividing the interval $[a, b]$ into $n$ subintervals, thereby dividing the solid into $n$ slabs as shown in the left part of Figure 6.2.6. If we assume that the width of the $k$th subinterval is $\Delta x_k$, then the volume of the $k$th slab can be approximated by the volume $A(x_k^*)\Delta x_k$ of a right cylinder of width (height) $\Delta x_k$ and cross-sectional area $A(x_k^*)$, where $x_k^*$ is a point in the $k$th subinterval (see the right part of Figure 6.2.6).

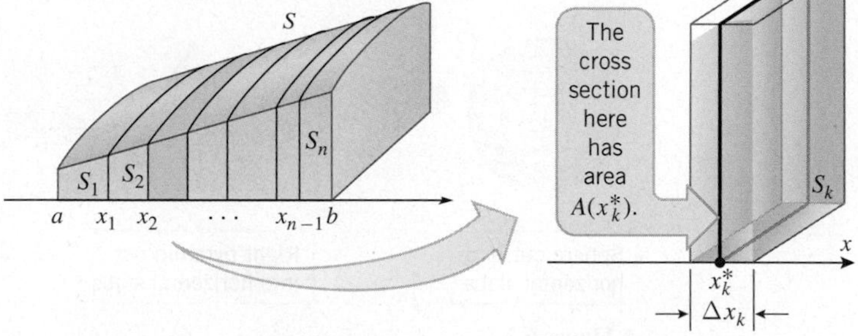


▶ **Figure 6.2.6**

Adding these approximations yields the following Riemann sum that approximates the volume $V$:

$$V \approx \sum_{k=1}^{n} A(x_k^*)\Delta x_k$$

Taking the limit as $n$ increases and the widths of all the subintervals approach zero yields the definite integral

$$V = \lim_{\max \Delta x_k \to 0} \sum_{k=1}^{n} A(x_k^*)\Delta x_k = \int_a^b A(x)\,dx$$

In summary, we have the following result.

It is understood in our calculations of volume that the units of volume are the cubed units of length [e.g., cubic inches ($\text{in}^3$) or cubic meters ($\text{m}^3$)].

**6.2.2 VOLUME FORMULA** Let $S$ be a solid bounded by two parallel planes perpendicular to the $x$-axis at $x = a$ and $x = b$. If, for each $x$ in $[a, b]$, the cross-sectional area of $S$ perpendicular to the $x$-axis is $A(x)$, then the volume of the solid is

$$V = \int_a^b A(x)\,dx \tag{3}$$

provided $A(x)$ is integrable.

There is a similar result for cross sections perpendicular to the $y$-axis.

**6.2.3 VOLUME FORMULA** Let $S$ be a solid bounded by two parallel planes perpendicular to the $y$-axis at $y = c$ and $y = d$. If, for each $y$ in $[c, d]$, the cross-sectional area of $S$ perpendicular to the $y$-axis is $A(y)$, then the volume of the solid is

$$V = \int_c^d A(y)\,dy \tag{4}$$

provided $A(y)$ is integrable.

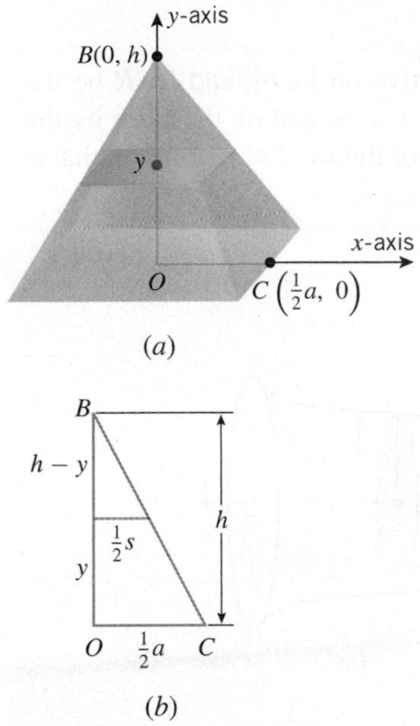


▲ Figure 6.2.7

In words, these formulas state:

*The volume of a solid can be obtained by integrating the cross-sectional area from one end of the solid to the other.*

▶ **Example 1** Derive the formula for the volume of a right pyramid whose altitude is $h$ and whose base is a square with sides of length $a$.

***Solution.*** As illustrated in Figure 6.2.7*a*, we introduce a rectangular coordinate system in which the $y$-axis passes through the apex and is perpendicular to the base, and the $x$-axis passes through the base and is parallel to a side of the base.

At any $y$ in the interval $[0, h]$ on the $y$-axis, the cross section perpendicular to the $y$-axis is a square. If $s$ denotes the length of a side of this square, then by similar triangles (Figure 6.2.7*b*)

$$\frac{\frac{1}{2}s}{\frac{1}{2}a} = \frac{h-y}{h} \quad \text{or} \quad s = \frac{a}{h}(h-y)$$

Thus, the area $A(y)$ of the cross section at $y$ is

$$A(y) = s^2 = \frac{a^2}{h^2}(h-y)^2$$

and by (4) the volume is

$$V = \int_0^h A(y)\,dy = \int_0^h \frac{a^2}{h^2}(h-y)^2\,dy = \frac{a^2}{h^2}\int_0^h (h-y)^2\,dy$$

$$= \frac{a^2}{h^2}\left[-\frac{1}{3}(h-y)^3\right]_{y=0}^{h} = \frac{a^2}{h^2}\left[0+\frac{1}{3}h^3\right] = \frac{1}{3}a^2h$$

That is, the volume is $\frac{1}{3}$ of the area of the base times the altitude. ◀

## SOLIDS OF REVOLUTION

A ***solid of revolution*** is a solid that is generated by revolving a plane region about a line that lies in the same plane as the region; the line is called the ***axis of revolution***. Many familiar solids are of this type (Figure 6.2.8).

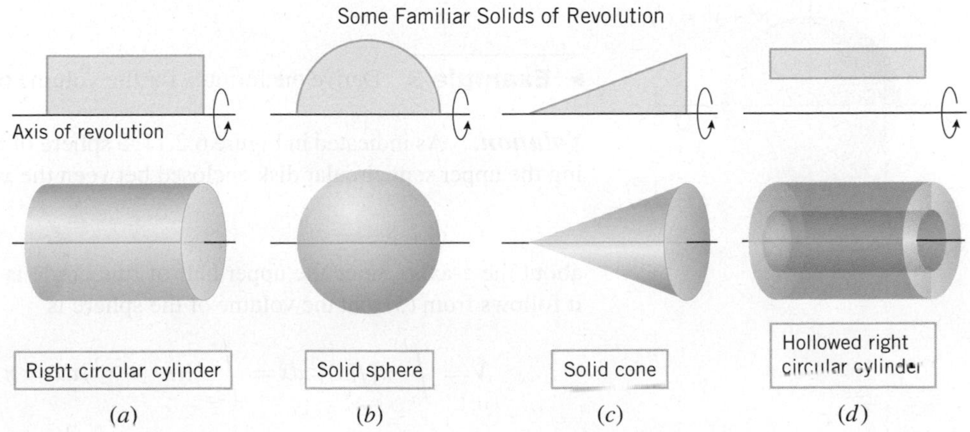


▶ Figure 6.2.8

## VOLUMES BY DISKS PERPENDICULAR TO THE *x*-AXIS

We will be interested in the following general problem.

**6.2.4 PROBLEM** Let $f$ be continuous and nonnegative on $[a, b]$, and let $R$ be the region that is bounded above by $y = f(x)$, below by the $x$-axis, and on the sides by the lines $x = a$ and $x = b$ (Figure 6.2.9*a*). Find the volume of the solid of revolution that is generated by revolving the region $R$ about the $x$-axis.

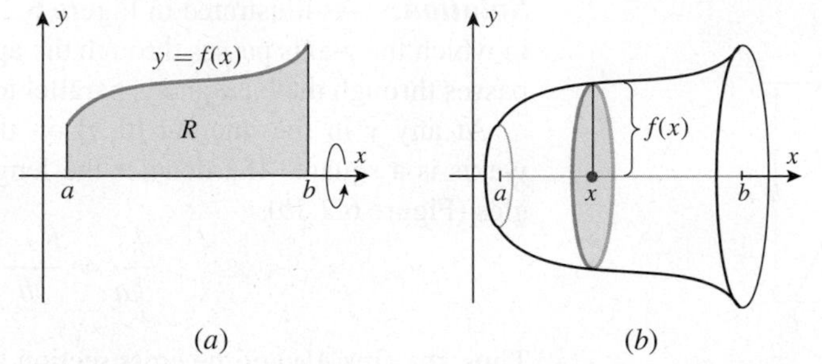

▶ **Figure 6.2.9**

We can solve this problem by slicing. For this purpose, observe that the cross section of the solid taken perpendicular to the $x$-axis at the point $x$ is a circular disk of radius $f(x)$ (Figure 6.2.9*b*). The area of this region is

$$A(x) = \pi[f(x)]^2$$

Thus, from (3) the volume of the solid is

$$V = \int_a^b \pi[f(x)]^2\, dx \tag{5}$$

Because the cross sections are disk shaped, the application of this formula is called the ***method of disks***.

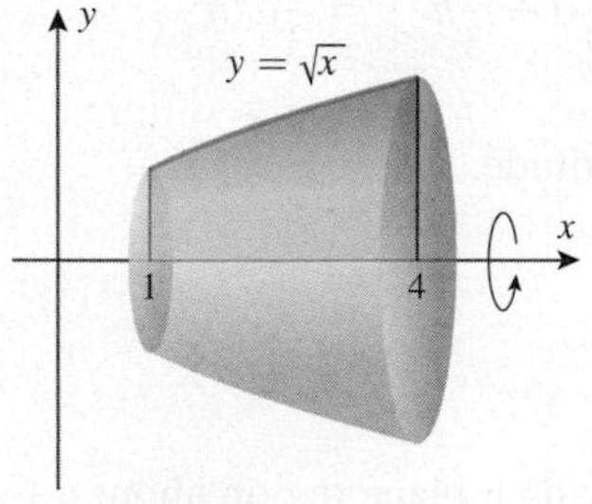

▲ **Figure 6.2.10**

▶ **Example 2** Find the volume of the solid that is obtained when the region under the curve $y = \sqrt{x}$ over the interval $[1, 4]$ is revolved about the $x$-axis (Figure 6.2.10).

***Solution.*** From (5), the volume is

$$V = \int_a^b \pi[f(x)]^2\, dx = \int_1^4 \pi x\, dx = \frac{\pi x^2}{2}\bigg]_1^4 = 8\pi - \frac{\pi}{2} = \frac{15\pi}{2} \blacktriangleleft$$

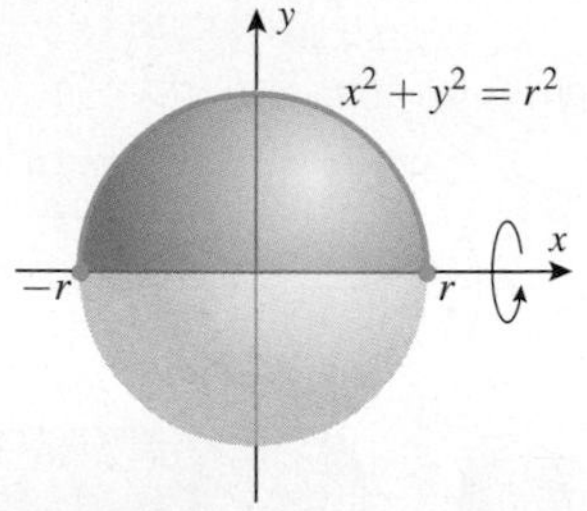

▲ **Figure 6.2.11**

▶ **Example 3** Derive the formula for the volume of a sphere of radius $r$.

***Solution.*** As indicated in Figure 6.2.11, a sphere of radius $r$ can be generated by revolving the upper semicircular disk enclosed between the $x$-axis and

$$x^2 + y^2 = r^2$$

about the $x$-axis. Since the upper half of this circle is the graph of $y = f(x) = \sqrt{r^2 - x^2}$, it follows from (5) that the volume of the sphere is

$$V = \int_a^b \pi[f(x)]^2\, dx = \int_{-r}^r \pi(r^2 - x^2)\, dx = \pi\left[r^2 x - \frac{x^3}{3}\right]_{-r}^r = \frac{4}{3}\pi r^3 \blacktriangleleft$$

## VOLUMES BY WASHERS PERPENDICULAR TO THE *x*-AXIS

Not all solids of revolution have solid interiors; some have holes or channels that create interior surfaces, as in Figure 6.2.8*d*. So we will also be interested in problems of the following type.

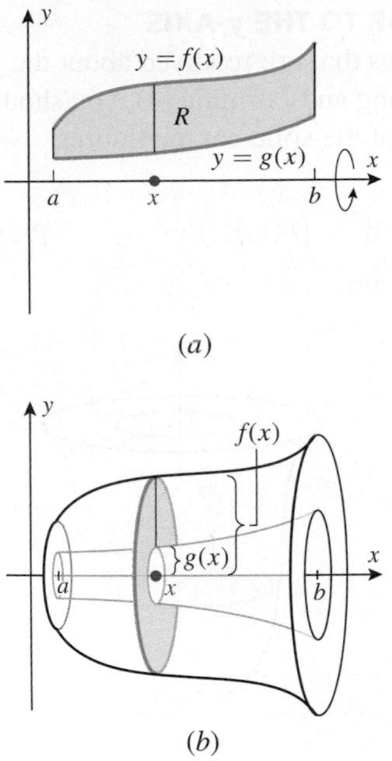


▲ Figure 6.2.12

> **6.2.5 PROBLEM** Let $f$ and $g$ be continuous and nonnegative on $[a, b]$, and suppose that $f(x) \geq g(x)$ for all $x$ in the interval $[a, b]$. Let $R$ be the region that is bounded above by $y = f(x)$, below by $y = g(x)$, and on the sides by the lines $x = a$ and $x = b$ (Figure 6.2.12*a*). Find the volume of the solid of revolution that is generated by revolving the region $R$ about the $x$-axis (Figure 6.2.12*b*).

We can solve this problem by slicing. For this purpose, observe that the cross section of the solid taken perpendicular to the $x$-axis at the point $x$ is the annular or "washer-shaped" region with inner radius $g(x)$ and outer radius $f(x)$ (Figure 6.2.12*b*); its area is

$$A(x) = \pi[f(x)]^2 - \pi[g(x)]^2 = \pi([f(x)]^2 - [g(x)]^2)$$

Thus, from (3) the volume of the solid is

$$V = \int_a^b \pi([f(x)]^2 - [g(x)]^2)\,dx \tag{6}$$

Because the cross sections are washer shaped, the application of this formula is called the ***method of washers***.

▶ **Example 4** Find the volume of the solid generated when the region between the graphs of the equations $f(x) = \frac{1}{2} + x^2$ and $g(x) = x$ over the interval $[0, 2]$ is revolved about the $x$-axis.

***Solution.*** First sketch the region (Figure 6.2.13*a*); then imagine revolving it about the $x$-axis (Figure 6.2.13*b*). From (6) the volume is

$$V = \int_a^b \pi([f(x)]^2 - [g(x)]^2)\,dx = \int_0^2 \pi([\tfrac{1}{2} + x^2]^2 - x^2)\,dx$$

$$= \int_0^2 \pi\left(\frac{1}{4} + x^4\right)dx = \pi\left[\frac{x}{4} + \frac{x^5}{5}\right]_0^2 = \frac{69\pi}{10} \quad ◀$$

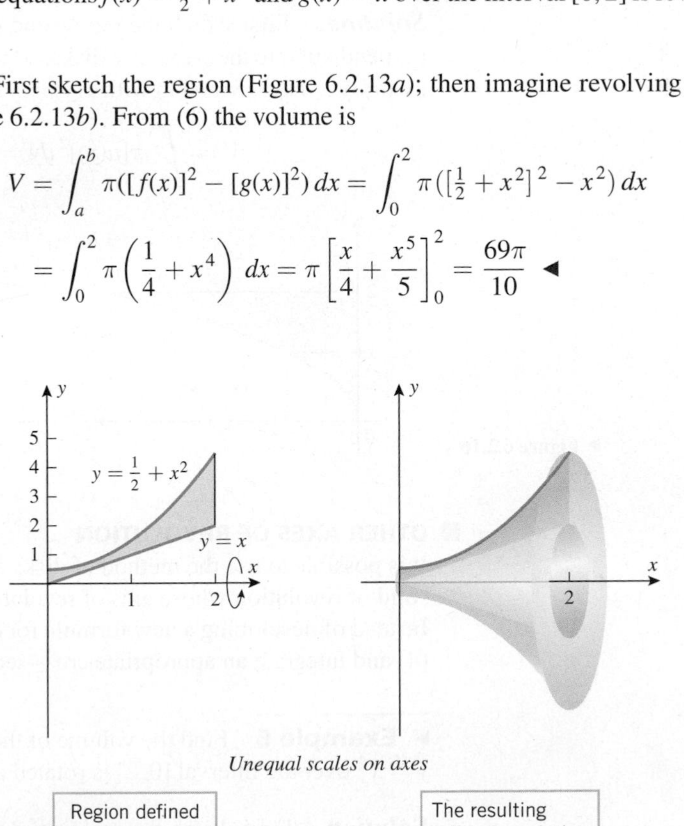


▶ Figure 6.2.13 (*a*) (*b*)

## VOLUMES BY DISKS AND WASHERS PERPENDICULAR TO THE *y*-AXIS

The methods of disks and washers have analogs for regions that are revolved about the $y$-axis (Figures 6.2.14 and 6.2.15). Using the method of slicing and Formula (4), you should be able to deduce the following formulas for the volumes of the solids in the figures.

$$V = \int_c^d \pi[u(y)]^2\,dy \quad \text{(Disks)} \qquad V = \int_c^d \pi([w(y)]^2 - [v(y)]^2)\,dy \quad \text{(Washers)} \tag{7–8}$$

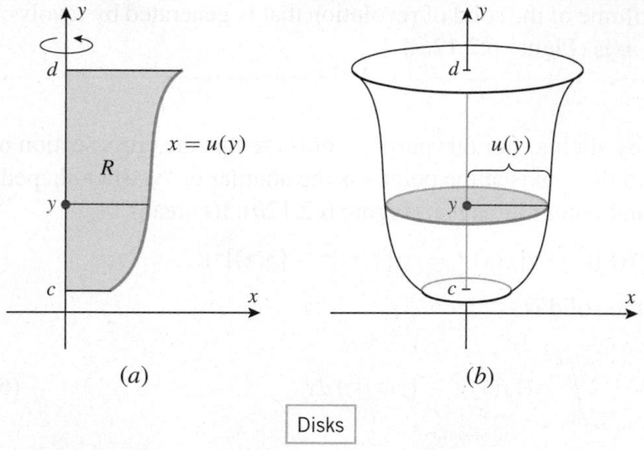


▲ Figure 6.2.14

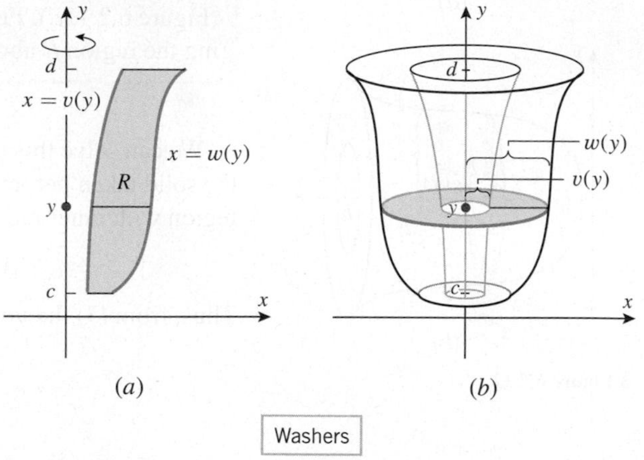


▲ Figure 6.2.15

► **Example 5** Find the volume of the solid generated when the region enclosed by $y = \sqrt{x}$, $y = 2$, and $x = 0$ is revolved about the $y$-axis.

***Solution.*** First sketch the region and the solid (Figure 6.2.16). The cross sections taken perpendicular to the $y$-axis are disks, so we will apply (7). But first we must rewrite $y = \sqrt{x}$ as $x = y^2$. Thus, from (7) with $u(y) = y^2$, the volume is

$$V = \int_c^d \pi[u(y)]^2\,dy = \int_0^2 \pi y^4\,dy = \left.\frac{\pi y^5}{5}\right]_0^2 = \frac{32\pi}{5} \quad ◄$$

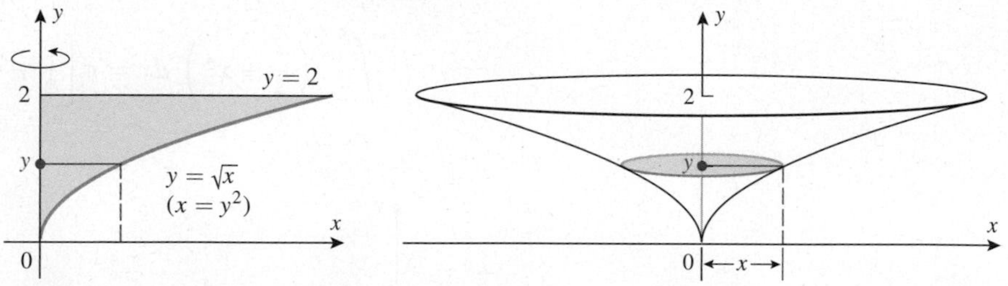


► Figure 6.2.16

## OTHER AXES OF REVOLUTION

It is possible to use the method of disks and the method of washers to find the volume of a solid of revolution whose axis of revolution is a line other than one of the coordinate axes. Instead of developing a new formula for each situation, we will appeal to Formulas (3) and (4) and integrate an appropriate cross-sectional area to find the volume.

► **Example 6** Find the volume of the solid generated when the region under the curve $y = x^2$ over the interval $[0, 2]$ is rotated about the line $y = -1$.

***Solution.*** First sketch the region and the axis of revolution; then imagine revolving the region about the axis (Figure 6.2.17). At each $x$ in the interval $0 \le x \le 2$, the cross section of the solid perpendicular to the axis $y = -1$ is a washer with outer radius $x^2 + 1$ and inner radius 1. Since the area of this washer is

$$A(x) = \pi([x^2 + 1]^2 - 1^2) = \pi(x^4 + 2x^2)$$

it follows by (3) that the volume of the solid is

$$V = \int_0^2 A(x)\,dx = \int_0^2 \pi(x^4 + 2x^2)\,dx = \pi\left[\frac{1}{5}x^5 + \frac{2}{3}x^3\right]_0^2 = \frac{176\pi}{15} \blacktriangleleft$$

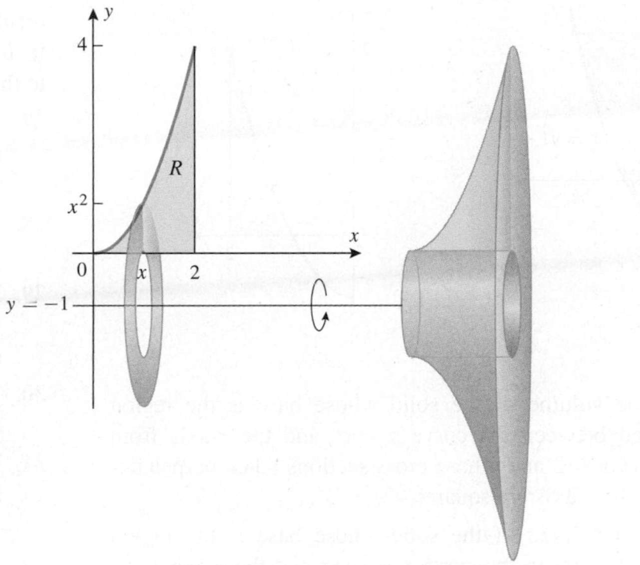


▶ **Figure 6.2.17**

## ✓ QUICK CHECK EXERCISES 6.2 *(See page 358 for answers.)*

1. A solid $S$ extends along the $x$-axis from $x = 1$ to $x = 3$. For $x$ between 1 and 3, the cross-sectional area of $S$ perpendicular to the $x$-axis is $3x^2$. An integral expression for the volume of $S$ is ________. The value of this integral is ________.

2. A solid $S$ is generated by revolving the region between the $x$-axis and the curve $y = \sqrt{\sin x}$ $(0 \le x \le \pi)$ about the $x$-axis.
   (a) For $x$ between 0 and $\pi$, the cross-sectional area of $S$ perpendicular to the $x$-axis at $x$ is $A(x) =$ ________.
   (b) An integral expression for the volume of $S$ is ________.
   (c) The value of the integral in part (b) is ________.

3. A solid $S$ is generated by revolving the region enclosed by the line $y = 2x + 1$ and the curve $y = x^2 + 1$ about the $x$-axis.
   (a) For $x$ between ________ and ________, the cross-sectional area of $S$ perpendicular to the $x$-axis at $x$ is $A(x) =$ ________.
   (b) An integral expression for the volume of $S$ is ________.

4. A solid $S$ is generated by revolving the region enclosed by the line $y = x + 1$ and the curve $y = x^2 + 1$ about the $y$-axis.
   (a) For $y$ between ________ and ________, the cross-sectional area of $S$ perpendicular to the $y$-axis at $y$ is $A(y) =$ ________.
   (b) An integral expression for the volume of $S$ is ________.

## EXERCISE SET 6.2 [C] CAS

**1–8** Find the volume of the solid that results when the shaded region is revolved about the indicated axis. ■

**1.**

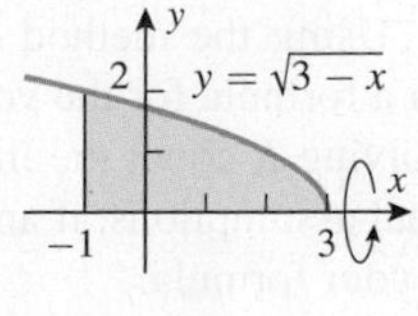


**2.**

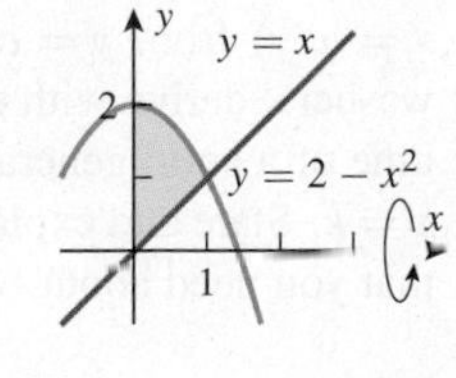


**3.**

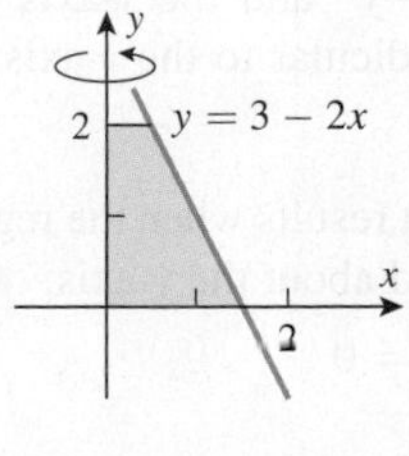


**4.**

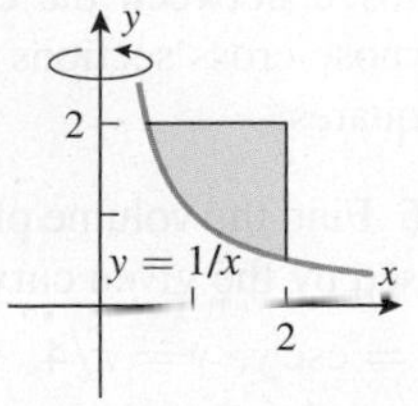

**5.**

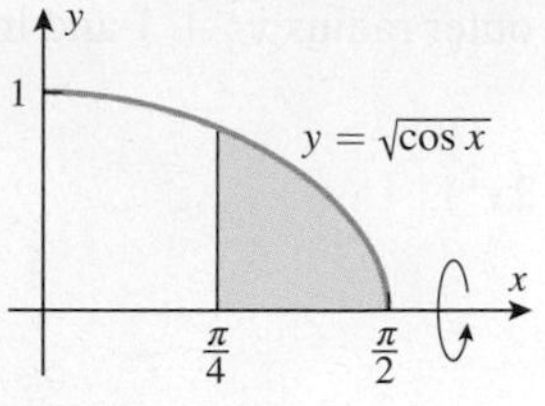


**6.**

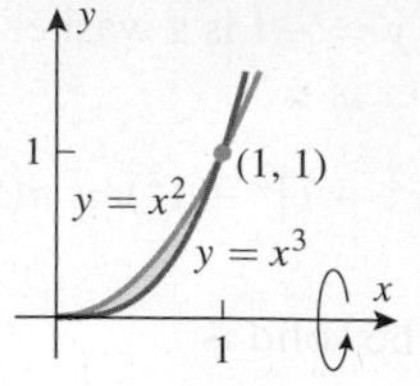


**7.**

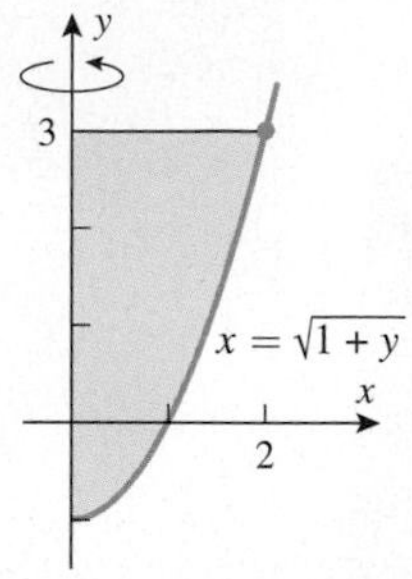


**8.**

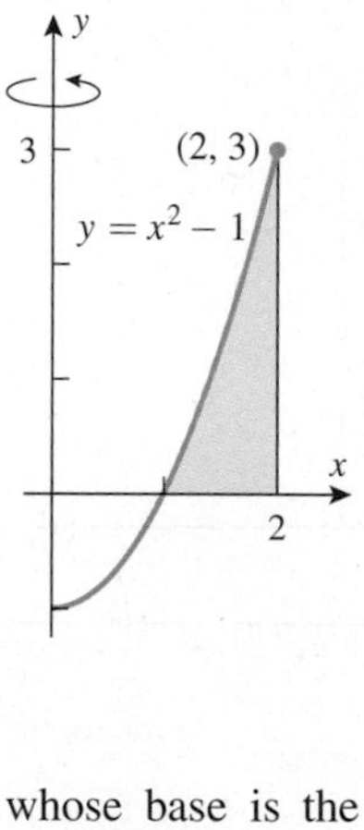


**9.** Find the volume of the solid whose base is the region bounded between the curve $y = x^2$ and the $x$-axis from $x = 0$ to $x = 2$ and whose cross sections taken perpendicular to the $x$-axis are squares.

**10.** Find the volume of the solid whose base is the region bounded between the curve $y = \sec x$ and the $x$-axis from $x = \pi/4$ to $x = \pi/3$ and whose cross sections taken perpendicular to the $x$-axis are squares.

**11–18** Find the volume of the solid that results when the region enclosed by the given curves is revolved about the $x$-axis. ■

**11.** $y = \sqrt{25 - x^2},\ y = 3$

**12.** $y = 9 - x^2,\ y = 0$

**13.** $x = \sqrt{y},\ x = y/4$

**14.** $y = \sin x,\ y = \cos x,\ x = 0,\ x = \pi/4$
[*Hint:* Use the identity $\cos 2x = \cos^2 x - \sin^2 x$.]

**15.** $y = e^x,\ y = 0,\ x = 0,\ x = \ln 3$

**16.** $y = e^{-2x},\ y = 0,\ x = 0,\ x = 1$

**17.** $y = \dfrac{1}{\sqrt{4 + x^2}},\ x = -2,\ x = 2,\ y = 0$

**18.** $y = \dfrac{e^{3x}}{\sqrt{1 + e^{6x}}},\ x = 0,\ x = 1,\ y = 0$

**19.** Find the volume of the solid whose base is the region bounded between the curve $y = x^3$ and the $y$-axis from $y = 0$ to $y = 1$ and whose cross sections taken perpendicular to the $y$-axis are squares.

**20.** Find the volume of the solid whose base is the region enclosed between the curve $x = 1 - y^2$ and the $y$-axis and whose cross sections taken perpendicular to the $y$-axis are squares.

**21–26** Find the volume of the solid that results when the region enclosed by the given curves is revolved about the $y$-axis. ■

**21.** $x = \csc y,\ y = \pi/4,\ y = 3\pi/4,\ x = 0$

**22.** $y = x^2,\ x = y^2$

**23.** $x = y^2,\ x = y + 2$

**24.** $x = 1 - y^2,\ x = 2 + y^2,\ y = -1,\ y = 1$

**25.** $y = \ln x,\ x = 0,\ y = 0,\ y = 1$

**26.** $y = \sqrt{\dfrac{1 - x^2}{x^2}}\quad (x > 0),\ x = 0,\ y = 0,\ y = 2$

**27–30 True–False** Determine whether the statement is true or false. Explain your answer. [In these exercises, assume that a solid $S$ of volume $V$ is bounded by two parallel planes perpendicular to the $x$-axis at $x = a$ and $x = b$ and that for each $x$ in $[a, b]$, $A(x)$ denotes the cross-sectional area of $S$ perpendicular to the $x$-axis.] ■

**27.** If each cross section of $S$ perpendicular to the $x$-axis is a square, then $S$ is a rectangular parallelepiped (i.e., is box shaped).

**28.** If each cross section of $S$ is a disk or a washer, then $S$ is a solid of revolution.

**29.** If $x$ is in centimeters (cm), then $A(x)$ must be a quadratic function of $x$, since units of $A(x)$ will be square centimeters ($cm^2$).

**30.** The average value of $A(x)$ on the interval $[a, b]$ is given by $V/(b - a)$.

**31.** Find the volume of the solid that results when the region above the $x$-axis and below the ellipse

$$\frac{x^2}{a^2} + \frac{y^2}{b^2} = 1 \quad (a > 0, b > 0)$$

is revolved about the $x$-axis.

**32.** Let $V$ be the volume of the solid that results when the region enclosed by $y = 1/x$, $y = 0$, $x = 2$, and $x = b\ (0 < b < 2)$ is revolved about the $x$-axis. Find the value of $b$ for which $V = 3$.

**33.** Find the volume of the solid generated when the region enclosed by $y = \sqrt{x + 1}$, $y = \sqrt{2x}$, and $y = 0$ is revolved about the $x$-axis. [*Hint:* Split the solid into two parts.]

**34.** Find the volume of the solid generated when the region enclosed by $y = \sqrt{x}$, $y = 6 - x$, and $y = 0$ is revolved about the $x$-axis. [*Hint:* Split the solid into two parts.]

**FOCUS ON CONCEPTS**

**35.** Suppose that $f$ is a continuous function on $[a, b]$, and let $R$ be the region between the curve $y = f(x)$ and the line $y = k$ from $x = a$ to $x = b$. Using the method of disks, derive with explanation a formula for the volume of a solid generated by revolving $R$ about the line $y = k$. State and explain additional assumptions, if any, that you need about $f$ for your formula.

**36.** Suppose that $v$ and $w$ are continuous functions on $[c, d]$, and let $R$ be the region between the curves $x = v(y)$ and $x = w(y)$ from $y = c$ to $y = d$. Using the method of washers, derive with explanation a formula for the volume of a solid generated by revolving $R$ about the line $x = k$. State and explain additional assumptions, if any, that you need about $v$ and $w$ for your formula.

37. Consider the solid generated by revolving the shaded region in Exercise 1 about the line $y = 2$.
(a) Make a conjecture as to which is larger: the volume of this solid or the volume of the solid in Exercise 1. Explain the basis of your conjecture.
(b) Check your conjecture by calculating this volume and comparing it to the volume obtained in Exercise 1.

38. Consider the solid generated by revolving the shaded region in Exercise 4 about the line $x = 2.5$.
(a) Make a conjecture as to which is larger: the volume of this solid or the volume of the solid in Exercise 4. Explain the basis of your conjecture.
(b) Check your conjecture by calculating this volume and comparing it to the volume obtained in Exercise 4.

39. Find the volume of the solid that results when the region enclosed by $y = \sqrt{x}$, $y = 0$, and $x = 9$ is revolved about the line $x = 9$.

40. Find the volume of the solid that results when the region in Exercise 39 is revolved about the line $y = 3$.

41. Find the volume of the solid that results when the region enclosed by $x = y^2$ and $x = y$ is revolved about the line $y = -1$.

42. Find the volume of the solid that results when the region in Exercise 41 is revolved about the line $x = -1$.

43. Find the volume of the solid that results when the region enclosed by $y = x^2$ and $y = x^3$ is revolved about the line $x = 1$.

44. Find the volume of the solid that results when the region in Exercise 43 is revolved about the line $y = -1$.

45. A nose cone for a space reentry vehicle is designed so that a cross section, taken $x$ ft from the tip and perpendicular to the axis of symmetry, is a circle of radius $\frac{1}{4}x^2$ ft. Find the volume of the nose cone given that its length is 20 ft.

46. A certain solid is 1 ft high, and a horizontal cross section taken $x$ ft above the bottom of the solid is an annulus of inner radius $x^2$ ft and outer radius $\sqrt{x}$ ft. Find the volume of the solid.

47. Find the volume of the solid whose base is the region bounded between the curves $y = x$ and $y = x^2$, and whose cross sections perpendicular to the $x$-axis are squares.

48. The base of a certain solid is the region enclosed by $y = \sqrt{x}$, $y = 0$, and $x = 4$. Every cross section perpendicular to the $x$-axis is a semicircle with its diameter across the base. Find the volume of the solid.

49. In parts (a)–(c) find the volume of the solid whose base is enclosed by the circle $x^2 + y^2 = 1$ and whose cross sections taken perpendicular to the $x$-axis are
(a) semicircles (b) squares
(c) equilateral triangles.

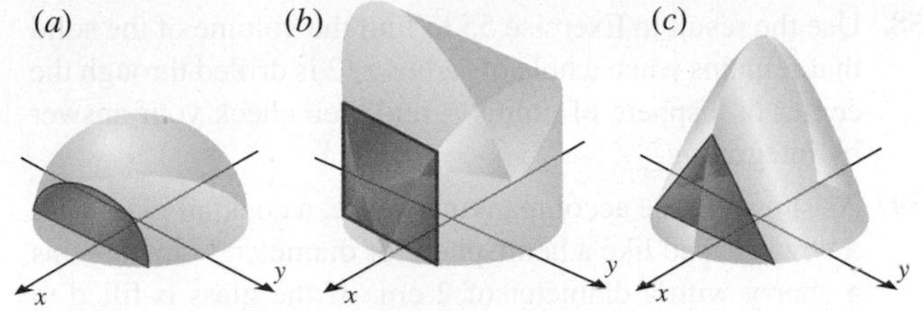


50. As shown in the accompanying figure, a cathedral dome is designed with three semicircular supports of radius $r$ so that each horizontal cross section is a regular hexagon. Show that the volume of the dome is $r^3\sqrt{3}$.

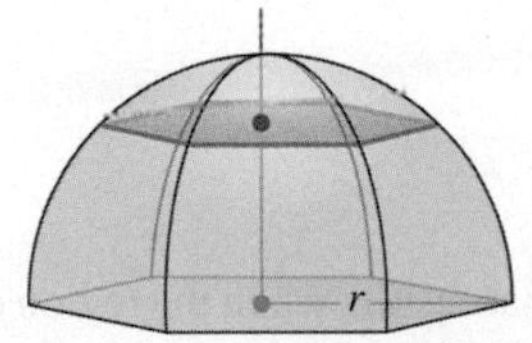

◀ **Figure Ex-50**

C 51–54 Use a CAS to estimate the volume of the solid that results when the region enclosed by the curves is revolved about the stated axis. ■

51. $y = \sin^8 x$, $y = 2x/\pi$, $x = 0$, $x = \pi/2$; $x$-axis

52. $y = \pi^2 \sin x \cos^3 x$, $y = 4x^2$, $x = 0$, $x = \pi/4$; $x$-axis

53. $y = e^x$, $x = 1$, $y = 1$; $y$-axis

54. $y = x\sqrt{\tan^{-1} x}$, $y = x$; $x$-axis

55. The accompanying figure shows a ***spherical cap*** of radius $\rho$ and height $h$ cut from a sphere of radius $r$. Show that the volume $V$ of the spherical cap can be expressed as
(a) $V = \frac{1}{3}\pi h^2(3r - h)$ (b) $V = \frac{1}{6}\pi h(3\rho^2 + h^2)$.

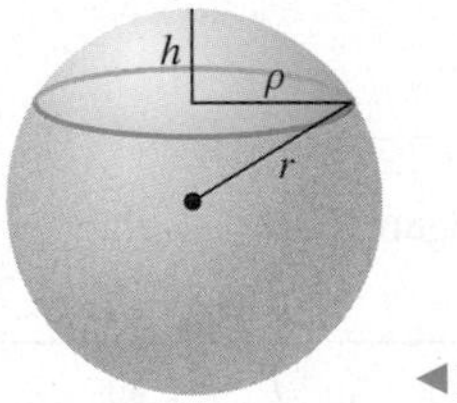

◀ **Figure Ex-55**

56. If fluid enters a hemispherical bowl with a radius of 10 ft at a rate of $\frac{1}{2}$ ft$^3$/min, how fast will the fluid be rising when the depth is 5 ft? [*Hint:* See Exercise 55.]

57. The accompanying figure shows the dimensions of a small lightbulb at 10 equally spaced points.
(a) Use formulas from geometry to make a rough estimate of the volume enclosed by the glass portion of the bulb.
(b) Use the average of left and right endpoint approximations to approximate the volume.

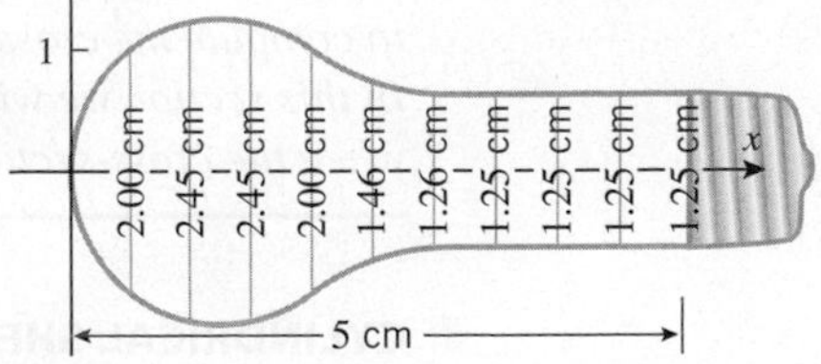

▲ **Figure Ex-57**

**58.** Use the result in Exercise 55 to find the volume of the solid that remains when a hole of radius $r/2$ is drilled through the center of a sphere of radius $r$, and then check your answer by integrating.

**59.** As shown in the accompanying figure, a cocktail glass with a bowl shaped like a hemisphere of diameter 8 cm contains a cherry with a diameter of 2 cm. If the glass is filled to a depth of $h$ cm, what is the volume of liquid it contains? [*Hint:* First consider the case where the cherry is partially submerged, then the case where it is totally submerged.]

◀ **Figure Ex-59**

**60.** Find the volume of the torus that results when the region enclosed by the circle of radius $r$ with center at $(h, 0)$, $h > r$, is revolved about the $y$-axis. [*Hint:* Use an appropriate formula from plane geometry to help evaluate the definite integral.]

**61.** A wedge is cut from a right circular cylinder of radius $r$ by two planes, one perpendicular to the axis of the cylinder and the other making an angle $\theta$ with the first. Find the volume of the wedge by slicing perpendicular to the $y$-axis as shown in the accompanying figure.

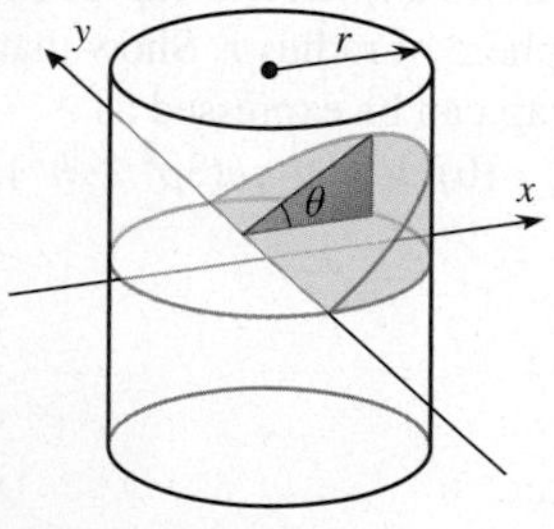


◀ **Figure Ex-61**

**62.** Find the volume of the wedge described in Exercise 61 by slicing perpendicular to the $x$-axis.

**63.** Two right circular cylinders of radius $r$ have axes that intersect at right angles. Find the volume of the solid common to the two cylinders. [*Hint:* One-eighth of the solid is sketched in the accompanying figure.]

**64.** In 1635 Bonaventura Cavalieri, a student of Galileo, stated the following result, called ***Cavalieri's principle***: *If two solids have the same height, and if the areas of their cross sections taken parallel to and at equal distances from their bases are always equal, then the solids have the same volume.* Use this result to find the volume of the oblique cylinder in the accompanying figure. (See Exercise 52 of Section 6.1 for a planar version of Cavalieri's principle.)

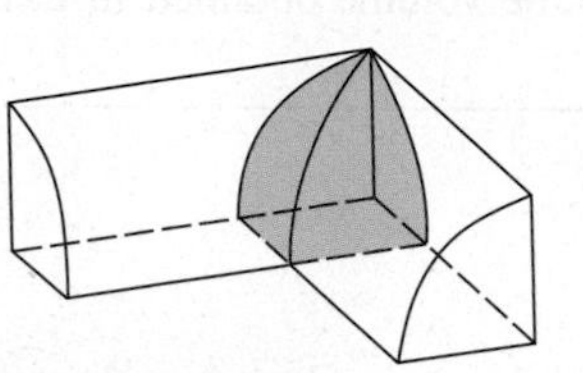

▲ **Figure Ex-63**

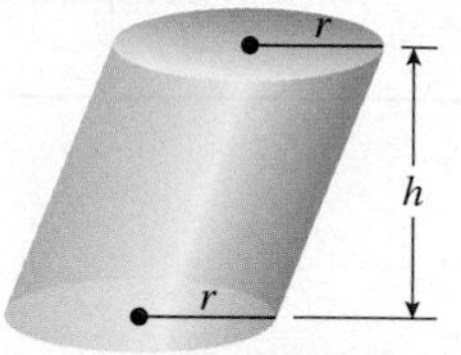


▲ **Figure Ex-64**

**65. Writing** Use the results of this section to derive Cavalieri's principle (Exercise 64).

**66. Writing** Write a short paragraph that explains how Formulas (4)–(8) may all be viewed as consequences of Formula (3).

✓ **QUICK CHECK ANSWERS 6.2** 1. $\int_1^3 3x^2\,dx$; 26 2. (a) $\pi \sin x$ (b) $\int_0^\pi \pi \sin x\,dx$ (c) $2\pi$
3. (a) 0; 2; $\pi[(2x+1)^2 - (x^2+1)^2] = \pi[-x^4 + 2x^2 + 4x]$ (b) $\int_0^2 \pi[-x^4 + 2x^2 + 4x]\,dx$
4. (a) 1; 2; $\pi[(y-1) - (y-1)^2] = \pi[-y^2 + 3y - 2]$ (b) $\int_1^2 \pi[-y^2 + 3y - 2]\,dy$

## 6.3 VOLUMES BY CYLINDRICAL SHELLS

*The methods for computing volumes that have been discussed so far depend on our ability to compute the cross-sectional area of the solid and to integrate that area across the solid. In this section we will develop another method for finding volumes that may be applicable when the cross-sectional area cannot be found or the integration is too difficult.*

### CYLINDRICAL SHELLS

In this section we will be interested in the following problem.

**6.3.1 PROBLEM** Let $f$ be continuous and nonnegative on $[a, b]$ $(0 \le a < b)$, and let $R$ be the region that is bounded above by $y = f(x)$, below by the $x$-axis, and on the sides by the lines $x = a$ and $x = b$. Find the volume $V$ of the solid of revolution $S$ that is generated by revolving the region $R$ about the $y$-axis (Figure 6.3.1).

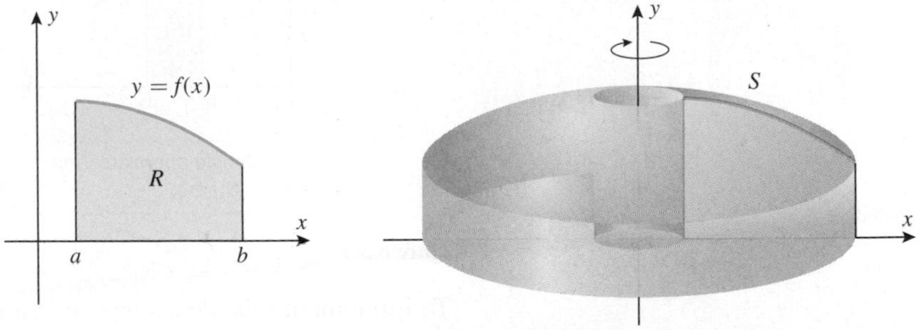


▶ **Figure 6.3.1**

Sometimes problems of the above type can be solved by the method of disks or washers perpendicular to the $y$-axis, but when that method is not applicable or the resulting integral is difficult, the *method of cylindrical shells*, which we will discuss here, will often work.

A ***cylindrical shell*** is a solid enclosed by two concentric right circular cylinders (Figure 6.3.2). The volume $V$ of a cylindrical shell with inner radius $r_1$, outer radius $r_2$, and height $h$ can be written as

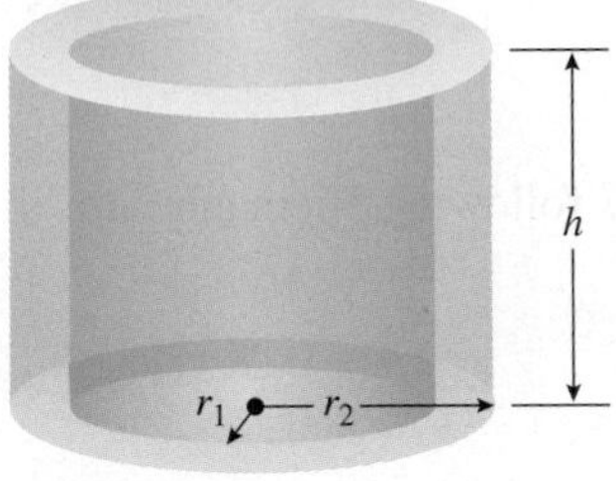


▲ **Figure 6.3.2**

$$
\begin{aligned}
V &= [\text{area of cross section}] \cdot [\text{height}] \\
&= (\pi r_2^2 - \pi r_1^2)h \\
&= \pi(r_2 + r_1)(r_2 - r_1)h \\
&= 2\pi \cdot \left[\tfrac{1}{2}(r_1 + r_2)\right] \cdot h \cdot (r_2 - r_1)
\end{aligned}
$$

But $\frac{1}{2}(r_1 + r_2)$ is the average radius of the shell and $r_2 - r_1$ is its thickness, so

$$V = 2\pi \cdot [\text{average radius}] \cdot [\text{height}] \cdot [\text{thickness}] \tag{1}$$

We will now show how this formula can be used to solve Problem 6.3.1. The underlying idea is to divide the interval $[a, b]$ into $n$ subintervals, thereby subdividing the region $R$ into $n$ strips, $R_1, R_2, \ldots, R_n$ (Figure 6.3.3*a*). When the region $R$ is revolved about the $y$-axis, these strips generate "tube-like" solids $S_1, S_2, \ldots, S_n$ that are nested one inside the other and together comprise the entire solid $S$ (Figure 6.3.3*b*). Thus, the volume $V$ of the solid can be obtained by adding together the volumes of the tubes; that is,

$$V = V(S_1) + V(S_2) + \cdots + V(S_n)$$

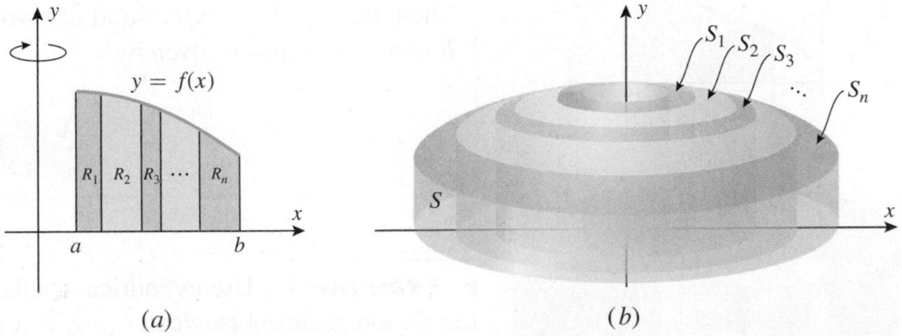


▶ **Figure 6.3.3**

As a rule, the tubes will have curved upper surfaces, so there will be no simple formulas for their volumes. However, if the strips are thin, then we can approximate each strip by a rectangle (Figure 6.3.4*a*). These rectangles, when revolved about the $y$-axis, will produce cylindrical shells whose volumes closely approximate the volumes of the tubes generated by the original strips (Figure 6.3.4*b*). We will show that by adding the volumes of the cylindrical shells we can obtain a Riemann sum that approximates the volume $V$, and by taking the limit of the Riemann sums we can obtain an integral for the exact volume $V$.

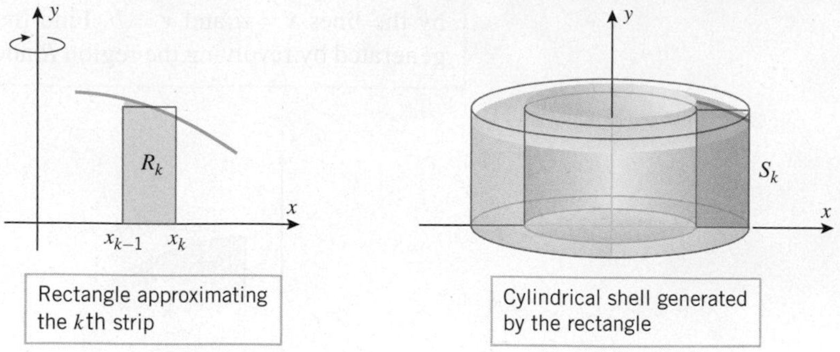


▶ **Figure 6.3.4** (a) (b)

To implement this idea, suppose that the $k$th strip extends from $x_{k-1}$ to $x_k$ and that the width of this strip is

$$\Delta x_k = x_k - x_{k-1}$$

If we let $x_k^*$ be the *midpoint* of the interval $[x_{k-1}, x_k]$, and if we construct a rectangle of height $f(x_k^*)$ over the interval, then revolving this rectangle about the $y$-axis produces a cylindrical shell of average radius $x_k^*$, height $f(x_k^*)$, and thickness $\Delta x_k$ (Figure 6.3.5). From (1), the volume $V_k$ of this cylindrical shell is

$$V_k = 2\pi x_k^* f(x_k^*)\Delta x_k$$

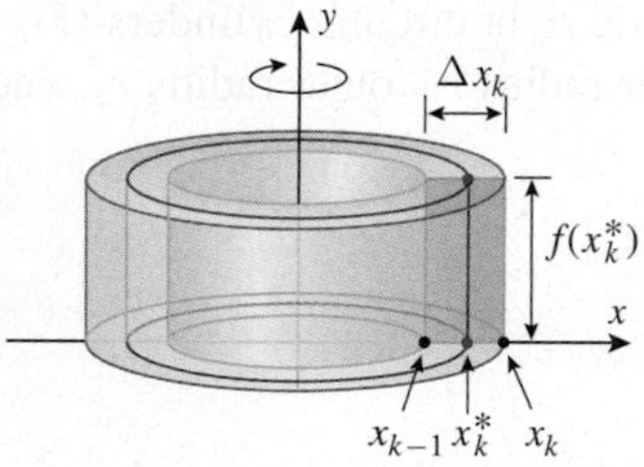


▲ **Figure 6.3.5**

Adding the volumes of the $n$ cylindrical shells yields the following Riemann sum that approximates the volume $V$:

$$V \approx \sum_{k=1}^{n} 2\pi x_k^* f(x_k^*)\Delta x_k$$

Taking the limit as $n$ increases and the widths of all the subintervals approach zero yields the definite integral

$$V = \lim_{\max \Delta x_k \to 0} \sum_{k=1}^{n} 2\pi x_k^* f(x_k^*)\Delta x_k = \int_a^b 2\pi x f(x)\,dx$$

In summary, we have the following result.

**6.3.2 VOLUME BY CYLINDRICAL SHELLS ABOUT THE $y$-AXIS** Let $f$ be continuous and nonnegative on $[a, b]$ $(0 \le a < b)$, and let $R$ be the region that is bounded above by $y = f(x)$, below by the $x$-axis, and on the sides by the lines $x = a$ and $x = b$. Then the volume $V$ of the solid of revolution that is generated by revolving the region $R$ about the $y$-axis is given by

$$V = \int_a^b 2\pi x f(x)\,dx \tag{2}$$

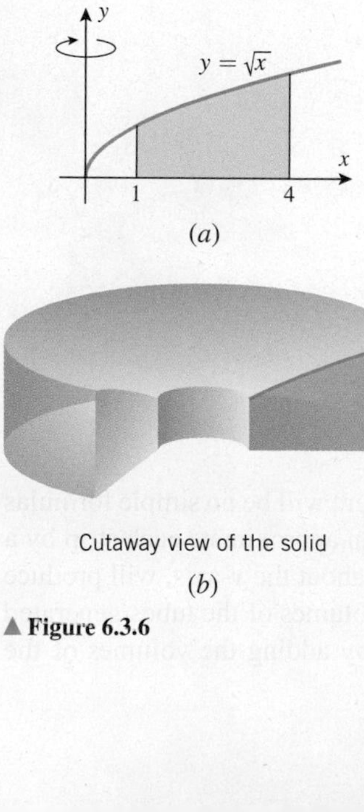


(a)

(b)

▲ **Figure 6.3.6**

▶ **Example 1** Use cylindrical shells to find the volume of the solid generated when the region enclosed between $y = \sqrt{x}$, $x = 1$, $x = 4$, and the $x$-axis is revolved about the $y$-axis.

***Solution.*** First sketch the region (Figure 6.3.6*a*); then imagine revolving it about the $y$-axis (Figure 6.3.6*b*). Since $f(x) = \sqrt{x}$, $a = 1$, and $b = 4$, Formula (2) yields

$$V = \int_1^4 2\pi x\sqrt{x}\,dx = 2\pi \int_1^4 x^{3/2}\,dx = \left[2\pi \cdot \frac{2}{5}x^{5/2}\right]_1^4 = \frac{4\pi}{5}[32 - 1] = \frac{124\pi}{5} \blacktriangleleft$$

## VARIATIONS OF THE METHOD OF CYLINDRICAL SHELLS

The method of cylindrical shells is applicable in a variety of situations that do not fit the conditions required by Formula (2). For example, the region may be enclosed between two curves, or the axis of revolution may be some line other than the $y$-axis. However, rather than develop a separate formula for every possible situation, we will give a general way of thinking about the method of cylindrical shells that can be adapted to each new situation as it arises.

For this purpose, we will need to reexamine the integrand in Formula (2): At each $x$ in the interval $[a, b]$, the vertical line segment from the $x$-axis to the curve $y = f(x)$ can be viewed as the cross section of the region $R$ at $x$ (Figure 6.3.7*a*). When the region $R$ is revolved about the $y$-axis, the cross section at $x$ sweeps out the *surface* of a right circular cylinder of height $f(x)$ and radius $x$ (Figure 6.3.7*b*). The area of this surface is

$$2\pi x f(x)$$

(Figure 6.3.7*c*), which is the integrand in (2). Thus, Formula (2) can be viewed informally in the following way.

**6.3.3 AN INFORMAL VIEWPOINT ABOUT CYLINDRICAL SHELLS** The volume $V$ of a solid of revolution that is generated by revolving a region $R$ about an axis can be obtained by integrating the area of the surface generated by an arbitrary cross section of $R$ taken parallel to the axis of revolution.

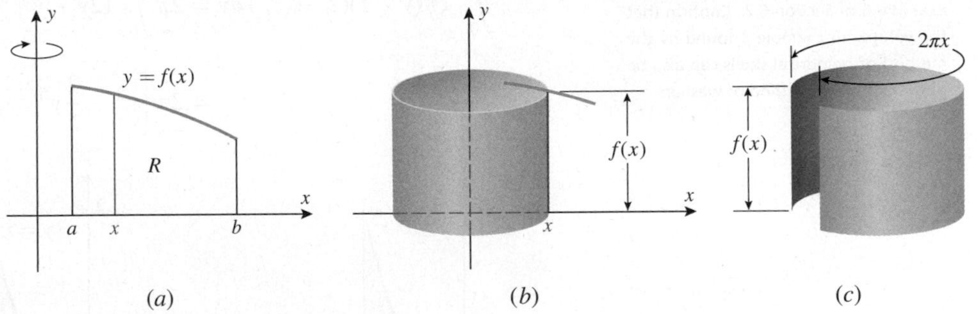


▶ **Figure 6.3.7**

The following examples illustrate how to apply this result in situations where Formula (2) is not applicable.

▶ **Example 2** Use cylindrical shells to find the volume of the solid generated when the region $R$ in the first quadrant enclosed between $y = x$ and $y = x^2$ is revolved about the $y$-axis (Figure 6.3.8*a*).

***Solution.*** As illustrated in part (*b*) of Figure 6.3.8, at each $x$ in $[0, 1]$ the cross section of $R$ parallel to the $y$-axis generates a cylindrical surface of height $x - x^2$ and radius $x$. Since the area of this surface is

$$2\pi x(x - x^2)$$

the volume of the solid is

$$V = \int_0^1 2\pi x(x - x^2)\,dx = 2\pi \int_0^1 (x^2 - x^3)\,dx$$

$$= 2\pi \left[\frac{x^3}{3} - \frac{x^4}{4}\right]_0^1 = 2\pi \left[\frac{1}{3} - \frac{1}{4}\right] = \frac{\pi}{6} \blacktriangleleft$$

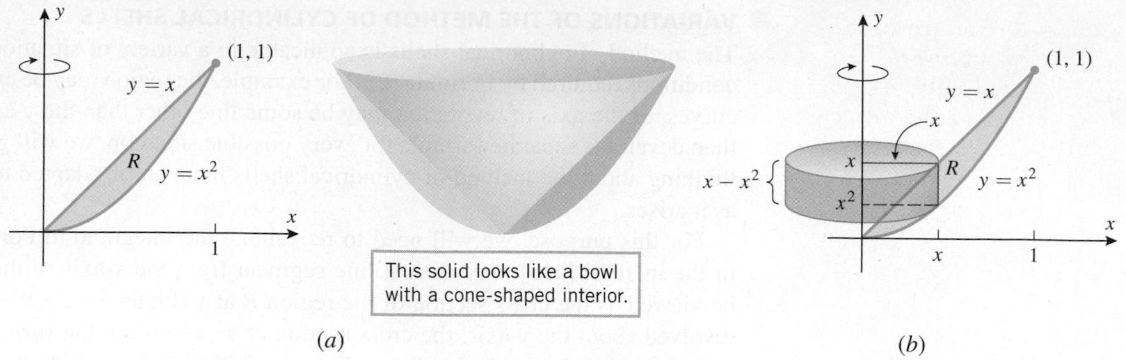

▲ Figure 6.3.8

▶ **Example 3** Use cylindrical shells to find the volume of the solid generated when the region $R$ under $y = x^2$ over the interval $[0, 2]$ is revolved about the line $y = -1$.

***Solution.*** First draw the axis of revolution; then imagine revolving the region about the axis (Figure 6.3.9*a*). As illustrated in Figure 6.3.9*b*, at each $y$ in the interval $0 \le y \le 4$, the cross section of $R$ parallel to the $x$-axis generates a cylindrical surface of height $2 - \sqrt{y}$ and radius $y + 1$. Since the area of this surface is

$$2\pi(y+1)(2-\sqrt{y})$$

it follows that the volume of the solid is

$$\int_0^4 2\pi(y+1)(2-\sqrt{y})\,dy = 2\pi\int_0^4 (2y - y^{3/2} + 2 - y^{1/2})\,dy$$

$$= 2\pi\left[y^2 - \frac{2}{5}y^{5/2} + 2y - \frac{2}{3}y^{3/2}\right]_0^4 = \frac{176\pi}{15} \blacktriangleleft$$

Note that the volume found in Example 3 agrees with the volume of the same solid found by the method of washers in Example 6 of Section 6.2. Confirm that the volume in Example 2 found by the method of cylindrical shells can also be obtained by the method of washers.

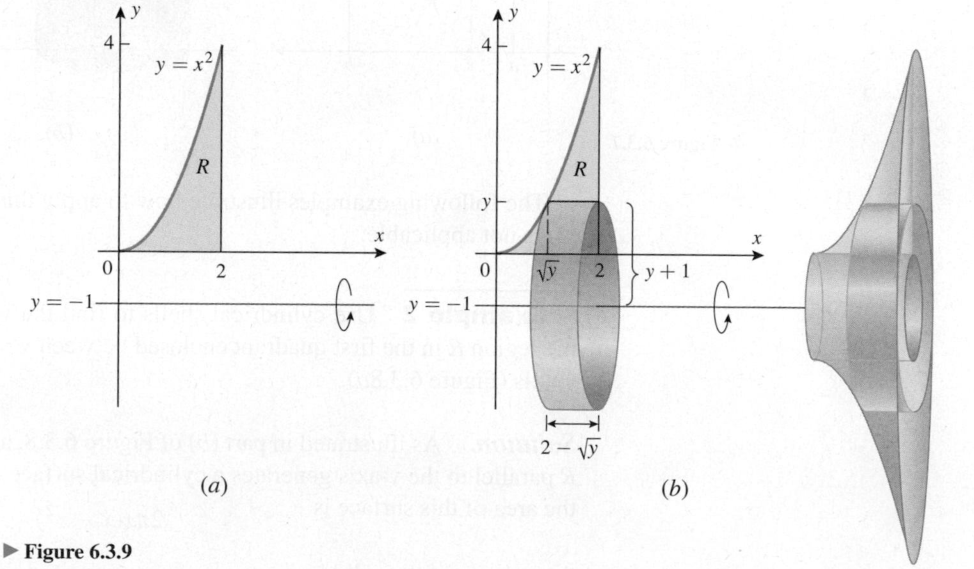

▶ Figure 6.3.9

## ✓ QUICK CHECK EXERCISES 6.3 (See page 364 for answers.)

**1.** Let $R$ be the region between the $x$-axis and the curve $y = 1 + \sqrt{x}$ for $1 \le x \le 4$.

(a) For $x$ between 1 and 4, the area of the cylindrical surface generated by revolving the vertical cross section of $R$ at $x$ about the $y$-axis is ______.

(b) Using cylindrical shells, an integral expression for the volume of the solid generated by revolving $R$ about the $y$-axis is ______.

2. Let $R$ be the region described in Quick Check Exercise 1.
 (a) For $x$ between 1 and 4, the area of the cylindrical surface generated by revolving the vertical cross section of $R$ at $x$ about the line $x = 5$ is ______.
 (b) Using cylindrical shells, an integral expression for the volume of the solid generated by revolving $R$ about the line $x = 5$ is ______.

3. A solid $S$ is generated by revolving the region enclosed by the curves $x = (y - 2)^2$ and $x = 4$ about the $x$-axis. Using cylindrical shells, an integral expression for the volume of $S$ is ______.

## EXERCISE SET 6.3 C CAS

**1–4** Use cylindrical shells to find the volume of the solid generated when the shaded region is revolved about the indicated axis. ■

1.
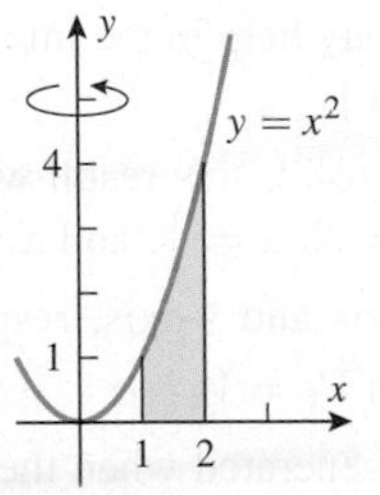


2.
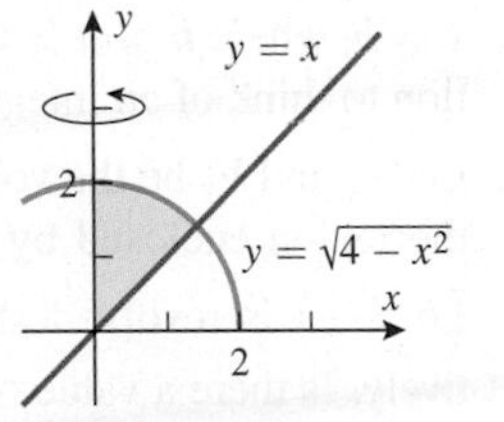


3.
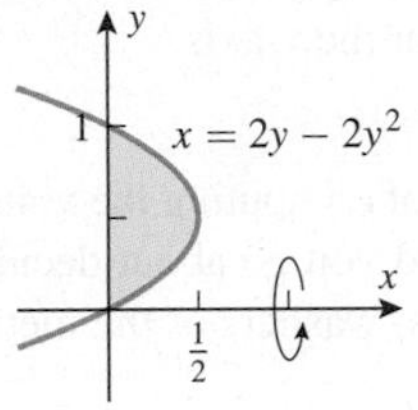


4.
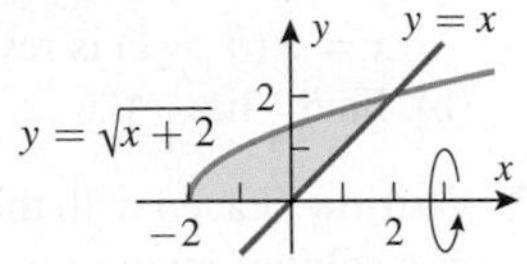


**5–12** Use cylindrical shells to find the volume of the solid generated when the region enclosed by the given curves is revolved about the $y$-axis. ■

5. $y = x^3,\ x = 1,\ y = 0$

6. $y = \sqrt{x},\ x = 4,\ x = 9,\ y = 0$

7. $y = 1/x,\ y = 0,\ x = 1,\ x = 3$

8. $y = \cos(x^2),\ x = 0,\ x = \frac{1}{2}\sqrt{\pi},\ y = 0$

9. $y = 2x - 1,\ y = -2x + 3,\ x = 2$

10. $y = 2x - x^2,\ y = 0$

11. $y = \dfrac{1}{x^2 + 1},\ x = 0,\ x = 1,\ y = 0$

12. $y = e^{x^2},\ x = 1,\ x = \sqrt{3},\ y = 0$

**13–16** Use cylindrical shells to find the volume of the solid generated when the region enclosed by the given curves is revolved about the $x$-axis. ■

13. $y^2 = x,\ y = 1,\ x = 0$

14. $x = 2y,\ y = 2,\ y = 3,\ x = 0$

15. $y = x^2,\ x = 1,\ y = 0$ 16. $xy = 4,\ x + y = 5$

**17–20 True–False** Determine whether the statement is true or false. Explain your answer. ■

17. The volume of a cylindrical shell is equal to the product of the thickness of the shell with the surface area of a cylinder whose height is that of the shell and whose radius is equal to the average of the inner and outer radii of the shell.

18. The method of cylindrical shells is a special case of the method of integration of cross-sectional area that was discussed in Section 6.2.

19. In the method of cylindrical shells, integration is over an interval on a coordinate axis that is *perpendicular* to the axis of revolution of the solid.

20. The Riemann sum approximation

$$V \approx \sum_{k=1}^{n} 2\pi x_k^* f(x_k^*)\Delta x_k \quad \left(\text{where } x_k^* = \frac{x_k + x_{k-1}}{2}\right)$$

for the volume of a solid of revolution is exact when $f$ is a constant function.

C 21. Use a CAS to find the volume of the solid generated when the region enclosed by $y = e^x$ and $y = 0$ for $1 \le x \le 2$ is revolved about the $y$-axis.

C 22. Use a CAS to find the volume of the solid generated when the region enclosed by $y = \cos x$, $y = 0$, and $x = 0$ for $0 \le x \le \pi/2$ is revolved about the $y$-axis.

C 23. Consider the region to the right of the $y$-axis, to the left of the vertical line $x = k$ $(0 < k < \pi)$, and between the curve $y = \sin x$ and the $x$-axis. Use a CAS to estimate the value of $k$ so that the solid generated by revolving the region about the $y$-axis has a volume of 8 cubic units.

**FOCUS ON CONCEPTS**

24. Let $R_1$ and $R_2$ be regions of the form shown in the accompanying figure. Use cylindrical shells to find a formula for the volume of the solid that results when
 (a) region $R_1$ is revolved about the $y$-axis
 (b) region $R_2$ is revolved about the $x$-axis.

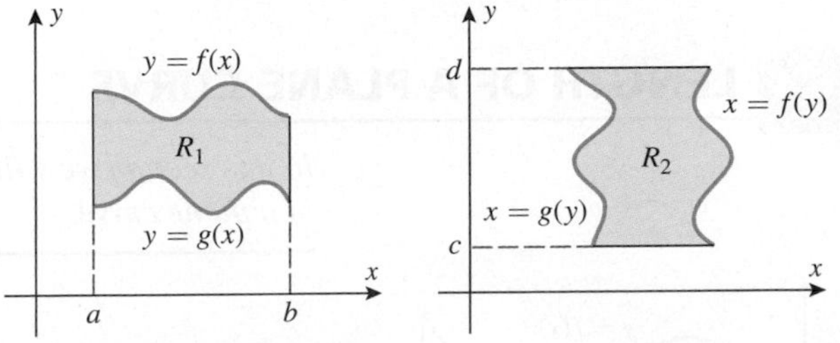


▲ **Figure Ex-24**

25. (a) Use cylindrical shells to find the volume of the solid that is generated when the region under the curve

$$y = x^3 - 3x^2 + 2x$$

over [0, 1] is revolved about the $y$-axis.

*(cont.)*

(b) For this problem, is the method of cylindrical shells easier or harder than the method of slicing discussed in the last section? Explain.

**26.** Let $f$ be continuous and nonnegative on $[a, b]$, and let $R$ be the region that is enclosed by $y = f(x)$ and $y = 0$ for $a \leq x \leq b$. Using the method of cylindrical shells, derive with explanation a formula for the volume of the solid generated by revolving $R$ about the line $x = k$, where $k \leq a$.

**27–28** Using the method of cylindrical shells, set up but do not evaluate an integral for the volume of the solid generated when the region $R$ is revolved about (a) the line $x = 1$ and (b) the line $y = -1$. ■

**27.** $R$ is the region bounded by the graphs of $y = x$, $y = 0$, and $x = 1$.

**28.** $R$ is the region in the first quadrant bounded by the graphs of $y = \sqrt{1 - x^2}$, $y = 0$, and $x = 0$.

**29.** Use cylindrical shells to find the volume of the solid that is generated when the region that is enclosed by $y = 1/x^3$, $x = 1$, $x = 2$, $y = 0$ is revolved about the line $x = -1$.

**30.** Use cylindrical shells to find the volume of the solid that is generated when the region that is enclosed by $y = x^3$, $y = 1$, $x = 0$ is revolved about the line $y = 1$.

**31.** Use cylindrical shells to find the volume of the cone generated when the triangle with vertices $(0, 0)$, $(0, r)$, $(h, 0)$, where $r > 0$ and $h > 0$, is revolved about the $x$-axis.

**32.** The region enclosed between the curve $y^2 = kx$ and the line $x = \frac{1}{4}k$ is revolved about the line $x = \frac{1}{2}k$. Use cylindrical shells to find the volume of the resulting solid. (Assume $k > 0$.)

**33.** As shown in the accompanying figure, a cylindrical hole is drilled all the way through the center of a sphere. Show that the volume of the remaining solid depends only on the length $L$ of the hole, not on the size of the sphere.

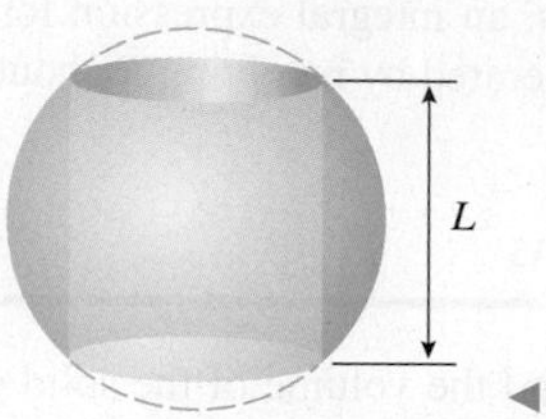

◄ **Figure Ex-33**

**34.** Use cylindrical shells to find the volume of the torus obtained by revolving the circle $x^2 + y^2 = a^2$ about the line $x = b$, where $b > a > 0$. [*Hint:* It may help in the integration to think of an integral as an area.]

**35.** Let $V_x$ and $V_y$ be the volumes of the solids that result when the region enclosed by $y = 1/x$, $y = 0$, $x = \frac{1}{2}$, and $x = b$ $\left(b > \frac{1}{2}\right)$ is revolved about the $x$-axis and $y$-axis, respectively. Is there a value of $b$ for which $V_x = V_y$?

**36.** (a) Find the volume $V$ of the solid generated when the region bounded by $y = 1/(1 + x^4)$, $y = 0$, $x = 1$, and $x = b\,(b > 1)$ is revolved about the $y$-axis.

(b) Find $\lim_{b \to +\infty} V$.

**37. Writing** Faced with the problem of computing the volume of a solid of revolution, how would you go about deciding whether to use the method of disks/washers or the method of cylindrical shells?

**38. Writing** With both the method of disks/washers and with the method of cylindrical shells, we integrate an "area" to get the volume of a solid of revolution. However, these two approaches differ in very significant ways. Write a brief paragraph that discusses these differences.

✓ **QUICK CHECK ANSWERS 6.3** **1.** (a) $2\pi x(1 + \sqrt{x})$ (b) $\int_1^4 2\pi x(1 + \sqrt{x})\,dx$ **2.** (a) $2\pi(5 - x)(1 + \sqrt{x})$ (b) $\int_1^4 2\pi(5 - x)(1 + \sqrt{x})\,dx$ **3.** $\int_0^4 2\pi y[4 - (y - 2)^2]\,dy$

# 6.4 LENGTH OF A PLANE CURVE

*In this section we will use the tools of calculus to study the problem of finding the length of a plane curve.*

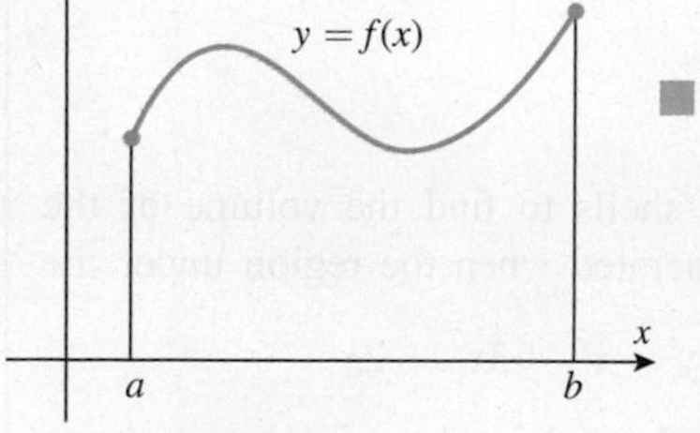

▲ **Figure 6.4.1**

## ■ ARC LENGTH

Our first objective is to define what we mean by the ***length*** (also called the ***arc length***) of a plane curve $y = f(x)$ over an interval $[a, b]$ (Figure 6.4.1). Once that is done we will be able to focus on the problem of computing arc lengths. To avoid some complications that would otherwise occur, we will impose the requirement that $f'$ be continuous on $[a, b]$, in which case we will say that $y = f(x)$ is a ***smooth curve*** on $[a, b]$ or that $f$ is a ***smooth function*** on $[a, b]$. Thus, we will be concerned with the following problem.

**6.4.1 ARC LENGTH PROBLEM** Suppose that $y = f(x)$ is a smooth curve on the interval $[a, b]$. Define and find a formula for the arc length $L$ of the curve $y = f(x)$ over the interval $[a, b]$.

Intuitively, you might think of the arc length of a curve as the number obtained by aligning a piece of string with the curve and then measuring the length of the string after it is straightened out.

To define the arc length of a curve we start by breaking the curve into small segments. Then we approximate the curve segments by line segments and add the lengths of the line segments to form a Riemann sum. Figure 6.4.2 illustrates how such line segments tend to become better and better approximations to a curve as the number of segments increases. As the number of segments increases, the corresponding Riemann sums approach a definite integral whose value we will take to be the arc length $L$ of the curve.

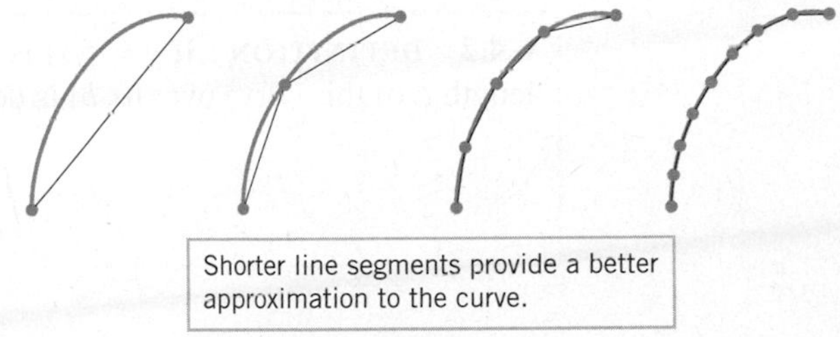


▶ **Figure 6.4.2**

To implement our idea for solving Problem 6.4.1, divide the interval $[a, b]$ into $n$ subintervals by inserting points $x_1, x_2, \ldots, x_{n-1}$ between $a = x_0$ and $b = x_n$. As shown in Figure 6.4.3*a*, let $P_0, P_1, \ldots, P_n$ be the points on the curve with $x$-coordinates $a = x_0$, $x_1, x_2, \ldots, x_{n-1}, b = x_n$ and join these points with straight line segments. These line segments form a ***polygonal path*** that we can regard as an approximation to the curve $y = f(x)$. As indicated in Figure 6.4.3*b*, the length $L_k$ of the $k$th line segment in the polygonal path is

$$L_k = \sqrt{(\Delta x_k)^2 + (\Delta y_k)^2} = \sqrt{(\Delta x_k)^2 + [f(x_k) - f(x_{k-1})]^2} \tag{1}$$

If we now add the lengths of these line segments, we obtain the following approximation to the length $L$ of the curve

$$L \approx \sum_{k=1}^{n} L_k = \sum_{k=1}^{n} \sqrt{(\Delta x_k)^2 + [f(x_k) - f(x_{k-1})]^2} \tag{2}$$

To put this in the form of a Riemann sum we will apply the Mean-Value Theorem (4.8.2). This theorem implies that there is a point $x_k^*$ between $x_{k-1}$ and $x_k$ such that

$$\frac{f(x_k) - f(x_{k-1})}{x_k - x_{k-1}} = f'(x_k^*) \quad \text{or} \quad f(x_k) - f(x_{k-1}) = f'(x_k^*)\Delta x_k$$

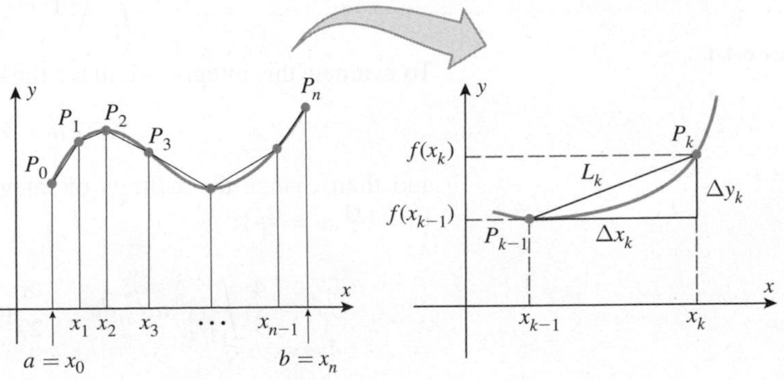


▶ **Figure 6.4.3** (*a*) (*b*)

and hence we can rewrite (2) as

$$L \approx \sum_{k=1}^{n} \sqrt{(\Delta x_k)^2 + [f'(x_k^*)]^2(\Delta x_k)^2} = \sum_{k=1}^{n} \sqrt{1 + [f'(x_k^*)]^2}\, \Delta x_k$$

Explain why the approximation in (2) cannot be greater than $L$.

Thus, taking the limit as $n$ increases and the widths of all the subintervals approach zero yields the following integral that defines the arc length $L$:

$$L = \lim_{\max \Delta x_k \to 0} \sum_{k=1}^{n} \sqrt{1 + [f'(x_k^*)]^2}\, \Delta x_k = \int_a^b \sqrt{1 + [f'(x)]^2}\, dx$$

In summary, we have the following definition.

**6.4.2 DEFINITION** If $y = f(x)$ is a smooth curve on the interval $[a, b]$, then the arc length $L$ of this curve over $[a, b]$ is defined as

$$L = \int_a^b \sqrt{1 + [f'(x)]^2}\, dx \tag{3}$$

This result provides both a definition and a formula for computing arc lengths. Where convenient, (3) can also be expressed as

$$L = \int_a^b \sqrt{1 + [f'(x)]^2}\, dx = \int_a^b \sqrt{1 + \left(\frac{dy}{dx}\right)^2}\, dx \tag{4}$$

Moreover, for a curve expressed in the form $x = g(y)$, where $g'$ is continuous on $[c, d]$, the arc length $L$ from $y = c$ to $y = d$ can be expressed as

$$L = \int_c^d \sqrt{1 + [g'(y)]^2}\, dy = \int_c^d \sqrt{1 + \left(\frac{dx}{dy}\right)^2}\, dy \tag{5}$$

► **Example 1** Find the arc length of the curve $y = x^{3/2}$ from $(1, 1)$ to $(2, 2\sqrt{2})$ (Figure 6.4.4) in two ways: (a) using Formula (4) and (b) using Formula (5).

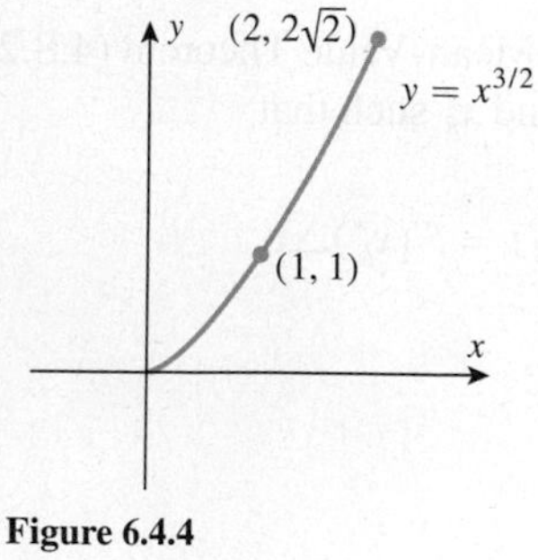


▲ Figure 6.4.4

***Solution (a).***

$$\frac{dy}{dx} = \frac{3}{2}x^{1/2}$$

and since the curve extends from $x = 1$ to $x = 2$, it follows from (4) that

$$L = \int_1^2 \sqrt{1 + \left(\tfrac{3}{2}x^{1/2}\right)^2}\, dx = \int_1^2 \sqrt{1 + \tfrac{9}{4}x}\, dx$$

To evaluate this integral we make the $u$-substitution

$$u = 1 + \tfrac{9}{4}x, \quad du = \tfrac{9}{4}\, dx$$

and then change the $x$-limits of integration $(x = 1, x = 2)$ to the corresponding $u$-limits $\left(u = \frac{13}{4}, u = \frac{22}{4}\right)$:

$$L = \frac{4}{9}\int_{13/4}^{22/4} u^{1/2}\, du = \frac{8}{27}u^{3/2}\Bigg]_{13/4}^{22/4} = \frac{8}{27}\left[\left(\frac{22}{4}\right)^{3/2} - \left(\frac{13}{4}\right)^{3/2}\right]$$

$$= \frac{22\sqrt{22} - 13\sqrt{13}}{27} \approx 2.09$$

***Solution (b).*** To apply Formula (5) we must first rewrite the equation $y = x^{3/2}$ so that $x$ is expressed as a function of $y$. This yields $x = y^{2/3}$ and

$$\frac{dx}{dy} = \frac{2}{3}y^{-1/3}$$

Since the curve extends from $y = 1$ to $y = 2\sqrt{2}$, it follows from (5) that

$$L = \int_1^{2\sqrt{2}} \sqrt{1 + \tfrac{4}{9}y^{-2/3}}\, dy = \frac{1}{3}\int_1^{2\sqrt{2}} y^{-1/3}\sqrt{9y^{2/3} + 4}\, dy$$

To evaluate this integral we make the $u$-substitution

$$u = 9y^{2/3} + 4, \quad du = 6y^{-1/3}\, dy$$

and change the $y$-limits of integration ($y = 1, y = 2\sqrt{2}$) to the corresponding $u$-limits ($u = 13, u = 22$). This gives

$$L = \frac{1}{18}\int_{13}^{22} u^{1/2}\, du = \frac{1}{27}u^{3/2}\Big]_{13}^{22} = \frac{1}{27}[(22)^{3/2} - (13)^{3/2}] = \frac{22\sqrt{22} - 13\sqrt{13}}{27}$$

The arc from the point $(1, 1)$ to the point $(2, 2\sqrt{2})$ in Figure 6.4.4 is nearly a straight line, so the arc length should be only slightly larger than the straight-line distance between these points. Show that this is so.

The answer in part (b) agrees with that in part (a); however, the integration in part (b) is more tedious. In problems where there is a choice between using (4) or (5), it is often the case that one of the formulas leads to a simpler integral than the other. ◄

## FINDING ARC LENGTH BY NUMERICAL METHODS

In the next chapter we will develop some techniques of integration that will enable us to find exact values of more integrals encountered in arc length calculations; however, generally speaking, most such integrals are impossible to evaluate in terms of elementary functions. In these cases one usually approximates the integral using a numerical method such as the midpoint approximation discussed in Section 5.4.

**TECHNOLOGY MASTERY**

If your calculating utility has a numerical integration capability, use it to confirm that the arc length $L$ in Example 2 is approximately $L \approx 3.8202$.

► **Example 2** From (4), the arc length of $y = \sin x$ from $x = 0$ to $x = \pi$ is given by the integral

$$L = \int_0^{\pi} \sqrt{1 + (\cos x)^2}\, dx$$

This integral cannot be evaluated in terms of elementary functions; however, using a calculating utility with a numerical integration capability yields the approximation $L \approx 3.8202$. ◄

## ✓QUICK CHECK EXERCISES 6.4 *(See page 370 for answers.)*

**1.** A function $f$ is smooth on $[a, b]$ if $f'$ is ______ on $[a, b]$.

**2.** If a function $f$ is smooth on $[a, b]$, then the length of the curve $y = f(x)$ over $[a, b]$ is ______.

**3.** The distance between points $(1, 0)$ and $(e, 1)$ is ______.

**4.** Let $L$ be the length of the curve $y = \ln x$ from $(1, 0)$ to $(e, 1)$.
(a) Integrating with respect to $x$, an integral expression for $L$ is ______.
(b) Integrating with respect to $y$, an integral expression for $L$ is ______.

## EXERCISE SET 6.4 [C] CAS

**1.** Use the Theorem of Pythagoras to find the length of the line segment $y = 2x$ from $(1, 2)$ to $(2, 4)$, and confirm that the value is consistent with the length computed using
(a) Formula (4) (b) Formula (5).

**2.** Use the Theorem of Pythagoras to find the length of the line segment $y = 5x$ from $(0, 0)$ and $(1, 5)$, and confirm that the value is consistent with the length computed using
(a) Formula (4) (b) Formula (5).

**3–8** Find the exact arc length of the curve over the interval. ■

**3.** $y = 3x^{3/2} - 1$ from $x = 0$ to $x = 1$

**4.** $x = \frac{1}{3}(y^2 + 2)^{3/2}$ from $y = 0$ to $y = 1$

**5.** $y = x^{2/3}$ from $x = 1$ to $x = 8$

**6.** $y = (x^6 + 8)/(16x^2)$ from $x = 2$ to $x = 3$

**7.** $24xy = y^4 + 48$ from $y = 2$ to $y = 4$

**8.** $x = \frac{1}{8}y^4 + \frac{1}{4}y^{-2}$ from $y = 1$ to $y = 4$

**9–12 True–False** Determine whether the statement is true or false. Explain your answer. ■

**9.** The graph of $y = \sqrt{1 - x^2}$ is a smooth curve on $[-1, 1]$.

**10.** The approximation

$$L \approx \sum_{k=1}^{n} \sqrt{(\Delta x_k)^2 + [f(x_k) - f(x_{k-1})]^2}$$

for arc length is not expressed in the form of a Riemann sum.

**11.** The approximation

$$L \approx \sum_{k=1}^{n} \sqrt{1 + [f'(x_k^*)]^2}\,\Delta x_k$$

for arc length is exact when $f$ is a linear function of $x$.

**12.** In our definition of the arc length for the graph of $y = f(x)$, we need $f'(x)$ to be a continuous function in order for $f$ to satisfy the hypotheses of the Mean-Value Theorem (4.8.2).

C **13–14** Express the exact arc length of the curve over the given interval as an integral that has been simplified to eliminate the radical, and then evaluate the integral using a CAS. ■

**13.** $y = \ln(\sec x)$ from $x = 0$ to $x = \pi/4$

**14.** $y = \ln(\sin x)$ from $x = \pi/4$ to $x = \pi/2$

**FOCUS ON CONCEPTS**

**15.** Consider the curve $y = x^{2/3}$.
(a) Sketch the portion of the curve between $x = -1$ and $x = 8$.
(b) Explain why Formula (4) cannot be used to find the arc length of the curve sketched in part (a).
(c) Find the arc length of the curve sketched in part (a).

**16.** The curve segment $y = x^2$ from $x = 1$ to $x = 2$ may also be expressed as the graph of $x = \sqrt{y}$ from $y = 1$ to $y = 4$. Set up two integrals that give the arc length of this curve segment, one by integrating with respect to $x$, and the other by integrating with respect to $y$. Demonstrate a substitution that verifies that these two integrals are equal.

**17.** Consider the curve segments $y = x^2$ from $x = \frac{1}{2}$ to $x = 2$ and $y = \sqrt{x}$ from $x = \frac{1}{4}$ to $x = 4$.
(a) Graph the two curve segments and use your graphs to explain why the lengths of these two curve segments should be equal.
(b) Set up integrals that give the arc lengths of the curve segments by integrating with respect to $x$. Demonstrate a substitution that verifies that these two integrals are equal.
(c) Set up integrals that give the arc lengths of the curve segments by integrating with respect to $y$.
(d) Approximate the arc length of each curve segment using Formula (2) with $n = 10$ equal subintervals.
(e) Which of the two approximations in part (d) is more accurate? Explain.
(f) Use the midpoint approximation with $n = 10$ subintervals to approximate each arc length integral in part (b).
(g) Use a calculating utility with numerical integration capabilities to approximate the arc length integrals in part (b) to four decimal places.

**18.** Follow the directions of Exercise 17 for the curve segments $y = x^{8/3}$ from $x = 10^{-3}$ to $x = 1$ and $y = x^{3/8}$ from $x = 10^{-8}$ to $x = 1$.

**19.** Follow the directions of Exercise 17 for the curve segment $y = \tan x$ from $x = 0$ to $x = \pi/3$ and for the curve segment $y = \tan^{-1} x$ from $x = 0$ to $x = \sqrt{3}$.

**20.** Let $y = f(x)$ be a smooth curve on the closed interval $[a, b]$. Prove that if $m$ and $M$ are nonnegative numbers such that $m \le |f'(x)| \le M$ for all $x$ in $[a, b]$, then the arc length $L$ of $y = f(x)$ over the interval $[a, b]$ satisfies the inequalities

$$(b - a)\sqrt{1 + m^2} \le L \le (b - a)\sqrt{1 + M^2}$$

**21.** Use the result of Exercise 20 to show that the arc length $L$ of $y = \sec x$ over the interval $0 \le x \le \pi/3$ satisfies

$$\frac{\pi}{3} \le L \le \frac{\pi}{3}\sqrt{13}$$

C **22.** A basketball player makes a successful shot from the free throw line. Suppose that the path of the ball from the moment of release to the moment it enters the hoop is described by

$$y = 2.15 + 2.09x - 0.41x^2, \quad 0 \le x \le 4.6$$

where $x$ is the horizontal distance (in meters) from the point of release, and $y$ is the vertical distance (in meters) above the floor. Use a CAS or a scientific calculator with a numerical integration capability to approximate the distance the ball travels from the moment it is released to the moment it enters the hoop. Round your answer to two decimal places.

C **23.** The central span of the Golden Gate Bridge in California is 4200 ft long and is suspended from cables that rise 500 ft above the roadway on either side. Approximately how long is the portion of a cable that lies between the support towers on one side of the roadway? [*Hint:* As suggested by the accompanying figure on the next page, assume the cable is modeled by a parabola $y = ax^2$ that passes through the point (2100, 500). Use a CAS or a calculating utility with a numerical integration capability to approximate the length of the cable. Round your answer to the nearest foot.]

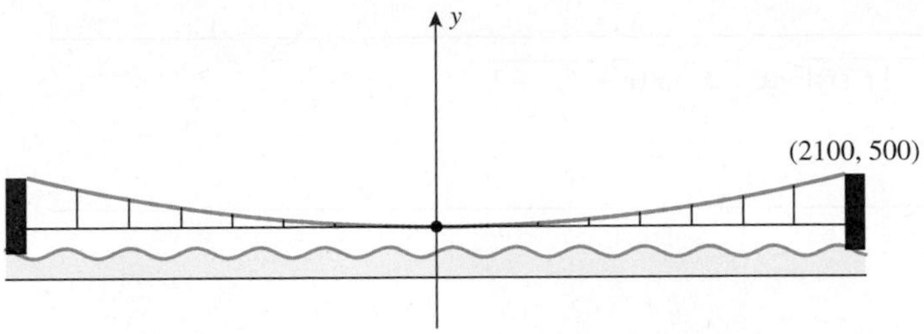


▲ Figure Ex-23

C 24. As shown in the accompanying figure, a horizontal beam with dimensions 2 in × 6 in × 16 ft is fixed at both ends and is subjected to a uniformly distributed load of 120 lb/ft. As a result of the load, the centerline of the beam undergoes a deflection that is described by

$$y = -1.67 \times 10^{-8}(x^4 - 2Lx^3 + L^2x^2)$$

($0 \le x \le 192$), where $L = 192$ is the length of the unloaded beam, $x$ is the horizontal distance along the beam measured in inches from the left end, and $y$ is the deflection of the centerline in inches.

(a) Graph $y$ versus $x$ for $0 \le x \le 192$.

(b) Find the maximum deflection of the centerline.

(c) Use a CAS or a calculator with a numerical integration capability to find the length of the centerline of the loaded beam. Round your answer to two decimal places.

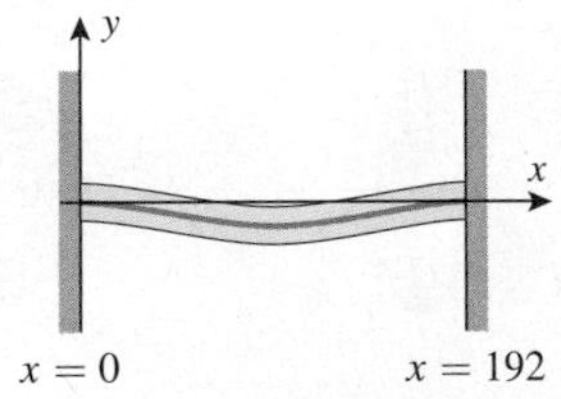


◀ Figure Ex-24

C 25. A golfer makes a successful chip shot to the green. Suppose that the path of the ball from the moment it is struck to the moment it hits the green is described by

$$y = 12.54x - 0.41x^2$$

where $x$ is the horizontal distance (in yards) from the point where the ball is struck, and $y$ is the vertical distance (in yards) above the fairway. Use a CAS or a calculating utility with a numerical integration capability to find the distance the ball travels from the moment it is struck to the moment it hits the green. Assume that the fairway and green are at the same level and round your answer to two decimal places.

**26–34** These exercises assume familiarity with the basic concepts of parametric curves. If needed, an introduction to this material is provided in Web Appendix M. ■

C 26. Assume that no segment of the curve

$$x = x(t), \quad y = y(t), \qquad (a \le t \le b)$$

is traced more than once as $t$ increases from $a$ to $b$. Divide the interval $[a, b]$ into $n$ subintervals by inserting points $t_1, t_2, \ldots, t_{n-1}$ between $a = t_0$ and $b = t_n$. Let $L$ denote the arc length of the curve. Give an informal argument for the approximation

$$L \approx \sum_{k=1}^{n} \sqrt{[x(t_k) - x(t_{k-1})]^2 + [y(t_k) - y(t_{k-1})]^2}$$

If $dx/dt$ and $dy/dt$ are continuous functions for $a \le t \le b$, then it can be shown that as $\max \Delta t_k \to 0$, this sum converges to

$$L = \int_a^b \sqrt{\left(\frac{dx}{dt}\right)^2 + \left(\frac{dy}{dt}\right)^2}\, dt$$

**27–32** Use the arc length formula from Exercise 26 to find the arc length of the curve. ■

27. $x = \frac{1}{3}t^3,\ y = \frac{1}{2}t^2 \quad (0 \le t \le 1)$

28. $x = (1+t)^2,\ y = (1+t)^3 \quad (0 \le t \le 1)$

29. $x = \cos 2t,\ y = \sin 2t \quad (0 \le t \le \pi/2)$

30. $x = \cos t + t \sin t,\ y = \sin t - t\cos t \quad (0 \le t \le \pi)$

31. $x = e^t \cos t,\ y = e^t \sin t \quad (0 \le t \le \pi/2)$

32. $x = e^t(\sin t + \cos t),\ y = e^t(\cos t - \sin t) \quad (1 \le t \le 4)$

C 33. (a) Show that the total arc length of the ellipse

$$x = 2\cos t, \quad y = \sin t \qquad (0 \le t \le 2\pi)$$

is given by

$$4\int_0^{\pi/2} \sqrt{1 + 3\sin^2 t}\, dt$$

(b) Use a CAS or a scientific calculator with a numerical integration capability to approximate the arc length in part (a). Round your answer to two decimal places.

(c) Suppose that the parametric equations in part (a) describe the path of a particle moving in the $xy$-plane, where $t$ is time in seconds and $x$ and $y$ are in centimeters. Use a CAS or a scientific calculator with a numerical integration capability to approximate the distance traveled by the particle from $t = 1.5$ s to $t = 4.8$ s. Round your answer to two decimal places.

34. Show that the total arc length of the ellipse $x = a\cos t$, $y = b \sin t$, $0 \le t \le 2\pi$ for $a > b > 0$ is given by

$$4a\int_0^{\pi/2} \sqrt{1 - k^2\cos^2 t}\, dt$$

where $k = \sqrt{a^2 - b^2}/a$.

35. **Writing** In our discussion of Arc Length Problem 6.4.1, we derived the approximation

$$L \approx \sum_{k=1}^{n} \sqrt{1 + [f'(x_k^*)]^2}\, \Delta x_k$$

Discuss the geometric meaning of this approximation. (Be sure to address the appearance of the derivative $f'$.)

36. **Writing** Give examples in which Formula (4) for arc length cannot be applied directly, and describe how you would go about finding the arc length of the curve in each case. (Discuss both the use of alternative formulas and the use of numerical methods.)

✓ **QUICK CHECK ANSWERS 6.4** 1. continuous 2. $\int_a^b \sqrt{1+[f'(x)]^2}\,dx$ 3. $\sqrt{(e-1)^2+1}$
4. (a) $\int_1^e \sqrt{1+(1/x)^2}\,dx$ (b) $\int_0^1 \sqrt{1+e^{2y}}\,dy$

## 6.5 AREA OF A SURFACE OF REVOLUTION

*In this section we will consider the problem of finding the area of a surface that is generated by revolving a plane curve about a line.*

### SURFACE AREA

A ***surface of revolution*** is a surface that is generated by revolving a plane curve about an axis that lies in the same plane as the curve. For example, the surface of a sphere can be generated by revolving a semicircle about its diameter, and the lateral surface of a right circular cylinder can be generated by revolving a line segment about an axis that is parallel to it (Figure 6.5.1).

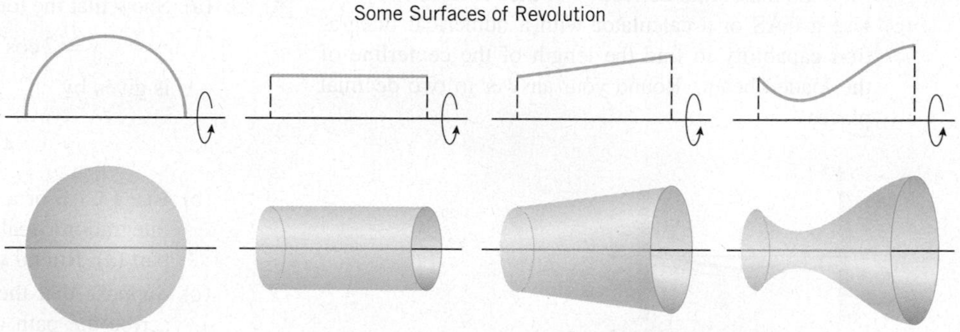


▶ **Figure 6.5.1**

In this section we will be concerned with the following problem.

**6.5.1 SURFACE AREA PROBLEM** Suppose that $f$ is a smooth, nonnegative function on $[a, b]$ and that a surface of revolution is generated by revolving the portion of the curve $y = f(x)$ between $x = a$ and $x = b$ about the $x$-axis (Figure 6.5.2). Define what is meant by the *area* $S$ of the surface, and find a formula for computing it.

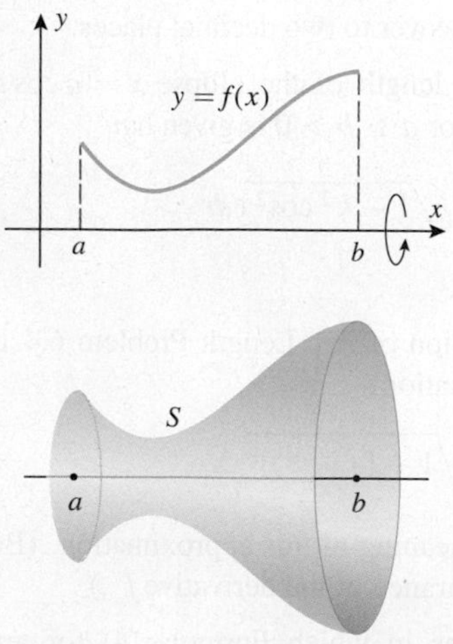


▲ **Figure 6.5.2**

To motivate an appropriate definition for the area $S$ of a surface of revolution, we will decompose the surface into small sections whose areas can be approximated by elementary formulas, add the approximations of the areas of the sections to form a Riemann sum that approximates $S$, and then take the limit of the Riemann sums to obtain an integral for the exact value of $S$.

To implement this idea, divide the interval $[a, b]$ into $n$ subintervals by inserting points $x_1, x_2, \ldots, x_{n-1}$ between $a = x_0$ and $b = x_n$. As illustrated in Figure 6.5.3*a*, the corresponding points on the graph of $f$ define a polygonal path that approximates the curve $y = f(x)$ over the interval $[a, b]$. As illustrated in Figure 6.5.3*b*, when this polygonal path is revolved about the $x$-axis, it generates a surface consisting of $n$ parts, each of which is a portion of a right circular cone called a ***frustum*** (from the Latin meaning "bit" or "piece"). Thus, the area of each part of the approximating surface can be obtained from the formula

$$S = \pi(r_1 + r_2)l \tag{1}$$

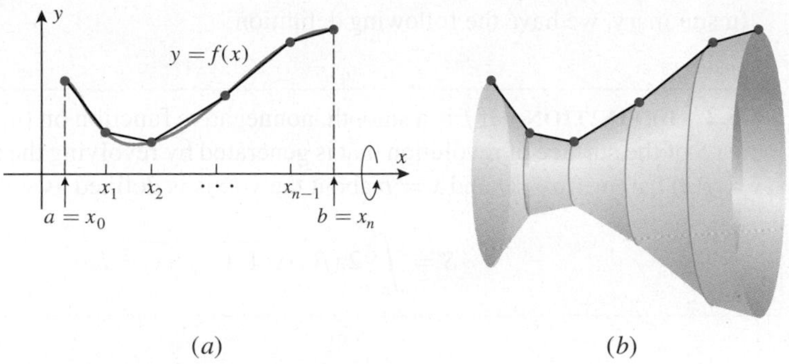


▲ **Figure 6.5.3**

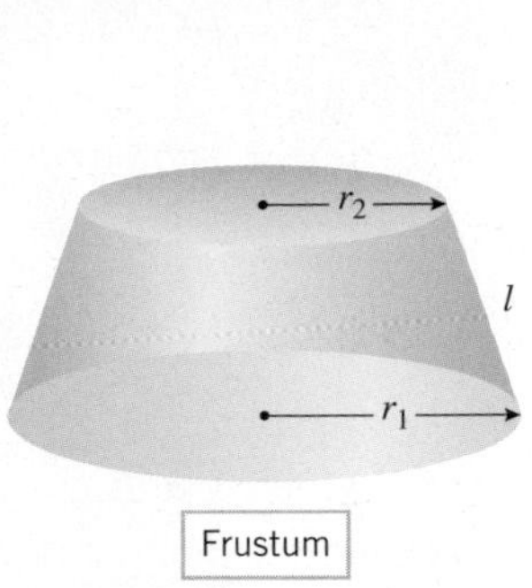


▲ **Figure 6.5.4**

for the lateral area $S$ of a frustum of slant height $l$ and base radii $r_1$ and $r_2$ (Figure 6.5.4). As suggested by Figure 6.5.5, the $k$th frustum has radii $f(x_{k-1})$ and $f(x_k)$ and height $\Delta x_k$. Its slant height is the length $L_k$ of the $k$th line segment in the polygonal path, which from Formula (1) of Section 6.4 is

$$L_k = \sqrt{(\Delta x_k)^2 + [f(x_k) - f(x_{k-1})]^2}$$

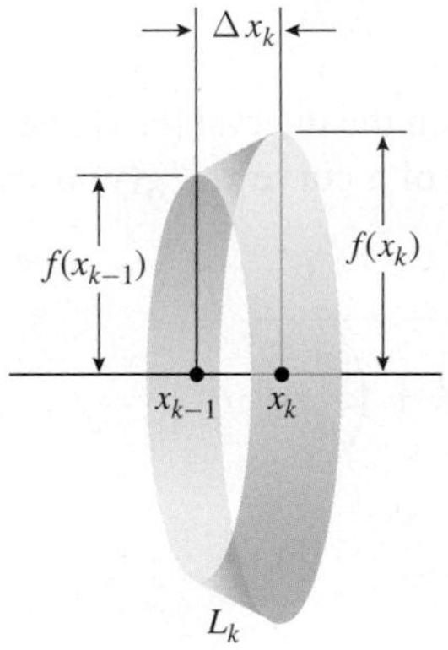


▲ **Figure 6.5.5**

This makes the lateral area $S_k$ of the $k$th frustum

$$S_k = \pi[f(x_{k-1}) + f(x_k)]\sqrt{(\Delta x_k)^2 + [f(x_k) - f(x_{k-1})]^2}$$

If we add these areas, we obtain the following approximation to the area $S$ of the entire surface:

$$S \approx \sum_{k=1}^{n} \pi[f(x_{k-1}) + f(x_k)]\sqrt{(\Delta x_k)^2 + [f(x_k) - f(x_{k-1})]^2} \tag{2}$$

To put this in the form of a Riemann sum we will apply the Mean-Value Theorem (4.8.2). This theorem implies that there is a point $x_k^*$ between $x_{k-1}$ and $x_k$ such that

$$\frac{f(x_k) - f(x_{k-1})}{x_k - x_{k-1}} = f'(x_k^*) \quad \text{or} \quad f(x_k) - f(x_{k-1}) = f'(x_k^*)\Delta x_k$$

and hence we can rewrite (2) as

$$\begin{aligned} S &\approx \sum_{k=1}^{n} \pi[f(x_{k-1}) + f(x_k)]\sqrt{(\Delta x_k)^2 + [f'(x_k^*)]^2(\Delta x_k)^2} \\ &= \sum_{k=1}^{n} \pi[f(x_{k-1}) + f(x_k)]\sqrt{1 + [f'(x_k^*)]^2}\,\Delta x_k \end{aligned} \tag{3}$$

However, this is not yet a Riemann sum because it involves the variables $x_{k-1}$ and $x_k$. To eliminate these variables from the expression, observe that the average value of the numbers $f(x_{k-1})$ and $f(x_k)$ lies between these numbers, so the continuity of $f$ and the Intermediate-Value Theorem (1.5.7) imply that there is a point $x_k^{**}$ between $x_{k-1}$ and $x_k$ such that

$$\tfrac{1}{2}[f(x_{k-1}) + f(x_k)] = f(x_k^{**})$$

Thus, (2) can be expressed as

$$S \approx \sum_{k=1}^{n} 2\pi f(x_k^{**})\sqrt{1 + [f'(x_k^*)]^2}\,\Delta x_k$$

Although this expression is close to a Riemann sum in form, it is not a true Riemann sum because it involves two variables $x_k^*$ and $x_k^{**}$, rather than $x_k^*$ alone. However, it is proved in advanced calculus courses that this has no effect on the limit because of the continuity of $f$. Thus, we can assume that $x_k^{**} = x_k^*$ when taking the limit, and this suggests that $S$ can be defined as

$$S = \lim_{\max \Delta x_k \to 0} \sum_{k=1}^{n} 2\pi f(x_k^{**})\sqrt{1 + [f'(x_k^*)]^2}\,\Delta x_k = \int_a^b 2\pi f(x)\sqrt{1 + [f'(x)]^2}\,dx$$

In summary, we have the following definition.

**6.5.2 DEFINITION** If $f$ is a smooth, nonnegative function on $[a, b]$, then the surface area $S$ of the surface of revolution that is generated by revolving the portion of the curve $y = f(x)$ between $x = a$ and $x = b$ about the $x$-axis is defined as

$$S = \int_a^b 2\pi f(x)\sqrt{1 + [f'(x)]^2}\, dx$$

This result provides both a definition and a formula for computing surface areas. Where convenient, this formula can also be expressed as

$$S = \int_a^b 2\pi f(x)\sqrt{1 + [f'(x)]^2}\, dx = \int_a^b 2\pi y\sqrt{1 + \left(\frac{dy}{dx}\right)^2}\, dx \tag{4}$$

Moreover, if $g$ is nonnegative and $x = g(y)$ is a smooth curve on the interval $[c, d]$, then the area of the surface that is generated by revolving the portion of a curve $x = g(y)$ between $y = c$ and $y = d$ about the $y$-axis can be expressed as

$$S = \int_c^d 2\pi g(y)\sqrt{1 + [g'(y)]^2}\, dy = \int_c^d 2\pi x\sqrt{1 + \left(\frac{dx}{dy}\right)^2}\, dy \tag{5}$$

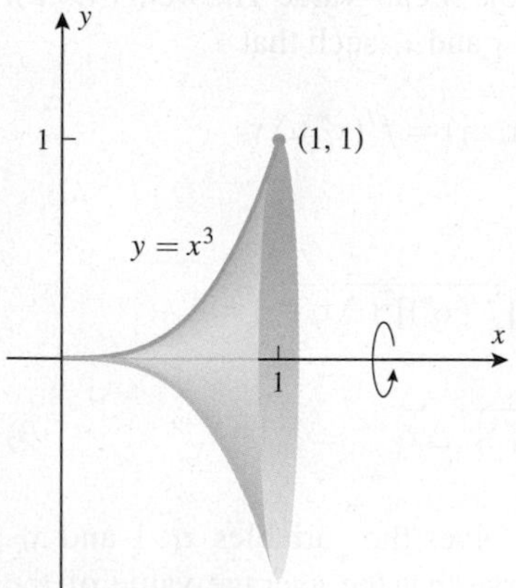

▲ Figure 6.5.6

**▶ Example 1** Find the area of the surface that is generated by revolving the portion of the curve $y = x^3$ between $x = 0$ and $x = 1$ about the $x$-axis.

***Solution.*** First sketch the curve; then imagine revolving it about the $x$-axis (Figure 6.5.6). Since $y = x^3$, we have $dy/dx = 3x^2$, and hence from (4) the surface area $S$ is

$$\begin{aligned}
S &= \int_0^1 2\pi y\sqrt{1 + \left(\frac{dy}{dx}\right)^2}\, dx \\
&= \int_0^1 2\pi x^3\sqrt{1 + (3x^2)^2}\, dx \\
&= 2\pi \int_0^1 x^3(1 + 9x^4)^{1/2}\, dx \\
&= \frac{2\pi}{36}\int_1^{10} u^{1/2}\, du \qquad \boxed{\begin{aligned} u &= 1 + 9x^4 \\ du &= 36x^3\, dx\end{aligned}} \\
&= \frac{2\pi}{36} \cdot \frac{2}{3} u^{3/2}\Big]_{u=1}^{10} = \frac{\pi}{27}(10^{3/2} - 1) \approx 3.56 \blacktriangleleft
\end{aligned}$$

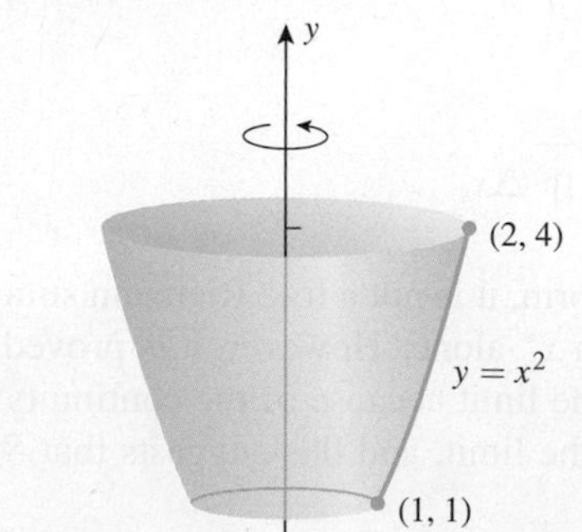

▲ Figure 6.5.7

**▶ Example 2** Find the area of the surface that is generated by revolving the portion of the curve $y = x^2$ between $x = 1$ and $x = 2$ about the $y$-axis.

***Solution.*** First sketch the curve; then imagine revolving it about the $y$-axis (Figure 6.5.7). Because the curve is revolved about the $y$-axis we will apply Formula (5). Toward this end, we rewrite $y = x^2$ as $x = \sqrt{y}$ and observe that the $y$-values corresponding to $x = 1$ and

$x = 2$ are $y = 1$ and $y = 4$. Since $x = \sqrt{y}$, we have $dx/dy = 1/(2\sqrt{y})$, and hence from (5) the surface area $S$ is

$$\begin{aligned} S &= \int_1^4 2\pi x \sqrt{1 + \left(\frac{dx}{dy}\right)^2}\, dy \\ &= \int_1^4 2\pi\sqrt{y}\sqrt{1 + \left(\frac{1}{2\sqrt{y}}\right)^2}\, dy \\ &= \pi \int_1^4 \sqrt{4y+1}\, dy \\ &= \frac{\pi}{4}\int_5^{17} u^{1/2}\, du \qquad \boxed{\begin{aligned} u &= 4y+1 \\ du &= 4\,dy \end{aligned}} \\ &= \frac{\pi}{4}\cdot\frac{2}{3}u^{3/2}\Big]_{u=5}^{17} = \frac{\pi}{6}(17^{3/2} - 5^{3/2}) \approx 30.85 \blacktriangleleft \end{aligned}$$

## ✓QUICK CHECK EXERCISES 6.5 (See page 375 for answers.)

1. If $f$ is a smooth, nonnegative function on $[a, b]$, then the surface area $S$ of the surface of revolution generated by revolving the portion of the curve $y = f(x)$ between $x = a$ and $x = b$ about the $x$-axis is ________.
2. The lateral area of the frustum with slant height $\sqrt{10}$ and base radii $r_1 = 1$ and $r_2 = 2$ is ________.
3. An integral expression for the area of the surface generated by rotating the line segment joining $(3, 1)$ and $(6, 2)$ about the $x$-axis is ________.
4. An integral expression for the area of the surface generated by rotating the line segment joining $(3, 1)$ and $(6, 2)$ about the $y$-axis is ________.

## EXERCISE SET 6.5 [C] CAS

**1–4** Find the area of the surface generated by revolving the given curve about the $x$-axis. ■

1. $y = 7x,\ 0 \le x \le 1$
2. $y = \sqrt{x},\ 1 \le x \le 4$
3. $y = \sqrt{4 - x^2},\ -1 \le x \le 1$
4. $x = \sqrt[3]{y},\ 1 \le y \le 8$

**5–8** Find the area of the surface generated by revolving the given curve about the $y$-axis. ■

5. $x = 9y + 1,\ 0 \le y \le 2$
6. $x = y^3,\ 0 \le y \le 1$
7. $x = \sqrt{9 - y^2},\ -2 \le y \le 2$
8. $x = 2\sqrt{1 - y},\ -1 \le y \le 0$

[C] **9–12** Use a CAS to find the exact area of the surface generated by revolving the curve about the stated axis. ■

9. $y = \sqrt{x} - \frac{1}{3}x^{3/2},\ 1 \le x \le 3$; $x$-axis
10. $y = \frac{1}{3}x^3 + \frac{1}{4}x^{-1},\ 1 \le x \le 2$; $x$-axis
11. $8xy^2 = 2y^6 + 1,\ 1 \le y \le 2$; $y$-axis
12. $x = \sqrt{16 - y},\ 0 \le y \le 15$; $y$-axis

[C] **13–16** Use a CAS or a calculating utility with a numerical integration capability to approximate the area of the surface generated by revolving the curve about the stated axis. Round your answer to two decimal places. ■

13. $y = \sin x,\ 0 \le x \le \pi$; $x$-axis
14. $x = \tan y,\ 0 \le y \le \pi/4$; $y$-axis
15. $y = e^x,\ 0 \le x \le 1$; $x$-axis
16. $y = e^x,\ 1 \le y \le e$; $y$-axis

**17–20 True–False** Determine whether the statement is true or false. Explain your answer. ■

17. The lateral surface area $S$ of a right circular cone with height $h$ and base radius $r$ is $S = \pi r\sqrt{r^2 + h^2}$.
18. The lateral surface area of a frustum of slant height $l$ and base radii $r_1$ and $r_2$ is equal to the lateral surface area of a right circular cylinder of height $l$ and radius equal to the average of $r_1$ and $r_2$.
19. The approximation
$$S \approx \sum_{k=1}^{n} 2\pi f(x_k^{**})\sqrt{1 + [f'(x_k^*)]^2}\, \Delta x_k$$
for surface area is exact if $f$ is a positive-valued constant function.

**20.** The expression

$$\sum_{k=1}^{n} 2\pi f(x_k^{**})\sqrt{1+[f'(x_k^*)]^2}\,\Delta x_k$$

is not a true Riemann sum for

$$\int_a^b 2\pi f(x)\sqrt{1+[f'(x)]^2}\,dx$$

**21–22** Approximate the area of the surface using Formula (2) with $n = 20$ subintervals of equal width. Round your answer to two decimal places. ■

**21.** The surface of Exercise 13.

**22.** The surface of Exercise 16.

**FOCUS ON CONCEPTS**

**23.** Assume that $y = f(x)$ is a smooth curve on the interval $[a, b]$ and assume that $f(x) \geq 0$ for $a \leq x \leq b$. Derive a formula for the surface area generated when the curve $y = f(x)$, $a \leq x \leq b$, is revolved about the line $y = -k\,(k > 0)$.

**24.** Would it be circular reasoning to use Definition 6.5.2 to find the surface area of a frustum of a right circular cone? Explain your answer.

**25.** Show that the area of the surface of a sphere of radius $r$ is $4\pi r^2$. [*Hint:* Revolve the semicircle $y = \sqrt{r^2 - x^2}$ about the $x$-axis.]

**26.** The accompanying figure shows a spherical cap of height $h$ cut from a sphere of radius $r$. Show that the surface area $S$ of the cap is $S = 2\pi rh$. [*Hint:* Revolve an appropriate portion of the circle $x^2 + y^2 = r^2$ about the $y$-axis.]

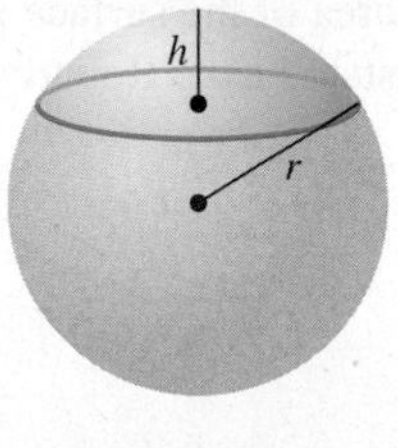


◀ **Figure Ex-26**

**27.** The portion of a sphere that is cut by two parallel planes is called a ***zone***. Use the result of Exercise 26 to show that the surface area of a zone depends on the radius of the sphere and the distance between the planes, but not on the location of the zone.

**28.** Let $y = f(x)$ be a smooth curve on the interval $[a, b]$ and assume that $f(x) \geq 0$ for $a \leq x \leq b$. By the Extreme-Value Theorem (4.4.2), the function $f$ has a maximum value $K$ and a minimum value $k$ on $[a, b]$. Prove: If $L$ is the arc length of the curve $y = f(x)$ between $x = a$ and $x = b$, and if $S$ is the area of the surface that is generated by revolving this curve about the $x$-axis, then

$$2\pi kL \leq S \leq 2\pi KL$$

**29.** Use the results of Exercise 28 above and Exercise 21 in Section 6.4 to show that the area $S$ of the surface generated by revolving the curve $y = \sec x$, $0 \leq x \leq \pi/3$, about the $x$-axis satisfies

$$\frac{2\pi^2}{3} \leq S \leq \frac{4\pi^2}{3}\sqrt{13}$$

**30.** Let $y = f(x)$ be a smooth curve on $[a, b]$ and assume that $f(x) \geq 0$ for $a \leq x \leq b$. Let $A$ be the area under the curve $y = f(x)$ between $x = a$ and $x = b$, and let $S$ be the area of the surface obtained when this section of curve is revolved about the $x$-axis.

(a) Prove that $2\pi A \leq S$.

(b) For what functions $f$ is $2\pi A = S$?

**31–37** These exercises assume familiarity with the basic concepts of parametric curves. If needed, an introduction to this material is provided in Web Appendix M. ■

**31–32** For these exercises, divide the interval $[a, b]$ into $n$ subintervals by inserting points $t_1, t_2, \ldots, t_{n-1}$ between $a = t_0$ and $b = t_n$, and assume that $x'(t)$ and $y'(t)$ are continuous functions and that no segment of the curve

$$x = x(t), \quad y = y(t) \qquad (a \leq t \leq b)$$

is traced more than once. ■

**31.** Let $S$ be the area of the surface generated by revolving the curve $x = x(t)$, $y = y(t)$ $(a \leq t \leq b)$ about the $x$-axis. Explain how $S$ can be approximated by

$$S \approx \sum_{k=1}^{n} (\pi[y(t_{k-1}) + y(t_k)] \times \sqrt{[x(t_k) - x(t_{k-1})]^2 + [y(t_k) - y(t_{k-1})]^2})$$

Using results from advanced calculus, it can be shown that as $\max \Delta t_k \to 0$, this sum converges to

$$S = \int_a^b 2\pi y(t)\sqrt{[x'(t)]^2 + [y'(t)]^2}\,dt \qquad \text{(A)}$$

**32.** Let $S$ be the area of the surface generated by revolving the curve $x = x(t)$, $y = y(t)$ $(a \leq t \leq b)$ about the $y$-axis. Explain how $S$ can be approximated by

$$S \approx \sum_{k=1}^{n} (\pi[x(t_{k-1}) + x(t_k)] \times \sqrt{[x(t_k) - x(t_{k-1})]^2 + [y(t_k) - y(t_{k-1})]^2})$$

Using results from advanced calculus, it can be shown that as $\max \Delta t_k \to 0$, this sum converges to

$$S = \int_a^b 2\pi x(t)\sqrt{[x'(t)]^2 + [y'(t)]^2}\,dt \qquad \text{(B)}$$

**33–37** Use Formulas (A) and (B) from Exercises 31 and 32. ■

**33.** Find the area of the surface generated by revolving the parametric curve $x = t^2$, $y = 2t\,(0 \leq t \leq 4)$ about the $x$-axis.

C **34.** Use a CAS to find the area of the surface generated by revolving the parametric curve

$$x = \cos^2 t, \quad y = 5\sin t \qquad (0 \leq t \leq \pi/2)$$

about the $x$-axis.

**35.** Find the area of the surface generated by revolving the parametric curve $x = t$, $y = 2t^2\,(0 \leq t \leq 1)$ about the $y$-axis.

**36.** Find the area of the surface generated by revolving the parametric curve $x = \cos^2 t$, $y = \sin^2 t\,(0 \leq t \leq \pi/2)$ about the $y$-axis.

**37.** By revolving the semicircle

$$x = r\cos t, \quad y = r\sin t \quad (0 \le t \le \pi)$$

about the $x$-axis, show that the surface area of a sphere of radius $r$ is $4\pi r^2$.

**38. Writing** Compare the derivation of Definition 6.5.2 with that of Definition 6.4.2. Discuss the geometric features that result in similarities in the two definitions.

**39. Writing** Discuss what goes wrong if we replace the frustums of right circular cones by right circular cylinders in the derivation of Definition 6.5.2.

✓ **QUICK CHECK ANSWERS 6.5** 1. $\int_a^b 2\pi f(x)\sqrt{1+[f'(x)]^2}\,dx$ 2. $3\sqrt{10}\,\pi$ 3. $\int_3^6 (2\pi)\left(\frac{x}{3}\right)\sqrt{\frac{10}{9}}\,dx = \int_3^6 \frac{2\sqrt{10}\,\pi}{9}x\,dx$ 4. $\int_1^2 (2\pi)(3y)\sqrt{10}\,dy$

## 6.6 WORK

*In this section we will use the integration tools developed in the preceding chapter to study some of the basic principles of "work," which is one of the fundamental concepts in physics and engineering.*

### THE ROLE OF WORK IN PHYSICS AND ENGINEERING

In this section we will be concerned with two related concepts, *work* and *energy*. To put these ideas in a familiar setting, when you push a stalled car for a certain distance you are performing work, and the effect of your work is to make the car move. The energy of motion caused by the work is called the *kinetic energy* of the car. The exact connection between work and kinetic energy is governed by a principle of physics called the *work–energy relationship*. Although we will touch on this idea in this section, a detailed study of the relationship between work and energy will be left for courses in physics and engineering. Our primary goal here will be to explain the role of integration in the study of work.

### WORK DONE BY A CONSTANT FORCE APPLIED IN THE DIRECTION OF MOTION

When a stalled car is pushed, the speed that the car attains depends on the force $F$ with which it is pushed and the distance $d$ over which that force is applied (Figure 6.6.1). Force and distance appear in the following definition of work.

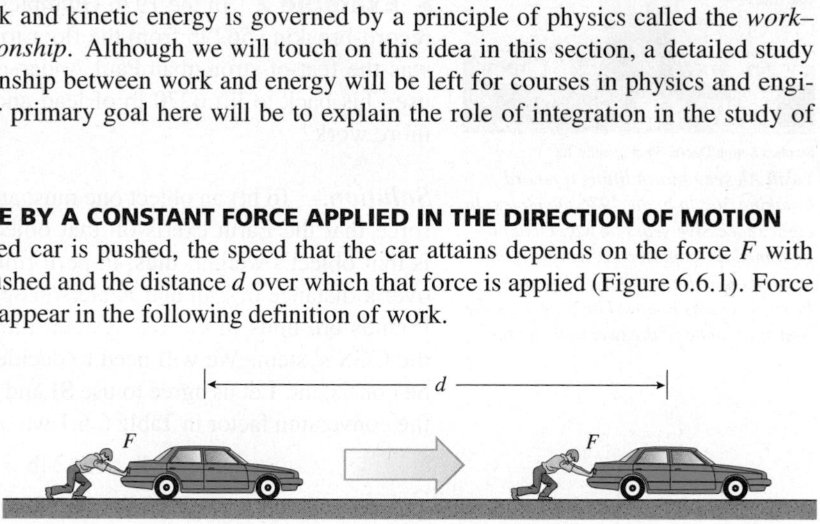


▶ **Figure 6.6.1**

**6.6.1 DEFINITION** If a constant force of magnitude $F$ is applied in the direction of motion of an object, and if that object moves a distance $d$, then we define the ***work*** $W$ performed by the force on the object to be

$$W = F \cdot d \tag{1}$$

If you push against an immovable object, such as a brick wall, you may tire yourself out, but you will not perform any work. Why?

Common units for measuring force are newtons (N) in the International System of Units (SI), dynes (dyn) in the centimeter-gram-second (CGS) system, and pounds (lb) in the British Engineering (BE) system. One newton is the force required to give a mass of 1 kg an acceleration of 1 $m/s^2$, one dyne is the force required to give a mass of 1 g an acceleration of 1 $cm/s^2$, and one pound of force is the force required to give a mass of 1 slug an acceleration of 1 $ft/s^2$.

It follows from Definition 6.6.1 that work has units of force times distance. The most common units of work are newton-meters (N·m), dyne-centimeters (dyn·cm), and foot-pounds (ft·lb). As indicated in Table 6.6.1, one newton-meter is also called a ***joule*** (J), and one dyne-centimeter is also called an ***erg***. One foot-pound is approximately 1.36 J.

**Table 6.6.1**

| SYSTEM | FORCE | × | DISTANCE | = | WORK |
|---|---|---|---|---|---|
| SI | newton (N) | | meter (m) | | joule (J) |
| CGS | dyne (dyn) | | centimeter (cm) | | erg |
| BE | pound (lb) | | foot (ft) | | foot-pound (ft·lb) |

CONVERSION FACTORS:

$1\text{ N} = 10^5\text{ dyn} \approx 0.225\text{ lb}$ $\quad$ $1\text{ lb} \approx 4.45\text{ N}$

$1\text{ J} = 10^7\text{ erg} \approx 0.738\text{ ft·lb}$ $\quad$ $1\text{ ft·lb} \approx 1.36\text{ J} = 1.36 \times 10^7\text{ erg}$

Stephen Sutton/Duomo Photography, Inc

*Vasili Alexeev shown lifting a record-breaking 562 lb in the 1976 Olympics. In eight successive years he won Olympic gold medals, captured six world championships, and broke 80 world records. In 1999 he was honored in Greece as the best sportsman of the twentieth century.*

▶ **Example 1** An object moves 5 ft along a line while subjected to a constant force of 100 lb in its direction of motion. The work done is

$$W = F \cdot d = 100 \cdot 5 = 500\text{ ft·lb}$$

An object moves 25 m along a line while subjected to a constant force of 4 N in its direction of motion. The work done is

$$W = F \cdot d = 4 \cdot 25 = 100\text{ N·m} = 100\text{ J} \blacktriangleleft$$

▶ **Example 2** In the 1976 Olympics, Vasili Alexeev astounded the world by lifting a record-breaking 562 lb from the floor to above his head (about 2 m). Equally astounding was the feat of strongman Paul Anderson, who in 1957 braced himself on the floor and used his back to lift 6270 lb of lead and automobile parts a distance of 1 cm. Who did more work?

***Solution.*** To lift an object one must apply sufficient force to overcome the gravitational force that the Earth exerts on that object. The force that the Earth exerts on an object is that object's weight; thus, in performing their feats, Alexeev applied a force of 562 lb over a distance of 2 m and Anderson applied a force of 6270 lb over a distance of 1 cm. Pounds are units in the BE system, meters are units in SI, and centimeters are units in the CGS system. We will need to decide on the measurement system we want to use and be consistent. Let us agree to use SI and express the work of the two men in joules. Using the conversion factor in Table 6.6.1 we obtain

$$562\text{ lb} \approx 562\text{ lb} \times 4.45\text{ N/lb} \approx 2500\text{ N}$$
$$6270\text{ lb} \approx 6270\text{ lb} \times 4.45\text{ N/lb} \approx 27{,}900\text{ N}$$

Using these values and the fact that 1 cm = 0.01 m we obtain

$$\text{Alexeev's work} = (2500\text{ N}) \times (2\text{ m}) = 5000\text{ J}$$
$$\text{Anderson's work} = (27{,}900\text{ N}) \times (0.01\text{ m}) = 279\text{ J}$$

Therefore, even though Anderson's lift required a tremendous upward force, it was applied over such a short distance that Alexeev did more work. ◀

## WORK DONE BY A VARIABLE FORCE APPLIED IN THE DIRECTION OF MOTION

Many important problems are concerned with finding the work done by a *variable* force that is applied in the direction of motion. For example, Figure 6.6.2*a* shows a spring in its natural state (neither compressed nor stretched). If we want to pull the block horizontally

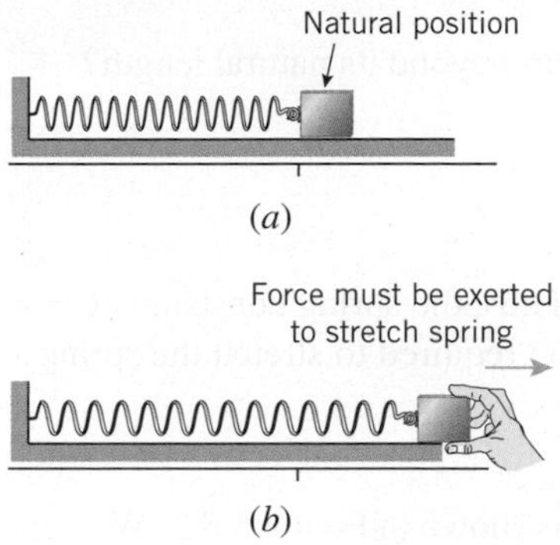


▲ **Figure 6.6.2**

(Figure 6.6.2*b*), then we would have to apply more and more force to the block to overcome the increasing force of the stretching spring. Thus, our next objective is to define what is meant by the work performed by a variable force and to find a formula for computing it. This will require calculus.

**6.6.2 PROBLEM** Suppose that an object moves in the positive direction along a coordinate line while subjected to a variable force $F(x)$ that is applied in the direction of motion. Define what is meant by the *work* $W$ performed by the force on the object as the object moves from $x = a$ to $x = b$, and find a formula for computing the work.

The basic idea for solving this problem is to break up the interval $[a, b]$ into subintervals that are sufficiently small that the force does not vary much on each subinterval. This will allow us to treat the force as constant on each subinterval and to approximate the work on each subinterval using Formula (1). By adding the approximations to the work on the subintervals, we will obtain a Riemann sum that approximates the work $W$ over the entire interval, and by taking the limit of the Riemann sums we will obtain an integral for $W$.

To implement this idea, divide the interval $[a, b]$ into $n$ subintervals by inserting points $x_1, x_2, \ldots, x_{n-1}$ between $a = x_0$ and $b = x_n$. We can use Formula (1) to approximate the work $W_k$ done in the $k$th subinterval by choosing any point $x_k^*$ in this interval and regarding the force to have a constant value $F(x_k^*)$ throughout the interval. Since the width of the $k$th subinterval is $x_k - x_{k-1} = \Delta x_k$, this yields the approximation

$$W_k \approx F(x_k^*)\Delta x_k$$

Adding these approximations yields the following Riemann sum that approximates the work $W$ done over the entire interval:

$$W \approx \sum_{k=1}^{n} F(x_k^*)\Delta x_k$$

Taking the limit as $n$ increases and the widths of all the subintervals approach zero yields the definite integral

$$W = \lim_{\max \Delta x_k \to 0} \sum_{k=1}^{n} F(x_k^*)\Delta x_k = \int_a^b F(x)\,dx$$

In summary, we have the following result.

**6.6.3 DEFINITION** Suppose that an object moves in the positive direction along a coordinate line over the interval $[a, b]$ while subjected to a variable force $F(x)$ that is applied in the direction of motion. Then we define the ***work*** $W$ performed by the force on the object to be

$$W = \int_a^b F(x)\,dx \tag{2}$$

***Hooke's law*** [Robert Hooke (1635–1703), English physicist] states that under appropriate conditions a spring that is stretched $x$ units beyond its natural length pulls back with a force

$$F(x) = kx$$

where $k$ is a constant (called the ***spring constant*** or ***spring stiffness***). The value of $k$ depends on such factors as the thickness of the spring and the material used in its composition. Since $k = F(x)/x$, the constant $k$ has units of force per unit length.

▶ **Example 3** A spring exerts a force of 5 N when stretched 1 m beyond its natural length.

(a) Find the spring constant $k$.

(b) How much work is required to stretch the spring 1.8 m beyond its natural length?

***Solution (a).*** From Hooke's law,

$$F(x) = kx$$

From the data, $F(x) = 5$ N when $x = 1$ m, so $5 = k \cdot 1$. Thus, the spring constant is $k = 5$ newtons per meter (N/m). This means that the force $F(x)$ required to stretch the spring $x$ meters is

$$F(x) = 5x \tag{3}$$

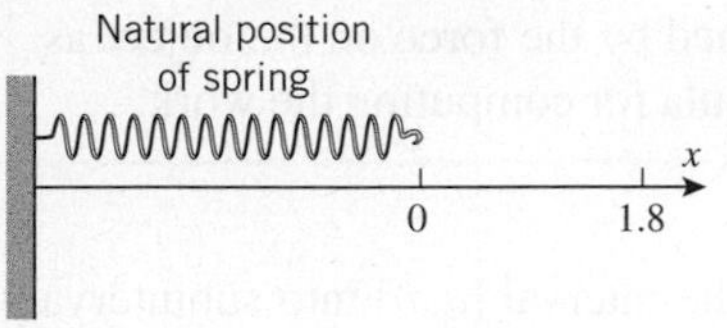


▲ **Figure 6.6.3**

***Solution (b).*** Place the spring along a coordinate line as shown in Figure 6.6.3. We want to find the work $W$ required to stretch the spring over the interval from $x = 0$ to $x = 1.8$. From (2) and (3) the work $W$ required is

$$W = \int_a^b F(x)\,dx = \int_0^{1.8} 5x\,dx = \frac{5x^2}{2}\bigg]_0^{1.8} = 8.1 \text{ J} \ ◀$$

NASA Marshall Space Flight Center Collection

*The International Space Station has had continuous human occupation since November 2, 2000 and is a cooperative effort of the United States, Russia, Europe, Japan, and Canada.*

► **Example 4** An astronaut's *weight* (or more precisely, *Earth weight*) is the force exerted on the astronaut by the Earth's gravity. As the astronaut moves upward into space, the gravitational pull of the Earth decreases, and hence so does his or her weight. If the Earth is assumed to be a sphere of radius 4000 mi, then it follows from Newton's Law of Universal Gravitation that an astronaut who weighs 150 lb on Earth will have a weight of

$$w(x) = \frac{2{,}400{,}000{,}000}{x^2} \text{ lb}, \quad x \geq 4000$$

at a distance of $x$ miles from the Earth's center (Exercise 25). Use this formula to estimate the work in foot-pounds required to lift the astronaut 220 miles upward to the International Space Station.

***Solution.*** Since the Earth has a radius of 4000 mi, the astronaut is lifted from a point that is 4000 mi from the Earth's center to a point that is 4220 mi from the Earth's center. Thus, from (2), the work $W$ required to lift the astronaut is

$$\begin{aligned}
W &= \int_{4000}^{4220} \frac{2{,}400{,}000{,}000}{x^2}\,dx \\
&= -\frac{2{,}400{,}000{,}000}{x}\bigg]_{4000}^{4220} \\
&\approx -568{,}720 + 600{,}000 \\
&= 31{,}280 \text{ mile-pounds} \\
&= (31{,}280 \text{ mi}\cdot\text{lb}) \times (5280 \text{ ft/mi}) \\
&\approx 1.65 \times 10^8 \text{ ft}\cdot\text{lb} \ ◀
\end{aligned}$$

## CALCULATING WORK FROM BASIC PRINCIPLES

Some problems cannot be solved by mechanically substituting into formulas, and one must return to basic principles to obtain solutions. This is illustrated in the next example.

► **Example 5** Figure 6.6.4*a* shows a conical container of radius 10 ft and height 30 ft. Suppose that this container is filled with water to a depth of 15 ft. How much work is required to pump all of the water out through a hole in the top of the container?

***Solution.*** Our strategy will be to divide the water into thin layers, approximate the work required to move each layer to the top of the container, add the approximations for the layers to obtain a Riemann sum that approximates the total work, and then take the limit of the Riemann sums to produce an integral for the total work.

To implement this idea, introduce an $x$-axis as shown in Figure 6.6.4$a$, and divide the water into $n$ layers with $\Delta x_k$ denoting the thickness of the $k$th layer. This division induces a partition of the interval [15, 30] into $n$ subintervals. Although the upper and lower surfaces of the $k$th layer are at different distances from the top, the difference will be small if the layer is thin, and we can reasonably assume that the entire layer is concentrated at a single point $x_k^*$ (Figure 6.6.4$a$). Thus, the work $W_k$ required to move the $k$th layer to the top of the container is approximately

$$W_k \approx F_k x_k^* \tag{4}$$

where $F_k$ is the force required to lift the $k$th layer. But the force required to lift the $k$th layer is the force needed to overcome gravity, and this is the same as the weight of the layer. If the layer is very thin, we can approximate the volume of the $k$th layer with the volume of a cylinder of height $\Delta x_k$ and radius $r_k$, where (by similar triangles)

$$\frac{r_k}{x_k^*} = \frac{10}{30} = \frac{1}{3}$$

or, equivalently, $r_k = x_k^*/3$ (Figure 6.6.4$b$). Therefore, the volume of the $k$th layer of water is approximately

$$\pi r_k^2 \Delta x_k = \pi (x_k^*/3)^2 \Delta x_k = \frac{\pi}{9}(x_k^*)^2 \Delta x_k$$

Since the weight density of water is 62.4 lb/ft$^3$, it follows that

$$F_k \approx \frac{62.4\pi}{9}(x_k^*)^2 \Delta x_k$$

Thus, from (4)

$$W_k \approx \left(\frac{62.4\pi}{9}(x_k^*)^2 \Delta x_k\right) x_k^* = \frac{62.4\pi}{9}(x_k^*)^3 \Delta x_k$$

and hence the work $W$ required to move all $n$ layers has the approximation

$$W = \sum_{k=1}^{n} W_k \approx \sum_{k=1}^{n} \frac{62.4\pi}{9}(x_k^*)^3 \Delta x_k$$

To find the *exact* value of the work we take the limit as max $\Delta x_k \to 0$. This yields

$$W = \lim_{\max \Delta x_k \to 0} \sum_{k=1}^{n} \frac{62.4\pi}{9}(x_k^*)^3 \Delta x_k = \int_{15}^{30} \frac{62.4\pi}{9} x^3\, dx$$

$$= \frac{62.4\pi}{9}\left(\frac{x^4}{4}\right)\Bigg]_{15}^{30} = 1{,}316{,}250\pi \approx 4{,}135{,}000 \text{ ft·lb} \blacktriangleleft$$

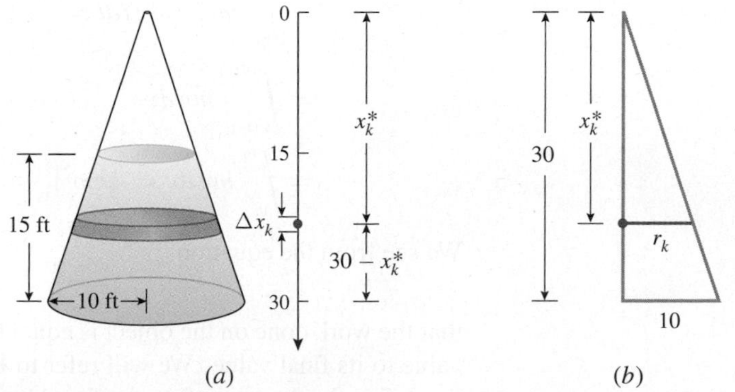


▶ **Figure 6.6.4**

## THE WORK–ENERGY RELATIONSHIP

When you see an object in motion, you can be certain that somehow work has been expended to create that motion. For example, when you drop a stone from a building, the stone gathers speed because the force of the Earth's gravity is performing work on it, and when a hockey player strikes a puck with a hockey stick, the work performed on the puck

Andrey Yurlov/Shutterstock

*The work performed by the skater's stick in a brief interval of time produces the blinding speed of the hockey puck.*

during the brief period of contact with the stick creates the enormous speed of the puck across the ice. However, experience shows that the speed obtained by an object depends not only on the amount of work done, but also on the mass of the object. For example, the work required to throw a 5 oz baseball 50 mi/h would accelerate a 10 lb bowling ball to less than 9 mi/h.

Using the method of substitution for definite integrals, we will derive a simple equation that relates the work done on an object to the object's mass and velocity. Furthermore, this equation will allow us to motivate an appropriate definition for the "energy of motion" of an object. As in Definition 6.6.3, we will assume that an object moves in the positive direction along a coordinate line over the interval $[a, b]$ while subjected to a force $F(x)$ that is applied in the direction of motion. We let $m$ denote the mass of the object, and we let $x = x(t)$, $v = v(t) = x'(t)$, and $a = a(t) = v'(t)$ denote the respective position, velocity, and acceleration of the object at time $t$. We will need the following important result from physics that relates the force acting on an object with the mass and acceleration of the object.

**6.6.4 NEWTON'S SECOND LAW OF MOTION** If an object with mass $m$ is subjected to a force $F$, then the object undergoes an acceleration $a$ that satisfies the equation

$$F = ma \tag{5}$$

It follows from Newton's Second Law of Motion that

$$F(x(t)) = ma(t) = mv'(t)$$

Assume that

$$x(t_0) = a \quad \text{and} \quad x(t_1) = b$$

with

$$v(t_0) = v_i \quad \text{and} \quad v(t_1) = v_f$$

the initial and final velocities of the object, respectively. Then

$$\begin{aligned}
W &= \int_a^b F(x)\,dx = \int_{x(t_0)}^{x(t_1)} F(x)\,dx \\
&= \int_{t_0}^{t_1} F(x(t))x'(t)\,dt && \boxed{\text{By Theorem 5.9.1 with } x = x(t),\ dx = x'(t)\,dt} \\
&= \int_{t_0}^{t_1} mv'(t)v(t)\,dt = \int_{t_0}^{t_1} mv(t)v'(t)\,dt \\
&= \int_{v(t_0)}^{v(t_1)} mv\,dv && \boxed{\text{By Theorem 5.9.1 with } v = v(t),\ dv = v'(t)\,dt} \\
&= \int_{v_i}^{v_f} mv\,dv = \tfrac{1}{2}mv^2\Big|_{v_i}^{v_f} = \tfrac{1}{2}mv_f^2 - \tfrac{1}{2}mv_i^2
\end{aligned}$$

We see from the equation

$$W = \tfrac{1}{2}mv_f^2 - \tfrac{1}{2}mv_i^2 \tag{6}$$

that the work done on the object is equal to the change in the quantity $\frac{1}{2}mv^2$ from its initial value to its final value. We will refer to Equation (6) as the ***work–energy relationship***. If we define the "energy of motion" or ***kinetic energy*** of our object to be given by

$$K = \tfrac{1}{2}mv^2 \tag{7}$$

then Equation (6) tells us that the work done on an object is equal to the *change* in the object's kinetic energy. Loosely speaking, we may think of work done on an object as being "transformed" into kinetic energy of the object. The units of kinetic energy are the same as the units of work. For example, in SI kinetic energy is measured in joules (J).

► **Example 6** A space probe of mass $m = 5.00 \times 10^4$ kg travels in deep space subjected only to the force of its own engine. Starting at a time when the speed of the probe is $v = 1.10 \times 10^4$ m/s, the engine is fired continuously over a distance of $2.50 \times 10^6$ m with a constant force of $4.00 \times 10^5$ N in the direction of motion. What is the final speed of the probe?

***Solution.*** Since the force applied by the engine is constant and in the direction of motion, the work $W$ expended by the engine on the probe is

$$W = \text{force} \times \text{distance} = (4.00 \times 10^5 \text{ N}) \times (2.50 \times 10^6 \text{ m}) = 1.00 \times 10^{12} \text{ J}$$

From (6), the final kinetic energy $K_f = \frac{1}{2}mv_f^2$ of the probe can be expressed in terms of the work $W$ and the initial kinetic energy $K_i = \frac{1}{2}mv_i^2$ as

$$K_f = W + K_i$$

Thus, from the known mass and initial speed we have

$$K_f = (1.00 \times 10^{12} \text{ J}) + \tfrac{1}{2}(5.00 \times 10^4 \text{ kg})(1.10 \times 10^4 \text{ m/s})^2 = 4.025 \times 10^{12} \text{ J}$$

The final kinetic energy is $K_f = \frac{1}{2}mv_f^2$, so the final speed of the probe is

$$v_f = \sqrt{\frac{2K_f}{m}} = \sqrt{\frac{2(4.025 \times 10^{12})}{5.00 \times 10^4}} \approx 1.27 \times 10^4 \text{ m/s} \blacktriangleleft$$

## ✓ QUICK CHECK EXERCISES 6.6 (See page 383 for answers.)

1. If a constant force of 5 lb moves an object 10 ft, then the work done by the force on the object is ________.
2. A newton-meter is also called a ________. A dyne-centimeter is also called an ________.
3. Suppose that an object moves in the positive direction along a coordinate line over the interval $[a, b]$. The work performed on the object by a variable force $F(x)$ applied in the direction of motion is $W =$ ________.
4. A force $F(x) = 10 - 2x$ N applied in the positive $x$-direction moves an object 3 m from $x = 2$ to $x = 5$. The work done by the force on the object is ________.

## EXERCISE SET 6.6

**FOCUS ON CONCEPTS**

1. A variable force $F(x)$ in the positive $x$-direction is graphed in the accompanying figure. Find the work done by the force on a particle that moves from $x = 0$ to $x = 3$.

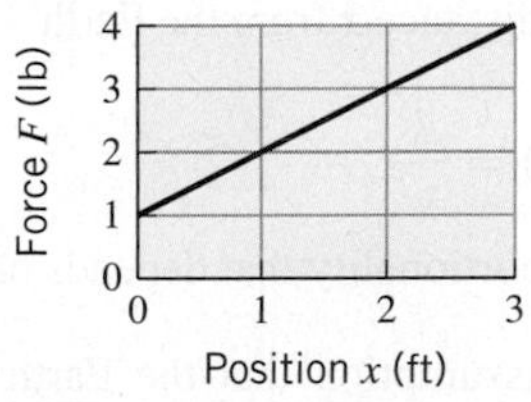

◄ **Figure Ex-1**

2. A variable force $F(x)$ in the positive $x$-direction is graphed in the accompanying figure. Find the work done by the force on a particle that moves from $x = 0$ to $x = 5$.

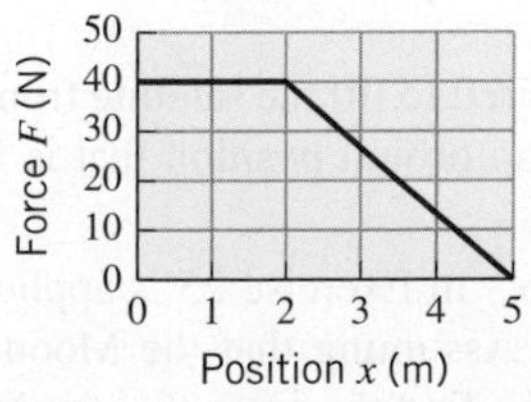

◄ **Figure Ex-2**

3. For the variable force $F(x)$ in Exercise 2, consider the distance $d$ for which the work done by the force on the particle when the particle moves from $x = 0$ to $x = d$ is half of the work done when the particle moves from $x = 0$ to $x = 5$. By inspecting the graph of $F$, is $d$ more or less than 2.5? Explain, and then find the exact value of $d$.

4. Suppose that a variable force $F(x)$ is applied in the positive $x$-direction so that an object moves from $x = a$ to $x = b$. Relate the work done by the force on the object and the average value of $F$ over $[a, b]$, and illustrate this relationship graphically.

5. A constant force of 10 lb in the positive $x$-direction is applied to a particle whose velocity versus time curve is shown in the accompanying figure. Find the work done by the force on the particle from time $t = 0$ to $t = 5$.

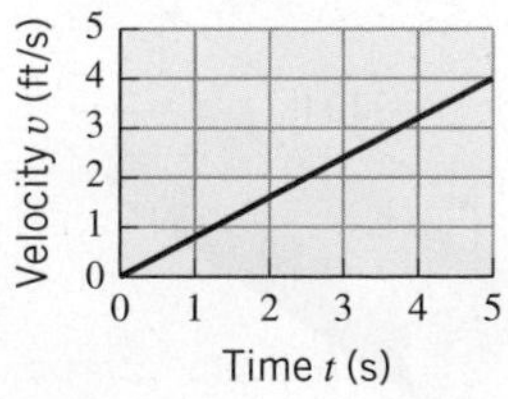

◄ **Figure Ex-5**

**6.** A spring exerts a force of 6 N when it is stretched from its natural length of 4 m to a length of $4\frac{1}{2}$ m. Find the work required to stretch the spring from its natural length to a length of 6 m.

**7.** A spring exerts a force of 100 N when it is stretched 0.2 m beyond its natural length. How much work is required to stretch the spring 0.8 m beyond its natural length?

**8.** A spring whose natural length is 15 cm exerts a force of 45 N when stretched to a length of 20 cm.
(a) Find the spring constant (in newtons/meter).
(b) Find the work that is done in stretching the spring 3 cm beyond its natural length.
(c) Find the work done in stretching the spring from a length of 20 cm to a length of 25 cm.

**9.** Assume that 10 ft·lb of work is required to stretch a spring 1 ft beyond its natural length. What is the spring constant?

**10–13 True–False** Determine whether the statement is true or false. Explain your answer. ■

**10.** In order to support the weight of a parked automobile, the surface of a driveway must do work against the force of gravity on the vehicle.

**11.** A force of 10 lb in the direction of motion of an object that moves 5 ft in 2 s does six times the work of a force of 10 lb in the direction of motion of an object that moves 5 ft in 12 s.

**12.** It follows from Hooke's law that in order to double the distance a spring is stretched beyond its natural length, four times as much work is required.

**13.** In the International System of Units, work and kinetic energy have the same units.

**14.** A cylindrical tank of radius 5 ft and height 9 ft is two-thirds filled with water. Find the work required to pump all the water over the upper rim.

**15.** Solve Exercise 14 assuming that the tank is half-filled with water.

**16.** A cone-shaped water reservoir is 20 ft in diameter across the top and 15 ft deep. If the reservoir is filled to a depth of 10 ft, how much work is required to pump all the water to the top of the reservoir?

**17.** The vat shown in the accompanying figure contains water to a depth of 2 m. Find the work required to pump all the water to the top of the vat. [Use 9810 N/m$^3$ as the weight density of water.]

**18.** The cylindrical tank shown in the accompanying figure is filled with a liquid weighing 50 lb/ft$^3$. Find the work required to pump all the liquid to a level 1 ft above the top of the tank.

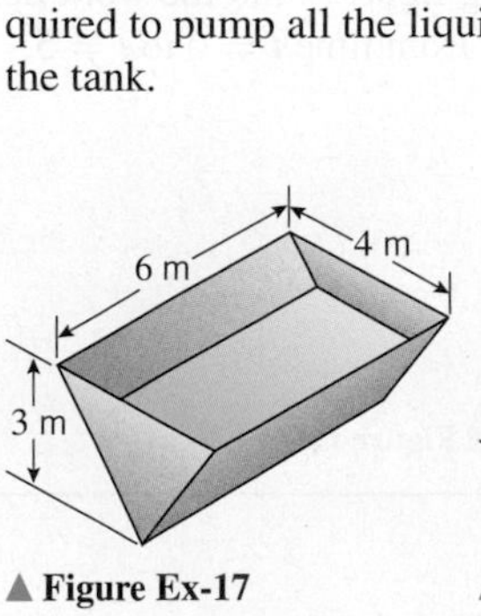

▲ **Figure Ex-17**

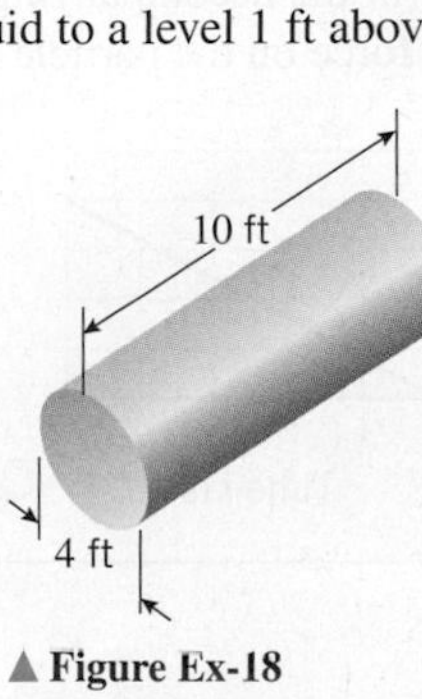

▲ **Figure Ex-18**

**19.** A swimming pool is built in the shape of a rectangular parallelepiped 10 ft deep, 15 ft wide, and 20 ft long.
(a) If the pool is filled to 1 ft below the top, how much work is required to pump all the water into a drain at the top edge of the pool?
(b) A one-horsepower motor can do 550 ft·lb of work per second. What size motor is required to empty the pool in 1 hour?

**20.** How much work is required to fill the swimming pool in Exercise 19 to 1 ft below the top if the water is pumped in through an opening located at the bottom of the pool?

**21.** A 100 ft length of steel chain weighing 15 lb/ft is dangling from a pulley. How much work is required to wind the chain onto the pulley?

**22.** A 3 lb bucket containing 20 lb of water is hanging at the end of a 20 ft rope that weighs 4 oz/ft. The other end of the rope is attached to a pulley. How much work is required to wind the length of rope onto the pulley, assuming that the rope is wound onto the pulley at a rate of 2 ft/s and that as the bucket is being lifted, water leaks from the bucket at a rate of 0.5 lb/s?

**23.** A rocket weighing 3 tons is filled with 40 tons of liquid fuel. In the initial part of the flight, fuel is burned off at a constant rate of 2 tons per 1000 ft of vertical height. How much work in foot-tons (ft·ton) is done lifting the rocket 3000 ft?

**24.** It follows from Coulomb's law in physics that two like electrostatic charges repel each other with a force inversely proportional to the square of the distance between them. Suppose that two charges $A$ and $B$ repel with a force of $k$ newtons when they are positioned at points $A(-a, 0)$ and $B(a, 0)$, where $a$ is measured in meters. Find the work $W$ required to move charge $A$ along the $x$-axis to the origin if charge $B$ remains stationary.

**25.** It follows from Newton's Law of Universal Gravitation that the gravitational force exerted by the Earth on an object above the Earth's surface varies inversely as the square of its distance from the Earth's center. Thus, an object's weight $w(x)$ is related to its distance $x$ from the Earth's center by a formula of the form

$$w(x) = \frac{k}{x^2}$$

where $k$ is a constant of proportionality that depends on the mass of the object.
(a) Use this fact and the assumption that the Earth is a sphere of radius 4000 mi to obtain the formula for $w(x)$ in Example 4.
(b) Find a formula for the weight $w(x)$ of a satellite that is $x$ mi from the Earth's surface if its weight on Earth is 6000 lb.
(c) How much work is required to lift the satellite from the surface of the Earth to an orbital position that is 1000 mi high?

**26.** (a) The formula $w(x) = k/x^2$ in Exercise 25 is applicable to all celestial bodies. Assuming that the Moon is a sphere of radius 1080 mi, find the force that the Moon exerts on an astronaut who is $x$ mi from the surface of the Moon if her weight on the Moon's surface is 20 lb.

*(cont.)*

(b) How much work is required to lift the astronaut to a point that is 10.8 mi above the Moon's surface?

**27.** The world's first commercial high-speed magnetic levitation (MAGLEV) train, a 30 km double-track project connecting Shanghai, China, to Pudong International Airport, began full revenue service in 2003. Suppose that a MAGLEV train has a mass $m = 4.00 \times 10^5$ kg and that starting at a time when the train has a speed of 20 m/s the engine applies a force of $6.40 \times 10^5$ N in the direction of motion over a distance of $3.00 \times 10^3$ m. Use the work–energy relationship (6) to find the final speed of the train.

**28.** Assume that a Mars probe of mass $m = 2.00 \times 10^3$ kg is subjected only to the force of its own engine. Starting at a time when the speed of the probe is $v = 1.00 \times 10^4$ m/s, the engine is fired continuously over a distance of $1.50 \times 10^5$ m with a constant force of $2.00 \times 10^5$ N in the direction of motion. Use the work–energy relationship (6) to find the final speed of the probe.

**29.** On August 10, 1972 a meteorite with an estimated mass of $4 \times 10^6$ kg and an estimated speed of 15 km/s skipped across the atmosphere above the western United States and Canada but fortunately did not hit the Earth.

(a) Assuming that the meteorite had hit the Earth with a speed of 15 km/s, what would have been its change in kinetic energy in joules (J)?

(b) Express the energy as a multiple of the explosive energy of 1 megaton of TNT, which is $4.2 \times 10^{15}$ J.

(c) The energy associated with the Hiroshima atomic bomb was 13 kilotons of TNT. To how many such bombs would the meteorite impact have been equivalent?

**30. Writing** After reading Examples 3–5, a student classifies work problems as either "pushing/pulling" or "pumping." Describe these categories in your own words and discuss the methods used to solve each type. Give examples to illustrate that these categories are not mutually exclusive.

**31. Writing** How might you recognize that a problem can be solved by means of the work–energy relationship? That is, what sort of "givens" and "unknowns" would suggest such a solution? Discuss two or three examples.

✓ **QUICK CHECK ANSWERS 6.6** 1. 50 ft·lb 2. joule; erg 3. $\int_a^b F(x)\,dx$ 4. 9 J

## 6.7 MOMENTS, CENTERS OF GRAVITY, AND CENTROIDS

*Suppose that a rigid physical body is acted on by a constant gravitational field. Because the body is composed of many particles, each of which is affected by gravity, the action of the gravitational field on the body consists of a large number of forces distributed over the entire body. However, it is a fact of physics that these individual forces can be replaced by a single force acting at a point called the* ***center of gravity*** *of the body. In this section we will show how integrals can be used to locate centers of gravity.*

### DENSITY AND MASS OF A LAMINA

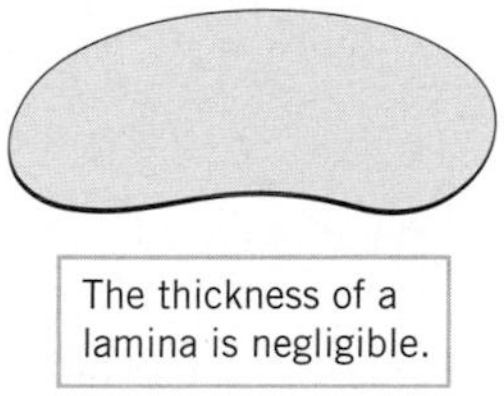

▲ Figure 6.7.1

Let us consider an idealized flat object that is thin enough to be viewed as a two-dimensional plane region (Figure 6.7.1). Such an object is called a ***lamina***. A lamina is called ***homogeneous*** if its composition is uniform throughout and ***inhomogeneous*** otherwise. We will consider homogeneous laminas in this section. Inhomogeneous laminas will be discussed in Chapter 14. The ***density*** of a *homogeneous* lamina is defined to be its mass per unit area. Thus, the density $\delta$ of a homogeneous lamina of mass $M$ and area $A$ is given by $\delta = M/A$. Notice that the mass $M$ of a homogeneous lamina can be expressed as

The units in Equation (1) are consistent since mass = (mass/area) × area.

$$M = \delta A \tag{1}$$

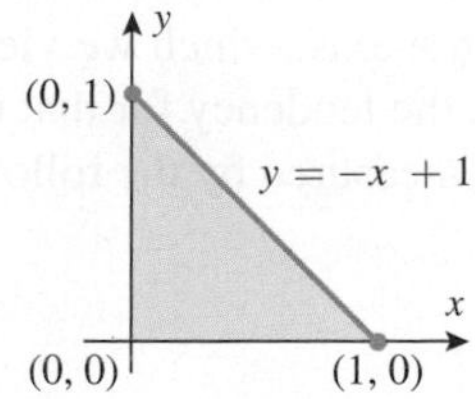

▲ Figure 6.7.2

► **Example 1** A triangular lamina with vertices (0, 0), (0, 1), and (1, 0) has density $\delta = 3$. Find its total mass.

***Solution.*** Referring to (1) and Figure 6.7.2, the mass $M$ of the lamina is

$$M = \delta A = 3 \cdot \frac{1}{2} = \frac{3}{2} \text{ (unit of mass)} \blacktriangleleft$$

## CENTER OF GRAVITY OF A LAMINA

Assume that the acceleration due to the force of gravity is constant and acts downward, and suppose that a lamina occupies a region $R$ in a horizontal $xy$-plane. It can be shown that there exists a unique point $(\bar{x}, \bar{y})$ (which may or may not belong to $R$) such that the effect of gravity on the lamina is "equivalent" to that of a single force acting at the point $(\bar{x}, \bar{y})$. This point is called the ***center of gravity*** of the lamina, and if it is in $R$, then the lamina will balance horizontally on the point of a support placed at $(\bar{x}, \bar{y})$. For example, the center of gravity of a homogeneous disk is at the center of the disk, and the center of gravity of a homogeneous rectangular region is at the center of the rectangle. For an irregularly shaped homogeneous lamina, locating the center of gravity requires calculus.

**6.7.1 PROBLEM** Let $f$ be a positive continuous function on the interval $[a, b]$. Suppose that a homogeneous lamina with constant density $\delta$ occupies a region $R$ in a horizontal $xy$-plane bounded by the graphs of $y = f(x)$, $y = 0$, $x = a$, and $x = b$. Find the coordinates $(\bar{x}, \bar{y})$ of the center of gravity of the lamina.

To motivate the solution, consider what happens if we try to balance the lamina on a knife-edge parallel to the $x$-axis. Suppose the lamina in Figure 6.7.3 is placed on a knife-edge along a line $y = c$ that does not pass through the center of gravity. Because the lamina behaves as if its entire mass is concentrated at the center of gravity $(\bar{x}, \bar{y})$, the lamina will be rotationally unstable and the force of gravity will cause a rotation about $y = c$. Similarly, the lamina will undergo a rotation if placed on a knife-edge along $y = d$. However, if the knife-edge runs along the line $y = \bar{y}$ through the center of gravity, the lamina will be in perfect balance. Similarly, the lamina will be in perfect balance on a knife-edge along the line $x = \bar{x}$ through the center of gravity. This suggests that the center of gravity of a lamina can be determined as the intersection of two lines of balance, one parallel to the $x$-axis and the other parallel to the $y$-axis. In order to find these lines of balance, we will need some preliminary results about rotations.

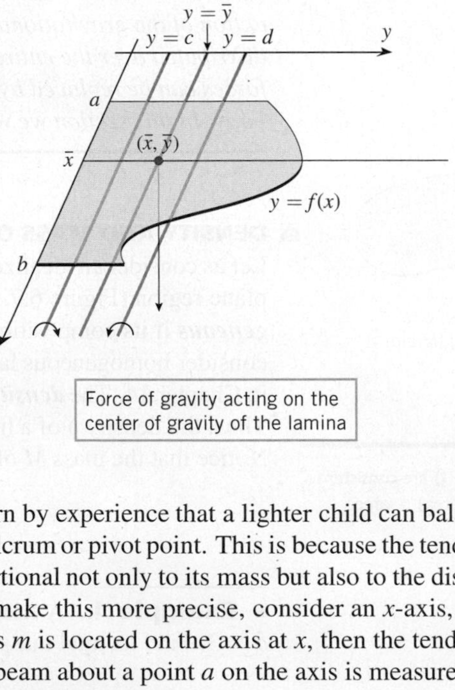

Force of gravity acting on the center of gravity of the lamina

▶ **Figure 6.7.3**

Children on a seesaw learn by experience that a lighter child can balance a heavier one by sitting farther from the fulcrum or pivot point. This is because the tendency for an object to produce rotation is proportional not only to its mass but also to the distance between the object and the fulcrum. To make this more precise, consider an $x$-axis, which we view as a weightless beam. If a mass $m$ is located on the axis at $x$, then the tendency for that mass to produce a rotation of the beam about a point $a$ on the axis is measured by the following quantity, called the ***moment of m about x = a***:

$$\begin{bmatrix}\text{moment of } m\\ \text{about } a\end{bmatrix} = m(x - a)$$

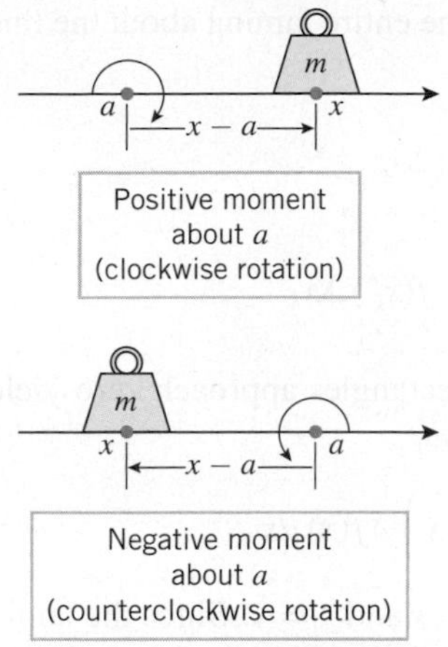

▲ **Figure 6.7.4**

The number $x - a$ is called the ***lever arm***. Depending on whether the mass is to the right or left of $a$, the lever arm is either the distance between $x$ and $a$ or the negative of this distance (Figure 6.7.4). Positive lever arms result in positive moments and clockwise rotations, and negative lever arms result in negative moments and counterclockwise rotations.

Suppose that masses $m_1, m_2, \ldots, m_n$ are located at $x_1, x_2, \ldots, x_n$ on a coordinate axis and a fulcrum is positioned at the point $a$ (Figure 6.7.5). Depending on whether the sum of the moments about $a$,

$$\sum_{k=1}^{n} m_k(x_k - a) = m_1(x_1 - a) + m_2(x_2 - a) + \cdots + m_n(x_n - a)$$

is positive, negative, or zero, a weightless beam along the axis will rotate clockwise about $a$, rotate counterclockwise about $a$, or balance perfectly. In the last case, the system of masses is said to be in ***equilibrium***.

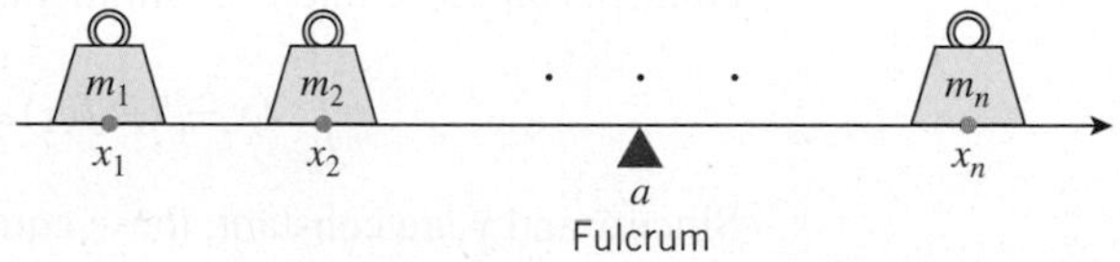

▶ **Figure 6.7.5**

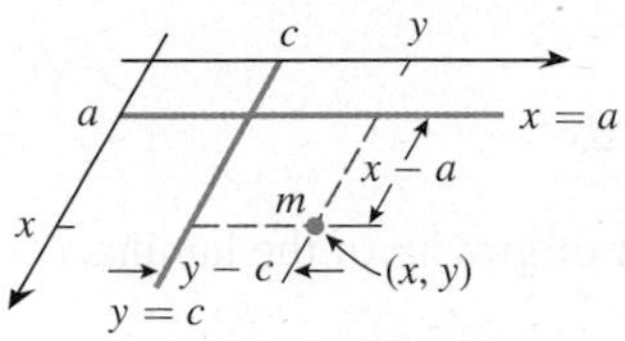

▲ **Figure 6.7.6**

The preceding ideas can be extended to masses distributed in two-dimensional space. If we imagine the $xy$-plane to be a weightless sheet supporting a mass $m$ located at a point $(x, y)$, then the tendency for the mass to produce a rotation of the sheet about the line $x = a$ is $m(x - a)$, called the ***moment of m about x = a***, and the tendency for the mass to produce a rotation about the line $y = c$ is $m(y - c)$, called the ***moment of m about y = c*** (Figure 6.7.6). In summary,

$$\begin{bmatrix}\text{moment of } m \\ \text{about the} \\ \text{line } x = a\end{bmatrix} = m(x - a) \quad \text{and} \quad \begin{bmatrix}\text{moment of } m \\ \text{about the} \\ \text{line } y = c\end{bmatrix} = m(y - c) \tag{2–3}$$

If a number of masses are distributed throughout the $xy$-plane, then the plane (viewed as a weightless sheet) will balance on a knife-edge along the line $x = a$ if the sum of the moments about the line is zero. Similarly, the plane will balance on a knife-edge along the line $y = c$ if the sum of the moments about that line are zero.

We are now ready to solve Problem 6.7.1. The basic idea for solving this problem is to divide the lamina into strips whose areas may be approximated by the areas of rectangles. These area approximations, along with Formulas (2) and (3), will allow us to create a Riemann sum that approximates the moment of the lamina about a horizontal or vertical line. By taking the limit of Riemann sums we will then obtain an integral for the moment of a lamina about a horizontal or vertical line. We observe that since the lamina balances on the lines $x = \bar{x}$ and $y = \bar{y}$, the moment of the lamina about those lines should be zero. This observation will enable us to calculate $\bar{x}$ and $\bar{y}$.

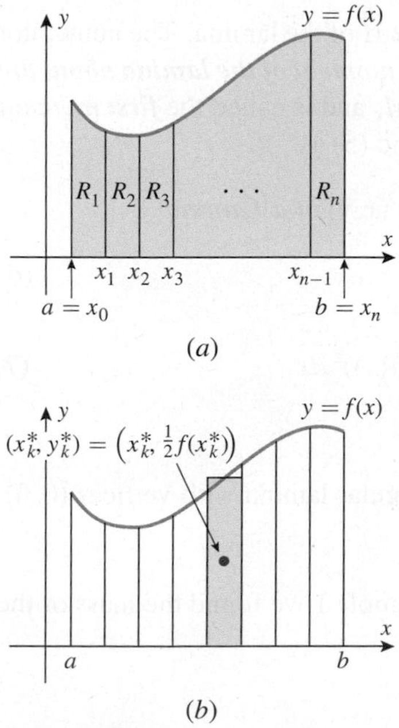

▲ **Figure 6.7.7**

To implement this idea, we divide the interval $[a, b]$ into $n$ subintervals by inserting the points $x_1, x_2, \ldots, x_{n-1}$ between $a = x_0$ and $b = x_n$. This has the effect of dividing the lamina $R$ into $n$ strips $R_1, R_2, \ldots, R_n$ (Figure 6.7.7$a$). Suppose that the $k$th strip extends from $x_{k-1}$ to $x_k$ and that the width of this strip is

$$\Delta x_k = x_k - x_{k-1}$$

We will let $x_k^*$ be the midpoint of the $k$th subinterval and we will approximate $R_k$ by a rectangle of width $\Delta x_k$ and height $f(x_k^*)$. From (1), the mass $\Delta M_k$ of this rectangle is $\Delta M_k = \delta f(x_k^*)\Delta x_k$, and we will assume that the rectangle behaves as if its entire mass is concentrated at its center $(x_k^*, y_k^*) = (x_k^*, \frac{1}{2}f(x_k^*))$ (Figure 6.7.7$b$). It then follows from (2) and (3) that the moments of $R_k$ about the lines $x = \bar{x}$ and $y = \bar{y}$ may be approximated by $(x_k^* - \bar{x})\Delta M_k$ and $(y_k^* - \bar{y})\Delta M_k$, respectively. Adding these approximations yields the following Riemann sums that approximate the moment of the entire lamina about the lines $x = \bar{x}$ and $y = \bar{y}$:

$$\sum_{k=1}^{n} (x_k^* - \bar{x})\Delta M_k = \sum_{k=1}^{n} (x_k^* - \bar{x})\delta f(x_k^*)\Delta x_k$$

$$\sum_{k=1}^{n} (y_k^* - \bar{y})\Delta M_k = \sum_{k=1}^{n} \left(\frac{f(x_k^*)}{2} - \bar{y}\right) \delta f(x_k^*)\Delta x_k$$

Taking the limits as $n$ increases and the widths of all the rectangles approach zero yields the definite integrals

$$\int_a^b (x - \bar{x})\delta f(x)\,dx \quad \text{and} \quad \int_a^b \left(\frac{f(x)}{2} - \bar{y}\right) \delta f(x)\,dx$$

that represent the moments of the lamina about the lines $x = \bar{x}$ and $y = \bar{y}$. Since the lamina balances on those lines, the moments of the lamina about those lines should be zero:

$$\int_a^b (x - \bar{x})\delta f(x)\,dx = \int_a^b \left(\frac{f(x)}{2} - \bar{y}\right) \delta f(x)\,dx = 0$$

Since $\bar{x}$ and $\bar{y}$ are constant, these equations can be rewritten as

$$\int_a^b \delta x f(x)\,dx = \bar{x}\int_a^b \delta f(x)\,dx$$

$$\int_a^b \frac{1}{2}\delta(f(x))^2\,dx = \bar{y}\int_a^b \delta f(x)\,dx$$

from which we obtain the following formulas for the center of gravity of the lamina:

***Center of Gravity $(\bar{x}, \bar{y})$ of a Lamina***

$$\bar{x} = \frac{\displaystyle\int_a^b \delta x f(x)\,dx}{\displaystyle\int_a^b \delta f(x)\,dx}, \qquad \bar{y} = \frac{\displaystyle\int_a^b \frac{1}{2}\delta(f(x))^2\,dx}{\displaystyle\int_a^b \delta f(x)\,dx} \tag{4–5}$$

Observe that in both formulas the denominator is the mass $M$ of the lamina. The numerator in the formula for $\bar{x}$ is denoted by $M_y$ and is called the ***first moment of the lamina about the y-axis***; the numerator of the formula for $\bar{y}$ is denoted by $M_x$ and is called the ***first moment of the lamina about the x-axis***. Thus, we can write (4) and (5) as

***Alternative Formulas for Center of Gravity $(\bar{x}, \bar{y})$ of a Lamina***

$$\bar{x} = \frac{M_y}{M} = \frac{1}{\text{mass of } R}\int_a^b \delta x f(x)\,dx \tag{6}$$

$$\bar{y} = \frac{M_x}{M} = \frac{1}{\text{mass of } R}\int_a^b \frac{1}{2}\delta(f(x))^2\,dx \tag{7}$$

▶ **Example 2** Find the center of gravity of the triangular lamina with vertices $(0, 0)$, $(0, 1)$, and $(1, 0)$ and density $\delta = 3$.

***Solution.*** The lamina is shown in Figure 6.7.2. In Example 1 we found the mass of the lamina to be

$$M = \frac{3}{2}$$

The moment of the lamina about the $y$-axis is

$$M_y = \int_0^1 \delta x f(x)\,dx = \int_0^1 3x(-x + 1)\,dx$$

$$= \int_0^1 (-3x^2 + 3x)\,dx = \left(-x^3 + \frac{3}{2}x^2\right)\Bigg]_0^1 = -1 + \frac{3}{2} = \frac{1}{2}$$

and the moment about the $x$-axis is

$$M_x = \int_0^1 \frac{1}{2}\delta(f(x))^2\,dx = \int_0^1 \frac{3}{2}(-x+1)^2\,dx$$
$$= \int_0^1 \frac{3}{2}(x^2 - 2x + 1)\,dx = \frac{3}{2}\left(\frac{1}{3}x^3 - x^2 + x\right)\bigg]_0^1 = \frac{3}{2}\left(\frac{1}{3}\right) = \frac{1}{2}$$

From (6) and (7),

$$\bar{x} = \frac{M_y}{M} = \frac{1/2}{3/2} = \frac{1}{3}, \qquad \bar{y} = \frac{M_x}{M} = \frac{1/2}{3/2} = \frac{1}{3}$$

so the center of gravity is $\left(\frac{1}{3}, \frac{1}{3}\right)$. ◀

In the case of a *homogeneous* lamina, the center of gravity of a lamina occupying the region $R$ is called the ***centroid of the region R***. Since the lamina is homogeneous, $\delta$ is constant. The factor $\delta$ in (4) and (5) may thus be moved through the integral signs and canceled, and (4) and (5) can be expressed as

Since the density factor has canceled, we may interpret the centroid as a ***geometric property*** of the region, and distinguish it from the center of gravity, which is a ***physical property*** of an idealized object that occupies the region.

***Centroid of a Region R***

$$\bar{x} = \frac{\displaystyle\int_a^b x f(x)\,dx}{\displaystyle\int_a^b f(x)\,dx} = \frac{1}{\text{area of } R}\int_a^b x f(x)\,dx \tag{8}$$

$$\bar{y} = \frac{\displaystyle\int_a^b \frac{1}{2}(f(x))^2\,dx}{\displaystyle\int_a^b f(x)\,dx} = \frac{1}{\text{area of } R}\int_a^b \frac{1}{2}(f(x))^2\,dx \tag{9}$$

► **Example 3** Find the centroid of the semicircular region in Figure 6.7.8.

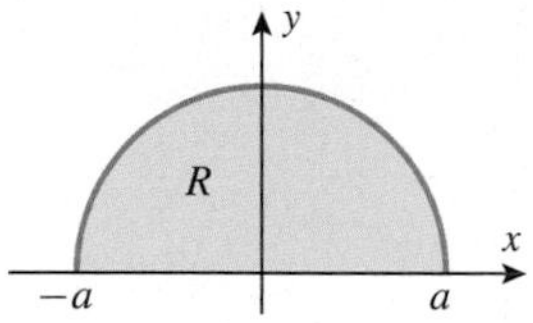

▲ **Figure 6.7.8**

***Solution.*** By symmetry, $\bar{x} = 0$ since the $y$-axis is obviously a line of balance. To find $\bar{y}$, first note that the equation of the semicircle is $y = f(x) = \sqrt{a^2 - x^2}$. From (9),

$$\bar{y} = \frac{1}{\text{area of } R}\int_{-a}^{a} \frac{1}{2}(f(x))^2\,dx = \frac{1}{\frac{1}{2}\pi a^2}\int_{-a}^{a} \frac{1}{2}(a^2 - x^2)\,dx$$
$$= \frac{1}{\pi a^2}\left(a^2 x - \frac{1}{3}x^3\right)\bigg]_{-a}^{a}$$
$$= \frac{1}{\pi a^2}\left[\left(a^3 - \frac{1}{3}a^3\right) - \left(-a^3 + \frac{1}{3}a^3\right)\right]$$
$$= \frac{1}{\pi a^2}\left(\frac{4a^3}{3}\right) = \frac{4a}{3\pi}$$

so the centroid is $(0, 4a/3\pi)$. ◀

## ■ OTHER TYPES OF REGIONS

The strategy used to find the center of gravity of the region in Problem 6.7.1 can be used to find the center of gravity of regions that are not of that form.

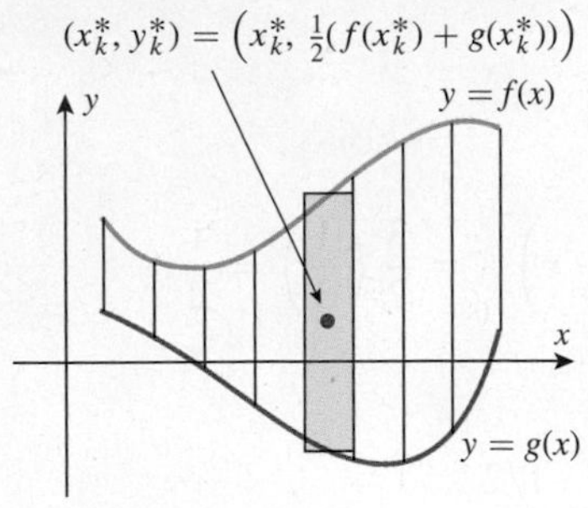

▲ Figure 6.7.9

Consider a homogeneous lamina that occupies the region $R$ between two continuous functions $f(x)$ and $g(x)$ over the interval $[a, b]$, where $f(x) \geq g(x)$ for $a \leq x \leq b$. To find the center of gravity of this lamina we can subdivide it into $n$ strips using lines parallel to the $y$-axis. If $x_k^*$ is the midpoint of the $k$th strip, the strip can be approximated by a rectangle of width $\Delta x_k$ and height $f(x_k^*) - g(x_k^*)$. We assume that the entire mass of the $k$th rectangle is concentrated at its center $(x_k^*, y_k^*) = (x_k^*, \frac{1}{2}(f(x_k^*) + g(x_k^*)))$ (Figure 6.7.9). Continuing the argument as in the solution of Problem 6.7.1, we find that the center of gravity of the lamina is

$$\bar{x} = \frac{\displaystyle\int_a^b x(f(x) - g(x))\,dx}{\displaystyle\int_a^b (f(x) - g(x))\,dx} = \frac{1}{\text{area of } R}\int_a^b x(f(x) - g(x))\,dx \tag{10}$$

$$\bar{y} = \frac{\displaystyle\int_a^b \frac{1}{2}\left([f(x)]^2 - [g(x)]^2\right)\,dx}{\displaystyle\int_a^b (f(x) - g(x))\,dx} = \frac{1}{\text{area of } R}\int_a^b \frac{1}{2}\left([f(x)]^2 - [g(x)]^2\right)\,dx \tag{11}$$

Note that the density of the lamina does not appear in Equations (10) and (11). This reflects the fact that the centroid is a geometric property of $R$.

▶ **Example 4** Find the centroid of the region $R$ enclosed between the curves $y = x^2$ and $y = x + 6$.

***Solution.*** To begin, we note that the two curves intersect when $x = -2$ and $x = 3$ and that $x + 6 \geq x^2$ over that interval (Figure 6.7.10). The area of $R$ is

$$\int_{-2}^{3} [(x + 6) - x^2]\,dx = \frac{125}{6}$$

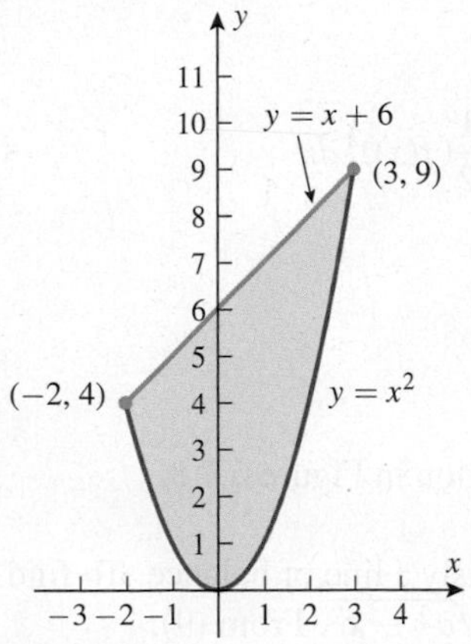

▲ Figure 6.7.10

From (10) and (11),

$$\begin{aligned}\bar{x} &= \frac{1}{\text{area of } R}\int_{-2}^{3} x[(x + 6) - x^2]\,dx \\ &= \frac{6}{125}\left(\frac{1}{3}x^3 + 3x^2 - \frac{1}{4}x^4\right)\Bigg]_{-2}^{3} \\ &= \frac{6}{125}\cdot\frac{125}{12} = \frac{1}{2}\end{aligned}$$

and

$$\begin{aligned}\bar{y} &= \frac{1}{\text{area of } R}\int_{-2}^{3} \frac{1}{2}((x + 6)^2 - (x^2)^2)\,dx \\ &= \frac{6}{125}\int_{-2}^{3} \frac{1}{2}(x^2 + 12x + 36 - x^4)\,dx \\ &= \frac{6}{125}\cdot\frac{1}{2}\left(\frac{1}{3}x^3 + 6x^2 + 36x - \frac{1}{5}x^5\right)\Bigg]_{-2}^{3} \\ &= \frac{6}{125}\cdot\frac{250}{3} = 4\end{aligned}$$

so the centroid of $R$ is $(\frac{1}{2}, 4)$. ◀

Suppose that $w$ is a continuous function of $y$ on an interval $[c, d]$ with $w(y) \geq 0$ for $c \leq y \leq d$. Consider a lamina that occupies a region $R$ bounded above by $y = d$, below by $y = c$, on the left by the $y$-axis, and on the right by $x = w(y)$ (Figure 6.7.11). To find the center of gravity of this lamina, we note that the roles of $x$ and $y$ in Problem 6.7.1 have been reversed. We now imagine the lamina to be subdivided into $n$ strips using lines parallel to the $x$-axis. We let $y_k^*$ be the midpoint of the $k$th subinterval and approximate the strip by

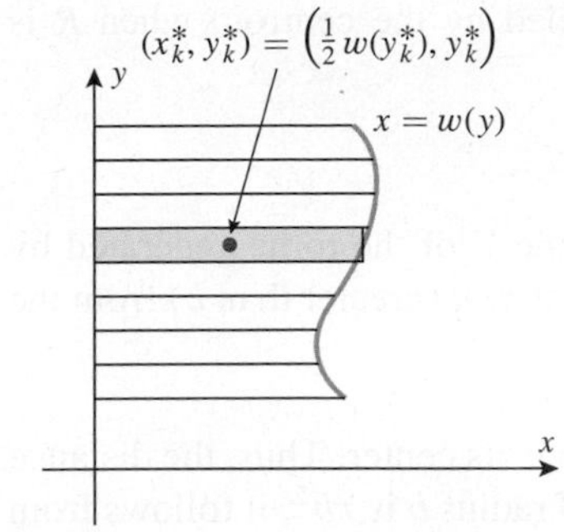


▲ Figure 6.7.11

a rectangle of width $\Delta y_k$ and height $w(y_k^*)$. We assume that the entire mass of the $k$th rectangle is concentrated at its center $(x_k^*, y_k^*) = (\frac{1}{2}w(y_k^*), y_k^*)$ (Figure 6.7.11). Continuing the argument as in the solution of Problem 6.7.1, we find that the center of gravity of the lamina is

$$\bar{x} = \frac{\displaystyle\int_c^d \frac{1}{2}(w(y))^2\, dy}{\displaystyle\int_c^d w(y)\, dy} = \frac{1}{\text{area of } R}\int_c^d \frac{1}{2}(w(y))^2\, dy \tag{12}$$

$$\bar{y} = \frac{\displaystyle\int_c^d yw(y)\, dy}{\displaystyle\int_c^d w(y)\, dy} = \frac{1}{\text{area of } R}\int_c^d yw(y)\, dy \tag{13}$$

Once again, the absence of the density in Equations (12) and (13) reflects the geometric nature of the centroid.

**▶ Example 5** Find the centroid of the region $R$ enclosed between the curves $y = \sqrt{x}$, $y = 1$, $y = 2$, and the $y$-axis (Figure 6.7.12).

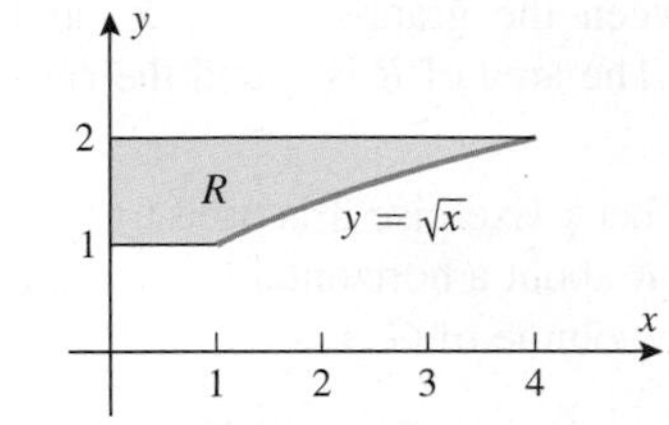


▲ Figure 6.7.12

***Solution.*** Note that $x = w(y) = y^2$ and that the area of $R$ is

$$\int_1^2 y^2\, dy = \frac{7}{3}$$

From (12) and (13),

$$\bar{x} = \frac{1}{\text{area of } R}\int_1^2 \frac{1}{2}(y^2)^2\, dy = \frac{3}{7}\cdot\frac{1}{10}y^5\bigg]_1^2 = \frac{3}{7}\cdot\frac{31}{10} = \frac{93}{70}$$

$$\bar{y} = \frac{1}{\text{area of } R}\int_1^2 y(y^2)\, dy = \frac{3}{7}\cdot\frac{1}{4}y^4\bigg]_1^2 = \frac{3}{7}\cdot\frac{15}{4} = \frac{45}{28}$$

so the centroid of $R$ is $(93/70, 45/28) \approx (1.329, 1.607)$. ◀

## THEOREM OF PAPPUS

The following theorem, due to the Greek mathematician Pappus, gives an important relationship between the centroid of a plane region $R$ and the volume of the solid generated when the region is revolved about a line.

> **6.7.2 THEOREM (*Theorem of Pappus*)** *If $R$ is a bounded plane region and $L$ is a line that lies in the plane of $R$ such that $R$ is entirely on one side of $L$, then the volume of the solid formed by revolving $R$ about $L$ is given by*
>
> $$\textit{volume} = (\textit{area of } R)\cdot\begin{pmatrix}\textit{distance traveled}\\ \textit{by the centroid}\end{pmatrix}$$

PROOF We prove this theorem in the special case where $L$ is the $y$-axis, the region $R$ is in the first quadrant, and the region $R$ is of the form given in Problem 6.7.1. (A more general proof will be outlined in the Exercises of Section 14.8.) In this case, the volume $V$ of the solid formed by revolving $R$ about $L$ can be found by the method of cylindrical shells (Section 6.3) to be

$$V = 2\pi\int_a^b xf(x)\, dx$$

Thus, it follows from (8) that

$$V = 2\pi\bar{x}[\text{area of } R]$$

This completes the proof since $2\pi\bar{x}$ is the distance traveled by the centroid when $R$ is revolved about the $y$-axis. ■

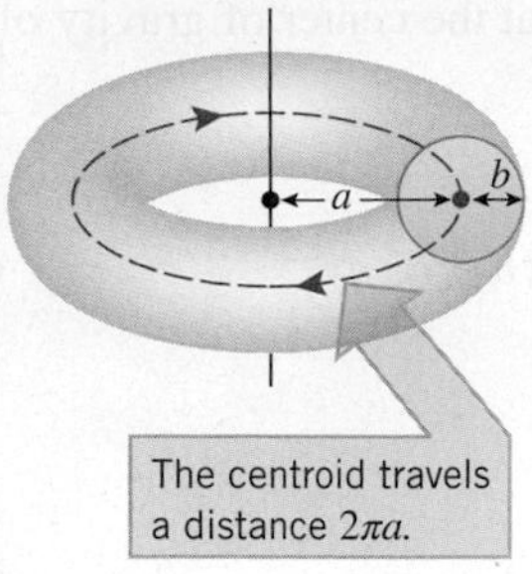


▲ **Figure 6.7.13**

▶ **Example 6** Use Pappus' Theorem to find the volume $V$ of the torus generated by revolving a circular region of radius $b$ about a line at a distance $a$ (greater than $b$) from the center of the circle (Figure 6.7.13).

***Solution.*** By symmetry, the centroid of a circular region is its center. Thus, the distance traveled by the centroid is $2\pi a$. Since the area of a circle of radius $b$ is $\pi b^2$, it follows from Pappus' Theorem that the volume of the torus is

$$V = (2\pi a)(\pi b^2) = 2\pi^2 ab^2 \blacktriangleleft$$

## ✓ QUICK CHECK EXERCISES 6.7 *(See page 392 for answers.)*

1. The total mass of a homogeneous lamina of area $A$ and density $\delta$ is ________.
2. A homogeneous lamina of mass $M$ and density $\delta$ occupies a region in the $xy$-plane bounded by the graphs of $y = f(x)$, $y = 0$, $x = a$, and $x = b$, where $f$ is a nonnegative continuous function defined on an interval $[a, b]$. The $x$-coordinate of the center of gravity of the lamina is $M_y/M$, where $M_y$ is called the ________ and is given by the integral ________.
3. Let $R$ be the region between the graphs of $y = x^2$ and $y = 2 - x$ for $0 \le x \le 1$. The area of $R$ is $\frac{7}{6}$ and the centroid of $R$ is ________.
4. If the region $R$ in Quick Check Exercise 3 is used to generate a solid $G$ by rotating $R$ about a horizontal line 6 units above its centroid, then the volume of $G$ is ________.

## EXERCISE SET 6.7 [C] CAS

**FOCUS ON CONCEPTS**

1. Masses $m_1 = 5$, $m_2 = 10$, and $m_3 = 20$ are positioned on a weightless beam as shown in the accompanying figure.
   (a) Suppose that the fulcrum is positioned at $x = 5$. Without computing the sum of moments about 5, determine whether the sum is positive, zero, or negative. Explain.
   (b) Where should the fulcrum be placed so that the beam is in equilibrium?

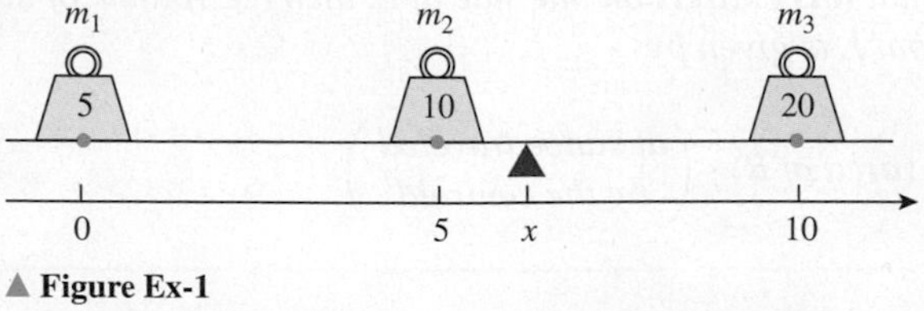


▲ **Figure Ex-1**

2. Masses $m_1 = 10$, $m_2 = 3$, $m_3 = 4$, and $m$ are positioned on a weightless beam, with the fulcrum positioned at point 4, as shown in the accompanying figure.
   (a) Suppose that $m = 14$. Without computing the sum of the moments about 4, determine whether the sum is positive, zero, or negative. Explain.
   (b) For what value of $m$ is the beam in equilibrium?

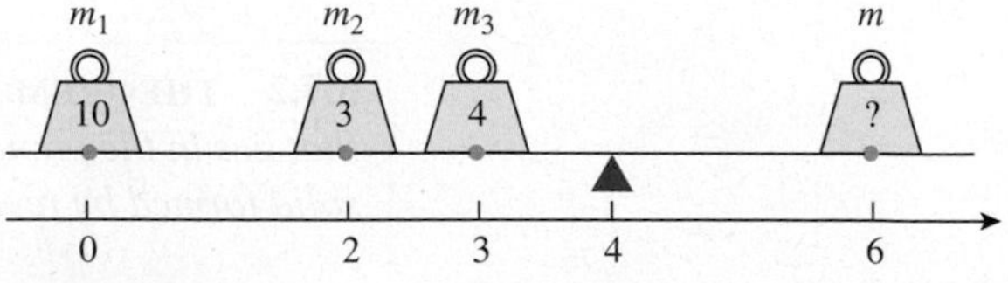


▲ **Figure Ex-2**

**Pappus of Alexandria (4th century A.D.)** Greek mathematician. Pappus lived during the early Christian era when mathematical activity was in a period of decline. His main contributions to mathematics appeared in a series of eight books called *The Collection* (written about 340 A.D.). This work, which survives only partially, contained some original results but was devoted mostly to statements, refinements, and proofs of results by earlier mathematicians. Pappus' Theorem, stated without proof in Book VII of *The Collection*, was probably known and proved in earlier times. This result is sometimes called Guldin's Theorem in recognition of the Swiss mathematician, Paul Guldin (1577–1643), who rediscovered it independently.

**3–6** Find the centroid of the region by inspection and confirm your answer by integrating. ■

**3.**

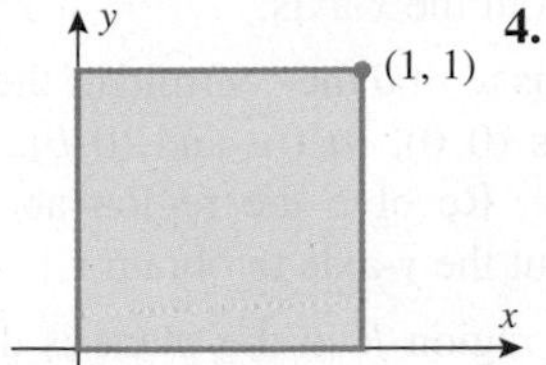


**4.**

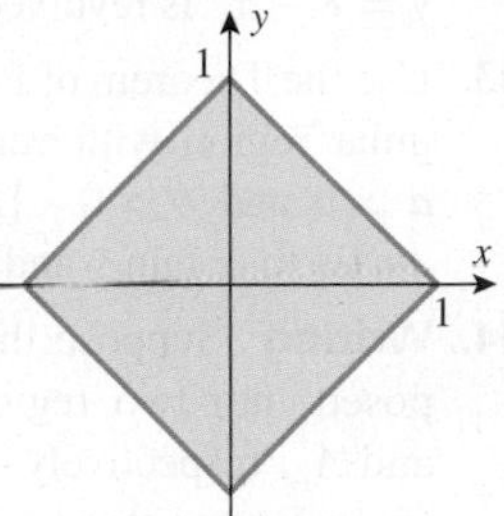


**5.**

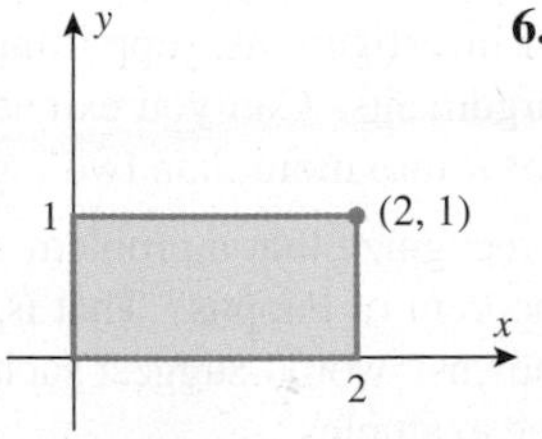


**6.**

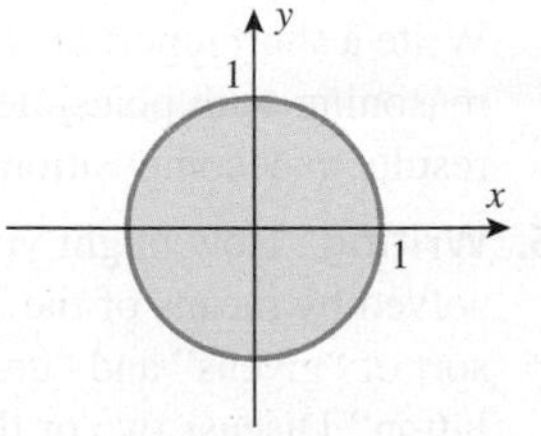


**7–20** Find the centroid of the region. ■

**7.**

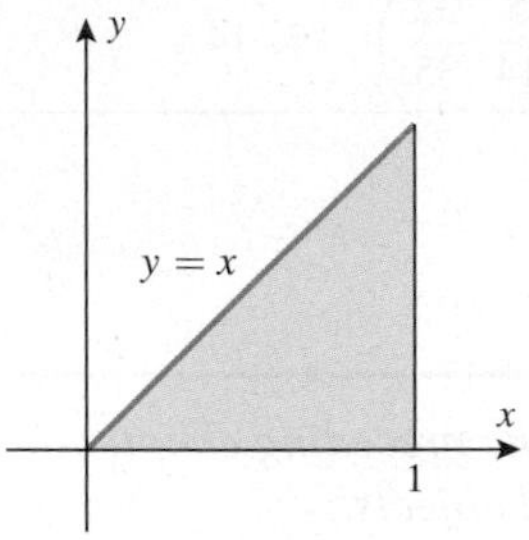


**8.**

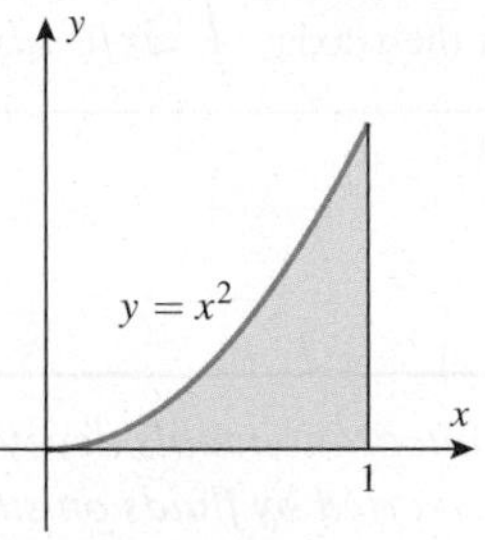


**9.**

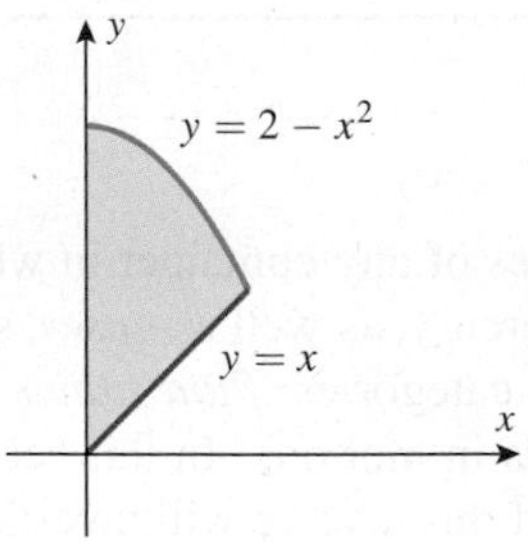


**10.**

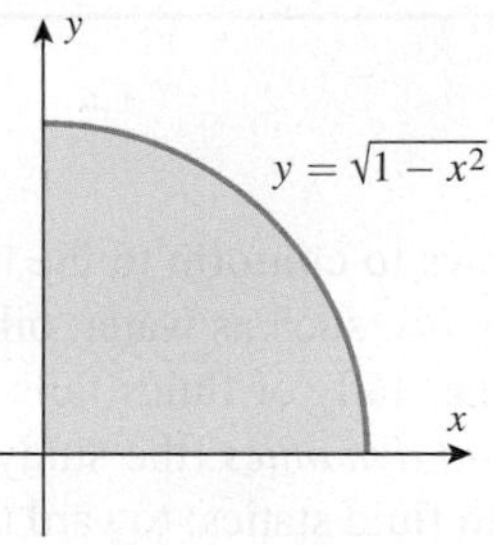


**11.** The triangle with vertices $(0, 0)$, $(2, 0)$, and $(0, 1)$.

**12.** The triangle with vertices $(0, 0)$, $(1, 1)$, and $(2, 0)$.

**13.** The region bounded by the graphs of $y = x^2$ and $x + y = 6$.

**14.** The region bounded on the left by the $y$-axis, on the right by the line $x = 2$, below by the parabola $y = x^2$, and above by the line $y = x + 6$.

**15.** The region bounded by the graphs of $y = x^2$ and $y = x + 2$.

**16.** The region bounded by the graphs of $y = x^2$ and $y = 1$.

**17.** The region bounded by the graphs of $y = \sqrt{x}$ and $y = x^2$.

**18.** The region bounded by the graphs of $x = 1/y$, $x = 0$, $y = 1$, and $y = 2$.

**19.** The region bounded by the graphs of $y = x$, $x = 1/y^2$, and $y = 2$.

**20.** The region bounded by the graphs of $xy = 4$ and $x + y = 5$.

**FOCUS ON CONCEPTS**

**21.** Use symmetry considerations to argue that the centroid of an isosceles triangle lies on the median to the base of the triangle.

**22.** Use symmetry considerations to argue that the centroid of an ellipse lies at the intersection of the major and minor axes of the ellipse.

**23–26** Find the mass and center of gravity of the lamina with density $\delta$. ■

**23.** A lamina bounded by the $x$-axis, the line $x = 1$, and the curve $y = \sqrt{x}$; $\delta = 2$.

**24.** A lamina bounded by the graph of $x = y^4$ and the line $x = 1$; $\delta = 15$.

**25.** A lamina bounded by the graph of $y = |x|$ and the line $y = 1$; $\delta = 3$.

**26.** A lamina bounded by the $x$-axis and the graph of the equation $y = 1 - x^2$; $\delta = 3$.

C **27–30** Use a CAS to find the mass and center of gravity of the lamina with density $\delta$. ■

**27.** A lamina bounded by $y = \sin x$, $y = 0$, $x = 0$, and $x = \pi$; $\delta = 4$.

**28.** A lamina bounded by $y = e^x$, $y = 0$, $x = 0$, and $x = 1$; $\delta = 1/(e - 1)$.

**29.** A lamina bounded by the graph of $y = \ln x$, the $x$-axis, and the line $x = 2$; $\delta = 1$.

**30.** A lamina bounded by the graphs of $y = \cos x$, $y = \sin x$, $x = 0$, and $x = \pi/4$; $\delta = 1 + \sqrt{2}$.

**31–34 True–False** Determine whether the statement is true or false. Explain your answer. [In Exercise 34, assume that the (rotated) square lies in the $xy$-plane to the right of the $y$-axis.] ■

**31.** The centroid of a rectangle is the intersection of the diagonals of the rectangle.

**32.** The centroid of a rhombus is the intersection of the diagonals of the rhombus.

**33.** The centroid of an equilateral triangle is the intersection of the medians of the triangle.

**34.** By rotating a square about its center, it is possible to change the volume of the solid of revolution generated by revolving the square about the $y$-axis.

**35.** Find the centroid of the triangle with vertices $(0, 0)$, $(a, b)$, and $(a, -b)$.

**36.** Prove that the centroid of a triangle is the point of intersection of the three medians of the triangle. [*Hint:* Choose coordinates so that the vertices of the triangle are located at $(0, -a)$, $(0, a)$, and $(b, c)$.]

**37.** Find the centroid of the isosceles trapezoid with vertices $(-a, 0)$, $(a, 0)$, $(-b, c)$, and $(b, c)$.

**38.** Prove that the centroid of a parallelogram is the point of intersection of the diagonals of the parallelogram. [*Hint:* Choose coordinates so that the vertices of the parallelogram are located at $(0, 0)$, $(0, a)$, $(b, c)$, and $(b, a + c)$.]

**39.** Use the Theorem of Pappus and the fact that the volume of a sphere of radius $a$ is $V = \frac{4}{3}\pi a^3$ to show that the centroid of the lamina that is bounded by the $x$-axis and the semicircle $y = \sqrt{a^2 - x^2}$ is $(0, 4a/(3\pi))$. (This problem was solved directly in Example 3.)

**40.** Use the Theorem of Pappus and the result of Exercise 39 to find the volume of the solid generated when the region bounded by the $x$-axis and the semicircle $y = \sqrt{a^2 - x^2}$ is revolved about
(a) the line $y = -a$ (b) the line $y = x - a$.

**41.** Use the Theorem of Pappus and the fact that the area of an ellipse with semiaxes $a$ and $b$ is $\pi ab$ to find the volume of the elliptical torus generated by revolving the ellipse

$$\frac{(x - k)^2}{a^2} + \frac{y^2}{b^2} = 1$$

about the $y$-axis. Assume that $k > a$.

**42.** Use the Theorem of Pappus to find the volume of the solid that is generated when the region enclosed by $y = x^2$ and $y = 8 - x^2$ is revolved about the $x$-axis.

**43.** Use the Theorem of Pappus to find the centroid of the triangular region with vertices $(0, 0)$, $(a, 0)$, and $(0, b)$, where $a > 0$ and $b > 0$. [*Hint:* Revolve the region about the $x$-axis to obtain $\bar{y}$ and about the $y$-axis to obtain $\bar{x}$.]

**44. Writing** Suppose that a region $R$ in the plane is decomposed into two regions $R_1$ and $R_2$ whose areas are $A_1$ and $A_2$, respectively, and whose centroids are $(\bar{x}_1, \bar{y}_1)$ and $(\bar{x}_2, \bar{y}_2)$, respectively. Investigate the problem of expressing the centroid of $R$ in terms of $A_1$, $A_2$, $(\bar{x}_1, \bar{y}_1)$, and $(\bar{x}_2, \bar{y}_2)$. Write a short report on your investigations, supporting your reasoning with plausible arguments. Can you extend your results to decompositions of $R$ into more than two regions?

**45. Writing** How might you recognize that a problem can be solved by means of the Theorem of Pappus? That is, what sort of "givens" and "unknowns" would suggest such a solution? Discuss two or three examples.

✓ **QUICK CHECK ANSWERS 6.7** 1. $\delta A$ 2. first moment about the $y$-axis; $\int_a^b \delta x f(x)\, dx$ 3. $\left(\frac{5}{14}, \frac{32}{35}\right)$ 4. $14\pi$

## 6.8 FLUID PRESSURE AND FORCE

*In this section we will use the integration tools developed in the preceding chapter to study the pressures and forces exerted by fluids on submerged objects.*

### WHAT IS A FLUID?

A ***fluid*** is a substance that flows to conform to the boundaries of any container in which it is placed. Fluids include *liquids*, such as water, oil, and mercury, as well as *gases*, such as helium, oxygen, and air. The study of fluids falls into two categories: *fluid statics* (the study of fluids at rest) and *fluid dynamics* (the study of fluids in motion). In this section we will be concerned only with fluid statics; toward the end of this text we will investigate problems in fluid dynamics.

Brand X Pictures/Jupiter Images/Getty Images

*Snowshoes prevent the woman from sinking by spreading her weight over a large area to reduce her pressure on the snow.*

### THE CONCEPT OF PRESSURE

The effect that a force has on an object depends on how that force is spread over the surface of the object. For example, when you walk on soft snow with boots, the weight of your body crushes the snow and you sink into it. However, if you put on a pair of snowshoes to spread the weight of your body over a greater surface area, then the weight of your body has less of a crushing effect on the snow. The concept that accounts for both the magnitude of a force and the area over which it is applied is called *pressure*.

**6.8.1 DEFINITION** If a force of magnitude $F$ is applied to a surface of area $A$, then we define the ***pressure*** $P$ exerted by the force on the surface to be

$$P = \frac{F}{A} \tag{1}$$

It follows from this definition that pressure has units of force per unit area. The most common units of pressure are newtons per square meter ($N/m^2$) in SI and pounds per square inch ($lb/in^2$) or pounds per square foot ($lb/ft^2$) in the BE system. As indicated in Table 6.8.1, one newton per square meter is called a *pascal* (Pa). A pressure of 1 Pa is quite small ($1\text{ Pa} = 1.45 \times 10^{-4}\text{ lb/in}^2$), so in countries using SI, tire pressure gauges are usually calibrated in kilopascals (kPa), which is 1000 pascals.

**Table 6.8.1**
UNITS OF FORCE AND PRESSURE

| SYSTEM | FORCE ÷ | AREA = | PRESSURE |
|---|---|---|---|
| SI | newton (N) | square meter ($m^2$) | pascal (Pa) |
| BE | pound (lb) | square foot ($ft^2$) | $lb/ft^2$ |
| BE | pound (lb) | square inch ($in^2$) | $lb/in^2$ (psi) |

CONVERSION FACTORS:
$1\text{ Pa} \approx 1.45 \times 10^{-4}\text{ lb/in}^2 \approx 2.09 \times 10^{-2}\text{ lb/ft}^2$
$1\text{ lb/in}^2 \approx 6.89 \times 10^3\text{ Pa}$ $\quad$ $1\text{ lb/ft}^2 \approx 47.9\text{ Pa}$

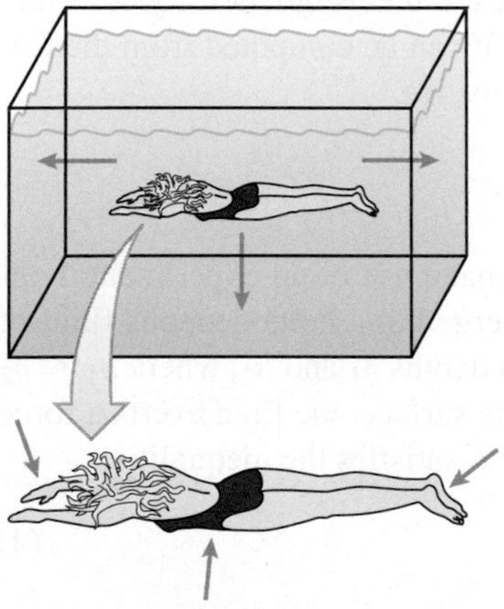
Fluid forces always act perpendicular to the surface of a submerged object.

▲ **Figure 6.8.1**

In this section we will be interested in pressures and forces on objects submerged in fluids. Pressures themselves have no directional characteristics, but the forces that they create always act perpendicular to the face of the submerged object. Thus, in Figure 6.8.1 the water pressure creates horizontal forces on the sides of the tank, vertical forces on the bottom of the tank, and forces that vary in direction, so as to be perpendicular to the different parts of the swimmer's body.

► **Example 1** Referring to Figure 6.8.1, suppose that the back of the swimmer's hand has a surface area of $8.4 \times 10^{-3}\text{ m}^2$ and that the pressure acting on it is $5.1 \times 10^4$ Pa (a realistic value near the bottom of a deep diving pool). Find the force that acts on the swimmer's hand.

***Solution.*** From (1), the force $F$ is

$$F = PA = (5.1 \times 10^4\text{ N/m}^2)(8.4 \times 10^{-3}\text{ m}^2) \approx 4.3 \times 10^2\text{ N}$$

This is quite a large force (nearly 100 lb in the BE system). ◄

**Blaise Pascal (1623–1662)** French mathematician and scientist. Pascal's mother died when he was three years old and his father, a highly educated magistrate, personally provided the boy's early education. Although Pascal showed an inclination for science and mathematics, his father refused to tutor him in those subjects until he mastered Latin and Greek. Pascal's sister and primary biographer claimed that he independently discovered the first thirty-two propositions of Euclid without ever reading a book on geometry. (However, it is generally agreed that the story is apocryphal.) Nevertheless, the precocious Pascal published a highly respected essay on conic sections by the time he was sixteen years old. Descartes, who read the essay, thought it so brilliant that he could not believe that it was written by such a young man. By age 18 his health began to fail and until his death he was in frequent pain. However, his creativity was unimpaired.

Pascal's contributions to physics include the discovery that air pressure decreases with altitude and the principle of fluid pressure that bears his name. However, the originality of his work is questioned by some historians. Pascal made major contributions to a branch of mathematics called "projective geometry," and he helped to develop probability theory through a series of letters with Fermat.

In 1646, Pascal's health problems resulted in a deep emotional crisis that led him to become increasingly concerned with religious matters. Although born a Catholic, he converted to a religious doctrine called Jansenism and spent most of his final years writing on religion and philosophy.

*[Image: Library of Congress Prints and Photographs Division; LC-USZ62-66287]*

Table 6.8.2

WEIGHT DENSITIES

| SI | N/m³ |
|---|---|
| Machine oil | 4708 |
| Gasoline | 6602 |
| Fresh water | 9810 |
| Seawater | 10,045 |
| Mercury | 133,416 |
| **BE SYSTEM** | **lb/ft³** |
| Machine oil | 30.0 |
| Gasoline | 42.0 |
| Fresh water | 62.4 |
| Seawater | 64.0 |
| Mercury | 849.0 |

All densities are affected by variations in temperature and pressure. Weight densities are also affected by variations in $g$.

## FLUID DENSITY

Scuba divers know that the pressure and forces on their bodies increase with the depth they dive. This is caused by the weight of the water and air above—the deeper the diver goes, the greater the weight above and so the greater the pressure and force exerted on the diver.

To calculate pressures and forces on submerged objects, we need to know something about the characteristics of the fluids in which they are submerged. For simplicity, we will assume that the fluids under consideration are *homogeneous*, by which we mean that any two samples of the fluid with the same volume have the same mass. It follows from this assumption that the mass per unit volume is a constant $\delta$ that depends on the physical characteristics of the fluid but not on the size or location of the sample; we call

$$\delta = \frac{m}{V} \tag{2}$$

the ***mass density*** of the fluid. Sometimes it is more convenient to work with weight per unit volume than with mass per unit volume. Thus, we define the ***weight density*** $\rho$ of a fluid to be

$$\rho = \frac{w}{V} \tag{3}$$

where $w$ is the weight of a fluid sample of volume $V$. Thus, if the weight density of a fluid is known, then the weight $w$ of a fluid sample of volume $V$ can be computed from the formula $w = \rho V$. Table 6.8.2 shows some typical weight densities.

## FLUID PRESSURE

To calculate fluid pressures and forces we will need to make use of an experimental observation. Suppose that a flat surface of area $A$ is submerged in a homogeneous fluid of weight density $\rho$ such that the entire surface lies between depths $h_1$ and $h_2$, where $h_1 \le h_2$ (Figure 6.8.2). Experiments show that on both sides of the surface, the fluid exerts a force that is perpendicular to the surface and whose magnitude $F$ satisfies the inequalities

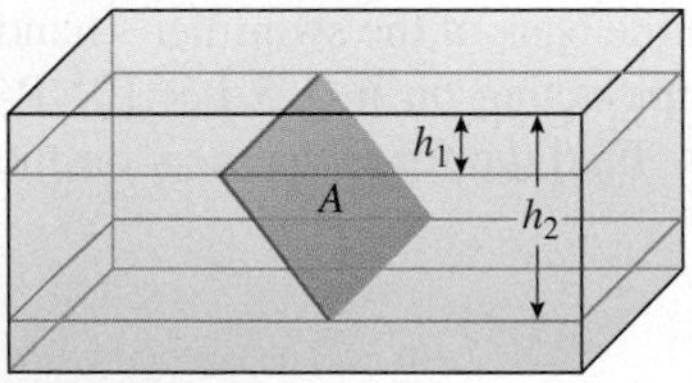

▲ Figure 6.8.2

$$\rho h_1 A \le F \le \rho h_2 A \tag{4}$$

Thus, it follows from (1) that the pressure $P = F/A$ on a given side of the surface satisfies the inequalities

$$\rho h_1 \le P \le \rho h_2 \tag{5}$$

Note that it is now a straightforward matter to calculate fluid force and pressure on a flat surface that is submerged *horizontally* at depth $h$, for then $h = h_1 = h_2$ and inequalities (4) and (5) become the *equalities*

$$F = \rho h A \tag{6}$$

and

$$P = \rho h \tag{7}$$

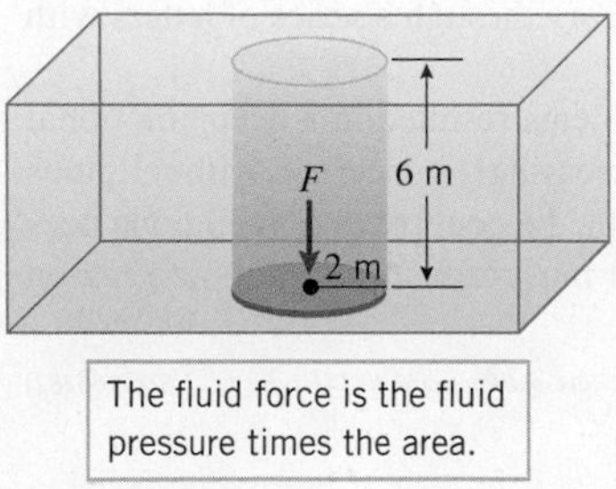

▲ Figure 6.8.3

► **Example 2** Find the fluid pressure and force on the top of a flat circular plate of radius 2 m that is submerged horizontally in water at a depth of 6 m (Figure 6.8.3).

***Solution.*** Since the weight density of water is $\rho = 9810\ \text{N/m}^3$, it follows from (7) that the fluid pressure is

$$P = \rho h = (9810)(6) = 58{,}860\ \text{Pa}$$

and it follows from (6) that the fluid force is

$$F = \rho h A = \rho h(\pi r^2) = (9810)(6)(4\pi) = 235{,}440\pi \approx 739{,}700\ \text{N} \blacktriangleleft$$

## FLUID FORCE ON A VERTICAL SURFACE

It was easy to calculate the fluid force on the horizontal plate in Example 2 because each point on the plate was at the same depth. The problem of finding the fluid force on a vertical surface is more complicated because the depth, and hence the pressure, is not constant over the surface. To find the fluid force on a vertical surface we will need calculus.

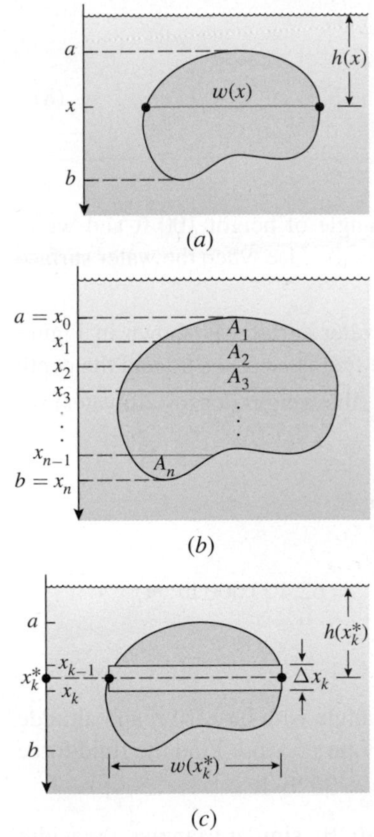

▲ **Figure 6.8.4**

**6.8.2 PROBLEM** Suppose that a flat surface is immersed vertically in a fluid of weight density $\rho$ and that the submerged portion of the surface extends from $x = a$ to $x = b$ along an $x$-axis whose positive direction is down (Figure 6.8.4*a*). For $a \le x \le b$, suppose that $w(x)$ is the width of the surface and that $h(x)$ is the depth of the point $x$. Define what is meant by the *fluid force* $F$ on the surface, and find a formula for computing it.

The basic idea for solving this problem is to divide the surface into horizontal strips whose areas may be approximated by areas of rectangles. These area approximations, along with inequalities (4), will allow us to create a Riemann sum that approximates the total force on the surface. By taking a limit of Riemann sums we will then obtain an integral for $F$.

To implement this idea, we divide the interval $[a, b]$ into $n$ subintervals by inserting the points $x_1, x_2, \ldots, x_{n-1}$ between $a = x_0$ and $b = x_n$. This has the effect of dividing the surface into $n$ strips of area $A_k$, $k = 1, 2, \ldots, n$ (Figure 6.8.4*b*). It follows from (4) that the force $F_k$ on the $k$th strip satisfies the inequalities

$$\rho h(x_{k-1})A_k \le F_k \le \rho h(x_k)A_k$$

or, equivalently,

$$h(x_{k-1}) \le \frac{F_k}{\rho A_k} \le h(x_k)$$

Since the depth function $h(x)$ increases linearly, there must exist a point $x_k^*$ between $x_{k-1}$ and $x_k$ such that

$$h(x_k^*) = \frac{F_k}{\rho A_k}$$

or, equivalently,

$$F_k = \rho h(x_k^*)A_k$$

We now approximate the area $A_k$ of the $k$th strip of the surface by the area of a rectangle of width $w(x_k^*)$ and height $\Delta x_k = x_k - x_{k-1}$ (Figure 6.8.4*c*). It follows that $F_k$ may be approximated as

$$F_k = \rho h(x_k^*)A_k \approx \rho h(x_k^*) \cdot \underbrace{w(x_k^*)\Delta x_k}_{\text{Area of rectangle}}$$

Adding these approximations yields the following Riemann sum that approximates the total force $F$ on the surface:

$$F = \sum_{k=1}^{n} F_k \approx \sum_{k=1}^{n} \rho h(x_k^*)w(x_k^*)\Delta x_k$$

Taking the limit as $n$ increases and the widths of all the subintervals approach zero yields the definite integral

$$F = \lim_{\max \Delta x_k \to 0} \sum_{k=1}^{n} \rho h(x_k^*)w(x_k^*)\Delta x_k = \int_a^b \rho h(x)w(x)\,dx$$

In summary, we have the following result.

**6.8.3 DEFINITION** Suppose that a flat surface is immersed vertically in a fluid of weight density $\rho$ and that the submerged portion of the surface extends from $x = a$ to $x = b$ along an $x$-axis whose positive direction is down (Figure 6.8.4*a*). For $a \le x \le b$, suppose that $w(x)$ is the width of the surface and that $h(x)$ is the depth of the point $x$. Then we define the ***fluid force*** $F$ on the surface to be

$$F = \int_a^b \rho h(x) w(x)\, dx \tag{8}$$

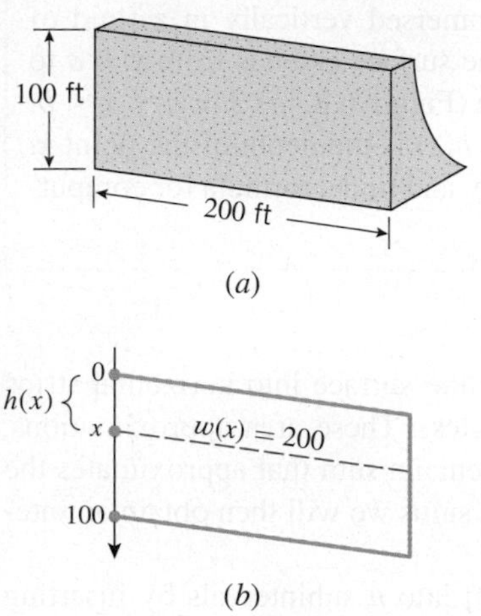

▲ **Figure 6.8.5**

► **Example 3** The face of a dam is a vertical rectangle of height 100 ft and width 200 ft (Figure 6.8.5*a*). Find the total fluid force exerted on the face when the water surface is level with the top of the dam.

***Solution.*** Introduce an $x$-axis with its origin at the water surface as shown in Figure 6.8.5*b*. At a point $x$ on this axis, the width of the dam in feet is $w(x) = 200$ and the depth in feet is $h(x) = x$. Thus, from (8) with $\rho = 62.4\ \text{lb/ft}^3$ (the weight density of water) we obtain as the total force on the face

$$F = \int_0^{100} (62.4)(x)(200)\, dx = 12{,}480 \int_0^{100} x\, dx$$

$$= 12{,}480 \left.\frac{x^2}{2}\right]_0^{100} = 62{,}400{,}000 \text{ lb} \blacktriangleleft$$

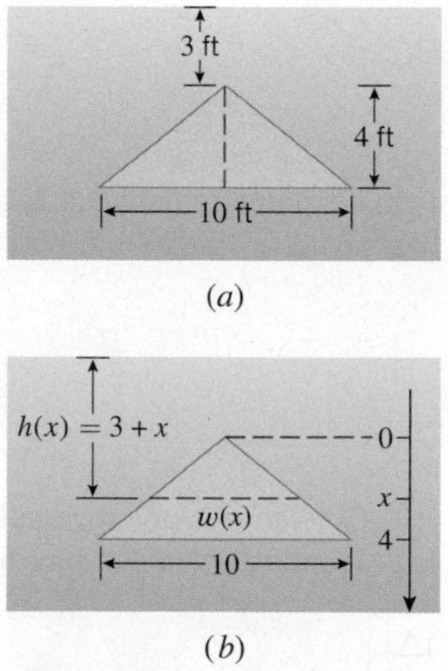

▲ **Figure 6.8.6**

► **Example 4** A plate in the form of an isosceles triangle with base 10 ft and altitude 4 ft is submerged vertically in machine oil as shown in Figure 6.8.6*a*. Find the fluid force $F$ against the plate surface if the oil has weight density $\rho = 30\ \text{lb/ft}^3$.

***Solution.*** Introduce an $x$-axis as shown in Figure 6.8.6*b*. By similar triangles, the width of the plate, in feet, at a depth of $h(x) = (3 + x)$ ft satisfies

$$\frac{w(x)}{10} = \frac{x}{4}, \quad \text{so} \quad w(x) = \frac{5}{2}x$$

Thus, it follows from (8) that the force on the plate is

$$F = \int_a^b \rho h(x) w(x)\, dx = \int_0^4 (30)(3 + x)\left(\frac{5}{2}x\right) dx$$

$$= 75 \int_0^4 (3x + x^2)\, dx = 75 \left[\frac{3x^2}{2} + \frac{x^3}{3}\right]_0^4 = 3400 \text{ lb} \blacktriangleleft$$

## ✓ QUICK CHECK EXERCISES 6.8 (See page 398 for answers.)

1. The pressure unit equivalent to a newton per square meter ($\text{N/m}^2$) is called a ______. The pressure unit psi stands for ______.

2. Given that the weight density of water is $9810\ \text{N/m}^3$, the fluid pressure on a rectangular 2 m × 3 m flat plate submerged horizontally in water at a depth of 10 m is ______. The fluid force on the plate is ______.

3. Suppose that a flat surface is immersed vertically in a fluid of weight density $\rho$ and that the submerged portion of the surface extends from $x = a$ to $x = b$ along an $x$-axis whose positive direction is down. If, for $a \le x \le b$, the surface has width $w(x)$ and depth $h(x)$, then the fluid force on the surface is $F =$ ______.

4. A rectangular plate 2 m wide and 3 m high is submerged vertically in water so that the top of the plate is 5 m below the water surface. An integral expression for the force of the water on the plate surface is $F =$ ______.

## EXERCISE SET 6.8

In this exercise set, refer to Table 6.8.2 for weight densities of fluids, where needed. ■

1. A flat rectangular plate is submerged horizontally in water.
   (a) Find the force (in lb) and the pressure (in $\text{lb/ft}^2$) on the top surface of the plate if its area is 100 $\text{ft}^2$ and the surface is at a depth of 5 ft.
   (b) Find the force (in N) and the pressure (in Pa) on the top surface of the plate if its area is 25 $\text{m}^2$ and the surface is at a depth of 10 m.
2. (a) Find the force (in N) on the deck of a sunken ship if its area is 160 $\text{m}^2$ and the pressure acting on it is $6.0 \times 10^5$ Pa.
   (b) Find the force (in lb) on a diver's face mask if its area is 60 $\text{in}^2$ and the pressure acting on it is 100 $\text{lb/in}^2$.

**3–8** The flat surfaces shown are submerged vertically in water. Find the fluid force against each surface. ■

3.
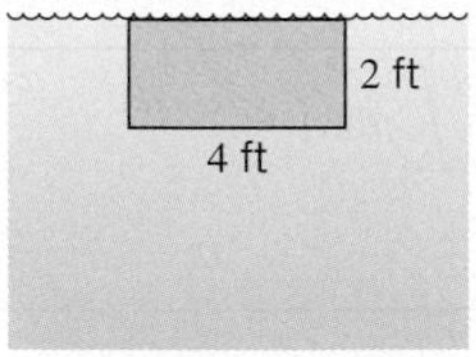


4.
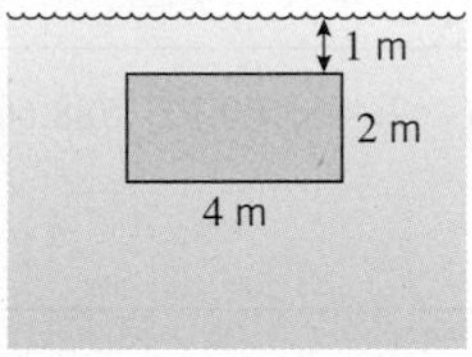


5.
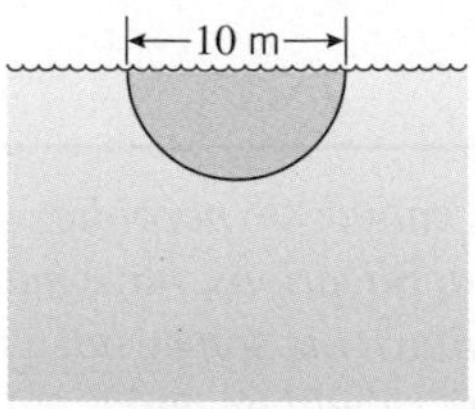


6.
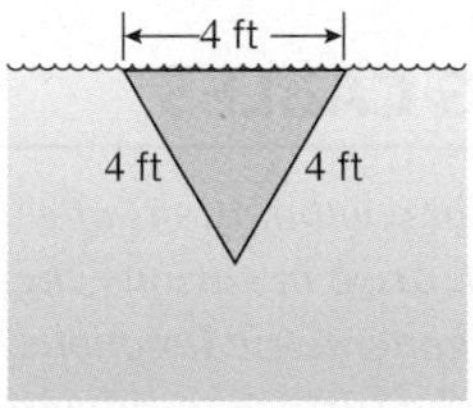


7.
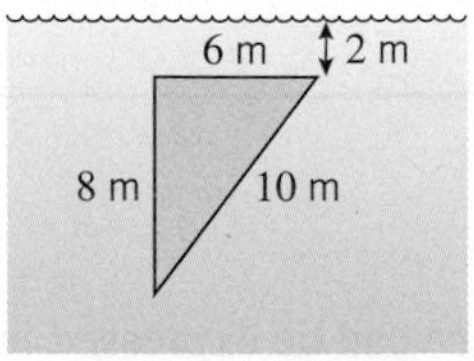


8.
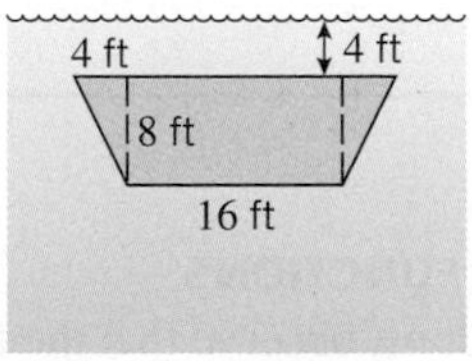


9. Suppose that a flat surface is immersed vertically in a fluid of weight density $\rho$. If $\rho$ is doubled, is the force on the plate also doubled? Explain your reasoning.
10. An oil tank is shaped like a right circular cylinder of diameter 4 ft. Find the total fluid force against one end when the axis is horizontal and the tank is half filled with oil of weight density 50 $\text{lb/ft}^3$.
11. A square plate of side $a$ feet is dipped in a liquid of weight density $\rho$ $\text{lb/ft}^3$. Find the fluid force on the plate if a vertex is at the surface and a diagonal is perpendicular to the surface.

**12–15 True–False** Determine whether the statement is true or false. Explain your answer. ■

12. In the International System of Units, pressure and force have the same units.
13. In a cylindrical water tank (with vertical axis), the fluid force on the base of the tank is equal to the weight of water in the tank.
14. In a rectangular water tank, the fluid force on any side of the tank must be less than the fluid force on the base of the tank.
15. In any water tank with a flat base, no matter what the shape of the tank, the fluid force on the base is at most equal to the weight of water in the tank.

**16–19** Formula (8) gives the fluid force on a flat surface immersed vertically in a fluid. More generally, if a flat surface is immersed so that it makes an angle of $0 \leq \theta < \pi/2$ with the vertical, then the fluid force on the surface is given by

$$F = \int_a^b \rho h(x) w(x) \sec\theta \, dx$$

Use this formula in these exercises. ■

16. Derive the formula given above for the fluid force on a flat surface immersed at an angle in a fluid.
17. The accompanying figure shows a rectangular swimming pool whose bottom is an inclined plane. Find the fluid force on the bottom when the pool is filled to the top.

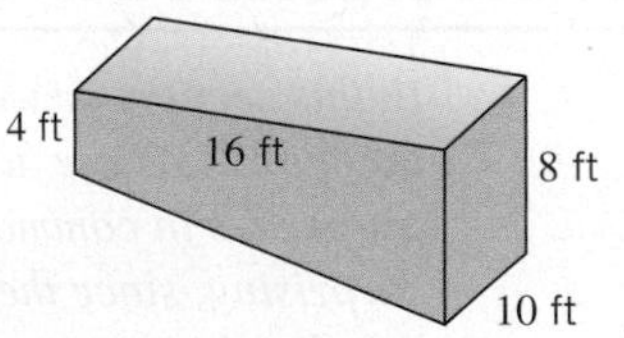


◀ **Figure Ex-17**

18. By how many feet should the water in the pool of Exercise 17 be lowered in order for the force on the bottom to be reduced by a factor of $\frac{1}{2}$?
19. The accompanying figure shows a dam whose face is an inclined rectangle. Find the fluid force on the face when the water is level with the top of this dam.

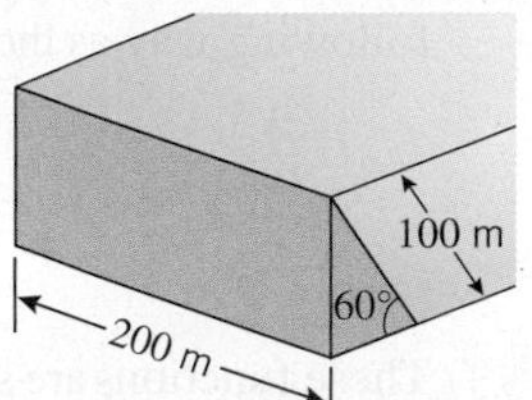


◀ **Figure Ex-19**

20. An observation window on a submarine is a square with 2 ft sides. Using $\rho_0$ for the weight density of seawater, find the fluid force on the window when the submarine has descended so that the window is vertical and its top is at a depth of $h$ feet.

**FOCUS ON CONCEPTS**

**21.** (a) Show: If the submarine in Exercise 20 descends vertically at a constant rate, then the fluid force on the window increases at a constant rate.
(b) At what rate is the force on the window increasing if the submarine is descending vertically at 20 ft/min?

**22.** (a) Let $D = D_a$ denote a disk of radius $a$ submerged in a fluid of weight density $\rho$ such that the center of $D$ is $h$ units below the surface of the fluid. For each value of $r$ in the interval $(0, a]$, let $D_r$ denote the disk of radius $r$ that is concentric with $D$. Select a side of the disk $D$ and define $P(r)$ to be the fluid pressure on the chosen side of $D_r$. Use (5) to prove that

$$\lim_{r\to 0^+} P(r) = \rho h$$

(b) Explain why the result in part (a) may be interpreted to mean that *fluid pressure at a given depth is the same in all directions*. (This statement is one version of a result known as ***Pascal's Principle***.)

**23. Writing** Suppose that we model the Earth's atmosphere as a "fluid." Atmospheric pressure at sea level is $P = 14.7$ lb/in$^2$ and the weight density of air at sea level is about $\rho = 4.66 \times 10^{-5}$ lb/in$^3$. With these numbers, what would Formula (7) yield as the height of the atmosphere above the Earth? Do you think this answer is reasonable? If not, explain how we might modify our assumptions to yield a more plausible answer.

**24. Writing** Suppose that the weight density $\rho$ of a fluid is a function $\rho = \rho(x)$ of the depth $x$ within the fluid. How do you think that Formula (7) for fluid pressure will need to be modified? Support your answer with plausible arguments.

✓ **QUICK CHECK ANSWERS 6.8** 1. pascal; pounds per square inch 2. 98,100 Pa; 588,600 N 3. $\int_a^b \rho h(x)w(x)\,dx$ 4. $\int_0^3 9810\,[(5+x)2]\,dx$

## 6.9 HYPERBOLIC FUNCTIONS AND HANGING CABLES

*In this section we will study certain combinations of $e^x$ and $e^{-x}$, called "hyperbolic functions." These functions, which arise in various engineering applications, have many properties in common with the trigonometric functions. This similarity is somewhat surprising, since there is little on the surface to suggest that there should be any relationship between exponential and trigonometric functions. This is because the relationship occurs within the context of complex numbers, a topic which we will leave for more advanced courses.*

### DEFINITIONS OF HYPERBOLIC FUNCTIONS

To introduce the hyperbolic functions, observe that the function $e^x$ can be expressed in the following way as the sum of an even function and an odd function:

$$e^x = \underbrace{\frac{e^x + e^{-x}}{2}}_{\text{Even}} + \underbrace{\frac{e^x - e^{-x}}{2}}_{\text{Odd}}$$

These functions are sufficiently important that there are names and notation associated with them: the odd function is called the *hyperbolic sine* of $x$ and the even function is called the *hyperbolic cosine* of $x$. They are denoted by

$$\sinh x = \frac{e^x - e^{-x}}{2} \quad \text{and} \quad \cosh x = \frac{e^x + e^{-x}}{2}$$

where sinh is pronounced "cinch" and cosh rhymes with "gosh." From these two building blocks we can create four more functions to produce the following set of six ***hyperbolic functions***.

The terms "tanh," "sech," and "csch" are pronounced "tanch," "seech," and "coseech," respectively.

**6.9.1 DEFINITION**

***Hyperbolic sine*** $\quad \sinh x = \dfrac{e^x - e^{-x}}{2}$

***Hyperbolic cosine*** $\quad \cosh x = \dfrac{e^x + e^{-x}}{2}$

***Hyperbolic tangent*** $\quad \tanh x = \dfrac{\sinh x}{\cosh x} = \dfrac{e^x - e^{-x}}{e^x + e^{-x}}$

***Hyperbolic cotangent*** $\quad \coth x = \dfrac{\cosh x}{\sinh x} = \dfrac{e^x + e^{-x}}{e^x - e^{-x}}$

***Hyperbolic secant*** $\quad \operatorname{sech} x = \dfrac{1}{\cosh x} = \dfrac{2}{e^x + e^{-x}}$

***Hyperbolic cosecant*** $\quad \operatorname{csch} x = \dfrac{1}{\sinh x} = \dfrac{2}{e^x - e^{-x}}$

**TECHNOLOGY MASTERY**

Computer algebra systems have built-in capabilities for evaluating hyperbolic functions directly, but some calculators do not. However, if you need to evaluate a hyperbolic function on a calculator, you can do so by expressing it in terms of exponential functions, as in Example 1.

## ▶ Example 1

$$\sinh 0 = \frac{e^0 - e^{-0}}{2} = \frac{1-1}{2} = 0$$

$$\cosh 0 = \frac{e^0 + e^{-0}}{2} = \frac{1+1}{2} = 1$$

$$\sinh 2 = \frac{e^2 - e^{-2}}{2} \approx 3.6269 \blacktriangleleft$$

### GRAPHS OF THE HYPERBOLIC FUNCTIONS

The graphs of the hyperbolic functions, which are shown in Figure 6.9.1, can be generated with a graphing utility, but it is worthwhile to observe that the general shape of the graph of

Jeremy Edwards/iStockphoto

*The design of the Gateway Arch in St. Louis is based on an inverted hyperbolic cosine curve (Exercise 73).*

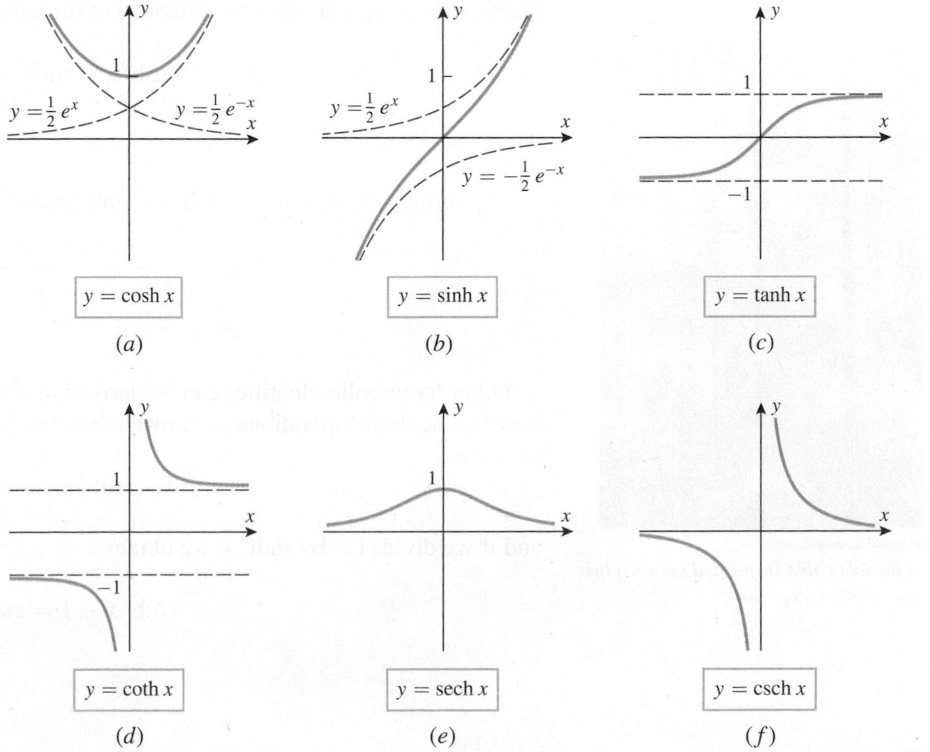


▲ **Figure 6.9.1**

$y = \cosh x$ can be obtained by sketching the graphs of $y = \frac{1}{2}e^x$ and $y = \frac{1}{2}e^{-x}$ separately and adding the corresponding $y$-coordinates [see part ($a$) of the figure]. Similarly, the general shape of the graph of $y = \sinh x$ can be obtained by sketching the graphs of $y = \frac{1}{2}e^x$ and $y = -\frac{1}{2}e^{-x}$ separately and adding corresponding $y$-coordinates [see part ($b$) of the figure].

Observe that $\sinh x$ has a domain of $(-\infty, +\infty)$ and a range of $(-\infty, +\infty)$, whereas $\cosh x$ has a domain of $(-\infty, +\infty)$ and a range of $[1, +\infty)$. Observe also that $y = \frac{1}{2}e^x$ and $y = \frac{1}{2}e^{-x}$ are ***curvilinear asymptotes*** for $y = \cosh x$ in the sense that the graph of $y = \cosh x$ gets closer and closer to the graph of $y = \frac{1}{2}e^x$ as $x \to +\infty$ and gets closer and closer to the graph of $y = \frac{1}{2}e^{-x}$ as $x \to -\infty$. (See Section 4.3.) Similarly, $y = \frac{1}{2}e^x$ is a curvilinear asymptote for $y = \sinh x$ as $x \to +\infty$ and $y = -\frac{1}{2}e^{-x}$ is a curvilinear asymptote as $x \to -\infty$. Other properties of the hyperbolic functions are explored in the exercises.

## HANGING CABLES AND OTHER APPLICATIONS

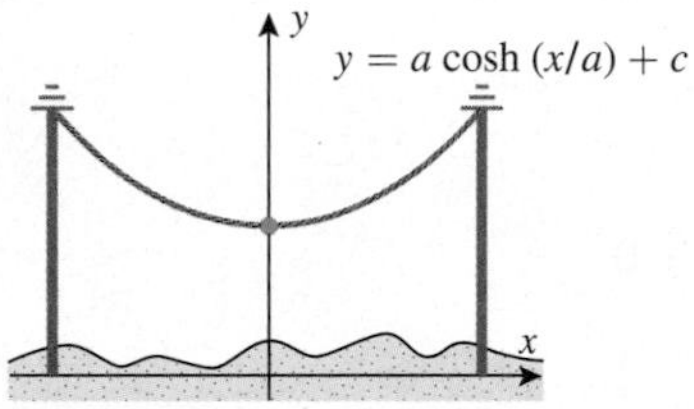


▲ **Figure 6.9.2**

Hyperbolic functions arise in vibratory motions inside elastic solids and more generally in many problems where mechanical energy is gradually absorbed by a surrounding medium. They also occur when a homogeneous, flexible cable is suspended between two points, as with a telephone line hanging between two poles. Such a cable forms a curve, called a ***catenary*** (from the Latin *catena*, meaning "chain"). If, as in Figure 6.9.2, a coordinate system is introduced so that the low point of the cable lies on the $y$-axis, then it can be shown using principles of physics that the cable has an equation of the form

$$y = a\cosh\left(\frac{x}{a}\right) + c$$

where the parameters $a$ and $c$ are determined by the distance between the poles and the composition of the cable.

## HYPERBOLIC IDENTITIES

The hyperbolic functions satisfy various identities that are similar to identities for trigonometric functions. The most fundamental of these is

$$\cosh^2 x - \sinh^2 x = 1 \tag{1}$$

which can be proved by writing

$$\begin{aligned}\cosh^2 x - \sinh^2 x &= (\cosh x + \sinh x)(\cosh x - \sinh x)\\ &= \left(\frac{e^x + e^{-x}}{2} + \frac{e^x - e^{-x}}{2}\right)\left(\frac{e^x + e^{-x}}{2} - \frac{e^x - e^{-x}}{2}\right)\\ &= e^x \cdot e^{-x} = 1\end{aligned}$$

hfng08/Depositphotos

*A flexible cable suspended between two poles forms a catenary.*

Other hyperbolic identities can be derived in a similar manner or, alternatively, by performing algebraic operations on known identities. For example, if we divide (1) by $\cosh^2 x$, we obtain

$$1 - \tanh^2 x = \operatorname{sech}^2 x$$

and if we divide (1) by $\sinh^2 x$, we obtain

$$\coth^2 x - 1 = \operatorname{csch}^2 x$$

The following theorem summarizes some of the more useful hyperbolic identities. The proofs of those not already obtained are left as exercises.

**6.9.2 THEOREM**

| | |
|---|---|
| $\cosh x + \sinh x = e^x$ | $\sinh(x + y) = \sinh x \cosh y + \cosh x \sinh y$ |
| $\cosh x - \sinh x = e^{-x}$ | $\cosh(x + y) = \cosh x \cosh y + \sinh x \sinh y$ |
| $\cosh^2 x - \sinh^2 x = 1$ | $\sinh(x - y) = \sinh x \cosh y - \cosh x \sinh y$ |
| $1 - \tanh^2 x = \operatorname{sech}^2 x$ | $\cosh(x - y) = \cosh x \cosh y - \sinh x \sinh y$ |
| $\coth^2 x - 1 = \operatorname{csch}^2 x$ | $\sinh 2x = 2 \sinh x \cosh x$ |
| $\cosh(-x) = \cosh x$ | $\cosh 2x = \cosh^2 x + \sinh^2 x$ |
| $\sinh(-x) = -\sinh x$ | $\cosh 2x = 2\sinh^2 x + 1 = 2\cosh^2 x - 1$ |

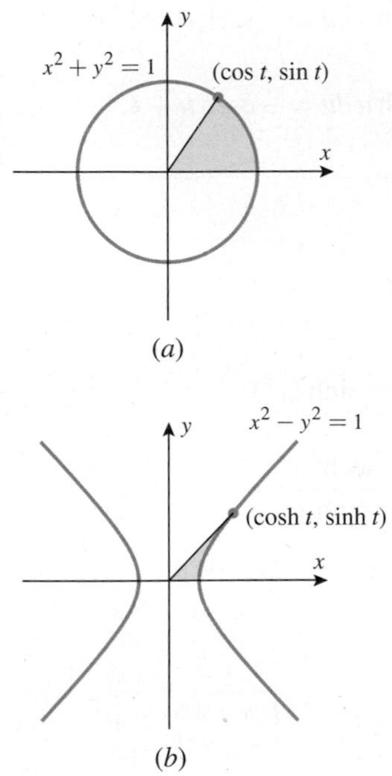

▲ **Figure 6.9.3**

## WHY THEY ARE CALLED HYPERBOLIC FUNCTIONS

Recall that the parametric equations

$$x = \cos t, \quad y = \sin t \qquad (0 \le t \le 2\pi)$$

represent the unit circle $x^2 + y^2 = 1$ (Figure 6.9.3*a*), as may be seen by writing

$$x^2 + y^2 = \cos^2 t + \sin^2 t = 1$$

If $0 \le t \le 2\pi$, then the parameter $t$ can be interpreted as the angle in radians from the positive $x$-axis to the point $(\cos t, \sin t)$ or, alternatively, as twice the shaded area of the sector in Figure 6.9.3*a* (verify). Analogously, the parametric equations

$$x = \cosh t, \quad y = \sinh t \qquad (-\infty < t < +\infty)$$

represent a portion of the curve $x^2 - y^2 = 1$, as may be seen by writing

$$x^2 - y^2 = \cosh^2 t - \sinh^2 t = 1$$

and observing that $x = \cosh t > 0$. This curve, which is shown in Figure 6.9.3*b*, is the right half of a larger curve called the ***unit hyperbola***; this is the reason why the functions in this section are called *hyperbolic* functions. It can be shown that if $t \ge 0$, then the parameter $t$ can be interpreted as twice the shaded area in Figure 6.9.3*b*. (We omit the details.)

## DERIVATIVE AND INTEGRAL FORMULAS

Derivative formulas for $\sinh x$ and $\cosh x$ can be obtained by expressing these functions in terms of $e^x$ and $e^{-x}$:

$$\frac{d}{dx}[\sinh x] = \frac{d}{dx}\left[\frac{e^x - e^{-x}}{2}\right] = \frac{e^x + e^{-x}}{2} = \cosh x$$

$$\frac{d}{dx}[\cosh x] = \frac{d}{dx}\left[\frac{e^x + e^{-x}}{2}\right] = \frac{e^x - e^{-x}}{2} = \sinh x$$

Derivatives of the remaining hyperbolic functions can be obtained by expressing them in terms of sinh and cosh and applying appropriate identities. For example,

$$\frac{d}{dx}[\tanh x] = \frac{d}{dx}\left[\frac{\sinh x}{\cosh x}\right] = \frac{\cosh x \frac{d}{dx}[\sinh x] - \sinh x \frac{d}{dx}[\cosh x]}{\cosh^2 x}$$

$$= \frac{\cosh^2 x - \sinh^2 x}{\cosh^2 x} = \frac{1}{\cosh^2 x} = \operatorname{sech}^2 x$$

The following theorem provides a complete list of the generalized derivative formulas and corresponding integration formulas for the hyperbolic functions.

**6.9.3 THEOREM**

$$\frac{d}{dx}[\sinh u] = \cosh u \frac{du}{dx} \qquad \int \cosh u\, du = \sinh u + C$$

$$\frac{d}{dx}[\cosh u] = \sinh u \frac{du}{dx} \qquad \int \sinh u\, du = \cosh u + C$$

$$\frac{d}{dx}[\tanh u] = \operatorname{sech}^2 u \frac{du}{dx} \qquad \int \operatorname{sech}^2 u\, du = \tanh u + C$$

$$\frac{d}{dx}[\coth u] = -\operatorname{csch}^2 u \frac{du}{dx} \qquad \int \operatorname{csch}^2 u\, du = -\coth u + C$$

$$\frac{d}{dx}[\operatorname{sech} u] = -\operatorname{sech} u \tanh u \frac{du}{dx} \qquad \int \operatorname{sech} u \tanh u\, du = -\operatorname{sech} u + C$$

$$\frac{d}{dx}[\operatorname{csch} u] = -\operatorname{csch} u \coth u \frac{du}{dx} \qquad \int \operatorname{csch} u \coth u\, du = -\operatorname{csch} u + C$$

**▶ Example 2**

$$\frac{d}{dx}[\cosh(x^3)] = \sinh(x^3) \cdot \frac{d}{dx}[x^3] = 3x^2 \sinh(x^3)$$

$$\frac{d}{dx}[\ln(\tanh x)] = \frac{1}{\tanh x} \cdot \frac{d}{dx}[\tanh x] = \frac{\operatorname{sech}^2 x}{\tanh x} \quad ◀$$

**▶ Example 3**

$$\int \sinh^5 x \cosh x\, dx = \tfrac{1}{6}\sinh^6 x + C \qquad \boxed{\begin{aligned} u &= \sinh x \\ du &= \cosh x\, dx \end{aligned}}$$

$$\begin{aligned} \int \tanh x\, dx &= \int \frac{\sinh x}{\cosh x}\, dx \\ &= \ln|\cosh x| + C \qquad \boxed{\begin{aligned} u &= \cosh x \\ du &= \sinh x\, dx \end{aligned}} \\ &= \ln(\cosh x) + C \end{aligned}$$

We were justified in dropping the absolute value signs since $\cosh x > 0$ for all $x$. ◀

**▶ Example 4** A 100 ft wire is attached at its ends to the tops of two 50 ft poles that are positioned 90 ft apart. How high above the ground is the middle of the wire?

***Solution.*** From above, the wire forms a catenary curve with equation

$$y = a\cosh\left(\frac{x}{a}\right) + c$$

where the origin is on the ground midway between the poles. Using Formula (4) of Section 6.4 for the length of the catenary, we have

$$
\begin{aligned}
100 &= \int_{-45}^{45} \sqrt{1+\left(\frac{dy}{dx}\right)^2}\, dx \\
&= 2\int_{0}^{45} \sqrt{1+\left(\frac{dy}{dx}\right)^2}\, dx && \text{By symmetry about the } y\text{-axis} \\
&= 2\int_{0}^{45} \sqrt{1+\sinh^2\left(\frac{x}{a}\right)}\, dx \\
&= 2\int_{0}^{45} \cosh\left(\frac{x}{a}\right) dx && \text{By (1) and the fact that } \cosh x > 0 \\
&= 2a \sinh\left(\frac{x}{a}\right)\bigg]_0^{45} = 2a\sinh\left(\frac{45}{a}\right)
\end{aligned}
$$

Using a calculating utility's numeric solver to solve

$$100 = 2a\sinh\left(\frac{45}{a}\right)$$

for $a$ gives $a \approx 56.01$. Then

$$50 = y(45) = 56.01\cosh\left(\frac{45}{56.01}\right) + c \approx 75.08 + c$$

so $c \approx -25.08$. Thus, the middle of the wire is $y(0) \approx 56.01 - 25.08 = 30.93$ ft above the ground (Figure 6.9.4). ◀

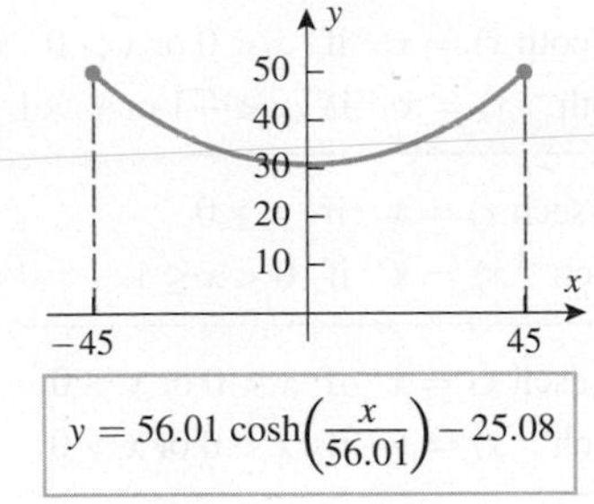


▲ **Figure 6.9.4**

## INVERSES OF HYPERBOLIC FUNCTIONS

Referring to Figure 6.9.1, it is evident that the graphs of $\sinh x$, $\tanh x$, $\coth x$, and $\operatorname{csch} x$ pass the horizontal line test, but the graphs of $\cosh x$ and $\operatorname{sech} x$ do not. In the latter case, restricting $x$ to be nonnegative makes the functions invertible (Figure 6.9.5). The graphs of the six inverse hyperbolic functions in Figure 6.9.6 were obtained by reflecting the graphs of the hyperbolic functions (with the appropriate restrictions) about the line $y = x$.

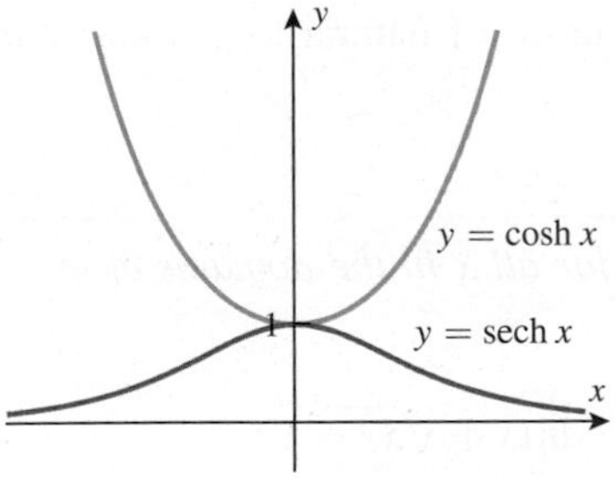


With the restriction that $x \geq 0$, the curves $y = \cosh x$ and $y = \operatorname{sech} x$ pass the horizontal line test.

▲ **Figure 6.9.5**

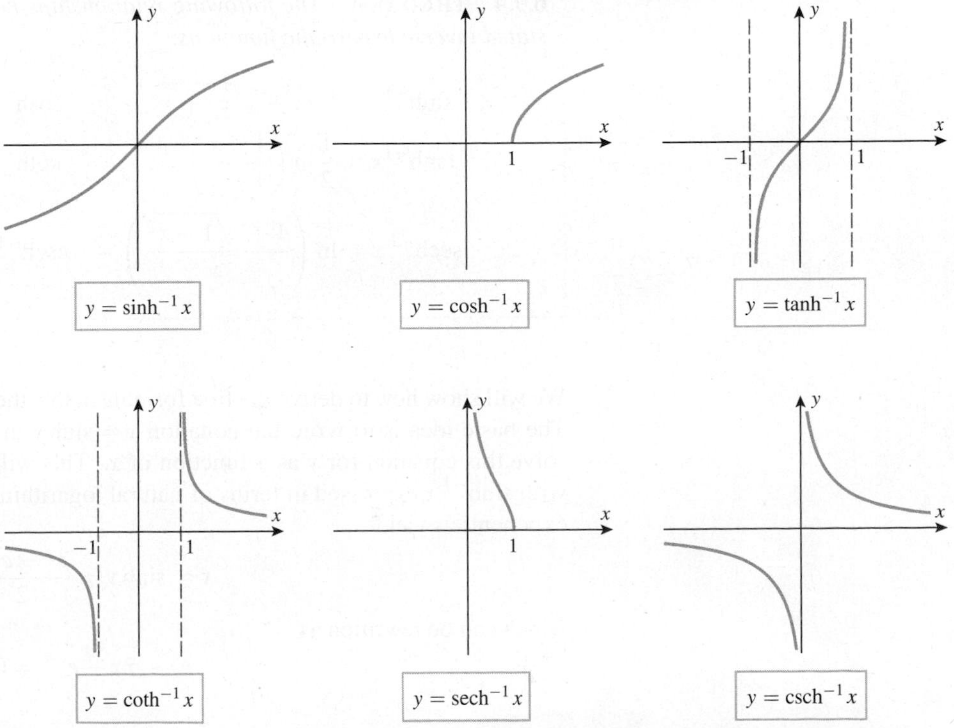


▶ **Figure 6.9.6**

Table 6.9.1 summarizes the basic properties of the inverse hyperbolic functions. You should confirm that the domains and ranges listed in this table agree with the graphs in Figure 6.9.6.

**Table 6.9.1**

PROPERTIES OF INVERSE HYPERBOLIC FUNCTIONS

| FUNCTION | DOMAIN | RANGE | BASIC RELATIONSHIPS |
|---|---|---|---|
| $\sinh^{-1} x$ | $(-\infty, +\infty)$ | $(-\infty, +\infty)$ | $\sinh^{-1}(\sinh x) = x$ if $-\infty < x < +\infty$<br>$\sinh(\sinh^{-1} x) = x$ if $-\infty < x < +\infty$ |
| $\cosh^{-1} x$ | $[1, +\infty)$ | $[0, +\infty)$ | $\cosh^{-1}(\cosh x) = x$ if $x \geq 0$<br>$\cosh(\cosh^{-1} x) = x$ if $x \geq 1$ |
| $\tanh^{-1} x$ | $(-1, 1)$ | $(-\infty, +\infty)$ | $\tanh^{-1}(\tanh x) = x$ if $-\infty < x < +\infty$<br>$\tanh(\tanh^{-1} x) = x$ if $-1 < x < 1$ |
| $\coth^{-1} x$ | $(-\infty, -1) \cup (1, +\infty)$ | $(-\infty, 0) \cup (0, +\infty)$ | $\coth^{-1}(\coth x) = x$ if $x < 0$ or $x > 0$<br>$\coth(\coth^{-1} x) = x$ if $x < -1$ or $x > 1$ |
| $\text{sech}^{-1} x$ | $(0, 1]$ | $[0, +\infty)$ | $\text{sech}^{-1}(\text{sech}\, x) = x$ if $x \geq 0$<br>$\text{sech}(\text{sech}^{-1} x) = x$ if $0 < x \leq 1$ |
| $\text{csch}^{-1} x$ | $(-\infty, 0) \cup (0, +\infty)$ | $(-\infty, 0) \cup (0, +\infty)$ | $\text{csch}^{-1}(\text{csch}\, x) = x$ if $x < 0$ or $x > 0$<br>$\text{csch}(\text{csch}^{-1} x) = x$ if $x < 0$ or $x > 0$ |

## LOGARITHMIC FORMS OF INVERSE HYPERBOLIC FUNCTIONS

Because the hyperbolic functions are expressible in terms of $e^x$, it should not be surprising that the inverse hyperbolic functions are expressible in terms of natural logarithms; the next theorem shows that this is so.

**6.9.4 THEOREM** *The following relationships hold for all x in the domains of the stated inverse hyperbolic functions:*

$$\sinh^{-1} x = \ln(x + \sqrt{x^2+1}) \qquad \cosh^{-1} x = \ln(x + \sqrt{x^2-1})$$

$$\tanh^{-1} x = \frac{1}{2}\ln\left(\frac{1+x}{1-x}\right) \qquad \coth^{-1} x = \frac{1}{2}\ln\left(\frac{x+1}{x-1}\right)$$

$$\text{sech}^{-1} x = \ln\left(\frac{1+\sqrt{1-x^2}}{x}\right) \qquad \text{csch}^{-1} x = \ln\left(\frac{1}{x} + \frac{\sqrt{1+x^2}}{|x|}\right)$$

We will show how to derive the first formula in this theorem and leave the rest as exercises. The basic idea is to write the equation $x = \sinh y$ in terms of exponential functions and solve this equation for $y$ as a function of $x$. This will produce the equation $y = \sinh^{-1} x$ with $\sinh^{-1} x$ expressed in terms of natural logarithms. Expressing $x = \sinh y$ in terms of exponentials yields

$$x = \sinh y = \frac{e^y - e^{-y}}{2}$$

which can be rewritten as

$$e^y - 2x - e^{-y} = 0$$

Multiplying this equation through by $e^y$ we obtain

$$e^{2y} - 2xe^y - 1 = 0$$

and applying the quadratic formula yields

$$e^y = \frac{2x \pm \sqrt{4x^2+4}}{2} = x \pm \sqrt{x^2+1}$$

Since $e^y > 0$, the solution involving the minus sign is extraneous and must be discarded. Thus,

$$e^y = x + \sqrt{x^2+1}$$

Taking natural logarithms yields

$$y = \ln(x + \sqrt{x^2+1}) \quad \text{or} \quad \sinh^{-1} x = \ln(x + \sqrt{x^2+1})$$

**▶ Example 5**

$$\sinh^{-1} 1 = \ln(1 + \sqrt{1^2+1}) = \ln(1+\sqrt{2}) \approx 0.8814$$

$$\tanh^{-1}\left(\frac{1}{2}\right) = \frac{1}{2}\ln\left(\frac{1+\frac{1}{2}}{1-\frac{1}{2}}\right) = \frac{1}{2}\ln 3 \approx 0.5493 \ ◀$$

## DERIVATIVES AND INTEGRALS INVOLVING INVERSE HYPERBOLIC FUNCTIONS

Show that the derivative of the function $\sinh^{-1} x$ can also be obtained by letting $y = \sinh^{-1} x$ and then differentiating $x = \sinh y$ implicitly.

Formulas for the derivatives of the inverse hyperbolic functions can be obtained from Theorem 6.9.4. For example,

$$\frac{d}{dx}[\sinh^{-1}x] = \frac{d}{dx}[\ln(x + \sqrt{x^2+1})] = \frac{1}{x+\sqrt{x^2+1}}\left(1 + \frac{x}{\sqrt{x^2+1}}\right)$$

$$= \frac{\sqrt{x^2+1}+x}{(x+\sqrt{x^2+1})(\sqrt{x^2+1})} = \frac{1}{\sqrt{x^2+1}}$$

This computation leads to two integral formulas, a formula that involves $\sinh^{-1} x$ and an equivalent formula that involves logarithms:

$$\int \frac{dx}{\sqrt{x^2+1}} = \sinh^{-1} x + C = \ln(x + \sqrt{x^2+1}) + C$$

The following two theorems list the generalized derivative formulas and corresponding integration formulas for the inverse hyperbolic functions. Some of the proofs appear as exercises.

**6.9.5 THEOREM**

$$\frac{d}{dx}(\sinh^{-1} u) = \frac{1}{\sqrt{1+u^2}}\frac{du}{dx} \qquad \frac{d}{dx}(\coth^{-1} u) = \frac{1}{1-u^2}\frac{du}{dx}, \quad |u| > 1$$

$$\frac{d}{dx}(\cosh^{-1} u) = \frac{1}{\sqrt{u^2-1}}\frac{du}{dx}, \quad u > 1 \qquad \frac{d}{dx}(\operatorname{sech}^{-1} u) = -\frac{1}{u\sqrt{1-u^2}}\frac{du}{dx}, \quad 0 < u < 1$$

$$\frac{d}{dx}(\tanh^{-1} u) = \frac{1}{1-u^2}\frac{du}{dx}, \quad |u| < 1 \qquad \frac{d}{dx}(\operatorname{csch}^{-1} u) = -\frac{1}{|u|\sqrt{1+u^2}}\frac{du}{dx}, \quad u \neq 0$$

**6.9.6 THEOREM** *If $a > 0$, then*

$$\int \frac{du}{\sqrt{a^2+u^2}} = \sinh^{-1}\left(\frac{u}{a}\right) + C \text{ or } \ln(u+\sqrt{u^2+a^2}) + C$$

$$\int \frac{du}{\sqrt{u^2-a^2}} = \cosh^{-1}\left(\frac{u}{a}\right) + C \text{ or } \ln(u+\sqrt{u^2-a^2}) + C, \; u > a$$

$$\int \frac{du}{a^2-u^2} = \begin{cases} \dfrac{1}{a}\tanh^{-1}\left(\dfrac{u}{a}\right) + C, & |u| < a \\ \dfrac{1}{a}\coth^{-1}\left(\dfrac{u}{a}\right) + C, & |u| > a \end{cases} \text{ or } \frac{1}{2a}\ln\left|\frac{a+u}{a-u}\right| + C, \; |u| \neq a$$

$$\int \frac{du}{u\sqrt{a^2-u^2}} = -\frac{1}{a}\operatorname{sech}^{-1}\left|\frac{u}{a}\right| + C \text{ or } -\frac{1}{a}\ln\left(\frac{a+\sqrt{a^2-u^2}}{|u|}\right) + C, \; 0 < |u| < a$$

$$\int \frac{du}{u\sqrt{a^2+u^2}} = -\frac{1}{a}\operatorname{csch}^{-1}\left|\frac{u}{a}\right| + C \text{ or } -\frac{1}{a}\ln\left(\frac{a+\sqrt{a^2+u^2}}{|u|}\right) + C, \; u \neq 0$$

► **Example 6** Evaluate $\displaystyle\int \frac{dx}{\sqrt{4x^2-9}}, \; x > \frac{3}{2}$.

***Solution.*** Let $u = 2x$. Thus, $du = 2\,dx$ and

$$\int \frac{dx}{\sqrt{4x^2-9}} = \frac{1}{2}\int \frac{2\,dx}{\sqrt{4x^2-9}} = \frac{1}{2}\int \frac{du}{\sqrt{u^2-3^2}}$$
$$= \frac{1}{2}\cosh^{-1}\left(\frac{u}{3}\right) + C = \frac{1}{2}\cosh^{-1}\left(\frac{2x}{3}\right) + C$$

Alternatively, we can use the logarithmic equivalent of $\cosh^{-1}(2x/3)$,

$$\cosh^{-1}\left(\frac{2x}{3}\right) = \ln(2x+\sqrt{4x^2-9}) - \ln 3$$

(verify), and express the answer as

$$\int \frac{dx}{\sqrt{4x^2-9}} = \frac{1}{2}\ln(2x+\sqrt{4x^2-9}) + C \;◄$$

## ✓ QUICK CHECK EXERCISES 6.9 *(See page 409 for answers.)*

1. $\cosh x =$ ______ $\sinh x =$ ______
$\tanh x =$ ______

2. Complete the table.

| | $\cosh x$ | $\sinh x$ | $\tanh x$ | $\coth x$ | $\operatorname{sech} x$ | $\operatorname{csch} x$ |
|---|---|---|---|---|---|---|
| DOMAIN | | | | | | |
| RANGE | | | | | | |

3. The parametric equations
$$x = \cosh t, \quad y = \sinh t \quad (-\infty < t < +\infty)$$
represent the right half of the curve called a ______. Eliminating the parameter, the equation of this curve is ______.

4. $\dfrac{d}{dx}[\cosh x] =$ ______ $\dfrac{d}{dx}[\sinh x] =$ ______
$\dfrac{d}{dx}[\tanh x] =$ ______

5. $\displaystyle\int \cosh x\,dx =$ ______ $\displaystyle\int \sinh x\,dx =$ ______
$\displaystyle\int \tanh x\,dx =$ ______

6. $\dfrac{d}{dx}[\cosh^{-1} x] =$ ______ $\dfrac{d}{dx}[\sinh^{-1} x] =$ ______
$\dfrac{d}{dx}[\tanh^{-1} x] =$ ______

## EXERCISE SET 6.9 Graphing Utility

**1–2** Approximate the expression to four decimal places. ■

1. (a) $\sinh 3$ (b) $\cosh(-2)$ (c) $\tanh(\ln 4)$
(d) $\sinh^{-1}(-2)$ (e) $\cosh^{-1} 3$ (f) $\tanh^{-1} \frac{3}{4}$

2. (a) $\operatorname{csch}(-1)$ (b) $\operatorname{sech}(\ln 2)$ (c) $\coth 1$
(d) $\operatorname{sech}^{-1} \frac{1}{2}$ (e) $\coth^{-1} 3$ (f) $\operatorname{csch}^{-1}(-\sqrt{3})$

3. Find the exact numerical value of each expression.
(a) $\sinh(\ln 3)$ (b) $\cosh(-\ln 2)$
(c) $\tanh(2\ln 5)$ (d) $\sinh(-3\ln 2)$

4. In each part, rewrite the expression as a ratio of polynomials.
(a) $\cosh(\ln x)$ (b) $\sinh(\ln x)$
(c) $\tanh(2\ln x)$ (d) $\cosh(-\ln x)$

5. In each part, a value for one of the hyperbolic functions is given at an unspecified positive number $x_0$. Use appropriate identities to find the exact values of the remaining five hyperbolic functions at $x_0$.
(a) $\sinh x_0 = 2$ (b) $\cosh x_0 = \frac{5}{4}$ (c) $\tanh x_0 = \frac{4}{5}$

6. Obtain the derivative formulas for csch $x$, sech $x$, and coth $x$ from the derivative formulas for sinh $x$, cosh $x$, and tanh $x$.

7. Find the derivatives of $\cosh^{-1} x$ and $\tanh^{-1} x$ by differentiating the formulas in Theorem 6.9.4.

8. Find the derivatives of $\sinh^{-1} x$, $\cosh^{-1} x$, and $\tanh^{-1} x$ by differentiating the equations $x = \sinh y$, $x = \cosh y$, and $x = \tanh y$ implicitly.

**9–28** Find $dy/dx$. ■

9. $y = \sinh(4x - 8)$
10. $y = \cosh(x^4)$
11. $y = \coth(\ln x)$
12. $y = \ln(\tanh 2x)$
13. $y = \operatorname{csch}(1/x)$
14. $y = \operatorname{sech}(e^{2x})$
15. $y = \sqrt{4x + \cosh^2(5x)}$
16. $y = \sinh^3(2x)$
17. $y = x^3 \tanh^2(\sqrt{x})$
18. $y = \sinh(\cos 3x)$
19. $y = \sinh^{-1}\left(\frac{1}{3}x\right)$
20. $y = \sinh^{-1}(1/x)$
21. $y = \ln(\cosh^{-1} x)$
22. $y = \cosh^{-1}(\sinh^{-1} x)$
23. $y = \dfrac{1}{\tanh^{-1} x}$
24. $y = (\coth^{-1} x)^2$
25. $y = \cosh^{-1}(\cosh x)$
26. $y = \sinh^{-1}(\tanh x)$
27. $y = e^x \operatorname{sech}^{-1}\sqrt{x}$
28. $y = (1 + x\operatorname{csch}^{-1} x)^{10}$

**29–44** Evaluate the integrals. ■

29. $\int \sinh^6 x \cosh x\, dx$
30. $\int \cosh(2x - 3)\, dx$
31. $\int \sqrt{\tanh x}\operatorname{sech}^2 x\, dx$
32. $\int \operatorname{csch}^2(3x)\, dx$
33. $\int \tanh x\, dx$
34. $\int \coth^2 x \operatorname{csch}^2 x\, dx$
35. $\int_{\ln 2}^{\ln 3} \tanh x \operatorname{sech}^3 x\, dx$
36. $\int_0^{\ln 3} \dfrac{e^x - e^{-x}}{e^x + e^{-x}}\, dx$
37. $\int \dfrac{dx}{\sqrt{1 + 9x^2}}$
38. $\int \dfrac{dx}{\sqrt{x^2 - 2}}$ $(x > \sqrt{2})$
39. $\int \dfrac{dx}{\sqrt{1 - e^{2x}}}$ $(x < 0)$
40. $\int \dfrac{\sin\theta\, d\theta}{\sqrt{1 + \cos^2\theta}}$
41. $\int \dfrac{dx}{x\sqrt{1 + 4x^2}}$
42. $\int \dfrac{dx}{\sqrt{9x^2 - 25}}$ $(x > 5/3)$
43. $\int_0^{1/2} \dfrac{dx}{1 - x^2}$
44. $\int_0^{\sqrt{3}} \dfrac{dt}{\sqrt{t^2 + 1}}$

**45–48 True–False** Determine whether the statement is true or false. Explain your answer. ■

45. The equation $\cosh x = \sinh x$ has no solutions.

46. Exactly two of the hyperbolic functions are bounded.

47. There is exactly one hyperbolic function $f(x)$ such that for all real numbers $a$, the equation $f(x) = a$ has a unique solution $x$.

48. The identities in Theorem 6.9.2 may be obtained from the corresponding trigonometric identities by replacing each trigonometric function with its hyperbolic analogue.

49. Find the area enclosed by $y = \sinh 2x$, $y = 0$, and $x = \ln 3$.

50. Find the volume of the solid that is generated when the region enclosed by $y = \operatorname{sech} x$, $y = 0$, $x = 0$, and $x = \ln 2$ is revolved about the $x$-axis.

51. Find the volume of the solid that is generated when the region enclosed by $y = \cosh 2x$, $y = \sinh 2x$, $x = 0$, and $x = 5$ is revolved about the $x$-axis.

52. Approximate the positive value of the constant $a$ such that the area enclosed by $y = \cosh ax$, $y = 0$, $x = 0$, and $x = 1$ is 2 square units. Express your answer to at least five decimal places.

53. Find the arc length of the catenary $y = \cosh x$ between $x = 0$ and $x = \ln 2$.

54. Find the arc length of the catenary $y = a\cosh(x/a)$ between $x = 0$ and $x = x_1$ $(x_1 > 0)$.

55. In parts (a)–(f) find the limits, and confirm that they are consistent with the graphs in Figures 6.9.1 and 6.9.6.
(a) $\lim_{x\to+\infty} \sinh x$ (b) $\lim_{x\to-\infty} \sinh x$
(c) $\lim_{x\to+\infty} \tanh x$ (d) $\lim_{x\to-\infty} \tanh x$
(e) $\lim_{x\to+\infty} \sinh^{-1} x$ (f) $\lim_{x\to 1^-} \tanh^{-1} x$

**FOCUS ON CONCEPTS**

56. Explain how to obtain the asymptotes for $y = \tanh x$ from the curvilinear asymptotes for $y = \cosh x$ and $y = \sinh x$.

57. Prove that $\sinh x$ is an odd function of $x$ and that $\cosh x$ is an even function of $x$, and check that this is consistent with the graphs in Figure 6.9.1.

**58–59** Prove the identities. ■

**58.** (a) $\cosh x + \sinh x = e^x$
(b) $\cosh x - \sinh x = e^{-x}$
(c) $\sinh(x + y) = \sinh x \cosh y + \cosh x \sinh y$
(d) $\sinh 2x = 2 \sinh x \cosh x$
(e) $\cosh(x + y) = \cosh x \cosh y + \sinh x \sinh y$
(f) $\cosh 2x = \cosh^2 x + \sinh^2 x$
(g) $\cosh 2x = 2 \sinh^2 x + 1$
(h) $\cosh 2x = 2 \cosh^2 x - 1$

**59.** (a) $1 - \tanh^2 x = \operatorname{sech}^2 x$
(b) $\tanh(x + y) = \dfrac{\tanh x + \tanh y}{1 + \tanh x \tanh y}$
(c) $\tanh 2x = \dfrac{2 \tanh x}{1 + \tanh^2 x}$

**60.** Prove:
(a) $\cosh^{-1} x = \ln(x + \sqrt{x^2 - 1}), \quad x \geq 1$
(b) $\tanh^{-1} x = \dfrac{1}{2} \ln\left(\dfrac{1 + x}{1 - x}\right), \quad -1 < x < 1.$

**61.** Use Exercise 60 to obtain the derivative formulas for $\cosh^{-1} x$ and $\tanh^{-1} x$.

**62.** Prove:

$$\operatorname{sech}^{-1} x = \cosh^{-1}(1/x), \quad 0 < x \leq 1$$
$$\coth^{-1} x = \tanh^{-1}(1/x), \quad |x| > 1$$
$$\operatorname{csch}^{-1} x = \sinh^{-1}(1/x), \quad x \neq 0$$

**63.** Use Exercise 62 to express the integral

$$\int \frac{du}{1 - u^2}$$

entirely in terms of $\tanh^{-1}$.

**64.** Show that
(a) $\dfrac{d}{dx}[\operatorname{sech}^{-1}|x|] = -\dfrac{1}{x\sqrt{1 - x^2}}$
(b) $\dfrac{d}{dx}[\operatorname{csch}^{-1}|x|] = -\dfrac{1}{x\sqrt{1 + x^2}}$.

**65.** In each part, find the limit.
(a) $\lim_{x \to +\infty} (\cosh^{-1} x - \ln x)$ (b) $\lim_{x \to +\infty} \dfrac{\cosh x}{e^x}$

**66.** Use the first and second derivatives to show that the graph of $y = \tanh^{-1} x$ is always increasing and has an inflection point at the origin.

**67.** The integration formulas for $1/\sqrt{u^2 - a^2}$ in Theorem 6.9.6 are valid for $u > a$. Show that the following formula is valid for $u < -a$:

$$\int \frac{du}{\sqrt{u^2 - a^2}} = -\cosh^{-1}\left(-\frac{u}{a}\right) + C \quad \text{or} \quad \ln\left|u + \sqrt{u^2 - a^2}\right| + C$$

**68.** Show that $(\sinh x + \cosh x)^n = \sinh nx + \cosh nx$.

**69.** Show that

$$\int_{-a}^{a} e^{tx}\, dx = \frac{2 \sinh at}{t}$$

**70.** A cable is suspended between two poles as shown in Figure 6.9.2. Assume that the equation of the curve formed by the cable is $y = a \cosh(x/a)$, where $a$ is a positive constant. Suppose that the $x$-coordinates of the points of support are $x = -b$ and $x = b$, where $b > 0$.
(a) Show that the length $L$ of the cable is given by

$$L = 2a \sinh \frac{b}{a}$$

(b) Show that the sag $S$ (the vertical distance between the highest and lowest points on the cable) is given by

$$S = a \cosh \frac{b}{a} - a$$

**71–72** These exercises refer to the hanging cable described in Exercise 70. ■

**71.** Assuming that the poles are 400 ft apart and the sag in the cable is 30 ft, approximate the length of the cable by approximating $a$. Express your final answer to the nearest tenth of a foot. [*Hint:* First let $u = 200/a$.]

**72.** Assuming that the cable is 120 ft long and the poles are 100 ft apart, approximate the sag in the cable by approximating $a$. Express your final answer to the nearest tenth of a foot. [*Hint:* First let $u = 50/a$.]

**73.** The design of the Gateway Arch in St. Louis, Missouri, by architect Eero Saarinan was implemented using equations provided by Dr. Hannskarl Badel. The equation used for the centerline of the arch was

$$y = 693.8597 - 68.7672 \cosh(0.0100333x) \text{ ft}$$

for $x$ between $-299.2239$ and $299.2239$.
(a) Use a graphing utility to graph the centerline of the arch.
(b) Find the length of the centerline to four decimal places.
(c) For what values of $x$ is the height of the arch 100 ft? Round your answers to four decimal places.
(d) Approximate, to the nearest degree, the acute angle that the tangent line to the centerline makes with the ground at the ends of the arch.

**74.** Suppose that a hollow tube rotates with a constant angular velocity of $\omega$ rad/s about a horizontal axis at one end of the tube, as shown in the accompanying figure. Assume that an object is free to slide without friction in the tube while the tube is rotating. Let $r$ be the distance from the object to the pivot point at time $t \geq 0$, and assume that the object is at rest and $r = 0$ when $t = 0$. It can be shown that if the tube is horizontal at time $t = 0$ and rotating as shown in the figure, then

$$r = \frac{g}{2\omega^2}[\sinh(\omega t) - \sin(\omega t)]$$

during the period that the object is in the tube. Assume that $t$ is in seconds and $r$ is in meters, and use $g = 9.8 \text{ m/s}^2$ and $\omega = 2$ rad/s.
(a) Graph $r$ versus $t$ for $0 \leq t \leq 1$.
(b) Assuming that the tube has a length of 1 m, approximately how long does it take for the object to reach the end of the tube?
(c) Use the result of part (b) to approximate $dr/dt$ at the instant that the object reaches the end of the tube.

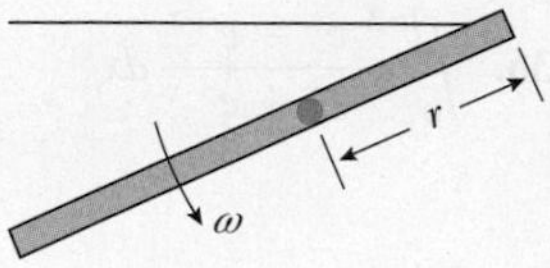

◀ **Figure Ex-74**

**75.** The accompanying figure shows a person pulling a boat by holding a rope of length $a$ attached to the bow and walking along the edge of a dock. If we assume that the rope is always tangent to the curve traced by the bow of the boat, then this curve, which is called a ***tractrix***, has the property that the segment of the tangent line between the curve and the $y$-axis has a constant length $a$. It can be proved that the equation of this tractrix is

$$y = a\,\operatorname{sech}^{-1}\frac{x}{a} - \sqrt{a^2 - x^2}$$

(a) Show that to move the bow of the boat to a point $(x, y)$, the person must walk a distance

$$D = a\,\operatorname{sech}^{-1}\frac{x}{a}$$

from the origin.

(b) If the rope has a length of 15 m, how far must the person walk from the origin to bring the boat 10 m from the dock? Round your answer to two decimal places.

(c) Find the distance traveled by the bow along the tractrix as it moves from its initial position to the point where it is 5 m from the dock.

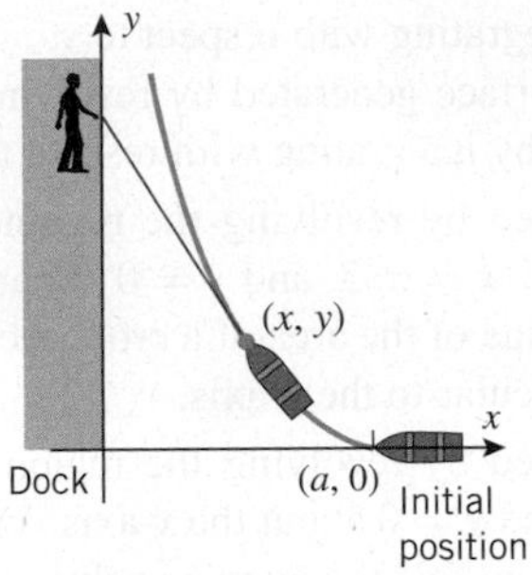


Figure Ex-75

**76.** The death rate for victims of a plague during the Bombay epidemic of 1905–1906 can be modeled by the formula $R(t) = 890\,\operatorname{sech}^2(0.2t - 3.4)$ deaths per week, where $0 \le t \le 30$ indicates the number of weeks since the outbreak of the disease. Use this model in each part.

(a) What was the maximum death rate? In what week did it occur?

(b) Estimate the number of deaths that occurred during the 30-week epidemic.

***Source:*** "Contributions to the Mathematical Theory of Epidemics," *Proceedings of the Royal Society London A*, Vol. 115, 1927, pp. 700–721, by W. O. Kermack and A. G. McKendrick.

**77. Writing** Suppose that, by analogy with the trigonometric functions, we *define* $\cosh t$ and $\sinh t$ geometrically using Figure 6.9.3*b*:

"For any real number $t$, define $x = \cosh t$ and $y = \sinh t$ to be the unique values of $x$ and $y$ such that

(i) $P(x, y)$ is on the right branch of the unit hyperbola $x^2 - y^2 = 1$;

(ii) $t$ and $y$ have the same sign (or are both 0);

(iii) the area of the region bounded by the $x$-axis, the right branch of the unit hyperbola, and the segment from the origin to $P$ is $|t|/2$."

Discuss what properties would first need to be verified in order for this to be a legitimate definition.

**78. Writing** Investigate what properties of $\cosh t$ and $\sinh t$ can be proved directly from the geometric definition in Exercise 77. Write a short description of the results of your investigation.

✓ **QUICK CHECK ANSWERS 6.9** **1.** $\dfrac{e^x + e^{-x}}{2}$; $\dfrac{e^x - e^{-x}}{2}$; $\dfrac{e^x - e^{-x}}{e^x + e^{-x}}$

**2.**

| | $\cosh x$ | $\sinh x$ | $\tanh x$ | $\coth x$ | $\operatorname{sech} x$ | $\operatorname{csch} x$ |
|---|---|---|---|---|---|---|
| DOMAIN | $(-\infty, +\infty)$ | $(-\infty, +\infty)$ | $(-\infty, +\infty)$ | $(-\infty, 0) \cup (0, +\infty)$ | $(-\infty, +\infty)$ | $(-\infty, 0) \cup (0, +\infty)$ |
| RANGE | $[1, +\infty)$ | $(-\infty, +\infty)$ | $(-1, 1)$ | $(-\infty, -1) \cup (1, +\infty)$ | $(0, 1]$ | $(-\infty, 0) \cup (0, +\infty)$ |

**3.** unit hyperbola; $x^2 - y^2 = 1$ **4.** $\sinh x$; $\cosh x$; $\operatorname{sech}^2 x$ **5.** $\sinh x + C$; $\cosh x + C$; $\ln(\cosh x) + C$

**6.** $\dfrac{1}{\sqrt{x^2 - 1}}$; $\dfrac{1}{\sqrt{1 + x^2}}$; $\dfrac{1}{1 - x^2}$

## CHAPTER 6 REVIEW EXERCISES

**1.** Describe the method of slicing for finding volumes, and use that method to derive an integral formula for finding volumes by the method of disks.

**2.** State an integral formula for finding a volume by the method of cylindrical shells, and use Riemann sums to derive the formula.

**3.** State an integral formula for finding the arc length of a smooth curve $y = f(x)$ over an interval $[a, b]$, and use Riemann sums to derive the formula.

**4.** State an integral formula for the work $W$ done by a variable force $F(x)$ applied in the direction of motion to an object moving from $x = a$ to $x = b$, and use Riemann sums to derive the formula.

**5.** State an integral formula for the fluid force $F$ exerted on a vertical flat surface immersed in a fluid of weight density $\rho$, and use Riemann sums to derive the formula.

**6.** Let $R$ be the region in the first quadrant enclosed by $y = x^2$, $y = 2 + x$, and $x = 0$. In each part, set up, but *do not* *evaluate*, an integral or a sum of integrals that will solve the problem.

(a) Find the area of $R$ by integrating with respect to $x$.
(b) Find the area of $R$ by integrating with respect to $y$.
(c) Find the volume of the solid generated by revolving $R$ about the $x$-axis by integrating with respect to $x$.
(d) Find the volume of the solid generated by revolving $R$ about the $x$-axis by integrating with respect to $y$.
(e) Find the volume of the solid generated by revolving $R$ about the $y$-axis by integrating with respect to $x$.
(f) Find the volume of the solid generated by revolving $R$ about the $y$-axis by integrating with respect to $y$.
(g) Find the volume of the solid generated by revolving $R$ about the line $y = -3$ by integrating with respect to $x$.
(h) Find the volume of the solid generated by revolving $R$ about the line $x = 5$ by integrating with respect to $x$.

**7.** (a) Set up a sum of definite integrals that represents the total shaded area between the curves $y = f(x)$ and $y = g(x)$ in the accompanying figure.
(b) Find the total area enclosed between $y = x^3$ and $y = x$ over the interval $[-1, 2]$.

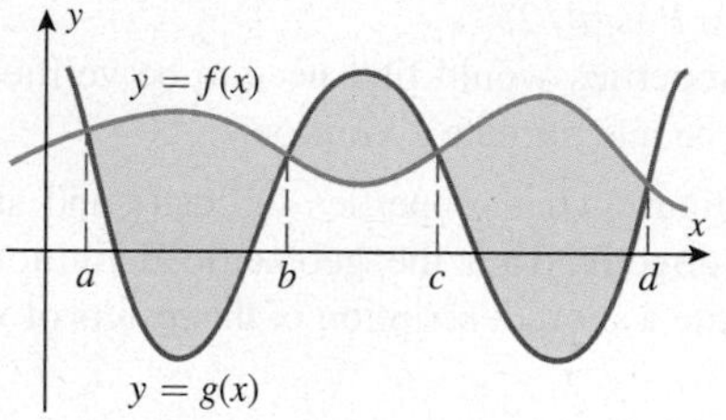


◀ **Figure Ex-7**

**8.** The accompanying figure shows velocity versus time curves for two cars that move along a straight track, accelerating from rest at a common starting line.
(a) How far apart are the cars after 60 seconds?
(b) How far apart are the cars after $T$ seconds, where $0 \le T \le 60$?

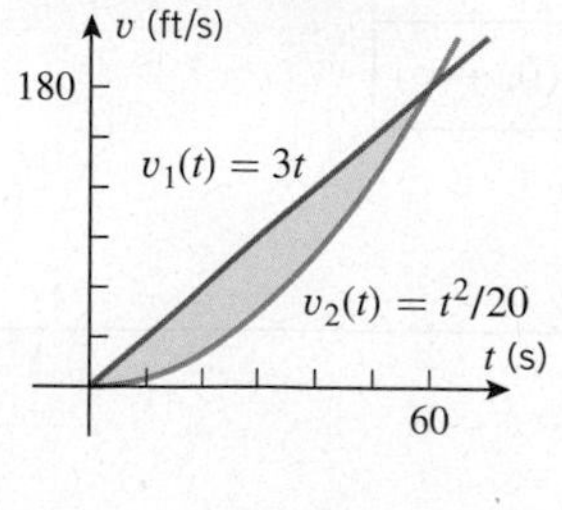


◀ **Figure Ex-8**

**9.** Let $R$ be the region enclosed by the curves $y = x^2 + 4$, $y = x^3$, and the $y$-axis. Find and evaluate a definite integral that represents the volume of the solid generated by revolving $R$ about the $x$-axis.

**10.** A football has the shape of the solid generated by revolving the region bounded between the $x$-axis and the parabola $y = 4R(x^2 - \frac{1}{4}L^2)/L^2$ about the $x$-axis. Find its volume.

**11.** Find the volume of the solid whose base is the region bounded between the curves $y = \sqrt{x}$ and $y = 1/\sqrt{x}$ for $1 \le x \le 4$ and whose cross sections perpendicular to the $x$-axis are squares.

**12.** Consider the region enclosed by $y = \sin^{-1} x$, $y = 0$, and $x = 1$. Set up, but *do not evaluate*, an integral that represents the volume of the solid generated by revolving the region about the $x$-axis using
(a) disks (b) cylindrical shells.

**13.** Find the arc length in the second quadrant of the curve $x^{2/3} + y^{2/3} = 4$ from $x = -8$ to $x = -1$.

**14.** Let $C$ be the curve $y = e^x$ between $x = 0$ and $x = \ln 10$. In each part, set up, but *do not evaluate*, an integral that solves the problem.
(a) Find the arc length of $C$ by integrating with respect to $x$.
(b) Find the arc length of $C$ by integrating with respect to $y$.

**15.** Find the area of the surface generated by revolving the curve $y = \sqrt{25 - x}$, $9 \le x \le 16$, about the $x$-axis.

**16.** Let $C$ be the curve $27x - y^3 = 0$ between $y = 0$ and $y = 2$. In each part, set up, but *do not evaluate*, an integral or a sum of integrals that solves the problem.
(a) Find the area of the surface generated by revolving $C$ about the $x$-axis by integrating with respect to $x$.
(b) Find the area of the surface generated by revolving $C$ about the $y$-axis by integrating with respect to $y$.
(c) Find the area of the surface generated by revolving $C$ about the line $y = -2$ by integrating with respect to $y$.

**17.** Consider the solid generated by revolving the region enclosed by $y = \sec x$, $x = 0$, $x = \pi/3$, and $y = 0$ about the $x$-axis. Find the average value of the area of a cross section of this solid taken perpendicular to the $x$-axis.

**18.** Consider the solid generated by revolving the region enclosed by $y = \sqrt{a^2 - x^2}$ and $y = 0$ about the $x$-axis. Without performing an integration, find the average value of the area of a cross section of this solid taken perpendicular to the $x$-axis.

**19.** (a) A spring exerts a force of 0.5 N when stretched 0.25 m beyond its natural length. Assuming that Hooke's law applies, how much work was performed in stretching the spring to this length?
(b) How far beyond its natural length can the spring be stretched with 25 J of work?

**20.** A boat is anchored so that the anchor is 150 ft below the surface of the water. In the water, the anchor weighs 2000 lb and the chain weighs 30 lb/ft. How much work is required to raise the anchor to the surface?

**21–22** Find the centroid of the region. ■

**21.** The region bounded by $y^2 = 4x$ and $y^2 = 8(x - 2)$.

**22.** The upper half of the ellipse $(x/a)^2 + (y/b)^2 = 1$.

**23.** In each part, set up, but *do not evaluate*, an integral that solves the problem.
(a) Find the fluid force exerted on a side of a box that has a 3 m square base and is filled to a depth of 1 m with a liquid of weight density $\rho$ N/m$^3$.
(b) Find the fluid force exerted by a liquid of weight density $\rho$ lb/ft$^3$ on a face of the vertical plate shown in part (*a*) of the accompanying figure.
(c) Find the fluid force exerted on the parabolic dam in part (*b*) of the accompanying figure by water that extends to the top of the dam.

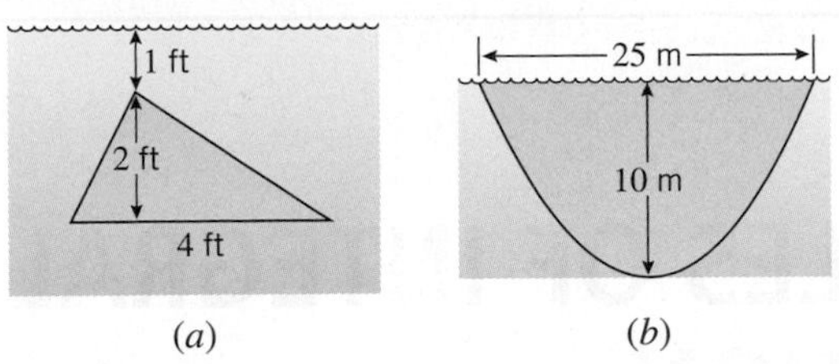


▲ **Figure Ex-23**

**24.** Show that for any constant $a$, the function $y = \sinh(ax)$ satisfies the equation $y'' = a^2 y$.

**25.** In each part, prove the identity.
(a) $\cosh 3x = 4\cosh^3 x - 3\cosh x$
(b) $\cosh \frac{1}{2}x = \sqrt{\frac{1}{2}(\cosh x + 1)}$
(c) $\sinh \frac{1}{2}x = \pm\sqrt{\frac{1}{2}(\cosh x - 1)}$

## CHAPTER 6 MAKING CONNECTIONS

**1.** Suppose that $f$ is a nonnegative function defined on $[0, 1]$ such that the area between the graph of $f$ and the interval $[0, 1]$ is $A_1$ and such that the area of the region $R$ between the graph of $g(x) = f(x^2)$ and the interval $[0, 1]$ is $A_2$. In each part, express your answer in terms of $A_1$ and $A_2$.
(a) What is the volume of the solid of revolution generated by revolving $R$ about the $y$-axis?
(b) Find a value of $a$ such that if the $xy$-plane were horizontal, the region $R$ would balance on the line $x = a$.

**2.** A water tank has the shape of a conical frustum with radius of the base 5 ft, radius of the top 10 ft and (vertical) height 15 ft. Suppose the tank is filled with water and consider the problem of finding the work required to pump all the water out through a hole in the top of the tank.
(a) Solve this problem using the method of Example 5 in Section 6.6.
(b) Solve this problem using Definition 6.6.3. [*Hint:* Think of the base as the head of a piston that expands to a watertight fit against the sides of the tank as the piston is pushed upward. What important result about water pressure do you need to use?]

**3.** A disk of radius $a$ is an inhomogeneous lamina whose density is a function $f(r)$ of the distance $r$ to the center of the lamina. Modify the argument used to derive the method of cylindrical shells to find a formula for the mass of the lamina.

**4.** Compare Formula (10) in Section 6.7 with Formula (8) in Section 6.8. Then give a plausible argument that the force on a flat surface immersed vertically in a fluid of constant weight density is equal to the product of the area of the surface and the pressure at the centroid of the surface. Conclude that the force on the surface is the same as if the surface were immersed horizontally at the depth of the centroid.

**5.** ***Archimedes' Principle*** states that a solid immersed in a fluid experiences a buoyant force equal to the weight of the fluid displaced by the solid.
(a) Use the results of Section 6.8 to verify Archimedes' Principle in the case of (i) a box-shaped solid with a pair of faces parallel to the surface of the fluid, (ii) a solid cylinder with vertical axis, and (iii) a cylindrical shell with vertical axis.
(b) Give a plausible argument for Archimedes' Principle in the case of a solid of revolution immersed in fluid such that the axis of revolution of the solid is vertical. [*Hint:* Approximate the solid by a union of cylindrical shells and use the result from part (a).]

Frederic Legrand - COMEO/Shutterstock

*The floating roof on the Stade de France sports complex is an ellipse. Finding the arc length of an ellipse involves numerical integration techniques introduced in this chapter.*

# 7 PRINCIPLES OF INTEGRAL EVALUATION

In earlier chapters we obtained many basic integration formulas as an immediate consequence of the corresponding differentiation formulas. For example, knowing that the derivative of sin $x$ is cos $x$ enabled us to deduce that the integral of cos $x$ is sin $x$. Subsequently, we expanded our integration repertoire by introducing the method of $u$-substitution. That method enabled us to integrate many functions by transforming the integrand of an unfamiliar integral into a familiar form. However, $u$-substitution alone is not adequate to handle the wide variety of integrals that arise in applications, so additional integration techniques are still needed. In this chapter we will discuss some of those techniques, and we will provide a more systematic procedure for attacking unfamiliar integrals. We will talk more about numerical approximations of definite integrals, and we will explore the idea of integrating over infinite intervals.

## 7.1 AN OVERVIEW OF INTEGRATION METHODS

*In this section we will give a brief overview of methods for evaluating integrals, and we will review the integration formulas that were discussed in earlier sections.*

### METHODS FOR APPROACHING INTEGRATION PROBLEMS

There are three basic approaches for evaluating unfamiliar integrals:

- **Technology**—CAS programs such as *Mathematica*, *Maple*, and the open source program *Sage* are capable of evaluating extremely complicated integrals, and such programs are increasingly available for both computers and handheld calculators.
- **Tables**—Prior to the development of CAS programs, scientists relied heavily on tables to evaluate difficult integrals arising in applications. Such tables were compiled over many years, incorporating the skills and experience of many people. One such table appears in the endpapers of this text, but more comprehensive tables appear in various reference books such as the *CRC Standard Mathematical Tables and Formulae*, CRC Press, Inc., 2002.
- **Transformation Methods**—Transformation methods are methods for converting unfamiliar integrals into familiar integrals. These include $u$-substitution, algebraic manipulation of the integrand, and other methods that we will discuss in this chapter.

None of the three methods is perfect; for example, CAS programs often encounter integrals that they cannot evaluate and they sometimes produce answers that are unnecessarily complicated, tables are not exhaustive and may not include a particular integral of interest, and transformation methods rely on human ingenuity that may prove to be inadequate in difficult problems.

In this chapter we will focus on transformation methods and tables, so it will *not be necessary* to have a CAS such as *Mathematica*, *Maple*, or *Sage*. However, if you have a CAS, then you can use it to confirm the results in the examples, and there are exercises that are designed to be solved with a CAS. If you have a CAS, keep in mind that many of the algorithms that it uses are based on the methods we will discuss here, so an understanding of these methods will help you to use your technology in a more informed way.

## A REVIEW OF FAMILIAR INTEGRATION FORMULAS

The following is a list of basic integrals that we have encountered thus far:

### CONSTANTS, POWERS, EXPONENTIALS

**1.** $\int du = u + C$

**2.** $\int a\,du = a\int du = au + C$

**3.** $\int u^r\,du = \dfrac{u^{r+1}}{r+1} + C,\ r \neq -1$

**4.** $\int \dfrac{du}{u} = \ln|u| + C$

**5.** $\int e^u\,du = e^u + C$

**6.** $\int b^u\,du = \dfrac{b^u}{\ln b} + C,\ b > 0, b \neq 1$

### TRIGONOMETRIC FUNCTIONS

**7.** $\int \sin u\,du = -\cos u + C$

**8.** $\int \cos u\,du = \sin u + C$

**9.** $\int \sec^2 u\,du = \tan u + C$

**10.** $\int \csc^2 u\,du = -\cot u + C$

**11.** $\int \sec u \tan u\,du = \sec u + C$

**12.** $\int \csc u \cot u\,du = -\csc u + C$

**13.** $\int \tan u\,du = -\ln|\cos u| + C$

**14.** $\int \cot u\,du = \ln|\sin u| + C$

### HYPERBOLIC FUNCTIONS

**15.** $\int \sinh u\,du = \cosh u + C$

**16.** $\int \cosh u\,du = \sinh u + C$

**17.** $\int \operatorname{sech}^2 u\,du = \tanh u + C$

**18.** $\int \operatorname{csch}^2 u\,du = -\coth u + C$

**19.** $\int \operatorname{sech} u \tanh u\,du = -\operatorname{sech} u + C$

**20.** $\int \operatorname{csch} u \coth u\,du = -\operatorname{csch} u + C$

### ALGEBRAIC FUNCTIONS ($a > 0$)

**21.** $\int \dfrac{du}{\sqrt{a^2 - u^2}} = \sin^{-1}\dfrac{u}{a} + C \qquad (|u| < a)$

**22.** $\int \dfrac{du}{a^2 + u^2} = \dfrac{1}{a}\tan^{-1}\dfrac{u}{a} + C$

**23.** $\int \dfrac{du}{u\sqrt{u^2 - a^2}} = \dfrac{1}{a}\sec^{-1}\left|\dfrac{u}{a}\right| + C \qquad (0 < a < |u|)$

**24.** $\int \dfrac{du}{\sqrt{a^2 + u^2}} = \ln(u + \sqrt{u^2 + a^2}) + C$

**25.** $\int \dfrac{du}{\sqrt{u^2 - a^2}} = \ln\left|u + \sqrt{u^2 - a^2}\right| + C \qquad (0 < a < |u|)$

**26.** $\int \dfrac{du}{a^2 - u^2} = \dfrac{1}{2a}\ln\left|\dfrac{a+u}{a-u}\right| + C$

**27.** $\int \dfrac{du}{u\sqrt{a^2 - u^2}} = -\dfrac{1}{a}\ln\left|\dfrac{a + \sqrt{a^2 - u^2}}{u}\right| + C \qquad (0 < |u| < a)$

**28.** $\int \dfrac{du}{u\sqrt{a^2 + u^2}} = -\dfrac{1}{a}\ln\left|\dfrac{a + \sqrt{a^2 + u^2}}{u}\right| + C$

**REMARK** Formula 25 is a generalization of a result in Theorem 6.9.6. Readers who did not cover Section 6.9 can ignore Formulas 24–28 for now, since we will develop other methods for obtaining them in this chapter.

## ✓ QUICK CHECK EXERCISES 7.1 (See page 415 for answers.)

1. Use algebraic manipulation and (if necessary) $u$-substitution to integrate the function.
   (a) $\int \frac{x+1}{x}\,dx =$ ______
   (b) $\int \frac{x+2}{x+1}\,dx =$ ______
   (c) $\int \frac{2x+1}{x^2+1}\,dx =$ ______
   (d) $\int xe^{3\ln x}\,dx =$ ______

2. Use trigonometric identities and (if necessary) $u$-substitution to integrate the function.
   (a) $\int \frac{1}{\csc x}\,dx =$ ______
   (b) $\int \frac{1}{\cos^2 x}\,dx =$ ______
   (c) $\int (\cot^2 x + 1)\,dx =$ ______
   (d) $\int \frac{1}{\sec x + \tan x}\,dx =$ ______

3. Integrate the function.
   (a) $\int \sqrt{x-1}\,dx =$ ______
   (b) $\int e^{2x+1}\,dx =$ ______
   (c) $\int (\sin^3 x\cos x + \sin x\cos^3 x)\,dx =$ ______
   (d) $\int \frac{1}{(e^x + e^{-x})^2}\,dx =$ ______

## EXERCISE SET 7.1

**1–30** Evaluate the integrals by making appropriate $u$-substitutions and applying the formulas reviewed in this section. ■

**1.** $\int (4-2x)^3\,dx$

**2.** $\int 3\sqrt{4+2x}\,dx$

**3.** $\int x\sec^2(x^2)\,dx$

**4.** $\int 4x\tan(x^2)\,dx$

**5.** $\int \frac{\sin 3x}{2+\cos 3x}\,dx$

**6.** $\int \frac{1}{9+4x^2}\,dx$

**7.** $\int e^x\sinh(e^x)\,dx$

**8.** $\int \frac{\sec(\ln x)\tan(\ln x)}{x}\,dx$

**9.** $\int e^{\tan x}\sec^2 x\,dx$

**10.** $\int \frac{x}{\sqrt{1-x^4}}\,dx$

**11.** $\int \cos^5 5x\sin 5x\,dx$

**12.** $\int \frac{\cos x}{\sin x\sqrt{\sin^2 x+1}}\,dx$

**13.** $\int \frac{e^x}{\sqrt{4+e^{2x}}}\,dx$

**14.** $\int \frac{e^{\tan^{-1}x}}{1+x^2}\,dx$

**15.** $\int \frac{e^{\sqrt{x-1}}}{\sqrt{x-1}}\,dx$

**16.** $\int (x+1)\cot(x^2+2x)\,dx$

**17.** $\int \frac{\cosh\sqrt{x}}{\sqrt{x}}\,dx$

**18.** $\int \frac{dx}{x(\ln x)^2}$

**19.** $\int \frac{dx}{\sqrt{x}\,3^{\sqrt{x}}}$

**20.** $\int \sec(\sin\theta)\tan(\sin\theta)\cos\theta\,d\theta$

**21.** $\int \frac{\operatorname{csch}^2(2/x)}{x^2}\,dx$

**22.** $\int \frac{dx}{\sqrt{x^2-4}}$

**23.** $\int \frac{e^{-x}}{4-e^{-2x}}\,dx$

**24.** $\int \frac{\cos(\ln x)}{x}\,dx$

**25.** $\int \frac{e^x}{\sqrt{1-e^{2x}}}\,dx$

**26.** $\int \frac{\sinh(x^{-1/2})}{x^{3/2}}\,dx$

**27.** $\int \frac{x}{\csc(x^2)}\,dx$

**28.** $\int \frac{e^x}{\sqrt{4-e^{2x}}}\,dx$

**29.** $\int x4^{-x^2}\,dx$

**30.** $\int 2^{\pi x}\,dx$

### FOCUS ON CONCEPTS

**31.** (a) Evaluate the integral $\int \sin x\cos x\,dx$ using the substitution $u = \sin x$.
(b) Evaluate the integral $\int \sin x\cos x\,dx$ using the identity $\sin 2x = 2\sin x\cos x$.
(c) Explain why your answers to parts (a) and (b) are consistent.

**32.** (a) Derive the identity
$$\frac{\operatorname{sech}^2 x}{1+\tanh^2 x} = \operatorname{sech} 2x$$
(b) Use the result in part (a) to evaluate $\int \operatorname{sech} x\,dx$.
(c) Derive the identity
$$\operatorname{sech} x = \frac{2e^x}{e^{2x}+1}$$
(d) Use the result in part (c) to evaluate $\int \operatorname{sech} x\,dx$.
(e) Explain why your answers to parts (b) and (d) are consistent.

**33.** (a) Derive the identity
$$\frac{\sec^2 x}{\tan x} = \frac{1}{\sin x\cos x}$$
(b) Use the identity $\sin 2x = 2\sin x\cos x$ along with the result in part (a) to evaluate $\int \csc x\,dx$.
(c) Use the identity $\cos x = \sin[(\pi/2) - x]$ along with your answer to part (a) to evaluate $\int \sec x\,dx$.

✓ **QUICK CHECK ANSWERS 7.1** 1. (a) $x+\ln|x|+C$ (b) $x+\ln|x+1|+C$ (c) $\ln(x^2+1)+\tan^{-1}x+C$ (d) $\frac{x^5}{5}+C$
2. (a) $-\cos x+C$ (b) $\tan x+C$ (c) $-\cot x+C$ (d) $\ln(1+\sin x)+C$ 3. (a) $\frac{2}{3}(x-1)^{3/2}+C$ (b) $\frac{1}{2}e^{2x+1}+C$ (c) $\frac{1}{2}\sin^2 x+C$
(d) $\frac{1}{4}\tanh x+C$

## 7.2 INTEGRATION BY PARTS

*In this section we will discuss an integration technique that is essentially an antiderivative formulation of the formula for differentiating a product of two functions.*

### THE PRODUCT RULE AND INTEGRATION BY PARTS

Our primary goal in this section is to develop a general method for attacking integrals of the form

$$\int f(x)g(x)\,dx$$

As a first step, let $G(x)$ be *any* antiderivative of $g(x)$. In this case $G'(x)=g(x)$, so the product rule for differentiating $f(x)G(x)$ can be expressed as

$$\frac{d}{dx}[f(x)G(x)]=f(x)G'(x)+f'(x)G(x)=f(x)g(x)+f'(x)G(x) \tag{1}$$

This implies that $f(x)G(x)$ is an antiderivative of the function on the right side of (1), so we can express (1) in integral form as

$$\int [f(x)g(x)+f'(x)G(x)]\,dx=f(x)G(x)$$

or, equivalently, as

$$\int f(x)g(x)\,dx=f(x)G(x)-\int f'(x)G(x)\,dx \tag{2}$$

This formula allows us to integrate $f(x)g(x)$ by integrating $f'(x)G(x)$ instead, and in many cases the net effect is to replace a difficult integration with an easier one. The application of this formula is called ***integration by parts***.

In practice, we usually rewrite (2) by letting

$$u=f(x),\quad du=f'(x)\,dx$$
$$v=G(x),\quad dv=G'(x)\,dx=g(x)\,dx$$

This yields the following alternative form for (2):

$$\int u\,dv=uv-\int v\,du \tag{3}$$

Note that in Example 1 we omitted the constant of integration in calculating $v$ from $dv$. Had we included a constant of integration, it would have eventually dropped out. This is always the case in integration by parts [Exercise 76(b)], so it is common to omit the constant at this stage of the computation. However, there are certain cases in which making a clever choice of a constant of integration to include with $v$ can simplify the computation of $\int v\,du$ (Exercises 77–79).

▶ **Example 1** Use integration by parts to evaluate $\int x\cos x\,dx$.

***Solution.*** We will apply Formula (3). The first step is to make a choice for $u$ and $dv$ to put the given integral in the form $\int u\,dv$. We will let

$$u=x \quad\text{and}\quad dv=\cos x\,dx$$

(Other possibilities will be considered later.) The second step is to compute $du$ from $u$ and $v$ from $dv$. This yields

$$du=dx \quad\text{and}\quad v=\int dv=\int \cos x\,dx=\sin x$$

The third step is to apply Formula (3). This yields

$$\int \underbrace{x}_{u}\ \underbrace{\cos x\,dx}_{dv} = \underbrace{x}_{u}\ \underbrace{\sin x}_{v} - \int \underbrace{\sin x}_{v}\ \underbrace{dx}_{du}$$
$$= x\sin x - (-\cos x) + C = x\sin x + \cos x + C \blacktriangleleft$$

## GUIDELINES FOR INTEGRATION BY PARTS

The main goal in integration by parts is to choose $u$ and $dv$ to obtain a new integral that is easier to evaluate than the original. In general, there are no hard and fast rules for doing this; it is mainly a matter of experience that comes from lots of practice. A strategy that often works is to choose $u$ and $dv$ so that $u$ becomes "simpler" when differentiated, while leaving a $dv$ that can be readily integrated to obtain $v$. Thus, for the integral $\int x\cos x\,dx$ in Example 1, both goals were achieved by letting $u = x$ and $dv = \cos x\,dx$. In contrast, $u = \cos x$ would not have been a good first choice in that example, since $du/dx = -\sin x$ is no simpler than $u$. Indeed, had we chosen

$$u = \cos x \qquad dv = x\,dx$$
$$du = -\sin x\,dx \qquad v = \int x\,dx = \frac{x^2}{2}$$

then we would have obtained

$$\int x\cos x\,dx = \frac{x^2}{2}\cos x - \int \frac{x^2}{2}(-\sin x)\,dx = \frac{x^2}{2}\cos x + \frac{1}{2}\int x^2\sin x\,dx$$

For this choice of $u$ and $dv$, the new integral is actually more complicated than the original.

There is another useful strategy for choosing $u$ and $dv$ that can be applied when the integrand is a product of two functions from *different* categories in the list

> The LIATE method is discussed in the article "A Technique for Integration by Parts," *American Mathematical Monthly*, Vol. 90, 1983, pp. 210–211, by Herbert Kasube.

**L**ogarithmic, **I**nverse trigonometric, **A**lgebraic, **T**rigonometric, **E**xponential

In this case you will often be successful if you take $u$ to be the function whose category occurs earlier in the list and take $dv$ to be the rest of the integrand. The acronym LIATE will help you to remember the order. The method does not work all the time, but it works often enough to be useful.

Note, for example, that the integrand in Example 1 consists of the product of the *algebraic* function $x$ and the *trigonometric* function $\cos x$. Thus, the LIATE method suggests that we should let $u = x$ and $dv = \cos x\,dx$, which proved to be a successful choice.

▶ **Example 2** Evaluate $\int xe^x\,dx$.

***Solution.*** In this case the integrand is the product of the algebraic function $x$ with the exponential function $e^x$. According to LIATE we should let

$$u = x \quad \text{and} \quad dv = e^x\,dx$$

so that

$$du = dx \quad \text{and} \quad v = \int e^x\,dx = e^x$$

Thus, from (3)

$$\int xe^x\,dx = \int u\,dv = uv - \int v\,du = xe^x - \int e^x\,dx = xe^x - e^x + C \blacktriangleleft$$

▶ **Example 3** Evaluate $\int \ln x\,dx$.

***Solution.*** One choice is to let $u = 1$ and $dv = \ln x\,dx$. But with this choice finding $v$ is equivalent to evaluating $\int \ln x\,dx$ and we have gained nothing. Therefore, the only reasonable choice is to let

$$u = \ln x \qquad dv = dx$$
$$du = \frac{1}{x}\,dx \qquad v = \int dx = x$$

With this choice it follows from (3) that

$$\int \ln x\,dx = \int u\,dv = uv - \int v\,du = x\ln x - \int dx = x\ln x - x + C \blacktriangleleft$$

## REPEATED INTEGRATION BY PARTS

It is sometimes necessary to use integration by parts more than once in the same problem.

▶ **Example 4** Evaluate $\int x^2 e^{-x}\,dx$.

***Solution.*** Let

$$u = x^2, \quad dv = e^{-x}\,dx, \quad du = 2x\,dx, \quad v = \int e^{-x}\,dx = -e^{-x}$$

so that from (3)

$$\begin{aligned}\int x^2 e^{-x}\,dx &= \int u\,dv = uv - \int v\,du \\ &= x^2(-e^{-x}) - \int -e^{-x}(2x)\,dx \\ &= -x^2e^{-x} + 2\int xe^{-x}\,dx \end{aligned} \tag{4}$$

The last integral is similar to the original except that we have replaced $x^2$ by $x$. Another integration by parts applied to $\int xe^{-x}\,dx$ will complete the problem. We let

$$u = x, \quad dv = e^{-x}\,dx, \quad du = dx, \quad v = \int e^{-x}\,dx = -e^{-x}$$

so that

$$\int xe^{-x}\,dx = x(-e^{-x}) - \int -e^{-x}\,dx = -xe^{-x} + \int e^{-x}\,dx = -xe^{-x} - e^{-x} + C$$

Finally, substituting this into the last line of (4) yields

$$\begin{aligned}\int x^2e^{-x}\,dx &= -x^2e^{-x} + 2\int xe^{-x}\,dx = -x^2e^{-x} + 2(-xe^{-x} - e^{-x}) + C \\ &= -(x^2 + 2x + 2)e^{-x} + C \blacktriangleleft\end{aligned}$$

The LIATE method suggests that integrals of the form

$$\int e^{ax}\sin bx\,dx \quad \text{and} \quad \int e^{ax}\cos bx\,dx$$

can be evaluated by letting $u = \sin bx$ or $u = \cos bx$ and $dv = e^{ax}\,dx$. However, this will require a technique that deserves special attention.

▶ **Example 5** Evaluate $\int e^x \cos x\,dx$.

***Solution.*** Let

$$u = \cos x, \quad dv = e^x\,dx, \quad du = -\sin x\,dx, \quad v = \int e^x\,dx = e^x$$

Thus,

$$\int e^x \cos x\,dx = \int u\,dv = uv - \int v\,du = e^x \cos x + \int e^x \sin x\,dx \tag{5}$$

Since the integral $\int e^x \sin x\,dx$ is similar in form to the original integral $\int e^x \cos x\,dx$, it seems that nothing has been accomplished. However, let us integrate this new integral by parts. We let

$$u = \sin x, \quad dv = e^x\,dx, \quad du = \cos x\,dx, \quad v = \int e^x\,dx = e^x$$

Thus,

$$\int e^x \sin x\,dx = \int u\,dv = uv - \int v\,du = e^x \sin x - \int e^x \cos x\,dx$$

Together with Equation (5) this yields

$$\int e^x \cos x\,dx = e^x \cos x + e^x \sin x - \int e^x \cos x\,dx \tag{6}$$

which is an equation we can solve for the unknown integral. We obtain

$$2\int e^x \cos x\,dx = e^x \cos x + e^x \sin x$$

and hence

$$\int e^x \cos x\,dx = \tfrac{1}{2}e^x \cos x + \tfrac{1}{2}e^x \sin x + C \blacktriangleleft$$

## A TABULAR METHOD FOR REPEATED INTEGRATION BY PARTS

Integrals of the form

$$\int p(x)f(x)\,dx$$

where $p(x)$ is a polynomial, can sometimes be evaluated using repeated integration by parts in which $u$ is taken to be $p(x)$ or one of its derivatives at each stage. Since $du$ is computed by differentiating $u$, the repeated differentiation of $p(x)$ will eventually produce 0, at which point you may be left with a simplified integration problem. A convenient method for organizing the computations into two columns is called ***tabular integration by parts***.

More information on tabular integration by parts can be found in the articles "Tabular Integration by Parts," *College Mathematics Journal*, Vol. 21, 1990, pp. 307–311, by David Horowitz and "More on Tabular Integration by Parts," *College Mathematics Journal*, Vol. 22, 1991, pp. 407–410, by Leonard Gillman.

***Tabular Integration by Parts***

**Step 1.** Differentiate $p(x)$ repeatedly until you obtain 0, and list the results in the first column.

**Step 2.** Integrate $f(x)$ repeatedly and list the results in the second column.

**Step 3.** Draw an arrow from each entry in the first column to the entry that is one row down in the second column.

**Step 4.** Label the arrows with alternating $+$ and $-$ signs, starting with a $+$.

**Step 5.** For each arrow, form the product of the expressions at its tip and tail and then multiply that product by $+1$ or $-1$ in accordance with the sign on the arrow. Add the results to obtain the value of the integral.

This process is illustrated in Figure 7.2.1 for the integral $\int (x^2 - x)\cos x\,dx$.

| REPEATED DIFFERENTIATION | | REPEATED INTEGRATION |
|---|---|---|
| $x^2 - x$ | $+$ | $\cos x$ |
| $2x - 1$ | $-$ | $\sin x$ |
| $2$ | $+$ | $-\cos x$ |
| $0$ | | $-\sin x$ |

$$\begin{aligned}\int (x^2 - x)\cos x\,dx &= (x^2 - x)\sin x + (2x - 1)\cos x - 2\sin x + C\\ &= (x^2 - x - 2)\sin x + (2x - 1)\cos x + C\end{aligned}$$

▶ **Figure 7.2.1**

▶ **Example 6** In Example 11 of Section 5.3 we evaluated $\int x^2\sqrt{x-1}\,dx$ using $u$-substitution. Evaluate this integral using tabular integration by parts.

***Solution.***

| REPEATED DIFFERENTIATION | | REPEATED INTEGRATION |
|---|---|---|
| $x^2$ | $+$ | $(x-1)^{1/2}$ |
| $2x$ | $-$ | $\frac{2}{3}(x-1)^{3/2}$ |
| $2$ | $+$ | $\frac{4}{15}(x-1)^{5/2}$ |
| $0$ | | $\frac{8}{105}(x-1)^{7/2}$ |

The result obtained in Example 6 looks quite different from that obtained in Example 11 of Section 5.3. Show that the two answers are equivalent.

Thus, it follows that

$$\int x^2\sqrt{x-1}\,dx = \tfrac{2}{3}x^2(x-1)^{3/2} - \tfrac{8}{15}x(x-1)^{5/2} + \tfrac{16}{105}(x-1)^{7/2} + C \blacktriangleleft$$

## INTEGRATION BY PARTS FOR DEFINITE INTEGRALS

For definite integrals the formula corresponding to (3) is

$$\int_a^b u\,dv = uv\Big]_a^b - \int_a^b v\,du \tag{7}$$

**REMARK** It is important to keep in mind that the variables $u$ and $v$ in this formula are functions of $x$ and that the limits of integration in (7) are limits on the variable $x$. Sometimes it is helpful to emphasize this by writing (7) as

$$\int_{x=a}^{b} u\,dv = uv\Big]_{x=a}^{b} - \int_{x=a}^{b} v\,du \tag{8}$$

The next example illustrates how integration by parts can be used to integrate the inverse trigonometric functions.

▶ **Example 7** Evaluate $\displaystyle\int_0^1 \tan^{-1} x\,dx$.

***Solution.*** Let

$$u = \tan^{-1} x, \quad dv = dx, \quad du = \frac{1}{1+x^2}\,dx, \quad v = x$$

Thus,

$$\int_0^1 \tan^{-1} x\,dx = \int_0^1 u\,dv = uv\Big]_0^1 - \int_0^1 v\,du$$

$$= x\tan^{-1} x\Big]_0^1 - \int_0^1 \frac{x}{1+x^2}\,dx$$

The limits of integration refer to $x$; that is, $x = 0$ and $x = 1$.

But

$$\int_0^1 \frac{x}{1+x^2}\,dx = \frac{1}{2}\int_0^1 \frac{2x}{1+x^2}\,dx = \frac{1}{2}\ln(1+x^2)\Big]_0^1 = \frac{1}{2}\ln 2$$

so

$$\int_0^1 \tan^{-1} x\,dx = x\tan^{-1} x\Big]_0^1 - \frac{1}{2}\ln 2 = \left(\frac{\pi}{4} - 0\right) - \frac{1}{2}\ln 2 = \frac{\pi}{4} - \ln\sqrt{2} \blacktriangleleft$$

## REDUCTION FORMULAS

Integration by parts can be used to derive ***reduction formulas*** for integrals. These are formulas that express an integral involving a power of a function in terms of an integral that involves a *lower* power of that function. For example, if $n$ is a positive integer and $n \geq 2$, then integration by parts can be used to obtain the reduction formulas

$$\int \sin^n x\,dx = -\frac{1}{n}\sin^{n-1} x\cos x + \frac{n-1}{n}\int \sin^{n-2} x\,dx \tag{9}$$

$$\int \cos^n x\,dx = \frac{1}{n}\cos^{n-1} x\sin x + \frac{n-1}{n}\int \cos^{n-2} x\,dx \tag{10}$$

To illustrate how such formulas can be obtained, let us derive (10). We begin by writing $\cos^n x$ as $\cos^{n-1} x \cdot \cos x$ and letting

$$u = \cos^{n-1} x \qquad dv = \cos x\,dx$$

$$du = (n-1)\cos^{n-2} x(-\sin x)\,dx \qquad v = \sin x$$

$$= -(n-1)\cos^{n-2} x\sin x\,dx$$

so that

$$\int \cos^n x\,dx = \int \cos^{n-1} x\cos x\,dx = \int u\,dv = uv - \int v\,du$$

$$= \cos^{n-1} x\sin x + (n-1)\int \sin^2 x\cos^{n-2} x\,dx$$

$$= \cos^{n-1} x\sin x + (n-1)\int (1-\cos^2 x)\cos^{n-2} x\,dx$$

$$= \cos^{n-1} x\sin x + (n-1)\int \cos^{n-2} x\,dx - (n-1)\int \cos^n x\,dx$$

Moving the last term on the right to the left side yields

$$n\int \cos^n x\,dx = \cos^{n-1} x\sin x + (n-1)\int \cos^{n-2} x\,dx$$

from which (10) follows. The derivation of reduction formula (9) is similar (Exercise 71).

Reduction formulas (9) and (10) reduce the exponent of sine (or cosine) by 2. Thus, if the formulas are applied repeatedly, the exponent can eventually be reduced to 0 if $n$ is even or 1 if $n$ is odd, at which point the integration can be completed. We will discuss this method in more detail in the next section, but for now, here is an example that illustrates how reduction formulas work.

► **Example 8** Evaluate $\int \cos^4 x\,dx$.

***Solution.*** From (10) with $n = 4$

$$\int \cos^4 x\,dx = \tfrac{1}{4}\cos^3 x \sin x + \tfrac{3}{4}\int \cos^2 x\,dx \qquad \boxed{\text{Now apply (10) with } n = 2.}$$

$$= \tfrac{1}{4}\cos^3 x \sin x + \tfrac{3}{4}\left(\tfrac{1}{2}\cos x \sin x + \tfrac{1}{2}\int dx\right)$$

$$= \tfrac{1}{4}\cos^3 x \sin x + \tfrac{3}{8}\cos x \sin x + \tfrac{3}{8}x + C \blacktriangleleft$$

## ✓QUICK CHECK EXERCISES 7.2 *(See page 423 for answers.)*

**1.** (a) If $G'(x) = g(x)$, then
$$\int f(x)g(x)\,dx = f(x)G(x) - \_\_\_\_\_\_$$
(b) If $u = f(x)$ and $v = G(x)$, then the formula in part (a) can be written in the form $\int u\,dv = \_\_\_\_\_\_$.

**2.** Find an appropriate choice of $u$ and $dv$ for integration by parts of each integral. Do not evaluate the integral.
(a) $\int x \ln x\,dx$; $u = \_\_\_\_\_\_$, $dv = \_\_\_\_\_\_$
(b) $\int (x-2)\sin x\,dx$; $u = \_\_\_\_\_\_$, $dv = \_\_\_\_\_\_$
(c) $\int \sin^{-1} x\,dx$; $u = \_\_\_\_\_\_$, $dv = \_\_\_\_\_\_$
(d) $\int \frac{x}{\sqrt{x-1}}\,dx$; $u = \_\_\_\_\_\_$, $dv = \_\_\_\_\_\_$

**3.** Use integration by parts to evaluate the integral.
(a) $\int xe^{2x}\,dx$ (b) $\int \ln(x-1)\,dx$
(c) $\int_0^{\pi/6} x \sin 3x\,dx$

**4.** Use a reduction formula to evaluate $\int \sin^3 x\,dx$.

## EXERCISE SET 7.2

**1–38** Evaluate the integral. ■

1. $\int xe^{-2x}\,dx$
2. $\int xe^{3x}\,dx$
3. $\int x^2e^x\,dx$
4. $\int x^2e^{-2x}\,dx$
5. $\int x\sin 3x\,dx$
6. $\int x\cos 2x\,dx$
7. $\int x^2\cos x\,dx$
8. $\int x^2\sin x\,dx$
9. $\int x\ln x\,dx$
10. $\int \sqrt{x}\ln x\,dx$
11. $\int (\ln x)^2\,dx$
12. $\int \frac{\ln x}{\sqrt{x}}\,dx$
13. $\int \ln(3x-2)\,dx$
14. $\int \ln(x^2+4)\,dx$
15. $\int \sin^{-1} x\,dx$
16. $\int \cos^{-1}(2x)\,dx$
17. $\int \tan^{-1}(3x)\,dx$
18. $\int x\tan^{-1} x\,dx$
19. $\int e^x\sin x\,dx$
20. $\int e^{3x}\cos 2x\,dx$
21. $\int \sin(\ln x)\,dx$
22. $\int \cos(\ln x)\,dx$
23. $\int x\sec^2 x\,dx$
24. $\int x\tan^2 x\,dx$
25. $\int x^3e^{x^2}\,dx$
26. $\int \frac{xe^x}{(x+1)^2}\,dx$
27. $\int_0^2 xe^{2x}\,dx$
28. $\int_0^1 xe^{-5x}\,dx$
29. $\int_1^e x^2\ln x\,dx$
30. $\int_{\sqrt{e}}^e \frac{\ln x}{x^2}\,dx$
31. $\int_{-1}^1 \ln(x+2)\,dx$
32. $\int_0^{\sqrt{3}/2} \sin^{-1} x\,dx$
33. $\int_2^4 \sec^{-1}\sqrt{\theta}\,d\theta$
34. $\int_1^2 x\sec^{-1} x\,dx$
35. $\int_0^\pi x\sin 2x\,dx$
36. $\int_0^\pi (x + x\cos x)\,dx$
37. $\int_1^3 \sqrt{x}\tan^{-1}\sqrt{x}\,dx$
38. $\int_0^2 \ln(x^2+1)\,dx$

**39–42 True–False** Determine whether the statement is true or false. Explain your answer. ■

**39.** The main goal in integration by parts is to choose $u$ and $dv$ to obtain a new integral that is easier to evaluate than the original.

**40.** Applying the LIATE strategy to evaluate $\int x^3 \ln x\,dx$, we should choose $u = x^3$ and $dv = \ln x\,dx$.

**41.** To evaluate $\int \ln e^x\,dx$ using integration by parts, choose $dv = e^x\,dx$.

**42.** Tabular integration by parts is useful for integrals of the form $\int p(x) f(x)\, dx$, where $p(x)$ is a polynomial and $f(x)$ can be repeatedly integrated.

**43–44** Evaluate the integral by making a $u$-substitution and then integrating by parts. ■

**43.** $\int e^{\sqrt{x}}\, dx$ **44.** $\int \cos \sqrt{x}\, dx$

**45.** Prove that tabular integration by parts gives the correct answer for

$$\int p(x) f(x)\, dx$$

where $p(x)$ is any *quadratic polynomial* and $f(x)$ is any function that can be repeatedly integrated.

**46.** The computations of any integral evaluated by repeated integration by parts can be organized using tabular integration by parts. Use this organization to evaluate $\int e^x \cos x\, dx$ in two ways: first by repeated differentiation of $\cos x$ (compare Example 5), and then by repeated differentiation of $e^x$.

**47–52** Evaluate the integral using tabular integration by parts. ■

**47.** $\int (3x^2 - x + 2)e^{-x}\, dx$ **48.** $\int (x^2 + x + 1) \sin x\, dx$

**49.** $\int 4x^4 \sin 2x\, dx$ **50.** $\int x^3 \sqrt{2x + 1}\, dx$

**51.** $\int e^{ax} \sin bx\, dx$ **52.** $\int e^{-3\theta} \sin 5\theta\, d\theta$

**53.** Consider the integral $\int \sin x \cos x\, dx$.

(a) Evaluate the integral two ways: first using integration by parts, and then using the substitution $u = \sin x$.

(b) Show that the results of part (a) are equivalent.

(c) Which of the two methods do you prefer? Discuss the reasons for your preference.

**54.** Evaluate the integral

$$\int_0^1 \frac{x^3}{\sqrt{x^2 + 1}}\, dx$$

using

(a) integration by parts

(b) the substitution $u = \sqrt{x^2 + 1}$.

**55.** (a) Find the area of the region enclosed by $y = \ln x$, the line $x = e$, and the $x$-axis.

(b) Find the volume of the solid generated when the region in part (a) is revolved about the $x$-axis.

**56.** Find the area of the region between $y = x \sin x$ and $y = x$ for $0 \le x \le \pi/2$.

**57.** Find the volume of the solid generated when the region between $y = \sin x$ and $y = 0$ for $0 \le x \le \pi$ is revolved about the $y$-axis.

**58.** Find the volume of the solid generated when the region enclosed between $y = \cos x$ and $y = 0$ for $0 \le x \le \pi/2$ is revolved about the $y$-axis.

**59.** A particle moving along the $x$-axis has velocity function $v(t) = t^3 \sin t$. How far does the particle travel from time $t = 0$ to $t = \pi$?

**60.** The study of sawtooth waves in electrical engineering leads to integrals of the form

$$\int_{-\pi/\omega}^{\pi/\omega} t \sin(k\omega t)\, dt$$

where $k$ is an integer and $\omega$ is a nonzero constant. Evaluate the integral.

**61–66** Suppose that during a period $t_0 \le t \le t_1$ years, a company has a continuous income stream at a rate of $I(t)$ dollars per year at time $t$ and that this income is invested at an annual rate of $r\%$, compounded continuously. The value (in dollars) of this income stream at the end of the time period $t_0 \le t \le t_1$, called the stream's *future value*, can be calculated using

$$FV = \int_{t_0}^{t_1} I(t)\, e^{r(t_1 - t)}\, dt$$

The *present value* (in dollars) of the income stream is given by

$$PV = \int_{t_0}^{t_1} I(t)\, e^{-r(t - t_0)}\, dt$$

The present value is the amount that, if put in the bank at time $t = t_0$ at $r\%$ compounded continuously, with no additional deposits, would result in a balance of $FV$ dollars at time $t = t_1$. That is,

$$FV = PV \times e^{r(t_1 - t_0)}$$

In each exercise, (a) find the future value $FV$ for the given income stream $I(t)$ and interest rate $r$ and time period $t_0 \le t \le t_1$; (b) find the present value $PV$ of the income stream over the time period; and (c) verify that $FV$ and $PV$ satisfy the relationship given above. ■

**61.** $I(t) = 1000 + 5t$; $r = 12\%$; $0 \le t \le 20$

**62.** $I(t) = 1000 + 5t$; $r = 12\%$; $5 \le t \le 20$

**63.** $I(t) = 20{,}000 - 200t^2$; $r = 5\%$; $0 \le t \le 10$

**64.** $I(t) = 20{,}000 - 200t^2$; $r = 5\%$; $2 \le t \le 10$

**65.** $I(t) = 2000t + 400e^{-t}$; $r = 8\%$; $0 \le t \le 10$

**66.** $I(t) = 2000t + 400e^{-t}$; $r = 8\%$; $0 \le t \le 25$

**67.** An entomologist studying an ant colony estimates its population density measured $x$ feet from the center of the colony is modeled by $d(x) = 3e^{-0.25x}$ thousand ants per square foot.

(a) Estimate the number of ants in a ring of width $\Delta x$ feet, $x$ feet from the center of the colony.

(b) According to this model, what is the population of ants within 6 feet of the center of the colony?

**68.** Repeat parts (a) and (b) of Exercise 67 for an ant population density modeled by $d(x) = (10 - x)e^{-0.4x}$ thousand ants per square foot, measured $x$ feet from the center of the colony.

**69.** Use reduction formula (9) to evaluate

(a) $\int \sin^4 x\, dx$ (b) $\int_0^{\pi/2} \sin^5 x\, dx$.

**70.** Use reduction formula (10) to evaluate

(a) $\int \cos^5 x\, dx$ (b) $\int_0^{\pi/2} \cos^6 x\, dx$.

**71.** Derive reduction formula (9).

**72.** In each part, use integration by parts or other methods to derive the reduction formula.

(a) $\int \sec^n x\,dx = \frac{\sec^{n-2} x \tan x}{n-1} + \frac{n-2}{n-1}\int \sec^{n-2} x\,dx$

(b) $\int \tan^n x\,dx = \frac{\tan^{n-1} x}{n-1} - \int \tan^{n-2} x\,dx$

(c) $\int x^n e^x\,dx = x^n e^x - n\int x^{n-1} e^x\,dx$

**73–75** Use the reduction formulas in Exercise 72 to evaluate the integrals. ■

**73.** (a) $\int \tan^4 x\,dx$ (b) $\int \sec^4 x\,dx$ (c) $\int x^3 e^x\,dx$

**74.** (a) $\int x^2 e^{3x}\,dx$ (b) $\int_0^1 xe^{-\sqrt{x}}\,dx$

[*Hint:* First make a substitution.]

**75.** Let $f$ be a function whose second derivative is continuous on $[-1, 1]$. Show that

$$\int_{-1}^{1} xf''(x)\,dx = f'(1) + f'(-1) - f(1) + f(-1)$$

**FOCUS ON CONCEPTS**

**76.** (a) In the integral $\int x\cos x\,dx$, let

$$u = x, \quad dv = \cos x\,dx,$$
$$du = dx, \quad v = \sin x + C_1$$

Show that the constant $C_1$ cancels out, thus giving the same solution obtained by omitting $C_1$.

(b) Show that in general

$$uv - \int v\,du = u(v + C_1) - \int (v + C_1)\,du$$

thereby justifying the omission of the constant of integration when calculating $v$ in integration by parts.

**77.** Evaluate $\int \ln(x+1)\,dx$ using integration by parts. Simplify the computation of $\int v\,du$ by introducing a constant of integration $C_1 = 1$ when going from $dv$ to $v$.

**78.** Evaluate $\int \ln(3x-2)\,dx$ using integration by parts. Simplify the computation of $\int v\,du$ by introducing a constant of integration $C_1 = -\frac{2}{3}$ when going from $dv$ to $v$. Compare your solution with your answer to Exercise 13.

**79.** Evaluate $\int x\tan^{-1} x\,dx$ using integration by parts. Simplify the computation of $\int v\,du$ by introducing a constant of integration $C_1 = \frac{1}{2}$ when going from $dv$ to $v$.

**80.** What equation results if integration by parts is applied to the integral

$$\int \frac{1}{x\ln x}\,dx$$

with the choices

$$u = \frac{1}{\ln x} \quad \text{and} \quad dv = \frac{1}{x}\,dx?$$

In what sense is this equation true? In what sense is it false?

**81. Writing** Explain how the product rule for derivatives and the technique of integration by parts are related.

**82. Writing** For what sort of problems are the integration techniques of substitution and integration by parts "competing" techniques? Describe situations, with examples, where each of these techniques would be preferred over the other.

✓ **QUICK CHECK ANSWERS 7.2** 1. (a) $\int f'(x)G(x)\,dx$ (b) $uv - \int v\,du$ 2. (a) $\ln x$; $x\,dx$ (b) $x-2$; $\sin x\,dx$ (c) $\sin^{-1} x$; $dx$ (d) $x$; $\frac{1}{\sqrt{x-1}}\,dx$ 3. (a) $\left(\frac{x}{2} - \frac{1}{4}\right)e^{2x} + C$ (b) $(x-1)\ln(x-1) - x + C$ (c) $\frac{1}{9}$ 4. $-\frac{1}{3}\sin^2 x\cos x - \frac{2}{3}\cos x + C$

# 7.3 INTEGRATING TRIGONOMETRIC FUNCTIONS

*In the last section we derived reduction formulas for integrating positive integer powers of sine, cosine, tangent, and secant. In this section we will show how to work with those reduction formulas, and we will discuss methods for integrating other kinds of integrals that involve trigonometric functions.*

## INTEGRATING POWERS OF SINE AND COSINE

We begin by recalling two reduction formulas from the preceding section.

$$\int \sin^n x\,dx = -\frac{1}{n}\sin^{n-1} x\cos x + \frac{n-1}{n}\int \sin^{n-2} x\,dx \qquad (1)$$

$$\int \cos^n x\,dx = \frac{1}{n}\cos^{n-1} x\sin x + \frac{n-1}{n}\int \cos^{n-2} x\,dx \qquad (2)$$

In the case where $n = 2$, these formulas yield

$$\int \sin^2 x\,dx = -\tfrac{1}{2}\sin x\cos x + \tfrac{1}{2}\int dx = \tfrac{1}{2}x - \tfrac{1}{2}\sin x\cos x + C \qquad (3)$$

$$\int \cos^2 x\,dx = \tfrac{1}{2}\cos x\sin x + \tfrac{1}{2}\int dx = \tfrac{1}{2}x + \tfrac{1}{2}\sin x\cos x + C \qquad (4)$$

Alternative forms of these integration formulas can be derived from the trigonometric identities

$$\sin^2 x = \tfrac{1}{2}(1 - \cos 2x) \quad \text{and} \quad \cos^2 x = \tfrac{1}{2}(1 + \cos 2x) \qquad (5\text{–}6)$$

which follow from the double-angle formulas

$$\cos 2x = 1 - 2\sin^2 x \quad \text{and} \quad \cos 2x = 2\cos^2 x - 1$$

These identities yield

$$\int \sin^2 x\,dx = \tfrac{1}{2}\int (1 - \cos 2x)\,dx = \tfrac{1}{2}x - \tfrac{1}{4}\sin 2x + C \qquad (7)$$

$$\int \cos^2 x\,dx = \tfrac{1}{2}\int (1 + \cos 2x)\,dx = \tfrac{1}{2}x + \tfrac{1}{4}\sin 2x + C \qquad (8)$$

Observe that the antiderivatives in Formulas (3) and (4) involve both sines and cosines, whereas those in (7) and (8) involve sines alone. However, the apparent discrepancy is easy to resolve by using the identity

$$\sin 2x = 2\sin x\cos x$$

to rewrite (7) and (8) in forms (3) and (4), or conversely.

In the case where $n = 3$, the reduction formulas for integrating $\sin^3 x$ and $\cos^3 x$ yield

$$\int \sin^3 x\,dx = -\tfrac{1}{3}\sin^2 x\cos x + \tfrac{2}{3}\int \sin x\,dx = -\tfrac{1}{3}\sin^2 x\cos x - \tfrac{2}{3}\cos x + C \qquad (9)$$

$$\int \cos^3 x\,dx = \tfrac{1}{3}\cos^2 x\sin x + \tfrac{2}{3}\int \cos x\,dx = \tfrac{1}{3}\cos^2 x\sin x + \tfrac{2}{3}\sin x + C \qquad (10)$$

If desired, Formula (9) can be expressed in terms of cosines alone by using the identity $\sin^2 x = 1 - \cos^2 x$, and Formula (10) can be expressed in terms of sines alone by using the identity $\cos^2 x = 1 - \sin^2 x$. We leave it for you to do this and confirm that

$$\int \sin^3 x\,dx = \tfrac{1}{3}\cos^3 x - \cos x + C \qquad (11)$$

$$\int \cos^3 x\,dx = \sin x - \tfrac{1}{3}\sin^3 x + C \qquad (12)$$

**TECHNOLOGY MASTERY**

The *Maple* CAS produces forms (11) and (12) when asked to integrate $\sin^3 x$ and $\cos^3 x$, but *Mathematica* produces

$$\int \sin^3 x\,dx = -\tfrac{3}{4}\cos x + \tfrac{1}{12}\cos 3x + C$$

$$\int \cos^3 x\,dx = \tfrac{3}{4}\sin x + \tfrac{1}{12}\sin 3x + C$$

Use trigonometric identities to reconcile the results of the two programs.

We leave it as an exercise to obtain the following formulas by first applying the reduction formulas, and then using appropriate trigonometric identities.

$$\int \sin^4 x\,dx = \tfrac{3}{8}x - \tfrac{1}{4}\sin 2x + \tfrac{1}{32}\sin 4x + C \qquad (13)$$

$$\int \cos^4 x\,dx = \tfrac{3}{8}x + \tfrac{1}{4}\sin 2x + \tfrac{1}{32}\sin 4x + C \qquad (14)$$

► **Example 1** Find the volume $V$ of the solid that is obtained when the region under the curve $y = \sin^2 x$ over the interval $[0, \pi]$ is revolved about the $x$-axis (Figure 7.3.1).

***Solution.*** Using the method of disks, Formula (5) of Section 6.2, and Formula (13) above yields

$$V = \int_0^{\pi} \pi\sin^4 x\,dx = \pi\left[\tfrac{3}{8}x - \tfrac{1}{4}\sin 2x + \tfrac{1}{32}\sin 4x\right]_0^{\pi} = \tfrac{3}{8}\pi^2 \;◄$$

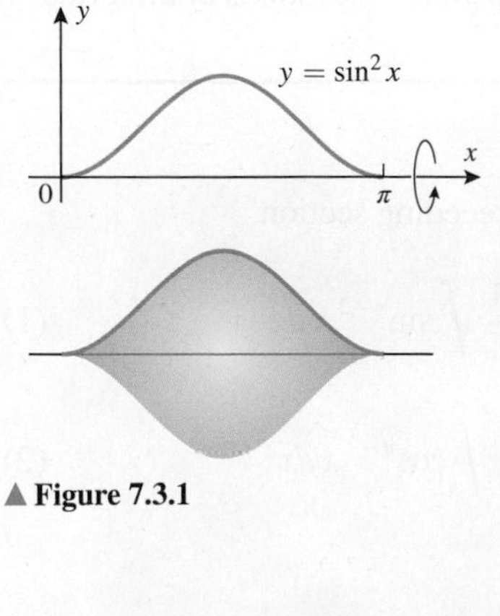


▲ **Figure 7.3.1**

## INTEGRATING PRODUCTS OF SINES AND COSINES

If $m$ and $n$ are positive integers, then the integral

$$\int \sin^m x \cos^n x \, dx$$

can be evaluated by one of the three procedures stated in Table 7.3.1, depending on whether $m$ and $n$ are odd or even.

**Table 7.3.1**

INTEGRATING PRODUCTS OF SINES AND COSINES

| $\int \sin^m x \cos^n x \, dx$ | PROCEDURE | RELEVANT IDENTITIES |
|---|---|---|
| $n$ odd | • Split off a factor of $\cos x$.<br>• Apply the relevant identity.<br>• Make the substitution $u = \sin x$. | $\cos^2 x = 1 - \sin^2 x$ |
| $m$ odd | • Split off a factor of $\sin x$.<br>• Apply the relevant identity.<br>• Make the substitution $u = \cos x$. | $\sin^2 x = 1 - \cos^2 x$ |
| $\begin{cases} m \text{ even} \\ n \text{ even} \end{cases}$ | • Use the relevant identities to reduce the powers on $\sin x$ and $\cos x$. | $\begin{cases} \sin^2 x = \frac{1}{2}(1 - \cos 2x) \\ \cos^2 x = \frac{1}{2}(1 + \cos 2x) \end{cases}$ |

► **Example 2** Evaluate

$$\text{(a)} \int \sin^4 x \cos^5 x \, dx \qquad \text{(b)} \int \sin^4 x \cos^4 x \, dx$$

***Solution (a).*** Since $n = 5$ is odd, we will follow the first procedure in Table 7.3.1:

$$\begin{aligned}
\int \sin^4 x \cos^5 x \, dx &= \int \sin^4 x \cos^4 x \cos x \, dx \\
&= \int \sin^4 x (1 - \sin^2 x)^2 \cos x \, dx \\
&= \int u^4 (1 - u^2)^2 \, du \\
&= \int (u^4 - 2u^6 + u^8) \, du \\
&= \tfrac{1}{5}u^5 - \tfrac{2}{7}u^7 + \tfrac{1}{9}u^9 + C \\
&= \tfrac{1}{5}\sin^5 x - \tfrac{2}{7}\sin^7 x + \tfrac{1}{9}\sin^9 x + C
\end{aligned}$$

***Solution (b).*** Since $m = n = 4$, both exponents are even, so we will follow the third procedure in Table 7.3.1:

$$\begin{aligned}
\int \sin^4 x \cos^4 x \, dx &= \int (\sin^2 x)^2 (\cos^2 x)^2 \, dx \\
&= \int \left(\tfrac{1}{2}[1 - \cos 2x]\right)^2 \left(\tfrac{1}{2}[1 + \cos 2x]\right)^2 dx \\
&= \tfrac{1}{16} \int (1 - \cos^2 2x)^2 \, dx \\
&= \tfrac{1}{16} \int \sin^4 2x \, dx \\
&= \tfrac{1}{32} \int \sin^4 u \, du \\
&= \tfrac{1}{32}\left(\tfrac{3}{8}u - \tfrac{1}{4}\sin 2u + \tfrac{1}{32}\sin 4u\right) + C \\
&= \tfrac{3}{128}x - \tfrac{1}{128}\sin 4x + \tfrac{1}{1024}\sin 8x + C \;◄
\end{aligned}$$

Note that this can be obtained more directly from the original integral using the identity $\sin x \cos x = \frac{1}{2}\sin 2x$.

$u = 2x$
$du = 2\,dx$ or $dx = \frac{1}{2}\,du$

Formula (13)

Integrals of the form

$$\int \sin mx \cos nx\,dx, \qquad \int \sin mx \sin nx\,dx, \qquad \int \cos mx \cos nx\,dx \tag{15}$$

can be found by using the trigonometric identities

$$\sin\alpha\cos\beta = \tfrac{1}{2}[\sin(\alpha-\beta)+\sin(\alpha+\beta)] \tag{16}$$

$$\sin\alpha\sin\beta = \tfrac{1}{2}[\cos(\alpha-\beta)-\cos(\alpha+\beta)] \tag{17}$$

$$\cos\alpha\cos\beta = \tfrac{1}{2}[\cos(\alpha-\beta)+\cos(\alpha+\beta)] \tag{18}$$

to express the integrand as a sum or difference of sines and cosines.

▶ **Example 3** Evaluate $\int \sin 7x \cos 3x\,dx$.

***Solution.*** Using (16) yields

$$\int \sin 7x\cos 3x\,dx = \tfrac{1}{2}\int(\sin 4x+\sin 10x)\,dx = -\tfrac{1}{8}\cos 4x - \tfrac{1}{20}\cos 10x + C \;◀$$

## INTEGRATING POWERS OF TANGENT AND SECANT

The procedures for integrating powers of tangent and secant closely parallel those for sine and cosine. The idea is to use the following reduction formulas (which were derived in Exercise 72 of Section 7.2) to reduce the exponent in the integrand until the resulting integral can be evaluated:

$$\int \tan^n x\,dx = \frac{\tan^{n-1}x}{n-1} - \int \tan^{n-2}x\,dx \tag{19}$$

$$\int \sec^n x\,dx = \frac{\sec^{n-2}x\tan x}{n-1} + \frac{n-2}{n-1}\int \sec^{n-2}x\,dx \tag{20}$$

In the case where $n$ is odd, the exponent can be reduced to 1, leaving us with the problem of integrating $\tan x$ or $\sec x$. These integrals are given by

$$\int \tan x\,dx = \ln|\sec x| + C \tag{21}$$

$$\int \sec x\,dx = \ln|\sec x + \tan x| + C \tag{22}$$

Formula (21) can be obtained by writing

$$\begin{aligned}\int \tan x\,dx &= \int \frac{\sin x}{\cos x}\,dx\\ &= -\ln|\cos x| + C \qquad \boxed{\begin{aligned}u&=\cos x\\ du&=-\sin x\,dx\end{aligned}}\\ &= \ln|\sec x| + C \qquad \boxed{\ln|\cos x| = -\ln\frac{1}{|\cos x|}}\end{aligned}$$

To obtain Formula (22) we write

$$\begin{aligned}\int \sec x\,dx &= \int \sec x\left(\frac{\sec x+\tan x}{\sec x+\tan x}\right)dx = \int \frac{\sec^2 x+\sec x\tan x}{\sec x+\tan x}\,dx\\ &= \ln|\sec x+\tan x| + C \qquad \boxed{\begin{aligned}u&=\sec x+\tan x\\ du&=(\sec^2 x+\sec x\tan x)\,dx\end{aligned}}\end{aligned}$$

The following basic integrals occur frequently and are worth noting:

$$\int \tan^2 x\,dx = \tan x - x + C \tag{23}$$

$$\int \sec^2 x\,dx = \tan x + C \tag{24}$$

Formula (24) is already known to us, since the derivative of $\tan x$ is $\sec^2 x$. Formula (23) can be obtained by applying reduction formula (19) with $n = 2$ (verify) or, alternatively, by using the identity

$$1 + \tan^2 x = \sec^2 x$$

to write

$$\int \tan^2 x\,dx = \int (\sec^2 x - 1)\,dx = \tan x - x + C$$

The formulas

$$\int \tan^3 x\,dx = \tfrac{1}{2}\tan^2 x - \ln|\sec x| + C \tag{25}$$

$$\int \sec^3 x\,dx = \tfrac{1}{2}\sec x \tan x + \tfrac{1}{2}\ln|\sec x + \tan x| + C \tag{26}$$

can be deduced from (21), (22), and reduction formulas (19) and (20) as follows:

$$\int \tan^3 x\,dx = \tfrac{1}{2}\tan^2 x - \int \tan x\,dx = \tfrac{1}{2}\tan^2 x - \ln|\sec x| + C$$

$$\int \sec^3 x\,dx = \tfrac{1}{2}\sec x \tan x + \tfrac{1}{2}\int \sec x\,dx = \tfrac{1}{2}\sec x \tan x + \tfrac{1}{2}\ln|\sec x + \tan x| + C$$

## INTEGRATING PRODUCTS OF TANGENTS AND SECANTS

If $m$ and $n$ are positive integers, then the integral

$$\int \tan^m x \sec^n x\,dx$$

can be evaluated by one of the three procedures stated in Table 7.3.2, depending on whether $m$ and $n$ are odd or even.

**Table 7.3.2**

INTEGRATING PRODUCTS OF TANGENTS AND SECANTS

| $\int \tan^m x \sec^n x\,dx$ | PROCEDURE | RELEVANT IDENTITIES |
|---|---|---|
| $n$ even | • Split off a factor of $\sec^2 x$.<br>• Apply the relevant identity.<br>• Make the substitution $u = \tan x$. | $\sec^2 x = \tan^2 x + 1$ |
| $m$ odd | • Split off a factor of $\sec x \tan x$.<br>• Apply the relevant identity.<br>• Make the substitution $u = \sec x$. | $\tan^2 x = \sec^2 x - 1$ |
| $\begin{cases} m \text{ even} \\ n \text{ odd} \end{cases}$ | • Use the relevant identities to reduce the integrand to powers of $\sec x$ alone.<br>• Then use the reduction formula for powers of $\sec x$. | $\tan^2 x = \sec^2 x - 1$ |

▶ **Example 4** Evaluate

$$\text{(a)} \int \tan^2 x \sec^4 x\, dx \qquad \text{(b)} \int \tan^3 x \sec^3 x\, dx \qquad \text{(c)} \int \tan^2 x \sec x\, dx$$

***Solution (a).*** Since $n = 4$ is even, we will follow the first procedure in Table 7.3.2:

$$\begin{aligned} \int \tan^2 x \sec^4 x\, dx &= \int \tan^2 x \sec^2 x \sec^2 x\, dx \\ &= \int \tan^2 x\,(\tan^2 x + 1) \sec^2 x\, dx \\ &= \int u^2(u^2 + 1)\, du \\ &= \tfrac{1}{5}u^5 + \tfrac{1}{3}u^3 + C = \tfrac{1}{5}\tan^5 x + \tfrac{1}{3}\tan^3 x + C \end{aligned}$$

***Solution (b).*** Since $m = 3$ is odd, we will follow the second procedure in Table 7.3.2:

$$\begin{aligned} \int \tan^3 x \sec^3 x\, dx &= \int \tan^2 x \sec^2 x\,(\sec x \tan x)\, dx \\ &= \int (\sec^2 x - 1) \sec^2 x\,(\sec x \tan x)\, dx \\ &= \int (u^2 - 1)u^2\, du \\ &= \tfrac{1}{5}u^5 - \tfrac{1}{3}u^3 + C = \tfrac{1}{5}\sec^5 x - \tfrac{1}{3}\sec^3 x + C \end{aligned}$$

***Solution (c).*** Since $m = 2$ is even and $n = 1$ is odd, we will follow the third procedure in Table 7.3.2:

$$\begin{aligned} \int \tan^2 x \sec x\, dx &= \int (\sec^2 x - 1) \sec x\, dx \\ &= \int \sec^3 x\, dx - \int \sec x\, dx \qquad \boxed{\text{See (26) and (22)}} \\ &= \tfrac{1}{2}\sec x \tan x + \tfrac{1}{2}\ln|\sec x + \tan x| - \ln|\sec x + \tan x| + C \\ &= \tfrac{1}{2}\sec x \tan x - \tfrac{1}{2}\ln|\sec x + \tan x| + C \end{aligned}$$ ◀

## AN ALTERNATIVE METHOD FOR INTEGRATING POWERS OF SINE, COSINE, TANGENT, AND SECANT

The methods in Tables 7.3.1 and 7.3.2 can sometimes be applied if $m = 0$ or $n = 0$ to integrate positive integer powers of sine, cosine, tangent, and secant without reduction formulas. For example, instead of using the reduction formula to integrate $\sin^3 x$, we can apply the second procedure in Table 7.3.1:

$$\begin{aligned} \int \sin^3 x\, dx &= \int (\sin^2 x) \sin x\, dx \\ &= \int (1 - \cos^2 x) \sin x\, dx \qquad \boxed{\begin{aligned} u &= \cos x \\ du &= -\sin x\, dx \end{aligned}} \\ &= -\int (1 - u^2)\, du \\ &= \tfrac{1}{3}u^3 - u + C = \tfrac{1}{3}\cos^3 x - \cos x + C \end{aligned}$$

which agrees with (11).

> With the aid of the identity
>
> $$1 + \cot^2 x = \csc^2 x$$
>
> the techniques in Table 7.3.2 can be adapted to evaluate integrals of the form
>
> $$\int \cot^m x \csc^n x\, dx$$
>
> It is also possible to derive reduction formulas for powers of cot and csc that are analogous to Formulas (19) and (20).

## MERCATOR'S MAP OF THE WORLD

The integral of $\sec x$ plays an important role in the design of navigational maps for charting nautical and aeronautical courses. Sailors and pilots usually chart their courses along paths

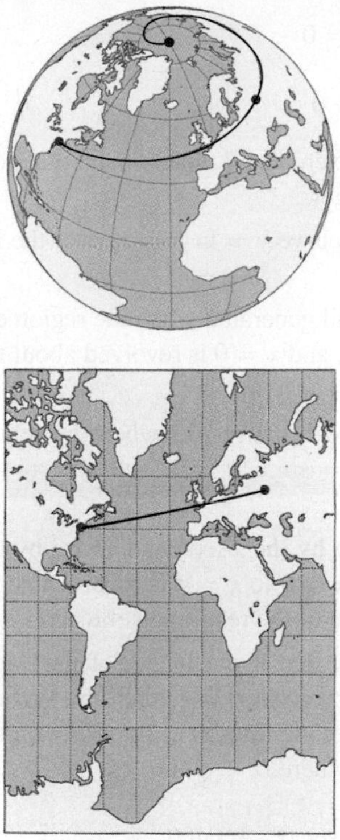

▲ **Figure 7.3.2** A flight path with constant compass heading from New York City to Moscow follows a spiral toward the North Pole but is a straight line segment on a Mercator projection.

with constant compass headings; for example, the course might be 30° northeast or 135° southeast. Except for courses that are parallel to the equator or run due north or south, a course with constant compass heading spirals around the Earth toward one of the poles (as in the top part of Figure 7.3.2). In 1569 the Flemish mathematician and geographer Gerhard Kramer (1512–1594) (better known by the Latin name Mercator) devised a world map, called the *Mercator projection*, in which spirals of constant compass headings appear as straight lines. This was extremely important because it enabled sailors to determine compass headings between two points by connecting them with a straight line on a map (as in the bottom part of Figure 7.3.2).

If the Earth is assumed to be a sphere of radius 4000 mi, then the lines of latitude at 1° increments are equally spaced about 70 mi apart (why?). However, in the Mercator projection, the lines of latitude become wider apart toward the poles, so that two widely spaced latitude lines near the poles may be actually the same distance apart on the Earth as two closely spaced latitude lines near the equator. It can be proved that on a Mercator map in which the equatorial line has length $L$, the vertical distance $D_\beta$ on the map between the equator (latitude 0°) and the line of latitude $\beta°$ is

$$D_\beta = \frac{L}{2\pi}\int_0^{\beta\pi/180} \sec x\, dx \tag{27}$$

## ✓ QUICK CHECK EXERCISES 7.3 (See page 431 for answers.)

**1.** Complete each trigonometric identity with an expression involving $\cos 2x$.

(a) $\sin^2 x =$ _______ (b) $\cos^2 x =$ _______

(c) $\cos^2 x - \sin^2 x =$ _______

**2.** Evaluate the integral.

(a) $\int \sec^2 x\, dx =$ _______

(b) $\int \tan^2 x\, dx =$ _______

(c) $\int \sec x\, dx =$ _______

(d) $\int \tan x\, dx =$ _______

**3.** Use the indicated substitution to rewrite the integral in terms of $u$. Do not evaluate the integral.

(a) $\int \sin^2 x \cos x\, dx;\ u = \sin x$

(b) $\int \sin^3 x \cos^2 x\, dx;\ u = \cos x$

(c) $\int \tan^3 x \sec^2 x\, dx;\ u = \tan x$

(d) $\int \tan^3 x \sec x\, dx;\ u = \sec x$

## EXERCISE SET 7.3

**1–52** Evaluate the integral. ■

**1.** $\int \cos^3 x \sin x\, dx$ **2.** $\int \sin^5 3x \cos 3x\, dx$

**3.** $\int \sin^2 5\theta\, d\theta$ **4.** $\int \cos^2 3x\, dx$

**5.** $\int \sin^3 a\theta\, d\theta$ **6.** $\int \cos^3 at\, dt$

**7.** $\int \sin ax \cos ax\, dx$ **8.** $\int \sin^3 x \cos^3 x\, dx$

**9.** $\int \sin^2 t \cos^3 t\, dt$ **10.** $\int \sin^3 x \cos^2 x\, dx$

**11.** $\int \sin^2 x \cos^2 x\, dx$ **12.** $\int \sin^2 x \cos^4 x\, dx$

**13.** $\int \sin 2x \cos 3x\, dx$ **14.** $\int \sin 3\theta \cos 2\theta\, d\theta$

**15.** $\int \sin x \cos (x/2)\, dx$ **16.** $\int \cos^{1/3} x \sin x\, dx$

**17.** $\int_0^{\pi/2} \cos^3 x\, dx$ **18.** $\int_0^{\pi/2} \sin^2 \frac{x}{2} \cos^2 \frac{x}{2}\, dx$

**19.** $\int_0^{\pi/3} \sin^4 3x \cos^3 3x\, dx$ **20.** $\int_{-\pi}^{\pi} \cos^2 5\theta\, d\theta$

**21.** $\int_0^{\pi/6} \sin 4x \cos 2x\, dx$ **22.** $\int_0^{2\pi} \sin^2 kx\, dx$

**23.** $\int \sec^2 (2x-1)\, dx$ **24.** $\int \tan 5x\, dx$

**25.** $\int e^{-x} \tan (e^{-x})\, dx$ **26.** $\int \cot 3x\, dx$

**27.** $\int \sec 4x\, dx$ **28.** $\int \frac{\sec (\sqrt{x})}{\sqrt{x}}\, dx$

**29.** $\int \tan^2 x \sec^2 x\, dx$ **30.** $\int \tan^5 x \sec^4 x\, dx$

**31.** $\int \tan 4x \sec^4 4x\, dx$ **32.** $\int \tan^4 \theta \sec^4 \theta\, d\theta$

**33.** $\int \sec^5 x \tan^3 x\, dx$ **34.** $\int \tan^5 \theta \sec \theta\, d\theta$

**35.** $\int \tan^4 x \sec x\, dx$ **36.** $\int \tan^2 x \sec^3 x\, dx$

**37.** $\int \tan t \sec^3 t\, dt$ **38.** $\int \tan x \sec^5 x\, dx$

**39.** $\int \sec^4 x\, dx$ **40.** $\int \sec^5 x\, dx$

**41.** $\int \tan^3 4x\, dx$ **42.** $\int \tan^4 x\, dx$

**43.** $\int \sqrt{\tan x} \sec^4 x\, dx$ **44.** $\int \tan x \sec^{3/2} x\, dx$

**45.** $\int_0^{\pi/8} \tan^2 2x\, dx$ **46.** $\int_0^{\pi/6} \sec^3 2\theta \tan 2\theta\, d\theta$

**47.** $\int_0^{\pi/2} \tan^5 \frac{x}{2}\, dx$ **48.** $\int_0^{1/4} \sec \pi x \tan \pi x\, dx$

**49.** $\int \cot^3 x \csc^3 x\, dx$ **50.** $\int \cot^2 3t \sec 3t\, dt$

**51.** $\int \cot^3 x\, dx$ **52.** $\int \csc^4 x\, dx$

**53–56 True–False** Determine whether the statement is true or false. Explain your answer. ■

**53.** To evaluate $\int \sin^5 x \cos^8 x\, dx$, use the trigonometric identity $\sin^2 x = 1 - \cos^2 x$ and the substitution $u = \cos x$.

**54.** To evaluate $\int \sin^8 x \cos^5 x\, dx$, use the trigonometric identity $\sin^2 x = 1 - \cos^2 x$ and the substitution $u = \cos x$.

**55.** The trigonometric identity

$$\sin \alpha \cos \beta = \tfrac{1}{2}[\sin(\alpha - \beta) + \sin(\alpha + \beta)]$$

is often useful for evaluating integrals of the form $\int \sin^m x \cos^n x\, dx$.

**56.** The integral $\int \tan^4 x \sec^5 x\, dx$ is equivalent to one whose integrand is a polynomial in $\sec x$.

**57.** Let $m$, $n$ be distinct nonnegative integers. Use Formulas (16)–(18) to prove:

(a) $\int_0^{2\pi} \sin mx \cos nx\, dx = 0$

(b) $\int_0^{2\pi} \cos mx \cos nx\, dx = 0$

(c) $\int_0^{2\pi} \sin mx \sin nx\, dx = 0.$

**58.** Evaluate the integrals in Exercise 57 when $m$ and $n$ denote the *same* nonnegative integer.

**59.** Find the arc length of the curve $y = \ln (\cos x)$ over the interval $[0, \pi/4]$.

**60.** Find the volume of the solid generated when the region enclosed by $y = \tan x$, $y = 1$, and $x = 0$ is revolved about the $x$-axis.

**61.** Find the volume of the solid that results when the region enclosed by $y = \cos x$, $y = \sin x$, $x = 0$, and $x = \pi/4$ is revolved about the $x$-axis.

**62.** The region bounded below by the $x$-axis and above by the portion of $y = \sin x$ from $x = 0$ to $x = \pi$ is revolved about the $x$-axis. Find the volume of the resulting solid.

**63.** Use Formula (27) to show that if the length of the equatorial line on a Mercator projection is $L$, then the vertical distance $D$ between the latitude lines at $\alpha°$ and $\beta°$ on the same side of the equator (where $\alpha < \beta$) is

$$D = \frac{L}{2\pi} \ln \left| \frac{\sec \beta° + \tan \beta°}{\sec \alpha° + \tan \alpha°} \right|$$

**64.** Suppose that the equator has a length of 100 cm on a Mercator projection. In each part, use the result in Exercise 63 to answer the question.

(a) What is the vertical distance on the map between the equator and the line at 25° north latitude?

(b) What is the vertical distance on the map between New Orleans, Louisiana, at 30° north latitude and Winnipeg, Canada, at 50° north latitude?

**FOCUS ON CONCEPTS**

**65.** (a) Show that

$$\int \csc x\, dx = -\ln |\csc x + \cot x| + C$$

(b) Show that the result in part (a) can also be written as

$$\int \csc x\, dx = \ln |\csc x - \cot x| + C$$

and

$$\int \csc x\, dx = \ln \left|\tan \tfrac{1}{2}x\right| + C$$

**66.** Rewrite $\sin x + \cos x$ in the form

$$A \sin (x + \phi)$$

and use your result together with Exercise 65 to evaluate

$$\int \frac{dx}{\sin x + \cos x}$$

**67.** Use the method of Exercise 66 to evaluate

$$\int \frac{dx}{a \sin x + b \cos x} \quad (a, b \text{ not both zero})$$

**68.** (a) Use Formula (9) in Section 7.2 to show that

$$\int_0^{\pi/2} \sin^n x\,dx = \frac{n-1}{n}\int_0^{\pi/2} \sin^{n-2} x\,dx \quad (n \geq 2)$$

(b) Use this result to derive the ***Wallis sine formulas***:

$$\int_0^{\pi/2} \sin^n x\,dx = \frac{\pi}{2}\cdot\frac{1\cdot 3\cdot 5\cdots(n-1)}{2\cdot 4\cdot 6\cdots n} \quad \left(\begin{matrix} n \text{ even} \\ \text{and} \geq 2\end{matrix}\right)$$

$$\int_0^{\pi/2} \sin^n x\,dx = \frac{2\cdot 4\cdot 6\cdots(n-1)}{3\cdot 5\cdot 7\cdots n} \quad \left(\begin{matrix} n \text{ odd} \\ \text{and} \geq 3\end{matrix}\right)$$

**69.** Use the Wallis formulas in Exercise 68 to evaluate

(a) $\int_0^{\pi/2} \sin^3 x\,dx$ (b) $\int_0^{\pi/2} \sin^4 x\,dx$

(c) $\int_0^{\pi/2} \sin^5 x\,dx$ (d) $\int_0^{\pi/2} \sin^6 x\,dx$.

**70.** Use Formula (10) in Section 7.2 and the method of Exercise 68 to derive the ***Wallis cosine formulas***:

$$\int_0^{\pi/2} \cos^n x\,dx = \frac{\pi}{2}\cdot\frac{1\cdot 3\cdot 5\cdots(n-1)}{2\cdot 4\cdot 6\cdots n} \quad \left(\begin{matrix} n \text{ even} \\ \text{and} \geq 2\end{matrix}\right)$$

$$\int_0^{\pi/2} \cos^n x\,dx = \frac{2\cdot 4\cdot 6\cdots(n-1)}{3\cdot 5\cdot 7\cdots n} \quad \left(\begin{matrix} n \text{ odd} \\ \text{and} \geq 3\end{matrix}\right)$$

**71. Writing** Describe the various approaches for evaluating integrals of the form

$$\int \sin^m x \cos^n x\,dx$$

Into what cases do these types of integrals fall? What procedures and identities are used in each case?

**72. Writing** Describe the various approaches for evaluating integrals of the form

$$\int \tan^m x \sec^n x\,dx$$

Into what cases do these types of integrals fall? What procedures and identities are used in each case?

---

✓ **QUICK CHECK ANSWERS 7.3** 1. (a) $\frac{1-\cos 2x}{2}$ (b) $\frac{1+\cos 2x}{2}$ (c) $\cos 2x$ 2. (a) $\tan x + C$ (b) $\tan x - x + C$ (c) $\ln|\sec x + \tan x| + C$ (d) $\ln|\sec x| + C$ 3. (a) $\int u^2\,du$ (b) $\int (u^2-1)u^2\,du$ (c) $\int u^3\,du$ (d) $\int (u^2-1)\,du$

---

# 7.4 TRIGONOMETRIC SUBSTITUTIONS

*In this section we will discuss a method for evaluating integrals containing radicals by making substitutions involving trigonometric functions. We will also show how integrals containing quadratic polynomials can sometimes be evaluated by completing the square.*

## THE METHOD OF TRIGONOMETRIC SUBSTITUTION

To start, we will be concerned with integrals that contain expressions of the form

$$\sqrt{a^2-x^2}, \quad \sqrt{x^2+a^2}, \quad \sqrt{x^2-a^2}$$

in which $a$ is a positive constant. The basic idea for evaluating such integrals is to make a substitution for $x$ that will eliminate the radical. For example, to eliminate the radical in the expression $\sqrt{a^2-x^2}$, we can make the substitution

$$x = a\sin\theta, \quad -\pi/2 \leq \theta \leq \pi/2 \tag{1}$$

which yields

$$\begin{aligned}\sqrt{a^2-x^2} &= \sqrt{a^2-a^2\sin^2\theta} = \sqrt{a^2(1-\sin^2\theta)} \\ &= a\sqrt{\cos^2\theta} = a|\cos\theta| = a\cos\theta\end{aligned}$$

$\cos\theta \geq 0$ since $-\pi/2 \leq \theta \leq \pi/2$

The restriction on $\theta$ in (1) serves two purposes—it enables us to replace $|\cos\theta|$ by $\cos\theta$ to simplify the calculations, and it also ensures that the substitutions can be rewritten as $\theta = \sin^{-1}(x/a)$, if needed.

► **Example 1** Evaluate $\displaystyle\int \frac{dx}{x^2\sqrt{4-x^2}}$.

***Solution.*** To eliminate the radical we make the substitution

$$x = 2\sin\theta, \quad dx = 2\cos\theta\,d\theta$$

This yields

$$\int \frac{dx}{x^2\sqrt{4-x^2}} = \int \frac{2\cos\theta\, d\theta}{(2\sin\theta)^2\sqrt{4-4\sin^2\theta}}$$

$$= \int \frac{2\cos\theta\, d\theta}{(2\sin\theta)^2(2\cos\theta)} = \frac{1}{4}\int \frac{d\theta}{\sin^2\theta}$$

$$= \frac{1}{4}\int \csc^2\theta\, d\theta = -\frac{1}{4}\cot\theta + C \qquad (2)$$

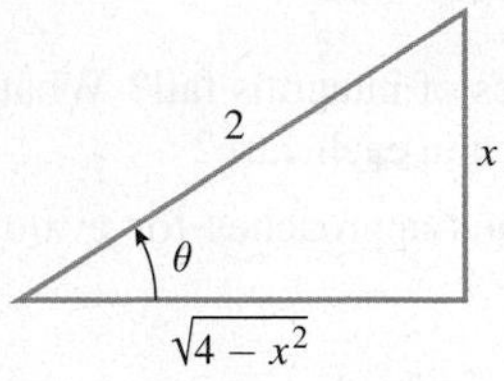


$x = 2\sin\theta$

▲ **Figure 7.4.1**

At this point we have completed the integration; however, because the original integral was expressed in terms of $x$, it is desirable to express $\cot\theta$ in terms of $x$ as well. This can be done using trigonometric identities, but the expression can also be obtained by writing the substitution $x = 2\sin\theta$ as $\sin\theta = x/2$ and representing it geometrically as in Figure 7.4.1. From that figure we obtain

$$\cot\theta = \frac{\sqrt{4-x^2}}{x}$$

Substituting this in (2) yields

$$\int \frac{dx}{x^2\sqrt{4-x^2}} = -\frac{1}{4}\frac{\sqrt{4-x^2}}{x} + C \blacktriangleleft$$

▶ **Example 2** Evaluate $\displaystyle\int_1^{\sqrt{2}} \frac{dx}{x^2\sqrt{4-x^2}}$.

***Solution.*** There are two possible approaches: we can make the substitution in the indefinite integral (as in Example 1) and then evaluate the definite integral using the $x$-limits of integration, or we can make the substitution in the definite integral and convert the $x$-limits to the corresponding $\theta$-limits.

**Method 1.**

Using the result from Example 1 with the $x$-limits of integration yields

$$\int_1^{\sqrt{2}} \frac{dx}{x^2\sqrt{4-x^2}} = -\frac{1}{4}\left[\frac{\sqrt{4-x^2}}{x}\right]_1^{\sqrt{2}} = -\frac{1}{4}\left[1-\sqrt{3}\right] = \frac{\sqrt{3}-1}{4}$$

**Method 2.**

The substitution $x = 2\sin\theta$ can be expressed as $x/2 = \sin\theta$ or $\theta = \sin^{-1}(x/2)$, so the $\theta$-limits that correspond to $x = 1$ and $x = \sqrt{2}$ are

$$x = 1: \quad \theta = \sin^{-1}(1/2) = \pi/6$$

$$x = \sqrt{2}: \quad \theta = \sin^{-1}(\sqrt{2}/2) = \pi/4$$

Thus, from (2) in Example 1 we obtain

$$\int_1^{\sqrt{2}} \frac{dx}{x^2\sqrt{4-x^2}} = \frac{1}{4}\int_{\pi/6}^{\pi/4} \csc^2\theta\, d\theta$$

Convert $x$-limits to $\theta$-limits.

$$= -\frac{1}{4}\left[\cot\theta\right]_{\pi/6}^{\pi/4} = -\frac{1}{4}\left[1-\sqrt{3}\right] = \frac{\sqrt{3}-1}{4} \blacktriangleleft$$

▶ **Example 3** Find the area of the ellipse

$$\frac{x^2}{a^2} + \frac{y^2}{b^2} = 1$$

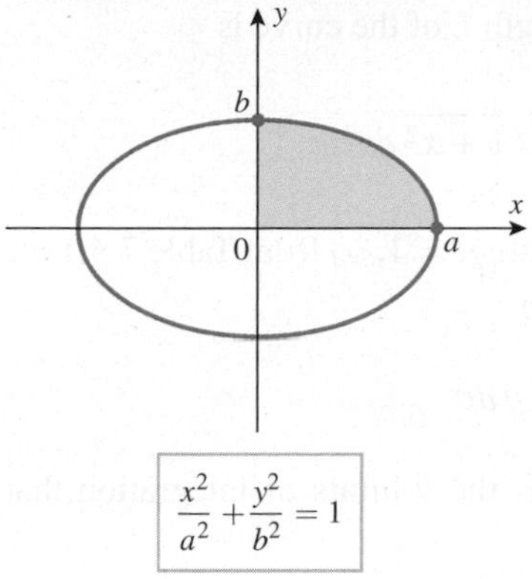


▲ Figure 7.4.2

***Solution.*** Because the ellipse is symmetric about both axes, its area $A$ is four times the area in the first quadrant (Figure 7.4.2). If we solve the equation of the ellipse for $y$ in terms of $x$, we obtain

$$y = \pm\frac{b}{a}\sqrt{a^2 - x^2}$$

where the positive square root gives the equation of the upper half. Thus, the area $A$ is given by

$$A = 4\int_0^a \frac{b}{a}\sqrt{a^2 - x^2}\,dx = \frac{4b}{a}\int_0^a \sqrt{a^2 - x^2}\,dx$$

To evaluate this integral, we will make the substitution $x = a\sin\theta$ (so $dx = a\cos\theta\,d\theta$) and convert the $x$-limits of integration to $\theta$-limits. Since the substitution can be expressed as $\theta = \sin^{-1}(x/a)$, the $\theta$-limits of integration are

$$x = 0: \quad \theta = \sin^{-1}(0) = 0$$

$$x = a: \quad \theta = \sin^{-1}(1) = \pi/2$$

Thus, we obtain

$$\begin{aligned} A &= \frac{4b}{a}\int_0^a \sqrt{a^2 - x^2}\,dx = \frac{4b}{a}\int_0^{\pi/2} \sqrt{a^2 - a^2\sin^2\theta} \cdot a\cos\theta\,d\theta \\ &= \frac{4b}{a}\int_0^{\pi/2} a\cos\theta \cdot a\cos\theta\,d\theta \\ &= 4ab\int_0^{\pi/2} \cos^2\theta\,d\theta = 4ab\int_0^{\pi/2} \frac{1}{2}(1 + \cos 2\theta)\,d\theta \\ &= 2ab\left[\theta + \frac{1}{2}\sin 2\theta\right]_0^{\pi/2} = 2ab\left[\frac{\pi}{2} - 0\right] = \pi ab \end{aligned}$$ ◀

**REMARK** In the special case where $a = b$, the ellipse becomes a circle of radius $a$, and the area formula becomes $A = \pi a^2$, as expected. It is worth noting that

$$\int_{-a}^{a} \sqrt{a^2 - x^2}\,dx = \tfrac{1}{2}\pi a^2 \qquad (3)$$

since this integral represents the area of the upper semicircle (Figure 7.4.3).

**TECHNOLOGY MASTERY**

If you have a calculating utility with a numerical integration capability, use it and Formula (3) to approximate $\pi$ to three decimal places.

Thus far, we have focused on using the substitution $x = a\sin\theta$ to evaluate integrals involving radicals of the form $\sqrt{a^2 - x^2}$. Table 7.4.1 summarizes this method and describes some other substitutions of this type.

**Table 7.4.1**

TRIGONOMETRIC SUBSTITUTIONS

| EXPRESSION IN THE INTEGRAND | SUBSTITUTION | RESTRICTION ON $\theta$ | SIMPLIFICATION |
|---|---|---|---|
| $\sqrt{a^2 - x^2}$ | $x = a\sin\theta$ | $-\pi/2 \le \theta \le \pi/2$ | $a^2 - x^2 = a^2 - a^2\sin^2\theta = a^2\cos^2\theta$ |
| $\sqrt{a^2 + x^2}$ | $x = a\tan\theta$ | $-\pi/2 < \theta < \pi/2$ | $a^2 + x^2 = a^2 + a^2\tan^2\theta = a^2\sec^2\theta$ |
| $\sqrt{x^2 - a^2}$ | $x = a\sec\theta$ | $\begin{cases} 0 \le \theta < \pi/2 & (\text{if } x \ge a) \\ \pi/2 < \theta \le \pi & (\text{if } x \le -a) \end{cases}$ | $x^2 - a^2 = a^2\sec^2\theta - a^2 = a^2\tan^2\theta$ |

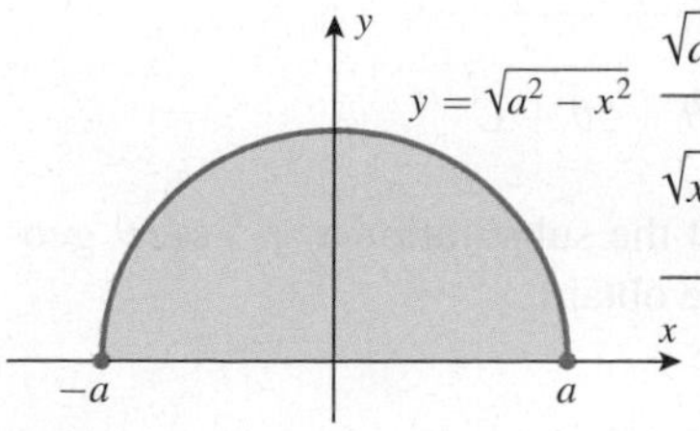


▲ Figure 7.4.3

▶ **Example 4** Find the arc length of the curve $y = x^2/2$ from $x = 0$ to $x = 1$ (Figure 7.4.4).

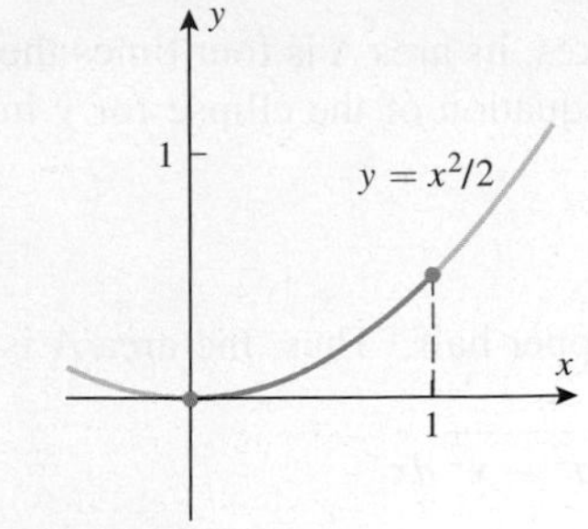


▲ **Figure 7.4.4**

***Solution.*** From Formula (4) of Section 6.4 the arc length $L$ of the curve is

$$L = \int_0^1 \sqrt{1 + \left(\frac{dy}{dx}\right)^2}\, dx = \int_0^1 \sqrt{1 + x^2}\, dx$$

The integrand involves a radical of the form $\sqrt{a^2 + x^2}$ with $a = 1$, so from Table 7.4.1 we make the substitution

$$x = \tan\theta, \quad -\pi/2 < \theta < \pi/2$$

$$\frac{dx}{d\theta} = \sec^2\theta \quad \text{or} \quad dx = \sec^2\theta\, d\theta$$

Since this substitution can be expressed as $\theta = \tan^{-1} x$, the $\theta$-limits of integration that correspond to the $x$-limits, $x = 0$ and $x = 1$, are

$$x = 0: \quad \theta = \tan^{-1} 0 = 0$$

$$x = 1: \quad \theta = \tan^{-1} 1 = \pi/4$$

Thus,

$$\begin{aligned}
L = \int_0^1 \sqrt{1 + x^2}\, dx &= \int_0^{\pi/4} \sqrt{1 + \tan^2\theta}\, \sec^2\theta\, d\theta \\
&= \int_0^{\pi/4} \sqrt{\sec^2\theta}\, \sec^2\theta\, d\theta \qquad \boxed{1 + \tan^2\theta = \sec^2\theta} \\
&= \int_0^{\pi/4} |\sec\theta| \sec^2\theta\, d\theta \\
&= \int_0^{\pi/4} \sec^3\theta\, d\theta \qquad \boxed{\sec\theta > 0 \text{ since } -\pi/2 < \theta < \pi/2} \\
&= \left[\tfrac{1}{2}\sec\theta\tan\theta + \tfrac{1}{2}\ln|\sec\theta + \tan\theta|\right]_0^{\pi/4} \qquad \boxed{\text{Formula (26) of Section 7.3}} \\
&= \tfrac{1}{2}\left[\sqrt{2} + \ln(\sqrt{2} + 1)\right] \approx 1.148 \blacktriangleleft
\end{aligned}$$

▶ **Example 5** Evaluate $\displaystyle\int \frac{\sqrt{x^2 - 25}}{x}\, dx$, assuming that $x \geq 5$.

***Solution.*** The integrand involves a radical of the form $\sqrt{x^2 - a^2}$ with $a = 5$, so from Table 7.4.1 we make the substitution

$$x = 5\sec\theta, \quad 0 \leq \theta < \pi/2$$

$$\frac{dx}{d\theta} = 5\sec\theta\tan\theta \quad \text{or} \quad dx = 5\sec\theta\tan\theta\, d\theta$$

Thus,

$$\begin{aligned}
\int \frac{\sqrt{x^2 - 25}}{x}\, dx &= \int \frac{\sqrt{25\sec^2\theta - 25}}{5\sec\theta}(5\sec\theta\tan\theta)\, d\theta \\
&= \int \frac{5|\tan\theta|}{5\sec\theta}(5\sec\theta\tan\theta)\, d\theta \\
&= 5\int \tan^2\theta\, d\theta \qquad \boxed{\tan\theta \geq 0 \text{ since } 0 \leq \theta < \pi/2} \\
&= 5\int (\sec^2\theta - 1)\, d\theta = 5\tan\theta - 5\theta + C
\end{aligned}$$

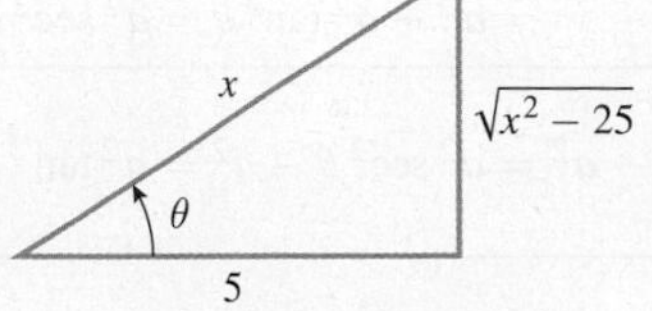


$x = 5\sec\theta$

▲ **Figure 7.4.5**

To express the solution in terms of $x$, we will represent the substitution $x = 5\sec\theta$ geometrically by the triangle in Figure 7.4.5, from which we obtain

$$\tan\theta = \frac{\sqrt{x^2 - 25}}{5}$$

From this and the fact that the substitution can be expressed as $\theta = \sec^{-1}(x/5)$, we obtain

$$\int \frac{\sqrt{x^2-25}}{x}\,dx = \sqrt{x^2-25} - 5\sec^{-1}\left(\frac{x}{5}\right) + C \blacktriangleleft$$

## INTEGRALS INVOLVING $ax^2 + bx + c$

Integrals that involve a quadratic expression $ax^2 + bx + c$, where $a \neq 0$ and $b \neq 0$, can often be evaluated by first completing the square, then making an appropriate substitution. The following example illustrates this idea.

**▶ Example 6** Evaluate $\displaystyle\int \frac{x}{x^2-4x+8}\,dx$.

***Solution.*** Completing the square yields

$$x^2 - 4x + 8 = (x^2 - 4x + 4) + 8 - 4 = (x-2)^2 + 4$$

Thus, the substitution

$$u = x - 2, \quad du = dx$$

yields

$$\int \frac{x}{x^2-4x+8}\,dx = \int \frac{x}{(x-2)^2+4}\,dx = \int \frac{u+2}{u^2+4}\,du$$

$$= \int \frac{u}{u^2+4}\,du + 2\int \frac{du}{u^2+4}$$

$$= \frac{1}{2}\int \frac{2u}{u^2+4}\,du + 2\int \frac{du}{u^2+4}$$

$$= \frac{1}{2}\ln(u^2+4) + 2\left(\frac{1}{2}\right)\tan^{-1}\frac{u}{2} + C$$

$$= \frac{1}{2}\ln[(x-2)^2+4] + \tan^{-1}\left(\frac{x-2}{2}\right) + C \blacktriangleleft$$

## ✓ QUICK CHECK EXERCISES 7.4 (See page 437 for answers.)

**1.** For each expression, give a trigonometric substitution that will eliminate the radical.
(a) $\sqrt{a^2-x^2}$ ______ (b) $\sqrt{a^2+x^2}$ ______
(c) $\sqrt{x^2-a^2}$ ______

**2.** If $x = 2\sec\theta$ and $0 < \theta < \pi/2$, then
(a) $\sin\theta =$ ______ (b) $\cos\theta =$ ______
(c) $\tan\theta =$ ______.

**3.** In each part, state the trigonometric substitution that you would try first to evaluate the integral. Do not evaluate the integral.
(a) $\int \sqrt{9+x^2}\,dx$ ______
(b) $\int \sqrt{9-x^2}\,dx$ ______
(c) $\int \sqrt{1-9x^2}\,dx$ ______
(d) $\int \sqrt{x^2-9}\,dx$ ______
(e) $\int \sqrt{9+3x^2}\,dx$ ______
(f) $\int \sqrt{1+(9x)^2}\,dx$ ______

**4.** In each part, determine the substitution $u$.
(a) $\displaystyle\int \frac{1}{x^2-2x+10}\,dx = \int \frac{1}{u^2+3^2}\,du$;
$u =$ ______
(b) $\int \sqrt{x^2-6x+8}\,dx = \int \sqrt{u^2-1}\,du$;
$u =$ ______
(c) $\int \sqrt{12-4x-x^2}\,dx = \int \sqrt{4^2-u^2}\,du$;
$u =$ ______

## EXERCISE SET 7.4 C CAS

**1–26** Evaluate the integral. ■

1. $\int \sqrt{4-x^2}\,dx$
2. $\int \sqrt{1-4x^2}\,dx$
3. $\int \frac{x^2}{\sqrt{16-x^2}}\,dx$
4. $\int \frac{dx}{x^2\sqrt{9-x^2}}$
5. $\int \frac{dx}{(4+x^2)^2}$
6. $\int \frac{x^2}{\sqrt{5+x^2}}\,dx$
7. $\int \frac{\sqrt{x^2-9}}{x}\,dx$
8. $\int \frac{dx}{x^2\sqrt{x^2-16}}$
9. $\int \frac{3x^3}{\sqrt{1-x^2}}\,dx$
10. $\int x^3\sqrt{5-x^2}\,dx$
11. $\int \frac{dx}{x^2\sqrt{9x^2-4}}$
12. $\int \frac{\sqrt{1+t^2}}{t}\,dt$
13. $\int \frac{dx}{(1-x^2)^{3/2}}$
14. $\int \frac{dx}{x^2\sqrt{x^2+25}}$
15. $\int \frac{dx}{\sqrt{x^2-9}}$
16. $\int \frac{dx}{1+2x^2+x^4}$
17. $\int \frac{dx}{(4x^2-9)^{3/2}}$
18. $\int \frac{3x^3}{\sqrt{x^2-25}}\,dx$
19. $\int e^x\sqrt{1-e^{2x}}\,dx$
20. $\int \frac{\cos\theta}{\sqrt{2-\sin^2\theta}}\,d\theta$
21. $\int_0^1 5x^3\sqrt{1-x^2}\,dx$
22. $\int_0^{1/2} \frac{dx}{(1-x^2)^2}$
23. $\int_{\sqrt{2}}^2 \frac{dx}{x^2\sqrt{x^2-1}}$
24. $\int_{\sqrt{2}}^2 \frac{\sqrt{2x^2-4}}{x}\,dx$
25. $\int_1^3 \frac{dx}{x^4\sqrt{x^2+3}}$
26. $\int_0^3 \frac{x^3}{(3+x^2)^{5/2}}\,dx$

**27–30 True–False** Determine whether the statement is true or false. Explain your answer. ■

27. An integrand involving a radical of the form $\sqrt{a^2-x^2}$ suggests the substitution $x = a\sin\theta$.
28. The trigonometric substitution $x = a\sin\theta$ is made with the restriction $0 \le \theta \le \pi$.
29. An integrand involving a radical of the form $\sqrt{x^2-a^2}$ suggests the substitution $x = a\cos\theta$.
30. The area enclosed by the ellipse $x^2+4y^2=1$ is $\pi/2$.

**FOCUS ON CONCEPTS**

31. The integral

$$\int \frac{x}{x^2+4}\,dx$$

can be evaluated either by a trigonometric substitution or by the substitution $u = x^2+4$. Do it both ways and show that the results are equivalent.

32. The integral

$$\int \frac{x^2}{x^2+4}\,dx$$

can be evaluated either by a trigonometric substitution or by algebraically rewriting the numerator of the integrand as $(x^2+4)-4$. Do it both ways and show that the results are equivalent.

33. Find the arc length of the curve $y = \ln x$ from $x = 1$ to $x = 2$.
34. Find the arc length of the curve $y = x^2$ from $x = 0$ to $x = 1$.
35. Find the area of the surface generated when the curve in Exercise 34 is revolved about the $x$-axis.
36. Find the volume of the solid generated when the region enclosed by $x = y(1-y^2)^{1/4}$, $y = 0$, $y = 1$, and $x = 0$ is revolved about the $y$-axis.

**37–48** Evaluate the integral. ■

37. $\int \frac{dx}{x^2-4x+5}$
38. $\int \frac{dx}{\sqrt{2x-x^2}}$
39. $\int \frac{dx}{\sqrt{3+2x-x^2}}$
40. $\int \frac{dx}{16x^2+16x+5}$
41. $\int \frac{dx}{\sqrt{x^2-6x+10}}$
42. $\int \frac{x}{x^2+2x+2}\,dx$
43. $\int \sqrt{3-2x-x^2}\,dx$
44. $\int \frac{e^x}{\sqrt{1+e^x+e^{2x}}}\,dx$
45. $\int \frac{dx}{2x^2+4x+7}$
46. $\int \frac{2x+3}{4x^2+4x+5}\,dx$
47. $\int_1^2 \frac{dx}{\sqrt{4x-x^2}}$
48. $\int_0^4 \sqrt{x(4-x)}\,dx$

C **49–50** There is a good chance that your CAS will not be able to evaluate these integrals as stated. If this is so, make a substitution that converts the integral into one that your CAS can evaluate. ■

49. $\int \cos x \sin x\sqrt{1-\sin^4 x}\,dx$
50. $\int (x\cos x + \sin x)\sqrt{1+x^2\sin^2 x}\,dx$
51. (a) Use the ***hyperbolic substitution*** $x = 3\sinh u$, the identity $\cosh^2 u - \sinh^2 u = 1$, and Theorem 6.9.4 to evaluate

$$\int \frac{dx}{\sqrt{x^2+9}}$$

(b) Evaluate the integral in part (a) using a trigonometric substitution and show that the result agrees with that obtained in part (a).

52. Use the hyperbolic substitutionn $x = \cosh u$, the identity $\sinh^2 u = \frac{1}{2}(\cosh 2u - 1)$, and the results referenced in Exercise 51 to evaluate

$$\int \sqrt{x^2-1}\,dx, \quad x \ge 1$$

**53. Writing** The trigonometric substitution $x = a\sin\theta$, $-\pi/2 \le \theta \le \pi/2$, is suggested for an integral whose integrand involves $\sqrt{a^2 - x^2}$. Discuss the implications of restricting $\theta$ to $\pi/2 \le \theta \le 3\pi/2$, and explain why the restriction $-\pi/2 \le \theta \le \pi/2$ should be preferred.

**54. Writing** The trigonometric substitution $x = a\cos\theta$ could also be used for an integral whose integrand involves $\sqrt{a^2 - x^2}$. Determine an appropriate restriction for $\theta$ with the substitution $x = a\cos\theta$, and discuss how to apply this substitution in appropriate integrals. Illustrate your discussion by evaluating the integral in Example 1 using a substitution of this type.

✓ **QUICK CHECK ANSWERS 7.4** 1. (a) $x = a\sin\theta$ (b) $x = a\tan\theta$ (c) $x = a\sec\theta$ 2. (a) $\dfrac{\sqrt{x^2-4}}{x}$ (b) $\dfrac{2}{x}$ (c) $\dfrac{\sqrt{x^2-4}}{2}$
3. (a) $x = 3\tan\theta$ (b) $x = 3\sin\theta$ (c) $x = \frac{1}{3}\sin\theta$ (d) $x = 3\sec\theta$ (e) $x = \sqrt{3}\tan\theta$ (f) $x = \frac{1}{9}\tan\theta$
4. (a) $x - 1$ (b) $x - 3$ (c) $x + 2$

## 7.5 INTEGRATING RATIONAL FUNCTIONS BY PARTIAL FRACTIONS

*Recall that a rational function is a ratio of two polynomials. In this section we will give a general method for integrating rational functions that is based on the idea of decomposing a rational function into a sum of simple rational functions that can be integrated by the methods studied in earlier sections.*

### PARTIAL FRACTIONS

In algebra, one learns to combine two or more fractions into a single fraction by finding a common denominator. For example,

$$\frac{2}{x-4} + \frac{3}{x+1} = \frac{2(x+1) + 3(x-4)}{(x-4)(x+1)} = \frac{5x-10}{x^2-3x-4} \tag{1}$$

However, for purposes of integration, the left side of (1) is preferable to the right side since each of the terms is easy to integrate:

$$\int \frac{5x-10}{x^2-3x-4}\,dx = \int \frac{2}{x-4}\,dx + \int \frac{3}{x+1}\,dx = 2\ln|x-4| + 3\ln|x+1| + C$$

Thus, it is desirable to have some method that will enable us to obtain the left side of (1), starting with the right side. To illustrate how this can be done, we begin by noting that on the left side the numerators are constants and the denominators are the factors of the denominator on the right side. Thus, to find the left side of (1), starting from the right side, we could factor the denominator of the right side and look for constants $A$ and $B$ such that

$$\frac{5x-10}{(x-4)(x+1)} = \frac{A}{x-4} + \frac{B}{x+1} \tag{2}$$

One way to find the constants $A$ and $B$ is to multiply (2) through by $(x-4)(x+1)$ to clear fractions. This yields

$$5x - 10 = A(x+1) + B(x-4) \tag{3}$$

This relationship holds for all $x$, so it holds in particular if $x = 4$ or $x = -1$. Substituting $x = 4$ in (3) makes the second term on the right drop out and yields the equation $10 = 5A$ or $A = 2$; and substituting $x = -1$ in (3) makes the first term on the right drop out and yields the equation $-15 = -5B$ or $B = 3$. Substituting these values in (2) we obtain

$$\frac{5x-10}{(x-4)(x+1)} = \frac{2}{x-4} + \frac{3}{x+1} \tag{4}$$

which agrees with (1).

A second method for finding the constants $A$ and $B$ is to multiply out the right side of (3) and collect like powers of $x$ to obtain

$$5x - 10 = (A+B)x + (A - 4B)$$

Since the polynomials on the two sides are identical, their corresponding coefficients must be the same. Equating the corresponding coefficients on the two sides yields the following system of equations in the unknowns $A$ and $B$:

$$\begin{aligned} A + B &= 5 \\ A - 4B &= -10 \end{aligned}$$

Solving this system yields $A = 2$ and $B = 3$ as before (verify).

The terms on the right side of (4) are called ***partial fractions*** of the expression on the left side because they each constitute *part* of that expression. To find those partial fractions we first had to make a guess about their form, and then we had to find the unknown constants. Our next objective is to extend this idea to general rational functions. For this purpose, suppose that $P(x)/Q(x)$ is a ***proper rational function***, by which we mean that the degree of the numerator is less than the degree of the denominator. There is a theorem in advanced algebra which states that every proper rational function can be expressed as a sum

$$\frac{P(x)}{Q(x)} = F_1(x) + F_2(x) + \cdots + F_n(x)$$

where $F_1(x), F_2(x), \ldots, F_n(x)$ are rational functions of the form

$$\frac{A}{(ax+b)^k} \quad \text{or} \quad \frac{Ax+B}{(ax^2+bx+c)^k}$$

in which the denominators are factors of $Q(x)$. The sum is called the ***partial fraction decomposition*** of $P(x)/Q(x)$, and the terms are called ***partial fractions***. As in our opening example, there are two parts to finding a partial fraction decomposition: determining the exact form of the decomposition and finding the unknown constants.

## FINDING THE FORM OF A PARTIAL FRACTION DECOMPOSITION

The first step in finding the form of the partial fraction decomposition of a proper rational function $P(x)/Q(x)$ is to factor $Q(x)$ completely into linear and irreducible quadratic factors, and then collect all repeated factors so that $Q(x)$ is expressed as a product of *distinct* factors of the form

$$(ax+b)^m \quad \text{and} \quad (ax^2+bx+c)^m$$

From these factors we can determine the form of the partial fraction decomposition using two rules that we will now discuss.

## LINEAR FACTORS

If all of the factors of $Q(x)$ are linear, then the partial fraction decomposition of $P(x)/Q(x)$ can be determined by using the following rule:

**LINEAR FACTOR RULE** For each factor of the form $(ax+b)^m$, the partial fraction decomposition contains the following sum of $m$ partial fractions:

$$\frac{A_1}{ax+b} + \frac{A_2}{(ax+b)^2} + \cdots + \frac{A_m}{(ax+b)^m}$$

where $A_1, A_2, \ldots, A_m$ are constants to be determined. In the case where $m = 1$, only the first term in the sum appears.

**▶ Example 1** Evaluate $\displaystyle\int \frac{dx}{x^2+x-2}$.

***Solution.*** The integrand is a proper rational function that can be written as

$$\frac{1}{x^2+x-2} = \frac{1}{(x-1)(x+2)}$$

The factors $x - 1$ and $x + 2$ are both linear and appear to the first power, so each contributes one term to the partial fraction decomposition by the linear factor rule. Thus, the decomposition has the form

$$\frac{1}{(x-1)(x+2)} = \frac{A}{x-1} + \frac{B}{x+2} \tag{5}$$

where $A$ and $B$ are constants to be determined. Multiplying this expression through by $(x-1)(x+2)$ yields

$$1 = A(x+2) + B(x-1) \tag{6}$$

As discussed earlier, there are two methods for finding $A$ and $B$: we can substitute values of $x$ that are chosen to make terms on the right drop out, or we can multiply out on the right and equate corresponding coefficients on the two sides to obtain a system of equations that can be solved for $A$ and $B$. We will use the first approach.

Setting $x = 1$ makes the second term in (6) drop out and yields $1 = 3A$ or $A = \frac{1}{3}$; and setting $x = -2$ makes the first term in (6) drop out and yields $1 = -3B$ or $B = -\frac{1}{3}$. Substituting these values in (5) yields the partial fraction decomposition

$$\frac{1}{(x-1)(x+2)} = \frac{\frac{1}{3}}{x-1} + \frac{-\frac{1}{3}}{x+2}$$

The integration can now be completed as follows:

$$\begin{aligned}\int \frac{dx}{(x-1)(x+2)} &= \frac{1}{3}\int \frac{dx}{x-1} - \frac{1}{3}\int \frac{dx}{x+2} \\ &= \frac{1}{3}\ln|x-1| - \frac{1}{3}\ln|x+2| + C = \frac{1}{3}\ln\left|\frac{x-1}{x+2}\right| + C \blacktriangleleft\end{aligned}$$

If the factors of $Q(x)$ are linear and none are repeated, as in the last example, then the recommended method for finding the constants in the partial fraction decomposition is to substitute appropriate values of $x$ to make terms drop out. However, if some of the linear factors are repeated, then it will not be possible to find all of the constants in this way. In this case the recommended procedure is to find as many constants as possible by substitution and then find the rest by equating coefficients. This is illustrated in the next example.

▶ **Example 2** Evaluate $\displaystyle\int \frac{2x+4}{x^3 - 2x^2}\,dx$.

***Solution.*** The integrand can be rewritten as

$$\frac{2x+4}{x^3-2x^2} = \frac{2x+4}{x^2(x-2)}$$

Although $x^2$ is a quadratic factor, it is *not* irreducible since $x^2 = xx$. Thus, by the linear factor rule, $x^2$ introduces two terms (since $m = 2$) of the form

$$\frac{A}{x} + \frac{B}{x^2}$$

and the factor $x - 2$ introduces one term (since $m = 1$) of the form

$$\frac{C}{x-2}$$

so the partial fraction decomposition is

$$\frac{2x+4}{x^2(x-2)} = \frac{A}{x} + \frac{B}{x^2} + \frac{C}{x-2} \tag{7}$$

Multiplying by $x^2(x-2)$ yields

$$2x + 4 = Ax(x-2) + B(x-2) + Cx^2 \tag{8}$$

which, after multiplying out and collecting like powers of $x$, becomes

$$2x + 4 = (A + C)x^2 + (-2A + B)x - 2B \tag{9}$$

Setting $x = 0$ in (8) makes the first and third terms drop out and yields $B = -2$, and setting $x = 2$ in (8) makes the first and second terms drop out and yields $C = 2$ (verify). However, there is no substitution in (8) that produces $A$ directly, so we look to Equation (9) to find this value. This can be done by equating the coefficients of $x^2$ on the two sides to obtain

$$A + C = 0 \quad \text{or} \quad A = -C = -2$$

Substituting the values $A = -2$, $B = -2$, and $C = 2$ in (7) yields the partial fraction decomposition

$$\frac{2x + 4}{x^2(x - 2)} = \frac{-2}{x} + \frac{-2}{x^2} + \frac{2}{x - 2}$$

Thus,

$$\int \frac{2x + 4}{x^2(x - 2)}\, dx = -2\int \frac{dx}{x} - 2\int \frac{dx}{x^2} + 2\int \frac{dx}{x - 2}$$

$$= -2\ln|x| + \frac{2}{x} + 2\ln|x - 2| + C = 2\ln\left|\frac{x - 2}{x}\right| + \frac{2}{x} + C \blacktriangleleft$$

## QUADRATIC FACTORS

If some of the factors of $Q(x)$ are irreducible quadratics, then the contribution of those factors to the partial fraction decomposition of $P(x)/Q(x)$ can be determined from the following rule:

> **QUADRATIC FACTOR RULE** For each factor of the form $(ax^2 + bx + c)^m$, the partial fraction decomposition contains the following sum of $m$ partial fractions:
>
> $$\frac{A_1x + B_1}{ax^2 + bx + c} + \frac{A_2x + B_2}{(ax^2 + bx + c)^2} + \cdots + \frac{A_mx + B_m}{(ax^2 + bx + c)^m}$$
>
> where $A_1, A_2, \ldots, A_m, B_1, B_2, \ldots, B_m$ are constants to be determined. In the case where $m = 1$, only the first term in the sum appears.

▶ **Example 3** Evaluate $\displaystyle\int \frac{x^2 + x - 2}{3x^3 - x^2 + 3x - 1}\, dx.$

***Solution.*** The denominator in the integrand can be factored by grouping:

$$3x^3 - x^2 + 3x - 1 = x^2(3x - 1) + (3x - 1) = (3x - 1)(x^2 + 1)$$

By the linear factor rule, the factor $3x - 1$ introduces one term, namely,

$$\frac{A}{3x - 1}$$

and by the quadratic factor rule, the factor $x^2 + 1$ introduces one term, namely,

$$\frac{Bx + C}{x^2 + 1}$$

Thus, the partial fraction decomposition is

$$\frac{x^2 + x - 2}{(3x - 1)(x^2 + 1)} = \frac{A}{3x - 1} + \frac{Bx + C}{x^2 + 1} \tag{10}$$

Multiplying by $(3x-1)(x^2+1)$ yields

$$x^2+x-2 = A(x^2+1)+(Bx+C)(3x-1) \tag{11}$$

We could find $A$ by substituting $x=\frac{1}{3}$ to make the last term drop out, and then find the rest of the constants by equating corresponding coefficients. However, in this case it is just as easy to find *all* of the constants by equating coefficients and solving the resulting system. For this purpose we multiply out the right side of (11) and collect like terms:

$$x^2+x-2 = (A+3B)x^2+(-B+3C)x+(A-C)$$

Equating corresponding coefficients gives

$$\begin{aligned} A + 3B \qquad &= 1 \\ -\,B + 3C &= 1 \\ A \qquad -\,C &= -2 \end{aligned}$$

To solve this system, subtract the third equation from the first to eliminate $A$. Then use the resulting equation together with the second equation to solve for $B$ and $C$. Finally, determine $A$ from the first or third equation. This yields (verify)

$$A=-\frac{7}{5},\quad B=\frac{4}{5},\quad C=\frac{3}{5}$$

Thus, (10) becomes

$$\frac{x^2+x-2}{(3x-1)(x^2+1)} = \frac{-\frac{7}{5}}{3x-1}+\frac{\frac{4}{5}x+\frac{3}{5}}{x^2+1}$$

and

$$\begin{aligned}\int \frac{x^2+x-2}{(3x-1)(x^2+1)}\,dx &= -\frac{7}{5}\int\frac{dx}{3x-1}+\frac{4}{5}\int\frac{x}{x^2+1}\,dx+\frac{3}{5}\int\frac{dx}{x^2+1} \\ &= -\frac{7}{15}\ln|3x-1|+\frac{2}{5}\ln(x^2+1)+\frac{3}{5}\tan^{-1}x+C \blacktriangleleft\end{aligned}$$

**TECHNOLOGY MASTERY**

Computer algebra systems have built-in capabilities for finding partial fraction decompositions. If you have a CAS, use it to find the decompositions in Examples 1, 2, and 3.

▶ **Example 4** Evaluate $\displaystyle\int \frac{3x^4+4x^3+16x^2+20x+9}{(x+2)(x^2+3)^2}\,dx$.

***Solution.*** Observe that the integrand is a proper rational function since the numerator has degree 4 and the denominator has degree 5. Thus, the method of partial fractions is applicable. By the linear factor rule, the factor $x+2$ introduces the single term

$$\frac{A}{x+2}$$

and by the quadratic factor rule, the factor $(x^2+3)^2$ introduces two terms (since $m=2$):

$$\frac{Bx+C}{x^2+3}+\frac{Dx+E}{(x^2+3)^2}$$

Thus, the partial fraction decomposition of the integrand is

$$\frac{3x^4+4x^3+16x^2+20x+9}{(x+2)(x^2+3)^2} = \frac{A}{x+2}+\frac{Bx+C}{x^2+3}+\frac{Dx+E}{(x^2+3)^2} \tag{12}$$

Multiplying by $(x+2)(x^2+3)^2$ yields

$$\begin{aligned}&3x^4+4x^3+16x^2+20x+9 \\ &\qquad = A(x^2+3)^2+(Bx+C)(x^2+3)(x+2)+(Dx+E)(x+2)\end{aligned} \tag{13}$$

which, after multiplying out and collecting like powers of $x$, becomes

$$\begin{aligned}&3x^4+4x^3+16x^2+20x+9 \\ &\qquad = (A+B)x^4+(2B+C)x^3+(6A+3B+2C+D)x^2 \\ &\qquad\quad +(6B+3C+2D+E)x+(9A+6C+2E)\end{aligned} \tag{14}$$

Equating corresponding coefficients in (14) yields the following system of five linear equations in five unknowns:

$$\begin{aligned} A + B &= 3 \\ 2B + C &= 4 \\ 6A + 3B + 2C + D &= 16 \\ 6B + 3C + 2D + E &= 20 \\ 9A + 6C + 2E &= 9 \end{aligned} \tag{15}$$

Efficient methods for solving systems of linear equations such as this are studied in a branch of mathematics called ***linear algebra***; those methods are outside the scope of this text. However, as a practical matter most linear systems of any size are solved by computer, and most computer algebra systems have commands that in many cases can solve linear systems exactly. In this particular case we can simplify the work by first substituting $x = -2$ in (13), which yields $A = 1$. Substituting this known value of $A$ in (15) yields the simpler system

$$\begin{aligned} B &= 2 \\ 2B + C &= 4 \\ 3B + 2C + D &= 10 \\ 6B + 3C + 2D + E &= 20 \\ 6C + 2E &= 0 \end{aligned} \tag{16}$$

This system can be solved by starting at the top and working down, first substituting $B = 2$ in the second equation to get $C = 0$, then substituting the known values of $B$ and $C$ in the third equation to get $D = 4$, and so forth. This yields

$$A = 1, \quad B = 2, \quad C = 0, \quad D = 4, \quad E = 0$$

Thus, (12) becomes

$$\frac{3x^4 + 4x^3 + 16x^2 + 20x + 9}{(x+2)(x^2+3)^2} = \frac{1}{x+2} + \frac{2x}{x^2+3} + \frac{4x}{(x^2+3)^2}$$

and so

$$\begin{aligned} &\int \frac{3x^4 + 4x^3 + 16x^2 + 20x + 9}{(x+2)(x^2+3)^2}\, dx \\ &\quad = \int \frac{dx}{x+2} + \int \frac{2x}{x^2+3}\, dx + 4\int \frac{x}{(x^2+3)^2}\, dx \\ &\quad = \ln|x+2| + \ln(x^2+3) - \frac{2}{x^2+3} + C \end{aligned}$$ ◀

## INTEGRATING IMPROPER RATIONAL FUNCTIONS

Although the method of partial fractions only applies to proper rational functions, an improper rational function can be integrated by performing a long division and expressing the function as the quotient plus the remainder over the divisor. The remainder over the divisor will be a proper rational function, which can then be decomposed into partial fractions. This idea is illustrated in the following example.

▶ **Example 5** Evaluate $\displaystyle\int \frac{3x^4 + 3x^3 - 5x^2 + x - 1}{x^2 + x - 2}\, dx.$

***Solution.*** The integrand is an improper rational function since the numerator has degree 4 and the denominator has degree 2. Thus, we first perform the long division

$$\begin{array}{r|l} & 3x^2 \qquad\quad + 1 \\ \hline x^2+x-2 & 3x^4+3x^3-5x^2+x-1 \\ & \underline{3x^4+3x^3-6x^2} \\ & \qquad\qquad\quad x^2+x-1 \\ & \qquad\qquad\quad \underline{x^2+x-2} \\ & \qquad\qquad\qquad\qquad\quad 1 \end{array}$$

It follows that the integrand can be expressed as

$$\frac{3x^4+3x^3-5x^2+x-1}{x^2+x-2} = (3x^2+1) + \frac{1}{x^2+x-2}$$

and hence

$$\int \frac{3x^4+3x^3-5x^2+x-1}{x^2+x-2}\,dx = \int (3x^2+1)\,dx + \int \frac{dx}{x^2+x-2}$$

The second integral on the right now involves a proper rational function and can thus be evaluated by a partial fraction decomposition. Using the result of Example 1 we obtain

$$\int \frac{3x^4+3x^3-5x^2+x-1}{x^2+x-2}\,dx = x^3+x+\frac{1}{3}\ln\left|\frac{x-1}{x+2}\right| + C \blacktriangleleft$$

## CONCLUDING REMARKS

There are some cases in which the method of partial fractions is inappropriate. For example, it would be inefficient to use partial fractions to perform the integration

$$\int \frac{3x^2+2}{x^3+2x-8}\,dx = \ln|x^3+2x-8| + C$$

since the substitution $u = x^3 + 2x - 8$ is more direct. Similarly, the integration

$$\int \frac{2x-1}{x^2+1}\,dx = \int \frac{2x}{x^2+1}\,dx - \int \frac{dx}{x^2+1} = \ln(x^2+1) - \tan^{-1}x + C$$

requires only a little algebra since the integrand is already in partial fraction form.

## ✓QUICK CHECK EXERCISES 7.5 *(See page 445 for answers.)*

**1.** A partial fraction is a rational function of the form ________ or of the form ________.

**2.** (a) What is a proper rational function?
(b) What condition must the degree of the numerator and the degree of the denominator of a rational function satisfy for the method of partial fractions to be applicable directly?
(c) If the condition in part (b) is not satisfied, what must you do if you want to use partial fractions?

**3.** Suppose that the function $f(x) = P(x)/Q(x)$ is a proper rational function.
(a) For each factor of $Q(x)$ of the form $(ax+b)^m$, the partial fraction decomposition of $f$ contains the following sum of $m$ partial fractions: ________
(b) For each factor of $Q(x)$ of the form $(ax^2+bx+c)^m$, where $ax^2+bx+c$ is an irreducible quadratic, the partial fraction decomposition of $f$ contains the following sum of $m$ partial fractions: ________

**4.** Complete the partial fraction decomposition.
(a) $\dfrac{-3}{(x+1)(2x-1)} = \dfrac{A}{x+1} - \dfrac{2}{2x-1}$
(b) $\dfrac{2x^2-3x}{(x^2+1)(3x+2)} = \dfrac{B}{3x+2} - \dfrac{1}{x^2+1}$

**5.** Evaluate the integral.
(a) $\displaystyle\int \frac{3}{(x+1)(1-2x)}\,dx$ (b) $\displaystyle\int \frac{2x^2-3x}{(x^2+1)(3x+2)}\,dx$

## EXERCISE SET 7.5 C CAS

**1–8** Write out the form of the partial fraction decomposition. (Do not find the numerical values of the coefficients.)

**1.** $\dfrac{3x-1}{(x-3)(x+4)}$ **2.** $\dfrac{5}{x(x^2-4)}$

**3.** $\dfrac{2x-3}{x^3-x^2}$ **4.** $\dfrac{x^2}{(x+2)^3}$

**5.** $\dfrac{1-x^2}{x^3(x^2+2)}$ **6.** $\dfrac{3x}{(x-1)(x^2+6)}$

**7.** $\dfrac{4x^3-x}{(x^2+5)^2}$ **8.** $\dfrac{1-3x^4}{(x-2)(x^2+1)^2}$

**9–34** Evaluate the integral.

**9.** $\displaystyle\int \frac{dx}{x^2-3x-4}$ **10.** $\displaystyle\int \frac{dx}{x^2-6x-7}$

**11.** $\displaystyle\int \frac{11x+17}{2x^2+7x-4}\,dx$ **12.** $\displaystyle\int \frac{5x-5}{3x^2-8x-3}\,dx$

**13.** $\displaystyle\int \frac{2x^2-9x-9}{x^3-9x}\,dx$ **14.** $\displaystyle\int \frac{dx}{x(x^2-1)}$

**15.** $\displaystyle\int \frac{x^2-8}{x+3}\,dx$ **16.** $\displaystyle\int \frac{x^2+1}{x-1}\,dx$

**17.** $\displaystyle\int \frac{3x^2-10}{x^2-4x+4}\,dx$ **18.** $\displaystyle\int \frac{x^2}{x^2-3x+2}\,dx$

**19.** $\displaystyle\int \frac{2x-3}{x^2-3x-10}\,dx$ **20.** $\displaystyle\int \frac{3x+1}{3x^2+2x-1}\,dx$

**21.** $\displaystyle\int \frac{x^5+x^2+2}{x^3-x}\,dx$ **22.** $\displaystyle\int \frac{x^5-4x^3+1}{x^3-4x}\,dx$

**23.** $\displaystyle\int \frac{2x^2+3}{x(x-1)^2}\,dx$ **24.** $\displaystyle\int \frac{3x^2-x+1}{x^3-x^2}\,dx$

**25.** $\displaystyle\int \frac{2x^2-10x+4}{(x+1)(x-3)^2}\,dx$ **26.** $\displaystyle\int \frac{2x^2-2x-1}{x^3-x^2}\,dx$

**27.** $\displaystyle\int \frac{x^2}{(x+1)^3}\,dx$ **28.** $\displaystyle\int \frac{2x^2+3x+3}{(x+1)^3}\,dx$

**29.** $\displaystyle\int \frac{2x^2-1}{(4x-1)(x^2+1)}\,dx$ **30.** $\displaystyle\int \frac{dx}{x^3+2x}$

**31.** $\displaystyle\int \frac{x^3+3x^2+x+9}{(x^2+1)(x^2+3)}\,dx$ **32.** $\displaystyle\int \frac{x^3+x^2+x+2}{(x^2+1)(x^2+2)}\,dx$

**33.** $\displaystyle\int \frac{x^3-2x^2+2x-2}{x^2+1}\,dx$

**34.** $\displaystyle\int \frac{x^4+6x^3+10x^2+x}{x^2+6x+10}\,dx$

**35–38 True–False** Determine whether the statement is true or false. Explain your answer.

**35.** The technique of partial fractions is used for integrals whose integrands are ratios of polynomials.

**36.** The integrand in

$$\int \frac{3x^4+5}{(x^2+1)^2}\,dx$$

is a proper rational function.

**37.** The partial fraction decomposition of

$$\frac{2x+3}{x^2} \quad \text{is} \quad \frac{2}{x}+\frac{3}{x^2}$$

**38.** If $f(x) = P(x)/(x+5)^3$ is a proper rational function, then the partial fraction decomposition of $f(x)$ has terms with constant numerators and denominators $(x+5)$, $(x+5)^2$, and $(x+5)^3$.

**39–42** Evaluate the integral by making a substitution that converts the integrand to a rational function.

**39.** $\displaystyle\int \frac{\cos\theta}{\sin^2\theta+4\sin\theta-5}\,d\theta$ **40.** $\displaystyle\int \frac{e^t}{e^{2t}-4}\,dt$

**41.** $\displaystyle\int \frac{e^{3x}}{e^{2x}+4}\,dx$ **42.** $\displaystyle\int \frac{5+2\ln x}{x(1+\ln x)^2}\,dx$

**43.** Find the volume of the solid generated when the region enclosed by $y = x^2/(9-x^2)$, $y=0$, $x=0$, and $x=2$ is revolved about the $x$-axis.

**44.** Find the area of the region under the curve $y = 1/(1+e^x)$, over the interval $[-\ln 5, \ln 5]$. [*Hint:* Make a substitution that converts the integrand to a rational function.]

C **45–46** Use a CAS to evaluate the integral in two ways: (i) integrate directly; (ii) use the CAS to find the partial fraction decomposition and integrate the decomposition. Integrate by hand to check the results.

**45.** $\displaystyle\int \frac{x^2+1}{(x^2+2x+3)^2}\,dx$

**46.** $\displaystyle\int \frac{x^5+x^4+4x^3+4x^2+4x+4}{(x^2+2)^3}\,dx$

C **47–48** Integrate by hand and check your answers using a CAS.

**47.** $\displaystyle\int \frac{dx}{x^4-3x^3-7x^2+27x-18}$

**48.** $\displaystyle\int \frac{dx}{16x^3-4x^2+4x-1}$

### FOCUS ON CONCEPTS

**49.** Show that

$$\int_0^1 \frac{x}{x^4+1}\,dx = \frac{\pi}{8}$$

**50.** Use partial fractions to derive the integration formula

$$\int \frac{1}{a^2-x^2}\,dx = \frac{1}{2a}\ln\left|\frac{a+x}{a-x}\right| + C$$

**51.** Suppose that $ax^2+bx+c$ is a quadratic polynomial and that the integration

$$\int \frac{1}{ax^2+bx+c}\,dx$$

produces a function with no inverse tangent terms. What does this tell you about the roots of the polynomial?

**52.** Suppose that $ax^2+bx+c$ is a quadratic polynomial and that the integration

$$\int \frac{1}{ax^2+bx+c}\,dx$$

produces a function with neither logarithmic nor inverse tangent terms. What does this tell you about the roots of the polynomial?

**53.** Does there exist a quadratic polynomial $ax^2 + bx + c$ such that the integration

$$\int \frac{x}{ax^2 + bx + c}\,dx$$

produces a function with no logarithmic terms? If so, give an example; if not, explain why no such polynomial can exist.

**54. Writing** Suppose that $P(x)$ is a cubic polynomial. State the general form of the partial fraction decomposition for

$$f(x) = \frac{P(x)}{(x+5)^4}$$

and state the implications of this decomposition for evaluating the integral $\int f(x)\,dx$.

**55. Writing** Consider the functions

$$f(x) = \frac{1}{x^2 - 4} \quad \text{and} \quad g(x) = \frac{x}{x^2 - 4}$$

Each of the integrals $\int f(x)\,dx$ and $\int g(x)\,dx$ can be evaluated using partial fractions and using at least one other integration technique. Demonstrate two different techniques for evaluating each of these integrals, and then discuss the considerations that would determine which technique you would use.

**✓QUICK CHECK ANSWERS 7.5** 1. $\dfrac{A}{(ax+b)^k}$; $\dfrac{Ax+B}{(ax^2+bx+c)^k}$ 2. (a) A proper rational function is a rational function in which the degree of the numerator is less than the degree of the denominator. (b) The degree of the numerator must be less than the degree of the denominator. (c) Divide the denominator into the numerator, which results in the sum of a polynomial and a proper rational function. 3. (a) $\dfrac{A_1}{ax+b} + \dfrac{A_2}{(ax+b)^2} + \cdots + \dfrac{A_m}{(ax+b)^m}$ (b) $\dfrac{A_1x+B_1}{ax^2+bx+c} + \dfrac{A_2x+B_2}{(ax^2+bx+c)^2} + \cdots + \dfrac{A_mx+B_m}{(ax^2+bx+c)^m}$ 4. (a) $A = 1$ (b) $B = 2$ 5. (a) $\displaystyle\int \frac{3}{(x+1)(1-2x)}\,dx = \ln\left|\frac{x+1}{1-2x}\right| + C$ (b) $\displaystyle\int \frac{2x^2-3x}{(x^2+1)(3x+2)}\,dx = \frac{2}{3}\ln|3x+2| - \tan^{-1}x + C$

## 7.6 USING COMPUTER ALGEBRA SYSTEMS AND TABLES OF INTEGRALS

*In this section we will discuss how to integrate using tables, and we will see some special substitutions to try when an integral doesn't match any of the forms in an integral table. In particular, we will discuss a method for integrating rational functions of* sin *x and* cos *x. We will also address some of the issues that relate to using computer algebra systems for integration. Readers who are not using computer algebra systems can skip that material.*

### INTEGRAL TABLES

Tables of integrals are useful for eliminating tedious hand computation. The endpapers of this text contain a relatively brief table of integrals that we will refer to as the ***Endpaper Integral Table***; more comprehensive tables are published in standard reference books such as the *CRC Standard Mathematical Tables and Formulae*, CRC Press, Inc., 2002.

All integral tables have their own scheme for classifying integrals according to the form of the integrand. For example, the Endpaper Integral Table classifies the integrals into 15 categories; *Basic Functions, Reciprocals of Basic Functions, Powers of Trigonometric Functions, Products of Trigonometric Functions*, and so forth. The first step in working with tables is to read through the classifications so that you understand the classification scheme and know where to look in the table for integrals of different types.

### PERFECT MATCHES

If you are lucky, the integral you are attempting to evaluate will match up perfectly with one of the forms in the table. However, when looking for matches you may have to make an adjustment for the variable of integration. For example, the integral

$$\int x^2 \sin x\,dx$$

is a perfect match with Formula (46) in the Endpaper Integral Table, except for the letter used for the variable of integration. Thus, to apply Formula (46) to the given integral we need to change the variable of integration in the formula from $u$ to $x$. With that minor modification we obtain

$$\int x^2 \sin x\, dx = 2x \sin x + (2 - x^2)\cos x + C$$

Here are some more examples of perfect matches.

**▶ Example 1** Use the Endpaper Integral Table to evaluate

(a) $\displaystyle\int \sin 7x \cos 2x\, dx$ (b) $\displaystyle\int x^2\sqrt{7+3x}\, dx$

(c) $\displaystyle\int \frac{\sqrt{2-x^2}}{x}\, dx$ (d) $\displaystyle\int (x^3 + 7x + 1)\sin \pi x\, dx$

***Solution (a).*** The integrand can be classified as a product of trigonometric functions. Thus, from Formula (40) with $m = 7$ and $n = 2$ we obtain

$$\int \sin 7x \cos 2x\, dx = -\frac{\cos 9x}{18} - \frac{\cos 5x}{10} + C$$

***Solution (b).*** The integrand can be classified as a power of $x$ multiplying $\sqrt{a+bx}$. Thus, from Formula (103) with $a = 7$ and $b = 3$ we obtain

$$\int x^2\sqrt{7+3x}\, dx = \frac{2}{2835}(135x^2 - 252x + 392)(7+3x)^{3/2} + C$$

***Solution (c).*** The integrand can be classified as a power of $x$ dividing $\sqrt{a^2 - x^2}$. Thus, from Formula (79) with $a = \sqrt{2}$ we obtain

$$\int \frac{\sqrt{2-x^2}}{x}\, dx = \sqrt{2-x^2} - \sqrt{2}\ln\left|\frac{\sqrt{2}+\sqrt{2-x^2}}{x}\right| + C$$

***Solution (d).*** The integrand can be classified as a polynomial multiplying a trigonometric function. Thus, we apply Formula (58) with $p(x) = x^3 + 7x + 1$ and $a = \pi$. The successive nonzero derivatives of $p(x)$ are

$$p'(x) = 3x^2 + 7, \quad p''(x) = 6x, \quad p'''(x) = 6$$

and so

$$\int (x^3 + 7x + 1)\sin \pi x\, dx$$
$$= -\frac{x^3 + 7x + 1}{\pi}\cos \pi x + \frac{3x^2 + 7}{\pi^2}\sin \pi x + \frac{6x}{\pi^3}\cos \pi x - \frac{6}{\pi^4}\sin \pi x + C \blacktriangleleft$$

## ■ MATCHES REQUIRING SUBSTITUTIONS

Sometimes an integral that does not match any table entry can be made to match by making an appropriate substitution.

**▶ Example 2** Use the Endpaper Integral Table to evaluate

(a) $\displaystyle\int e^{\pi x}\sin^{-1}(e^{\pi x})\, dx$ (b) $\displaystyle\int x\sqrt{x^2 - 4x + 5}\, dx$

***Solution (a).*** The integrand does not even come close to matching any of the forms in the table. However, a little thought suggests the substitution

$$u = e^{\pi x}, \quad du = \pi e^{\pi x}\, dx$$

from which we obtain

$$\int e^{\pi x}\sin^{-1}(e^{\pi x})\, dx = \frac{1}{\pi}\int \sin^{-1} u\, du$$

The integrand is now a basic function, and Formula (7) yields

$$\int e^{\pi x}\sin^{-1}(e^{\pi x})\,dx = \frac{1}{\pi}\left[u\sin^{-1}u + \sqrt{1-u^2}\right] + C$$
$$= \frac{1}{\pi}\left[e^{\pi x}\sin^{-1}(e^{\pi x}) + \sqrt{1-e^{2\pi x}}\right] + C$$

***Solution (b).*** Again, the integrand does not closely match any of the forms in the table. However, a little thought suggests that it may be possible to bring the integrand closer to the form $x\sqrt{x^2+a^2}$ by completing the square to eliminate the term involving $x$ inside the radical. Doing this yields

$$\int x\sqrt{x^2-4x+5}\,dx = \int x\sqrt{(x^2-4x+4)+1}\,dx = \int x\sqrt{(x-2)^2+1}\,dx \qquad (1)$$

At this point we are closer to the form $x\sqrt{x^2+a^2}$, but we are not quite there because of the $(x-2)^2$ rather than $x^2$ inside the radical. However, we can resolve that problem with the substitution

$$u = x-2, \quad du = dx$$

With this substitution we have $x = u+2$, so (1) can be expressed in terms of $u$ as

$$\int x\sqrt{x^2-4x+5}\,dx = \int (u+2)\sqrt{u^2+1}\,du = \int u\sqrt{u^2+1}\,du + 2\int \sqrt{u^2+1}\,du$$

The first integral on the right is now a perfect match with Formula (84) with $a = 1$, and the second is a perfect match with Formula (72) with $a = 1$. Thus, applying these formulas we obtain

$$\int x\sqrt{x^2-4x+5}\,dx = \tfrac{1}{3}(u^2+1)^{3/2} + 2\left[\tfrac{1}{2}u\sqrt{u^2+1} + \tfrac{1}{2}\ln\left(u+\sqrt{u^2+1}\right)\right] + C$$

If we now replace $u$ by $x-2$ (in which case $u^2+1 = x^2-4x+5$), we obtain

$$\int x\sqrt{x^2-4x+5}\,dx = \tfrac{1}{3}(x^2-4x+5)^{3/2} + (x-2)\sqrt{x^2-4x+5}$$
$$+ \ln\left(x-2+\sqrt{x^2-4x+5}\right) + C$$

Although correct, this form of the answer has an unnecessary mixture of radicals and fractional exponents. If desired, we can "clean up" the answer by writing

$$(x^2-4x+5)^{3/2} = (x^2-4x+5)\sqrt{x^2-4x+5}$$

from which it follows that (verify)

$$\int x\sqrt{x^2-4x+5}\,dx = \tfrac{1}{3}(x^2-x-1)\sqrt{x^2-4x+5}$$
$$+ \ln\left(x-2+\sqrt{x^2-4x+5}\right) + C \blacktriangleleft$$

## MATCHES REQUIRING REDUCTION FORMULAS

In cases where the entry in an integral table is a reduction formula, that formula will have to be applied first to reduce the given integral to a form in which it can be evaluated.

**▶ Example 3** Use the Endpaper Integral Table to evaluate $\displaystyle\int \frac{x^3}{\sqrt{1+x}}\,dx$.

***Solution.*** The integrand can be classified as a power of $x$ multiplying the reciprocal of $\sqrt{a+bx}$. Thus, from Formula (107) with $a = 1$, $b = 1$, and $n = 3$, followed by Formula (106), we obtain

$$\int \frac{x^3}{\sqrt{1+x}}\,dx = \frac{2x^3\sqrt{1+x}}{7} - \frac{6}{7}\int \frac{x^2}{\sqrt{1+x}}\,dx$$
$$= \frac{2x^3\sqrt{1+x}}{7} - \frac{6}{7}\left[\frac{2}{15}(3x^2-4x+8)\sqrt{1+x}\right] + C$$
$$= \left(\frac{2x^3}{7} - \frac{12x^2}{35} + \frac{16x}{35} - \frac{32}{35}\right)\sqrt{1+x} + C \blacktriangleleft$$

## SPECIAL SUBSTITUTIONS

The Endpaper Integral Table has numerous entries involving an exponent of $3/2$ or involving square roots (exponent $1/2$), but it has no entries with other fractional exponents. However, integrals involving fractional powers of $x$ can often be simplified by making the substitution $u = x^{1/n}$ in which $n$ is the least common multiple of the denominators of the exponents. The resulting integral will then involve integer powers of $u$.

► **Example 4** Evaluate

$$\text{(a)} \int \frac{\sqrt{x}}{1+\sqrt[3]{x}}\,dx \qquad \text{(b)} \int \sqrt{1+e^x}\,dx$$

***Solution (a).*** The integrand contains $x^{1/2}$ and $x^{1/3}$, so we make the substitution $u = x^{1/6}$, from which we obtain

$$x = u^6, \quad dx = 6u^5\,du$$

Thus,

$$\int \frac{\sqrt{x}}{1+\sqrt[3]{x}}\,dx = \int \frac{(u^6)^{1/2}}{1+(u^6)^{1/3}}(6u^5)\,du = 6\int \frac{u^8}{1+u^2}\,du$$

By long division

$$\frac{u^8}{1+u^2} = u^6 - u^4 + u^2 - 1 + \frac{1}{1+u^2}$$

from which it follows that

$$\begin{aligned}\int \frac{\sqrt{x}}{1+\sqrt[3]{x}}\,dx &= 6\int \left(u^6 - u^4 + u^2 - 1 + \frac{1}{1+u^2}\right) du \\ &= \tfrac{6}{7}u^7 - \tfrac{6}{5}u^5 + 2u^3 - 6u + 6\tan^{-1} u + C \\ &= \tfrac{6}{7}x^{7/6} - \tfrac{6}{5}x^{5/6} + 2x^{1/2} - 6x^{1/6} + 6\tan^{-1}(x^{1/6}) + C\end{aligned}$$

***Solution (b).*** The integral does not match any of the forms in the Endpaper Integral Table. However, the table does include several integrals containing $\sqrt{a+bu}$. This suggests the substitution $u = e^x$, from which we obtain

$$x = \ln u, \quad dx = \frac{1}{u}\,du$$

Thus, from Formula (110) with $a = 1$ and $b = 1$, followed by Formula (108), we obtain

$$\begin{aligned}\int \sqrt{1+e^x}\,dx &= \int \frac{\sqrt{1+u}}{u}\,du \\ &= 2\sqrt{1+u} + \int \frac{du}{u\sqrt{1+u}} \\ &= 2\sqrt{1+u} + \ln\left|\frac{\sqrt{1+u}-1}{\sqrt{1+u}+1}\right| + C \\ &= 2\sqrt{1+e^x} + \ln\left[\frac{\sqrt{1+e^x}-1}{\sqrt{1+e^x}+1}\right] + C \qquad \boxed{\text{Absolute value not needed}} \blacktriangleleft\end{aligned}$$

> Try finding the antiderivative in Example 4(b) using the substitution
>
> $u = \sqrt{1+e^x}$

Functions that consist of finitely many sums, differences, quotients, and products of $\sin x$ and $\cos x$ are called ***rational functions of*** $\sin x$ ***and*** $\cos x$. Some examples are

$$\frac{\sin x + 3\cos^2 x}{\cos x + 4\sin x}, \quad \frac{\sin x}{1+\cos x - \cos^2 x}, \quad \frac{3\sin^5 x}{1+4\sin x}$$

The Endpaper Integral Table gives a few formulas for integrating rational functions of $\sin x$ and $\cos x$ under the heading *Reciprocals of Basic Functions*. For example, it follows from Formula (18) that

$$\int \frac{1}{1+\sin x}\,dx = \tan x - \sec x + C \tag{2}$$

However, since the integrand is a rational function of $\sin x$, it may be desirable in a particular application to express the value of the integral in terms of $\sin x$ and $\cos x$ and rewrite (2) as

$$\int \frac{1}{1+\sin x}\,dx = \frac{\sin x - 1}{\cos x} + C$$

Many rational functions of $\sin x$ and $\cos x$ can be evaluated by an ingenious method that was discovered by the mathematician Karl Weierstrass (see p. 32 for biography). The idea is to make the substitution

$$u = \tan(x/2), \quad -\pi/2 < x/2 < \pi/2$$

from which it follows that

$$x = 2\tan^{-1} u, \quad dx = \frac{2}{1+u^2}\,du$$

To implement this substitution we need to express $\sin x$ and $\cos x$ in terms of $u$. For this purpose we will use the identities

$$\sin x = 2\sin(x/2)\cos(x/2) \tag{3}$$

$$\cos x = \cos^2(x/2) - \sin^2(x/2) \tag{4}$$

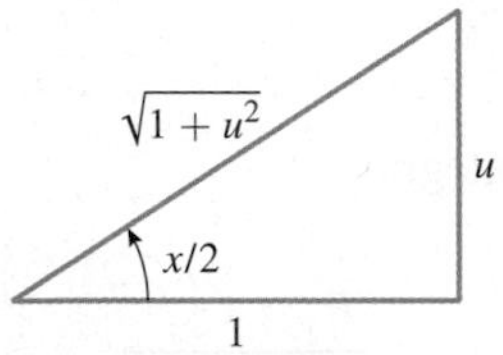

▲ **Figure 7.6.1**

and the following relationships suggested by Figure 7.6.1:

$$\sin(x/2) = \frac{u}{\sqrt{1+u^2}} \quad \text{and} \quad \cos(x/2) = \frac{1}{\sqrt{1+u^2}}$$

Substituting these expressions in (3) and (4) yields

$$\sin x = 2\left(\frac{u}{\sqrt{1+u^2}}\right)\left(\frac{1}{\sqrt{1+u^2}}\right) = \frac{2u}{1+u^2}$$

$$\cos x = \left(\frac{1}{\sqrt{1+u^2}}\right)^2 - \left(\frac{u}{\sqrt{1+u^2}}\right)^2 = \frac{1-u^2}{1+u^2}$$

In summary, we have shown that the substitution $u = \tan(x/2)$ can be implemented in a rational function of $\sin x$ and $\cos x$ by letting

$$\sin x = \frac{2u}{1+u^2}, \quad \cos x = \frac{1-u^2}{1+u^2}, \quad dx = \frac{2}{1+u^2}\,du \tag{5}$$

▶ **Example 5** Evaluate $\displaystyle\int \frac{dx}{1-\sin x+\cos x}$.

***Solution.*** The integrand is a rational function of $\sin x$ and $\cos x$ that does not match any of the formulas in the Endpaper Integral Table, so we make the substitution $u = \tan(x/2)$. Thus, from (5) we obtain

$$\int \frac{dx}{1-\sin x+\cos x} = \int \frac{\dfrac{2\,du}{1+u^2}}{1-\left(\dfrac{2u}{1+u^2}\right)+\left(\dfrac{1-u^2}{1+u^2}\right)}$$

$$= \int \frac{2\,du}{(1+u^2)-2u+(1-u^2)}$$

$$= \int \frac{du}{1-u} = -\ln|1-u| + C = -\ln|1-\tan(x/2)| + C \quad ◀$$

The substitution $u = \tan(x/2)$ will convert any rational function of $\sin x$ and $\cos x$ to an ordinary rational function of $u$. However, the method can lead to cumbersome partial fraction decompositions, so it may be worthwhile to consider other methods as well when hand computations are being used.

## INTEGRATING WITH COMPUTER ALGEBRA SYSTEMS

Integration tables are rapidly giving way to computerized integration using computer algebra systems. However, as with many powerful tools, a knowledgeable operator is an important component of the system.

Sometimes computer algebra systems do not produce the most general form of the indefinite integral. For example, the integral formula

$$\int \frac{dx}{x-1} = \ln|x-1| + C$$

which can be obtained by inspection or by using the substitution $u = x - 1$, is valid for $x > 1$ or for $x < 1$. However, not all computer algebra systems produce this form of the answer. Some typical answers produced by various implementations of *Mathematica*, *Maple*, and the CAS on a handheld calculator are

$$\ln(-1+x), \quad \ln(x-1), \quad \ln(|x-1|)$$

Observe that none of the systems include the constant of integration—the answer produced is a particular antiderivative and not the most general antiderivative (indefinite integral). Observe also that only one of these answers includes the absolute value signs; the antiderivatives produced by the other systems are valid only for $x > 1$. All systems, however, are able to calculate the definite integral

$$\int_0^{1/2} \frac{dx}{x-1} = -\ln 2$$

correctly. Now let us examine how these systems handle the integral

$$\int x\sqrt{x^2-4x+5}\,dx = \tfrac{1}{3}(x^2-x-1)\sqrt{x^2-4x+5} + \ln\left(x-2+\sqrt{x^2-4x+5}\right) \tag{6}$$

which we obtained in Example 2(b) (with the constant of integration included). Some CAS implementations produce this result in slightly different algebraic forms, but a version of *Maple* produces the result

$$\int x\sqrt{x^2-4x+5}\,dx = \tfrac{1}{3}(x^2-4x+5)^{3/2} + \tfrac{1}{2}(2x-4)\sqrt{x^2-4x+5} + \sinh^{-1}(x-2)$$

This can be rewritten as (6) by expressing the fractional exponent in radical form and expressing $\sinh^{-1}(x-2)$ in logarithmic form using Theorem 6.9.4 (verify). A version of *Mathematica* produces the result

$$\int x\sqrt{x^2-4x+5}\,dx = \tfrac{1}{3}(x^2-x-1)\sqrt{x^2-4x+5} - \sinh^{-1}(2-x)$$

which can be rewritten in form (6) by using Theorem 6.9.4 together with the identity $\sinh^{-1}(-x) = -\sinh^{-1}x$ (verify).

Computer algebra systems can sometimes produce inconvenient or unnatural answers to integration problems. For example, various computer algebra systems produced the following results when asked to integrate $(x+1)^7$:

$$\frac{(x+1)^8}{8}, \quad \frac{1}{8}x^8 + x^7 + \frac{7}{2}x^6 + 7x^5 + \frac{35}{4}x^4 + 7x^3 + \frac{7}{2}x^2 + x \tag{7}$$

> Expanding the expression
>
> $$\frac{(x+1)^8}{8}$$
>
> produces a constant term of $\frac{1}{8}$, whereas the second expression in (7) has no constant term. What is the explanation?

The first form is in keeping with the hand computation

$$\int (x+1)^7\,dx = \frac{(x+1)^8}{8} + C$$

that uses the substitution $u = x + 1$, whereas the second form is based on expanding $(x+1)^7$ and integrating term by term.

In Example 2(a) of Section 7.3 we showed that

$$\int \sin^4 x\cos^5 x\,dx = \tfrac{1}{5}\sin^5 x - \tfrac{2}{7}\sin^7 x + \tfrac{1}{9}\sin^9 x + C$$

However, a version of *Mathematica* integrates this as

$$\tfrac{3}{128}\sin x - \tfrac{1}{192}\sin 3x - \tfrac{1}{320}\sin 5x + \tfrac{1}{1792}\sin 7x + \tfrac{1}{2304}\sin 9x$$

whereas other computer algebra systems essentially integrate it as

$$-\tfrac{1}{9}\sin^3 x\cos^6 x - \tfrac{1}{21}\sin x\cos^6 x + \tfrac{1}{105}\cos^4 x\sin x + \tfrac{4}{315}\cos^2 x\sin x + \tfrac{8}{315}\sin x$$

Although these three results look quite different, they can be obtained from one another using appropriate trigonometric identities.

## COMPUTER ALGEBRA SYSTEMS HAVE LIMITATIONS

A computer algebra system combines a set of integration rules (such as substitution) with a library of functions that it can use to construct antiderivatives. Such libraries contain elementary functions, such as polynomials, rational functions, trigonometric functions, as well as various nonelementary functions that arise in engineering, physics, and other applied fields. Just as our Endpaper Integral Table has only 121 indefinite integrals, these libraries are not exhaustive of all possible integrands. If the system cannot manipulate the integrand to a form matching one in its library, the program will give some indication that it cannot evaluate the integral. For example, when asked to evaluate the integral

$$\int (1+\ln x)\sqrt{1+(x\ln x)^2}\,dx \tag{8}$$

all of the systems mentioned above respond by displaying some form of the unevaluated integral as an answer, indicating that they could not perform the integration.

**TECHNOLOGY MASTERY**

Sometimes integrals that cannot be evaluated by a CAS in their given form can be evaluated by first rewriting them in a different form or by making a substitution. If you have a CAS, make a $u$-substitution in (8) that will enable you to evaluate the integral with your CAS. Then evaluate the integral.

Sometimes computer algebra systems respond by expressing an integral in terms of another integral. For example, if you try to integrate $e^{x^2}$ using *Mathematica*, *Maple*, or *Sage*, you will obtain an expression involving erf (which stands for ***error function***). The function erf($x$) is defined as

$$\operatorname{erf}(x) = \frac{2}{\sqrt{\pi}}\int_0^x e^{-t^2}\,dt$$

so all three programs essentially rewrite the given integral in terms of a closely related integral. From one point of view this is what we did in integrating $1/x$, since the natural logarithm function is (formally) defined as

$$\ln x = \int_1^x \frac{1}{t}\,dt$$

(see Section 5.10).

▶ **Example 6** A particle moves along an $x$-axis in such a way that its velocity $v(t)$ at time $t$ is

$$v(t) = 30\cos^7 t\sin^4 t \quad (t \ge 0)$$

Graph the position versus time curve for the particle, given that the particle is at $x = 1$ when $t = 0$.

***Solution.*** Since $dx/dt = v(t)$ and $x = 1$ when $t = 0$, the position function $x(t)$ is given by

$$x(t) = 1 + \int_0^t v(s)\,ds$$

Some computer algebra systems will allow this expression to be entered directly into a command for plotting functions, but it is often more efficient to perform the integration first. The authors' integration utility yields

$$\begin{aligned} x &= \int 30\cos^7 t\sin^4 t\,dt \\ &= -\tfrac{30}{11}\sin^{11} t + 10\sin^9 t - \tfrac{90}{7}\sin^7 t + 6\sin^5 t + C \end{aligned}$$

where we have added the required constant of integration. Using the initial condition $x(0) = 1$, we substitute the values $x = 1$ and $t = 0$ into this equation to find that $C = 1$, so

$$x(t) = -\tfrac{30}{11}\sin^{11} t + 10\sin^9 t - \tfrac{90}{7}\sin^7 t + 6\sin^5 t + 1 \quad (t \ge 0)$$

The graph of $x$ versus $t$ is shown in Figure 7.6.2. ◀

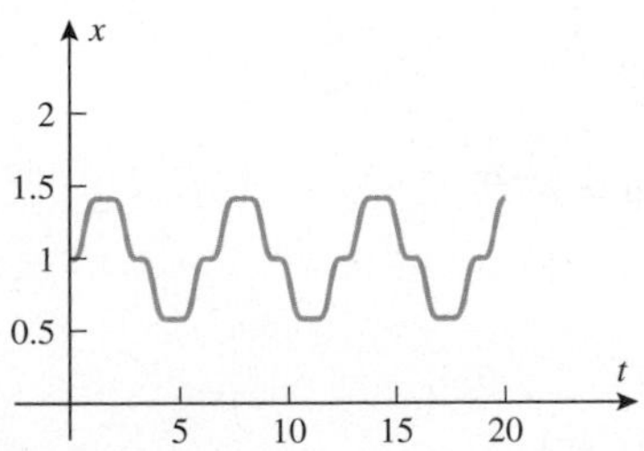


▲ **Figure 7.6.2**

## ✓ QUICK CHECK EXERCISES 7.6 *(See page 454 for answers.)*

1. Find an integral formula in the Endpaper Integral Table that can be used to evaluate the integral. Do not evaluate the integral.
   (a) $\int \frac{2x}{3x+4}\,dx$ ________
   (b) $\int \frac{1}{x\sqrt{5x-4}}\,dx$ ________
   (c) $\int x\sqrt{3x+2}\,dx$ ________
   (d) $\int x^2 \ln x\,dx$ ________
2. In each part, make the indicated $u$-substitution, and then find an integral formula in the Endpaper Integral Table that can be used to evaluate the integral. Do not evaluate the integral.
   (a) $\int \frac{x}{1+e^{x^2}}\,dx;\ u=x^2$ ________
   (b) $\int e^{\sqrt{x}}\,dx;\ u=\sqrt{x}$ ________
   (c) $\int \frac{e^x}{1+\sin(e^x)}\,dx;\ u=e^x$ ________
   (d) $\int \frac{1}{(1-4x^2)^{3/2}}\,dx;\ u=2x$ ________
3. In each part, use the Endpaper Integral Table to evaluate the integral. (If necessary, first make an appropriate substitution or complete the square.)
   (a) $\int \frac{1}{4-x^2}\,dx =$ ________
   (b) $\int \cos 2x \cos x\,dx =$ ________
   (c) $\int \frac{e^{3x}}{\sqrt{1-e^{2x}}}\,dx =$ ________
   (d) $\int \frac{x}{x^2-4x+8}\,dx =$ ________

## EXERCISE SET 7.6 [C] CAS

[C] **1–24** (a) Use the Endpaper Integral Table to evaluate the given integral. (b) If you have a CAS, use it to evaluate the integral, and then confirm that the result is equivalent to the one that you found in part (a). ■

1. $\int \frac{4x}{3x-1}\,dx$
2. $\int \frac{x}{(4-5x)^2}\,dx$
3. $\int \frac{1}{x(2x+5)}\,dx$
4. $\int \frac{1}{x^2(1-5x)}\,dx$
5. $\int x\sqrt{2x+3}\,dx$
6. $\int \frac{x}{\sqrt{2-x}}\,dx$
7. $\int \frac{1}{x\sqrt{4-3x}}\,dx$
8. $\int \frac{1}{x\sqrt{3x-4}}\,dx$
9. $\int \frac{1}{16-x^2}\,dx$
10. $\int \frac{1}{x^2-9}\,dx$
11. $\int \sqrt{x^2-3}\,dx$
12. $\int \frac{\sqrt{x^2-5}}{x^2}\,dx$
13. $\int \frac{x^2}{\sqrt{x^2+4}}\,dx$
14. $\int \frac{1}{x^2\sqrt{x^2-2}}\,dx$
15. $\int \sqrt{9-x^2}\,dx$
16. $\int \frac{\sqrt{4-x^2}}{x^2}\,dx$
17. $\int \frac{\sqrt{4-x^2}}{x}\,dx$
18. $\int \frac{1}{x\sqrt{6x-x^2}}\,dx$
19. $\int \sin 3x \sin 4x\,dx$
20. $\int \sin 2x \cos 5x\,dx$
21. $\int x^3 \ln x\,dx$
22. $\int \frac{\ln x}{\sqrt{x^3}}\,dx$
23. $\int e^{-2x}\sin 3x\,dx$
24. $\int e^x \cos 2x\,dx$

[C] **25–36** (a) Make the indicated $u$-substitution, and then use the Endpaper Integral Table to evaluate the integral. (b) If you have a CAS, use it to evaluate the integral, and then confirm that the result is equivalent to the one that you found in part (a). ■

25. $\int \frac{e^{4x}}{(4-3e^{2x})^2}\,dx,\ u=e^{2x}$
26. $\int \frac{\sin 2x}{(\cos 2x)(3-\cos 2x)}\,dx,\ u=\cos 2x$
27. $\int \frac{1}{\sqrt{x}(9x+4)}\,dx,\ u=3\sqrt{x}$
28. $\int \frac{\cos 4x}{9+\sin^2 4x}\,dx,\ u=\sin 4x$
29. $\int \frac{1}{\sqrt{4x^2-9}}\,dx,\ u=2x$
30. $\int x\sqrt{2x^4+3}\,dx,\ u=\sqrt{2}x^2$
31. $\int \frac{4x^5}{\sqrt{2-4x^4}}\,dx,\ u=2x^2$
32. $\int \frac{1}{x^2\sqrt{3-4x^2}}\,dx,\ u=2x$
33. $\int \frac{\sin^2(\ln x)}{x}\,dx,\ u=\ln x$
34. $\int e^{-2x}\cos^2(e^{-2x})\,dx,\ u=e^{-2x}$
35. $\int xe^{-2x}\,dx,\ u=-2x$
36. $\int \ln(3x+1)\,dx,\ u=3x+1$

C **37–48** (a) Make an appropriate $u$-substitution, and then use the Endpaper Integral Table to evaluate the integral. (b) If you have a CAS, use it to evaluate the integral (no substitution), and then confirm that the result is equivalent to that in part (a).

**37.** $\int \frac{\cos 3x}{(\sin 3x)(\sin 3x + 1)^2}\,dx$

**38.** $\int \frac{\ln x}{x\sqrt{4\ln x - 1}}\,dx$

**39.** $\int \frac{x}{16x^4 - 1}\,dx$

**40.** $\int \frac{e^x}{3 - 4e^{2x}}\,dx$

**41.** $\int e^x\sqrt{3 - 4e^{2x}}\,dx$

**42.** $\int \frac{\sqrt{4 - 9x^2}}{x^2}\,dx$

**43.** $\int \sqrt{5x - 9x^2}\,dx$

**44.** $\int \frac{1}{x\sqrt{x - 5x^2}}\,dx$

**45.** $\int 4x \sin 2x\,dx$

**46.** $\int \cos\sqrt{x}\,dx$

**47.** $\int e^{-\sqrt{x}}\,dx$

**48.** $\int x\ln(2 + x^2)\,dx$

C **49–52** (a) Complete the square, make an appropriate $u$-substitution, and then use the Endpaper Integral Table to evaluate the integral. (b) If you have a CAS, use it to evaluate the integral (no substitution or square completion), and then confirm that the result is equivalent to that in part (a).

**49.** $\int \frac{1}{x^2 + 6x - 7}\,dx$

**50.** $\int \sqrt{3 - 2x - x^2}\,dx$

**51.** $\int \frac{x}{\sqrt{5 + 4x - x^2}}\,dx$

**52.** $\int \frac{x}{x^2 + 6x + 13}\,dx$

C **53–64** (a) Make an appropriate $u$-substitution of the form $u = x^{1/n}$ or $u = (x + a)^{1/n}$, and then evaluate the integral. (b) If you have a CAS, use it to evaluate the integral, and then confirm that the result is equivalent to the one that you found in part (a).

**53.** $\int x\sqrt{x - 2}\,dx$

**54.** $\int \frac{x}{\sqrt{x + 1}}\,dx$

**55.** $\int x^5\sqrt{x^3 + 1}\,dx$

**56.** $\int \frac{1}{x\sqrt{x^3 - 1}}\,dx$

**57.** $\int \frac{dx}{x - \sqrt[3]{x}}$

**58.** $\int \frac{dx}{\sqrt{x} + \sqrt[3]{x}}$

**59.** $\int \frac{dx}{x(1 - x^{1/4})}$

**60.** $\int \frac{\sqrt{x}}{x + 1}\,dx$

**61.** $\int \frac{dx}{x^{1/2} - x^{1/3}}$

**62.** $\int \frac{1 + \sqrt{x}}{1 - \sqrt{x}}\,dx$

**63.** $\int \frac{x^3}{\sqrt{1 + x^2}}\,dx$

**64.** $\int \frac{x}{(x + 3)^{1/5}}\,dx$

C **65–70** (a) Make $u$-substitution (5) to convert the integrand to a rational function of $u$, and then evaluate the integral. (b) If you have a CAS, use it to evaluate the integral (no substitution), and then confirm that the result is equivalent to that in part (a).

**65.** $\int \frac{dx}{1 + \sin x + \cos x}$

**66.** $\int \frac{dx}{2 + \sin x}$

**67.** $\int \frac{d\theta}{1 - \cos\theta}$

**68.** $\int \frac{dx}{4\sin x - 3\cos x}$

**69.** $\int \frac{dx}{\sin x + \tan x}$

**70.** $\int \frac{\sin x}{\sin x + \tan x}\,dx$

**71–72** Use any method to solve for $x$.

**71.** $\int_2^x \frac{1}{t(4 - t)}\,dt = 0.5,\ 2 < x < 4$

**72.** $\int_1^x \frac{1}{t\sqrt{2t - 1}}\,dt = 1,\ x > \frac{1}{2}$

**73–76** Use any method to find the area of the region enclosed by the curves.

**73.** $y = \sqrt{25 - x^2},\ y = 0,\ x = 0,\ x = 4$

**74.** $y = \sqrt{9x^2 - 4},\ y = 0,\ x = 2$

**75.** $y = \frac{1}{25 - 16x^2},\ y = 0,\ x = 0,\ x = 1$

**76.** $y = \sqrt{x}\ln x,\ y = 0,\ x = 4$

**77–80** Use any method to find the volume of the solid generated when the region enclosed by the curves is revolved about the $y$-axis.

**77.** $y = \cos x,\ y = 0,\ x = 0,\ x = \pi/2$

**78.** $y = \sqrt{x - 4},\ y = 0,\ x = 8$

**79.** $y = e^{-x},\ y = 0,\ x = 0,\ x = 3$

**80.** $y = \ln x,\ y = 0,\ x = 5$

**81–82** Use any method to find the arc length of the curve.

**81.** $y = 2x^2,\ 0 \le x \le 2$

**82.** $y = 3\ln x,\ 1 \le x \le 3$

**83–84** Use any method to find the area of the surface generated by revolving the curve about the $x$-axis.

**83.** $y = \sin x,\ 0 \le x \le \pi$

**84.** $y = 1/x,\ 1 \le x \le 4$

C **85–86** Information is given about the motion of a particle moving along a coordinate line.

(a) Use a CAS to find the position function of the particle for $t \ge 0$.

(b) Graph the position versus time curve.

**85.** $v(t) = 20\cos^6 t\sin^3 t,\ s(0) = 2$

**86.** $a(t) = e^{-t}\sin 2t\sin 4t,\ v(0) = 0,\ s(0) = 10$

**FOCUS ON CONCEPTS**

**87.** (a) Use the substitution $u = \tan(x/2)$ to show that

$$\int \sec x\,dx = \ln\left|\frac{1 + \tan(x/2)}{1 - \tan(x/2)}\right| + C$$

and confirm that this is consistent with Formula (22) of Section 7.3.

(b) Use the result in part (a) to show that

$$\int \sec x\,dx = \ln\left|\tan\left(\frac{\pi}{4} + \frac{x}{2}\right)\right| + C$$

**88.** Use the substitution $u = \tan(x/2)$ to show that

$$\int \csc x\,dx = \frac{1}{2}\ln\left[\frac{1-\cos x}{1+\cos x}\right] + C$$

and confirm that this is consistent with the result in Exercise 65(a) of Section 7.3.

**89.** Find a substitution that can be used to integrate rational functions of $\sinh x$ and $\cosh x$ and use your substitution to evaluate

$$\int \frac{dx}{2\cosh x + \sinh x}$$

without expressing the integrand in terms of $e^x$ and $e^{-x}$.

C **90–93** Some integrals that can be evaluated by hand cannot be evaluated by all computer algebra systems. Evaluate the integral by hand, and determine if it can be evaluated on your CAS. ■

**90.** $\displaystyle\int \frac{x^3}{\sqrt{1-x^8}}\,dx$

**91.** $\displaystyle\int (\cos^{32} x \sin^{30} x - \cos^{30} x \sin^{32} x)\,dx$

**92.** $\displaystyle\int \sqrt{x - \sqrt{x^2-4}}\,dx$ [*Hint:* $\frac{1}{2}(\sqrt{x+2} - \sqrt{x-2})^2 = ?$]

**93.** $\displaystyle\int \frac{1}{x^{10}+x}\,dx$

[*Hint:* Rewrite the denominator as $x^{10}(1+x^{-9})$.]

C **94.** Let

$$f(x) = \frac{-2x^5 + 26x^4 + 15x^3 + 6x^2 + 20x + 43}{x^6 - x^5 - 18x^4 - 2x^3 - 39x^2 - x - 20}$$

(a) Use a CAS to factor the denominator, and then write down the form of the partial fraction decomposition. You need not find the values of the constants.

(b) Check your answer in part (a) by using the CAS to find the partial fraction decomposition of $f$.

(c) Integrate $f$ by hand, and then check your answer by integrating with the CAS.

✓ **QUICK CHECK ANSWERS 7.6** 1. (a) Formula (60) (b) Formula (108) (c) Formula (102) (d) Formula (50) 2. (a) Formula (25) (b) Formula (51) (c) Formula (18) (d) Formula (97) 3. (a) $\frac{1}{4}\ln\left|\frac{x+2}{x-2}\right| + C$ (b) $\frac{1}{6}\sin 3x + \frac{1}{2}\sin x + C$ (c) $-\frac{e^x}{2}\sqrt{1-e^{2x}} + \frac{1}{2}\sin^{-1} e^x + C$ (d) $\frac{1}{2}\ln(x^2-4x+8) + \tan^{-1}\frac{x-2}{2} + C$

# 7.7 NUMERICAL INTEGRATION; SIMPSON'S RULE

*If it is necessary to evaluate a definite integral of a function for which an antiderivative cannot be found, then one must settle for some kind of numerical approximation of the integral. In Section 5.4 we considered three such approximations in the context of areas—left endpoint approximation, right endpoint approximation, and midpoint approximation. In this section we will extend those methods to general definite integrals, and we will develop some new methods that often provide more accuracy with less computation. We will also discuss the errors that arise in integral approximations.*

## ■ A REVIEW OF RIEMANN SUM APPROXIMATIONS

Recall from Section 5.5 that the definite integral of a continuous function $f$ over an interval $[a, b]$ may be computed as

$$\int_a^b f(x)\,dx = \lim_{\max \Delta x_k \to 0} \sum_{k=1}^{n} f(x_k^*)\Delta x_k$$

where the sum that appears on the right side is called a Riemann sum. In this formula, $\Delta x_k$ is the width of the $k$th subinterval of a partition $a = x_0 < x_1 < x_2 < \cdots < x_n = b$ of $[a, b]$ into $n$ subintervals, and $x_k^*$ denotes an arbitrary point in the $k$th subinterval. If we take all subintervals of the same width, so that $\Delta x_k = (b-a)/n$, then as $n$ increases the Riemann sum will eventually be a good approximation to the definite integral. We denote this by writing

$$\int_a^b f(x)\,dx \approx \left(\frac{b-a}{n}\right)[f(x_1^*) + f(x_2^*) + \cdots + f(x_n^*)] \tag{1}$$

If we denote the values of $f$ at the endpoints of the subintervals by

$$y_0 = f(a), \quad y_1 = f(x_1), \quad y_2 = f(x_2), \ldots, y_{n-1} = f(x_{n-1}), \quad y_n = f(x_n)$$

and the values of $f$ at the midpoints of the subintervals by

$$y_{m_1}, y_{m_2}, \ldots, y_{m_n}$$

then it follows from (1) that the left endpoint, right endpoint, and midpoint approximations discussed in Section 5.4 can be expressed as shown in Table 7.7.1. Although we originally obtained these results for nonnegative functions in the context of approximating areas, they are applicable to any function that is continuous on $[a, b]$.

**Table 7.7.1**

| LEFT ENDPOINT APPROXIMATION | RIGHT ENDPOINT APPROXIMATION | MIDPOINT APPROXIMATION |
|---|---|---|
| $\int_a^b f(x)\,dx \approx \left(\frac{b-a}{n}\right)[y_0 + y_1 + \cdots + y_{n-1}]$ | $\int_a^b f(x)\,dx \approx \left(\frac{b-a}{n}\right)[y_1 + y_2 + \cdots + y_n]$ | $\int_a^b f(x)\,dx \approx \left(\frac{b-a}{n}\right)[y_{m_1} + y_{m_2} + \cdots + y_{m_n}]$ |
| 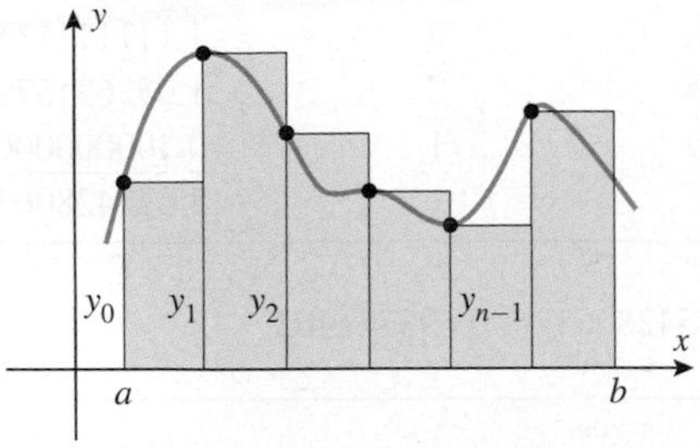 | 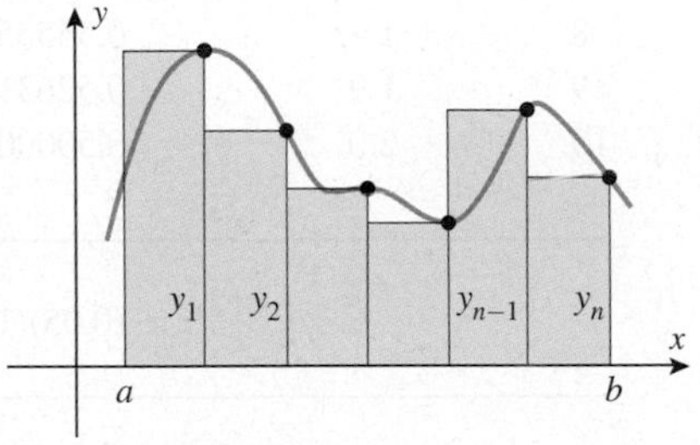 | 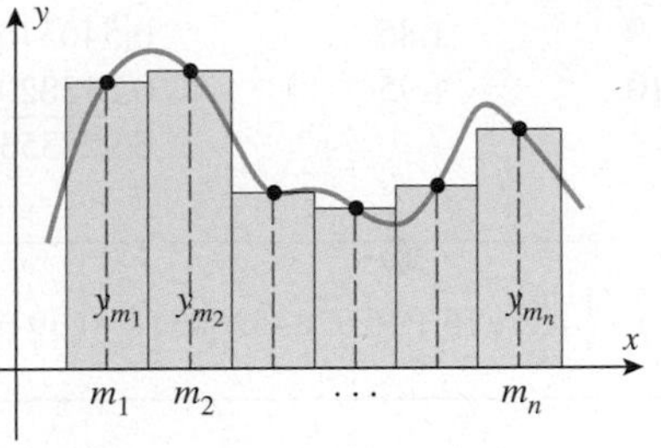 |







## TRAPEZOIDAL APPROXIMATION

It will be convenient in this section to denote the left endpoint, right endpoint, and midpoint approximations with $n$ subintervals by $L_n$, $R_n$, and $M_n$, respectively. Of the three approximations, the midpoint approximation is most widely used in applications. If we take the average of $L_n$ and $R_n$, then we obtain another important approximation denoted by

$$T_n = \tfrac{1}{2}(L_n + R_n)$$

called the ***trapezoidal approximation***:

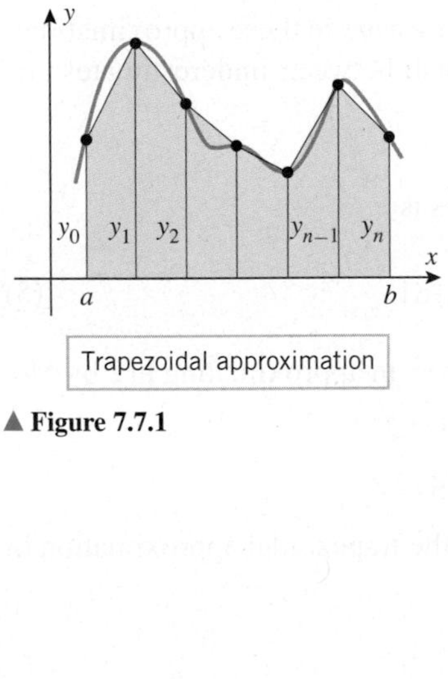


Trapezoidal approximation

▲ **Figure 7.7.1**

***Trapezoidal Approximation***

$$\int_a^b f(x)\,dx \approx T_n = \left(\frac{b-a}{2n}\right)[y_0 + 2y_1 + \cdots + 2y_{n-1} + y_n] \qquad (2)$$

The name "trapezoidal approximation" results from the fact that in the case where $f$ is nonnegative on the interval of integration, the approximation $T_n$ is the sum of the trapezoidal areas shown in Figure 7.7.1 (see Exercise 51).

▶ **Example 1** In Table 7.7.2 we have approximated

$$\ln 2 = \int_1^2 \frac{1}{x}\,dx$$

using the midpoint approximation and the trapezoidal approximation.* In each case we used $n = 10$ subdivisions of the interval $[1, 2]$, so that

$$\underbrace{\frac{b-a}{n} = \frac{2-1}{10} = 0.1}_{\text{Midpoint}} \quad \text{and} \quad \underbrace{\frac{b-a}{2n} = \frac{2-1}{20} = 0.05}_{\text{Trapezoidal}} \quad ◀$$

*Throughout this section we will show numerical values to nine places to the right of the decimal point. If your calculating utility does not show this many places, then you will need to make the appropriate adjustments. What is important here is that you understand the principles being discussed.

**Table 7.7.2**

MIDPOINT AND TRAPEZOIDAL APPROXIMATIONS FOR $\int_1^2 \frac{1}{x}\,dx$

| MIDPOINT APPROXIMATION | | | TRAPEZOIDAL APPROXIMATION | | | | |
|---|---|---|---|---|---|---|---|
| $i$ | MIDPOINT $m_i$ | $y_{m_i} = f(m_i) = 1/m_i$ | $i$ | ENDPOINT $x_i$ | $y_i = f(x_i) = 1/x_i$ | MULTIPLIER $w_i$ | $w_i y_i$ |
| 1 | 1.05 | 0.952380952 | 0 | 1.0 | 1.000000000 | 1 | 1.000000000 |
| 2 | 1.15 | 0.869565217 | 1 | 1.1 | 0.909090909 | 2 | 1.818181818 |
| 3 | 1.25 | 0.800000000 | 2 | 1.2 | 0.833333333 | 2 | 1.666666667 |
| 4 | 1.35 | 0.740740741 | 3 | 1.3 | 0.769230769 | 2 | 1.538461538 |
| 5 | 1.45 | 0.689655172 | 4 | 1.4 | 0.714285714 | 2 | 1.428571429 |
| 6 | 1.55 | 0.645161290 | 5 | 1.5 | 0.666666667 | 2 | 1.333333333 |
| 7 | 1.65 | 0.606060606 | 6 | 1.6 | 0.625000000 | 2 | 1.250000000 |
| 8 | 1.75 | 0.571428571 | 7 | 1.7 | 0.588235294 | 2 | 1.176470588 |
| 9 | 1.85 | 0.540540541 | 8 | 1.8 | 0.555555556 | 2 | 1.111111111 |
| 10 | 1.95 | 0.512820513 | 9 | 1.9 | 0.526315789 | 2 | 1.052631579 |
| | | 6.928353603 | 10 | 2.0 | 0.500000000 | 1 | 0.500000000 |
| | | | | | | | 13.875428063 |
| $\int_1^2 \frac{1}{x}\,dx \approx (0.1)(6.928353603) \approx 0.692835360$ | | | $\int_1^2 \frac{1}{x}\,dx \approx (0.05)(13.875428063) \approx 0.693771403$ | | | | |

## COMPARISON OF THE MIDPOINT AND TRAPEZOIDAL APPROXIMATIONS

We define the ***errors*** in the midpoint and trapezoidal approximations to be

$$E_M = \int_a^b f(x)\,dx - M_n \quad \text{and} \quad E_T = \int_a^b f(x)\,dx - T_n \qquad (3\text{–}4)$$

respectively, and we define $|E_M|$ and $|E_T|$ to be the ***absolute errors*** in these approximations. The absolute errors are nonnegative and do not distinguish between underestimates and overestimates.

By rewriting (3) and (4) in the form

$$\int_a^b f(x)\,dx = \text{approximation} + \text{error}$$

we see that positive values of $E_M$ and $E_T$ correspond to underestimates and negative values to overestimates.

▶ **Example 2** The value of ln 2 to nine decimal places is

$$\ln 2 = \int_1^2 \frac{1}{x}\,dx \approx 0.693147181 \qquad (5)$$

so we see from Tables 7.7.2 and 7.7.3 that the absolute errors in approximating ln 2 by $M_{10}$ and $T_{10}$ are

$$|E_M| = |\ln 2 - M_{10}| \approx 0.000311821$$
$$|E_T| = |\ln 2 - T_{10}| \approx 0.000624222$$

Thus, the midpoint approximation is more accurate than the trapezoidal approximation in this case. ◀

**Table 7.7.3**

| ln 2 (NINE DECIMAL PLACES) | APPROXIMATION | ERROR |
|---|---|---|
| 0.693147181 | $M_{10} \approx 0.692835360$ | $E_M = \ln 2 - M_{10} \approx 0.000311821$ |
| 0.693147181 | $T_{10} \approx 0.693771403$ | $E_T = \ln 2 - T_{10} \approx -0.000624222$ |

It is not accidental in Example 2 that the midpoint approximation of ln 2 was more accurate than the trapezoidal approximation. To see why this is so, we first need to look at the midpoint approximation from another point of view. To simplify our explanation, we will assume that $f$ is nonnegative on $[a, b]$, though the conclusions we reach will be true without this assumption.

If $f$ is a differentiable function, then the midpoint approximation is sometimes called the ***tangent line approximation*** because for each subinterval of $[a, b]$ the area of the rectangle used in the midpoint approximation is equal to the area of the trapezoid whose upper boundary is the tangent line to $y = f(x)$ at the midpoint of the subinterval (Figure 7.7.2). The equality of these areas follows from the fact that the shaded areas in the figure are congruent. We will now show how this point of view about midpoint approximations can be used to establish useful criteria for determining which of $M_n$ or $T_n$ produces the better approximation of a given integral.

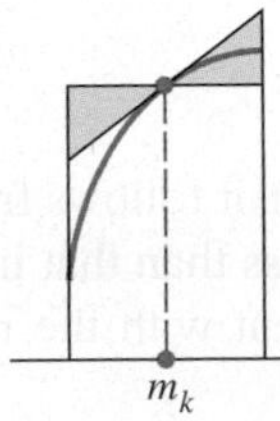


The shaded triangles have equal areas.

▲ **Figure 7.7.2**

In Figure 7.7.3*a* we have isolated a subinterval of $[a, b]$ on which the graph of a function $f$ is concave down, and we have shaded the areas that represent the errors in the midpoint and trapezoidal approximations over the subinterval. In Figure 7.7.3*b* we show a succession of four illustrations which make it evident that the error from the midpoint approximation is less than that from the trapezoidal approximation. If the graph of $f$ were concave up, analogous figures would lead to the same conclusion. (This argument, due to Frank Buck, appeared in *The College Mathematics Journal*, Vol. 16, No. 1, 1985.)

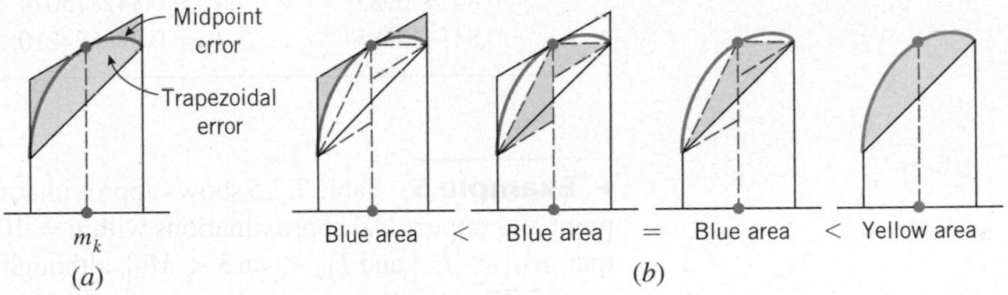


▲ **Figure 7.7.3**

Justify the conclusions in each step of Figure 7.7.3*b*.

Figure 7.7.3*a* also suggests that on a subinterval where the graph is concave down, the midpoint approximation is larger than the value of the integral and the trapezoidal approximation is smaller. On an interval where the graph is concave up it is the other way around. In summary, we have the following result, which we state without formal proof:

**7.7.1 THEOREM** *Let $f$ be continuous on $[a, b]$, and let $|E_M|$ and $|E_T|$ be the absolute errors that result from the midpoint and trapezoidal approximations of $\int_a^b f(x)\,dx$ using $n$ subintervals.*

(*a*) *If the graph of $f$ is either concave up or concave down on $(a, b)$, then $|E_M| < |E_T|$, that is, the absolute error from the midpoint approximation is less than that from the trapezoidal approximation.*

(*b*) *If the graph of $f$ is concave down on $(a, b)$, then*

$$T_n < \int_a^b f(x)\,dx < M_n$$

(*c*) *If the graph of $f$ is concave up on $(a, b)$, then*

$$M_n < \int_a^b f(x)\,dx < T_n$$

▶ **Example 3** Since the graph of $f(x) = 1/x$ is continuous on the interval $[1, 2]$ and concave up on the interval $(1, 2)$, it follows from part (*a*) of Theorem 7.7.1 that $M_n$ will always provide a better approximation than $T_n$ for

$$\int_1^2 \frac{1}{x}\,dx = \ln 2$$

Moreover, if follows from part (c) of Theorem 7.7.1 that $M_n < \ln 2 < T_n$ for every positive integer $n$. Note that this is consistent with our computations in Example 2. ◂

**WARNING**

Do not conclude that the midpoint approximation is always better than the trapezoidal approximation; the trapezoidal approximation may be better if the function changes concavity on the interval of integration.

▸ **Example 4** The midpoint and trapezoidal approximations can be used to approximate sin 1 by using the integral

$$\sin 1 = \int_0^1 \cos x\, dx$$

Since $f(x) = \cos x$ is continuous on $[0, 1]$ and concave down on $(0, 1)$, it follows from parts (a) and (b) of Theorem 7.7.1 that the absolute error in $M_n$ will be less than that in $T_n$, and that $T_n < \sin 1 < M_n$ for every positive integer $n$. This is consistent with the results in Table 7.7.4 for $n = 5$ (intermediate computations are omitted). ◂

**Table 7.7.4**

| sin 1 (NINE DECIMAL PLACES) | APPROXIMATION | ERROR |
|---|---|---|
| 0.841470985 | $M_5 \approx 0.842875074$ | $E_M = \sin 1 - M_5 \approx -0.001404089$ |
| 0.841470985 | $T_5 \approx 0.838664210$ | $E_T = \sin 1 - T_5 \approx 0.002806775$ |

▸ **Example 5** Table 7.7.5 shows approximations for $\sin 3 = \int_0^3 \cos x\, dx$ using the midpoint and trapezoidal approximations with $n = 10$ subdivisions of the interval $[0, 3]$. Note that $|E_M| < |E_T|$ and $T_{10} < \sin 3 < M_{10}$, although these results are not guaranteed by Theorem 7.7.1 since $f(x) = \cos x$ changes concavity on the interval $[0, 3]$. ◂

**Table 7.7.5**

| sin 3 (NINE DECIMAL PLACES) | APPROXIMATION | ERROR |
|---|---|---|
| 0.141120008 | $M_{10} \approx 0.141650601$ | $E_M = \sin 3 - M_{10} \approx -0.000530592$ |
| 0.141120008 | $T_{10} \approx 0.140060017$ | $E_T = \sin 3 - T_{10} \approx 0.001059991$ |

## SIMPSON'S RULE

When the left and right endpoint approximations are averaged to produce the trapezoidal approximation, a better approximation often results. We now see how a weighted average of the midpoint and trapezoidal approximations can yield an even better approximation.

The numerical evidence in Tables 7.7.3, 7.7.4, and 7.7.5 reveals that $E_T \approx -2E_M$, so that $2E_M + E_T \approx 0$ in these instances. This suggests that

$$\begin{aligned} 3\int_a^b f(x)\,dx &= 2\int_a^b f(x)\,dx + \int_a^b f(x)\,dx \\ &= 2(M_k + E_M) + (T_k + E_T) \\ &= (2M_k + T_k) + (2E_M + E_T) \\ &\approx 2M_k + T_k \end{aligned}$$

This gives

$$\int_a^b f(x)\,dx \approx \tfrac{1}{3}(2M_k + T_k) \tag{6}$$

The midpoint approximation $M_k$ in (6) requires the evaluation of $f$ at $k$ points in the interval $[a, b]$, and the trapezoidal approximation $T_k$ in (6) requires the evaluation of $f$ at $k + 1$ points in $[a, b]$. Thus, $\frac{1}{3}(2M_k + T_k)$ uses $2k + 1$ values of $f$, taken at equally spaced points in the interval $[a, b]$. These points are obtained by partitioning $[a, b]$ into $2k$ equal subintervals indicated by the left endpoints, right endpoints, and midpoints used in $T_k$ and $M_k$,

**WARNING**

Note that in (7) the subscript $n$ in $S_n$ is always *even* since it is twice the value of the subscripts for the corresponding midpoint and trapezoidal approximations. For example,

$$S_{10} = \tfrac{1}{3}(2M_5 + T_5)$$

and

$$S_{20} = \tfrac{1}{3}(2M_{10} + T_{10})$$

respectively. Setting $n = 2k$, we use $S_n$ to denote the weighted average of $M_k$ and $T_k$ in (6). That is,

$$S_n = S_{2k} = \tfrac{1}{3}(2M_k + T_k) \quad \text{or} \quad S_n = \tfrac{1}{3}(2M_{n/2} + T_{n/2}) \tag{7}$$

Table 7.7.6 displays the approximations $S_n$ corresponding to the data in Tables 7.7.3 to 7.7.5.

**Table 7.7.6**

| FUNCTION VALUE (NINE DECIMAL PLACES) | APPROXIMATION | ERROR |
|---|---|---|
| $\ln 2 \approx 0.693147181$ | $\int_1^2 (1/x)\,dx \approx S_{20} = \frac{1}{3}(2M_{10} + T_{10}) \approx 0.693147375$ | –0.000000194 |
| $\sin 1 \approx 0.841470985$ | $\int_0^1 \cos x\,dx \approx S_{10} = \frac{1}{3}(2M_5 + T_5) \approx 0.841471453$ | –0.000000468 |
| $\sin 3 \approx 0.141120008$ | $\int_0^3 \cos x\,dx \approx S_{20} = \frac{1}{3}(2M_{10} + T_{10}) \approx 0.141120406$ | –0.000000398 |

Using the midpoint approximation formula in Table 7.7.1 and Formula (2) for the trapezoidal approximation, we can derive a similar formula for $S_n$. We start by partitioning the interval $[a, b]$ into an *even* number of equal subintervals. If $n$ is the number of subintervals, then each subinterval has length $(b - a)/n$. Label the endpoints of these subintervals successively by $a = x_0, x_1, x_2, \ldots, x_n = b$. Then $x_0, x_2, x_4, \ldots, x_n$ define a partition of $[a, b]$ into $n/2$ equal intervals, each of length $2(b - a)/n$, and the midpoints of these subintervals are $x_1, x_3, x_5, \ldots, x_{n-1}$, respectively, as illustrated in Figure 7.7.4. Using $y_i = f(x_i)$, we have

$$\begin{aligned} 2M_{n/2} &= 2\left(\frac{2(b-a)}{n}\right)[y_1 + y_3 + \cdots + y_{n-1}] \\ &= \left(\frac{b-a}{n}\right)[4y_1 + 4y_3 + \cdots + 4y_{n-1}] \end{aligned}$$

Noting that $(b - a)/[2(n/2)] = (b - a)/n$, we can express $T_{n/2}$ as

$$T_{n/2} = \left(\frac{b-a}{n}\right)[y_0 + 2y_2 + 2y_4 + \cdots + 2y_{n-2} + y_n]$$

Thus, $S_n = \frac{1}{3}(2M_{n/2} + T_{n/2})$ can be expressed as

$$S_n = \frac{1}{3}\left(\frac{b-a}{n}\right)[y_0 + 4y_1 + 2y_2 + 4y_3 + 2y_4 + \cdots + 2y_{n-2} + 4y_{n-1} + y_n] \tag{8}$$

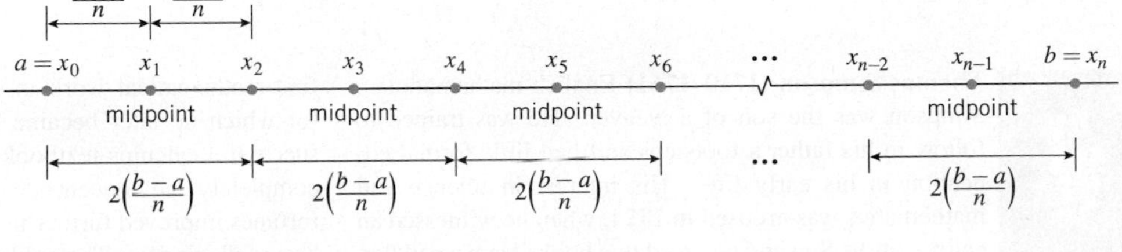


▶ **Figure 7.7.4**

The approximation

$$\int_a^b f(x)\,dx \approx S_n \tag{9}$$

with $S_n$ as given in (8) is known as ***Simpson's rule***. We denote the error in this approximation by

$$E_S = \int_a^b f(x)\,dx - S_n \tag{10}$$

As before, the absolute error in the approximation (9) is given by $|E_S|$.

► **Example 6** In Table 7.7.7 we have used Simpson's rule with $n = 10$ subintervals to obtain the approximation

$$\ln 2 = \int_1^2 \frac{1}{x}\,dx \approx S_{10} = 0.693150231$$

For this approximation,

$$\frac{1}{3}\left(\frac{b-a}{n}\right) = \frac{1}{3}\left(\frac{2-1}{10}\right) = \frac{1}{30}$$

**Table 7.7.7**

AN APPROXIMATION TO ln 2 USING SIMPSON'S RULE

| $i$ | ENDPOINT $x_i$ | $y_i = f(x_i) = 1/x_i$ | MULTIPLIER $w_i$ | $w_i y_i$ |
|---|---|---|---|---|
| 0 | 1.0 | 1.000000000 | 1 | 1.000000000 |
| 1 | 1.1 | 0.909090909 | 4 | 3.636363636 |
| 2 | 1.2 | 0.833333333 | 2 | 1.666666667 |
| 3 | 1.3 | 0.769230769 | 4 | 3.076923077 |
| 4 | 1.4 | 0.714285714 | 2 | 1.428571429 |
| 5 | 1.5 | 0.666666667 | 4 | 2.666666667 |
| 6 | 1.6 | 0.625000000 | 2 | 1.250000000 |
| 7 | 1.7 | 0.588235294 | 4 | 2.352941176 |
| 8 | 1.8 | 0.555555556 | 2 | 1.111111111 |
| 9 | 1.9 | 0.526315789 | 4 | 2.105263158 |
| 10 | 2.0 | 0.500000000 | 1 | 0.500000000 |
| | | | | 20.794506921 |

$$\int_1^2 \frac{1}{x}\,dx \approx \left(\tfrac{1}{30}\right)(20.794506921) \approx 0.693150231$$

Although $S_{10}$ is a weighted average of $M_5$ and $T_5$, it makes sense to compare $S_{10}$ to $M_{10}$ and $T_{10}$, since the sums for these three approximations involve the same number of terms. Using the values for $M_{10}$ and $T_{10}$ from Example 2 and the value for $S_{10}$ in Table 7.7.7, we have

$$|E_M| = |\ln 2 - M_{10}| \approx |0.693147181 - 0.692835360| = 0.000311821$$

$$|E_T| = |\ln 2 - T_{10}| \approx |0.693147181 - 0.693771403| = 0.000624222$$

$$|E_S| = |\ln 2 - S_{10}| \approx |0.693147181 - 0.693150231| = 0.000003050$$

Comparing these absolute errors, it is clear that $S_{10}$ is a much more accurate approximation of ln 2 than either $M_{10}$ or $T_{10}$. ◄

**Thomas Simpson (1710–1761)** English mathematician. Simpson was the son of a weaver. He was trained to follow in his father's footsteps and had little formal education in his early life. His interest in science and mathematics was aroused in 1724, when he witnessed an eclipse of the Sun and received two books from a peddler, one on astrology and the other on arithmetic. Simpson quickly absorbed their contents and soon became a successful local fortune teller. His improved financial situation enabled him to give up weaving and marry his landlady. Then in 1733 some mysterious "unfortunate incident" forced him to move. He settled in Derby, where he taught in an evening school and worked at weaving during the day. In 1736 he moved to London and published his first mathematical work in a periodical called the *Ladies' Diary* (of which he later became the editor). In 1737 he published a successful calculus textbook that enabled him to give up weaving completely and concentrate on textbook writing and teaching. His fortunes improved further in 1740 when one Robert Heath accused him of plagiarism. The publicity was marvelous, and Simpson proceeded to dash off a succession of best-selling textbooks: *Algebra* (ten editions plus translations), *Geometry* (twelve editions plus translations), *Trigonometry* (five editions plus translations), and numerous others. It is interesting to note that Simpson did not discover the rule that bears his name—it was a well-known result by Simpson's time.

*[Image: © John Wiley & Sons, Inc; drawn by Patrick Francisco]*

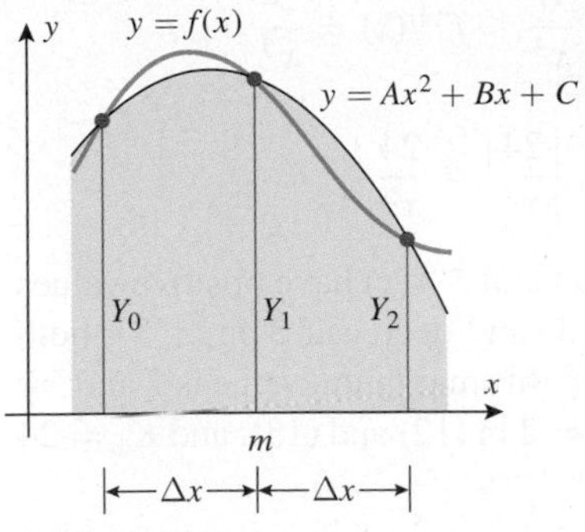


▲ **Figure 7.7.5**

## GEOMETRIC INTERPRETATION OF SIMPSON'S RULE

The midpoint (or tangent line) approximation and the trapezoidal approximation for a definite integral are based on approximating a segment of the curve $y = f(x)$ by line segments. Intuition suggests that we might improve on these approximations using parabolic arcs rather than line segments, thereby accounting for concavity of the curve $y = f(x)$ more closely.

At the heart of this idea is a formula, sometimes called the ***one-third rule***. The one-third rule expresses a definite integral of a quadratic function $g(x) = Ax^2 + Bx + C$ in terms of the values $Y_0$, $Y_1$, and $Y_2$ of $g$ at the left endpoint, midpoint, and right endpoint, respectively, of the interval of integration $[m - \Delta x, m + \Delta x]$ (see Figure 7.7.5):

$$\int_{m-\Delta x}^{m+\Delta x} (Ax^2 + Bx + C)\,dx = \frac{\Delta x}{3}[Y_0 + 4Y_1 + Y_2] \tag{11}$$

Verification of the one-third rule is left for the reader (Exercise 53). By applying the one-third rule to subintervals $[x_{2k-2}, x_{2k}]$, $k = 1, \ldots, n/2$, one arrives at Formula (8) for Simpson's rule (Exercise 54). Thus, Simpson's rule corresponds to the integral of a piecewise-quadratic approximation to $f(x)$.

## ERROR BOUNDS

With all the methods studied in this section, there are two sources of error: the *intrinsic* or *truncation error* due to the approximation formula, and the *roundoff error* introduced in the calculations. In general, increasing $n$ reduces the truncation error but increases the roundoff error, since more computations are required for larger $n$. In practical applications, it is important to know how large $n$ must be taken to ensure that a specified degree of accuracy is obtained. The analysis of roundoff error is complicated and will not be considered here. However, the following theorems, which are proved in books on numerical analysis, provide upper bounds on the truncation errors in the midpoint, trapezoidal, and Simpson's rule approximations.

**7.7.2 THEOREM** ***(Midpoint and Trapezoidal Error Bounds)*** *If $f''$ is continuous on $[a, b]$ and if $K_2$ is the maximum value of $|f''(x)|$ on $[a, b]$, then*

$$(a)\quad |E_M| = \left|\int_a^b f(x)\,dx - M_n\right| \le \frac{(b-a)^3K_2}{24n^2} \tag{12}$$

$$(b)\quad |E_T| = \left|\int_a^b f(x)\,dx - T_n\right| \le \frac{(b-a)^3K_2}{12n^2} \tag{13}$$

**7.7.3 THEOREM** ***(Simpson Error Bound)*** *If $f^{(4)}$ is continuous on $[a, b]$ and if $K_4$ is the maximum value of $|f^{(4)}(x)|$ on $[a, b]$, then*

$$|E_S| = \left|\int_a^b f(x)\,dx - S_n\right| \le \frac{(b-a)^5K_4}{180n^4} \tag{14}$$

▶ **Example 7** Find an upper bound on the absolute error that results from approximating

$$\ln 2 = \int_1^2 \frac{1}{x}\,dx$$

using (a) the midpoint approximation $M_{10}$, (b) the trapezoidal approximation $T_{10}$, and (c) Simpson's rule $S_{10}$, each with $n = 10$ subintervals.

***Solution.*** We will apply Formulas (12), (13), and (14) with

$$f(x) = \frac{1}{x}, \quad a = 1, \quad b = 2, \quad \text{and} \quad n = 10$$

We have

$$f'(x) = -\frac{1}{x^2}, \quad f''(x) = \frac{2}{x^3}, \quad f'''(x) = -\frac{6}{x^4}, \quad f^{(4)}(x) = \frac{24}{x^5}$$

Thus,

$$|f''(x)| = \left|\frac{2}{x^3}\right| = \frac{2}{x^3}, \quad |f^{(4)}(x)| = \left|\frac{24}{x^5}\right| = \frac{24}{x^5}$$

Note that the upper bounds calculated in Example 7 are consistent with the values $|E_M|$, $|E_T|$, and $|E_S|$ calculated in Example 6 but are considerably greater than those values. It is quite common that the upper bounds on the absolute errors given in Theorems 7.7.2 and 7.7.3 substantially exceed the actual absolute errors. However, that does not diminish the utility of these bounds.

where we have dropped the absolute values because $f''(x)$ and $f^{(4)}(x)$ have positive values for $1 \le x \le 2$. Since $|f''(x)|$ and $|f^{(4)}(x)|$ are continuous and decreasing on $[1, 2]$, both functions have their maximum values at $x = 1$; for $|f''(x)|$ this maximum value is 2 and for $|f^{(4)}(x)|$ the maximum value is 24. Thus we can take $K_2 = 2$ in (12) and (13), and $K_4 = 24$ in (14). This yields

$$|E_M| \le \frac{(b-a)^3 K_2}{24n^2} = \frac{1^3 \cdot 2}{24 \cdot 10^2} \approx 0.000833333$$

$$|E_T| \le \frac{(b-a)^3 K_2}{12n^2} = \frac{1^3 \cdot 2}{12 \cdot 10^2} \approx 0.001666667$$

$$|E_S| \le \frac{(b-a)^5 K_4}{180n^4} = \frac{1^5 \cdot 24}{180 \cdot 10^4} \approx 0.000013333 \blacktriangleleft$$

► **Example 8** How many subintervals should be used in approximating

$$\ln 2 = \int_1^2 \frac{1}{x}\,dx$$

by Simpson's rule for five decimal-place accuracy?

***Solution.*** To obtain five decimal-place accuracy, we must choose the number of subintervals so that

$$|E_S| \le 0.000005 = 5 \times 10^{-6}$$

From (14), this can be achieved by taking $n$ in Simpson's rule to satisfy

$$\frac{(b-a)^5 K_4}{180n^4} \le 5 \times 10^{-6}$$

Taking $a = 1, b = 2$, and $K_4 = 24$ (found in Example 7) in this inequality yields

$$\frac{1^5 \cdot 24}{180 \cdot n^4} \le 5 \times 10^{-6}$$

which, on taking reciprocals, can be rewritten as

$$n^4 \ge \frac{2 \times 10^6}{75} = \frac{8 \times 10^4}{3}$$

Thus,

$$n \ge \frac{20}{\sqrt[4]{6}} \approx 12.779$$

Since $n$ must be an even integer, the smallest value of $n$ that satisfies this requirement is $n = 14$. Thus, the approximation $S_{14}$ using 14 subintervals will produce five decimal-place accuracy. ◄

**REMARK** In cases where it is difficult to find the values of $K_2$ and $K_4$ in Formulas (12), (13), and (14), these constants may be replaced by any larger constants. For example, suppose that a constant $K$ can be easily found with the certainty that $|f''(x)| < K$ on the interval. Then $K_2 \le K$ and

$$|E_T| \le \frac{(b-a)^3 K_2}{12n^2} \le \frac{(b-a)^3 K}{12n^2} \tag{15}$$

so the right side of (15) is also an upper bound on the value of $|E_T|$. Using $K$, however, will likely increase the computed value of $n$ needed for a given error tolerance. Many applications involve the resolution of competing practical issues, illustrated here through the trade-off between the convenience of finding a crude bound for $|f''(x)|$ versus the efficiency of using the smallest possible $n$ for a desired accuracy.

▶ **Example 9** How many subintervals should be used in approximating

$$\int_0^1 \cos(x^2)\, dx$$

by the midpoint approximation for three decimal-place accuracy?

***Solution.*** To obtain three decimal-place accuracy, we must choose $n$ so that

$$|E_M| \leq 0.0005 = 5 \times 10^{-4} \tag{16}$$

From (12) with $f(x) = \cos(x^2)$, $a = 0$, and $b = 1$, an upper bound on $|E_M|$ is given by

$$|E_M| \leq \frac{K_2}{24n^2} \tag{17}$$

where $|K_2|$ is the maximum value of $|f''(x)|$ on the interval [0, 1]. However,

$$f'(x) = -2x\sin(x^2)$$
$$f''(x) = -4x^2\cos(x^2) - 2\sin(x^2) = -[4x^2\cos(x^2) + 2\sin(x^2)]$$

so that

$$|f''(x)| = |4x^2\cos(x^2) + 2\sin(x^2)| \tag{18}$$

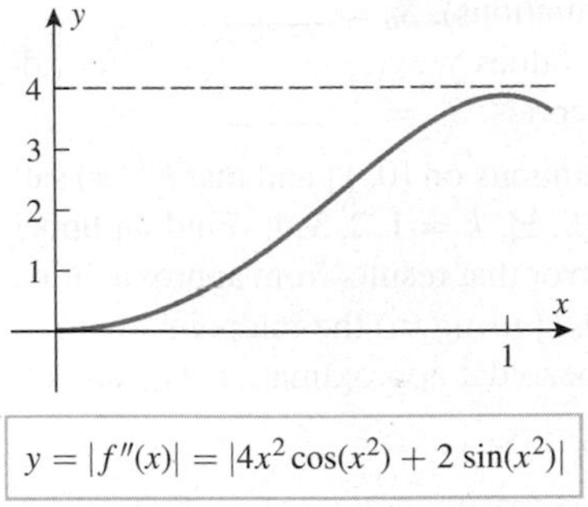


▲ **Figure 7.7.6**

It would be tedious to look for the maximum value of this function on the interval [0, 1]. For $x$ in [0, 1], it is easy to see that each of the expressions $x^2$, $\cos(x^2)$, and $\sin(x^2)$ is bounded in absolute value by 1, so $|4x^2\cos(x^2) + 2\sin(x^2)| \leq 4 + 2 = 6$ on [0, 1]. We can improve on this by using a graphing utility to sketch $|f''(x)|$, as shown in Figure 7.7.6. It is evident from the graph that

$$|f''(x)| < 4 \quad \text{for} \quad 0 \leq x \leq 1$$

Thus, it follows from (17) that

$$|E_M| \leq \frac{K_2}{24n^2} < \frac{4}{24n^2} = \frac{1}{6n^2}$$

and hence we can satisfy (16) by choosing $n$ so that

$$\frac{1}{6n^2} < 5 \times 10^{-4}$$

which, on taking reciprocals, can be written as

$$n^2 > \frac{10^4}{30} \quad \text{or} \quad n > \frac{10^2}{\sqrt{30}} \approx 18.257$$

The smallest integer value of $n$ satisfying this inequality is $n = 19$. Thus, the midpoint approximation $M_{19}$ using 19 subintervals will produce three decimal-place accuracy. ◀

## A COMPARISON OF THE THREE METHODS

Of the three methods studied in this section, Simpson's rule generally produces more accurate results than the midpoint or trapezoidal approximations for the same amount of work. To make this plausible, let us express (12), (13), and (14) in terms of the subinterval width

$$\Delta x = \frac{b-a}{n}$$

We obtain

$$|E_M| \leq \frac{1}{24}K_2(b-a)(\Delta x)^2 \tag{19}$$

$$|E_T| \leq \frac{1}{12}K_2(b-a)(\Delta x)^2 \tag{20}$$

$$|E_S| \leq \frac{1}{180}K_4(b-a)(\Delta x)^4 \tag{21}$$

(verify). For Simpson's rule, the upper bound on the absolute error is proportional to $(\Delta x)^4$, whereas the upper bound on the absolute error for the midpoint and trapezoidal approximations is proportional to $(\Delta x)^2$. Thus, reducing the interval width by a factor of 10, for example, reduces the error bound by a factor of 100 for the midpoint and trapezoidal approximations but reduces the error bound by a factor of 10,000 for Simpson's rule. This suggests that, as $n$ increases, the accuracy of Simpson's rule improves much more rapidly than that of the other approximations.

As a final note, observe that if $f(x)$ is a polynomial of degree 3 or less, then we have $f^{(4)}(x) = 0$ for all $x$, so $K_4 = 0$ in (14) and consequently $|E_S| = 0$. Thus, Simpson's rule gives exact results for polynomials of degree 3 or less. Similarly, the midpoint and trapezoidal approximations give exact results for polynomials of degree 1 or less. (You should also be able to see that this is so geometrically.)

## ✓QUICK CHECK EXERCISES 7.7

(See page 467 for answers.)

1. Let $T_n$ be the trapezoidal approximation for the definite integral of $f(x)$ over an interval $[a, b]$ using $n$ subintervals.
   (a) Expressed in terms of $L_n$ and $R_n$ (the left and right endpoint approximations), $T_n =$ ________.
   (b) Expressed in terms of the function values $y_0, y_1, \ldots, y_n$ at the endpoints of the subintervals, $T_n =$ ________.
2. Let $I$ denote the definite integral of $f$ over an interval $[a, b]$ with $T_n$ and $M_n$ the respective trapezoidal and midpoint approximations of $I$ for a given $n$. Assume that the graph of $f$ is concave up on the interval $[a, b]$ and order the quantities $T_n$, $M_n$, and $I$ from smallest to largest: ________ < ________ < ________.
3. Let $S_6$ be the Simpson's rule approximation for $\int_a^b f(x)\,dx$ using $n = 6$ subintervals.
   (a) Expressed in terms of $M_3$ and $T_3$ (the midpoint and trapezoidal approximations), $S_6 =$ ________.
   (b) Using the function values $y_0, y_1, y_2, \ldots, y_6$ at the endpoints of the subintervals, $S_6 =$ ________.
4. Assume that $f^{(4)}$ is continuous on $[0, 1]$ and that $f^{(k)}(x)$ satisfies $|f^{(k)}(x)| \le 1$ on $[0, 1]$, $k = 1, 2, 3, 4$. Find an upper bound on the absolute error that results from approximating the integral of $f$ over $[0, 1]$ using (a) the midpoint approximation $M_{10}$; (b) the trapezoidal approximation $T_{10}$; and (c) Simpson's rule $S_{10}$.
5. Approximate $\displaystyle\int_1^3 \frac{1}{x^2}\,dx$ using the indicated method.
   (a) $M_1 =$ ________ (b) $T_1 =$ ________
   (c) $S_2 =$ ________

## EXERCISE SET 7.7 C CAS

**1–6** Approximate the integral using (a) the midpoint approximation $M_{10}$, (b) the trapezoidal approximation $T_{10}$, and (c) Simpson's rule approximation $S_{20}$ using Formula (7). In each case, find the exact value of the integral and approximate the absolute error. Express your answers to at least four decimal places. ■

1. $\displaystyle\int_0^3 \sqrt{x+1}\,dx$
2. $\displaystyle\int_4^9 \frac{1}{\sqrt{x}}\,dx$
3. $\displaystyle\int_0^{\pi/2} \cos x\,dx$
4. $\displaystyle\int_0^2 \sin x\,dx$
5. $\displaystyle\int_1^3 e^{-2x}\,dx$
6. $\displaystyle\int_0^3 \frac{1}{3x+1}\,dx$

**7–12** Use inequalities (12), (13), and (14) to find upper bounds on the errors in parts (a), (b), and (c) of the indicated exercise. ■

7. Exercise 1
8. Exercise 2
9. Exercise 3
10. Exercise 4
11. Exercise 5
12. Exercise 6

**13–18** Use inequalities (12), (13), and (14) to find a number $n$ of subintervals for (a) the midpoint approximation $M_n$, (b) the trapezoidal approximation $T_n$, and (c) Simpson's rule approximation $S_n$ to ensure that the absolute error will be less than the given value. ■

13. Exercise 1; $5 \times 10^{-4}$
14. Exercise 2; $5 \times 10^{-4}$
15. Exercise 3; $10^{-3}$
16. Exercise 4; $10^{-3}$
17. Exercise 5; $10^{-4}$
18. Exercise 6; $10^{-4}$

**19–22 True–False** Determine whether the statement is true or false. Explain your answer. ■

19. The midpoint approximation, $M_n$, is the average of the left and right endpoint approximations, $L_n$ and $R_n$, respectively.
20. If $f(x)$ is concave down on the interval $(a, b)$, then the trapezoidal approximation $T_n$ underestimates $\int_a^b f(x)\,dx$.
21. The Simpson's rule approximation $S_{50}$ for $\int_a^b f(x)\,dx$ is a weighted average of the approximations $M_{50}$ and $T_{50}$, where $M_{50}$ is given twice the weight of $T_{50}$ in the average.
22. Simpson's rule approximation $S_{50}$ for $\int_a^b f(x)\,dx$ corresponds to $\int_a^b q(x)\,dx$, where the graph of $q$ is composed of 25 parabolic segments joined at points on the graph of $f$.

**23–24** Find a function $g(x)$ of the form

$$g(x) = Ax^2 + Bx + C$$

whose graph contains the points $(m - \Delta x,\ f(m - \Delta x))$, $(m, f(m))$, and $(m + \Delta x, f(m + \Delta x))$, for the given function $f(x)$ and the given values of $m$ and $\Delta x$. Then verify Formula (11):

$$\int_{m-\Delta x}^{m+\Delta x} g(x)\,dx = \frac{\Delta x}{3}[Y_0 + 4Y_1 + Y_2]$$

where $Y_0 = f(m - \Delta x)$, $Y_1 = f(m)$, and $Y_2 = f(m + \Delta x)$. ■

**23.** $f(x) = \dfrac{1}{x}$; $m = 3, \Delta x = 1$

**24.** $f(x) = \sin^2(\pi x)$; $m = \frac{1}{6}, \Delta x = \frac{1}{6}$

**25–30** Approximate the integral using Simpson's rule $S_{10}$ and compare your answer to that produced by a calculating utility with a numerical integration capability. Express your answers to at least four decimal places. ■

**25.** $\displaystyle\int_{-1}^{1} e^{-x^2}\,dx$ **26.** $\displaystyle\int_{0}^{3} \frac{x}{\sqrt{2x^3+1}}\,dx$

**27.** $\displaystyle\int_{-1}^{2} x\sqrt{2+x^3}\,dx$ **28.** $\displaystyle\int_{0}^{\pi} \frac{x}{2+\sin x}\,dx$

**29.** $\displaystyle\int_{0}^{1} \cos(x^2)\,dx$ **30.** $\displaystyle\int_{1}^{2} (\ln x)^{3/2}\,dx$

**31–32** The exact value of the given integral is $\pi$ (verify). Approximate the integral using (a) the midpoint approximation $M_{10}$, (b) the trapezoidal approximation $T_{10}$, and (c) Simpson's rule approximation $S_{20}$ using Formula (7). Approximate the absolute error and express your answers to at least four decimal places. ■

**31.** $\displaystyle\int_{0}^{2} \frac{8}{x^2+4}\,dx$ **32.** $\displaystyle\int_{0}^{3} \frac{4}{9}\sqrt{9-x^2}\,dx$

**33.** In Example 8 we showed that taking $n = 14$ subdivisions ensures that the approximation of

$$\ln 2 = \int_{1}^{2} \frac{1}{x}\,dx$$

by Simpson's rule is accurate to five decimal places. Confirm this by comparing the approximation of ln 2 produced by Simpson's rule with $n = 14$ to the value produced directly by your calculating utility.

**34.** In each part, determine whether a trapezoidal approximation would be an underestimate or an overestimate for the definite integral.

(a) $\displaystyle\int_{0}^{1} \cos(x^2)\,dx$ (b) $\displaystyle\int_{3/2}^{2} \cos(x^2)\,dx$

**35–36** Find a value of $n$ to ensure that the absolute error in approximating the integral by the midpoint approximation will be less than $10^{-4}$. Estimate the absolute error, and express your answers to at least four decimal places. ■

**35.** $\displaystyle\int_{0}^{2} x\sin x\,dx$ **36.** $\displaystyle\int_{0}^{1} e^{\cos x}\,dx$

**37–38** Show that the inequalities (12) and (13) are of no value in finding an upper bound on the absolute error that results from approximating the integral using either the midpoint approximation or the trapezoidal approximation. ■

**37.** $\displaystyle\int_{0}^{1} x\sqrt{x}\,dx$ **38.** $\displaystyle\int_{0}^{1} \sin\sqrt{x}\,dx$

**39–40** Use Simpson's rule approximation $S_{10}$ to approximate the length of the curve over the stated interval. Express your answers to at least four decimal places. ■

**39.** $y = \sin x$ from $x = 0$ to $x = \pi$

**40.** $y = x^{-2}$ from $x = 1$ to $x = 2$

**FOCUS ON CONCEPTS**

**41.** A graph of the speed $v$ versus time $t$ curve for a test run of a BMW 335i is shown in the accompanying figure. Estimate the speeds at times $t = 0, 5, 10, 15, 20, 25, 30$ s from the graph, convert to ft/s using 1 mi/h $= \frac{22}{15}$ ft/s, and use these speeds and Simpson's rule to approximate the number of feet traveled during the first 30 s. Round your answer to the nearest foot. [*Hint:* Distance traveled $= \int_0^{30} v(t)\,dt$.]

**Source:** Data from *Car and Driver Magazine*, September 2010.

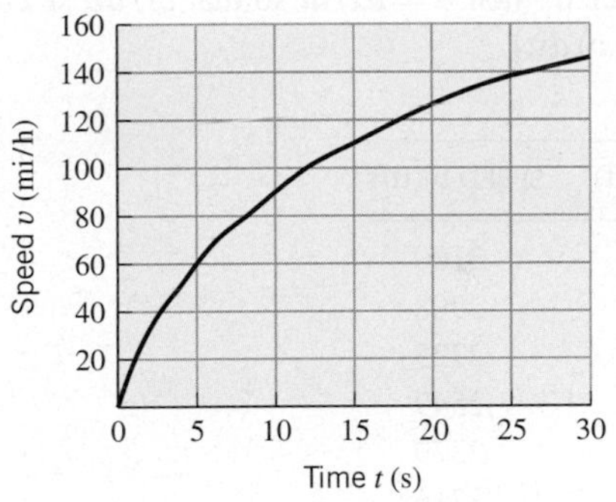


◀ **Figure Ex-41**

**42.** A graph of the acceleration $a$ versus time $t$ for an object moving on a straight line is shown in the accompanying figure. Estimate the accelerations at $t = 0, 1, 2, \ldots, 8$ seconds (s) from the graph and use Simpson's rule to approximate the change in velocity from $t = 0$ to $t = 8$ s. Round your answer to the nearest tenth cm/s. [*Hint:* Change in velocity $= \int_0^8 a(t)\,dt$.]

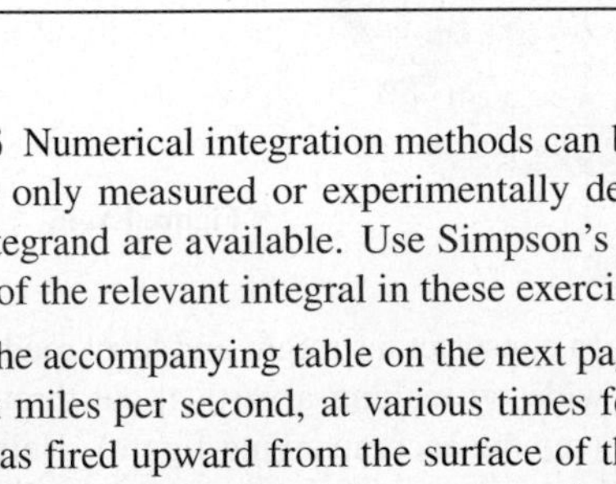


◀ **Figure Ex-42**

**43–46** Numerical integration methods can be used in problems where only measured or experimentally determined values of the integrand are available. Use Simpson's rule to estimate the value of the relevant integral in these exercises. ■

**43.** The accompanying table on the next page gives the speeds, in miles per second, at various times for a test rocket that was fired upward from the surface of the Earth. Use these values to approximate the number of miles traveled during the first 180 s. Round your answer to the nearest tenth of a mile. [*Hint:* Distance traveled $= \int_0^{180} v(t)\,dt$.]

| TIME $t$ (s) | SPEED $v$ (mi/s) |
|---|---|
| 0 | 0.00 |
| 30 | 0.03 |
| 60 | 0.08 |
| 90 | 0.16 |
| 120 | 0.27 |
| 150 | 0.42 |
| 180 | 0.65 |

◀ **Table Ex-43**

**44.** The accompanying table gives the speeds of a bullet at various distances from the muzzle of a rifle. Use these values to approximate the number of seconds for the bullet to travel 1800 ft. Express your answer to the nearest hundredth of a second. [*Hint:* If $v$ is the speed of the bullet and $x$ is the distance traveled, then $v = dx/dt$ so that $dt/dx = 1/v$ and $t = \int_0^{1800} (1/v)\, dx$.]

| DISTANCE $x$ (ft) | SPEED $v$ (ft/s) |
|---|---|
| 0 | 3100 |
| 300 | 2908 |
| 600 | 2725 |
| 900 | 2549 |
| 1200 | 2379 |
| 1500 | 2216 |
| 1800 | 2059 |

◀ **Table Ex-44**

**45.** Measurements of a pottery shard recovered from an archaeological dig reveal that the shard came from a pot with a flat bottom and circular cross sections (see the accompanying figure). The figure shows interior radius measurements of the shard made every 4 cm from the bottom of the pot to the top. Use those values to approximate the interior volume of the pot to the nearest tenth of a liter (1 L = 1000 cm$^3$). [*Hint:* Use 6.2.3 (volume by cross sections) to set up an appropriate integral for the volume.]

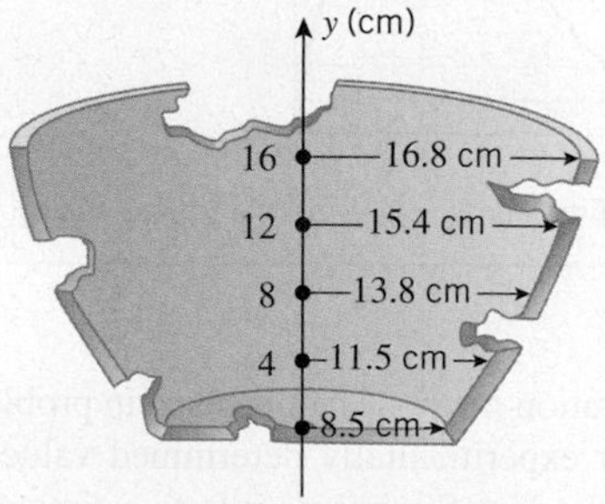


◀ **Figure Ex-45**

**46.** Engineers want to construct a straight and level road 600 ft long and 75 ft wide by making a vertical cut through an intervening hill (see the accompanying figure). Heights of the hill above the centerline of the proposed road, as obtained at various points from a contour map of the region, are shown in the accompanying figure. To estimate the construction costs, the engineers need to know the volume of earth that must be removed. Approximate this volume, rounded to the nearest cubic foot. [*Hint:* First set up an integral for the cross-sectional area of the cut along the centerline of the road, then assume that the height of the hill does not vary between the centerline and edges of the road.]

| HORIZONTAL DISTANCE $x$ (ft) | HEIGHT $h$ (ft) |
|---|---|
| 0 | 0 |
| 100 | 7 |
| 200 | 16 |
| 300 | 24 |
| 400 | 25 |
| 500 | 16 |
| 600 | 0 |

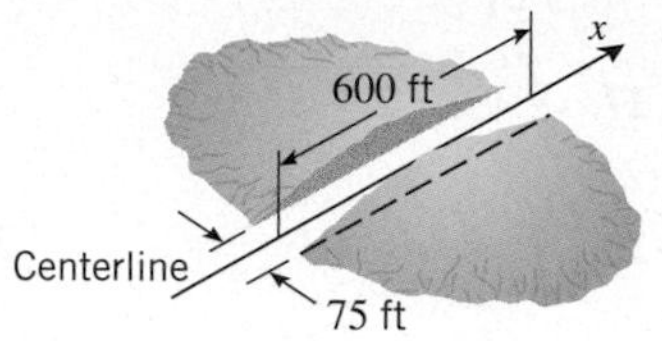


▲ **Figure Ex-46**

C **47.** Let $f(x) = \cos(x^2)$.

(a) Use a CAS to approximate the maximum value of $|f''(x)|$ on the interval $[0, 1]$.

(b) How large must $n$ be in the midpoint approximation of $\int_0^1 f(x)\, dx$ to ensure that the absolute error is less than $5 \times 10^{-4}$? Compare your result with that obtained in Example 9.

(c) Estimate the integral using the midpoint approximation with the value of $n$ obtained in part (b).

C **48.** Let $f(x) = \sqrt{1 + x^3}$.

(a) Use a CAS to approximate the maximum value of $|f''(x)|$ on the interval $[0, 1]$.

(b) How large must $n$ be in the trapezoidal approximation of $\int_0^1 f(x)\, dx$ to ensure that the absolute error is less than $10^{-3}$?

(c) Estimate the integral using the trapezoidal approximation with the value of $n$ obtained in part (b).

C **49.** Let $f(x) = \cos(x - x^2)$.

(a) Use a CAS to approximate the maximum value of $|f^{(4)}(x)|$ on the interval $[0, 1]$.

(b) How large must the value of $n$ be in the approximation $S_n$ of $\int_0^1 f(x)\, dx$ by Simpson's rule to ensure that the absolute error is less than $10^{-4}$?

(c) Estimate the integral using Simpson's rule approximation $S_n$ with the value of $n$ obtained in part (b).

C **50.** Let $f(x) = \sqrt{2 + x^3}$.

(a) Use a CAS to approximate the maximum value of $|f^{(4)}(x)|$ on the interval $[0, 1]$.

(b) How large must the value of $n$ be in the approximation $S_n$ of $\int_0^1 f(x)\, dx$ by Simpson's rule to ensure that the absolute error is less than $10^{-6}$?

(c) Estimate the integral using Simpson's rule approximation $S_n$ with the value of $n$ obtained in part (b).

**FOCUS ON CONCEPTS**

**51.** (a) Verify that the average of the left and right endpoint approximations as given in Table 7.7.1 gives Formula (2) for the trapezoidal approximation.

(b) Suppose that $f$ is a continuous nonnegative function on the interval $[a, b]$ and partition $[a, b]$ with equally spaced points, $a = x_0 < x_1 < \cdots < x_n = b$. Find the area of the trapezoid under the line segment joining points $(x_k, f(x_k))$ and $(x_{k+1}, f(x_{k+1}))$ and above the interval $[x_k, x_{k+1}]$. Show that the right side of Formula (2) is the sum of these trapezoidal areas (Figure 7.7.1).

**52.** Let $f$ be a function that is positive, continuous, decreasing, and concave down on the interval $[a, b]$. Assuming that $[a, b]$ is subdivided into $n$ equal subintervals, arrange the following approximations of $\int_a^b f(x)\,dx$ in order of increasing value: left endpoint, right endpoint, midpoint, and trapezoidal.

**53.** Suppose that $\Delta x > 0$ and $g(x) = Ax^2 + Bx + C$. Let $m$ be a number and set $Y_0 = g(m - \Delta x)$, $Y_1 = g(m)$, and $Y_2 = g(m + \Delta x)$. Verify Formula (11):

$$\int_{m-\Delta x}^{m+\Delta x} g(x)\,dx = \frac{\Delta x}{3}[Y_0 + 4Y_1 + Y_2]$$

**54.** Suppose that $f$ is a continuous nonnegative function on the interval $[a, b]$, $n$ is even, and $[a, b]$ is partitioned using $n + 1$ equally spaced points, $a = x_0 < x_1 < \cdots < x_n = b$. Set $y_0 = f(x_0)$, $y_1 = f(x_1), \ldots, y_n = f(x_n)$. Let $g_1, g_2, \ldots, g_{n/2}$ be the quadratic functions of the form $g_i(x) = Ax^2 + Bx + C$ so that

- the graph of $g_1$ passes through the points $(x_0, y_0)$, $(x_1, y_1)$, and $(x_2, y_2)$;
- the graph of $g_2$ passes through the points $(x_2, y_2)$, $(x_3, y_3)$, and $(x_4, y_4)$;
- ...
- the graph of $g_{n/2}$ passes through the points $(x_{n-2}, y_{n-2})$, $(x_{n-1}, y_{n-1})$, and $(x_n, y_n)$.

Verify that Formula (8) computes the area under a piecewise quadratic function by showing that

$$\sum_{j=1}^{n/2}\left(\int_{x_{2j-2}}^{x_{2j}} g_j(x)\,dx\right) = \frac{1}{3}\left(\frac{b-a}{n}\right)[y_0 + 4y_1 + 2y_2 + 4y_3 + 2y_4 + \cdots + 2y_{n-2} + 4y_{n-1} + y_n]$$

**55. Writing** Discuss two different circumstances under which numerical integration is necessary.

**56. Writing** For the numerical integration methods of this section, better accuracy of an approximation was obtained by increasing the number of subdivisions of the interval. Another strategy is to use the same number of subintervals, but to select subintervals of differing lengths. Discuss a scheme for doing this to approximate $\int_0^4 \sqrt{x}\,dx$ using a trapezoidal approximation with 4 subintervals. Comment on the advantages and disadvantages of your scheme.

**✓ QUICK CHECK ANSWERS 7.7** 1. (a) $\frac{1}{2}(L_n + R_n)$ (b) $\left(\frac{b-a}{2n}\right)[y_0 + 2y_1 + \cdots + 2y_{n-1} + y_n]$ 2. $M_n < I < T_n$ 3. (a) $\frac{2}{3}M_3 + \frac{1}{3}T_3$ (b) $\left(\frac{b-a}{18}\right)(y_0 + 4y_1 + 2y_2 + 4y_3 + 2y_4 + 4y_5 + y_6)$ 4. (a) $\frac{1}{2400}$ (b) $\frac{1}{1200}$ (c) $\frac{1}{1{,}800{,}000}$ 5. (a) $M_1 = \frac{1}{2}$ (b) $T_1 = \frac{10}{9}$ (c) $S_2 = \frac{19}{27}$

## 7.8 IMPROPER INTEGRALS

*Up to now we have focused on definite integrals with continuous integrands and finite intervals of integration. In this section we will extend the concept of a definite integral to include infinite intervals of integration and integrands that become infinite within the interval of integration.*

### IMPROPER INTEGRALS

It is assumed in the definition of the definite integral

$$\int_a^b f(x)\,dx$$

that $[a, b]$ is a finite interval and that the limit that defines the integral exists; that is, the function $f$ is integrable. We observed in Theorems 5.5.2 and 5.5.8 that continuous functions are integrable, as are bounded functions with finitely many points of discontinuity. We also observed in Theorem 5.5.8 that functions that are not bounded on the interval of integration are not integrable. Thus, for example, a function with a vertical asymptote within the interval of integration would not be integrable.

Our main objective in this section is to extend the concept of a definite integral to allow for infinite intervals of integration and integrands with vertical asymptotes within the interval of integration. We will call the vertical asymptotes ***infinite discontinuities***, and we will call integrals with infinite intervals of integration or infinite discontinuities within the interval of integration ***improper integrals***. Here are some examples:

- Improper integrals with infinite intervals of integration:

$$\int_1^{+\infty} \frac{dx}{x^2}, \quad \int_{-\infty}^{0} e^x\,dx, \quad \int_{-\infty}^{+\infty} \frac{dx}{1+x^2}$$

- Improper integrals with infinite discontinuities in the interval of integration:

$$\int_{-3}^{3} \frac{dx}{x^2}, \quad \int_{1}^{2} \frac{dx}{x-1}, \quad \int_{0}^{\pi} \tan x\,dx$$

- Improper integrals with infinite discontinuities and infinite intervals of integration:

$$\int_0^{+\infty} \frac{dx}{\sqrt{x}}, \quad \int_{-\infty}^{+\infty} \frac{dx}{x^2-9}, \quad \int_1^{+\infty} \sec x\,dx$$

## INTEGRALS OVER INFINITE INTERVALS

To motivate a reasonable definition for improper integrals of the form

$$\int_a^{+\infty} f(x)\,dx$$

let us begin with the case where $f$ is continuous and nonnegative on $[a, +\infty)$, so we can think of the integral as the area under the curve $y = f(x)$ over the interval $[a, +\infty)$ (Figure 7.8.1). At first, you might be inclined to argue that this area is infinite because the region has infinite extent. However, such an argument would be based on vague intuition rather than precise mathematical logic, since the concept of area has only been defined over intervals of *finite extent*. Thus, before we can make any reasonable statements about the area of the region in Figure 7.8.1, we need to begin by defining what we mean by the area of this region. For that purpose, it will help to focus on a specific example.

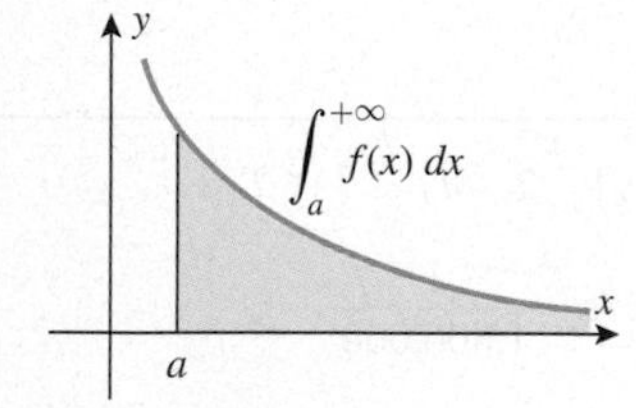

▲ Figure 7.8.1

Suppose we are interested in the area $A$ of the region that lies below the curve $y = 1/x^2$ and above the interval $[1, +\infty)$ on the $x$-axis. Instead of trying to find the entire area at once, let us begin by calculating the portion of the area that lies above a finite interval $[1, b]$, where $b > 1$ is arbitrary. That area is

$$\int_1^b \frac{dx}{x^2} = -\frac{1}{x}\bigg]_1^b = 1 - \frac{1}{b}$$

(Figure 7.8.2). If we now allow $b$ to increase so that $b \to +\infty$, then the portion of the area over the interval $[1, b]$ will begin to fill out the area over the entire interval $[1, +\infty)$ (Figure 7.8.3), and hence we can reasonably define the area $A$ under $y = 1/x^2$ over the interval $[1, +\infty)$ to be

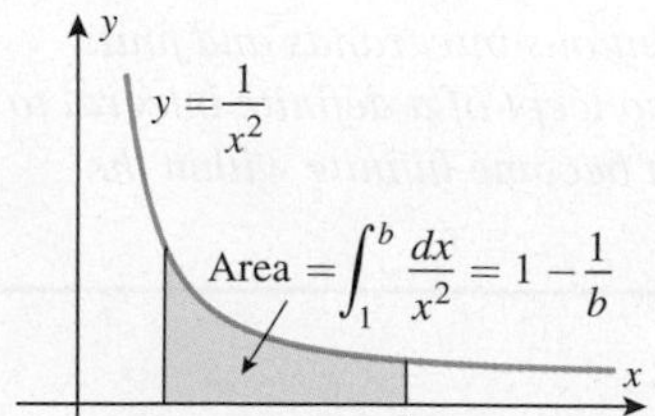

▲ Figure 7.8.2

$$A = \int_1^{+\infty} \frac{dx}{x^2} = \lim_{b\to+\infty} \int_1^b \frac{dx}{x^2} = \lim_{b\to+\infty} \left(1 - \frac{1}{b}\right) = 1 \tag{1}$$

Thus, the area has a finite value of 1 and is not infinite as we first conjectured.

With the preceding discussion as our guide, we make the following definition (which is applicable to functions with both positive and negative values).

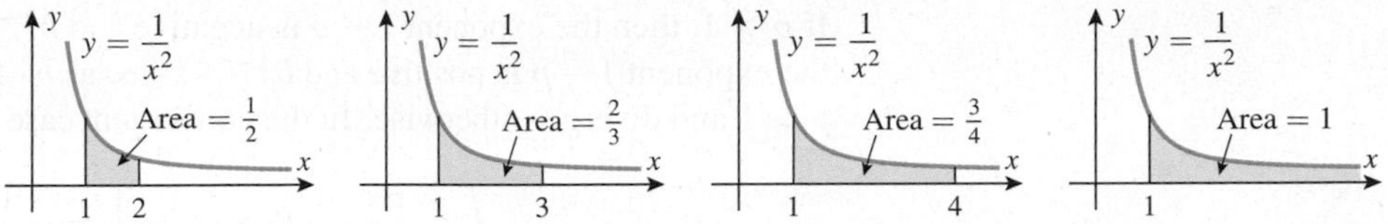


▶ Figure 7.8.3

If $f$ is nonnegative over the interval $[a, +\infty)$, then the improper integral in Definition 7.8.1 can be interpreted to be the area under the graph of $f$ over the interval $[a, +\infty)$. If the integral converges, then the area is finite and equal to the value of the integral, and if the integral diverges, then the area is regarded to be infinite.

**7.8.1 DEFINITION** The ***improper integral of f over the interval*** $[a, +\infty)$ is defined to be

$$\int_a^{+\infty} f(x)\,dx = \lim_{b\to+\infty} \int_a^b f(x)\,dx$$

In the case where the limit exists, the improper integral is said to ***converge***, and the limit is defined to be the value of the integral. In the case where the limit does not exist, the improper integral is said to ***diverge***, and it is not assigned a value.

▶ **Example 1** Evaluate

$$\text{(a)} \int_1^{+\infty} \frac{dx}{x^3} \qquad \text{(b)} \int_1^{+\infty} \frac{dx}{x}$$

***Solution (a).*** Following the definition, we replace the infinite upper limit by a finite upper limit $b$, and then take the limit of the resulting integral. This yields

$$\int_1^{+\infty} \frac{dx}{x^3} = \lim_{b\to+\infty} \int_1^b \frac{dx}{x^3} = \lim_{b\to+\infty} \left[-\frac{1}{2x^2}\right]_1^b = \lim_{b\to+\infty} \left(\frac{1}{2} - \frac{1}{2b^2}\right) = \frac{1}{2}$$

Since the limit is finite, the integral converges and its value is $1/2$.

***Solution (b).***

$$\int_1^{+\infty} \frac{dx}{x} = \lim_{b\to+\infty} \int_1^b \frac{dx}{x} = \lim_{b\to+\infty} [\ln x]_1^b = \lim_{b\to+\infty} \ln b = +\infty$$

In this case the integral diverges and hence has no value. ◀

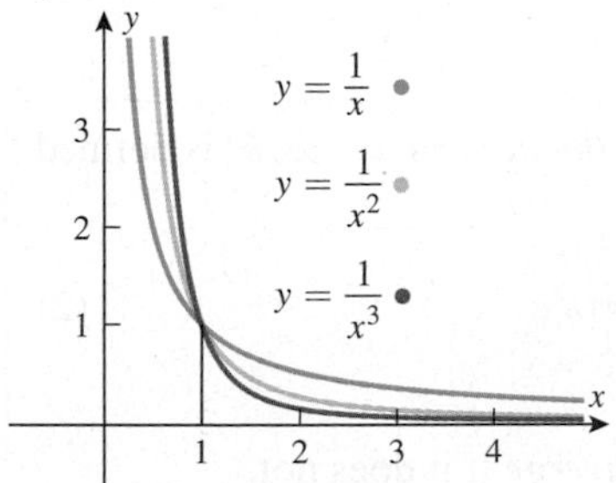


▲ Figure 7.8.4

Because the functions $1/x^3$, $1/x^2$, and $1/x$ are nonnegative over the interval $[1, +\infty)$, it follows from (1) and the last example that over this interval the area under $y = 1/x^3$ is $\frac{1}{2}$, the area under $y = 1/x^2$ is 1, and the area under $y = 1/x$ is infinite. However, on the surface the graphs of the three functions seem very much alike (Figure 7.8.4), and there is nothing to suggest why one of the areas should be infinite and the other two finite. One explanation is that $1/x^3$ and $1/x^2$ approach zero more rapidly than $1/x$ as $x\to+\infty$, so that the area over the interval $[1, b]$ accumulates less rapidly under the curves $y = 1/x^3$ and $y = 1/x^2$ than under $y = 1/x$ as $b\to+\infty$, and the difference is just enough that the first two areas are finite and the third is infinite.

▶ **Example 2** For what values of $p$ does the integral $\displaystyle\int_1^{+\infty} \frac{dx}{x^p}$ converge?

***Solution.*** We know from the preceding example that the integral diverges if $p = 1$, so let us assume that $p \neq 1$. In this case we have

$$\int_1^{+\infty} \frac{dx}{x^p} = \lim_{b\to+\infty} \int_1^b x^{-p}\,dx = \lim_{b\to+\infty} \left.\frac{x^{1-p}}{1-p}\right]_1^b = \lim_{b\to+\infty} \left[\frac{b^{1-p}}{1-p} - \frac{1}{1-p}\right]$$

If $p > 1$, then the exponent $1 - p$ is negative and $b^{1-p} \to 0$ as $b \to +\infty$; and if $p < 1$, then the exponent $1 - p$ is positive and $b^{1-p} \to +\infty$ as $b \to +\infty$. Thus, the integral converges if $p > 1$ and diverges otherwise. In the convergent case the value of the integral is

$$\int_1^{+\infty} \frac{dx}{x^p} = \left[0 - \frac{1}{1-p}\right] = \frac{1}{p-1} \quad (p > 1) \blacktriangleleft$$

The following theorem summarizes this result.

**7.8.2 THEOREM**

$$\int_1^{+\infty} \frac{dx}{x^p} = \begin{cases} \dfrac{1}{p-1} & \textit{if} \quad p > 1 \\ \textit{diverges} & \textit{if} \quad p \le 1 \end{cases}$$

▶ **Example 3** Evaluate $\displaystyle\int_0^{+\infty} (1 - x)e^{-x}\, dx$.

***Solution.*** We begin by evaluating the indefinite integral using integration by parts. Setting $u = 1 - x$ and $dv = e^{-x}\, dx$ yields

$$\int (1 - x)e^{-x}\, dx = -e^{-x}(1 - x) - \int e^{-x}\, dx = -e^{-x} + xe^{-x} + e^{-x} + C = xe^{-x} + C$$

Thus,

$$\int_0^{+\infty} (1 - x)e^{-x}\, dx = \lim_{b \to +\infty} \int_0^b (1 - x)e^{-x}\, dx = \lim_{b \to +\infty} \left[xe^{-x}\right]_0^b = \lim_{b \to +\infty} \frac{b}{e^b}$$

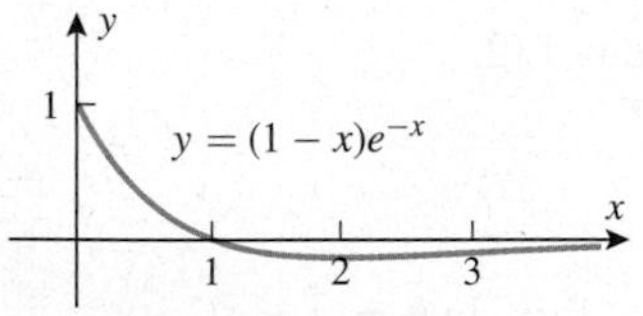


The net signed area between the graph and the interval $[0, +\infty)$ is zero.

▲ **Figure 7.8.5**

The limit is an indeterminate form of type $\infty/\infty$, so we will apply L'Hôpital's rule by differentiating the numerator and denominator with respect to $b$. This yields

$$\int_0^{+\infty} (1 - x)e^{-x}\, dx = \lim_{b \to +\infty} \frac{1}{e^b} = 0$$

We can interpret this to mean that the net signed area between the graph of $y = (1 - x)e^{-x}$ and the interval $[0, +\infty)$ is 0 (Figure 7.8.5). ◀

If $f$ is nonnegative over the interval $(-\infty, +\infty)$, then the improper integral

$$\int_{-\infty}^{+\infty} f(x)\, dx$$

can be interpreted to be the area under the graph of $f$ over the interval $(-\infty, +\infty)$. The area is finite and equal to the value of the integral if the integral converges and is infinite if it diverges.

**7.8.3 DEFINITION** The ***improper integral of $f$ over the interval*** $(-\infty, b]$ is defined to be

$$\int_{-\infty}^{b} f(x)\, dx = \lim_{a \to -\infty} \int_a^b f(x)\, dx \tag{2}$$

The integral is said to ***converge*** if the limit exists and ***diverge*** if it does not.

The ***improper integral of $f$ over the interval*** $(-\infty, +\infty)$ is defined as

$$\int_{-\infty}^{+\infty} f(x)\, dx = \int_{-\infty}^{c} f(x)\, dx + \int_c^{+\infty} f(x)\, dx \tag{3}$$

where $c$ is any real number. The improper integral is said to ***converge*** if *both* terms converge and ***diverge*** if *either* term diverges.

Although we usually choose $c = 0$ in (3), the choice does not matter because it can be proved that neither the convergence nor the value of the integral is affected by the choice of $c$.

▶ **Example 4** Evaluate $\displaystyle\int_{-\infty}^{+\infty} \frac{dx}{1+x^2}$.

***Solution.*** We will evaluate the integral by choosing $c = 0$ in (3). With this value for $c$ we obtain

$$\int_0^{+\infty} \frac{dx}{1+x^2} = \lim_{b\to+\infty} \int_0^b \frac{dx}{1+x^2} = \lim_{b\to+\infty} \Big[\tan^{-1} x\Big]_0^b = \lim_{b\to+\infty} (\tan^{-1} b) = \frac{\pi}{2}$$

$$\int_{-\infty}^{0} \frac{dx}{1+x^2} = \lim_{a\to-\infty} \int_a^0 \frac{dx}{1+x^2} = \lim_{a\to-\infty} \Big[\tan^{-1} x\Big]_a^0 = \lim_{a\to-\infty} (-\tan^{-1} a) = \frac{\pi}{2}$$

Thus, the integral converges and its value is

$$\int_{-\infty}^{+\infty} \frac{dx}{1+x^2} = \int_{-\infty}^{0} \frac{dx}{1+x^2} + \int_0^{+\infty} \frac{dx}{1+x^2} = \frac{\pi}{2} + \frac{\pi}{2} = \pi$$

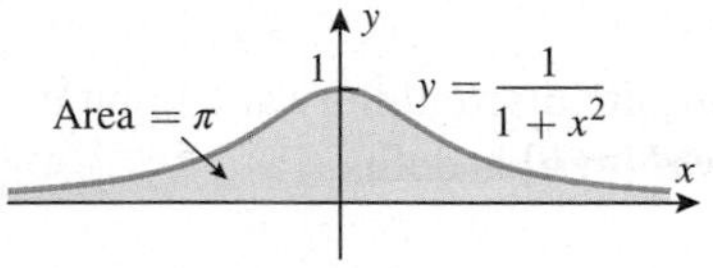


▲ **Figure 7.8.6**

Since the integrand is nonnegative on the interval $(-\infty, +\infty)$, the integral represents the area of the region shown in Figure 7.8.6. ◀

## INTEGRALS WHOSE INTEGRANDS HAVE INFINITE DISCONTINUITIES

Next we will consider improper integrals whose integrands have infinite discontinuities. We will start with the case where the interval of integration is a finite interval $[a, b]$ and the infinite discontinuity occurs at the right-hand endpoint.

To motivate an appropriate definition for such an integral let us consider the case where $f$ is nonnegative on $[a, b]$, so we can interpret the improper integral $\int_a^b f(x)\,dx$ as the area of the region in Figure 7.8.7*a*. The problem of finding the area of this region is complicated by the fact that it extends indefinitely in the positive $y$-direction. However, instead of trying to find the entire area at once, we can proceed indirectly by calculating the portion of the area over the interval $[a, k]$, where $a \le k < b$, and then letting $k$ approach $b$ to fill out the area of the entire region (Figure 7.8.7*b*). Motivated by this idea, we make the following definition.

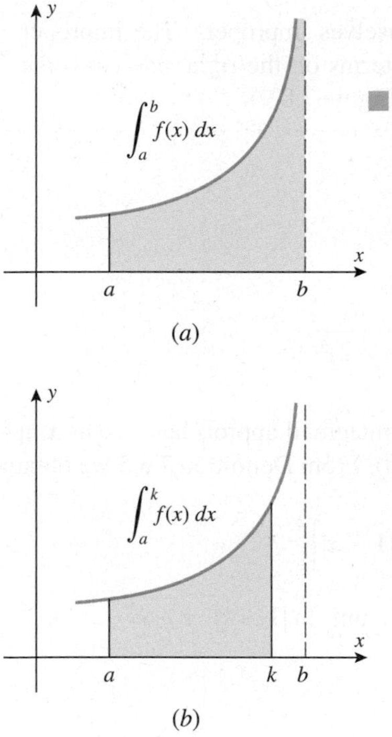


▲ **Figure 7.8.7**

**7.8.4 DEFINITION** If $f$ is continuous on the interval $[a, b]$, except for an infinite discontinuity at $b$, then the ***improper integral of f over the interval* [*a*, *b*]** is defined as

$$\int_a^b f(x)\,dx = \lim_{k\to b^-} \int_a^k f(x)\,dx \tag{4}$$

In the case where the indicated limit exists, the improper integral is said to ***converge***, and the limit is defined to be the value of the integral. In the case where the limit does not exist, the improper integral is said to ***diverge***, and it is not assigned a value.

▶ **Example 5** Evaluate $\displaystyle\int_0^1 \frac{dx}{\sqrt{1-x}}$.

***Solution.*** The integral is improper because the integrand approaches $+\infty$ as $x$ approaches the upper limit 1 from the left (Figure 7.8.8). From (4),

$$\int_0^1 \frac{dx}{\sqrt{1-x}} = \lim_{k\to1^-} \int_0^k \frac{dx}{\sqrt{1-x}} = \lim_{k\to1^-} \Big[-2\sqrt{1-x}\Big]_0^k$$

$$= \lim_{k\to1^-} \Big[-2\sqrt{1-k}+2\Big] = 2 \; ◀$$

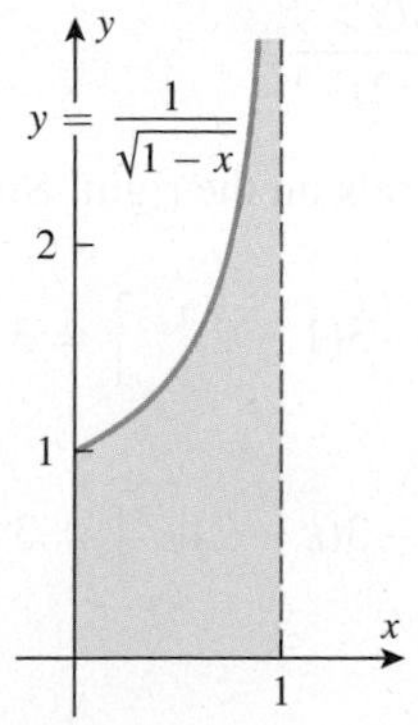


▲ **Figure 7.8.8**

Improper integrals with an infinite discontinuity at the left-hand endpoint or inside the interval of integration are defined as follows.

**7.8.5 DEFINITION** If $f$ is continuous on the interval $[a, b]$, except for an infinite discontinuity at $a$, then the ***improper integral of f over the interval*** $[a, b]$ is defined as

$$\int_a^b f(x)\,dx = \lim_{k \to a^+} \int_k^b f(x)\,dx \tag{5}$$

The integral is said to ***converge*** if the indicated limit exists and ***diverge*** if it does not.

If $f$ is continuous on the interval $[a, b]$, except for an infinite discontinuity at a point $c$ in $(a, b)$, then the ***improper integral of f over the interval*** $[a, b]$ is defined as

$$\int_a^b f(x)\,dx = \int_a^c f(x)\,dx + \int_c^b f(x)\,dx \tag{6}$$

where the two integrals on the right side are themselves improper. The improper integral on the left side is said to ***converge*** if *both* terms on the right side converge and ***diverge*** if *either* term on the right side diverges (Figure 7.8.9).

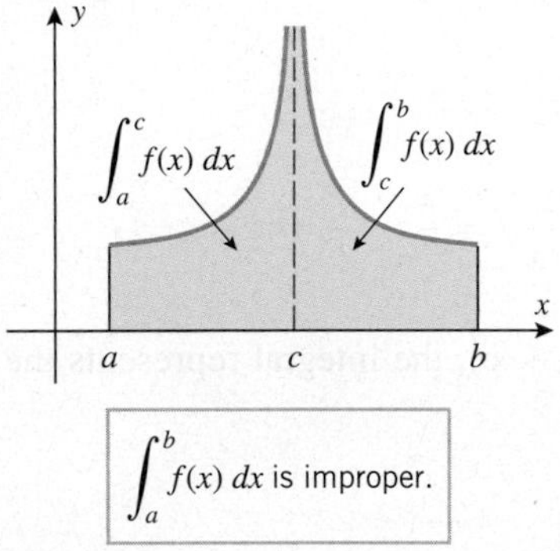


▲ **Figure 7.8.9**

**▶ Example 6** Evaluate

$$\text{(a)} \int_1^2 \frac{dx}{1-x} \qquad \text{(b)} \int_1^4 \frac{dx}{(x-2)^{2/3}}$$

***Solution (a).*** The integral is improper because the integrand approaches $-\infty$ as $x$ approaches the lower limit 1 from the right (Figure 7.8.10). From Definition 7.8.5 we obtain

$$\begin{aligned}\int_1^2 \frac{dx}{1-x} &= \lim_{k \to 1^+} \int_k^2 \frac{dx}{1-x} = \lim_{k \to 1^+} \Big[-\ln|1-x|\Big]_k^2 \\ &= \lim_{k \to 1^+} [-\ln|-1| + \ln|1-k|] = \lim_{k \to 1^+} \ln|1-k| = -\infty\end{aligned}$$

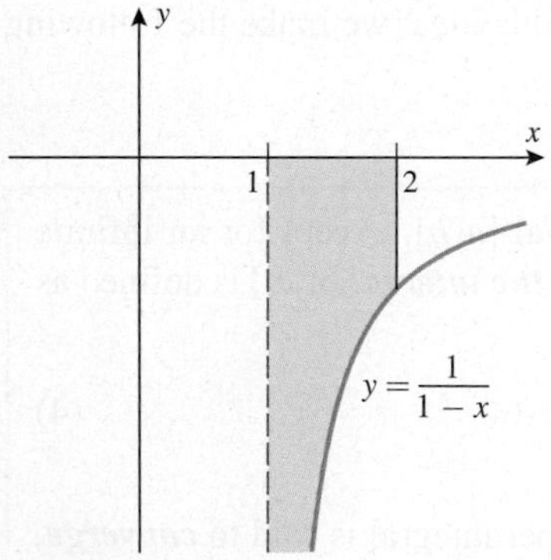


▲ **Figure 7.8.10**

so the integral diverges.

***Solution (b).*** The integral is improper because the integrand approaches $+\infty$ at $x = 2$, which is inside the interval of integration. From Definition 7.8.5 we obtain

$$\int_1^4 \frac{dx}{(x-2)^{2/3}} = \int_1^2 \frac{dx}{(x-2)^{2/3}} + \int_2^4 \frac{dx}{(x-2)^{2/3}} \tag{7}$$

and we must investigate the convergence of both improper integrals on the right. Since

$$\int_1^2 \frac{dx}{(x-2)^{2/3}} = \lim_{k \to 2^-} \int_1^k \frac{dx}{(x-2)^{2/3}} = \lim_{k \to 2^-} \Big[3(k-2)^{1/3} - 3(1-2)^{1/3}\Big] = 3$$

$$\int_2^4 \frac{dx}{(x-2)^{2/3}} = \lim_{k \to 2^+} \int_k^4 \frac{dx}{(x-2)^{2/3}} = \lim_{k \to 2^+} \Big[3(4-2)^{1/3} - 3(k-2)^{1/3}\Big] = 3\sqrt[3]{2}$$

we have from (7) that

$$\int_1^4 \frac{dx}{(x-2)^{2/3}} = 3 + 3\sqrt[3]{2} \blacktriangleleft$$

**WARNING** It is sometimes tempting to apply the Fundamental Theorem of Calculus directly to an improper integral without taking the appropriate limits. To illustrate what can go wrong with this procedure, suppose we fail to recognize that the integral

$$\int_0^2 \frac{dx}{(x-1)^2} \tag{8}$$

is improper and mistakenly evaluate this integral as

$$-\frac{1}{x-1}\bigg]_0^2 = -1-(1) = -2$$

This result is clearly incorrect because the integrand is never negative and hence the integral cannot be negative! To evaluate (8) correctly we should first write

$$\int_0^2 \frac{dx}{(x-1)^2} = \int_0^1 \frac{dx}{(x-1)^2} + \int_1^2 \frac{dx}{(x-1)^2}$$

and then treat each term as an improper integral. For the first term,

$$\int_0^1 \frac{dx}{(x-1)^2} = \lim_{k\to 1^-}\int_0^k \frac{dx}{(x-1)^2} = \lim_{k\to 1^-}\left[-\frac{1}{k-1}-1\right] = +\infty$$

so (8) diverges.

## ARC LENGTH AND SURFACE AREA USING IMPROPER INTEGRALS

In Definitions 6.4.2 and 6.5.2 for arc length and surface area we required the function $f$ to be smooth (continuous first derivative) to ensure the integrability in the resulting formula. However, smoothness is overly restrictive since some of the most basic formulas in geometry involve functions that are not smooth but lead to convergent improper integrals. Accordingly, let us agree to extend the definitions of arc length and surface area to allow functions that are not smooth, but for which the resulting integral in the formula converges.

► **Example 7** Derive the formula for the circumference of a circle of radius $r$.

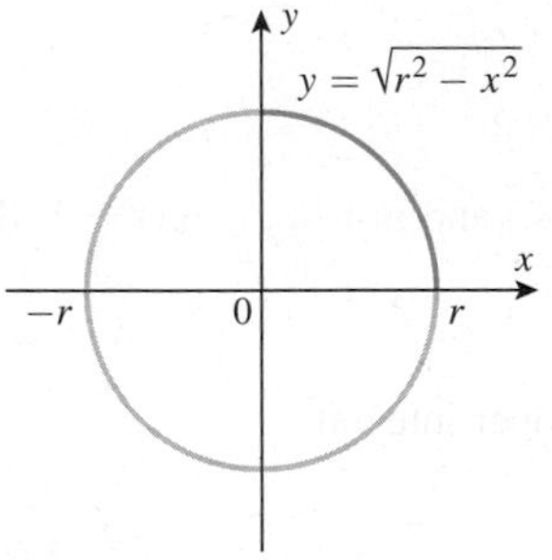

▲ **Figure 7.8.11**

***Solution.*** For convenience, let us assume that the circle is centered at the origin, in which case its equation is $x^2+y^2=r^2$. We will find the arc length of the portion of the circle that lies in the first quadrant and then multiply by 4 to obtain the total circumference (Figure 7.8.11).

Since the equation of the upper semicircle is $y=\sqrt{r^2-x^2}$, it follows from Formula (4) of Section 6.4 that the circumference $C$ is

$$\begin{aligned} C &= 4\int_0^r \sqrt{1+(dy/dx)^2}\,dx = 4\int_0^r \sqrt{1+\left(-\frac{x}{\sqrt{r^2-x^2}}\right)^2}\,dx \\ &= 4r\int_0^r \frac{dx}{\sqrt{r^2-x^2}} \end{aligned}$$

This integral is improper because of the infinite discontinuity at $x=r$, and hence we evaluate it by writing

$$\begin{aligned} C &= 4r\lim_{k\to r^-}\int_0^k \frac{dx}{\sqrt{r^2-x^2}} \\ &= 4r\lim_{k\to r^-}\left[\sin^{-1}\left(\frac{x}{r}\right)\right]_0^k \\ &= 4r\lim_{k\to r^-}\left[\sin^{-1}\left(\frac{k}{r}\right)-\sin^{-1}0\right] \\ &= 4r[\sin^{-1}1-\sin^{-1}0] = 4r\left(\frac{\pi}{2}-0\right) = 2\pi r \end{aligned}$$ ◄

Formula (77) in the Endpaper Integral Table

## ✓ QUICK CHECK EXERCISES 7.8 (See page 477 for answers.)

**1.** In each part, determine whether the integral is improper, and if so, explain why. Do not evaluate the integrals.

(a) $\int_{\pi/4}^{3\pi/4} \cot x\,dx$ (b) $\int_{\pi/4}^{\pi} \cot x\,dx$

(c) $\int_{0}^{+\infty} \frac{1}{x^2+1}\,dx$ (d) $\int_{1}^{+\infty} \frac{1}{x^2-1}\,dx$

**2.** Express each improper integral in Quick Check Exercise 1 in terms of one or more appropriate limits. Do not evaluate the limits.

**3.** The improper integral

$$\int_{1}^{+\infty} x^{-p}\,dx$$

converges to ________ provided ________.

**4.** Evaluate the integrals that converge.

(a) $\int_{0}^{+\infty} e^{-x}\,dx$ (b) $\int_{0}^{+\infty} e^{x}\,dx$

(c) $\int_{0}^{1} \frac{1}{x^3}\,dx$ (d) $\int_{0}^{1} \frac{1}{\sqrt[3]{x^2}}\,dx$

## EXERCISE SET 7.8 Graphing Utility C CAS

**1.** In each part, determine whether the integral is improper, and if so, explain why.

(a) $\int_{1}^{5} \frac{dx}{x-3}$ (b) $\int_{1}^{5} \frac{dx}{x+3}$ (c) $\int_{0}^{1} \ln x\,dx$

(d) $\int_{1}^{+\infty} e^{-x}\,dx$ (e) $\int_{-\infty}^{+\infty} \frac{dx}{\sqrt[3]{x-1}}$ (f) $\int_{0}^{\pi/4} \tan x\,dx$

**2.** In each part, determine all values of $p$ for which the integral is improper.

(a) $\int_{0}^{1} \frac{dx}{x^p}$ (b) $\int_{1}^{2} \frac{dx}{x-p}$ (c) $\int_{0}^{1} e^{-px}\,dx$

**3–32** Evaluate the integrals that converge. ■

**3.** $\int_{0}^{+\infty} e^{-2x}\,dx$

**4.** $\int_{-1}^{+\infty} \frac{x}{1+x^2}\,dx$

**5.** $\int_{3}^{+\infty} \frac{2}{x^2-1}\,dx$

**6.** $\int_{0}^{+\infty} xe^{-x^2}\,dx$

**7.** $\int_{e}^{+\infty} \frac{1}{x\ln^3 x}\,dx$

**8.** $\int_{2}^{+\infty} \frac{1}{x\sqrt{\ln x}}\,dx$

**9.** $\int_{-\infty}^{0} \frac{dx}{(2x-1)^3}$

**10.** $\int_{-\infty}^{3} \frac{dx}{x^2+9}$

**11.** $\int_{-\infty}^{0} e^{3x}\,dx$

**12.** $\int_{-\infty}^{0} \frac{e^x\,dx}{3-2e^x}$

**13.** $\int_{-\infty}^{+\infty} x\,dx$

**14.** $\int_{-\infty}^{+\infty} \frac{x}{\sqrt{x^2+2}}\,dx$

**15.** $\int_{-\infty}^{+\infty} \frac{x}{(x^2+3)^2}\,dx$

**16.** $\int_{-\infty}^{+\infty} \frac{e^{-t}}{1+e^{-2t}}\,dt$

**17.** $\int_{0}^{4} \frac{dx}{(x-4)^2}$

**18.** $\int_{0}^{8} \frac{dx}{\sqrt[3]{x}}$

**19.** $\int_{0}^{\pi/2} \tan x\,dx$

**20.** $\int_{0}^{4} \frac{dx}{\sqrt{4-x}}$

**21.** $\int_{0}^{1} \frac{dx}{\sqrt{1-x^2}}$

**22.** $\int_{-3}^{1} \frac{x\,dx}{\sqrt{9-x^2}}$

**23.** $\int_{\pi/3}^{\pi/2} \frac{\sin x}{\sqrt{1-2\cos x}}\,dx$

**24.** $\int_{0}^{\pi/4} \frac{\sec^2 x}{1-\tan x}\,dx$

**25.** $\int_{0}^{3} \frac{dx}{x-2}$

**26.** $\int_{-2}^{2} \frac{dx}{x^2}$

**27.** $\int_{-1}^{8} x^{-1/3}\,dx$

**28.** $\int_{0}^{1} \frac{dx}{(x-1)^{2/3}}$

**29.** $\int_{0}^{+\infty} \frac{1}{x^2}\,dx$

**30.** $\int_{1}^{+\infty} \frac{dx}{x\sqrt{x^2-1}}$

**31.** $\int_{0}^{1} \frac{dx}{\sqrt{x}(x+1)}$

**32.** $\int_{0}^{+\infty} \frac{dx}{\sqrt{x}(x+1)}$

**33–36 True–False** Determine whether the statement is true or false. Explain your answer. ■

**33.** $\int_{1}^{+\infty} x^{-4/3}\,dx$ converges to 3.

**34.** If $f$ is continuous on $[a, +\infty)$ and $\lim_{x\to+\infty} f(x) = 1$, then $\int_a^{+\infty} f(x)\,dx$ converges.

**35.** $\int_{1}^{2} \frac{1}{x(x-3)}\,dx$ is an improper integral.

**36.** $\int_{-1}^{1} \frac{1}{x^3}\,dx = 0$

**37–40** Make the $u$-substitution and evaluate the resulting definite integral. ■

**37.** $\int_{0}^{+\infty} \frac{e^{-\sqrt{x}}}{\sqrt{x}}\,dx$; $u = \sqrt{x}$ [*Note:* $u\to+\infty$ as $x\to+\infty$.]

**38.** $\int_{12}^{+\infty} \frac{dx}{\sqrt{x}(x+4)}$; $u = \sqrt{x}$ [*Note:* $u\to+\infty$ as $x\to+\infty$.]

**39.** $\int_{0}^{+\infty} \frac{e^{-x}}{\sqrt{1-e^{-x}}}\,dx$; $u = 1-e^{-x}$
[*Note:* $u\to 1$ as $x\to+\infty$.]

**40.** $\int_{0}^{+\infty} \frac{e^{-x}}{\sqrt{1-e^{-2x}}}\,dx$; $u = e^{-x}$

C **41–42** Express the improper integral as a limit, and then evaluate that limit with a CAS. Confirm the answer by evaluating the integral directly with the CAS. ■

**41.** $\int_0^{+\infty} e^{-x}\cos x\,dx$ **42.** $\int_0^{+\infty} xe^{-3x}\,dx$

C **43.** In each part, try to evaluate the integral exactly with a CAS. If your result is not a simple numerical answer, then use the CAS to find a numerical approximation of the integral.

(a) $\int_{-\infty}^{+\infty} \frac{1}{x^8+x+1}\,dx$ (b) $\int_0^{+\infty} \frac{1}{\sqrt{1+x^3}}\,dx$

(c) $\int_1^{+\infty} \frac{\ln x}{e^x}\,dx$ (d) $\int_1^{+\infty} \frac{\sin x}{x^2}\,dx$

C **44.** In each part, confirm the result with a CAS.

(a) $\int_0^{+\infty} \frac{\sin x}{\sqrt{x}}\,dx = \sqrt{\frac{\pi}{2}}$ (b) $\int_{-\infty}^{+\infty} e^{-x^2}\,dx = \sqrt{\pi}$

(c) $\int_0^1 \frac{\ln x}{1+x}\,dx = -\frac{\pi^2}{12}$

**45.** Find the length of the curve $y=(4-x^{2/3})^{3/2}$ over the interval $[0,8]$.

**46.** Find the length of the curve $y=\sqrt{4-x^2}$ over the interval $[0,2]$.

**47–48** Use L'Hôpital's rule to help evaluate the improper integral. ■

**47.** $\int_0^1 \ln x\,dx$ **48.** $\int_1^{+\infty} \frac{\ln x}{x^2}\,dx$

**49.** Find the area of the region between the $x$-axis and the curve $y=e^{-3x}$ for $x\geq 0$.

**50.** Find the area of the region between the $x$-axis and the curve $y=8/(x^2-4)$ for $x\geq 4$.

**51.** Suppose that the region between the $x$-axis and the curve $y=e^{-x}$ for $x\geq 0$ is revolved about the $x$-axis.
(a) Find the volume of the solid that is generated.
(b) Find the surface area of the solid.

**FOCUS ON CONCEPTS**

**52.** Suppose that $f$ and $g$ are continuous functions and that

$$0\leq f(x)\leq g(x)$$

if $x\geq a$. Give a reasonable informal argument using areas to explain why the following results are true.
(a) If $\int_a^{+\infty} f(x)\,dx$ diverges, then $\int_a^{+\infty} g(x)\,dx$ diverges.
(b) If $\int_a^{+\infty} g(x)\,dx$ converges, then $\int_a^{+\infty} f(x)\,dx$ converges and $\int_a^{+\infty} f(x)\,dx \leq \int_a^{+\infty} g(x)\,dx$.

[*Note:* The results in this exercise are sometimes called ***comparison tests*** for improper integrals.]

**53–56** Use the results in Exercise 52. ■

**53.** (a) Confirm graphically and algebraically that

$$e^{-x^2}\leq e^{-x} \quad (x\geq 1)$$

(b) Evaluate the integral

$$\int_1^{+\infty} e^{-x}\,dx$$

(c) What does the result obtained in part (b) tell you about the integral

$$\int_1^{+\infty} e^{-x^2}\,dx?$$

**54.** (a) Confirm graphically and algebraically that

$$\frac{1}{2x+1}\leq \frac{e^x}{2x+1} \quad (x\geq 0)$$

(b) Evaluate the integral

$$\int_0^{+\infty} \frac{dx}{2x+1}$$

(c) What does the result obtained in part (b) tell you about the integral

$$\int_0^{+\infty} \frac{e^x}{2x+1}\,dx?$$

**55.** Let $R$ be the region to the right of $x=1$ that is bounded by the $x$-axis and the curve $y=1/x$. When this region is revolved about the $x$-axis it generates a solid whose surface is known as ***Gabriel's Horn*** (for reasons that should be clear from the accompanying figure). Show that the solid has a finite volume but its surface has an infinite area. [*Note:* It has been suggested that if one could saturate the interior of the solid with paint and allow it to seep through to the surface, then one could paint an infinite surface with a finite amount of paint! What do you think?]

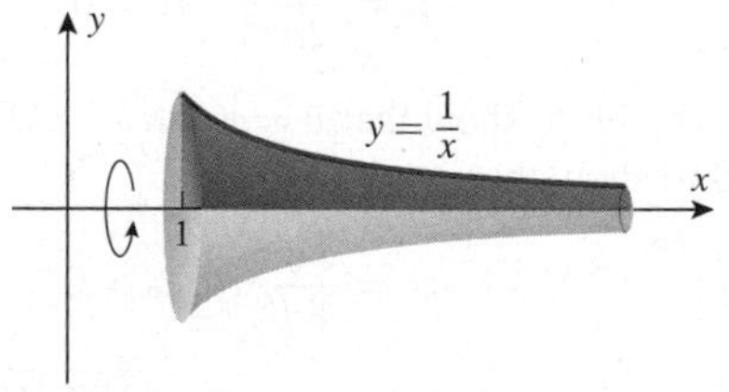


◄ **Figure Ex-55**

**56.** In each part, use Exercise 52 to determine whether the integral converges or diverges. If it converges, then use part (b) of that exercise to find an upper bound on the value of the integral.

(a) $\int_2^{+\infty} \frac{\sqrt{x^3+1}}{x}\,dx$ (b) $\int_2^{+\infty} \frac{x}{x^5+1}\,dx$

(c) $\int_0^{+\infty} \frac{xe^x}{2x+1}\,dx$

**FOCUS ON CONCEPTS**

**57.** Sketch the region whose area is

$$\int_0^{+\infty} \frac{dx}{1+x^2}$$

and use your sketch to show that

$$\int_0^{+\infty} \frac{dx}{1+x^2} = \int_0^1 \sqrt{\frac{1-y}{y}}\,dy$$

**58.** (a) Give a reasonable informal argument, based on areas, that explains why the integrals

$$\int_0^{+\infty} \sin x\,dx \quad \text{and} \quad \int_0^{+\infty} \cos x\,dx$$

diverge.

(b) Show that $\displaystyle\int_0^{+\infty} \frac{\cos\sqrt{x}}{\sqrt{x}}\,dx$ diverges.

**59.** In electromagnetic theory, the magnetic potential at a point on the axis of a circular coil is given by

$$u = \frac{2\pi NIr}{k}\int_a^{+\infty} \frac{dx}{(r^2+x^2)^{3/2}}$$

where $N, I, r, k$, and $a$ are constants. Find $u$.

C **60.** The *average speed*, $\bar{v}$, of the molecules of an ideal gas is given by

$$\bar{v} = \frac{4}{\sqrt{\pi}}\left(\frac{M}{2RT}\right)^{3/2}\int_0^{+\infty} v^3 e^{-Mv^2/(2RT)}\,dv$$

and the *root-mean-square speed*, $v_{\text{rms}}$, by

$$v_{\text{rms}}^2 = \frac{4}{\sqrt{\pi}}\left(\frac{M}{2RT}\right)^{3/2}\int_0^{+\infty} v^4 e^{-Mv^2/(2RT)}\,dv$$

where $v$ is the molecular speed, $T$ is the gas temperature, $M$ is the molecular weight of the gas, and $R$ is the gas constant.

(a) Use a CAS to show that

$$\int_0^{+\infty} x^3 e^{-a^2x^2}\,dx = \frac{1}{2a^4}, \quad a > 0$$

and use this result to show that $\bar{v} = \sqrt{8RT/(\pi M)}$.

(b) Use a CAS to show that

$$\int_0^{+\infty} x^4 e^{-a^2x^2}\,dx = \frac{3\sqrt{\pi}}{8a^5}, \quad a > 0$$

and use this result to show that $v_{\text{rms}} = \sqrt{3RT/M}$.

**61–62** Medication can be administered to a patient using a variety of methods. For a given method, let $c(t)$ denote the concentration of medication in the patient's bloodstream (measured in mg/L) $t$ hours after the dose is given. The area under the curve $c = c(t)$ over the time interval $[0, +\infty)$ indicates the "availability" of the medication for the patient's body. Determine which method provides the greater availability. ■

**61.** Method 1: $c_1(t) = 5(e^{-0.2t} - e^{-t})$;
Method 2: $c_2(t) = 4(e^{-0.2t} - e^{-3t})$

**62.** Method 1: $c_1(t) = 6(e^{-0.4t} - e^{-1.3t})$;
Method 2: $c_2(t) = 5(e^{-0.4t} - e^{-3t})$

**63.** In Exercise 25 of Section 6.6, we determined the work required to lift a 6000 lb satellite to an orbital position that is 1000 mi above the Earth's surface. The ideas discussed in that exercise will be needed here.

(a) Find a definite integral that represents the work required to lift a 6000 lb satellite to a position $b$ miles above the Earth's surface.

(b) Find a definite integral that represents the work required to lift a 6000 lb satellite an "infinite distance" above the Earth's surface. Evaluate the integral. [*Note:* The result obtained here is sometimes called the work required to "escape" the Earth's gravity.]

**64–65** A ***transform*** is a formula that converts or "transforms" one function into another. Transforms are used in applications to convert a difficult problem into an easier problem whose solution can then be used to solve the original difficult problem. The ***Laplace transform*** of a function $f(t)$, which plays an important role in the study of differential equations, is denoted by $\mathscr{L}\{f(t)\}$ and is defined by

$$\mathscr{L}\{f(t)\} = \int_0^{+\infty} e^{-st} f(t)\,dt$$

In this formula $s$ is treated as a constant in the integration process; thus, the Laplace transform has the effect of transforming $f(t)$ into a function of $s$. Use this formula in these exercises. ■

**64.** Show that

(a) $\mathscr{L}\{1\} = \dfrac{1}{s}, \ s > 0$ (b) $\mathscr{L}\{e^{2t}\} = \dfrac{1}{s-2}, \ s > 2$

(c) $\mathscr{L}\{\sin t\} = \dfrac{1}{s^2+1}, \ s > 0$

(d) $\mathscr{L}\{\cos t\} = \dfrac{s}{s^2+1}, \ s > 0.$

**65.** In each part, find the Laplace transform.

(a) $f(t) = t, \ s > 0$ (b) $f(t) = t^2, \ s > 0$

(c) $f(t) = \begin{cases} 0, & t < 3 \\ 1, & t \geq 3 \end{cases}, \ s > 0$

C **66.** Later in the text, we will show that

$$\int_0^{+\infty} e^{-x^2}\,dx = \tfrac{1}{2}\sqrt{\pi}$$

Confirm that this is reasonable by using a CAS or a calculator with a numerical integration capability.

**67.** Use the result in Exercise 66 to show that

(a) $\displaystyle\int_{-\infty}^{+\infty} e^{-ax^2}\,dx = \sqrt{\frac{\pi}{a}}, \ a > 0$

(b) $\displaystyle\frac{1}{\sqrt{2\pi}\sigma}\int_{-\infty}^{+\infty} e^{-x^2/2\sigma^2}\,dx = 1, \ \sigma > 0.$

**68–69** A convergent improper integral over an infinite interval can be approximated by first replacing the infinite limit(s) of integration by finite limit(s), then using a numerical integration technique, such as Simpson's rule, to approximate the integral with finite limit(s). This technique is illustrated in these exercises. ■

**68.** Suppose that the integral in Exercise 66 is approximated by first writing it as

$$\int_0^{+\infty} e^{-x^2}\,dx = \int_0^{K} e^{-x^2}\,dx + \int_K^{+\infty} e^{-x^2}\,dx$$

then dropping the second term, and then applying Simpson's rule to the integral

$$\int_0^{K} e^{-x^2}\,dx$$

The resulting approximation has two sources of error: the error from Simpson's rule and the error

$$E = \int_K^{+\infty} e^{-x^2}\,dx$$

that results from discarding the second term. We call $E$ the ***truncation error***.

(a) Approximate the integral in Exercise 66 by applying Simpson's rule with $n = 10$ subdivisions to the integral

$$\int_0^3 e^{-x^2}\,dx$$

Round your answer to four decimal places and compare it to $\frac{1}{2}\sqrt{\pi}$ rounded to four decimal places.

(b) Use the result that you obtained in Exercise 52 and the fact that $e^{-x^2} \le \frac{1}{3}xe^{-x^2}$ for $x \ge 3$ to show that the truncation error for the approximation in part (a) satisfies $0 < E < 2.1 \times 10^{-5}$.

**69.** (a) It can be shown that

$$\int_0^{+\infty} \frac{1}{x^6+1}\,dx = \frac{\pi}{3}$$

Approximate this integral by applying Simpson's rule with $n = 20$ subdivisions to the integral

$$\int_0^4 \frac{1}{x^6+1}\,dx$$

Round your answer to three decimal places and compare it to $\pi/3$ rounded to three decimal places.

(b) Use the result that you obtained in Exercise 52 and the fact that $1/(x^6+1) < 1/x^6$ for $x \ge 4$ to show that the truncation error for the approximation in part (a) satisfies $0 < E < 2 \times 10^{-4}$.

**70.** For what values of $p$ does $\int_0^{+\infty} e^{px}\,dx$ converge?

**71.** Show that $\int_0^1 dx/x^p$ converges if $p < 1$ and diverges if $p \ge 1$.

C **72.** It is sometimes possible to convert an improper integral into a "proper" integral having the same value by making an appropriate substitution. Evaluate the following integral by making the indicated substitution, and investigate what happens if you evaluate the integral directly using a CAS.

$$\int_0^1 \sqrt{\frac{1+x}{1-x}}\,dx;\quad u = \sqrt{1-x}$$

**73–74** Transform the given improper integral into a proper integral by making the stated $u$-substitution; then approximate the proper integral by Simpson's rule with $n = 10$ subdivisions. Round your answer to three decimal places. ■

**73.** $\displaystyle\int_0^1 \frac{\cos x}{\sqrt{x}}\,dx;\ u = \sqrt{x}$

**74.** $\displaystyle\int_0^1 \frac{\sin x}{\sqrt{1-x}}\,dx;\ u = \sqrt{1-x}$

**75. Writing** What is "improper" about an integral over an infinite interval? Explain why Definition 5.5.1 for $\int_a^b f(x)\,dx$ fails for $\int_a^{+\infty} f(x)\,dx$. Discuss a strategy for assigning a value to $\int_a^{+\infty} f(x)\,dx$.

**76. Writing** What is "improper" about a definite integral over an interval on which the integrand has an infinite discontinuity? Explain why Definition 5.5.1 for $\int_a^b f(x)\,dx$ fails if the graph of $f$ has a vertical asymptote at $x = a$. Discuss a strategy for assigning a value to $\int_a^b f(x)\,dx$ in this circumstance.

---

✓ **QUICK CHECK ANSWERS 7.8** 1. (a) proper (b) improper, since $\cot x$ has an infinite discontinuity at $x = \pi$ (c) improper, since there is an infinite interval of integration (d) improper, since there is an infinite interval of integration and the integrand has an infinite discontinuity at $x = 1$ 2. (b) $\lim_{b\to\pi^-} \int_{\pi/4}^b \cot x\,dx$ (c) $\lim_{b\to+\infty} \int_0^b \frac{1}{x^2+1}\,dx$ (d) $\lim_{a\to 1^+} \int_a^2 \frac{1}{x^2-1}\,dx + \lim_{b\to+\infty} \int_2^b \frac{1}{x^2-1}\,dx$ 3. $\frac{1}{p-1}$; $p > 1$ 4. (a) 1 (b) diverges (c) diverges (d) 3

---

## CHAPTER 7 REVIEW EXERCISES

**1–6** Evaluate the given integral with the aid of an appropriate $u$-substitution. ■

**1.** $\int \sqrt{4+9x}\,dx$

**2.** $\int \frac{1}{\sec \pi x}\,dx$

**3.** $\int \sqrt{\cos x}\sin x\,dx$

**4.** $\int \frac{dx}{x\ln x}$

**5.** $\int x\tan^2(x^2)\sec^2(x^2)\,dx$

**6.** $\int_0^9 \frac{\sqrt{x}}{x+9}\,dx$

**7.** (a) Evaluate the integral

$$\int \frac{1}{\sqrt{2x - x^2}}\,dx$$

three ways: using the substitution $u = \sqrt{x}$, using the substitution $u = \sqrt{2-x}$, and completing the square.

(b) Show that the answers in part (a) are equivalent.

**8.** Evaluate the integral $\displaystyle\int_0^1 \frac{x^3}{\sqrt{x^2+1}}\,dx$

(a) using integration by parts

(b) using the substitution $u = \sqrt{x^2+1}$.

**9–12** Use integration by parts to evaluate the integral. ■

**9.** $\int xe^{-x}\,dx$

**10.** $\int x\sin 2x\,dx$

**11.** $\int \ln(2x+3)\,dx$ **12.** $\int_0^{1/2} \tan^{-1}(2x)\,dx$

**13.** Evaluate $\int 8x^4 \cos 2x\,dx$ using tabular integration by parts.

**14.** A particle moving along the $x$-axis has velocity function $v(t) = t^2 e^{-t}$. How far does the particle travel from time $t = 0$ to $t = 5$?

**15–20** Evaluate the integral. ■

**15.** $\int \sin^2 5\theta\,d\theta$ **16.** $\int \sin^3 2x \cos^2 2x\,dx$

**17.** $\int \sin x \cos 2x\,dx$ **18.** $\int_0^{\pi/6} \sin 2x \cos 4x\,dx$

**19.** $\int \sin^4 2x\,dx$ **20.** $\int x\cos^5(x^2)\,dx$

**21–26** Evaluate the integral by making an appropriate trigonometric substitution. ■

**21.** $\int \frac{x^2}{\sqrt{9-x^2}}\,dx$ **22.** $\int \frac{dx}{x^2\sqrt{16-x^2}}$

**23.** $\int \frac{dx}{\sqrt{x^2-1}}$ **24.** $\int \frac{x^2}{\sqrt{x^2-25}}\,dx$

**25.** $\int \frac{x^2}{\sqrt{9+x^2}}\,dx$ **26.** $\int \frac{\sqrt{1+4x^2}}{x}\,dx$

**27–32** Evaluate the integral using the method of partial fractions. ■

**27.** $\int \frac{dx}{x^2+3x-4}$ **28.** $\int \frac{dx}{x^2+8x+7}$

**29.** $\int \frac{x^2+2}{x+2}\,dx$ **30.** $\int \frac{x^2+x-16}{(x-1)(x-3)^2}\,dx$

**31.** $\int \frac{x^2}{(x+2)^3}\,dx$ **32.** $\int \frac{dx}{x^3+x}$

**33.** Consider the integral $\int \frac{1}{x^3-x}\,dx$.

(a) Evaluate the integral using the substitution $x = \sec\theta$. For what values of $x$ is your result valid?

(b) Evaluate the integral using the substitution $x = \sin\theta$. For what values of $x$ is your result valid?

(c) Evaluate the integral using the method of partial fractions. For what values of $x$ is your result valid?

**34.** Find the area of the region that is enclosed by the curves $y = (x-3)/(x^3+x^2)$, $y = 0$, $x = 1$, and $x = 2$.

**35–40** Use the Endpaper Integral Table to evaluate the integral. ■

**35.** $\int \sin 7x \cos 9x\,dx$ **36.** $\int (x^3 - x^2)e^{-x}\,dx$

**37.** $\int x\sqrt{x - x^2}\,dx$ **38.** $\int \frac{dx}{x\sqrt{4x+3}}$

**39.** $\int \tan^2 2x\,dx$ **40.** $\int \frac{3x-1}{2+x^2}\,dx$

**41–42** Approximate the integral using (a) the midpoint approximation $M_{10}$, (b) the trapezoidal approximation $T_{10}$, and (c) Simpson's rule approximation $S_{20}$. In each case, find the exact value of the integral and approximate the absolute error. Express your answers to at least four decimal places. ■

**41.** $\int_1^3 \frac{1}{\sqrt{x+1}}\,dx$ **42.** $\int_{-1}^1 \frac{1}{1+x^2}\,dx$

**43–44** Use inequalities (12), (13), and (14) of Section 7.7 to find upper bounds on the errors in parts (a), (b), or (c) of the indicated exercise. ■

**43.** Exercise 41 **44.** Exercise 42

**45–46** Use inequalities (12), (13), and (14) of Section 7.7 to find a number $n$ of subintervals for (a) the midpoint approximation $M_n$, (b) the trapezoidal approximation $T_n$, and (c) Simpson's rule approximation $S_n$ to ensure the absolute error will be less than $10^{-4}$. ■

**45.** Exercise 41 **46.** Exercise 42

**47–50** Evaluate the integral if it converges. ■

**47.** $\int_0^{+\infty} e^{-x}\,dx$ **48.** $\int_{-\infty}^{2} \frac{dx}{x^2+4}$

**49.** $\int_0^9 \frac{dx}{\sqrt{9-x}}$ **50.** $\int_0^1 \frac{1}{2x-1}\,dx$

**51.** Find the area that is enclosed between the $x$-axis and the curve $y = (\ln x - 1)/x^2$ for $x \geq e$.

**52.** Find the volume of the solid that is generated when the region between the $x$-axis and the curve $y = e^{-x}$ for $x \geq 0$ is revolved about the $y$-axis.

**53.** Find a positive value of $a$ that satisfies the equation

$$\int_0^{+\infty} \frac{1}{x^2+a^2}\,dx = 1$$

**54.** Consider the following methods for evaluating integrals: $u$-substitution, integration by parts, partial fractions, reduction formulas, and trigonometric substitutions. In each part, state the approach that you would try first to evaluate the integral. If none of them seems appropriate, then say so. You need not evaluate the integral.

(a) $\int x\sin x\,dx$ (b) $\int \cos x \sin x\,dx$

(c) $\int \tan^7 x\,dx$ (d) $\int \tan^7 x \sec^2 x\,dx$

(e) $\int \frac{3x^2}{x^3+1}\,dx$ (f) $\int \frac{3x^2}{(x+1)^3}\,dx$

(g) $\int \tan^{-1} x\,dx$ (h) $\int \sqrt{4-x^2}\,dx$

(i) $\int x\sqrt{4-x^2}\,dx$

**55–74** Evaluate the integral. ■

**55.** $\int \frac{dx}{(3+x^2)^{3/2}}$ **56.** $\int x\cos 3x\,dx$

**57.** $\int_0^{\pi/4} \tan^7\theta\,d\theta$ **58.** $\int \frac{\cos\theta}{\sin^2\theta - 6\sin\theta + 12}\,d\theta$

**59.** $\int \sin^2 2x \cos^3 2x\,dx$ **60.** $\int_0^4 \frac{1}{(x-3)^2}\,dx$

**61.** $\int e^{2x}\cos 3x\,dx$ **62.** $\int_{-1/\sqrt{2}}^{1/\sqrt{2}} (1-2x^2)^{3/2}\,dx$

**63.** $\int \frac{dx}{(x-1)(x+2)(x-3)}$ **64.** $\int_0^{1/3} \frac{dx}{(4-9x^2)^2}$

65. $\int_4^8 \frac{\sqrt{x-4}}{x}\,dx$

66. $\int_0^{\ln 2} \sqrt{e^x - 1}\,dx$

67. $\int \frac{1}{\sqrt{e^x+1}}\,dx$

68. $\int \frac{dx}{x(x^2+x+1)}$

69. $\int_0^{1/2} \sin^{-1} x\,dx$

70. $\int \tan^5 4x \sec^4 4x\,dx$

71. $\int \frac{x+3}{\sqrt{x^2+2x+2}}\,dx$

72. $\int \frac{\sec^2\theta}{\tan^3\theta - \tan^2\theta}\,d\theta$

73. $\int_a^{+\infty} \frac{x}{(x^2+1)^2}\,dx$

74. $\int_0^{+\infty} \frac{dx}{a^2+b^2x^2}, \quad a, b > 0$

## CHAPTER 7 MAKING CONNECTIONS

C CAS

1. Recall from Theorem 3.3.1 and the discussion preceding it that if $f'(x) > 0$, then the function $f$ is increasing and has an inverse function. Parts (a), (b), and (c) of this problem show that if this condition is satisfied and if $f'$ is continuous, then a definite integral of $f^{-1}$ can be expressed in terms of a definite integral of $f$.
   (a) Use integration by parts to show that
   $$\int_a^b f(x)\,dx = bf(b) - af(a) - \int_a^b xf'(x)\,dx$$
   (b) Use the result in part (a) to show that if $y = f(x)$, then
   $$\int_a^b f(x)\,dx = bf(b) - af(a) - \int_{f(a)}^{f(b)} f^{-1}(y)\,dy$$
   (c) Show that if we let $\alpha = f(a)$ and $\beta = f(b)$, then the result in part (b) can be written as
   $$\int_\alpha^\beta f^{-1}(x)\,dx = \beta f^{-1}(\beta) - \alpha f^{-1}(\alpha) - \int_{f^{-1}(\alpha)}^{f^{-1}(\beta)} f(x)\,dx$$

2. In each part, use the result in Exercise 1 to obtain the equation, and then confirm that the equation is correct by performing the integrations.
   (a) $\int_0^{1/2} \sin^{-1} x\,dx = \frac{1}{2}\sin^{-1}\left(\frac{1}{2}\right) - \int_0^{\pi/6} \sin x\,dx$
   (b) $\int_e^{e^2} \ln x\,dx = (2e^2 - e) - \int_1^2 e^x\,dx$

3. The ***Gamma function***, $\Gamma(x)$, is defined as
   $$\Gamma(x) = \int_0^{+\infty} t^{x-1}e^{-t}\,dt$$
   It can be shown that this improper integral converges if and only if $x > 0$.
   (a) Find $\Gamma(1)$.
   (b) Prove: $\Gamma(x+1) = x\Gamma(x)$ for all $x > 0$. [*Hint:* Use integration by parts.]
   (c) Use the results in parts (a) and (b) to find $\Gamma(2)$, $\Gamma(3)$, and $\Gamma(4)$; and then make a conjecture about $\Gamma(n)$ for positive integer values of $n$.
   (d) Show that $\Gamma\left(\frac{1}{2}\right) = \sqrt{\pi}$. [*Hint:* See Exercise 66 of Section 7.8.]
   (e) Use the results obtained in parts (b) and (d) to show that $\Gamma\left(\frac{3}{2}\right) = \frac{1}{2}\sqrt{\pi}$ and $\Gamma\left(\frac{5}{2}\right) = \frac{3}{4}\sqrt{\pi}$.

4. Refer to the Gamma function defined in Exercise 3 to show that
   (a) $\int_0^1 (\ln x)^n\,dx = (-1)^n\Gamma(n+1), \quad n > 0$
   [*Hint:* Let $t = -\ln x$.]
   (b) $\int_0^{+\infty} e^{-x^n}\,dx = \Gamma\left(\frac{n+1}{n}\right), \quad n > 0.$
   [*Hint:* Let $t = x^n$. Use the result in Exercise 3(b).]

C 5. A ***simple pendulum*** consists of a mass that swings in a vertical plane at the end of a massless rod of length $L$, as shown in the accompanying figure. Suppose that a simple pendulum is displaced through an angle $\theta_0$ and released from rest. It can be shown that in the absence of friction, the time $T$ required for the pendulum to make one complete back-and-forth swing, called the ***period***, is given by
   $$T = \sqrt{\frac{8L}{g}}\int_0^{\theta_0} \frac{1}{\sqrt{\cos\theta - \cos\theta_0}}\,d\theta \qquad (1)$$
   where $\theta = \theta(t)$ is the angle the pendulum makes with the vertical at time $t$. The improper integral in (1) is difficult to evaluate numerically. By a substitution outlined below it can be shown that the period can be expressed as
   $$T = 4\sqrt{\frac{L}{g}}\int_0^{\pi/2} \frac{1}{\sqrt{1-k^2\sin^2\phi}}\,d\phi \qquad (2)$$
   where $k = \sin(\theta_0/2)$. The integral in (2) is called a ***complete elliptic integral of the first kind*** and is more easily evaluated by numerical methods.
   (a) Obtain (2) from (1) by substituting
   $$\cos\theta = 1 - 2\sin^2(\theta/2)$$
   $$\cos\theta_0 = 1 - 2\sin^2(\theta_0/2)$$
   $$k = \sin(\theta_0/2)$$
   and then making the change of variable
   $$\sin\phi = \frac{\sin(\theta/2)}{\sin(\theta_0/2)} = \frac{\sin(\theta/2)}{k}$$
   (b) Use (2) and the numerical integration capability of your CAS to estimate the period of a simple pendulum for which $L = 1.5$ ft, $\theta_0 = 20°$, and $g = 32$ ft/s$^2$.

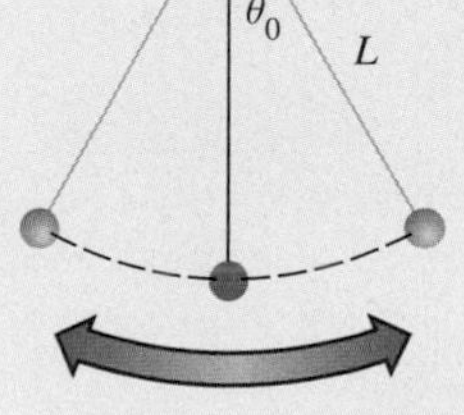


Figure Ex-5

## EXPANDING THE CALCULUS HORIZON

To learn how numerical integration can be applied to the cost analysis of an engineering project, see the module entitled **Railroad Design** at:

**www.wiley.com/college/anton**

8

# MATHEMATICAL MODELING WITH DIFFERENTIAL EQUATIONS

Photo by Milton Bell, catalog # Lu1-mb1, Texas Archeological Research Laboratory, The University of Texas at Austin

*In the 1920s, excavation of an archeological site in Folsom, New Mexico, uncovered a collection of prehistoric stone spearheads now known as "Folsom points." In 1950, carbon dating of charred bison bones found nearby confirmed that human hunters lived in the area between 9000 B.C. and 8000 B.C. We will study carbon dating in this chapter.*

Many fundamental laws of science and engineering can be expressed in the form of differential equations. In this chapter we will describe some important mathematical models that involve differential equations, and we will discuss methods for solving some of the basic types of differential equations. In addition, we will return to the concept of a slope field and we will describe an associated numerical method for generating approximate solutions to certain differential equations.

## 8.1 MODELING WITH DIFFERENTIAL EQUATIONS

*In this section we will introduce some basic terminology and concepts concerning differential equations. We will also discuss the general idea of modeling with differential equations, and we will encounter important models that can be applied to demography, medicine, ecology, and physics.*

### TERMINOLOGY

Recall from Section 5.2 that a ***differential equation*** is an equation involving one or more derivatives of an unknown function. In this section we will denote the unknown function by $y = y(x)$ unless the differential equation arises from an applied problem involving time, in which case we will denote it by $y = y(t)$. The ***order*** of a differential equation is the order of the highest derivative that it contains. Some examples are given in Table 8.1.1. The last two equations in that table are expressed in "prime" notation, which does not specify the independent variable explicitly. However, you will usually be able to tell from the equation itself or from the context in which it arises whether to interpret $y'$ as $dy/dx$ or $dy/dt$.

Table 8.1.1

| DIFFERENTIAL EQUATION | ORDER |
|---|---|
| $\frac{dy}{dx} = 3y$ | 1 |
| $\frac{d^2y}{dx^2} - 6\frac{dy}{dx} + 8y = 0$ | 2 |
| $\frac{d^3y}{dt^3} - t\frac{dy}{dt} + (t^2 - 1)y = e^t$ | 3 |
| $y' - y = e^{2x}$ | 1 |
| $y'' + y' = \cos t$ | 2 |

### SOLUTIONS OF DIFFERENTIAL EQUATIONS

A function $y = y(x)$ is a ***solution*** of a differential equation on an open interval if the equation is satisfied identically on the interval when $y$ and its derivatives are substituted into the equation. For example, $y = e^{2x}$ is a solution of the differential equation

$$\frac{dy}{dx} - y = e^{2x} \tag{1}$$

on the interval $(-\infty, +\infty)$, since substituting $y$ and its derivative into the left side of this equation yields

$$\frac{dy}{dx} - y = \frac{d}{dx}[e^{2x}] - e^{2x} = 2e^{2x} - e^{2x} = e^{2x}$$

for all real values of $x$. However, this is not the only solution on $(-\infty, +\infty)$; for example, the function

$$y = e^{2x} + Ce^{x} \tag{2}$$

is also a solution for every real value of the constant $C$, since

$$\frac{dy}{dx} - y = \frac{d}{dx}[e^{2x} + Ce^{x}] - (e^{2x} + Ce^{x}) = (2e^{2x} + Ce^{x}) - (e^{2x} + Ce^{x}) = e^{2x}$$

After developing some techniques for solving equations such as (1), we will be able to show that *all* solutions of (1) on $(-\infty, +\infty)$ can be obtained by substituting values for the constant $C$ in (2). On a given interval, a solution of a differential equation from which all solutions on that interval can be derived by substituting values for arbitrary constants is called a ***general solution*** of the equation on the interval. Thus (2) is a general solution of (1) on the interval $(-\infty, +\infty)$.

The first-order equation (1) has a single arbitrary constant in its general solution (2). Usually, the general solution of an $n$th-order differential equation will contain $n$ arbitrary constants. This is plausible, since $n$ integrations are needed to recover a function from its $n$th derivative.

The graph of a solution of a differential equation is called an ***integral curve*** for the equation, so the general solution of a differential equation produces a family of integral curves corresponding to the different possible choices for the arbitrary constants. For example, Figure 8.1.1 shows some integral curves for (1), which were obtained by assigning values to the arbitrary constant in (2).

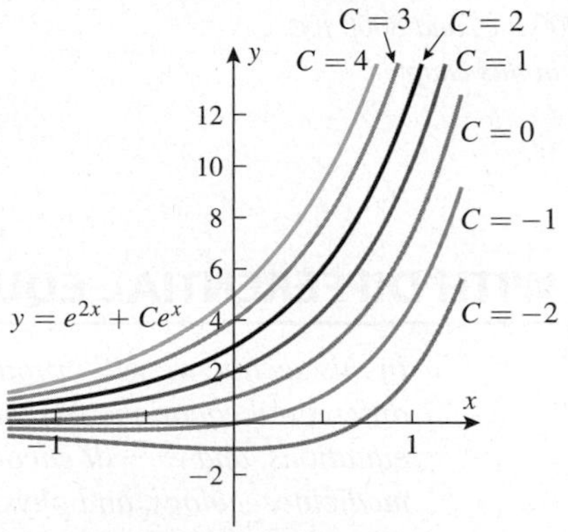


Integral curves for $\frac{dy}{dx} - y = e^{2x}$

▶ **Figure 8.1.1**

## INITIAL-VALUE PROBLEMS

When an applied problem leads to a differential equation, there are usually conditions in the problem that determine specific values for the arbitrary constants. As a rule of thumb, it requires $n$ conditions to determine values for all $n$ arbitrary constants in the general solution of an $n$th-order differential equation (one condition for each constant). For a first-order equation, the single arbitrary constant can be determined by specifying the value of the unknown function $y(x)$ at an arbitrary $x$-value $x_0$, say $y(x_0) = y_0$. This is called an ***initial condition***, and the problem of solving a first-order equation subject to an initial condition is called a ***first-order initial-value problem***. Geometrically, the initial condition $y(x_0) = y_0$ has the effect of isolating the integral curve that passes through the point $(x_0, y_0)$ from the complete family of integral curves.

▶ **Example 1** The solution of the initial-value problem

$$\frac{dy}{dx} - y = e^{2x}, \quad y(0) = 3$$

can be obtained by substituting the initial condition $x = 0, y = 3$ in the general solution (2) to find $C$. We obtain

$$3 = e^{0} + Ce^{0} = 1 + C$$

Thus, $C = 2$, and the solution of the initial-value problem, which is obtained by substituting this value of $C$ in (2), is

$$y = e^{2x} + 2e^x$$

Geometrically, this solution is realized as the integral curve in Figure 8.1.1 that passes through the point $(0, 3)$. ◀

Since many important principles in the physical and social sciences involve rates of change, such principles can often be modeled by differential equations. Here are some examples of the modeling process.

## UNINHIBITED POPULATION GROWTH

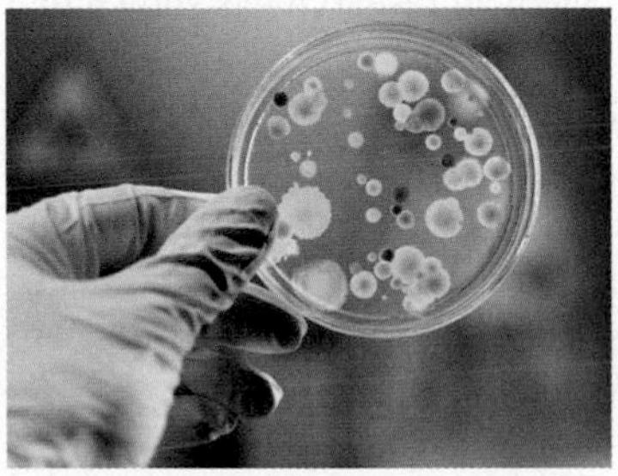

AndreasReh/iStockphoto

*When the number of bacteria is small, an uninhibited population growth model can be used to model the growth of bacteria in a petri dish.*

One of the simplest models of population growth is based on the observation that when populations (people, plants, bacteria, and fruit flies, for example) are not constrained by environmental limitations, they tend to grow at a rate that is proportional to the size of the population—the larger the population, the more rapidly it grows.

To translate this principle into a mathematical model, suppose that $y = y(t)$ denotes the population at time $t$. At each point in time, the rate of increase of the population with respect to time is $dy/dt$, so the assumption that the rate of growth is proportional to the population is described by the differential equation

$$\frac{dy}{dt} = ky \tag{3}$$

where $k$ is a positive constant of proportionality that can usually be determined experimentally. Thus, if the population is known at some point in time, say $y = y_0$ at time $t = 0$, then a formula for the population $y(t)$ can be obtained by solving the initial-value problem

$$\frac{dy}{dt} = ky, \quad y(0) = y_0$$

## INHIBITED POPULATION GROWTH; LOGISTIC MODELS

The uninhibited population growth model was predicated on the assumption that the population $y = y(t)$ was not constrained by the environment. While this assumption is reasonable as long as the size of the population is relatively small, environmental effects become increasingly important as the population grows. In general, populations grow within ecological systems that can only support a certain number of individuals; the number $L$ of such individuals is called the ***carrying capacity*** of the system. When $y > L$, the population exceeds the capacity of the ecological system and tends to decrease toward $L$; when $y < L$, the population is below the capacity of the ecological system and tends to increase toward $L$; when $y = L$, the population is in balance with the capacity of the ecological system and tends to remain stable.

To translate this into a mathematical model, we must look for a differential equation in which $y > 0$, $L > 0$, and

$$\frac{dy}{dt} < 0 \text{ if } \frac{y}{L} > 1, \qquad \frac{dy}{dt} > 0 \text{ if } \frac{y}{L} < 1, \qquad \frac{dy}{dt} = 0 \text{ if } \frac{y}{L} = 1$$

Moreover, when the population is far below the carrying capacity (i.e., $y/L \approx 0$), then the environmental constraints should have little effect, and the growth rate should behave like the uninhibited population model. Thus, we want

$$\frac{dy}{dt} \approx ky \text{ if } \frac{y}{L} \approx 0$$

A simple differential equation that meets all of these requirements is

$$\frac{dy}{dt} = k\left(1 - \frac{y}{L}\right)y$$

where $k$ is a positive constant of proportionality. Thus if $k$ and $L$ can be determined experimentally, and if the population is known at some point, say $y(0) = y_0$, then a formula for the population $y(t)$ can be determined by solving the initial-value problem

$$\frac{dy}{dt} = k\left(1 - \frac{y}{L}\right)y, \quad y(0) = y_0 \tag{4}$$

This theory of population growth is due to the Belgian mathematician P. F. Verhulst (1804–1849), who introduced it in 1838 and described it as "logistic growth."* Thus, the differential equation in (4) is called the ***logistic differential equation***, and the growth model described by (4) is called the ***logistic model***.

## PHARMACOLOGY

When a drug (say, penicillin or aspirin) is administered to an individual, it enters the bloodstream and then is absorbed by the body over time. Medical research has shown that the amount of a drug that is present in the bloodstream tends to decrease at a rate that is proportional to the amount of the drug present—the more of the drug that is present in the bloodstream, the more rapidly it is absorbed by the body.

To translate this principle into a mathematical model, suppose that $y = y(t)$ is the amount of the drug present in the bloodstream at time $t$. At each point in time, the rate of change in $y$ with respect to $t$ is $dy/dt$, so the assumption that the rate of decrease is proportional to the amount $y$ in the bloodstream translates into the differential equation

$$\frac{dy}{dt} = -ky \tag{5}$$

where $k$ is a positive constant of proportionality that depends on the drug and can be determined experimentally. The negative sign is required because $y$ decreases with time. Thus, if the initial dosage of the drug is known, say $y = y_0$ at time $t = 0$, then a formula for $y(t)$ can be obtained by solving the initial-value problem

$$\frac{dy}{dt} = -ky, \quad y(0) = y_0$$

## SPREAD OF DISEASE

Suppose that a disease begins to spread in a population of $L$ individuals. Logic suggests that at each point in time the rate at which the disease spreads will depend on how many individuals are already affected and how many are not—as more individuals are affected, the opportunity to spread the disease tends to increase, but at the same time there are fewer individuals who are not affected, so the opportunity to spread the disease tends to decrease. Thus, there are two conflicting influences on the rate at which the disease spreads.

To translate this into a mathematical model, suppose that $y = y(t)$ is the number of individuals who have the disease at time $t$, so of necessity the number of individuals who do not have the disease at time $t$ is $L - y$. As the value of $y$ increases, the value of $L - y$ decreases, so the conflicting influences of the two factors on the rate of spread $dy/dt$ are taken into account by the differential equation

$$\frac{dy}{dt} = ky(L - y)$$

Show that the model for the spread of disease can be viewed as a logistic model with constant of proportionality $kL$ by rewriting (6) appropriately.

where $k$ is a positive constant of proportionality that depends on the nature of the disease and the behavior patterns of the individuals and can be determined experimentally. Thus, if the number of affected individuals is known at some point in time, say $y = y_0$ at time $t = 0$, then a formula for $y(t)$ can be obtained by solving the initial-value problem

$$\frac{dy}{dt} = ky(L - y), \quad y(0) = y_0 \tag{6}$$

* Verhulst's model fell into obscurity for nearly a hundred years because he did not have sufficient census data to test its validity. However, interest in the model was revived during the 1930s when biologists used it successfully to describe the growth of fruit fly and flour beetle populations. Verhulst himself used the model to predict that an upper limit of Belgium's population would be approximately 9,400,000. In 2006 the population was about 10,379,000.

## NEWTON'S LAW OF COOLING

If a hot object is placed into a cool environment, the object will cool at a rate proportional to the difference in temperature between the object and the environment. Similarly, if a cold object is placed into a warm environment, the object will warm at a rate that is again proportional to the difference in temperature between the object and the environment. Together, these observations comprise a result known as *Newton's Law of Cooling*. (Newton's Law of Cooling appeared previously in the exercises of Section 2.2 and was mentioned briefly in Section 5.8.) To translate this into a mathematical model, suppose that $T = T(t)$ is the temperature of the object at time $t$ and that $T_e$ is the temperature of the environment, which is assumed to be constant. Since the rate of change $dT/dt$ is proportional to $T - T_e$, we have

$$\frac{dT}{dt} = k(T - T_e)$$

where $k$ is a constant of proportionality. Moreover, since $dT/dt$ is positive when $T < T_e$, and is negative when $T > T_e$, the sign of $k$ must be *negative*. Thus if the temperature of the object is known at some time, say $T = T_0$ at time $t = 0$, then a formula for the temperature $T(t)$ can be obtained by solving the initial-value problem

$$\frac{dT}{dt} = k(T - T_e), \quad T(0) = T_0 \tag{7}$$

## VIBRATIONS OF SPRINGS

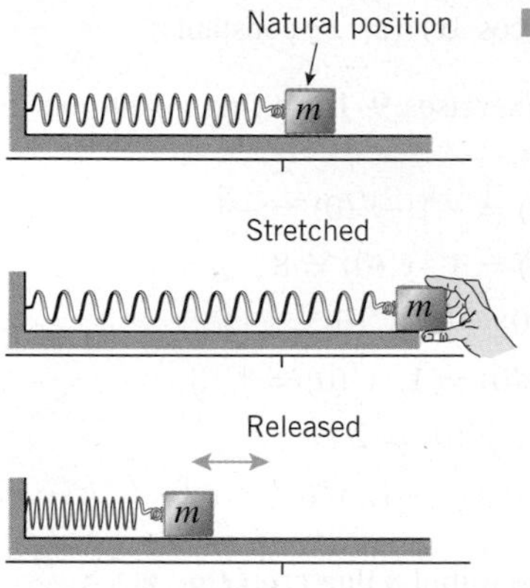

▲ **Figure 8.1.2**

▲ **Figure 8.1.3**

We conclude this section with an engineering model that leads to a second-order differential equation.

As shown in Figure 8.1.2, consider a block of mass $m$ attached to the end of a horizontal spring. Assume that the block is then set into vibratory motion by pulling the spring beyond its natural position and releasing it at time $t = 0$. We will be interested in finding a mathematical model that describes the vibratory motion of the block over time.

To translate this problem into mathematical form, we introduce a horizontal $x$-axis whose positive direction is to the right and whose origin is at the right end of the spring when the spring is in its natural position (Figure 8.1.3). Our goal is to find a model for the coordinate $x = x(t)$ of the point of attachment of the block to the spring as a function of time. In developing this model, we will assume that the only force on the mass $m$ is the restoring force of the spring, and we will ignore the influence of other forces such as friction, air resistance, and so forth. Recall from Hooke's Law (Section 6.6) that when the connection point has coordinate $x(t)$, the restoring force is $-kx(t)$, where $k$ is the spring constant. [The negative sign is due to the fact that the restoring force is to the left when $x(t)$ is positive, and the restoring force is to the right when $x(t)$ is negative.] It follows from Newton's Second Law of Motion [Equation (5) of Section 6.6] that this restoring force is equal to the product of the mass $m$ and the acceleration $d^2x/dt^2$ of the mass. In other words, we have

$$m\frac{d^2x}{dt^2} = -kx$$

which is a second-order differential equation for $x$. If at time $t = 0$ the mass is released from rest at position $x(0) = x_0$, then a formula for $x(t)$ can be found by solving the initial-value problem

$$m\frac{d^2x}{dt^2} = -kx, \quad x(0) = x_0, \quad x'(0) = 0 \tag{8}$$

[If at time $t = 0$ the mass is given an initial velocity $v_0 \neq 0$, then the condition $x'(0) = 0$ must be replaced by $x'(0) = v_0$.]

## ✓ QUICK CHECK EXERCISES 8.1 (See page 487 for answers.)

1. Match each differential equation with its family of solutions.

(a) $x\frac{dy}{dx} = y$ ______ (i) $y = x^2 + C$

(b) $y'' = 4y$ ______ (ii) $y = C_1 \sin 2x + C_2 \cos 2x$

(c) $\frac{dy}{dx} = 2x$ ______ (iii) $y = C_1e^{2x} + C_2e^{-2x}$

(d) $\frac{d^2y}{dx^2} = -4y$ ______ (iv) $y = Cx$

2. If $y = C_1e^{2x} + C_2xe^{2x}$ is the general solution of a differential equation, then the order of the equation is ______, and a solution to the differential equation that satisfies the initial conditions $y(0) = 1, y'(0) = 4$ is given by $y =$ ______.

3. The graph of a differentiable function $y = y(x)$ passes through the point $(0, 1)$ and at every point $P(x, y)$ on the graph the tangent line is perpendicular to the line through $P$ and the origin. Find an initial-value problem whose solution is $y(x)$.

4. A glass of ice water with a temperature of 36°F is placed in a room with a constant temperature of 68°F. Assuming that Newton's Law of Cooling applies, find an initial-value problem whose solution is the temperature of water $t$ minutes after it is placed in the room. [*Note:* The differential equation will involve a constant of proportionality.]

## EXERCISE SET 8.1

1. Confirm that $y = 3e^{x^3}$ is a solution of the initial-value problem $y' = 3x^2y, y(0) = 3$.

2. Confirm that $y = \frac{1}{4}x^4 + 2\cos x + 1$ is a solution of the initial-value problem $y' = x^3 - 2\sin x, y(0) = 3$.

**3–4** State the order of the differential equation, and confirm that the functions in the given family are solutions. ■

3. (a) $(1+x)\dfrac{dy}{dx} = y;\ y = c(1+x)$
(b) $y'' + y = 0;\ y = c_1 \sin t + c_2 \cos t$

4. (a) $2\dfrac{dy}{dx} + y = x - 1;\ y = ce^{-x/2} + x - 3$
(b) $y'' - y = 0;\ y = c_1e^t + c_2e^{-t}$

**5–8 True–False** Determine whether the statement is true or false. Explain your answer. ■

5. The equation
$$\left(\frac{dy}{dx}\right)^2 = \frac{dy}{dx} + 2y$$
is an example of a second-order differential equation.

6. The differential equation
$$\frac{dy}{dx} = 2y + 1$$
has a solution that is constant.

7. We expect the general solution of the differential equation
$$\frac{d^3y}{dx^3} + 3\frac{d^2y}{dx^2} - \frac{dy}{dx} + 4y = 0$$
to involve three arbitrary constants.

8. If every solution to a differential equation can be expressed in the form $y = Ae^{x+b}$ for some choice of constants $A$ and $b$, then the differential equation must be of second order.

**9–14** In each part, verify that the functions are solutions of the differential equation by substituting the functions into the equation. ■

9. $y'' + y' - 2y = 0$
(a) $e^{-2x}$ and $e^x$
(b) $c_1e^{-2x} + c_2e^x$ ($c_1, c_2$ constants)

10. $y'' - y' - 6y = 0$
(a) $e^{-2x}$ and $e^{3x}$
(b) $c_1e^{-2x} + c_2e^{3x}$ ($c_1, c_2$ constants)

11. $y'' - 4y' + 4y = 0$
(a) $e^{2x}$ and $xe^{2x}$
(b) $c_1e^{2x} + c_2xe^{2x}$ ($c_1, c_2$ constants)

12. $y'' - 8y' + 16y = 0$
(a) $e^{4x}$ and $xe^{4x}$
(b) $c_1e^{4x} + c_2xe^{4x}$ ($c_1, c_2$ constants)

13. $y'' + 4y = 0$
(a) $\sin 2x$ and $\cos 2x$
(b) $c_1 \sin 2x + c_2 \cos 2x$ ($c_1, c_2$ constants)

14. $y'' + 4y' + 13y = 0$
(a) $e^{-2x}\sin 3x$ and $e^{-2x}\cos 3x$
(b) $e^{-2x}(c_1 \sin 3x + c_2 \cos 3x)$ ($c_1, c_2$ constants)

**15–20** Use the results of Exercises 9–14 to find a solution to the initial-value problem. ■

15. $y'' + y' - 2y = 0,\ y(0) = -1,\ y'(0) = -4$

16. $y'' - y' - 6y = 0,\ y(0) = 1,\ y'(0) = 8$

17. $y'' - 4y' + 4y = 0,\ y(0) = 2,\ y'(0) = 2$

18. $y'' - 8y' + 16y = 0,\ y(0) = 1,\ y'(0) = 1$

19. $y'' + 4y = 0,\ y(0) = 1,\ y'(0) = 2$

20. $y'' + 4y' + 13y = 0,\ y(0) = -1,\ y'(0) = -1$

**21–26** Find a solution to the initial-value problem. ■

21. $y' + 4x = 2,\ y(0) = 3$

22. $y'' + 6x = 0,\ y(0) = 1,\ y'(0) = 2$

23. $y' - y^2 = 0,\ y(1) = 2$ [*Hint:* Assume the solution has an inverse function $x = x(y)$. Find, and solve, a differential equation that involves $x'(y)$.]

24. $y' = 1 + y^2,\ y(0) = 0$ (See Exercise 23.)

25. $x^2y' + 2xy = 0,\ y(1) = 2$ [*Hint:* Interpret the left-hand side of the equation as the derivative of a product of two functions.]

26. $xy' + y = e^x,\ y(1) = 1 + e$ (See Exercise 25.)

**FOCUS ON CONCEPTS**

27. (a) Suppose that a quantity $y = y(t)$ increases at a rate that is proportional to the square of the amount present, and suppose that at time $t = 0$, the amount present is $y_0$. Find an initial-value problem whose solution is $y(t)$.
(b) Suppose that a quantity $y = y(t)$ decreases at a rate that is proportional to the square of the amount present, and suppose that at a time $t = 0$, the amount present is $y_0$. Find an initial-value problem whose solution is $y(t)$.

28. (a) Suppose that a quantity $y = y(t)$ changes in such a way that $dy/dt = k\sqrt{y}$, where $k > 0$. Describe how $y$ changes in words.
(b) Suppose that a quantity $y = y(t)$ changes in such a way that $dy/dt = -ky^3$, where $k > 0$. Describe how $y$ changes in words.

29. (a) Suppose that a particle moves along an $s$-axis in such a way that its velocity $v(t)$ is always half of $s(t)$. Find a differential equation whose solution is $s(t)$.
(b) Suppose that an object moves along an $s$-axis in such a way that its acceleration $a(t)$ is always twice the velocity. Find a differential equation whose solution is $s(t)$.

30. Suppose that a body moves along an $s$-axis through a resistive medium in such a way that the velocity $v = v(t)$ decreases at a rate that is twice the square of the velocity.
(a) Find a differential equation whose solution is the velocity $v(t)$.
(b) Find a differential equation whose solution is the position $s(t)$.

31. Consider a solution $y = y(t)$ to the uninhibited population growth model.
(a) Use Equation (3) to explain why $y$ will be an increasing function of $t$.
(b) Use Equation (3) to explain why the graph $y = y(t)$ will be concave up.

32. Consider the logistic model for population growth.
(a) Explain why there are two constant solutions to this model.
(b) For what size of the population will the population be growing most rapidly?

33. Consider the model for the spread of disease.
(a) Explain why there are two constant solutions to this model.
(b) For what size of the infected population is the disease spreading most rapidly?

34. Explain why there is exactly one constant solution to the Newton's Law of Cooling model.

35. Show that if $c_1$ and $c_2$ are any constants, the function

$$x = x(t) = c_1 \cos\left(\sqrt{\frac{k}{m}}\,t\right) + c_2 \sin\left(\sqrt{\frac{k}{m}}\,t\right)$$

is a solution to the differential equation for the vibrating spring. (The corresponding motion of the spring is referred to as ***simple harmonic motion***.)

36. (a) Use the result of Exercise 35 to solve the initial-value problem in (8).
(b) Find the amplitude, period, and frequency of your answer to part (a), and interpret each of these in terms of the motion of the spring.

37. **Writing** Select one of the models in this section and write a paragraph that discusses conditions under which the model would not be appropriate. How might you modify the model to take those conditions into account?

**✓ QUICK CHECK ANSWERS 8.1** 1. (a) (iv) (b) (iii) (c) (i) (d) (ii) 2. 2; $e^{2x} + 2xe^{2x}$ 3. $\dfrac{dy}{dx} = -\dfrac{x}{y}$, $y(0) = 1$ 4. $\dfrac{dT}{dt} = k(T - 68)$, $T(0) = 36$

# 8.2 SEPARATION OF VARIABLES

*In this section we will discuss a method, called "separation of variables," that can be used to solve a large class of first-order differential equations of a particular form. We will use this method to investigate mathematical models for exponential growth and decay, including population models and carbon dating.*

## FIRST-ORDER SEPARABLE EQUATIONS

We will now consider a method of solution that can often be applied to first-order equations that are expressible in the form

$$h(y)\frac{dy}{dx} = g(x) \tag{1}$$

Such first-order equations are said to be ***separable***. Some examples of separable equations are given in Table 8.2.1. The name "separable" arises from the fact that Equation (1) can be rewritten in the differential form

$$h(y)\,dy = g(x)\,dx \tag{2}$$

in which the expressions involving $x$ and $y$ appear on opposite sides. The process of rewriting (1) in form (2) is called ***separating variables***.

Some writers define a separable equation to be one that can be written in the form $dy/dx = G(x)H(y)$. Explain why this is equivalent to our definition.

**Table 8.2.1**

| EQUATION | FORM (1) | $h(y)$ | $g(x)$ |
|---|---|---|---|
| $\dfrac{dy}{dx} = \dfrac{x}{y}$ | $y\dfrac{dy}{dx} = x$ | $y$ | $x$ |
| $\dfrac{dy}{dx} = x^2y^3$ | $\dfrac{1}{y^3}\dfrac{dy}{dx} = x^2$ | $\dfrac{1}{y^3}$ | $x^2$ |
| $\dfrac{dy}{dx} = y$ | $\dfrac{1}{y}\dfrac{dy}{dx} = 1$ | $\dfrac{1}{y}$ | $1$ |
| $\dfrac{dy}{dx} = y - \dfrac{y}{x}$ | $\dfrac{1}{y}\dfrac{dy}{dx} = 1 - \dfrac{1}{x}$ | $\dfrac{1}{y}$ | $1 - \dfrac{1}{x}$ |

To motivate a method for solving separable equations, assume that $h(y)$ and $g(x)$ are continuous functions of their respective variables, and let $H(y)$ and $G(x)$ denote antiderivatives of $h(y)$ and $g(x)$, respectively. Consider the equation that results if we integrate both sides of (2), the left side with respect to $y$ and the right side with respect to $x$. We then have

$$\int h(y)\,dy = \int g(x)\,dx \tag{3}$$

or, equivalently,

$$H(y) = G(x) + C \tag{4}$$

where we consolidated the constants of integration into a single constant. We claim that a differentiable function $y = y(x)$ is a solution to (1) if and only if $y$ satisfies Equation (4) for some choice of the constant $C$.

Suppose that $y = y(x)$ is a solution to (1). It then follows from the chain rule that

$$\frac{d}{dx}[H(y)] = \frac{dH}{dy}\frac{dy}{dx} = h(y)\frac{dy}{dx} = g(x) = \frac{dG}{dx} \tag{5}$$

Since the functions $H(y)$ and $G(x)$ have the same derivative with respect to $x$, they must differ by a constant (Theorem 4.8.3). It then follows that $y$ satisfies (4) for an appropriate choice of $C$. Conversely, if $y = y(x)$ is defined implicitly by Equation (4), then implicit differentiation shows that (5) is satisfied, and thus $y(x)$ is a solution to (1) (Exercise 67). Because of this, it is common practice to refer to Equation (4) as the "solution" to (1).

In summary, we have the following procedure for solving (1), called ***separation of variables***:

***Separation of Variables***

**Step 1.** Separate the variables in (1) by rewriting the equation in the differential form

$$h(y)\,dy = g(x)\,dx$$

**Step 2.** Integrate both sides of the equation in Step 1 (the left side with respect to $y$ and the right side with respect to $x$),

$$\int h(y)\,dy = \int g(x)\,dx$$

and consolidate the constants of integration into a single constant.

**Step 3.** The equation that results from Step 2 will be equivalent to

$$H(y) = G(x) + C$$

where $H(y)$ is an antiderivative of $h(y)$ and $G(x)$ is an antiderivative of $g(x)$. If it is not too demanding, solve this equation explicitly for $y$ in terms of $x$ or for $x$ in terms of $y$. Otherwise, leave the solution to the separable differential equation in implicit form.

**▶ Example 1** Solve the differential equation

$$\frac{dy}{dx} = -4xy^2$$

and then solve the initial-value problem

$$\frac{dy}{dx} = -4xy^2, \quad y(0) = 1$$

For an initial-value problem in which the differential equation is separable, you can either use the initial condition to solve for $C$, as in Example 1, or replace the indefinite integrals in Step 2 by definite integrals (Exercise 68).

***Solution.*** For $y \neq 0$ we can write the differential equation in form (1) as

$$\frac{1}{y^2}\frac{dy}{dx} = -4x$$

Separating variables and integrating yields

$$\frac{1}{y^2}\,dy = -4x\,dx$$

$$\int \frac{1}{y^2}\,dy = \int -4x\,dx$$

or

$$-\frac{1}{y} = -2x^2 + C$$

Solving for $y$ as a function of $x$, we obtain

$$y = \frac{1}{2x^2 - C}$$

The initial condition $y(0) = 1$ requires that $y = 1$ when $x = 0$. Substituting these values into our solution yields $C = -1$ (verify). Thus, a solution to the initial-value problem is

$$y = \frac{1}{2x^2 + 1} \tag{6}$$

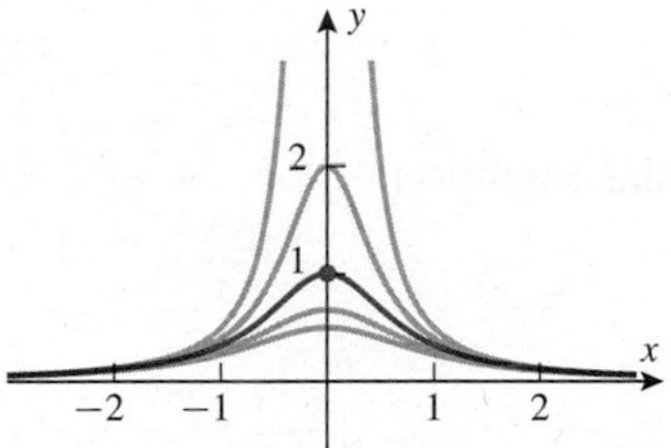


Integral curves for $\dfrac{dy}{dx} = -4xy^2$

▲ **Figure 8.2.1**

Some integral curves and our solution of the initial-value problem are graphed in Figure 8.2.1. ◀

One aspect of our solution to Example 1 deserves special comment. Had the initial condition been $y(0) = 0$ instead of $y(0) = 1$, the method we used would have failed to yield a solution to the resulting initial-value problem (Exercise 25). This is due to the fact that we assumed $y \neq 0$ in order to rewrite the equation $dy/dx = -4xy^2$ in the form

$$\frac{1}{y^2}\frac{dy}{dx} = -4x$$

It is important to be aware of such assumptions when manipulating a differential equation algebraically.

**▶ Example 2** Solve the initial-value problem

$$(4y - \cos y)\frac{dy}{dx} - 3x^2 = 0, \quad y(0) = 0$$

The solution of an initial-value problem in $x$ and $y$ can sometimes be expressed explicitly as a function of $x$ [as in Formula (6) of Example 1], or explicitly as a function of $y$ [as in Formula (8) of Example 2]. However, sometimes the solution cannot be expressed in either such form, so the only option is to express it implicitly as an equation in $x$ and $y$.

***Solution.*** We can write the differential equation in form (1) as

$$(4y - \cos y)\frac{dy}{dx} = 3x^2$$

Separating variables and integrating yields

$$(4y - \cos y)\,dy = 3x^2\,dx$$

$$\int (4y - \cos y)\,dy = \int 3x^2\,dx$$

or

$$2y^2 - \sin y = x^3 + C \tag{7}$$

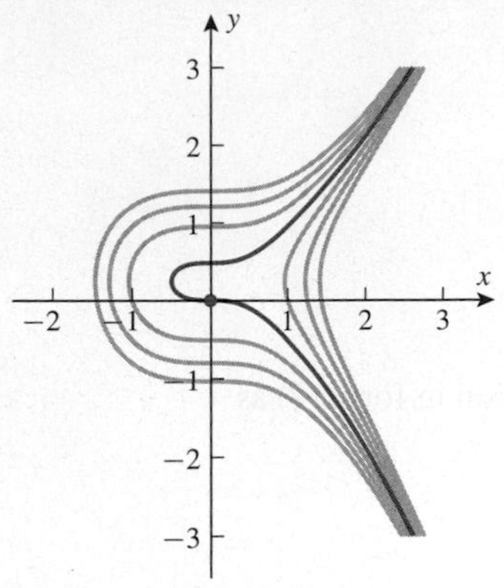


▲ **Figure 8.2.2**

**TECHNOLOGY MASTERY**

Some computer algebra systems can graph implicit equations. Figure 8.2.2 shows the graphs of (7) for $C = 0, \pm1, \pm2$, and $\pm3$. If you have a CAS that can graph implicit equations, try to duplicate this figure.

For the initial-value problem, the initial condition $y(0) = 0$ requires that $y = 0$ if $x = 0$. Substituting these values into (7) to determine the constant of integration yields $C = 0$ (verify). Thus, the solution of the initial-value problem is

$$2y^2 - \sin y = x^3$$

or

$$x = \sqrt[3]{2y^2 - \sin y} \blacktriangleleft \tag{8}$$

Some integral curves and the solution of the initial-value problem in Example 2 are graphed in Figure 8.2.2.

Initial-value problems often result from geometrical questions, as in the following example.

▶ **Example 3** Find a curve in the $xy$-plane that passes through $(0, 3)$ and whose tangent line at a point $(x, y)$ has slope $2x/y^2$.

***Solution.*** Since the slope of the tangent line is $dy/dx$, we have

$$\frac{dy}{dx} = \frac{2x}{y^2} \tag{9}$$

and, since the curve passes through $(0, 3)$, we have the initial condition

$$y(0) = 3$$

Equation (9) is separable and can be written as

$$y^2\,dy = 2x\,dx$$

so

$$\int y^2\,dy = \int 2x\,dx \quad \text{or} \quad \tfrac{1}{3}y^3 = x^2 + C$$

It follows from the initial condition that $y = 3$ if $x = 0$. Substituting these values into the last equation yields $C = 9$ (verify), so the equation of the desired curve is

$$\tfrac{1}{3}y^3 = x^2 + 9 \quad \text{or} \quad y = (3x^2 + 27)^{1/3} \blacktriangleleft$$

## EXPONENTIAL GROWTH AND DECAY MODELS

The population growth and pharmacology models developed in Section 8.1 are examples of a general class of models called *exponential models*. In general, exponential models arise in situations where a quantity increases or decreases at a rate that is proportional to the amount of the quantity present. More precisely, we make the following definition.

**8.2.1 DEFINITION** A quantity $y = y(t)$ is said to have an ***exponential growth model*** if it increases at a rate that is proportional to the amount of the quantity present, and it is said to have an ***exponential decay model*** if it decreases at a rate that is proportional to the amount of the quantity present. Thus, for an exponential growth model, the quantity $y(t)$ satisfies an equation of the form

$$\frac{dy}{dt} = ky \quad (k > 0) \tag{10}$$

and for an exponential decay model, the quantity $y(t)$ satisfies an equation of the form

$$\frac{dy}{dt} = -ky \quad (k > 0) \tag{11}$$

The constant $k$ is called the ***growth constant*** or the ***decay constant***, as appropriate.

Equations (10) and (11) are separable since they have the form of (1), but with $t$ rather than $x$ as the independent variable. To illustrate how these equations can be solved, suppose that a positive quantity $y = y(t)$ has an exponential growth model and that we know the amount of the quantity at some point in time, say $y = y_0$ when $t = 0$. Thus, a formula for $y(t)$ can be obtained by solving the initial-value problem

$$\frac{dy}{dt} = ky, \quad y(0) = y_0$$

Separating variables and integrating yields

$$\int \frac{1}{y}\, dy = \int k\, dt$$

or (since $y > 0$)

$$\ln y = kt + C \tag{12}$$

The initial condition implies that $y = y_0$ when $t = 0$. Substituting these values in (12) yields $C = \ln y_0$ (verify). Thus,

$$\ln y = kt + \ln y_0$$

from which it follows that

$$y = e^{\ln y} = e^{kt + \ln y_0}$$

or, equivalently,

$$y = y_0 e^{kt} \tag{13}$$

We leave it for you to show that if $y = y(t)$ has an exponential decay model, and if $y(0) = y_0$, then

$$y = y_0 e^{-kt} \tag{14}$$

## INTERPRETING THE GROWTH AND DECAY CONSTANTS

The significance of the constant $k$ in Formulas (13) and (14) can be understood by reexamining the differential equations that gave rise to these formulas. For example, in the case of the exponential growth model, Equation (10) can be rewritten as

$$k = \frac{dy/dt}{y} \tag{15}$$

which states that the growth rate as a fraction of the entire population remains constant over time, and this constant is $k$. For this reason, $k$ is called the ***relative growth rate*** of the population. It is usual to express the relative growth rate as a percentage. Thus, a relative growth rate of 3% per unit of time in an exponential growth model means that $k = 0.03$. Similarly, the constant $k$ in an exponential decay model is called the ***relative decay rate***.

It is standard practice in applications to call (15) the *growth rate*, even though it is misleading (the growth rate is $dy/dt$). However, the practice is so common that we will follow it here.

► **Example 4** According to the U.S. Census Bureau, the world population at the beginning of 2014 was about 7.1 billion and growing at a rate of about 1.08% per year. Assuming an exponential growth model, estimate the world population at the beginning of the year 2030.

***Solution.*** We assume that the population at the beginning of 2014 was 7.1 billion and let

$t$ = time elapsed from the beginning of 2014 (in years)

$y$ = world population (in billions)

The beginning of 2014 corresponds to $t = 0$ so that

$$y_0 = y(0) = 7.1 \text{ billion}$$

Since the growth rate is 1.08% ($k = 0.0108$), it follows from (13) that the world population at time $t$ will be

$$y = y_0 e^{kt} = 7.1e^{0.0108t} \tag{16}$$

The beginning of the year 2030 corresponds to an elapsed time of $t = 16$ years ($2030 - 2014 = 16$). It follows from (16) that the world population at the start of year 2030 will be

$$y(16) = 7.1e^{0.0108(16)} \approx 8.4$$

which is a population of approximately 8.4 billion. ◄

In Example 4 the growth rate was given, so there was no need to calculate it. If the growth rate or decay rate is unknown, then it can be calculated using the initial condition and the value of $y$ at another point in time (Exercise 44).

## DOUBLING TIME AND HALF-LIFE

If a quantity $y$ has an exponential growth model, then the time required for the original size to double is called the ***doubling time***, and if $y$ has an exponential decay model, then the

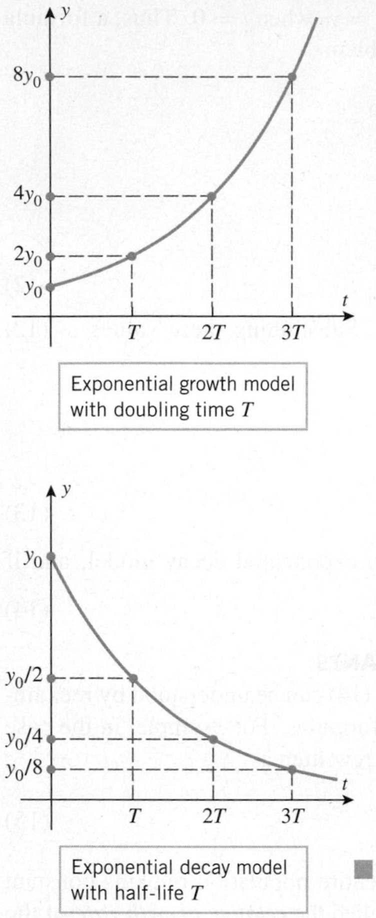

▲ Figure 8.2.3

time required for the original size to reduce by half is called the ***half-life***. As it turns out, doubling time and half-life depend only on the growth or decay rate and not on the amount present initially. To see why this is so, suppose that $y = y(t)$ has an exponential growth model

$$y = y_0 e^{kt} \tag{17}$$

and let $T$ denote the amount of time required for $y$ to double in size. Thus, at time $t = T$ the value of $y$ will be $2y_0$, and hence from (17)

$$2y_0 = y_0 e^{kT} \quad \text{or} \quad e^{kT} = 2$$

Taking the natural logarithm of both sides yields $kT = \ln 2$, which implies that the doubling time is

$$T = \frac{1}{k} \ln 2 \tag{18}$$

We leave it as an exercise to show that Formula (18) also gives the half-life of an exponential decay model. Observe that this formula does not involve the initial amount $y_0$, so that in an exponential growth or decay model, the quantity $y$ doubles (or reduces by half) every $T$ units (Figure 8.2.3).

▶ **Example 5** It follows from (18) that with a continued growth of 1.08% per year, the doubling time for the world population will be

$$T = \frac{1}{0.0108} \ln 2 \approx 64$$

or approximately 64 years. Thus, with a continued 1.08% annual growth rate the population of 7.1 billion in 2014 will double to 14.2 billion in 2078 and will double again to 28.4 billion by 2142. ◀

## RADIOACTIVE DECAY

It is a fact of physics that radioactive elements disintegrate spontaneously in a process called ***radioactive decay***. Experimentation has shown that the rate of disintegration is proportional to the amount of the element present, which implies that the amount $y = y(t)$ of a radioactive element present as a function of time has an exponential decay model.

Every radioactive element has a specific half-life; for example, the half-life of radioactive carbon-14 is about 5730 years. Thus, from (18), the decay constant for this element is

$$k = \frac{1}{T} \ln 2 = \frac{\ln 2}{5730} \approx 0.000121$$

and this implies that if there are $y_0$ units of carbon-14 present at time $t = 0$, then the number of units present after $t$ years will be approximately

$$y(t) = y_0 e^{-0.000121t} \tag{19}$$

▶ **Example 6** If 100 grams of radioactive carbon-14 are stored in a cave for 1000 years, how many grams will be left at that time?

***Solution.*** From (19) with $y_0 = 100$ and $t = 1000$, we obtain

$$y(1000) = 100e^{-0.000121(1000)} = 100e^{-0.121} \approx 88.6$$

Thus, about 88.6 grams will be left. ◀

## CARBON DATING

When the nitrogen in the Earth's upper atmosphere is bombarded by cosmic radiation, the radioactive element carbon-14 is produced. This carbon-14 combines with oxygen to form carbon dioxide, which is ingested by plants, which in turn are eaten by animals. In this way all living plants and animals absorb quantities of radioactive carbon-14. In 1947 the American nuclear scientist W. F. Libby* proposed the theory that the percentage of

* W. F. Libby, "Radiocarbon Dating," *American Scientist*, Vol. 44, 1956, pp. 98–112.

carbon-14 in the atmosphere and in living tissues of plants is the same. When a plant or animal dies, the carbon-14 in the tissue begins to decay. Thus, the age of an artifact that contains plant or animal material can be estimated by determining what percentage of its original carbon-14 content remains. Various procedures, called ***carbon dating*** or ***carbon-14 dating***, have been developed for measuring this percentage.

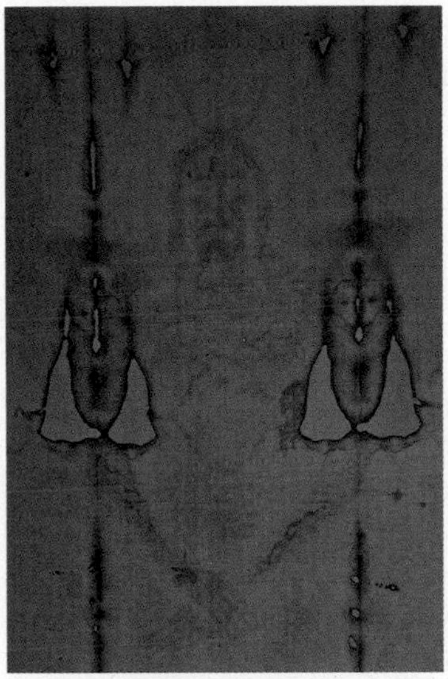

perseomedusa/Depositphotos

*The Shroud of Turin*

► **Example 7** In 1988 the Vatican authorized the British Museum to date a cloth relic known as the Shroud of Turin, possibly the burial shroud of Jesus of Nazareth. This cloth, which first surfaced in 1356, contains the negative image of a human body that was widely believed to be that of Jesus. The report of the British Museum showed that the fibers in the cloth contained between 92% and 93% of their original carbon-14. Use this information to estimate the age of the shroud.

***Solution.*** From (19), the fraction of the original carbon-14 that remains after $t$ years is

$$\frac{y(t)}{y_0} = e^{-0.000121t}$$

Taking the natural logarithm of both sides and solving for $t$, we obtain

$$t = -\frac{1}{0.000121}\ln\left(\frac{y(t)}{y_0}\right)$$

Thus, taking $y(t)/y_0$ to be 0.93 and 0.92, we obtain

$$t = -\frac{1}{0.000121}\ln(0.93) \approx 600$$

$$t = -\frac{1}{0.000121}\ln(0.92) \approx 689$$

This means that when the test was done in 1988, the shroud was between 600 and 689 years old, thereby placing its origin between 1299 A.D. and 1388 A.D. Thus, if one accepts the validity of carbon-14 dating, the Shroud of Turin cannot be the burial shroud of Jesus of Nazareth. ◄

## ✓ QUICK CHECK EXERCISES 8.2 *(See page 498 for answers.)*

1. Solve the first-order separable equation
$$h(y)\frac{dy}{dx} = g(x)$$
by completing the following steps:

Step 1. Separate the variables by writing the equation in the differential form ________.

Step 2. Integrate both sides of the equation in Step 1: ________.

Step 3. If $H(y)$ is any antiderivative of $h(y)$, $G(x)$ is any antiderivative of $g(x)$, and $C$ is an unspecified constant, then, as suggested by Step 2, the equation ________ will generally define a family of solutions to $h(y)\,dy/dx = g(x)$ implicitly.

2. Suppose that a quantity $y = y(t)$ has an exponential growth model with growth constant $k > 0$.
(a) $y(t)$ satisfies a first-order differential equation of the form $dy/dt =$ ________.
(b) In terms of $k$, the doubling time of the quantity is ________.
(c) If $y_0 = y(0)$ is the initial amount of the quantity, then an explicit formula for $y(t)$ is given by $y(t) =$ ________.

3. Suppose that a quantity $y = y(t)$ has an exponential decay model with decay constant $k > 0$.
(a) $y(t)$ satisfies a first-order differential equation of the form $dy/dt =$ ________.
(b) In terms of $k$, the half-life of the quantity is ________.
(c) If $y_0 = y(0)$ is the initial amount of the quantity, then an explicit formula for $y(t)$ is given by $y(t) =$ ________.

4. The initial-value problem
$$\frac{dy}{dx} = -\frac{x}{y}, \quad y(0) = 1$$
has solution $y(x) =$ ________.

## EXERCISE SET 8.2 Graphing Utility C CAS

**1–10** Solve the differential equation by separation of variables. Where reasonable, express the family of solutions as explicit functions of $x$. ■

1. $\dfrac{dy}{dx} = \dfrac{y}{x}$
2. $\dfrac{dy}{dx} = 2(1+y^2)x$
3. $\dfrac{\sqrt{1+x^2}}{1+y}\dfrac{dy}{dx} = -x$
4. $(1+x^4)\dfrac{dy}{dx} = \dfrac{x^3}{y}$
5. $(2+2y^2)y' = e^x y$
6. $y' = -xy$
7. $e^{-y}\sin x - y'\cos^2 x = 0$
8. $y' - (1+x)(1+y^2) = 0$
9. $\dfrac{dy}{dx} - \dfrac{y^2-y}{\sin x} = 0$
10. $y - \dfrac{dy}{dx}\sec x = 0$

**11–14** Solve the initial-value problem by separation of variables. ■

11. $y' = \dfrac{3x^2}{2y+\cos y}, \quad y(0) = \pi$
12. $y' - xe^y = 2e^y, \quad y(0) = 0$
13. $\dfrac{dy}{dt} = \dfrac{2t+1}{2y-2}, \quad y(0) = -1$
14. $y'\cosh^2 x - y\cosh 2x = 0, \quad y(0) = 3$
15. (a) Sketch some typical integral curves of the differential equation $y' = y/2x$.
    (b) Find an equation for the integral curve that passes through the point $(2, 1)$.
16. (a) Sketch some typical integral curves of the differential equation $y' = -x/y$.
    (b) Find an equation for the integral curve that passes through the point $(3, 4)$.

**17–18** Solve the differential equation and then use a graphing utility to generate five integral curves for the equation. ■

17. $(x^2+4)\dfrac{dy}{dx} + xy = 0$
18. $(\cos y)y' = \cos x$

C **19–20** Solve the differential equation. If you have a CAS with implicit plotting capability, use the CAS to generate five integral curves for the equation. ■

19. $y' = \dfrac{x^2}{1-y^2}$
20. $y' = \dfrac{y}{1+y^2}$

**21–24 True–False** Determine whether the statement is true or false. Explain your answer. ■

21. Every differential equation of the form $y' = f(y)$ is separable.
22. A differential equation of the form
$$h(x)\frac{dy}{dx} = g(y)$$
is not separable.
23. If a radioactive element has a half-life of 1 minute, and if a container holds 32 g of the element at 1:00 P.M., then the amount remaining at 1:05 P.M. will be 1 g.
24. If a population is growing exponentially, then the time it takes the population to quadruple is independent of the size of the population.
25. Suppose that the initial condition in Example 1 had been $y(0) = 0$. Show that none of the solutions generated in Example 1 satisfy this initial condition, and then solve the initial-value problem
$$\frac{dy}{dx} = -4xy^2, \quad y(0) = 0$$
Why does the method of Example 1 fail to produce this particular solution?
26. Find all ordered pairs $(x_0, y_0)$ such that if the initial condition in Example 1 is replaced by $y(x_0) = y_0$, the solution of the resulting initial-value problem is defined for all real numbers.
27. Find an equation of a curve with $x$-intercept 2 whose tangent line at any point $(x, y)$ has slope $xe^{-y}$.
28. Use a graphing utility to generate a curve that passes through the point $(1, 1)$ and whose tangent line at $(x, y)$ is perpendicular to the line through $(x, y)$ with slope $-2y/(3x^2)$.
29. Suppose that an initial population of 10,000 bacteria grows exponentially at a rate of 2% per hour and that $y = y(t)$ is the number of bacteria present $t$ hours later.
    (a) Find an initial-value problem whose solution is $y(t)$.
    (b) Find a formula for $y(t)$.
    (c) How long does it take for the initial population of bacteria to double?
    (d) How long does it take for the population of bacteria to reach 45,000?
30. A cell of the bacterium *E. coli* divides into two cells every 20 minutes when placed in a nutrient culture. Let $y = y(t)$ be the number of cells that are present $t$ minutes after a single cell is placed in the culture. Assume that the growth of the bacteria is approximated by an exponential growth model.
    (a) Find an initial-value problem whose solution is $y(t)$.
    (b) Find a formula for $y(t)$.
    (c) How many cells are present after 2 hours?
    (d) How long does it take for the number of cells to reach 1,000,000?
31. Radon-222 is a radioactive gas with a half-life of 3.83 days. This gas is a health hazard because it tends to get trapped in the basements of houses, and many health officials suggest that homeowners seal their basements to prevent entry of the gas. Assume that $5.0 \times 10^7$ radon atoms are trapped in a basement at the time it is sealed and that $y(t)$ is the number of atoms present $t$ days later.
    (a) Find an initial-value problem whose solution is $y(t)$.
    (b) Find a formula for $y(t)$.
    (c) How many atoms will be present after 30 days?
    (d) How long will it take for 90% of the original quantity of gas to decay?
32. Methylmercury is a toxic compound that can lead to neurological problems and an increased risk of heart disease. It takes about 50 days for the human body to eliminate 50% of a given quantity of the compound from the system. Suppose a test shows that there are 600 micrograms of

methylmercury in a person's body and that $y(t)$ is the number of micrograms present $t$ days later. Assume that $y(t)$ has an exponential decay model with a half-life of 50 days and that no additional methylmercury is absorbed from the environment.
(a) Find an initial-value problem whose solution is $y(t)$.
(b) Find a formula for $y(t)$.
(c) How many milligrams will be present after 4 weeks?
(d) How long will it take for 70% of the methylmercury to be eliminated from the person's body?

**33.** Suppose that 100 fruit flies are placed in a breeding container that can support at most 10,000 flies. Assuming that the population grows exponentially at a rate of 2% per day, how long will it take for the container to reach capacity?

**34.** Suppose that the town of Grayrock had a population of 10,000 in 2014 and a population of 12,000 in 2019. Assuming an exponential growth model, in what year will the population reach 20,000?

**35.** A scientist wants to determine the half-life of a certain radioactive substance. She determines that in exactly 5 days a 10.0-milligram sample of the substance decays to 3.5 milligrams. Based on these data, what is the half-life?

**36.** Suppose that 30% of a certain radioactive substance decays in 5 years.
(a) What is the half-life of the substance in years?
(b) Suppose that a certain quantity of this substance is stored in a cave. What percentage of it will remain after $t$ years?

**FOCUS ON CONCEPTS**

**37.** (a) Make a conjecture about the effect on the graphs of $y = y_0e^{kt}$ and $y = y_0e^{-kt}$ of varying $k$ and keeping $y_0$ fixed. Confirm your conjecture with a graphing utility.
(b) Make a conjecture about the effect on the graphs of $y = y_0e^{kt}$ and $y = y_0e^{-kt}$ of varying $y_0$ and keeping $k$ fixed. Confirm your conjecture with a graphing utility.

**38.** (a) What effect does increasing $y_0$ and keeping $k$ fixed have on the doubling time or half-life of an exponential model? Justify your answer.
(b) What effect does increasing $k$ and keeping $y_0$ fixed have on the doubling time and half-life of an exponential model? Justify your answer.

**39.** (a) There is a trick, called the ***Rule of 70***, that can be used to get a quick estimate of the doubling time or half-life of an exponential model. According to this rule, the doubling time or half-life is roughly 70 divided by the percentage growth or decay rate. For example, we showed in Example 5 that with a continued growth rate of 1.08% per year the world population would double every 64 years. This result agrees with the Rule of 70, since $70/1.08 \approx 64.8$. Explain why this rule works.
(b) Use the Rule of 70 to estimate the doubling time of a population that grows exponentially at a rate of 1% per year.
(c) Use the Rule of 70 to estimate the half-life of a population that decreases exponentially at a rate of 3.5% per hour.
(d) Use the Rule of 70 to estimate the growth rate that would be required for a population growing exponentially to double every 10 years.

**40.** Find a formula for the tripling time of an exponential growth model.

**41.** In 1950, a research team digging near Folsom, New Mexico, found charred bison bones along with some leaf-shaped projectile points (called the "Folsom points") that had been made by a Paleo-Indian hunting culture. It was clear from the evidence that the bison had been cooked and eaten by the makers of the points, so that carbon-14 dating of the bones made it possible for the researchers to determine when the hunters roamed North America. Tests showed that the bones contained between 27% and 30% of their original carbon-14. Use this information to show that the hunters lived roughly between 9000 B.C. and 8000 B.C.

**42.** (a) Use a graphing utility to make a graph of $p_{\text{rem}}$ versus $t$, where $p_{\text{rem}}$ is the percentage of carbon-14 that remains in an artifact after $t$ years.
(b) Use the graph to estimate the percentage of carbon-14 that would have to have been present in the 1988 test of the Shroud of Turin for it to have been the burial shroud of Jesus of Nazareth (see Example 7).

**43.** (a) It is currently accepted that the half-life of carbon-14 might vary $\pm 40$ years from its nominal value of 5730 years. Does this variation make it possible that the Shroud of Turin dates to the time of Jesus of Nazareth (see Example 7)?
(b) Review the subsection of Section 3.5 entitled Error Propagation, and then estimate the percentage error that results in the computed age of an artifact from an $r$% error in the half-life of carbon-14.

**44.** Suppose that a quantity $y$ has an exponential growth model $y = y_0e^{kt}$ or an exponential decay model $y = y_0e^{-kt}$, and it is known that $y = y_1$ if $t = t_1$. In each case find a formula for $k$ in terms of $y_0$, $y_1$, and $t_1$, assuming that $t_1 \neq 0$.

**45.** (a) Show that if a quantity $y = y(t)$ has an exponential model, and if $y(t_1) = y_1$ and $y(t_2) = y_2$, then the doubling time or the half-life $T$ is

$$T = \left| \frac{(t_2 - t_1)\ln 2}{\ln(y_2/y_1)} \right|$$

(b) In a certain 1-hour period the number of bacteria in a colony increases by 25%. Assuming an exponential growth model, what is the doubling time for the colony?

**46.** Suppose that $P$ dollars is invested at an annual interest rate of $r \times 100\%$. If the accumulated interest is credited to the account at the end of the year, then the interest is said to be *compounded annually*; if it is credited at the end of each 6-month period, then it is said to be *compounded*

*semiannually*; and if it is credited at the end of each 3-month period, then it is said to be *compounded quarterly*. The more frequently the interest is compounded, the better it is for the investor since more of the interest is itself earning interest.
(a) Show that if interest is compounded $n$ times a year at equally spaced intervals, then the value $A$ of the investment after $t$ years is
$$A = P\left(1 + \frac{r}{n}\right)^{nt}$$
(b) One can imagine interest to be compounded each day, each hour, each minute, and so forth. Carried to the limit one can conceive of interest compounded at each instant of time; this is called ***continuous compounding***. Thus, from part (a), the value $A$ of $P$ dollars after $t$ years when invested at an annual rate of $r \times 100\%$, compounded continuously, is
$$A = \lim_{n\to+\infty} P\left(1 + \frac{r}{n}\right)^{nt}$$
Use the fact that $\lim_{x\to 0}(1+x)^{1/x} = e$ to prove that $A = Pe^{rt}$.
(c) Use the result in part (b) to show that money invested at continuous compound interest increases at a rate proportional to the amount present.

**47.** (a) If \$1000 is invested at 8% per year compounded continuously (Exercise 46), what will the investment be worth after 5 years?
(b) If it is desired that an investment at 8% per year compounded continuously should have a value of \$10,000 after 10 years, how much should be invested now?
(c) How long does it take for an investment at 8% per year compounded continuously to double in value?

**48.** What is the effective annual interest rate for an interest rate of $r$% per year compounded continuously?

**49.** Assume that $y = y(t)$ satisfies the logistic equation with $y_0 = y(0)$ the initial value of $y$.
(a) Use separation of variables to derive the solution
$$y = \frac{y_0 L}{y_0 + (L - y_0)e^{-kt}}$$
(b) Use part (a) to show that $\lim_{t\to+\infty} y(t) = L$.

**50.** Use your answer to Exercise 49 to derive a solution to the model for the spread of disease [Equation (6) of Section 8.1].

**51.** The graph of a solution to the logistic equation is known as a ***logistic curve***, and if $y_0 > 0$, it has one of four general shapes, depending on the relationship between $y_0$ and $L$. In each part, assume that $k = 1$ and use a graphing utility to plot a logistic curve satisfying the given condition.
(a) $y_0 > L$ (b) $y_0 = L$
(c) $L/2 \le y_0 < L$ (d) $0 < y_0 < L/2$

**52–53** The graph of a logistic model
$$y = \frac{y_0 L}{y_0 + (L - y_0)e^{-kt}}$$
is shown. Estimate $y_0$, $L$, and $k$. ■

**52.**
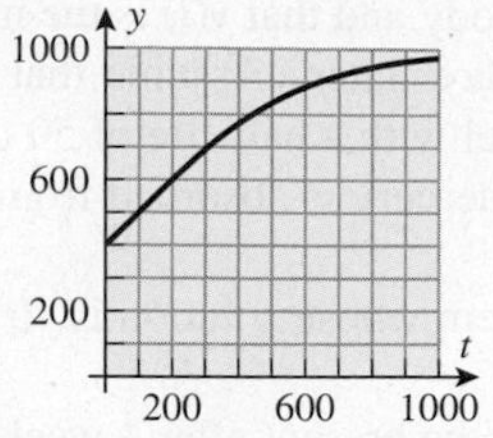


**53.**
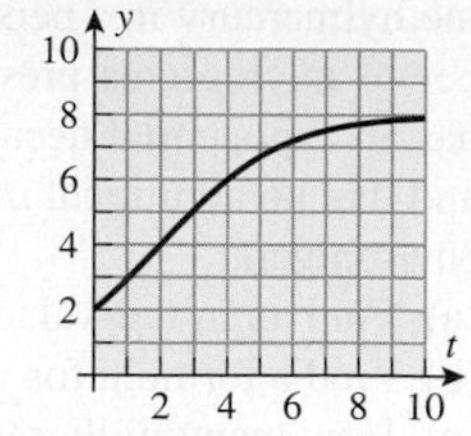


**54.** Plot a solution to the initial-value problem
$$\frac{dy}{dt} = 0.98\left(1 - \frac{y}{5}\right)y, \quad y_0 = 1$$

**55.** Suppose that the growth of a population $y = y(t)$ is given by the logistic equation
$$y = \frac{60}{5 + 7e^{-t}}$$
(a) What is the population at time $t = 0$?
(b) What is the carrying capacity $L$?
(c) What is the constant $k$?
(d) When does the population reach half of the carrying capacity?
(e) Find an initial-value problem whose solution is $y(t)$.

**56.** Suppose that the growth of a population $y = y(t)$ is given by the logistic equation
$$y = \frac{1000}{1 + 999e^{-0.9t}}$$
(a) What is the population at time $t = 0$?
(b) What is the carrying capacity $L$?
(c) What is the constant $k$?
(d) When does the population reach 75% of the carrying capacity?
(e) Find an initial-value problem whose solution is $y(t)$.

**57.** Suppose that a university residence hall houses 1000 students. Following the semester break, 20 students in the hall return with the flu, and 5 days later 35 students have the flu.
(a) Use the result of Exercise 50 to find the number of students who will have the flu $t$ days after returning to school.
(b) Make a table that illustrates how the flu spreads day to day over a 2-week period.
(c) Use a graphing utility to generate a graph that illustrates how the flu spreads over a 2-week period.

**58.** Suppose that at time $t = 0$ an object with temperature $T_0$ is placed in a room with constant temperature $T_a$. If $T_0 < T_a$, then the temperature of the object will increase, and if $T_0 > T_a$, then the temperature will decrease. Assuming that Newton's Law of Cooling applies, show that in both cases the temperature $T(t)$ at time $t$ is given by
$$T(t) = T_a + (T_0 - T_a)e^{-kt}$$
where $k$ is a positive constant.

**59.** A cup of water with a temperature of 95°C is placed in a room with a constant temperature of 21°C.
(a) Assuming that Newton's Law of Cooling applies, use the result of Exercise 58 to find the temperature of the water $t$ minutes after it is placed in the room. [*Note:* The solution will involve a constant of proportionality.]

(*cont.*)

(b) How many minutes will it take for the water to reach a temperature of 51 °C if it cools to 85 °C in 1 minute?

**60.** A glass of lemonade with a temperature of 40 °F is placed in a room with a constant temperature of 70 °F, and 1 hour later its temperature is 52 °F. Show that $t$ hours after the lemonade is placed in the room its temperature is approximated by $T = 70 - 30e^{-0.5t}$.

**61.** A rocket, fired upward from rest at time $t = 0$, has an initial mass of $m_0$ (including its fuel). Assuming that the fuel is consumed at a constant rate $k$, the mass $m$ of the rocket, while fuel is being burned, will be given by $m = m_0 - kt$. It can be shown that if air resistance is neglected and the fuel gases are expelled at a constant speed $c$ relative to the rocket, then the velocity $v$ of the rocket will satisfy the equation

$$m\frac{dv}{dt} = ck - mg$$

where $g$ is the acceleration due to gravity.

(a) Find $v(t)$ keeping in mind that the mass $m$ is a function of $t$.

(b) Suppose that the fuel accounts for 80% of the initial mass of the rocket and that all of the fuel is consumed in 100 s. Find the velocity of the rocket in meters per second at the instant the fuel is exhausted. [*Note:* Take $g = 9.8 \text{ m/s}^2$ and $c = 2500 \text{ m/s}$.]

**62.** A bullet of mass $m$, fired straight up with an initial velocity of $v_0$, is slowed by the force of gravity and a drag force of air resistance $kv^2$, where $k$ is a positive constant. As the bullet moves upward, its velocity $v$ satisfies the equation

$$m\frac{dv}{dt} = -(kv^2 + mg)$$

where $g$ is the constant acceleration due to gravity.

(a) Show that if $x = x(t)$ is the height of the bullet above the barrel opening at time $t$, then

$$mv\frac{dv}{dx} = -(kv^2 + mg)$$

(b) Express $x$ in terms of $v$ given that $x = 0$ when $v = v_0$.

(c) Assuming that

$$v_0 = 988 \text{ m/s}, \quad g = 9.8 \text{ m/s}^2$$
$$m = 3.56 \times 10^{-3} \text{ kg}, \quad k = 7.3 \times 10^{-6} \text{ kg/m}$$

use the result in part (b) to find out how high the bullet rises. [*Hint:* Find the velocity of the bullet at its highest point.]

**63–64** Suppose that a tank containing a liquid is vented to the air at the top and has an outlet at the bottom through which the liquid can drain. It follows from ***Torricelli's law*** in physics that if the outlet is opened at time $t = 0$, then at each instant the depth of the liquid $h(t)$ and the area $A(h)$ of the liquid's surface are related by

$$A(h)\frac{dh}{dt} = -k\sqrt{h}$$

where $k$ is a positive constant that depends on such factors as the viscosity of the liquid and the cross-sectional area of the outlet. Use this result in these exercises, assuming that $h$ is in feet, $A(h)$ is in square feet, and $t$ is in seconds. ■

**63.** Suppose that the cylindrical tank in the accompanying figure is filled to a depth of 4 feet at time $t = 0$ and that the constant in Torricelli's law is $k = 0.025$.

(a) Find $h(t)$.

(b) How many minutes will it take for the tank to drain completely?

**64.** Follow the directions of Exercise 63 for the cylindrical tank in the accompanying figure, assuming that the tank is filled to a depth of 4 feet at time $t = 0$ and that the constant in Torricelli's law is $k = 0.025$.

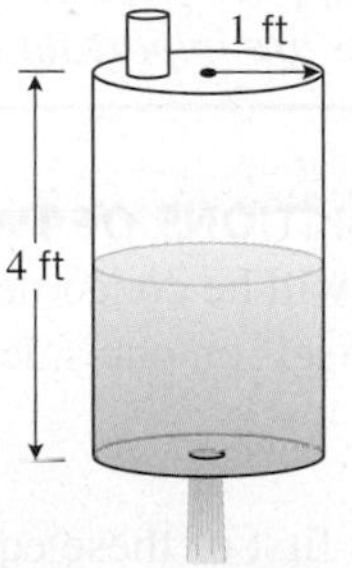


▲ **Figure Ex-63**

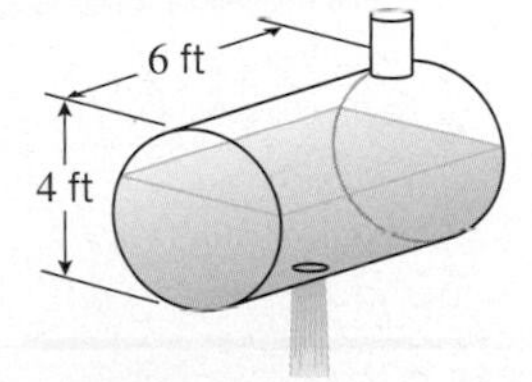


▲ **Figure Ex-64**

**65.** Suppose that a particle moving along the $x$-axis encounters a resisting force that results in an acceleration of $a = dv/dt = -\frac{1}{32}v^2$. If $x = 0$ cm and $v = 128$ cm/s at time $t = 0$, find the velocity $v$ and position $x$ as a function of $t$ for $t \geq 0$.

**66.** Suppose that a particle moving along the $x$-axis encounters a resisting force that results in an acceleration of $a = dv/dt = -0.02\sqrt{v}$. Given that $x = 0$ cm and $v = 9$ cm/s at time $t = 0$, find the velocity $v$ and position $x$ as a function of $t$ for $t \geq 0$.

**FOCUS ON CONCEPTS**

**67.** Use implicit differentiation to prove that any differentiable function defined implicitly by Equation (4) will be a solution to (1).

**68.** Prove that a solution to the initial-value problem

$$h(y)\frac{dy}{dx} = g(x), \quad y(x_0) = y_0$$

is defined implicitly by the equation

$$\int_{y_0}^{y} h(r)\,dr = \int_{x_0}^{x} g(s)\,ds$$

**69.** Let $L$ denote a tangent line at $(x, y)$ to a solution of Equation (1), and let $(x_1, y_1)$, $(x_2, y_2)$ denote any two points on $L$. Prove that Equation (2) is satisfied by $dy = \Delta y = y_2 - y_1$ and $dx = \Delta x = x_2 - x_1$.

**70. Writing** A student objects to the method of separation of variables because it often produces an equation in $x$ and $y$ instead of an explicit function $y = f(x)$. Discuss the pros and cons of this student's position.

**71. Writing** A student objects to Step 2 in the method of separation of variables because one side of the equation is integrated with respect to $x$ while the other side is integrated with respect to $y$. Answer this student's objection. [*Hint:* Recall the method of integration by substitution.]

✓ **QUICK CHECK ANSWERS 8.2** 1. Step 1: $h(y)\,dy = g(x)\,dx$; Step 2: $\int h(y)\,dy = \int g(x)\,dx$; Step 3: $H(y) = G(x) + C$ 2. (a) $ky$ (b) $\frac{\ln 2}{k}$ (c) $y_0e^{kt}$ 3. (a) $-ky$ (b) $\frac{\ln 2}{k}$ (c) $y_0e^{-kt}$ 4. $y = \sqrt{1 - x^2}$

## 8.3 SLOPE FIELDS; EULER'S METHOD

*In this section we will reexamine the concept of a slope field and we will discuss a method for approximating solutions of first-order equations numerically. Numerical approximations are important in cases where the differential equation cannot be solved exactly.*

### FUNCTIONS OF TWO VARIABLES

We will be concerned here with first-order equations that are expressed with the derivative by itself on one side of the equation. For example,

$$y' = x^3 \quad \text{and} \quad y' = \sin(xy)$$

In applied problems involving time, it is usual to use $t$ as the independent variable, in which case one would be concerned with equations of the form $y' = f(t, y)$, where $y' = dy/dt$.

The first of these equations involves only $x$ on the right side, so it has the form $y' = f(x)$. However, the second equation involves both $x$ and $y$ on the right side, so it has the form $y' = f(x, y)$, where the symbol $f(x, y)$ stands for a function of the two variables $x$ and $y$. Later in the text we will study functions of two variables in more depth, but for now it will suffice to think of $f(x, y)$ as a formula that produces a unique output when values of $x$ and $y$ are given as inputs. For example, if

$$f(x, y) = x^2 + 3y$$

and if the inputs are $x = 2$ and $y = -4$, then the output is

$$f(2, -4) = 2^2 + 3(-4) = 4 - 12 = -8$$

### SLOPE FIELDS

In Section 5.2 we introduced the concept of a slope field in the context of differential equations of the form $y' = f(x)$; the same principles apply to differential equations of the form

$$y' = f(x, y)$$

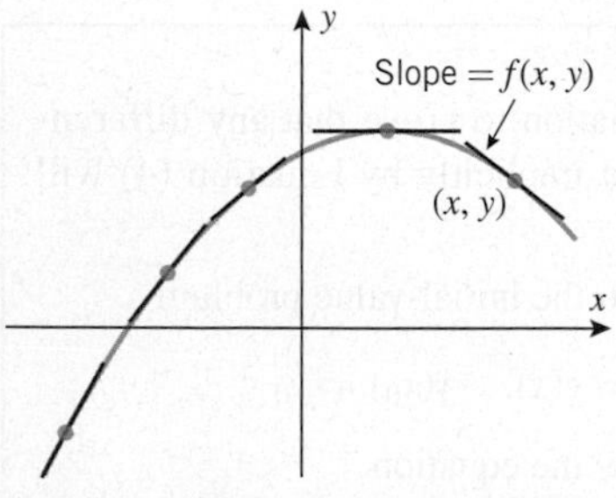


At each point $(x, y)$ on an integral curve of $y' = f(x, y)$, the tangent line has slope $f(x, y)$.

▲ **Figure 8.3.1**

To see why this is so, let us review the basic idea. If we interpret $y'$ as the slope of a tangent line, then the differential equation states that at each point $(x, y)$ on an integral curve, the slope of the tangent line is equal to the value of $f$ at that point (Figure 8.3.1). For example, suppose that $f(x, y) = y - x$, in which case we have the differential equation

$$y' = y - x \tag{1}$$

A geometric description of the set of integral curves can be obtained by choosing a rectangular grid of points in the $xy$-plane, calculating the slopes of the tangent lines to the integral curves at the gridpoints, and drawing small segments of the tangent lines through those points. The resulting picture is called a ***slope field*** or a ***direction field*** for the differential equation because it shows the "slope" or "direction" of the integral curves at the gridpoints. The more gridpoints that are used, the better the description of the integral curves. For example, Figure 8.3.2 shows two slope fields for (1)—the first was obtained by hand calculation using the 49 gridpoints shown in the accompanying table, and the second, which gives a clearer picture of the integral curves, was obtained using 625 gridpoints and a CAS.

It so happens that Equation (1) can be solved exactly using a method we will introduce in Section 8.4. We leave it for you to confirm that the general solution of this equation is

$$y = x + 1 + Ce^x \tag{2}$$

Confirm that the first slope field in Figure 8.3.2 is consistent with the accompanying table in that figure.

Figure 8.3.3 shows some of the integral curves superimposed on the slope field. Note that it was not necessary to have the general solution to construct the slope field. Indeed,

VALUES of $f(x, y) = y - x$

| | $y=-3$ | $y=-2$ | $y=-1$ | $y=0$ | $y=1$ | $y=2$ | $y=3$ |
|---|---|---|---|---|---|---|---|
| $x=-3$ | 0 | 1 | 2 | 3 | 4 | 5 | 6 |
| $x=-2$ | −1 | 0 | 1 | 2 | 3 | 4 | 5 |
| $x=-1$ | −2 | −1 | 0 | 1 | 2 | 3 | 4 |
| $x=0$ | −3 | −2 | −1 | 0 | 1 | 2 | 3 |
| $x=1$ | −4 | −3 | −2 | −1 | 0 | 1 | 2 |
| $x=2$ | −5 | −4 | −3 | −2 | −1 | 0 | 1 |
| $x=3$ | −6 | −5 | −4 | −3 | −2 | −1 | 0 |

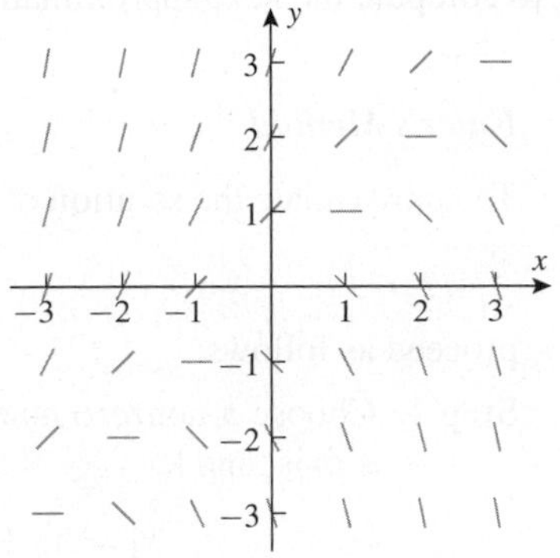


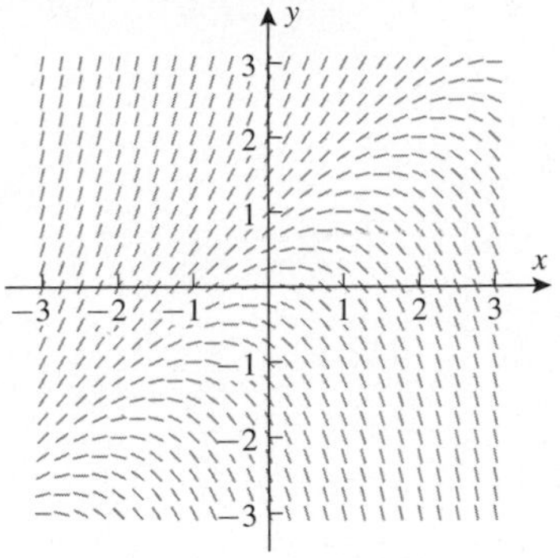


▲ Figure 8.3.2

slope fields are important precisely because they can be constructed in cases where the differential equation cannot be solved exactly.

## EULER'S METHOD

Consider an initial-value problem of the form

$$y' = f(x, y), \quad y(x_0) = y_0$$

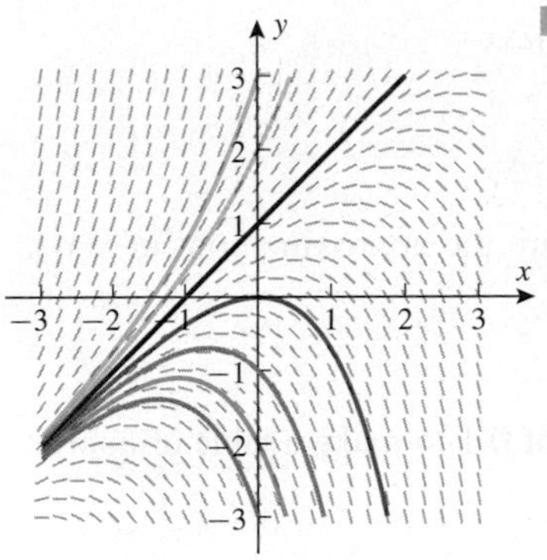


▲ Figure 8.3.3

The slope field for the differential equation $y' = f(x, y)$ gives us a way to visualize the solution of the initial-value problem, since the graph of the solution is the integral curve that passes through the point $(x_0, y_0)$. The slope field will also help us to develop a method for approximating the solution to the initial-value problem numerically.

We will not attempt to approximate $y(x)$ for all values of $x$; rather, we will choose some small increment $\Delta x$ and focus on approximating the values of $y(x)$ at a succession of $x$-values spaced $\Delta x$ units apart, starting from $x_0$. We will denote these $x$-values by

$$x_1 = x_0 + \Delta x, \quad x_2 = x_1 + \Delta x, \quad x_3 = x_2 + \Delta x, \quad x_4 = x_3 + \Delta x, \ldots$$

and we will denote the approximations of $y(x)$ at these points by

$$y_1 \approx y(x_1), \quad y_2 \approx y(x_2), \quad y_3 \approx y(x_3), \quad y_4 \approx y(x_4), \ldots$$

The technique that we will describe for obtaining these approximations is called ***Euler's Method***. Although there are better approximation methods available, many of them use Euler's Method as a starting point, so the underlying concepts are important to understand.

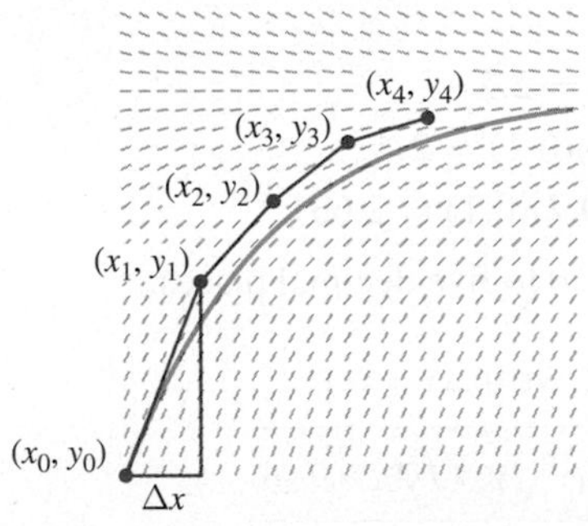


▲ Figure 8.3.4

The basic idea behind Euler's Method is to start at the known initial point $(x_0, y_0)$ and draw a line segment in the direction determined by the slope field until we reach the point $(x_1, y_1)$ with $x$-coordinate $x_1 = x_0 + \Delta x$ (Figure 8.3.4). If $\Delta x$ is small, then it is reasonable to expect that this line segment will not deviate much from the integral curve $y = y(x)$, and thus $y_1$ should closely approximate $y(x_1)$. To obtain the subsequent approximations, we repeat the process using the slope field as a guide at each step. Starting at the endpoint $(x_1, y_1)$, we draw a line segment determined by the slope field until we reach the point $(x_2, y_2)$ with $x$-coordinate $x_2 = x_1 + \Delta x$, and from that point we draw a line segment determined by the slope field to the point $(x_3, y_3)$ with $x$-coordinate $x_3 = x_2 + \Delta x$, and so forth. As indicated in Figure 8.3.4, this procedure produces a polygonal path that tends to follow the integral curve closely, so it is reasonable to expect that the $y$-values $y_2, y_3, y_4, \ldots$ will closely approximate $y(x_2), y(x_3), y(x_4), \ldots$.

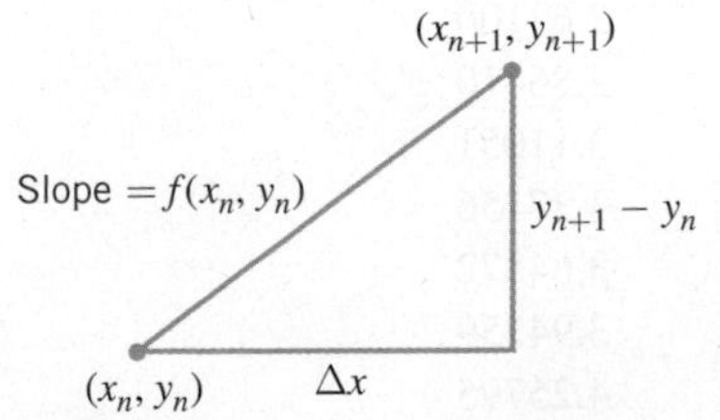


▲ Figure 8.3.5

To explain how the approximations $y_1, y_2, y_3, \ldots$ can be computed, let us focus on a typical line segment. As indicated in Figure 8.3.5, assume that we have found the point $(x_n, y_n)$, and we are trying to determine the next point $(x_{n+1}, y_{n+1})$, where $x_{n+1} = x_n + \Delta x$. Since the slope of the line segment joining the points is determined by the slope field at the starting point, the slope is $f(x_n, y_n)$, and hence

$$\frac{y_{n+1} - y_n}{x_{n+1} - x_n} = \frac{y_{n+1} - y_n}{\Delta x} = f(x_n, y_n)$$

which we can rewrite as

$$y_{n+1} = y_n + f(x_n, y_n)\Delta x$$

This formula, which is the heart of Euler's Method, tells us how to use each approximation to compute the next approximation.

***Euler's Method***

To approximate the solution of the initial-value problem

$$y' = f(x, y), \quad y(x_0) = y_0$$

proceed as follows:

**Step 1.** Choose a nonzero number $\Delta x$ to serve as an ***increment*** or ***step size*** along the $x$-axis, and let

$$x_1 = x_0 + \Delta x, \quad x_2 = x_1 + \Delta x, \quad x_3 = x_2 + \Delta x, \ldots$$

**Step 2.** Compute successively

$$\begin{aligned} y_1 &= y_0 + f(x_0, y_0)\Delta x \\ y_2 &= y_1 + f(x_1, y_1)\Delta x \\ y_3 &= y_2 + f(x_2, y_2)\Delta x \\ &\vdots \\ y_{n+1} &= y_n + f(x_n, y_n)\Delta x \end{aligned}$$

The numbers $y_1, y_2, y_3, \ldots$ in these equations are the approximations of $y(x_1)$, $y(x_2)$, $y(x_3)$, ....

► **Example 1** Use Euler's Method with a step size of 0.1 to make a table of approximate values of the solution of the initial-value problem

$$y' = y - x, \quad y(0) = 2 \tag{3}$$

over the interval $0 \le x \le 1$.

***Solution.*** In this problem we have $f(x, y) = y - x$, $x_0 = 0$, and $y_0 = 2$. Moreover, since the step size is 0.1, the $x$-values at which the approximate values will be obtained are

$$x_1 = 0.1, \quad x_2 = 0.2, \quad x_3 = 0.3, \ldots, \quad x_9 = 0.9, \quad x_{10} = 1$$

The first three approximations are

$$\begin{aligned} y_1 &= y_0 + f(x_0, y_0)\Delta x = 2 + (2 - 0)(0.1) = 2.2 \\ y_2 &= y_1 + f(x_1, y_1)\Delta x = 2.2 + (2.2 - 0.1)(0.1) = 2.41 \\ y_3 &= y_2 + f(x_2, y_2)\Delta x = 2.41 + (2.41 - 0.2)(0.1) = 2.631 \end{aligned}$$

Here is a way of organizing all 10 approximations rounded to five decimal places:

EULER'S METHOD FOR $y' = y - x$, $y(0) = 2$ WITH $\Delta x = 0.1$

| $n$ | $x_n$ | $y_n$ | $f(x_n, y_n)\Delta x$ | $y_{n+1} = y_n + f(x_n, y_n)\Delta x$ |
|---|---|---|---|---|
| 0 | 0 | 2.00000 | 0.20000 | 2.20000 |
| 1 | 0.1 | 2.20000 | 0.21000 | 2.41000 |
| 2 | 0.2 | 2.41000 | 0.22100 | 2.63100 |
| 3 | 0.3 | 2.63100 | 0.23310 | 2.86410 |
| 4 | 0.4 | 2.86410 | 0.24641 | 3.11051 |
| 5 | 0.5 | 3.11051 | 0.26105 | 3.37156 |
| 6 | 0.6 | 3.37156 | 0.27716 | 3.64872 |
| 7 | 0.7 | 3.64872 | 0.29487 | 3.94359 |
| 8 | 0.8 | 3.94359 | 0.31436 | 4.25795 |
| 9 | 0.9 | 4.25795 | 0.33579 | 4.59374 |
| 10 | 1.0 | 4.59374 | — | — |

Observe that each entry in the last column becomes the next entry in the third column. This is reminiscent of Newton's Method in which each successive approximation is used to find the next. ◀

## ACCURACY OF EULER'S METHOD

As a rule of thumb, the absolute error in an approximation produced by Euler's Method is proportional to the step size. Thus, reducing the step size by half reduces the absolute and percentage errors by roughly half. However, reducing the step size increases the amount of computation, thereby increasing the potential for more roundoff error. Such matters are discussed in courses on differential equations or numerical analysis.

It follows from (3) and the initial condition $y(0) = 2$ that the exact solution of the initial-value problem in Example 1 is

$$y = x + 1 + e^x$$

Thus, in this case we can compare the approximate values of $y(x)$ produced by Euler's Method with decimal approximations of the exact values (Table 8.3.1). In Table 8.3.1 the ***absolute error*** is calculated as

$$|\text{exact value} - \text{approximation}|$$

and the ***percentage error*** as

$$\frac{|\text{exact value} - \text{approximation}|}{|\text{exact value}|} \times 100\%$$

**Table 8.3.1**

| $x$ | EXACT SOLUTION | EULER APPROXIMATION | ABSOLUTE ERROR | PERCENTAGE ERROR |
|---|---|---|---|---|
| 0 | 2.00000 | 2.00000 | 0.00000 | 0.00 |
| 0.1 | 2.20517 | 2.20000 | 0.00517 | 0.23 |
| 0.2 | 2.42140 | 2.41000 | 0.01140 | 0.47 |
| 0.3 | 2.64986 | 2.63100 | 0.01886 | 0.71 |
| 0.4 | 2.89182 | 2.86410 | 0.02772 | 0.96 |
| 0.5 | 3.14872 | 3.11051 | 0.03821 | 1.21 |
| 0.6 | 3.42212 | 3.37156 | 0.05056 | 1.48 |
| 0.7 | 3.71375 | 3.64872 | 0.06503 | 1.75 |
| 0.8 | 4.02554 | 3.94359 | 0.08195 | 2.04 |
| 0.9 | 4.35960 | 4.25795 | 0.10165 | 2.33 |
| 1.0 | 4.71828 | 4.59374 | 0.12454 | 2.64 |

Notice that the absolute error tends to increase as $x$ moves away from $x_0$.

## ✓QUICK CHECK EXERCISES 8.3 *(See page 504 for answers.)*

1. Match each differential equation with its slope field.
   (a) $y' = 2xy^2$ ______ (b) $y' = e^{-y}$ ______
   (c) $y' = y$ ______ (d) $y' = 2xy$ ______

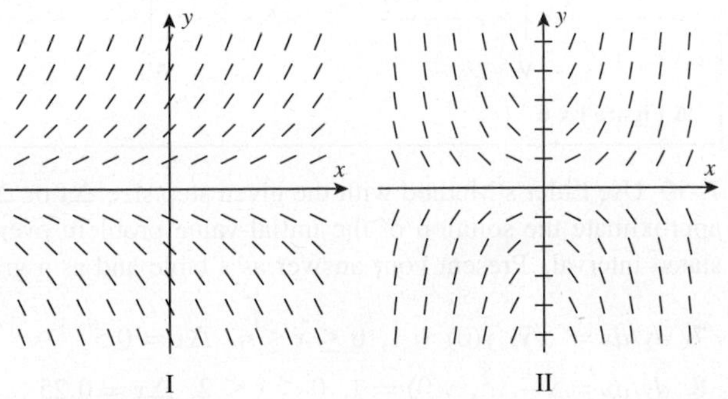


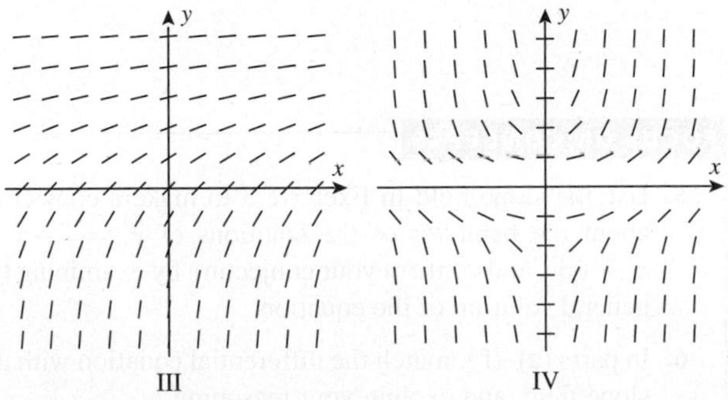


▲ **Figure Ex-1**

2. The slope field for $y' = y/x$ at the 16 gridpoints $(x, y)$, where $x = -2, -1, 1, 2$ and $y = -2, -1, 1, 2$ is shown in

the accompanying figure. Use this slope field and geometric reasoning to find the integral curve that passes through the point (1, 2).

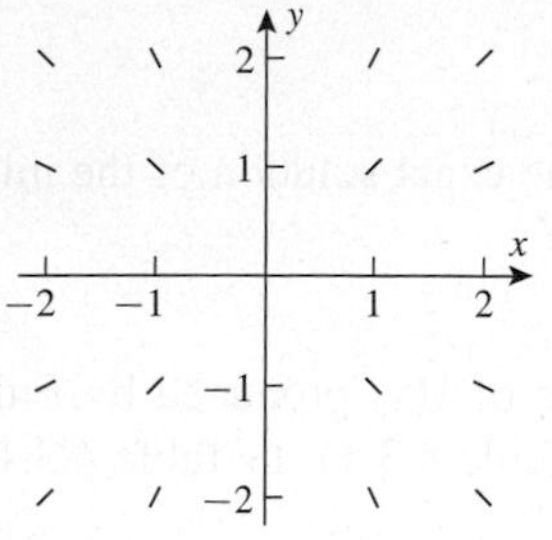


◀ **Figure Ex-2**

3. When using Euler's Method on the initial-value problem $y' = f(x, y)$, $y(x_0) = y_0$, we obtain $y_{n+1}$ from $y_n$, $x_n$, and $\Delta x$ by means of the formula $y_{n+1} =$ ________.

4. Consider the initial-value problem $y' = y$, $y(0) = 1$.
(a) Use Euler's Method with two steps to approximate $y(1)$.
(b) What is the exact value of $y(1)$?

## EXERCISE SET 8.3 Graphing Utility

**1.** Sketch the slope field for $y' = xy/4$ at the 25 gridpoints $(x, y)$, where $x = -2, -1, \ldots, 2$ and $y = -2, -1, \ldots, 2$.

**2.** Sketch the slope field for $y' + y = 2$ at the 25 gridpoints $(x, y)$, where $x = 0, 1, \ldots, 4$ and $y = 0, 1, \ldots, 4$.

**3.** A slope field for the differential equation $y' = 1 - y$ is shown in the accompanying figure. In each part, sketch the graph of the solution that satisfies the initial condition.
(a) $y(0) = -1$ (b) $y(0) = 1$ (c) $y(0) = 2$

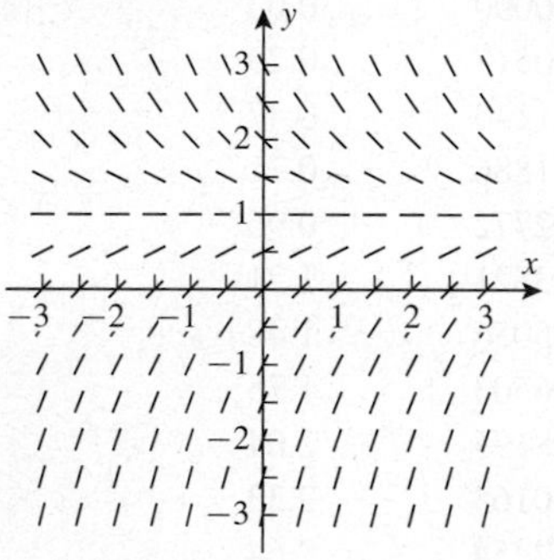


◀ **Figure Ex-3**

**4.** Solve the initial-value problems in Exercise 3, and use a graphing utility to confirm that the integral curves for these solutions are consistent with the sketches you obtained from the slope field.

**FOCUS ON CONCEPTS**

**5.** Use the slope field in Exercise 3 to make a conjecture about the behavior of the solutions of $y' = 1 - y$ as $x \to +\infty$, and confirm your conjecture by examining the general solution of the equation.

**6.** In parts (a)–(f), match the differential equation with the slope field, and explain your reasoning.
(a) $y' = 1/x$ (b) $y' = 1/y$
(c) $y' = e^{-x^2}$ (d) $y' = y^2 - 1$
(e) $y' = \dfrac{x + y}{x - y}$ (f) $y' = (\sin x)(\sin y)$

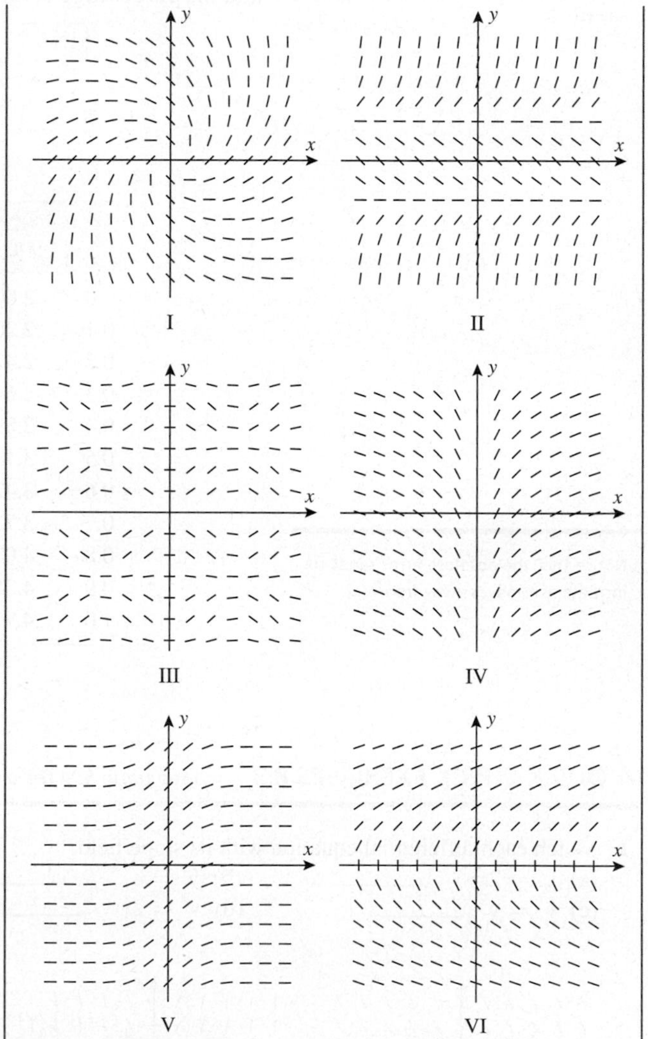


▲ **Figure Ex-6**

**7–10** Use Euler's Method with the given step size $\Delta x$ or $\Delta t$ to approximate the solution of the initial-value problem over the stated interval. Present your answer as a table and as a graph. ■

**7.** $dy/dx = \sqrt[3]{y}$, $y(0) = 1$, $0 \le x \le 4$, $\Delta x = 0.5$

**8.** $dy/dx = x - y^2$, $y(0) = 1$, $0 \le x \le 2$, $\Delta x = 0.25$

**9.** $dy/dt = \cos y,\ y(0) = 1,\ 0 \le t \le 2,\ \Delta t = 0.5$

**10.** $dy/dt = e^{-y},\ y(0) = 0,\ 0 \le t \le 1,\ \Delta t = 0.1$

**11.** Consider the initial-value problem

$$y' = \sin \pi t, \quad y(0) = 0$$

Use Euler's Method with five steps to approximate $y(1)$.

**12–15 True–False** Determine whether the statement is true or false. Explain your answer. ■

**12.** If the graph of $y = f(x)$ is an integral curve for a slope field, then so is any vertical translation of this graph.

**13.** Every integral curve for the slope field $dy/dx = e^{xy}$ is the graph of an increasing function of $x$.

**14.** Every integral curve for the slope field $dy/dx = e^y$ is concave up.

**15.** If $p(y)$ is a cubic polynomial in $y$, then the slope field $dy/dx = p(y)$ has an integral curve that is a horizontal line.

**FOCUS ON CONCEPTS**

**16.** (a) Show that the solution of the initial-value problem $y' = e^{-x^2}, y(0) = 0$ is

$$y(x) = \int_0^x e^{-t^2}\, dt$$

(b) Use Euler's Method with $\Delta x = 0.05$ to approximate the value of

$$y(1) = \int_0^1 e^{-t^2}\, dt$$

and compare the answer to that produced by a calculating utility with a numerical integration capability.

**17.** The accompanying figure shows a slope field for the differential equation $y' = -x/y$.

(a) Use the slope field to estimate $y\left(\frac{1}{2}\right)$ for the solution that satisfies the given initial condition $y(0) = 1$.

(b) Compare your estimate to the exact value of $y\left(\frac{1}{2}\right)$.

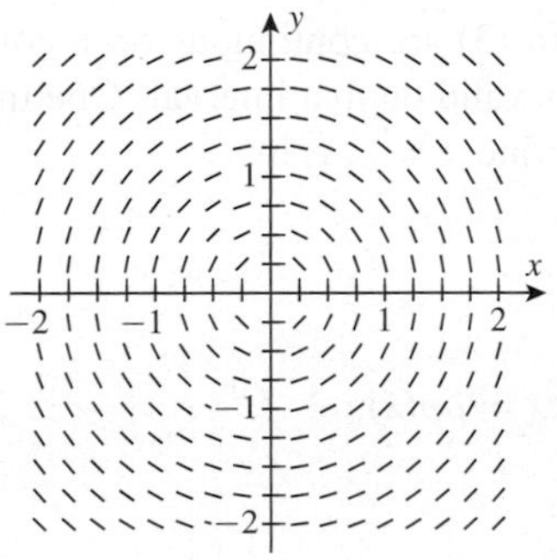


◀ **Figure Ex-17**

**18.** Refer to slope field II in Quick Check Exercise 1.

(a) Does the slope field appear to have a horizontal line as an integral curve?

(b) Use the differential equation for the slope field to verify your answer to part (a).

**19.** Refer to the slope field in Exercise 3 and consider the integral curve through $(0, -1)$.

(a) Use the slope field to estimate where the integral curve intersects the $x$-axis.

(b) Compare your estimate in part (a) with the exact value of the $x$-intercept for the integral curve.

**20.** Consider the initial-value problem

$$\frac{dy}{dx} = \frac{\sqrt{y}}{2}, \quad y(0) = 1$$

(a) Use Euler's Method with step sizes of $\Delta x = 0.2$, $0.1$, and $0.05$ to obtain three approximations of $y(1)$.

(b) Find $y(1)$ exactly.

**21.** A slope field of the form $y' = f(y)$ is said to be ***autonomous***.

(a) Explain why the tangent segments along any horizontal line will be parallel for an autonomous slope field.

(b) The word *autonomous* means "independent." In what sense is an autonomous slope field independent?

(c) Suppose that $G(y)$ is an antiderivative of $1/[f(y)]$ and that $C$ is a constant. Explain why any differentiable function defined implicitly by $G(y) - x = C$ will be a solution to the equation $y' = f(y)$.

**22.** (a) Solve the equation $y' = \sqrt{y}$ and show that every nonconstant solution has a graph that is everywhere concave up.

(b) Explain how the conclusion in part (a) may be obtained directly from the equation $y' = \sqrt{y}$ without solving.

**23.** (a) Find a slope field whose integral curve through $(1, 1)$ satisfies $xy^3 - x^2y = 0$ by differentiating this equation implicitly.

(b) Prove that if $y(x)$ is any integral curve of the slope field in part (a), then $x[y(x)]^3 - x^2y(x)$ will be a constant function.

(c) Find an equation that implicitly defines the integral curve through $(-1, -1)$ of the slope field in part (a).

**24.** (a) Find a slope field whose integral curve through $(0, 0)$ satisfies $xe^y + ye^x = 0$ by differentiating this equation implicitly.

(b) Prove that if $y(x)$ is any integral curve of the slope field in part (a), then $xe^{y(x)} + y(x)e^x$ will be a constant function.

(c) Find an equation that implicitly defines the integral curve through $(1, 1)$ of the slope field in part (a).

**25.** Consider the initial-value problem $y' = y,\ y(0) = 1$, and let $y_n$ denote the approximation of $y(1)$ using Euler's Method with $n$ steps.

(a) What would you conjecture is the exact value of $\lim_{n\to+\infty} y_n$? Explain your reasoning.

(b) Find an explicit formula for $y_n$ and use it to verify your conjecture in part (a).

**26. Writing** Explain the connection between Euler's Method and the local linear approximation discussed in Section 3.5.

**27. Writing** Given a slope field, what features of an integral curve might be discussed from the slope field? Apply your ideas to the slope field in Exercise 3.

✓ QUICK CHECK ANSWERS 8.3 1. (a) IV (b) III (c) I (d) II 2. $y = 2x, x > 0$ 3. $y_n + f(x_n, y_n)\Delta x$ 4. (a) 2.25 (b) $e$

## 8.4 FIRST-ORDER DIFFERENTIAL EQUATIONS AND APPLICATIONS

*In this section we will discuss a general method that can be used to solve a large class of first-order differential equations. We will use this method to solve differential equations related to the problems of mixing liquids and free fall retarded by air resistance.*

### FIRST-ORDER LINEAR EQUATIONS

The simplest first-order equations are those that can be written in the form

$$\frac{dy}{dx} = q(x) \tag{1}$$

Such equations can often be solved by integration. For example, if

$$\frac{dy}{dx} = x^3 \tag{2}$$

then

$$y = \int x^3\,dx = \frac{x^4}{4} + C$$

is the general solution of (2) on the interval $(-\infty, +\infty)$. More generally, a first-order differential equation is called ***linear*** if it is expressible in the form

$$\frac{dy}{dx} + p(x)y = q(x) \tag{3}$$

Equation (1) is the special case of (3) that results when the function $p(x)$ is identically 0. Some other examples of first-order linear differential equations are

$$\frac{dy}{dx} + x^2y = e^x, \qquad \frac{dy}{dx} + (\sin x)y + x^3 = 0, \qquad \frac{dy}{dx} + 5y = 2$$

$p(x) = x^2, q(x) = e^x$ | $p(x) = \sin x, q(x) = -x^3$ | $p(x) = 5, q(x) = 2$

We will assume that the functions $p(x)$ and $q(x)$ in (3) are continuous on a common interval, and we will look for a general solution that is valid on that interval. One method for doing this is based on the observation that if we define $\mu = \mu(x)$ by

$$\mu = e^{\int p(x)\,dx} \tag{4}$$

then

$$\frac{d\mu}{dx} = e^{\int p(x)\,dx} \cdot \frac{d}{dx}\int p(x)\,dx = \mu p(x)$$

Thus,

$$\frac{d}{dx}(\mu y) = \mu\frac{dy}{dx} + \frac{d\mu}{dx}y = \mu\frac{dy}{dx} + \mu p(x)y \tag{5}$$

If (3) is multiplied through by $\mu$, it becomes

$$\mu\frac{dy}{dx} + \mu p(x)y = \mu q(x)$$

Combining this with (5) we have

$$\frac{d}{dx}(\mu y) = \mu q(x) \tag{6}$$

This equation can be solved for $y$ by integrating both sides with respect to $x$ and then dividing through by $\mu$ to obtain

$$y = \frac{1}{\mu}\int \mu q(x)\,dx \tag{7}$$

which is a general solution of (3) on the interval. The function $\mu$ in (4) is called an ***integrating factor*** for (3), and this method for finding a general solution of (3) is called the ***method of integrating factors***. Although one could simply memorize Formula (7), we recommend solving first-order linear equations by actually carrying out the steps used to derive this formula:

***The Method of Integrating Factors***

**Step 1.** Calculate the integrating factor

$$\mu = e^{\int p(x)\,dx}$$

Since any $\mu$ will suffice, we can take the constant of integration to be zero in this step.

**Step 2.** Multiply both sides of (3) by $\mu$ and express the result as

$$\frac{d}{dx}(\mu y) = \mu q(x)$$

**Step 3.** Integrate both sides of the equation obtained in Step 2 and then solve for $y$. Be sure to include a constant of integration in this step.

▶ **Example 1** Solve the differential equation

$$\frac{dy}{dx} - y = e^{2x}$$

***Solution.*** Comparing the given equation to (3), we see that we have a first-order linear equation with $p(x) = -1$ and $q(x) = e^{2x}$. These coefficients are continuous on the interval $(-\infty, +\infty)$, so the method of integrating factors will produce a general solution on this interval. The first step is to compute the integrating factor. This yields

$$\mu = e^{\int p(x)\,dx} = e^{\int (-1)\,dx} = e^{-x}$$

Next we multiply both sides of the given equation by $\mu$ to obtain

$$e^{-x}\frac{dy}{dx} - e^{-x}y = e^{-x}e^{2x}$$

which we can rewrite as

$$\frac{d}{dx}[e^{-x}y] = e^{x}$$

Integrating both sides of this equation with respect to $x$ we obtain

$$e^{-x}y = e^{x} + C$$

Finally, solving for $y$ yields the general solution

$$y = e^{2x} + Ce^{x} \blacktriangleleft$$

Confirm that the solution obtained in Example 1 agrees with that obtained by substituting the integrating factor into Formula (7).

A differential equation of the form

$$P(x)\frac{dy}{dx} + Q(x)y = R(x)$$

can be solved by dividing through by $P(x)$ to put the equation in the form of (3) and then applying the method of integrating factors. However, the resulting solution will only be valid on intervals where $p(x) = Q(x)/P(x)$ and $q(x) = R(x)/P(x)$ are both continuous.

▶ **Example 2** Solve the initial-value problem

$$x\frac{dy}{dx} - y = x, \quad y(1) = 2$$

***Solution.*** This differential equation can be written in the form of (3) by dividing through by $x$. This yields

$$\frac{dy}{dx} - \frac{1}{x}y = 1 \tag{8}$$

where $q(x) = 1$ is continuous on $(-\infty, +\infty)$ and $p(x) = -1/x$ is continuous on $(-\infty, 0)$ and $(0, +\infty)$. Since we need $p(x)$ and $q(x)$ to be continuous on a common interval, and since our initial condition requires a solution for $x = 1$, we will find a general solution of (8) on the interval $(0, +\infty)$. On this interval we have $|x| = x$, so that

$$\int p(x)\,dx = -\int \frac{1}{x}\,dx = -\ln|x| = -\ln x$$

Taking the constant of integration to be 0

Thus, an integrating factor that will produce a general solution on the interval $(0, +\infty)$ is

$$\mu = e^{\int p(x)\,dx} = e^{-\ln x} = e^{\ln(1/x)} = \frac{1}{x}$$

Multiplying both sides of Equation (8) by this integrating factor yields

$$\frac{1}{x}\frac{dy}{dx} - \frac{1}{x^2}y = \frac{1}{x}$$

or

$$\frac{d}{dx}\left[\frac{1}{x}y\right] = \frac{1}{x}$$

Therefore, on the interval $(0, +\infty)$,

$$\frac{1}{x}y = \int \frac{1}{x}\,dx = \ln x + C$$

from which it follows that

$$y = x\ln x + Cx \tag{9}$$

The initial condition $y(1) = 2$ requires that $y = 2$ if $x = 1$. Substituting these values into (9) and solving for $C$ yields $C = 2$ (verify), so the solution of the initial-value problem is

$$y = x\ln x + 2x \quad ◀$$

It is not accidental that the initial-value problem in Example 2 has a unique solution. If the coefficients of (3) are continuous on an open interval that contains the point $x_0$, then for any $y_0$ there will be a unique solution of (3) on that interval that satisfies the initial condition $y(x_0) = y_0$ [Exercise 29(b)].

We conclude this section with some applications of first-order differential equations.

## MIXING PROBLEMS

In a typical mixing problem, a tank is filled to a specified level with a solution that contains a known amount of some soluble substance (say salt). The thoroughly stirred solution is allowed to drain from the tank at a known rate, and at the same time a solution with a known concentration of the soluble substance is added to the tank at a known rate that may or may not differ from the draining rate. As time progresses, the amount of the soluble substance in the tank will generally change, and the usual mixing problem seeks to determine the amount of the substance in the tank at a specified time. This type of problem serves as a model for many kinds of problems: discharge and filtration of pollutants in a river, injection and absorption of medication in the bloodstream, and migrations of species into and out of an ecological system, for example.

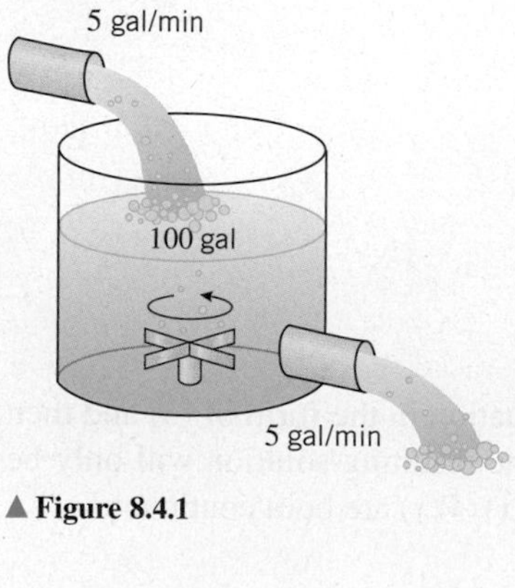

▲ **Figure 8.4.1**

▶ **Example 3** At time $t = 0$, a tank contains 4 lb of salt dissolved in 100 gal of water. Suppose that brine containing 2 lb of salt per gallon of brine is allowed to enter the tank at a rate of 5 gal/min and that the mixed solution is drained from the tank at the same rate (Figure 8.4.1). Find the amount of salt in the tank after 10 minutes.

***Solution.*** Let $y(t)$ be the amount of salt (in pounds) after $t$ minutes. We are given that $y(0) = 4$, and we want to find $y(10)$. We will begin by finding a differential equation that is satisfied by $y(t)$. To do this, observe that $dy/dt$, which is the rate at which the amount of salt in the tank changes with time, can be expressed as

$$\frac{dy}{dt} = \text{rate in} - \text{rate out} \tag{10}$$

where *rate in* is the rate at which salt enters the tank and *rate out* is the rate at which salt leaves the tank. But the rate at which salt enters the tank is

$$\text{rate in} = (2 \text{ lb/gal}) \cdot (5 \text{ gal/min}) = 10 \text{ lb/min}$$

Since brine enters and drains from the tank at the same rate, the volume of brine in the tank stays constant at 100 gal. Thus, after $t$ minutes have elapsed, the tank contains $y(t)$ lb of salt per 100 gal of brine, and hence the rate at which salt leaves the tank at that instant is

$$\text{rate out} = \left(\frac{y(t)}{100} \text{ lb/gal}\right) \cdot (5 \text{ gal/min}) = \frac{y(t)}{20} \text{ lb/min}$$

Therefore, (10) can be written as

$$\frac{dy}{dt} = 10 - \frac{y}{20} \quad \text{or} \quad \frac{dy}{dt} + \frac{y}{20} = 10$$

which is a first-order linear differential equation satisfied by $y(t)$. Since we are given that $y(0) = 4$, the function $y(t)$ can be obtained by solving the initial-value problem

$$\frac{dy}{dt} + \frac{y}{20} = 10, \quad y(0) = 4$$

The integrating factor for the differential equation is

$$\mu = e^{\int (1/20)\, dt} = e^{t/20}$$

If we multiply the differential equation through by $\mu$, then we obtain

$$\frac{d}{dt}(e^{t/20} y) = 10e^{t/20}$$

$$e^{t/20} y = \int 10e^{t/20}\, dt = 200e^{t/20} + C$$

$$y(t) = 200 + Ce^{-t/20} \tag{11}$$

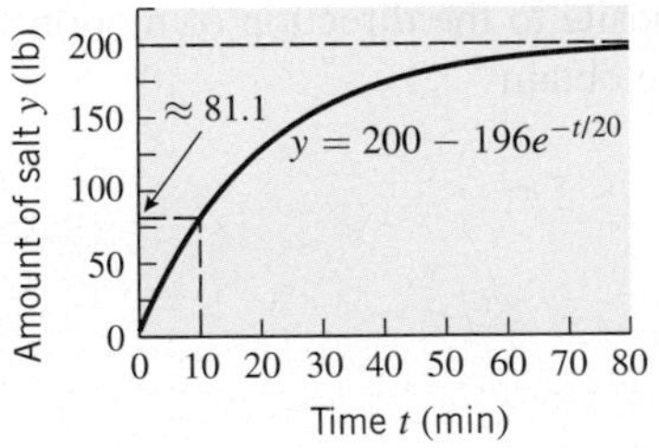


▲ **Figure 8.4.2**

The initial condition states that $y = 4$ when $t = 0$. Substituting these values into (11) and solving for $C$ yields $C = -196$ (verify), so

$$y(t) = 200 - 196e^{-t/20} \tag{12}$$

The graph of (12) is shown in Figure 8.4.2. At time $t = 10$ the amount of salt in the tank is

$$y(10) = 200 - 196e^{-0.5} \approx 81.1 \text{ lb} \blacktriangleleft$$

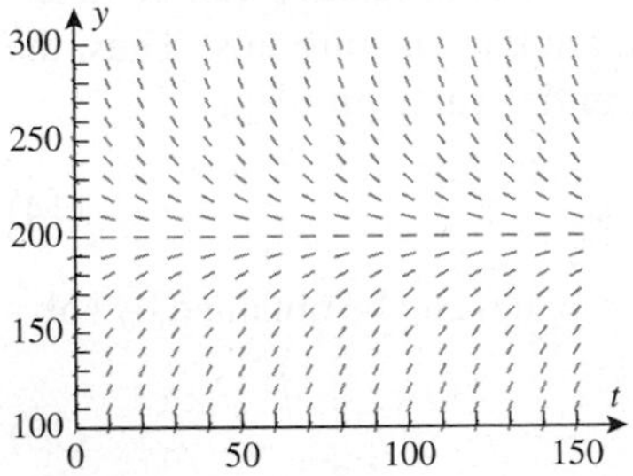


▲ **Figure 8.4.3**

Notice that it follows from (11) that

$$\lim_{t \to +\infty} y(t) = 200$$

for all values of $C$, so regardless of the amount of salt that is present in the tank initially, the amount of salt in the tank will eventually stabilize at 200 lb. This can also be seen geometrically from the slope field for the differential equation shown in Figure 8.4.3. This slope field suggests the following: If the amount of salt present in the tank is greater than 200 lb initially, then the amount of salt will decrease steadily over time toward a limiting value of 200 lb; and if the amount of salt is less than 200 lb initially, then it will increase steadily toward a limiting value of 200 lb. The slope field also suggests that if the amount present initially is exactly 200 lb, then the amount of salt in the tank will stay constant at 200 lb. This can also be seen from (11), since $C = 0$ in this case (verify).

The graph shown in Figure 8.4.2 suggests that $y(t) \to 200$ as $t \to +\infty$. This means that over an extended period of time the amount of salt in the tank tends toward 200 lb. Give an informal physical argument to explain why this result is to be expected.

## A MODEL OF FREE-FALL MOTION RETARDED BY AIR RESISTANCE

In Section 5.7 we considered the free-fall model of an object moving along a vertical axis near the surface of the Earth. It was assumed in that model that there is no air resistance and that the only force acting on the object is the Earth's gravity. Our goal here is to find a model that takes air resistance into account. For this purpose we make the following assumptions:

- The object moves along a vertical $s$-axis whose origin is at the surface of the Earth and whose positive direction is up (Figure 5.7.7).
- At time $t = 0$ the height of the object is $s_0$ and the velocity is $v_0$.
- The only forces on the object are the force $F_G = -mg$ of the Earth's gravity acting down and the force $F_R$ of air resistance acting opposite to the direction of motion. The force $F_R$ is called the ***drag force***.

In the case of free-fall motion retarded by air resistance, the net force acting on the object is

$$F_G + F_R = -mg + F_R$$

and the acceleration is $d^2s/dt^2$, so Newton's Second Law of Motion [Equation (5) of Section 6.6] implies that

$$-mg + F_R = m\frac{d^2s}{dt^2} \tag{13}$$

Experimentation has shown that the force $F_R$ of air resistance depends on the shape of the object and its speed—the greater the speed, the greater the drag force. There are many possible models for air resistance, but one of the most basic assumes that the drag force $F_R$ is proportional to the velocity of the object, that is,

$$F_R = -cv$$

where $c$ is a positive constant that depends on the object's shape and properties of the air.* (The minus sign ensures that the drag force is opposite to the direction of motion.) Substituting this in (13) and writing $d^2s/dt^2$ as $dv/dt$, we obtain

$$-mg - cv = m\frac{dv}{dt}$$

Dividing by $m$ and rearranging we obtain

$$\frac{dv}{dt} + \frac{c}{m}v = -g$$

which is a first-order linear differential equation in the unknown function $v = v(t)$ with $p(t) = c/m$ and $q(t) = -g$ [see (3)]. For a specific object, the coefficient $c$ can be determined experimentally, so we will assume that $m$, $g$, and $c$ are known constants. Thus, the velocity function $v = v(t)$ can be obtained by solving the initial-value problem

$$\frac{dv}{dt} + \frac{c}{m}v = -g, \quad v(0) = v_0 \tag{14}$$

Once the velocity function is found, the position function $s = s(t)$ can be obtained by solving the initial-value problem

$$\frac{ds}{dt} = v(t), \quad s(0) = s_0 \tag{15}$$

In Exercise 25 we will ask you to solve (14) and show that

$$v(t) = e^{-ct/m}\left(v_0 + \frac{mg}{c}\right) - \frac{mg}{c} \tag{16}$$

Note that

$$\lim_{t\to+\infty} v(t) = -\frac{mg}{c} \tag{17}$$

---

* Other common models assume that $F_R = -cv^2$ or, more generally, $F_R = -cv^p$ for some value of $p$.

(verify). Thus, the speed $|v(t)|$ does not increase indefinitely, as in free fall; rather, because of the air resistance, it approaches a finite limiting speed $v_\tau$ given by

$$v_\tau = \left|-\frac{mg}{c}\right| = \frac{mg}{c} \tag{18}$$

This is called the ***terminal speed*** of the object, and (17) is called its ***terminal velocity***.

**REMARK** Intuition suggests that near the limiting velocity, the velocity $v(t)$ changes very slowly; that is, $dv/dt \approx 0$. Thus, it should not be surprising that the limiting velocity can be obtained informally from (14) by setting $dv/dt = 0$ in the differential equation and solving for $v$. This yields

$$v = -\frac{mg}{c}$$

which agrees with (17).

## ✓QUICK CHECK EXERCISES 8.4 *(See page 511 for answers.)*

1. Solve the first-order linear differential equation
$$\frac{dy}{dx} + p(x)y = q(x)$$
by completing the following steps:

Step 1. Calculate the integrating factor $\mu =$ ______.
Step 2. Multiply both sides of the equation by the integrating factor and express the result as
$$\frac{d}{dx}[\_\_\_\_\_\_] = \_\_\_\_\_\_$$
Step 3. Integrate both sides of the equation obtained in Step 2 and solve for $y =$ ______.

2. An integrating factor for
$$\frac{dy}{dx} + \frac{y}{x} = q(x)$$
is ______.

3. At time $t = 0$, a tank contains 30 oz of salt dissolved in 60 gal of water. Then brine containing 5 oz of salt per gallon of brine is allowed to enter the tank at a rate of 3 gal/min and the mixed solution is drained from the tank at the same rate. Give an initial-value problem satisfied by the amount of salt $y(t)$ in the tank at time $t$. Do not solve the problem.

## EXERCISE SET 8.4 Graphing Utility

**1–6** Solve the differential equation by the method of integrating factors. ■

1. $\dfrac{dy}{dx} + 4y = e^{-3x}$
2. $\dfrac{dy}{dx} + 2xy = x$
3. $y' + y = \cos(e^x)$
4. $2\dfrac{dy}{dx} + 4y = 1$
5. $(x^2+1)\dfrac{dy}{dx} + xy = 0$
6. $\dfrac{dy}{dx} + y + \dfrac{1}{1-e^x} = 0$

**7–10** Solve the initial-value problem. ■

7. $x\dfrac{dy}{dx} + y = x, \quad y(1) = 2$
8. $x\dfrac{dy}{dx} - y = x^2, \quad y(1) = -1$
9. $\dfrac{dy}{dx} - 2xy = 2x, \quad y(0) = 3$
10. $\dfrac{dy}{dt} + y = 2, \quad y(0) = 1$

**11–14 True–False** Determine whether the statement is true or false. Explain your answer. ■

11. If $y_1$ and $y_2$ are two solutions to a first-order linear differential equation, then $y = y_1 + y_2$ is also a solution.
12. If the first-order linear differential equation
$$\frac{dy}{dx} + p(x)y = q(x)$$
has a solution that is a constant function, then $q(x)$ is a constant multiple of $p(x)$.
13. In a mixing problem, we expect the concentration of the dissolved substance within the tank to approach a finite limit over time.
14. In our model for free-fall motion retarded by air resistance, the terminal velocity is proportional to the weight of the falling object.
15. A slope field for the differential equation $y' = 2y - x$ is shown in the accompanying figure on the next page. In each

part, sketch the graph of the solution that satisfies the initial condition.

(a) $y(1) = 1$ (b) $y(0) = -1$ (c) $y(-1) = 0$

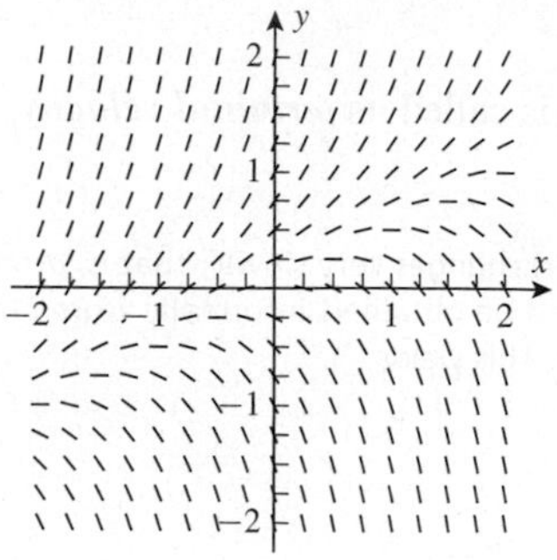

◀ **Figure Ex-15**

**16.** Solve the initial-value problems in Exercise 15, and use a graphing utility to confirm that the integral curves for these solutions are consistent with the sketches you obtained from the slope field.

**FOCUS ON CONCEPTS**

**17.** Use the slope field in Exercise 15 to make a conjecture about the effect of $y_0$ on the behavior of the solution of the initial-value problem $y' = 2y - x, y(0) = y_0$ as $x \to +\infty$, and check your conjecture by examining the solution of the initial-value problem.

**18.** Consider the slope field in Exercise 15.

(a) Use Euler's Method with $\Delta x = 0.1$ to estimate $y(\frac{1}{2})$ for the solution that satisfies the initial condition $y(0) = 1$.

(b) Would you conjecture your answer in part (a) to be greater than or less than the actual value of $y(\frac{1}{2})$? Explain.

(c) Check your conjecture in part (b) by finding the exact value of $y(\frac{1}{2})$.

**19.** (a) Use Euler's Method with a step size of $\Delta x = 0.2$ to approximate the solution of the initial-value problem

$$y' = x + y, \quad y(0) = 1$$

over the interval $0 \le x \le 1$.

(b) Solve the initial-value problem exactly, and calculate the error and the percentage error in each of the approximations in part (a).

(c) Sketch the exact solution and the approximate solution together.

**20.** It was stated at the end of Section 8.3 that reducing the step size in Euler's Method by half reduces the error in each approximation by about half. Confirm that the error in $y(1)$ is reduced by about half if a step size of $\Delta x = 0.1$ is used in Exercise 19.

**21.** At time $t = 0$, a tank contains 25 oz of salt dissolved in 50 gal of water. Then brine containing 4 oz of salt per gallon of brine is allowed to enter the tank at a rate of 2 gal/min and the mixed solution is drained from the tank at the same rate.

(a) How much salt is in the tank at an arbitrary time $t$?

(b) How much salt is in the tank after 25 min?

**22.** A tank initially contains 200 gal of pure water. Then at time $t = 0$ brine containing 5 lb of salt per gallon of brine is allowed to enter the tank at a rate of 20 gal/min and the mixed solution is drained from the tank at the same rate.

(a) How much salt is in the tank at an arbitrary time $t$?

(b) How much salt is in the tank after 30 min?

**23.** Fish is a rich source of protein and omega-3 fatty acids. However, some fish, such as shark, swordfish, and tuna, contain high concentrations of methylmercury and should be eaten only in moderation. For example, suppose a man starts a new diet in which he consumes 425 grams of albacore tuna per week (roughly equivalent to three 5 oz cans). His body will absorb about 145 micrograms ($\mu$g) of methylmercury from the tuna. On the other hand, approximately 9% of any given quantity of methylmercury within his system will be eliminated in a week. Assume that there are 300 $\mu$g of methylmercury in his body when he begins the diet and that afterwards his tuna consumption is the only source of additional amounts of the compound. Let $y(t)$ denote the number of micrograms of methylmercury in his body $t$ weeks after the start of his diet.

(a) Find an initial-value problem whose solution is $y(t)$. [*Hint:* Model this as a mixing problem.]

(b) Find a formula for $y(t)$.

(c) Suppose the man weighs 160 lb. According to U.S. EPA guidelines, the amount of methylmercury within his body should be at or below 569 $\mu$g to avoid toxicity. Based upon your solution to part (b), determine whether the man should modify his diet.

**24.** The concentration of methylmercury in "light" tuna is one-third that of albacore tuna. Repeat Exercise 23 under the assumption that the man consumes light tuna instead of albacore tuna. (Assume his body will absorb 145/3 $\mu$g of methylmercury per week from the tuna.)

**25.** (a) Use the method of integrating factors to derive solution (16) to the initial-value problem (14). [*Note:* Keep in mind that $c$, $m$, and $g$ are constants.]

(b) Show that (16) can be expressed in terms of the terminal speed (18) as

$$v(t) = e^{-gt/v_\tau}(v_0 + v_\tau) - v_\tau$$

(c) Show that if $s(0) = s_0$, then the position function of the object can be expressed as

$$s(t) = s_0 - v_\tau t + \frac{v_\tau}{g}(v_0 + v_\tau)(1 - e^{-gt/v_\tau})$$

**26.** Suppose a fully equipped skydiver weighing 240 lb has a terminal speed of 120 ft/s with a closed parachute and 24 ft/s with an open parachute. Suppose further that this skydiver is dropped from an airplane at an altitude of 10,000 ft, falls for 25 s with a closed parachute, and then falls the rest of the way with an open parachute.

(a) Assuming that the skydiver's initial vertical velocity is zero, use Exercise 25 to find the skydiver's vertical velocity and height at the time the parachute opens. [*Note:* Take $g = 32$ ft/s$^2$.]

(b) Use a calculating utility to find a numerical solution for the total time that the skydiver is in the air.

**27.** The accompanying figure is a schematic diagram of a basic $RL$ series electrical circuit that contains a power source with a time-dependent voltage of $V(t)$ volts (V), a resistor with a constant resistance of $R$ ohms ($\Omega$), and an inductor with a constant inductance of $L$ henrys (H). If you don't know anything about electrical circuits, don't worry; all you need to know is that electrical theory states that a current of $I(t)$ amperes (A) flows through the circuit where $I(t)$ satisfies the differential equation

$$L\frac{dI}{dt} + RI = V(t)$$

(a) Find $I(t)$ if $R = 10\,\Omega$, $L = 5$ H, $V$ is a constant 20 V, and $I(0) = 0$ A.
(b) What happens to the current over a long period of time?

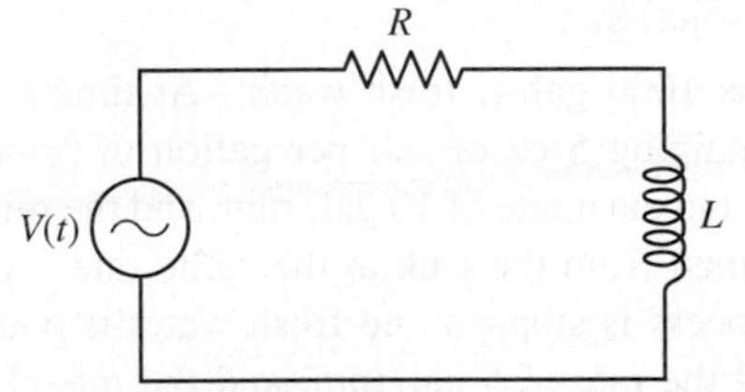


◀ Figure Ex-27

**28.** Find $I(t)$ for the electrical circuit in Exercise 27 if $R = 6\,\Omega$, $L = 3$ H, $V(t) = 3\sin t$ V, and $I(0) = 15$ A.

**FOCUS ON CONCEPTS**

**29.** (a) Prove that any function $y = y(x)$ defined by Equation (7) will be a solution to (3).
(b) Consider the initial-value problem

$$\frac{dy}{dx} + p(x)y = q(x), \quad y(x_0) = y_0$$

where the functions $p(x)$ and $q(x)$ are both continuous on some open interval. Using the general solution for a first-order linear equation, prove that this initial-value problem has a unique solution on the interval.

**30.** (a) Prove that solutions need not be unique for nonlinear initial-value problems by finding two solutions to

$$y\frac{dy}{dx} = x, \quad y(0) = 0$$

(b) Prove that solutions need not exist for nonlinear initial-value problems by showing that there is no solution for

$$y\frac{dy}{dx} = -x, \quad y(0) = 0$$

**31. Writing** Explain why the quantity $\mu$ in the *Method of Integrating Factors* is called an "integrating factor" and explain its role in this method.

**32. Writing** Suppose that a given first-order differential equation can be solved both by the method of integrating factors and by separation of variables. Discuss the advantages and disadvantages of each method.

✓ **QUICK CHECK ANSWERS 8.4** 1. Step 1: $e^{\int p(x)\,dx}$; Step 2: $\mu y$, $\mu q(x)$; Step 3: $\frac{1}{\mu}\int \mu q(x)\,dx$ 2. $x$ 3. $\frac{dy}{dt} + \frac{y}{20} = 15$, $y(0) = 30$

## CHAPTER 8 REVIEW EXERCISES

C CAS

**1.** Classify the following first-order differential equations as separable, linear, both, or neither.
(a) $\frac{dy}{dx} - 3y = \sin x$ (b) $\frac{dy}{dx} + xy = x$
(c) $y\frac{dy}{dx} - x = 1$ (d) $\frac{dy}{dx} + xy^2 = \sin(xy)$

**2.** Which of the given differential equations are separable?
(a) $\frac{dy}{dx} = f(x)g(y)$ (b) $\frac{dy}{dx} = \frac{f(x)}{g(y)}$
(c) $\frac{dy}{dx} = f(x) + g(y)$ (d) $\frac{dy}{dx} = \sqrt{f(x)g(y)}$

**3–5** Solve the differential equation by the method of separation of variables. ■

**3.** $\frac{dy}{dx} = (1 + y^2)x^2$ **4.** $3\tan y - \frac{dy}{dx}\sec x = 0$

**5.** $(1 + y^2)y' = e^x y$

**6–8** Solve the initial-value problem by the method of separation of variables. ■

**6.** $y' = 1 + y^2$, $y(0) = 1$ **7.** $y' = \frac{y^5}{x(1 + y^4)}$, $y(1) = 1$

**8.** $y' = 4y^2\sec^2 2x$, $y(\pi/8) = 1$

**9.** Sketch the integral curve of $y' = -2xy^2$ that passes through the point $(0, 1)$.

**10.** Sketch the integral curve of $2yy' = 1$ that passes through the point $(0, 1)$ and the integral curve that passes through the point $(0, -1)$.

**11.** Sketch the slope field for $y' = xy/8$ at the 25 gridpoints $(x, y)$, where $x = 0, 1, \ldots, 4$ and $y = 0, 1, \ldots, 4$.

**12.** Solve the differential equation $y' = xy/8$, and find a family of integral curves for the slope field in Exercise 11.

**13–14** Use Euler's Method with the given step size $\Delta x$ to approximate the solution of the initial-value problem over the stated interval. Present your answer as a table and as a graph. ■

**13.** $dy/dx = \sqrt{y},\ y(0) = 1,\ 0 \le x \le 4,\ \Delta x = 0.5$

**14.** $dy/dx = \sin y,\ y(0) = 1,\ 0 \le x \le 2,\ \Delta x = 0.5$

**15.** Consider the initial-value problem

$$y' = \cos 2\pi t, \quad y(0) = 1$$

Use Euler's Method with five steps to approximate $y(1)$.

**16.** Cloth found in an Egyptian pyramid contains 78.5% of its original carbon-14. Estimate the age of the cloth.

**17.** In each part, find an exponential growth model $y = y_0 e^{kt}$ that satisfies the stated conditions.
(a) $y_0 = 2$; doubling time $T = 5$
(b) $y(0) = 5$; growth rate 1.5%
(c) $y(1) = 1$; $y(10) = 100$
(d) $y(1) = 1$; doubling time $T = 5$

**18.** Suppose that an initial population of 5000 bacteria grows exponentially at a rate of 1% per hour and that $y = y(t)$ is the number of bacteria present after $t$ hours.
(a) Find an initial-value problem whose solution is $y(t)$.
(b) Find a formula for $y(t)$.
(c) What is the doubling time for the population?
(d) How long does it take for the population of bacteria to reach 30,000?

**19–20** Solve the differential equation by the method of integrating factors. ■

**19.** $\dfrac{dy}{dx} + 3y = e^{-2x}$ **20.** $\dfrac{dy}{dx} + y - \dfrac{1}{1 + e^x} = 0$

**21–23** Solve the initial-value problem by the method of integrating factors. ■

**21.** $y' - xy = x,\ y(0) = 3$

**22.** $xy' + 2y = 4x^2,\ y(1) = 2$

**23.** $y' \cosh x + y \sinh x = \cosh^2 x,\ y(0) = 2$

C **24.** (a) Solve the initial-value problem

$$y' - y = x \sin 3x, \quad y(0) = 1$$

by the method of integrating factors, using a CAS to perform any difficult integrations.
(b) Use the CAS to solve the initial-value problem directly, and confirm that the answer is consistent with that obtained in part (a).
(c) Graph the solution.

**25.** A tank contains 1000 gal of fresh water. At time $t = 0$ min, brine containing 5 oz of salt per gallon of brine is poured into the tank at a rate of 10 gal/min, and the mixed solution is drained from the tank at the same rate. After 15 min that process is stopped and fresh water is poured into the tank at the rate of 5 gal/min, and the mixed solution is drained from the tank at the same rate. Find the amount of salt in the tank at time $t = 30$ min.

**26.** Suppose that a room containing 1200 ft$^3$ of air is free of carbon monoxide. At time $t = 0$ cigarette smoke containing 4% carbon monoxide is introduced at the rate of 0.1 ft$^3$/min, and the well-circulated mixture is vented from the room at the same rate.
(a) Find a formula for the percentage of carbon monoxide in the room at time $t$.
(b) Extended exposure to air containing 0.012% carbon monoxide is considered dangerous. How long will it take to reach this level?

***Source:*** This is based on a problem from William E. Boyce and Richard C. DiPrima, *Elementary Differential Equations*, 7th ed., John Wiley & Sons, New York, 2001.

## CHAPTER 8 MAKING CONNECTIONS

**1.** Consider the first-order differential equation

$$\frac{dy}{dx} + py = q$$

where $p$ and $q$ are constants. If $y = y(x)$ is a solution to this equation, define $u = u(x) = q - py(x)$.
(a) Without solving the differential equation, show that $u$ grows exponentially as a function of $x$ if $p < 0$, and decays exponentially as a function of $x$ if $0 < p$.
(b) Use the result of part (a) and Equations (13–14) of Section 8.2 to solve the initial-value problem

$$\frac{dy}{dx} + 2y = 4, \quad y(0) = -1$$

**2.** Consider a differential equation of the form

$$\frac{dy}{dx} = f(ax + by + c)$$

where $f$ is a function of a single variable. If $y = y(x)$ is a solution to this equation, define $u = u(x) = ax + by(x) + c$.
(a) Find a separable differential equation that is satisfied by the function $u$.
(b) Use your answer to part (a) to solve

$$\frac{dy}{dx} = \frac{1}{x + y}$$

**3.** A first-order differential equation is ***homogeneous*** if it can be written in the form

$$\frac{dy}{dx} = f\left(\frac{y}{x}\right) \quad \text{for } x \neq 0$$

where $f$ is a function of a single variable. If $y = y(x)$ is a solution to a first-order homogeneous differential equation, define $u = u(x) = y(x)/x$.

(a) Find a separable differential equation that is satisfied by the function $u$.

(b) Use your answer to part (a) to solve

$$\frac{dy}{dx} = \frac{x - y}{x + y}$$

**4.** A first-order differential equation is called a ***Bernoulli equation*** if it can be written in the form

$$\frac{dy}{dx} + p(x)y = q(x)y^n \quad \text{for } n \neq 0, 1$$

If $y = y(x)$ is a solution to a Bernoulli equation, define $u = u(x) = [y(x)]^{1-n}$.

(a) Find a first-order linear differential equation that is satisfied by $u$.

(b) Use your answer to part (a) to solve the initial-value problem

$$x\frac{dy}{dx} - y = -2xy^2, \quad y(1) = \frac{1}{2}$$

MDoubrava/iStockphoto

*Perspective creates the illusion that the sequence of railroad ties continues indefinitely but converges toward a single point infinitely far away.*

# 9

# INFINITE SERIES

In this chapter we will be concerned with infinite series, which are sums that involve infinitely many terms. Since it is impossible to add up infinitely many numbers directly, one goal will be to define exactly what we mean by the sum of an infinite series. However, unlike finite sums, it turns out that not all infinite series actually have a sum, so we will need to develop tools for determining which infinite series have sums and which do not. Once the basic ideas have been developed we will begin to apply our work; we will show how infinite series are used to evaluate such quantities as $\ln 2$, $e$, $\sin 3^\circ$, and $\pi$, how they are used to create functions, and finally, how they are used to model physical laws.

## 9.1 SEQUENCES

*In everyday language, the term "sequence" means a succession of things in a definite order—chronological order, size order, or logical order, for example. In mathematics, the term "sequence" is commonly used to denote a succession of numbers whose order is determined by a rule or a function. In this section, we will develop some of the basic ideas concerning sequences of numbers.*

### DEFINITION OF A SEQUENCE

Stated informally, an ***infinite sequence***, or more simply a ***sequence***, is an unending succession of numbers, called ***terms***. It is understood that the terms have a definite order; that is, there is a first term $a_1$, a second term $a_2$, a third term $a_3$, a fourth term $a_4$, and so forth. Such a sequence would typically be written as

$$a_1, a_2, a_3, a_4, \ldots$$

where the dots are used to indicate that the sequence continues indefinitely. Some specific examples are

$$1, 2, 3, 4, \ldots, \qquad 1, \tfrac{1}{2}, \tfrac{1}{3}, \tfrac{1}{4}, \ldots,$$

$$2, 4, 6, 8, \ldots, \qquad 1, -1, 1, -1, \ldots$$

Each of these sequences has a definite pattern that makes it easy to generate additional terms if we assume that those terms follow the same pattern as the displayed terms. However, the most common way to specify a sequence is to give a rule or formula that relates each term in the sequence to its term number. For example, in the sequence

$$2, 4, 6, 8, \ldots$$

each term is twice the term number; that is, the $n$th term in the sequence is given by the formula $2n$. We denote this by writing the sequence as

$$2, 4, 6, 8, \ldots, 2n, \ldots$$

We refer to $2n$ as the *general term* of this sequence. Now, if we want to know a specific term in the sequence, we need only substitute its term number in the formula for the general term. For example, the 37th term in the sequence is $2 \cdot 37 = 74$.

**Table 9.1.1**

| TERM NUMBER | 1 | 2 | 3 | 4 | ⋯ | $n$ | ⋯ |
|---|---|---|---|---|---|---|---|
| TERM | $\frac{1}{2}$ | $\frac{2}{3}$ | $\frac{3}{4}$ | $\frac{4}{5}$ | ⋯ | $\frac{n}{n+1}$ | ⋯ |

**Table 9.1.2**

| TERM NUMBER | 1 | 2 | 3 | 4 | ⋯ | $n$ | ⋯ |
|---|---|---|---|---|---|---|---|
| TERM | $\frac{1}{2}$ | $\frac{1}{2^2}$ | $\frac{1}{2^3}$ | $\frac{1}{2^4}$ | ⋯ | $\frac{1}{2^n}$ | ⋯ |

**Table 9.1.3**

| TERM NUMBER | 1 | 2 | 3 | 4 | ⋯ | $n$ | ⋯ |
|---|---|---|---|---|---|---|---|
| TERM | 1 | 3 | 5 | 7 | ⋯ | $2n-1$ | ⋯ |

A sequence cannot be uniquely determined from a few initial terms. For example, the sequence whose general term is

$$f(n) = \tfrac{1}{3}(3 - 5n + 6n^2 - n^3)$$

has 1, 3, and 5 as its first three terms, but its fourth term is also 5.

▶ **Example 1** In each part, find the general term of the sequence.

(a) $\frac{1}{2}, \frac{2}{3}, \frac{3}{4}, \frac{4}{5}, \ldots$ (b) $\frac{1}{2}, \frac{1}{4}, \frac{1}{8}, \frac{1}{16}, \ldots$

(c) $\frac{1}{2}, -\frac{2}{3}, \frac{3}{4}, -\frac{4}{5}, \ldots$ (d) $1, 3, 5, 7, \ldots$

***Solution (a).*** In Table 9.1.1, the four known terms have been placed below their term numbers, from which we see that the numerator is the same as the term number and the denominator is one greater than the term number. This suggests that the general term has numerator $n$ and denominator $n + 1$, as indicated in the table.

***Solution (b).*** In Table 9.1.2, the denominators of the four known terms have been expressed as powers of 2 and the first four terms have been placed below their term numbers, from which we see that the exponent in the denominator is the same as the term number. This suggests that the general term is $1/2^n$, as indicated in the table.

***Solution (c).*** This sequence is identical to that in part (a), except for the alternating signs. Thus, the $n$th term in the sequence can be obtained by multiplying the $n$th term in part (a) by $(-1)^{n+1}$. This factor produces the correct alternating signs, since its successive values, starting with $n = 1$, are $1, -1, 1, -1, \ldots$. Thus, the sequence can be written as

$$\frac{1}{2}, -\frac{2}{3}, \frac{3}{4}, -\frac{4}{5}, \ldots, (-1)^{n+1}\frac{n}{n+1}, \ldots$$

and has general term $(-1)^{n+1}\frac{n}{n+1}$.

***Solution (d).*** In Table 9.1.3, the four known terms have been placed below their term numbers, from which we see that each term is one less than twice its term number. This suggests that the general term in the sequence is $2n - 1$, as indicated in the table. ◀

When the general term of a sequence

$$a_1, a_2, a_3, \ldots, a_n, \ldots \tag{1}$$

is known, there is no need to write out the initial terms, and it is common to write only the general term enclosed in braces. Thus, (1) might be written as

$$\{a_n\}_{n=1}^{+\infty} \quad \text{or as} \quad \{a_n\}_{n=1}^{\infty}$$

For example, here are the four sequences in Example 1 expressed in brace notation.

| SEQUENCE | BRACE NOTATION |
|---|---|
| $\frac{1}{2}, \frac{2}{3}, \frac{3}{4}, \frac{4}{5}, \ldots, \frac{n}{n+1}, \ldots$ | $\left\{\frac{n}{n+1}\right\}_{n=1}^{+\infty}$ |
| $\frac{1}{2}, \frac{1}{4}, \frac{1}{8}, \frac{1}{16}, \ldots, \frac{1}{2^n}, \ldots$ | $\left\{\frac{1}{2^n}\right\}_{n=1}^{+\infty}$ |
| $\frac{1}{2}, -\frac{2}{3}, \frac{3}{4}, -\frac{4}{5}, \ldots, (-1)^{n+1}\frac{n}{n+1}, \ldots$ | $\left\{(-1)^{n+1}\frac{n}{n+1}\right\}_{n=1}^{+\infty}$ |
| $1, 3, 5, 7, \ldots, 2n-1, \ldots$ | $\{2n-1\}_{n=1}^{+\infty}$ |

The letter $n$ in (1) is called the ***index*** for the sequence. It is not essential to use $n$ for the index; any letter not reserved for another purpose can be used. Moreover, it is not essential to start the index at 1; sometimes it is more convenient to start it at 0 (or some other integer). For example, consider the sequence

$$1, \frac{1}{2}, \frac{1}{2^2}, \frac{1}{2^3}, \ldots$$

One way to write this sequence is

$$\left\{\frac{1}{2^{n-1}}\right\}_{n=1}^{+\infty}$$

However, the general term will be simpler if we think of the initial term in the sequence as the zeroth term, in which case we can write the sequence as

$$\left\{\frac{1}{2^n}\right\}_{n=0}^{+\infty}$$

We began this section by describing a sequence as an unending succession of numbers. We are now in a position to provide a more precise definition. Note that Table 9.1.1 can be interpreted as a tabular description of a function whose domain is the set of positive integers $n$ and whose outputs are $f(n) = n/(n+1)$. Similarly, the notation

$$\left\{\frac{1}{2^n}\right\}_{n=0}^{+\infty}$$

can be regarded as a description of the function $g$ whose domain is the set of nonnegative integers $n$ and whose outputs are $g(n) = 1/2^n$. These observations suggest the following formal definition of a sequence.

**9.1.1 DEFINITION** A ***sequence*** is a function whose domain is a set of integers.

Typically, the domain of a sequence is the set of positive integers or the set of nonnegative integers. We will regard the expression $\{a_n\}_{n=1}^{+\infty}$ to be an alternative notation for the function $f(n) = a_n, n = 1, 2, 3, \ldots$, and we will regard $\{a_n\}_{n=0}^{+\infty}$ to be an alternative notation for the function $f(n) = a_n, n = 0, 1, 2, 3, \ldots$.

## GRAPHS OF SEQUENCES

Since sequences are functions, it makes sense to talk about the graph of a sequence. For example, the graph of the sequence $\{1/n\}_{n=1}^{+\infty}$ is the graph of the equation

$$y = \frac{1}{n}, \quad n = 1, 2, 3, \ldots$$

Because the right side of this equation is defined only for positive integer values of $n$, the graph consists of a succession of isolated points (Figure 9.1.1*a*). This is different from the graph of

$$y = \frac{1}{x}, \quad x \geq 1$$

which is a continuous curve (Figure 9.1.1*b*).

When the starting value for the index of a sequence is not relevant to the discussion, it is common to use a notation such as $\{a_n\}$ in which there is no reference to the starting value of $n$. We can distinguish between different sequences by using different letters for their general terms; thus, $\{a_n\}$, $\{b_n\}$, and $\{c_n\}$ denote three different sequences.

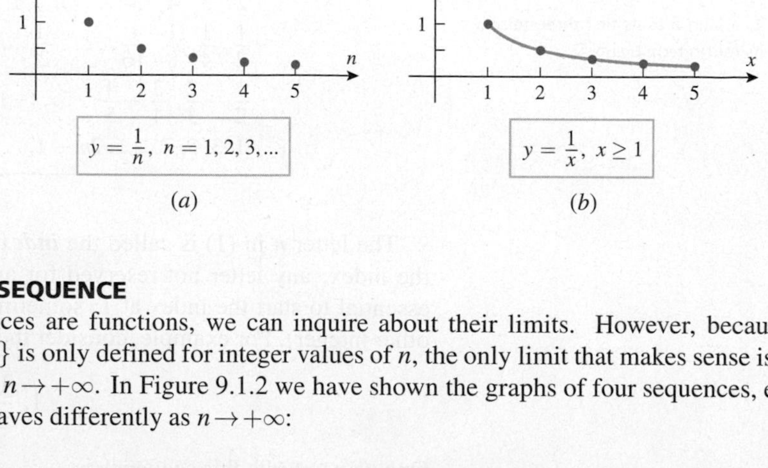


▶ **Figure 9.1.1** (*a*) (*b*)

## LIMIT OF A SEQUENCE

Since sequences are functions, we can inquire about their limits. However, because a sequence $\{a_n\}$ is only defined for integer values of $n$, the only limit that makes sense is the limit of $a_n$ as $n \to +\infty$. In Figure 9.1.2 we have shown the graphs of four sequences, each of which behaves differently as $n \to +\infty$:

- The terms in the sequence $\{n + 1\}$ increase without bound.
- The terms in the sequence $\{(-1)^{n+1}\}$ oscillate between $-1$ and 1.

- The terms in the sequence $\{n/(n+1)\}$ increase toward a "limiting value" of 1.
- The terms in the sequence $\{1+\left(-\frac{1}{2}\right)^n\}$ also tend toward a "limiting value" of 1, but do so in an oscillatory fashion.

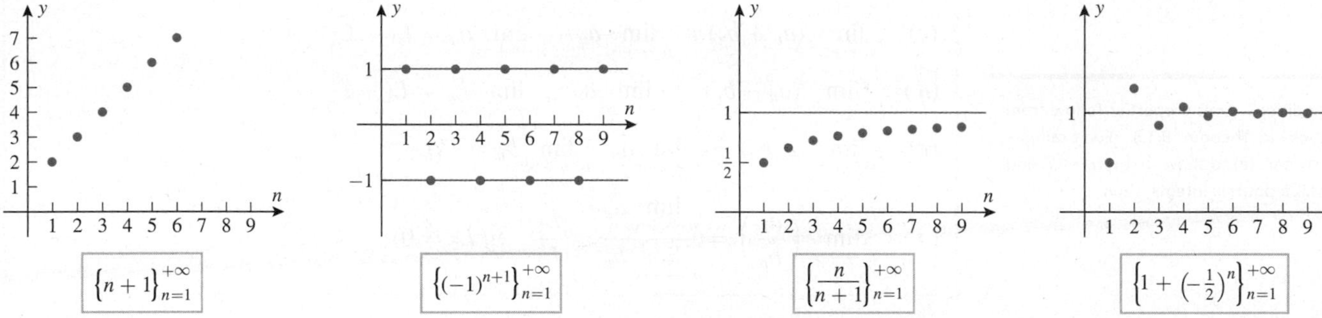


▲ **Figure 9.1.2**

Informally speaking, the limit of a sequence $\{a_n\}$ is intended to describe how $a_n$ behaves as $n \to +\infty$. To be more specific, we will say that *a sequence* $\{a_n\}$ *approaches a limit* $L$ *if the terms in the sequence eventually become arbitrarily close to* $L$. Geometrically, this means that for any positive number $\epsilon$ there is a point in the sequence after which all terms lie between the lines $y = L - \epsilon$ and $y = L + \epsilon$ (Figure 9.1.3).

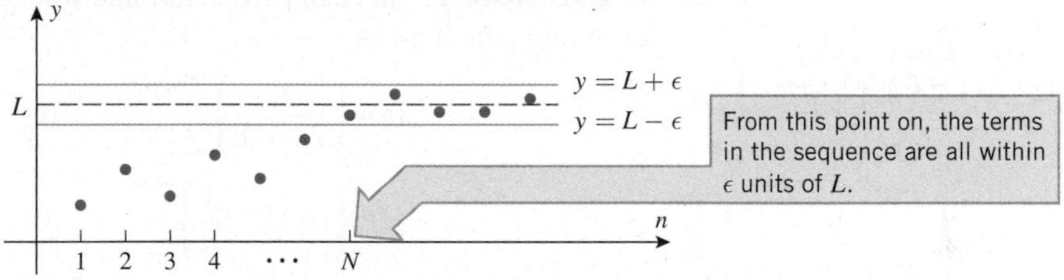


► **Figure 9.1.3**

The following definition makes these ideas precise.

> **9.1.2 DEFINITION** A sequence $\{a_n\}$ is said to ***converge*** to the ***limit*** $L$ if given any $\epsilon > 0$, there is a positive integer $N$ such that $|a_n - L| < \epsilon$ for $n \geq N$. In this case we write
>
> $$\lim_{n\to+\infty} a_n = L$$
>
> A sequence that does not converge to some finite limit is said to ***diverge***.

How would you define these limits?

$$\lim_{n\to+\infty} a_n = +\infty$$

$$\lim_{n\to+\infty} a_n = -\infty$$

► **Example 2** The first two sequences in Figure 9.1.2 diverge, and the second two converge to 1; that is,

$$\lim_{n\to+\infty} \frac{n}{n+1} = 1 \quad \text{and} \quad \lim_{n\to+\infty} \left[1+\left(-\tfrac{1}{2}\right)^n\right] = 1 \blacktriangleleft$$

The following theorem, which we state without proof, shows that the familiar properties of limits apply to sequences. This theorem ensures that the algebraic techniques used to find limits of the form $\lim_{x\to+\infty}$ can also be used for limits of the form $\lim_{n\to+\infty}$.

**9.1.3 THEOREM** *Suppose that the sequences $\{a_n\}$ and $\{b_n\}$ converge to limits $L_1$ and $L_2$, respectively, and c is a constant. Then:*

(a) $\lim\limits_{n\to+\infty} c = c$

(b) $\lim\limits_{n\to+\infty} ca_n = c\lim\limits_{n\to+\infty} a_n = cL_1$

(c) $\lim\limits_{n\to+\infty} (a_n + b_n) = \lim\limits_{n\to+\infty} a_n + \lim\limits_{n\to+\infty} b_n = L_1 + L_2$

(d) $\lim\limits_{n\to+\infty} (a_n - b_n) = \lim\limits_{n\to+\infty} a_n - \lim\limits_{n\to+\infty} b_n = L_1 - L_2$

(e) $\lim\limits_{n\to+\infty} (a_n b_n) = \lim\limits_{n\to+\infty} a_n \cdot \lim\limits_{n\to+\infty} b_n = L_1 L_2$

(f) $\lim\limits_{n\to+\infty} \left(\dfrac{a_n}{b_n}\right) = \dfrac{\lim\limits_{n\to+\infty} a_n}{\lim\limits_{n\to+\infty} b_n} = \dfrac{L_1}{L_2}$ (*if* $L_2 \neq 0$)

Additional limit properties follow from those in Theorem 9.1.3. For example, use part (e) to show that if $a_n \to L$ and $m$ is a positive integer, then

$$\lim_{n\to+\infty} (a_n)^m = L^m$$

If the general term of a sequence is $f(n)$, where $f(x)$ is a function defined on the entire interval $[1, +\infty)$, then the values of $f(n)$ can be viewed as "sample values" of $f(x)$ taken at the positive integers. Thus,

$$\text{if } f(x)\to L \text{ as } x\to+\infty, \quad \text{then} \quad f(n)\to L \text{ as } n\to+\infty$$

(Figure 9.1.4*a*). However, the converse is not true; that is, one cannot infer that $f(x)\to L$ as $x\to+\infty$ from the fact that $f(n)\to L$ as $n\to+\infty$ (Figure 9.1.4*b*).

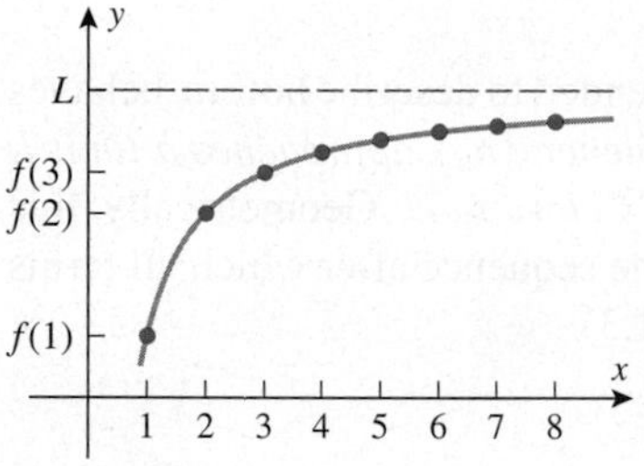


If $f(x) \to L$ as $x \to +\infty$, then $f(n) \to L$ as $n \to +\infty$.

(*a*)

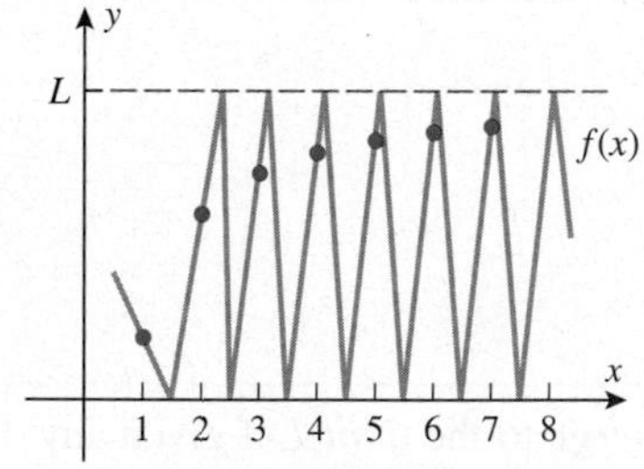


$f(n) \to L$ as $n \to +\infty$, but $f(x)$ diverges by oscillation as $x \to +\infty$.

(*b*)

▲ **Figure 9.1.4**

► **Example 3** In each part, determine whether the sequence converges or diverges by examining the limit as $n\to+\infty$.

(a) $\left\{\dfrac{n}{2n+1}\right\}_{n=1}^{+\infty}$ (b) $\left\{(-1)^{n+1}\dfrac{n}{2n+1}\right\}_{n=1}^{+\infty}$

(c) $\left\{(-1)^{n+1}\dfrac{1}{n}\right\}_{n=1}^{+\infty}$ (d) $\{8-2n\}_{n=1}^{+\infty}$

***Solution (a).*** Dividing numerator and denominator by $n$ and using Theorem 9.1.3 yields

$$\lim_{n\to+\infty} \frac{n}{2n+1} = \lim_{n\to+\infty} \frac{1}{2+1/n} = \frac{\lim\limits_{n\to+\infty} 1}{\lim\limits_{n\to+\infty} (2+1/n)} = \frac{\lim\limits_{n\to+\infty} 1}{\lim\limits_{n\to+\infty} 2 + \lim\limits_{n\to+\infty} 1/n}$$

$$= \frac{1}{2+0} = \frac{1}{2}$$

Thus, the sequence converges to $\frac{1}{2}$.

***Solution (b).*** This sequence is the same as that in part (a), except for the factor of $(-1)^{n+1}$, which oscillates between $+1$ and $-1$. Thus, the terms in this sequence oscillate between positive and negative values, with the odd-numbered terms being identical to those in part (a) and the even-numbered terms being the negatives of those in part (a). Since the sequence in part (a) has a limit of $\frac{1}{2}$, it follows that the odd-numbered terms in this sequence approach $\frac{1}{2}$, and the even-numbered terms approach $-\frac{1}{2}$. Therefore, this sequence has no limit—it diverges.

***Solution (c).*** Since $1/n\to 0$, the product $(-1)^{n+1}(1/n)$ oscillates between positive and negative values, with the odd-numbered terms approaching 0 through positive values and the even-numbered terms approaching 0 through negative values. Thus,

$$\lim_{n\to+\infty} (-1)^{n+1}\frac{1}{n} = 0$$

so the sequence converges to 0.

***Solution (d).*** $\lim\limits_{n\to+\infty} (8-2n) = -\infty$, so the sequence $\{8-2n\}_{n=1}^{+\infty}$ diverges. ◄

▶ **Example 4** In each part, determine whether the sequence converges, and if so, find its limit.

$$\text{(a) } 1, \frac{1}{2}, \frac{1}{2^2}, \frac{1}{2^3}, \ldots, \frac{1}{2^n}, \ldots \qquad \text{(b) } 1, 2, 2^2, 2^3, \ldots, 2^n, \ldots$$

***Solution.*** Replacing $n$ by $x$ in the first sequence produces the power function $(1/2)^x$, and replacing $n$ by $x$ in the second sequence produces the power function $2^x$. Now recall that if $0 < b < 1$, then $b^x \to 0$ as $x \to +\infty$, and if $b > 1$, then $b^x \to +\infty$ as $x \to +\infty$ (Figure 1.8.1). Thus,

$$\lim_{n\to+\infty} \frac{1}{2^n} = 0 \quad \text{and} \quad \lim_{n\to+\infty} 2^n = +\infty$$

So, the sequence $\{1/2^n\}$ converges to 0, but the sequence $\{2^n\}$ diverges. ◀

▶ **Example 5** Find the limit of the sequence $\left\{\dfrac{n}{e^n}\right\}_{n=1}^{+\infty}$.

***Solution.*** The expression

$$\lim_{n\to+\infty} \frac{n}{e^n}$$

is an indeterminate form of type $\infty/\infty$, so L'Hôpital's rule is indicated. However, we cannot apply this rule directly to $n/e^n$ because the functions $n$ and $e^n$ have been defined here only at the positive integers, and hence are not differentiable functions. To circumvent this problem we extend the domains of these functions to all real numbers, here implied by replacing $n$ by $x$, and apply L'Hôpital's rule to the limit of the quotient $x/e^x$. This yields

$$\lim_{x\to+\infty} \frac{x}{e^x} = \lim_{x\to+\infty} \frac{1}{e^x} = 0$$

from which we can conclude that

$$\lim_{n\to+\infty} \frac{n}{e^n} = 0 \;◀$$

▶ **Example 6** Show that $\lim\limits_{n\to+\infty} \sqrt[n]{n} = 1$.

***Solution.***

$$\lim_{n\to+\infty} \sqrt[n]{n} = \lim_{n\to+\infty} n^{1/n} = \lim_{n\to+\infty} e^{(1/n)\ln n} = e^0 = 1$$

By L'Hôpital's rule applied to $(1/x)\ln x$ ◀

Sometimes the even-numbered and odd-numbered terms of a sequence behave sufficiently differently that it is desirable to investigate their convergence separately. The following theorem, whose proof is omitted, is helpful for that purpose.

**9.1.4 THEOREM** *A sequence converges to a limit L if and only if the sequences of even-numbered terms and odd-numbered terms both converge to L.*

▶ **Example 7** The sequence

$$\frac{1}{2}, \frac{1}{3}, \frac{1}{2^2}, \frac{1}{3^2}, \frac{1}{2^3}, \frac{1}{3^3}, \ldots$$

converges to 0, since the even-numbered terms and the odd-numbered terms both converge to 0, and the sequence

$$1, \tfrac{1}{2}, 1, \tfrac{1}{3}, 1, \tfrac{1}{4}, \ldots$$

diverges, since the odd-numbered terms converge to 1 and the even-numbered terms converge to 0. ◀

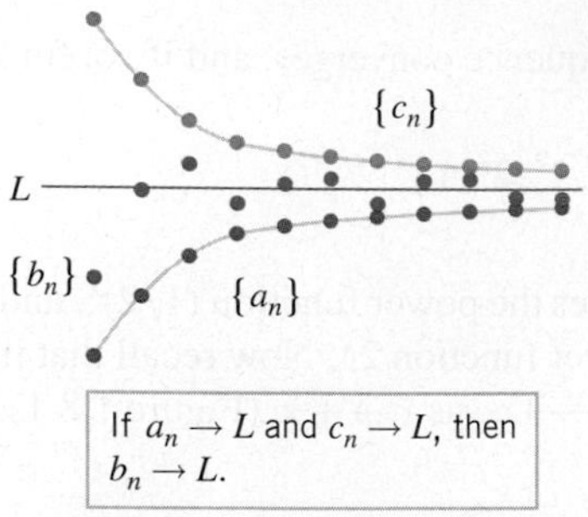


▲ **Figure 9.1.5**

## THE SQUEEZING THEOREM FOR SEQUENCES

The following theorem, illustrated in Figure 9.1.5, is an adaptation of the Squeezing Theorem (1.6.2) to sequences. This theorem will be useful for finding limits of sequences that cannot be obtained directly. The proof is omitted.

**9.1.5 THEOREM** *(The Squeezing Theorem for Sequences)* *Let $\{a_n\}$, $\{b_n\}$, and $\{c_n\}$ be sequences such that*

$$a_n \le b_n \le c_n \quad (\textit{for all values of } n \textit{ beyond some index } N)$$

*If the sequences $\{a_n\}$ and $\{c_n\}$ have a common limit $L$ as $n \to +\infty$, then $\{b_n\}$ also has the limit $L$ as $n \to +\infty$.*

Recall that if $n$ is a positive integer, then $n!$ (read "$n$ factorial") is the product of the first $n$ positive integers. In addition, it is convenient to define $0! = 1$.

▶ **Example 8** Use numerical evidence to make a conjecture about the limit of the sequence

$$\left\{\frac{n!}{n^n}\right\}_{n=1}^{+\infty}$$

and then confirm that your conjecture is correct.

**Table 9.1.4**

| $n$ | $\dfrac{n!}{n^n}$ |
|---|---|
| 1 | 1.0000000000 |
| 2 | 0.5000000000 |
| 3 | 0.2222222222 |
| 4 | 0.0937500000 |
| 5 | 0.0384000000 |
| 6 | 0.0154320988 |
| 7 | 0.0061198990 |
| 8 | 0.0024032593 |
| 9 | 0.0009366567 |
| 10 | 0.0003628800 |
| 11 | 0.0001399059 |
| 12 | 0.0000537232 |

***Solution.*** Table 9.1.4, which was obtained with a calculating utility, suggests that the limit of the sequence may be 0. To confirm this we need to examine the limit of

$$a_n = \frac{n!}{n^n}$$

as $n \to +\infty$. Although this is an indeterminate form of type $\infty/\infty$, L'Hôpital's rule is not helpful because we have no definition of $x!$ for values of $x$ that are not integers. However, let us write out some of the initial terms and the general term in the sequence:

$$a_1 = 1, \quad a_2 = \frac{1 \cdot 2}{2 \cdot 2} = \frac{1}{2}, \quad a_3 = \frac{1 \cdot 2 \cdot 3}{3 \cdot 3 \cdot 3} = \frac{2}{9} < \frac{1}{3}, \quad a_4 = \frac{1 \cdot 2 \cdot 3 \cdot 4}{4 \cdot 4 \cdot 4 \cdot 4} = \frac{3}{32} < \frac{1}{4}, \ldots$$

If $n > 1$, the general term of the sequence can be rewritten as

$$a_n = \frac{1 \cdot 2 \cdot 3 \cdots n}{n \cdot n \cdot n \cdots n} = \frac{1}{n}\left(\frac{2 \cdot 3 \cdots n}{n \cdot n \cdots n}\right)$$

from which it follows that $a_n \le 1/n$ (why?). It is now evident that

$$0 \le a_n \le \frac{1}{n}$$

However, the two outside expressions have a limit of 0 as $n \to +\infty$; thus, the Squeezing Theorem for Sequences implies that $a_n \to 0$ as $n \to +\infty$, which confirms our conjecture. ◀

The following theorem is often useful for finding the limit of a sequence with both positive and negative terms—it states that if the sequence $\{|a_n|\}$ that is obtained by taking the absolute value of each term in the sequence $\{a_n\}$ converges to 0, then $\{a_n\}$ also converges to 0.

**9.1.6 THEOREM** *If* $\lim\limits_{n \to +\infty} |a_n| = 0$, *then* $\lim\limits_{n \to +\infty} a_n = 0$.

**PROOF** Depending on the sign of $a_n$, either $a_n = |a_n|$ or $a_n = -|a_n|$. Thus, in all cases we have

$$-|a_n| \le a_n \le |a_n|$$

However, the limit of the two outside terms is 0, and hence the limit of $a_n$ is 0 by the Squeezing Theorem for Sequences. ■

▶ **Example 9** Consider the sequence

$$1, -\frac{1}{2}, \frac{1}{2^2}, -\frac{1}{2^3}, \ldots, (-1)^n\frac{1}{2^n}, \ldots$$

If we take the absolute value of each term, we obtain the sequence

$$1, \frac{1}{2}, \frac{1}{2^2}, \frac{1}{2^3}, \ldots, \frac{1}{2^n}, \ldots$$

which, as shown in Example 4, converges to 0. Thus, from Theorem 9.1.6 we have

$$\lim_{n\to+\infty}\left[(-1)^n\frac{1}{2^n}\right] = 0 \blacktriangleleft$$

## SEQUENCES DEFINED RECURSIVELY

Some sequences do not arise from a formula for the general term, but rather from a formula or set of formulas that specify how to generate each term in the sequence from terms that precede it; such sequences are said to be defined ***recursively***, and the defining formulas are called ***recursion formulas***. A good example is the mechanic's rule for approximating square roots. In Exercise 25 of Section 4.7 you were asked to show that

$$x_1 = 1, \quad x_{n+1} = \frac{1}{2}\left(x_n + \frac{a}{x_n}\right) \tag{2}$$

describes the sequence produced by Newton's Method to approximate $\sqrt{a}$ as a zero of the function $f(x) = x^2 - a$. Table 9.1.5 shows the first five terms in an application of the mechanic's rule to approximate $\sqrt{2}$.

It would take us too far afield to investigate the convergence of sequences defined recursively, but we will conclude this section with a useful technique that can sometimes be used to compute limits of such sequences.

**Table 9.1.5**

| $n$ | $x_1 = 1,\quad x_{n+1} = \frac{1}{2}\left(x_n + \frac{2}{x_n}\right)$ | DECIMAL APPROXIMATION |
|---|---|---|
| | $x_1 = 1$ (Starting value) | 1.00000000000 |
| 1 | $x_2 = \frac{1}{2}\left[1 + \frac{2}{1}\right] = \frac{3}{2}$ | 1.50000000000 |
| 2 | $x_3 = \frac{1}{2}\left[\frac{3}{2} + \frac{2}{3/2}\right] = \frac{17}{12}$ | 1.41666666667 |
| 3 | $x_4 = \frac{1}{2}\left[\frac{17}{12} + \frac{2}{17/12}\right] = \frac{577}{408}$ | 1.41421568627 |
| 4 | $x_5 = \frac{1}{2}\left[\frac{577}{408} + \frac{2}{577/408}\right] = \frac{665{,}857}{470{,}832}$ | 1.41421356237 |
| 5 | $x_6 = \frac{1}{2}\left[\frac{665{,}857}{470{,}832} + \frac{2}{665{,}857/470{,}832}\right] = \frac{886{,}731{,}088{,}897}{627{,}013{,}566{,}048}$ | 1.41421356237 |

▶ **Example 10** Assuming that the sequence in Table 9.1.5 converges, show that the limit is $\sqrt{2}$.

***Solution.*** Assume that $x_n \to L$, where $L$ is to be determined. Since $n+1 \to +\infty$ as $n \to +\infty$, it is also true that $x_{n+1} \to L$ as $n \to +\infty$. Thus, if we take the limit of the expression

$$x_{n+1} = \frac{1}{2}\left(x_n + \frac{2}{x_n}\right)$$

as $n \to +\infty$, we obtain

$$L = \frac{1}{2}\left(L + \frac{2}{L}\right)$$

which can be rewritten as $L^2 = 2$. The negative solution of this equation is extraneous because $x_n > 0$ for all $n$, so $L = \sqrt{2}$. ◄

## ✓ QUICK CHECK EXERCISES 9.1

(See page 524 for answers.)

1. Consider the sequence 4, 6, 8, 10, 12, . . . .
   (a) If $\{a_n\}_{n=1}^{+\infty}$ denotes this sequence, then $a_1 =$ ________, $a_4 =$ ________, and $a_7 =$ ________. The general term is $a_n =$ ________.
   (b) If $\{b_n\}_{n=0}^{+\infty}$ denotes this sequence, then $b_0 =$ ________, $b_4 =$ ________, and $b_8 =$ ________. The general term is $b_n =$ ________.
2. What does it mean to say that a sequence $\{a_n\}$ converges?
3. Consider sequences $\{a_n\}$ and $\{b_n\}$, where $a_n \to 2$ as $n \to +\infty$ and $b_n = (-1)^n$. Determine which of the following sequences converge and which diverge. If a sequence converges, indicate its limit.
   (a) $\{b_n\}$ (b) $\{3a_n - 1\}$ (c) $\{b_n^2\}$
   (d) $\{a_n + b_n\}$ (e) $\left\{\dfrac{1}{a_n^2 + 3}\right\}$ (f) $\left\{\dfrac{b_n}{1000}\right\}$
4. Suppose that $\{a_n\}$, $\{b_n\}$, and $\{c_n\}$ are sequences such that $a_n \le b_n \le c_n$ for all $n \ge 10$, and that $\{a_n\}$ and $\{c_n\}$ both converge to 12. Then the ________ Theorem for Sequences implies that $\{b_n\}$ converges to ________.

## EXERCISE SET 9.1

Graphing Utility

1. In each part, find a formula for the general term of the sequence, starting with $n = 1$.
   (a) $1, \frac{1}{3}, \frac{1}{9}, \frac{1}{27}, \ldots$ (b) $1, -\frac{1}{3}, \frac{1}{9}, -\frac{1}{27}, \ldots$
   (c) $\frac{1}{2}, \frac{3}{4}, \frac{5}{6}, \frac{7}{8}, \ldots$ (d) $\frac{1}{\sqrt{\pi}}, \frac{4}{\sqrt[3]{\pi}}, \frac{9}{\sqrt[4]{\pi}}, \frac{16}{\sqrt[5]{\pi}}, \ldots$
2. In each part, find two formulas for the general term of the sequence, one starting with $n = 1$ and the other with $n = 0$.
   (a) $1, -r, r^2, -r^3, \ldots$ (b) $r, -r^2, r^3, -r^4, \ldots$
3. (a) Write out the first four terms of the sequence $\{1 + (-1)^n\}$, starting with $n = 0$.
   (b) Write out the first four terms of the sequence $\{\cos n\pi\}$, starting with $n = 0$.
   (c) Use the results in parts (a) and (b) to express the general term of the sequence 4, 0, 4, 0, . . . in two different ways, starting with $n = 0$.
4. In each part, find a formula for the general term using factorials and starting with $n = 1$.
   (a) $1 \cdot 2, 1 \cdot 2 \cdot 3 \cdot 4, 1 \cdot 2 \cdot 3 \cdot 4 \cdot 5 \cdot 6, 1 \cdot 2 \cdot 3 \cdot 4 \cdot 5 \cdot 6 \cdot 7 \cdot 8, \ldots$
   (b) $1, 1 \cdot 2 \cdot 3, 1 \cdot 2 \cdot 3 \cdot 4 \cdot 5, 1 \cdot 2 \cdot 3 \cdot 4 \cdot 5 \cdot 6 \cdot 7, \ldots$

**5–6** Let $f$ be the function $f(x) = \cos\left(\frac{\pi}{2}x\right)$ and define sequences $\{a_n\}$ and $\{b_n\}$ by $a_n = f(2n)$ and $b_n = f(2n+1)$. ■

5. (a) Does $\lim_{x \to +\infty} f(x)$ exist? Explain.
   (b) Evaluate $a_1, a_2, a_3, a_4$, and $a_5$.
   (c) Does $\{a_n\}$ converge? If so, find its limit.
6. (a) Evaluate $b_1, b_2, b_3, b_4$, and $b_5$.
   (b) Does $\{b_n\}$ converge? If so, find its limit.
   (c) Does $\{f(n)\}$ converge? If so, find its limit.

**7–22** Write out the first five terms of the sequence, determine whether the sequence converges, and if so find its limit. ■

7. $\left\{\dfrac{n}{n+2}\right\}_{n=1}^{+\infty}$
8. $\left\{\dfrac{n^2}{2n+1}\right\}_{n=1}^{+\infty}$
9. $\{2\}_{n=1}^{+\infty}$
10. $\left\{\ln\left(\dfrac{1}{n}\right)\right\}_{n=1}^{+\infty}$
11. $\left\{\dfrac{\ln n}{n}\right\}_{n=1}^{+\infty}$
12. $\left\{n \sin \dfrac{\pi}{n}\right\}_{n=1}^{+\infty}$
13. $\{1 + (-1)^n\}_{n=1}^{+\infty}$
14. $\left\{\dfrac{(-1)^{n+1}}{n^2}\right\}_{n=1}^{+\infty}$
15. $\left\{(-1)^n \dfrac{2n^3}{n^3+1}\right\}_{n=1}^{+\infty}$
16. $\left\{\dfrac{n}{2^n}\right\}_{n=1}^{+\infty}$
17. $\left\{\dfrac{(n+1)(n+2)}{2n^2}\right\}_{n=1}^{+\infty}$
18. $\left\{\dfrac{\pi^n}{4^n}\right\}_{n=1}^{+\infty}$
19. $\{n^2 e^{-n}\}_{n=1}^{+\infty}$
20. $\{\sqrt{n^2+3n} - n\}_{n=1}^{+\infty}$
21. $\left\{\left(\dfrac{n+3}{n+1}\right)^n\right\}_{n=1}^{+\infty}$
22. $\left\{\left(1 - \dfrac{2}{n}\right)^n\right\}_{n=1}^{+\infty}$

**23–30** Find the general term of the sequence, starting with $n = 1$, determine whether the sequence converges, and if so find its limit. ■

23. $\frac{1}{2}, \frac{3}{4}, \frac{5}{6}, \frac{7}{8}, \ldots$
24. $0, \frac{1}{2^2}, \frac{2}{3^2}, \frac{3}{4^2}, \ldots$
25. $\frac{1}{3}, -\frac{1}{9}, \frac{1}{27}, -\frac{1}{81}, \ldots$
26. $-1, 2, -3, 4, -5, \ldots$
27. $\left(1 - \frac{1}{2}\right), \left(\frac{1}{3} - \frac{1}{2}\right), \left(\frac{1}{3} - \frac{1}{4}\right), \left(\frac{1}{5} - \frac{1}{4}\right), \ldots$
28. $3, \frac{3}{2}, \frac{3}{2^2}, \frac{3}{2^3}, \ldots$
29. $(\sqrt{2} - \sqrt{3}), (\sqrt{3} - \sqrt{4}), (\sqrt{4} - \sqrt{5}), \ldots$
30. $\frac{1}{3^5}, -\frac{1}{3^6}, \frac{1}{3^7}, -\frac{1}{3^8}, \ldots$

**31–34 True–False** Determine whether the statement is true or false. Explain your answer. ■

**31.** Sequences are functions.

**32.** If $\{a_n\}$ and $\{b_n\}$ are sequences such that $\{a_n + b_n\}$ converges, then $\{a_n\}$ and $\{b_n\}$ converge.

**33.** If $\{a_n\}$ diverges, then $a_n \to +\infty$ or $a_n \to -\infty$.

**34.** If the graph of $y = f(x)$ has a horizontal asymptote as $x \to +\infty$, then the sequence $\{f(n)\}$ converges.

**35–36** Use numerical evidence to make a conjecture about the limit of the sequence, and then use the Squeezing Theorem for Sequences (Theorem 9.1.5) to confirm that your conjecture is correct. ■

**35.** $\lim\limits_{n\to+\infty} \dfrac{\sin^2 n}{n}$ **36.** $\lim\limits_{n\to+\infty} \left(\dfrac{1+n}{2n}\right)^n$

**FOCUS ON CONCEPTS**

**37.** Give two examples of sequences, all of whose terms are between $-10$ and 10, that do not converge. Use graphs of your sequences to explain their properties.

**38.** (a) Suppose that $f$ satisfies $\lim_{x\to 0^+} f(x) = +\infty$. Is it possible that the sequence $\{f(1/n)\}$ converges? Explain.

(b) Find a function $f$ such that $\lim_{x\to 0^+} f(x)$ does not exist but the sequence $\{f(1/n)\}$ converges.

**39.** (a) Starting with $n = 1$, write out the first six terms of the sequence $\{a_n\}$, where

$$a_n = \begin{cases} 1, & \text{if } n \text{ is odd} \\ n, & \text{if } n \text{ is even} \end{cases}$$

(b) Starting with $n = 1$, and considering the even and odd terms separately, find a formula for the general term of the sequence

$$1, \frac{1}{2^2}, 3, \frac{1}{2^4}, 5, \frac{1}{2^6}, \ldots$$

(c) Starting with $n = 1$, and considering the even and odd terms separately, find a formula for the general term of the sequence

$$1, \frac{1}{3}, \frac{1}{3}, \frac{1}{5}, \frac{1}{5}, \frac{1}{7}, \frac{1}{7}, \frac{1}{9}, \frac{1}{9}, \ldots$$

(d) Determine whether the sequences in parts (a), (b), and (c) converge. For those that do, find the limit.

**40.** For what positive values of $b$ does the sequence $b, 0, b^2, 0, b^3, 0, b^4, \ldots$ converge? Justify your answer.

**41.** Assuming that the sequence given in Formula (2) of this section converges, use the method of Example 10 to show that the limit of this sequence is $\sqrt{a}$.

**42.** Consider the sequence

$$a_1 = \sqrt{6}$$
$$a_2 = \sqrt{6+\sqrt{6}}$$
$$a_3 = \sqrt{6+\sqrt{6+\sqrt{6}}}$$
$$a_4 = \sqrt{6+\sqrt{6+\sqrt{6+\sqrt{6}}}}$$
$$\vdots$$

(a) Find a recursion formula for $a_{n+1}$.

(b) Assuming that the sequence converges, use the method of Example 10 to find the limit.

**43.** Each year on his birthday Tim's grandmother deposits \$20 into a "birthday account" that earns an annual interest rate of 10%. The year's interest is added to the account at the same time as that year's deposit.

(a) Let $a_n$ denote the amount in the savings account after $n$ years with $a_0 = 20$ (dollars) the very first deposit on the day of Tim's birth. Find a recursion formula for $a_{n+1}$. (Assume that no money is ever withdrawn from the account.)

(b) Use the formula from part (a) to determine how much money will be in the account when Tim is 40 years old.

**44.** Prove that the sequence $a_n$ defined recursively in the preceding exercise is given explicitly by the formula $a_n = 20(11 \cdot (1.1)^n - 10), n \geq 0$.

**45.** (a) Suppose that a study of coho salmon suggests the population model

$$p_{n+1} = \frac{2.08p_n}{1 + 0.00018p_n}$$

where $p_0 = 10{,}000$ is the number of salmon at the start of the study and $p_n$ is the population $n$ years later. Based upon this model, what will the population of salmon be 10 years after the start of the study?

(b) Find a value of an initial population $p_0 > 0$ of coho salmon such that, with the recursion formula in part (a), the population remains fixed at $p_0$ from year to year.

**46.** (a) Prove that the sequence $p_n$ defined recursively in part (a) of the preceding exercise is given explicitly by

$$p_n = \frac{60{,}000 \cdot (2.08)^n}{10 \cdot (2.08)^n - 4}, \quad n \geq 0$$

(b) Use the result of part (a) to determine $\lim_{n\to+\infty} p_n$.

**47.** (a) Use a graphing utility to generate the graph of the equation $y = (2^x + 3^x)^{1/x}$, and then use the graph to make a conjecture about the limit of the sequence

$$\{(2^n + 3^n)^{1/n}\}_{n=1}^{+\infty}$$

(b) Confirm your conjecture by calculating the limit.

**48.** Consider the sequence $\{a_n\}_{n=1}^{+\infty}$ whose $n$th term is

$$a_n = \frac{1}{n}\sum_{k=1}^{n} \frac{1}{1+(k/n)}$$

Show that $\lim_{n\to+\infty} a_n = \ln 2$ by interpreting $a_n$ as the Riemann sum of a definite integral.

**49.** The sequence whose terms are 1, 1, 2, 3, 5, 8, 13, 21, ... is called the ***Fibonacci sequence*** in honor of the Italian mathematician Leonardo ("Fibonacci") da Pisa (c. 1170–1250). This sequence has the property that after starting with two 1's, each term is the sum of the preceding two.

(a) Denoting the sequence by $\{a_n\}$ and starting with $a_1 = 1$ and $a_2 = 1$, show that

$$\frac{a_{n+2}}{a_{n+1}} = 1 + \frac{a_n}{a_{n+1}} \quad \text{if } n \geq 1$$

(b) Give a reasonable informal argument to show that if the sequence $\{a_{n+1}/a_n\}$ converges to some limit $L$, then the sequence $\{a_{n+2}/a_{n+1}\}$ must also converge to $L$.

(c) Assuming that the sequence $\{a_{n+1}/a_n\}$ converges, show that its limit is $(1+\sqrt{5})/2$.

**50.** If we accept the fact that the sequence $\{1/n\}_{n=1}^{+\infty}$ converges to the limit $L = 0$, then according to Definition 9.1.2, for every $\epsilon > 0$ there exists a positive integer $N$ such that $|a_n - L| = |(1/n) - 0| < \epsilon$ when $n \geq N$. In each part, find the smallest possible value of $N$ for the given value of $\epsilon$.

(a) $\epsilon = 0.5$ (b) $\epsilon = 0.1$ (c) $\epsilon = 0.001$

**51.** If we accept the fact that the sequence

$$\left\{\frac{n}{n+1}\right\}_{n=1}^{+\infty}$$

converges to the limit $L = 1$, then according to Definition 9.1.2, for every $\epsilon > 0$ there exists an integer $N$ such that

$$|a_n - L| = \left|\frac{n}{n+1} - 1\right| < \epsilon$$

when $n \geq N$. In each part, find the smallest value of $N$ for the given value of $\epsilon$.

(a) $\epsilon = 0.25$ (b) $\epsilon = 0.1$ (c) $\epsilon = 0.001$

**52.** Use Definition 9.1.2 to prove that

(a) the sequence $\{1/n\}_{n=1}^{+\infty}$ converges to 0

(b) the sequence $\left\{\frac{n}{n+1}\right\}_{n=1}^{+\infty}$ converges to 1.

**53. Writing** Discuss, with examples, various ways that a sequence could diverge.

**54. Writing** Discuss the convergence of the sequence $\{r^n\}$ considering the cases $|r| < 1$, $|r| > 1$, $r = 1$, and $r = -1$ separately.

✓ **QUICK CHECK ANSWERS 9.1** 1. (a) 4; 10; 16; $2n+2$ (b) 4; 12; 20; $2n+4$ 2. $\lim_{n\to+\infty} a_n$ exists 3. (a) diverges (b) converges to 5 (c) converges to 1 (d) diverges (e) converges to $\frac{1}{7}$ (f) diverges 4. Squeezing; 12

## 9.2 MONOTONE SEQUENCES

*There are many situations in which it is important to know whether a sequence converges, but the value of the limit is not relevant to the problem at hand. In this section we will study several techniques that can be used to determine whether a sequence converges.*

### ■ TERMINOLOGY

We begin with some terminology.

**9.2.1 DEFINITION** A sequence $\{a_n\}_{n=1}^{+\infty}$ is called

| | |
|---|---|
| ***strictly increasing*** if | $a_1 < a_2 < a_3 < \cdots < a_n < \cdots$ |
| ***increasing*** if | $a_1 \leq a_2 \leq a_3 \leq \cdots \leq a_n \leq \cdots$ |
| ***strictly decreasing*** if | $a_1 > a_2 > a_3 > \cdots > a_n > \cdots$ |
| ***decreasing*** if | $a_1 \geq a_2 \geq a_3 \geq \cdots \geq a_n \geq \cdots$ |

A sequence that is either increasing or decreasing is said to be ***monotone***, and a sequence that is either strictly increasing or strictly decreasing is said to be ***strictly monotone***.

Note that an increasing sequence need not be strictly increasing, and a decreasing sequence need not be strictly decreasing.

Some examples are given in Table 9.2.1 and their corresponding graphs are shown in Figure 9.2.1. The first and second sequences in Table 9.2.1 are strictly monotone; the third and fourth sequences are monotone but not strictly monotone; and the fifth sequence is neither strictly monotone nor monotone.

**Table 9.2.1**

| SEQUENCE | DESCRIPTION |
|---|---|
| $\frac{1}{2}, \frac{2}{3}, \frac{3}{4}, \ldots, \frac{n}{n+1}, \ldots$ | Strictly increasing |
| $1, \frac{1}{2}, \frac{1}{3}, \ldots, \frac{1}{n}, \ldots$ | Strictly decreasing |
| $1, 1, 2, 2, 3, 3, \ldots$ | Increasing; not strictly increasing |
| $1, 1, \frac{1}{2}, \frac{1}{2}, \frac{1}{3}, \frac{1}{3}, \ldots$ | Decreasing; not strictly decreasing |
| $1, -\frac{1}{2}, \frac{1}{3}, -\frac{1}{4}, \ldots, (-1)^{n+1}\frac{1}{n}, \ldots$ | Neither increasing nor decreasing |

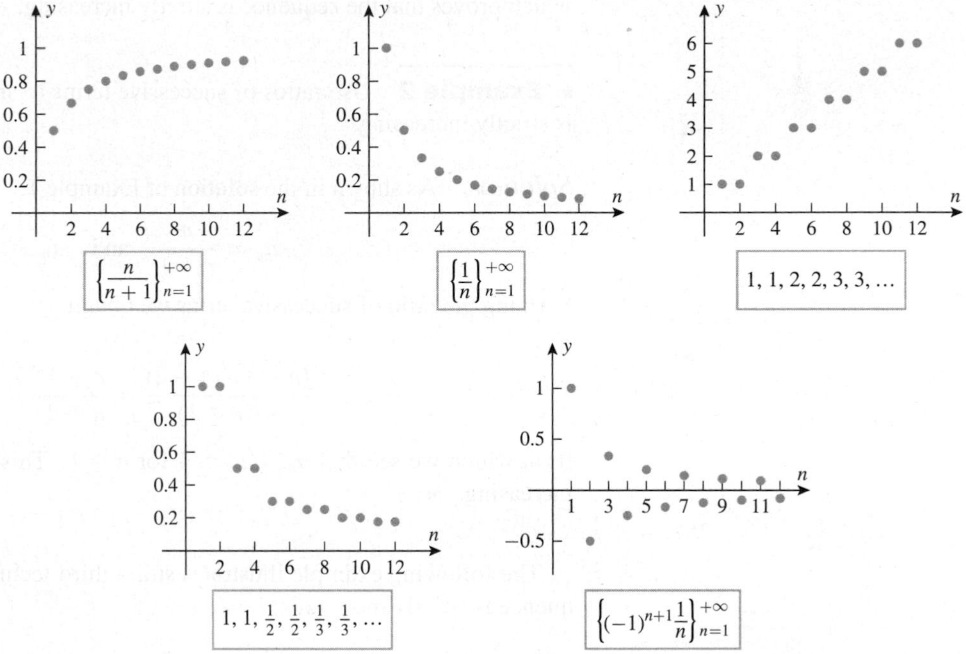


▲ **Figure 9.2.1**

Can a sequence be both increasing and decreasing? Explain.

## TESTING FOR MONOTONICITY

Frequently, one can *guess* whether a sequence is monotone or strictly monotone by writing out some of the initial terms. However, to be certain that the guess is correct, one must give a precise mathematical argument. Table 9.2.2 provides two ways of doing this, one based on differences of successive terms and the other on ratios of successive terms. It is assumed in the latter case that the terms are positive. One must show that the specified conditions hold for *all* pairs of successive terms.

**Table 9.2.2**

| DIFFERENCE BETWEEN SUCCESSIVE TERMS | RATIO OF SUCCESSIVE TERMS | CONCLUSION |
|---|---|---|
| $a_{n+1} - a_n > 0$ | $a_{n+1}/a_n > 1$ | Strictly increasing |
| $a_{n+1} - a_n < 0$ | $a_{n+1}/a_n < 1$ | Strictly decreasing |
| $a_{n+1} - a_n \geq 0$ | $a_{n+1}/a_n \geq 1$ | Increasing |
| $a_{n+1} - a_n \leq 0$ | $a_{n+1}/a_n \leq 1$ | Decreasing |

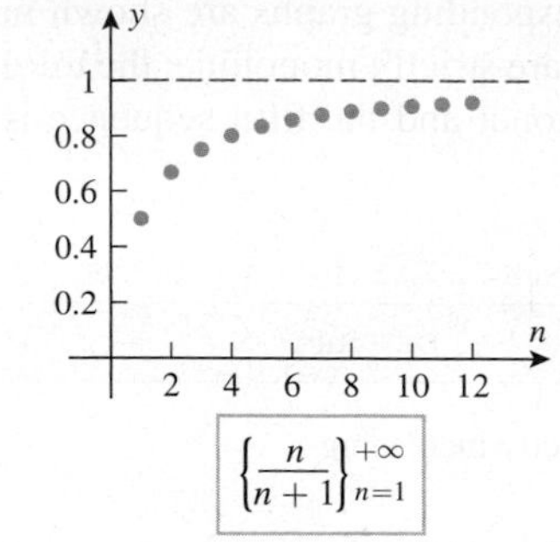


▲ **Figure 9.2.2**

**▶ Example 1** Use differences of successive terms to show that

$$\frac{1}{2}, \frac{2}{3}, \frac{3}{4}, \ldots, \frac{n}{n+1}, \ldots$$

(Figure 9.2.2) is a strictly increasing sequence.

***Solution.*** The pattern of the initial terms suggests that the sequence is strictly increasing. To prove that this is so, let

$$a_n = \frac{n}{n+1}$$

We can obtain $a_{n+1}$ by replacing $n$ by $n+1$ in this formula. This yields

$$a_{n+1} = \frac{n+1}{(n+1)+1} = \frac{n+1}{n+2}$$

Thus, for $n \geq 1$

$$a_{n+1} - a_n = \frac{n+1}{n+2} - \frac{n}{n+1} = \frac{n^2+2n+1-n^2-2n}{(n+1)(n+2)} = \frac{1}{(n+1)(n+2)} > 0$$

which proves that the sequence is strictly increasing. ◀

**▶ Example 2** Use ratios of successive terms to show that the sequence in Example 1 is strictly increasing.

***Solution.*** As shown in the solution of Example 1,

$$a_n = \frac{n}{n+1} \quad \text{and} \quad a_{n+1} = \frac{n+1}{n+2}$$

Forming the ratio of successive terms we obtain

$$\frac{a_{n+1}}{a_n} = \frac{(n+1)/(n+2)}{n/(n+1)} = \frac{n+1}{n+2} \cdot \frac{n+1}{n} = \frac{n^2+2n+1}{n^2+2n} \tag{1}$$

from which we see that $a_{n+1}/a_n > 1$ for $n \geq 1$. This proves that the sequence is strictly increasing. ◀

The following example illustrates still a third technique for determining whether a sequence is strictly monotone.

**▶ Example 3** In Examples 1 and 2 we proved that the sequence

$$\frac{1}{2}, \frac{2}{3}, \frac{3}{4}, \ldots, \frac{n}{n+1}, \ldots$$

is strictly increasing by considering the difference and ratio of successive terms. Alternatively, we can proceed as follows. Let

$$f(x) = \frac{x}{x+1}$$

so that the $n$th term in the given sequence is $a_n = f(n)$. The function $f$ is increasing for $x \geq 1$ since

$$f'(x) = \frac{(x+1)(1) - x(1)}{(x+1)^2} = \frac{1}{(x+1)^2} > 0$$

Thus,

$$a_n = f(n) < f(n+1) = a_{n+1}$$

which proves that the given sequence is strictly increasing. ◀

**Table 9.2.3**

| DERIVATIVE OF $f$ FOR $x \geq 1$ | CONCLUSION FOR THE SEQUENCE WITH $a_n = f(n)$ |
|---|---|
| $f'(x) > 0$ | Strictly increasing |
| $f'(x) < 0$ | Strictly decreasing |
| $f'(x) \geq 0$ | Increasing |
| $f'(x) \leq 0$ | Decreasing |

In general, if $f(n) = a_n$ is the $n$th term of a sequence, and if $f$ is differentiable for $x \geq 1$, then the results in Table 9.2.3 can be used to investigate the monotonicity of the sequence.

## PROPERTIES THAT HOLD EVENTUALLY

Sometimes a sequence will behave erratically at first and then settle down into a definite pattern. For example, the sequence

$$9, -8, -17, 12, 1, 2, 3, 4, \ldots \tag{2}$$

is strictly increasing from the fifth term on, but the sequence as a whole cannot be classified as strictly increasing because of the erratic behavior of the first four terms. To describe such sequences, we introduce the following terminology.

> **9.2.2 DEFINITION** If discarding finitely many terms from the beginning of a sequence produces a sequence with a certain property, then the original sequence is said to have that property ***eventually***.

For example, although we cannot say that sequence (2) is strictly increasing, we can say that it is eventually strictly increasing.

▶ **Example 4** Show that the sequence $\left\{\dfrac{10^n}{n!}\right\}_{n=1}^{+\infty}$ is eventually strictly decreasing.

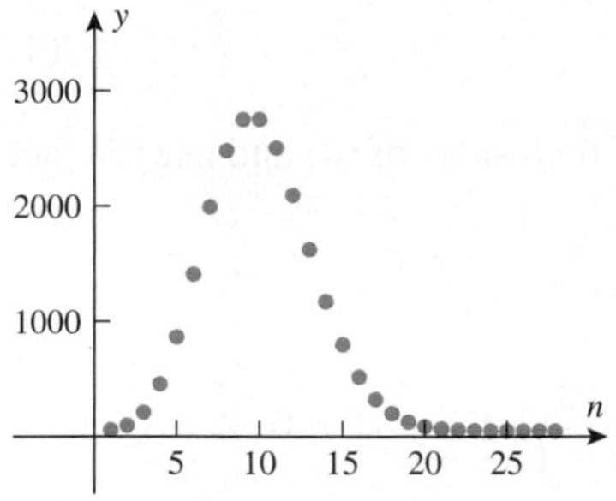


$\left\{10^n/n!\right\}_{n=1}^{+\infty}$

▲ **Figure 9.2.3**

***Solution.*** We have

$$a_n = \frac{10^n}{n!} \quad \text{and} \quad a_{n+1} = \frac{10^{n+1}}{(n+1)!}$$

so

$$\frac{a_{n+1}}{a_n} = \frac{10^{n+1}/(n+1)!}{10^n/n!} = \frac{10^{n+1}n!}{10^n(n+1)!} = 10\frac{n!}{(n+1)n!} = \frac{10}{n+1} \tag{3}$$

From (3), $a_{n+1}/a_n < 1$ for all $n \geq 10$, so the sequence is eventually strictly decreasing, as confirmed by the graph in Figure 9.2.3. ◀

## AN INTUITIVE VIEW OF CONVERGENCE

Informally stated, the convergence or divergence of a sequence does not depend on the behavior of its *initial terms*, but rather on how the terms behave *eventually*. For example, the sequence

$$3, -9, -13, 17, 1, \frac{1}{2}, \frac{1}{3}, \frac{1}{4}, \ldots$$

eventually behaves like the sequence

$$1, \frac{1}{2}, \frac{1}{3}, \ldots, \frac{1}{n}, \ldots$$

and hence has a limit of 0.

## CONVERGENCE OF MONOTONE SEQUENCES

The following two theorems, whose proofs are discussed at the end of this section, show that a monotone sequence either converges or becomes infinite—divergence by oscillation cannot occur.

> **9.2.3 THEOREM** *If a sequence $\{a_n\}$ is eventually increasing, then there are two possibilities:*
>
> (a) *There is a constant M, called an* ***upper bound*** *for the sequence, such that $a_n \leq M$ for all n, in which case the sequence converges to a limit L satisfying $L \leq M$.*
>
> (b) *No upper bound exists, in which case $\lim_{n\to+\infty} a_n = +\infty$.*

> Theorems 9.2.3 and 9.2.4 are examples of ***existence theorems***; they tell us whether a limit exists, but they do not provide a method for finding it.

**9.2.4 THEOREM** *If a sequence $\{a_n\}$ is eventually decreasing, then there are two possibilities:*

*(a) There is a constant M, called a* ***lower bound*** *for the sequence, such that $a_n \geq M$ for all n, in which case the sequence converges to a limit L satisfying $L \geq M$.*

*(b) No lower bound exists, in which case $\lim_{n\to+\infty} a_n = -\infty$.*

▶ **Example 5** Show that the sequence $\left\{\dfrac{10^n}{n!}\right\}_{n=1}^{+\infty}$ converges and find its limit.

***Solution.*** We showed in Example 4 that the sequence is eventually strictly decreasing. Since all terms in the sequence are positive, it is bounded below by $M = 0$, and hence Theorem 9.2.4 guarantees that it converges to a nonnegative limit $L$. However, the limit is not evident directly from the formula $10^n/n!$ for the $n$th term, so we will need some ingenuity to obtain it.

It follows from Formula (3) of Example 4 that successive terms in the given sequence are related by the recursion formula

$$a_{n+1} = \frac{10}{n+1}a_n \tag{4}$$

where $a_n = 10^n/n!$. We will take the limit as $n\to+\infty$ of both sides of (4) and use the fact that

$$\lim_{n\to+\infty} a_{n+1} = \lim_{n\to+\infty} a_n = L$$

We obtain

$$L = \lim_{n\to+\infty} a_{n+1} = \lim_{n\to+\infty}\left(\frac{10}{n+1}a_n\right) = \lim_{n\to+\infty}\frac{10}{n+1}\lim_{n\to+\infty} a_n = 0 \cdot L = 0$$

so that

$$L = \lim_{n\to+\infty}\frac{10^n}{n!} = 0 \blacktriangleleft$$

In the exercises we will show that the technique illustrated in the last example can be adapted to obtain

$$\lim_{n\to+\infty}\frac{x^n}{n!} = 0 \tag{5}$$

for any real value of $x$ (Exercise 31). This result will be useful in our later work.

## ■ THE COMPLETENESS AXIOM

In this text we have accepted the familiar properties of real numbers without proof, and indeed, we have not even attempted to define the term *real number*. Although this is sufficient for many purposes, it was recognized by the late nineteenth century that the study of limits and functions in calculus requires a precise axiomatic formulation of the real numbers analogous to the axiomatic development of Euclidean geometry. Although we will not attempt to pursue this development, we will need to discuss one of the axioms about real numbers in order to prove Theorems 9.2.3 and 9.2.4. But first we will introduce some terminology.

If $S$ is a nonempty set of real numbers, then we call $u$ an ***upper bound*** for $S$ if $u$ is greater than or equal to every number in $S$, and we call $l$ a ***lower bound*** for $S$ if $l$ is smaller than or equal to every number in $S$. For example, if $S$ is the set of numbers in the interval $(1, 3)$, then $u = 10$, 4, 3.2, and 3 are upper bounds for $S$ and $l = -10$, 0, 0.5, and 1 are lower bounds for $S$. Observe also that $u = 3$ is the smallest of all upper bounds and $l = 1$ is the largest of all lower bounds. The existence of a smallest upper bound and a largest lower bound for $S$ is not accidental; it is a consequence of the following axiom.

**9.2.5 AXIOM** (*The Completeness Axiom*) *If a nonempty set S of real numbers has an upper bound, then it has a smallest upper bound (called the* ***least upper bound****), and if a nonempty set S of real numbers has a lower bound, then it has a largest lower bound (called the* ***greatest lower bound****).*

**PROOF OF THEOREM 9.2.3**

(a) We will prove the result for increasing sequences, and leave it for the reader to adapt the argument to sequences that are eventually increasing. Assume there exists a number $M$ such that $a_n \le M$ for $n = 1, 2, \ldots$. Then $M$ is an upper bound for the set of terms in the sequence. By the Completeness Axiom there is a least upper bound for the terms; call it $L$. Now let $\epsilon$ be any positive number. Since $L$ is the least upper bound for the terms, $L - \epsilon$ is not an upper bound for the terms, which means that there is at least one term $a_N$ such that

$$a_N > L - \epsilon$$

Moreover, since $\{a_n\}$ is an increasing sequence, we must have

$$a_n \ge a_N > L - \epsilon \tag{6}$$

when $n \ge N$. But $a_n$ cannot exceed $L$ since $L$ is an upper bound for the terms. This observation together with (6) tells us that $L \ge a_n > L - \epsilon$ for $n \ge N$, so all terms from the $N$th on are within $\epsilon$ units of $L$. This is exactly the requirement to have

$$\lim_{n\to+\infty} a_n = L$$

Finally, $L \le M$ since $M$ is an upper bound for the terms and $L$ is the least upper bound. This proves part (a).

(b) If there is no number $M$ such that $a_n \le M$ for $n = 1, 2, \ldots$, then no matter how large we choose $M$, there is a term $a_N$ such that

$$a_N > M$$

and, since the sequence is increasing,

$$a_n \ge a_N > M$$

when $n \ge N$. Thus, the terms in the sequence become arbitrarily large as $n$ increases. That is,

$$\lim_{n\to+\infty} a_n = +\infty \quad \blacksquare$$

We omit the proof of Theorem 9.2.4 since it is similar to that of 9.2.3.

## ✓ QUICK CHECK EXERCISES 9.2

*(See page 531 for answers.)*

**1.** Classify each sequence as (I) increasing, (D) decreasing, or (N) neither increasing nor decreasing.

_____ $\{2n\}$ _____ $\{2^{-n}\}$

_____ $\left\{\dfrac{5-n}{n^2}\right\}$ _____ $\left\{\dfrac{-1}{n^2}\right\}$

_____ $\left\{\dfrac{(-1)^n}{n^2}\right\}$

**2.** Classify each sequence as (M) monotonic, (S) strictly monotonic, or (N) not monotonic.

_____ $\{n + (-1)^n\}$ _____ $\{2n + (-1)^n\}$

_____ $\{3n + (-1)^n\}$

**3.** Since

$$\frac{n/[2(n+1)]}{(n-1)/(2n)} = \frac{n^2}{n^2-1} > \_\_\_\_\_$$

the sequence $\{(n-1)/(2n)\}$ is strictly _____.

**4.** Since

$$\frac{d}{dx}[(x-8)^2] > 0 \text{ for } x > \_\_\_\_\_$$

the sequence $\{(n-8)^2\}$ is _____ strictly _____.

## EXERCISE SET 9.2

**1–6** Use the difference $a_{n+1} - a_n$ to show that the given sequence $\{a_n\}$ is strictly increasing or strictly decreasing. ■

**1.** $\left\{\frac{1}{n}\right\}_{n=1}^{+\infty}$ **2.** $\left\{1 - \frac{1}{n}\right\}_{n=1}^{+\infty}$ **3.** $\left\{\frac{n}{2n+1}\right\}_{n=1}^{+\infty}$

**4.** $\left\{\frac{n}{4n-1}\right\}_{n=1}^{+\infty}$ **5.** $\{n - 2^n\}_{n=1}^{+\infty}$ **6.** $\{n - n^2\}_{n=1}^{+\infty}$

**7–12** Use the ratio $a_{n+1}/a_n$ to show that the given sequence $\{a_n\}$ is strictly increasing or strictly decreasing. ■

**7.** $\left\{\frac{n}{2n+1}\right\}_{n=1}^{+\infty}$ **8.** $\left\{\frac{2^n}{1+2^n}\right\}_{n=1}^{+\infty}$ **9.** $\{ne^{-n}\}_{n=1}^{+\infty}$

**10.** $\left\{\frac{10^n}{(2n)!}\right\}_{n=1}^{+\infty}$ **11.** $\left\{\frac{n^n}{n!}\right\}_{n=1}^{+\infty}$ **12.** $\left\{\frac{5^n}{2^{(n^2)}}\right\}_{n=1}^{+\infty}$

**13–16 True–False** Determine whether the statement is true or false. Explain your answer. ■

**13.** If $a_{n+1} - a_n > 0$ for all $n \geq 1$, then the sequence $\{a_n\}$ is strictly increasing.

**14.** A sequence $\{a_n\}$ is monotone if $a_{n+1} - a_n \neq 0$ for all $n \geq 1$.

**15.** Any bounded sequence converges.

**16.** If $\{a_n\}$ is eventually increasing, then $a_{100} < a_{200}$.

**17–20** Use differentiation to show that the given sequence is strictly increasing or strictly decreasing. ■

**17.** $\left\{\frac{n}{2n+1}\right\}_{n=1}^{+\infty}$ **18.** $\left\{\frac{\ln(n+2)}{n+2}\right\}_{n=1}^{+\infty}$

**19.** $\{\tan^{-1} n\}_{n=1}^{+\infty}$ **20.** $\{ne^{-2n}\}_{n=1}^{+\infty}$

**21–24** Show that the given sequence is eventually strictly increasing or eventually strictly decreasing. ■

**21.** $\{2n^2 - 7n\}_{n=1}^{+\infty}$ **22.** $\left\{\frac{n}{n^2+10}\right\}_{n=1}^{+\infty}$

**23.** $\left\{\frac{n!}{3^n}\right\}_{n=1}^{+\infty}$ **24.** $\{n^5 e^{-n}\}_{n=1}^{+\infty}$

**FOCUS ON CONCEPTS**

**25.** Suppose that $\{a_n\}$ is a monotone sequence such that $1 \leq a_n \leq 2$ for all $n$. Must the sequence converge? If so, what can you say about the limit?

**26.** Suppose that $\{a_n\}$ is a monotone sequence such that $a_n \leq 2$ for all $n$. Must the sequence converge? If so, what can you say about the limit?

**27.** Let $\{a_n\}$ be the sequence defined recursively by $a_1 = \sqrt{2}$ and $a_{n+1} = \sqrt{2 + a_n}$ for $n \geq 1$.
(a) List the first three terms of the sequence.
(b) Show that $a_n < 2$ for $n \geq 1$.
(c) Show that $a_{n+1}^2 - a_n^2 = (2 - a_n)(1 + a_n)$ for $n \geq 1$.
(d) Use the results in parts (b) and (c) to show that $\{a_n\}$ is a strictly increasing sequence. [*Hint:* If $x$ and $y$ are positive real numbers such that $x^2 - y^2 > 0$, then it follows by factoring that $x - y > 0$.]
(e) Show that $\{a_n\}$ converges and find its limit $L$.

**28.** Let $\{a_n\}$ be the sequence defined recursively by $a_1 = 1$ and $a_{n+1} = \frac{1}{2}[a_n + (3/a_n)]$ for $n \geq 1$.
(a) Show that $a_n \geq \sqrt{3}$ for $n \geq 2$. [*Hint:* What is the minimum value of $\frac{1}{2}[x + (3/x)]$ for $x > 0$?]
(b) Show that $\{a_n\}$ is eventually decreasing. [*Hint:* Examine $a_{n+1} - a_n$ or $a_{n+1}/a_n$ and use the result in part (a).]
(c) Show that $\{a_n\}$ converges and find its limit $L$.

**29–30** The Beverton–Holt model is used to describe changes in a population from one generation to the next under certain assumptions. If the population in generation $n$ is given by $x_n$, the Beverton–Holt model predicts that the population in the next generation satisfies

$$x_{n+1} = \frac{RKx_n}{K + (R-1)x_n}$$

for some positive constants $R$ and $K$ with $R > 1$. These exercises explore some properties of this population model. ■

**29.** Let $\{x_n\}$ be the sequence of population values defined recursively by $x_1 = 60$, and for $n \geq 1, x_{n+1}$ is given by the Beverton–Holt model with $R = 10$ and $K = 300$.
(a) List the first four terms of the sequence $\{x_n\}$.
(b) If $0 < x_n < 300$, show that $0 < x_{n+1} < 300$. Conclude that $0 < x_n < 300$ for $n \geq 1$.
(c) Show that $\{x_n\}$ is increasing.
(d) Show that $\{x_n\}$ converges and find its limit $L$.

**30.** Let $\{x_n\}$ be a sequence of population values defined recursively by the Beverton–Holt model for which $x_1 > K$. Assume that the constants $R$ and $K$ satisfy $R > 1$ and $K > 0$.
(a) If $x_n > K$, show that $x_{n+1} > K$. Conclude that $x_n > K$ for all $n \geq 1$.
(b) Show that $\{x_n\}$ is decreasing.
(c) Show that $\{x_n\}$ converges and find its limit $L$.

**31.** The goal of this exercise is to establish Formula (5), namely,

$$\lim_{n\to+\infty} \frac{x^n}{n!} = 0$$

Let $a_n = |x|^n/n!$ and observe that the case where $x = 0$ is obvious, so we will focus on the case where $x \neq 0$.
(a) Show that

$$a_{n+1} = \frac{|x|}{n+1}a_n$$

(b) Show that the sequence $\{a_n\}$ is eventually strictly decreasing.
(c) Show that the sequence $\{a_n\}$ converges.

**32.** (a) Compare appropriate areas in the accompanying figure to deduce the following inequalities for $n \geq 2$:

$$\int_1^n \ln x\,dx < \ln n! < \int_1^{n+1} \ln x\,dx$$

(*cont.*)

(b) Use the result in part (a) to show that
$$\frac{n^n}{e^{n-1}} < n! < \frac{(n+1)^{n+1}}{e^n}, \quad n > 1$$

(c) Use the Squeezing Theorem for Sequences (Theorem 9.1.5) and the result in part (b) to show that
$$\lim_{n\to+\infty} \frac{\sqrt[n]{n!}}{n} = \frac{1}{e}$$

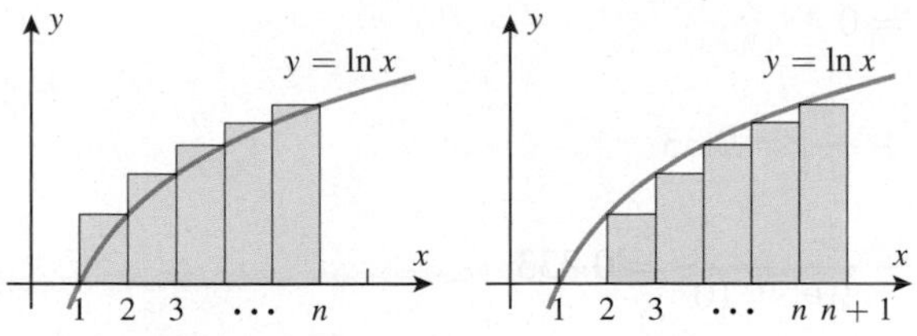


▲ **Figure Ex-32**

**33.** Use the left inequality in Exercise 32(b) to show that
$$\lim_{n\to+\infty} \sqrt[n]{n!} = +\infty$$

**34. Writing** Give an example of an increasing sequence that is not eventually strictly increasing. What can you conclude about the terms of any such sequence? Explain.

**35. Writing** Discuss the appropriate use of "eventually" for various properties of sequences. For example, which is a useful expression: "eventually bounded" or "eventually monotone"?

✓ **QUICK CHECK ANSWERS 9.2** 1. I; D; N; I; N 2. N; M; S 3. 1; increasing 4. 8; eventually; increasing

## 9.3 INFINITE SERIES

*The purpose of this section is to discuss sums that contain infinitely many terms. The most familiar examples of such sums occur in the decimal representations of real numbers. For example, when we write $\frac{1}{3}$ in the decimal form $\frac{1}{3} = 0.3333\ldots$, we mean*
$$\frac{1}{3} = 0.3 + 0.03 + 0.003 + 0.0003 + \cdots$$
*which suggests that the decimal representation of $\frac{1}{3}$ can be viewed as a sum of infinitely many real numbers.*

### SUMS OF INFINITE SERIES

Our first objective is to define what is meant by the "sum" of infinitely many real numbers. We begin with some terminology.

**9.3.1 DEFINITION** An ***infinite series*** is an expression that can be written in the form
$$\sum_{k=1}^{\infty} u_k = u_1 + u_2 + u_3 + \cdots + u_k + \cdots$$
The numbers $u_1, u_2, u_3, \ldots$ are called the ***terms*** of the series.

Since it is impossible to add infinitely many numbers together directly, sums of infinite series are defined and computed by an indirect limiting process. To motivate the basic idea, consider the decimal
$$0.3333\ldots \qquad (1)$$
This can be viewed as the infinite series
$$0.3 + 0.03 + 0.003 + 0.0003 + \cdots$$

or, equivalently,

$$\frac{3}{10}+\frac{3}{10^2}+\frac{3}{10^3}+\frac{3}{10^4}+\cdots \qquad (2)$$

Since (1) is the decimal expansion of $\frac{1}{3}$, any reasonable definition for the sum of an infinite series should yield $\frac{1}{3}$ for the sum of (2). To obtain such a definition, consider the following sequence of (finite) sums:

$$\begin{aligned}
s_1 &= \frac{3}{10} = 0.3\\
s_2 &= \frac{3}{10}+\frac{3}{10^2} = 0.33\\
s_3 &= \frac{3}{10}+\frac{3}{10^2}+\frac{3}{10^3} = 0.333\\
s_4 &= \frac{3}{10}+\frac{3}{10^2}+\frac{3}{10^3}+\frac{3}{10^4} = 0.3333\\
&\ \vdots
\end{aligned}$$

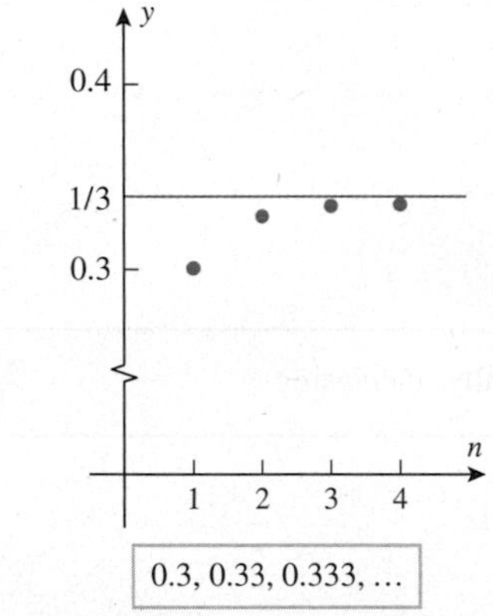


▲ **Figure 9.3.1**

The sequence of numbers $s_1, s_2, s_3, s_4, \ldots$ satisfies $s_n \to \frac{1}{3}$ as $n \to +\infty$ (Figure 9.3.1). This suggests that we define the sum of the series (2) by $\lim_{n\to+\infty} s_n$. In other words, we construct a sequence of (finite) sums and take a limit, instead of attempting to sum the series directly.

Motivated by the preceding example, we are now ready to define the general concept of the "sum" of an infinite series

$$u_1+u_2+u_3+\cdots+u_k+\cdots$$

We begin with some terminology: Let $s_n$ denote the sum of the initial terms of the series, up to and including the term with index $n$. Thus,

$$\begin{aligned}
s_1 &= u_1\\
s_2 &= u_1+u_2\\
s_3 &= u_1+u_2+u_3\\
&\ \vdots\\
s_n &= u_1+u_2+u_3+\cdots+u_n = \sum_{k=1}^{n} u_k
\end{aligned}$$

The number $s_n$ is called the ***nth partial sum*** of the series and the sequence $\{s_n\}_{n=1}^{+\infty}$ is called the ***sequence of partial sums***.

As $n$ increases, the partial sum $s_n = u_1+u_2+\cdots+u_n$ includes more and more terms of the series. Thus, if $s_n$ tends toward a limit as $n\to+\infty$, it is reasonable to view this limit as the sum of *all* the terms in the series. This suggests the following definition.

**WARNING**

In everyday language the words "sequence" and "series" are often used interchangeably. However, in mathematics there is a distinction between these two words—a sequence is a *succession* whereas a series is a *sum*. It is essential that you keep this distinction in mind.

**9.3.2 DEFINITION** Let $\{s_n\}$ be the sequence of partial sums of the series

$$u_1+u_2+u_3+\cdots+u_k+\cdots$$

If the sequence $\{s_n\}$ converges to a limit $S$, then the series is said to ***converge*** to $S$, and $S$ is called the ***sum*** of the series. We denote this by writing

$$S=\sum_{k=1}^{\infty} u_k$$

If the sequence of partial sums diverges, then the series is said to ***diverge***. A divergent series has no sum.

▶ **Example 1** Determine whether the series

$$1 - 1 + 1 - 1 + 1 - 1 + \cdots$$

converges or diverges. If it converges, find the sum.

***Solution.*** It is tempting to conclude that the sum of the series is zero by arguing that the positive and negative terms cancel one another. However, this is *not correct*; the problem is that algebraic operations that hold for finite sums do not carry over to infinite series in all cases. Later, we will discuss conditions under which familiar algebraic operations can be applied to infinite series, but for this example we turn directly to Definition 9.3.2. The partial sums are

$$s_1 = 1$$
$$s_2 = 1 - 1 = 0$$
$$s_3 = 1 - 1 + 1 = 1$$
$$s_4 = 1 - 1 + 1 - 1 = 0$$

and so forth. Thus, the sequence of partial sums is

$$1, 0, 1, 0, 1, 0, \ldots$$

(Figure 9.3.2). Since this is a divergent sequence, the given series diverges and consequently has no sum. ◀

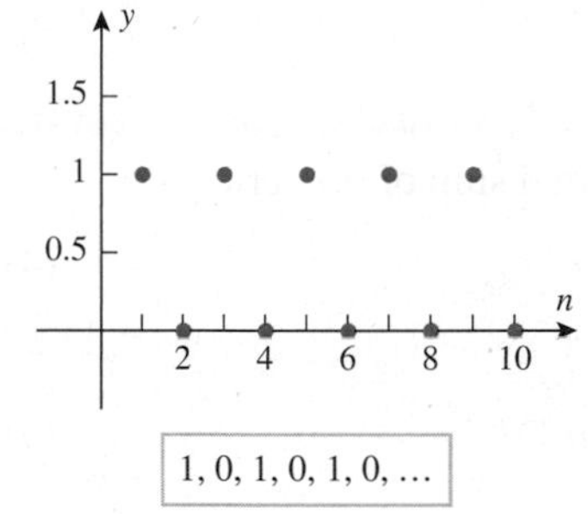

▲ Figure 9.3.2

## GEOMETRIC SERIES

In many important series, each term is obtained by multiplying the preceding term by some fixed constant. Thus, if the initial term of the series is $a$ and each term is obtained by multiplying the preceding term by $r$, then the series has the form

$$\sum_{k=0}^{\infty} ar^k = a + ar + ar^2 + ar^3 + \cdots + ar^k + \cdots \quad (a \neq 0) \tag{3}$$

Such series are called ***geometric series***, and the number $r$ is called the ***ratio*** for the series. Here are some examples:

$$1 + 2 + 4 + 8 + \cdots + 2^k + \cdots \qquad a = 1, r = 2$$

$$\frac{3}{10} + \frac{3}{10^2} + \frac{3}{10^3} + \cdots + \frac{3}{10^k} + \cdots \qquad a = \tfrac{3}{10}, r = \tfrac{1}{10}$$

$$\frac{1}{2} - \frac{1}{4} + \frac{1}{8} - \frac{1}{16} + \cdots + (-1)^{k+1}\frac{1}{2^k} + \cdots \qquad a = \tfrac{1}{2}, r = -\tfrac{1}{2}$$

$$1 + 1 + 1 + \cdots + 1 + \cdots \qquad a = 1, r = 1$$

$$1 - 1 + 1 - 1 + \cdots + (-1)^{k+1} + \cdots \qquad a = 1, r = -1$$

$$1 + x + x^2 + x^3 + \cdots + x^k + \cdots \qquad a = 1, r = x$$

Sometimes it is desirable to start the index of summation of an infinite series at $k = 0$ rather than $k = 1$, in which case we would call $u_0$ the *zeroth term* and $s_0 = u_0$ the *zeroth partial sum*. One can prove that changing the starting value for the index of summation of an infinite series has no effect on the convergence, the divergence, or the sum. If we had started the index at $k = 1$ in (3), then the series would be expressed as

$$\sum_{k=1}^{\infty} ar^{k-1}$$

Since this expression is more complicated than (3), we started the index at $k = 0$.

The following theorem is the fundamental result on convergence of geometric series.

**9.3.3 THEOREM** *A geometric series*

$$\sum_{k=0}^{\infty} ar^k = a + ar + ar^2 + \cdots + ar^k + \cdots \quad (a \neq 0)$$

*converges if* $|r| < 1$ *and diverges if* $|r| \geq 1$. *If the series converges, then the sum is*

$$\sum_{k=0}^{\infty} ar^k = \frac{a}{1 - r}$$

**PROOF** Let us treat the case $|r| = 1$ first. If $r = 1$, then the series is

$$a + a + a + a + \cdots$$

so the $n$th partial sum is $s_n = (n+1)a$ and

$$\lim_{n\to+\infty} s_n = \lim_{n\to+\infty} (n+1)a = \pm\infty$$

(the sign depending on whether $a$ is positive or negative). This proves divergence. If $r = -1$, the series is

$$a - a + a - a + \cdots$$

so the sequence of partial sums is

$$a, 0, a, 0, a, 0, \ldots$$

which diverges.

Now let us consider the case where $|r| \neq 1$. The $n$th partial sum of the series is

$$s_n = a + ar + ar^2 + \cdots + ar^n \tag{4}$$

Multiplying both sides of (4) by $r$ yields

$$rs_n = ar + ar^2 + \cdots + ar^n + ar^{n+1} \tag{5}$$

and subtracting (5) from (4) gives

$$s_n - rs_n = a - ar^{n+1}$$

or

$$(1-r)s_n = a - ar^{n+1} \tag{6}$$

Since $r \neq 1$ in the case we are considering, this can be rewritten as

$$s_n = \frac{a - ar^{n+1}}{1-r} = \frac{a}{1-r}(1 - r^{n+1}) \tag{7}$$

Note that (4) is an open form for $s_n$, while (7) is a closed form for $s_n$. In general, one needs a closed form to calculate the limit.

If $|r| < 1$, then $r^{n+1}$ goes to 0 as $n\to+\infty$ (can you see why?), so $\{s_n\}$ converges. From (7)

$$\lim_{n\to+\infty} s_n = \frac{a}{1-r}$$

If $|r| > 1$, then either $r > 1$ or $r < -1$. In the case $r > 1$, $r^{n+1}$ increases without bound as $n\to+\infty$, and in the case $r < -1$, $r^{n+1}$ oscillates between positive and negative values that grow in magnitude, so $\{s_n\}$ diverges in both cases. ■

► **Example 2** In each part, determine whether the series converges, and if so find its sum.

$$\text{(a)} \sum_{k=0}^{\infty} \frac{5}{4^k} \qquad \text{(b)} \sum_{k=1}^{\infty} 3^{2k}5^{1-k}$$

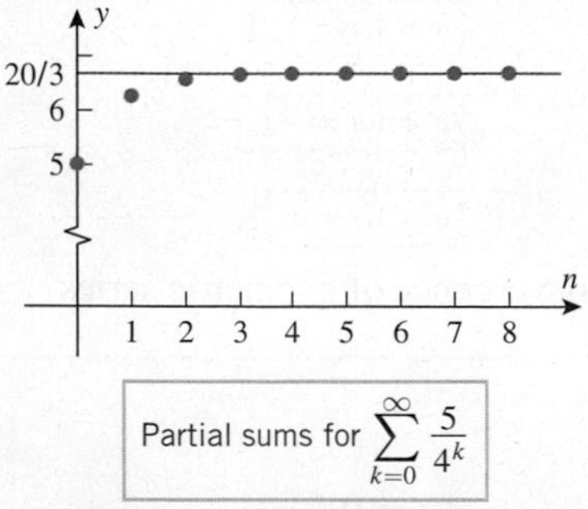


▲ **Figure 9.3.3**

***Solution (a).*** This is a geometric series with $a = 5$ and $r = \frac{1}{4}$. Since $|r| = \frac{1}{4} < 1$, the series converges and the sum is

$$\frac{a}{1-r} = \frac{5}{1-\frac{1}{4}} = \frac{20}{3}$$

(Figure 9.3.3).

***Solution (b).*** This is a geometric series in concealed form, since we can rewrite it as

$$\sum_{k=1}^{\infty} 3^{2k}5^{1-k} = \sum_{k=1}^{\infty} \frac{9^k}{5^{k-1}} = \sum_{k=1}^{\infty} 9\left(\frac{9}{5}\right)^{k-1}$$

Since $r = \frac{9}{5} > 1$, the series diverges. ◄

**TECHNOLOGY MASTERY**

Computer algebra systems have commands for finding sums of convergent series. If you have a CAS, use it to compute the sums in Examples 2 and 3.

▶ **Example 3** Find the rational number represented by the repeating decimal

$$0.784784784\ldots$$

***Solution.*** We can write

$$0.784784784\ldots = 0.784 + 0.000784 + 0.000000784 + \cdots$$

so the given decimal is the sum of a geometric series with $a = 0.784$ and $r = 0.001$. Thus,

$$0.784784784\ldots = \frac{a}{1-r} = \frac{0.784}{1-0.001} = \frac{0.784}{0.999} = \frac{784}{999} \blacktriangleleft$$

▶ **Example 4** In each part, find all values of $x$ for which the series converges, and find the sum of the series for those values of $x$.

$$\text{(a)} \sum_{k=0}^{\infty} x^k \qquad \text{(b)}\ 3 - \frac{3x}{2} + \frac{3x^2}{4} - \frac{3x^3}{8} + \cdots + \frac{3(-1)^k}{2^k}x^k + \cdots$$

***Solution (a).*** The expanded form of the series is

$$\sum_{k=0}^{\infty} x^k = 1 + x + x^2 + \cdots + x^k + \cdots$$

The series is a geometric series with $a = 1$ and $r = x$, so it converges if $|x| < 1$ and diverges otherwise. When the series converges its sum is

$$\sum_{k=0}^{\infty} x^k = \frac{1}{1-x}$$

***Solution (b).*** This is a geometric series with $a = 3$ and $r = -x/2$. It converges if $|-x/2| < 1$, or equivalently, when $|x| < 2$. When the series converges its sum is

$$\sum_{k=0}^{\infty} 3\left(-\frac{x}{2}\right)^k = \frac{3}{1-\left(-\frac{x}{2}\right)} = \frac{6}{2+x} \blacktriangleleft$$

## TELESCOPING SUMS

▶ **Example 5** Determine whether the series

$$\sum_{k=1}^{\infty} \frac{1}{k(k+1)} = \frac{1}{1\cdot 2} + \frac{1}{2\cdot 3} + \frac{1}{3\cdot 4} + \frac{1}{4\cdot 5} + \cdots$$

converges or diverges. If it converges, find the sum.

***Solution.*** The $n$th partial sum of the series is

$$s_n = \sum_{k=1}^{n} \frac{1}{k(k+1)} = \frac{1}{1\cdot 2} + \frac{1}{2\cdot 3} + \frac{1}{3\cdot 4} + \cdots + \frac{1}{n(n+1)}$$

We will begin by rewriting $s_n$ in closed form. This can be accomplished by using the method of partial fractions to obtain (verify)

$$\frac{1}{k(k+1)} = \frac{1}{k} - \frac{1}{k+1}$$

from which we obtain the sum

$$\begin{aligned} s_n &= \sum_{k=1}^{n}\left(\frac{1}{k}-\frac{1}{k+1}\right) \\ &= \left(1-\frac{1}{2}\right)+\left(\frac{1}{2}-\frac{1}{3}\right)+\left(\frac{1}{3}-\frac{1}{4}\right)+\cdots+\left(\frac{1}{n}-\frac{1}{n+1}\right) \\ &= 1+\left(-\frac{1}{2}+\frac{1}{2}\right)+\left(-\frac{1}{3}+\frac{1}{3}\right)+\cdots+\left(-\frac{1}{n}+\frac{1}{n}\right)-\frac{1}{n+1} \\ &= 1-\frac{1}{n+1} \end{aligned} \tag{8}$$

The sum in (8) is an example of a ***telescoping sum***. The name is derived from the fact that in simplifying the sum, one term in each parenthetical expression cancels one term in the next parenthetical expression, until the entire sum collapses (like a folding telescope) into just two terms.

Thus,

$$\sum_{k=1}^{\infty}\frac{1}{k(k+1)} = \lim_{n\to+\infty} s_n = \lim_{n\to+\infty}\left(1-\frac{1}{n+1}\right) = 1 \blacktriangleleft$$

## HARMONIC SERIES

One of the most important of all diverging series is the ***harmonic series***,

$$\sum_{k=1}^{\infty}\frac{1}{k} = 1+\frac{1}{2}+\frac{1}{3}+\frac{1}{4}+\frac{1}{5}+\cdots$$

which arises in connection with the overtones produced by a vibrating musical string. It is not immediately evident that this series diverges. However, the divergence will become apparent when we examine the partial sums in detail. Because the terms in the series are all positive, the partial sums

$$s_1 = 1,\quad s_2 = 1+\frac{1}{2},\quad s_3 = 1+\frac{1}{2}+\frac{1}{3},\quad s_4 = 1+\frac{1}{2}+\frac{1}{3}+\frac{1}{4},\ldots$$

form a strictly increasing sequence

$$s_1 < s_2 < s_3 < \cdots < s_n < \cdots$$

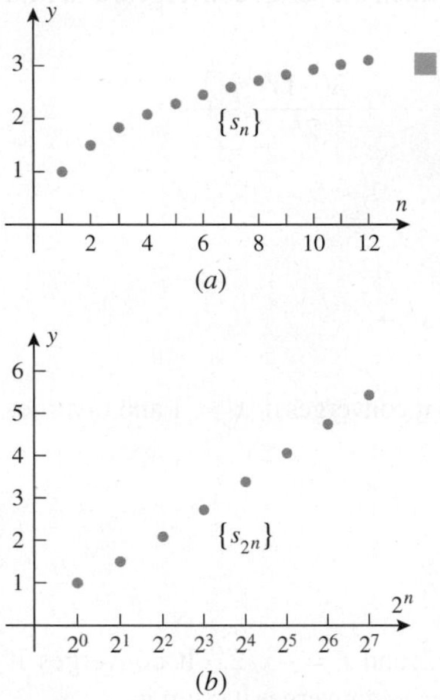


Partial sums for the harmonic series

▲ **Figure 9.3.4**

(Figure 9.3.4*a*). Thus, by Theorem 9.2.3 we can prove divergence by demonstrating that there is no constant $M$ that is greater than or equal to *every* partial sum. To this end, we will consider some selected partial sums, namely, $s_2, s_4, s_8, s_{16}, s_{32}, \ldots$. Note that the subscripts are successive powers of 2, so that these are the partial sums of the form $s_{2^n}$ (Figure 9.3.4*b*). These partial sums satisfy the inequalities

$$\begin{aligned} s_2 &= 1+\tfrac{1}{2} > \tfrac{1}{2}+\tfrac{1}{2} = \tfrac{2}{2} \\ s_4 &= s_2+\tfrac{1}{3}+\tfrac{1}{4} > s_2+\left(\tfrac{1}{4}+\tfrac{1}{4}\right) = s_2+\tfrac{1}{2} > \tfrac{3}{2} \\ s_8 &= s_4+\tfrac{1}{5}+\tfrac{1}{6}+\tfrac{1}{7}+\tfrac{1}{8} > s_4+\left(\tfrac{1}{8}+\tfrac{1}{8}+\tfrac{1}{8}+\tfrac{1}{8}\right) = s_4+\tfrac{1}{2} > \tfrac{4}{2} \\ s_{16} &= s_8+\tfrac{1}{9}+\tfrac{1}{10}+\tfrac{1}{11}+\tfrac{1}{12}+\tfrac{1}{13}+\tfrac{1}{14}+\tfrac{1}{15}+\tfrac{1}{16} \\ &> s_8+\left(\tfrac{1}{16}+\tfrac{1}{16}+\tfrac{1}{16}+\tfrac{1}{16}+\tfrac{1}{16}+\tfrac{1}{16}+\tfrac{1}{16}+\tfrac{1}{16}\right) = s_8+\tfrac{1}{2} > \tfrac{5}{2} \\ &\vdots \\ s_{2^n} &> \frac{n+1}{2} \end{aligned}$$

If $M$ is any constant, we can find a positive integer $n$ such that $(n+1)/2 > M$. But for this $n$

$$s_{2^n} > \frac{n+1}{2} > M$$

so that no constant $M$ is greater than or equal to *every* partial sum of the harmonic series. This proves divergence.

This divergence proof, which predates the discovery of calculus, is due to a French bishop and teacher, Nicole Oresme (1323–1382). This series eventually attracted the interest of Johann and Jakob Bernoulli (p. 612) and led them to begin thinking about the general concept of convergence, which was a new idea at that time.

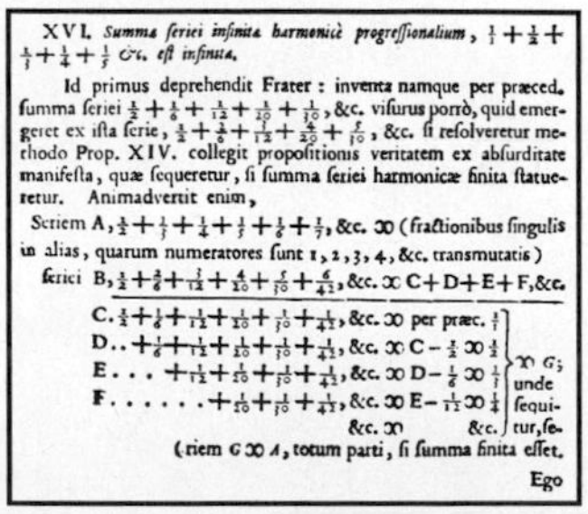

XVI. *Summa ſeriei infinita harmonicè progreſſionalium*, $\frac{1}{1}+\frac{1}{2}+\frac{1}{3}+\frac{1}{4}+\frac{1}{5}$ *&c. eſt infinita.*

Id primus deprehendit Frater: inventa namque per præced. ſumma ſeriei $\frac{1}{2}+\frac{1}{6}+\frac{1}{12}+\frac{1}{20}+\frac{1}{30}$, &c. viſurus porrò, quid emergeret ex iſta ſerie, $\frac{1}{2}+\frac{2}{6}+\frac{3}{12}+\frac{4}{20}+\frac{5}{30}$, &c. ſi reſolveretur methodo Prop. XIV. collegit propoſitionis veritatem ex abſurditate manifeſta, quæ ſequeretur, ſi ſumma ſeriei harmonicæ finita ſtatueretur. Animadvertit enim,

Seriem A, $\frac{1}{2}+\frac{1}{3}+\frac{1}{4}+\frac{1}{5}+\frac{1}{6}+\frac{1}{7}$, &c. ∞ (fractionibus ſingulis in alias, quarum numeratores ſunt 1, 2, 3, 4, &c. transmutatis) ſeriei B, $\frac{1}{2}+\frac{2}{6}+\frac{3}{12}+\frac{4}{20}+\frac{5}{30}+\frac{6}{42}$, &c. ∞ C+D+E+F, &c.

C. $\frac{1}{2}+\frac{1}{6}+\frac{1}{12}+\frac{1}{20}+\frac{1}{30}+\frac{1}{42}$, &c. ∞ per præc. $\frac{1}{1}$
D. . $+\frac{1}{6}+\frac{1}{12}+\frac{1}{20}+\frac{1}{30}+\frac{1}{42}$, &c. ∞ C $-\frac{1}{2}$ ∞ $\frac{1}{2}$
E. . . $+\frac{1}{12}+\frac{1}{20}+\frac{1}{30}+\frac{1}{42}$, &c. ∞ D $-\frac{1}{6}$ ∞ $\frac{1}{3}$
F. . . . . . $+\frac{1}{20}+\frac{1}{30}+\frac{1}{42}$, &c. ∞ E $-\frac{1}{12}$ ∞ $\frac{1}{4}$
&c. ∞ &c.
} ∞ G; unde ſequitur, ſeriem G ∞ A, totum parti, ſi ſumma finita eſſet.

Ego

Courtesy The Lilly Library, Indiana University, Bloomington, Indiana

*This is a proof of the divergence of the harmonic series, as it appeared in an appendix of Jakob Bernoulli's posthumous publication,* Ars Conjectandi, *which appeared in 1713.*

## ✓ QUICK CHECK EXERCISES 9.3 (See page 539 for answers.)

1. In mathematics, the terms "sequence" and "series" have different meanings: a ________ is a succession, whereas a ________ is a sum.

2. Consider the series
$$\sum_{k=1}^{\infty} \frac{1}{2^k}$$
If $\{s_n\}$ is the sequence of partial sums for this series, then $s_1 =$ ________, $s_2 =$ ________, $s_3 =$ ________, $s_4 =$ ________, and $s_n =$ ________.

3. What does it mean to say that a series $\sum u_k$ *converges*?

4. A geometric series is a series of the form
$$\sum_{k=0}^{\infty} \text{\_\_\_\_\_\_\_\_}$$
This series converges to ________ if ________. This series diverges if ________.

5. The harmonic series has the form
$$\sum_{k=1}^{\infty} \text{\_\_\_\_\_\_\_\_}$$
Does the harmonic series converge or diverge?

## EXERCISE SET 9.3 C CAS

**1–2** In each part, find exact values for the first four partial sums, find a closed form for the $n$th partial sum, and determine whether the series converges by calculating the limit of the $n$th partial sum. If the series converges, then state its sum. ■

1. (a) $2 + \frac{2}{5} + \frac{2}{5^2} + \cdots + \frac{2}{5^{k-1}} + \cdots$
   (b) $\frac{1}{4} + \frac{2}{4} + \frac{2^2}{4} + \cdots + \frac{2^{k-1}}{4} + \cdots$
   (c) $\frac{1}{2 \cdot 3} + \frac{1}{3 \cdot 4} + \frac{1}{4 \cdot 5} + \cdots + \frac{1}{(k+1)(k+2)} + \cdots$

2. (a) $\sum_{k=1}^{\infty} \left(\frac{1}{4}\right)^k$ (b) $\sum_{k=1}^{\infty} 4^{k-1}$ (c) $\sum_{k=1}^{\infty} \left(\frac{1}{k+3} - \frac{1}{k+4}\right)$

**3–14** Determine whether the series converges, and if so find its sum. ■

3. $\sum_{k=1}^{\infty} \left(-\frac{3}{4}\right)^{k-1}$

4. $\sum_{k=1}^{\infty} \left(\frac{2}{3}\right)^{k+2}$

5. $\sum_{k=1}^{\infty} (-1)^{k-1} \frac{7}{6^{k-1}}$

6. $\sum_{k=1}^{\infty} \left(-\frac{3}{2}\right)^{k+1}$

7. $\sum_{k=1}^{\infty} \frac{1}{(k+2)(k+3)}$

8. $\sum_{k=1}^{\infty} \left(\frac{1}{2^k} - \frac{1}{2^{k+1}}\right)$

9. $\sum_{k=1}^{\infty} \frac{1}{9k^2 + 3k - 2}$

10. $\sum_{k=2}^{\infty} \frac{1}{k^2 - 1}$

11. $\sum_{k=3}^{\infty} \frac{1}{k-2}$

12. $\sum_{k=5}^{\infty} \left(\frac{e}{\pi}\right)^{k-1}$

13. $\sum_{k=1}^{\infty} \frac{4^{k+2}}{7^{k-1}}$

14. $\sum_{k=1}^{\infty} 5^{3k} 7^{1-k}$

15. Match a series from one of Exercises 3, 5, 7, or 9 with the graph of its sequence of partial sums.

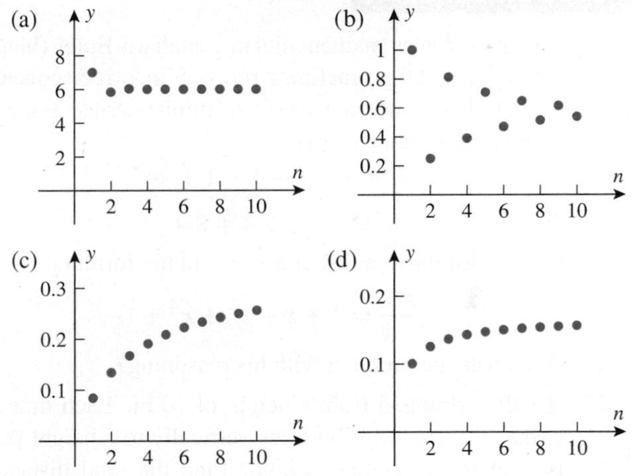


16. Match a series from one of Exercises 4, 6, 8, or 10 with the graph of its sequence of partial sums.

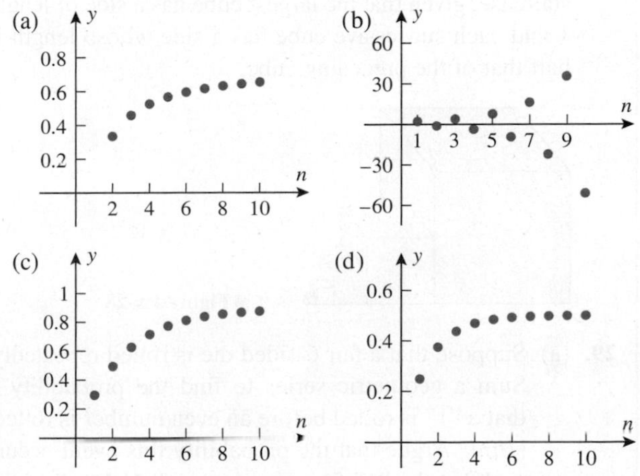

**17–20 True–False** Determine whether the statement is true or false. Explain your answer. ■

**17.** An infinite series converges if its sequence of terms converges.

**18.** The geometric series $a + ar + ar^2 + \cdots + ar^n + \cdots$ converges provided $|r| < 1$.

**19.** The harmonic series diverges.

**20.** An infinite series converges if its sequence of partial sums is bounded and monotone.

**21–24** Express the repeating decimal as a fraction. ■

**21.** 0.9999 . . .  **22.** 0.4444 . . .

**23.** 5.373737 . . .  **24.** 0.451141414 . . .

**25.** Recall that a *terminating decimal* is a decimal whose digits are all 0 from some point on ($0.5 = 0.50000\ldots$, for example). Show that a decimal of the form $0.a_1a_2\ldots a_n9999\ldots$, where $a_n \neq 9$, can be expressed as a terminating decimal.

**FOCUS ON CONCEPTS**

**26.** The great Swiss mathematician Leonhard Euler (biography on p. 66) sometimes reached incorrect conclusions in his pioneering work on infinite series. For example, Euler deduced that

$$\tfrac{1}{2} = 1 - 1 + 1 - 1 + \cdots$$

and

$$-1 = 1 + 2 + 4 + 8 + \cdots$$

by substituting $x = -1$ and $x = 2$ in the formula

$$\frac{1}{1-x} = 1 + x + x^2 + x^3 + \cdots$$

What was the problem with his reasoning?

**27.** A ball is dropped from a height of 10 m. Each time it strikes the ground it bounces vertically to a height that is $\frac{3}{4}$ of the preceding height. Find the total distance the ball will travel if it is assumed to bounce infinitely often.

**28.** The accompanying figure shows an "infinite staircase" constructed from cubes. Find the total volume of the staircase, given that the largest cube has a side of length 1 and each successive cube has a side whose length is half that of the preceding cube.

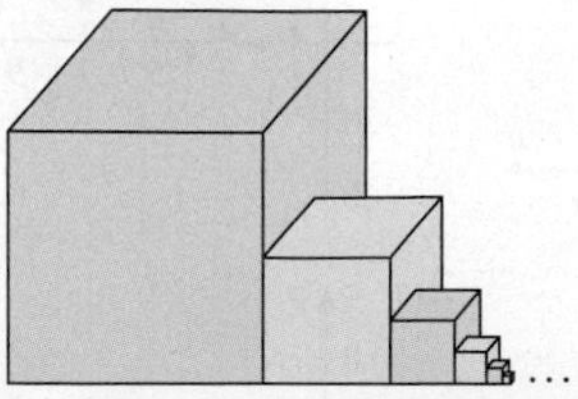

◀ **Figure Ex-28**

**29.** (a) Suppose that a fair 6-sided die is rolled repeatedly. Sum a geometric series to find the probability $p$ that a "1" is rolled before an even number is rolled. [*Hint*: Argue that the probability this event occurs *and* that the "1" first appears on the $k$th roll of the die is $p_k = (1/3)^{k-1}(1/6)$, $k = 1, 2, \ldots$. Then argue that $p = \sum_{k=1}^{\infty} p_k$.]

(b) Show how to compute the probability in part (a) without summing a series.

**30.** (a) Suppose that a fair 6-sided die is rolled repeatedly. Sum a geometric series to find the probability $p$ that a "1" or "2" is rolled before a "4", "5", or "6" is rolled.

(b) Show how to compute the probability in part (a) without summing a series.

**31.** In each part, find a closed form for the $n$th partial sum of the series, and determine whether the series converges. If so, find its sum.

(a) $\ln\frac{1}{2} + \ln\frac{2}{3} + \ln\frac{3}{4} + \cdots + \ln\frac{k}{k+1} + \cdots$

(b) $\ln\left(1 - \frac{1}{4}\right) + \ln\left(1 - \frac{1}{9}\right) + \ln\left(1 - \frac{1}{16}\right) + \cdots + \ln\left(1 - \frac{1}{(k+1)^2}\right) + \cdots$

**32.** Use geometric series to show that

(a) $\displaystyle\sum_{k=0}^{\infty} (-1)^k x^k = \frac{1}{1+x}$ if $-1 < x < 1$

(b) $\displaystyle\sum_{k=0}^{\infty} (x-3)^k = \frac{1}{4-x}$ if $2 < x < 4$

(c) $\displaystyle\sum_{k=0}^{\infty} (-1)^k x^{2k} = \frac{1}{1+x^2}$ if $-1 < x < 1$.

**33.** In each part, find all values of $x$ for which the series converges, and find the sum of the series for those values of $x$.

(a) $x - x^3 + x^5 - x^7 + x^9 - \cdots$

(b) $\dfrac{1}{x^2} + \dfrac{2}{x^3} + \dfrac{4}{x^4} + \dfrac{8}{x^5} + \dfrac{16}{x^6} + \cdots$

(c) $e^{-x} + e^{-2x} + e^{-3x} + e^{-4x} + e^{-5x} + \cdots$

**34.** Show that for all real values of $x$

$$\sin x - \frac{1}{2}\sin^2 x + \frac{1}{4}\sin^3 x - \frac{1}{8}\sin^4 x + \cdots = \frac{2\sin x}{2+\sin x}$$

**35.** Let $a_1$ be any real number, and let $\{a_n\}$ be the sequence defined recursively by

$$a_{n+1} = \tfrac{1}{2}(a_n + 1)$$

Make a conjecture about the limit of the sequence, and confirm your conjecture by expressing $a_n$ in terms of $a_1$ and taking the limit.

**36.** Show: $\displaystyle\sum_{k=1}^{\infty} \frac{\sqrt{k+1} - \sqrt{k}}{\sqrt{k^2+k}} = 1.$

**37.** Show: $\displaystyle\sum_{k=1}^{\infty} \left(\frac{1}{k} - \frac{1}{k+2}\right) = \frac{3}{2}.$

**38.** Show: $\dfrac{1}{1\cdot 3}+\dfrac{1}{2\cdot 4}+\dfrac{1}{3\cdot 5}+\cdots=\dfrac{3}{4}$.

**39.** Show: $\dfrac{1}{1\cdot 3}+\dfrac{1}{3\cdot 5}+\dfrac{1}{5\cdot 7}+\cdots=\dfrac{1}{2}$.

**40.** In his *Treatise on the Configurations of Qualities and Motions* (written in the 1350s), the French Bishop of Lisieux, Nicole Oresme, used a geometric method to find the sum of the series

$$\sum_{k=1}^{\infty}\frac{k}{2^k}=\frac{1}{2}+\frac{2}{4}+\frac{3}{8}+\frac{4}{16}+\cdots$$

In part (*a*) of the accompanying figure, each term in the series is represented by the area of a rectangle, and in part (*b*) the configuration in part (*a*) has been divided into rectangles with areas $A_1, A_2, A_3, \ldots$. Find the sum $A_1 + A_2 + A_3 + \cdots$.

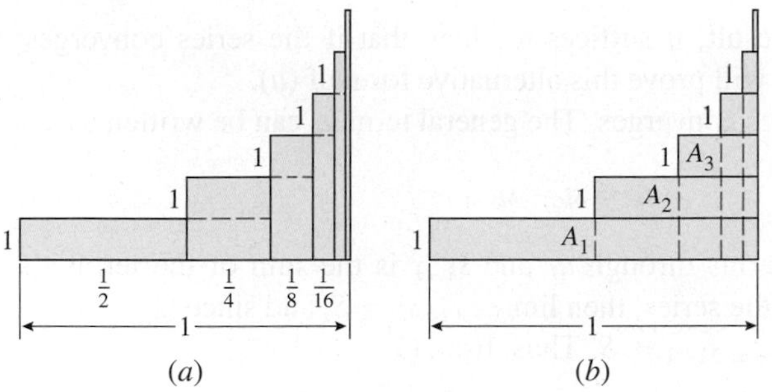


▲ **Figure Ex-40**

**41.** As shown in the accompanying figure, suppose that an angle $\theta$ is bisected using a straightedge and compass to produce ray $R_1$, then the angle between $R_1$ and the initial side is bisected to produce ray $R_2$. Thereafter, rays $R_3$, $R_4$, $R_5, \ldots$ are constructed in succession by bisecting the angle between the preceding two rays. Show that the sequence of angles that these rays make with the initial side has a limit of $\theta/3$.

***Source:*** This problem is based on "Trisection of an Angle in an Infinite Number of Steps" by Eric Kincannon, which appeared in *The College Mathematics Journal*, Vol. 21, No. 5, November 1990.

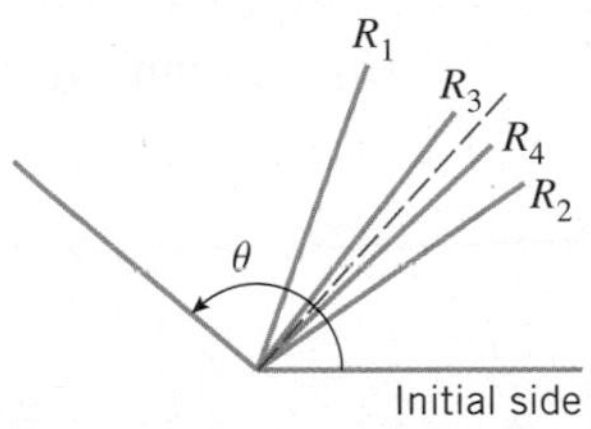


◀ **Figure Ex-41**

C **42.** In each part, use a CAS to find the sum of the series if it converges, and then confirm the result by hand calculation.

(a) $\displaystyle\sum_{k=1}^{\infty}(-1)^{k+1}2^k3^{2-k}$ (b) $\displaystyle\sum_{k=1}^{\infty}\frac{3^{3k}}{5^{k-1}}$ (c) $\displaystyle\sum_{k=1}^{\infty}\frac{1}{4k^2-1}$

**43. Writing** Discuss the similarities and differences between what it means for a sequence to converge and what it means for a series to converge.

**44. Writing** Read about Zeno's dichotomy paradox in an appropriate reference work and relate the paradox in a setting that is familiar to you. Discuss a connection between the paradox and geometric series.

---

✓ **QUICK CHECK ANSWERS 9.3** 1. sequence; series 2. $\frac{1}{2};\frac{3}{4};\frac{7}{8};\frac{15}{16}; 1-\frac{1}{2^n}$ 3. The sequence of partial sums converges. 4. $ar^k$ $(a\neq 0)$; $\frac{a}{1-r}$; $|r|<1$; $|r|\geq 1$ 5. $\frac{1}{k}$; diverge

---

## 9.4 CONVERGENCE TESTS

*In the last section we showed how to find the sum of a series by finding a closed form for the nth partial sum and taking its limit. However, it is relatively rare that one can find a closed form for the nth partial sum of a series, so alternative methods are needed for finding the sum of a series. One possibility is to prove that the series converges, and then to approximate the sum by a partial sum with sufficiently many terms to achieve the desired degree of accuracy. In this section we will develop various tests that can be used to determine whether a given series converges or diverges.*

### THE DIVERGENCE TEST

In stating general results about convergence or divergence of series, it is convenient to use the notation $\sum u_k$ as a generic notation for a series, thus avoiding the issue of whether the sum begins with $k = 0$ or $k = 1$ or some other value. Indeed, we will see shortly that the starting index value is irrelevant to the issue of convergence. The $k$th term in an infinite series $\sum u_k$ is called the ***general term*** of the series. The following theorem establishes a relationship between the limit of the general term and the convergence properties of a series.

**9.4.1 THEOREM** ***(The Divergence Test)***

*(a) If* $\lim_{k\to+\infty} u_k \neq 0$, *then the series* $\sum u_k$ *diverges.*

*(b) If* $\lim_{k\to+\infty} u_k = 0$, *then the series* $\sum u_k$ *may either converge or diverge.*

**PROOF** ***(a)*** To prove this result, it suffices to show that if the series converges, then $\lim_{k\to+\infty} u_k = 0$ (why?). We will prove this alternative form of *(a)*.

Let us assume that the series converges. The general term $u_k$ can be written as

$$u_k = s_k - s_{k-1} \tag{1}$$

where $s_k$ is the sum of the terms through $u_k$ and $s_{k-1}$ is the sum of the terms through $u_{k-1}$. If $S$ denotes the sum of the series, then $\lim_{k\to+\infty} s_k = S$, and since $(k-1)\to+\infty$ as $k\to+\infty$, we also have $\lim_{k\to+\infty} s_{k-1} = S$. Thus, from (1)

$$\lim_{k\to+\infty} u_k = \lim_{k\to+\infty} (s_k - s_{k-1}) = S - S = 0$$

**PROOF** ***(b)*** To prove this result, it suffices to produce both a convergent series and a divergent series for which $\lim_{k\to+\infty} u_k = 0$. The following series both have this property:

$$\frac{1}{2} + \frac{1}{2^2} + \cdots + \frac{1}{2^k} + \cdots \quad \text{and} \quad 1 + \frac{1}{2} + \frac{1}{3} + \cdots + \frac{1}{k} + \cdots$$

The first is a convergent geometric series and the second is the divergent harmonic series. ■

**WARNING**

The converse of Theorem 9.4.2 is false; that is, showing that

$$\lim_{k\to+\infty} u_k = 0$$

does not prove that $\sum u_k$ converges, since this property may hold for divergent as well as convergent series. This is illustrated in the proof of part *(b)* of Theorem 9.4.1.

The alternative form of part *(a)* given in the preceding proof is sufficiently important that we state it separately for future reference.

**9.4.2 THEOREM** *If the series* $\sum u_k$ *converges, then* $\lim_{k\to+\infty} u_k = 0$.

► **Example 1** The series

$$\sum_{k=1}^{\infty} \frac{k}{k+1} = \frac{1}{2} + \frac{2}{3} + \frac{3}{4} + \cdots + \frac{k}{k+1} + \cdots$$

diverges since

$$\lim_{k\to+\infty} \frac{k}{k+1} = \lim_{k\to+\infty} \frac{1}{1+1/k} = 1 \neq 0 \ ◄$$

## ALGEBRAIC PROPERTIES OF INFINITE SERIES

For brevity, the proof of the following result is omitted.

See Exercises 27 and 28 for an exploration of what happens when $\sum u_k$ or $\sum v_k$ diverge.

**9.4.3 THEOREM**

*(a) If $\sum u_k$ and $\sum v_k$ are convergent series, then $\sum (u_k + v_k)$ and $\sum (u_k - v_k)$ are convergent series and the sums of these series are related by*

$$\sum_{k=1}^{\infty} (u_k + v_k) = \sum_{k=1}^{\infty} u_k + \sum_{k=1}^{\infty} v_k$$

$$\sum_{k=1}^{\infty} (u_k - v_k) = \sum_{k=1}^{\infty} u_k - \sum_{k=1}^{\infty} v_k$$

*(b) If c is a nonzero constant, then the series $\sum u_k$ and $\sum cu_k$ both converge or both diverge. In the case of convergence, the sums are related by*

$$\sum_{k=1}^{\infty} cu_k = c\sum_{k=1}^{\infty} u_k$$

*(c) Convergence or divergence is unaffected by deleting a finite number of terms from a series; in particular, for any positive integer K, the series*

$$\sum_{k=1}^{\infty} u_k = u_1 + u_2 + u_3 + \cdots$$

$$\sum_{k=K}^{\infty} u_k = u_K + u_{K+1} + u_{K+2} + \cdots$$

*both converge or both diverge.*

**WARNING**

Do not read too much into part (c) of Theorem 9.4.3. Although convergence is not affected when finitely many terms are deleted from the beginning of a convergent series, the *sum* of the series is changed by the removal of those terms.

► **Example 2** Find the sum of the series

$$\sum_{k=1}^{\infty} \left( \frac{3}{4^k} - \frac{2}{5^{k-1}} \right)$$

***Solution.*** The series

$$\sum_{k=1}^{\infty} \frac{3}{4^k} = \frac{3}{4} + \frac{3}{4^2} + \frac{3}{4^3} + \cdots$$

is a convergent geometric series $\left(a = \frac{3}{4}, r = \frac{1}{4}\right)$, and the series

$$\sum_{k=1}^{\infty} \frac{2}{5^{k-1}} = 2 + \frac{2}{5} + \frac{2}{5^2} + \frac{2}{5^3} + \cdots$$

is also a convergent geometric series $\left(a = 2, r = \frac{1}{5}\right)$. Thus, from Theorems 9.4.3(*a*) and 9.3.3 the given series converges and

$$\sum_{k=1}^{\infty} \left( \frac{3}{4^k} - \frac{2}{5^{k-1}} \right) = \sum_{k=1}^{\infty} \frac{3}{4^k} - \sum_{k=1}^{\infty} \frac{2}{5^{k-1}}$$

$$= \frac{\frac{3}{4}}{1 - \frac{1}{4}} - \frac{2}{1 - \frac{1}{5}} = -\frac{3}{2} \blacktriangleleft$$

**▶ Example 3** Determine whether the following series converge or diverge.

$$\text{(a)} \sum_{k=1}^{\infty} \frac{5}{k} = 5 + \frac{5}{2} + \frac{5}{3} + \cdots + \frac{5}{k} + \cdots \qquad \text{(b)} \sum_{k=10}^{\infty} \frac{1}{k} = \frac{1}{10} + \frac{1}{11} + \frac{1}{12} + \cdots$$

***Solution.*** The first series is a constant times the divergent harmonic series, and hence diverges by part (*b*) of Theorem 9.4.3. The second series results by deleting the first nine terms from the divergent harmonic series, and hence diverges by part (*c*) of Theorem 9.4.3. ◀

## THE INTEGRAL TEST

The expressions

$$\sum_{k=1}^{\infty} \frac{1}{k^2} \quad \text{and} \quad \int_1^{+\infty} \frac{1}{x^2}\,dx$$

are related in that the integrand in the improper integral results when the index $k$ in the general term of the series is replaced by $x$ and the limits of summation in the series are replaced by the corresponding limits of integration. The following theorem shows that there is a relationship between the convergence of the series and the integral.

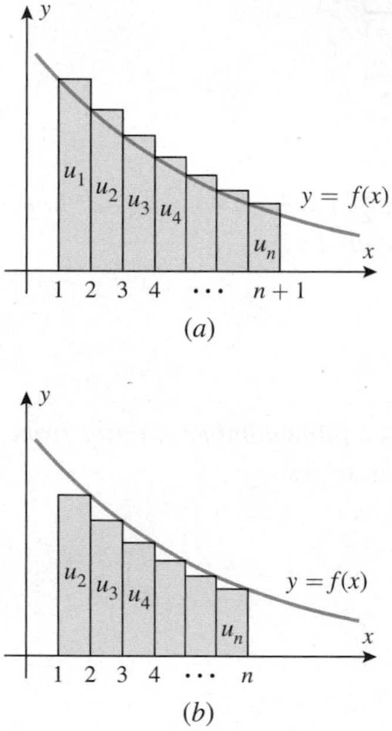


▲ **Figure 9.4.1**

> **9.4.4 THEOREM (*The Integral Test*)** *Let $\sum u_k$ be a series with positive terms. If $f$ is a function that is decreasing and continuous on an interval $[a, +\infty)$ and such that $u_k = f(k)$ for all $k \geq a$, then*
>
> $$\sum_{k=1}^{\infty} u_k \quad \textit{and} \quad \int_a^{+\infty} f(x)\,dx$$
>
> *both converge or both diverge.*

The proof of the integral test is deferred to the end of this section. However, the gist of the proof is captured in Figure 9.4.1: if the integral diverges, then so does the series (Figure 9.4.1*a*), and if the integral converges, then so does the series (Figure 9.4.1*b*).

**▶ Example 4** Show that the integral test applies, and use the integral test to determine whether the following series converge or diverge.

$$\text{(a)} \sum_{k=1}^{\infty} \frac{1}{k} \qquad \text{(b)} \sum_{k=1}^{\infty} \frac{1}{k^2}$$

***Solution (a).*** We already know that this is the divergent harmonic series, so the integral test will simply illustrate another way of establishing the divergence.

Note first that the series has positive terms, so the integral test is applicable. If we replace $k$ by $x$ in the general term $1/k$, we obtain the function $f(x) = 1/x$, which is decreasing and continuous for $x \geq 1$ (as required to apply the integral test with $a = 1$). Since

$$\int_1^{+\infty} \frac{1}{x}\,dx = \lim_{b \to +\infty} \int_1^b \frac{1}{x}\,dx = \lim_{b \to +\infty} [\ln b - \ln 1] = +\infty$$

the integral diverges and consequently so does the series.

***Solution (b).*** Note first that the series has positive terms, so the integral test is applicable. If we replace $k$ by $x$ in the general term $1/k^2$, we obtain the function $f(x) = 1/x^2$, which is decreasing and continuous for $x \geq 1$. Since

$$\int_1^{+\infty} \frac{1}{x^2}\,dx = \lim_{b \to +\infty} \int_1^b \frac{dx}{x^2} = \lim_{b \to +\infty} \left[-\frac{1}{x}\right]_1^b = \lim_{b \to +\infty} \left[1 - \frac{1}{b}\right] = 1$$

the integral converges and consequently the series converges by the integral test with $a = 1$. ◀

**WARNING**

In part (b) of Example 4, do not erroneously conclude that the sum of the series is 1 because the value of the corresponding integral is 1. You can see that this is not so since the sum of the first two terms alone exceeds 1. Later, we will see that the sum of the series is actually $\pi^2/6$.

## p-SERIES

The series in Example 4 are special cases of a class of series called ***p*-series** or ***hyperharmonic series***. A $p$-series is an infinite series of the form

$$\sum_{k=1}^{\infty} \frac{1}{k^p} = 1 + \frac{1}{2^p} + \frac{1}{3^p} + \cdots + \frac{1}{k^p} + \cdots$$

where $p > 0$. Examples of $p$-series are

$$\sum_{k=1}^{\infty} \frac{1}{k} = 1 + \frac{1}{2} + \frac{1}{3} + \cdots + \frac{1}{k} + \cdots \qquad p = 1$$

$$\sum_{k=1}^{\infty} \frac{1}{k^2} = 1 + \frac{1}{2^2} + \frac{1}{3^2} + \cdots + \frac{1}{k^2} + \cdots \qquad p = 2$$

$$\sum_{k=1}^{\infty} \frac{1}{\sqrt{k}} = 1 + \frac{1}{\sqrt{2}} + \frac{1}{\sqrt{3}} + \cdots + \frac{1}{\sqrt{k}} + \cdots \qquad p = \tfrac{1}{2}$$

The following theorem tells when a $p$-series converges.

**9.4.5 THEOREM** ***(Convergence of p-Series)***

$$\sum_{k=1}^{\infty} \frac{1}{k^p} = 1 + \frac{1}{2^p} + \frac{1}{3^p} + \cdots + \frac{1}{k^p} + \cdots$$

*converges if* $p > 1$ *and diverges if* $0 < p \leq 1$.

**PROOF** To establish this result when $p \neq 1$, we will use the integral test.

$$\int_1^{+\infty} \frac{1}{x^p}\,dx = \lim_{b\to+\infty} \int_1^b x^{-p}\,dx = \lim_{b\to+\infty} \left.\frac{x^{1-p}}{1-p}\right]_1^b = \lim_{b\to+\infty} \left[\frac{b^{1-p}}{1-p} - \frac{1}{1-p}\right]$$

Assume first that $p > 1$. Then $1 - p < 0$, so $b^{1-p} \to 0$ as $b \to +\infty$. Thus, the integral converges [its value is $-1/(1-p)$] and consequently the series also converges.

Now assume that $0 < p < 1$. It follows that $1 - p > 0$ and $b^{1-p} \to +\infty$ as $b \to +\infty$, so the integral and the series diverge. The case $p = 1$ is the harmonic series, which was previously shown to diverge. ■

**▶ Example 5**

$$1 + \frac{1}{\sqrt[3]{2}} + \frac{1}{\sqrt[3]{3}} + \cdots + \frac{1}{\sqrt[3]{k}} + \cdots$$

diverges since it is a $p$-series with $p = \frac{1}{3} < 1$. ◀

## PROOF OF THE INTEGRAL TEST

Before we can prove the integral test, we need a basic result about convergence of series with *nonnegative* terms. If $u_1 + u_2 + u_3 + \cdots + u_k + \cdots$ is such a series, then its sequence of partial sums is increasing, that is,

$$s_1 \leq s_2 \leq s_3 \leq \cdots \leq s_n \leq \cdots$$

Thus, from Theorem 9.2.3 the sequence of partial sums converges to a limit $S$ if and only if it has some upper bound $M$, in which case $S \leq M$. If no upper bound exists, then the sequence of partial sums diverges. Since convergence of the sequence of partial sums corresponds to convergence of the series, we have the following theorem.

**9.4.6 THEOREM** *If $\sum u_k$ is a series with nonnegative terms, and if there is a constant M such that*

$$s_n = u_1 + u_2 + \cdots + u_n \leq M$$

*for every n, then the series converges and the sum S satisfies $S \leq M$. If no such M exists, then the series diverges.*

In words, this theorem implies that *a series with nonnegative terms converges if and only if its sequence of partial sums is bounded above.*

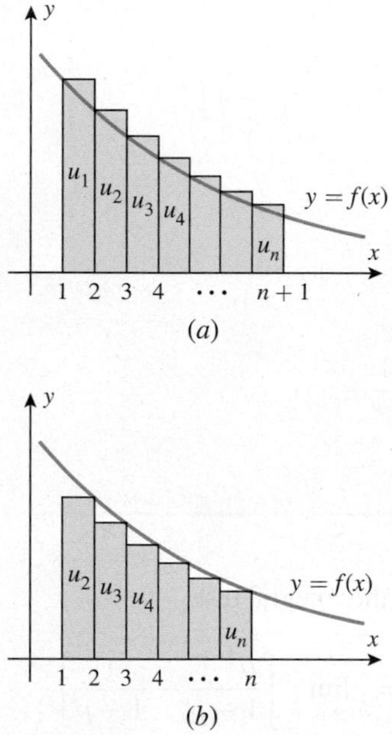

▲ **Figure 9.4.2**

**PROOF OF THEOREM 9.4.4** We need only show that the series converges when the integral converges and that the series diverges when the integral diverges. For simplicity, we will limit the proof to the case where $a = 1$. Assume that $f(x)$ satisfies the hypotheses of the theorem for $x \geq 1$. Since

$$f(1) = u_1, f(2) = u_2, \ldots, f(n) = u_n, \ldots$$

the values of $u_1, u_2, \ldots, u_n, \ldots$ can be interpreted as the areas of the rectangles shown in Figure 9.4.2.

The following inequalities result by comparing the areas under the curve $y = f(x)$ to the areas of the rectangles in Figure 9.4.2 for $n > 1$:

$$\int_1^{n+1} f(x)\,dx < u_1 + u_2 + \cdots + u_n = s_n \qquad \text{Figure 9.4.2}a$$

$$s_n - u_1 = u_2 + u_3 + \cdots + u_n < \int_1^n f(x)\,dx \qquad \text{Figure 9.4.2}b$$

These inequalities can be combined as

$$\int_1^{n+1} f(x)\,dx < s_n < u_1 + \int_1^n f(x)\,dx \tag{2}$$

If the integral $\int_1^{+\infty} f(x)\,dx$ converges to a finite value $L$, then from the right-hand inequality in (2)

$$s_n < u_1 + \int_1^n f(x)\,dx < u_1 + \int_1^{+\infty} f(x)\,dx = u_1 + L$$

Thus, each partial sum is less than the finite constant $u_1 + L$, and the series converges by Theorem 9.4.6. On the other hand, if the integral $\int_1^{+\infty} f(x)\,dx$ diverges, then

$$\lim_{n\to+\infty} \int_1^{n+1} f(x)\,dx = +\infty$$

so that from the left-hand inequality in (2), $s_n \to +\infty$ as $n \to +\infty$. This implies that the series also diverges. ■

## ✓ QUICK CHECK EXERCISES 9.4 *(See page 546 for answers.)*

1. The divergence test says that if ______ $\neq 0$, then the series $\sum u_k$ diverges.

2. Given that

$$a_1 = 3, \quad \sum_{k=1}^{\infty} a_k = 1, \quad \text{and} \quad \sum_{k=1}^{\infty} b_k = 5$$

it follows that

$$\sum_{k=2}^{\infty} a_k = \text{\_\_\_\_\_\_} \quad \text{and} \quad \sum_{k=1}^{\infty} (2a_k + b_k) = \text{\_\_\_\_\_\_}$$

3. Since $\int_1^{+\infty} (1/\sqrt{x})\,dx = +\infty$, the ______ test applied to the series $\sum_{k=1}^{\infty}$ ______ shows that this series ______.

4. A $p$-series is a series of the form

$$\sum_{k=1}^{\infty} \text{\_\_\_\_\_\_}$$

This series converges if ______. This series diverges if ______.

## EXERCISE SET 9.4 Graphing Utility C CAS

**1.** Use Theorem 9.4.3 to find the sum of each series.

(a) $\left(\frac{1}{2}+\frac{1}{4}\right)+\left(\frac{1}{2^2}+\frac{1}{4^2}\right)+\cdots+\left(\frac{1}{2^k}+\frac{1}{4^k}\right)+\cdots$

(b) $\sum_{k=1}^{\infty}\left(\frac{1}{5^k}-\frac{1}{k(k+1)}\right)$

**2.** Use Theorem 9.4.3 to find the sum of each series.

(a) $\sum_{k=2}^{\infty}\left[\frac{1}{k^2-1}-\frac{7}{10^{k-1}}\right]$ (b) $\sum_{k=1}^{\infty}\left[7^{-k}3^{k+1}-\frac{2^{k+1}}{5^k}\right]$

**3–4** For each given $p$-series, identify $p$ and determine whether the series converges. ■

**3.** (a) $\sum_{k=1}^{\infty}\frac{1}{k^3}$ (b) $\sum_{k=1}^{\infty}\frac{1}{\sqrt{k}}$ (c) $\sum_{k=1}^{\infty}k^{-1}$ (d) $\sum_{k=1}^{\infty}k^{-2/3}$

**4.** (a) $\sum_{k=1}^{\infty}k^{-4/3}$ (b) $\sum_{k=1}^{\infty}\frac{1}{\sqrt[4]{k}}$ (c) $\sum_{k=1}^{\infty}\frac{1}{\sqrt[3]{k^5}}$ (d) $\sum_{k=1}^{\infty}\frac{1}{k^{\pi}}$

**5–6** Apply the divergence test and state what it tells you about the series. ■

**5.** (a) $\sum_{k=1}^{\infty}\frac{k^2+k+3}{2k^2+1}$ (b) $\sum_{k=1}^{\infty}\left(1+\frac{1}{k}\right)^k$

(c) $\sum_{k=1}^{\infty}\cos k\pi$ (d) $\sum_{k=1}^{\infty}\frac{1}{k!}$

**6.** (a) $\sum_{k=1}^{\infty}\frac{k}{e^k}$ (b) $\sum_{k=1}^{\infty}\ln k$

(c) $\sum_{k=1}^{\infty}\frac{1}{\sqrt{k}}$ (d) $\sum_{k=1}^{\infty}\frac{\sqrt{k}}{\sqrt{k}+3}$

**7–8** Confirm that the integral test is applicable and use it to determine whether the series converges. ■

**7.** (a) $\sum_{k=1}^{\infty}\frac{1}{5k+2}$ (b) $\sum_{k=1}^{\infty}\frac{1}{1+9k^2}$

**8.** (a) $\sum_{k=1}^{\infty}\frac{k}{1+k^2}$ (b) $\sum_{k=1}^{\infty}\frac{1}{(4+2k)^{3/2}}$

**9–24** Determine whether the series converges. ■

**9.** $\sum_{k=1}^{\infty}\frac{1}{k+6}$ **10.** $\sum_{k=1}^{\infty}\frac{3}{5k}$ **11.** $\sum_{k=1}^{\infty}\frac{1}{\sqrt{k+5}}$

**12.** $\sum_{k=1}^{\infty}\frac{1}{\sqrt[k]{e}}$ **13.** $\sum_{k=1}^{\infty}\frac{1}{\sqrt[3]{2k-1}}$ **14.** $\sum_{k=3}^{\infty}\frac{\ln k}{k}$

**15.** $\sum_{k=1}^{\infty}\frac{k}{\ln(k+1)}$ **16.** $\sum_{k=1}^{\infty}ke^{-k^2}$ **17.** $\sum_{k=1}^{\infty}\left(1+\frac{1}{k}\right)^{-k}$

**18.** $\sum_{k=1}^{\infty}\frac{k^2+1}{k^2+3}$ **19.** $\sum_{k=1}^{\infty}\frac{\tan^{-1}k}{1+k^2}$ **20.** $\sum_{k=1}^{\infty}\frac{1}{\sqrt{k^2+1}}$

**21.** $\sum_{k=1}^{\infty}k^2\sin^2\left(\frac{1}{k}\right)$ **22.** $\sum_{k=1}^{\infty}k^2e^{-k^3}$

**23.** $\sum_{k=5}^{\infty}7k^{-1.01}$ **24.** $\sum_{k=1}^{\infty}\operatorname{sech}^2 k$

**25–26** Use the integral test to investigate the relationship between the value of $p$ and the convergence of the series. ■

**25.** $\sum_{k=2}^{\infty}\frac{1}{k(\ln k)^p}$ **26.** $\sum_{k=3}^{\infty}\frac{1}{k(\ln k)[\ln(\ln k)]^p}$

**FOCUS ON CONCEPTS**

**27.** Suppose that the series $\sum u_k$ converges and the series $\sum v_k$ diverges. Show that the series $\sum(u_k+v_k)$ and $\sum(u_k-v_k)$ both diverge. [*Hint:* Assume that $\sum(u_k+v_k)$ converges and use Theorem 9.4.3 to obtain a contradiction.]

**28.** Find examples to show that if the series $\sum u_k$ and $\sum v_k$ both diverge, then the series $\sum(u_k+v_k)$ and $\sum(u_k-v_k)$ may either converge or diverge.

**29–30** Use the results of Exercises 27 and 28, if needed, to determine whether each series converges or diverges. ■

**29.** (a) $\sum_{k=1}^{\infty}\left[\left(\frac{2}{3}\right)^{k-1}+\frac{1}{k}\right]$ (b) $\sum_{k=1}^{\infty}\left[\frac{1}{3k+2}-\frac{1}{k^{3/2}}\right]$

**30.** (a) $\sum_{k=2}^{\infty}\left[\frac{1}{k(\ln k)^2}-\frac{1}{k^2}\right]$ (b) $\sum_{k=2}^{\infty}\left[ke^{-k^2}+\frac{1}{k\ln k}\right]$

**31–34 True–False** Determine whether the statement is true or false. Explain your answer. ■

**31.** If $\sum u_k$ converges to $L$, then $\sum(1/u_k)$ converges to $1/L$.

**32.** If $\sum cu_k$ diverges for some constant $c$, then $\sum u_k$ must diverge.

**33.** The integral test can be used to prove that a series diverges.

**34.** The series $\sum_{k=1}^{\infty}\frac{1}{p^k}$ is a $p$-series.

C **35.** Use a CAS to confirm that

$$\sum_{k=1}^{\infty}\frac{1}{k^2}=\frac{\pi^2}{6} \quad\text{and}\quad \sum_{k=1}^{\infty}\frac{1}{k^4}=\frac{\pi^4}{90}$$

and then use these results in each part to find the sum of the series.

(a) $\sum_{k=1}^{\infty}\frac{3k^2-1}{k^4}$ (b) $\sum_{k=3}^{\infty}\frac{1}{k^2}$ (c) $\sum_{k=2}^{\infty}\frac{1}{(k-1)^4}$

**36–40** Exercise 36 will show how a partial sum can be used to obtain upper and lower bounds on the sum of a series when the hypotheses of the integral test are satisfied. This result will be needed in Exercises 37–40. ■

**36.** (a) Let $\sum_{k=1}^{\infty} u_k$ be a convergent series with positive terms, and let $f$ be a function that is decreasing and continuous on $[n, +\infty)$ and such that $u_k = f(k)$ for $k \geq n$. Use an area argument and the accompanying figure to show that

$$\int_{n+1}^{+\infty} f(x)\,dx < \sum_{k=n+1}^{\infty} u_k < \int_{n}^{+\infty} f(x)\,dx$$

(b) Show that if $S$ is the sum of the series $\sum_{k=1}^{\infty} u_k$ and $s_n$ is the $n$th partial sum, then

$$s_n + \int_{n+1}^{+\infty} f(x)\,dx < S < s_n + \int_{n}^{+\infty} f(x)\,dx$$

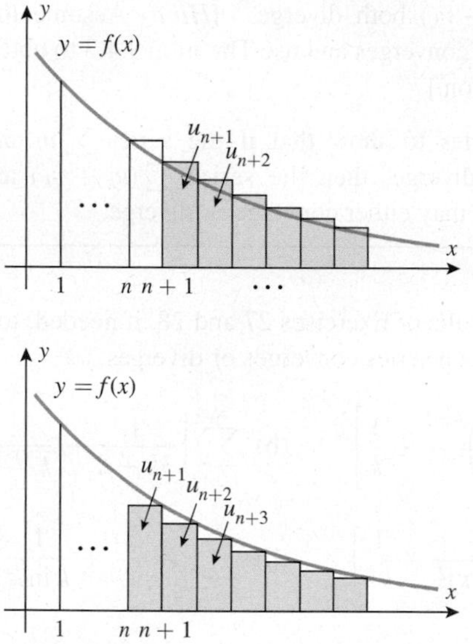


◀ **Figure Ex-36**

**37.** (a) It was stated in Exercise 35 that

$$\sum_{k=1}^{\infty} \frac{1}{k^2} = \frac{\pi^2}{6}$$

Show that if $s_n$ is the $n$th partial sum of this series, then

$$s_n + \frac{1}{n+1} < \frac{\pi^2}{6} < s_n + \frac{1}{n}$$

(b) Calculate $s_3$ exactly, and then use the result in part (a) to show that

$$\frac{29}{18} < \frac{\pi^2}{6} < \frac{61}{36}$$

(c) Use a calculating utility to confirm that the inequalities in part (b) are correct.

(d) Find upper and lower bounds on the error that results if the sum of the series is approximated by the 10th partial sum.

**38.** In each part, find upper and lower bounds on the error that results if the sum of the series is approximated by the 10th partial sum.

(a) $\sum_{k=1}^{\infty} \frac{1}{(2k+1)^2}$ (b) $\sum_{k=1}^{\infty} \frac{1}{k^2+1}$ (c) $\sum_{k=1}^{\infty} \frac{k}{e^k}$

**39.** It was stated in Exercise 35 that

$$\sum_{k=1}^{\infty} \frac{1}{k^4} = \frac{\pi^4}{90}$$

(a) Let $s_n$ be the $n$th partial sum of the series above. Show that

$$s_n + \frac{1}{3(n+1)^3} < \frac{\pi^4}{90} < s_n + \frac{1}{3n^3}$$

(b) We can use a partial sum of the series to approximate $\pi^4/90$ to three decimal-place accuracy by capturing the sum of the series in an interval of length 0.001 (or less). Find the smallest value of $n$ such that the interval containing $\pi^4/90$ in part (a) has a length of 0.001 or less.

(c) Approximate $\pi^4/90$ to three decimal places using the midpoint of an interval of width at most 0.001 that contains the sum of the series. Use a calculating utility to confirm that your answer is within 0.0005 of $\pi^4/90$.

**40.** We showed in Section 9.3 that the harmonic series $\sum_{k=1}^{\infty} 1/k$ diverges. Our objective in this problem is to demonstrate that although the partial sums of this series approach $+\infty$, they increase extremely slowly.

(a) Use inequality (2) to show that for $n \geq 2$

$$\ln(n+1) < s_n < 1 + \ln n$$

(b) Use the inequalities in part (a) to find upper and lower bounds on the sum of the first million terms in the series.

(c) Show that the sum of the first billion terms in the series is less than 22.

(d) Find a value of $n$ so that the sum of the first $n$ terms is greater than 100.

**41.** Use a graphing utility to confirm that the integral test applies to the series $\sum_{k=1}^{\infty} k^2 e^{-k}$, and then determine whether the series converges.

C **42.** (a) Show that the hypotheses of the integral test are satisfied by the series $\sum_{k=1}^{\infty} 1/(k^3+1)$.

(b) Use a CAS and the integral test to confirm that the series converges.

(c) Construct a table of partial sums for $n = 10, 20, 30, \ldots, 100$, showing at least six decimal places.

(d) Based on your table, make a conjecture about the sum of the series to three decimal-place accuracy.

(e) Use part (b) of Exercise 36 to check your conjecture.

✓ **QUICK CHECK ANSWERS 9.4** 1. $\lim_{k \to +\infty} u_k$ 2. $-2$; 7 3. integral; $\frac{1}{\sqrt{k}}$; diverges 4. $\frac{1}{k^p}$; $p > 1$; $0 < p \leq 1$

# 9.5 THE COMPARISON, RATIO, AND ROOT TESTS

*In this section we will develop some more basic convergence tests for series with nonnegative terms. Later, we will use some of these tests to study the convergence of Taylor series.*

## THE COMPARISON TEST

We will begin with a test that is useful in its own right and is also the building block for other important convergence tests. The underlying idea of this test is to use the known convergence or divergence of a series to deduce the convergence or divergence of another series.

It is not essential in Theorem 9.5.1 that the condition $a_k \le b_k$ hold for all $k$, as stated; the conclusions of the theorem remain true if this condition is eventually true.

**9.5.1 THEOREM (*The Comparison Test*)** *Let $\sum_{k=1}^{\infty} a_k$ and $\sum_{k=1}^{\infty} b_k$ be series with nonnegative terms and suppose that*

$$a_1 \le b_1, a_2 \le b_2, a_3 \le b_3, \ldots, a_k \le b_k, \ldots$$

(a) *If the "bigger series" $\Sigma b_k$ converges, then the "smaller series" $\Sigma a_k$ also converges.*

(b) *If the "smaller series" $\Sigma a_k$ diverges, then the "bigger series" $\Sigma b_k$ also diverges.*

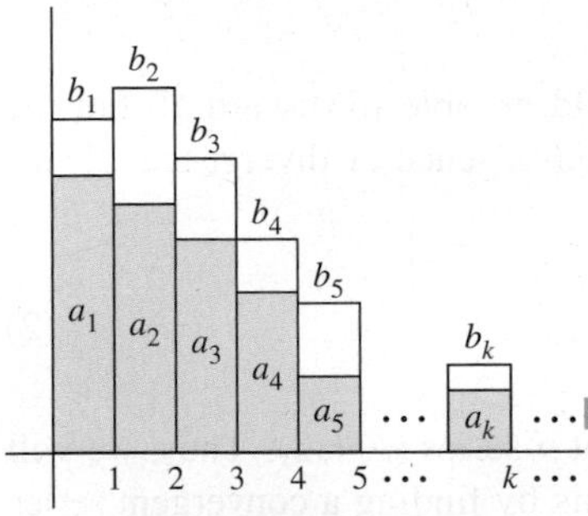


For each rectangle, $a_k$ denotes the area of the blue portion and $b_k$ denotes the combined area of the white and blue portions.

▲ **Figure 9.5.1**

We have left the proof of this theorem for the exercises; however, it is easy to visualize why the theorem is true by interpreting the terms in the series as areas of rectangles (Figure 9.5.1). The comparison test states that if the total area $\sum b_k$ is finite, then the total area $\sum a_k$ must also be finite; and if the total area $\sum a_k$ is infinite, then the total area $\sum b_k$ must also be infinite.

## USING THE COMPARISON TEST

There are two steps required for using the comparison test to determine whether a series $\sum u_k$ with positive terms converges:

**Step 1.** Guess at whether the series $\sum u_k$ converges or diverges.

**Step 2.** Find a series that proves the guess to be correct. That is, if we guess that $\sum u_k$ diverges, we must find a divergent series whose terms are "smaller" than the corresponding terms of $\sum u_k$, and if we guess that $\sum u_k$ converges, we must find a convergent series whose terms are "bigger" than the corresponding terms of $\sum u_k$.

In most cases, the series $\sum u_k$ being considered will have its general term $u_k$ expressed as a fraction. To help with the guessing process in the first step, we have formulated two principles that are based on the form of the denominator for $u_k$. These principles sometimes *suggest* whether a series is likely to converge or diverge. We have called these "informal principles" because they are not intended as formal theorems. In fact, we will not guarantee that they *always* work. However, they work often enough to be useful.

**9.5.2 INFORMAL PRINCIPLE** *Constant terms in the denominator of $u_k$ can usually be deleted without affecting the convergence or divergence of the series.*

> **9.5.3 INFORMAL PRINCIPLE** *If a polynomial in k appears as a factor in the numerator or denominator of $u_k$, all but the leading term in the polynomial can usually be discarded without affecting the convergence or divergence of the series.*

▶ **Example 1** Use the comparison test to determine whether the following series converge or diverge.

$$\text{(a)} \sum_{k=1}^{\infty} \frac{1}{\sqrt{k} - \frac{1}{2}} \qquad \text{(b)} \sum_{k=1}^{\infty} \frac{1}{2k^2 + k}$$

***Solution (a).*** According to Principle 9.5.2, we should be able to drop the constant in the denominator without affecting the convergence or divergence. Thus, the given series is likely to behave like

$$\sum_{k=1}^{\infty} \frac{1}{\sqrt{k}} \tag{1}$$

which is a divergent $p$-series $\left(p = \frac{1}{2}\right)$. Thus, we will guess that the given series diverges and try to prove this by finding a divergent series that is "smaller" than the given series. However, series (1) does the trick since

$$\frac{1}{\sqrt{k} - \frac{1}{2}} > \frac{1}{\sqrt{k}} \quad \text{for } k = 1, 2, \ldots$$

Thus, we have proved that the given series diverges.

***Solution (b).*** According to Principle 9.5.3, we should be able to discard all but the leading term in the polynomial without affecting the convergence or divergence. Thus, the given series is likely to behave like

$$\sum_{k=1}^{\infty} \frac{1}{2k^2} = \frac{1}{2} \sum_{k=1}^{\infty} \frac{1}{k^2} \tag{2}$$

which converges since it is a constant times a convergent $p$-series ($p = 2$). Thus, we will guess that the given series converges and try to prove this by finding a convergent series that is "bigger" than the given series. However, series (2) does the trick since

$$\frac{1}{2k^2 + k} < \frac{1}{2k^2} \quad \text{for } k = 1, 2, \ldots$$

Thus, we have proved that the given series converges. ◀

## THE LIMIT COMPARISON TEST

In the last example, Principles 9.5.2 and 9.5.3 provided the guess about convergence or divergence as well as the series needed to apply the comparison test. Unfortunately, it is not always so straightforward to find the series required for comparison, so we will now consider an alternative to the comparison test that is usually easier to apply. The proof is given in Web Appendix L.

> **9.5.4 THEOREM (*The Limit Comparison Test*)** *Let $\sum a_k$ and $\sum b_k$ be series with positive terms and suppose that*
>
> $$\rho = \lim_{k \to +\infty} \frac{a_k}{b_k}$$
>
> *If $\rho$ is finite and $\rho > 0$, then the series both converge or both diverge.*

The cases where $\rho = 0$ or $\rho = +\infty$ are discussed in the exercises (Exercise 56).

To use the limit comparison test we must again first guess at the convergence or divergence of $\sum a_k$ and then find a series $\sum b_k$ that supports our guess. The following example illustrates this principle.

▶ **Example 2** Use the limit comparison test to determine whether the following series converge or diverge.

$$\text{(a)} \sum_{k=1}^{\infty} \frac{1}{\sqrt{k}+1} \qquad \text{(b)} \sum_{k=1}^{\infty} \frac{1}{2k^2+k} \qquad \text{(c)} \sum_{k=1}^{\infty} \frac{3k^3-2k^2+4}{k^7-k^3+2}$$

***Solution (a).*** As in Example 1, Principle 9.5.2 suggests that the series is likely to behave like the divergent $p$-series (1). To prove that the given series diverges, we will apply the limit comparison test with

$$a_k = \frac{1}{\sqrt{k}+1} \quad \text{and} \quad b_k = \frac{1}{\sqrt{k}}$$

We obtain

$$\rho = \lim_{k\to+\infty} \frac{a_k}{b_k} = \lim_{k\to+\infty} \frac{\sqrt{k}}{\sqrt{k}+1} = \lim_{k\to+\infty} \frac{1}{1+\dfrac{1}{\sqrt{k}}} = 1$$

Since $\rho$ is finite and positive, it follows from Theorem 9.5.4 that the given series diverges.

***Solution (b).*** As in Example 1, Principle 9.5.3 suggests that the series is likely to behave like the convergent series (2). To prove that the given series converges, we will apply the limit comparison test with

$$a_k = \frac{1}{2k^2+k} \quad \text{and} \quad b_k = \frac{1}{2k^2}$$

We obtain

$$\rho = \lim_{k\to+\infty} \frac{a_k}{b_k} = \lim_{k\to+\infty} \frac{2k^2}{2k^2+k} = \lim_{k\to+\infty} \frac{2}{2+\dfrac{1}{k}} = 1$$

Since $\rho$ is finite and positive, it follows from Theorem 9.5.4 that the given series converges, which agrees with the conclusion reached in Example 1 using the comparison test.

***Solution (c).*** From Principle 9.5.3, the series is likely to behave like

$$\sum_{k=1}^{\infty} \frac{3k^3}{k^7} = \sum_{k=1}^{\infty} \frac{3}{k^4} \tag{3}$$

which converges since it is a constant times a convergent $p$-series. Thus, the given series is likely to converge. To prove this, we will apply the limit comparison test to series (3) and the given series. We obtain

$$\rho = \lim_{k\to+\infty} \frac{\dfrac{3k^3-2k^2+4}{k^7-k^3+2}}{\dfrac{3}{k^4}} = \lim_{k\to+\infty} \frac{3k^7-2k^6+4k^4}{3k^7-3k^3+6} = 1$$

Since $\rho$ is finite and nonzero, it follows from Theorem 9.5.4 that the given series converges, since (3) converges. ◀

## THE RATIO TEST

The comparison test and the limit comparison test hinge on first making a guess about convergence and then finding an appropriate series for comparison, both of which can be difficult tasks in cases where Principles 9.5.2 and 9.5.3 cannot be applied. In such cases the next test can often be used, since it works exclusively with the terms of the given series—it requires neither an initial guess about convergence nor the discovery of a series for comparison. Its proof is given in Web Appendix L.

**9.5.5 THEOREM (*The Ratio Test*)** *Let $\sum u_k$ be a series with positive terms and suppose that*

$$\rho = \lim_{k\to+\infty} \frac{u_{k+1}}{u_k}$$

(a) *If $\rho < 1$, the series converges.*

(b) *If $\rho > 1$ or $\rho = +\infty$, the series diverges.*

(c) *If $\rho = 1$, the series may converge or diverge, so that another test must be tried.*

▶ **Example 3** Each of the following series has positive terms, so the ratio test applies. In each part, use the ratio test to determine whether the following series converge or diverge.

$$\text{(a) } \sum_{k=1}^{\infty} \frac{1}{k!} \qquad \text{(b) } \sum_{k=1}^{\infty} \frac{k}{2^k} \qquad \text{(c) } \sum_{k=1}^{\infty} \frac{k^k}{k!} \qquad \text{(d) } \sum_{k=3}^{\infty} \frac{(2k)!}{4^k} \qquad \text{(e) } \sum_{k=1}^{\infty} \frac{1}{2k-1}$$

***Solution (a).*** The series converges, since

$$\rho = \lim_{k\to+\infty} \frac{u_{k+1}}{u_k} = \lim_{k\to+\infty} \frac{1/(k+1)!}{1/k!} = \lim_{k\to+\infty} \frac{k!}{(k+1)!} = \lim_{k\to+\infty} \frac{1}{k+1} = 0 < 1$$

***Solution (b).*** The series converges, since

$$\rho = \lim_{k\to+\infty} \frac{u_{k+1}}{u_k} = \lim_{k\to+\infty} \frac{k+1}{2^{k+1}} \cdot \frac{2^k}{k} = \frac{1}{2} \lim_{k\to+\infty} \frac{k+1}{k} = \frac{1}{2} < 1$$

***Solution (c).*** The series diverges, since

$$\rho = \lim_{k\to+\infty} \frac{u_{k+1}}{u_k} = \lim_{k\to+\infty} \frac{(k+1)^{k+1}}{(k+1)!} \cdot \frac{k!}{k^k} = \lim_{k\to+\infty} \frac{(k+1)^k}{k^k} = \lim_{k\to+\infty} \left(1 + \frac{1}{k}\right)^k = e > 1$$

See Formula (4) of Section 1.8

***Solution (d).*** The series diverges, since

$$\rho = \lim_{k\to+\infty} \frac{u_{k+1}}{u_k} = \lim_{k\to+\infty} \frac{[2(k+1)]!}{4^{k+1}} \cdot \frac{4^k}{(2k)!} = \lim_{k\to+\infty} \left(\frac{(2k+2)!}{(2k)!} \cdot \frac{1}{4}\right)$$

$$= \lim_{k\to+\infty} \left(\frac{(2k+2)(2k+1)(2k)!}{(2k)!} \cdot \frac{1}{4}\right) = \frac{1}{4} \lim_{k\to+\infty} (2k+2)(2k+1) = +\infty$$

***Solution (e).*** The ratio test is of no help since

$$\rho = \lim_{k\to+\infty} \frac{u_{k+1}}{u_k} = \lim_{k\to+\infty} \frac{1}{2(k+1)-1} \cdot \frac{2k-1}{1} = \lim_{k\to+\infty} \frac{2k-1}{2k+1} = 1$$

However, the integral test proves that the series diverges since

$$\int_1^{+\infty} \frac{dx}{2x-1} = \lim_{b\to+\infty} \int_1^b \frac{dx}{2x-1} = \lim_{b\to+\infty} \frac{1}{2} \ln(2x-1) \Big]_1^b = +\infty$$

Both the comparison test and the limit comparison test would also have worked here (verify). ◀

## THE ROOT TEST

In cases where it is difficult or inconvenient to find the limit required for the ratio test, the next test is sometimes useful. Since its proof is similar to the proof of the ratio test, we will omit it.

**9.5.6 THEOREM (*The Root Test*)** *Let $\sum u_k$ be a series with positive terms and suppose that*

$$\rho = \lim_{k\to+\infty} \sqrt[k]{u_k} = \lim_{k\to+\infty} (u_k)^{1/k}$$

(*a*) *If $\rho < 1$, the series converges.*

(*b*) *If $\rho > 1$ or $\rho = +\infty$, the series diverges.*

(*c*) *If $\rho = 1$, the series may converge or diverge, so that another test must be tried.*

▸ **Example 4** Use the root test to determine whether the following series converge or diverge.

$$\text{(a)} \sum_{k=2}^{\infty} \left(\frac{4k-5}{2k+1}\right)^k \qquad \text{(b)} \sum_{k=1}^{\infty} \frac{1}{(\ln(k+1))^k}$$

***Solution (a).*** The series diverges, since

$$\rho = \lim_{k\to+\infty} (u_k)^{1/k} = \lim_{k\to+\infty} \frac{4k-5}{2k+1} = 2 > 1$$

***Solution (b).*** The series converges, since

$$\rho = \lim_{k\to+\infty} (u_k)^{1/k} = \lim_{k\to+\infty} \frac{1}{\ln(k+1)} = 0 < 1 \blacktriangleleft$$

## ✓QUICK CHECK EXERCISES 9.5

(See page 553 for answers.)

**1–4** Select between *converges* or *diverges* to fill the first blank.

**1.** The series

$$\sum_{k=1}^{\infty} \frac{2k^2+1}{2k^{8/3}-1}$$

________ by comparison with the $p$-series $\sum_{k=1}^{\infty}$ ________.

**2.** Since

$$\lim_{k\to+\infty} \frac{(k+1)^3/3^{k+1}}{k^3/3^k} = \lim_{k\to+\infty} \frac{\left(1+\frac{1}{k}\right)^3}{3} = \frac{1}{3}$$

the series $\sum_{k=1}^{\infty} k^3/3^k$ ________ by the ________ test.

**3.** Since

$$\lim_{k\to+\infty} \frac{(k+1)!/3^{k+1}}{k!/3^k} = \lim_{k\to+\infty} \frac{k+1}{3} = +\infty$$

the series $\sum_{k=1}^{\infty} k!/3^k$ ________ by the ________ test.

**4.** Since

$$\lim_{k\to+\infty} \left(\frac{1}{k^{k/2}}\right)^{1/k} = \lim_{k\to+\infty} \frac{1}{k^{1/2}} = 0$$

the series $\sum_{k=1}^{\infty} 1/k^{k/2}$ ________ by the ________ test.

## EXERCISE SET 9.5

**1–2** Make a guess about the convergence or divergence of the series, and confirm your guess using the comparison test. ■

**1.** (a) $\displaystyle\sum_{k=1}^{\infty} \frac{1}{5k^2-k}$ (b) $\displaystyle\sum_{k=1}^{\infty} \frac{3}{k-\frac{1}{4}}$

**2.** (a) $\displaystyle\sum_{k=2}^{\infty} \frac{k+1}{k^2-k}$ (b) $\displaystyle\sum_{k=1}^{\infty} \frac{2}{k^4+k}$

**3.** In each part, use the comparison test to show that the series converges.

(a) $\displaystyle\sum_{k=1}^{\infty} \frac{1}{3^k+5}$ (b) $\displaystyle\sum_{k=1}^{\infty} \frac{5\sin^2 k}{k!}$

**4.** In each part, use the comparison test to show that the series diverges.

(a) $\displaystyle\sum_{k=1}^{\infty} \frac{\ln k}{k}$ (b) $\displaystyle\sum_{k=1}^{\infty} \frac{k}{k^{3/2}-\frac{1}{2}}$

**5–10** Use the limit comparison test to determine whether the series converges. ■

5. $\sum_{k=1}^{\infty} \frac{4k^2 - 2k + 6}{8k^7 + k - 8}$ 6. $\sum_{k=1}^{\infty} \frac{1}{9k + 6}$

7. $\sum_{k=1}^{\infty} \frac{5}{3^k + 1}$ 8. $\sum_{k=1}^{\infty} \frac{k(k+3)}{(k+1)(k+2)(k+5)}$

9. $\sum_{k=1}^{\infty} \frac{1}{\sqrt[3]{8k^2 - 3k}}$ 10. $\sum_{k=1}^{\infty} \frac{1}{(2k+3)^{17}}$

**11–16** Use the ratio test to determine whether the series converges. If the test is inconclusive, then say so. ■

11. $\sum_{k=1}^{\infty} \frac{3^k}{k!}$ 12. $\sum_{k=1}^{\infty} \frac{4^k}{k^2}$ 13. $\sum_{k=1}^{\infty} \frac{1}{5k}$

14. $\sum_{k=1}^{\infty} k\left(\frac{1}{2}\right)^k$ 15. $\sum_{k=1}^{\infty} \frac{k!}{k^3}$ 16. $\sum_{k=1}^{\infty} \frac{k}{k^2 + 1}$

**17–20** Use the root test to determine whether the series converges. If the test is inconclusive, then say so. ■

17. $\sum_{k=1}^{\infty} \left(\frac{3k+2}{2k-1}\right)^k$ 18. $\sum_{k=1}^{\infty} \left(\frac{k}{100}\right)^k$

19. $\sum_{k=1}^{\infty} \frac{k}{5^k}$ 20. $\sum_{k=1}^{\infty} (1 - e^{-k})^k$

**21–24 True–False** Determine whether the statement is true or false. Explain your answer. ■

21. The limit comparison test decides convergence based on a limit of the quotient of consecutive terms in a series.

22. If $\lim_{k \to +\infty} (u_{k+1}/u_k) = 5$, then $\sum u_k$ diverges.

23. If $\lim_{k \to +\infty} (k^2 u_k) = 5$, then $\sum u_k$ converges.

24. The root test decides convergence based on a limit of $k$th roots of terms in the sequence of partial sums for a series.

**25–49** Use any method to determine whether the series converges. ■

25. $\sum_{k=0}^{\infty} \frac{7^k}{k!}$ 26. $\sum_{k=1}^{\infty} \frac{1}{2k+1}$ 27. $\sum_{k=1}^{\infty} \frac{k^2}{5^k}$

28. $\sum_{k=1}^{\infty} \frac{k!\,10^k}{3^k}$ 29. $\sum_{k=1}^{\infty} k^{50} e^{-k}$ 30. $\sum_{k=1}^{\infty} \frac{k^2}{k^3 + 1}$

31. $\sum_{k=1}^{\infty} \frac{\sqrt{k}}{k^3 + 1}$ 32. $\sum_{k=1}^{\infty} \frac{4}{2 + 3^k k}$

33. $\sum_{k=1}^{\infty} \frac{1}{\sqrt{k(k+1)}}$ 34. $\sum_{k=1}^{\infty} \frac{2 + (-1)^k}{5^k}$

35. $\sum_{k=1}^{\infty} \frac{2 + \sqrt{k}}{(k+1)^3 - 1}$ 36. $\sum_{k=1}^{\infty} \frac{4 + |\cos x|}{k^3}$

37. $\sum_{k=1}^{\infty} \frac{1}{1 + \sqrt{k}}$ 38. $\sum_{k=1}^{\infty} \frac{k!}{k^k}$ 39. $\sum_{k=1}^{\infty} \frac{\ln k}{e^k}$

40. $\sum_{k=1}^{\infty} \frac{k!}{e^{k^2}}$ 41. $\sum_{k=0}^{\infty} \frac{(k+4)!}{4!\,k!\,4^k}$ 42. $\sum_{k=1}^{\infty} \left(\frac{k}{k+1}\right)^{k^2}$

43. $\sum_{k=1}^{\infty} \frac{1}{4 + 2^{-k}}$ 44. $\sum_{k=1}^{\infty} \frac{\sqrt{k}\ln k}{k^3 + 1}$ 45. $\sum_{k=1}^{\infty} \frac{\tan^{-1} k}{k^2}$

46. $\sum_{k=1}^{\infty} \frac{5^k + k}{k! + 3}$ 47. $\sum_{k=0}^{\infty} \frac{(k!)^2}{(2k)!}$ 48. $\sum_{k=1}^{\infty} \frac{[\pi(k+1)]^k}{k^{k+1}}$

49. $\sum_{k=1}^{\infty} \frac{\ln k}{3^k}$

50. For what positive values of $\alpha$ does the series $\sum_{k=1}^{\infty} (\alpha^k / k^\alpha)$ converge?

**51–52** Find the general term of the series and use the ratio test to show that the series converges. ■

51. $1 + \frac{1 \cdot 2}{1 \cdot 3} + \frac{1 \cdot 2 \cdot 3}{1 \cdot 3 \cdot 5} + \frac{1 \cdot 2 \cdot 3 \cdot 4}{1 \cdot 3 \cdot 5 \cdot 7} + \cdots$

52. $1 + \frac{1 \cdot 3}{3!} + \frac{1 \cdot 3 \cdot 5}{5!} + \frac{1 \cdot 3 \cdot 5 \cdot 7}{7!} + \cdots$

53. Show that $\ln x < \sqrt{x}$ if $x > 0$, and use this result to investigate the convergence of

(a) $\sum_{k=1}^{\infty} \frac{\ln k}{k^2}$ (b) $\sum_{k=2}^{\infty} \frac{1}{(\ln k)^2}$

**FOCUS ON CONCEPTS**

54. (a) Make a conjecture about the convergence of the series $\sum_{k=1}^{\infty} \sin(\pi/k)$ by considering the local linear approximation of $\sin x$ at $x = 0$.
(b) Try to confirm your conjecture using the limit comparison test.

55. (a) We will see later that the polynomial $1 - x^2/2$ is the "local quadratic" approximation for $\cos x$ at $x = 0$. Make a conjecture about the convergence of the series

$$\sum_{k=1}^{\infty} \left[1 - \cos\left(\frac{1}{k}\right)\right]$$

by considering this approximation.
(b) Try to confirm your conjecture using the limit comparison test.

56. Let $\sum a_k$ and $\sum b_k$ be series with positive terms. Prove:
(a) If $\lim_{k \to +\infty} (a_k/b_k) = 0$ and $\sum b_k$ converges, then $\sum a_k$ converges.
(b) If $\lim_{k \to +\infty} (a_k/b_k) = +\infty$ and $\sum b_k$ diverges, then $\sum a_k$ diverges.

57. Use Theorem 9.4.6 to prove the comparison test (Theorem 9.5.1).

58. **Writing** What does the ratio test tell you about the convergence of a geometric series? Discuss similarities between geometric series and series to which the ratio test applies.

59. **Writing** Given an infinite series, discuss a strategy for deciding what convergence test to use.

✓ **QUICK CHECK ANSWERS 9.5** 1. diverges; $1/k^{2/3}$ 2. converges; ratio 3. diverges; ratio 4. converges; root

## 9.6 ALTERNATING SERIES; ABSOLUTE AND CONDITIONAL CONVERGENCE

*Up to now we have focused exclusively on series with nonnegative terms. In this section we will discuss series that contain both positive and negative terms.*

### ALTERNATING SERIES

Series whose terms alternate between positive and negative, called ***alternating series***, are of special importance. Some examples are

$$\sum_{k=1}^{\infty}(-1)^{k+1}\frac{1}{k} = 1 - \frac{1}{2} + \frac{1}{3} - \frac{1}{4} + \frac{1}{5} - \cdots$$

$$\sum_{k=1}^{\infty}(-1)^{k}\frac{1}{k} = -1 + \frac{1}{2} - \frac{1}{3} + \frac{1}{4} - \frac{1}{5} + \cdots$$

In general, an alternating series has one of the following two forms:

$$\sum_{k=1}^{\infty}(-1)^{k+1}a_k = a_1 - a_2 + a_3 - a_4 + \cdots \tag{1}$$

$$\sum_{k=1}^{\infty}(-1)^{k}a_k = -a_1 + a_2 - a_3 + a_4 - \cdots \tag{2}$$

where the $a_k$'s are assumed to be positive in both cases.

The following theorem is the key result on convergence of alternating series.

It is not essential for condition (*a*) in Theorem 9.6.1 to hold for all terms; an alternating series will converge if condition (*b*) is true and condition (*a*) holds eventually.

**9.6.1 THEOREM (*Alternating Series Test*)** *An alternating series of either form* (1) *or form* (2) *converges if the following two conditions are satisfied:*

(*a*) $a_1 \geq a_2 \geq a_3 \geq \cdots \geq a_k \geq \cdots$

(*b*) $\lim_{k\to+\infty} a_k = 0$

**PROOF** We will consider only alternating series of form (1). The idea of the proof is to show that if conditions (*a*) and (*b*) hold, then the sequences of even-numbered and odd-numbered partial sums converge to a common limit $S$. It will then follow from Theorem 9.1.4 that the entire sequence of partial sums converges to $S$.

Figure 9.6.1 shows how successive partial sums satisfying conditions (*a*) and (*b*) appear when plotted on a horizontal axis. The even-numbered partial sums

$$s_2, s_4, s_6, s_8, \ldots, s_{2n}, \ldots$$

form an increasing sequence bounded above by $a_1$, and the odd-numbered partial sums

$$s_1, s_3, s_5, \ldots, s_{2n-1}, \ldots$$

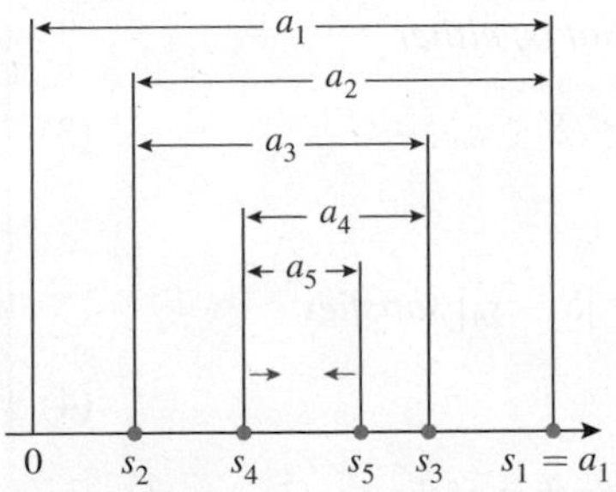


▲ **Figure 9.6.1**

form a decreasing sequence bounded below by 0. Thus, by Theorems 9.2.3 and 9.2.4, the even-numbered partial sums converge to some limit $S_E$ and the odd-numbered partial sums converge to some limit $S_O$. To complete the proof we must show that $S_E = S_O$. But the $(2n)$-th term in the series is $-a_{2n}$, so that $s_{2n} - s_{2n-1} = -a_{2n}$, which can be written as

$$s_{2n-1} = s_{2n} + a_{2n}$$

However, $2n \to +\infty$ and $2n - 1 \to +\infty$ as $n \to +\infty$, so that

$$S_O = \lim_{n\to+\infty} s_{2n-1} = \lim_{n\to+\infty} (s_{2n} + a_{2n}) = S_E + 0 = S_E$$

which completes the proof. ■

If an alternating series violates condition (*b*) of the alternating series test, then the series must diverge by the divergence test (Theorem 9.4.1).

▶ **Example 1** Use the alternating series test to show that the following series converge.

$$\text{(a)}\ \sum_{k=1}^{\infty} (-1)^{k+1}\frac{1}{k} \qquad \text{(b)}\ \sum_{k=1}^{\infty} (-1)^{k+1}\frac{k+3}{k(k+1)}$$

***Solution (a).*** The two conditions in the alternating series test are satisfied since

$$a_k = \frac{1}{k} > \frac{1}{k+1} = a_{k+1} \quad \text{and} \quad \lim_{k\to+\infty} a_k = \lim_{k\to+\infty} \frac{1}{k} = 0$$

The series in part (a) of Example 1 is called the ***alternating harmonic series***. Note that this series converges, whereas the harmonic series diverges.

***Solution (b).*** The two conditions in the alternating series test are satisfied since

$$\frac{a_{k+1}}{a_k} = \frac{k+4}{(k+1)(k+2)} \cdot \frac{k(k+1)}{k+3} = \frac{k^2+4k}{k^2+5k+6} = \frac{k^2+4k}{(k^2+4k)+(k+6)} < 1$$

so

$$a_k > a_{k+1}$$

and

$$\lim_{k\to+\infty} a_k = \lim_{k\to+\infty} \frac{k+3}{k(k+1)} = \lim_{k\to+\infty} \frac{\dfrac{1}{k} + \dfrac{3}{k^2}}{1 + \dfrac{1}{k}} = 0 \ ◀$$

## APPROXIMATING SUMS OF ALTERNATING SERIES

The following theorem is concerned with the error that results when the sum of an alternating series is approximated by a partial sum.

**9.6.2 THEOREM** *If an alternating series satisfies the hypotheses of the alternating series test, and if $S$ is the sum of the series, then:*

(*a*) *$S$ lies between any two successive partial sums; that is, either*

$$s_n \le S \le s_{n+1} \quad \text{or} \quad s_{n+1} \le S \le s_n \tag{3}$$

*depending on which partial sum is larger.*

(*b*) *If $S$ is approximated by $s_n$, then the absolute error $|S - s_n|$ satisfies*

$$|S - s_n| \le a_{n+1} \tag{4}$$

*Moreover, the sign of the error $S - s_n$ is the same as that of the coefficient of $a_{n+1}$.*

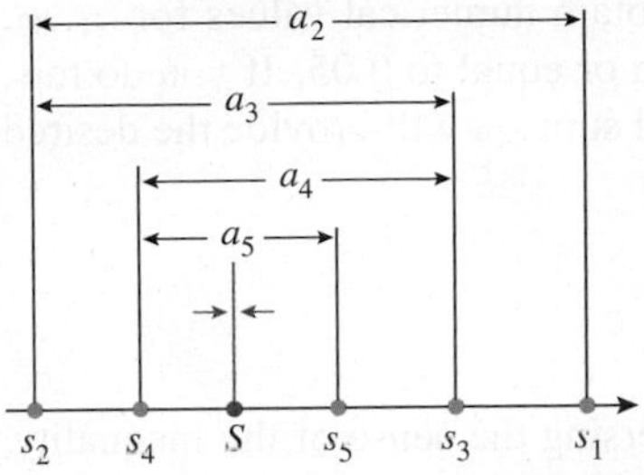


▲ Figure 9.6.2

**PROOF** We will prove the theorem for series of form (1). Referring to Figure 9.6.2 and keeping in mind our observation in the proof of Theorem 9.6.1 that the odd-numbered partial sums form a decreasing sequence converging to $S$ and the even-numbered partial sums form an increasing sequence converging to $S$, we see that successive partial sums oscillate from one side of $S$ to the other in smaller and smaller steps with the odd-numbered partial sums being larger than $S$ and the even-numbered partial sums being smaller than $S$. Thus, depending on whether $n$ is even or odd, we have

$$s_n \le S \le s_{n+1} \quad \text{or} \quad s_{n+1} \le S \le s_n$$

which proves (3). Moreover, in either case we have

$$|S - s_n| \le |s_{n+1} - s_n| \tag{5}$$

But $s_{n+1} - s_n = \pm a_{n+1}$ (the sign depending on whether $n$ is even or odd). Thus, it follows from (5) that $|S - s_n| \le a_{n+1}$, which proves (4). Finally, since the odd-numbered partial sums are larger than $S$ and the even-numbered partial sums are smaller than $S$, it follows that $S - s_n$ has the same sign as the coefficient of $a_{n+1}$ (verify). ■

**REMARK** In words, inequality (4) states that for a series satisfying the hypotheses of the alternating series test, the magnitude of the error that results from approximating $S$ by $s_n$ is at most that of the first term that is *not* included in the partial sum. Also, note that if $a_1 > a_2 > \cdots > a_k > \cdots$, then inequality (4) can be strengthened to $|S - s_n| < a_{n+1}$.

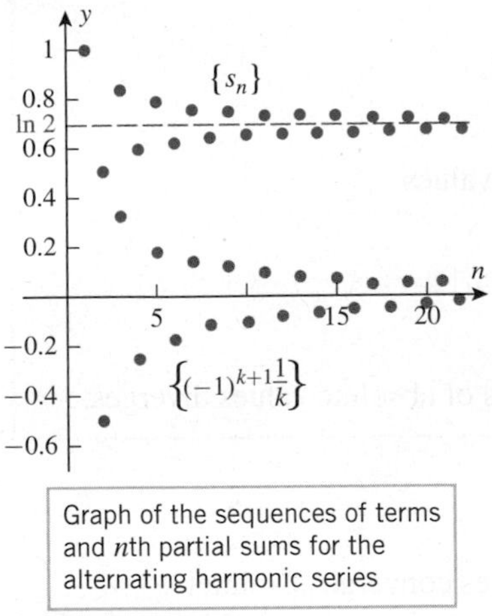


▲ Figure 9.6.3

► **Example 2** Later in this chapter we will show that the sum of the alternating harmonic series is

$$\ln 2 = 1 - \frac{1}{2} + \frac{1}{3} - \frac{1}{4} + \cdots + (-1)^{k+1}\frac{1}{k} + \cdots$$

This is illustrated in Figure 9.6.3.

(a) Accepting this to be so, find an upper bound on the magnitude of the error that results if ln 2 is approximated by the sum of the first eight terms in the series.

(b) Find a partial sum that approximates ln 2 to one decimal-place accuracy (the nearest tenth).

***Solution (a).*** It follows from the strengthened form of (4) that

$$|\ln 2 - s_8| < a_9 = \frac{1}{9} < 0.12 \tag{6}$$

As a check, let us compute $s_8$ exactly. We obtain

$$s_8 = 1 - \frac{1}{2} + \frac{1}{3} - \frac{1}{4} + \frac{1}{5} - \frac{1}{6} + \frac{1}{7} - \frac{1}{8} = \frac{533}{840}$$

Thus, with the help of a calculator

$$|\ln 2 - s_8| = \left|\ln 2 - \frac{533}{840}\right| \approx 0.059$$

This shows that the error is well under the estimate provided by upper bound (6).

***Solution (b).*** For one decimal-place accuracy, we must choose a value of $n$ for which $|\ln 2 - s_n| \le 0.05$. However, it follows from the strengthened form of (4) that

$$|\ln 2 - s_n| < a_{n+1}$$

so it suffices to choose $n$ so that $a_{n+1} \le 0.05$.

One way to find $n$ is to use a calculating utility to obtain numerical values for $a_1, a_2, a_3, \ldots$ until you encounter the first value that is less than or equal to 0.05. If you do this, you will find that it is $a_{20} = 0.05$; this tells us that partial sum $s_{19}$ will provide the desired accuracy. Another way to find $n$ is to solve the inequality

$$\frac{1}{n+1} \leq 0.05$$

algebraically. We can do this by taking reciprocals, reversing the sense of the inequality, and then simplifying to obtain $n \geq 19$. Thus, $s_{19}$ will provide the required accuracy, which is consistent with the previous result.

With the help of a calculating utility, the value of $s_{19}$ is approximately $s_{19} \approx 0.7$ and the value of $\ln 2$ obtained directly is approximately $\ln 2 \approx 0.69$, which agrees with $s_{19}$ when rounded to one decimal place. ◄

As Example 2 illustrates, the alternating harmonic series does not provide an efficient way to approximate ln 2, since too many terms and hence too much computation is required to achieve reasonable accuracy. Later, we will develop better ways to approximate logarithms.

## ABSOLUTE CONVERGENCE

The series

$$1 - \frac{1}{2} - \frac{1}{2^2} + \frac{1}{2^3} + \frac{1}{2^4} - \frac{1}{2^5} - \frac{1}{2^6} + \cdots$$

does not fit in any of the categories studied so far—it has mixed signs but is not alternating. We will now develop some convergence tests that can be applied to such series.

**9.6.3 DEFINITION** A series

$$\sum_{k=1}^{\infty} u_k = u_1 + u_2 + \cdots + u_k + \cdots$$

is said to ***converge absolutely*** if the series of absolute values

$$\sum_{k=1}^{\infty} |u_k| = |u_1| + |u_2| + \cdots + |u_k| + \cdots$$

converges and is said to ***diverge absolutely*** if the series of absolute values diverges.

► **Example 3** Determine whether the following series converge absolutely.

(a) $1 - \frac{1}{2} - \frac{1}{2^2} + \frac{1}{2^3} + \frac{1}{2^4} - \frac{1}{2^5} - \cdots$  (b) $1 - \frac{1}{2} + \frac{1}{3} - \frac{1}{4} + \frac{1}{5} - \cdots$

***Solution (a).*** The series of absolute values is the convergent geometric series

$$1 + \frac{1}{2} + \frac{1}{2^2} + \frac{1}{2^3} + \frac{1}{2^4} + \frac{1}{2^5} + \cdots$$

so the given series converges absolutely.

***Solution (b).*** The series of absolute values is the divergent harmonic series

$$1 + \frac{1}{2} + \frac{1}{3} + \frac{1}{4} + \frac{1}{5} + \cdots$$

so the given series diverges absolutely. ◄

It is important to distinguish between the notions of convergence and absolute convergence. For example, the series in part (b) of Example 3 converges, since it is the alternating harmonic series, yet we demonstrated that it does not converge absolutely. However, the following theorem shows that *if a series converges absolutely, then it converges.*

Theorem 9.6.4 provides a way of inferring convergence of a series with positive and negative terms from a related series with nonnegative terms (the series of absolute values). This is important because most of the convergence tests that we have developed apply only to series with nonnegative terms.

**9.6.4 THEOREM** *If the series*

$$\sum_{k=1}^{\infty} |u_k| = |u_1| + |u_2| + \cdots + |u_k| + \cdots$$

*converges, then so does the series*

$$\sum_{k=1}^{\infty} u_k = u_1 + u_2 + \cdots + u_k + \cdots$$

**PROOF** We will write the series $\sum u_k$ as

$$\sum_{k=1}^{\infty} u_k = \sum_{k=1}^{\infty} [(u_k + |u_k|) - |u_k|] \tag{7}$$

We are assuming that $\sum |u_k|$ converges, so that if we can show that $\sum (u_k + |u_k|)$ converges, then it will follow from (7) and Theorem 9.4.3(*a*) that $\sum u_k$ converges. However, the value of $u_k + |u_k|$ is either 0 or $2|u_k|$, depending on the sign of $u_k$. Thus, in all cases it is true that

$$0 \le u_k + |u_k| \le 2|u_k|$$

But $\sum 2|u_k|$ converges, since it is a constant times the convergent series $\sum |u_k|$; hence $\sum (u_k + |u_k|)$ converges by the comparison test. ■

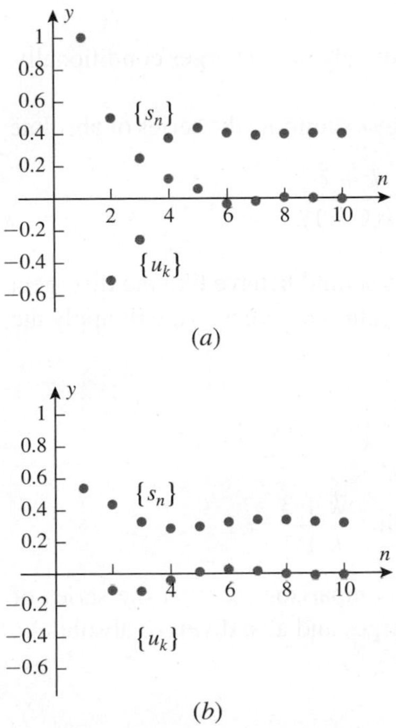


Graphs of the sequences of terms and $n$th partial sums for the series in Example 4

▲ **Figure 9.6.4**

► **Example 4** Show that the following series converge.

(a) $1 - \dfrac{1}{2} - \dfrac{1}{2^2} + \dfrac{1}{2^3} + \dfrac{1}{2^4} - \dfrac{1}{2^5} - \dfrac{1}{2^6} + \cdots$ (b) $\displaystyle\sum_{k=1}^{\infty} \frac{\cos k}{k^2}$

***Solution (a).*** Observe that this is not an alternating series because the signs alternate in pairs after the first term. Thus, we have no convergence test that can be applied directly. However, we showed in Example 3(a) that the series converges absolutely, so Theorem 9.6.4 implies that it converges (Figure 9.6.4*a*).

***Solution (b).*** With the help of a calculating utility, you will be able to verify that the signs of the terms in this series vary irregularly. Thus, we will test for absolute convergence. The series of absolute values is

$$\sum_{k=1}^{\infty} \left| \frac{\cos k}{k^2} \right|$$

However,

$$\left| \frac{\cos k}{k^2} \right| \le \frac{1}{k^2}$$

But $\sum 1/k^2$ is a convergent $p$-series ($p = 2$), so the series of absolute values converges by the comparison test. Thus, the given series converges absolutely and hence converges (Figure 9.6.4$b$). ◀

## CONDITIONAL CONVERGENCE

Although Theorem 9.6.4 is a useful tool for series that converge absolutely, it provides no information about the convergence or divergence of a series that diverges absolutely. For example, consider the two series

$$1 - \frac{1}{2} + \frac{1}{3} - \frac{1}{4} + \cdots + (-1)^{k+1}\frac{1}{k} + \cdots \tag{8}$$

$$-1 - \frac{1}{2} - \frac{1}{3} - \frac{1}{4} - \cdots - \frac{1}{k} - \cdots \tag{9}$$

Both of these series diverge absolutely, since in each case the series of absolute values is the divergent harmonic series

$$1 + \frac{1}{2} + \frac{1}{3} + \cdots + \frac{1}{k} + \cdots$$

However, series (8) converges, since it is the alternating harmonic series, and series (9) diverges, since it is a constant times the divergent harmonic series. As a matter of terminology, a series that converges but diverges absolutely is said to ***converge conditionally*** (or to be ***conditionally convergent***). Thus, (8) is a conditionally convergent series.

▶ **Example 5** In Example 1(b) we used the alternating series test to show that the series

$$\sum_{k=1}^{\infty} (-1)^{k+1}\frac{k+3}{k(k+1)}$$

converges. Determine whether this series converges absolutely or converges conditionally.

***Solution.*** We test the series for absolute convergence by examining the series of absolute values:

$$\sum_{k=1}^{\infty} \left| (-1)^{k+1}\frac{k+3}{k(k+1)} \right| = \sum_{k=1}^{\infty} \frac{k+3}{k(k+1)}$$

Principle 9.5.3 suggests that the series of absolute values should behave like the divergent $p$-series with $p = 1$. To prove that the series of absolute values diverges, we will apply the limit comparison test with

$$a_k = \frac{k+3}{k(k+1)} \quad \text{and} \quad b_k = \frac{1}{k}$$

We obtain

$$\rho = \lim_{k\to+\infty} \frac{a_k}{b_k} = \lim_{k\to+\infty} \frac{k(k+3)}{k(k+1)} = \lim_{k\to+\infty} \frac{k+3}{k+1} = 1$$

Since $\rho$ is finite and positive, it follows from the limit comparison test that the series of absolute values diverges. Thus, the original series converges and also diverges absolutely, and so converges conditionally. ◀

## THE RATIO TEST FOR ABSOLUTE CONVERGENCE

Although one cannot generally infer convergence or divergence of a series from absolute divergence, the following variation of the ratio test provides a way of deducing divergence from absolute divergence in certain situations. We omit the proof.

**9.6.5 THEOREM** ***(Ratio Test for Absolute Convergence)*** *Let $\sum u_k$ be a series with nonzero terms and suppose that*

$$\rho = \lim_{k\to+\infty} \frac{|u_{k+1}|}{|u_k|}$$

*(a) If $\rho < 1$, then the series $\sum u_k$ converges absolutely and therefore converges.*

*(b) If $\rho > 1$ or if $\rho = +\infty$, then the series $\sum u_k$ diverges.*

*(c) If $\rho = 1$, no conclusion about convergence or absolute convergence can be drawn from this test.*

▶ **Example 6** Use the ratio test for absolute convergence to determine whether the series converges.

$$\text{(a)} \sum_{k=1}^{\infty} (-1)^k \frac{2^k}{k!} \qquad \text{(b)} \sum_{k=1}^{\infty} (-1)^k \frac{(2k-1)!}{3^k}$$

***Solution (a).*** Taking the absolute value of the general term $u_k$ we obtain

$$|u_k| = \left|(-1)^k \frac{2^k}{k!}\right| = \frac{2^k}{k!}$$

Thus,

$$\rho = \lim_{k\to+\infty} \frac{|u_{k+1}|}{|u_k|} = \lim_{k\to+\infty} \frac{2^{k+1}}{(k+1)!} \cdot \frac{k!}{2^k} = \lim_{k\to+\infty} \frac{2}{k+1} = 0 < 1$$

which implies that the series converges absolutely and therefore converges.

***Solution (b).*** Taking the absolute value of the general term $u_k$ we obtain

$$|u_k| = \left|(-1)^k \frac{(2k-1)!}{3^k}\right| = \frac{(2k-1)!}{3^k}$$

Thus,

$$\rho = \lim_{k\to+\infty} \frac{|u_{k+1}|}{|u_k|} = \lim_{k\to+\infty} \frac{[2(k+1)-1]!}{3^{k+1}} \cdot \frac{3^k}{(2k-1)!}$$

$$= \lim_{k\to+\infty} \frac{1}{3} \cdot \frac{(2k+1)!}{(2k-1)!} = \frac{1}{3} \lim_{k\to+\infty} (2k)(2k+1) = +\infty$$

which implies that the series diverges. ◀

## ■ SUMMARY OF CONVERGENCE TESTS

We conclude this section with a summary of convergence tests that can be used for reference. The skill of selecting a good test is developed through lots of practice. In some instances a test may be inconclusive, so another test must be tried.

**Summary of Convergence Tests**

| NAME | STATEMENT | COMMENTS |
|---|---|---|
| **Divergence Test** (9.4.1) | If $\lim_{k\to+\infty} u_k \neq 0$, then $\sum u_k$ diverges. | If $\lim_{k\to+\infty} u_k = 0$, then $\sum u_k$ may or may not converge. |
| **Integral Test** (9.4.4) | Let $\sum u_k$ be a series with positive terms. If $f$ is a function that is decreasing and continuous on an interval $[a, +\infty)$ and such that $u_k = f(k)$ for all $k \geq a$, then $\sum_{k=1}^{\infty} u_k$ and $\int_a^{+\infty} f(x)\,dx$ both converge or both diverge. | This test only applies to series that have positive terms. Try this test when $f(x)$ is easy to integrate. |
| **Comparison Test** (9.5.1) | Let $\sum_{k=1}^{\infty} a_k$ and $\sum_{k=1}^{\infty} b_k$ be series with nonnegative terms such that $a_1 \leq b_1, a_2 \leq b_2, \ldots, a_k \leq b_k, \ldots$ If $\sum b_k$ converges, then $\sum a_k$ converges, and if $\sum a_k$ diverges, then $\sum b_k$ diverges. | This test only applies to series with nonnegative terms. Try this test as a last resort; other tests are often easier to apply. |
| **Limit Comparison Test** (9.5.4) | Let $\sum a_k$ and $\sum b_k$ be series with positive terms and let $\rho = \lim_{k\to+\infty} \frac{a_k}{b_k}$ If $0 < \rho < +\infty$, then both series converge or both diverge. | This is easier to apply than the comparison test, but still requires some skill in choosing the series $\sum b_k$ for comparison. |
| **Ratio Test** (9.5.5) | Let $\sum u_k$ be a series with positive terms and suppose that $\rho = \lim_{k\to+\infty} \frac{u_{k+1}}{u_k}$ (a) Series converges if $\rho < 1$. (b) Series diverges if $\rho > 1$ or $\rho = +\infty$. (c) The test is inconclusive if $\rho = 1$. | Try this test when $u_k$ involves factorials or $k$th powers. |
| **Root Test** (9.5.6) | Let $\sum u_k$ be a series with positive terms and suppose that $\rho = \lim_{k\to+\infty} \sqrt[k]{u_k}$ (a) The series converges if $\rho < 1$. (b) The series diverges if $\rho > 1$ or $\rho = +\infty$. (c) The test is inconclusive if $\rho = 1$. | Try this test when $u_k$ involves $k$th powers. |
| **Alternating Series Test** (9.6.1) | If $a_k > 0$ for $k = 1, 2, 3, \ldots$, then the series $a_1 - a_2 + a_3 - a_4 + \cdots$ $-a_1 + a_2 - a_3 + a_4 - \cdots$ converge if the following conditions hold: (a) $a_1 \geq a_2 \geq a_3 \geq \cdots$ (b) $\lim_{k\to+\infty} a_k = 0$ | This test applies only to alternating series. |
| **Ratio Test for Absolute Convergence** (9.6.5) | Let $\sum u_k$ be a series with nonzero terms and suppose that $\rho = \lim_{k\to+\infty} \frac{\lvert u_{k+1}\rvert}{\lvert u_k\rvert}$ (a) The series converges absolutely if $\rho < 1$. (b) The series diverges if $\rho > 1$ or $\rho = +\infty$. (c) The test is inconclusive if $\rho = 1$. | The series need not have positive terms and need not be alternating to use this test. |

## ✓QUICK CHECK EXERCISES 9.6 (See page 563 for answers.)

1. What characterizes an *alternating* series?

2. (a) The series
$$\sum_{k=1}^{\infty} \frac{(-1)^{k+1}}{k^2}$$
converges by the alternating series test since ______ and ______.

(b) If
$$S = \sum_{k=1}^{\infty} \frac{(-1)^{k+1}}{k^2} \quad \text{and} \quad s_9 = \sum_{k=1}^{9} \frac{(-1)^{k+1}}{k^2}$$
then $|S - s_9| <$ ______.

3. Classify each sequence as conditionally convergent, absolutely convergent, or divergent.

(a) $\sum_{k=1}^{\infty} (-1)^{k+1} \frac{1}{k}$: ______

(b) $\sum_{k=1}^{\infty} (-1)^k \frac{3k-1}{9k+15}$: ______

(c) $\sum_{k=1}^{\infty} (-1)^k \frac{1}{k(k+2)}$: ______

(d) $\sum_{k=1}^{\infty} (-1)^{k+1} \frac{1}{\sqrt[4]{k^3}}$: ______

4. Given that
$$\lim_{k\to+\infty} \frac{(k+1)^4/4^{k+1}}{k^4/4^k} = \lim_{k\to+\infty} \frac{\left(1+\frac{1}{k}\right)^4}{4} = \frac{1}{4}$$
is the series $\sum_{k=1}^{\infty} (-1)^k k^4/4^k$ conditionally convergent, absolutely convergent, or divergent?

## EXERCISE SET 9.6 C CAS

**1–2** Show that the series converges by confirming that it satisfies the hypotheses of the alternating series test (Theorem 9.6.1).

1. $\sum_{k=1}^{\infty} \frac{(-1)^{k+1}}{2k+1}$

2. $\sum_{k=1}^{\infty} (-1)^{k+1} \frac{k}{3^k}$

**3–6** Determine whether the alternating series converges; justify your answer.

3. $\sum_{k=1}^{\infty} (-1)^{k+1} \frac{k+1}{3k+1}$

4. $\sum_{k=1}^{\infty} (-1)^{k+1} \frac{k+1}{\sqrt{k}+1}$

5. $\sum_{k=1}^{\infty} (-1)^{k+1} e^{-k}$

6. $\sum_{k=3}^{\infty} (-1)^k \frac{\ln k}{k}$

**7–12** Use the ratio test for absolute convergence (Theorem 9.6.5) to determine whether the series converges or diverges. If the test is inconclusive, say so.

7. $\sum_{k=1}^{\infty} \left(-\frac{3}{5}\right)^k$

8. $\sum_{k=1}^{\infty} (-1)^{k+1} \frac{2^k}{k!}$

9. $\sum_{k=1}^{\infty} (-1)^{k+1} \frac{3^k}{k^2}$

10. $\sum_{k=1}^{\infty} (-1)^k \frac{k}{5^k}$

11. $\sum_{k=1}^{\infty} (-1)^k \frac{k^3}{e^k}$

12. $\sum_{k=1}^{\infty} (-1)^{k+1} \frac{k^k}{k!}$

**13–28** Classify each series as absolutely convergent, conditionally convergent, or divergent.

13. $\sum_{k=1}^{\infty} \frac{(-1)^{k+1}}{3k}$

14. $\sum_{k=1}^{\infty} \frac{(-1)^{k+1}}{k^{4/3}}$

15. $\sum_{k=1}^{\infty} \frac{(-4)^k}{k^2}$

16. $\sum_{k=1}^{\infty} \frac{(-1)^{k+1}}{k!}$

17. $\sum_{k=1}^{\infty} \frac{\cos k\pi}{k}$

18. $\sum_{k=3}^{\infty} \frac{(-1)^k \ln k}{k}$

19. $\sum_{k=1}^{\infty} (-1)^{k+1} \frac{k+2}{k(k+3)}$

20. $\sum_{k=1}^{\infty} \frac{(-1)^{k+1} k^2}{k^3+1}$

21. $\sum_{k=1}^{\infty} \sin \frac{k\pi}{2}$

22. $\sum_{k=1}^{\infty} \frac{\sin k}{k^3}$

23. $\sum_{k=2}^{\infty} \frac{(-1)^k}{k \ln k}$

24. $\sum_{k=1}^{\infty} \frac{(-1)^k}{\sqrt{k(k+1)}}$

25. $\sum_{k=2}^{\infty} \left(-\frac{1}{\ln k}\right)^k$

26. $\sum_{k=1}^{\infty} \frac{k \cos k\pi}{k^2+1}$

27. $\sum_{k=1}^{\infty} \frac{(-1)^{k+1} k!}{(2k-1)!}$

28. $\sum_{k=1}^{\infty} (-1)^{k+1} \frac{3^{2k-1}}{k^2+1}$

**29–32 True–False** Determine whether the statement is true or false. Explain your answer.

29. An alternating series is one whose terms alternate between even and odd.

30. If a series satisfies the hypothesis of the alternating series test, then the sequence of partial sums of the series oscillates between overestimates and underestimates for the sum of the series.

31. If a series converges, then either it converges absolutely or it converges conditionally.

32. If $\sum (u_k)^2$ converges, then $\sum u_k$ converges absolutely.

**33–36** Each series satisfies the hypotheses of the alternating series test. For the stated value of $n$, find an upper bound on the absolute error that results if the sum of the series is approximated by the $n$th partial sum. ■

**33.** $\sum_{k=1}^{\infty} \frac{(-1)^{k+1}}{k}$; $n = 7$

**34.** $\sum_{k=1}^{\infty} \frac{(-1)^{k+1}}{k!}$; $n = 5$

**35.** $\sum_{k=1}^{\infty} \frac{(-1)^{k+1}}{\sqrt{k}}$; $n = 99$

**36.** $\sum_{k=1}^{\infty} \frac{(-1)^{k+1}}{(k+1)\ln(k+1)}$; $n = 3$

**37–40** Each series satisfies the hypotheses of the alternating series test. Find a value of $n$ for which the $n$th partial sum is ensured to approximate the sum of the series to the stated accuracy. ■

**37.** $\sum_{k=1}^{\infty} \frac{(-1)^{k+1}}{k}$; $|\text{error}| < 0.0001$

**38.** $\sum_{k=1}^{\infty} \frac{(-1)^{k+1}}{k!}$; $|\text{error}| < 0.00001$

**39.** $\sum_{k=1}^{\infty} \frac{(-1)^{k+1}}{\sqrt{k}}$; two decimal places

**40.** $\sum_{k=1}^{\infty} \frac{(-1)^{k+1}}{(k+1)\ln(k+1)}$; one decimal place

**41–42** Find an upper bound on the absolute error that results if $s_{10}$ is used to approximate the sum of the given *geometric* series. Compute $s_{10}$ rounded to four decimal places and compare this value with the exact sum of the series. ■

**41.** $\frac{3}{4} - \frac{3}{8} + \frac{3}{16} - \frac{3}{32} + \cdots$

**42.** $1 - \frac{2}{3} + \frac{4}{9} - \frac{8}{27} + \cdots$

**43–46** Each series satisfies the hypotheses of the alternating series test. Approximate the sum of the series to two decimal-place accuracy. ■

**43.** $1 - \frac{1}{3!} + \frac{1}{5!} - \frac{1}{7!} + \cdots$

**44.** $1 - \frac{1}{2!} + \frac{1}{4!} - \frac{1}{6!} + \cdots$

**45.** $\frac{1}{1 \cdot 2} - \frac{1}{2 \cdot 2^2} + \frac{1}{3 \cdot 2^3} - \frac{1}{4 \cdot 2^4} + \cdots$

**46.** $\frac{1}{1^5 + 4 \cdot 1} - \frac{1}{3^5 + 4 \cdot 3} + \frac{1}{5^5 + 4 \cdot 5} - \frac{1}{7^5 + 4 \cdot 7} + \cdots$

**FOCUS ON CONCEPTS**

C **47.** The purpose of this exercise is to show that the error bound in part (*b*) of Theorem 9.6.2 can be overly conservative in certain cases.

(a) Use a CAS to confirm that

$$\frac{\pi}{4} = 1 - \frac{1}{3} + \frac{1}{5} - \frac{1}{7} + \cdots$$

(b) Use the CAS to show that $|(\pi/4) - s_{25}| < 10^{-2}$.

(c) According to the error bound in part (*b*) of Theorem 9.6.2, what value of $n$ is required to ensure that $|(\pi/4) - s_n| < 10^{-2}$?

**48.** Prove: If a series $\sum a_k$ converges absolutely, then the series $\sum {a_k}^2$ converges.

**49.** (a) Find examples to show that if $\sum a_k$ converges, then $\sum {a_k}^2$ may diverge or converge.

(b) Find examples to show that if $\sum {a_k}^2$ converges, then $\sum a_k$ may diverge or converge.

**50.** Let $\sum u_k$ be a series and define series $\sum p_k$ and $\sum q_k$ so that

$$p_k = \begin{cases} u_k, & u_k > 0 \\ 0, & u_k \le 0 \end{cases} \quad \text{and} \quad q_k = \begin{cases} 0, & u_k \ge 0 \\ -u_k, & u_k < 0 \end{cases}$$

(a) Show that $\sum u_k$ converges absolutely if and only if $\sum p_k$ and $\sum q_k$ both converge.

(b) Show that if one of $\sum p_k$ or $\sum q_k$ converges and the other diverges, then $\sum u_k$ diverges.

(c) Show that if $\sum u_k$ converges conditionally, then both $\sum p_k$ and $\sum q_k$ diverge.

**51.** It can be proved that the terms of any conditionally convergent series can be rearranged to give either a divergent series or a conditionally convergent series whose sum is any given number $S$. For example, we stated in Example 2 that

$$\ln 2 = 1 - \frac{1}{2} + \frac{1}{3} - \frac{1}{4} + \frac{1}{5} - \frac{1}{6} + \cdots$$

Show that we can rearrange this series so that its sum is $\frac{1}{2}\ln 2$ by rewriting it as

$$\left(1 - \frac{1}{2} - \frac{1}{4}\right) + \left(\frac{1}{3} - \frac{1}{6} - \frac{1}{8}\right) + \left(\frac{1}{5} - \frac{1}{10} - \frac{1}{12}\right) + \cdots$$

[*Hint:* Add the first two terms in each grouping.]

**52–54** Exercise 51 illustrates that one of the nuances of "conditional" convergence is that the sum of a series that converges conditionally depends on the order that the terms of the series are summed. Absolutely convergent series are more dependable, however. It can be proved that any series that is constructed from an absolutely convergent series by rearranging the terms will also be absolutely convergent and has the same sum as the original series. Use this fact together with parts (*a*) and (*b*) of Theorem 9.4.3 in these exercises. ■

**52.** It was stated in Exercise 35 of Section 9.4 that

$$\frac{\pi^2}{6} = 1 + \frac{1}{2^2} + \frac{1}{3^2} + \frac{1}{4^2} + \cdots$$

Use this to show that

$$\frac{\pi^2}{8} = 1 + \frac{1}{3^2} + \frac{1}{5^2} + \frac{1}{7^2} + \cdots$$

**53.** Use the series for $\pi^2/6$ given in the preceding exercise to show that

$$\frac{\pi^2}{12} = 1 - \frac{1}{2^2} + \frac{1}{3^2} - \frac{1}{4^2} + \cdots$$

**54.** It was stated in Exercise 35 of Section 9.4 that

$$\frac{\pi^4}{90} = 1 + \frac{1}{2^4} + \frac{1}{3^4} + \frac{1}{4^4} + \cdots$$

Use this to show that

$$\frac{\pi^4}{96} = 1 + \frac{1}{3^4} + \frac{1}{5^4} + \frac{1}{7^4} + \cdots$$

**55. Writing** Consider the series

$$1 - \frac{1}{2} + \frac{2}{3} - \frac{1}{3} + \frac{2}{4} - \frac{1}{4} + \frac{2}{5} - \frac{1}{5} + \cdots$$

Determine whether this series converges and use this series as an example in a discussion of the importance of hypotheses (*a*) and (*b*) of the alternating series test (Theorem 9.6.1).

**56. Writing** Discuss the ways that conditional convergence is "conditional." In particular, describe how one could rearrange the terms of a conditionally convergent series $\sum u_k$ so that the resulting series diverges, either to $+\infty$ or to $-\infty$. [*Hint:* See Exercise 50.]

✓ **QUICK CHECK ANSWERS 9.6** 1. Terms alternate between positive and negative. 2. (a) $1 \geq \frac{1}{4} \geq \frac{1}{9} \geq \cdots \geq \frac{1}{k^2} \geq \frac{1}{(k+1)^2} \geq \cdots$; $\lim_{k\to+\infty} \frac{1}{k^2} = 0$ (b) $\frac{1}{100}$ 3. (a) conditionally convergent (b) divergent (c) absolutely convergent (d) conditionally convergent 4. absolutely convergent

## 9.7 MACLAURIN AND TAYLOR POLYNOMIALS

*In a local linear approximation the tangent line to the graph of a function is used to obtain a linear approximation of the function near the point of tangency. In this section we will consider how one might improve on the accuracy of local linear approximations by using higher-order polynomials as approximating functions. We will also investigate the error associated with such approximations.*

### LOCAL QUADRATIC APPROXIMATIONS

Recall from Formula (1) in Section 3.5 that the local linear approximation of a function $f$ at $x_0$ is

$$f(x) \approx f(x_0) + f'(x_0)(x - x_0) \tag{1}$$

In this formula, the approximating function

$$p(x) = f(x_0) + f'(x_0)(x - x_0)$$

is a first-degree polynomial satisfying $p(x_0) = f(x_0)$ and $p'(x_0) = f'(x_0)$ (verify). Thus, the local linear approximation of $f$ at $x_0$ has the property that its value and the value of its first derivative match those of $f$ at $x_0$.

If the graph of a function $f$ has a pronounced "bend" at $x_0$, then we can expect that the accuracy of the local linear approximation of $f$ at $x_0$ will decrease rapidly as we progress away from $x_0$ (Figure 9.7.1). One way to deal with this problem is to approximate the function $f$ at $x_0$ by a polynomial $p$ of degree 2 with the property that the value of $p$ and the values of its first two derivatives match those of $f$ at $x_0$. This ensures that the graphs of $f$ and $p$ not only have the same tangent line at $x_0$, but they also bend in the same direction at $x_0$ (both concave up or concave down). As a result, we can expect that the graph of $p$ will remain close to the graph of $f$ over a larger interval around $x_0$ than the graph of the local linear approximation. The polynomial $p$ is called the ***local quadratic approximation of f at $x = x_0$***.

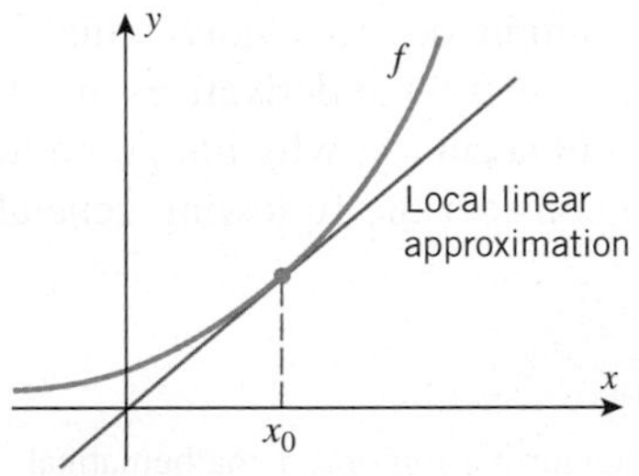

▲ Figure 9.7.1

To illustrate this idea, let us try to find a formula for the local quadratic approximation of a function $f$ at $x = 0$. This approximation has the form

$$f(x) \approx c_0 + c_1 x + c_2 x^2 \tag{2}$$

where $c_0$, $c_1$, and $c_2$ must be chosen so that the values of

$$p(x) = c_0 + c_1 x + c_2 x^2$$

and its first two derivatives match those of $f$ at 0. Thus, we want

$$p(0) = f(0), \quad p'(0) = f'(0), \quad p''(0) = f''(0) \tag{3}$$

But the values of $p(0)$, $p'(0)$, and $p''(0)$ are as follows:

$$\begin{aligned} p(x) &= c_0 + c_1x + c_2x^2 & \qquad p(0) &= c_0 \\ p'(x) &= c_1 + 2c_2x & \qquad p'(0) &= c_1 \\ p''(x) &= 2c_2 & \qquad p''(0) &= 2c_2 \end{aligned}$$

Thus, it follows from (3) that

$$c_0 = f(0), \quad c_1 = f'(0), \quad c_2 = \frac{f''(0)}{2}$$

and substituting these in (2) yields the following formula for the local quadratic approximation of $f$ at $x = 0$:

$$f(x) \approx f(0) + f'(0)x + \frac{f''(0)}{2}x^2 \tag{4}$$

**▶ Example 1** Find the local linear and quadratic approximations of $e^x$ at $x = 0$, and graph $e^x$ and the two approximations together.

***Solution.*** If we let $f(x) = e^x$, then $f'(x) = f''(x) = e^x$; and hence

$$f(0) = f'(0) = f''(0) = e^0 = 1$$

Thus, from (4) the local quadratic approximation of $e^x$ at $x = 0$ is

$$e^x \approx 1 + x + \frac{x^2}{2}$$

and the local linear approximation (which is the linear part of the local quadratic approximation) is

$$e^x \approx 1 + x$$

The graphs of $e^x$ and the two approximations are shown in Figure 9.7.2. As expected, the local quadratic approximation is more accurate than the local linear approximation near $x = 0$. ◀

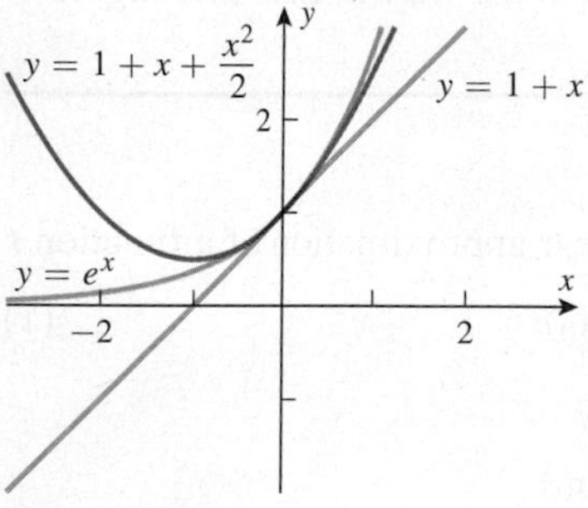

▲ **Figure 9.7.2**

## MACLAURIN POLYNOMIALS

It is natural to ask whether one can improve on the accuracy of a local quadratic approximation by using a polynomial of degree 3. Specifically, one might look for a polynomial of degree 3 with the property that its value and the values of its first three derivatives match those of $f$ at a point; and if this provides an improvement in accuracy, why not go on to polynomials of even higher degree? Thus, we are led to consider the following general problem.

**Colin Maclaurin (1698–1746)** Scottish mathematician. Maclaurin's father, a minister, died when the boy was only six months old, and his mother when he was nine years old. He was then raised by an uncle who was also a minister. Maclaurin entered Glasgow University as a divinity student but switched to mathematics after one year. He received his Master's degree at age 17 and, in spite of his youth, began teaching at Marischal College in Aberdeen, Scotland. He met Isaac Newton during a visit to London in 1719 and from that time on became Newton's disciple. During that era, some of Newton's analytic methods were bitterly attacked by major mathematicians and much of Maclaurin's important mathematical work resulted from his efforts to defend Newton's ideas geometrically. Maclaurin's work, *A Treatise of Fluxions* (1742), was the first systematic formulation of Newton's methods. The treatise was so carefully done that it was a standard of mathematical rigor in calculus until the work of Cauchy in 1821. Maclaurin was also an outstanding experimentalist; he devised numerous ingenious mechanical devices, made important astronomical observations, performed actuarial computations for insurance societies, and helped to improve maps of the islands around Scotland.

*[Image: Engraving by R. Page, 1814/Wellcome Library, London]*

**9.7.1 PROBLEM** Given a function $f$ that can be differentiated $n$ times at $x = x_0$, find a polynomial $p$ of degree $n$ with the property that the value of $p$ and the values of its first $n$ derivatives match those of $f$ at $x_0$.

We will begin by solving this problem in the case where $x_0 = 0$. Thus, we want a polynomial

$$p(x) = c_0 + c_1x + c_2x^2 + c_3x^3 + \cdots + c_nx^n \tag{5}$$

such that

$$f(0) = p(0), \quad f'(0) = p'(0), \quad f''(0) = p''(0), \ldots, \quad f^{(n)}(0) = p^{(n)}(0) \tag{6}$$

But

$$\begin{aligned} p(x) &= c_0 + c_1x + c_2x^2 + c_3x^3 + \cdots + c_nx^n \\ p'(x) &= c_1 + 2c_2x + 3c_3x^2 + \cdots + nc_nx^{n-1} \\ p''(x) &= 2c_2 + 3\cdot 2c_3x + \cdots + n(n-1)c_nx^{n-2} \\ p'''(x) &= 3\cdot 2c_3 + \cdots + n(n-1)(n-2)c_nx^{n-3} \\ &\vdots \\ p^{(n)}(x) &= n(n-1)(n-2)\cdots(1)c_n \end{aligned}$$

Thus, to satisfy (6) we must have

$$\begin{aligned} f(0) &= p(0) = c_0 \\ f'(0) &= p'(0) = c_1 \\ f''(0) &= p''(0) = 2c_2 = 2!c_2 \\ f'''(0) &= p'''(0) = 3\cdot 2c_3 = 3!c_3 \\ &\vdots \\ f^{(n)}(0) &= p^{(n)}(0) = n(n-1)(n-2)\cdots(1)c_n = n!c_n \end{aligned}$$

which yields the following values for the coefficients of $p(x)$:

$$c_0 = f(0), \quad c_1 = f'(0), \quad c_2 = \frac{f''(0)}{2!}, \quad c_3 = \frac{f'''(0)}{3!}, \ldots, \quad c_n = \frac{f^{(n)}(0)}{n!}$$

The polynomial that results by using these coefficients in (5) is called the *nth Maclaurin polynomial for f*.

Local linear approximations and local quadratic approximations at $x = 0$ of a function $f$ are special cases of the MacLaurin polynomials for $f$. Verify that $f(x) \approx p_1(x)$ is the local linear approximation of $f$ at $x = 0$, and $f(x) \approx p_2(x)$ is the local quadratic approximation at $x = 0$.

**9.7.2 DEFINITION** If $f$ can be differentiated $n$ times at 0, then we define the ***nth Maclaurin polynomial for f*** to be

$$p_n(x) = f(0) + f'(0)x + \frac{f''(0)}{2!}x^2 + \frac{f'''(0)}{3!}x^3 + \cdots + \frac{f^{(n)}(0)}{n!}x^n \tag{7}$$

Note that the polynomial in (7) has the property that its value and the values of its first $n$ derivatives match the values of $f$ and its first $n$ derivatives at $x = 0$.

▶ **Example 2** Find the Maclaurin polynomials $p_0$, $p_1$, $p_2$, $p_3$, and $p_n$ for $e^x$.

***Solution.*** Let $f(x) = e^x$. Thus,

$$f'(x) = f''(x) = f'''(x) = \cdots = f^{(n)}(x) = e^x$$

and

$$f(0) = f'(0) = f''(0) = f'''(0) = \cdots = f^{(n)}(0) = e^0 = 1$$

Therefore,

$$p_0(x) = f(0) = 1$$

$$p_1(x) = f(0) + f'(0)x = 1 + x$$

$$p_2(x) = f(0) + f'(0)x + \frac{f''(0)}{2!}x^2 = 1 + x + \frac{x^2}{2!} = 1 + x + \frac{1}{2}x^2$$

$$p_3(x) = f(0) + f'(0)x + \frac{f''(0)}{2!}x^2 + \frac{f'''(0)}{3!}x^3$$

$$= 1 + x + \frac{x^2}{2!} + \frac{x^3}{3!} = 1 + x + \frac{1}{2}x^2 + \frac{1}{6}x^3$$

$$p_n(x) = f(0) + f'(0)x + \frac{f''(0)}{2!}x^2 + \cdots + \frac{f^{(n)}(0)}{n!}x^n$$

$$= 1 + x + \frac{x^2}{2!} + \cdots + \frac{x^n}{n!} \blacktriangleleft$$

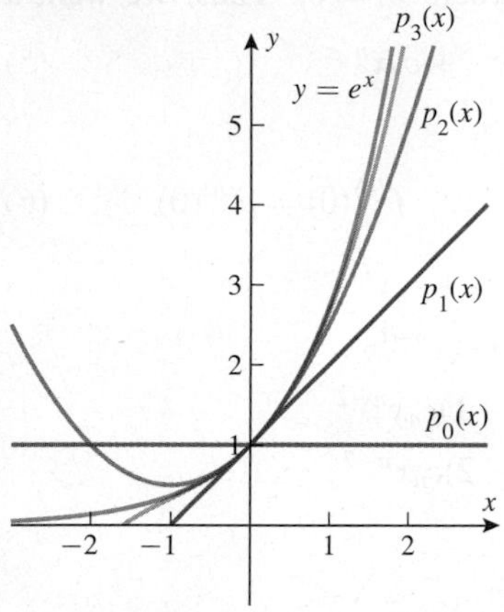

▲ Figure 9.7.3

Figure 9.7.3 shows the graph of $e^x$ (in blue) and the graph of the first four Maclaurin polynomials. Note that the graphs of $p_1(x)$, $p_2(x)$, and $p_3(x)$ are virtually indistinguishable from the graph of $e^x$ near $x = 0$, so these polynomials are good approximations of $e^x$ for $x$ near 0. However, the farther $x$ is from 0, the poorer these approximations become. This is typical of the Maclaurin polynomials for a function $f(x)$; they provide good approximations of $f(x)$ near 0, but the accuracy diminishes as $x$ progresses away from 0. It is usually the case that the higher the degree of the polynomial, the larger the interval on which it provides a specified accuracy. Accuracy issues will be investigated later.

▶ **Example 3** Find the $n$th Maclaurin polynomials for

(a) $\sin x$ (b) $\cos x$

***Solution (a).*** In the Maclaurin polynomials for $\sin x$, only the odd powers of $x$ appear explicitly. To see this, let $f(x) = \sin x$; thus,

$$\begin{aligned} f(x) &= \sin x & f(0) &= 0 \\ f'(x) &= \cos x & f'(0) &= 1 \\ f''(x) &= -\sin x & f''(0) &= 0 \\ f'''(x) &= -\cos x & f'''(0) &= -1 \end{aligned}$$

**Augustin Louis Cauchy (1789–1857)** French mathematician. Cauchy's early education was acquired from his father, a barrister and master of the classics. Cauchy entered L'Ecole Polytechnique in 1805 to study engineering, but because of poor health, was advised to concentrate on mathematics. His major mathematical work began in 1811 with a series of brilliant solutions to some difficult outstanding problems. In 1814 he wrote a treatise on integrals that was to become the basis for modern complex variable theory; in 1816 there followed a classic paper on wave propagation in liquids that won a prize from the French Academy; and in 1822 he wrote a paper that formed the basis of modern elasticity theory. Cauchy's mathematical contributions for the next 35 years were brilliant and staggering in quantity, over 700 papers filling 26 modern volumes. Cauchy's work initiated the era of modern analysis. He brought to mathematics standards of precision and rigor undreamed of by Leibniz and Newton.

Cauchy's life was inextricably tied to the political upheavals of the time. A strong partisan of the Bourbons, he left his wife and children in 1830 to follow the Bourbon king Charles X into exile. For his loyalty he was made a baron by the ex-king. Cauchy eventually returned to France, but refused to accept a university position until the government waived its requirement that he take a loyalty oath.

It is difficult to get a clear picture of the man. Devoutly Catholic, he sponsored charitable work for unwed mothers, criminals, and relief for Ireland. Yet other aspects of his life cast him in an unfavorable light. The Norwegian mathematician Abel described him as, "mad, infinitely Catholic, and bigoted." Some writers praise his teaching, yet others say he rambled incoherently and, according to a report of the day, he once devoted an entire lecture to extracting the square root of seventeen to ten decimal places by a method well known to his students. In any event, Cauchy is undeniably one of the greatest minds in the history of science.

*[Image: Lithograph by Z. Belliard after J. Roller/Wellcome Library, London]*

Since $f^{(4)}(x) = \sin x = f(x)$, the pattern 0, 1, 0, −1 will repeat as we evaluate successive derivatives at 0. Therefore, the successive Maclaurin polynomials for $\sin x$ are

$$\begin{aligned}
p_0(x) &= 0\\
p_1(x) &= 0 + x\\
p_2(x) &= 0 + x + 0\\
p_3(x) &= 0 + x + 0 - \frac{x^3}{3!}\\
p_4(x) &= 0 + x + 0 - \frac{x^3}{3!} + 0\\
p_5(x) &= 0 + x + 0 - \frac{x^3}{3!} + 0 + \frac{x^5}{5!}\\
p_6(x) &= 0 + x + 0 - \frac{x^3}{3!} + 0 + \frac{x^5}{5!} + 0\\
p_7(x) &= 0 + x + 0 - \frac{x^3}{3!} + 0 + \frac{x^5}{5!} + 0 - \frac{x^7}{7!}
\end{aligned}$$

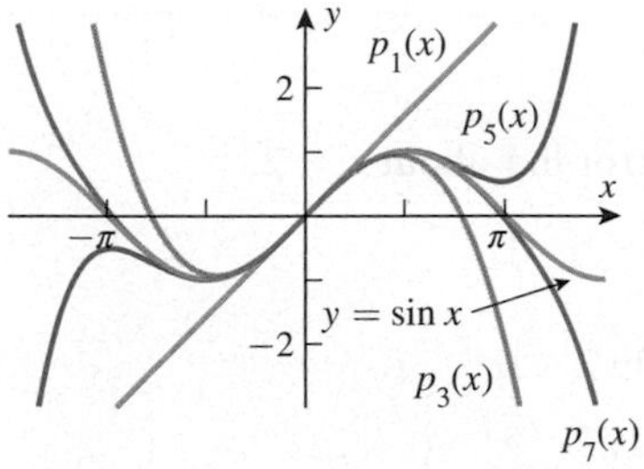


▲ **Figure 9.7.4**

Because of the zero terms, each even-order Maclaurin polynomial [after $p_0(x)$] is the same as the preceding odd-order Maclaurin polynomial. That is,

$$p_{2k+1}(x) = p_{2k+2}(x) = x - \frac{x^3}{3!} + \frac{x^5}{5!} - \frac{x^7}{7!} + \cdots + (-1)^k \frac{x^{2k+1}}{(2k+1)!} \quad (k = 0, 1, 2, \ldots)$$

The graphs of $\sin x, p_1(x), p_3(x), p_5(x)$, and $p_7(x)$ are shown in Figure 9.7.4.

***Solution (b).*** In the Maclaurin polynomials for $\cos x$, only the even powers of $x$ appear explicitly; the computations are similar to those in part (a). The reader should be able to show that

$$\begin{aligned}
p_0(x) &= p_1(x) = 1\\
p_2(x) &= p_3(x) = 1 - \frac{x^2}{2!}\\
p_4(x) &= p_5(x) = 1 - \frac{x^2}{2!} + \frac{x^4}{4!}\\
p_6(x) &= p_7(x) = 1 - \frac{x^2}{2!} + \frac{x^4}{4!} - \frac{x^6}{6!}
\end{aligned}$$

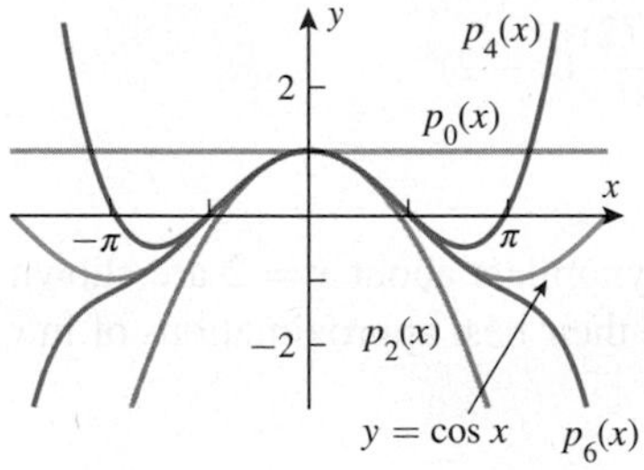


▲ **Figure 9.7.5**

In general, the Maclaurin polynomials for $\cos x$ are given by

$$p_{2k}(x) = p_{2k+1}(x) = 1 - \frac{x^2}{2!} + \frac{x^4}{4!} - \frac{x^6}{6!} + \cdots + (-1)^k \frac{x^{2k}}{(2k)!} \quad (k = 0, 1, 2, \ldots)$$

The graphs of $\cos x$, $p_0(x)$, $p_2(x)$, $p_4(x)$, and $p_6(x)$ are shown in Figure 9.7.5. ◀

## TAYLOR POLYNOMIALS

Up to now we have focused on approximating a function $f$ in the vicinity of $x = 0$. Now we will consider the more general case of approximating $f$ in the vicinity of an arbitrary domain value $x_0$. The basic idea is the same as before; we want to find an $n$th-degree polynomial $p$ with the property that its value and the values of its first $n$ derivatives match those of $f$ at $x_0$. However, rather than expressing $p(x)$ in powers of $x$, it will simplify the computations if we express it in powers of $x - x_0$; that is,

$$p(x) = c_0 + c_1(x - x_0) + c_2(x - x_0)^2 + \cdots + c_n(x - x_0)^n \quad (8)$$

We will leave it as an exercise for you to imitate the computations used in the case where $x_0 = 0$ to show that

$$c_0 = f(x_0),\quad c_1 = f'(x_0),\quad c_2 = \frac{f''(x_0)}{2!},\quad c_3 = \frac{f'''(x_0)}{3!}, \ldots,\quad c_n = \frac{f^{(n)}(x_0)}{n!}$$

Substituting these values in (8) we obtain a polynomial called the *nth Taylor polynomial about $x = x_0$ for $f$.*

Local linear approximations and local quadratic approximations at $x = x_0$ of a function $f$ are special cases of the Taylor polynomials for $f$. Verify that $f(x) \approx p_1(x)$ is the local linear approximation of $f$ at $x = x_0$, and $f(x) \approx p_2(x)$ is the local quadratic approximation at $x = x_0$.

**9.7.3 DEFINITION** If $f$ can be differentiated $n$ times at $x_0$, then we define the ***nth Taylor polynomial for f about $x = x_0$*** to be

$$p_n(x) = f(x_0) + f'(x_0)(x - x_0) + \frac{f''(x_0)}{2!}(x - x_0)^2 + \frac{f'''(x_0)}{3!}(x - x_0)^3 + \cdots + \frac{f^{(n)}(x_0)}{n!}(x - x_0)^n \tag{9}$$

The Maclaurin polynomials are the special cases of the Taylor polynomials in which $x_0 = 0$. Thus, theorems about Taylor polynomials also apply to Maclaurin polynomials.

**▶ Example 4** Find the first four Taylor polynomials for $\ln x$ about $x = 2$.

***Solution.*** Let $f(x) = \ln x$. Thus,

$$\begin{aligned}
f(x) &= \ln x & f(2) &= \ln 2\\
f'(x) &= 1/x & f'(2) &= 1/2\\
f''(x) &= -1/x^2 & f''(2) &= -1/4\\
f'''(x) &= 2/x^3 & f'''(2) &= 1/4
\end{aligned}$$

Substituting in (9) with $x_0 = 2$ yields

$$\begin{aligned}
p_0(x) &= f(2) = \ln 2\\
p_1(x) &= f(2) + f'(2)(x-2) = \ln 2 + \tfrac{1}{2}(x-2)\\
p_2(x) &= f(2) + f'(2)(x-2) + \frac{f''(2)}{2!}(x-2)^2 = \ln 2 + \tfrac{1}{2}(x-2) - \tfrac{1}{8}(x-2)^2\\
p_3(x) &= f(2) + f'(2)(x-2) + \frac{f''(2)}{2!}(x-2)^2 + \frac{f'''(2)}{3!}(x-2)^3\\
&= \ln 2 + \tfrac{1}{2}(x-2) - \tfrac{1}{8}(x-2)^2 + \tfrac{1}{24}(x-2)^3
\end{aligned}$$

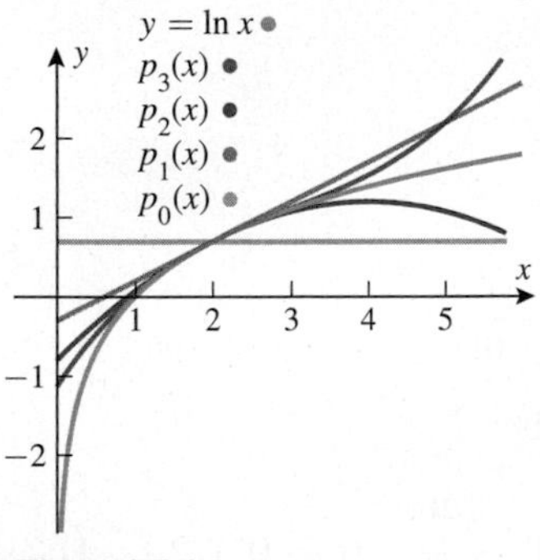

▲ Figure 9.7.6

The graph of $\ln x$ (in blue) and its first four Taylor polynomials about $x = 2$ are shown in Figure 9.7.6. As expected, these polynomials produce their best approximations of $\ln x$ near 2. ◀

**Brook Taylor (1685–1731)** English mathematician. Taylor was born of well-to-do parents. Musicians and artists were entertained frequently in the Taylor home, which undoubtedly had a lasting influence on him. In later years, Taylor published a definitive work on the mathematical theory of perspective and obtained major mathematical results about the vibrations of strings. There also exists an unpublished work, *On Musick*, that was intended to be part of a joint paper with Isaac Newton. Taylor's life was scarred with unhappiness, illness, and tragedy. Because his first wife was not rich enough to suit his father, the two men argued bitterly and parted ways. Subsequently, his wife died in childbirth. Then, after he remarried, his second wife also died in childbirth, though his daughter survived. Taylor's most productive period was from 1714 to 1719, during which time he wrote on a wide range of subjects—magnetism, capillary action, thermometers, perspective, and calculus. In his final years, Taylor devoted his writing efforts to religion and philosophy. According to Taylor, the results that bear his name were motivated by coffeehouse conversations about works of Newton on planetary motion and works of Halley ("Halley's comet") on roots of polynomials. Unfortunately, Taylor's writing style was so terse and hard to understand that he never received credit for many of his innovations.

*[Image: Line engraving after R. Earlom/Wellcome Library, London]*

## SIGMA NOTATION FOR TAYLOR AND MACLAURIN POLYNOMIALS

Frequently, we will want to express Formula (9) in sigma notation. To do this, we use the notation $f^{(k)}(x_0)$ to denote the $k$th derivative of $f$ at $x = x_0$, and we make the convention that $f^{(0)}(x_0)$ denotes $f(x_0)$. This enables us to write

$$\sum_{k=0}^{n} \frac{f^{(k)}(x_0)}{k!}(x-x_0)^k = f(x_0) + f'(x_0)(x-x_0) + \frac{f''(x_0)}{2!}(x-x_0)^2 + \cdots + \frac{f^{(n)}(x_0)}{n!}(x-x_0)^n \qquad (10)$$

In particular, we can write the $n$th Maclaurin polynomial for $f(x)$ as

$$\sum_{k=0}^{n} \frac{f^{(k)}(0)}{k!}x^k = f(0) + f'(0)x + \frac{f''(0)}{2!}x^2 + \cdots + \frac{f^{(n)}(0)}{n!}x^n \qquad (11)$$

▶ **Example 5** Find the $n$th Maclaurin polynomial for

$$\frac{1}{1-x}$$

and express it in sigma notation.

***Solution.*** Let $f(x) = 1/(1-x)$. The values of $f$ and its first $k$ derivatives at $x = 0$ are as follows:

$$\begin{aligned}
f(x) &= \frac{1}{1-x} & f(0) &= 1 = 0! \\
f'(x) &= \frac{1}{(1-x)^2} & f'(0) &= 1 = 1! \\
f''(x) &= \frac{2}{(1-x)^3} & f''(0) &= 2 = 2! \\
f'''(x) &= \frac{3\cdot 2}{(1-x)^4} & f'''(0) &= 3! \\
f^{(4)}(x) &= \frac{4\cdot 3\cdot 2}{(1-x)^5} & f^{(4)}(0) &= 4! \\
&\vdots & &\vdots \\
f^{(k)}(x) &= \frac{k!}{(1-x)^{k+1}} & f^{(k)}(0) &= k!
\end{aligned}$$

**TECHNOLOGY MASTERY**

Computer algebra systems have commands for generating Taylor polynomials of any specified degree. If you have a CAS, use it to find some of the Maclaurin and Taylor polynomials in Examples 3, 4, and 5.

Thus, substituting $f^{(k)}(0) = k!$ into Formula (11) yields the $n$th Maclaurin polynomial for $1/(1-x)$:

$$p_n(x) = \sum_{k=0}^{n} x^k = 1 + x + x^2 + \cdots + x^n \quad (n = 0, 1, 2, \ldots) \blacktriangleleft$$

▶ **Example 6** Find the $n$th Taylor polynomial for $1/x$ about $x = 1$ and express it in sigma notation.

***Solution.*** Let $f(x) = 1/x$. The computations are similar to those in Example 5. We leave it for you to show that

$$f(1) = 1, \quad f'(1) = -1, \quad f''(1) = 2!, \quad f'''(1) = -3!,$$
$$f^{(4)}(1) = 4!, \ldots, \quad f^{(k)}(1) = (-1)^k k!$$

Thus, substituting $f^{(k)}(1) = (-1)^k k!$ into Formula (10) with $x_0 = 1$ yields the $n$th Taylor polynomial for $1/x$:

$$\sum_{k=0}^{n} (-1)^k (x-1)^k = 1 - (x-1) + (x-1)^2 - (x-1)^3 + \cdots + (-1)^n (x-1)^n \blacktriangleleft$$

## THE nTH REMAINDER

It will be convenient to have a notation for the error in the approximation $f(x) \approx p_n(x)$. Accordingly, we will let $R_n(x)$ denote the difference between $f(x)$ and its $n$th Taylor polynomial; that is,

$$R_n(x) = f(x) - p_n(x) = f(x) - \sum_{k=0}^{n} \frac{f^{(k)}(x_0)}{k!}(x - x_0)^k \tag{12}$$

This can also be written as

$$f(x) = p_n(x) + R_n(x) = \sum_{k=0}^{n} \frac{f^{(k)}(x_0)}{k!}(x - x_0)^k + R_n(x) \tag{13}$$

The function $R_n(x)$ is called the ***nth remainder*** for the Taylor series of $f$, and Formula (13) is called ***Taylor's formula with remainder***.

Finding a bound for $R_n(x)$ gives an indication of the accuracy of the approximation $p_n(x) \approx f(x)$. The following theorem, which is proved in Web Appendix L, provides such a bound.

**9.7.4 THEOREM** (***The Remainder Estimation Theorem***) *If the function $f$ can be differentiated $n+1$ times on an interval containing the number $x_0$, and if $M$ is an upper bound for $|f^{(n+1)}(x)|$ on the interval, that is, $|f^{(n+1)}(x)| \le M$ for all $x$ in the interval, then*

$$|R_n(x)| \le \frac{M}{(n+1)!}|x - x_0|^{n+1} \tag{14}$$

*for all $x$ in the interval.*

The bound for $|R_n(x)|$ in (14) is called the ***Lagrange error bound***.

► **Example 7** Use an $n$th Maclaurin polynomial for $e^x$ to approximate $e$ to five decimal-place accuracy.

***Solution.*** We note first that the exponential function $e^x$ has derivatives of all orders for every real number $x$. From Example 2, the $n$th Maclaurin polynomial for $e^x$ is

$$\sum_{k=0}^{n} \frac{x^k}{k!} = 1 + x + \frac{x^2}{2!} + \cdots + \frac{x^n}{n!}$$

from which we have

$$e = e^1 \approx \sum_{k=0}^{n} \frac{1^k}{k!} = 1 + 1 + \frac{1}{2!} + \cdots + \frac{1}{n!}$$

Thus, our problem is to determine how many terms to include in a Maclaurin polynomial for $e^x$ to achieve five decimal-place accuracy; that is, we want to choose $n$ so that the absolute value of the $n$th remainder at $x = 1$ satisfies

$$|R_n(1)| \le 0.000005$$

To determine $n$ we use the Remainder Estimation Theorem with $f(x) = e^x, x = 1, x_0 = 0$, and the interval $[0, 1]$. In this case it follows from (14) that

$$|R_n(1)| \le \frac{M}{(n+1)!} \cdot |1 - 0|^{n+1} = \frac{M}{(n+1)!} \tag{15}$$

where $M$ is an upper bound on the value of $f^{(n+1)}(x) = e^x$ for $x$ in the interval $[0, 1]$. However, $e^x$ is an increasing function, so its maximum value on the interval $[0, 1]$ occurs at $x = 1$; that is, $e^x \le e$ on this interval. Thus, we can take $M = e$ in (15) to obtain

$$|R_n(1)| \le \frac{e}{(n+1)!} \tag{16}$$

Unfortunately, this inequality is not very useful because it involves $e$, which is the very quantity we are trying to approximate. However, if we accept that $e < 3$, then we can replace (16) with the following less precise, but more easily applied, inequality:

$$|R_n(1)| \le \frac{3}{(n+1)!}$$

Thus, we can achieve five decimal-place accuracy by choosing $n$ so that

$$\frac{3}{(n+1)!} \le 0.000005 \quad \text{or} \quad (n+1)! \ge 600{,}000$$

Since $9! = 362{,}880$ and $10! = 3{,}628{,}800$, the smallest value of $n$ that meets this criterion is $n = 9$. Thus, to five decimal-place accuracy

$$e \approx 1 + 1 + \frac{1}{2!} + \frac{1}{3!} + \frac{1}{4!} + \frac{1}{5!} + \frac{1}{6!} + \frac{1}{7!} + \frac{1}{8!} + \frac{1}{9!} \approx 2.71828$$

As a check, a calculator's 12-digit representation of $e$ is $e \approx 2.71828182846$, which agrees with the preceding approximation when rounded to five decimal places. ◀

► **Example 8** Use the Remainder Estimation Theorem to find an interval containing $x = 0$ throughout which $f(x) = \cos x$ can be approximated by $p(x) = 1 - (x^2/2!)$ to three decimal-place accuracy.

***Solution.*** We note first that $f(x) = \cos x$ has derivatives of all orders for every real number $x$, so the first hypothesis of the Remainder Estimation Theorem is satisfied over any interval that we choose. The given polynomial $p(x)$ is both the second and the third Maclaurin polynomial for $\cos x$; we will choose the degree $n$ of the polynomial to be as large as possible, so we will take $n = 3$. Our problem is to determine an interval on which the absolute value of the third remainder at $x$ satisfies

$$|R_3(x)| \le 0.0005$$

We will use the Remainder Estimation Theorem with $f(x) = \cos x$, $n = 3$, and $x_0 = 0$. It follows from (14) that

$$|R_3(x)| \le \frac{M}{(3+1)!}|x - 0|^{3+1} = \frac{M|x|^4}{24} \tag{17}$$

where $M$ is an upper bound for $|f^{(4)}(x)| = |\cos x|$. Since $|\cos x| \le 1$ for every real number $x$, we can take $M = 1$ in (17) to obtain

$$|R_3(x)| \le \frac{|x|^4}{24} \tag{18}$$

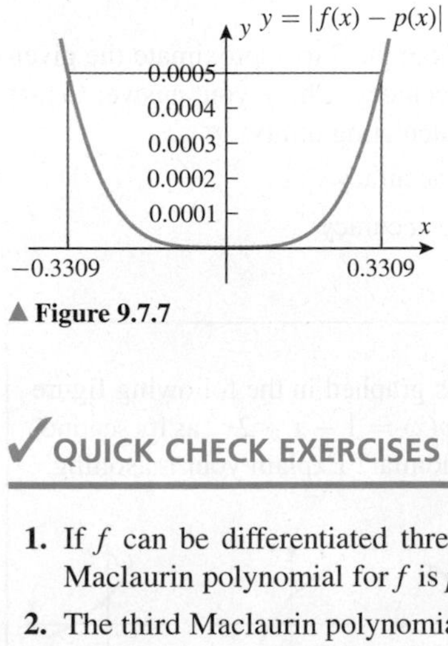


▲ **Figure 9.7.7**

Thus we can achieve three decimal-place accuracy by choosing values of $x$ for which

$$\frac{|x|^4}{24} \le 0.0005 \quad \text{or} \quad |x| \le 0.3309$$

so the interval $[-0.3309, 0.3309]$ is one option. We can check this answer by graphing $|f(x) - p(x)|$ over the interval $[-0.3309, 0.3309]$ (Figure 9.7.7). ◀

## ✓ QUICK CHECK EXERCISES 9.7 *(See page 573 for answers.)*

**1.** If $f$ can be differentiated three times at 0, then the third Maclaurin polynomial for $f$ is $p_3(x) =$ ________.

**2.** The third Maclaurin polynomial for $f(x) = e^{2x}$ is

$$p_3(x) = \_\_\_\_ + \_\_\_\_\, x + \_\_\_\_\, x^2 + \_\_\_\_\, x^3$$

**3.** If $f(2) = 3$, $f'(2) = -4$, and $f''(2) = 10$, then the second Taylor polynomial for $f$ about $x = 2$ is $p_2(x) =$ ________.

**4.** The third Taylor polynomial for $f(x) = x^5$ about $x = -1$ is

$$p_3(x) = \_\_\_\_ + \_\_\_\_\,(x+1) + \_\_\_\_\,(x+1)^2 + \_\_\_\_\,(x+1)^3$$

5. (a) If a function $f$ has $n$th Taylor polynomial $p_n(x)$ about $x = x_0$, then the $n$th remainder $R_n(x)$ is defined by $R_n(x) =$ ______.

(b) Suppose that a function $f$ can be differentiated five times on an interval containing the number $x_0 = 2$ andthat $|f^{(5)}(x)| \le 20$ for all $x$ in the interval. Then the fourth remainder satisfies $|R_4(x)| \le$ ______ for all $x$ in the interval.

## EXERCISE SET 9.7 Graphing Utility

**1–2** In each part, find the local quadratic approximation of $f$ at $x = x_0$, and use that approximation to find the local linear approximation of $f$ at $x_0$. Use a graphing utility to graph $f$ and the two approximations on the same screen. ■

1. (a) $f(x) = e^{-x}$; $x_0 = 0$ (b) $f(x) = \cos x$; $x_0 = 0$
2. (a) $f(x) = \sin x$; $x_0 = \pi/2$ (b) $f(x) = \sqrt{x}$; $x_0 = 1$
3. (a) Find the local quadratic approximation of $\sqrt{x}$ at $x_0 = 1$.
   (b) Use the result obtained in part (a) to approximate $\sqrt{1.1}$, and compare your approximation to that produced directly by your calculating utility. [*Note:* See Example 1 of Section 3.5.]
4. (a) Find the local quadratic approximation of $\cos x$ at $x_0 = 0$.
   (b) Use the result obtained in part (a) to approximate $\cos 2°$, and compare the approximation to that produced directly by your calculating utility.
5. Use an appropriate local quadratic approximation to approximate $\tan 61°$, and compare the result to that produced directly by your calculating utility.
6. Use an appropriate local quadratic approximation to approximate $\sqrt{36.03}$, and compare the result to that produced directly by your calculating utility.

**7–16** Find the Maclaurin polynomials of orders $n = 0, 1, 2, 3,$ and 4, and then find the $n$th Maclaurin polynomials for the function in sigma notation. ■

7. $e^{-x}$ 8. $e^{ax}$ 9. $\cos \pi x$
10. $\sin \pi x$ 11. $\ln(1 + x)$ 12. $\dfrac{1}{1+x}$
13. $\cosh x$ 14. $\sinh x$ 15. $x \sin x$
16. $xe^x$

**17–24** Find the Taylor polynomials of orders $n = 0, 1, 2, 3,$ and 4 about $x = x_0$, and then find the $n$th Taylor polynomial for the function in sigma notation. ■

17. $e^x$; $x_0 = 1$ 18. $e^{-x}$; $x_0 = \ln 2$
19. $\dfrac{1}{x}$; $x_0 = -1$ 20. $\dfrac{1}{x+2}$; $x_0 = 3$
21. $\sin \pi x$; $x_0 = \dfrac{1}{2}$ 22. $\cos x$; $x_0 = \dfrac{\pi}{2}$
23. $\ln x$; $x_0 = 1$ 24. $\ln x$; $x_0 = e$
25. (a) Find the third Maclaurin polynomial for
$$f(x) = 1 + 2x - x^2 + x^3$$
   (b) Find the third Taylor polynomial about $x = 1$ for
$$f(x) = 1 + 2(x-1) - (x-1)^2 + (x-1)^3$$
26. (a) Find the $n$th Maclaurin polynomial for
$$f(x) = c_0 + c_1x + c_2x^2 + \cdots + c_nx^n$$
   (b) Find the $n$th Taylor polynomial about $x = 1$ for
$$f(x) = c_0 + c_1(x-1) + c_2(x-1)^2 + \cdots + c_n(x-1)^n$$

**27–30** Find the first four distinct Taylor polynomials about $x = x_0$, and use a graphing utility to graph the given function and the Taylor polynomials on the same screen. ■

27. $f(x) = e^{-2x}$; $x_0 = 0$ 28. $f(x) = \sin x$; $x_0 = \pi/2$
29. $f(x) = \cos x$; $x_0 = \pi$ 30. $\ln(x + 1)$; $x_0 = 0$

**31–34 True–False** Determine whether the statement is true or false. Explain your answer. ■

31. The equation of a tangent line to a differentiable function is a first-degree Taylor polynomial for that function.
32. The graph of a function $f$ and the graph of its Maclaurin polynomial have a common $y$-intercept.
33. If $p_6(x)$ is the sixth-degree Taylor polynomial for a function $f$ about $x = x_0$, then $p_6^{(4)}(x_0) = 4!f^{(4)}(x_0)$.
34. If $p_4(x)$ is the fourth-degree Maclaurin polynomial for $e^x$, then
$$|e^2 - p_4(2)| \le \frac{9}{5!}$$

**35–36** Use the method of Example 7 to approximate the given expression to the specified accuracy. Check your answer to that produced directly by your calculating utility. ■

35. $\sqrt{e}$; four decimal-place accuracy
36. $1/e$; three decimal-place accuracy

**FOCUS ON CONCEPTS**

37. Which of the functions graphed in the following figure is most likely to have $p(x) = 1 - x + 2x^2$ as its second-order Maclaurin polynomial? Explain your reasoning.

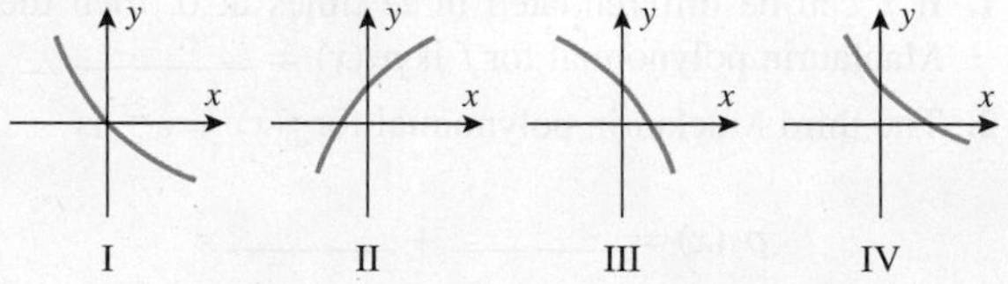

**38.** Suppose that the values of a function $f$ and its first three derivatives at $x = 1$ are

$$f(1) = 2, \quad f'(1) = -3, \quad f''(1) = 0, \quad f'''(1) = 6$$

Find as many Taylor polynomials for $f$ as you can about $x = 1$.

**39.** Let $p_1(x)$ and $p_2(x)$ be the local linear and local quadratic approximations of $f(x) = e^{\sin x}$ at $x = 0$.
(a) Use a graphing utility to generate the graphs of $f(x)$, $p_1(x)$, and $p_2(x)$ on the same screen for $-1 \le x \le 1$.
(b) Construct a table of values of $f(x)$, $p_1(x)$, and $p_2(x)$ for $x = -1.00, -0.75, -0.50, -0.25, 0, 0.25, 0.50, 0.75, 1.00$. Round the values to three decimal places.
(c) Generate the graph of $|f(x) - p_1(x)|$, and use the graph to determine an interval on which $p_1(x)$ approximates $f(x)$ with an error of at most $\pm 0.01$. [*Suggestion:* Review the discussion relating to Figure 3.5.4.]
(d) Generate the graph of $|f(x) - p_2(x)|$, and use the graph to determine an interval on which $p_2(x)$ approximates $f(x)$ with an error of at most $\pm 0.01$.

**40.** (a) The accompanying figure shows a sector of radius $r$ and central angle $2\alpha$. Assuming that the angle $\alpha$ is small, use the local quadratic approximation of $\cos\alpha$ at $\alpha = 0$ to show that $x \approx r\alpha^2/2$.
(b) Assuming that the Earth is a sphere of radius 4000 mi, use the result in part (a) to approximate the maximum amount by which a 100 mi arc along the equator will diverge from its chord.

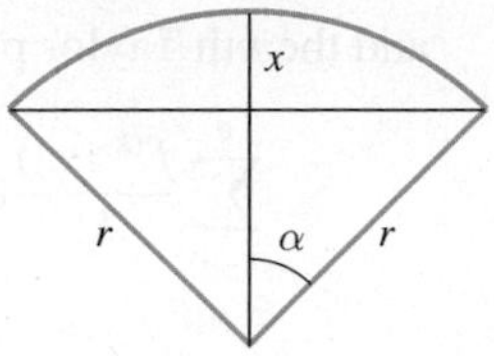


**Figure Ex-40**

**41.** (a) Find an interval $[0, b]$ over which $e^x$ can be approximated by $1 + x + (x^2/2!)$ to three decimal-place accuracy throughout the interval.
(b) Check your answer in part (a) by graphing

$$\left| e^x - \left(1 + x + \frac{x^2}{2!}\right) \right|$$

over the interval you obtained.

**42.** Show that the $n$th Taylor polynomial for $\sinh x$ about $x = \ln 4$ is

$$\sum_{k=0}^{n} \frac{16 - (-1)^k}{8k!}(x - \ln 4)^k$$

**43–46** Use the Remainder Estimation Theorem to find an interval containing $x = 0$ over which $f(x)$ can be approximated by $p(x)$ to three decimal-place accuracy throughout the interval. Check your answer by graphing $|f(x) - p(x)|$ over the interval you obtained. ■

**43.** $f(x) = \sin x;\ p(x) = x - \dfrac{x^3}{3!}$

**44.** $f(x) = \cos x;\ p(x) = 1 - \dfrac{x^2}{2!} + \dfrac{x^4}{4!}$

**45.** $f(x) = \dfrac{1}{1 + x^2};\ p(x) = 1 - x^2 + x^4$

**46.** $f(x) = \ln(1 + x);\ p(x) = x - \dfrac{x^2}{2} + \dfrac{x^3}{3}$

✓ **QUICK CHECK ANSWERS 9.7** **1.** $f(0) + f'(0)x + \dfrac{f''(0)}{2!}x^2 + \dfrac{f'''(0)}{3!}x^3$ **2.** $1; 2; 2; \frac{4}{3}$ **3.** $3 - 4(x - 2) + 5(x - 2)^2$ **4.** $-1; 5; -10; 10$ **5.** (a) $f(x) - p_n(x)$ (b) $\frac{1}{6}|x - 2|^5$

## 9.8 MACLAURIN AND TAYLOR SERIES; POWER SERIES

*Recall from the last section that the nth Taylor polynomial $p_n(x)$ at $x = x_0$ for a function $f$ was defined so its value and the values of its first n derivatives match those of $f$ at $x_0$. This being the case, it is reasonable to expect that for values of $x$ near $x_0$ the values of $p_n(x)$ will become better and better approximations of $f(x)$ as n increases, and may possibly converge to $f(x)$ as $n \to +\infty$. We will explore this idea in this section.*

### ■ MACLAURIN AND TAYLOR SERIES

In Section 9.7 we defined the $n$th Maclaurin polynomial for a function $f$ as

$$\sum_{k=0}^{n} \frac{f^{(k)}(0)}{k!}x^k = f(0) + f'(0)x + \frac{f''(0)}{2!}x^2 + \cdots + \frac{f^{(n)}(0)}{n!}x^n$$

and the $n$th Taylor polynomial for $f$ about $x = x_0$ as

$$\sum_{k=0}^{n} \frac{f^{(k)}(x_0)}{k!}(x-x_0)^k = f(x_0) + f'(x_0)(x-x_0) + \frac{f''(x_0)}{2!}(x-x_0)^2 + \cdots + \frac{f^{(n)}(x_0)}{n!}(x-x_0)^n$$

It is not a big step to extend the notions of Maclaurin and Taylor polynomials to series by not stopping the summation index at $n$. Thus, we have the following definition.

**9.8.1 DEFINITION** If $f$ has derivatives of all orders at $x_0$, then we call the series

$$\sum_{k=0}^{\infty} \frac{f^{(k)}(x_0)}{k!}(x-x_0)^k = f(x_0) + f'(x_0)(x-x_0) + \frac{f''(x_0)}{2!}(x-x_0)^2 + \cdots + \frac{f^{(k)}(x_0)}{k!}(x-x_0)^k + \cdots \quad (1)$$

the ***Taylor series for f about x = x₀***. In the special case where $x_0 = 0$, this series becomes

$$\sum_{k=0}^{\infty} \frac{f^{(k)}(0)}{k!}x^k = f(0) + f'(0)x + \frac{f''(0)}{2!}x^2 + \cdots + \frac{f^{(k)}(0)}{k!}x^k + \cdots \quad (2)$$

in which case we call it the ***Maclaurin series for f***.

Note that the $n$th Maclaurin and Taylor polynomials are the $n$th partial sums for the corresponding Maclaurin and Taylor series.

▶ **Example 1** Find the Maclaurin series for

(a) $e^x$ (b) $\sin x$ (c) $\cos x$ (d) $\dfrac{1}{1-x}$

***Solution (a).*** In Example 2 of Section 9.7 we found that the $n$th Maclaurin polynomial for $e^x$ is

$$p_n(x) = \sum_{k=0}^{n} \frac{x^k}{k!} = 1 + x + \frac{x^2}{2!} + \cdots + \frac{x^n}{n!}$$

Thus, the Maclaurin series for $e^x$ is

$$\sum_{k=0}^{\infty} \frac{x^k}{k!} = 1 + x + \frac{x^2}{2!} + \cdots + \frac{x^k}{k!} + \cdots$$

***Solution (b).*** In Example 3(a) of Section 9.7 we found that the Maclaurin polynomials for $\sin x$ are given by

$$p_{2k+1}(x) = p_{2k+2}(x) = x - \frac{x^3}{3!} + \frac{x^5}{5!} - \frac{x^7}{7!} + \cdots + (-1)^k \frac{x^{2k+1}}{(2k+1)!} \quad (k = 0, 1, 2, \ldots)$$

Thus, the Maclaurin series for $\sin x$ is

$$\sum_{k=0}^{\infty} (-1)^k \frac{x^{2k+1}}{(2k+1)!} = x - \frac{x^3}{3!} + \frac{x^5}{5!} - \frac{x^7}{7!} + \cdots + (-1)^k \frac{x^{2k+1}}{(2k+1)!} + \cdots$$

***Solution (c).*** In Example 3(b) of Section 9.7 we found that the Maclaurin polynomials for $\cos x$ are given by

$$p_{2k}(x) = p_{2k+1}(x) = 1 - \frac{x^2}{2!} + \frac{x^4}{4!} - \frac{x^6}{6!} + \cdots + (-1)^k \frac{x^{2k}}{(2k)!} \quad (k = 0, 1, 2, \ldots)$$

Thus, the Maclaurin series for $\cos x$ is

$$\sum_{k=0}^{\infty} (-1)^k \frac{x^{2k}}{(2k)!} = 1 - \frac{x^2}{2!} + \frac{x^4}{4!} - \frac{x^6}{6!} + \cdots + (-1)^k \frac{x^{2k}}{(2k)!} + \cdots$$

***Solution (d).*** In Example 5 of Section 9.7 we found that the $n$th Maclaurin polynomial for $1/(1-x)$ is

$$p_n(x) = \sum_{k=0}^{n} x^k = 1 + x + x^2 + \cdots + x^n \quad (n = 0, 1, 2, \ldots)$$

Thus, the Maclaurin series for $1/(1-x)$ is

$$\sum_{k=0}^{\infty} x^k = 1 + x + x^2 + \cdots + x^k + \cdots \quad ◀$$

▶ **Example 2** Find the Taylor series for $1/x$ about $x = 1$.

***Solution.*** In Example 6 of Section 9.7 we found that the $n$th Taylor polynomial for $1/x$ about $x = 1$ is

$$\sum_{k=0}^{n} (-1)^k (x-1)^k = 1 - (x-1) + (x-1)^2 - (x-1)^3 + \cdots + (-1)^n (x-1)^n$$

Thus, the Taylor series for $1/x$ about $x = 1$ is

$$\sum_{k=0}^{\infty} (-1)^k (x-1)^k = 1 - (x-1) + (x-1)^2 - (x-1)^3 + \cdots + (-1)^k (x-1)^k + \cdots \quad ◀$$

## POWER SERIES IN *x*

Maclaurin and Taylor series differ from the series that we have considered in Sections 9.3 to 9.6 in that their terms are not merely constants, but instead involve a variable. These are examples of *power series*, which we now define.

If $c_0, c_1, c_2, \ldots$ are constants and $x$ is a variable, then a series of the form

$$\sum_{k=0}^{\infty} c_k x^k = c_0 + c_1 x + c_2 x^2 + \cdots + c_k x^k + \cdots \tag{3}$$

is called a ***power series in x***. Some examples are

$$\sum_{k=0}^{\infty} x^k = 1 + x + x^2 + x^3 + \cdots$$

$$\sum_{k=0}^{\infty} \frac{x^k}{k!} = 1 + x + \frac{x^2}{2!} + \frac{x^3}{3!} + \cdots$$

$$\sum_{k=0}^{\infty} (-1)^k \frac{x^{2k}}{(2k)!} = 1 - \frac{x^2}{2!} + \frac{x^4}{4!} - \frac{x^6}{6!} + \cdots$$

From Example 1, these are the Maclaurin series for the functions $1/(1-x)$, $e^x$, and $\cos x$, respectively. Indeed, every Maclaurin series

$$\sum_{k=0}^{\infty} \frac{f^{(k)}(0)}{k!} x^k = f(0) + f'(0)x + \frac{f''(0)}{2!} x^2 + \cdots + \frac{f^{(k)}(0)}{k!} x^k + \cdots$$

is a power series in $x$.

## RADIUS AND INTERVAL OF CONVERGENCE

If a numerical value is substituted for $x$ in a power series $\sum c_k x^k$, then the resulting series of numbers may either converge or diverge. This leads to the problem of determining the set of $x$-values for which a given power series converges; this is called its ***convergence set***.

Observe that every power series in $x$ converges at $x = 0$, since substituting this value in (3) produces the series

$$c_0 + 0 + 0 + 0 + \cdots + 0 + \cdots$$

whose sum is $c_0$. In some cases $x = 0$ may be the only number in the convergence set; in other cases the convergence set is some finite or infinite interval containing $x = 0$. This is the content of the following theorem, whose proof will be omitted.

**9.8.2 THEOREM** *For any power series in $x$, exactly one of the following is true:*

(*a*) *The series converges only for $x = 0$.*

(*b*) *The series converges absolutely (and hence converges) for all real values of $x$.*

(*c*) *The series converges absolutely (and hence converges) for all $x$ in some finite open interval $(-R, R)$ and diverges if $x < -R$ or $x > R$. At either of the values $x = R$ or $x = -R$, the series may converge absolutely, converge conditionally, or diverge, depending on the particular series.*

This theorem states that the convergence set for a power series in $x$ is always an interval centered at $x = 0$ (possibly just the value $x = 0$ itself or possibly infinite). For this reason, the convergence set of a power series in $x$ is called the ***interval of convergence***. In the case where the convergence set is the single value $x = 0$ we say that the series has ***radius of convergence* 0**, in the case where the convergence set is $(-\infty, +\infty)$ we say that the series has ***radius of convergence* $+\infty$**, and in the case where the convergence set extends between $-R$ and $R$ we say that the series has ***radius of convergence R*** (Figure 9.8.1).

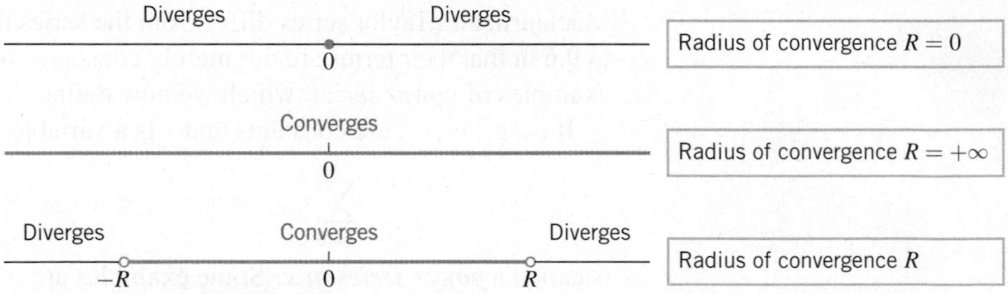


▶ **Figure 9.8.1**

## FINDING THE INTERVAL OF CONVERGENCE

The usual procedure for finding the interval of convergence of a power series is to apply the ratio test for absolute convergence (Theorem 9.6.5). The following example illustrates how this works.

▶ **Example 3** Find the interval of convergence and radius of convergence of the following power series.

$$\text{(a)} \sum_{k=0}^{\infty} x^k \qquad \text{(b)} \sum_{k=0}^{\infty} \frac{x^k}{k!} \qquad \text{(c)} \sum_{k=0}^{\infty} k!\,x^k \qquad \text{(d)} \sum_{k=0}^{\infty} \frac{(-1)^k x^k}{3^k(k+1)}$$

***Solution (a).*** Applying the ratio test for absolute convergence to the given series, we obtain

$$\rho = \lim_{k\to+\infty}\left|\frac{u_{k+1}}{u_k}\right| = \lim_{k\to+\infty}\left|\frac{x^{k+1}}{x^k}\right| = \lim_{k\to+\infty}|x| = |x|$$

so the series converges absolutely if $\rho = |x| < 1$ and diverges if $\rho = |x| > 1$. The test is inconclusive if $|x| = 1$ (i.e., if $x = 1$ or $x = -1$), which means that we will have to investigate convergence at these values separately. At these values the series becomes

$$\sum_{k=0}^{\infty} 1^k = 1 + 1 + 1 + 1 + \cdots \qquad \boxed{x = 1}$$

$$\sum_{k=0}^{\infty} (-1)^k = 1 - 1 + 1 - 1 + \cdots \qquad \boxed{x = -1}$$

both of which diverge; thus, the interval of convergence for the given power series is $(-1, 1)$, and the radius of convergence is $R = 1$.

***Solution (b).*** Applying the ratio test for absolute convergence to the given series, we obtain

$$\rho = \lim_{k\to+\infty}\left|\frac{u_{k+1}}{u_k}\right| = \lim_{k\to+\infty}\left|\frac{x^{k+1}}{(k+1)!}\cdot\frac{k!}{x^k}\right| = \lim_{k\to+\infty}\left|\frac{x}{k+1}\right| = 0$$

Since $\rho < 1$ for all $x$, the series converges absolutely for all $x$. Thus, the interval of convergence is $(-\infty, +\infty)$ and the radius of convergence is $R = +\infty$.

***Solution (c).*** If $x \neq 0$, then the ratio test for absolute convergence yields

$$\rho = \lim_{k\to+\infty}\left|\frac{u_{k+1}}{u_k}\right| = \lim_{k\to+\infty}\left|\frac{(k+1)!x^{k+1}}{k!x^k}\right| = \lim_{k\to+\infty}|(k+1)x| = +\infty$$

Therefore, the series diverges for all nonzero values of $x$. Thus, the interval of convergence is the single value $x = 0$ and the radius of convergence is $R = 0$.

***Solution (d).*** Since $|(-1)^k| = |(-1)^{k+1}| = 1$, we obtain

$$\begin{aligned}\rho = \lim_{k\to+\infty}\left|\frac{u_{k+1}}{u_k}\right| &= \lim_{k\to+\infty}\left|\frac{x^{k+1}}{3^{k+1}(k+2)}\cdot\frac{3^k(k+1)}{x^k}\right| \\ &= \lim_{k\to+\infty}\left[\frac{|x|}{3}\cdot\left(\frac{k+1}{k+2}\right)\right] \\ &= \frac{|x|}{3}\lim_{k\to+\infty}\left(\frac{1+(1/k)}{1+(2/k)}\right) = \frac{|x|}{3}\end{aligned}$$

The ratio test for absolute convergence implies that the series converges absolutely if $|x| < 3$ and diverges if $|x| > 3$. The ratio test fails to provide any information when $|x| = 3$, so the cases $x = -3$ and $x = 3$ need separate analyses. Substituting $x = -3$ in the given series yields

$$\sum_{k=0}^{\infty}\frac{(-1)^k(-3)^k}{3^k(k+1)} = \sum_{k=0}^{\infty}\frac{(-1)^k(-1)^k3^k}{3^k(k+1)} = \sum_{k=0}^{\infty}\frac{1}{k+1}$$

which is the divergent harmonic series $1 + \frac{1}{2} + \frac{1}{3} + \frac{1}{4} + \cdots$. Substituting $x = 3$ in the given series yields

$$\sum_{k=0}^{\infty}\frac{(-1)^k3^k}{3^k(k+1)} = \sum_{k=0}^{\infty}\frac{(-1)^k}{k+1} = 1 - \frac{1}{2} + \frac{1}{3} - \frac{1}{4} + \cdots$$

which is the conditionally convergent alternating harmonic series. Thus, the interval of convergence for the given series is $(-3, 3]$ and the radius of convergence is $R = 3$. ◀

## POWER SERIES IN $x - x_0$

If $x_0$ is a constant, and if $x$ is replaced by $x - x_0$ in (3), then the resulting series has the form

$$\sum_{k=0}^{\infty} c_k(x-x_0)^k = c_0 + c_1(x-x_0) + c_2(x-x_0)^2 + \cdots + c_k(x-x_0)^k + \cdots$$

This is called a ***power series in x − x₀***. Some examples are

$$\sum_{k=0}^{\infty} \frac{(x-1)^k}{k+1} = 1 + \frac{(x-1)}{2} + \frac{(x-1)^2}{3} + \frac{(x-1)^3}{4} + \cdots \qquad \boxed{x_0 = 1}$$

$$\sum_{k=0}^{\infty} \frac{(-1)^k(x+3)^k}{k!} = 1 - (x+3) + \frac{(x+3)^2}{2!} - \frac{(x+3)^3}{3!} + \cdots \qquad \boxed{x_0 = -3}$$

The first of these is a power series in $x - 1$ and the second is a power series in $x + 3$. Note that a power series in $x$ is a power series in $x - x_0$ in which $x_0 = 0$. More generally, the Taylor series

$$\sum_{k=0}^{\infty} \frac{f^{(k)}(x_0)}{k!}(x-x_0)^k$$

is a power series in $x - x_0$.

The main result on convergence of a power series in $x - x_0$ can be obtained by substituting $x - x_0$ for $x$ in Theorem 9.8.2. This leads to the following theorem.

**9.8.3 THEOREM** *For a power series $\sum c_k(x-x_0)^k$, exactly one of the following statements is true:*

(a) *The series converges only for $x = x_0$.*

(b) *The series converges absolutely (and hence converges) for all real values of x.*

(c) *The series converges absolutely (and hence converges) for all x in some finite open interval $(x_0 - R, x_0 + R)$ and diverges if $x < x_0 - R$ or $x > x_0 + R$. At either of the values $x = x_0 - R$ or $x = x_0 + R$, the series may converge absolutely, converge conditionally, or diverge, depending on the particular series.*

It follows from this theorem that the set of values for which a power series in $x - x_0$ converges is always an interval centered at $x = x_0$; we call this the ***interval of convergence*** (Figure 9.8.2). In part (*a*) of Theorem 9.8.3 the interval of convergence reduces to the single value $x = x_0$, in which case we say that the series has ***radius of convergence*** $\boldsymbol{R = 0}$; in part (*b*) the interval of convergence is infinite (the entire real line), in which case

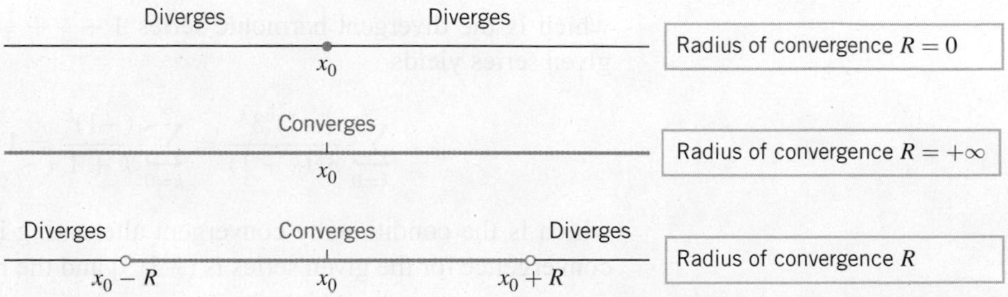


▶ **Figure 9.8.2**

we say that the series has ***radius of convergence R*** $= +\infty$; and in part ($c$) the interval extends between $x_0 - R$ and $x_0 + R$, in which case we say that the series has ***radius of convergence R***.

**► Example 4** Find the interval of convergence and radius of convergence of the series

$$\sum_{k=1}^{\infty} \frac{(x-5)^k}{k^2}$$

***Solution.*** We apply the ratio test for absolute convergence.

$$\rho = \lim_{k\to+\infty}\left|\frac{u_{k+1}}{u_k}\right| = \lim_{k\to+\infty}\left|\frac{(x-5)^{k+1}}{(k+1)^2}\cdot\frac{k^2}{(x-5)^k}\right|$$

$$= \lim_{k\to+\infty}\left[|x-5|\left(\frac{k}{k+1}\right)^2\right]$$

$$= |x-5|\lim_{k\to+\infty}\left(\frac{1}{1+(1/k)}\right)^2 = |x-5|$$

Thus, the series converges absolutely if $|x-5| < 1$, or $-1 < x-5 < 1$, or $4 < x < 6$. The series diverges if $x < 4$ or $x > 6$.

To determine the convergence behavior at the endpoints $x = 4$ and $x = 6$, we substitute these values in the given series. If $x = 6$, the series becomes

$$\sum_{k=1}^{\infty}\frac{1^k}{k^2} = \sum_{k=1}^{\infty}\frac{1}{k^2} = 1 + \frac{1}{2^2} + \frac{1}{3^2} + \frac{1}{4^2} + \cdots$$

which is a convergent $p$-series ($p = 2$). If $x = 4$, the series becomes

$$\sum_{k=1}^{\infty}\frac{(-1)^k}{k^2} = -1 + \frac{1}{2^2} - \frac{1}{3^2} + \frac{1}{4^2} - \cdots$$

Since this series converges absolutely, the interval of convergence for the given series is $[4, 6]$. The radius of convergence is $R = 1$ (Figure 9.8.3). ◄

It will always be a waste of time to test for convergence at the endpoints of the interval of convergence using the ratio test, since $\rho$ will always be 1 at those points if

$$\lim_{k\to+\infty}\left|\frac{u_{k+1}}{u_k}\right|$$

exists. Explain why this must be so.

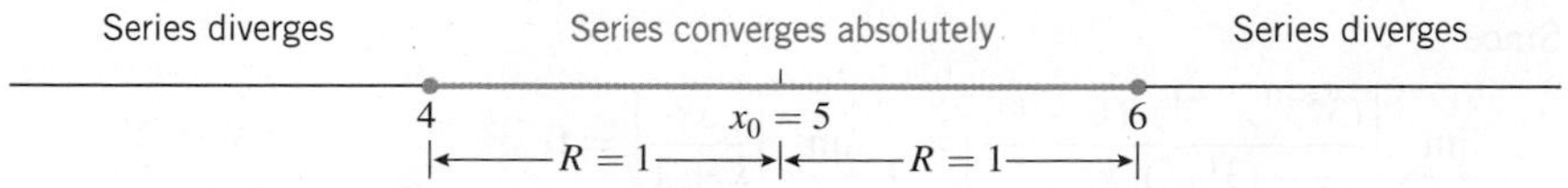


► **Figure 9.8.3**

## FUNCTIONS DEFINED BY POWER SERIES

If a function $f$ is expressed as a power series on some interval, then we say that the power series ***represents*** $f$ on that interval. For example, we saw in Example 4($a$) of Section 9.3 that

$$\frac{1}{1-x} = \sum_{k=0}^{\infty} x^k$$

if $|x| < 1$, so this power series represents the function $1/(1-x)$ on the interval $-1 < x < 1$.

Sometimes new functions actually originate as power series, and the properties of the functions are developed by working with their power series representations. For example, the functions

$$J_0(x) = \sum_{k=0}^{\infty} \frac{(-1)^k x^{2k}}{2^{2k}(k!)^2} = 1 - \frac{x^2}{2^2(1!)^2} + \frac{x^4}{2^4(2!)^2} - \frac{x^6}{2^6(3!)^2} + \cdots \quad (4)$$

and

$$J_1(x) = \sum_{k=0}^{\infty} \frac{(-1)^k x^{2k+1}}{2^{2k+1}(k!)(k+1)!} = \frac{x}{2} - \frac{x^3}{2^3(1!)(2!)} + \frac{x^5}{2^5(2!)(3!)} - \cdots \quad (5)$$

which are called ***Bessel functions*** in honor of the German mathematician and astronomer Friedrich Wilhelm Bessel (1784–1846), arise naturally in the study of planetary motion and in various problems that involve heat flow.

To find the domains of these functions, we must determine where their defining power series converge. For example, in the case of $J_0(x)$ we have

$$\rho = \lim_{k\to+\infty} \left|\frac{u_{k+1}}{u_k}\right| = \lim_{k\to+\infty} \left|\frac{x^{2(k+1)}}{2^{2(k+1)}[(k+1)!]^2} \cdot \frac{2^{2k}(k!)^2}{x^{2k}}\right|$$

$$= \lim_{k\to+\infty} \left|\frac{x^2}{4(k+1)^2}\right| = 0 < 1$$

so the series converges for all $x$; that is, the domain of $J_0(x)$ is $(-\infty, +\infty)$. We leave it as an exercise (Exercise 61) to show that the power series for $J_1(x)$ also converges for all $x$. Computer-generated graphs of $J_0(x)$ and $J_1(x)$ are shown in Figure 9.8.4.

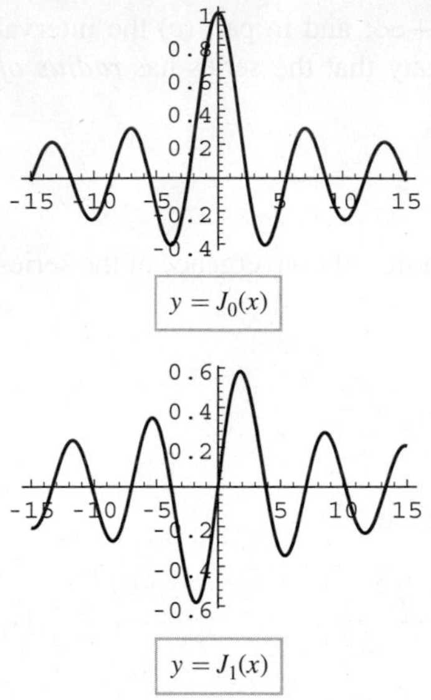


*Generated by Mathematica*

▲ **Figure 9.8.4**

**TECHNOLOGY MASTERY**

Many computer algebra systems have the Bessel functions as part of their libraries. If you have a CAS with Bessel functions, use it to generate the graphs in Figure 9.8.4.

## ✓QUICK CHECK EXERCISES 9.8 *(See page 582 for answers.)*

**1.** If $f$ has derivatives of all orders at $x_0$, then the Taylor series for $f$ about $x = x_0$ is defined to be

$$\sum_{k=0}^{\infty} \underline{\qquad\qquad}$$

**2.** Since

$$\lim_{k\to+\infty} \left|\frac{2^{k+1}x^{k+1}}{2^k x^k}\right| = 2|x|$$

the radius of convergence for the infinite series $\sum_{k=0}^{\infty} 2^k x^k$ is ________.

**3.** Since

$$\lim_{k\to+\infty} \left|\frac{(3^{k+1}x^{k+1})/(k+1)!}{(3^k x^k)/k!}\right| = \lim_{k\to+\infty} \left|\frac{3x}{k+1}\right| = 0$$

the interval of convergence for the series $\sum_{k=0}^{\infty} (3^k/k!)x^k$ is ________.

**4.** (a) Since

$$\lim_{k\to+\infty} \left|\frac{(x-4)^{k+1}/\sqrt{k+1}}{(x-4)^k/\sqrt{k}}\right| = \lim_{k\to+\infty} \left|\sqrt{\frac{k}{k+1}}(x-4)\right|$$

$$= |x-4|$$

the radius of convergence for the infinite series $\sum_{k=1}^{\infty} (1/\sqrt{k})(x-4)^k$ is ________.

(b) When $x = 3$,

$$\sum_{k=1}^{\infty} \frac{1}{\sqrt{k}}(x-4)^k = \sum_{k=1}^{\infty} \frac{1}{\sqrt{k}}(-1)^k$$

Does this series converge or diverge?

(c) When $x = 5$,

$$\sum_{k=1}^{\infty} \frac{1}{\sqrt{k}}(x-4)^k = \sum_{k=1}^{\infty} \frac{1}{\sqrt{k}}$$

Does this series converge or diverge?

(d) The interval of convergence for the infinite series $\sum_{k=1}^{\infty} (1/\sqrt{k})(x-4)^k$ is ________.

## EXERCISE SET 9.8 Graphing Utility C CAS

**1–10** Use sigma notation to write the Maclaurin series for the function. ■

**1.** $e^{-x}$ **2.** $e^{ax}$ **3.** $\cos \pi x$ **4.** $\sin \pi x$

**5.** $\ln(1+x)$ **6.** $\dfrac{1}{1+x}$ **7.** $\cosh x$

**8.** $\sinh x$ **9.** $x \sin x$ **10.** $xe^{x}$

**11–18** Use sigma notation to write the Taylor series about $x = x_0$ for the function. ■

**11.** $e^x;\ x_0 = 1$ **12.** $e^{-x};\ x_0 = \ln 2$

**13.** $\dfrac{1}{x};\ x_0 = -1$ **14.** $\dfrac{1}{x+2};\ x_0 = 3$

**15.** $\sin \pi x;\ x_0 = \dfrac{1}{2}$ **16.** $\cos x;\ x_0 = \dfrac{\pi}{2}$

**17.** $\ln x;\ x_0 = 1$ **18.** $\ln x;\ x_0 = e$

**19–22** Find the interval of convergence of the power series, and find a familiar function that is represented by the power series on that interval. ■

**19.** $1 - x + x^2 - x^3 + \cdots + (-1)^k x^k + \cdots$

**20.** $1 + x^2 + x^4 + \cdots + x^{2k} + \cdots$

**21.** $1 + (x-2) + (x-2)^2 + \cdots + (x-2)^k + \cdots$

**22.** $1 - (x+3) + (x+3)^2 - (x+3)^3$
$+ \cdots + (-1)^k(x+3)^k| \ldots$

**23.** Suppose that the function $f$ is represented by the power series

$$f(x) = 1 - \frac{x}{2} + \frac{x^2}{4} - \frac{x^3}{8} + \cdots + (-1)^k \frac{x^k}{2^k} + \cdots$$

(a) Find the domain of $f$. (b) Find $f(0)$ and $f(1)$.

**24.** Suppose that the function $f$ is represented by the power series

$$f(x) = 1 - \frac{x-5}{3} + \frac{(x-5)^2}{3^2} - \frac{(x-5)^3}{3^3} + \cdots$$

(a) Find the domain of $f$. (b) Find $f(3)$ and $f(6)$.

**25–28 True–False** Determine whether the statement is true or false. Explain your answer. ■

**25.** If a power series in $x$ converges conditionally at $x = 3$, then the series converges if $|x| < 3$ and diverges if $|x| > 3$.

**26.** The ratio test is often useful to determine convergence at the endpoints of the interval of convergence of a power series.

**27.** The Maclaurin series for a polynomial function has radius of convergence $+\infty$.

**28.** The series $\sum_{k=0}^{\infty} \dfrac{x^k}{k!}$ converges if $|x| < 1$.

**29–50** Find the radius of convergence and the interval of convergence. ■

**29.** $\sum_{k=0}^{\infty} \dfrac{x^k}{k+1}$ **30.** $\sum_{k=0}^{\infty} 3^k x^k$ **31.** $\sum_{k=0}^{\infty} \dfrac{(-1)^k x^k}{k!}$

**32.** $\sum_{k=0}^{\infty} \dfrac{k!}{2^k} x^k$ **33.** $\sum_{k=1}^{\infty} \dfrac{5^k}{k^2} x^k$ **34.** $\sum_{k=2}^{\infty} \dfrac{x^k}{\ln k}$

**35.** $\sum_{k=1}^{\infty} \dfrac{x^k}{k(k+1)}$ **36.** $\sum_{k=0}^{\infty} \dfrac{(-2)^k x^{k+1}}{k+1}$

**37.** $\sum_{k=1}^{\infty} (-1)^{k-1} \dfrac{x^k}{\sqrt{k}}$ **38.** $\sum_{k=0}^{\infty} \dfrac{(-1)^k x^{2k}}{(2k)!}$

**39.** $\sum_{k=0}^{\infty} \dfrac{3^k}{k!} x^k$ **40.** $\sum_{k=2}^{\infty} (-1)^{k+1} \dfrac{x^k}{k(\ln k)^2}$

**41.** $\sum_{k=0}^{\infty} \dfrac{x^k}{1+k^2}$ **42.** $\sum_{k=0}^{\infty} (-1)^k \dfrac{x^{2k+1}}{(2k+1)!}$

**43.** $\sum_{k=0}^{\infty} \left(\dfrac{3}{4}\right)^k (x+5)^k$ **44.** $\sum_{k=0}^{\infty} \dfrac{(x-3)^k}{2^k}$

**45.** $\sum_{k=1}^{\infty} (-1)^{k+1} \dfrac{(x+1)^k}{k}$ **46.** $\sum_{k=0}^{\infty} (-1)^k \dfrac{(x-4)^k}{(k+1)^2}$

**47.** $\sum_{k=1}^{\infty} (-1)^k \dfrac{(x+1)^{2k+1}}{k^2+4}$ **48.** $\sum_{k=1}^{\infty} \dfrac{(2k+1)!}{k^3} (x-2)^k$

**49.** $\sum_{k=0}^{\infty} \dfrac{\pi^k (x-1)^{2k}}{(2k+1)!}$ **50.** $\sum_{k=0}^{\infty} \dfrac{(2x-3)^k}{4^{2k}}$

**51.** Use the root test to find the interval of convergence of

$$\sum_{k=2}^{\infty} \frac{x^k}{(\ln k)^k}$$

**52.** Find the domain of the function

$$f(x) = \sum_{k=1}^{\infty} \frac{1 \cdot 3 \cdot 5 \cdots (2k-1)}{(2k-2)!} x^k$$

**53.** Show that the series

$$1 - \frac{x}{2!} + \frac{x^2}{4!} - \frac{x^3}{6!} + \cdots$$

is the Maclaurin series for the function

$$f(x) = \begin{cases} \cos \sqrt{x}, & x \geq 0 \\ \cosh \sqrt{-x}, & x < 0 \end{cases}$$

[*Hint:* Use the Maclaurin series for $\cos x$ and $\cosh x$ to obtain series for $\cos \sqrt{x}$, where $x \geq 0$, and $\cosh \sqrt{-x}$, where $x \leq 0$.]

**FOCUS ON CONCEPTS**

**54.** If a function $f$ is represented by a power series on an interval, then the graphs of the partial sums can be used as approximations to the graph of $f$.

(a) Use a graphing utility to generate the graph of $1/(1-x)$ together with the graphs of the first four partial sums of its Maclaurin series over the interval $(-1, 1)$.

*(cont.)*

(b) In general terms, where are the graphs of the partial sums the most accurate?

55. Prove:
(a) If $f$ is an even function, then all odd powers of $x$ in its Maclaurin series have coefficient 0.
(b) If $f$ is an odd function, then all even powers of $x$ in its Maclaurin series have coefficient 0.

56. Suppose that the power series $\sum c_k(x-x_0)^k$ has radius of convergence $R$ and $p$ is a nonzero constant. What can you say about the radius of convergence of the power series $\sum pc_k(x-x_0)^k$? Explain your reasoning. [*Hint:* See Theorem 9.4.3.]

57. Suppose that the power series $\sum c_k(x-x_0)^k$ has a finite radius of convergence $R$, and the power series $\sum d_k(x-x_0)^k$ has a radius of convergence of $+\infty$. What can you say about the radius of convergence of $\sum(c_k+d_k)(x-x_0)^k$? Explain your reasoning.

58. Suppose that the power series $\sum c_k(x-x_0)^k$ has a finite radius of convergence $R_1$ and the power series $\sum d_k(x-x_0)^k$ has a finite radius of convergence $R_2$. What can you say about the radius of convergence of $\sum(c_k+d_k)(x-x_0)^k$? Explain your reasoning. [*Hint:* The case $R_1=R_2$ requires special attention.]

59. Show that if $p$ is a positive integer, then the power series

$$\sum_{k=0}^{\infty}\frac{(pk)!}{(k!)^p}x^k$$

has a radius of convergence of $1/p^p$.

60. Show that if $p$ and $q$ are positive integers, then the power series

$$\sum_{k=0}^{\infty}\frac{(k+p)!}{k!(k+q)!}x^k$$

has a radius of convergence of $+\infty$.

61. Show that the power series representation of the Bessel function $J_1(x)$ converges for all $x$ [Formula (5)].

62. Approximate the values of the Bessel functions $J_0(x)$ and $J_1(x)$ at $x=1$, each to four decimal-place accuracy.

C 63. If the constant $p$ in the general $p$-series is replaced by a variable $x$ for $x>1$, then the resulting function is called the ***Riemann zeta function*** and is denoted by

$$\zeta(x)=\sum_{k=1}^{\infty}\frac{1}{k^x}$$

(a) Let $s_n$ be the $n$th partial sum of the series for $\zeta(3.7)$. Find $n$ such that $s_n$ approximates $\zeta(3.7)$ to two decimal-place accuracy, and calculate $s_n$ using this value of $n$. [*Hint:* Use the right inequality in Exercise 36(b) of Section 9.4 with $f(x)=1/x^{3.7}$.]
(b) Determine whether your CAS can evaluate the Riemann zeta function directly. If so, compare the value produced by the CAS to the value of $s_n$ obtained in part (a).

64. Prove: If $\lim_{k\to+\infty}|c_k|^{1/k}=L$, where $L\neq 0$, then $1/L$ is the radius of convergence of the power series $\sum_{k=0}^{\infty}c_kx^k$.

65. Prove: If the power series $\sum_{k=0}^{\infty}c_kx^k$ has radius of convergence $R$, then the series $\sum_{k=0}^{\infty}c_kx^{2k}$ has radius of convergence $\sqrt{R}$.

66. Prove: If the interval of convergence of the series $\sum_{k=0}^{\infty}c_k(x-x_0)^k$ is $(x_0-R, x_0+R]$, then the series converges conditionally at $x_0+R$.

67. **Writing** The sine function can be defined geometrically from the unit circle or analytically from its Maclaurin series. Discuss the advantages of each representation with regard to providing information about the sine function.

✓ **QUICK CHECK ANSWERS 9.8** 1. $\dfrac{f^{(k)}(x_0)}{k!}(x-x_0)^k$ 2. $\dfrac{1}{2}$ 3. $(-\infty,+\infty)$ 4. (a) 1 (b) converges (c) diverges (d) $(3,5)$

# 9.9 CONVERGENCE OF TAYLOR SERIES

*In this section we will investigate when a Taylor series for a function converges to that function on some interval, and we will consider how Taylor series can be used to approximate values of trigonometric, exponential, and logarithmic functions.*

## THE CONVERGENCE PROBLEM FOR TAYLOR SERIES

Recall that the $n$th Taylor polynomial for a function $f$ about $x=x_0$ has the property that its value and the values of its first $n$ derivatives match those of $f$ at $x_0$. As $n$ increases, more and more derivatives match up, so it is reasonable to hope that for values of $x$ near $x_0$ the values of the Taylor polynomials might converge to the value of $f(x)$; that is,

$$f(x)=\lim_{n\to+\infty}\sum_{k=0}^{n}\frac{f^{(k)}(x_0)}{k!}(x-x_0)^k \tag{1}$$

However, the $n$th Taylor polynomial for $f$ is the $n$th partial sum of the Taylor series for $f$, so (1) is equivalent to stating that the Taylor series for $f$ converges at $x$, and its sum is $f(x)$. Thus, we are led to consider the following problem.

Problem 9.9.1 is concerned not only with whether the Taylor series of a function $f$ converges, but also whether it converges to the function $f$ itself. Indeed, it is possible for a Taylor series of a function $f$ to converge to values different from $f(x)$ for certain values of $x$ (Exercise 14).

**9.9.1 PROBLEM** Given a function $f$ that has derivatives of all orders at $x = x_0$, determine whether there is an open interval containing $x_0$ such that $f(x)$ is the sum of its Taylor series about $x = x_0$ at each point in the interval; that is,

$$f(x) = \sum_{k=0}^{\infty} \frac{f^{(k)}(x_0)}{k!}(x - x_0)^k \tag{2}$$

for all values of $x$ in the interval.

One way to show that (1) holds is to show that

$$\lim_{n \to +\infty} \left[ f(x) - \sum_{k=0}^{n} \frac{f^{(k)}(x_0)}{k!}(x - x_0)^k \right] = 0$$

However, the difference appearing on the left side of this equation is the $n$th remainder for the Taylor series [Formula (12) of Section 9.7]. Thus, we have the following result.

**9.9.2 THEOREM** *The equality*

$$f(x) = \sum_{k=0}^{\infty} \frac{f^{(k)}(x_0)}{k!}(x - x_0)^k$$

*holds at a point $x$ if and only if* $\lim_{n \to +\infty} R_n(x) = 0$.

## ESTIMATING THE *n*TH REMAINDER

It is relatively rare that one can prove directly that $R_n(x) \to 0$ as $n \to +\infty$. Usually, this is proved indirectly by finding appropriate bounds on $|R_n(x)|$ and applying the Squeezing Theorem for Sequences. The Remainder Estimation Theorem (Theorem 9.7.4) provides a useful bound for this purpose. Recall that this theorem asserts that if $M$ is an upper bound for $|f^{(n+1)}(x)|$ on an interval containing $x_0$, then

$$|R_n(x)| \le \frac{M}{(n+1)!}|x - x_0|^{n+1} \tag{3}$$

for all $x$ in that interval.

The following example illustrates how the Remainder Estimation Theorem is applied.

▶ **Example 1** Show that the Maclaurin series for $\cos x$ converges to $\cos x$ for all $x$; that is,

$$\cos x = \sum_{k=0}^{\infty} (-1)^k \frac{x^{2k}}{(2k)!} = 1 - \frac{x^2}{2!} + \frac{x^4}{4!} - \frac{x^6}{6!} + \cdots \qquad (-\infty < x < +\infty)$$

***Solution.*** From Theorem 9.9.2 we must show that $R_n(x) \to 0$ for all $x$ as $n \to +\infty$. For this purpose let $f(x) = \cos x$, so that for all $x$ we have

$$f^{(n+1)}(x) = \pm \cos x \quad \text{or} \quad f^{(n+1)}(x) = \pm \sin x$$

In all cases we have $|f^{(n+1)}(x)| \le 1$, so we can apply (3) with $M = 1$ and $x_0 = 0$ to conclude that

$$0 \le |R_n(x)| \le \frac{|x|^{n+1}}{(n+1)!} \tag{4}$$

The method of Example 1 can be easily modified to prove that the Taylor series for $\sin x$ and $\cos x$ about any point $x = x_0$ converge to $\sin x$ and $\cos x$, respectively, for all $x$ (Exercises 21 and 22). For reference, some of the most important Maclaurin series are listed in Table 9.9.1 at the end of this section.

However, it follows from Formula (5) of Section 9.2 with $n+1$ in place of $n$ and $|x|$ in place of $x$ that

$$\lim_{n\to+\infty} \frac{|x|^{n+1}}{(n+1)!} = 0 \tag{5}$$

Using this result and the Squeezing Theorem for Sequences (Theorem 9.1.5), it follows from (4) that $|R_n(x)| \to 0$ and hence that $R_n(x) \to 0$ as $n \to +\infty$ (Theorem 9.1.6). Since this is true for all $x$, we have proved that the Maclaurin series for $\cos x$ converges to $\cos x$ for all $x$. This is illustrated in Figure 9.9.1, where we can see how successive partial sums approximate the cosine curve more and more closely. ◀

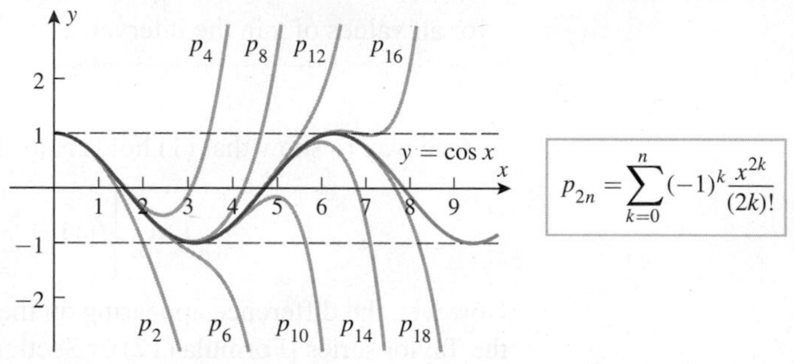


▶ **Figure 9.9.1**

## APPROXIMATING TRIGONOMETRIC FUNCTIONS

In general, to approximate the value of a function $f$ at a point $x$ using a Taylor series, there are two basic questions that must be answered:

- About what point $x_0$ should the Taylor series be expanded?
- How many terms in the series should be used to achieve the desired accuracy?

In response to the first question, $x_0$ needs to be a point at which the derivatives of $f$ can be evaluated easily, since these values are needed for the coefficients in the Taylor series. Furthermore, if the function $f$ is being evaluated at $x$, then $x_0$ should be chosen as close as possible to $x$, since Taylor series tend to converge more rapidly near $x_0$. For example, to approximate $\sin 3^\circ$ $(= \pi/60$ radians), it would be reasonable to take $x_0 = 0$, since $\pi/60$ is close to 0 and the derivatives of $\sin x$ are easy to evaluate at 0. On the other hand, to approximate $\sin 85^\circ$ $(= 17\pi/36$ radians), it would be more natural to take $x_0 = \pi/2$, since $17\pi/36$ is close to $\pi/2$ and the derivatives of $\sin x$ are easy to evaluate at $\pi/2$.

In response to the second question posed above, the number of terms required to achieve a specific accuracy needs to be determined on a problem-by-problem basis. The next example gives two methods for doing this.

▶ **Example 2** Use the Maclaurin series for $\sin x$ to approximate $\sin 3^\circ$ to five decimal-place accuracy.

***Solution.*** In the Maclaurin series

$$\sin x = \sum_{k=0}^{\infty} (-1)^k \frac{x^{2k+1}}{(2k+1)!} = x - \frac{x^3}{3!} + \frac{x^5}{5!} - \frac{x^7}{7!} + \cdots \tag{6}$$

the angle $x$ is assumed to be in radians (because the differentiation formulas for the trigonometric functions were derived with this assumption). Since $3^\circ = \pi/60$ radians, it follows from (6) that

$$\sin 3^\circ = \sin\frac{\pi}{60} = \left(\frac{\pi}{60}\right) - \frac{(\pi/60)^3}{3!} + \frac{(\pi/60)^5}{5!} - \frac{(\pi/60)^7}{7!} + \cdots \tag{7}$$

We must now determine how many terms in the series are required to achieve five decimal-place accuracy. We will consider two possible approaches, one using the Remainder Estimation Theorem (Theorem 9.7.4) and the other using the fact that (7) satisfies the hypotheses of the alternating series test (Theorem 9.6.1).

**Method 1.** (*The Remainder Estimation Theorem*)

Since we want to achieve five decimal-place accuracy, our goal is to choose $n$ so that the absolute value of the $n$th remainder at $x = \pi/60$ does not exceed $0.000005 = 5 \times 10^{-6}$; that is,

$$\left| R_n\left(\frac{\pi}{60}\right) \right| \leq 0.000005 \tag{8}$$

However, if we let $f(x) = \sin x$, then $f^{(n+1)}(x)$ is either $\pm \sin x$ or $\pm \cos x$, and in either case $|f^{(n+1)}(x)| \leq 1$ for all $x$. Thus, it follows from the Remainder Estimation Theorem with $M = 1$, $x_0 = 0$, and $x = \pi/60$ that

$$\left| R_n\left(\frac{\pi}{60}\right) \right| \leq \frac{(\pi/60)^{n+1}}{(n+1)!}$$

Thus, we can satisfy (8) by choosing $n$ so that

$$\frac{(\pi/60)^{n+1}}{(n+1)!} \leq 0.000005$$

With the help of a calculating utility you can verify that the smallest value of $n$ that meets this criterion is $n = 3$. Thus, to achieve five decimal-place accuracy we need only keep terms up to the third power in (7). This yields

$$\sin 3^\circ \approx \left(\frac{\pi}{60}\right) - \frac{(\pi/60)^3}{3!} \approx 0.05234 \tag{9}$$

(verify). As a check, a calculator gives $\sin 3^\circ \approx 0.05233595624$, which agrees with (9) when rounded to five decimal places.

**Method 2.** (*The Alternating Series Test*)

We leave it for you to check that (7) satisfies the hypotheses of the alternating series test (Theorem 9.6.1).

Let $s_n$ denote the sum of the terms in (7) up to and including the $n$th power of $\pi/60$. Since the exponents in the series are odd integers, the integer $n$ must be odd, and the exponent of the first term *not* included in the sum $s_n$ must be $n + 2$. Thus, it follows from part (*b*) of Theorem 9.6.2 that

$$|\sin 3^\circ - s_n| < \frac{(\pi/60)^{n+2}}{(n+2)!}$$

This means that for five decimal-place accuracy we must look for the first positive odd integer $n$ such that

$$\frac{(\pi/60)^{n+2}}{(n+2)!} \leq 0.000005$$

With the help of a calculating utility you can verify that the smallest value of $n$ that meets this criterion is $n = 3$. This agrees with the result obtained above using the Remainder Estimation Theorem and hence leads to approximation (9) as before. ◄

## ROUNDOFF AND TRUNCATION ERROR

There are two types of errors that occur when computing with series. The first, called ***truncation error***, is the error that results when a series is approximated by a partial sum; and the second, called ***roundoff error***, is the error that arises from approximations in numerical computations. For example, in our derivation of (9) we took $n = 3$ to keep the truncation error below 0.000005. However, to evaluate the partial sum we had to approximate $\pi$, thereby introducing roundoff error. Had we not exercised some care in choosing this approximation, the roundoff error could easily have degraded the final result.

Methods for estimating and controlling roundoff error are studied in a branch of mathematics called ***numerical analysis***. However, as a rule of thumb, to achieve $n$ decimal-place accuracy in a final result, all intermediate calculations must be accurate to at least $n+1$ decimal places. Thus, in (9) at least six decimal-place accuracy in $\pi$ is required to achieve the five decimal-place accuracy in the final numerical result. As a practical matter, a good working procedure is to perform all intermediate computations with the maximum number of digits that your calculating utility can handle and then round at the end.

## APPROXIMATING EXPONENTIAL FUNCTIONS

▶ **Example 3** Show that the Maclaurin series for $e^x$ converges to $e^x$ for all $x$; that is,

$$e^x = \sum_{k=0}^{\infty} \frac{x^k}{k!} = 1 + x + \frac{x^2}{2!} + \frac{x^3}{3!} + \cdots + \frac{x^k}{k!} + \cdots \qquad (-\infty < x < +\infty)$$

***Solution.*** Let $f(x) = e^x$, so that

$$f^{(n+1)}(x) = e^x$$

We want to show that $R_n(x) \to 0$ as $n \to +\infty$ for all $x$ in the interval $-\infty < x < +\infty$. However, it will be helpful here to consider the cases $x \le 0$ and $x > 0$ separately. If $x \le 0$, then we will take the interval in the Remainder Estimation Theorem (Theorem 9.7.4) to be $[x, 0]$, and if $x > 0$, then we will take it to be $[0, x]$. Since $f^{(n+1)}(x) = e^x$ is an increasing function, it follows that if $c$ is in the interval $[x, 0]$, then

$$|f^{(n+1)}(c)| \le |f^{(n+1)}(0)| = e^0 = 1$$

and if $c$ is in the interval $[0, x]$, then

$$|f^{(n+1)}(c)| \le |f^{(n+1)}(x)| = e^x$$

Thus, we can apply Theorem 9.7.4 with $M = 1$ in the case where $x \le 0$ and with $M = e^x$ in the case where $x > 0$. This yields

$$0 \le |R_n(x)| \le \frac{|x|^{n+1}}{(n+1)!} \qquad \text{if } x \le 0$$

$$0 \le |R_n(x)| \le e^x \frac{|x|^{n+1}}{(n+1)!} \qquad \text{if } x > 0$$

Thus, in both cases it follows from (5) and the Squeezing Theorem for Sequences that $|R_n(x)| \to 0$ as $n \to +\infty$, which in turn implies that $R_n(x) \to 0$ as $n \to +\infty$. Since this is true for all $x$, we have proved that the Maclaurin series for $e^x$ converges to $e^x$ for all $x$. ◀

Since the Maclaurin series for $e^x$ converges to $e^x$ for all $x$, we can use partial sums of the Maclaurin series to approximate powers of $e$ to arbitrary precision. Recall that in Example 7 of Section 9.7 we were able to use the Remainder Estimation Theorem to determine that evaluating the ninth Maclaurin polynomial for $e^x$ at $x = 1$ yields an approximation for $e$ with five decimal-place accuracy:

$$e \approx 1 + 1 + \frac{1}{2!} + \frac{1}{3!} + \frac{1}{4!} + \frac{1}{5!} + \frac{1}{6!} + \frac{1}{7!} + \frac{1}{8!} + \frac{1}{9!} \approx 2.71828$$

## APPROXIMATING LOGARITHMS

The Maclaurin series

$$\ln(1+x) = x - \frac{x^2}{2} + \frac{x^3}{3} - \frac{x^4}{4} + \cdots \qquad (-1 < x \le 1) \tag{10}$$

is the starting point for the approximation of natural logarithms. Unfortunately, the usefulness of this series is limited because of its slow convergence and the restriction $-1 < x \le 1$. However, if we replace $x$ by $-x$ in this series, we obtain

$$\ln(1-x) = -x - \frac{x^2}{2} - \frac{x^3}{3} - \frac{x^4}{4} - \cdots \qquad (-1 \le x < 1) \tag{11}$$

and on subtracting (11) from (10) we obtain

$$\ln\left(\frac{1+x}{1-x}\right) = 2\left(x + \frac{x^3}{3} + \frac{x^5}{5} + \frac{x^7}{7} + \cdots\right) \qquad (-1 < x < 1) \tag{12}$$

In Example 2 of Section 9.6, we stated without proof that

$$\ln 2 = 1 - \frac{1}{2} + \frac{1}{3} - \frac{1}{4} + \frac{1}{5} - \cdots$$

This result can be obtained by letting $x = 1$ in (10), but as indicated in the text discussion, this series converges too slowly to be of practical use.

Series (12), first obtained by James Gregory in 1668, can be used to compute the natural logarithm of any positive number $y$ by letting

$$y = \frac{1+x}{1-x}$$

or, equivalently,

$$x = \frac{y-1}{y+1} \tag{13}$$

and noting that $-1 < x < 1$. For example, to compute $\ln 2$ we let $y = 2$ in (13), which yields $x = \frac{1}{3}$. Substituting this value in (12) gives

$$\ln 2 = 2\left[\frac{1}{3} + \frac{\left(\frac{1}{3}\right)^3}{3} + \frac{\left(\frac{1}{3}\right)^5}{5} + \frac{\left(\frac{1}{3}\right)^7}{7} + \cdots\right] \tag{14}$$

In Exercise 19 we will ask you to show that five decimal-place accuracy can be achieved using the partial sum with terms up to and including the 13th power of $\frac{1}{3}$. Thus, to five decimal-place accuracy

$$\ln 2 \approx 2\left[\frac{1}{3} + \frac{\left(\frac{1}{3}\right)^3}{3} + \frac{\left(\frac{1}{3}\right)^5}{5} + \frac{\left(\frac{1}{3}\right)^7}{7} + \cdots + \frac{\left(\frac{1}{3}\right)^{13}}{13}\right] \approx 0.69315$$

(verify). As a check, a calculator gives $\ln 2 \approx 0.69314718056$, which agrees with the preceding approximation when rounded to five decimal places.

**James Gregory (1638–1675)** Scottish mathematician and astronomer. Gregory, the son of a minister, was famous in his time as the inventor of the Gregorian reflecting telescope, so named in his honor. Although he is not generally ranked with the great mathematicians, much of his work relating to calculus was studied by Leibniz and Newton and undoubtedly influenced some of their discoveries. There is a manuscript, discovered posthumously, which shows that Gregory had anticipated Taylor series well before Taylor.

*[Image: Engraving by William Holl/Wellcome Library, London]*

## APPROXIMATING $\pi$

In the next section we will show that

$$\tan^{-1} x = x - \frac{x^3}{3} + \frac{x^5}{5} - \frac{x^7}{7} + \cdots \qquad (-1 \le x \le 1) \tag{15}$$

Letting $x = 1$, we obtain

$$\frac{\pi}{4} = \tan^{-1} 1 = 1 - \frac{1}{3} + \frac{1}{5} - \frac{1}{7} + \cdots$$

or

$$\pi = 4\left[1 - \frac{1}{3} + \frac{1}{5} - \frac{1}{7} + \cdots\right]$$

This famous series, obtained by Leibniz in 1674, converges too slowly to be of computational value. A more practical procedure for approximating $\pi$ uses the identity

$$\frac{\pi}{4} = \tan^{-1}\frac{1}{2} + \tan^{-1}\frac{1}{3} \tag{16}$$

which was derived in Exercise 40 of Section 1.7. By using this identity and series (15) to approximate $\tan^{-1}\frac{1}{2}$ and $\tan^{-1}\frac{1}{3}$, the value of $\pi$ can be approximated efficiently to any degree of accuracy.

## BINOMIAL SERIES

If $m$ is a real number, then the Maclaurin series for $(1+x)^m$ is called the ***binomial series***; it is given by

$$1+mx+\frac{m(m-1)}{2!}x^2+\frac{m(m-1)(m-2)}{3!}x^3+\cdots+\frac{m(m-1)\cdots(m-k+1)}{k!}x^k+\cdots$$

In the case where $m$ is a nonnegative integer, the function $f(x)=(1+x)^m$ is a polynomial of degree $m$, so

$$f^{(m+1)}(0)=f^{(m+2)}(0)=f^{(m+3)}(0)=\cdots=0$$

and the binomial series reduces to the familiar binomial expansion

$$(1+x)^m=1+mx+\frac{m(m-1)}{2!}x^2+\frac{m(m-1)(m-2)}{3!}x^3+\cdots+x^m$$

which is valid for $-\infty<x<+\infty$.

Let $f(x)=(1+x)^m$. Verify that

$$f(0)=1$$
$$f'(0)=m$$
$$f''(0)=m(m-1)$$
$$f'''(0)=m(m-1)(m-2)$$
$$\vdots$$
$$f^{(k)}(0)=m(m-1)\cdots(m-k+1)$$

It can be proved that if $m$ is not a nonnegative integer, then the binomial series converges to $(1+x)^m$ if $|x|<1$. Thus, for such values of $x$

$$(1+x)^m=1+mx+\frac{m(m-1)}{2!}x^2+\cdots+\frac{m(m-1)\cdots(m-k+1)}{k!}x^k+\cdots \qquad (17)$$

or in sigma notation,

$$(1+x)^m=1+\sum_{k=1}^{\infty}\frac{m(m-1)\cdots(m-k+1)}{k!}x^k \quad \text{if } |x|<1 \qquad (18)$$

► **Example 4** Find binomial series for

$$\text{(a)}\ \frac{1}{(1+x)^2} \qquad \text{(b)}\ \frac{1}{\sqrt{1+x}}$$

***Solution (a).*** Since the general term of the binomial series is complicated, you may find it helpful to write out some of the beginning terms of the series, as in Formula (17), to see developing patterns. Substituting $m=-2$ in this formula yields

$$\begin{aligned}\frac{1}{(1+x)^2}=(1+x)^{-2}&=1+(-2)x+\frac{(-2)(-3)}{2!}x^2\\&\quad+\frac{(-2)(-3)(-4)}{3!}x^3+\frac{(-2)(-3)(-4)(-5)}{4!}x^4+\cdots\\&=1-2x+\frac{3!}{2!}x^2-\frac{4!}{3!}x^3+\frac{5!}{4!}x^4-\cdots\\&=1-2x+3x^2-4x^3+5x^4-\cdots\\&=\sum_{k=0}^{\infty}(-1)^k(k+1)x^k\end{aligned}$$

***Solution (b).*** Substituting $m=-\frac{1}{2}$ in (17) yields

$$\begin{aligned}\frac{1}{\sqrt{1+x}}&=1-\frac{1}{2}x+\frac{\left(-\frac{1}{2}\right)\left(-\frac{1}{2}-1\right)}{2!}x^2+\frac{\left(-\frac{1}{2}\right)\left(-\frac{1}{2}-1\right)\left(-\frac{1}{2}-2\right)}{3!}x^3+\cdots\\&=1-\frac{1}{2}x+\frac{1\cdot 3}{2^2\cdot 2!}x^2-\frac{1\cdot 3\cdot 5}{2^3\cdot 3!}x^3+\cdots\\&=1+\sum_{k=1}^{\infty}(-1)^k\frac{1\cdot 3\cdot 5\cdots(2k-1)}{2^k k!}x^k\end{aligned}$$ ◄

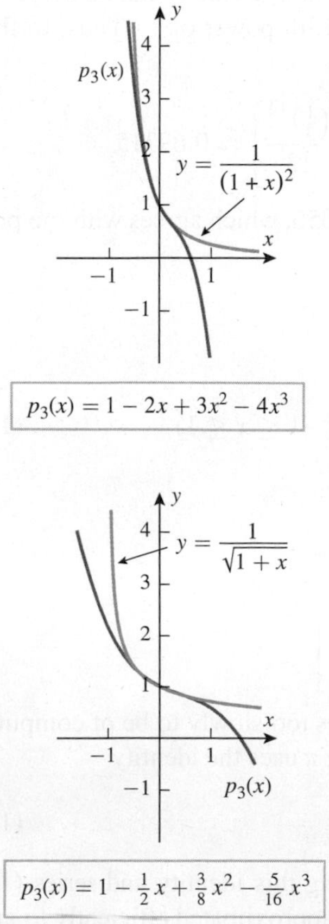

▲ **Figure 9.9.2**

Figure 9.9.2 shows the graphs of the functions in Example 4 compared to their third-degree Maclaurin polynomials.

## SOME IMPORTANT MACLAURIN SERIES

For reference, Table 9.9.1 lists the Maclaurin series for some of the most important functions, together with a specification of the intervals over which the Maclaurin series converge to those functions. Some of these results are derived in the exercises and others will be derived in the next section using some special techniques that we will develop.

**Table 9.9.1**

SOME IMPORTANT MACLAURIN SERIES

| MACLAURIN SERIES | INTERVAL OF CONVERGENCE |
|---|---|
| $\dfrac{1}{1-x}=\sum_{k=0}^{\infty} x^k = 1+x+x^2+x^3+\cdots$ | $-1<x<1$ |
| $\dfrac{1}{1+x^2}=\sum_{k=0}^{\infty} (-1)^k x^{2k} = 1-x^2+x^4-x^6+\cdots$ | $-1<x<1$ |
| $e^x=\sum_{k=0}^{\infty} \dfrac{x^k}{k!} = 1+x+\dfrac{x^2}{2!}+\dfrac{x^3}{3!}+\dfrac{x^4}{4!}+\cdots$ | $-\infty<x<+\infty$ |
| $\sin x=\sum_{k=0}^{\infty} (-1)^k \dfrac{x^{2k+1}}{(2k+1)!} = x-\dfrac{x^3}{3!}+\dfrac{x^5}{5!}-\dfrac{x^7}{7!}+\cdots$ | $-\infty<x<+\infty$ |
| $\cos x=\sum_{k=0}^{\infty} (-1)^k \dfrac{x^{2k}}{(2k)!} = 1-\dfrac{x^2}{2!}+\dfrac{x^4}{4!}-\dfrac{x^6}{6!}+\cdots$ | $-\infty<x<+\infty$ |
| $\ln(1+x)=\sum_{k=1}^{\infty} (-1)^{k+1} \dfrac{x^k}{k} = x-\dfrac{x^2}{2}+\dfrac{x^3}{3}-\dfrac{x^4}{4}+\cdots$ | $-1<x\le 1$ |
| $\tan^{-1} x=\sum_{k=0}^{\infty} (-1)^k \dfrac{x^{2k+1}}{2k+1} = x-\dfrac{x^3}{3}+\dfrac{x^5}{5}-\dfrac{x^7}{7}+\cdots$ | $-1\le x\le 1$ |
| $\sinh x=\sum_{k=0}^{\infty} \dfrac{x^{2k+1}}{(2k+1)!} = x+\dfrac{x^3}{3!}+\dfrac{x^5}{5!}+\dfrac{x^7}{7!}+\cdots$ | $-\infty<x<+\infty$ |
| $\cosh x=\sum_{k=0}^{\infty} \dfrac{x^{2k}}{(2k)!} = 1+\dfrac{x^2}{2!}+\dfrac{x^4}{4!}+\dfrac{x^6}{6!}+\cdots$ | $-\infty<x<+\infty$ |
| $(1+x)^m = 1+\sum_{k=1}^{\infty} \dfrac{m(m-1)\cdots(m-k+1)}{k!}x^k$ | $-1<x<1$* $(m\neq 0,1,2,\ldots)$ |

*The behavior at the endpoints depends on $m$: For $m>0$ the series converges absolutely at both endpoints; for $m\le -1$ the series diverges at both endpoints; and for $-1<m<0$ the series converges conditionally at $x=1$ and diverges at $x=-1$.

## ✓ QUICK CHECK EXERCISES 9.9

(See page 591 for answers.)

1. $\cos x = \sum_{k=0}^{\infty}$ ________

2. $e^x = \sum_{k=0}^{\infty}$ ________

3. $\ln(1+x) = \sum_{k=1}^{\infty}$ ________ for $x$ in the interval ________.

4. If $m$ is a real number but not a nonnegative integer, the *binomial series*
$$1+\sum_{k=1}^{\infty} \text{________}$$
converges to $(1+x)^m$ if $|x| <$ ________.

## EXERCISE SET 9.9

Graphing Utility   C CAS

1. Use the Remainder Estimation Theorem and the method of Example 1 to prove that the Taylor series for $\sin x$ about $x=\pi/4$ converges to $\sin x$ for all $x$.

2. Use the Remainder Estimation Theorem and the method of Example 3 to prove that the Taylor series for $e^x$ about $x=1$ converges to $e^x$ for all $x$.

**3–10** Approximate the specified function value as indicated and check your work by comparing your answer to the function value produced directly by your calculating utility. ■

**3.** Approximate $\sin 4^\circ$ to five decimal-place accuracy using both of the methods given in Example 2.

**4.** Approximate $\cos 3^\circ$ to three decimal-place accuracy using both of the methods given in Example 2.

**5.** Approximate $\cos 0.1$ to five decimal-place accuracy using the Maclaurin series for $\cos x$.

**6.** Approximate $\tan^{-1} 0.1$ to three decimal-place accuracy using the Maclaurin series for $\tan^{-1} x$.

**7.** Approximate $\sin 85^\circ$ to four decimal-place accuracy using an appropriate Taylor series.

**8.** Approximate $\cos(-175^\circ)$ to four decimal-place accuracy using a Taylor series.

**9.** Approximate $\sinh 0.5$ to three decimal-place accuracy using the Maclaurin series for $\sinh x$.

**10.** Approximate $\cosh 0.1$ to three decimal-place accuracy using the Maclaurin series for $\cosh x$.

**11.** (a) Use Formula (12) in the text to find a series that converges to $\ln 1.25$.
(b) Approximate $\ln 1.25$ using the first two terms of the series. Round your answer to three decimal places, and compare the result to that produced directly by your calculating utility.

**12.** (a) Use Formula (12) to find a series that converges to $\ln 3$.
(b) Approximate $\ln 3$ using the first two terms of the series. Round your answer to three decimal places, and compare the result to that produced directly by your calculating utility.

**FOCUS ON CONCEPTS**

**13.** (a) Use the Maclaurin series for $\tan^{-1} x$ to approximate $\tan^{-1}\frac{1}{2}$ and $\tan^{-1}\frac{1}{3}$ to three decimal-place accuracy.
(b) Use the results in part (a) and Formula (16) to approximate $\pi$.
(c) Would you be willing to guarantee that your answer in part (b) is accurate to three decimal places? Explain your reasoning.
(d) Compare your answer in part (b) to that produced by your calculating utility.

**14.** The purpose of this exercise is to show that the Taylor series of a function $f$ may possibly converge to a value different from $f(x)$ for certain values of $x$. Let

$$f(x) = \begin{cases} e^{-1/x^2}, & x \neq 0 \\ 0, & x = 0 \end{cases}$$

(a) Use the definition of a derivative to show that $f'(0) = 0$.
(b) With some difficulty it can be shown that if $n \geq 2$, then $f^{(n)}(0) = 0$. Accepting this fact, show that the Maclaurin series of $f$ converges for all $x$ but converges to $f(x)$ only at $x = 0$.

**15.** (a) Find an upper bound on the error that can result if $\cos x$ is approximated by $1 - (x^2/2!) + (x^4/4!)$ over the interval $[-0.2, 0.2]$.
(b) Check your answer in part (a) by graphing

$$\left|\cos x - \left(1 - \frac{x^2}{2!} + \frac{x^4}{4!}\right)\right|$$

over the interval.

**16.** (a) Find an upper bound on the error that can result if $\ln(1 + x)$ is approximated by $x$ over the interval $[-0.01, 0.01]$.
(b) Check your answer in part (a) by graphing

$$|\ln(1 + x) - x|$$

over the interval.

**17.** Use Formula (17) for the binomial series to obtain the Maclaurin series for

(a) $\dfrac{1}{1+x}$ (b) $\sqrt[3]{1+x}$ (c) $\dfrac{1}{(1+x)^3}$.

**18.** If $m$ is any real number, and $k$ is a nonnegative integer, then we define the ***binomial coefficient***

$$\binom{m}{k} \text{ by the formulas } \binom{m}{0} = 1 \text{ and}$$

$$\binom{m}{k} = \frac{m(m-1)(m-2)\cdots(m-k+1)}{k!}$$

for $k \geq 1$. Express Formula (17) in the text in terms of binomial coefficients.

**19.** In this exercise we will use the Remainder Estimation Theorem to determine the number of terms that are required in Formula (14) to approximate $\ln 2$ to five decimal-place accuracy. For this purpose let

$$f(x) = \ln\frac{1+x}{1-x} = \ln(1+x) - \ln(1-x) \quad (-1 < x < 1)$$

(a) Show that

$$f^{(n+1)}(x) = n!\left[\frac{(-1)^n}{(1+x)^{n+1}} + \frac{1}{(1-x)^{n+1}}\right]$$

(b) Use the result in part (a) to show that

$$|f^{(n+1)}(x)| \leq n!\left[\frac{1}{(1+x)^{n+1}} + \frac{1}{(1-x)^{n+1}}\right]$$

(c) Since we want to achieve five decimal-place accuracy, our goal is to choose $n$ so that the absolute value of the $n$th remainder at $x = \frac{1}{3}$ does not exceed the value $0.000005 = 0.5 \times 10^{-5}$; that is, $\left|R_n\left(\frac{1}{3}\right)\right| \leq 0.000005$. Use the Remainder Estimation Theorem to show that this condition will be satisfied if $n$ is chosen so that

$$\frac{M}{(n+1)!}\left(\frac{1}{3}\right)^{n+1} \leq 0.000005$$

where $|f^{(n+1)}(x)| \leq M$ on the interval $\left[0, \frac{1}{3}\right]$.
(d) Use the result in part (b) to show that $M$ can be taken as

$$M = n!\left[1 + \frac{1}{\left(\frac{2}{3}\right)^{n+1}}\right]$$

*(cont.)*

(e) Use the results in parts (c) and (d) to show that five decimal-place accuracy will be achieved if $n$ satisfies

$$\frac{1}{n+1}\left[\left(\frac{1}{3}\right)^{n+1}+\left(\frac{1}{2}\right)^{n+1}\right] \le 0.000005$$

and then show that the smallest value of $n$ that satisfies this condition is $n = 13$.

**20.** Use Formula (12) and the method of Exercise 19 to approximate $\ln\left(\frac{5}{3}\right)$ to five decimal-place accuracy. Then check your work by comparing your answer to that produced directly by your calculating utility.

**21.** Prove: The Taylor series for $\cos x$ about any value $x = x_0$ converges to $\cos x$ for all $x$.

**22.** Prove: The Taylor series for $\sin x$ about any value $x = x_0$ converges to $\sin x$ for all $x$.

**23.** Research has shown that the proportion $p$ of the population with IQs (intelligence quotients) between $\alpha$ and $\beta$ is approximately

$$p = \frac{1}{16\sqrt{2\pi}}\int_{\alpha}^{\beta} e^{-\frac{1}{2}\left(\frac{x-100}{16}\right)^2}\,dx$$

Use the first three terms of an appropriate Maclaurin series to estimate the proportion of the population that has IQs between 100 and 110.

C **24.** (a) In 1706 the British astronomer and mathematician John Machin discovered the following formula for $\pi/4$, called ***Machin's formula***:

$$\frac{\pi}{4} = 4\tan^{-1}\frac{1}{5} - \tan^{-1}\frac{1}{239}$$

Use a CAS to approximate $\pi/4$ using Machin's formula to 25 decimal places.

(b) In 1914 the brilliant Indian mathematician Srinivasa Ramanujan (1887–1920) showed that

$$\frac{1}{\pi} = \frac{\sqrt{8}}{9801}\sum_{k=0}^{\infty}\frac{(4k)!(1103+26{,}390k)}{(k!)^4 396^{4k}}$$

Use a CAS to compute the first four partial sums in ***Ramanujan's formula***.

✓ QUICK CHECK ANSWERS 9.9 1. $(-1)^k\dfrac{x^{2k}}{(2k)!}$ 2. $\dfrac{x^k}{k!}$ 3. $(-1)^{k+1}\dfrac{x^k}{k}$; $(-1, 1]$ 4. $\dfrac{m(m-1)\cdots(m-k+1)}{k!}x^k$; 1

# 9.10 DIFFERENTIATING AND INTEGRATING POWER SERIES; MODELING WITH TAYLOR SERIES

*In this section we will discuss methods for finding power series for derivatives and integrals of functions, and we will discuss some practical methods for finding Taylor series that can be used in situations where it is difficult or impossible to find the series directly.*

## DIFFERENTIATING POWER SERIES

We begin by considering the following problem.

**9.10.1 PROBLEM** Suppose that a function $f$ is represented by a power series on an open interval. How can we use the power series to find the derivative of $f$ on that interval?

The solution to this problem can be motivated by considering the Maclaurin series for $\sin x$:

$$\sin x = x - \frac{x^3}{3!} + \frac{x^5}{5!} - \frac{x^7}{7!} + \cdots \qquad (-\infty < x < +\infty)$$

Of course, we already know that the derivative of $\sin x$ is $\cos x$; however, we are concerned here with using the Maclaurin series to deduce this. The solution is easy—all we need to do is differentiate the Maclaurin series term by term and observe that the resulting series is the Maclaurin series for $\cos x$:

$$\frac{d}{dx}\left[x - \frac{x^3}{3!} + \frac{x^5}{5!} - \frac{x^7}{7!} + \cdots\right] = 1 - 3\frac{x^2}{3!} + 5\frac{x^4}{5!} - 7\frac{x^6}{7!} + \cdots$$

$$= 1 - \frac{x^2}{2!} + \frac{x^4}{4!} - \frac{x^6}{6!} + \cdots = \cos x$$

Here is another example.

$$\frac{d}{dx}[e^x] = \frac{d}{dx}\left[1 + x + \frac{x^2}{2!} + \frac{x^3}{3!} + \frac{x^4}{4!} + \cdots\right]$$

$$= 1 + 2\frac{x}{2!} + 3\frac{x^2}{3!} + 4\frac{x^3}{4!} + \cdots = 1 + x + \frac{x^2}{2!} + \frac{x^3}{3!} + \cdots = e^x$$

The preceding computations suggest that if a function $f$ is represented by a power series on an open interval, then a power series representation of $f'$ on that interval can be obtained by differentiating the power series for $f$ term by term. This is stated more precisely in the following theorem, which we give without proof.

**9.10.2 THEOREM** (*Differentiation of Power Series*) *Suppose that a function $f$ is represented by a power series in $x - x_0$ that has a nonzero radius of convergence $R$; that is,*

$$f(x) = \sum_{k=0}^{\infty} c_k(x - x_0)^k \qquad (x_0 - R < x < x_0 + R)$$

*Then:*

(*a*) *The function $f$ is differentiable on the interval $(x_0 - R, x_0 + R)$.*

(*b*) *If the power series representation for $f$ is differentiated term by term, then the resulting series has radius of convergence $R$ and converges to $f'$ on the interval $(x_0 - R, x_0 + R)$; that is,*

$$f'(x) = \sum_{k=0}^{\infty} \frac{d}{dx}[c_k(x - x_0)^k] \qquad (x_0 - R < x < x_0 + R)$$

This theorem has an important implication about the differentiability of functions that are represented by power series. According to the theorem, the power series for $f'$ has the same radius of convergence as the power series for $f$, and this means that the theorem can be applied to $f'$ as well as $f$. However, if we do this, then we conclude that $f'$ is differentiable on the interval $(x_0 - R, x_0 + R)$, and the power series for $f''$ has the same radius of convergence as the power series for $f$ and $f'$. We can now repeat this process ad infinitum, applying the theorem successively to $f'', f''', \ldots, f^{(n)}, \ldots$ to conclude that $f$ has derivatives of all orders on the interval $(x_0 - R, x_0 + R)$. Thus, we have established the following result.

**9.10.3 THEOREM** *If a function $f$ can be represented by a power series in $x - x_0$ with a nonzero radius of convergence $R$, then $f$ has derivatives of all orders on the interval $(x_0 - R, x_0 + R)$.*

In short, it is only the most "well-behaved" functions that can be represented by power series; that is, if a function $f$ does not possess derivatives of all orders on an interval $(x_0 - R, x_0 + R)$, then it cannot be represented by a power series in $x - x_0$ on that interval.

► **Example 1** In Section 9.8, we showed that the Bessel function $J_0(x)$, represented by the power series

$$J_0(x) = \sum_{k=0}^{\infty} \frac{(-1)^k x^{2k}}{2^{2k}(k!)^2} \tag{1}$$

has radius of convergence $+\infty$ [see Formula (4) of that section and the related discussion]. Thus, $J_0(x)$ has derivatives of all orders on the interval $(-\infty, +\infty)$, and these can be obtained by differentiating the series term by term. For example, if we write (1) as

$$J_0(x) = 1 + \sum_{k=1}^{\infty} \frac{(-1)^k x^{2k}}{2^{2k}(k!)^2}$$

and differentiate term by term, we obtain

See Exercise 45 for a relationship between $J_0'(x)$ and $J_1(x)$.

$$J_0'(x) = \sum_{k=1}^{\infty} \frac{(-1)^k (2k) x^{2k-1}}{2^{2k}(k!)^2} = \sum_{k=1}^{\infty} \frac{(-1)^k x^{2k-1}}{2^{2k-1} k!(k-1)!}$$ ◄

**REMARK** The computations in this example use some techniques that are worth noting. First, when a power series is expressed in sigma notation, the formula for the general term of the series will often not be of a form that can be used for differentiating the constant term. Thus, if the series has a nonzero constant term, as here, it is usually a good idea to split it off from the summation before differentiating. Second, observe how we simplified the final formula by canceling the factor $k$ from one of the factorials in the denominator. This is a standard simplification technique.

## INTEGRATING POWER SERIES

Since the derivative of a function that is represented by a power series can be obtained by differentiating the series term by term, it should not be surprising that an antiderivative of a function represented by a power series can be obtained by integrating the series term by term. For example, we know that $\sin x$ is an antiderivative of $\cos x$. Here is how this result can be obtained by integrating the Maclaurin series for $\cos x$ term by term:

$$\begin{aligned}\int \cos x\, dx &= \int \left[1 - \frac{x^2}{2!} + \frac{x^4}{4!} - \frac{x^6}{6!} + \cdots\right] dx \\ &= \left[x - \frac{x^3}{3(2!)} + \frac{x^5}{5(4!)} - \frac{x^7}{7(6!)} + \cdots\right] + C \\ &= \left[x - \frac{x^3}{3!} + \frac{x^5}{5!} - \frac{x^7}{7!} + \cdots\right] + C = \sin x + C\end{aligned}$$

The same idea applies to definite integrals. For example, by direct integration we have

$$\int_0^1 \frac{dx}{1+x^2} = \tan^{-1} x \Big]_0^1 = \tan^{-1} 1 - \tan 0 = \frac{\pi}{4} - 0 = \frac{\pi}{4}$$

and we will show later in this section that

$$\frac{\pi}{4} = 1 - \frac{1}{3} + \frac{1}{5} - \frac{1}{7} + \cdots \tag{2}$$

Thus,

$$\int_0^1 \frac{dx}{1+x^2} = 1 - \frac{1}{3} + \frac{1}{5} - \frac{1}{7} + \cdots$$

Here is how this result can be obtained by integrating the Maclaurin series for $1/(1+x^2)$ term by term (see Table 9.9.1):

$$\begin{aligned}\int_0^1 \frac{dx}{1+x^2} &= \int_0^1 [1 - x^2 + x^4 - x^6 + \cdots]\, dx \\ &= x - \frac{x^3}{3} + \frac{x^5}{5} - \frac{x^7}{7} + \cdots \Big]_0^1 = 1 - \frac{1}{3} + \frac{1}{5} - \frac{1}{7} + \cdots\end{aligned}$$

The preceding computations are justified by the following theorem, which we give without proof.

Theorems 9.10.2 and 9.10.4 tell us how to use a power series representation of a function $f$ to produce power series representations of $f'(x)$ and $\int f(x)\,dx$ that have the same radius of convergence as $f$. However, the *intervals* of convergence for these series may not be the same because their convergence behavior may differ at the endpoints of the interval. (See Exercises 25 and 26.)

**9.10.4 THEOREM** ***(Integration of Power Series)*** *Suppose that a function $f$ is represented by a power series in $x - x_0$ that has a nonzero radius of convergence $R$; that is,*

$$f(x) = \sum_{k=0}^{\infty} c_k(x - x_0)^k \qquad (x_0 - R < x < x_0 + R)$$

*(a) If the power series representation of $f$ is integrated term by term, then the resulting series has radius of convergence $R$ and converges to an antiderivative for $f(x)$ on the interval $(x_0 - R, x_0 + R)$; that is,*

$$\int f(x)\,dx = \sum_{k=0}^{\infty}\left[\frac{c_k}{k+1}(x - x_0)^{k+1}\right] + C \qquad (x_0 - R < x < x_0 + R)$$

*(b) If $\alpha$ and $\beta$ are points in the interval $(x_0 - R, x_0 + R)$, and if the power series representation of $f$ is integrated term by term from $\alpha$ to $\beta$, then the resulting series converges absolutely on the interval $(x_0 - R, x_0 + R)$ and*

$$\int_{\alpha}^{\beta} f(x)\,dx = \sum_{k=0}^{\infty}\left[\int_{\alpha}^{\beta} c_k(x - x_0)^k\,dx\right]$$

## POWER SERIES REPRESENTATIONS MUST BE TAYLOR SERIES

For many functions it is difficult or impossible to find the derivatives that are required to obtain a Taylor series. For example, to find the Maclaurin series for $1/(1 + x^2)$ directly would require some tedious derivative computations (try it). A more practical approach is to substitute $-x^2$ for $x$ in the geometric series

$$\frac{1}{1 - x} = 1 + x + x^2 + x^3 + x^4 + \cdots \qquad (-1 < x < 1)$$

to obtain

$$\frac{1}{1 + x^2} = 1 - x^2 + x^4 - x^6 + x^8 - \cdots$$

However, there are two questions of concern with this procedure:

- Where does the power series that we obtained for $1/(1 + x^2)$ actually converge to $1/(1 + x^2)$?
- How do we know that the power series we have obtained is actually the Maclaurin series for $1/(1 + x^2)$?

The first question is easy to resolve. Since the geometric series converges to $1/(1 - x)$ if $|x| < 1$, the second series will converge to $1/(1 + x^2)$ if $|-x^2| < 1$ or $|x^2| < 1$. However, this is true if and only if $|x| < 1$, so the power series we obtained for the function $1/(1 + x^2)$ converges to this function if $-1 < x < 1$.

The second question is more difficult to answer and leads us to the following general problem.

**9.10.5 PROBLEM** Suppose that a function $f$ is represented by a power series in $x - x_0$ that has a nonzero radius of convergence. What relationship exists between the given power series and the Taylor series for $f$ about $x = x_0$?

The answer is that they are the same; and here is the theorem that proves it.

Theorem 9.10.6 tells us that no matter how we arrive at a power series representation of a function $f$, be it by substitution, by differentiation, by integration, or by some algebraic process, that series will be the Taylor series for $f$ about $x = x_0$, provided the series converges to $f$ on some open interval containing $x_0$.

**9.10.6 THEOREM** *If a function $f$ is represented by a power series in $x - x_0$ on some open interval containing $x_0$, then that power series is the Taylor series for $f$ about $x = x_0$.*

**PROOF** Suppose that

$$f(x) = c_0 + c_1(x - x_0) + c_2(x - x_0)^2 + \cdots + c_k(x - x_0)^k + \cdots$$

for all $x$ in some open interval containing $x_0$. To prove that this is the Taylor series for $f$ about $x = x_0$, we must show that

$$c_k = \frac{f^{(k)}(x_0)}{k!} \quad \text{for} \quad k = 0, 1, 2, 3, \ldots$$

However, the assumption that the series converges to $f(x)$ on an open interval containing $x_0$ ensures that it has a nonzero radius of convergence $R$; hence we can differentiate term by term in accordance with Theorem 9.10.2. Thus,

$$\begin{aligned} f(x) &= c_0 + c_1(x - x_0) + c_2(x - x_0)^2 + c_3(x - x_0)^3 + c_4(x - x_0)^4 + \cdots \\ f'(x) &= c_1 + 2c_2(x - x_0) + 3c_3(x - x_0)^2 + 4c_4(x - x_0)^3 + \cdots \\ f''(x) &= 2!c_2 + (3 \cdot 2)c_3(x - x_0) + (4 \cdot 3)c_4(x - x_0)^2 + \cdots \\ f'''(x) &= 3!c_3 + (4 \cdot 3 \cdot 2)c_4(x - x_0) + \cdots \\ &\vdots \end{aligned}$$

On substituting $x = x_0$, all the powers of $x - x_0$ drop out, leaving

$$f(x_0) = c_0, \quad f'(x_0) = c_1, \quad f''(x_0) = 2!c_2, \quad f'''(x_0) = 3!c_3, \ldots$$

from which we obtain

$$c_0 = f(x_0), \quad c_1 = f'(x_0), \quad c_2 = \frac{f''(x_0)}{2!}, \quad c_3 = \frac{f'''(x_0)}{3!}, \ldots$$

which shows that the coefficients $c_0, c_1, c_2, c_3, \ldots$ are precisely the coefficients in the Taylor series about $x_0$ for $f(x)$. ■

## SOME PRACTICAL WAYS TO FIND TAYLOR SERIES

▶ **Example 2** Find Taylor series for the given functions about the given $x_0$.

$$\text{(a) } e^{-x^2}, \quad x_0 = 0 \qquad \text{(b) } \ln x, \quad x_0 = 1 \qquad \text{(c) } \frac{1}{x}, \quad x_0 = 1$$

***Solution (a).*** The simplest way to find the Maclaurin series for $e^{-x^2}$ is to substitute $-x^2$ for $x$ in the Maclaurin series

$$e^x = 1 + x + \frac{x^2}{2!} + \frac{x^3}{3!} + \frac{x^4}{4!} + \cdots \tag{3}$$

to obtain

$$e^{-x^2} = 1 - x^2 + \frac{x^4}{2!} - \frac{x^6}{3!} + \frac{x^8}{4!} - \cdots$$

Since (3) converges for all values of $x$, so will the series for $e^{-x^2}$.

***Solution (b).*** We begin with the Maclaurin series for $\ln(1+x)$, which can be found in Table 9.9.1:

$$\ln(1+x) = x - \frac{x^2}{2} + \frac{x^3}{3} - \frac{x^4}{4} + \cdots \qquad (-1 < x \le 1)$$

Substituting $x-1$ for $x$ in this series gives

$$\ln(1+[x-1]) = \ln x = (x-1) - \frac{(x-1)^2}{2} + \frac{(x-1)^3}{3} - \frac{(x-1)^4}{4} + \cdots \qquad (4)$$

Since the original series converges when $-1 < x \le 1$, the interval of convergence for (4) will be $-1 < x - 1 \le 1$ or, equivalently, $0 < x \le 2$.

***Solution (c).*** Since $1/x$ is the derivative of $\ln x$, we can differentiate the series for $\ln x$ found in (b) to obtain

$$\begin{aligned}\frac{1}{x} &= 1 - \frac{2(x-1)}{2} + \frac{3(x-1)^2}{3} - \frac{4(x-1)^3}{4} + \cdots \\ &= 1 - (x-1) + (x-1)^2 - (x-1)^3 + \cdots \end{aligned} \qquad (5)$$

By Theorem 9.10.2, we know that the radius of convergence for (5) is the same as that for (4), which is $R = 1$. Thus the interval of convergence for (5) must be at least $0 < x < 2$. Since the behaviors of (4) and (5) may differ at the endpoints $x = 0$ and $x = 2$, those must be checked separately. When $x = 0$, (5) becomes

$$1 - (-1) + (-1)^2 - (-1)^3 + \cdots = 1 + 1 + 1 + 1 + \cdots$$

which diverges by the divergence test. Similarly, when $x = 2$, (5) becomes

$$1 - 1 + 1^2 - 1^3 + \cdots = 1 - 1 + 1 - 1 + \cdots$$

which also diverges by the divergence test. Thus the interval of convergence for (5) is $0 < x < 2$. ◀

**▶ Example 3** Find the Maclaurin series for $\tan^{-1} x$.

***Solution.*** It would be tedious to find the Maclaurin series directly. A better approach is to start with the formula

$$\int \frac{1}{1+x^2}\,dx = \tan^{-1} x + C$$

and integrate the Maclaurin series

$$\frac{1}{1+x^2} = 1 - x^2 + x^4 - x^6 + x^8 - \cdots \qquad (-1 < x < 1)$$

term by term. This yields

$$\tan^{-1} x + C = \int \frac{1}{1+x^2}\,dx = \int [1 - x^2 + x^4 - x^6 + x^8 - \cdots]\,dx$$

or

$$\tan^{-1} x = \left[x - \frac{x^3}{3} + \frac{x^5}{5} - \frac{x^7}{7} + \frac{x^9}{9} - \cdots\right] - C$$

The constant of integration can be evaluated by substituting $x = 0$ and using the condition $\tan^{-1} 0 = 0$. This gives $C = 0$, so that

$$\tan^{-1} x = x - \frac{x^3}{3} + \frac{x^5}{5} - \frac{x^7}{7} + \frac{x^9}{9} - \cdots \qquad (-1 < x < 1) \qquad (6)$$

◀

**REMARK** Observe that neither Theorem 9.10.2 nor Theorem 9.10.3 addresses what happens at the endpoints of the interval of convergence. However, it can be proved that if the Taylor series for $f$ about $x = x_0$ converges to $f(x)$ for all $x$ in the interval $(x_0 - R, x_0 + R)$, and if the Taylor series converges at the right endpoint $x_0 + R$, then the value that it converges to at that point is the limit of $f(x)$ as $x \to x_0 + R$ from the left; and if the Taylor series converges at the left endpoint $x_0 - R$, then the value that it converges to at that point is the limit of $f(x)$ as $x \to x_0 - R$ from the right.

For example, the Maclaurin series for $\tan^{-1}x$ given in (6) converges at both $x = -1$ and $x = 1$, since the hypotheses of the alternating series test (Theorem 9.6.1) are satisfied at those points. Thus, the continuity of $\tan^{-1}x$ on the interval $[-1, 1]$ implies that at $x = 1$ the Maclaurin series converges to

$$\lim_{x\to 1^-} \tan^{-1}x = \tan^{-1}1 = \frac{\pi}{4}$$

and at $x = -1$ it converges to

$$\lim_{x\to -1^+} \tan^{-1}x = \tan^{-1}(-1) = -\frac{\pi}{4}$$

This shows that the Maclaurin series for $\tan^{-1}x$ actually converges to $\tan^{-1}x$ on the closed interval $-1 \le x \le 1$. Moreover, the convergence at $x = 1$ establishes Formula (2).

## APPROXIMATING DEFINITE INTEGRALS USING TAYLOR SERIES

Taylor series provide an alternative to Simpson's rule and other numerical methods for approximating definite integrals.

▶ **Example 4** Approximate the integral

$$\int_0^1 e^{-x^2}\,dx$$

to three decimal-place accuracy by expanding the integrand in a Maclaurin series and integrating term by term.

***Solution.*** We found in Example 2(a) that the Maclaurin series for $e^{-x^2}$ is

$$e^{-x^2} = 1 - x^2 + \frac{x^4}{2!} - \frac{x^6}{3!} + \frac{x^8}{4!} - \cdots$$

Therefore,

$$\begin{aligned}\int_0^1 e^{-x^2}\,dx &= \int_0^1 \left[1 - x^2 + \frac{x^4}{2!} - \frac{x^6}{3!} + \frac{x^8}{4!} - \cdots\right] dx \\ &= \left[x - \frac{x^3}{3} + \frac{x^5}{5(2!)} - \frac{x^7}{7(3!)} + \frac{x^9}{9(4!)} - \cdots\right]_0^1 \\ &= 1 - \frac{1}{3} + \frac{1}{5\cdot 2!} - \frac{1}{7\cdot 3!} + \frac{1}{9\cdot 4!} - \cdots \\ &= \sum_{k=0}^{\infty} \frac{(-1)^k}{(2k+1)k!}\end{aligned}$$

Since this series clearly satisfies the hypotheses of the alternating series test (Theorem 9.6.1), it follows from Theorem 9.6.2 that if we approximate the integral by $s_n$ (the $n$th partial sum of the series), then

$$\left|\int_0^1 e^{-x^2}\,dx - s_n\right| < \frac{1}{[2(n+1)+1](n+1)!} = \frac{1}{(2n+3)(n+1)!}$$

Thus, for three decimal-place accuracy we must choose $n$ such that

$$\frac{1}{(2n+3)(n+1)!} \le 0.0005 = 5 \times 10^{-4}$$

With the help of a calculating utility you can show that the smallest value of $n$ that satisfies this condition is $n = 5$. Thus, the value of the integral to three decimal-place accuracy is

$$\int_0^1 e^{-x^2}\,dx \approx 1 - \frac{1}{3} + \frac{1}{5\cdot 2!} - \frac{1}{7\cdot 3!} + \frac{1}{9\cdot 4!} - \frac{1}{11\cdot 5!} \approx 0.747$$

What advantages does the method of Example 4 have over Simpson's rule? What are its disadvantages?

As a check, a calculator with a built-in numerical integration capability produced the approximation 0.746824, which agrees with our result when rounded to three decimal places. ◀

## FINDING TAYLOR SERIES BY MULTIPLICATION AND DIVISION

The following examples illustrate some algebraic techniques that are sometimes useful for finding Taylor series.

**▶ Example 5** Find the first three nonzero terms in the Maclaurin series for the function $f(x) = e^{-x^2}\tan^{-1} x$.

$$\begin{array}{r} 1 - x^2 + \frac{x^4}{2} - \cdots \\ \times\quad x - \frac{x^3}{3} + \frac{x^5}{5} - \cdots \\ \hline x - x^3 + \frac{x^5}{2} - \cdots \\ -\frac{x^3}{3} + \frac{x^5}{3} - \frac{x^7}{6} + \cdots \\ \frac{x^5}{5} - \frac{x^7}{5} + \cdots \\ \hline x - \frac{4}{3}x^3 + \frac{31}{30}x^5 - \cdots \end{array}$$

*Solution.* Using the series for $e^{-x^2}$ and $\tan^{-1} x$ obtained in Examples 2 and 3 gives

$$e^{-x^2}\tan^{-1} x = \left(1 - x^2 + \frac{x^4}{2} - \cdots\right)\left(x - \frac{x^3}{3} + \frac{x^5}{5} - \cdots\right)$$

Multiplying, as shown in the margin, we obtain

$$e^{-x^2}\tan^{-1} x = x - \frac{4}{3}x^3 + \frac{31}{30}x^5 - \cdots$$

More terms in the series can be obtained by including more terms in the factors. Moreover, one can prove that a series obtained by this method converges at each point in the intersection of the intervals of convergence of the factors (and possibly on a larger interval). Thus, we can be certain that the series we have obtained converges for all $x$ in the interval $-1 \le x \le 1$ (why?). ◀

$$\begin{array}{r|l} & x + \frac{x^3}{3} + \frac{2x^5}{15} + \cdots \\ \hline 1 - \frac{x^2}{2} + \frac{x^4}{24} - \cdots & x - \frac{x^3}{6} + \frac{x^5}{120} - \cdots \\ & x - \frac{x^3}{2} + \frac{x^5}{24} - \cdots \\ \hline & \frac{x^3}{3} - \frac{x^5}{30} + \cdots \\ & \frac{x^3}{3} - \frac{x^5}{6} + \cdots \\ \hline & \frac{2x^5}{15} + \cdots \end{array}$$

**▶ Example 6** Find the first three nonzero terms in the Maclaurin series for $\tan x$.

*Solution.* Using the first three terms in the Maclaurin series for $\sin x$ and $\cos x$, we can express $\tan x$ as

$$\tan x = \frac{\sin x}{\cos x} = \frac{x - \dfrac{x^3}{3!} + \dfrac{x^5}{5!} - \cdots}{1 - \dfrac{x^2}{2!} + \dfrac{x^4}{4!} - \cdots}$$

Dividing, as shown in the margin, we obtain

$$\tan x = x + \frac{x^3}{3} + \frac{2x^5}{15} + \cdots \quad ◀$$

**TECHNOLOGY MASTERY**

If you have a CAS, use its capability for multiplying and dividing polynomials to perform the computations in Examples 5 and 6.

## MODELING PHYSICAL LAWS WITH TAYLOR SERIES

Taylor series provide an important way of modeling physical laws. To illustrate the idea we will consider the problem of modeling the period of a simple pendulum (Figure 9.10.1). As explained in Chapter 7 Making Connections Exercise 5, the period $T$ of such a pendulum is given by

$$T = 4\sqrt{\frac{L}{g}}\int_0^{\pi/2} \frac{1}{\sqrt{1 - k^2\sin^2\phi}}\,d\phi \tag{7}$$

where

$L$ = length of the supporting rod
$g$ = acceleration due to gravity
$k = \sin(\theta_0/2)$, where $\theta_0$ is the initial angle of displacement from the vertical

The integral, which is called a ***complete elliptic integral of the first kind***, cannot be expressed in terms of elementary functions and is often approximated by numerical methods.

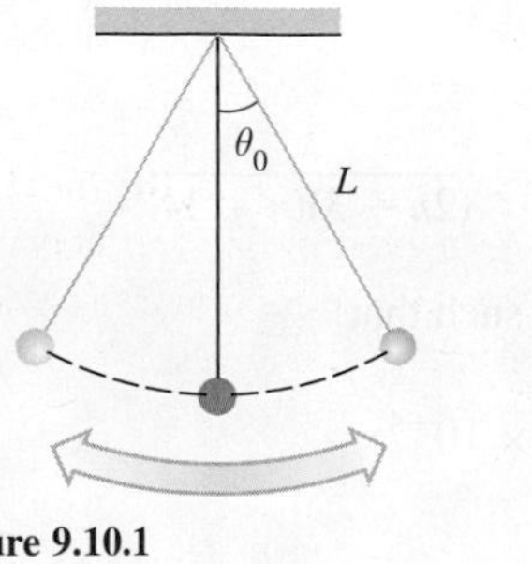


▲ **Figure 9.10.1**

Unfortunately, numerical values are so specific that they often give little insight into general physical principles. However, if we expand the integrand of (7) in a series and integrate term by term, then we can generate an infinite series that can be used to construct various mathematical models for the period $T$ that give a deeper understanding of the behavior of the pendulum.

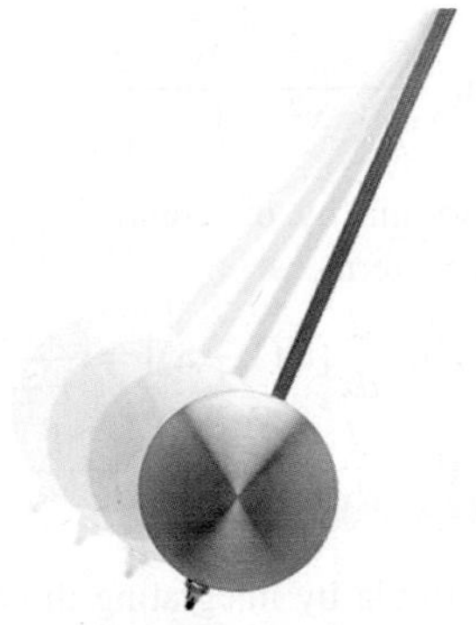

Gary S Chapman/Getty Images

*Understanding the motion of a pendulum played a critical role in the advance of accurate timekeeping with the development of the pendulum clock in the seventeenth century.*

To obtain a series for the integrand, we will substitute $-k^2 \sin^2 \phi$ for $x$ in the binomial series for $1/\sqrt{1+x}$ that we derived in Example 4(b) of Section 9.9. If we do this, then we can rewrite (7) as

$$T = 4\sqrt{\frac{L}{g}} \int_0^{\pi/2} \left[1 + \frac{1}{2}k^2 \sin^2 \phi + \frac{1 \cdot 3}{2^2 2!}k^4 \sin^4 \phi + \frac{1 \cdot 3 \cdot 5}{2^3 3!}k^6 \sin^6 \phi + \cdots\right] d\phi \tag{8}$$

If we integrate term by term, then we can produce a series that converges to the period $T$. However, one of the most important cases of pendulum motion occurs when the initial displacement is small, in which case all subsequent displacements are small, and we can assume that $k = \sin(\theta_0/2) \approx 0$. In this case we expect the convergence of the series for $T$ to be rapid, and we can approximate the sum of the series by dropping all but the constant term in (8). This yields

$$T = 2\pi\sqrt{\frac{L}{g}} \tag{9}$$

which is called the ***first-order model*** of $T$ or the model for ***small vibrations***. This model can be improved on by using more terms in the series. For example, if we use the first two terms in the series, we obtain the ***second-order model***

$$T = 2\pi\sqrt{\frac{L}{g}}\left(1 + \frac{k^2}{4}\right) \tag{10}$$

(verify).

## ✓ QUICK CHECK EXERCISES 9.10 *(See page 602 for answers.)*

1. The Maclaurin series for $e^{-x^2}$ obtained by substituting $-x^2$ for $x$ in the series
$$e^x = \sum_{k=0}^{\infty} \frac{x^k}{k!}$$
is $e^{-x^2} = \sum_{k=0}^{\infty}$ ______.

2. $$\frac{d}{dx}\left[\sum_{k=1}^{\infty} (-1)^{k+1}\frac{x^k}{k}\right] = \text{\_\_\_\_\_} + \text{\_\_\_\_\_}\,x + \text{\_\_\_\_\_}\,x^2 + \text{\_\_\_\_\_}\,x^3 + \cdots = \sum_{k=0}^{\infty} \text{\_\_\_\_\_}$$

3. $$\left(\sum_{k=0}^{\infty} \frac{x^k}{k!}\right)\left(\sum_{k=0}^{\infty} \frac{x^k}{k+1}\right) = \left(1 + x + \frac{x^2}{2!} + \cdots\right)\left(1 + \frac{x}{2} + \frac{x^2}{3} + \cdots\right) = \text{\_\_\_\_\_} + \text{\_\_\_\_\_}\,x + \text{\_\_\_\_\_}\,x^2 + \cdots$$

4. Suppose that $f(1) = 4$ and $f'(x) = \sum_{k=0}^{\infty} \frac{(-1)^k}{(k+1)!}(x-1)^k$
(a) $f''(1) =$ ______
(b) $f(x) =$ ______ + ______ $(x-1)$ + ______ $(x-1)^2$ + ______ $(x-1)^3 + \cdots$ = ______ + $\sum_{k=1}^{\infty}$ ______

## EXERCISE SET 9.10 [C] CAS

1. In each part, obtain the Maclaurin series for the function by making an appropriate substitution in the Maclaurin series for $1/(1-x)$. Include the general term in your answer, and state the radius of convergence of the series.
(a) $\dfrac{1}{1+x}$ (b) $\dfrac{1}{1-x^2}$ (c) $\dfrac{1}{1-2x}$ (d) $\dfrac{1}{2-x}$

2. In each part, obtain the Maclaurin series for the function by making an appropriate substitution in the Maclaurin series for $\ln(1+x)$. Include the general term in your answer, and state the radius of convergence of the series.
(a) $\ln(1-x)$ (b) $\ln(1+x^2)$
(c) $\ln(1+2x)$ (d) $\ln(2+x)$

3. In each part, obtain the first four nonzero terms of the Maclaurin series for the function by making an appropriate substitution in one of the binomial series obtained in Example 4 of Section 9.9.
(a) $(2+x)^{-1/2}$ (b) $(1-x^2)^{-2}$

4. (a) Use the Maclaurin series for $1/(1-x)$ to find the Maclaurin series for $1/(a-x)$, where $a \neq 0$, and state the radius of convergence of the series.
(b) Use the binomial series for $1/(1+x)^2$ obtained in Example 4 of Section 9.9 to find the first four nonzero terms in the Maclaurin series for $1/(a+x)^2$, where $a \neq 0$, and state the radius of convergence of the series.

**5–8** Find the first four nonzero terms of the Maclaurin series for the function by making an appropriate substitution in a known Maclaurin series and performing any algebraic operations that are required. State the radius of convergence of the series. ■

5. (a) $\sin 2x$ (b) $e^{-2x}$ (c) $e^{x^2}$ (d) $x^2 \cos \pi x$

6. (a) $\cos 2x$ (b) $x^2 e^x$ (c) $xe^{-x}$ (d) $\sin(x^2)$

7. (a) $\dfrac{x^2}{1+3x}$ (b) $x \sinh 2x$ (c) $x(1-x^2)^{3/2}$

8. (a) $\dfrac{x}{x-1}$ (b) $3\cosh(x^2)$ (c) $\dfrac{x}{(1+2x)^3}$

**9–10** Find the first four nonzero terms of the Maclaurin series for the function by using an appropriate trigonometric identity or property of logarithms and then substituting in a known Maclaurin series. ■

9. (a) $\sin^2 x$ (b) $\ln[(1+x^3)^{12}]$

10. (a) $\cos^2 x$ (b) $\ln\left(\dfrac{1-x}{1+x}\right)$

11. (a) Use a known Maclaurin series to find the Taylor series of $1/x$ about $x=1$ by expressing this function as
$$\frac{1}{x} = \frac{1}{1-(1-x)}$$
(b) Find the interval of convergence of the Taylor series.

12. Use the method of Exercise 11 to find the Taylor series of $1/x$ about $x = x_0$, and state the interval of convergence of the Taylor series.

**13–14** Find the first four nonzero terms of the Maclaurin series for the function by multiplying the Maclaurin series of the factors. ■

13. (a) $e^x \sin x$ (b) $\sqrt{1+x}\ln(1+x)$

14. (a) $e^{-x^2}\cos x$ (b) $(1+x^2)^{4/3}(1+x)^{1/3}$

**15–16** Find the first four nonzero terms of the Maclaurin series for the function by dividing appropriate Maclaurin series. ■

15. (a) $\sec x \left(= \dfrac{1}{\cos x}\right)$ (b) $\dfrac{\sin x}{e^x}$

16. (a) $\dfrac{\tan^{-1} x}{1+x}$ (b) $\dfrac{\ln(1+x)}{1-x}$

17. Use the Maclaurin series for $e^x$ and $e^{-x}$ to derive the Maclaurin series for $\sinh x$ and $\cosh x$. Include the general terms in your answers and state the radius of convergence of each series.

18. Use the Maclaurin series for $\sinh x$ and $\cosh x$ to obtain the first four nonzero terms in the Maclaurin series for $\tanh x$.

**19–20** Find the first five nonzero terms of the Maclaurin series for the function by using partial fractions and a known Maclaurin series. ■

19. $\dfrac{4x-2}{x^2-1}$

20. $\dfrac{x^3+x^2+2x-2}{x^2-1}$

**21–22** Confirm the derivative formula by differentiating the appropriate Maclaurin series term by term. ■

21. (a) $\dfrac{d}{dx}[\cos x] = -\sin x$ (b) $\dfrac{d}{dx}[\ln(1+x)] = \dfrac{1}{1+x}$

22. (a) $\dfrac{d}{dx}[\sinh x] = \cosh x$ (b) $\dfrac{d}{dx}[\tan^{-1} x] = \dfrac{1}{1+x^2}$

**23–24** Confirm the integration formula by integrating the appropriate Maclaurin series term by term. ■

23. (a) $\displaystyle\int e^x\,dx = e^x + C$
(b) $\displaystyle\int \sinh x\,dx = \cosh x + C$

24. (a) $\displaystyle\int \sin x\,dx = -\cos x + C$
(b) $\displaystyle\int \frac{1}{1+x}\,dx = \ln(1+x) + C$

25. Consider the series
$$\sum_{k=0}^{\infty} \frac{x^{k+1}}{(k+1)(k+2)}$$
Determine the intervals of convergence for this series and for the series obtained by differentiating this series term by term.

26. Consider the series
$$\sum_{k=1}^{\infty} \frac{(-3)^k}{k} x^k$$
Determine the intervals of convergence for this series and for the series obtained by integrating this series term by term.

27. (a) Use the Maclaurin series for $1/(1-x)$ to find the Maclaurin series for
$$f(x) = \frac{x}{1-x^2}$$
(b) Use the Maclaurin series obtained in part (a) to find $f^{(5)}(0)$ and $f^{(6)}(0)$.
(c) What can you say about the value of $f^{(n)}(0)$?

28. Let $f(x) = x^2 \cos 2x$. Use the method of Exercise 27 to find $f^{(99)}(0)$.

**29–30** The limit of an indeterminate form as $x \to x_0$ can sometimes be found by expanding the functions involved in Taylor series about $x = x_0$ and taking the limit of the series term by term. Use this method to find the limits in these exercises. ■

29. (a) $\displaystyle\lim_{x\to 0} \frac{\sin x}{x}$ (b) $\displaystyle\lim_{x\to 0} \frac{\tan^{-1} x - x}{x^3}$

30. (a) $\displaystyle\lim_{x\to 0} \frac{1-\cos x}{\sin x}$ (b) $\displaystyle\lim_{x\to 0} \frac{\ln\sqrt{1+x} - \sin 2x}{x}$

**31–34** Use Maclaurin series to approximate the integral to three decimal-place accuracy. ■

**31.** $\int_0^1 \sin(x^2)\,dx$ **32.** $\int_0^{1/2} \tan^{-1}(2x^2)\,dx$

**33.** $\int_0^{0.2} \sqrt[3]{1+x^4}\,dx$ **34.** $\int_0^{1/2} \frac{dx}{\sqrt[4]{x^2+1}}$

**FOCUS ON CONCEPTS**

**35.** (a) Find the Maclaurin series for $e^{x^4}$. What is the radius of convergence?

(b) Explain two different ways to use the Maclaurin series for $e^{x^4}$ to find a series for $x^3e^{x^4}$. Confirm that both methods produce the same series.

**36.** (a) Differentiate the Maclaurin series for $1/(1-x)$, and use the result to show that

$$\sum_{k=1}^{\infty} kx^k = \frac{x}{(1-x)^2} \quad \text{for } -1 < x < 1$$

(b) Integrate the Maclaurin series for $1/(1-x)$, and use the result to show that

$$\sum_{k=1}^{\infty} \frac{x^k}{k} = -\ln(1-x) \quad \text{for } -1 < x < 1$$

(c) Use the result in part (b) to show that

$$\sum_{k=1}^{\infty} (-1)^{k+1}\frac{x^k}{k} = \ln(1+x) \quad \text{for } -1 < x < 1$$

(d) Show that the series in part (c) converges if $x = 1$.

(e) Use the remark following Example 3 to show that

$$\sum_{k=1}^{\infty} (-1)^{k+1}\frac{x^k}{k} = \ln(1+x) \quad \text{for } -1 < x \le 1$$

**37.** Use the results in Exercise 36 to find the sum of the series.

(a) $\sum_{k=1}^{\infty} \frac{k}{3^k} = \frac{1}{3} + \frac{2}{3^2} + \frac{3}{3^3} + \frac{4}{3^4} + \cdots$

(b) $\sum_{k=1}^{\infty} \frac{1}{k(4^k)} = \frac{1}{4} + \frac{1}{2(4^2)} + \frac{1}{3(4^3)} + \frac{1}{4(4^4)} + \cdots$

**38.** Use the results in Exercise 36 to find the sum of each series.

(a) $\sum_{k=1}^{\infty} (-1)^{k+1}\frac{1}{k} = 1 - \frac{1}{2} + \frac{1}{3} - \frac{1}{4} + \cdots$

(b) $\sum_{k=1}^{\infty} \frac{(e-1)^k}{ke^k} = \frac{e-1}{e} + \frac{(e-1)^2}{2(e^2)} - \frac{(e-1)^3}{3(e^3)} + \cdots$

**39.** (a) Use the relationship

$$\int \frac{1}{\sqrt{1+x^2}}\,dx = \sinh^{-1} x + C$$

to find the first four nonzero terms in the Maclaurin series for $\sinh^{-1} x$.

(b) Express the series in sigma notation.

(c) What is the radius of convergence?

**40.** (a) Use the relationship

$$\int \frac{1}{\sqrt{1-x^2}}\,dx = \sin^{-1} x + C$$

to find the first four nonzero terms in the Maclaurin series for $\sin^{-1} x$.

(b) Express the series in sigma notation.

(c) What is the radius of convergence?

**41.** We showed by Formula (19) of Section 8.2 that if there are $y_0$ units of radioactive carbon-14 present at time $t = 0$, then the number of units present $t$ years later is

$$y(t) = y_0e^{-0.000121t}$$

(a) Express $y(t)$ as a Maclaurin series.

(b) Use the first two terms in the series to show that the number of units present after 1 year is approximately $(0.999879)y_0$.

(c) Compare this to the value produced by the formula for $y(t)$.

C **42.** Suppose that a simple pendulum with a length of $L = 1$ meter is given an initial displacement of $\theta_0 = 5°$ from the vertical.

(a) Approximate the period $T$ of the pendulum using Formula (9) for the first-order model of $T$. [*Note:* Take $g = 9.8\ \text{m/s}^2$.]

(b) Approximate the period of the pendulum using Formula (10) for the second-order model.

(c) Use the numerical integration capability of a CAS to approximate the period of the pendulum from Formula (7), and compare it to the values obtained in parts (a) and (b).

**43.** Use the first three nonzero terms in Formula (8) and the Wallis sine formula in the Endpaper Integral Table (Formula 122) to obtain a model for the period of a simple pendulum.

**44.** Recall that the gravitational force exerted by the Earth on an object is called the object's *weight* (or more precisely, its *Earth weight*). If an object of mass $m$ is on the surface of the Earth (mean sea level), then the magnitude of its weight is $mg$, where $g$ is the acceleration due to gravity at the Earth's surface. A more general formula for the magnitude of the gravitational force that the Earth exerts on an object of mass $m$ is

$$F = \frac{mgR^2}{(R+h)^2}$$

where $R$ is the radius of the Earth and $h$ is the height of the object above the Earth's surface.

(a) Use the binomial series for $1/(1+x)^2$ obtained in Example 4 of Section 9.9 to express $F$ as a Maclaurin series in powers of $h/R$.

(b) Show that if $h = 0$, then $F = mg$.

(c) Show that if $h/R \approx 0$, then $F \approx mg - (2mgh/R)$. [*Note:* The quantity $2mgh/R$ can be thought of as a "correction term" for the weight that takes the object's height above the Earth's surface into account.]

(d) If we assume that the Earth is a sphere of radius $R = 4000$ mi at mean sea level, by approximately what percentage does a person's weight change in going from mean sea level to the top of Mt. Everest (29,028 ft)?

**45.** (a) Show that the Bessel function $J_0(x)$ given by Formula (4) of Section 9.8 satisfies the differential equation $xy'' + y' + xy = 0$. (This is called the ***Bessel equation of order zero.***)

(cont.)

(b) Show that the Bessel function $J_1(x)$ given by Formula (5) of Section 9.8 satisfies the differential equation $x^2y'' + xy' + (x^2 - 1)y = 0$. (This is called the ***Bessel equation of order one***.)

(c) Show that $J_0'(x) = -J_1(x)$.

**46.** Prove: If the power series $\sum_{k=0}^{\infty} a_k x^k$ and $\sum_{k=0}^{\infty} b_k x^k$ have the same sum on an interval $(-r, r)$, then $a_k = b_k$ for all values of $k$.

**47. Writing** Evaluate the limit

$$\lim_{x\to 0} \frac{x - \sin x}{x^3}$$

in two ways: using L'Hôpital's rule and by replacing $\sin x$ by its Maclaurin series. Discuss how the use of a series can give qualitative information about how the value of an indeterminate limit is approached.

✓ **QUICK CHECK ANSWERS 9.10** 1. $(-1)^k \frac{x^{2k}}{k!}$ 2. 1; −1; 1; −1; $(-1)^k x^k$ 3. 1; $\frac{3}{2}$; $\frac{4}{3}$ 4. (a) $-\frac{1}{2}$ (b) 4; 1; $-\frac{1}{4}$; $\frac{1}{18}$; 4; $(-1)^{k+1}\frac{(x-1)^k}{k\cdot(k!)}$

## CHAPTER 9 REVIEW EXERCISES

**1.** What is the difference between an infinite sequence and an infinite series?

**2.** What is meant by the sum of an infinite series?

**3.** (a) What is a geometric series? Give some examples of convergent and divergent geometric series.

(b) What is a $p$-series? Give some examples of convergent and divergent $p$-series.

**4.** State conditions under which an alternating series is guaranteed to converge.

**5.** (a) What does it mean to say that an infinite series converges absolutely?

(b) What relationship exists between convergence and absolute convergence of an infinite series?

**6.** State the Remainder Estimation Theorem, and describe some of its uses.

**7.** If a power series in $x - x_0$ has radius of convergence $R$, what can you say about the set of $x$-values at which the series converges?

**8.** (a) Write down the formula for the Maclaurin series for $f$ in sigma notation.

(b) Write down the formula for the Taylor series for $f$ about $x = x_0$ in sigma notation.

**9.** Are the following statements true or false? If true, state a theorem to justify your conclusion; if false, then give a counterexample.

(a) If $\sum u_k$ converges, then $u_k \to 0$ as $k \to +\infty$.

(b) If $u_k \to 0$ as $k \to +\infty$, then $\sum u_k$ converges.

(c) If $f(n) = a_n$ for $n = 1, 2, 3, \ldots$, and if $a_n \to L$ as $n \to +\infty$, then $f(x) \to L$ as $x \to +\infty$.

(d) If $f(n) = a_n$ for $n = 1, 2, 3, \ldots$, and if $f(x) \to L$ as $x \to +\infty$, then $a_n \to L$ as $n \to +\infty$.

(e) If $0 < a_n < 1$, then $\{a_n\}$ converges.

(f) If $0 < u_k < 1$, then $\sum u_k$ converges.

(g) If $\sum u_k$ and $\sum v_k$ converge, then $\sum (u_k + v_k)$ diverges.

(h) If $\sum u_k$ and $\sum v_k$ diverge, then $\sum (u_k - v_k)$ converges.

(i) If $0 \le u_k \le v_k$ and $\sum v_k$ converges, then $\sum u_k$ converges.

(j) If $0 \le u_k \le v_k$ and $\sum u_k$ diverges, then $\sum v_k$ diverges.

(k) If an infinite series converges, then it converges absolutely.

(l) If an infinite series diverges absolutely, then it diverges.

**10.** State whether each of the following is true or false. Justify your answers.

(a) The function $f(x) = x^{1/3}$ has a Maclaurin series.

(b) $1 + \frac{1}{2} - \frac{1}{2} + \frac{1}{3} - \frac{1}{3} + \frac{1}{4} - \frac{1}{4} + \cdots = 1$

(c) $1 + \frac{1}{2} - \frac{1}{2} + \frac{1}{2} - \frac{1}{2} + \frac{1}{2} - \frac{1}{2} + \cdots = 1$

**11.** Find the general term of the sequence, starting with $n = 1$, determine whether the sequence converges, and if so find its limit.

(a) $\frac{3}{2^2 - 1^2}, \frac{4}{3^2 - 2^2}, \frac{5}{4^2 - 3^2}, \ldots$

(b) $\frac{1}{3}, -\frac{2}{5}, \frac{3}{7}, -\frac{4}{9}, \ldots$

**12.** Suppose that the sequence $\{a_k\}$ is defined recursively by

$$a_0 = c, \quad a_{k+1} = \sqrt{a_k}$$

Assuming that the sequence converges, find its limit if

(a) $c = \frac{1}{2}$ (b) $c = \frac{3}{2}$.

**13.** Show that the sequence is eventually strictly monotone.

(a) $\{(n - 10)^4\}_{n=0}^{+\infty}$ (b) $\left\{\frac{100^n}{(2n)!(n!)}\right\}_{n=1}^{+\infty}$

**14.** (a) Give an example of a bounded sequence that diverges.

(b) Give an example of a monotonic sequence that diverges.

**15–20** Use any method to determine whether the series converge. ■

**15.** (a) $\sum_{k=1}^{\infty} \frac{1}{5^k}$ (b) $\sum_{k=1}^{\infty} \frac{1}{5^k + 1}$

**16.** (a) $\sum_{k=1}^{\infty} (-1)^k \frac{k+4}{k^2+k}$ (b) $\sum_{k=1}^{\infty} (-1)^{k+1} \left(\frac{k+2}{3k-1}\right)^k$

**17.** (a) $\sum_{k=1}^{\infty} \frac{1}{k^3+2k+1}$ (b) $\sum_{k=1}^{\infty} \frac{1}{(3+k)^{2/5}}$

**18.** (a) $\sum_{k=1}^{\infty} \frac{\ln k}{k\sqrt{k}}$ (b) $\sum_{k=1}^{\infty} \frac{k^{4/3}}{8k^2+5k+1}$

**19.** (a) $\sum_{k=1}^{\infty} \frac{9}{\sqrt{k}+1}$ (b) $\sum_{k=1}^{\infty} \frac{\cos(1/k)}{k^2}$

**20.** (a) $\sum_{k=1}^{\infty} \frac{k^{-1/2}}{2+\sin^2 k}$ (b) $\sum_{k=1}^{\infty} \frac{(-1)^{k+1}}{k^2+1}$

**21.** Find the exact error that results when the sum of the geometric series $\sum_{k=0}^{\infty}(1/5)^k$ is approximated by the sum of the first 100 terms in the series.

**22.** Suppose that $\sum_{k=1}^{n} u_k = 2 - \frac{1}{n}$. Find

(a) $u_{100}$ (b) $\lim_{k\to+\infty} u_k$ (c) $\sum_{k=1}^{\infty} u_k$.

**23.** In each part, determine whether the series converges; if so, find its sum.

(a) $\sum_{k=1}^{\infty}\left(\frac{3}{2^k}-\frac{2}{3^k}\right)$ (b) $\sum_{k=1}^{\infty}[\ln(k+1)-\ln k]$

(c) $\sum_{k=1}^{\infty}\frac{1}{k(k+2)}$ (d) $\sum_{k=1}^{\infty}[\tan^{-1}(k+1)-\tan^{-1}k]$

**24.** It can be proved that

$$\lim_{n\to+\infty}\sqrt[n]{n!}=+\infty \quad\text{and}\quad \lim_{n\to+\infty}\frac{\sqrt[n]{n!}}{n}=\frac{1}{e}$$

In each part, use these limits and the root test to determine whether the series converges.

(a) $\sum_{k=0}^{\infty}\frac{2^k}{k!}$ (b) $\sum_{k=0}^{\infty}\frac{k^k}{k!}$

**25.** Let $a$, $b$, and $p$ be positive constants. For which values of $p$ does the series $\sum_{k=1}^{\infty}\frac{1}{(a+bk)^p}$ converge?

**26.** Find the interval of convergence of

$$\sum_{k=0}^{\infty}\frac{(x-x_0)^k}{b^k} \quad (b>0)$$

**27.** (a) Show that $k^k \geq k!$.

(b) Use the comparison test to show that $\sum_{k=1}^{\infty}k^{-k}$ converges.

(c) Use the root test to show that the series converges.

**28.** Does the series $1-\frac{2}{3}+\frac{3}{5}-\frac{4}{7}+\frac{5}{9}+\cdots$ converge? Justify your answer.

**29.** (a) Find the first five Maclaurin polynomials of the function $p(x)=1-7x+5x^2+4x^3$.

(b) Make a general statement about the Maclaurin polynomials of a polynomial of degree $n$.

**30.** Show that the approximation

$$\sin x \approx x - \frac{x^3}{3!}+\frac{x^5}{5!}$$

is accurate to four decimal places if $0 \leq x \leq \pi/4$.

**31.** Use a Maclaurin series and properties of alternating series to show that $|\ln(1+x)-x| \leq x^2/2$ if $0<x<1$.

**32.** Use Maclaurin series to approximate the integral

$$\int_0^1 \frac{1-\cos x}{x}\,dx$$

to three decimal-place accuracy.

**33.** In parts (a)–(d), find the sum of the series by associating it with some Maclaurin series.

(a) $2+\frac{4}{2!}+\frac{8}{3!}+\frac{16}{4!}+\cdots$

(b) $\pi-\frac{\pi^3}{3!}+\frac{\pi^5}{5!}-\frac{\pi^7}{7!}+\cdots$

(c) $1-\frac{e^2}{2!}+\frac{e^4}{4!}-\frac{e^6}{6!}+\cdots$

(d) $1-\ln 3+\frac{(\ln 3)^2}{2!}-\frac{(\ln 3)^3}{3!}+\cdots$

**34.** In each part, write out the first four terms of the series, and then find the radius of convergence.

(a) $\sum_{k=1}^{\infty}\frac{1\cdot 2\cdot 3\cdots k}{1\cdot 4\cdot 7\cdots(3k-2)}x^k$

(b) $\sum_{k=1}^{\infty}(-1)^k\frac{1\cdot 2\cdot 3\cdots k}{1\cdot 3\cdot 5\cdots(2k-1)}x^{2k+1}$

**35.** Use an appropriate Taylor series for $\sqrt[3]{x}$ to approximate $\sqrt[3]{28}$ to three decimal-place accuracy, and check your answer by comparing it to that produced directly by your calculating utility.

**36.** Differentiate the Maclaurin series for $xe^x$ and use the result to show that

$$\sum_{k=0}^{\infty}\frac{k+1}{k!}=2e$$

**37.** Use the supplied Maclaurin series for $\sin x$ and $\cos x$ to find the first four nonzero terms of the Maclaurin series for the given functions.

$$\sin x = \sum_{k=0}^{\infty}(-1)^k\frac{x^{2k+1}}{(2k+1)!}$$

$$\cos x = \sum_{k=0}^{\infty}(-1)^k\frac{x^{2k}}{(2k)!}$$

(a) $\sin x\cos x$ (b) $\frac{1}{2}\sin 2x$

## CHAPTER 9 MAKING CONNECTIONS

1. As shown in the accompanying figure, suppose that lines $L_1$ and $L_2$ form an angle $\theta$, $0 < \theta < \pi/2$, at their point of intersection $P$. A point $P_0$ is chosen that is on $L_1$ and $a$ units from $P$. Starting from $P_0$ a zig-zag path is constructed by successively going back and forth between $L_1$ and $L_2$ along a perpendicular from one line to the other. Find the following sums in terms of $\theta$ and $a$.
(a) $P_0P_1 + P_1P_2 + P_2P_3 + \cdots$
(b) $P_0P_1 + P_2P_3 + P_4P_5 + \cdots$
(c) $P_1P_2 + P_3P_4 + P_5P_6 + \cdots$

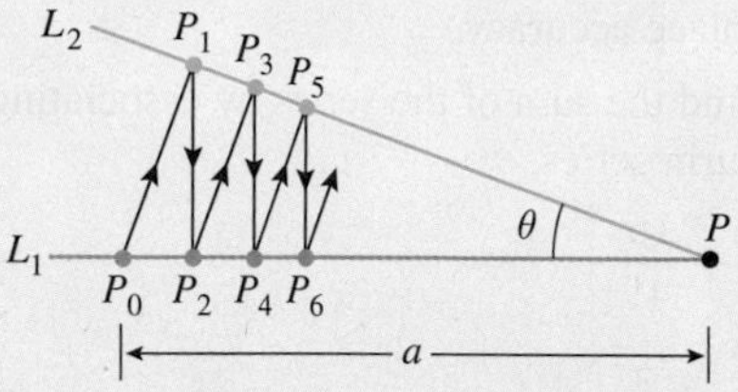

◀ Figure Ex-1

2. (a) Find $A$ and $B$ such that
$$\frac{6^k}{(3^{k+1}-2^{k+1})(3^k-2^k)} = \frac{2^kA}{3^k-2^k} + \frac{2^kB}{3^{k+1}-2^{k+1}}$$
(b) Use the result in part (a) to find a closed form for the $n$th partial sum of the series
$$\sum_{k=1}^{\infty} \frac{6^k}{(3^{k+1}-2^{k+1})(3^k-2^k)}$$
and then find the sum of the series.

**Source:** This exercise is adapted from a problem that appeared in the Forty-Fifth Annual William Lowell Putnam Competition.

3. Show that the alternating $p$-series
$$1 - \frac{1}{2^p} + \frac{1}{3^p} - \frac{1}{4^p} + \cdots + (-1)^{k+1}\frac{1}{k^p} + \cdots$$
converges absolutely if $p > 1$, converges conditionally if $0 < p \le 1$, and diverges if $p \le 0$.

4. As illustrated in the accompanying figure, a bug, starting at point $A$ on a 180 cm wire, walks the length of the wire, stops and walks in the opposite direction for half the length of the wire, stops again and walks in the opposite direction for one-third the length of the wire, stops again and walks in the opposite direction for one-fourth the length of the wire, and so forth until it stops for the 1000th time.
(a) Give upper and lower bounds on the distance between the bug and point $A$ when it finally stops. [*Hint:* As stated in Example 2 of Section 9.6, assume that the sum of the alternating harmonic series is ln 2.]
(b) Give upper and lower bounds on the total distance that the bug has traveled when it finally stops. [*Hint:* Use inequality (2) of Section 9.4.]

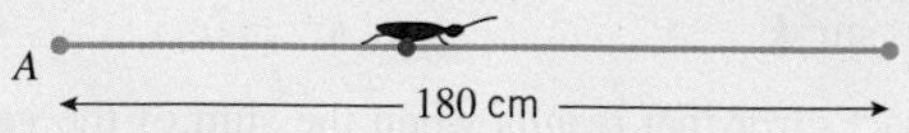

▲ Figure Ex-4

5. In Section 6.6 we defined the kinetic energy $K$ of a particle with mass $m$ and velocity $v$ to be $K = \frac{1}{2}mv^2$ [see Formula (7) of that section]. In this formula the mass $m$ is assumed to be constant, and $K$ is called the ***Newtonian kinetic energy***. However, in Albert Einstein's relativity theory the mass $m$ increases with the velocity and the kinetic energy $K$ is given by the formula
$$K = m_0c^2\left[\frac{1}{\sqrt{1-(v/c)^2}} - 1\right]$$
in which $m_0$ is the mass of the particle when its velocity is zero, and $c$ is the speed of light. This is called the ***relativistic kinetic energy***. Use an appropriate binomial series to show that if the velocity is small compared to the speed of light (i.e., $v/c \approx 0$), then the Newtonian and relativistic kinetic energies are in close agreement.

6. In Section 8.4 we studied the motion of a falling object that has mass $m$ and is retarded by air resistance. We showed that if the initial velocity is $v_0$ and the drag force $F_R$ is proportional to the velocity, that is, $F_R = -cv$, then the velocity of the object at time $t$ is
$$v(t) = e^{-ct/m}\left(v_0 + \frac{mg}{c}\right) - \frac{mg}{c}$$
where $g$ is the acceleration due to gravity [see Formula (16) of Section 8.4].
(a) Use a Maclaurin series to show that if $ct/m \approx 0$, then the velocity can be approximated as
$$v(t) \approx v_0 - \left(\frac{cv_0}{m} + g\right)t$$
(b) Improve on the approximation in part (a).

## EXPANDING THE CALCULUS HORIZON

To learn how ecologists use mathematical models based on the process of iteration to study the growth and decline of animal populations, see the module entitled **Iteration and Dynamical Systems** at:

**www.wiley.com/college/anton**

windujedi/iStockphoto

*Mathematical curves, such as the spirals in the center of a sunflower, can be described conveniently using ideas developed in this chapter.*

# 10

# PARAMETRIC AND POLAR CURVES; CONIC SECTIONS

In this chapter we will study alternative ways of expressing curves in the plane. We will begin by studying parametric curves: curves described in terms of component functions. This study will include methods for finding tangent lines to parametric curves. We will then introduce polar coordinate systems and discuss methods for finding tangent lines to polar curves, arc length of polar curves, and areas enclosed by polar curves. Our attention will then turn to a review of the basic properties of conic sections: parabolas, ellipses, and hyperbolas. Finally, we will consider conic sections in the context of polar coordinates and discuss some applications in astronomy.

## 10.1 PARAMETRIC EQUATIONS; TANGENT LINES AND ARC LENGTH FOR PARAMETRIC CURVES

*Graphs of functions must pass the vertical line test, a limitation that excludes curves with self-intersections or even such basic curves as circles. In this section we will study an alternative method for describing curves algebraically that is not subject to the severe restriction of the vertical line test. We will then derive formulas required to find slopes, tangent lines, and arc lengths of these parametric curves. We will conclude with an investigation of a classic parametric curve known as the cycloid.*

### PARAMETRIC EQUATIONS

Suppose that a particle moves along a curve $C$ in the $xy$-plane in such a way that its $x$- and $y$-coordinates, as functions of time, are

$$x = f(t), \quad y = g(t)$$

We call these the ***parametric equations*** of motion for the particle and refer to $C$ as the ***trajectory*** of the particle or the ***graph*** of the equations (Figure 10.1.1). The variable $t$ is called the ***parameter*** for the equations.

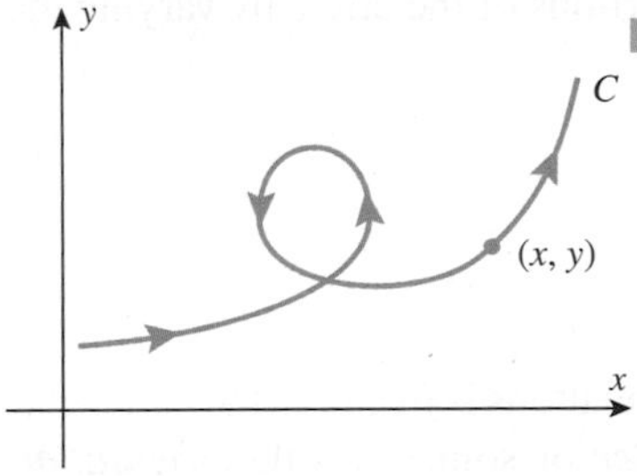


A moving particle with trajectory $C$

▲ **Figure 10.1.1**

► **Example 1** Sketch the trajectory over the time interval $0 \le t \le 10$ of the particle whose parametric equations of motion are

$$x = t - 3\sin t, \quad y = 4 - 3\cos t \tag{1}$$

***Solution.*** One way to sketch the trajectory is to choose a representative succession of times, plot the $(x, y)$ coordinates of points on the trajectory at those times, and connect the points with a smooth curve. The trajectory in Figure 10.1.2 was obtained in this way from the data in Table 10.1.1 in which the approximate coordinates of the particle are given at time increments of 1 unit. Observe that there is no $t$-axis in the picture; the values of $t$ appear only as labels on the plotted points, and even these are usually omitted unless it is important to emphasize the locations of the particle at specific times. ◄

**TECHNOLOGY MASTERY**

Read the documentation for your graphing utility to learn how to graph parametric equations, and then generate the trajectory in Example 1. Explore the behavior of the particle beyond time $t = 10$.

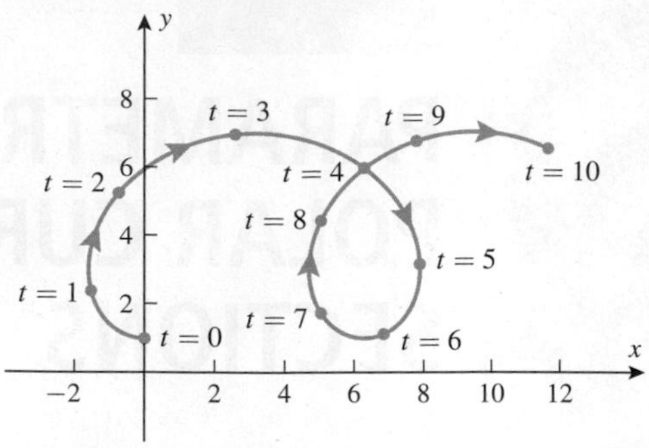


▲ Figure 10.1.2

Table 10.1.1

| t | x | y |
|---|---|---|
| 0 | 0.0 | 1.0 |
| 1 | −1.5 | 2.4 |
| 2 | −0.7 | 5.2 |
| 3 | 2.6 | 7.0 |
| 4 | 6.3 | 6.0 |
| 5 | 7.9 | 3.1 |
| 6 | 6.8 | 1.1 |
| 7 | 5.0 | 1.7 |
| 8 | 5.0 | 4.4 |
| 9 | 7.8 | 6.7 |
| 10 | 11.6 | 6.5 |

Although parametric equations commonly arise in problems of motion with time as the parameter, they arise in other contexts as well. Thus, unless the problem dictates that the parameter $t$ in the equations

$$x = f(t), \quad y = g(t)$$

represents time, it should be viewed simply as an independent variable that varies over some interval of real numbers. (In fact, there is no need to use the letter $t$ for the parameter; any letter not reserved for another purpose can be used.) If no restrictions on the parameter are stated explicitly or implied by the equations, then it is understood that it varies from $-\infty$ to $+\infty$. To indicate that a parameter $t$ is restricted to an interval $[a, b]$, we will write

$$x = f(t), \quad y = g(t) \qquad (a \le t \le b)$$

► **Example 2** Find the graph of the parametric equations

$$x = \cos t, \quad y = \sin t \qquad (0 \le t \le 2\pi) \tag{2}$$

***Solution.*** One way to find the graph is to eliminate the parameter $t$ by noting that

$$x^2 + y^2 = \sin^2 t + \cos^2 t = 1$$

Thus, the graph is contained in the unit circle $x^2 + y^2 = 1$. Geometrically, the parameter $t$ can be interpreted as the angle swept out by the radial line from the origin to the point $(x, y) = (\cos t, \sin t)$ on the unit circle (Figure 10.1.3). As $t$ increases from 0 to $2\pi$, the point traces the circle counterclockwise, starting at $(1, 0)$ when $t = 0$ and completing one full revolution when $t = 2\pi$. One can obtain different portions of the circle by varying the interval over which the parameter varies. For example,

$$x = \cos t, \quad y = \sin t \qquad (0 \le t \le \pi) \tag{3}$$

represents just the upper semicircle in Figure 10.1.3. ◄

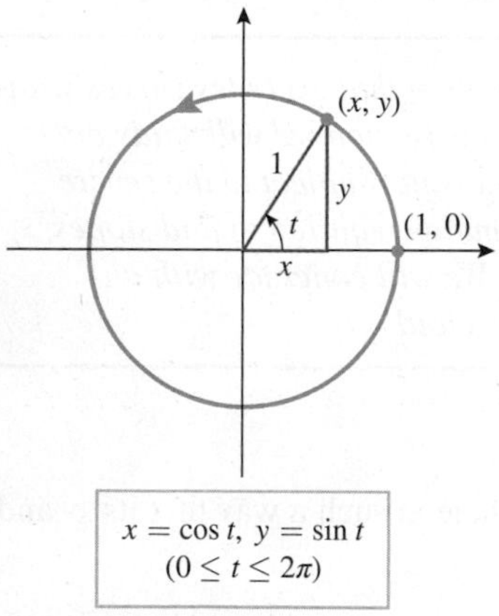


▲ Figure 10.1.3

## ORIENTATION

The direction in which the graph of a pair of parametric equations is traced as the parameter increases is called the ***direction of increasing parameter*** or sometimes the ***orientation*** imposed on the curve by the equations. Thus, we make a distinction between a ***curve***, which is a set of points, and a ***parametric curve***, which is a curve with an orientation imposed on it by a set of parametric equations. For example, we saw in Example 2 that the circle represented parametrically by (2) is traced counterclockwise as $t$ increases and hence has *counterclockwise orientation*. As shown in Figures 10.1.2 and 10.1.3, the orientation of a parametric curve can be indicated by arrowheads.

To obtain parametric equations for the unit circle with *clockwise orientation*, we can replace $t$ by $-t$ in (2) and use the identities $\cos(-t) = \cos t$ and $\sin(-t) = -\sin t$. This yields

$$x = \cos t, \quad y = -\sin t \qquad (0 \le t \le 2\pi)$$

Here, the circle is traced clockwise by a point that starts at $(1, 0)$ when $t = 0$ and completes one full revolution when $t = 2\pi$ (Figure 10.1.4).

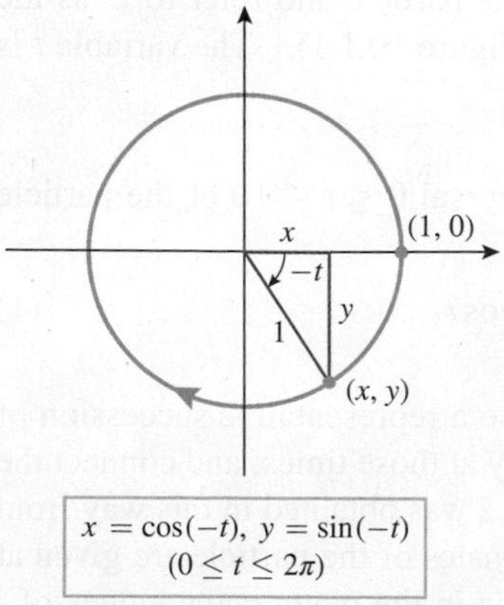


▲ Figure 10.1.4

**TECHNOLOGY MASTERY** When parametric equations are graphed using a calculator, the orientation can often be determined by watching the direction in which the graph is traced on the screen. However, many computers graph so fast that it is often hard to discern the orientation. See if you can use your graphing utility to confirm that (3) has a counterclockwise orientation.

▶ **Example 3** Graph the parametric curve

$$x = 2t - 3, \quad y = 6t - 7$$

by eliminating the parameter, and indicate the orientation on the graph.

***Solution.*** To eliminate the parameter we will solve the first equation for $t$ as a function of $x$, and then substitute this expression for $t$ into the second equation:

$$t = \left(\tfrac{1}{2}\right)(x + 3)$$
$$y = 6\left(\tfrac{1}{2}\right)(x + 3) - 7$$
$$y = 3x + 2$$

Thus, the graph is a line of slope 3 and $y$-intercept 2. To find the orientation we must look to the original equations; the direction of increasing $t$ can be deduced by observing that $x$ increases as $t$ increases *or* by observing that $y$ increases as $t$ increases. Either piece of information tells us that the line is traced left to right as shown in Figure 10.1.5. ◀

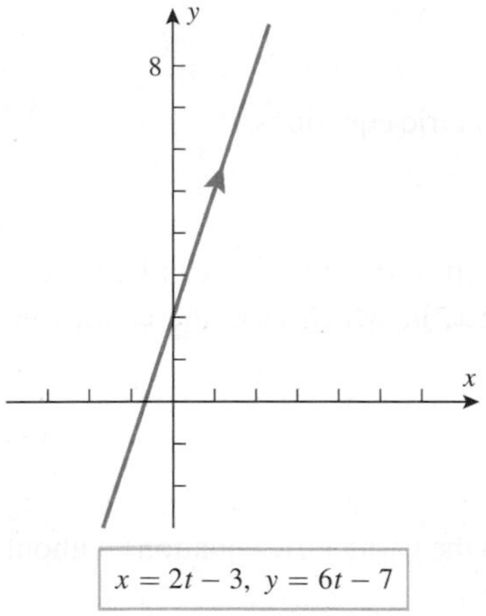

▲ **Figure 10.1.5**

**REMARK** Not all parametric equations produce curves with definite orientations; if the equations are badly behaved, then the point tracing the curve may leap around sporadically or move back and forth, failing to determine a definite direction. For example, if

$$x = \sin t, \quad y = \sin^2 t$$

then the point $(x, y)$ moves along the parabola $y = x^2$. However, the value of $x$ varies periodically between $-1$ and 1, so the point $(x, y)$ moves periodically back and forth along the parabola between the points $(-1, 1)$ and $(1, 1)$ (as shown in Figure 10.1.6). Later in the text we will discuss restrictions that eliminate such erratic behavior, but for now we will just avoid such complications.

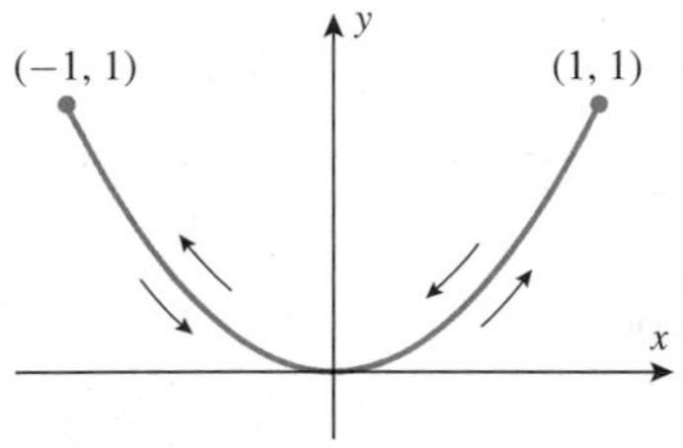

▲ **Figure 10.1.6**

## EXPRESSING ORDINARY FUNCTIONS PARAMETRICALLY

An equation $y = f(x)$ can be expressed in parametric form by introducing the parameter $t = x$; this yields the parametric equations

$$x = t, \quad y = f(t)$$

For example, the portion of the curve $y = \cos x$ over the interval $[-2\pi, 2\pi]$ can be expressed parametrically as

$$x = t, \quad y = \cos t \quad (-2\pi \le t \le 2\pi)$$

(Figure 10.1.7).

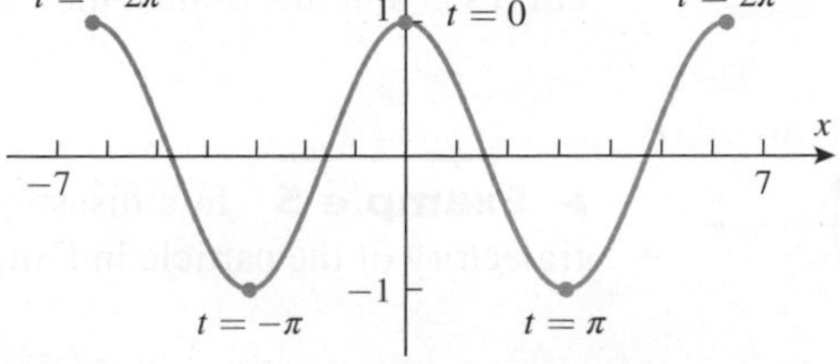

▶ **Figure 10.1.7**

If a function $f$ is one-to-one, then it has an inverse function $f^{-1}$. In this case the equation $y = f^{-1}(x)$ is equivalent to $x = f(y)$. We can express the graph of $f^{-1}$ in parametric form by introducing the parameter $y = t$; this yields the parametric equations

$$x = f(t), \quad y = t$$

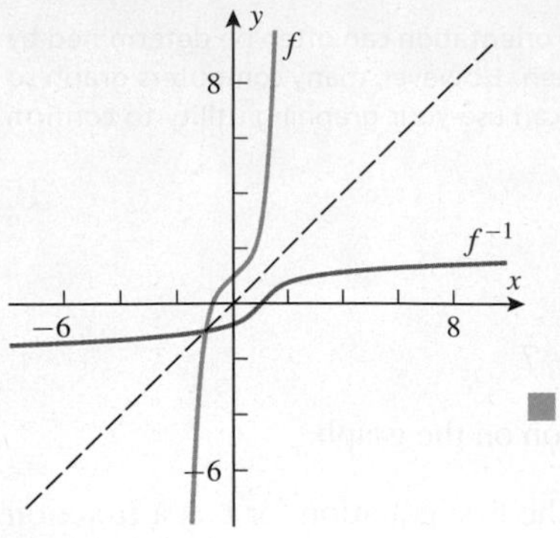

▲ **Figure 10.1.8**

For example, Figure 10.1.8 shows the graph of $f(x) = x^5 + x + 1$ and its inverse. The graph of $f$ can be repesented parametrically as

$$x = t, \quad y = t^5 + t + 1$$

and the graph of $f^{-1}$ can be represented parametrically as

$$x = t^5 + t + 1, \quad y = t$$

## TANGENT LINES TO PARAMETRIC CURVES

We will be concerned with curves that are given by parametric equations

$$x = f(t), \quad y = g(t)$$

in which $f(t)$ and $g(t)$ have continuous first derivatives with respect to $t$. It can be proved that if $dx/dt \neq 0$, then $y$ is a differentiable function of $x$, in which case the chain rule implies that

$$\frac{dy}{dx} = \frac{dy/dt}{dx/dt} \tag{4}$$

This formula makes it possible to find $dy/dx$ directly from the parametric equations without eliminating the parameter.

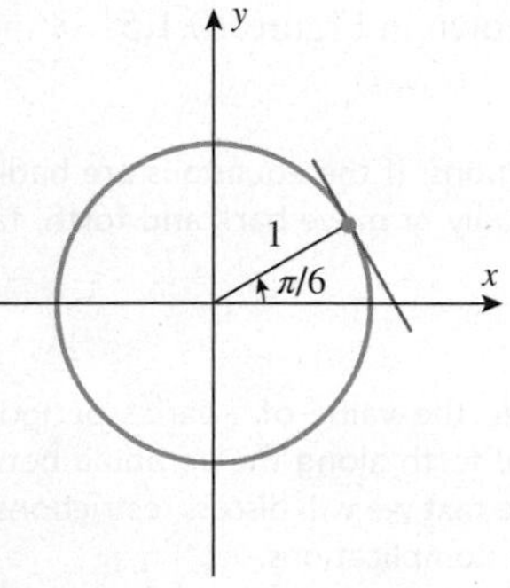

▲ **Figure 10.1.9**

► **Example 4** Find the slope of the tangent line to the unit circle

$$x = \cos t, \quad y = \sin t \quad (0 \leq t \leq 2\pi)$$

at the point where $t = \pi/6$ (Figure 10.1.9).

***Solution.*** From (4), the slope at a general point on the circle is

$$\frac{dy}{dx} = \frac{dy/dt}{dx/dt} = \frac{\cos t}{-\sin t} = -\cot t \tag{5}$$

Thus, the slope at $t = \pi/6$ is

$$\left.\frac{dy}{dx}\right|_{t=\pi/6} = -\cot\frac{\pi}{6} = -\sqrt{3} \blacktriangleleft$$

Note that Formula (5) makes sense geometrically because the radius from the origin to the point $P(\cos t, \sin t)$ has slope $m = \tan t$. Thus the tangent line at $P$, being perpendicular to the radius, has slope

$$-\frac{1}{m} = -\frac{1}{\tan t} = -\cot t$$

(Figure 10.1.10).

It follows from Formula (4) that the tangent line to a parametric curve will be horizontal at those points where $dy/dt = 0$ and $dx/dt \neq 0$, since $dy/dx = 0$ at such points. Two different situations occur when $dx/dt = 0$. At points where $dx/dt = 0$ and $dy/dt \neq 0$, the right side of (4) has a nonzero numerator and a zero denominator; we will agree that the curve has ***infinite slope*** and a ***vertical tangent line*** at such points. At points where $dx/dt$ and $dy/dt$ are both zero, the right side of (4) becomes an indeterminate form; we call such points ***singular points***. No general statement can be made about the behavior of parametric curves at singular points; they must be analyzed case by case.

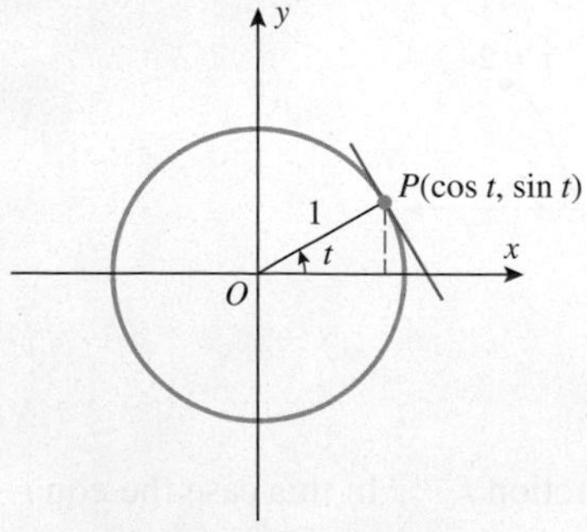

Radius $OP$ has slope $m = \tan t$.

▲ **Figure 10.1.10**

► **Example 5** In a disastrous first flight, an experimental paper airplane follows the trajectory of the particle in Example 1:

$$x = t - 3\sin t, \quad y = 4 - 3\cos t \quad (t \geq 0)$$

but crashes into a wall at time $t = 10$ (Figure 10.1.11).

(a) At what times was the airplane flying horizontally?

(b) At what times was it flying vertically?

***Solution (a).*** The airplane was flying horizontally at those times when $dy/dt = 0$ and $dx/dt \neq 0$. From the given trajectory we have

$$\frac{dy}{dt} = 3\sin t \quad \text{and} \quad \frac{dx}{dt} = 1 - 3\cos t \tag{6}$$

Setting $dy/dt = 0$ yields the equation $3\sin t = 0$, or, more simply, $\sin t = 0$. This equation has four solutions in the time interval $0 \le t < 10$:

$$t = 0, \quad t = \pi, \quad t = 2\pi, \quad t = 3\pi$$

Stanislovas Kairys/iStockphoto

*The complicated motion of a paper airplane is best described mathematically using parametric equations.*

Since $dx/dt = 1 - 3\cos t \neq 0$ for these values of $t$ (verify), the airplane was flying horizontally at times

$$t = 0, \quad t = \pi \approx 3.14, \quad t = 2\pi \approx 6.28, \quad \text{and} \quad t = 3\pi \approx 9.42$$

which is consistent with Figure 10.1.11.

***Solution (b).*** The airplane was flying vertically at those times when $dx/dt = 0$ and $dy/dt \neq 0$. Setting $dx/dt = 0$ in (6) yields the equation

$$1 - 3\cos t = 0 \quad \text{or} \quad \cos t = \tfrac{1}{3}$$

This equation has three solutions in the time interval $0 \le t \le 10$ (Figure 10.1.12):

$$t = \cos^{-1}\tfrac{1}{3}, \quad t = 2\pi - \cos^{-1}\tfrac{1}{3}, \quad t = 2\pi + \cos^{-1}\tfrac{1}{3}$$

Since $dy/dt = 3\sin t$ is not zero at these points (why?), it follows that the airplane was flying vertically at times

$$t = \cos^{-1}\tfrac{1}{3} \approx 1.23, \quad t \approx 2\pi - 1.23 \approx 5.05, \quad t \approx 2\pi + 1.23 \approx 7.51$$

which again is consistent with Figure 10.1.11. ◀

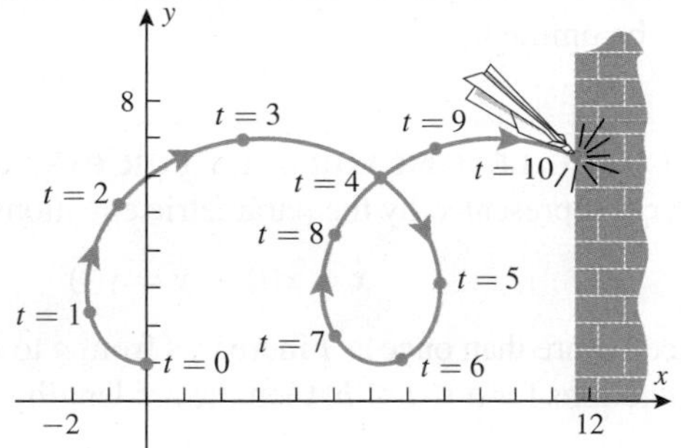


▲ Figure 10.1.11

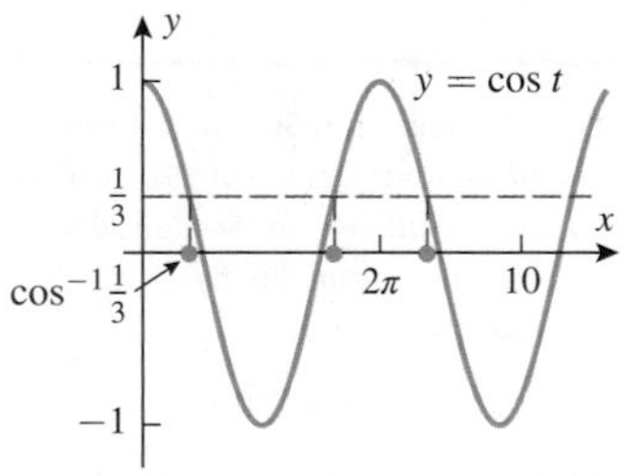


▲ Figure 10.1.12

**▶ Example 6** The curve represented by the parametric equations

$$x = t^2, \quad y = t^3 \qquad (-\infty < t < +\infty)$$

is called a ***semicubical parabola***. The parameter $t$ can be eliminated by cubing $x$ and squaring $y$, from which it follows that $y^2 = x^3$. The graph of this equation, shown in Figure 10.1.13, consists of two branches: an upper branch obtained by graphing $y = x^{3/2}$ and a lower branch obtained by graphing $y = -x^{3/2}$. The two branches meet at the origin, which corresponds to $t = 0$ in the parametric equations. This is a singular point because the derivatives $dx/dt = 2t$ and $dy/dt = 3t^2$ are both zero there. ◀

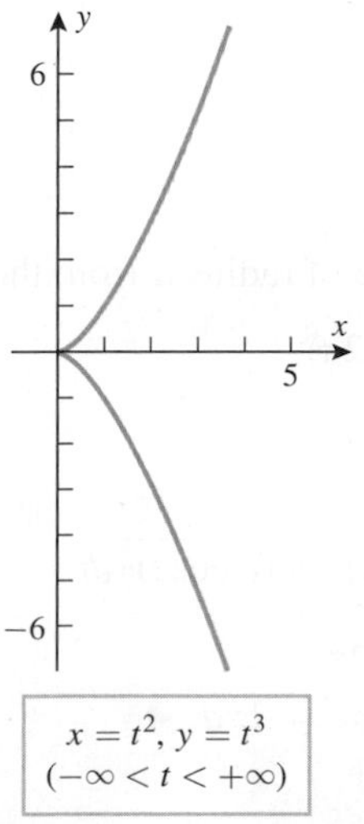


▲ Figure 10.1.13

**▶ Example 7** Without eliminating the parameter, find $dy/dx$ and $d^2y/dx^2$ at $(1, 1)$ and $(1, -1)$ on the semicubical parabola given by the parametric equations in Example 6.

***Solution.*** From (4) we have

$$\frac{dy}{dx} = \frac{dy/dt}{dx/dt} = \frac{3t^2}{2t} = \frac{3}{2}t \qquad (t \neq 0) \tag{7}$$

**WARNING**

Although it is true that

$$\frac{dy}{dx} = \frac{dy/dt}{dx/dt}$$

you cannot conclude that $d^2y/dx^2$ is the quotient of $d^2y/dt^2$ and $d^2x/dt^2$. To illustrate that this conclusion is erroneous, show that for the parametric curve in Example 7,

$$\left.\frac{d^2y}{dx^2}\right|_{t=1} \neq \left.\frac{d^2y/dt^2}{d^2x/dt^2}\right|_{t=1}$$

and from (4) applied to $y' = dy/dx$ we have

$$\frac{d^2y}{dx^2} = \frac{dy'}{dx} = \frac{dy'/dt}{dx/dt} = \frac{3/2}{2t} = \frac{3}{4t} \tag{8}$$

Since the point (1, 1) on the curve corresponds to $t = 1$ in the parametric equations, it follows from (7) and (8) that

$$\left.\frac{dy}{dx}\right|_{t=1} = \frac{3}{2} \quad \text{and} \quad \left.\frac{d^2y}{dx^2}\right|_{t=1} = \frac{3}{4}$$

Similarly, the point $(1, -1)$ corresponds to $t = -1$ in the parametric equations, so applying (7) and (8) again yields

$$\left.\frac{dy}{dx}\right|_{t=-1} = -\frac{3}{2} \quad \text{and} \quad \left.\frac{d^2y}{dx^2}\right|_{t=-1} = -\frac{3}{4}$$

Note that the values we obtained for the first and second derivatives are consistent with the graph in Figure 10.1.13, since at (1, 1) on the upper branch the tangent line has positive slope and the curve is concave up, and at $(1, -1)$ on the lower branch the tangent line has negative slope and the curve is concave down.

Finally, observe that we were able to apply Formulas (7) and (8) for both $t = 1$ and $t = -1$, even though the points (1, 1) and $(1, -1)$ lie on different branches. In contrast, had we chosen to perform the same computations by eliminating the parameter, we would have had to obtain separate derivative formulas for $y = x^{3/2}$ and $y = -x^{3/2}$. ◂

## ARC LENGTH OF PARAMETRIC CURVES

The following result provides a formula for finding the arc length of a curve from parametric equations for the curve. Its derivation is similar to that of Formula (3) in Section 6.4 and will be omitted.

Formulas (4) and (5) in Section 6.4 can be viewed as special cases of (9). For example, Formula (4) in Section 6.4 can be obtained from (9) by writing $y = f(x)$ parametrically as

$$x = t, \quad y = f(t)$$

and Formula (5) in Section 6.4 can be obtained by writing $x = g(y)$ parametrically as

$$x = g(t), \quad y = t$$

**10.1.1 ARC LENGTH FORMULA FOR PARAMETRIC CURVES** If no segment of the curve represented by the parametric equations

$$x = x(t), \quad y = y(t) \qquad (a \le t \le b)$$

is traced more than once as $t$ increases from $a$ to $b$, and if $dx/dt$ and $dy/dt$ are continuous functions for $a \le t \le b$, then the arc length $L$ of the curve is given by

$$L = \int_a^b \sqrt{\left(\frac{dx}{dt}\right)^2 + \left(\frac{dy}{dt}\right)^2}\, dt \tag{9}$$

▸ **Example 8** Use (9) to find the circumference of a circle of radius $a$ from the parametric equations

$$x = a\cos t, \quad y = a\sin t \qquad (0 \le t \le 2\pi)$$

***Solution.***

$$L = \int_0^{2\pi} \sqrt{\left(\frac{dx}{dt}\right)^2 + \left(\frac{dy}{dt}\right)^2}\, dt = \int_0^{2\pi} \sqrt{(-a\sin t)^2 + (a\cos t)^2}\, dt$$

$$= \int_0^{2\pi} a\, dt = at\Big]_0^{2\pi} = 2\pi a \;◂$$

## THE CYCLOID (THE APPLE OF DISCORD)

The results of this section can be used to investigate a curve known as a ***cycloid***. This curve, which is one of the most significant in the history of mathematics, can be generated by a point on a circle that rolls along a straight line (Figure 10.1.14). This curve has a fascinating history, which we will discuss shortly; but first we will show how to obtain parametric equations for it. For this purpose, let us assume that the circle has radius $a$ and rolls along the positive $x$-axis of a rectangular coordinate system. Let $P(x, y)$ be the point on the circle that traces the cycloid, and assume that $P$ is initially at the origin. We will take as our parameter the angle $\theta$ that is swept out by the radial line to $P$ as the circle rolls (Figure 10.1.14). It is standard here to regard $\theta$ as positive, even though it is generated by a clockwise rotation.

The motion of $P$ is a combination of the movement of the circle's center parallel to the $x$-axis and the rotation of $P$ about the center. As the radial line sweeps out an angle $\theta$, the point $P$ traverses an arc of length $a\theta$, and the circle moves a distance $a\theta$ along the $x$-axis. Thus, as suggested by Figure 10.1.15, the center moves to the point $(a\theta, a)$, and the coordinates of $P$ are

$$x = a\theta - a\sin\theta, \quad y = a - a\cos\theta \tag{10}$$

These are the equations of the cycloid in terms of the parameter $\theta$.

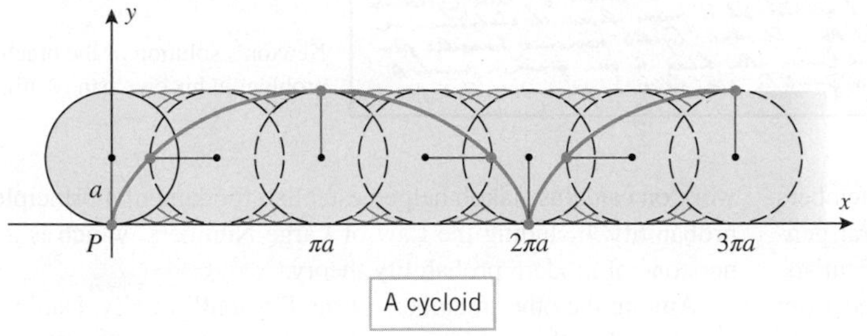


▲ Figure 10.1.14

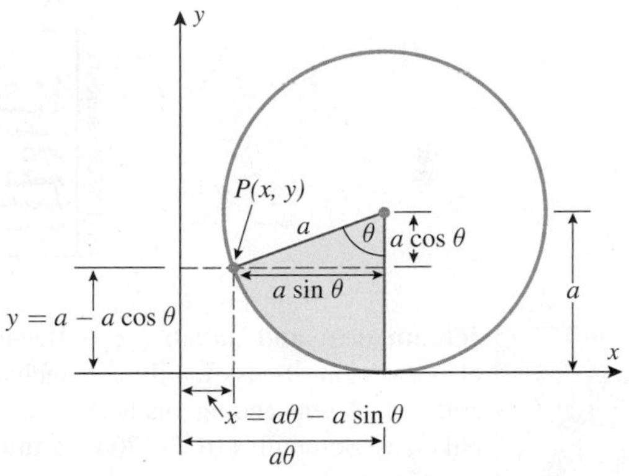


▲ Figure 10.1.15

One of the reasons the cycloid is important in the history of mathematics is that the study of its properties helped to spur the development of early versions of differentiation and integration. Work on the cycloid was carried out by some of the most famous names in seventeenth century mathematics, including Johann and Jakob Bernoulli, Descartes, L'Hôpital, Newton, and Leibniz. The curve was named the "cycloid" by the Italian mathematician and astronomer, Galileo, who spent over 40 years investigating its properties. An early problem of interest was that of constructing tangent lines to the cycloid. This problem was first solved by Descartes, and then by Fermat, whom Descartes had challenged with the question. A modern solution to this problem follows directly from the parametric equations (10) and Formula (4). For example, using Formula (4), it is straightforward to show that the $x$-intercepts of the cycloid are cusps and that there is a horizontal tangent line to the cycloid halfway between adjacent $x$-intercepts (Exercise 60).

Another early problem was determining the arc length of an arch of the cycloid. This was solved in 1658 by the famous British architect and mathematician, Sir Christopher Wren. He showed that the arc length of one arch of the cycloid is exactly eight times the radius of the generating circle. [For a solution to this problem using Formula (9), see Exercise 71.]

The cycloid is also important historically because it provides the solution to two famous mathematical problems—the ***brachistochrone problem*** (from Greek words meaning "shortest time") and the ***tautochrone problem*** (from Greek words meaning "equal time"). The brachistochrone problem is to determine the shape of a wire along which a bead might slide from a point $P$ to another point $Q$, not directly below, in the *shortest time*. The tautochrone problem is to find the shape of a wire from $P$ to $Q$ such that two beads started at any points on the wire between $P$ and $Q$ reach $Q$ in the *same amount of time*. The solution to both problems turns out to be an inverted cycloid (Figure 10.1.16).

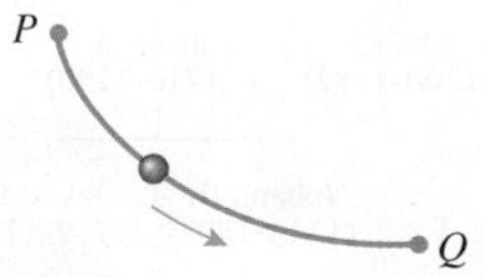


▲ Figure 10.1.16

In June of 1696, Johann Bernoulli posed the brachistochrone problem in the form of a challenge to other mathematicians. At first, one might conjecture that the wire should form a straight line, since that shape results in the shortest distance from $P$ to $Q$. However, the inverted cycloid allows the bead to fall more rapidly at first, building up sufficient speed to reach $Q$ in the shortest time, even though it travels a longer distance. The problem was solved by Newton, Leibniz, and L'Hôpital, as well as by Johann Bernoulli and his older brother Jakob; it was formulated and solved *incorrectly* years earlier by Galileo, who thought the answer was a circular arc. In fact, Johann was so impressed with his brother Jakob's solution that he claimed it to be his own. (This was just one of many disputes about the cycloid that eventually led to the curve being known as the "apple of discord.") One solution of the brachistochrone problem leads to the differential equation

$$\left(1+\left(\frac{dy}{dx}\right)^2\right)y = 2a \tag{11}$$

where $a$ is a positive constant. We leave it as an exercise (Exercise 72) to show that the cycloid provides a solution to this differential equation.

NYPL/Science Source/Getty Images

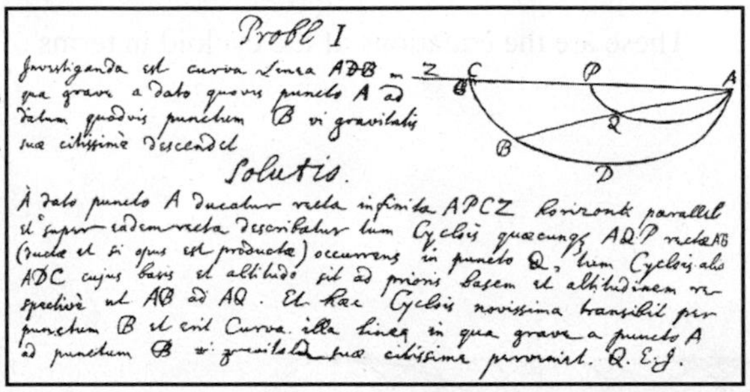


Newton's solution of the brachistochrone problem in his own handwriting

**Johann** (left) **and Jakob** (right) **Bernoulli** Members of an amazing Swiss family that included several generations of outstanding mathematicians and scientists. Nikolaus Bernoulli (1623–1708), a druggist, fled from Antwerp to escape religious persecution and ultimately settled in Basel, Switzerland. There he had three sons, Jakob I (also called Jacques or James), Nikolaus, and Johann I (also called Jean or John). The Roman numerals are used to distinguish family members with identical names (see the family tree below). Following Newton and Leibniz, the Bernoulli brothers, Jakob I and Johann I, are considered by some to be the two most important founders of calculus. Jakob I was self-taught in mathematics. His father wanted him to study for the ministry, but he turned to mathematics and in 1686 became a professor at the University of Basel. When he started working in mathematics, he knew nothing of Newton's and Leibniz' work. He eventually became familiar with Newton's results, but because so little of Leibniz' work was published, Jakob duplicated many of Leibniz' results.

Jakob's younger brother Johann I was urged to enter into business by his father. Instead, he turned to medicine and studied mathematics under the guidance of his older brother. He eventually became a mathematics professor at Gröningen in Holland, and then, when Jakob died in 1705, Johann succeeded him as mathematics professor at Basel. Throughout their lives, Jakob I and Johann I had a mutual passion for criticizing each other's work, which frequently erupted into ugly confrontations. Leibniz tried to mediate the disputes, but Jakob, who resented Leibniz' superior intellect, accused him of siding with Johann, and thus Leibniz became entangled in the arguments. The brothers often worked on common problems that they posed as challenges to one another. Johann, interested in gaining fame, often used unscrupulous means to make himself appear the originator of his brother's results; Jakob occasionally retaliated. Thus, it is often difficult to determine who deserves credit for many results. However, both men made major contributions to the development of calculus. In addition to his work on calculus, Jakob helped establish fundamental principles in probability, including the Law of Large Numbers, which is a cornerstone of modern probability theory.

Among the other members of the Bernoulli family, Daniel, son of Johann I, is the most famous. He was a professor of mathematics at St. Petersburg Academy in Russia and subsequently a professor of anatomy and then physics at Basel. He did work in calculus and probability, but is best known for his work in physics. A basic law of fluid flow, called Bernoulli's principle, is named in his honor. He won the annual prize of the French Academy 10 times for work on vibrating strings, tides of the sea, and kinetic theory of gases.

Johann II succeeded his father as professor of mathematics at Basel. His research was on the theory of heat and sound. Nikolaus I was a mathematician and law scholar who worked on probability and series. On the recommendation of Leibniz, he was appointed professor of mathematics at Padua and then went to Basel as a professor of logic and then law. Nikolaus II was professor of jurisprudence in Switzerland and then professor of mathematics at St. Petersburg Academy. Johann III was a professor of mathematics and astronomy in Berlin and Jakob II succeeded his uncle Daniel as professor of mathematics at St. Petersburg Academy in Russia. Truly an incredible family!

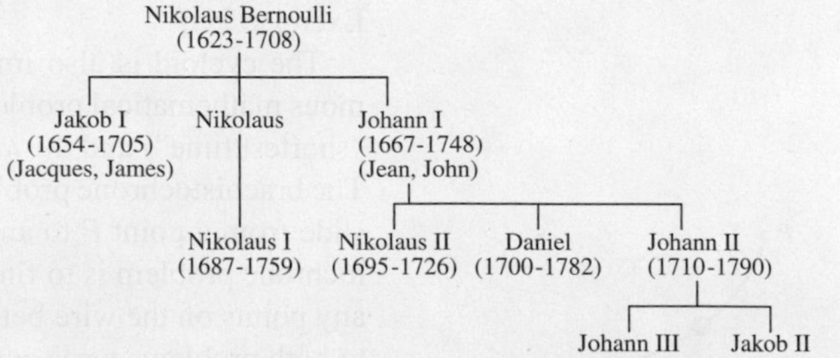


[*Image: © John Wiley & Sons, Inc.; drawn by Patrick Francisco and Jamie Zuccaro*]

## ✓ QUICK CHECK EXERCISES 10.1 (See page 617 for answers.)

1. Find parametric equations for a circle of radius 2, centered at (3, 5).

2. The graph of the curve described by the parametric equations $x = 4t - 1, y = 3t + 2$ is a straight line with slope ______ and $y$-intercept ______.

3. Suppose that a parametric curve $C$ is given by the equations $x = f(t), y = g(t)$ for $0 \le t \le 1$. Find parametric equations for $C$ that reverse the direction the curve is traced as the parameter increases from 0 to 1.

4. To find $dy/dx$ directly from the parametric equations
$$x = f(t), \quad y = g(t)$$
we can use the formula $dy/dx =$ ______.

5. Let $L$ be the length of the curve
$$x = \ln t, \quad y = \sin t \qquad (1 \le t \le \pi)$$
An integral expression for $L$ is ______.

## EXERCISE SET 10.1 Graphing Utility C CAS

1. (a) By eliminating the parameter, sketch the trajectory over the time interval $0 \le t \le 5$ of the particle whose parametric equations of motion are
$$x = t - 1, \quad y = t + 1$$
(b) Indicate the direction of motion on your sketch.
(c) Make a table of $x$- and $y$-coordinates of the particle at times $t = 0, 1, 2, 3, 4, 5$.
(d) Mark the position of the particle on the curve at the times in part (c), and label those positions with the values of $t$.

2. (a) By eliminating the parameter, sketch the trajectory over the time interval $0 \le t \le 1$ of the particle whose parametric equations of motion are
$$x = \cos(\pi t), \quad y = \sin(\pi t)$$
(b) Indicate the direction of motion on your sketch.
(c) Make a table of $x$- and $y$-coordinates of the particle at times $t = 0, 0.25, 0.5, 0.75, 1$.
(d) Mark the position of the particle on the curve at the times in part (c), and label those positions with the values of $t$.

**3–12** Sketch the curve by eliminating the parameter, and indicate the direction of increasing $t$. ■

3. $x = 3t - 4, \; y = 6t + 2$
4. $x = t - 3, \; y = 3t - 7 \quad (0 \le t \le 3)$
5. $x = 2\cos t, \; y = 5\sin t \quad (0 \le t \le 2\pi)$
6. $x = \sqrt{t}, \; y = 2t + 4$
7. $x = 3 + 2\cos t, \; y = 2 + 4\sin t \quad (0 \le t \le 2\pi)$
8. $x = \sec t, \; y = \tan t \quad (\pi \le t < 3\pi/2)$
9. $x = \cos 2t, \; y = \sin t \quad (-\pi/2 \le t \le \pi/2)$
10. $x = 4t + 3, \; y = 16t^2 - 9$
11. $x = 2\sin^2 t, \; y = 3\cos^2 t \quad (0 \le t \le \pi/2)$
12. $x = \sec^2 t, \; y = \tan^2 t \quad (0 \le t < \pi/2)$

**13–18** Find parametric equations for the curve, and check your work by generating the curve with a graphing utility. ■

13. A circle of radius 5, centered at the origin, oriented clockwise.

14. The portion of the circle $x^2 + y^2 = 1$ that lies in the third quadrant, oriented counterclockwise.

15. A vertical line intersecting the $x$-axis at $x = 2$, oriented upward.

16. The ellipse $x^2/4 + y^2/9 = 1$, oriented counterclockwise.

17. The portion of the parabola $x = y^2$ joining $(1, -1)$ and $(1, 1)$, oriented down to up.

18. The circle of radius 4, centered at $(1, -3)$, oriented counterclockwise.

19. (a) Use a graphing utility to generate the trajectory of a housefly whose equations of motion over the time interval $0 \le t \le 5$ are
$$x = 6t - \tfrac{1}{2}t^3, \quad y = 1 + \tfrac{1}{2}t^2$$
(b) Make a table of $x$- and $y$-coordinates of the fly at times $t = 0, 1, 2, 3, 4, 5$.
(c) At what times is the fly on the $y$-axis?
(d) During what time interval is $y < 5$?
(e) At what time does the $x$-coordinate of the housefly reach a maximum?

20. (a) Use a graphing utility to generate the trajectory of a paper airplane whose equations of motion for $t \ge 0$ are
$$x = t - 2\sin t, \quad y = 3 - 2\cos t$$
(b) Assuming that the plane flies in a room in which the floor is at $y = 0$, explain why the plane will not crash into the floor. [For simplicity, ignore the physical size of the plane by treating it as a particle.]
(c) How high must the ceiling be to ensure that the plane does not touch or crash into it?

**21–22** Graph the equation using a graphing utility. ■

21. (a) $x = y^2 + 2y + 1$
(b) $x = \sin y, \; -2\pi \le y \le 2\pi$

22. (a) $x = y + 2y^3 - y^5$
(b) $x = \tan y, \; -\pi/2 < y < \pi/2$

**FOCUS ON CONCEPTS**

23. In each part, match the parametric equation with one of the curves labeled (I)–(VI), and explain your reasoning.
(a) $x = \sqrt{t}, \; y = \sin 3t$ (b) $x = 2\cos t, \; y = 3\sin t$
(c) $x = t\cos t, \; y = t\sin t$

*(cont.)*

(d) $x = \dfrac{3t}{1+t^3},\ y = \dfrac{3t^2}{1+t^3}$

(e) $x = \dfrac{t^3}{1+t^2},\ y = \dfrac{2t^2}{1+t^2}$

(f) $x = \frac{1}{2}\cos t,\ y = \sin 2t$

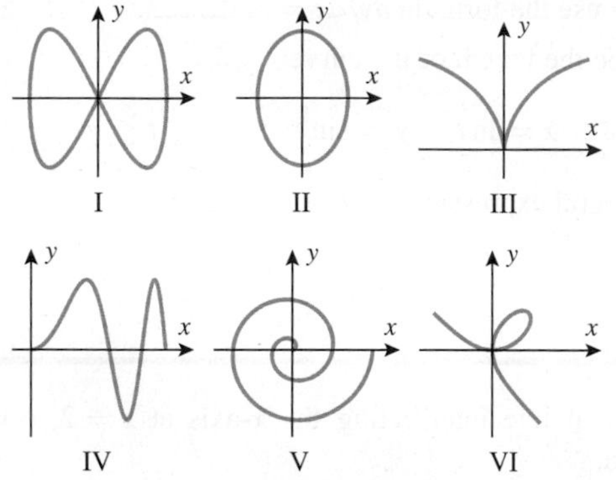


▲ Figure Ex-23

**24.** (a) Identify the orientation of the curves in Exercise 23.
(b) Explain why the parametric curve

$$x = t^2, \quad y = t^4 \quad (-1 \le t \le 1)$$

does not have a definite orientation.

**25.** (a) Suppose that the line segment from the point $P(x_0, y_0)$ to $Q(x_1, y_1)$ is represented parametrically by

$$x = x_0 + (x_1 - x_0)t, \quad y = y_0 + (y_1 - y_0)t \quad (0 \le t \le 1)$$

and that $R(x, y)$ is the point on the line segment corresponding to a specified value of $t$ (see the accompanying figure). Show that $t = r/q$, where $r$ is the distance from $P$ to $R$ and $q$ is the distance from $P$ to $Q$.
(b) What value of $t$ produces the midpoint between points $P$ and $Q$?
(c) What value of $t$ produces the point that is three-fourths of the way from $P$ to $Q$?

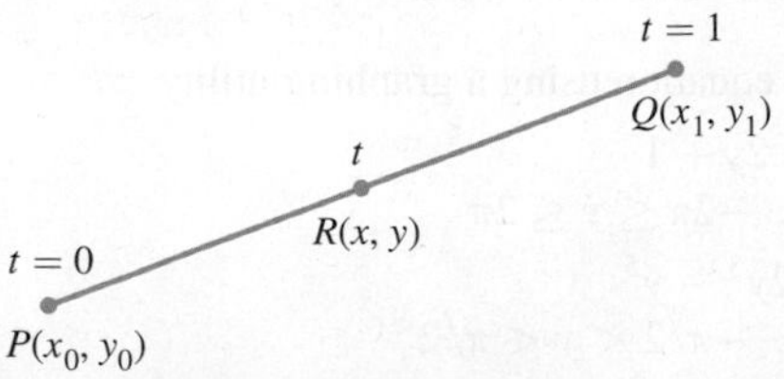


◀ Figure Ex-25

**26.** Find parametric equations for the line segment joining $P(2, -1)$ and $Q(3, 1)$, and use the result in Exercise 25 to find
(a) the midpoint between $P$ and $Q$
(b) the point that is one-fourth of the way from $P$ to $Q$
(c) the point that is three-fourths of the way from $P$ to $Q$.

**27.** (a) Show that the line segment joining the points $(x_0, y_0)$ and $(x_1, y_1)$ can be represented parametrically as

$$x = x_0 + (x_1 - x_0)\frac{t - t_0}{t_1 - t_0}, \quad y = y_0 + (y_1 - y_0)\frac{t - t_0}{t_1 - t_0} \quad (t_0 \le t \le t_1)$$

(b) Which way is the line segment oriented?
(c) Find parametric equations for the line segment traced from $(3, -1)$ to $(1, 4)$ as $t$ varies from 1 to 2, and check your result with a graphing utility.

**28.** (a) By eliminating the parameter, show that if $a$ and $c$ are not both zero, then the graph of the parametric equations

$$x = at + b, \quad y = ct + d \quad (t_0 \le t \le t_1)$$

is a line segment.
(b) Sketch the parametric curve

$$x = 2t - 1, \quad y = t + 1 \quad (1 \le t \le 2)$$

and indicate its orientation.
(c) What can you say about the line in part (a) if $a$ or $c$ (but not both) is zero?
(d) What do the equations represent if $a$ and $c$ are both zero?

**29–32** Use a graphing utility and parametric equations to display the graphs of $f$ and $f^{-1}$ on the same screen. ■

**29.** $f(x) = x^3 + 0.2x - 1, \quad -1 \le x \le 2$

**30.** $f(x) = \sqrt{x^2 + 2} + x, \quad -5 \le x \le 5$

**31.** $f(x) = \cos(\cos 0.5x), \quad 0 \le x \le 3$

**32.** $f(x) = x + \sin x, \quad 0 \le x \le 6$

**33–36 True–False** Determine whether the statement is true or false. Explain your answer. ■

**33.** The equation $y = 1 - x^2$ can be described parametrically by $x = \sin t$, $y = \cos^2 t$.

**34.** The graph of the parametric equations $x = f(t)$, $y = t$ is the reflection of the graph of $y = f(x)$ about the $x$-axis.

**35.** For the parametric curve $x = x(t)$, $y = 3t^4 - 2t^3$, the derivative of $y$ with respect to $x$ is computed by

$$\frac{dy}{dx} = \frac{12t^3 - 6t^2}{x'(t)}$$

**36.** The curve represented by the parametric equations

$$x = t^3, \quad y = t + t^6 \quad (-\infty < t < +\infty)$$

is concave down for $t < 0$.

**37.** Parametric curves can be defined piecewise by using different formulas for different values of the parameter. Sketch the curve that is represented piecewise by the parametric equations

$$\begin{cases} x = 2t, & y = 4t^2 \quad \left(0 \le t \le \frac{1}{2}\right) \\ x = 2 - 2t, & y = 2t \quad \left(\frac{1}{2} \le t \le 1\right) \end{cases}$$

**38.** Find parametric equations for the rectangle in the accompanying figure, assuming that the rectangle is traced counterclockwise as $t$ varies from 0 to 1, starting at $\left(\frac{1}{2}, \frac{1}{2}\right)$ when $t = 0$. [*Hint:* Represent the rectangle piecewise, letting $t$ vary from 0 to $\frac{1}{4}$ for the first edge, from $\frac{1}{4}$ to $\frac{1}{2}$ for the second edge, and so forth.]

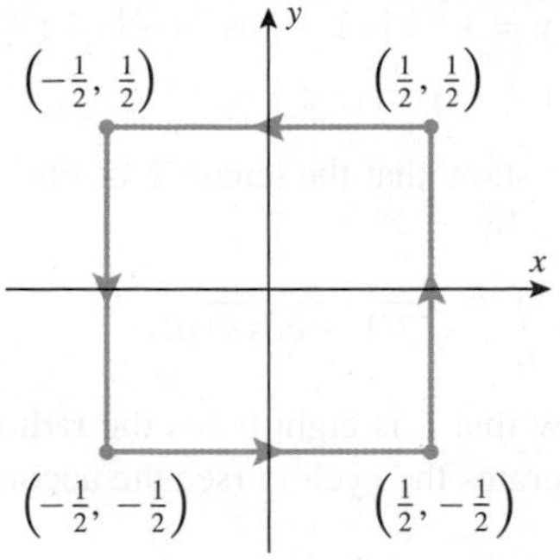

◀ **Figure Ex-38**

**39.** (a) Find parametric equations for the ellipse that is centered at the origin and has intercepts $(4, 0)$, $(-4, 0)$, $(0, 3)$, and $(0, -3)$.
(b) Find parametric equations for the ellipse that results by translating the ellipse in part (a) so that its center is at $(-1, 2)$.
(c) Confirm your results in parts (a) and (b) using a graphing utility.

**40.** We will show later in the text that if a projectile is fired from ground level with an initial speed of $v_0$ meters per second at an angle $\alpha$ with the horizontal, and if air resistance is neglected, then its position after $t$ seconds, relative to the coordinate system in the accompanying figure is

$$x = (v_0 \cos \alpha)t, \quad y = (v_0 \sin \alpha)t - \tfrac{1}{2}gt^2$$

where $g \approx 9.8 \text{ m/s}^2$.
(a) By eliminating the parameter, show that the trajectory lies on the graph of a quadratic polynomial.
(b) Use a graphing utility to sketch the trajectory if $\alpha = 30°$ and $v_0 = 1000$ m/s.
(c) Using the trajectory in part (b), how high does the shell rise?
(d) Using the trajectory in part (b), how far does the shell travel horizontally?

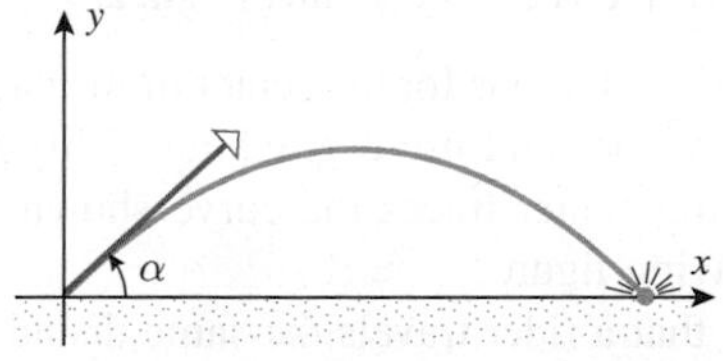

◀ **Figure Ex-40**

**FOCUS ON CONCEPTS**

**41.** (a) Find the slope of the tangent line to the parametric curve $x = t/2$, $y = t^2 + 1$ at $t = -1$ and at $t = 1$ without eliminating the parameter.
(b) Check your answers in part (a) by eliminating the parameter and differentiating an appropriate function of $x$.

**42.** (a) Find the slope of the tangent line to the parametric curve $x = 3\cos t$, $y = 4\sin t$ at $t = \pi/4$ and at $t = 7\pi/4$ without eliminating the parameter.
(b) Check your answers in part (a) by eliminating the parameter and differentiating an appropriate function of $x$.

**43.** For the parametric curve in Exercise 41, make a conjecture about the sign of $d^2y/dx^2$ at $t = -1$ and at $t = 1$, and confirm your conjecture without eliminating the parameter.

**44.** For the parametric curve in Exercise 42, make a conjecture about the sign of $d^2y/dx^2$ at $t = \pi/4$ and at $t = 7\pi/4$, and confirm your conjecture without eliminating the parameter.

**45–50** Find $dy/dx$ and $d^2y/dx^2$ at the given point without eliminating the parameter. ■

**45.** $x = \sqrt{t}$, $y = 2t + 4$; $t = 1$

**46.** $x = \frac{1}{2}t^2 + 1$, $y = \frac{1}{3}t^3 - t$; $t = 2$

**47.** $x = \sec t$, $y = \tan t$; $t = \pi/3$

**48.** $x = \sinh t$, $y = \cosh t$; $t = 0$

**49.** $x = \theta + \cos\theta$, $y = 1 + \sin\theta$; $\theta = \pi/6$

**50.** $x = \cos\phi$, $y = 3\sin\phi$; $\phi = 5\pi/6$

**51.** (a) Find the equation of the tangent line to the curve

$$x = e^t, \quad y = e^{-t}$$

at $t = 1$ without eliminating the parameter.
(b) Find the equation of the tangent line in part (a) by eliminating the parameter.

**52.** (a) Find the equation of the tangent line to the curve

$$x = 2t + 4, \quad y = 8t^2 - 2t + 4$$

at $t = 1$ without eliminating the parameter.
(b) Find the equation of the tangent line in part (a) by eliminating the parameter.

**53–54** Find all values of $t$ at which the parametric curve has (a) a horizontal tangent line and (b) a vertical tangent line. ■

**53.** $x = 2\sin t$, $y = 4\cos t$ $(0 \le t \le 2\pi)$

**54.** $x = 2t^3 - 15t^2 + 24t + 7$, $y = t^2 + t + 1$

**55.** In the mid-1850s the French physicist Jules Antoine Lissajous (1822–1880) became interested in parametric equations of the form

$$x = \sin at, \quad y = \sin bt$$

in the course of studying vibrations that combine two perpendicular sinusoidal motions. If $a/b$ is a rational number, then the combined effect of the oscillations is a periodic motion along a path called a ***Lissajous curve***.
(a) Use a graphing utility to generate the complete graph of the Lissajous curves corresponding to $a = 1, b = 2$; $a = 2, b = 3$; $a = 3, b = 4$; and $a = 4, b = 5$.
(b) The Lissajous curve

$$x = \sin t, \quad y = \sin 2t \quad (0 \le t \le 2\pi)$$

crosses itself at the origin (see Figure Ex-55 on the next page). Find equations for the two tangent lines at the origin.

**56.** The ***prolate cycloid***

$$x = 2 - \pi\cos t, \quad y = 2t - \pi\sin t \quad (-\pi \le t \le \pi)$$

crosses itself at a point on the $x$-axis (see the accompanying figure on the next page). Find equations for the two tangent lines at that point.

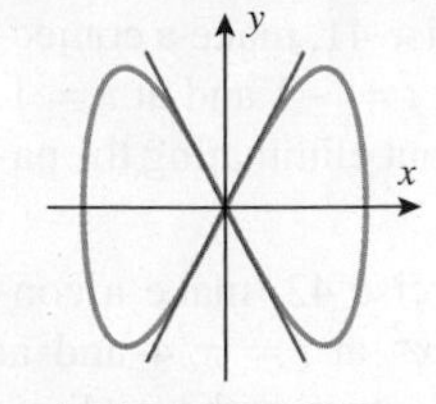

▲ Figure Ex-55

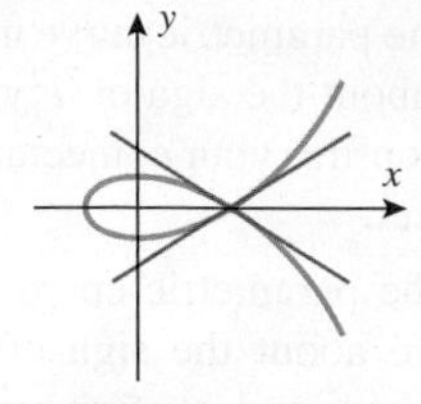

▲ Figure Ex-56

**57.** Show that the curve $x = t^2$, $y = t^3 - 4t$ intersects itself at the point (4, 0), and find equations for the two tangent lines to the curve at the point of intersection.

**58.** Show that the curve with parametric equations

$$x = t^2 - 3t + 5, \quad y = t^3 + t^2 - 10t + 9$$

intersects itself at the point (3, 1), and find equations for the two tangent lines to the curve at the point of intersection.

**59.** (a) Use a graphing utility to generate the graph of the parametric curve

$$x = \cos^3 t, \quad y = \sin^3 t \qquad (0 \le t \le 2\pi)$$

and make a conjecture about the values of $t$ at which singular points occur.

(b) Confirm your conjecture in part (a) by calculating appropriate derivatives.

**60.** Verify that the cycloid described by Formula (10) has cusps at its $x$-intercepts and horizontal tangent lines at midpoints between adjacent $x$-intercepts (see Figure 10.1.14).

**61.** (a) What is the slope of the tangent line at time $t$ to the trajectory of the paper airplane in Example 5?

(b) What was the airplane's approximate angle of inclination when it crashed into the wall?

**62.** Suppose that a bee follows the trajectory

$$x = t - 2\cos t, \quad y = 2 - 2\sin t \qquad (0 \le t \le 10)$$

(a) At what times was the bee flying horizontally?

(b) At what times was the bee flying vertically?

**63.** Consider the family of curves described by the parametric equations

$$x = a\cos t + h, \quad y = b\sin t + k \qquad (0 \le t < 2\pi)$$

where $a \ne 0$ and $b \ne 0$. Describe the curves in this family if

(a) $h$ and $k$ are fixed but $a$ and $b$ can vary

(b) $a$ and $b$ are fixed but $h$ and $k$ can vary

(c) $a = 1$ and $b = 1$, but $h$ and $k$ vary so that $h = k + 1$.

**64.** (a) Use a graphing utility to study how the curves in the family

$$x = 2a\cos^2 t, \quad y = 2a\cos t \sin t \qquad (-2\pi < t < 2\pi)$$

change as $a$ varies from 0 to 5.

(b) Confirm your conclusion algebraically.

(c) Write a brief paragraph that describes your findings.

**65–70** Find the exact arc length of the curve over the stated interval. ■

**65.** $x = t^2$, $y = \frac{1}{3}t^3 \quad (0 \le t \le 1)$

**66.** $x = \sqrt{t} - 2$, $y = 2t^{3/4} \quad (1 \le t \le 16)$

**67.** $x = \cos 3t$, $y = \sin 3t \quad (0 \le t \le \pi)$

**68.** $x = \sin t + \cos t$, $y = \sin t - \cos t \quad (0 \le t \le \pi)$

**69.** $x = e^{2t}(\sin t + \cos t)$, $y = e^{2t}(\sin t - \cos t)\ (-1 \le t \le 1)$

**70.** $x = 2\sin^{-1} t$, $y = \ln(1 - t^2) \quad \left(0 \le t \le \frac{1}{2}\right)$

C **71.** (a) Use Formula (9) to show that the length $L$ of one arch of a cycloid is given by

$$L = a\int_0^{2\pi} \sqrt{2(1 - \cos\theta)}\, d\theta$$

(b) Use a CAS to show that $L$ is eight times the radius of the wheel that generates the cycloid (see the accompanying figure).

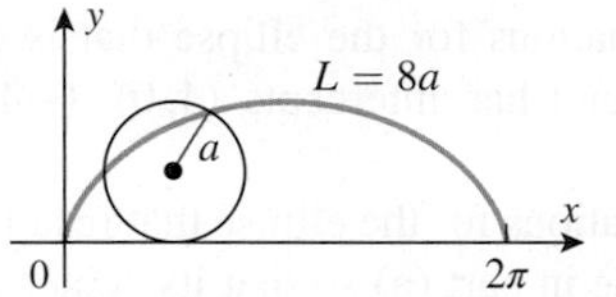

◀ Figure Ex-71

**72.** Use the parametric equations in Formula (10) to verify that the cycloid provides one solution to the differential equation

$$\left(1 + \left(\frac{dy}{dx}\right)^2\right) y = 2a$$

where $a$ is a positive constant.

**FOCUS ON CONCEPTS**

**73.** The amusement park rides illustrated in the accompanying figure consist of two connected rotating arms of length 1—an inner arm that rotates counterclockwise at 1 radian per second and an outer arm that can be programmed to rotate either clockwise at 2 radians per second (the Scrambler ride) or counterclockwise at 2 radians per second (the Calypso ride). The center of the rider cage is at the end of the outer arm.

(a) Show that in the Scrambler ride the center of the cage has parametric equations

$$x = \cos t + \cos 2t, \quad y = \sin t - \sin 2t$$

(b) Find parametric equations for the center of the cage in the Calypso ride, and use a graphing utility to confirm that the center traces the curve shown in the accompanying figure.

(c) Do you think that a rider travels the same distance in one revolution of the Scrambler ride as in one revolution of the Calypso ride? Justify your conclusion.

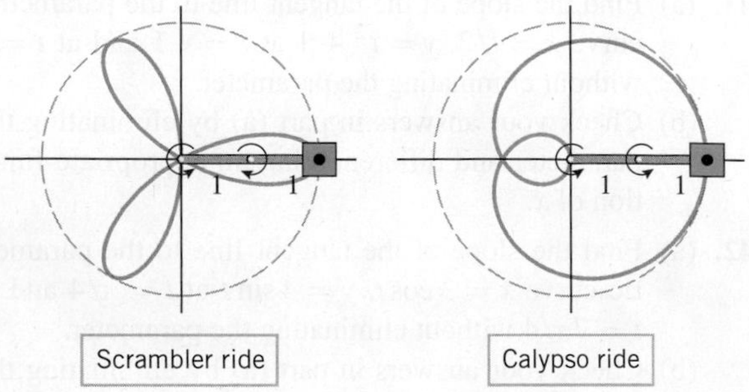

▲ Figure Ex-73

**74.** (a) If a thread is unwound from a fixed circle while being held taut (i.e., tangent to the circle), then the end of the thread traces a curve called an ***involute of a circle***. Show that if the circle is centered at the origin, has radius $a$, and the end of the thread is initially at the point $(a, 0)$, then the involute can be expressed parametrically as

$$x = a(\cos\theta + \theta\sin\theta), \quad y = a(\sin\theta - \theta\cos\theta)$$

where $\theta$ is the angle shown in part (*a*) of the accompanying figure.

(b) Assuming that the dog in part (*b*) of the accompanying figure unwinds its leash while keeping it taut, for what values of $\theta$ in the interval $0 \le \theta \le 2\pi$ will the dog be walking North? South? East? West?

(c) Use a graphing utility to generate the curve traced by the dog, and show that it is consistent with your answer in part (*b*).

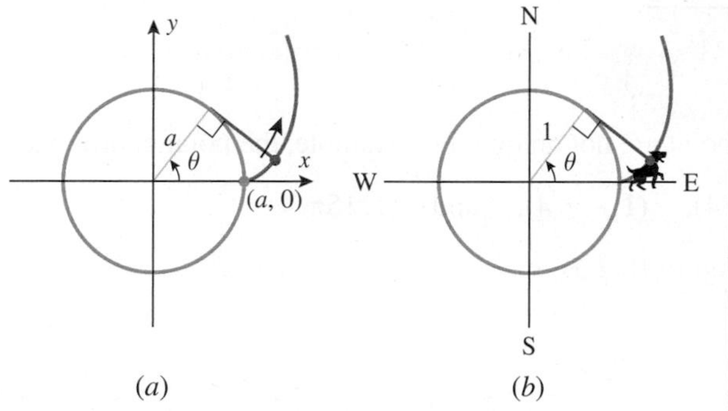


▲ **Figure Ex-74**

**75–80** If $f'(t)$ and $g'(t)$ are continuous functions, and if no segment of the curve

$$x = f(t), \quad y = g(t) \qquad (a \le t \le b)$$

is traced more than once, then it can be shown that the area of the surface generated by revolving this curve about the $x$-axis is

$$S = \int_a^b 2\pi y\sqrt{\left(\frac{dx}{dt}\right)^2 + \left(\frac{dy}{dt}\right)^2}\, dt$$

and the area of the surface generated by revolving the curve about the $y$-axis is

$$S = \int_a^b 2\pi x\sqrt{\left(\frac{dx}{dt}\right)^2 + \left(\frac{dy}{dt}\right)^2}\, dt$$

[The derivations are similar to those used to obtain Formulas (4) and (5) in Section 6.5.] Use the formulas above in these exercises. ■

**75.** Find the area of the surface generated by revolving $x = t^2$, $y = 3t$ $(0 \le t \le 2)$ about the $x$-axis.

**76.** Find the area of the surface generated by revolving the curve $x = e^t\cos t$, $y = e^t\sin t$ $(0 \le t \le \pi/2)$ about the $x$-axis.

**77.** Find the area of the surface generated by revolving the curve $x = \cos^2 t$, $y = \sin^2 t$ $(0 \le t \le \pi/2)$ about the $y$-axis.

**78.** Find the area of the surface generated by revolving $x = 6t$, $y = 4t^2$ $(0 \le t \le 1)$ about the $y$-axis.

**79.** By revolving the semicircle

$$x = r\cos t, \quad y = r\sin t \qquad (0 \le t \le \pi)$$

about the $x$-axis, show that the surface area of a sphere of radius $r$ is $4\pi r^2$.

**80.** The equations

$$x = a\phi - a\sin\phi, \quad y = a - a\cos\phi \qquad (0 \le \phi \le 2\pi)$$

represent one arch of a cycloid. Show that the surface area generated by revolving this curve about the $x$-axis is given by $S = 64\pi a^2/3$.

**81. Writing** Consult appropriate reference works and write an essay on American mathematician Nathaniel Bowditch (1773–1838) and his investigation of ***Bowditch curves*** (better known as Lissajous curves; see Exercise 55).

**82. Writing** What are some of the advantages of expressing a curve parametrically rather than in the form $y = f(x)$?

---

✓ **QUICK CHECK ANSWERS 10.1** 1. $x = 3 + 2\cos t$, $y = 5 + 2\sin t$ $(0 \le t \le 2\pi)$ 2. $\frac{3}{4}$; 2.75 3. $x = f(1 - t)$, $y = g(1 - t)$ 4. $\dfrac{dy/dt}{dx/dt} = \dfrac{g'(t)}{f'(t)}$ 5. $\displaystyle\int_1^{\pi} \sqrt{(1/t)^2 + \cos^2 t}\, dt$

---

## 10.2 POLAR COORDINATES

*Up to now we have specified the location of a point in the plane by means of coordinates relative to two perpendicular coordinate axes. However, sometimes a moving point has a special affinity for some fixed point, such as a planet moving in an orbit under the central attraction of the Sun. In such cases, the path of the particle is best described by its angular direction and its distance from the fixed point. In this section we will discuss a new kind of coordinate system that is based on this idea.*

## POLAR COORDINATE SYSTEMS

A ***polar coordinate system*** in a plane consists of a fixed point $O$, called the ***pole*** (or ***origin***), and a ray emanating from the pole, called the ***polar axis***. In such a coordinate system we can associate with each point $P$ in the plane a pair of ***polar coordinates*** $(r, \theta)$, where $r$ is the distance from $P$ to the pole and $\theta$ is an angle from the polar axis to the ray $OP$ (Figure 10.2.1). The number $r$ is called the ***radial coordinate*** of $P$ and the number $\theta$ the ***angular coordinate*** (or ***polar angle***) of $P$. In Figure 10.2.2, the points $(6, \pi/4)$, $(5, 2\pi/3)$, $(3, 5\pi/4)$, and $(4, 11\pi/6)$ are plotted in polar coordinate systems. If $P$ is the pole, then $r = 0$, but there is no clearly defined polar angle. We will agree that an arbitrary angle can be used in this case; that is, $(0, \theta)$ are polar coordinates of the pole for all choices of $\theta$.

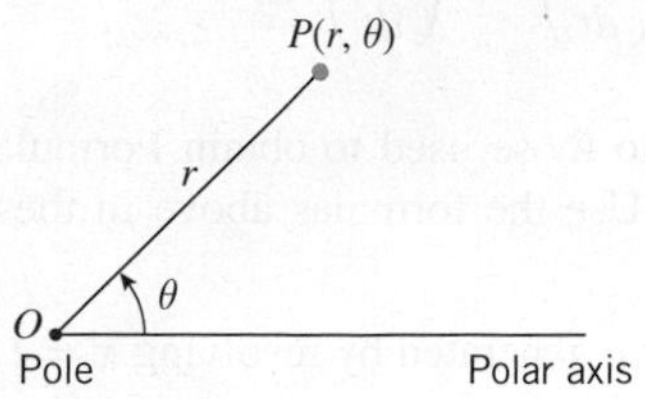

▲ **Figure 10.2.1**

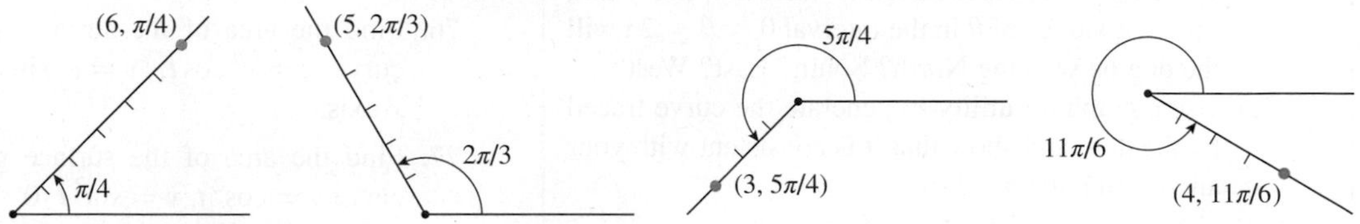

▲ **Figure 10.2.2**

The polar coordinates of a point are not unique. For example, the polar coordinates

$$(1, 7\pi/4), \quad (1, -\pi/4), \quad \text{and} \quad (1, 15\pi/4)$$

all represent the same point (Figure 10.2.3).

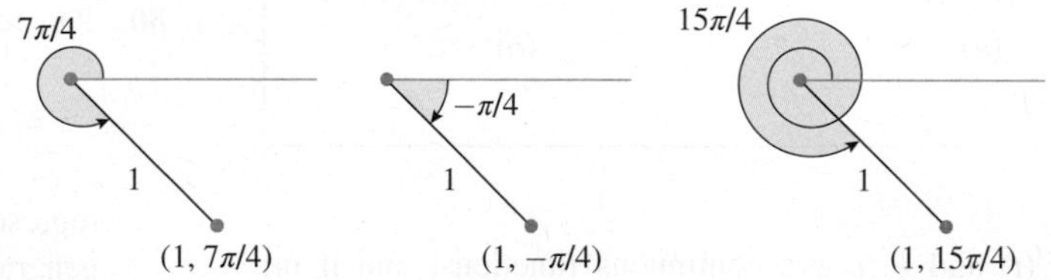

▶ **Figure 10.2.3**

In general, if a point $P$ has polar coordinates $(r, \theta)$, then

$$(r, \theta + 2n\pi) \quad \text{and} \quad (r, \theta - 2n\pi)$$

are also polar coordinates of $P$ for any nonnegative integer $n$. Thus, every point has infinitely many pairs of polar coordinates.

As defined above, the radial coordinate $r$ of a point $P$ is nonnegative, since it represents the distance from $P$ to the pole. However, it will be convenient to allow for negative values of $r$ as well. To motivate an appropriate definition, consider the point $P$ with polar coordinates $(3, 5\pi/4)$. As shown in Figure 10.2.4, we can reach this point by rotating the polar axis through an angle of $5\pi/4$ and then moving 3 units from the pole along the terminal side of the angle, or we can reach the point $P$ by rotating the polar axis through an angle of $\pi/4$ and then moving 3 units from the pole along the extension of the terminal side. This suggests that the point $(3, 5\pi/4)$ might also be denoted by $(-3, \pi/4)$, with the minus sign serving to indicate that the point is on the *extension* of the angle's terminal side rather than on the terminal side itself.

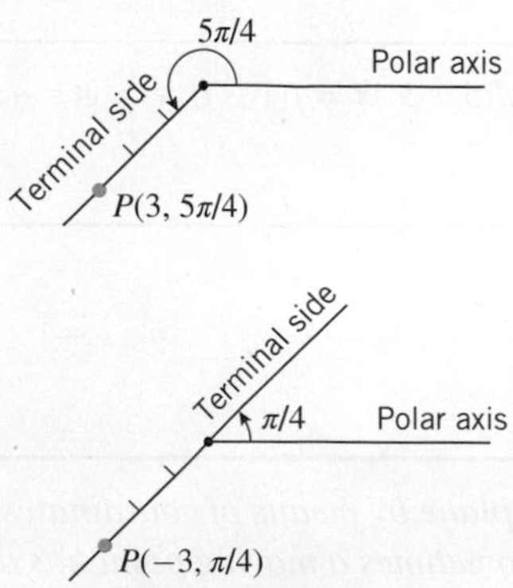

▲ **Figure 10.2.4**

In general, the terminal side of the angle $\theta + \pi$ is the extension of the terminal side of $\theta$, so we define negative radial coordinates by agreeing that

$$(-r, \theta) \quad \text{and} \quad (r, \theta + \pi)$$

are polar coordinates of the same point.

## RELATIONSHIP BETWEEN POLAR AND RECTANGULAR COORDINATES

Frequently, it will be useful to superimpose a rectangular $xy$-coordinate system on top of a polar coordinate system, making the positive $x$-axis coincide with the polar axis. If this is done, then every point $P$ will have both rectangular coordinates $(x, y)$ and polar coordinates $(r, \theta)$. As suggested by Figure 10.2.5, these coordinates are related by the equations

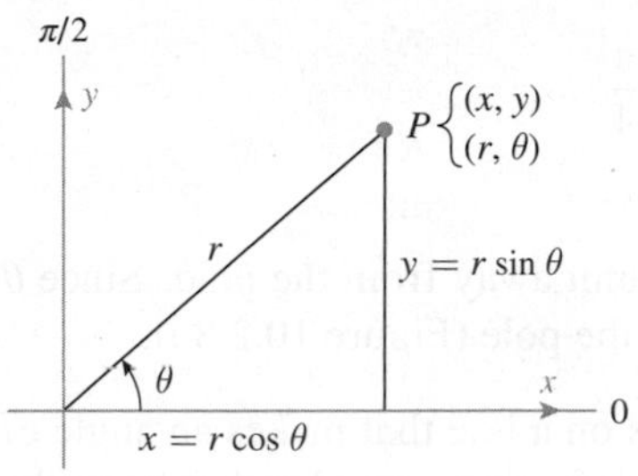

▲ **Figure 10.2.5**

$$x = r\cos\theta, \quad y = r\sin\theta \tag{1}$$

These equations are well suited for finding $x$ and $y$ when $r$ and $\theta$ are known. However, to find $r$ and $\theta$ when $x$ and $y$ are known, it is preferable to use the identities $\sin^2\theta + \cos^2\theta = 1$ and $\tan\theta = \sin\theta/\cos\theta$ to rewrite (1) as

$$r^2 = x^2 + y^2, \quad \tan\theta = \frac{y}{x} \tag{2}$$

▶ **Example 1** Find the rectangular coordinates of the point $P$ whose polar coordinates are $(r, \theta) = (6, 2\pi/3)$ (Figure 10.2.6).

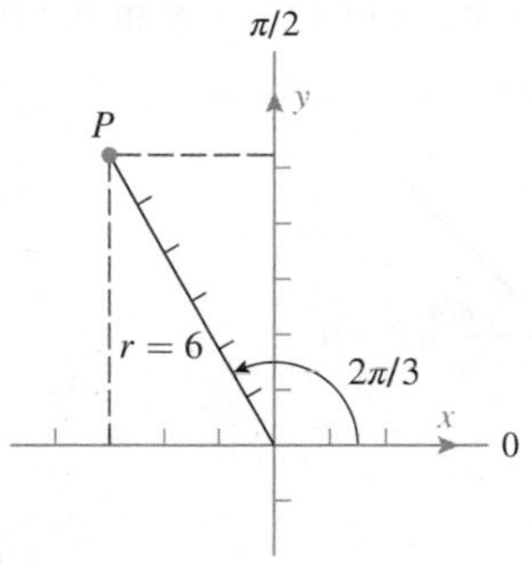

▲ **Figure 10.2.6**

***Solution.*** Substituting the polar coordinates $r = 6$ and $\theta = 2\pi/3$ in (1) yields

$$x = 6\cos\frac{2\pi}{3} = 6\left(-\frac{1}{2}\right) = -3$$

$$y = 6\sin\frac{2\pi}{3} = 6\left(\frac{\sqrt{3}}{2}\right) = 3\sqrt{3}$$

Thus, the rectangular coordinates of $P$ are $(x, y) = (-3, 3\sqrt{3})$. ◀

▶ **Example 2** Find polar coordinates of the point $P$ whose rectangular coordinates are $(-2, -2\sqrt{3})$ (Figure 10.2.7).

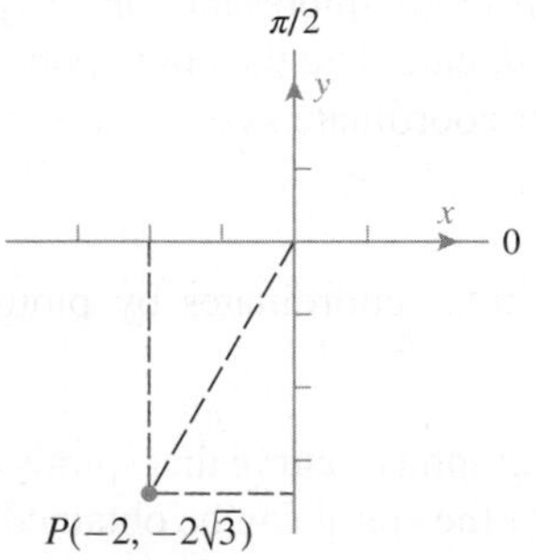

▲ **Figure 10.2.7**

***Solution.*** We will find the polar coordinates $(r, \theta)$ of $P$ that satisfy the conditions $r > 0$ and $0 \le \theta < 2\pi$. From the first equation in (2),

$$r^2 = x^2 + y^2 = (-2)^2 + (-2\sqrt{3})^2 = 4 + 12 = 16$$

so $r = 4$. From the second equation in (2),

$$\tan\theta = \frac{y}{x} = \frac{-2\sqrt{3}}{-2} = \sqrt{3}$$

From this and the fact that $(-2, -2\sqrt{3})$ lies in the third quadrant, it follows that the angle satisfying the requirement $0 \le \theta < 2\pi$ is $\theta = 4\pi/3$. Thus, $(r, \theta) = (4, 4\pi/3)$ are polar coordinates of $P$. All other polar coordinates of $P$ are expressible in the form

$$\left(4, \frac{4\pi}{3} + 2n\pi\right) \quad \text{or} \quad \left(-4, \frac{\pi}{3} + 2n\pi\right)$$

where $n$ is an integer. ◀

## GRAPHS IN POLAR COORDINATES

We will now consider the problem of graphing equations in $r$ and $\theta$, where $\theta$ is assumed to be measured in radians. Some examples of such equations are

$$r = 1, \quad \theta = \pi/4, \quad r = \theta, \quad r = \sin\theta, \quad r = \cos 2\theta$$

In a rectangular coordinate system the graph of an equation in $x$ and $y$ consists of all points whose coordinates $(x, y)$ satisfy the equation. However, in a polar coordinate system, points have infinitely many different pairs of polar coordinates, so that a given point may have some polar coordinates that satisfy an equation and others that do not. Given an equation in $r$ and $\theta$, we define its ***graph in polar coordinates*** to consist of all points with *at least one* pair of coordinates $(r, \theta)$ that satisfy the equation.

► **Example 3** Sketch the graphs of

$$\text{(a) } r = 1 \qquad \text{(b) } \theta = \frac{\pi}{4}$$

in polar coordinates.

***Solution (a).*** For all values of $\theta$, the point $(1, \theta)$ is 1 unit away from the pole. Since $\theta$ is arbitrary, the graph is the circle of radius 1 centered at the pole (Figure 10.2.8*a*).

***Solution (b).*** For all values of $r$, the point $(r, \pi/4)$ lies on a line that makes an angle of $\pi/4$ with the polar axis (Figure 10.2.8*b*). Positive values of $r$ correspond to points on the line in the first quadrant and negative values of $r$ to points on the line in the third quadrant. Thus, in absence of any restriction on $r$, the graph is the entire line. Observe, however, that had we imposed the restriction $r \geq 0$, the graph would have been just the ray in the first quadrant. ◄

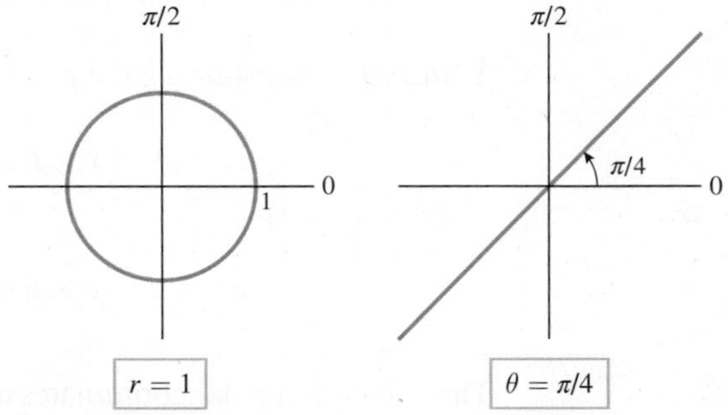


► **Figure 10.2.8** (*a*) (*b*)

Equations $r = f(\theta)$ that express $r$ as a function of $\theta$ are especially important. One way to graph such an equation is to choose some typical values of $\theta$, calculate the corresponding values of $r$, and then plot the resulting pairs $(r, \theta)$ in a polar coordinate system. The next two examples illustrate this process.

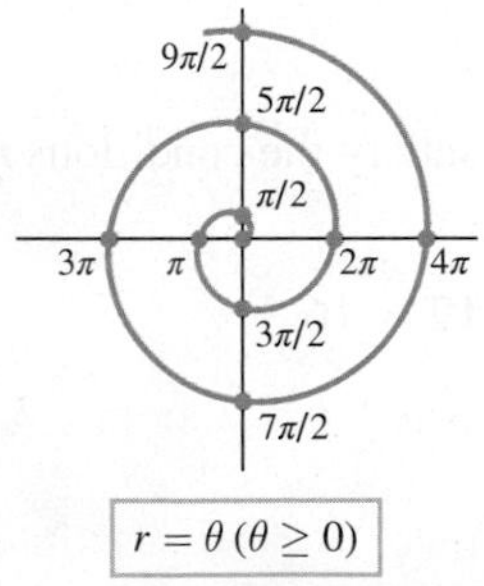


▲ **Figure 10.2.9**

Graph the spiral $r = \theta\ (\theta \leq 0)$. Compare your graph to that in Figure 10.2.9.

► **Example 4** Sketch the graph of $r = \theta\ (\theta \geq 0)$ in polar coordinates by plotting points.

***Solution.*** Observe that as $\theta$ increases, so does $r$; thus, the graph is a curve that spirals out from the pole as $\theta$ increases. A reasonably accurate sketch of the spiral can be obtained by plotting the points that correspond to values of $\theta$ that are integer multiples of $\pi/2$, keeping in mind that the value of $r$ is always equal to the value of $\theta$ (Figure 10.2.9). ◄

► **Example 5** Sketch the graph of the equation $r = \sin\theta$ in polar coordinates by plotting points.

***Solution.*** Table 10.2.1 shows the coordinates of points on the graph at increments of $\pi/6$.

These points are plotted in Figure 10.2.10. Note, however, that there are 13 points listed in the table but only 6 distinct plotted points. This is because the pairs from $\theta = \pi$ on yield duplicates of the preceding points. For example, $(-1/2, 7\pi/6)$ and $(1/2, \pi/6)$ represent the same point. ◄

**Table 10.2.1**

| $\theta$ (RADIANS) | $0$ | $\frac{\pi}{6}$ | $\frac{\pi}{3}$ | $\frac{\pi}{2}$ | $\frac{2\pi}{3}$ | $\frac{5\pi}{6}$ | $\pi$ | $\frac{7\pi}{6}$ | $\frac{4\pi}{3}$ | $\frac{3\pi}{2}$ | $\frac{5\pi}{4}$ | $\frac{11\pi}{6}$ | $2\pi$ |
|---|---|---|---|---|---|---|---|---|---|---|---|---|---|
| $r = \sin\theta$ | $0$ | $\frac{1}{2}$ | $\frac{\sqrt{3}}{2}$ | $1$ | $\frac{\sqrt{3}}{2}$ | $\frac{1}{2}$ | $0$ | $-\frac{1}{2}$ | $-\frac{\sqrt{3}}{2}$ | $-1$ | $-\frac{\sqrt{3}}{2}$ | $-\frac{1}{2}$ | $0$ |
| $(r, \theta)$ | $(0, 0)$ | $\left(\frac{1}{2}, \frac{\pi}{6}\right)$ | $\left(\frac{\sqrt{3}}{2}, \frac{\pi}{3}\right)$ | $\left(1, \frac{\pi}{2}\right)$ | $\left(\frac{\sqrt{3}}{2}, \frac{2\pi}{3}\right)$ | $\left(\frac{1}{2}, \frac{5\pi}{6}\right)$ | $(0, \pi)$ | $\left(-\frac{1}{2}, \frac{7\pi}{6}\right)$ | $\left(-\frac{\sqrt{3}}{2}, \frac{4\pi}{3}\right)$ | $\left(-1, \frac{3\pi}{2}\right)$ | $\left(-\frac{\sqrt{3}}{2}, \frac{5\pi}{3}\right)$ | $\left(-\frac{1}{2}, \frac{11\pi}{6}\right)$ | $(0, 2\pi)$ |

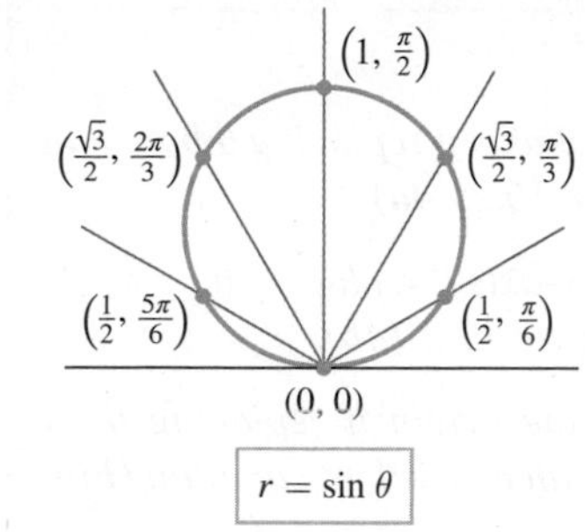


▲ **Figure 10.2.10**

Observe that the points in Figure 10.2.10 appear to lie on a circle. We can confirm that this is so by expressing the polar equation $r = \sin\theta$ in terms of $x$ and $y$. To do this, we multiply the equation through by $r$ to obtain

$$r^2 = r\sin\theta$$

which now allows us to apply Formulas (1) and (2) to rewrite the equation as

$$x^2 + y^2 = y$$

Rewriting this equation as $x^2 + y^2 - y = 0$ and then completing the square yields

$$x^2 + \left(y - \tfrac{1}{2}\right)^2 = \tfrac{1}{4}$$

which is a circle of radius $\frac{1}{2}$ centered at the point $\left(0, \frac{1}{2}\right)$ in the $xy$-plane.

It is often useful to view the equation $r = f(\theta)$ as an equation in rectangular coordinates (rather than polar coordinates) and graphed in a rectangular $\theta r$-coordinate system. For example, Figure 10.2.11 shows the graph of $r = \sin\theta$ displayed using rectangular $\theta r$-coordinates. This graph can actually help to visualize how the polar graph in Figure 10.2.10 is generated:

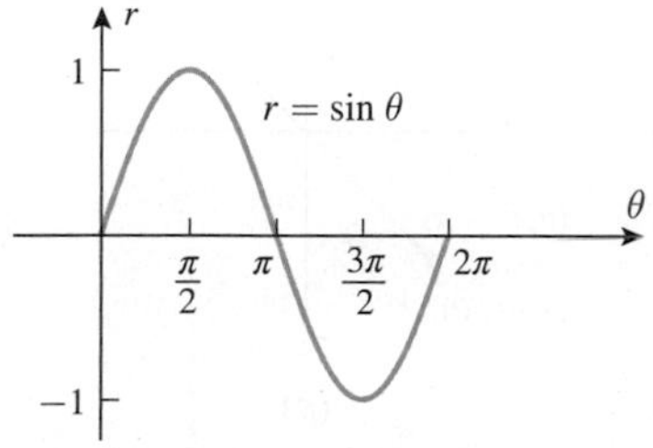


▲ **Figure 10.2.11**

- At $\theta = 0$ we have $r = 0$, which corresponds to the pole $(0, 0)$ on the polar graph.
- As $\theta$ varies from 0 to $\pi/2$, the value of $r$ increases from 0 to 1, so the point $(r, \theta)$ moves along the circle from the pole to the high point at $(1, \pi/2)$.
- As $\theta$ varies from $\pi/2$ to $\pi$, the value of $r$ decreases from 1 back to 0, so the point $(r, \theta)$ moves along the circle from the high point back to the pole.
- As $\theta$ varies from $\pi$ to $3\pi/2$, the values of $r$ are negative, varying from 0 to $-1$. Thus, the point $(r, \theta)$ moves along the circle from the pole to the high point at $(1, \pi/2)$, which is the same as the point $(-1, 3\pi/2)$. This duplicates the motion that occurred for $0 \le \theta \le \pi/2$.
- As $\theta$ varies from $3\pi/2$ to $2\pi$, the value of $r$ varies from $-1$ to 0. Thus, the point $(r, \theta)$ moves along the circle from the high point back to the pole, duplicating the motion that occurred for $\pi/2 \le \theta \le \pi$.

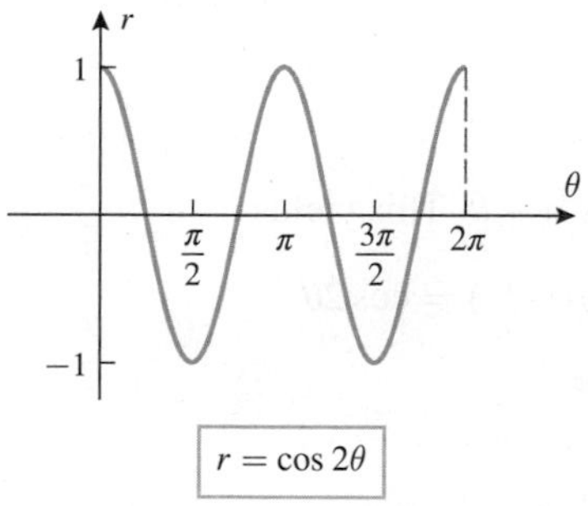


▲ **Figure 10.2.12**

▶ **Example 6** Sketch the graph of $r = \cos 2\theta$ in polar coordinates.

***Solution.*** Instead of plotting points, we will use the graph of $r = \cos 2\theta$ in rectangular coordinates (Figure 10.2.12) to visualize how the polar graph of this equation is generated. The analysis and the resulting polar graph are shown in Figure 10.2.13. This curve is called a *four-petal rose*. ◀

## SYMMETRY TESTS

Observe that the polar graph of $r = \cos 2\theta$ in Figure 10.2.13 is symmetric about the $x$-axis and the $y$-axis. This symmetry could have been predicted from the following theorem, which is suggested by Figure 10.2.14 (we omit the proof).

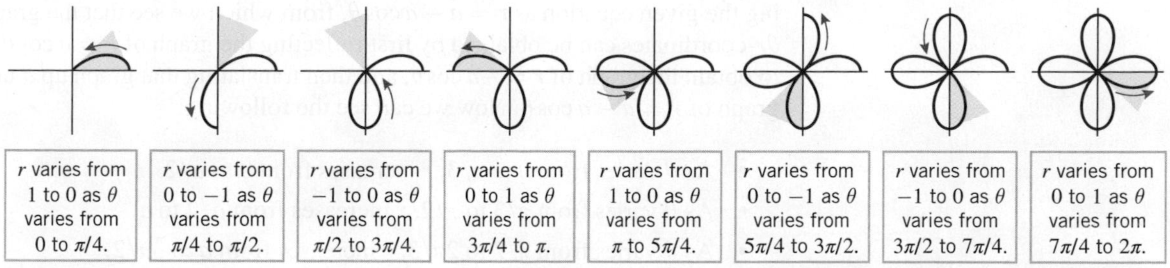


▲ **Figure 10.2.13**

The converse of each part of Theorem 10.2.1 is false. See Exercise 79.

**10.2.1 THEOREM (*Symmetry Tests*)**

(*a*) *A curve in polar coordinates is symmetric about the x-axis if replacing $\theta$ by $-\theta$ in its equation produces an equivalent equation (Figure 10.2.14a).*

(*b*) *A curve in polar coordinates is symmetric about the y-axis if replacing $\theta$ by $\pi - \theta$ in its equation produces an equivalent equation (Figure 10.2.14b).*

(*c*) *A curve in polar coordinates is symmetric about the origin if replacing $\theta$ by $\theta + \pi$, or replacing r by $-r$ in its equation produces an equivalent equation (Figure 10.2.14c).*

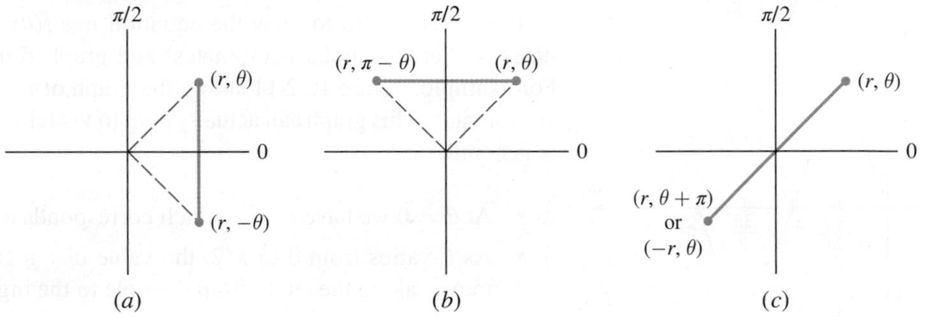


▶ Figure 10.2.14

**▶ Example 7** Use Theorem 10.2.1 to confirm that the graph of $r = \cos 2\theta$ in Figure 10.2.13 is symmetric about the $x$-axis and $y$-axis.

A graph that is symmetric about both the $x$-axis and the $y$-axis is also symmetric about the origin. Use Theorem 10.2.1(c) to verify that the curve in Example 7 is symmetric about the origin.

***Solution.*** To test for symmetry about the $x$-axis, we replace $\theta$ by $-\theta$. This yields

$$r = \cos(-2\theta) = \cos 2\theta$$

Thus, replacing $\theta$ by $-\theta$ does not alter the equation.

To test for symmetry about the $y$-axis, we replace $\theta$ by $\pi - \theta$. This yields

$$r = \cos 2(\pi - \theta) = \cos(2\pi - 2\theta) = \cos(-2\theta) = \cos 2\theta$$

Thus, replacing $\theta$ by $\pi - \theta$ does not alter the equation. ◀

**▶ Example 8** Sketch the graph of $r = a(1 - \cos\theta)$ in polar coordinates, assuming $a$ to be a positive constant.

***Solution.*** Observe first that replacing $\theta$ by $-\theta$ does not alter the equation, so we know in advance that the graph is symmetric about the polar axis. Thus, if we graph the upper half of the curve, then we can obtain the lower half by reflection about the polar axis.

As in our previous examples, we will first graph the equation in rectangular $\theta r$-coordinates. This graph, which is shown in Figure 10.2.15$a$, can be obtained by rewriting the given equation as $r = a - a\cos\theta$, from which we see that the graph in rectangular $\theta r$-coordinates can be obtained by first reflecting the graph of $r = a\cos\theta$ about the $x$-axis to obtain the graph of $r = -a\cos\theta$, and then translating that graph up $a$ units to obtain the graph of $r = a - a\cos\theta$. Now we can see the following:

- As $\theta$ varies from 0 to $\pi/3$, $r$ increases from 0 to $a/2$.
- As $\theta$ varies from $\pi/3$ to $\pi/2$, $r$ increases from $a/2$ to $a$.
- As $\theta$ varies from $\pi/2$ to $2\pi/3$, $r$ increases from $a$ to $3a/2$.
- As $\theta$ varies from $2\pi/3$ to $\pi$, $r$ increases from $3a/2$ to $2a$.

This produces the polar curve shown in Figure 10.2.15$b$. The rest of the curve can be obtained by continuing the preceding analysis from $\pi$ to $2\pi$ or, as noted above, by reflecting the portion already graphed about the $x$-axis (Figure 10.2.15$c$). This heart-shaped curve is called a ***cardioid*** (from the Greek word *kardia* meaning "heart"). ◄

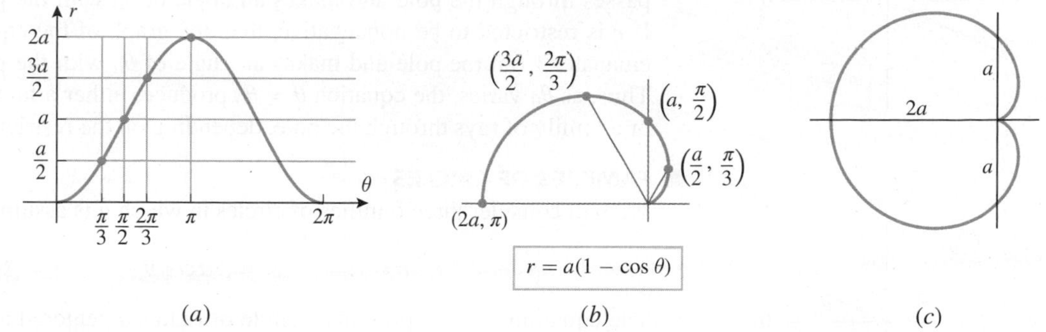


▲ **Figure 10.2.15**

► **Example 9** Sketch the graph of $r^2 = 4\cos 2\theta$ in polar coordinates.

***Solution.*** This equation does not express $r$ as a function of $\theta$, since solving for $r$ in terms of $\theta$ yields two functions:

$$r = 2\sqrt{\cos 2\theta} \quad \text{and} \quad r = -2\sqrt{\cos 2\theta}$$

Thus, to graph the equation $r^2 = 4\cos 2\theta$ we will have to graph the two functions separately and then combine those graphs.

We will start with the graph of $r = 2\sqrt{\cos 2\theta}$. Observe first that this equation is not changed if we replace $\theta$ by $-\theta$ or if we replace $\theta$ by $\pi - \theta$. Thus, the graph is symmetric about the $x$-axis and the $y$-axis. This means that the entire graph can be obtained by graphing the portion in the first quadrant, reflecting that portion about the $y$-axis to obtain the portion in the second quadrant, and then reflecting those two portions about the $x$-axis to obtain the portions in the third and fourth quadrants.

To begin the analysis, we will graph the equation $r = 2\sqrt{\cos 2\theta}$ in rectangular $\theta r$-coordinates (see Figure 10.2.16$a$). Note that there are gaps in that graph over the intervals $\pi/4 < \theta < 3\pi/4$ and $5\pi/4 < \theta < 7\pi/4$ because $\cos 2\theta$ is negative for those values of $\theta$. From this graph we can see the following:

- As $\theta$ varies from 0 to $\pi/4$, $r$ decreases from 2 to 0.
- As $\theta$ varies from $\pi/4$ to $\pi/2$, no points are generated on the polar graph.

This produces the portion of the graph shown in Figure 10.2.16$b$. As noted above, we can complete the graph by a reflection about the $y$-axis followed by a reflection about the $x$-axis (Figure 10.2.16$c$). The resulting propeller-shaped graph is called a ***lemniscate*** (from the Greek word *lemniscos* for a looped ribbon resembling the number 8). We leave it for you to verify that the equation $r = 2\sqrt{\cos 2\theta}$ has the same graph as $r = -2\sqrt{\cos 2\theta}$, but traced in a diagonally opposite manner. Thus, the graph of the equation $r^2 = 4\cos 2\theta$ consists of two identical superimposed lemniscates. ◄

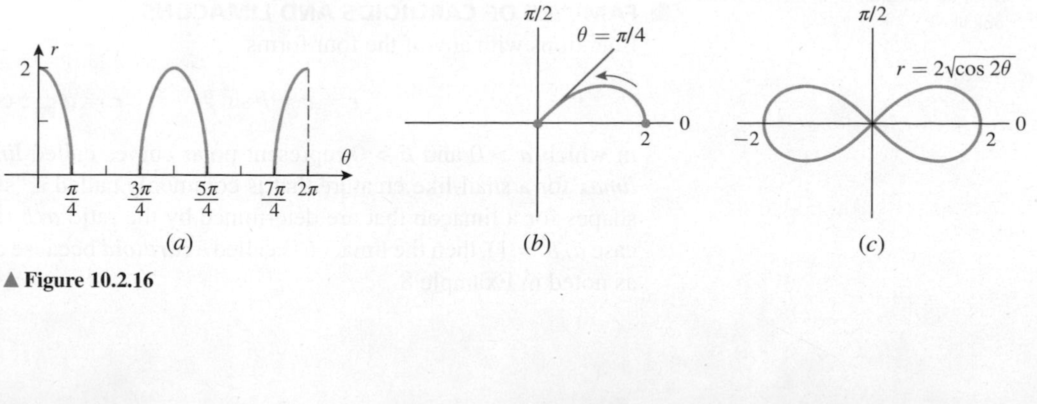


▲ **Figure 10.2.16**

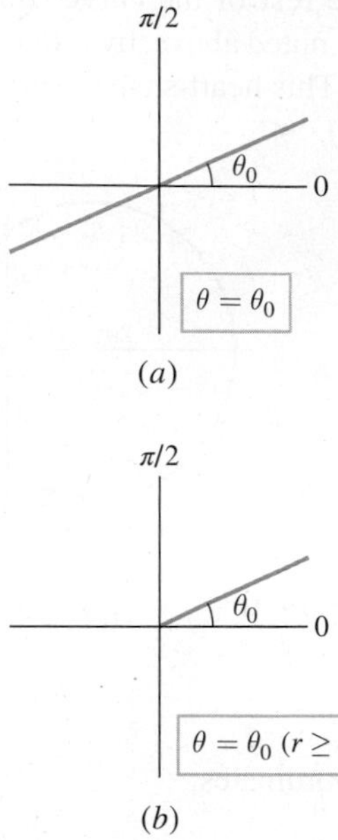

▲ Figure 10.2.17

## FAMILIES OF LINES AND RAYS THROUGH THE POLE

If $\theta_0$ is a fixed angle, then for all values of $r$ the point $(r, \theta_0)$ lies on the line that makes an angle of $\theta = \theta_0$ with the polar axis; and, conversely, every point on this line has a pair of polar coordinates of the form $(r, \theta_0)$. Thus, the equation $\theta = \theta_0$ represents the line that passes through the pole and makes an angle of $\theta_0$ with the polar axis (Figure 10.2.17*a*). If $r$ is restricted to be nonnegative, then the graph of the equation $\theta = \theta_0$ is the ray that emanates from the pole and makes an angle of $\theta_0$ with the polar axis (Figure 10.2.17*b*). Thus, as $\theta_0$ varies, the equation $\theta = \theta_0$ produces either a family of lines through the pole or a family of rays through the pole, depending on the restrictions on $r$.

## FAMILIES OF CIRCLES

We will consider three families of circles in which $a$ is assumed to be a positive constant:

$$r = a \qquad r = 2a\cos\theta \qquad r = 2a\sin\theta \tag{3–5}$$

The equation $r = a$ represents a circle of radius $a$ centered at the pole (Figure 10.2.18*a*). Thus, as $a$ varies, this equation produces a family of circles centered at the pole. For families (4) and (5), recall from plane geometry that a triangle that is inscribed in a circle with a diameter of the circle for a side must be a right triangle. Thus, as indicated in Figures 10.2.18*b* and 10.2.18*c*, the equation $r = 2a\cos\theta$ represents a circle of radius $a$, centered on the $x$-axis and tangent to the $y$-axis at the origin; similarly, the equation $r = 2a\sin\theta$ represents a circle of radius $a$, centered on the $y$-axis and tangent to the $x$-axis at the origin. Thus, as $a$ varies, Equations (4) and (5) produce the families illustrated in Figures 10.2.18*d* and 10.2.18*e*.

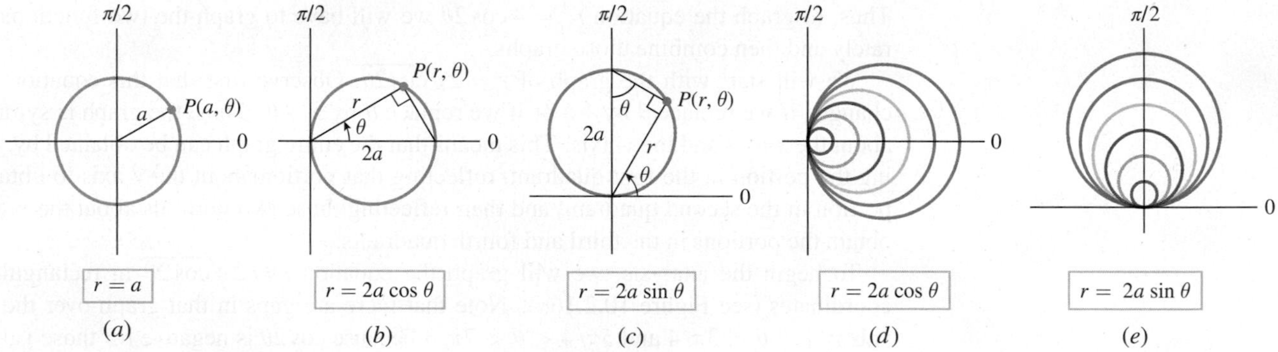

▲ Figure 10.2.18

Observe that replacing $\theta$ by $-\theta$ does not change the equation $r = 2a\cos\theta$ and that replacing $\theta$ by $\pi - \theta$ does not change the equation $r = 2a\sin\theta$. This explains why the circles in Figure 10.2.18*d* are symmetric about the $x$-axis and those in Figure 10.2.18e are symmetric about the $y$-axis.

## FAMILIES OF ROSE CURVES

In polar coordinates, equations of the form

$$r = a\sin n\theta \qquad r = a\cos n\theta \tag{6–7}$$

in which $a > 0$ and $n$ is a positive integer represent families of flower-shaped curves called ***roses*** (Figure 10.2.19). The rose consists of $n$ equally spaced petals of radius $a$ if $n$ is odd and $2n$ equally spaced petals of radius $a$ if $n$ is even. It can be shown that a rose with an even number of petals is traced out exactly once as $\theta$ varies over the interval $0 \le \theta < 2\pi$ and a rose with an odd number of petals is traced out exactly once as $\theta$ varies over the interval $0 \le \theta < \pi$ (Exercise 78). A four-petal rose of radius 1 was graphed in Example 6.

What do the graphs of one-petal roses look like?

## FAMILIES OF CARDIOIDS AND LIMAÇONS

Equations with any of the four forms

$$r = a \pm b\sin\theta \qquad r = a \pm b\cos\theta \tag{8–9}$$

in which $a > 0$ and $b > 0$ represent polar curves called ***limaçons*** (from the Latin word *limax* for a snail-like creature that is commonly called a "slug"). There are four possible shapes for a limaçon that are determined by the ratio $a/b$ (Figure 10.2.20). If $a = b$ (the case $a/b = 1$), then the limaçon is called a ***cardioid*** because of its heart-shaped appearance, as noted in Example 8.

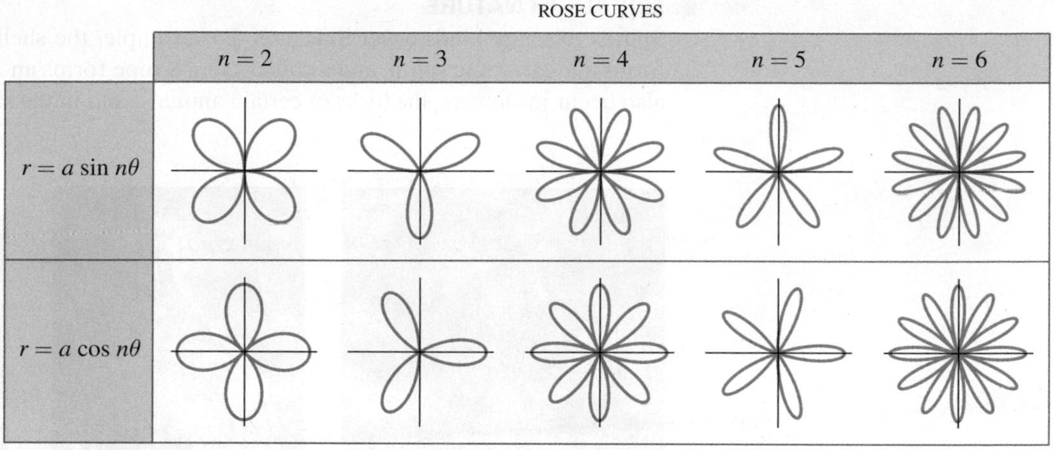


▲ **Figure 10.2.19**

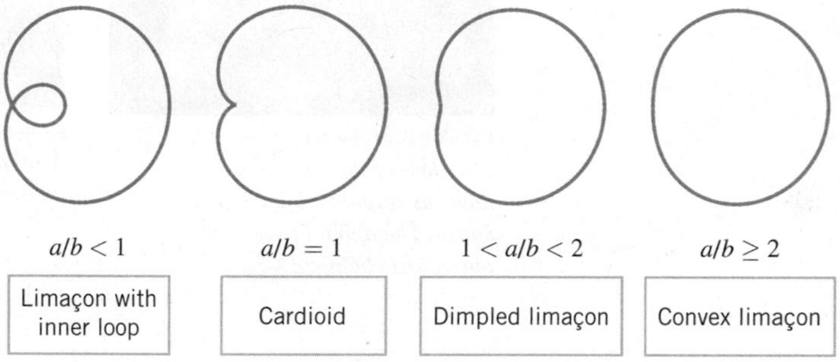


▶ **Figure 10.2.20**

▶ **Example 10** Figure 10.2.21 shows the family of limaçons $r = a + \cos\theta$ with the constant $a$ varying from 0.25 to 2.50 in steps of 0.25. In keeping with Figure 10.2.20, the limaçons evolve from the loop type to the convex type. As $a$ increases from the starting value of 0.25, the loops get smaller and smaller until the cardioid is reached at $a = 1$. As $a$ increases further, the limaçons evolve through the dimpled type into the convex type. ◀

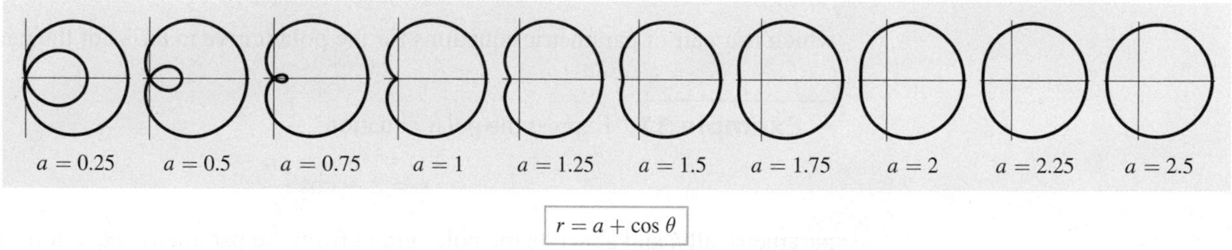


▲ **Figure 10.2.21**

## ■ FAMILIES OF SPIRALS

A ***spiral*** is a curve that coils around a central point. Spirals generally have "left-hand" and "right-hand" versions that coil in opposite directions, depending on the restrictions on the polar angle and the signs of constants that appear in their equations. Some of the more common types of spirals are shown in Figure 10.2.22 for nonnegative values of $\theta$, $a$, and $b$.

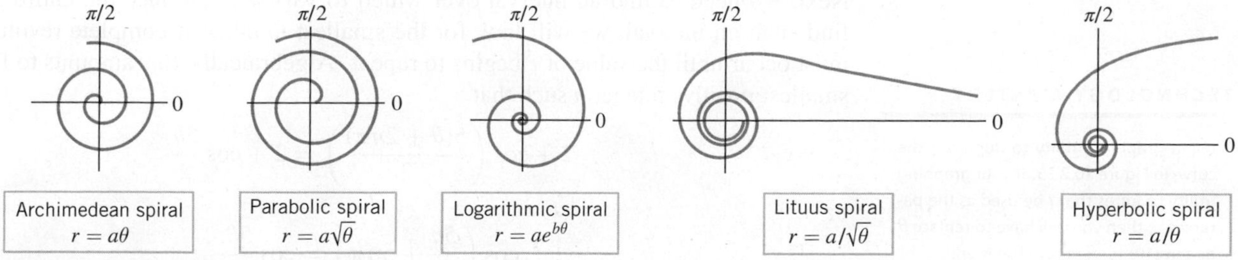


▲ **Figure 10.2.22**

## SPIRALS IN NATURE

Spirals of many kinds occur in nature. For example, the shell of the chambered nautilus forms a logarithmic spiral, and a coiled sailor's rope forms an Archimedean spiral. Spirals also occur in flowers, the tusks of certain animals, and in the shapes of galaxies.

Kaz Chiba/Getty Images

*The shell of the chambered nautilus reveals a logarithmic spiral. The animal lives in the outermost chamber.*

megasquib/iStockphoto

*A sailor's coiled rope forms an Archimedean spiral.*

tose/iStockphoto

*A spiral galaxy.*

## GENERATING POLAR CURVES WITH GRAPHING UTILITIES

For polar curves that are too complicated for hand computation, graphing utilities can be used. Although many graphing utilities are capable of graphing polar curves directly, some are not. However, if a graphing utility is capable of graphing parametric equations, then it can be used to graph a polar curve $r = f(\theta)$ by converting this equation to parametric form. This can be done by substituting $f(\theta)$ for $r$ in (1). This yields

$$x = f(\theta)\cos\theta, \quad y = f(\theta)\sin\theta \tag{10}$$

which is a pair of parametric equations for the polar curve in terms of the parameter $\theta$.

**▶ Example 11** Express the polar equation

$$r = 2 + \cos\frac{5\theta}{2}$$

parametrically, and generate the polar graph from the parametric equations using a graphing utility.

***Solution.*** Substituting the given expression for $r$ in $x = r\cos\theta$ and $y = r\sin\theta$ yields the parametric equations

$$x = \left[2 + \cos\frac{5\theta}{2}\right]\cos\theta, \quad y = \left[2 + \cos\frac{5\theta}{2}\right]\sin\theta$$

Next, we need to find an interval over which to vary $\theta$ to produce the entire graph. To find such an interval, we will look for the smallest number of complete revolutions that must occur until the value of $r$ begins to repeat. Algebraically, this amounts to finding the smallest positive integer $n$ such that

$$2 + \cos\left(\frac{5(\theta + 2n\pi)}{2}\right) = 2 + \cos\frac{5\theta}{2}$$

or

$$\cos\left(\frac{5\theta}{2} + 5n\pi\right) = \cos\frac{5\theta}{2}$$

**TECHNOLOGY MASTERY**

Use a graphing utility to duplicate the curve in Figure 10.2.23. If your graphing utility requires that $t$ be used as the parameter, then you will have to replace $\theta$ by $t$ in (10) to generate the graph.

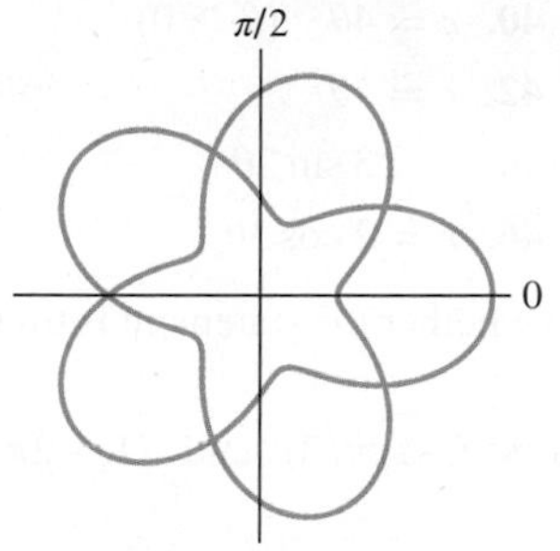


▲ **Figure 10.2.23**

For this equality to hold, the quantity $5n\pi$ must be an even multiple of $\pi$; the smallest $n$ for which this occurs is $n = 2$. Thus, the entire graph will be traced in two revolutions, which means it can be generated from the parametric equations

$$x = \left[2 + \cos\frac{5\theta}{2}\right]\cos\theta, \quad y = \left[2 + \cos\frac{5\theta}{2}\right]\sin\theta \qquad (0 \le \theta \le 4\pi)$$

This yields the graph in Figure 10.2.23. ◀

## ✓ QUICK CHECK EXERCISES 10.2 *(See page 630 for answers.)*

**1.** (a) Rectangular coordinates of a point $(x, y)$ may be recovered from its polar coordinates $(r, \theta)$ by means of the equations $x =$ ______ and $y =$ ______.

(b) Polar coordinates $(r, \theta)$ may be recovered from rectangular coordinates $(x, y)$ by means of the equations $r^2 =$ ______ and $\tan\theta =$ ______.

**2.** Find the rectangular coordinates of the points whose polar coordinates are given.
(a) $(4, \pi/3)$ (b) $(2, -\pi/6)$
(c) $(6, -2\pi/3)$ (d) $(4, 5\pi/4)$

**3.** In each part, find polar coordinates satisfying the stated conditions for the point whose rectangular coordinates are $(1, \sqrt{3})$.
(a) $r \ge 0$ and $0 \le \theta < 2\pi$
(b) $r \le 0$ and $0 \le \theta < 2\pi$

**4.** In each part, state the name that describes the polar curve most precisely: a rose, a line, a circle, a limaçon, a cardioid, a spiral, a lemniscate, or none of these.
(a) $r = 1 - \theta$ (b) $r = 1 + 2\sin\theta$
(c) $r = \sin 2\theta$ (d) $r = \cos^2\theta$
(e) $r = \csc\theta$ (f) $r = 2 + 2\cos\theta$
(g) $r = -2\sin\theta$

## EXERCISE SET 10.2 ⊠ Graphing Utility

**1–2** Plot the points in polar coordinates. ■

**1.** (a) $(3, \pi/4)$ (b) $(5, 2\pi/3)$ (c) $(1, \pi/2)$
(d) $(4, 7\pi/6)$ (e) $(-6, -\pi)$ (f) $(-1, 9\pi/4)$

**2.** (a) $(2, -\pi/3)$ (b) $(3/2, -7\pi/4)$ (c) $(-3, 3\pi/2)$
(d) $(-5, -\pi/6)$ (e) $(2, 4\pi/3)$ (f) $(0, \pi)$

**3–4** Find the rectangular coordinates of the points whose polar coordinates are given. ■

**3.** (a) $(6, \pi/6)$ (b) $(7, 2\pi/3)$ (c) $(-6, -5\pi/6)$
(d) $(0, -\pi)$ (e) $(7, 17\pi/6)$ (f) $(-5, 0)$

**4.** (a) $(-2, \pi/4)$ (b) $(6, -\pi/4)$ (c) $(4, 9\pi/4)$
(d) $(3, 0)$ (e) $(-4, -3\pi/2)$ (f) $(0, 3\pi)$

**5.** In each part, a point is given in rectangular coordinates. Find two pairs of polar coordinates for the point, one pair satisfying $r \ge 0$ and $0 \le \theta < 2\pi$, and the second pair satisfying $r \ge 0$ and $-2\pi < \theta \le 0$.
(a) $(-5, 0)$ (b) $(2\sqrt{3}, -2)$ (c) $(0, -2)$
(d) $(-8, -8)$ (e) $(-3, 3\sqrt{3})$ (f) $(1, 1)$

**6.** In each part, find polar coordinates satisfying the stated conditions for the point whose rectangular coordinates are $(-\sqrt{3}, 1)$.
(a) $r \ge 0$ and $0 \le \theta < 2\pi$
(b) $r \le 0$ and $0 \le \theta < 2\pi$
(c) $r \ge 0$ and $-2\pi < \theta \le 0$
(d) $r \le 0$ and $-\pi < \theta \le \pi$

**7–8** Use a calculating utility, where needed, to approximate the polar coordinates of the points whose rectangular coordinates are given. ■

**7.** (a) $(3, 4)$ (b) $(6, -8)$ (c) $(-1, \tan^{-1} 1)$

**8.** (a) $(-3, 4)$ (b) $(-3, 1.7)$ (c) $\left(2, \sin^{-1}\frac{1}{2}\right)$

**9–10** Identify the curve by transforming the given polar equation to rectangular coordinates. ■

**9.** (a) $r = 2$ (b) $r\sin\theta = 4$
(c) $r = 3\cos\theta$ (d) $r = \dfrac{6}{3\cos\theta + 2\sin\theta}$

**10.** (a) $r = 5\sec\theta$ (b) $r = 2\sin\theta$
(c) $r = 4\cos\theta + 4\sin\theta$ (d) $r = \sec\theta\tan\theta$

**11–12** Express the given equations in polar coordinates. ■

**11.** (a) $x = 3$ (b) $x^2 + y^2 = 7$
(c) $x^2 + y^2 + 6y = 0$ (d) $9xy = 4$

**12.** (a) $y = -3$ (b) $x^2 + y^2 = 5$
(c) $x^2 + y^2 + 4x = 0$ (d) $x^2(x^2 + y^2) = y^2$

**FOCUS ON CONCEPTS**

**13–16** A graph is given in a rectangular $\theta r$-coordinate system. Sketch the corresponding graph in polar coordinates. ■

**13.**

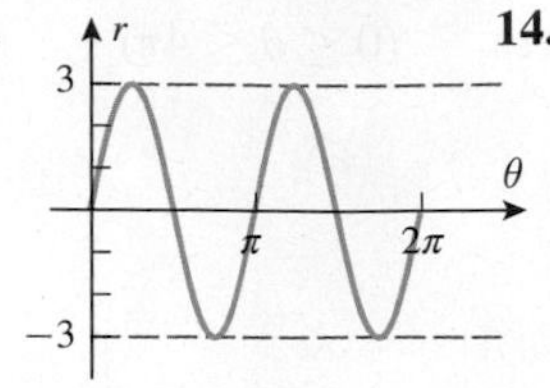

**14.**

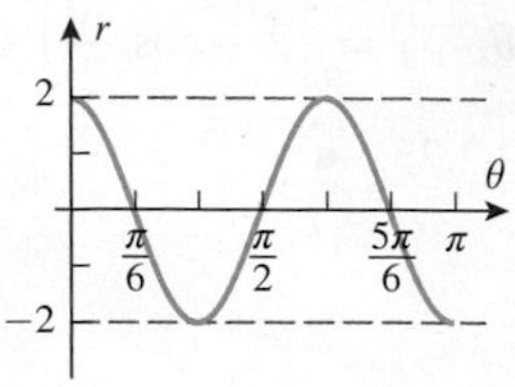

**15.**

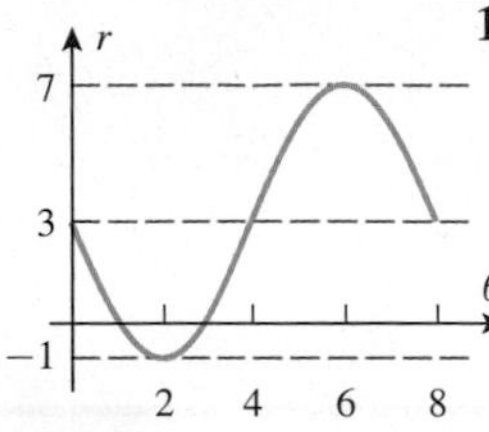

**16.**

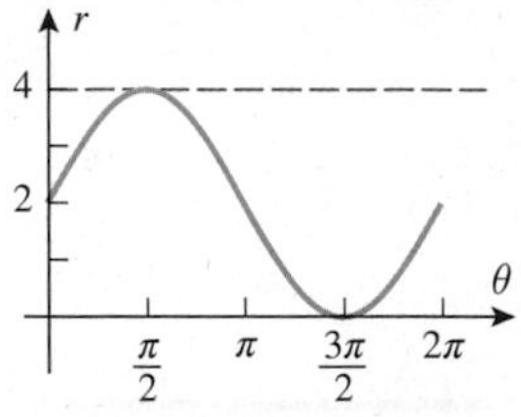

**17–20** Find an equation for the given polar graph. [*Note:* Numeric labels on these graphs represent distances to the origin.] ■

**17.** (a) (b) (c)

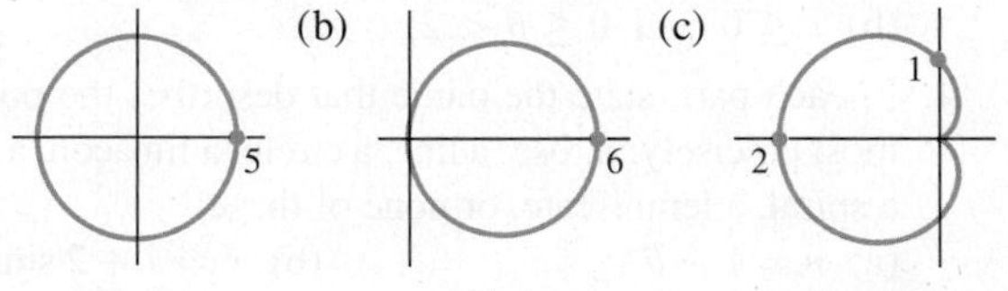

Circle Circle Cardioid

**18.** (a) (b) (c)

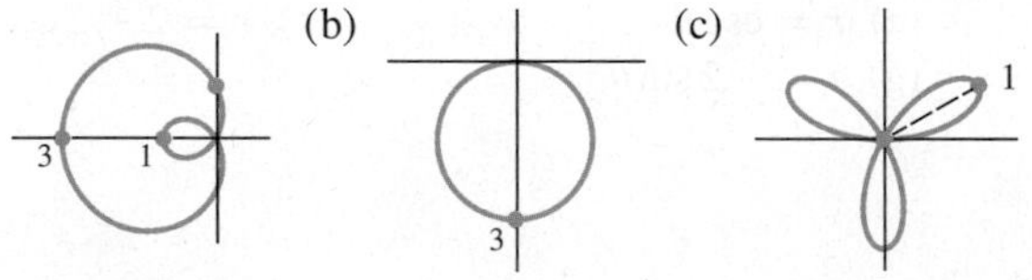

Limaçon Circle Three-petal rose

**19.** (a) (b) (c)

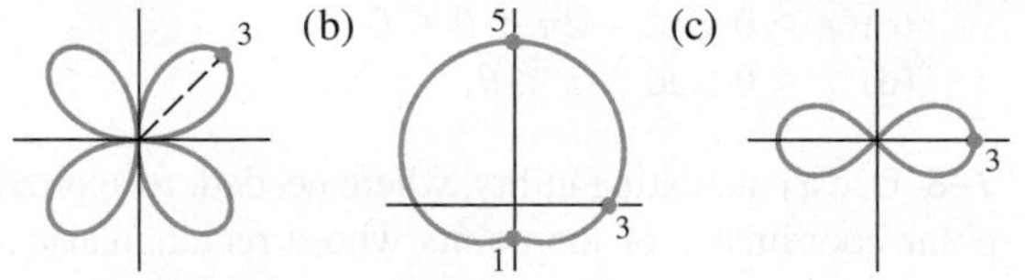

Four-petal rose Limaçon Lemniscate

**20.** (a) (b) (c)

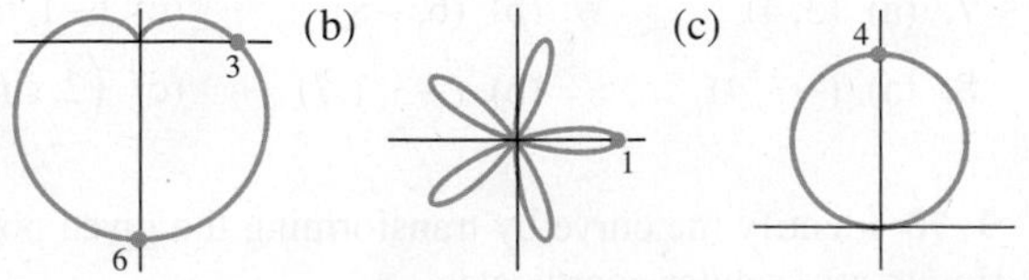

Cardioid Five-petal rose Circle

**21–46** Sketch the curve in polar coordinates. ■

**21.** $\theta = \dfrac{\pi}{3}$ **22.** $\theta = -\dfrac{3\pi}{4}$ **23.** $r = 3$

**24.** $r = 4\cos\theta$ **25.** $r = 6\sin\theta$ **26.** $r - 2 = 2\cos\theta$

**27.** $r = 3(1 + \sin\theta)$ **28.** $r = 5 - 5\sin\theta$

**29.** $r = 4 - 4\cos\theta$ **30.** $r = 1 + 2\sin\theta$

**31.** $r = -1 - \cos\theta$ **32.** $r = 4 + 3\cos\theta$

**33.** $r = 3 - \sin\theta$ **34.** $r = 3 + 4\cos\theta$

**35.** $r - 5 = 3\sin\theta$ **36.** $r = 5 - 2\cos\theta$

**37.** $r = -3 - 4\sin\theta$ **38.** $r^2 = \cos 2\theta$

**39.** $r^2 = 16\sin 2\theta$ **40.** $r = 4\theta \quad (\theta \geq 0)$

**41.** $r = 4\theta \quad (\theta \leq 0)$ **42.** $r = 4\theta$

**43.** $r = -2\cos 2\theta$ **44.** $r = 3\sin 2\theta$

**45.** $r = 9\sin 4\theta$ **46.** $r = 2\cos 3\theta$

**47–50 True–False** Determine whether the statement is true or false. Explain your answer. ■

**47.** The polar coordinate pairs $(-1, \pi/3)$ and $(1, -2\pi/3)$ describe the same point.

**48.** If the graph of $r = f(\theta)$ drawn in rectangular $\theta r$-coordinates is symmetric about the $r$-axis, then the graph of $r = f(\theta)$ drawn in polar coordinates is symmetric about the $x$-axis.

**49.** The portion of the polar graph of $r = \sin 2\theta$ for values of $\theta$ between $\pi/2$ and $\pi$ is contained in the second quadrant.

**50.** The graph of a dimpled limaçon passes through the polar origin.

**51–55** Determine a shortest parameter interval on which a complete graph of the polar equation can be generated, and then use a graphing utility to generate the polar graph. ■

**51.** $r = \cos\dfrac{\theta}{2}$ **52.** $r = \sin\dfrac{\theta}{2}$

**53.** $r = 1 - 2\sin\dfrac{\theta}{4}$ **54.** $r = 0.5 + \cos\dfrac{\theta}{3}$

**55.** $r = \cos\dfrac{\theta}{5}$

**56.** The accompanying figure shows the graph of the "butterfly curve"

$$r = e^{\cos\theta} - 2\cos 4\theta + \sin^3\frac{\theta}{4}$$

Determine a shortest parameter interval on which the complete butterfly can be generated, and then check your answer using a graphing utility.

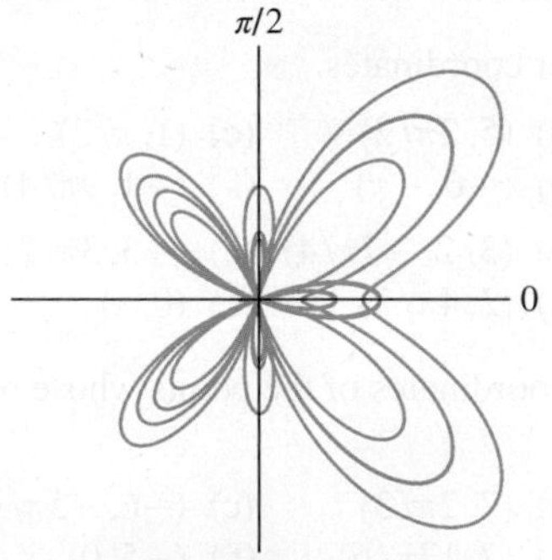


◀ **Figure Ex-56**

**57.** The accompanying figure shows the Archimedean spiral $r = \theta/2$ produced with a graphing calculator.

(a) What interval of values for $\theta$ do you think was used to generate the graph?

(b) Duplicate the graph with your own graphing utility.

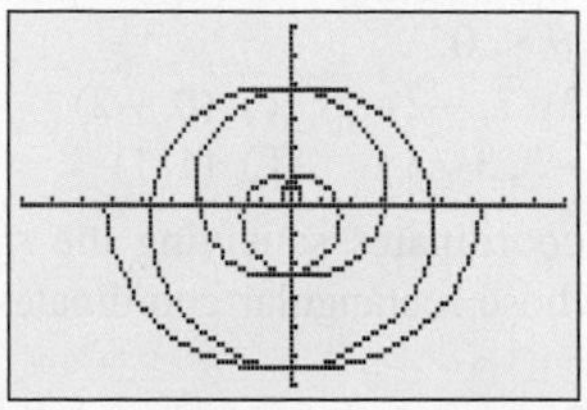

$[-9, 9] \times [-6, 6]$
$x$Scl $= 1$, $y$Scl $= 1$

◀ **Figure Ex-57**

**58.** Find equations for the two families of circles in the accompanying figure.

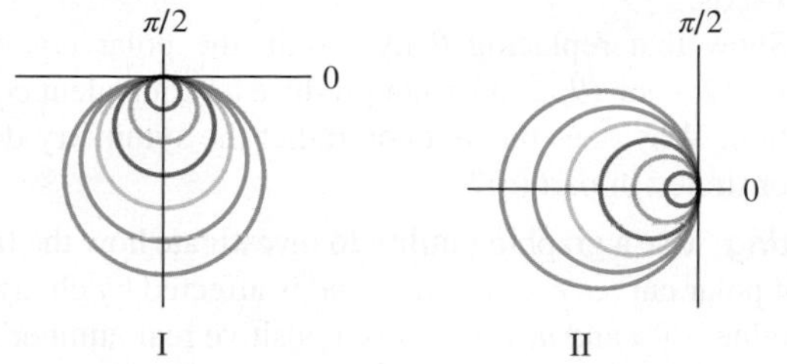


▲ **Figure Ex-58**

**59.** (a) Show that if $a$ varies, then the polar equation

$$r = a\sec\theta \quad (-\pi/2 < \theta < \pi/2)$$

describes a family of lines perpendicular to the polar axis.

(b) Show that if $b$ varies, then the polar equation

$$r = b\csc\theta \quad (0 < \theta < \pi)$$

describes a family of lines parallel to the polar axis.

**FOCUS ON CONCEPTS**

**60.** The accompanying figure shows graphs of the Archimedean spiral $r = \theta$ and the parabolic spiral $r = \sqrt{\theta}$. Which is which? Explain your reasoning.

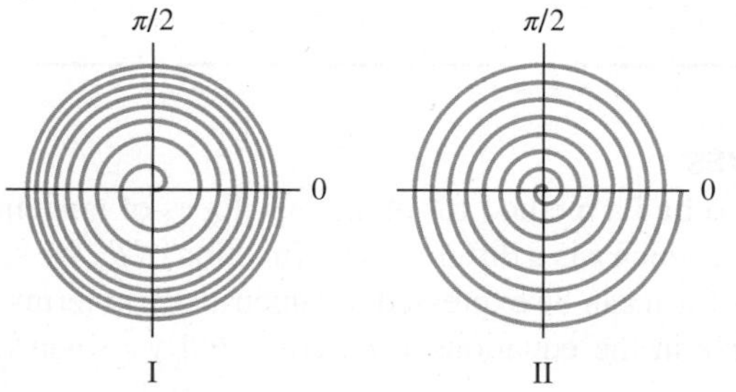


▲ **Figure Ex-60**

**61–62** A polar graph of $r = f(\theta)$ is given over the stated interval. Sketch the graph of

(a) $r = f(-\theta)$ (b) $r = f\left(\theta - \frac{\pi}{2}\right)$

(c) $r = f\left(\theta + \frac{\pi}{2}\right)$ (d) $r = -f(\theta)$. ■

**61.** $0 \le \theta \le \pi/2$ **62.** $\pi/2 \le \theta \le \pi$

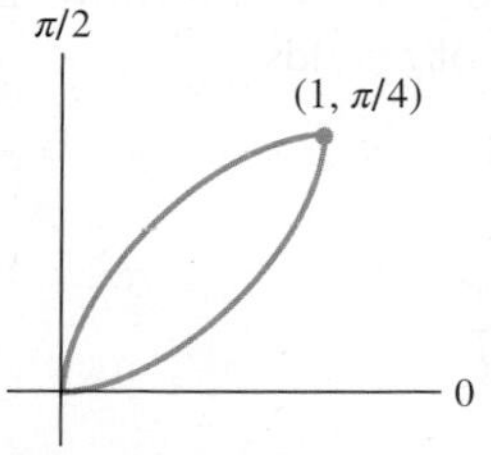


▲ **Figure Ex-61**

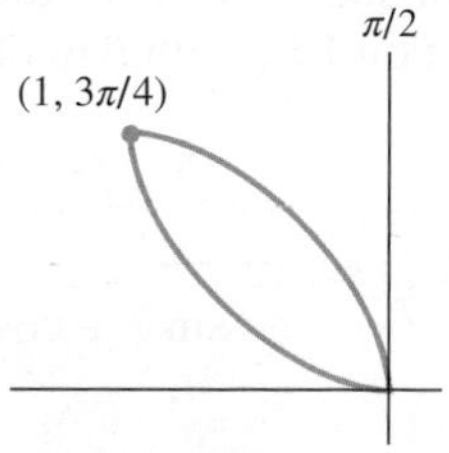


▲ **Figure Ex-62**

**63–64** Use the polar graph from the indicated exercise to sketch the graph of

(a) $r = f(\theta) + 1$ (b) $r = 2f(\theta) - 1$. ■

**63.** Exercise 61 **64.** Exercise 62

**65.** Show that if the polar graph of $r = f(\theta)$ is rotated counterclockwise around the origin through an angle $\alpha$, then $r = f(\theta - \alpha)$ is an equation for the rotated curve. [*Hint:* If $(r_0, \theta_0)$ is any point on the original graph, then $(r_0, \theta_0 + \alpha)$ is a point on the rotated graph.]

**66.** Use the result in Exercise 65 to find an equation for the lemniscate that results when the lemniscate in Example 9 is rotated counterclockwise through an angle of $\pi/2$.

**67.** Use the result in Exercise 65 to find an equation for the cardioid $r = 1 + \cos\theta$ after it has been rotated through the given angle, and check your answer with a graphing utility.

(a) $\frac{\pi}{4}$ (b) $\frac{\pi}{2}$ (c) $\pi$ (d) $\frac{5\pi}{4}$

**68.** (a) Show that if $A$ and $B$ are not both zero, then the graph of the polar equation

$$r = A\sin\theta + B\cos\theta$$

is a circle. Find its radius.

(b) Derive Formulas (4) and (5) from the formula given in part (a).

**69.** Find the highest point on the cardioid $r = 1 + \cos\theta$.

**70.** Find the leftmost point on the upper half of the cardioid $r = 1 + \cos\theta$.

**71.** Show that in a polar coordinate system the distance $d$ between the points $(r_1, \theta_1)$ and $(r_2, \theta_2)$ is

$$d = \sqrt{r_1^2 + r_2^2 - 2r_1r_2\cos(\theta_1 - \theta_2)}$$

**72–74** Use the formula obtained in Exercise 71 to find the distance between the two points indicated in polar coordinates. ■

**72.** $(3, \pi/6)$ and $(2, \pi/3)$

**73.** Successive tips of the four-petal rose $r = \cos 2\theta$. Check your answer using geometry.

**74.** Successive tips of the three-petal rose $r = \sin 3\theta$. Check your answer using trigonometry.

**75.** In the late seventeenth century the Italian astronomer Giovanni Domenico Cassini (1625–1712) introduced the family of curves

$$(x^2 + y^2 + a^2)^2 - b^4 - 4a^2x^2 = 0 \quad (a > 0, b > 0)$$

in his studies of the relative motions of the Earth and the Sun. These curves, which are called ***Cassini ovals***, have one of the three basic shapes shown in the accompanying figure.

(a) Show that if $a = b$, then the polar equation of the Cassini oval is $r^2 = 2a^2\cos 2\theta$, which is a lemniscate.

(b) Use the formula in Exercise 71 to show that the lemniscate in part (a) is the curve traced by a point that moves in such a way that the product of its distances from the polar points $(a, 0)$ and $(a, \pi)$ is $a^2$.

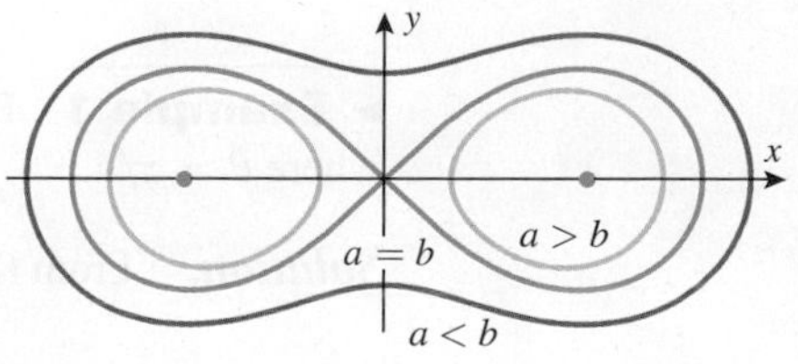


▲ **Figure Ex-75**

**76–77** Vertical and horizontal asymptotes of polar curves can sometimes be detected by investigating the behavior of $x = r\cos\theta$ and $y = r\sin\theta$ as $\theta$ varies. This idea is used in these exercises. ■

**76.** Show that the ***hyperbolic spiral*** $r = 1/\theta\ (\theta > 0)$ has a horizontal asymptote at $y = 1$ by showing that $y \to 1$ and $x \to +\infty$ as $\theta \to 0^+$. Confirm this result by generating the spiral with a graphing utility.

**77.** Show that the spiral $r = 1/\theta^2$ does not have any horizontal asymptotes.

**78.** Prove that a rose with an even number of petals is traced out exactly once as $\theta$ varies over the interval $0 \le \theta < 2\pi$ and a rose with an odd number of petals is traced out exactly once as $\theta$ varies over the interval $0 \le \theta < \pi$.

**79.** (a) Use a graphing utility to confirm that the graph of $r = 2 - \sin(\theta/2)\ (0 \le \theta \le 4\pi)$ is symmetric about the $x$-axis.

(b) Show that replacing $\theta$ by $-\theta$ in the polar equation $r = 2 - \sin(\theta/2)$ does not produce an equivalent equation. Why does this not contradict the symmetry demonstrated in part (a)?

**80. Writing** Use a graphing utility to investigate how the family of polar curves $r = 1 + a\cos n\theta$ is affected by changing the values of $a$ and $n$, where $a$ is a positive real number and $n$ is a positive integer. Write a brief paragraph to explain your conclusions.

**81. Writing** Do some research and write a short report on the properties of a "cardioid microphone." Explain the significance of the term "cardioid," and describe a scenario in which such a microphone would be useful.

---

**✓ QUICK CHECK ANSWERS 10.2** 1. (a) $r\cos\theta$; $r\sin\theta$ (b) $x^2 + y^2$; $y/x$
2. (a) $(2, 2\sqrt{3})$ (b) $(\sqrt{3}, -1)$ (c) $(-3, -3\sqrt{3})$ (d) $(-2\sqrt{2}, -2\sqrt{2})$ 3. (a) $(2, \pi/3)$ (b) $(-2, 4\pi/3)$
4. (a) spiral (b) limaçon (c) rose (d) none of these (e) line (f) cardioid (g) circle

---

## 10.3 TANGENT LINES, ARC LENGTH, AND AREA FOR POLAR CURVES

*In this section we will derive the formulas required to find slopes, tangent lines, and arc lengths of polar curves. We will then show how to find areas of regions that are bounded by polar curves.*

### ■ TANGENT LINES TO POLAR CURVES

Our first objective in this section is to find a method for obtaining slopes of tangent lines to polar curves of the form $r = f(\theta)$ in which $r$ is a differentiable function of $\theta$. We showed in the last section that a curve of this form can be expressed parametrically in terms of the parameter $\theta$ by substituting $f(\theta)$ for $r$ in the equations $x = r\cos\theta$ and $y = r\sin\theta$. This yields

$$x = f(\theta)\cos\theta, \quad y = f(\theta)\sin\theta$$

from which we obtain

$$\begin{aligned}\frac{dx}{d\theta} &= -f(\theta)\sin\theta + f'(\theta)\cos\theta = -r\sin\theta + \frac{dr}{d\theta}\cos\theta \\ \frac{dy}{d\theta} &= f(\theta)\cos\theta + f'(\theta)\sin\theta = r\cos\theta + \frac{dr}{d\theta}\sin\theta\end{aligned} \tag{1}$$

Thus, if $dx/d\theta$ and $dy/d\theta$ are continuous and if $dx/d\theta \ne 0$, then $y$ is a differentiable function of $x$, and Formula (4) in Section 10.1 with $\theta$ in place of $t$ yields

$$\frac{dy}{dx} = \frac{dy/d\theta}{dx/d\theta} = \frac{r\cos\theta + \sin\theta\dfrac{dr}{d\theta}}{-r\sin\theta + \cos\theta\dfrac{dr}{d\theta}} \tag{2}$$

**▶ Example 1** Find the slope of the tangent line to the circle $r = 4\cos\theta$ at the point where $\theta = \pi/4$.

***Solution.*** From (2) with $r = 4\cos\theta$, so that $dr/d\theta = -4\sin\theta$, we obtain

$$\frac{dy}{dx} = \frac{4\cos^2\theta - 4\sin^2\theta}{-8\sin\theta\cos\theta} = -\frac{\cos^2\theta - \sin^2\theta}{2\sin\theta\cos\theta}$$

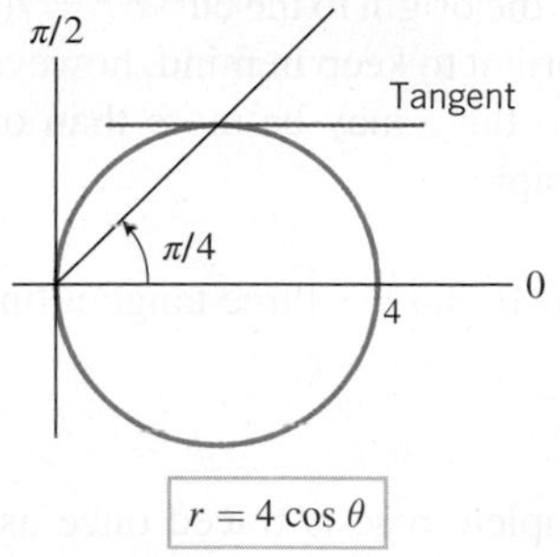


▲ Figure 10.3.1

Using the double-angle formulas for sine and cosine,

$$\frac{dy}{dx} = -\frac{\cos 2\theta}{\sin 2\theta} = -\cot 2\theta$$

Thus, at the point where $\theta = \pi/4$ the slope of the tangent line is

$$m = \left.\frac{dy}{dx}\right|_{\theta=\pi/4} = -\cot\frac{\pi}{2} = 0$$

which implies that the circle has a horizontal tangent line at the point where $\theta = \pi/4$ (Figure 10.3.1). ◀

▶ **Example 2** Find the points on the cardioid $r = 1 - \cos\theta$ at which there is a horizontal tangent line, a vertical tangent line, or a singular point.

***Solution.*** A horizontal tangent line will occur where $dy/d\theta = 0$ and $dx/d\theta \neq 0$, a vertical tangent line where $dy/d\theta \neq 0$ and $dx/d\theta = 0$, and a singular point where $dy/d\theta = 0$ and $dx/d\theta = 0$. We could find these derivatives from the formulas in (1). However, an alternative approach is to go back to basic principles and express the cardioid parametrically by substituting $r = 1 - \cos\theta$ in the conversion formulas $x = r\cos\theta$ and $y = r\sin\theta$. This yields

$$x = (1-\cos\theta)\cos\theta, \quad y = (1-\cos\theta)\sin\theta \qquad (0 \le \theta \le 2\pi)$$

Differentiating these equations with respect to $\theta$ and then simplifying yields (verify)

$$\frac{dx}{d\theta} = \sin\theta(2\cos\theta - 1), \quad \frac{dy}{d\theta} = (1-\cos\theta)(1+2\cos\theta)$$

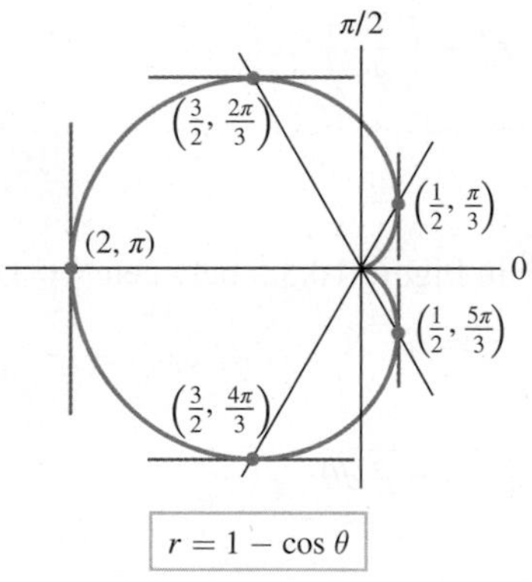


▲ Figure 10.3.2

Thus, $dx/d\theta = 0$ if $\sin\theta = 0$ or $\cos\theta = \frac{1}{2}$, and $dy/d\theta = 0$ if $\cos\theta = 1$ or $\cos\theta = -\frac{1}{2}$. We leave it for you to solve these equations and show that the solutions of $dx/d\theta = 0$ on the interval $0 \le \theta \le 2\pi$ are

$$\frac{dx}{d\theta} = 0: \quad \theta = 0, \ \frac{\pi}{3}, \ \pi, \ \frac{5\pi}{3}, \ 2\pi$$

and the solutions of $dy/d\theta = 0$ on the interval $0 \le \theta \le 2\pi$ are

$$\frac{dy}{d\theta} = 0: \quad \theta = 0, \ \frac{2\pi}{3}, \ \frac{4\pi}{3}, \ 2\pi$$

Thus, horizontal tangent lines occur at $\theta = 2\pi/3$ and $\theta = 4\pi/3$; vertical tangent lines occur at $\theta = \pi/3$, $\pi$, and $5\pi/3$; and singular points occur at $\theta = 0$ and $\theta = 2\pi$ (Figure 10.3.2). Note, however, that $r = 0$ at both singular points, so there is really only one singular point on the cardioid—the pole. ◀

## ■ TANGENT LINES TO POLAR CURVES AT THE ORIGIN

Formula (2) reveals some useful information about the behavior of a polar curve $r = f(\theta)$ that passes through the origin. If we assume that $r = 0$ and $dr/d\theta \neq 0$ when $\theta = \theta_0$, then it follows from Formula (2) that the slope of the tangent line to the curve at $\theta = \theta_0$ is

$$\frac{dy}{dx} = \frac{0 + \sin\theta_0 \dfrac{dr}{d\theta}}{0 + \cos\theta_0 \dfrac{dr}{d\theta}} = \frac{\sin\theta_0}{\cos\theta_0} = \tan\theta_0$$

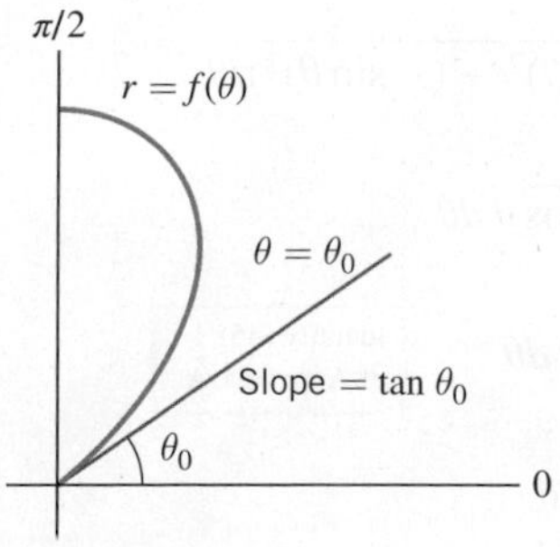


▲ Figure 10.3.3

(Figure 10.3.3). However, $\tan\theta_0$ is also the slope of the line $\theta = \theta_0$, so we can conclude that this line is tangent to the curve at the origin. Thus, we have established the following result.

**10.3.1 THEOREM** *If the polar curve $r = f(\theta)$ passes through the origin at $\theta = \theta_0$, and if $dr/d\theta \neq 0$ at $\theta = \theta_0$, then the line $\theta = \theta_0$ is tangent to the curve at the origin.*

This theorem tells us that equations of the tangent lines at the origin to the curve $r = f(\theta)$ can be obtained by solving the equation $f(\theta) = 0$. It is important to keep in mind, however, that $r = f(\theta)$ may be zero for more than one value of $\theta$, so there may be more than one tangent line at the origin. This is illustrated in the next example.

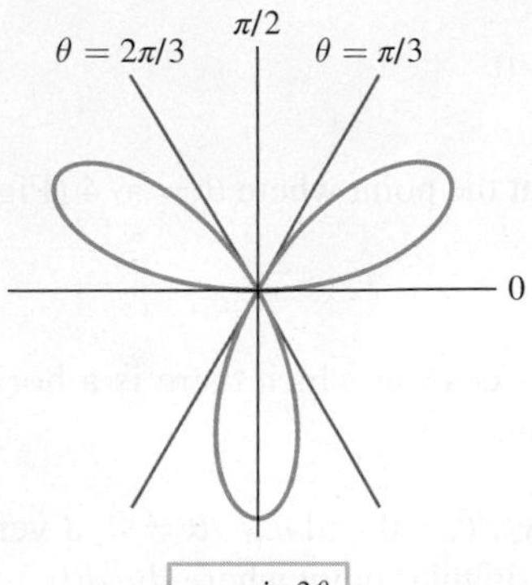

▲ **Figure 10.3.4**

► **Example 3** The three-petal rose $r = \sin 3\theta$ in Figure 10.3.4 has three tangent lines at the origin, which can be found by solving the equation

$$\sin 3\theta = 0$$

It was shown in Exercise 78 of Section 10.2 that the complete rose is traced once as $\theta$ varies over the interval $0 \le \theta < \pi$, so we need only look for solutions in this interval. We leave it for you to confirm that these solutions are

$$\theta = 0, \quad \theta = \frac{\pi}{3}, \quad \text{and} \quad \theta = \frac{2\pi}{3}$$

Since $dr/d\theta = 3\cos 3\theta \neq 0$ for these values of $\theta$, these three lines are tangent to the rose at the origin, which is consistent with the figure. ◄

## ARC LENGTH OF A POLAR CURVE

A formula for the arc length of a polar curve $r = f(\theta)$ can be derived by expressing the curve in parametric form and applying Formula (9) of Section 10.1 for the arc length of a parametric curve. We leave it as an exercise to show the following.

**10.3.2 ARC LENGTH FORMULA FOR POLAR CURVES** If no segment of the polar curve $r = f(\theta)$ is traced more than once as $\theta$ increases from $\alpha$ to $\beta$, and if $dr/d\theta$ is continuous for $\alpha \le \theta \le \beta$, then the arc length $L$ from $\theta = \alpha$ to $\theta = \beta$ is

$$L = \int_{\alpha}^{\beta} \sqrt{[f(\theta)]^2 + [f'(\theta)]^2}\, d\theta = \int_{\alpha}^{\beta} \sqrt{r^2 + \left(\frac{dr}{d\theta}\right)^2}\, d\theta \tag{3}$$

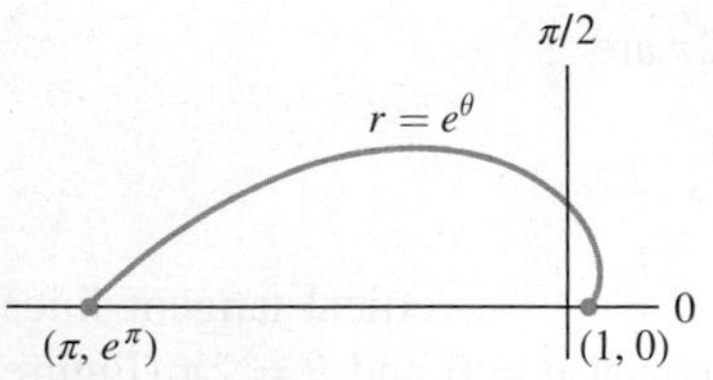

▲ **Figure 10.3.5**

► **Example 4** Find the arc length of the spiral $r = e^{\theta}$ in Figure 10.3.5 between $\theta = 0$ and $\theta = \pi$.

***Solution.***

$$L = \int_{\alpha}^{\beta} \sqrt{r^2 + \left(\frac{dr}{d\theta}\right)^2}\, d\theta = \int_{0}^{\pi} \sqrt{(e^{\theta})^2 + (e^{\theta})^2}\, d\theta$$

$$= \int_{0}^{\pi} \sqrt{2}\, e^{\theta}\, d\theta = \sqrt{2}\, e^{\theta}\Big]_{0}^{\pi} = \sqrt{2}(e^{\pi} - 1) \approx 31.3 \text{ ◄}$$

► **Example 5** Find the total arc length of the cardioid $r = 1 + \cos\theta$.

***Solution.*** The cardioid is traced out once as $\theta$ varies from $\theta = 0$ to $\theta = 2\pi$. Thus,

$$L = \int_{\alpha}^{\beta} \sqrt{r^2 + \left(\frac{dr}{d\theta}\right)^2}\, d\theta = \int_{0}^{2\pi} \sqrt{(1 + \cos\theta)^2 + (-\sin\theta)^2}\, d\theta$$

$$= \sqrt{2} \int_{0}^{2\pi} \sqrt{1 + \cos\theta}\, d\theta$$

$$= 2 \int_{0}^{2\pi} \sqrt{\cos^2 \tfrac{1}{2}\theta}\, d\theta \qquad \text{Identity (45) of Appendix A}$$

$$= 2 \int_{0}^{2\pi} \left|\cos \tfrac{1}{2}\theta\right|\, d\theta$$

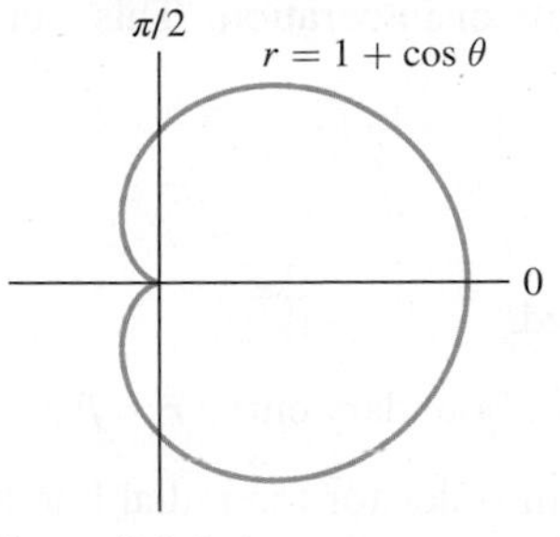


▲ Figure 10.3.6

Since $\cos \frac{1}{2}\theta$ changes sign at $\pi$, we must split the last integral into the sum of two integrals: the integral from 0 to $\pi$ plus the integral from $\pi$ to $2\pi$. However, the integral from $\pi$ to $2\pi$ is equal to the integral from 0 to $\pi$, since the cardioid is symmetric about the polar axis (Figure 10.3.6). Thus,

$$L = 2\int_0^{2\pi} \left|\cos \tfrac{1}{2}\theta\right| d\theta = 4\int_0^{\pi} \cos \tfrac{1}{2}\theta \, d\theta = 8 \sin \tfrac{1}{2}\theta \Big]_0^{\pi} = 8 \blacktriangleleft$$

## AREA IN POLAR COORDINATES

We begin our investigation of area in polar coordinates with a simple case.

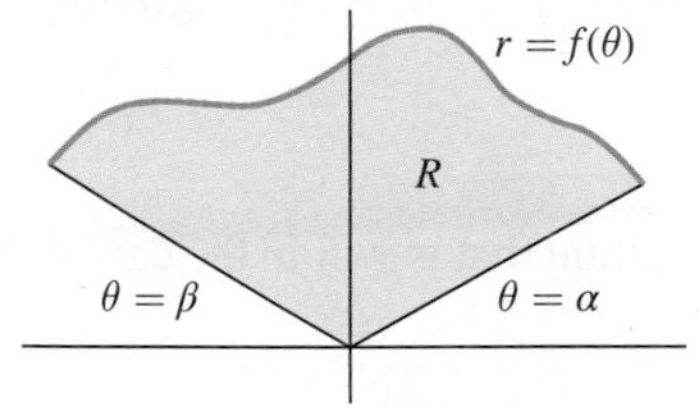


▲ Figure 10.3.7

**10.3.3 AREA PROBLEM IN POLAR COORDINATES** Suppose that $\alpha$ and $\beta$ are angles that satisfy the condition

$$\alpha < \beta \leq \alpha + 2\pi$$

and suppose that $f(\theta)$ is continuous and nonnegative for $\alpha \leq \theta \leq \beta$. Find the area of the region $R$ enclosed by the polar curve $r = f(\theta)$ and the rays $\theta = \alpha$ and $\theta = \beta$ (Figure 10.3.7).

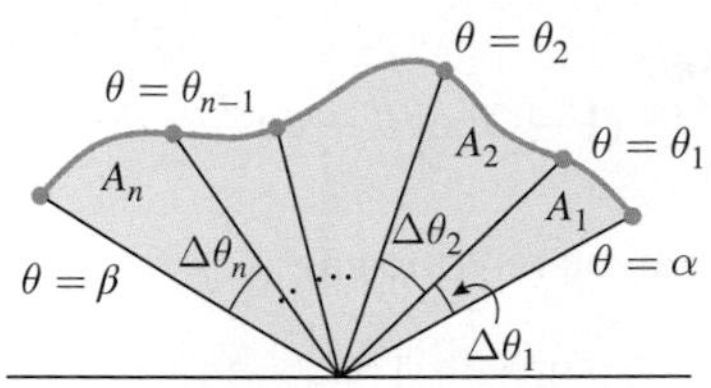


▲ Figure 10.3.8

In rectangular coordinates we obtained areas under curves by dividing the region into an increasing number of vertical strips, approximating the strips by rectangles, and taking a limit. In polar coordinates rectangles are clumsy to work with, and it is better to partition the region into ***wedges*** by using rays

$$\theta = \theta_1,\ \theta = \theta_2,\ \ldots,\ \theta = \theta_{n-1}$$

such that

$$\alpha < \theta_1 < \theta_2 < \cdots < \theta_{n-1} < \beta$$

(Figure 10.3.8). As shown in that figure, the rays divide the region $R$ into $n$ wedges with areas $A_1, A_2, \ldots, A_n$ and central angles $\Delta\theta_1, \Delta\theta_2, \ldots, \Delta\theta_n$. The area of the entire region can be written as

$$A = A_1 + A_2 + \cdots + A_n = \sum_{k=1}^{n} A_k \tag{4}$$

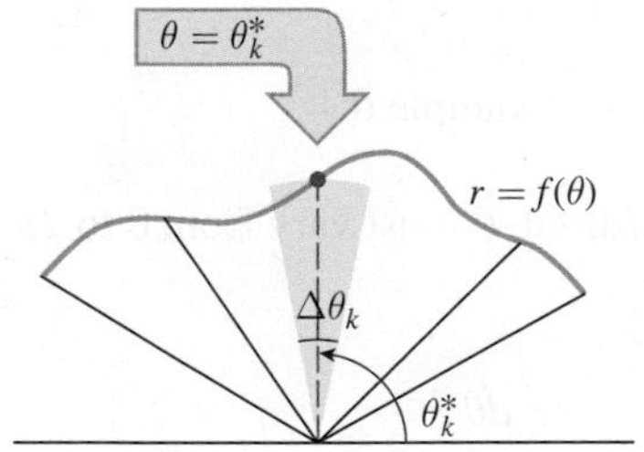


▲ Figure 10.3.9

If $\Delta\theta_k$ is small, then we can approximate the area $A_k$ of the $k$th wedge by the area of a sector with central angle $\Delta\theta_k$ and radius $f(\theta_k^*)$, where $\theta = \theta_k^*$ is any ray that lies in the $k$th wedge (Figure 10.3.9). Thus, from (4) and Formula (5) of Appendix A for the area of a sector, we obtain

$$A = \sum_{k=1}^{n} A_k \approx \sum_{k=1}^{n} \tfrac{1}{2}[f(\theta_k^*)]^2 \Delta\theta_k \tag{5}$$

If we now increase $n$ in such a way that $\max \Delta\theta_k \to 0$, then the sectors will become better and better approximations of the wedges and it is reasonable to expect that (5) will approach the exact value of the area $A$ (Figure 10.3.10); that is,

$$A = \lim_{\max \Delta\theta_k \to 0} \sum_{k=1}^{n} \tfrac{1}{2}[f(\theta_k^*)]^2 \Delta\theta_k = \int_{\alpha}^{\beta} \tfrac{1}{2}[f(\theta)]^2 \, d\theta$$

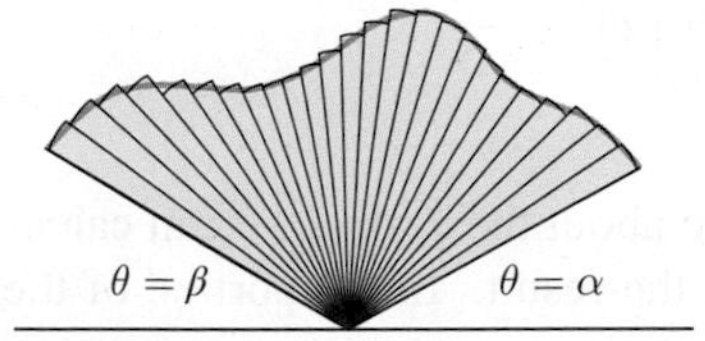


▲ Figure 10.3.10

Note that the discussion above can easily be adapted to the case where $f(\theta)$ is nonpositive for $\alpha \leq \theta \leq \beta$. We summarize this result below.

**10.3.4 AREA IN POLAR COORDINATES** If $\alpha$ and $\beta$ are angles that satisfy the condition

$$\alpha < \beta \leq \alpha + 2\pi$$

and if $f(\theta)$ is continuous and either nonnegative or nonpositive for $\alpha \leq \theta \leq \beta$, then the area $A$ of the region $R$ enclosed by the polar curve $r = f(\theta)$ $(\alpha \leq \theta \leq \beta)$ and the lines $\theta = \alpha$ and $\theta = \beta$ is

$$A = \int_{\alpha}^{\beta} \tfrac{1}{2}[f(\theta)]^2 \, d\theta = \int_{\alpha}^{\beta} \tfrac{1}{2} r^2 \, d\theta \tag{6}$$

The hardest part of applying (6) is determining the limits of integration. This can be done as follows:

**Area in Polar Coordinates: Limits of Integration**

**Step 1.** Sketch the region $R$ whose area is to be determined.

**Step 2.** Draw an arbitrary "radial line" from the pole to the boundary curve $r = f(\theta)$.

**Step 3.** Ask, "Over what interval of values must $\theta$ vary in order for the radial line to sweep out the region $R$?"

**Step 4.** Your answer in Step 3 will determine the lower and upper limits of integration.

▶ **Example 6** Find the area of the region in the first quadrant that is within the cardioid $r = 1 - \cos\theta$.

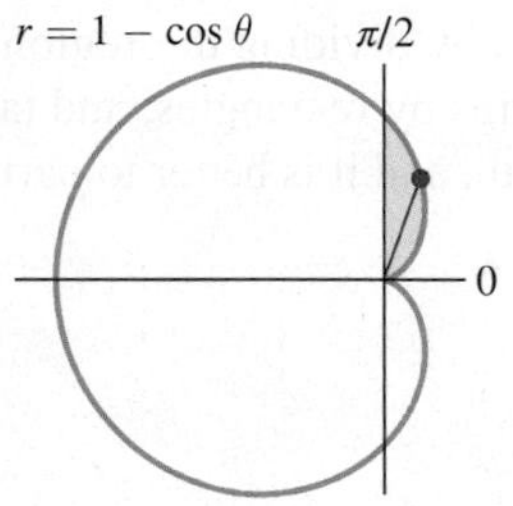


The shaded region is swept out by the radial line as $\theta$ varies from 0 to $\pi/2$.

▲ **Figure 10.3.11**

***Solution.*** The region and a typical radial line are shown in Figure 10.3.11. For the radial line to sweep out the region, $\theta$ must vary from 0 to $\pi/2$. Thus, from (6) with $\alpha = 0$ and $\beta = \pi/2$, we obtain

$$A = \int_0^{\pi/2} \frac{1}{2} r^2 \, d\theta = \frac{1}{2}\int_0^{\pi/2} (1 - \cos\theta)^2 \, d\theta = \frac{1}{2}\int_0^{\pi/2} (1 - 2\cos\theta + \cos^2\theta) \, d\theta$$

With the help of the identity $\cos^2\theta = \frac{1}{2}(1 + \cos 2\theta)$, this can be rewritten as

$$A = \frac{1}{2}\int_0^{\pi/2} \left(\frac{3}{2} - 2\cos\theta + \frac{1}{2}\cos 2\theta\right) d\theta = \frac{1}{2}\left[\frac{3}{2}\theta - 2\sin\theta + \frac{1}{4}\sin 2\theta\right]_0^{\pi/2} = \frac{3}{8}\pi - 1 \blacktriangleleft$$

▶ **Example 7** Find the entire area within the cardioid of Example 6.

***Solution.*** For the radial line to sweep out the entire cardioid, $\theta$ must vary from 0 to $2\pi$. Thus, from (6) with $\alpha = 0$ and $\beta = 2\pi$,

$$A = \int_0^{2\pi} \frac{1}{2} r^2 \, d\theta = \frac{1}{2}\int_0^{2\pi} (1 - \cos\theta)^2 \, d\theta$$

If we proceed as in Example 6, this reduces to

$$A = \frac{1}{2}\int_0^{2\pi} \left(\frac{3}{2} - 2\cos\theta + \frac{1}{2}\cos 2\theta\right) d\theta = \frac{3\pi}{2}$$

***Alternative Solution.*** Since the cardioid is symmetric about the $x$-axis, we can calculate the portion of the area above the $x$-axis and double the result. In the portion of the cardioid above the $x$-axis, $\theta$ ranges from 0 to $\pi$, so that

$$A = 2\int_0^{\pi} \frac{1}{2} r^2 \, d\theta = \int_0^{\pi} (1 - \cos\theta)^2 \, d\theta = \frac{3\pi}{2} \blacktriangleleft$$

## USING SYMMETRY

Although Formula (6) is applicable if $r = f(\theta)$ is negative, area computations can sometimes be simplified by using symmetry to restrict the limits of integration to intervals where $r \geq 0$. This is illustrated in the next example.

▶ **Example 8** Find the area of the region enclosed by the rose curve $r = \cos 2\theta$.

***Solution.*** Referring to Figure 10.2.13 and using symmetry, the area in the first quadrant that is swept out for $0 \le \theta \le \pi/4$ is one-eighth of the total area inside the rose. Thus, from Formula (6)

$$\begin{aligned} A &= 8\int_0^{\pi/4} \frac{1}{2}r^2\,d\theta = 4\int_0^{\pi/4} \cos^2 2\theta\,d\theta \\ &= 4\int_0^{\pi/4} \frac{1}{2}(1+\cos 4\theta)\,d\theta = 2\int_0^{\pi/4}(1+\cos 4\theta)\,d\theta \\ &= 2\theta + \frac{1}{2}\sin 4\theta\Big]_0^{\pi/4} = \frac{\pi}{2} \end{aligned}$$ ◀

Sometimes the most natural way to satisfy the restriction $\alpha < \beta \le \alpha + 2\pi$ required by Formula (6) is to use a negative value for $\alpha$. For example, suppose that we are interested in finding the area of the shaded region in Figure 10.3.12*a*. The first step would be to determine the intersections of the cardioid $r = 4 + 4\cos\theta$ and the circle $r = 6$, since this information is needed for the limits of integration. To find the points of intersection, we can equate the two expressions for $r$. This yields

$$4 + 4\cos\theta = 6 \quad \text{or} \quad \cos\theta = \frac{1}{2}$$

which is satisfied by the positive angles

$$\theta = \frac{\pi}{3} \quad \text{and} \quad \theta = \frac{5\pi}{3}$$

However, there is a problem here because the radial lines to the circle and cardioid do not sweep through the shaded region shown in Figure 10.3.12*b* as $\theta$ varies over the interval $\pi/3 \le \theta \le 5\pi/3$. There are two ways to circumvent this problem—one is to take advantage of the symmetry by integrating over the interval $0 \le \theta \le \pi/3$ and doubling the result, and the second is to use a negative lower limit of integration and integrate over the interval $-\pi/3 \le \theta \le \pi/3$ (Figure 10.3.12*c*). The two methods are illustrated in the next example.

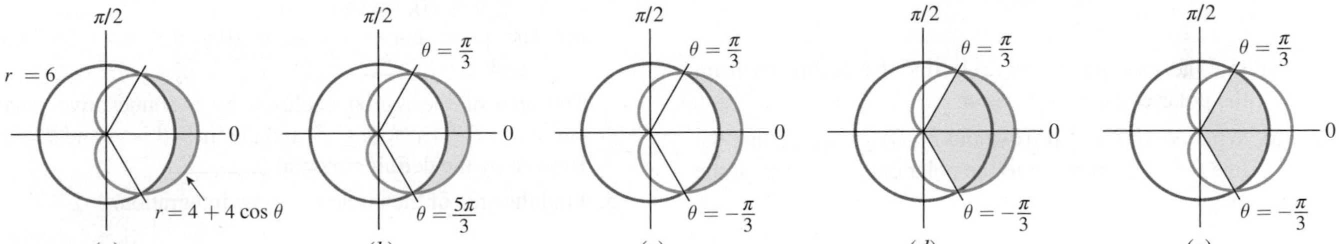


▲ **Figure 10.3.12**

► **Example 9** Find the area of the region that is inside of the cardioid $r = 4 + 4\cos\theta$ and outside of the circle $r = 6$.

***Solution Using a Negative Angle.*** The area of the region can be obtained by subtracting the areas in Figures 10.3.12*d* and 10.3.12*e*:

$$\begin{aligned} A &= \int_{-\pi/3}^{\pi/3} \frac{1}{2}(4+4\cos\theta)^2\,d\theta - \int_{-\pi/3}^{\pi/3} \frac{1}{2}(6)^2\,d\theta \\ &= \int_{-\pi/3}^{\pi/3} \frac{1}{2}[(4+4\cos\theta)^2 - 36]\,d\theta = \int_{-\pi/3}^{\pi/3} (16\cos\theta + 8\cos^2\theta - 10)\,d\theta \\ &= [16\sin\theta + (4\theta + 2\sin 2\theta) - 10\theta]_{-\pi/3}^{\pi/3} = 18\sqrt{3} - 4\pi \end{aligned}$$

Area inside cardioid minus area inside circle.

***Solution Using Symmetry.*** Using symmetry, we can calculate the area above the polar axis and double it. This yields (verify)

$$A = 2\int_0^{\pi/3} \frac{1}{2}[(4+4\cos\theta)^2 - 36]\,d\theta = 2(9\sqrt{3} - 2\pi) = 18\sqrt{3} - 4\pi$$

which agrees with the preceding result. ◀

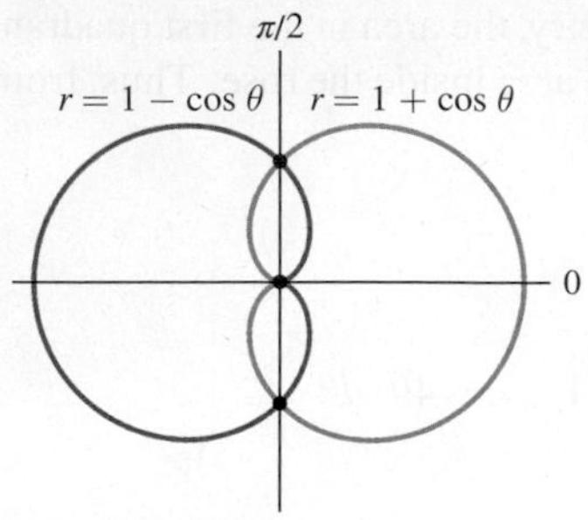


▲ Figure 10.3.13

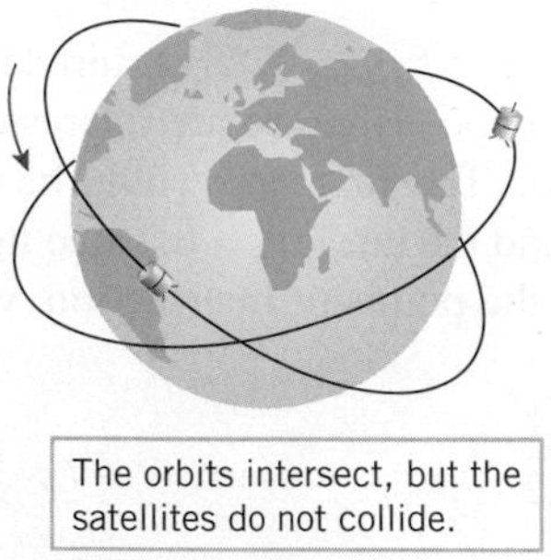


▲ Figure 10.3.14

## INTERSECTIONS OF POLAR GRAPHS

In the last example we found the intersections of the cardioid and circle by equating their expressions for $r$ and solving for $\theta$. However, because a point can be represented in different ways in polar coordinates, this procedure will not always produce all of the intersections. For example, the cardioids

$$r = 1 - \cos\theta \quad \text{and} \quad r = 1 + \cos\theta \tag{7}$$

intersect at three points: the pole, the point $(1, \pi/2)$, and the point $(1, 3\pi/2)$ (Figure 10.3.13). Equating the right-hand sides of the equations in (7) yields $1 - \cos\theta = 1 + \cos\theta$ or $\cos\theta = 0$, so

$$\theta = \frac{\pi}{2} + k\pi, \quad k = 0, \pm 1, \pm 2, \ldots$$

Substituting any of these values in (7) yields $r = 1$, so that we have found only two distinct points of intersection, $(1, \pi/2)$ and $(1, 3\pi/2)$; the pole has been missed. This problem occurs because the two cardioids pass through the pole at different values of $\theta$—the cardioid $r = 1 - \cos\theta$ passes through the pole at $\theta = 0$, and the cardioid $r = 1 + \cos\theta$ passes through the pole at $\theta = \pi$.

The situation with the cardioids is analogous to two satellites circling the Earth in intersecting orbits (Figure 10.3.14). The satellites will not collide unless they reach the same point at the same time. In general, when looking for intersections of polar curves, it is a good idea to graph the curves to determine how many intersections there should be.

## ✓ QUICK CHECK EXERCISES 10.3 (See page 639 for answers.)

1. (a) To obtain $dy/dx$ directly from the polar equation $r = f(\theta)$, we can use the formula

$$\frac{dy}{dx} = \frac{dy/d\theta}{dx/d\theta} = \underline{\qquad\qquad}$$

(b) Use the formula in part (a) to find $dy/dx$ directly from the polar equation $r = \csc\theta$.

2. (a) What conditions on $f(\theta_0)$ and $f'(\theta_0)$ guarantee that the line $\theta = \theta_0$ is tangent to the polar curve $r = f(\theta)$ at the origin?

(b) What are the values of $\theta_0$ in $[0, 2\pi]$ at which the lines $\theta = \theta_0$ are tangent at the origin to the four-petal rose $r = \cos 2\theta$?

3. (a) To find the arc length $L$ of the polar curve $r = f(\theta)$ $(\alpha \le \theta \le \beta)$, we can use the formula $L =$ ______.

(b) The polar curve $r = \sec\theta$ $(0 \le \theta \le \pi/4)$ has arc length $L =$ ______.

4. The area of the region enclosed by a nonnegative polar curve $r = f(\theta)$ $(\alpha \le \theta \le \beta)$ and the lines $\theta = \alpha$ and $\theta = \beta$ is given by the definite integral ______.

5. Find the area of the circle $r = a$ by integration.

## EXERCISE SET 10.3 Graphing Utility C CAS

**1–6** Find the slope of the tangent line to the polar curve for the given value of $\theta$. ■

1. $r = 2\sin\theta;\ \theta = \pi/6$
2. $r = 1 + \cos\theta;\ \theta = \pi/2$
3. $r = 1/\theta;\ \theta = 2$
4. $r = a\sec 2\theta;\ \theta = \pi/6$
5. $r = \sin 3\theta;\ \theta = \pi/4$
6. $r = 4 - 3\sin\theta;\ \theta = \pi$

**7–8** Calculate the slopes of the tangent lines indicated in the accompanying figures. ■

7. $r = 2 + 2\sin\theta$
8. $r = 1 - 2\sin\theta$

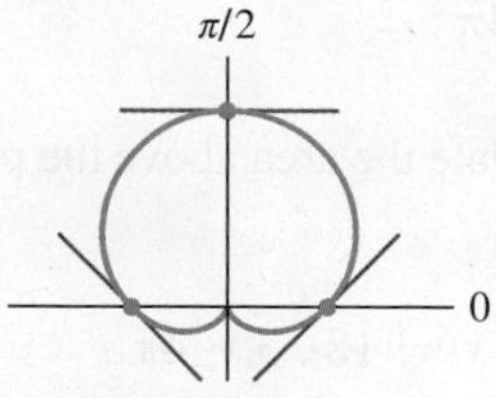


▲ Figure Ex-7

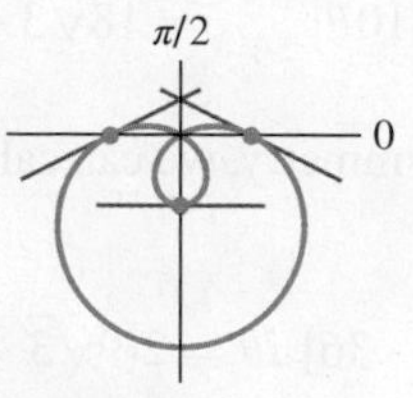


▲ Figure Ex-8

**9–10** Find polar coordinates of all points at which the polar curve has a horizontal or a vertical tangent line. ■

9. $r = a(1 + \cos\theta)$
10. $r = a\sin\theta$

**11–12** Use a graphing utility to make a conjecture about the number of points on the polar curve at which there is a horizontal tangent line, and confirm your conjecture by finding appropriate derivatives. ■

11. $r = \sin\theta\cos^2\theta$
12. $r = 1 - 2\sin\theta$

**13–18** Sketch the polar curve and find polar equations of the tangent lines to the curve at the pole. ■

13. $r = 2\cos 3\theta$
14. $r = 4\sin\theta$
15. $r = 4\sqrt{\cos 2\theta}$
16. $r = \sin 2\theta$
17. $r = 1 - 2\cos\theta$
18. $r = 2\theta$

**19–22** Use Formula (3) to calculate the arc length of the polar curve. ■

19. The entire circle $r = a$

**20.** The entire circle $r = 2a\cos\theta$

**21.** The entire cardioid $r = a(1 - \cos\theta)$

**22.** $r = e^{3\theta}$ from $\theta = 0$ to $\theta = 2$

**23.** (a) Show that the arc length of one petal of the rose $r = \cos n\theta$ is given by

$$2\int_0^{\pi/(2n)} \sqrt{1 + (n^2 - 1)\sin^2 n\theta}\, d\theta$$

(b) Use the numerical integration capability of a calculating utility to approximate the arc length of one petal of the four-petal rose $r = \cos 2\theta$.

(c) Use the numerical integration capability of a calculating utility to approximate the arc length of one petal of the $n$-petal rose $r = \cos n\theta$ for $n = 2, 3, 4, \ldots, 20$; then make a conjecture about the limit of these arc lengths as $n \to +\infty$.

**24.** (a) Sketch the spiral $r = e^{-\theta/8}$ $(0 \le \theta < +\infty)$.

(b) Find an improper integral for the total arc length of the spiral.

(c) Show that the integral converges and find the total arc length of the spiral.

**25.** Write down, but do not evaluate, an integral for the area of each shaded region.

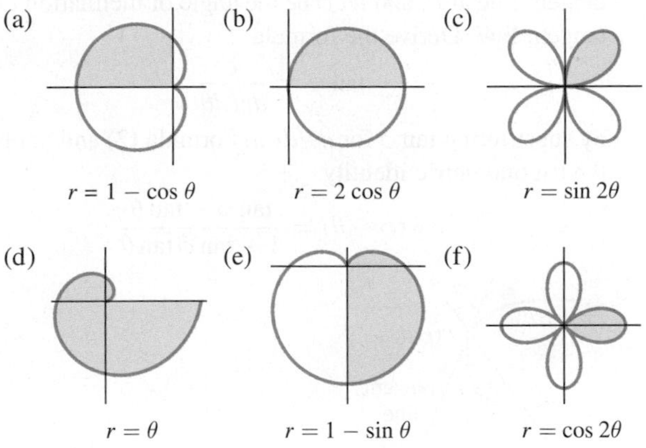


**26.** Find the area of the shaded region in Exercise 25(d).

**27.** In each part, find the area of the circle by integration.
(a) $r = 2a\sin\theta$ (b) $r = 2a\cos\theta$

**28.** (a) Show that $r = 2\sin\theta + 2\cos\theta$ is a circle.

(b) Find the area of the circle using a geometric formula and then by integration.

**29–34** Find the area of the region described. ■

**29.** The region that is enclosed by the cardioid $r = 2 + 2\sin\theta$.

**30.** The region in the first quadrant within the cardioid $r = 1 + \cos\theta$.

**31.** The region enclosed by the rose $r = 4\cos 3\theta$.

**32.** The region enclosed by the rose $r = 2\sin 2\theta$.

**33.** The region enclosed by the inner loop of the limaçon $r = 1 + 2\cos\theta$. [*Hint:* $r \le 0$ over the interval of integration.]

**34.** The region swept out by a radial line from the pole to the curve $r = 2/\theta$ as $\theta$ varies over the interval $1 \le \theta \le 3$.

**35–38** Find the area of the shaded region. ■

**35.**

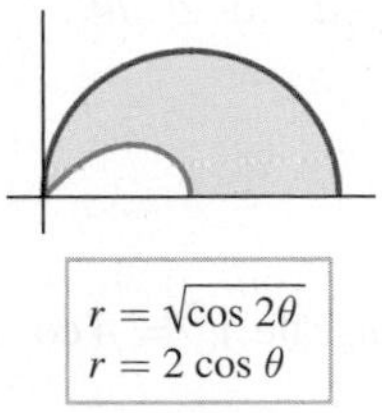


**36.**

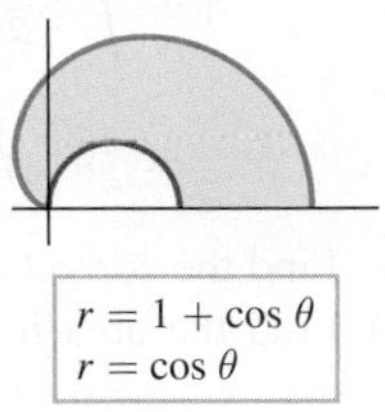


**37.**

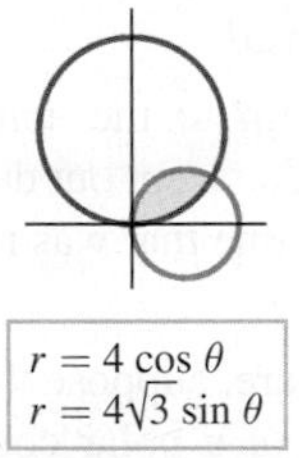


**38.**

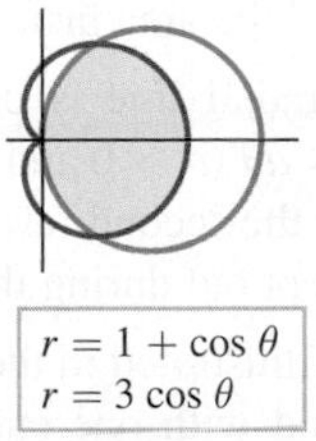


**39–46** Find the area of the region described. ■

**39.** The region inside the circle $r = 3\sin\theta$ and outside the cardioid $r = 1 + \sin\theta$.

**40.** The region outside the cardioid $r = 2 - 2\cos\theta$ and inside the circle $r = 4$.

**41.** The region inside the cardioid $r = 2 + 2\cos\theta$ and outside the circle $r = 3$.

**42.** The region that is common to the circles $r = 2\cos\theta$ and $r = 2\sin\theta$.

**43.** The region between the loops of the limaçon $r = \frac{1}{2} + \cos\theta$.

**44.** The region inside the cardioid $r = 2 + 2\cos\theta$ and to the right of the line $r\cos\theta = \frac{3}{2}$.

**45.** The region inside the circle $r = 2$ and to the right of the line $r = \sqrt{2}\sec\theta$.

**46.** The region inside the rose $r = 2a\cos 2\theta$ and outside the circle $r = a\sqrt{2}$.

**47–50 True–False** Determine whether the statement is true or false. Explain your answer. ■

**47.** The $x$-axis is tangent to the polar curve $r = \cos(\theta/2)$ at $\theta = 3\pi$.

**48.** The arc length of the polar curve $r = \sqrt{\theta}$ for $0 \le \theta \le \pi/2$ is given by

$$L = \int_0^{\pi/2} \sqrt{1 + \frac{1}{4\theta}}\, d\theta$$

**49.** The area of a sector with central angle $\theta$ taken from a circle of radius $r$ is $\theta r^2$.

**50.** The expression

$$\frac{1}{2}\int_{-\pi/4}^{\pi/4} (1 - \sqrt{2}\cos\theta)^2\, d\theta$$

computes the area enclosed by the inner loop of the limaçon $r = 1 - \sqrt{2}\cos\theta$.

**FOCUS ON CONCEPTS**

**51.** (a) Find the error: The area that is inside the lemniscate $r^2 = a^2 \cos 2\theta$ is

$$A = \int_0^{2\pi} \tfrac{1}{2} r^2 \, d\theta = \int_0^{2\pi} \tfrac{1}{2} a^2 \cos 2\theta \, d\theta$$

$$= \tfrac{1}{4} a^2 \sin 2\theta \Big]_0^{2\pi} = 0$$

(b) Find the correct area.

(c) Find the area inside the lemniscate $r^2 = 4\cos 2\theta$ and outside the circle $r = \sqrt{2}$.

**52.** Find the area inside the curve $r^2 = \sin 2\theta$.

**53.** A radial line is drawn from the origin to the spiral $r = a\theta$ ($a > 0$ and $\theta \geq 0$). Find the area swept out during the second revolution of the radial line that was not swept out during the first revolution.

**54.** As illustrated in the accompanying figure, suppose that a rod with one end fixed at the pole of a polar coordinate system rotates counterclockwise at the constant rate of 1 rad/s. At time $t = 0$ a bug on the rod is 10 mm from the pole and is moving outward along the rod at the constant speed of 2 mm/s.

(a) Find an equation of the form $r = f(\theta)$ for the path of motion of the bug, assuming that $\theta = 0$ when $t = 0$.

(b) Find the distance the bug travels along the path in part (a) during the first 5 s. Round your answer to the nearest tenth of a millimeter.

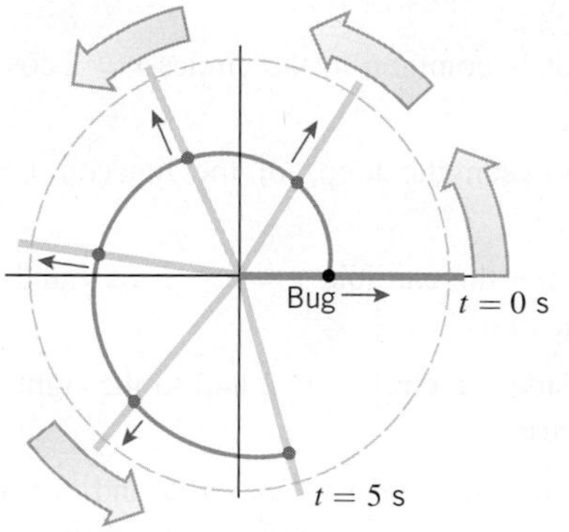


◀ **Figure Ex-54**

**55.** (a) Show that the Folium of Descartes $x^3 - 3xy + y^3 = 0$ can be expressed in polar coordinates as

$$r = \frac{3 \sin\theta \cos\theta}{\cos^3\theta + \sin^3\theta}$$

(b) Use a CAS to show that the area inside of the loop is $\frac{3}{2}$ (Figure 3.1.3*a*).

**56.** (a) What is the area that is enclosed by one petal of the rose $r = a\cos n\theta$ if $n$ is an even integer?

(b) What is the area that is enclosed by one petal of the rose $r = a\cos n\theta$ if $n$ is an odd integer?

(c) Use a CAS to show that the total area enclosed by the rose $r = a\cos n\theta$ is $\pi a^2/2$ if the number of petals is even. [*Hint:* See Exercise 78 of Section 10.2.]

(d) Use a CAS to show that the total area enclosed by the rose $r = a\cos n\theta$ is $\pi a^2/4$ if the number of petals is odd.

**57.** One of the most famous problems in Greek antiquity was "squaring the circle," that is, using a straightedge and compass to construct a square whose area is equal to that of a given circle. It was proved in the nineteenth century that no such construction is possible. However, show that the shaded areas in the accompanying figure are equal, thereby "squaring the crescent."

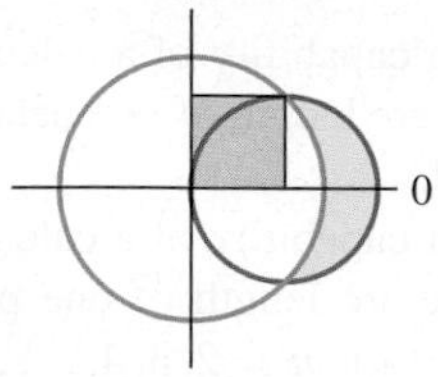


◀ **Figure Ex-57**

**58.** Use a graphing utility to generate the polar graph of the equation $r = \cos 3\theta + 2$, and find the area that it encloses.

**59.** Use a graphing utility to generate the graph of the ***bifolium*** $r = 2\cos\theta \sin^2\theta$, and find the area of the upper loop.

**60.** Use Formula (9) of Section 10.1 to derive the arc length formula for polar curves, Formula (3).

**61.** As illustrated in the accompanying figure, let $P(r, \theta)$ be a point on the polar curve $r = f(\theta)$, let $\psi$ be the smallest counterclockwise angle from the extended radius $OP$ to the tangent line at $P$, and let $\phi$ be the angle of inclination of the tangent line. Derive the formula

$$\tan\psi = \frac{r}{dr/d\theta}$$

by substituting $\tan\phi$ for $dy/dx$ in Formula (2) and applying the trigonometric identity

$$\tan(\phi - \theta) = \frac{\tan\phi - \tan\theta}{1 + \tan\phi \tan\theta}$$

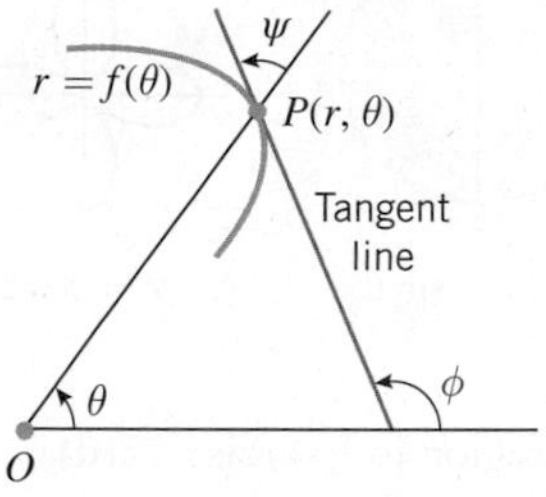


◀ **Figure Ex-61**

**62–63** Use the formula for $\psi$ obtained in Exercise 61. ■

**62.** (a) Use the trigonometric identity

$$\tan\frac{\theta}{2} = \frac{1 - \cos\theta}{\sin\theta}$$

to show that if $(r, \theta)$ is a point on the cardioid

$$r = 1 - \cos\theta \quad (0 \leq \theta < 2\pi)$$

then $\psi = \theta/2$.

(b) Sketch the cardioid and show the angle $\psi$ at the points where the cardioid crosses the $y$-axis.

(c) Find the angle $\psi$ at the points where the cardioid crosses the $y$-axis.

**63.** Show that for a logarithmic spiral $r = ae^{b\theta}$, the angle from the radial line to the tangent line is constant along the spiral (see the accompanying figure). [*Note:* For this reason, logarithmic spirals are sometimes called ***equiangular spirals***.]

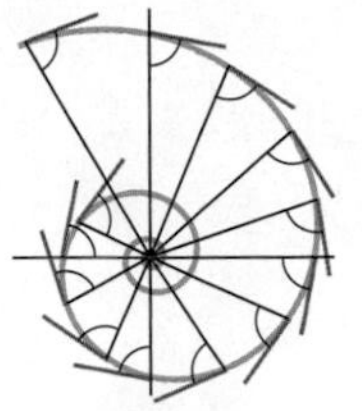

◀ Figure Ex-63

64. (a) In the discussion associated with Exercises 75–80 of Section 10.1, formulas were given for the area of the surface of revolution that is generated by revolving a parametric curve about the $x$-axis or $y$-axis. Use those formulas to derive the following formulas for the areas of the surfaces of revolution that are generated by revolving the portion of the polar curve $r = f(\theta)$ from $\theta = \alpha$ to $\theta = \beta$ about the polar axis and about the line $\theta = \pi/2$:

$$S = \int_{\alpha}^{\beta} 2\pi r \sin\theta \sqrt{r^2 + \left(\frac{dr}{d\theta}\right)^2}\, d\theta \quad \text{About } \theta = 0$$

$$S = \int_{\alpha}^{\beta} 2\pi r \cos\theta \sqrt{r^2 + \left(\frac{dr}{d\theta}\right)^2}\, d\theta \quad \text{About } \theta = \pi/2$$

(b) State conditions under which these formulas hold.

**65–68** Sketch the surface, and use the formulas in Exercise 64 to find the surface area. ■

65. The surface generated by revolving the circle $r = \cos\theta$ about the line $\theta = \pi/2$.

66. The surface generated by revolving the spiral $r = e^{\theta}$ $(0 \le \theta \le \pi/2)$ about the line $\theta = \pi/2$.

67. The "apple" generated by revolving the upper half of the cardioid $r = 1 - \cos\theta$ $(0 \le \theta \le \pi)$ about the polar axis.

68. The sphere of radius $a$ generated by revolving the semicircle $r = a$ in the upper half-plane about the polar axis.

69. **Writing**

(a) Show that if $0 \le \theta_1 < \theta_2 \le \pi$ and if $r_1$ and $r_2$ are positive, then the area $A$ of a triangle with vertices $(0, 0)$, $(r_1, \theta_1)$, and $(r_2, \theta_2)$ is

$$A = \tfrac{1}{2} r_1 r_2 \sin(\theta_2 - \theta_1)$$

(b) Use the formula obtained in part (a) to describe an approach to answer Area Problem 10.3.3 that uses an approximation of the region $R$ by triangles instead of circular wedges. Reconcile your approach with Formula (6).

70. **Writing** In order to find the area of a region bounded by two polar curves it is often necessary to determine their points of intersection. Give an example to illustrate that the points of intersection of curves $r = f(\theta)$ and $r = g(\theta)$ may not coincide with solutions to $f(\theta) = g(\theta)$. Discuss some strategies for determining intersection points of polar curves and provide examples to illustrate your strategies.

✓ **QUICK CHECK ANSWERS 10.3** 1. (a) $\dfrac{r\cos\theta + \sin\theta \dfrac{dr}{d\theta}}{-r\sin\theta + \cos\theta \dfrac{dr}{d\theta}}$ (b) $\dfrac{dy}{dx} = 0$ 2. (a) $f(\theta_0) = 0$, $f'(\theta_0) \neq 0$ (b) $\theta_0 = \dfrac{\pi}{4}, \dfrac{3\pi}{4}, \dfrac{5\pi}{4}, \dfrac{7\pi}{4}$ 3. (a) $\displaystyle\int_{\alpha}^{\beta} \sqrt{r^2 + \left(\frac{dr}{d\theta}\right)^2}\, d\theta$ (b) 1 4. $\displaystyle\int_{\alpha}^{\beta} \tfrac{1}{2}[f(\theta)]^2\, d\theta = \int_{\alpha}^{\beta} \tfrac{1}{2} r^2\, d\theta$ 5. $\displaystyle\int_{0}^{2\pi} \tfrac{1}{2} a^2\, d\theta = \pi a^2$

# 10.4 CONIC SECTIONS

*In this section* we will discuss some of the basic geometric properties of parabolas, ellipses, and hyperbolas. These curves play an important role in calculus and also arise naturally in a broad range of applications in such fields as planetary motion, design of telescopes and antennas, geodetic positioning, and medicine, to name a few.*

## ■ CONIC SECTIONS

Circles, ellipses, parabolas, and hyperbolas are called ***conic sections*** or ***conics*** because they can be obtained as intersections of a plane with a double-napped circular cone (Figure 10.4.1). If the plane passes through the vertex of the double-napped cone, then the intersection is a point, a pair of intersecting lines, or a single line. These are called ***degenerate conic sections***.

* Some students may already be familiar with the material in this section, in which case it can be treated as a review. Instructors who want to spend some additional time on precalculus review may want to allocate more than one lecture on this material.

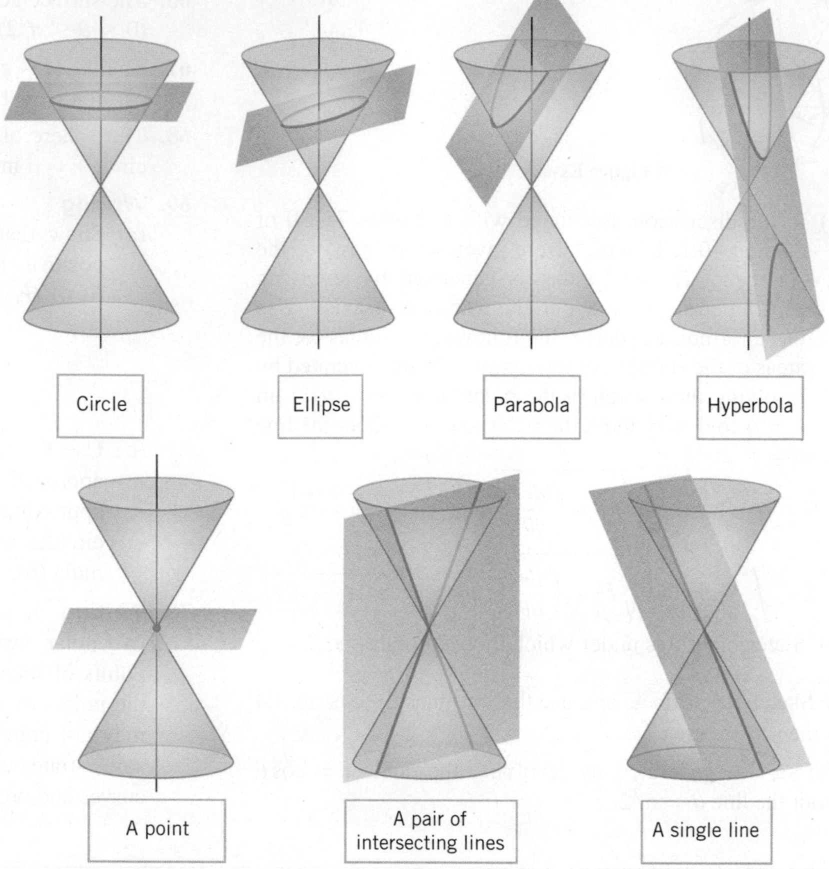

▲ Figure 10.4.1

## DEFINITIONS OF THE CONIC SECTIONS

Although we could derive properties of parabolas, ellipses, and hyperbolas by defining them as intersections with a double-napped cone, it will be better suited to calculus if we begin with equivalent definitions that are based on their geometric properties.

**10.4.1 DEFINITION** A ***parabola*** is the set of all points in the plane that are equidistant from a fixed line and a fixed point not on the line.

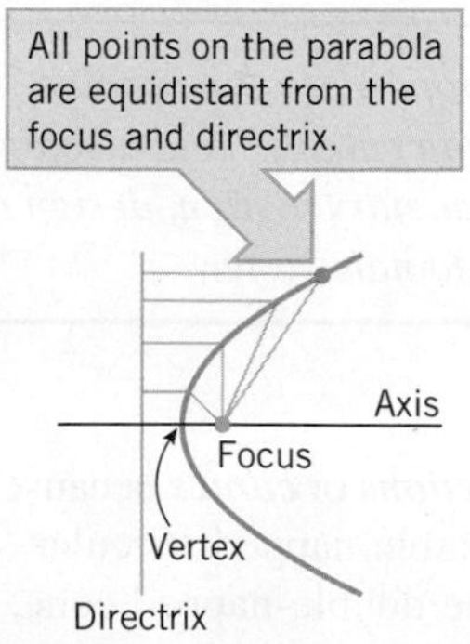

▲ Figure 10.4.2

The line is called the ***directrix*** of the parabola, and the point is called the ***focus*** (Figure 10.4.2). A parabola is symmetric about the line that passes through the focus at right angles to the directrix. This line, called the ***axis*** or the ***axis of symmetry*** of the parabola, intersects the parabola at a point called the ***vertex***.

**10.4.2 DEFINITION** An ***ellipse*** is the set of all points in the plane, the sum of whose distances from two fixed points is a given positive constant that is greater than the distance between the fixed points.

The two fixed points are called the ***foci*** (plural of "focus") of the ellipse, and the midpoint of the line segment joining the foci is called the ***center*** (Figure 10.4.3*a*). To help visualize Definition 10.4.2, imagine that two ends of a string are tacked to the foci and a pencil traces a curve as it is held tight against the string (Figure 10.4.3*b*). The resulting curve will be an ellipse since the sum of the distances to the foci is a constant, namely, the total length of the string. Note that if the foci coincide, the ellipse reduces to a circle. For ellipses other than circles, the line segment through the foci and across the ellipse is called the ***major axis*** (Figure 10.4.3*c*), and the line segment across the ellipse, through the center, and perpendicular to the major axis is called the ***minor axis***. The endpoints of the major axis are called ***vertices***.

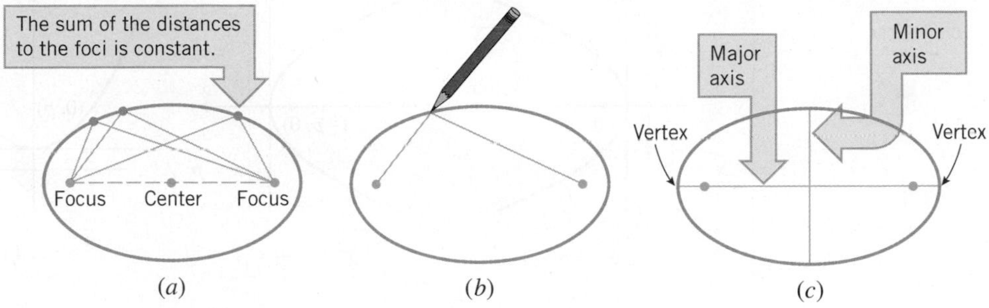


▶ **Figure 10.4.3**

**10.4.3 DEFINITION** A ***hyperbola*** is the set of all points in the plane, the difference of whose distances from two fixed distinct points is a given positive constant that is less than the distance between the fixed points.

The two fixed points are called the ***foci*** of the hyperbola, and the term "difference" that is used in the definition is understood to mean the distance to the farther focus minus the distance to the closer focus. As a result, the points on the hyperbola form two ***branches***, each "wrapping around" the closer focus (Figure 10.4.4*a*). The midpoint of the line segment joining the foci is called the ***center*** of the hyperbola, the line through the foci is called the ***focal axis***, and the line through the center that is perpendicular to the focal axis is called the ***conjugate axis***. The hyperbola intersects the focal axis at two points called the ***vertices***.

Associated with every hyperbola is a pair of lines, called the ***asymptotes*** of the hyperbola. These lines intersect at the center of the hyperbola and have the property that as a point $P$ moves along the hyperbola away from the center, the vertical distance between $P$ and one of the asymptotes approaches zero (Figure 10.4.4*b*).

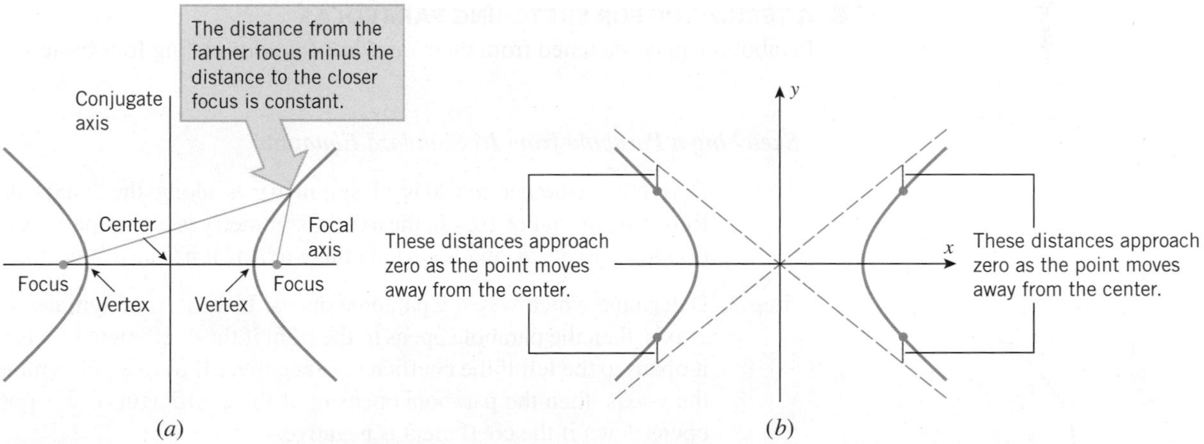


▲ **Figure 10.4.4**

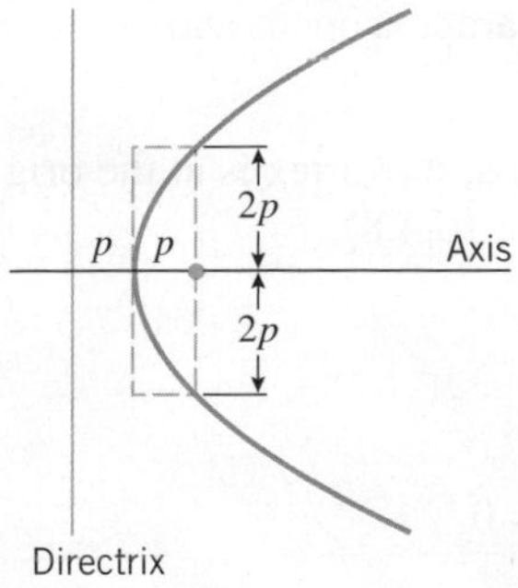


▲ **Figure 10.4.5**

## ■ EQUATIONS OF PARABOLAS IN STANDARD POSITION

It is traditional in the study of parabolas to denote the distance between the focus and the vertex by $p$. The vertex is equidistant from the focus and the directrix, so the distance between the vertex and the directrix is also $p$; consequently, the distance between the focus and the directrix is $2p$ (Figure 10.4.5). As illustrated in that figure, the parabola passes through two of the corners of a box that extends from the vertex to the focus along the axis of symmetry and extends $2p$ units above and $2p$ units below the axis of symmetry.

The equation of a parabola is simplest if the vertex is the origin and the axis of symmetry is along the $x$-axis or $y$-axis. The four possible such orientations are shown in Figure 10.4.6. These are called the ***standard positions*** of a parabola, and the resulting equations are called the ***standard equations*** of a parabola.

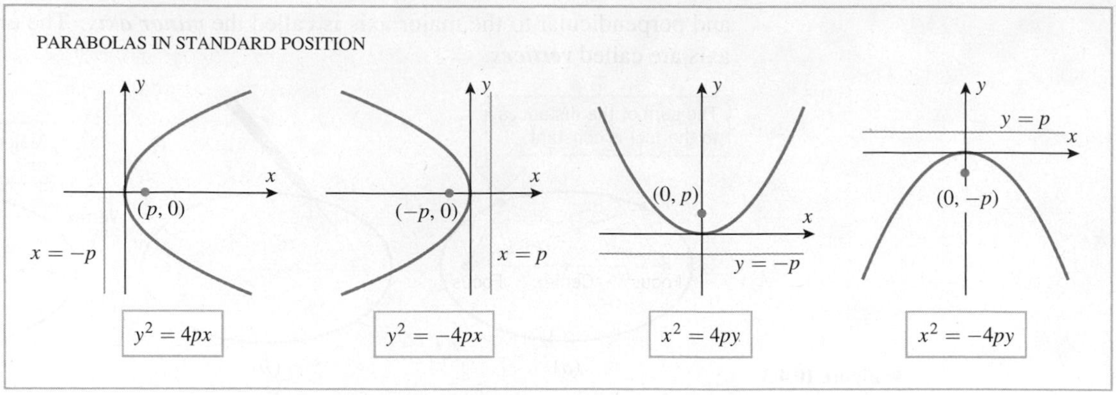


▲ Figure 10.4.6

To illustrate how the equations in Figure 10.4.6 are obtained, we will derive the equation for the parabola with focus $(p, 0)$ and directrix $x = -p$. Let $P(x, y)$ be any point on the parabola. Since $P$ is equidistant from the focus and directrix, the distances $PF$ and $PD$ in Figure 10.4.7 are equal; that is,

$$PF = PD \tag{1}$$

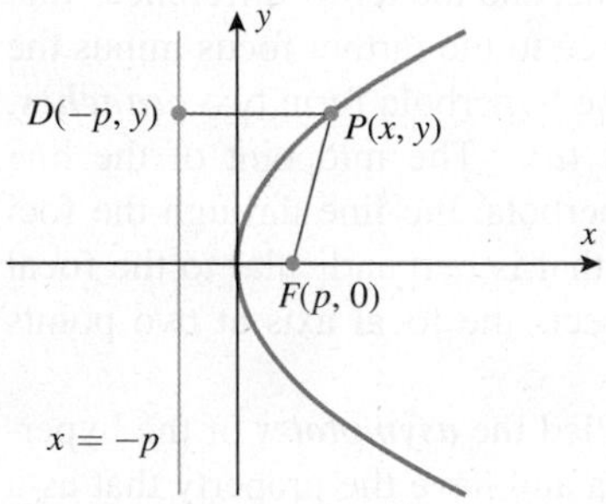


▲ Figure 10.4.7

where $D(-p, y)$ is the foot of the perpendicular from $P$ to the directrix. From the distance formula, the distances $PF$ and $PD$ are

$$PF = \sqrt{(x-p)^2 + y^2} \quad \text{and} \quad PD = \sqrt{(x+p)^2} \tag{2}$$

Substituting in (1) and squaring yields

$$(x-p)^2 + y^2 = (x+p)^2 \tag{3}$$

and after simplifying

$$y^2 = 4px \tag{4}$$

The derivations of the other equations in Figure 10.4.6 are similar.

## A TECHNIQUE FOR SKETCHING PARABOLAS

Parabolas can be sketched from their *standard equations* using four basic steps:

***Sketching a Parabola from Its Standard Equation***

**Step 1.** Determine whether the axis of symmetry is along the $x$-axis or the $y$-axis. Referring to Figure 10.4.6, the axis of symmetry is along the $x$-axis if the equation has a $y^2$-term, and it is along the $y$-axis if it has an $x^2$-term.

**Step 2.** Determine which way the parabola opens. If the axis of symmetry is along the $x$-axis, then the parabola opens to the right if the coefficient of $x$ is positive, and it opens to the left if the coefficient is negative. If the axis of symmetry is along the $y$-axis, then the parabola opens up if the coefficient of $y$ is positive, and it opens down if the coefficient is negative.

**Step 3.** Determine the value of $p$ and draw a box extending $p$ units from the origin along the axis of symmetry in the direction in which the parabola opens and extending $2p$ units on each side of the axis of symmetry.

**Step 4.** Using the box as a guide, sketch the parabola so that its vertex is at the origin and it passes through the corners of the box (Figure 10.4.8).

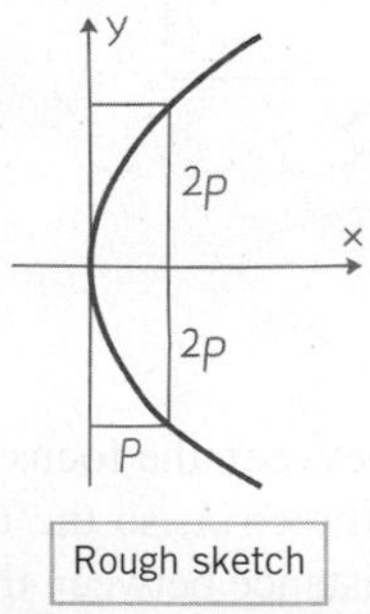


▲ Figure 10.4.8

▶ **Example 1** Sketch the graphs of the parabolas

$$\text{(a) } x^2 = 12y \qquad \text{(b) } y^2 + 8x = 0$$

and show the focus and directrix of each.

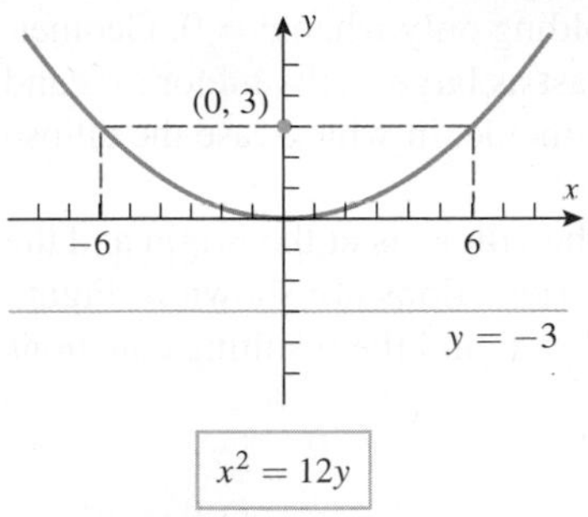

▲ Figure 10.4.9

***Solution (a).*** This equation involves $x^2$, so the axis of symmetry is along the $y$-axis, and the coefficient of $y$ is positive, so the parabola opens upward. From the coefficient of $y$, we obtain $4p = 12$ or $p = 3$. Drawing a box extending $p = 3$ units up from the origin and $2p = 6$ units to the left and $2p = 6$ units to the right of the $y$-axis, then using corners of the box as a guide, yields the graph in Figure 10.4.9.

The focus is $p = 3$ units from the vertex along the axis of symmetry in the direction in which the parabola opens, so its coordinates are $(0, 3)$. The directrix is perpendicular to the axis of symmetry at a distance of $p = 3$ units from the vertex on the opposite side from the focus, so its equation is $y = -3$.

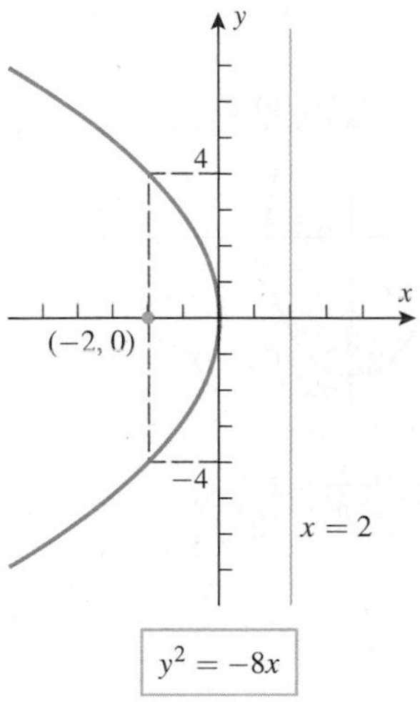

▲ Figure 10.4.10

***Solution (b).*** We first rewrite the equation in the standard form

$$y^2 = -8x$$

This equation involves $y^2$, so the axis of symmetry is along the $x$-axis, and the coefficient of $x$ is negative, so the parabola opens to the left. From the coefficient of $x$ we obtain $4p = 8$, so $p = 2$. Drawing a box extending $p = 2$ units left from the origin and $2p = 4$ units above and $2p = 4$ units below the $x$-axis, then using corners of the box as a guide, yields the graph in Figure 10.4.10. ◀

▶ **Example 2** Find an equation of the parabola that is symmetric about the $y$-axis, has its vertex at the origin, and passes through the point $(5, 2)$.

***Solution.*** Since the parabola is symmetric about the $y$-axis and has its vertex at the origin, the equation is of the form

$$x^2 = 4py \quad \text{or} \quad x^2 = -4py$$

where the sign depends on whether the parabola opens up or down. But the parabola must open up since it passes through the point $(5, 2)$, which lies in the first quadrant. Thus, the equation is of the form

$$x^2 = 4py \tag{5}$$

Since the parabola passes through $(5, 2)$, we must have $5^2 = 4p \cdot 2$ or $4p = \frac{25}{2}$. Therefore, (5) becomes

$$x^2 = \tfrac{25}{2}y \quad ◀$$

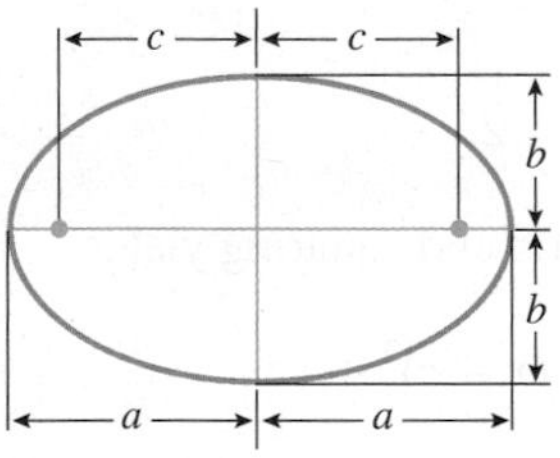

▲ Figure 10.4.11

## EQUATIONS OF ELLIPSES IN STANDARD POSITION

It is traditional in the study of ellipses to denote the length of the major axis by $2a$, the length of the minor axis by $2b$, and the distance between the foci by $2c$ (Figure 10.4.11). The number $a$ is called the ***semimajor axis*** and the number $b$ the ***semiminor axis*** (standard but odd terminology, since $a$ and $b$ are numbers, not geometric axes).

There is a basic relationship between the numbers $a$, $b$, and $c$ that can be obtained by examining the sum of the distances to the foci from a point $P$ at the end of the major axis and from a point $Q$ at the end of the minor axis (Figure 10.4.12). From Definition 10.4.2, these sums must be equal, so we obtain

$$2\sqrt{b^2 + c^2} = (a - c) + (a + c)$$

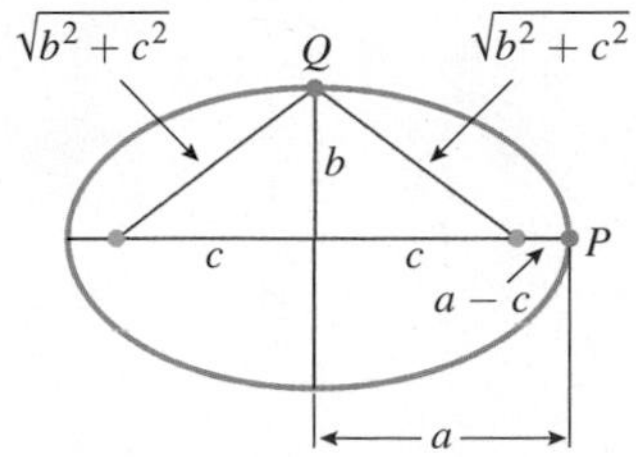

▲ Figure 10.4.12

from which it follows that

$$a = \sqrt{b^2 + c^2} \tag{6}$$

or, equivalently,

$$c = \sqrt{a^2 - b^2} \tag{7}$$

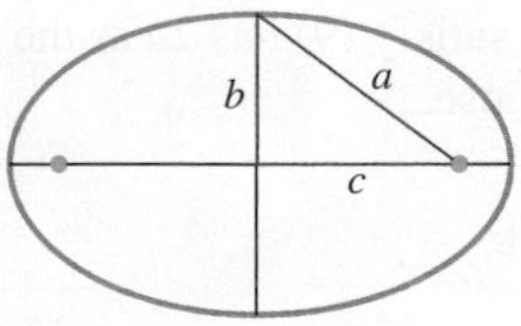

▲ Figure 10.4.13

From (6), the distance from a focus to an end of the minor axis is $a$ (Figure 10.4.13), which implies that for *all* points on the ellipse the sum of the distances to the foci is $2a$.

It also follows from (6) that $a \geq b$ with the equality holding only when $c = 0$. Geometrically, this means that the major axis of an ellipse is at least as large as the minor axis and that the two axes have equal length only when the foci coincide, in which case the ellipse is a circle.

The equation of an ellipse is simplest if the center of the ellipse is at the origin and the foci are on the $x$-axis or $y$-axis. The two possible such orientations are shown in Figure 10.4.14. These are called the ***standard positions*** of an ellipse, and the resulting equations are called the ***standard equations*** of an ellipse.

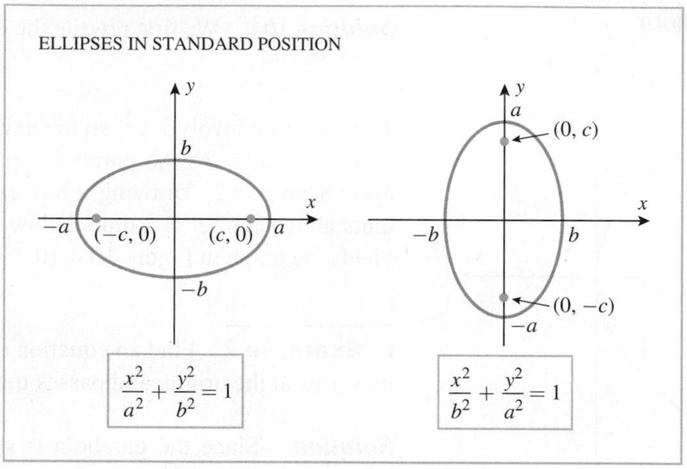


▶ **Figure 10.4.14**

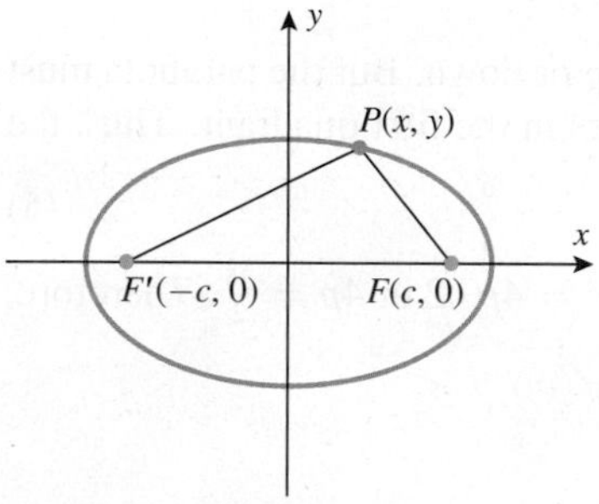


▲ **Figure 10.4.15**

To illustrate how the equations in Figure 10.4.14 are obtained, we will derive the equation for the ellipse with foci on the $x$-axis. Let $P(x, y)$ be any point on that ellipse. Since the sum of the distances from $P$ to the foci is $2a$, it follows (Figure 10.4.15) that

$$PF' + PF = 2a$$

so

$$\sqrt{(x+c)^2 + y^2} + \sqrt{(x-c)^2 + y^2} = 2a$$

Transposing the second radical to the right side of the equation and squaring yields

$$(x+c)^2 + y^2 = 4a^2 - 4a\sqrt{(x-c)^2 + y^2} + (x-c)^2 + y^2$$

and, on simplifying,

$$\sqrt{(x-c)^2 + y^2} = a - \frac{c}{a}x \tag{8}$$

Squaring again and simplifying yields

$$\frac{x^2}{a^2} + \frac{y^2}{a^2 - c^2} = 1$$

which, by virtue of (6), can be written as

$$\frac{x^2}{a^2} + \frac{y^2}{b^2} = 1 \tag{9}$$

Conversely, it can be shown that any point whose coordinates satisfy (9) has $2a$ as the sum of its distances from the foci, so that such a point is on the ellipse.

## ■ A TECHNIQUE FOR SKETCHING ELLIPSES

Ellipses can be sketched from their *standard equations* using three basic steps:

*Sketching an Ellipse from Its Standard Equation*

**Step 1.** Determine whether the major axis is on the $x$-axis or the $y$-axis. This can be ascertained from the sizes of the denominators in the equation. Referring to Figure 10.4.14, and keeping in mind that $a^2 > b^2$ (since $a > b$), the major axis is along the $x$-axis if $x^2$ has the larger denominator, and it is along the $y$-axis if $y^2$ has the larger denominator. If the denominators are equal, the ellipse is a circle.

**Step 2.** Determine the values of $a$ and $b$ and draw a box extending $a$ units on each side of the center along the major axis and $b$ units on each side of the center along the minor axis.

**Step 3.** Using the box as a guide, sketch the ellipse so that its center is at the origin and it touches the sides of the box where the sides intersect the coordinate axes (Figure 10.4.16).

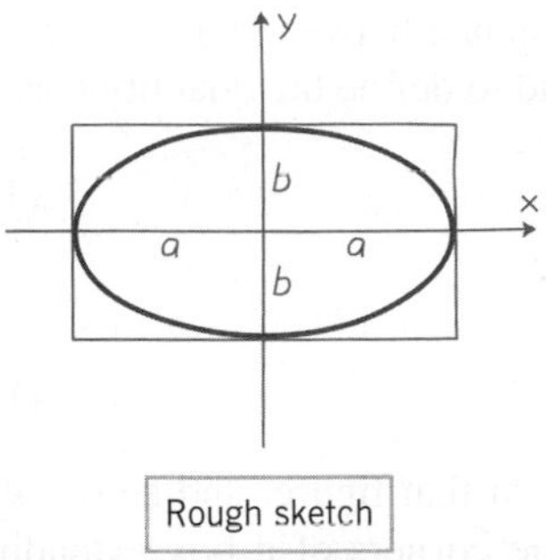

▲ Figure 10.4.16

▶ **Example 3** Sketch the graphs of the ellipses

$$\text{(a)}\ \frac{x^2}{9} + \frac{y^2}{16} = 1 \qquad \text{(b)}\ x^2 + 2y^2 = 4$$

showing the foci of each.

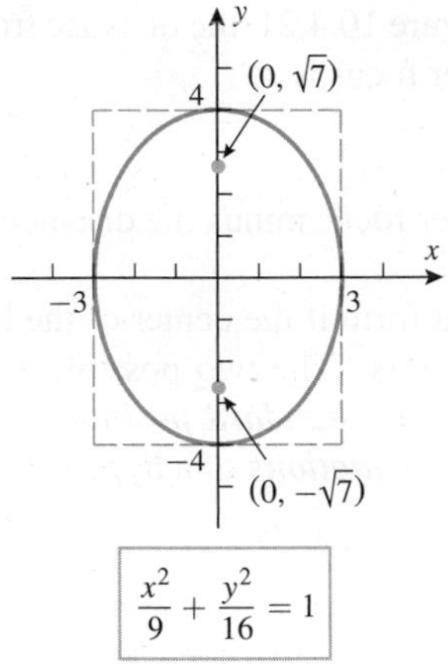

▲ Figure 10.4.17

***Solution (a).*** Since $y^2$ has the larger denominator, the major axis is along the $y$-axis. Moreover, since $a^2 > b^2$, we must have $a^2 = 16$ and $b^2 = 9$, so

$$a = 4 \quad \text{and} \quad b = 3$$

Drawing a box extending 4 units on each side of the origin along the $y$-axis and 3 units on each side of the origin along the $x$-axis as a guide yields the graph in Figure 10.4.17.

The foci lie $c$ units on each side of the center along the major axis, where $c$ is given by (7). From the values of $a^2$ and $b^2$ above, we obtain

$$c = \sqrt{a^2 - b^2} = \sqrt{16 - 9} = \sqrt{7} \approx 2.6$$

Thus, the coordinates of the foci are $(0, \sqrt{7})$ and $(0, -\sqrt{7})$, since they lie on the $y$-axis.

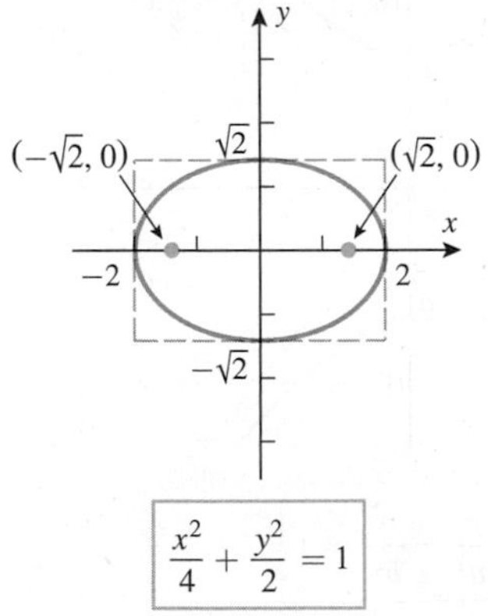

▲ Figure 10.4.18

***Solution (b).*** We first rewrite the equation in the standard form

$$\frac{x^2}{4} + \frac{y^2}{2} = 1$$

Since $x^2$ has the larger denominator, the major axis lies along the $x$-axis, and we have $a^2 = 4$ and $b^2 = 2$. Drawing a box extending $a = 2$ units on each side of the origin along the $x$-axis and extending $b = \sqrt{2} \approx 1.4$ units on each side of the origin along the $y$-axis as a guide yields the graph in Figure 10.4.18.

From (7), we obtain

$$c = \sqrt{a^2 - b^2} = \sqrt{2} \approx 1.4$$

Thus, the coordinates of the foci are $(\sqrt{2}, 0)$ and $(-\sqrt{2}, 0)$, since they lie on the $x$-axis. ◀

▶ **Example 4** Find an equation for the ellipse with foci $(0, \pm 2)$ and major axis with endpoints $(0, \pm 4)$.

***Solution.*** From Figure 10.4.14, the equation has the form

$$\frac{x^2}{b^2} + \frac{y^2}{a^2} = 1$$

and from the given information, $a = 4$ and $c = 2$. It follows from (6) that

$$b^2 = a^2 - c^2 = 16 - 4 = 12$$

so the equation of the ellipse is

$$\frac{x^2}{12} + \frac{y^2}{16} = 1 \blacktriangleleft$$

## EQUATIONS OF HYPERBOLAS IN STANDARD POSITION

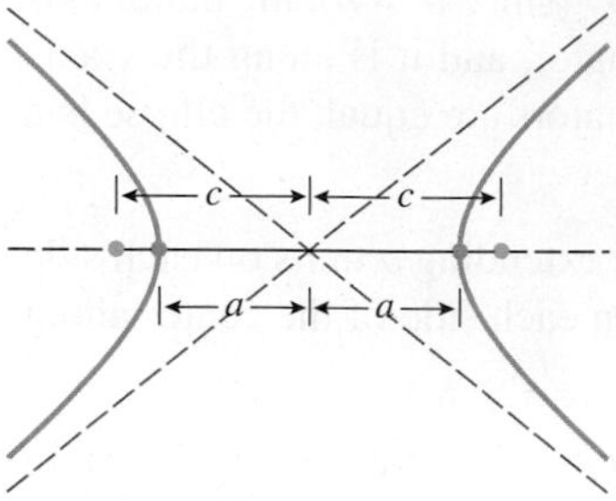


▲ **Figure 10.4.19**

It is traditional in the study of hyperbolas to denote the distance between the vertices by $2a$, the distance between the foci by $2c$ (Figure 10.4.19), and to define the quantity $b$ as

$$b = \sqrt{c^2 - a^2} \tag{10}$$

This relationship, which can also be expressed as

$$c = \sqrt{a^2 + b^2} \tag{11}$$

is pictured geometrically in Figure 10.4.20. As illustrated in that figure, and as we will show later in this section, the asymptotes pass through the corners of a box extending $b$ units on each side of the center along the conjugate axis and $a$ units on each side of the center along the focal axis. The number $a$ is called the ***semifocal axis*** of the hyperbola and the number $b$ the ***semiconjugate axis***. (As with the semimajor and semiminor axes of an ellipse, these are numbers, not geometric axes.)

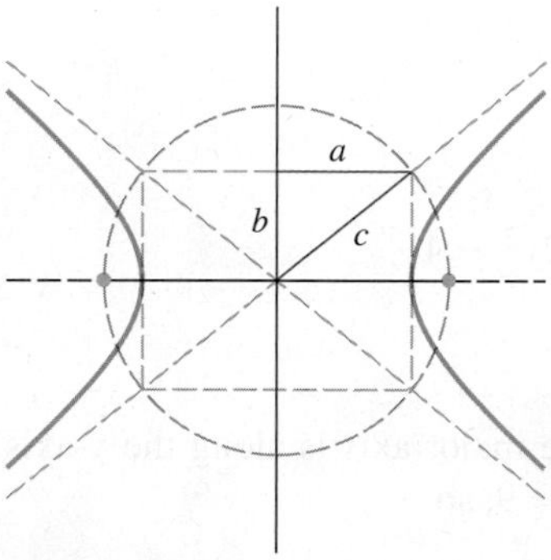


▲ **Figure 10.4.20**

If $V$ is one vertex of a hyperbola, then, as illustrated in Figure 10.4.21, the distance from $V$ to the farther focus minus the distance from $V$ to the closer focus is

$$[(c - a) + 2a] - (c - a) = 2a$$

Thus, for *all* points on a hyperbola, the distance to the farther focus minus the distance to the closer focus is $2a$.

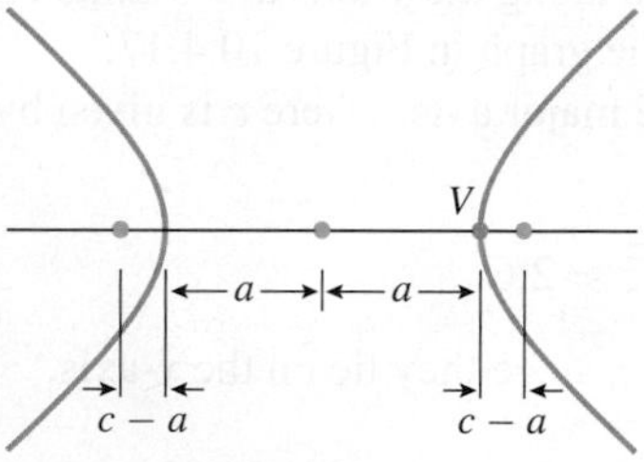


▲ **Figure 10.4.21**

The equation of a hyperbola has an especially convenient form if the center of the hyperbola is at the origin and the foci are on the $x$-axis or $y$-axis. The two possible such orientations are shown in Figure 10.4.22. These are called the ***standard positions*** of a hyperbola, and the resulting equations are called the ***standard equations*** of a hyperbola.

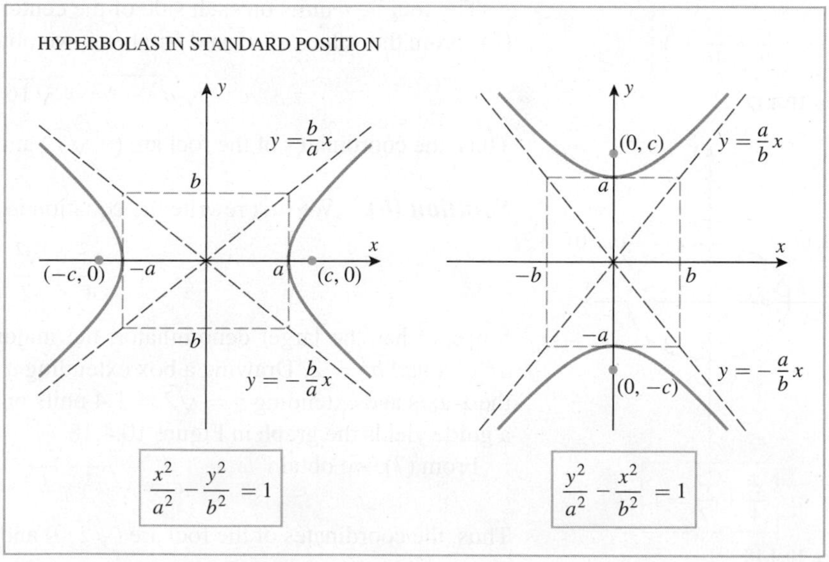


▶ **Figure 10.4.22**

The derivations of these equations are similar to those already given for parabolas and ellipses, so we will leave them as exercises. However, to illustrate how the equations of the asymptotes are derived, we will derive those equations for the hyperbola

$$\frac{x^2}{a^2} - \frac{y^2}{b^2} = 1$$

We can rewrite this equation as

$$y^2 = \frac{b^2}{a^2}(x^2 - a^2)$$

which is equivalent to the pair of equations

$$y = \frac{b}{a}\sqrt{x^2 - a^2} \quad \text{and} \quad y = -\frac{b}{a}\sqrt{x^2 - a^2}$$

Thus, in the first quadrant, the vertical distance between the line $y = (b/a)x$ and the hyperbola can be written as

$$\frac{b}{a}x - \frac{b}{a}\sqrt{x^2 - a^2}$$

(Figure 10.4.23). But this distance tends to zero as $x \to +\infty$ since

$$\lim_{x \to +\infty} \left(\frac{b}{a}x - \frac{b}{a}\sqrt{x^2 - a^2}\right) = \lim_{x \to +\infty} \frac{b}{a}\left(x - \sqrt{x^2 - a^2}\right)$$

$$= \lim_{x \to +\infty} \frac{b}{a} \frac{\left(x - \sqrt{x^2 - a^2}\right)\left(x + \sqrt{x^2 - a^2}\right)}{x + \sqrt{x^2 - a^2}}$$

$$= \lim_{x \to +\infty} \frac{ab}{x + \sqrt{x^2 - a^2}} = 0$$

The analysis in the remaining quadrants is similar.

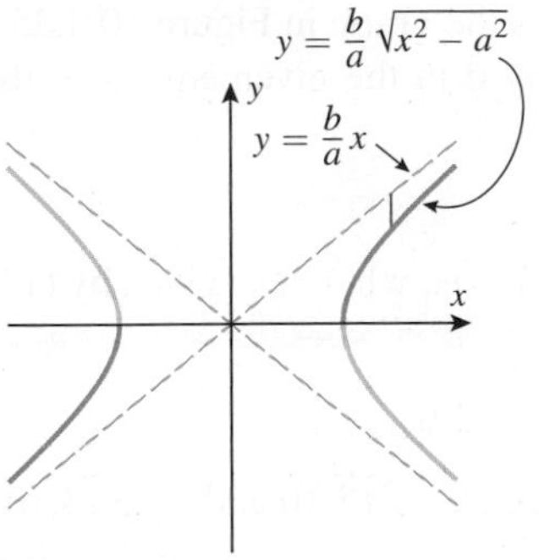


▲ Figure 10.4.23

## A QUICK WAY TO FIND ASYMPTOTES

There is a trick that can be used to avoid memorizing the equations of the asymptotes of a hyperbola. They can be obtained, when needed, by replacing 1 by 0 on the right side of the hyperbola equation, and then solving for $y$ in terms of $x$. For example, for the hyperbola

$$\frac{x^2}{a^2} - \frac{y^2}{b^2} = 1$$

we would write

$$\frac{x^2}{a^2} - \frac{y^2}{b^2} = 0 \quad \text{or} \quad y^2 = \frac{b^2}{a^2}x^2 \quad \text{or} \quad y = \pm\frac{b}{a}x$$

which are the equations for the asymptotes.

## A TECHNIQUE FOR SKETCHING HYPERBOLAS

Hyperbolas can be sketched from their *standard equations* using four basic steps:

***Sketching a Hyperbola from Its Standard Equation***

**Step 1.** Determine whether the focal axis is on the $x$-axis or the $y$-axis. This can be ascertained from the location of the minus sign in the equation. Referring to Figure 10.4.22, the focal axis is along the $x$-axis when the minus sign precedes the $y^2$-term, and it is along the $y$-axis when the minus sign precedes the $x^2$-term.

**Step 2.** Determine the values of $a$ and $b$ and draw a box extending $a$ units on either side of the center along the focal axis and $b$ units on either side of the center along the conjugate axis. (The squares of $a$ and $b$ can be read directly from the equation.)

**Step 3.** Draw the asymptotes along the diagonals of the box.

**Step 4.** Using the box and the asymptotes as a guide, sketch the graph of the hyperbola (Figure 10.4.24).

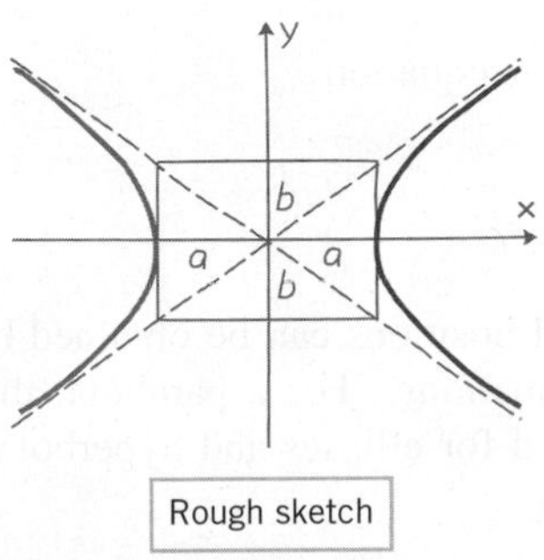


▲ Figure 10.4.24

► **Example 5** Sketch the graphs of the hyperbolas

$$\text{(a)}\ \frac{x^2}{4} - \frac{y^2}{9} = 1 \qquad \text{(b)}\ y^2 - x^2 = 1$$

showing their vertices, foci, and asymptotes.

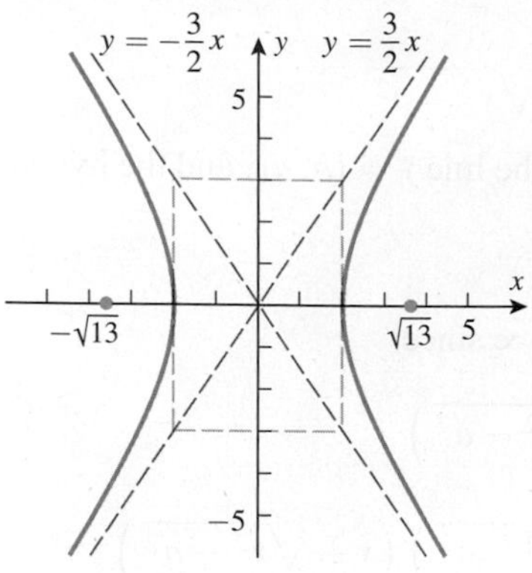


▲ **Figure 10.4.25**

***Solution (a).*** The minus sign precedes the $y^2$-term, so the focal axis is along the $x$-axis. From the denominators in the equation we obtain

$$a^2 = 4 \quad \text{and} \quad b^2 = 9$$

Since $a$ and $b$ are positive, we must have $a = 2$ and $b = 3$. Recalling that the vertices lie $a$ units on each side of the center on the focal axis, it follows that their coordinates in this case are $(2, 0)$ and $(-2, 0)$. Drawing a box extending $a = 2$ units along the $x$-axis on each side of the origin and $b = 3$ units on each side of the origin along the $y$-axis, then drawing the asymptotes along the diagonals of the box as a guide, yields the graph in Figure 10.4.25.

To obtain equations for the asymptotes, we replace 1 by 0 in the given equation; this yields

$$\frac{x^2}{4} - \frac{y^2}{9} = 0 \quad \text{or} \quad y = \pm\frac{3}{2}x$$

The foci lie $c$ units on each side of the center along the focal axis, where $c$ is given by (11). From the values of $a^2$ and $b^2$ above we obtain

$$c = \sqrt{a^2 + b^2} = \sqrt{4 + 9} = \sqrt{13} \approx 3.6$$

Since the foci lie on the $x$-axis in this case, their coordinates are $(\sqrt{13}, 0)$ and $(-\sqrt{13}, 0)$.

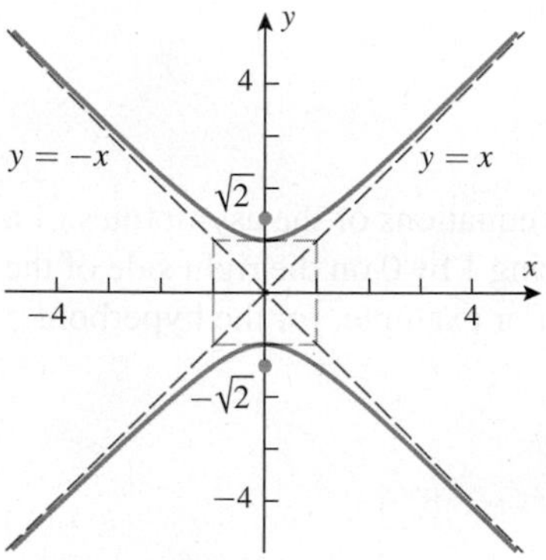


▲ **Figure 10.4.26**

***Solution (b).*** The minus sign precedes the $x^2$-term, so the focal axis is along the $y$-axis. From the denominators in the equation we obtain $a^2 = 1$ and $b^2 = 1$, from which it follows that

$$a = 1 \quad \text{and} \quad b = 1$$

Thus, the vertices are at $(0, -1)$ and $(0, 1)$. Drawing a box extending $a = 1$ unit on either side of the origin along the $y$-axis and $b = 1$ unit on either side of the origin along the $x$-axis, then drawing the asymptotes, yields the graph in Figure 10.4.26. Since the box is actually a square, the asymptotes are perpendicular and have equations $y = \pm x$. This can also be seen by replacing 1 by 0 in the given equation, which yields $y^2 - x^2 = 0$ or $y = \pm x$. Also,

$$c = \sqrt{a^2 + b^2} = \sqrt{1 + 1} = \sqrt{2}$$

so the foci, which lie on the $y$-axis, are $(0, -\sqrt{2})$ and $(0, \sqrt{2})$. ◀

A hyperbola in which $a = b$, as in part (b) of Example 5, is called an ***equilateral hyperbola***. Such hyperbolas always have perpendicular asymptotes.

▶ **Example 6** Find the equation of the hyperbola with vertices $(0, \pm 8)$ and asymptotes $y = \pm\frac{4}{3}x$.

***Solution.*** Since the vertices are on the $y$-axis, the equation of the hyperbola has the form $(y^2/a^2) - (x^2/b^2) = 1$ and the asymptotes are

$$y = \pm\frac{a}{b}x$$

From the locations of the vertices we have $a = 8$, so the given equations of the asymptotes yield

$$y = \pm\frac{a}{b}x = \pm\frac{8}{b}x = \pm\frac{4}{3}x$$

from which it follows that $b = 6$. Thus, the hyperbola has the equation

$$\frac{y^2}{64} - \frac{x^2}{36} = 1 \ ◀$$

## TRANSLATED CONICS

Equations of conics that are translated from their standard positions can be obtained by replacing $x$ by $x - h$ and $y$ by $y - k$ in their standard equations. For a parabola, this translates the vertex from the origin to the point $(h, k)$; and for ellipses and hyperbolas, this translates the center from the origin to the point $(h, k)$.

***Parabolas with vertex (h, k) and axis parallel to x-axis***

$$(y - k)^2 = 4p(x - h) \quad \text{[Opens right]} \qquad (12)$$

$$(y - k)^2 = -4p(x - h) \quad \text{[Opens left]} \qquad (13)$$

***Parabolas with vertex (h, k) and axis parallel to y-axis***

$$(x-h)^2 = 4p(y-k) \quad \text{[Opens up]} \tag{14}$$

$$(x-h)^2 = -4p(y-k) \quad \text{[Opens down]} \tag{15}$$

***Ellipse with center (h, k) and major axis parallel to x-axis***

$$\frac{(x-h)^2}{a^2} + \frac{(y-k)^2}{b^2} = 1 \quad [b < a] \tag{16}$$

***Ellipse with center (h, k) and major axis parallel to y-axis***

$$\frac{(x-h)^2}{b^2} + \frac{(y-k)^2}{a^2} = 1 \quad [b < a] \tag{17}$$

***Hyperbola with center (h, k) and focal axis parallel to x-axis***

$$\frac{(x-h)^2}{a^2} - \frac{(y-k)^2}{b^2} = 1 \tag{18}$$

***Hyperbola with center (h, k) and focal axis parallel to y-axis***

$$\frac{(y-k)^2}{a^2} - \frac{(x-h)^2}{b^2} = 1 \tag{19}$$

▶ **Example 7** Find an equation for the parabola that has its vertex at $(1, 2)$ and its focus at $(4, 2)$.

***Solution.*** Since the focus and vertex are on a horizontal line, and since the focus is to the right of the vertex, the parabola opens to the right and its equation has the form

$$(y-k)^2 = 4p(x-h)$$

Since the vertex and focus are 3 units apart, we have $p = 3$, and since the vertex is at $(h, k) = (1, 2)$, we obtain

$$(y-2)^2 = 12(x-1) \ ◀$$

Sometimes the equations of translated conics occur in expanded form, in which case we are faced with the problem of identifying the graph of a quadratic equation in $x$ and $y$:

$$Ax^2 + Cy^2 + Dx + Ey + F = 0 \tag{20}$$

The basic procedure for determining the nature of such a graph is to complete the squares of the quadratic terms and then try to match up the resulting equation with one of the forms of a translated conic.

▶ **Example 8** Describe the graph of the equation

$$y^2 - 8x - 6y - 23 = 0$$

***Solution.*** The equation involves quadratic terms in $y$ but none in $x$, so we first take all of the $y$-terms to one side:

$$y^2 - 6y = 8x + 23$$

Next, we complete the square on the $y$-terms by adding 9 to both sides:

$$(y-3)^2 = 8x + 32$$

Finally, we factor out the coefficient of the $x$-term to obtain

$$(y-3)^2 = 8(x+4)$$

This equation is of form (12) with $h = -4, k = 3$, and $p = 2$, so the graph is a parabola with vertex $(-4, 3)$ opening to the right. Since $p = 2$, the focus is 2 units to the right of the vertex, which places it at the point $(-2, 3)$; and the directrix is 2 units to the left of the vertex, which means that its equation is $x = -6$. The parabola is shown in Figure 10.4.27. ◀

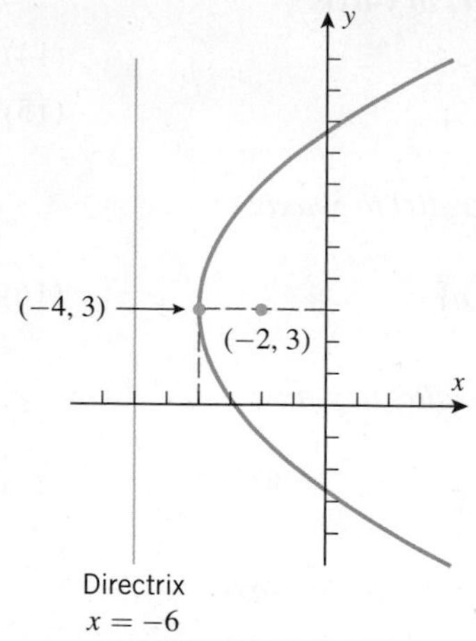


$y^2 - 8x - 6y - 23 = 0$

▲ Figure 10.4.27

▶ **Example 9** Describe the graph of the equation

$$16x^2 + 9y^2 - 64x - 54y + 1 = 0$$

***Solution.*** This equation involves quadratic terms in both $x$ and $y$, so we will group the $x$-terms and the $y$-terms on one side and put the constant on the other:

$$(16x^2 - 64x) + (9y^2 - 54y) = -1$$

Next, factor out the coefficients of $x^2$ and $y^2$ and complete the squares:

$$16(x^2 - 4x + 4) + 9(y^2 - 6y + 9) = -1 + 64 + 81$$

or

$$16(x - 2)^2 + 9(y - 3)^2 = 144$$

Finally, divide through by 144 to introduce a 1 on the right side:

$$\frac{(x-2)^2}{9} + \frac{(y-3)^2}{16} = 1$$

This is an equation of form (17), with $h = 2, k = 3, a^2 = 16$, and $b^2 = 9$. Thus, the graph of the equation is an ellipse with center $(2, 3)$ and major axis parallel to the $y$-axis. Since $a = 4$, the major axis extends 4 units above and 4 units below the center, so its endpoints are $(2, 7)$ and $(2, -1)$ (Figure 10.4.28). Since $b = 3$, the minor axis extends 3 units to the left and 3 units to the right of the center, so its endpoints are $(-1, 3)$ and $(5, 3)$. Since

$$c = \sqrt{a^2 - b^2} = \sqrt{16 - 9} = \sqrt{7}$$

the foci lie $\sqrt{7}$ units above and below the center, placing them at the points $(2, 3 + \sqrt{7})$ and $(2, 3 - \sqrt{7})$. ◀

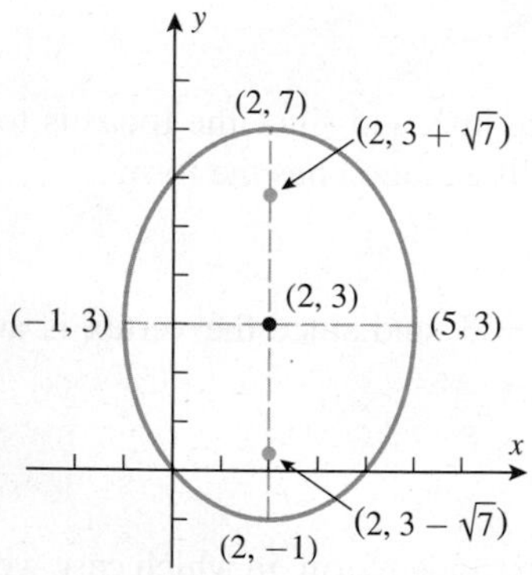


$16x^2 + 9y^2 - 64x - 54y + 1 = 0$

▲ Figure 10.4.28

▶ **Example 10** Describe the graph of the equation

$$x^2 - y^2 - 4x + 8y - 21 = 0$$

***Solution.*** This equation involves quadratic terms in both $x$ and $y$, so we will group the $x$-terms and the $y$-terms on one side and put the constant on the other:

$$(x^2 - 4x) - (y^2 - 8y) = 21$$

We leave it for you to verify by completing the squares that this equation can be written as

$$\frac{(x-2)^2}{9} - \frac{(y-4)^2}{9} = 1 \qquad (21)$$

This is an equation of form (18) with $h = 2, k = 4, a^2 = 9$, and $b^2 = 9$. Thus, the equation represents a hyperbola with center $(2, 4)$ and focal axis parallel to the $x$-axis. Since $a = 3$, the vertices are located 3 units to the left and 3 units to the right of the center, or at the points $(-1, 4)$ and $(5, 4)$. From (11), $c = \sqrt{a^2 + b^2} = \sqrt{9 + 9} = 3\sqrt{2}$, so the foci are located $3\sqrt{2}$ units to the left and right of the center, or at the points $(2 - 3\sqrt{2}, 4)$ and $(2 + 3\sqrt{2}, 4)$.

The equations of the asymptotes may be found using the trick of replacing 1 by 0 in (21) to obtain

$$\frac{(x-2)^2}{9} - \frac{(y-4)^2}{9} = 0$$

This can be written as $y - 4 = \pm(x - 2)$, which yields the asymptotes

$$y = x + 2 \quad \text{and} \quad y = -x + 6$$

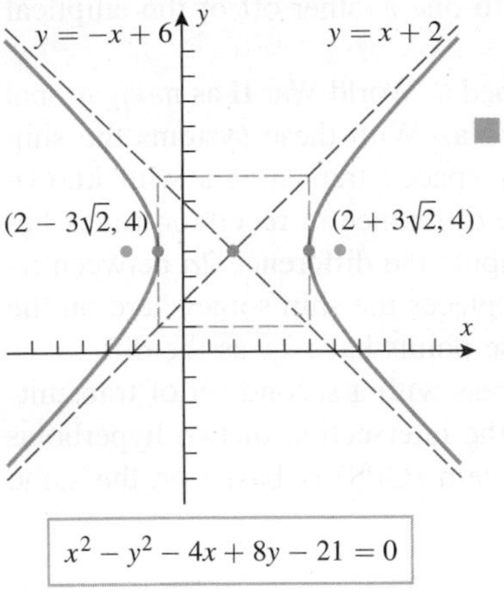


▲ **Figure 10.4.29**

With the aid of a box extending $a = 3$ units left and right of the center and $b = 3$ units above and below the center, we obtain the sketch in Figure 10.4.29. ◄

## REFLECTION PROPERTIES OF THE CONIC SECTIONS

Parabolas, ellipses, and hyperbolas have certain reflection properties that make them extremely valuable in various applications. In the exercises we will ask you to prove the following results.

**10.4.4 THEOREM** (*Reflection Property of Parabolas*) *The tangent line at a point P on a parabola makes equal angles with the line through P parallel to the axis of symmetry and the line through P and the focus (Figure 10.4.30a).*

**10.4.5 THEOREM** (*Reflection Property of Ellipses*) *A line tangent to an ellipse at a point P makes equal angles with the lines joining P to the foci (Figure 10.4.30b).*

**10.4.6 THEOREM** (*Reflection Property of Hyperbolas*) *A line tangent to a hyperbola at a point P makes equal angles with the lines joining P to the foci (Figure 10.4.30c).*

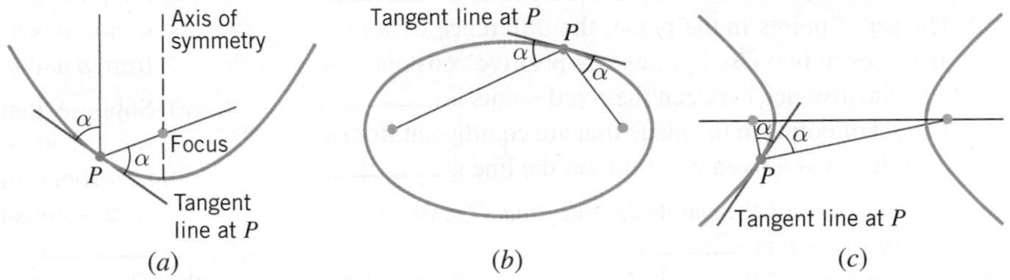


► **Figure 10.4.30**

## APPLICATIONS OF THE CONIC SECTIONS

Mike Norton/iStockphoto

*Incoming signals are reflected by the parabolic antenna to the receiver at the focus.*

Fermat's principle in optics implies that light reflects off of a surface at an angle equal to its angle of incidence. (See Exercise 64 in Section 4.5.) In particular, if a reflecting surface is generated by revolving a parabola about its axis of symmetry, it follows from Theorem 10.4.4 that all light rays entering parallel to the axis will be reflected to the focus (Figure 10.4.31*a*); conversely, if a light source is located at the focus, then the reflected rays will all be parallel to the axis (Figure 10.4.31*b*). This principle is used in certain telescopes to reflect the approximately parallel rays of light from the stars and planets off of a parabolic mirror to an eyepiece at the focus; and the parabolic reflectors in flashlights and automobile headlights utilize this principle to form a parallel beam of light rays from a bulb placed at the focus. The same optical principles apply to radar signals and sound waves, which explains the parabolic shape of many antennas.

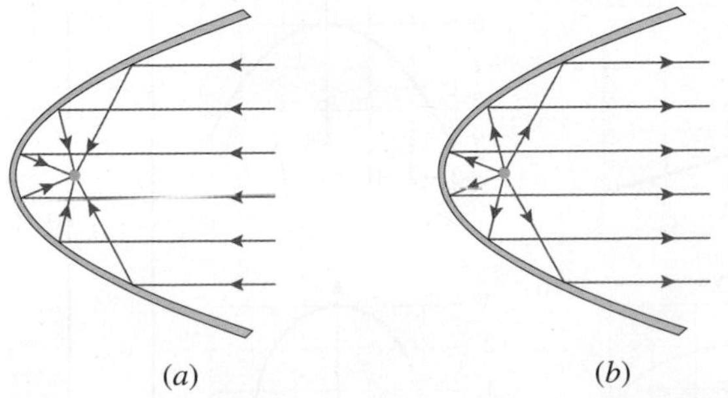


► **Figure 10.4.31**

Visitors to various rooms in the United States Capitol Building and in St. Paul's Cathedral in London are often astonished by the "whispering gallery" effect in which two people at opposite ends of the room can hear one another's whispers very clearly. Such rooms have ceilings with elliptical cross sections and common foci. Thus, when the two people

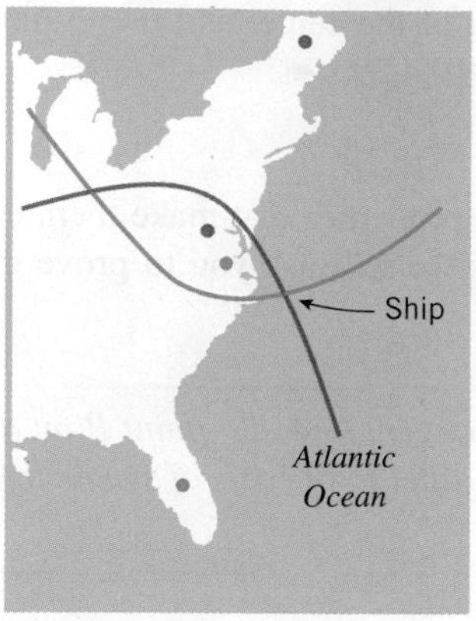


▲ **Figure 10.4.32**

stand at the foci, their whispers are reflected directly to one another off of the elliptical ceiling.

***Hyperbolic navigation systems***, which were developed in World War II as navigational aids to ships, are based on the definition of a hyperbola. With these systems the ship receives synchronized radio signals from two widely spaced transmitters with known positions. The ship's electronic receiver measures the difference in reception times between the signals and then uses that difference to compute the difference $2a$ between its distances from the two transmitters. This information places the ship somewhere on the hyperbola whose foci are at the transmitters and whose points have $2a$ as the difference in their distances from the foci. By repeating the process with a second set of transmitters, the position of the ship can be approximated as the intersection of two hyperbolas (Figure 10.4.32). [The modern global positioning system (GPS) is based on the same principle.]

## ✓ QUICK CHECK EXERCISES 10.4 *(See page 656 for answers.)*

**1.** Identify the conic.
 (a) The set of points in the plane, the sum of whose distances to two fixed points is a positive constant greater than the distance between the fixed points is ______.
 (b) The set of points in the plane, the difference of whose distances to two fixed points is a positive constant less than the distance between the fixed points is ______.
 (c) The set of points in the plane that are equidistant from a fixed line and a fixed point not on the line is ______.

**2.** (a) The equation of the parabola with focus $(p, 0)$ and directrix $x = -p$ is ______.
 (b) The equation of the parabola with focus $(0, p)$ and directrix $y = -p$ is ______.

**3.** (a) Suppose that an ellipse has semimajor axis $a$ and semiminor axis $b$. Then for all points on the ellipse, the sum of the distances to the foci is equal to ______.
 (b) The two standard equations of an ellipse with semimajor axis $a$ and semiminor axis $b$ are ______ and ______.
 (c) Suppose that an ellipse has semimajor axis $a$, semiminor axis $b$, and foci $(\pm c, 0)$. Then $c$ may be obtained from $a$ and $b$ by the equation $c =$ ______.

**4.** (a) Suppose that a hyperbola has semifocal axis $a$ and semiconjugate axis $b$. Then for all points on the hyperbola, the difference of the distance to the farther focus minus the distance to the closer focus is equal to ______.
 (b) The two standard equations of a hyperbola with semifocal axis $a$ and semiconjugate axis $b$ are ______ and ______.
 (c) Suppose that a hyperbola in standard position has semifocal axis $a$, semiconjugate axis $b$, and foci $(\pm c, 0)$. Then $c$ may be obtained from $a$ and $b$ by the equation $c =$ ______. The equations of the asymptotes of this hyperbola are $y = \pm$ ______.

## EXERCISE SET 10.4 Graphing Utility C CAS

### FOCUS ON CONCEPTS

**1.** In parts (a)–(f), find the equation of the conic.

(a)
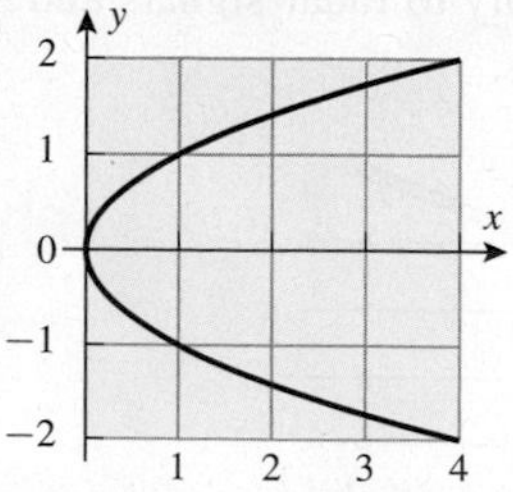

(b)
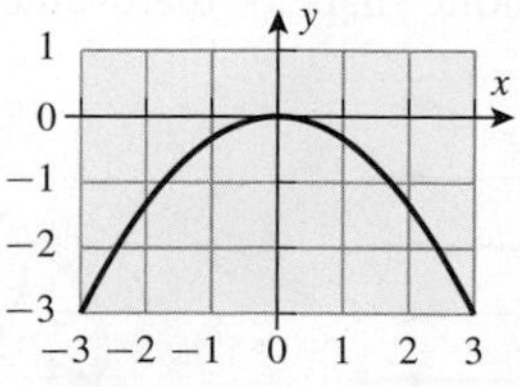

(c)
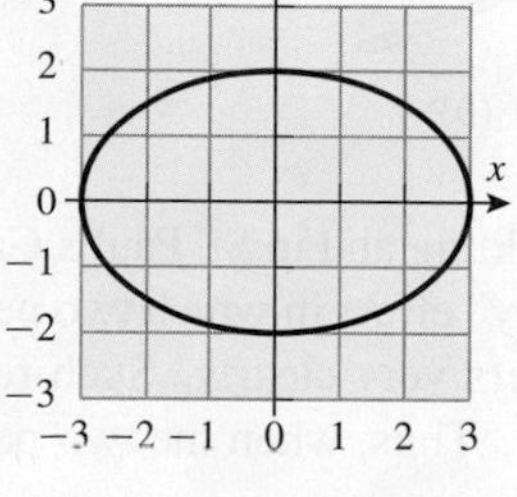

(d)
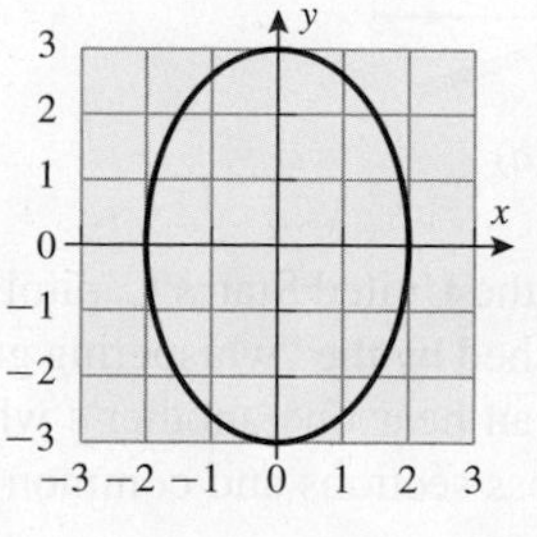

(e)
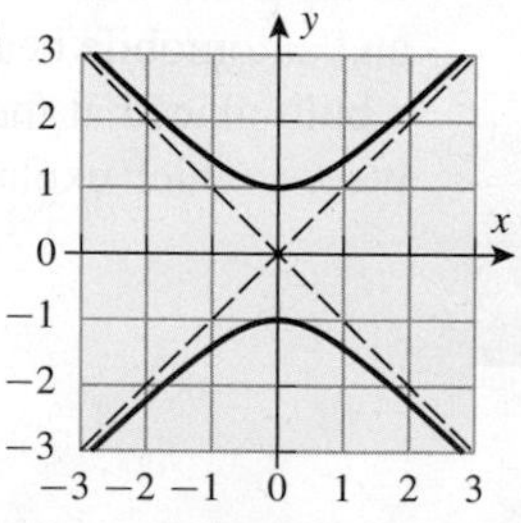

(f)
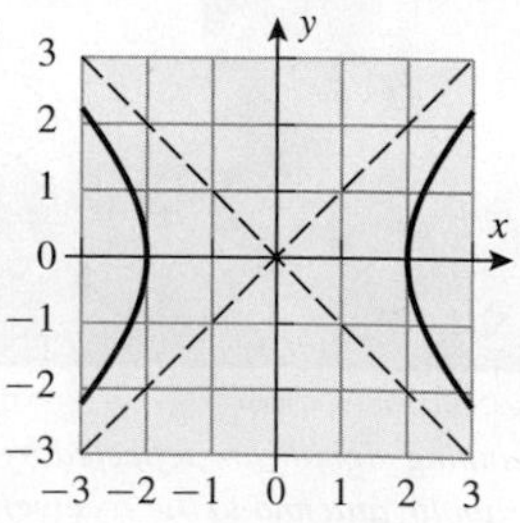

**2.** (a) Find the focus and directrix for each parabola in Exercise 1.
 (b) Find the foci of the ellipses in Exercise 1.
 (c) Find the foci and the equations of the asymptotes of the hyperbolas in Exercise 1.

**3–6** Sketch the parabola, and label the focus, vertex, and directrix. ■

**3.** (a) $y^2 = 4x$ (b) $x^2 = -8y$

4. (a) $y^2 = -10x$ (b) $x^2 = 4y$

5. (a) $(y-1)^2 = -12(x+4)$ (b) $(x-1)^2 = 2\left(y - \frac{1}{2}\right)$

6. (a) $y^2 - 6y - 2x + 1 = 0$ (b) $y = 4x^2 + 8x + 5$

**7–10** Sketch the ellipse, and label the foci, vertices, and ends of the minor axis. ■

7. (a) $\frac{x^2}{16} + \frac{y^2}{9} = 1$ (b) $9x^2 + y^2 = 9$

8. (a) $\frac{x^2}{25} + \frac{y^2}{4} = 1$ (b) $4x^2 + y^2 = 36$

9. (a) $(x+3)^2 + 4(y-5)^2 = 16$
(b) $\frac{1}{4}x^2 + \frac{1}{9}(y+2)^2 - 1 = 0$

10. (a) $9x^2 + 4y^2 - 18x + 24y + 9 = 0$
(b) $5x^2 + 9y^2 + 20x - 54y = -56$

**11–14** Sketch the hyperbola, and label the vertices, foci, and asymptotes. ■

11. (a) $\frac{x^2}{16} - \frac{y^2}{9} = 1$ (b) $9y^2 - x^2 = 36$

12. (a) $\frac{y^2}{9} - \frac{x^2}{25} = 1$ (b) $16x^2 - 25y^2 = 400$

13. (a) $\frac{(y+4)^2}{3} - \frac{(x-2)^2}{5} = 1$
(b) $16(x+1)^2 - 8(y-3)^2 = 16$

14. (a) $x^2 - 4y^2 + 2x + 8y - 7 = 0$
(b) $16x^2 - y^2 - 32x - 6y = 57$

**15–18** Find an equation for the parabola that satisfies the given conditions. ■

15. (a) Vertex (0, 0); focus (3, 0).
(b) Vertex (0, 0); directrix $y = \frac{1}{4}$.

16. (a) Focus (6, 0); directrix $x = -6$.
(b) Focus (1, 1); directrix $y = -2$.

17. Axis $y = 0$; passes through (3, 2) and $(2, -\sqrt{2})$.

18. Vertex $(5, -3)$; axis parallel to the $y$-axis; passes through (9, 5).

**19–22** Find an equation for the ellipse that satisfies the given conditions. ■

19. (a) Ends of major axis $(\pm 3, 0)$; ends of minor axis $(0, \pm 2)$.
(b) Length of minor axis 8; foci $(0, \pm 3)$.

20. (a) Foci $(\pm 1, 0)$; $b = \sqrt{2}$.
(b) $c = 2\sqrt{3}$; $a = 4$; center at the origin; foci on a coordinate axis (two answers).

21. (a) Ends of major axis $(0, \pm 6)$; passes through $(-3, 2)$.
(b) Foci $(-1, 1)$ and $(-1, 3)$; minor axis of length 4.

22. (a) Center at (0, 0); major and minor axes along the coordinate axes; passes through (3, 2) and (1, 6).
(b) Foci (2, 1) and $(2, -3)$; major axis of length 6.

**23–26** Find an equation for a hyperbola that satisfies the given conditions. [*Note:* In some cases there may be more than one hyperbola.] ■

23. (a) Vertices $(\pm 2, 0)$; foci $(\pm 3, 0)$.
(b) Vertices $(0, \pm 2)$; asymptotes $y = \pm\frac{2}{3}x$.

24. (a) Asymptotes $y = \pm\frac{3}{2}x$; $b = 4$.
(b) Foci $(0, \pm 5)$; asymptotes $y = \pm 2x$.

25. (a) Asymptotes $y = \pm\frac{3}{4}x$; $c = 5$.
(b) Foci $(\pm 3, 0)$; asymptotes $y = \pm 2x$.

26. (a) Vertices (0, 6) and (6, 6); foci 10 units apart.
(b) Asymptotes $y = x - 2$ and $y = -x + 4$; passes through the origin.

**27–30 True–False** Determine whether the statement is true or false. Explain your answer. ■

27. A hyperbola is the set of all points in the plane that are equidistant from a fixed line and a fixed point not on the line.

28. If an ellipse is not a circle, then the foci of an ellipse lie on the major axis of the ellipse.

29. If a parabola has equation $y^2 = 4px$, where $p$ is a positive constant, then the perpendicular distance from the parabola's focus to its directrix is $p$.

30. The hyperbola $(y^2/a^2) - x^2 = 1$ has asymptotes the lines $y = \pm x/a$.

31. (a) As illustrated in the accompanying figure, a parabolic arch spans a road 40 ft wide. How high is the arch if a center section of the road 20 ft wide has a minimum clearance of 12 ft?
(b) How high would the center be if the arch were the upper half of an ellipse?

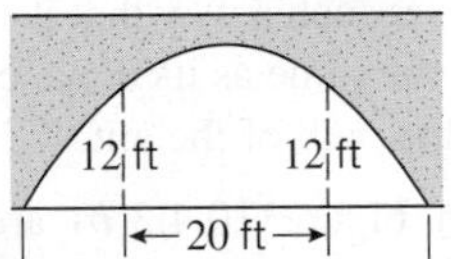

◀ **Figure Ex-31**

32. (a) Find an equation for the parabolic arch with base $b$ and height $h$, shown in the accompanying figure.
(b) Find the area under the arch.

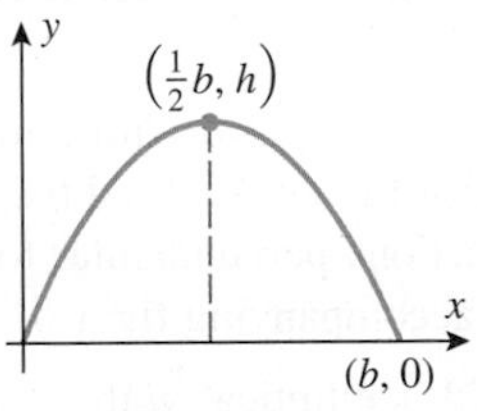

◀ **Figure Ex-32**

33. Show that the vertex is the closest point on a parabola to the focus. [*Suggestion:* Introduce a convenient coordinate system and use Definition 10.4.1.]

34. As illustrated in the accompanying figure on the next page, suppose that a comet moves in a parabolic orbit with the Sun at its focus and that the line from the Sun to the comet makes an angle of 60° with the axis of the parabola when the comet is 40 million miles from the center of the Sun. Use the result in Exercise 33 to determine how close the comet will come to the center of the Sun.

35. For the parabolic reflector in the accompanying figure on the next page, how far from the vertex should the light source be placed to produce a beam of parallel rays?

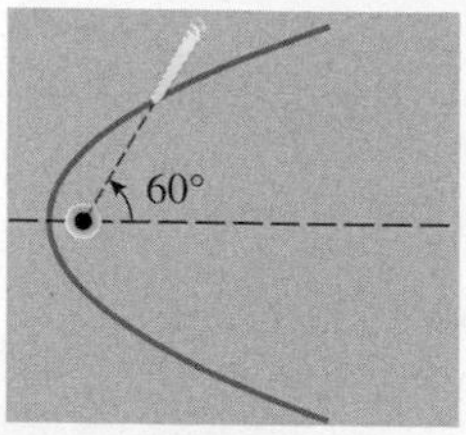


▲ Figure Ex-34

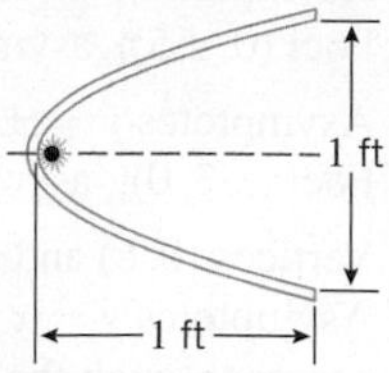


▲ Figure Ex-35

**36.** (a) Show that the right and left branches of the hyperbola

$$\frac{x^2}{a^2} - \frac{y^2}{b^2} = 1$$

can be represented parametrically as

$$x = a\cosh t, \quad y = b\sinh t \qquad (-\infty < t < +\infty)$$
$$x = -a\cosh t, \quad y = b\sinh t \qquad (-\infty < t < +\infty)$$

(b) Use a graphing utility to generate both branches of the hyperbola $x^2 - y^2 = 1$ on the same screen.

**37.** (a) Show that the right and left branches of the hyperbola

$$\frac{x^2}{a^2} - \frac{y^2}{b^2} = 1$$

can be represented parametrically as

$$x = a\sec t, \quad y = b\tan t \qquad (-\pi/2 < t < \pi/2)$$
$$x = -a\sec t, \quad y = b\tan t \qquad (-\pi/2 < t < \pi/2)$$

(b) Use a graphing utility to generate both branches of the hyperbola $x^2 - y^2 = 1$ on the same screen.

**38.** An ant is walking on the $xy$–plane is such a way that its distance to the point $(2, 4)$ is always the same as its distance to the $x$–axis. Find an equation for the path of the ant.

**39.** Suppose that the thumbtacks in Figure 10.4.3($b$) are at points $(4, 1)$ and $(4, 5)$ and that the length of the string is 12 units. Find an equation for the curve sketched out by the pencil.

**40.** Find the equation of the hyperbola traced by a point that moves so that the difference between its distances to $(0, 0)$ and $(1, 1)$ is 1.

**41.** Suppose that the base of a solid is elliptical with a major axis of length 9 and a minor axis of length 4. Find the volume of the solid if the cross sections perpendicular to the major axis are squares (see the accompanying figure).

**42.** Suppose that the base of a solid is elliptical with a major axis of length 9 and a minor axis of length 4. Find the volume of the solid if the cross sections perpendicular to the minor axis are equilateral triangles (see the accompanying figure).

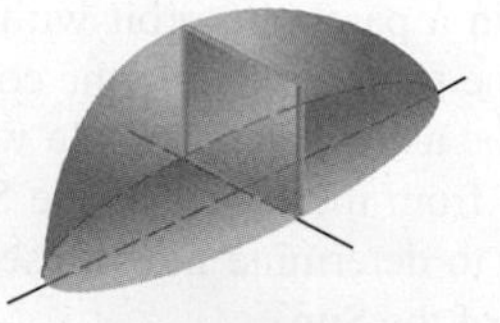

▲ Figure Ex-41

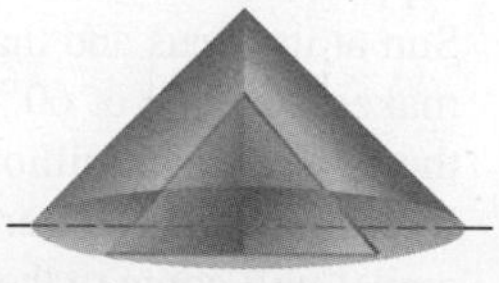

▲ Figure Ex-42

**43.** Show that an ellipse with semimajor axis $a$ and semiminor axis $b$ has area $A = \pi ab$.

**FOCUS ON CONCEPTS**

**44.** Show that if a plane is not parallel to the axis of a right circular cylinder, then the intersection of the plane and cylinder is an ellipse (possibly a circle). [*Hint:* Let $\theta$ be the angle shown in the accompanying figure, introduce coordinate axes as shown, and express $x'$ and $y'$ in terms of $x$ and $y$.]

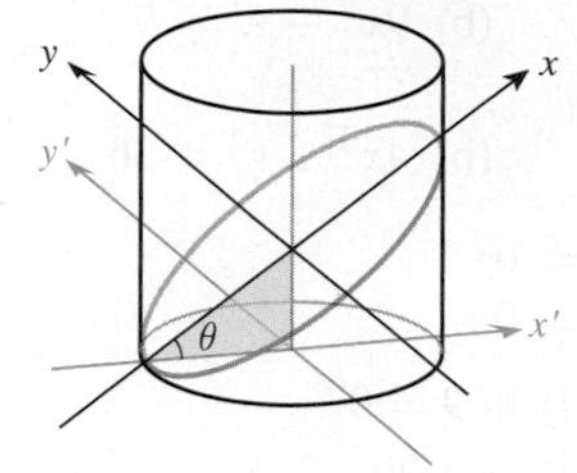


◀ Figure Ex-44

**45.** As illustrated in the accompanying figure, a carpenter needs to cut an elliptical hole in a sloped roof through which a circular vent pipe of diameter $D$ is to be inserted vertically. The carpenter wants to draw the outline of the hole on the roof using a pencil, two tacks, and a piece of string (as in Figure 10.4.3$b$). The center point of the ellipse is known, and common sense suggests that its major axis must be perpendicular to the drip line of the roof. The carpenter needs to determine the length $L$ of the string and the distance $T$ between a tack and the center point. The architect's plans show that the pitch of the roof is $p$ (pitch = rise over run; see the accompanying figure). Find $T$ and $L$ in terms of $D$ and $p$.

***Source:*** This exercise is based on an article by William H. Enos, which appeared in the *Mathematics Teacher*, Feb. 1991, p. 148.

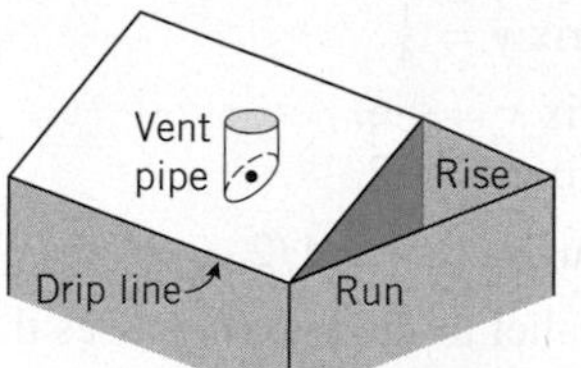


◀ Figure Ex-45

**46.** As illustrated in the accompanying figure, suppose that two observers are stationed at the points $F_1(c, 0)$ and $F_2(-c, 0)$ in an $xy$-coordinate system. Suppose also that the sound of an explosion in the $xy$-plane is heard by the $F_1$ observer $t$ seconds before it is heard by the $F_2$ observer. Assuming that the speed of sound is a constant $v$, show that the explosion occurred somewhere on the hyperbola

$$\frac{x^2}{v^2t^2/4} - \frac{y^2}{c^2 - (v^2t^2/4)} = 1$$

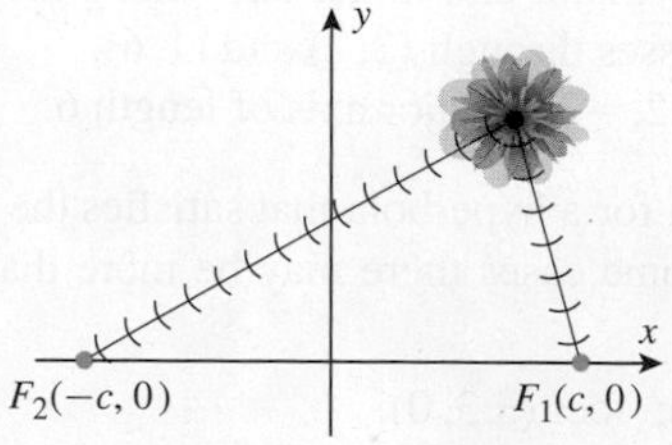


◀ Figure Ex-46

**47.** As illustrated in the accompanying figure, suppose that two transmitting stations are positioned 100 km apart at points $F_1(50, 0)$ and $F_2(-50, 0)$ on a straight shoreline in an $xy$-coordinate system. Suppose also that a ship is traveling parallel to the shoreline but 200 km at sea. Find the coordinates of the ship if the stations transmit a pulse simultaneously, but the pulse from station $F_1$ is received by the ship 100 microseconds sooner than the pulse from station $F_2$. [Assume that the pulses travel at the speed of light (299,792,458 m/s).]

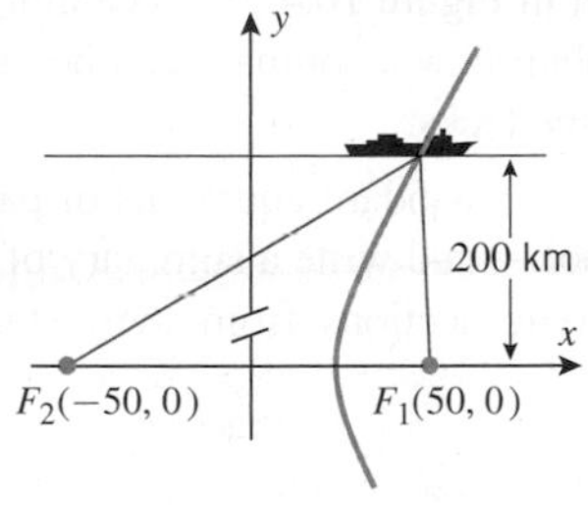

◀ **Figure Ex-47**

**48.** A nuclear cooling tower is to have a height of $h$ feet and the shape of the solid that is generated by revolving the region $R$ enclosed by the right branch of the hyperbola $1521x^2 - 225y^2 = 342{,}225$ and the lines $x = 0$, $y = -h/2$, and $y = h/2$ about the $y$-axis.
(a) Find the volume of the tower.
(b) Find the lateral surface area of the tower.

**49.** Let $R$ be the region that is above the $x$-axis and enclosed between the curve $b^2x^2 - a^2y^2 = a^2b^2$ and the line $x = \sqrt{a^2 + b^2}$.
(a) Sketch the solid generated by revolving $R$ about the $x$-axis, and find its volume.
(b) Sketch the solid generated by revolving $R$ about the $y$-axis, and find its volume.

C **50.** As illustrated in the accompanying figure, the tank of an oil truck is 18 ft long and has elliptical cross sections that are 6 ft wide and 4 ft high.
(a) Show that the volume $V$ of oil in the tank (in cubic feet) when it is filled to a depth of $h$ feet is

$$V = 27\left[4\sin^{-1}\frac{h-2}{2} + (h-2)\sqrt{4h - h^2} + 2\pi\right]$$

(b) Use the numerical root-finding capability of a CAS to determine how many inches from the bottom of a dipstick the calibration marks should be placed to indicate when the tank is $\frac{1}{4}$, $\frac{1}{2}$, and $\frac{3}{4}$ full.

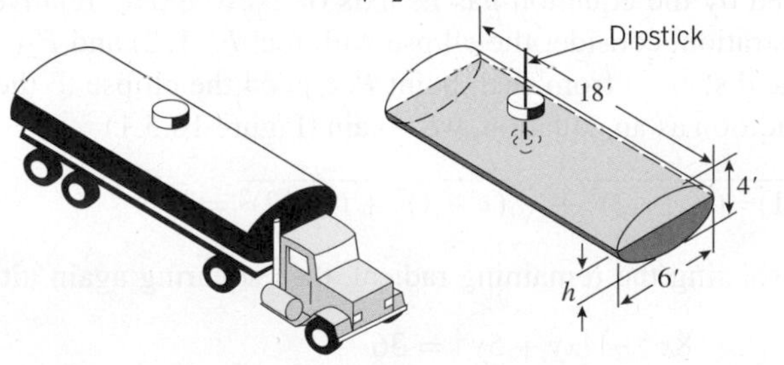

▲ **Figure Ex-50**

**51.** Prove: The line tangent to the parabola $x^2 = 4py$ at the point $(x_0, y_0)$ is $x_0x = 2p(y + y_0)$.

**52.** Prove: The line tangent to the ellipse
$$\frac{x^2}{a^2} + \frac{y^2}{b^2} = 1$$
at the point $(x_0, y_0)$ has the equation
$$\frac{xx_0}{a^2} + \frac{yy_0}{b^2} = 1$$

**53.** Prove: The line tangent to the hyperbola
$$\frac{x^2}{a^2} - \frac{y^2}{b^2} = 1$$
at the point $(x_0, y_0)$ has the equation
$$\frac{xx_0}{a^2} - \frac{yy_0}{b^2} = 1$$

**54.** Use the results in Exercises 52 and 53 to show that if an ellipse and a hyperbola have the same foci, then at each point of intersection their tangent lines are perpendicular.

**55.** Find two values of $k$ such that the line $x + 2y = k$ is tangent to the ellipse $x^2 + 4y^2 = 8$. Find the points of tangency.

**56.** Find the coordinates of all points on the hyperbola
$$4x^2 - y^2 = 4$$
where the two lines that pass through the point and the foci are perpendicular.

**57.** A line tangent to the hyperbola $4x^2 - y^2 = 36$ intersects the $y$-axis at the point $(0, 4)$. Find the point(s) of tangency.

**58.** Consider the second-degree equation
$$Ax^2 + Cy^2 + Dx + Ey + F = 0$$
where $A$ and $C$ are not both 0. Show by completing the square:
(a) If $AC > 0$, then the equation represents an ellipse, a circle, a point, or has no graph.
(b) If $AC < 0$, then the equation represents a hyperbola or a pair of intersecting lines.
(c) If $AC = 0$, then the equation represents a parabola, a pair of parallel lines, or has no graph.

**59.** In each part, use the result in Exercise 58 to make a statement about the graph of the equation, and then check your conclusion by completing the square and identifying the graph.
(a) $x^2 - 5y^2 - 2x - 10y - 9 = 0$
(b) $x^2 - 3y^2 - 6y - 3 = 0$
(c) $4x^2 + 8y^2 + 16x + 16y + 20 = 0$
(d) $3x^2 + y^2 + 12x + 2y + 13 = 0$
(e) $x^2 + 8x + 2y + 14 = 0$
(f) $5x^2 + 40x + 2y + 94 = 0$

**60.** Derive the equation $x^2 = 4py$ in Figure 10.4.6.

**61.** Derive the equation $(x^2/b^2) + (y^2/a^2) = 1$ given in Figure 10.4.14.

**62.** Derive the equation $(x^2/a^2) - (y^2/b^2) = 1$ given in Figure 10.4.22.

**63.** Prove Theorem 10.4.4. [*Hint:* Choose coordinate axes so that the parabola has the equation $x^2 = 4py$. Show that the tangent line at $P(x_0, y_0)$ intersects the $y$-axis at $Q(0, -y_0)$ and that the triangle whose three vertices are at $P$, $Q$, and the focus is isosceles.]

**64.** Given two intersecting lines, let $L_2$ be the line with the larger angle of inclination $\phi_2$, and let $L_1$ be the line with the smaller angle of inclination $\phi_1$. We define the ***angle*** $\boldsymbol{\theta}$ ***between*** $\boldsymbol{L_1}$ ***and*** $\boldsymbol{L_2}$ by $\theta = \phi_2 - \phi_1$. (See the accompanying figure.)

(a) Prove: If $L_1$ and $L_2$ are not perpendicular, then

$$\tan\theta = \frac{m_2 - m_1}{1 + m_1 m_2}$$

where $L_1$ and $L_2$ have slopes $m_1$ and $m_2$.

(b) Prove Theorem 10.4.5. [*Hint:* Introduce coordinates so that the equation $(x^2/a^2) + (y^2/b^2) = 1$ describes the ellipse, and use part (a).]

(c) Prove Theorem 10.4.6. [*Hint:* Introduce coordinates so that the equation $(x^2/a^2) - (y^2/b^2) = 1$ describes the hyperbola, and use part (a).]

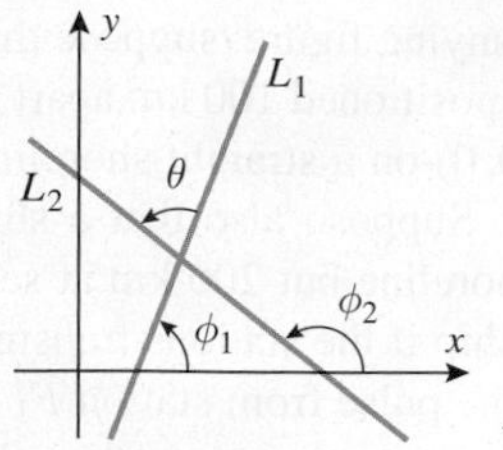

◀ **Figure Ex-64**

**65. Writing** Suppose that you want to draw an ellipse that has given values for the lengths of the major and minor axes by using the method shown in Figure 10.4.3*b*. Assuming that the axes are drawn, explain how a compass can be used to locate the positions for the tacks.

**66. Writing** List the forms for standard equations of parabolas, ellipses, and hyperbolas, and write a summary of techniques for sketching conic sections from their standard equations.

✓ **QUICK CHECK ANSWERS 10.4** 1. (a) an ellipse (b) a hyperbola (c) a parabola 2. (a) $y^2 = 4px$ (b) $x^2 = 4py$ 3. (a) $2a$ (b) $\dfrac{x^2}{a^2} + \dfrac{y^2}{b^2} = 1$; $\dfrac{x^2}{b^2} + \dfrac{y^2}{a^2} = 1$ (c) $\sqrt{a^2 - b^2}$ 4. (a) $2a$ (b) $\dfrac{x^2}{a^2} - \dfrac{y^2}{b^2} = 1$; $\dfrac{y^2}{a^2} - \dfrac{x^2}{b^2} = 1$ (c) $\sqrt{a^2 + b^2}$; $\dfrac{b}{a}x$

# 10.5 ROTATION OF AXES; SECOND-DEGREE EQUATIONS

*In the preceding section we obtained equations of conic sections with axes parallel to the coordinate axes. In this section we will study the equations of conics that are "tilted" relative to the coordinate axes. This will lead us to investigate rotations of coordinate axes.*

## QUADRATIC EQUATIONS IN *x* AND *y*

We saw in Examples 8 to 10 of the preceding section that equations of the form

$$Ax^2 + Cy^2 + Dx + Ey + F = 0 \tag{1}$$

can represent conic sections. Equation (1) is a special case of the more general equation

$$Ax^2 + Bxy + Cy^2 + Dx + Ey + F = 0 \tag{2}$$

which, if $A$, $B$, and $C$ are not all zero, is called a ***quadratic equation*** in $x$ and $y$. It is usually the case that the graph of any second-degree equation is a conic section. If $B = 0$, then (2) reduces to (1) and the conic section has its axis or axes parallel to the coordinate axes. However, if $B \neq 0$, then (2) contains a ***cross-product term*** $Bxy$, and the graph of the conic section represented by the equation has its axis or axes "tilted" relative to the coordinate axes. As an illustration, consider the ellipse with foci $F_1(1, 2)$ and $F_2(-1, -2)$ and such that the sum of the distances from each point $P(x, y)$ on the ellipse to the foci is 6 units. Expressing this condition as an equation, we obtain (Figure 10.5.1)

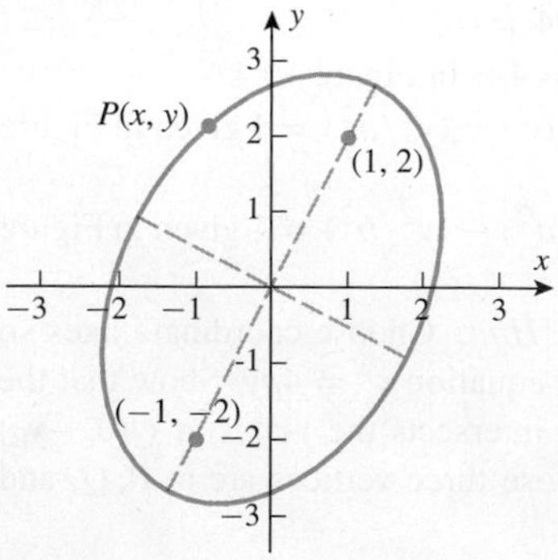

▲ **Figure 10.5.1**

$$\sqrt{(x-1)^2 + (y-2)^2} + \sqrt{(x+1)^2 + (y+2)^2} = 6$$

Squaring both sides, then isolating the remaining radical, then squaring again ultimately yields

$$8x^2 - 4xy + 5y^2 = 36$$

as the equation of the ellipse. This is of form (2) with $A = 8$, $B = -4$, $C = 5$, $D = 0$, $E = 0$, and $F = -36$.

## ROTATION OF AXES

To study conics that are tilted relative to the coordinate axes it is frequently helpful to rotate the coordinate axes, so that the rotated coordinate axes are parallel to the axes of the conic. Before we can discuss the details, we need to develop some ideas about rotation of coordinate axes.

In Figure 10.5.2*a* the axes of an $xy$-coordinate system have been rotated about the origin through an angle $\theta$ to produce a new $x'y'$-coordinate system. As shown in the figure, each point $P$ in the plane has coordinates $(x', y')$ as well as coordinates $(x, y)$. To see how the two are related, let $r$ be the distance from the common origin to the point $P$, and let $\alpha$ be the angle shown in Figure 10.5.2*b*. It follows that

$$x = r\cos(\theta+\alpha), \quad y = r\sin(\theta+\alpha) \tag{3}$$

and

$$x' = r\cos\alpha, \quad y' = r\sin\alpha \tag{4}$$

Using familiar trigonometric identities, the relationships in (3) can be written as

$$x = r\cos\theta\cos\alpha - r\sin\theta\sin\alpha$$
$$y = r\sin\theta\cos\alpha + r\cos\theta\sin\alpha$$

and on substituting (4) in these equations we obtain the following relationships called the ***rotation equations***:

$$\begin{aligned} x &= x'\cos\theta - y'\sin\theta \\ y &= x'\sin\theta + y'\cos\theta \end{aligned} \tag{5}$$

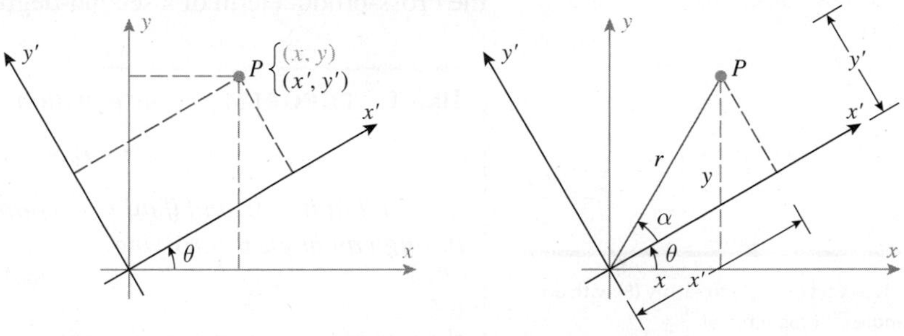


▶ **Figure 10.5.2**

▶ **Example 1** Suppose that the axes of an $xy$-coordinate system are rotated through an angle of $\theta = 45°$ to obtain an $x'y'$-coordinate system. Find the equation of the curve

$$x^2 - xy + y^2 - 6 = 0$$

in $x'y'$-coordinates.

***Solution.*** Substituting $\sin\theta = \sin 45° = 1/\sqrt{2}$ and $\cos\theta = \cos 45° = 1/\sqrt{2}$ in (5) yields the rotation equations

$$x = \frac{x'}{\sqrt{2}} - \frac{y'}{\sqrt{2}} \quad \text{and} \quad y = \frac{x'}{\sqrt{2}} + \frac{y'}{\sqrt{2}}$$

Substituting these into the given equation yields

$$\left(\frac{x'}{\sqrt{2}} - \frac{y'}{\sqrt{2}}\right)^2 - \left(\frac{x'}{\sqrt{2}} - \frac{y'}{\sqrt{2}}\right)\left(\frac{x'}{\sqrt{2}} + \frac{y'}{\sqrt{2}}\right) + \left(\frac{x'}{\sqrt{2}} + \frac{y'}{\sqrt{2}}\right)^2 - 6 = 0$$

or

$$\frac{x'^2 - 2x'y' + y'^2 - x'^2 + y'^2 + x'^2 + 2x'y' + y'^2}{2} = 6$$

or

$$\frac{x'^2}{12} + \frac{y'^2}{4} = 1$$

which is the equation of an ellipse (Figure 10.5.3). ◀

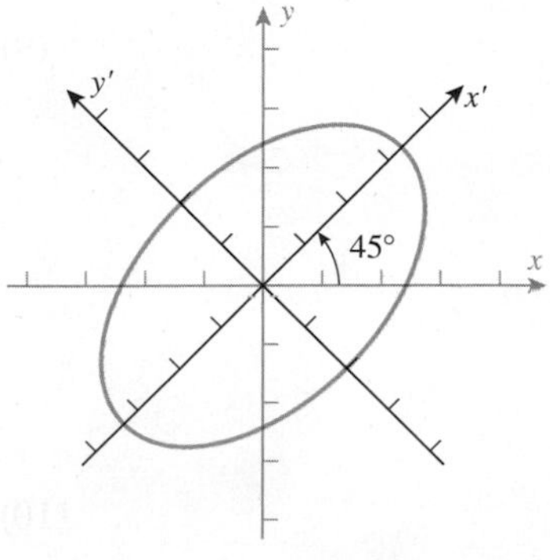


$x^2 - xy + y^2 - 6 = 0$

▲ **Figure 10.5.3**

If the rotation equations (5) are solved for $x'$ and $y'$ in terms of $x$ and $y$, one obtains (Exercise 16):

$$\begin{aligned} x' &= x\cos\theta + y\sin\theta \\ y' &= -x\sin\theta + y\cos\theta \end{aligned} \tag{6}$$

**▶ Example 2** Find the new coordinates of the point $(2, 4)$ if the coordinate axes are rotated through an angle of $\theta = 30°$.

***Solution.*** Using the rotation equations in (6) with $x = 2$, $y = 4$, $\cos\theta = \cos 30° = \sqrt{3}/2$, and $\sin\theta = \sin 30° = 1/2$, we obtain

$$\begin{aligned} x' &= 2(\sqrt{3}/2) + 4(1/2) = \sqrt{3} + 2 \\ y' &= -2(1/2) + 4(\sqrt{3}/2) = -1 + 2\sqrt{3} \end{aligned}$$

Thus, the new coordinates are $(\sqrt{3} + 2, -1 + 2\sqrt{3})$. ◀

## ELIMINATING THE CROSS-PRODUCT TERM

In Example 1 we were able to identify the curve $x^2 - xy + y^2 - 6 = 0$ as an ellipse because the rotation of axes eliminated the $xy$-term, thereby reducing the equation to a familiar form. This occurred because the new $x'y'$-axes were aligned with the axes of the ellipse. The following theorem tells how to determine an appropriate rotation of axes to eliminate the cross-product term of a second-degree equation in $x$ and $y$.

**10.5.1 THEOREM** *If the equation*

$$Ax^2 + Bxy + Cy^2 + Dx + Ey + F = 0 \tag{7}$$

*is such that $B \neq 0$, and if an $x'y'$-coordinate system is obtained by rotating the $xy$-axes through an angle $\theta$ satisfying*

$$\cot 2\theta = \frac{A - C}{B} \tag{8}$$

*then, in $x'y'$-coordinates, Equation (7) will have the form*

$$A'x'^2 + C'y'^2 + D'x' + E'y' + f' = 0$$

It is always possible to satisfy (8) with an angle $\theta$ in the interval

$$0 < \theta < \pi/2$$

We will always choose $\theta$ in this way.

**PROOF** Substituting (5) into (7) and simplifying yields

$$A'x'^2 + B'x'y' + C'y'^2 + D'x' + E'y' + f' = 0$$

where

$$\begin{aligned} A' &= A\cos^2\theta + B\cos\theta\sin\theta + C\sin^2\theta \\ B' &= B(\cos^2\theta - \sin^2\theta) + 2(C - A)\sin\theta\cos\theta \\ C' &= A\sin^2\theta - B\sin\theta\cos\theta + C\cos^2\theta \\ D' &= D\cos\theta + E\sin\theta \\ E' &= -D\sin\theta + E\cos\theta \\ f' &= F \end{aligned} \tag{9}$$

(Verify.) To complete the proof we must show that $B' = 0$ if

$$\cot 2\theta = \frac{A - C}{B}$$

or, equivalently,

$$\frac{\cos 2\theta}{\sin 2\theta} = \frac{A - C}{B} \tag{10}$$

However, by using the trigonometric double-angle formulas, we can rewrite $B'$ in the form

$$B' = B\cos 2\theta - (A - C)\sin 2\theta$$

Thus, $B' = 0$ if $\theta$ satisfies (10). ■

► **Example 3** Identify and sketch the curve $xy = 1$.

***Solution.*** As a first step, we will rotate the coordinate axes to eliminate the cross-product term. Comparing the given equation to (7), we have

$$A = 0, \quad B = 1, \quad C = 0$$

Thus, the desired angle of rotation must satisfy

$$\cot 2\theta = \frac{A - C}{B} = \frac{0 - 0}{1} = 0$$

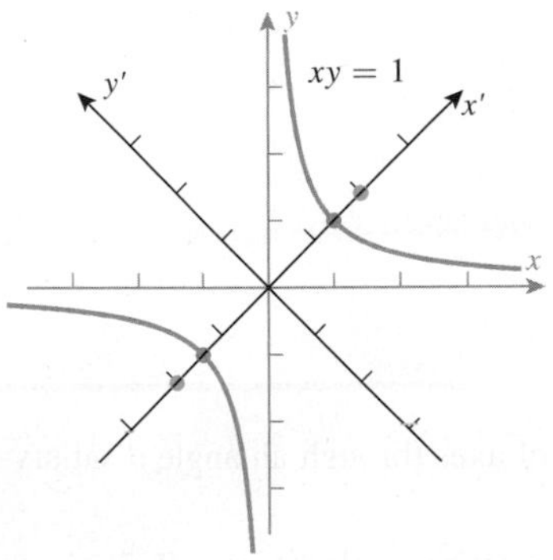

▲ **Figure 10.5.4**

This condition can be met by taking $2\theta = \pi/2$ or $\theta = \pi/4 = 45°$. Making the substitutions $\cos\theta = \cos 45° = 1/\sqrt{2}$ and $\sin\theta = \sin 45° = 1/\sqrt{2}$ in (5) yields

$$x = \frac{x'}{\sqrt{2}} - \frac{y'}{\sqrt{2}} \quad \text{and} \quad y = \frac{x'}{\sqrt{2}} + \frac{y'}{\sqrt{2}}$$

Substituting these in the equation $xy = 1$ yields

$$\left(\frac{x'}{\sqrt{2}} - \frac{y'}{\sqrt{2}}\right)\left(\frac{x'}{\sqrt{2}} + \frac{y'}{\sqrt{2}}\right) = 1 \quad \text{or} \quad \frac{x'^2}{2} - \frac{y'^2}{2} = 1$$

which is the equation in the $x'y'$-coordinate system of an equilateral hyperbola with vertices at $(\sqrt{2}, 0)$ and $(-\sqrt{2}, 0)$ in that coordinate system (Figure 10.5.4). ◄

In problems where it is inconvenient to solve

$$\cot 2\theta = \frac{A - C}{B}$$

for $\theta$, the values of $\sin\theta$ and $\cos\theta$ needed for the rotation equations can be obtained by first calculating $\cos 2\theta$ and then computing $\sin\theta$ and $\cos\theta$ from the identities

$$\sin\theta = \sqrt{\frac{1 - \cos 2\theta}{2}} \quad \text{and} \quad \cos\theta = \sqrt{\frac{1 + \cos 2\theta}{2}}$$

► **Example 4** Identify and sketch the curve

$$153x^2 - 192xy + 97y^2 - 30x - 40y - 200 = 0$$

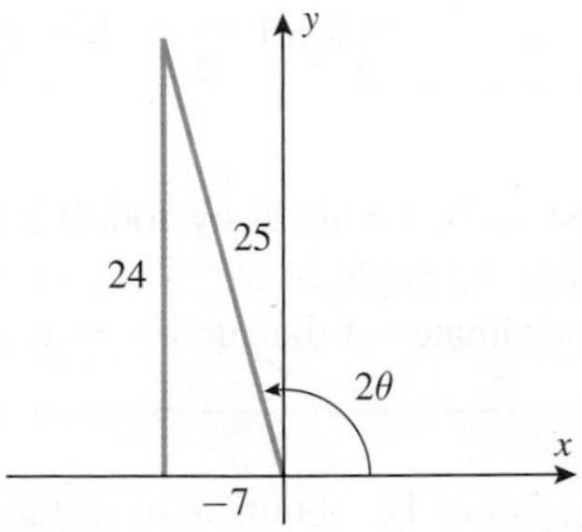

▲ **Figure 10.5.5**

***Solution.*** We have $A = 153$, $B = -192$, and $C = 97$, so

$$\cot 2\theta = \frac{A - C}{B} = -\frac{56}{192} = -\frac{7}{24}$$

Since $\theta$ is to be chosen in the range $0 < \theta < \pi/2$, this relationship is represented by the triangle in Figure 10.5.5. From that triangle we obtain $\cos 2\theta = -\frac{7}{25}$, which implies that

$$\cos\theta = \sqrt{\frac{1 + \cos 2\theta}{2}} = \sqrt{\frac{1 - \frac{7}{25}}{2}} = \frac{3}{5}$$

$$\sin\theta = \sqrt{\frac{1 - \cos 2\theta}{2}} = \sqrt{\frac{1 + \frac{7}{25}}{2}} = \frac{4}{5}$$

Substituting these values in (5) yields the rotation equations

$$x = \tfrac{3}{5}x' - \tfrac{4}{5}y' \quad \text{and} \quad y = \tfrac{4}{5}x' + \tfrac{3}{5}y'$$

and substituting these in turn in the given equation yields

$$\tfrac{153}{25}(3x' - 4y')^2 - \tfrac{192}{25}(3x' - 4y')(4x' + 3y') + \tfrac{97}{25}(4x' + 3y')^2$$
$$- \tfrac{30}{5}(3x' - 4y') - \tfrac{40}{5}(4x' + 3y') - 200 = 0$$

There is a method for deducing the kind of curve represented by a second-degree equation directly from the equation itself without rotating coordinate axes. For a discussion of this topic, see the section on the ***discriminant*** that appears in Web Appendix O.

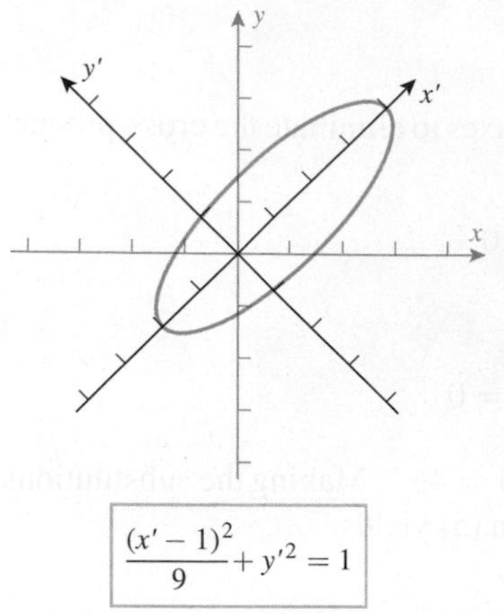


▲ Figure 10.5.6

which simplifies to

$$25x'^2 + 225y'^2 - 50x' - 200 = 0$$

or

$$x'^2 + 9y'^2 - 2x' - 8 = 0$$

Completing the square yields

$$\frac{(x'-1)^2}{9} + y'^2 = 1$$

which is the equation in the $x'y'$-coordinate system of an ellipse with center $(1, 0)$ in that coordinate system and semiaxes $a = 3$ and $b = 1$ (Figure 10.5.6). ◄

## ✓QUICK CHECK EXERCISES 10.5 *(See page 661 for answers.)*

1. Suppose that an $xy$-coordinate system is rotated $\theta$ radians to produce a new $x'y'$-coordinate system.
   (a) $x$ and $y$ may be obtained from $x'$, $y'$, and $\theta$ using the rotation equations $x =$ ______ and $y =$ ______.
   (b) $x'$ and $y'$ may be obtained from $x$, $y$, and $\theta$ using the equations $x' =$ ______ and $y' =$ ______.
2. If the equation
$$Ax^2 + Bxy + Cy^2 + Dx + Ey + F = 0$$
is such that $B \neq 0$, then the $xy$-term in this equation can be eliminated by a rotation of axes through an angle $\theta$ satisfying $\cot 2\theta =$ ______.
3. In each part, determine a rotation angle $\theta$ that will eliminate the $xy$-term.
   (a) $2x^2 + xy + 2y^2 + x - y = 0$
   (b) $x^2 + 2\sqrt{3}xy + 3y^2 - 2x + y = 1$
   (c) $3x^2 + \sqrt{3}xy + 2y^2 + y = 0$
4. Express $2x^2 + xy + 2y^2 = 1$ in the $x'y'$-coordinate system obtained by rotating the $xy$-coordinate system through the angle $\theta = \pi/4$.

## EXERCISE SET 10.5

1. Let an $x'y'$-coordinate system be obtained by rotating an $xy$-coordinate system through an angle of $\theta = 60°$.
   (a) Find the $x'y'$-coordinates of the point whose $xy$-coordinates are $(-2, 6)$.
   (b) Find an equation of the curve $\sqrt{3}xy + y^2 = 6$ in $x'y'$-coordinates.
   (c) Sketch the curve in part (b), showing both $xy$-axes and $x'y'$-axes.
2. Let an $x'y'$-coordinate system be obtained by rotating an $xy$-coordinate system through an angle of $\theta = 30°$.
   (a) Find the $x'y'$-coordinates of the point whose $xy$-coordinates are $(1, -\sqrt{3})$.
   (b) Find an equation of the curve $2x^2 + 2\sqrt{3}xy = 3$ in $x'y'$-coordinates.
   (c) Sketch the curve in part (b), showing both $xy$-axes and $x'y'$-axes.

**3–12** Rotate the coordinate axes to remove the $xy$-term. Then identify the type of conic and sketch its graph. ■

3. $xy = -9$
4. $x^2 - xy + y^2 - 2 = 0$
5. $x^2 + 4xy - 2y^2 - 6 = 0$
6. $31x^2 + 10\sqrt{3}xy + 21y^2 - 144 = 0$
7. $x^2 + 2\sqrt{3}xy + 3y^2 + 2\sqrt{3}x - 2y = 0$
8. $34x^2 - 24xy + 41y^2 - 25 = 0$
9. $9x^2 - 24xy + 16y^2 - 80x - 60y + 100 = 0$
10. $5x^2 - 6xy + 5y^2 - 8\sqrt{2}x + 8\sqrt{2}y = 8$
11. $52x^2 - 72xy + 73y^2 + 40x + 30y - 75 = 0$
12. $6x^2 + 24xy - y^2 - 12x + 26y + 11 = 0$
13. Let an $x'y'$-coordinate system be obtained by rotating an $xy$-coordinate system through an angle of 45°. Use (6) to find an equation of the curve $3x'^2 + y'^2 = 6$ in $xy$-coordinates.
14. Let an $x'y'$-coordinate system be obtained by rotating an $xy$-coordinate system through an angle of 30°. Use (5) to find an equation in $x'y'$-coordinates of the curve $y = x^2$.

**FOCUS ON CONCEPTS**

15. Let an $x'y'$-coordinate system be obtained by rotating an $xy$-coordinate system through an angle $\theta$. Prove: For every value of $\theta$, the equation $x^2 + y^2 = r^2$ becomes the equation $x'^2 + y'^2 = r^2$. Give a geometric explanation.
16. Derive (6) by solving the rotation equations in (5) for $x'$ and $y'$ in terms of $x$ and $y$.
17. Let an $x'y'$-coordinate system be obtained by rotating an $xy$-coordinate system through an angle $\theta$. Explain how to find the $xy$-coordinates of a point whose $x'y'$-coordinates are known.

**18.** Let an $x'y'$-coordinate system be obtained by rotating an $xy$-coordinate system through an angle $\theta$. Explain how to find the $xy$-equation of a line whose $x'y'$-equation is known.

**19–22** Show that the graph of the given equation is a parabola. Find its vertex, focus, and directrix. ■

**19.** $x^2 + 2xy + y^2 + 4\sqrt{2}x - 4\sqrt{2}y = 0$

**20.** $x^2 - 2\sqrt{3}xy + 3y^2 - 8\sqrt{3}x - 8y = 0$

**21.** $9x^2 - 24xy + 16y^2 - 80x - 60y + 100 = 0$

**22.** $x^2 + 2\sqrt{3}xy + 3y^2 + 16\sqrt{3}x - 16y - 96 = 0$

**23–26** Show that the graph of the given equation is an ellipse. Find its foci, vertices, and the ends of its minor axis. ■

**23.** $288x^2 - 168xy + 337y^2 - 3600 = 0$

**24.** $25x^2 - 14xy + 25y^2 - 288 = 0$

**25.** $31x^2 + 10\sqrt{3}xy + 21y^2 - 32x + 32\sqrt{3}y - 80 = 0$

**26.** $43x^2 - 14\sqrt{3}xy + 57y^2 - 36\sqrt{3}x - 36y - 540 = 0$

**27–30** Show that the graph of the given equation is a hyperbola. Find its foci, vertices, and asymptotes. ■

**27.** $x^2 - 10\sqrt{3}xy + 11y^2 + 64 = 0$

**28.** $17x^2 - 312xy + 108y^2 - 900 = 0$

**29.** $32y^2 - 52xy - 7x^2 + 72\sqrt{5}x - 144\sqrt{5}y + 900 = 0$

**30.** $2\sqrt{2}y^2 + 5\sqrt{2}xy + 2\sqrt{2}x^2 + 18x + 18y + 36\sqrt{2} = 0$

**31.** Show that the graph of the equation

$$\sqrt{x} + \sqrt{y} = 1$$

is a portion of a parabola. [*Hint:* First rationalize the equation and then perform a rotation of axes.]

**FOCUS ON CONCEPTS**

**32.** Derive the expression for $B'$ in (9).

**33.** Use (9) to prove that $B^2 - 4AC = B'^2 - 4A'C'$ for all values of $\theta$.

**34.** Use (9) to prove that $A + C = A' + C'$ for all values of $\theta$.

**35.** Prove: If $A = C$ in (7), then the cross-product term can be eliminated by rotating through 45°.

**36.** Prove: If $B \neq 0$, then the graph of $x^2 + Bxy + F = 0$ is a hyperbola if $F \neq 0$ and two intersecting lines if $F = 0$.

✓ **QUICK CHECK ANSWERS 10.5** 1. (a) $x'\cos\theta - y'\sin\theta$; $x'\sin\theta + y'\cos\theta$ (b) $x\cos\theta + y\sin\theta$; $-x\sin\theta + y\cos\theta$ 2. $\dfrac{A-C}{B}$ 3. (a) $\dfrac{\pi}{4}$ (b) $\dfrac{\pi}{3}$ (c) $\dfrac{\pi}{6}$ 4. $5x'^2 + 3y'^2 = 2$

# 10.6 CONIC SECTIONS IN POLAR COORDINATES

*It will be shown later in the text that if an object moves in a gravitational field that is directed toward a fixed point (such as the center of the Sun), then the path of that object must be a conic section with the fixed point at a focus. For example, planets in our solar system move along elliptical paths with the Sun at a focus, and the comets move along parabolic, elliptical, or hyperbolic paths with the Sun at a focus, depending on the conditions under which they were born. For applications of this type it is usually desirable to express the equations of the conic sections in polar coordinates with the pole at a focus. In this section we will show how to do this.*

## THE FOCUS–DIRECTRIX CHARACTERIZATION OF CONICS

To obtain polar equations for the conic sections we will need the following theorem.

**10.6.1 THEOREM** (***Focus–Directrix Property of Conics***) *Suppose that a point P moves in the plane determined by a fixed point (called the* ***focus****) and a fixed line (called the* ***directrix****), where the focus does not lie on the directrix. If the point moves in such a way that its distance to the focus divided by its distance to the directrix is some constant e (called the* ***eccentricity****), then the curve traced by the point is a conic section. Moreover, the conic is*

*(a) a parabola if* $e = 1$ *(b) an ellipse if* $0 < e < 1$ *(c) a hyperbola if* $e > 1$.

It is an unfortunate historical accident that the letter $e$ is used for the base of the natural logarithm as well as for the eccentricity of conic sections. However, as a practical matter the appropriate interpretation will usually be clear from the context in which the letter is used.

We will not give a formal proof of this theorem; rather, we will use the specific cases in Figure 10.6.1 to illustrate the basic ideas. For the parabola, we will take the directrix to be $x = -p$, as usual; and for the ellipse and the hyperbola we will take the directrix to

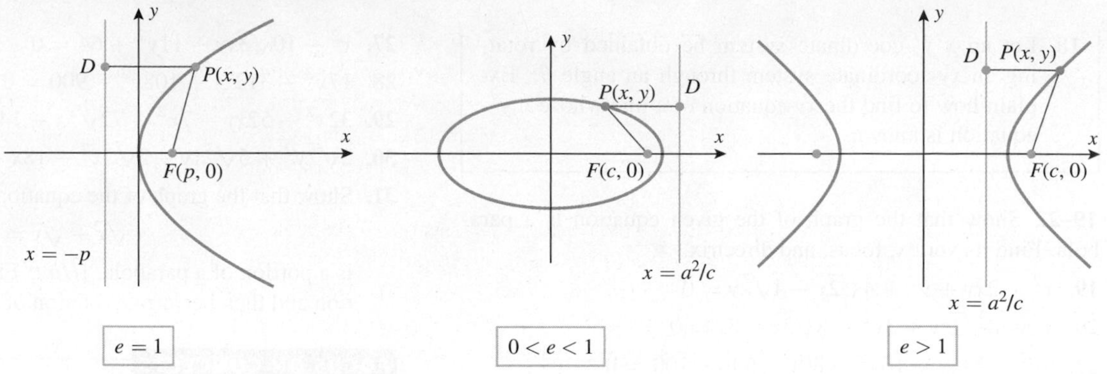


▲ Figure 10.6.1

be $x = a^2/c$. We want to show in all three cases that if $P$ is a point on the graph, $F$ is the focus, and $D$ is the directrix, then the ratio $PF/PD$ is some constant $e$, where $e = 1$ for the parabola, $0 < e < 1$ for the ellipse, and $e > 1$ for the hyperbola. We will give the arguments for the parabola and ellipse and leave the argument for the hyperbola as an exercise.

For the parabola, the distance $PF$ to the focus is equal to the distance $PD$ to the directrix, so that $PF/PD = 1$, which is what we wanted to show. For the ellipse, we rewrite Equation (8) of Section 10.4 as

$$\sqrt{(x-c)^2 + y^2} = a - \frac{c}{a}x = \frac{c}{a}\left(\frac{a^2}{c} - x\right)$$

But the expression on the left side is the distance $PF$, and the expression in the parentheses on the right side is the distance $PD$, so we have shown that

$$PF = \frac{c}{a}PD$$

Thus, $PF/PD$ is constant, and the eccentricity is

$$e = \frac{c}{a} \tag{1}$$

If we rule out the degenerate case where $a = 0$ or $c = 0$, then it follows from Formula (7) of Section 10.4 that $0 < c < a$, so $0 < e < 1$, which is what we wanted to show.

We will leave it as an exercise to show that the eccentricity of the hyperbola in Figure 10.6.1 is also given by Formula (1), but in this case it follows from Formula (11) of Section 10.4 that $c > a$, so $e > 1$.

## ECCENTRICITY OF AN ELLIPSE AS A MEASURE OF FLATNESS

The eccentricity of an ellipse can be viewed as a measure of its flatness—as $e$ approaches 0 the ellipses become more and more circular, and as $e$ approaches 1 they become more and more flat (Figure 10.6.2). Table 10.6.1 shows the orbital eccentricities of various celestial objects. Note that most of the planets actually have fairly circular orbits.

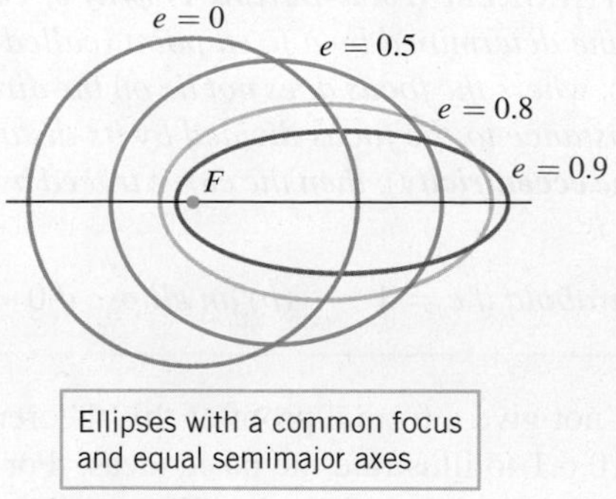


▲ Figure 10.6.2

**Table 10.6.1**

| CELESTIAL BODY | ECCENTRICITY |
|---|---|
| Mercury | 0.206 |
| Venus | 0.007 |
| Earth | 0.017 |
| Mars | 0.093 |
| Jupiter | 0.048 |
| Saturn | 0.056 |
| Uranus | 0.046 |
| Neptune | 0.010 |
| Pluto | 0.249 |
| Halley's comet | 0.970 |

## POLAR EQUATIONS OF CONICS

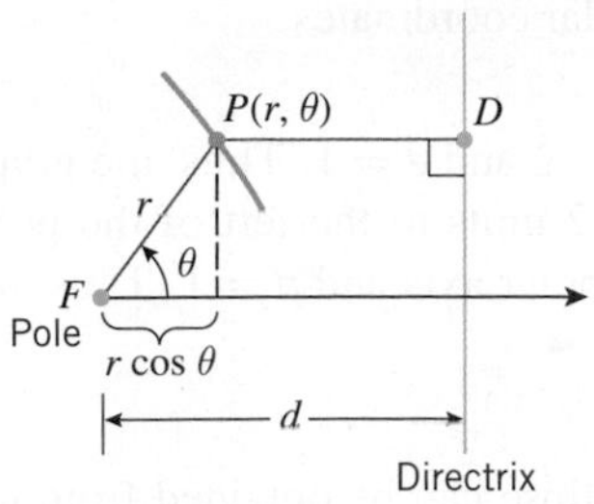

▲ **Figure 10.6.3**

Our next objective is to derive polar equations for the conic sections from their focus–directrix characterizations. We will assume that the focus is at the pole and the directrix is either parallel or perpendicular to the polar axis. If the directrix is parallel to the polar axis, then it can be above or below the pole; and if the directrix is perpendicular to the polar axis, then it can be to the left or right of the pole. Thus, there are four cases to consider. We will derive the formulas for the case in which the directrix is perpendicular to the polar axis and to the right of the pole.

As illustrated in Figure 10.6.3, let us assume that the directrix is perpendicular to the polar axis and $d$ units to the right of the pole, where the constant $d$ is known. If $P$ is a point on the conic and if the eccentricity of the conic is $e$, then it follows from Theorem 10.6.1 that $PF/PD = e$ or, equivalently, that

$$PF = ePD \tag{2}$$

However, it is evident from Figure 10.6.3 that $PF = r$ and $PD = d - r\cos\theta$. Thus, (2) can be written as

$$r = e(d - r\cos\theta)$$

which can be solved for $r$ and expressed as

$$r = \frac{ed}{1 + e\cos\theta}$$

(verify). Observe that this single polar equation can represent a parabola, an ellipse, or a hyperbola, depending on the value of $e$. In contrast, the rectangular equations for these conics all have different forms. The derivations in the other three cases are similar.

**10.6.2 THEOREM** *If a conic section with eccentricity e is positioned in a polar coordinate system so that its focus is at the pole and the corresponding directrix is d units from the pole and is either parallel or perpendicular to the polar axis, then the equation of the conic has one of four possible forms, depending on its orientation:*

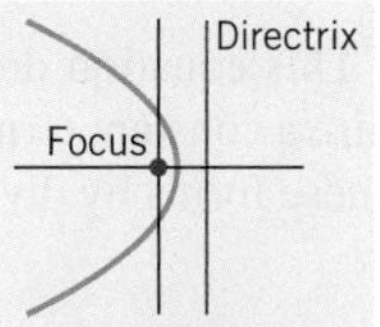


$$r = \frac{ed}{1 + e\cos\theta}$$

Directrix right of pole

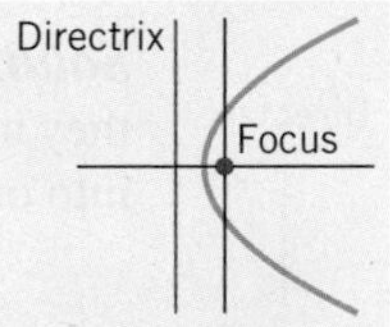


$$r = \frac{ed}{1 - e\cos\theta} \tag{3–4}$$

Directrix left of pole

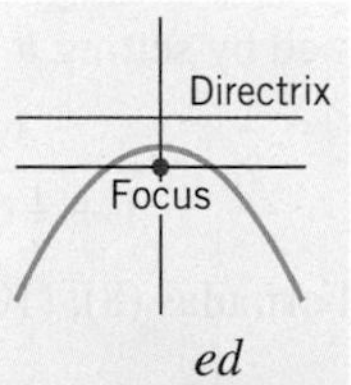


$$r = \frac{ed}{1 + e\sin\theta}$$

Directrix above pole

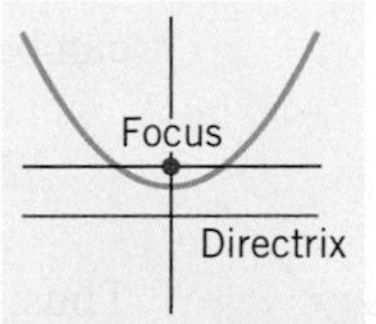


$$r = \frac{ed}{1 - e\sin\theta} \tag{5–6}$$

Directrix below pole

## SKETCHING CONICS IN POLAR COORDINATES

Precise graphs of conic sections in polar coordinates can be generated with graphing utilities. However, it is often useful to be able to make quick sketches of these graphs that show their orientations and give some sense of their dimensions. The orientation of a conic relative to the polar axis can be deduced by matching its equation with one of the four forms in Theorem 10.6.2. The key dimensions of a parabola are determined by the constant $p$ (Figure 10.4.5) and those of ellipses and hyperbolas by the constants $a$, $b$, and $c$ (Figures 10.4.11 and 10.4.20). Thus, we need to show how these constants can be obtained from the polar equations.

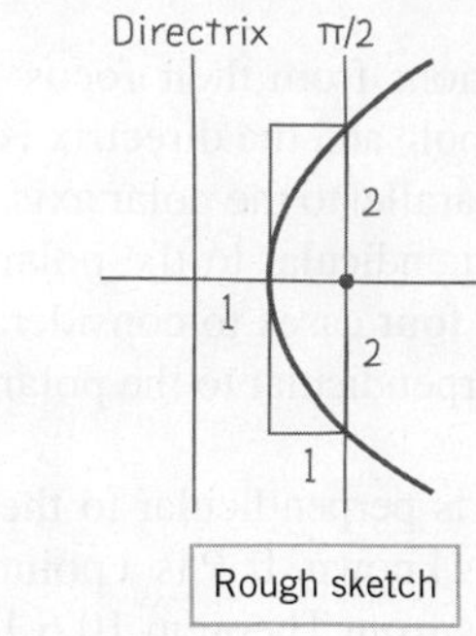


▲ **Figure 10.6.4**

► **Example 1** Sketch the graph of $r = \dfrac{2}{1 - \cos\theta}$ in polar coordinates.

***Solution.*** The equation is an exact match to (4) with $d = 2$ and $e = 1$. Thus, the graph is a parabola with the focus at the pole and the directrix 2 units to the left of the pole. This tells us that the parabola opens to the right along the polar axis and $p = 1$. Thus, the parabola looks roughly like that sketched in Figure 10.6.4. ◄

All of the important geometric information about an ellipse can be obtained from the values of $a$, $b$, and $c$ in Figure 10.6.5. One way to find these values from the polar equation of an ellipse is based on finding the distances from the focus to the vertices. As shown in the figure, let $r_0$ be the distance from the focus to the closest vertex and $r_1$ the distance to the farthest vertex. Thus,

$$r_0 = a - c \quad \text{and} \quad r_1 = a + c \tag{7}$$

from which it follows that

$$a = \tfrac{1}{2}(r_1 + r_0) \qquad c = \tfrac{1}{2}(r_1 - r_0) \tag{8–9}$$

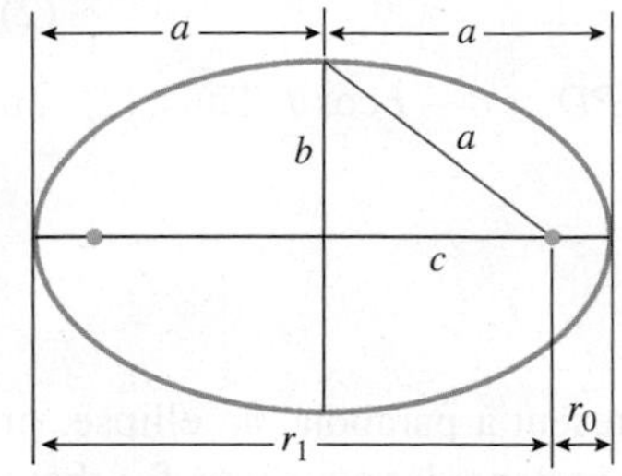


▲ **Figure 10.6.5**

In words, Formula (8) states that $a$ is the ***arithmetic average*** (also called the ***arithmetic mean***) of $r_0$ and $r_1$, and Formula (10) states that $b$ is the ***geometric mean*** of $r_0$ and $r_1$.

Moreover, it also follows from (7) that

$$r_0 r_1 = a^2 - c^2 = b^2$$

Thus,

$$b = \sqrt{r_0 r_1} \tag{10}$$

► **Example 2** Find the constants $a$, $b$, and $c$ for the ellipse $r = \dfrac{6}{2 + \cos\theta}$.

***Solution.*** This equation does not match any of the forms in Theorem 10.6.2 because they all require a constant term of 1 in the denominator. However, we can put the equation into one of these forms by dividing the numerator and denominator by 2 to obtain

$$r = \frac{3}{1 + \frac{1}{2}\cos\theta}$$

This is an exact match to (3) with $d = 6$ and $e = \frac{1}{2}$, so the graph is an ellipse with the directrix 6 units to the right of the pole. The distance $r_0$ from the focus to the closest vertex can be obtained by setting $\theta = 0$ in this equation, and the distance $r_1$ to the farthest vertex can be obtained by setting $\theta = \pi$. This yields

$$r_0 = \frac{3}{1 + \frac{1}{2}\cos 0} = \frac{3}{\frac{3}{2}} = 2, \quad r_1 = \frac{3}{1 + \frac{1}{2}\cos\pi} = \frac{3}{\frac{1}{2}} = 6$$

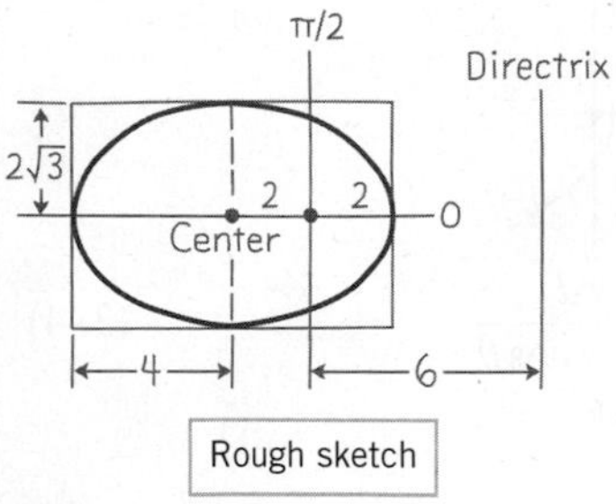


▲ **Figure 10.6.6**

Thus, from Formulas (8), (10), and (9), respectively, we obtain

$$a = \tfrac{1}{2}(r_1 + r_0) = 4, \quad b = \sqrt{r_0 r_1} = 2\sqrt{3}, \quad c = \tfrac{1}{2}(r_1 - r_0) = 2$$

The ellipse looks roughly like that sketched in Figure 10.6.6. ◄

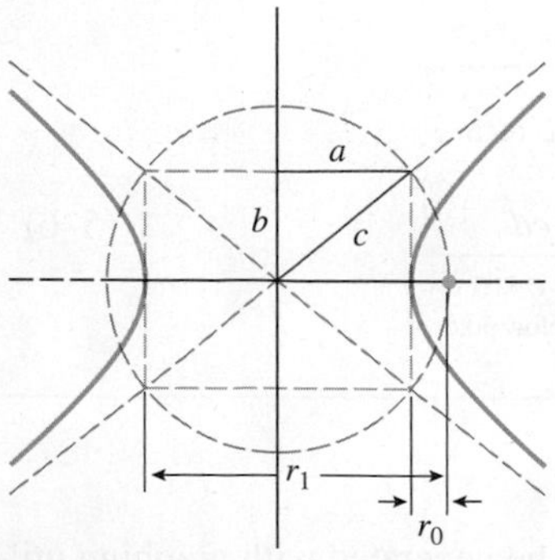


▲ **Figure 10.6.7**

All of the important information about a hyperbola can be obtained from the values of $a$, $b$, and $c$ in Figure 10.6.7. As with the ellipse, one way to find these values from the polar equation of a hyperbola is based on finding the distances from the focus to the vertices. As shown in the figure, let $r_0$ be the distance from the focus to the closest vertex and $r_1$ the distance to the farthest vertex. Thus,

$$r_0 = c - a \quad \text{and} \quad r_1 = c + a \tag{11}$$

from which it follows that

$$a = \tfrac{1}{2}(r_1 - r_0) \qquad c = \tfrac{1}{2}(r_1 + r_0) \tag{12–13}$$

In words, Formula (13) states that $c$ is the ***arithmetic mean*** of $r_0$ and $r_1$, and Formula (14) states that $b$ is the ***geometric mean*** of $r_0$ and $r_1$.

Moreover, it also follows from (11) that

$$r_0 r_1 = c^2 - a^2 = b^2$$

from which it follows that

$$b = \sqrt{r_0 r_1} \tag{14}$$

▶ **Example 3** Sketch the graph of $r = \dfrac{2}{1 + 2\sin\theta}$ in polar coordinates.

***Solution.*** This equation is an exact match to (5) with $d = 1$ and $e = 2$. Thus, the graph is a hyperbola with its directrix 1 unit above the pole. However, it is not so straightforward to compute the values of $r_0$ and $r_1$, since hyperbolas in polar coordinates are generated in a strange way as $\theta$ varies from 0 to $2\pi$. This can be seen from Figure 10.6.8*a*, which is the graph of the given equation in rectangular $\theta r$-coordinates. It follows from this graph that the corresponding polar graph is generated in pieces (see Figure 10.6.8*b*):

- As $\theta$ varies over the interval $0 \le \theta < 7\pi/6$, the value of $r$ is positive and varies from 2 down to $2/3$ and then to $+\infty$, which generates part of the lower branch.
- As $\theta$ varies over the interval $7\pi/6 < \theta \le 3\pi/2$, the value of $r$ is negative and varies from $-\infty$ to $-2$, which generates the right part of the upper branch.
- As $\theta$ varies over the interval $3\pi/2 \le \theta < 11\pi/6$, the value of $r$ is negative and varies from $-2$ to $-\infty$, which generates the left part of the upper branch.
- As $\theta$ varies over the interval $11\pi/6 < \theta \le 2\pi$, the value of $r$ is positive and varies from $+\infty$ to 2, which fills in the missing piece of the lower right branch.

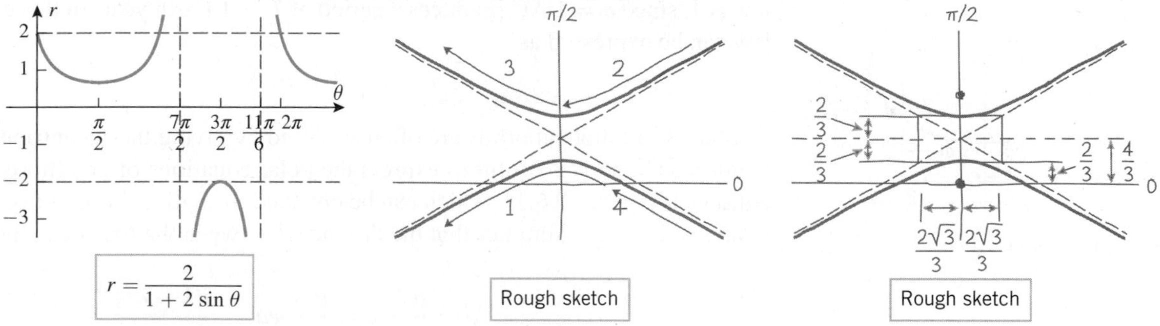


(*a*) (*b*) (*c*)

▲ **Figure 10.6.8**

To obtain a rough sketch of a hyperbola, it is generally sufficient to locate the center, the asymptotes, and the points where $\theta = 0$, $\theta = \pi/2$, $\theta = \pi$, and $\theta = 3\pi/2$.

It is now clear that we can obtain $r_0$ by setting $\theta = \pi/2$ and $r_1$ by setting $\theta = 3\pi/2$. Keeping in mind that $r_0$ and $r_1$ are positive, this yields

$$r_0 = \frac{2}{1 + 2\sin(\pi/2)} = \frac{2}{3}, \quad r_1 = \left|\frac{2}{1 + 2\sin(3\pi/2)}\right| = \left|\frac{2}{-1}\right| = 2$$

Thus, from Formulas (12), (14), and (13), respectively, we obtain

$$a = \frac{1}{2}(r_1 - r_0) = \frac{2}{3}, \quad b = \sqrt{r_0 r_1} = \frac{2\sqrt{3}}{3}, \quad c = \frac{1}{2}(r_1 + r_0) = \frac{4}{3}$$

Thus, the hyperbola looks roughly like that sketched in Figure 10.6.8*c*. ◀

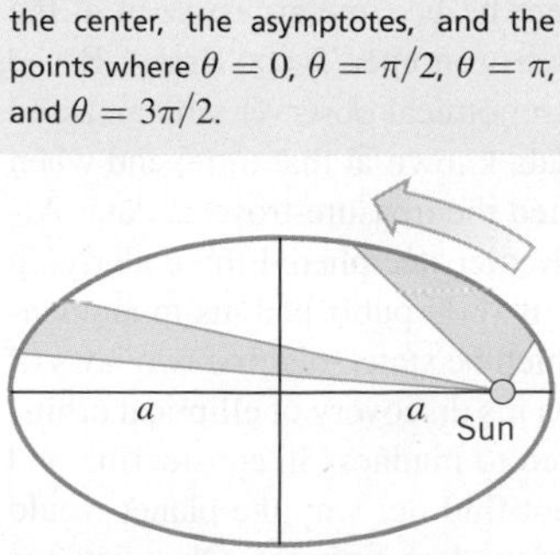


Equal areas are swept out in equal times, and the square of the period $T$ is proportional to $a^3$.

▲ **Figure 10.6.9**

## APPLICATIONS IN ASTRONOMY

In 1609 Johannes Kepler published a book known as *Astronomia Nova* (or sometimes *Commentaries on the Motions of Mars*) in which he succeeded in distilling thousands of years of observational astronomy into three beautiful laws of planetary motion (Figure 10.6.9).

**10.6.3 KEPLER'S LAWS**

- First law (***Law of Orbits***). Each planet moves in an elliptical orbit with the Sun at a focus.
- Second law (***Law of Areas***). The radial line from the center of the Sun to the center of a planet sweeps out equal areas in equal times.
- Third law (***Law of Periods***). The square of a planet's period (the time it takes the planet to complete one orbit about the Sun) is proportional to the cube of the semimajor axis of its orbit.

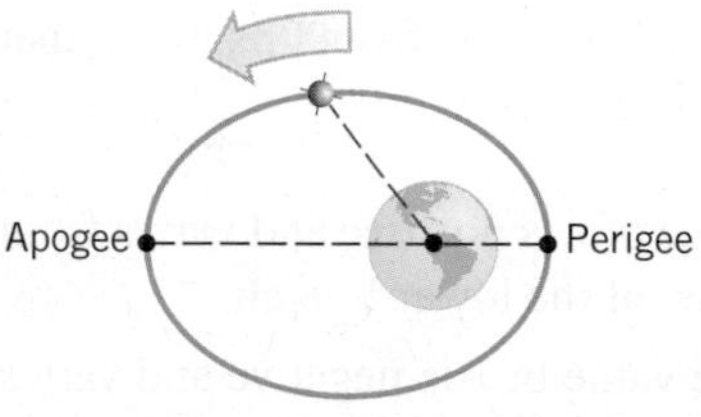

▲ **Figure 10.6.10**

Kepler's laws, although stated for planetary motion around the Sun, apply to all orbiting celestial bodies that are subjected to a *single* central gravitational force—artificial satellites subjected only to the central force of Earth's gravity and moons subjected only to the central gravitational force of a planet, for example. Later in the text we will derive Kepler's laws from basic principles, but for now we will show how they can be used in basic astronomical computations.

In an elliptical orbit, the closest point to the focus is called the ***perigee*** and the farthest point the ***apogee*** (Figure 10.6.10). The distances from the focus to the perigee and apogee are called the ***perigee distance*** and ***apogee distance***, respectively. For orbits around the Sun, it is more common to use the terms ***perihelion*** and ***aphelion***, rather than perigee and apogee, and to measure time in Earth years and distances in astronomical units (AU), where 1 AU is the semimajor axis $a$ of the Earth's orbit (approximately $150 \times 10^6$ km or $92.9 \times 10^6$ mi). With this choice of units, the constant of proportionality in Kepler's third law is 1, since $a = 1$ AU produces a period of $T = 1$ Earth year. In this case Kepler's third law can be expressed as

$$T = a^{3/2} \tag{15}$$

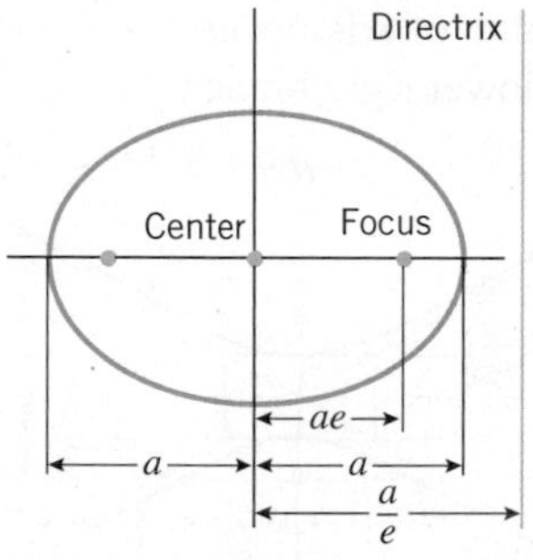

▲ **Figure 10.6.11**

Shapes of elliptical orbits are often specified by giving the eccentricity $e$ and the semimajor axis $a$, so it is useful to express the polar equations of an ellipse in terms of these constants. Figure 10.6.11, which can be obtained from the ellipse in Figure 10.6.1 and the relationship $c = ea$, implies that the distance $d$ between the focus and the directrix is

$$d = \frac{a}{e} - c = \frac{a}{e} - ea = \frac{a(1-e^2)}{e} \tag{16}$$

**Johannes Kepler (1571–1630)** German astronomer and physicist. Kepler, whose work provided our contemporary view of planetary motion, led a fascinating but ill-starred life. His alcoholic father made him work in a family-owned tavern as a child, later withdrawing him from elementary school and hiring him out as a field laborer, where the boy contracted smallpox, permanently crippling his hands and impairing his eyesight. In later years, Kepler's first wife and several children died, his mother was accused of witchcraft, and being a Protestant he was often subjected to persecution by Catholic authorities. He was often impoverished, eking out a living as an astrologer and prognosticator. Looking back on his unhappy childhood, Kepler described his father as "criminally inclined" and "quarrelsome" and his mother as "garrulous" and "bad-tempered." However, it was his mother who left an indelible mark on the six-year-old Kepler by showing him the comet of 1577; and in later life he personally prepared her defense against the witchcraft charges. Kepler became acquainted with the work of Copernicus as a student at the University of Tübingen, where he received his master's degree in 1591. He continued on as a theological student, but at the urging of the university officials he abandoned his clerical studies and accepted a position as a mathematician and teacher in Graz, Austria. However, he was expelled from the city when it came under Catholic control, and in 1600 he finally moved on to Prague, where he became an assistant at the observatory of the famous Danish astronomer Tycho Brahe. Brahe was a brilliant and meticulous astronomical observer who amassed the most accurate astronomical data known at that time; and when Brahe died in 1601 Kepler inherited the treasure-trove of data. After eight years of intense labor, Kepler deciphered the underlying principles buried in the data and in 1609 published his monumental work, *Astronomia Nova*, in which he stated his first two laws of planetary motion. Commenting on his discovery of elliptical orbits, Kepler wrote, "I was almost driven to madness in considering and calculating this matter. I could not find out why the planet would rather go on an elliptical orbit (rather than a circle). Oh ridiculous me!" It ultimately remained for Isaac Newton to discover the laws of gravitation that explained the reason for elliptical orbits.

*[Image: Nicku/Depositphotos]*

from which it follows that $ed = a(1 - e^2)$. Thus, depending on the orientation of the ellipse, the formulas in Theorem 10.6.2 can be expressed in terms of $a$ and $e$ as

$$r = \frac{a(1 - e^2)}{1 \pm e\cos\theta} \qquad r = \frac{a(1 - e^2)}{1 \pm e\sin\theta} \tag{17–18}$$

| $r = \frac{a(1 - e^2)}{1 \pm e\cos\theta}$ | $r = \frac{a(1 - e^2)}{1 \pm e\sin\theta}$ |
|---|---|
| +: Directrix right of pole | +: Directrix above pole |
| −: Directrix left of pole | −: Directrix below pole |

Moreover, it is evident from Figure 10.6.11 that the distances from the focus to the closest and farthest vertices can be expressed in terms of $a$ and $e$ as

$$r_0 = a - ea = a(1 - e) \quad \text{and} \quad r_1 = a + ea = a(1 + e) \tag{19–20}$$

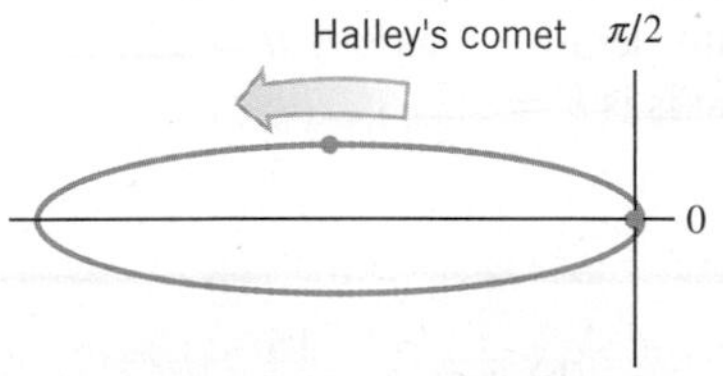


▲ **Figure 10.6.12**

Stocktrek/Getty Images

*Halley's comet photographed April 21, 1910 in Peru.*

▶ **Example 4** Halley's comet (last seen in 1986) has an eccentricity of 0.97 and a semimajor axis of $a = 18.1$ AU.

(a) Find the equation of its orbit in the polar coordinate system shown in Figure 10.6.12.

(b) Find the period of its orbit.

(c) Find its perihelion and aphelion distances.

***Solution (a).*** From (17), the polar equation of the orbit has the form

$$r = \frac{a(1 - e^2)}{1 + e\cos\theta}$$

But $a(1 - e^2) = 18.1[1 - (0.97)^2] \approx 1.07$. Thus, the equation of the orbit is

$$r = \frac{1.07}{1 + 0.97\cos\theta}$$

***Solution (b).*** From (15), with $a = 18.1$, the period of the orbit is

$$T = (18.1)^{3/2} \approx 77 \text{ years}$$

***Solution (c).*** Since the perihelion and aphelion distances are the distances to the closest and farthest vertices, respectively, it follows from (19) and (20) that

$$r_0 = a - ea = a(1 - e) = 18.1(1 - 0.97) \approx 0.543 \text{ AU}$$
$$r_1 = a + ea = a(1 + e) = 18.1(1 + 0.97) \approx 35.7 \text{ AU}$$

or since 1 AU $\approx 150 \times 10^6$ km, the perihelion and aphelion distances in kilometers are

$$r_0 = 18.1(1 - 0.97)(150 \times 10^6) \approx 81{,}500{,}000 \text{ km}$$
$$r_1 = 18.1(1 + 0.97)(150 \times 10^6) \approx 5{,}350{,}000{,}000 \text{ km} \blacktriangleleft$$

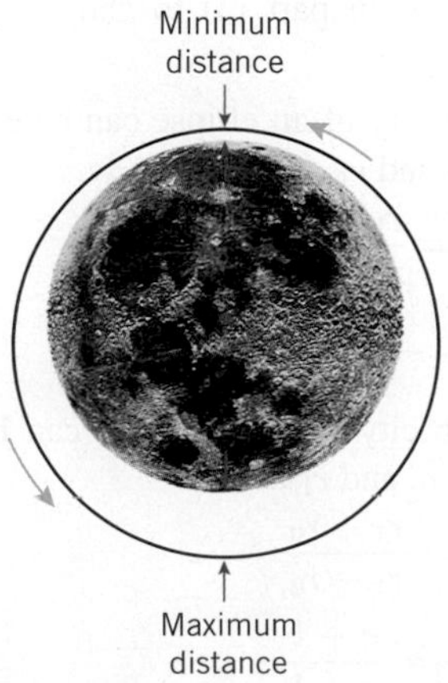


▲ **Figure 10.6.13**

[*Image: NASA*]

▶ **Example 5** An Apollo lunar lander orbits the Moon in an elliptic orbit with eccentricity $e = 0.12$ and semimajor axis $a = 2015$ km. Assuming the Moon to be a sphere of radius 1740 km, find the minimum and maximum heights of the lander above the lunar surface (Figure 10.6.13).

***Solution.*** If we let $r_0$ and $r_1$ denote the minimum and maximum distances from the center of the Moon, then the minimum and maximum distances from the surface of the Moon will be

$$d_{\text{min}} = r_0 - 1740$$
$$d_{\text{max}} = r_1 - 1740$$

or from Formulas (19) and (20)

$$d_{\text{min}} = r_0 - 1740 = a(1 - e) - 1740 = 2015(0.88) - 1740 = 33.2 \text{ km}$$
$$d_{\text{max}} = r_1 - 1740 = a(1 + e) - 1740 = 2015(1.12) - 1740 = 516.8 \text{ km} \blacktriangleleft$$

## ✓ QUICK CHECK EXERCISES 10.6 *(See page 669 for answers.)*

1. In each part, name the conic section described.
   (a) The set of points whose distance to the point (2, 3) is half the distance to the line $x + y = 1$ is ________.
   (b) The set of points whose distance to the point (2, 3) is equal to the distance to the line $x + y = 1$ is ________.
   (c) The set of points whose distance to the point (2, 3) is twice the distance to the line $x + y = 1$ is ________.

2. In each part: (i) Identify the polar graph as a parabola, an ellipse, or a hyperbola; (ii) state whether the directrix is above, below, to the left, or to the right of the pole; and (iii) find the distance from the pole to the directrix.
   (a) $r = \dfrac{1}{4 + \cos\theta}$ (b) $r = \dfrac{1}{1 - 4\cos\theta}$
   (c) $r = \dfrac{1}{4 + 4\sin\theta}$ (d) $r = \dfrac{4}{1 - \sin\theta}$

3. If the distance from a vertex of an ellipse to the nearest focus is $r_0$, and if the distance from that vertex to the farthest focus is $r_1$, then the semimajor axis is $a =$ ________ and the semiminor axis is $b =$ ________.

4. If the distance from a vertex of a hyperbola to the nearest focus is $r_0$, and if the distance from that vertex to the farthest focus is $r_1$, then the semifocal axis is $a =$ ________ and the semiconjugate axis is $b =$ ________.

## EXERCISE SET 10.6 Graphing Utility

**1–2** Find the eccentricity and the distance from the pole to the directrix, and sketch the graph in polar coordinates. ■

1. (a) $r = \dfrac{3}{2 - 2\cos\theta}$ (b) $r = \dfrac{3}{2 + \sin\theta}$

2. (a) $r = \dfrac{4}{2 + 3\cos\theta}$ (b) $r = \dfrac{5}{3 + 3\sin\theta}$

**3–4** Use Formulas (3)–(6) to identify the type of conic and its orientation. Check your answer by generating the graph with a graphing utility. ■

3. (a) $r = \dfrac{8}{1 - \sin\theta}$ (b) $r = \dfrac{16}{4 + 3\sin\theta}$

4. (a) $r = \dfrac{4}{2 - 3\sin\theta}$ (b) $r = \dfrac{12}{4 + \cos\theta}$

**5–6** Find a polar equation for the conic that has its focus at the pole and satisfies the stated conditions. Points are in polar coordinates and directrices in rectangular coordinates for simplicity. (In some cases there may be more than one conic that satisfies the conditions.) ■

5. (a) Ellipse; $e = \frac{3}{4}$; directrix $x = 2$.
   (b) Parabola; directrix $x = 1$.
   (c) Hyperbola; $e = \frac{4}{3}$; directrix $y = 3$.

6. (a) Ellipse; ends of major axis $(2, \pi/2)$ and $(6, 3\pi/2)$.
   (b) Parabola; vertex $(2, \pi)$.
   (c) Hyperbola; $e = \sqrt{2}$; vertex $(2, 0)$.

**7–8** Find the distances from the pole to the vertices, and then apply Formulas (8)–(10) to find the equation of the ellipse in rectangular coordinates. ■

7. (a) $r = \dfrac{6}{2 + \sin\theta}$ (b) $r = \dfrac{1}{2 - \cos\theta}$

8. (a) $r = \dfrac{6}{5 + 2\cos\theta}$ (b) $r = \dfrac{8}{4 - 3\sin\theta}$

**9–10** Find the distances from the pole to the vertices, and then apply Formulas (12)–(14) to find the equation of the hyperbola in rectangular coordinates. ■

9. (a) $r = \dfrac{3}{1 + 2\sin\theta}$ (b) $r = \dfrac{5}{2 - 3\cos\theta}$

10. (a) $r = \dfrac{4}{1 - 2\sin\theta}$ (b) $r = \dfrac{15}{2 + 8\cos\theta}$

**11–12** Find a polar equation for the ellipse that has its focus at the pole and satisfies the stated conditions. ■

11. (a) Directrix to the right of the pole; $a = 8$; $e = \frac{1}{2}$.
    (b) Directrix below the pole; $a = 4$; $e = \frac{3}{5}$.

12. (a) Directrix to the left of the pole; $b = 4$; $e = \frac{3}{5}$.
    (b) Directrix above the pole; $c = 5$; $e = \frac{1}{5}$.

13. Find the polar equation of an equilateral hyperbola with a focus at the pole and vertex (5, 0).

**FOCUS ON CONCEPTS**

14. Prove that a hyperbola is an equilateral hyperbola if and only if $e = \sqrt{2}$.

15. (a) Show that the coordinates of the point $P$ on the hyperbola in Figure 10.6.1 satisfy the equation
    $$\sqrt{(x - c)^2 + y^2} = \frac{c}{a}x - a$$
    (b) Use the result obtained in part (a) to show that $PF/PD = c/a$.

16. (a) Show that the eccentricity of an ellipse can be expressed in terms of $r_0$ and $r_1$ as
    $$e = \frac{r_1 - r_0}{r_1 + r_0}$$
    (b) Show that $\dfrac{r_1}{r_0} = \dfrac{1 + e}{1 - e}$

17. (a) Show that the eccentricity of a hyperbola can be expressed in terms of $r_0$ and $r_1$ as
    $$e = \frac{r_1 + r_0}{r_1 - r_0}$$
    (b) Show that $\dfrac{r_1}{r_0} = \dfrac{e + 1}{e - 1}$

18. (a) Sketch the curves
    $$r = \frac{1}{1 + \cos\theta} \quad \text{and} \quad r = \frac{1}{1 - \cos\theta}$$
    (b) Find polar coordinates of the intersections of the curves in part (a).

*(cont.)*

(c) Show that the curves are *orthogonal*, that is, their tangent lines are perpendicular at the points of intersection.

**19–22 True–False** Determine whether the statement is true or false. Explain your answer. ■

**19.** If an ellipse is not a circle, then the eccentricity of the ellipse is less than one.

**20.** A parabola has eccentricity greater than one.

**21.** If one ellipse has foci that are farther apart than those of a second ellipse, then the eccentricity of the first is greater than that of the second.

**22.** If $d$ is a positive constant, then the conic section with polar equation

$$r = \frac{d}{1 + \cos\theta}$$

is a parabola.

**23–28** Use the following values, where needed:

radius of the Earth $= 4000$ mi $= 6440$ km

1 year (Earth year) $= 365$ days (Earth days)

1 AU $= 92.9 \times 10^6$ mi $= 150 \times 10^6$ km ■

**23.** The dwarf planet Pluto has eccentricity $e = 0.249$ and semimajor axis $a = 39.5$ AU.
(a) Find the period $T$ in years.
(b) Find the perihelion and aphelion distances.
(c) Choose a polar coordinate system with the center of the Sun at the pole, and find a polar equation of Pluto's orbit in that coordinate system.
(d) Make a sketch of the orbit with reasonably accurate proportions.

**24.** (a) Let $a$ be the semimajor axis of a planet's orbit around the Sun, and let $T$ be its period. Show that if $T$ is measured in days and $a$ is measured in kilometers, then $T = (365 \times 10^{-9})(a/150)^{3/2}$.
(b) Use the result in part (a) to find the period of the planet Mercury in days, given that its semimajor axis is $a = 57.95 \times 10^6$ km.
(c) Choose a polar coordinate system with the Sun at the pole, and find an equation for the orbit of Mercury in that coordinate system given that the eccentricity of the orbit is $e = 0.206$.
(d) Use a graphing utility to generate the orbit of Mercury from the equation obtained in part (c).

**25.** The Hale–Bopp comet, discovered independently on July 23, 1995 by Alan Hale and Thomas Bopp, has an orbital eccentricity of $e = 0.9951$ and a period of 2380 years.
(a) Find its semimajor axis in astronomical units (AU).
(b) Find its perihelion and aphelion distances.
(c) Choose a polar coordinate system with the center of the Sun at the pole, and find an equation for the Hale–Bopp orbit in that coordinate system.
(d) Make a sketch of the Hale–Bopp orbit with reasonably accurate proportions.

**26.** Mars has a perihelion distance of 204,520,000 km and an aphelion distance of 246,280,000 km.
(a) Use these data to calculate the eccentricity, and compare your answer to the value given in Table 10.6.1.
(b) Find the period of Mars.
(c) Choose a polar coordinate system with the center of the Sun at the pole, and find an equation for the orbit of Mars in that coordinate system.
(d) Use a graphing utility to generate the orbit of Mars from the equation obtained in part (c).

**27.** *Vanguard 1* was launched in March 1958 into an orbit around the Earth with eccentricity $e = 0.21$ and semimajor axis 8864.5 km. Find the minimum and maximum heights of *Vanguard 1* above the surface of the Earth.

**28.** The planet Jupiter is believed to have a rocky core of radius 10,000 km surrounded by two layers of hydrogen—a 40,000 km thick layer of compressed metallic-like hydrogen and a 20,000 km thick layer of ordinary molecular hydrogen. The visible features, such as the Great Red Spot, are at the outer surface of the molecular hydrogen layer. On November 6, 1997 the spacecraft *Galileo* was placed in a Jovian orbit to study the moon Europa. The orbit had eccentricity 0.814580 and semimajor axis 3,514,918.9 km. Find *Galileo*'s minimum and maximum heights above the molecular hydrogen layer (see the accompanying figure).

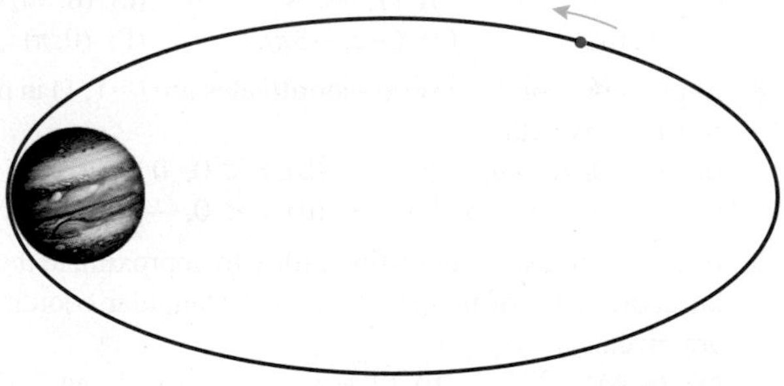

*Not to scale*

▲ **Figure Ex-28**
[*Image: NASA*]

**29. Writing** Discuss how a hyperbola's eccentricity $e$ affects the shape of the hyperbola. How is the shape affected as $e$ approaches 1? As $e$ approaches $+\infty$? Draw some pictures to illustrate your conclusions.

**30. Writing** Discuss the relationship between the eccentricity $e$ of an ellipse and the distance $z$ between the directrix and center of the ellipse. For example, if the foci remain fixed, what happens to $z$ as $e$ approaches 0?

✓ **QUICK CHECK ANSWERS 10.6** **1.** (a) an ellipse (b) a parabola (c) a hyperbola **2.** (a) (i) ellipse (ii) to the right of the pole (iii) distance $= 1$ (b) (i) hyperbola (ii) to the left of the pole (iii) distance $= \frac{1}{4}$ (c) (i) parabola (ii) above the pole (iii) distance $= \frac{1}{4}$ (d) (i) parabola (ii) below the pole (iii) distance $= 4$ **3.** $\frac{1}{2}(r_1 + r_0)$; $\sqrt{r_0 r_1}$ **4.** $\frac{1}{2}(r_1 - r_0)$; $\sqrt{r_0 r_1}$

## CHAPTER 10 REVIEW EXERCISES

Graphing Utility

1. Find parametric equations for the portion of the circle $x^2+y^2=2$ that lies outside the first quadrant, oriented clockwise. Check your work by generating the curve with a graphing utility.

2. (a) Suppose that the equations $x=f(t)$, $y=g(t)$ describe a curve $C$ as $t$ increases from 0 to 1. Find parametric equations that describe the same curve $C$ but traced in the opposite direction as $t$ increases from 0 to 1.
(b) Check your work using the parametric graphing feature of a graphing utility by generating the line segment between $(1, 2)$ and $(4, 0)$ in both possible directions as $t$ increases from 0 to 1.

3. (a) Find the slope of the tangent line to the parametric curve $x=t^2+1$, $y=t/2$ at $t=-1$ and $t=1$ without eliminating the parameter.
(b) Check your answers in part (a) by eliminating the parameter and differentiating a function of $x$.

4. Find $dy/dx$ and $d^2y/dx^2$ at $t=2$ for the parametric curve $x=\frac{1}{2}t^2$, $y=\frac{1}{3}t^3$.

5. Find all values of $t$ at which a tangent line to the parametric curve $x=2\cos t$, $y=4\sin t$ is
(a) horizontal (b) vertical.

6. Find the exact arc length of the curve

$$x=1-5t^4,\quad y=4t^5-1\qquad(0\le t\le 1)$$

7. In each part, find the rectangular coordinates of the point whose polar coordinates are given.
(a) $(-8, \pi/4)$ (b) $(7, -\pi/4)$ (c) $(8, 9\pi/4)$
(d) $(5, 0)$ (e) $(-2, -3\pi/2)$ (f) $(0, \pi)$

8. Express the point whose $xy$-coordinates are $(-1, 1)$ in polar coordinates with
(a) $r>0,\ 0\le\theta<2\pi$ (b) $r<0,\ 0\le\theta<2\pi$
(c) $r>0,\ -\pi<\theta\le\pi$ (d) $r<0,\ -\pi<\theta\le\pi$.

9. In each part, use a calculating utility to approximate the polar coordinates of the point whose rectangular coordinates are given.
(a) $(4, 3)$ (b) $(2, -5)$ (c) $(1, \tan^{-1} 1)$

10. In each part, state the name that describes the polar curve most precisely: a rose, a line, a circle, a limaçon, a cardioid, a spiral, a lemniscate, or none of these.
(a) $r=3\cos\theta$ (b) $r=\cos 3\theta$
(c) $r=\dfrac{3}{\cos\theta}$ (d) $r=3-\cos\theta$
(e) $r=1-3\cos\theta$ (f) $r^2=3\cos\theta$
(g) $r=(3\cos\theta)^2$ (h) $r=1+3\theta$

11. In each part, identify the curve by converting the polar equation to rectangular coordinates. Assume that $a>0$.
(a) $r=a\sec^2\dfrac{\theta}{2}$ (b) $r^2\cos 2\theta=a^2$
(c) $r=4\csc\left(\theta-\dfrac{\pi}{4}\right)$ (d) $r=4\cos\theta+8\sin\theta$

12. In each part, express the given equation in polar coordinates.
(a) $x=7$ (b) $x^2+y^2=9$
(c) $x^2+y^2-6y=0$ (d) $4xy=9$

13–17 Sketch the curve in polar coordinates. ■

13. $\theta=\dfrac{\pi}{6}$ 14. $r=6\cos\theta$

15. $r=3(1-\sin\theta)$ 16. $r^2=\sin 2\theta$

17. $r=3-\cos\theta$

18. (a) Show that the maximum value of the $y$-coordinate of points on the curve $r=1/\sqrt{\theta}$ for $\theta$ in the interval $(0, \pi]$ occurs when $\tan\theta=2\theta$.
(b) Use a calculating utility to solve the equation in part (a) to at least four decimal-place accuracy.
(c) Use the result of part (b) to approximate the maximum value of $y$ for $0<\theta\le\pi$.

19. (a) Find the minimum and maximum $x$-coordinates of points on the cardioid $r=1-\cos\theta$.
(b) Find the minimum and maximum $y$-coordinates of points on the cardioid in part (a).

20. Determine the slope of the tangent line to the polar curve $r=1+\sin\theta$ at $\theta=\pi/4$.

21. A parametric curve of the form

$$x=a\cot t+b\cos t,\quad y=a+b\sin t\qquad(0<t<2\pi)$$

is called a ***conchoid of Nicomedes*** (see the accompanying figure for the case $0<a<b$).
(a) Describe how the conchoid

$$x=\cot t+4\cos t,\quad y=1+4\sin t$$

is generated as $t$ varies over the interval $0<t<2\pi$.
(b) Find the horizontal asymptote of the conchoid given in part (a).
(c) For what values of $t$ does the conchoid in part (a) have a horizontal tangent line? A vertical tangent line?
(d) Find a polar equation $r=f(\theta)$ for the conchoid in part (a), and then find polar equations for the tangent lines to the conchoid at the pole.

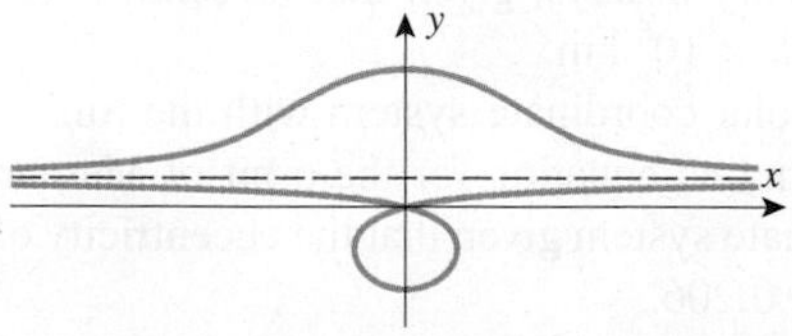


◀ **Figure Ex-21**

22. (a) Find the arc length of the polar curve $r=1/\theta$ for $\pi/4\le\theta\le\pi/2$.
(b) What can you say about the arc length of the portion of the curve that lies inside the circle $r=1$?

23. Find the area of the region that is enclosed by the cardioid $r=2+2\cos\theta$.

24. Find the area of the region in the first quadrant within the cardioid $r=1+\sin\theta$.

25. Find the area of the region that is common to the circles $r=1$, $r=2\cos\theta$, and $r=2\sin\theta$.

26. Find the area of the region that is inside the cardioid $r=a(1+\sin\theta)$ and outside the circle $r=a\sin\theta$.

**27–30** Sketch the parabola, and label the focus, vertex, and directrix. ■

**27.** $y^2 = 6x$ **28.** $x^2 = -9y$

**29.** $(y + 1)^2 = -7(x - 4)$ **30.** $\left(x - \frac{1}{2}\right)^2 = 2(y - 1)$

**31–34** Sketch the ellipse, and label the foci, the vertices, and the ends of the minor axis. ■

**31.** $\dfrac{x^2}{4} + \dfrac{y^2}{25} = 1$ **32.** $4x^2 + 9y^2 = 36$

**33.** $9(x - 1)^2 + 16(y - 3)^2 = 144$

**34.** $3(x + 2)^2 + 4(y + 1)^2 = 12$

**35–37** Sketch the hyperbola, and label the vertices, foci, and asymptotes. ■

**35.** $\dfrac{x^2}{16} - \dfrac{y^2}{4} = 1$ **36.** $9y^2 - 4x^2 = 36$

**37.** $\dfrac{(x - 2)^2}{9} - \dfrac{(y - 4)^2}{4} = 1$

**38.** In each part, sketch the graph of the conic section with reasonably accurate proportions.
(a) $x^2 - 4x + 8y + 36 = 0$
(b) $3x^2 + 4y^2 - 30x - 8y + 67 = 0$
(c) $4x^2 - 5y^2 - 8x - 30y - 21 = 0$

**39–41** Find an equation for the conic described. ■

**39.** A parabola with vertex $(0, 0)$ and focus $(0, -4)$.

**40.** An ellipse with the ends of the major axis $(0, \pm\sqrt{5})$ and the ends of the minor axis $(\pm 1, 0)$.

**41.** A hyperbola with vertices $(0, \pm 3)$ and asymptotes $y = \pm x$.

**42.** It can be shown in the accompanying figure that hanging cables form parabolic arcs rather than catenaries if they are subjected to uniformly distributed downward forces along their length. For example, if the weight of the roadway in a suspension bridge is assumed to be uniformly distributed along the supporting cables, then the cables can be modeled by parabolas.
(a) Assuming a parabolic model, find an equation for the cable in the accompanying figure, taking the $y$-axis to be vertical and the origin at the low point of the cable.
(b) Find the length of the cable between the supports.

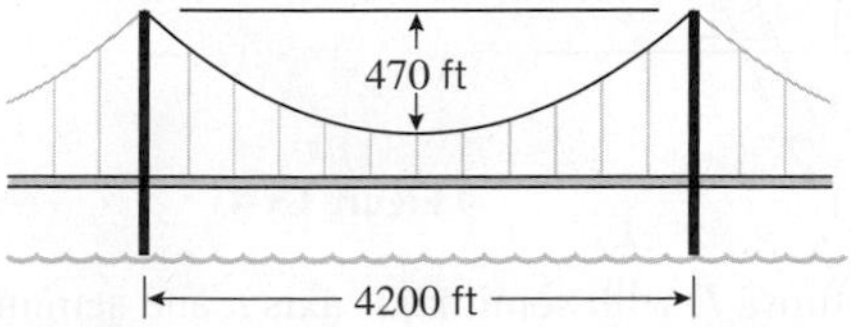


▲ **Figure Ex-42**

**43.** It will be shown later in this text that if a projectile is launched with speed $v_0$ at an angle $\alpha$ with the horizontal and at a height $y_0$ above ground level, then the resulting trajectory relative to the coordinate system in the accompanying figure will have parametric equations

$$x = (v_0 \cos\alpha)t, \quad y = y_0 + (v_0 \sin\alpha)t - \tfrac{1}{2}gt^2$$

where $g$ is the acceleration due to gravity.
(a) Show that the trajectory is a parabola.
(b) Find the coordinates of the vertex.

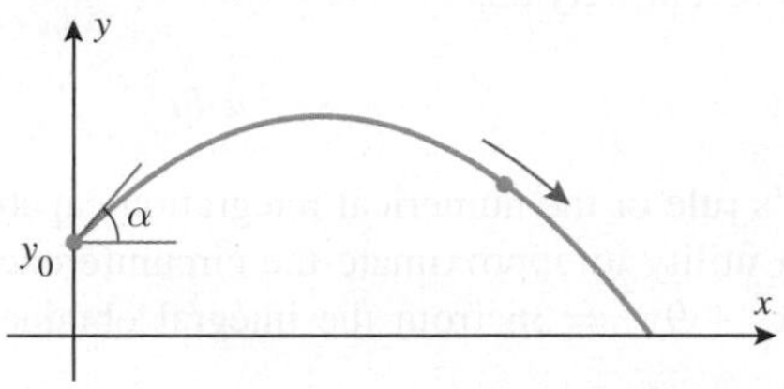


◀ **Figure Ex-43**

**44.** Mickey Mantle is recognized as baseball's unofficial king of long home runs. On April 17, 1953 Mantle blasted a pitch by Chuck Stobbs of the hapless Washington Senators out of Griffith Stadium, just clearing the 50 ft wall at the 391 ft marker in left center. Assuming that the ball left the bat at a height of 3 ft above the ground and at an angle of 45°, use the parametric equations in Exercise 43 with $g = 32\ \text{ft/s}^2$ to find
(a) the speed of the ball as it left the bat
(b) the maximum height of the ball
(c) the distance along the ground from home plate to where the ball struck the ground.

**45–47** Rotate the coordinate axes to remove the $xy$-term, and then name the conic. ■

**45.** $x^2 + y^2 - 3xy - 3 = 0$

**46.** $7x^2 + 2\sqrt{3}xy + 5y^2 - 4 = 0$

**47.** $4\sqrt{5}x^2 + 4\sqrt{5}xy + \sqrt{5}y^2 + 5x - 10y = 0$

**48.** Rotate the coordinate axes to show that the graph of

$$17x^2 - 312xy + 108y^2 + 1080x - 1440y + 4500 = 0$$

is a hyperbola. Then find its vertices, foci, and asymptotes.

**49.** In each part: (i) Identify the polar graph as a parabola, an ellipse, or a hyperbola; (ii) state whether the directrix is above, below, to the left, or to the right of the pole; and (iii) find the distance from the pole to the directrix.
(a) $r = \dfrac{1}{3 + \cos\theta}$ (b) $r = \dfrac{1}{1 - 3\cos\theta}$
(c) $r = \dfrac{1}{3(1 + \sin\theta)}$ (d) $r = \dfrac{3}{1 - \sin\theta}$

**50–51** Find an equation in $xy$-coordinates for the conic section that satisfies the given conditions. ■

**50.** (a) Ellipse with eccentricity $e = \frac{2}{7}$ and ends of the minor axis at the points $(0, \pm 3)$.
(b) Parabola with vertex at the origin, focus on the $y$-axis, and directrix passing through the point $(7, 4)$.
(c) Hyperbola that has the same foci as the ellipse $3x^2 + 16y^2 = 48$ and asymptotes $y = \pm 2x/3$.

**51.** (a) Ellipse with center $(-3, 2)$, vertex $(2, 2)$, and eccentricity $e = \frac{4}{5}$.
(b) Parabola with focus $(-2, -2)$ and vertex $(-2, 0)$.
(c) Hyperbola with vertex $(-1, 7)$ and asymptotes $y - 5 = \pm 8(x + 1)$.

**52.** Use the parametric equations $x = a\cos t$, $y = b\sin t$ to show that the circumference $C$ of an ellipse with semimajor axis $a$ and eccentricity $e$ is

$$C = 4a\int_0^{\pi/2}\sqrt{1 - e^2\sin^2 u}\,du$$

**53.** Use Simpson's rule or the numerical integration capability of a graphing utility to approximate the circumference of the ellipse $4x^2 + 9y^2 = 36$ from the integral obtained in Exercise 52.

**54.** (a) Calculate the eccentricity of the Earth's orbit, given that the ratio of the distance between the center of the Earth and the center of the Sun at perihelion to the distance between the centers at aphelion is $\frac{59}{61}$.

(b) Find the distance between the center of the Earth and the center of the Sun at perihelion, given that the average value of the perihelion and aphelion distances between the centers is 93 million miles.

(c) Use the result in Exercise 52 and Simpson's rule or the numerical integration capability of a graphing utility to approximate the distance that the Earth travels in 1 year (one revolution around the Sun).

## CHAPTER 10 MAKING CONNECTIONS

C CAS

C **1.** Recall from Section 5.10 that the Fresnel sine and cosine functions are defined as

$$S(x) = \int_0^x \sin\left(\frac{\pi t^2}{2}\right) dt \quad\text{and}\quad C(x) = \int_0^x \cos\left(\frac{\pi t^2}{2}\right) dt$$

The following parametric curve, which is used to study amplitudes of light waves in optics, is called a ***clothoid*** or ***Cornu spiral*** in honor of the French scientist Marie Alfred Cornu (1841–1902):

$$x = C(t) = \int_0^t \cos\left(\frac{\pi u^2}{2}\right) du$$
$$(-\infty < t < +\infty)$$
$$y = S(t) = \int_0^t \sin\left(\frac{\pi u^2}{2}\right) du$$

(a) Use a CAS to graph the Cornu spiral.

(b) Describe the behavior of the spiral as $t \to +\infty$ and as $t \to -\infty$.

(c) Find the arc length of the spiral for $-1 \le t \le 1$.

**2.** (a) The accompanying figure shows an ellipse with semimajor axis $a$ and semiminor axis $b$. Express the coordinates of the points $P$, $Q$, and $R$ in terms of $t$.

(b) How does the geometric interpretation of the parameter $t$ differ between a circle

$$x = a\cos t, \quad y = a\sin t$$

and an ellipse

$$x = a\cos t, \quad y = b\sin t?$$

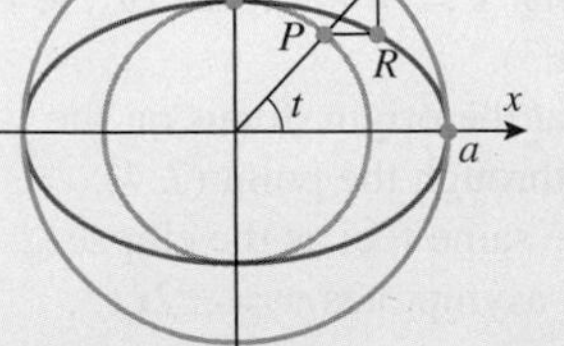


◀ Figure Ex-2

**3.** The accompanying figure shows Kepler's method for constructing a parabola. A piece of string the length of the left edge of the drafting triangle is tacked to the vertex $Q$ of the triangle and the other end to a fixed point $F$. A pencil holds the string taut against the base of the triangle as the edge opposite $Q$ slides along a horizontal line $L$ below $F$. Show that the pencil traces an arc of a parabola with focus $F$ and directrix $L$.

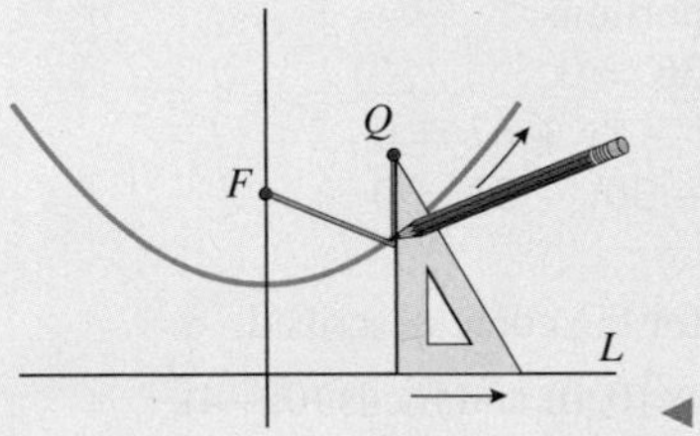


◀ Figure Ex-3

**4.** The accompanying figure shows a method for constructing a hyperbola. A corner of a ruler is pinned to a fixed point $F_1$ and the ruler is free to rotate about that point. A piece of string whose length is less than that of the ruler is tacked to a point $F_2$ and to the free corner $Q$ of the ruler on the same edge as $F_1$. A pencil holds the string taut against the top edge of the ruler as the ruler rotates about the point $F_1$. Show that the pencil traces an arc of a hyperbola with foci $F_1$ and $F_2$.

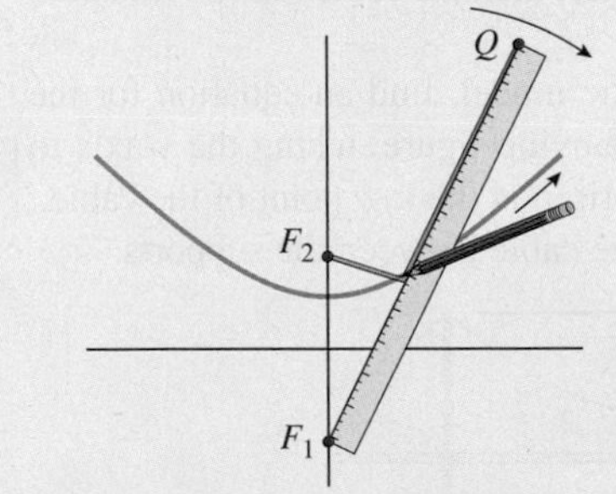


◀ Figure Ex-4

**5.** Consider an ellipse $E$ with semimajor axis $a$ and semiminor axis $b$, and set $c = \sqrt{a^2 - b^2}$.

(a) Show that the ellipsoid that results when $E$ is revolved about its major axis has volume $V = \frac{4}{3}\pi ab^2$ and surface area

$$S = 2\pi ab\left(\frac{b}{a} + \frac{a}{c}\sin^{-1}\frac{c}{a}\right)$$

(b) Show that the ellipsoid that results when $E$ is revolved about its minor axis has volume $V = \frac{4}{3}\pi a^2 b$ and surface area

$$S = 2\pi ab\left(\frac{a}{b} + \frac{b}{c}\ln\frac{a+c}{b}\right)$$

## EXPANDING THE CALCULUS HORIZON

To learn how polar coordinates and conic sections can be used to analyze the possibility of a collision between a comet and Earth, see the module entitled **Comet Collision** at:

www.wiley.com/college/anton

nadi555/Depositphotos

*To describe fully the motion of a boat, one must specify its speed and direction of motion at each instant. Speed and direction together describe a "vector" quantity. We will study vectors in this chapter.*

# 11 THREE-DIMENSIONAL SPACE; VECTORS

In this chapter we will discuss rectangular coordinate systems in three dimensions, and we will study the analytic geometry of lines, planes, and other basic surfaces. The second theme of this chapter is the study of vectors. These are the mathematical objects that physicists and engineers use to study forces, displacements, and velocities of objects moving on curved paths. More generally, vectors are used to represent all physical entities that involve both a magnitude and a direction for their complete description. We will introduce various algebraic operations on vectors, and we will apply these operations to problems involving force, work, and rotational tendencies in two and three dimensions. Finally, we will discuss cylindrical and spherical coordinate systems, which are appropriate in problems that involve various kinds of symmetries and also have specific applications in navigation and celestial mechanics.

## 11.1 RECTANGULAR COORDINATES IN 3-SPACE; SPHERES; CYLINDRICAL SURFACES

*In this section we will discuss coordinate systems in three-dimensional space and some basic facts about surfaces in three dimensions.*

### RECTANGULAR COORDINATE SYSTEMS

In the remainder of this text we will call three-dimensional space ***3-space***, two-dimensional space (a plane) ***2-space***, and one-dimensional space (a line) ***1-space***. Just as points in 2-space can be placed in one-to-one correspondence with pairs of real numbers using two perpendicular coordinate lines, so points in 3-space can be placed in one-to-one correspondence with triples of real numbers by using three mutually perpendicular coordinate lines, called the ***x-axis***, the ***y-axis***, and the ***z-axis***, positioned so that their origins coincide (Figure 11.1.1). The three coordinate axes form a three-dimensional ***rectangular coordinate system*** (or ***Cartesian coordinate system***). The point of intersection of the coordinate axes is called the ***origin*** of the coordinate system.

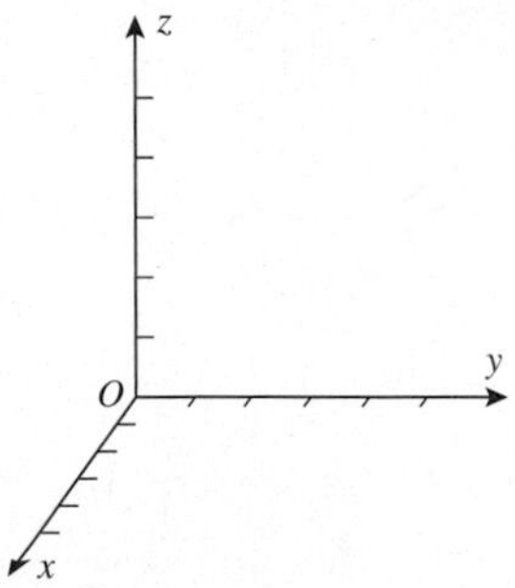


▲ **Figure 11.1.1**

Rectangular coordinate systems in 3-space fall into two categories: ***left-handed*** and ***right-handed***. A right-handed system has the property that when the fingers of the right hand are cupped so that they curve from the positive $x$-axis toward the positive $y$-axis, the thumb points (roughly) in the direction of the positive $z$-axis (Figure 11.1.2). A similar property holds for a left-handed coordinate system (Figure 11.1.2). We will use only right-handed coordinate systems in this text.

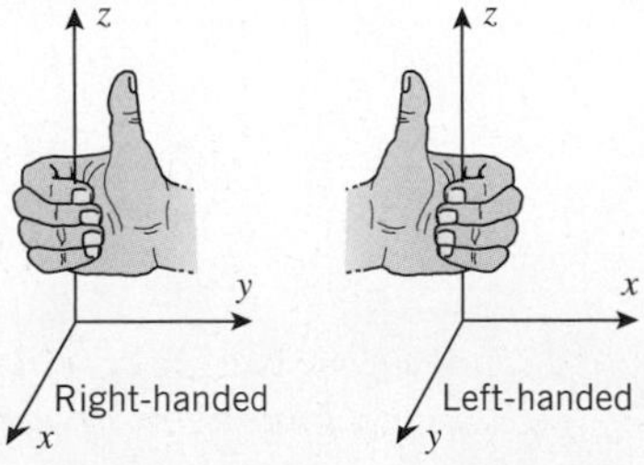


▲ **Figure 11.1.2**

The coordinate axes, taken in pairs, determine three ***coordinate planes***: the ***xy-plane***, the ***xz-plane***, and the ***yz-plane*** (Figure 11.1.3). To each point $P$ in 3-space we can assign a triple of real numbers by passing three planes through $P$ parallel to the coordinate planes and letting $a$, $b$, and $c$ be the coordinates of the intersections of those planes with the $x$-axis, $y$-axis, and $z$-axis, respectively (Figure 11.1.4). We call $a$, $b$, and $c$ the ***x-coordinate***, ***y-coordinate***, and ***z-coordinate*** of $P$, respectively, and we denote the point $P$ by $(a, b, c)$ or by $P(a, b, c)$. Figure 11.1.5 shows the points $(4, 5, 6)$ and $(-3, 2, -4)$.

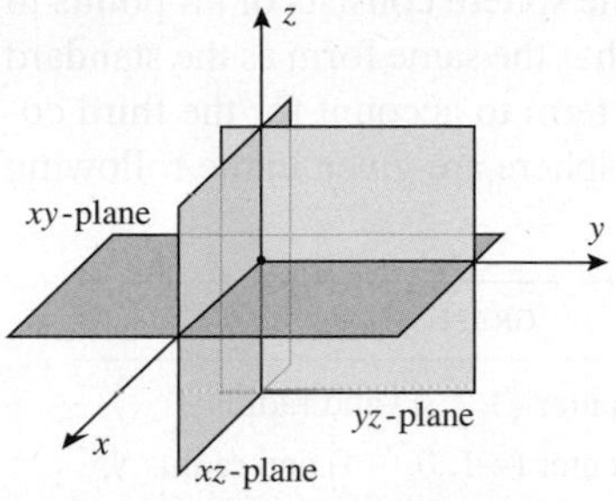

▲ Figure 11.1.3

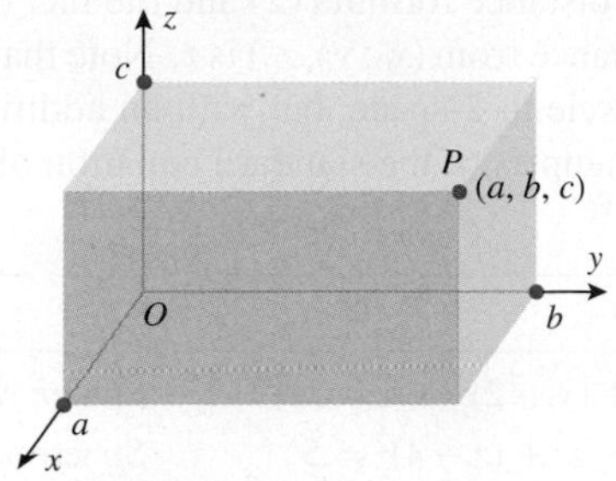

▲ Figure 11.1.4

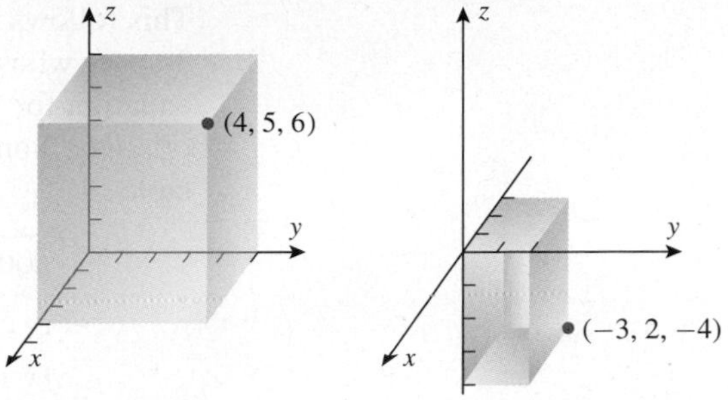

▲ Figure 11.1.5

Just as the coordinate axes in a two-dimensional coordinate system divide 2-space into four quadrants, so the coordinate planes of a three-dimensional coordinate system divide 3-space into eight parts, called ***octants***. The set of points with three positive coordinates forms the ***first octant***; the remaining octants have no standard numbering.

You should be able to visualize the following facts about three-dimensional rectangular coordinate systems:

| REGION | DESCRIPTION |
|---|---|
| $xy$-plane | Consists of all points of the form $(x, y, 0)$ |
| $xz$-plane | Consists of all points of the form $(x, 0, z)$ |
| $yz$-plane | Consists of all points of the form $(0, y, z)$ |
| $x$-axis | Consists of all points of the form $(x, 0, 0)$ |
| $y$-axis | Consists of all points of the form $(0, y, 0)$ |
| $z$-axis | Consists of all points of the form $(0, 0, z)$ |

## DISTANCE IN 3-SPACE; SPHERES

Recall that in 2-space the distance $d$ between the points $P_1(x_1, y_1)$ and $P_2(x_2, y_2)$ is

$$d = \sqrt{(x_2 - x_1)^2 + (y_2 - y_1)^2} \tag{1}$$

The distance formula in 3-space has the same form, but it has a third term to account for the added dimension. (We will see that this is a common occurrence in extending formulas from 2-space to 3-space.) The distance between the points $P_1(x_1, y_1, z_1)$ and $P_2(x_2, y_2, z_2)$ is

$$d = \sqrt{(x_2 - x_1)^2 + (y_2 - y_1)^2 + (z_2 - z_1)^2} \tag{2}$$

We leave the proof of (2) as an exercise (Exercise 7).

▶ **Example 1** Find the distance $d$ between the points $(2, 3, -1)$ and $(4, -1, 3)$.

***Solution.*** From Formula (2)

$$d = \sqrt{(4-2)^2 + (-1-3)^2 + (3+1)^2} = \sqrt{36} = 6 \blacktriangleleft$$

In an $xy$-coordinate system, the set of points $(x, y)$ whose coordinates satisfy an equation in $x$ and $y$ is called the ***graph*** of the equation. Analogously, in an $xyz$-coordinate system, the set of points $(x, y, z)$ whose coordinates satisfy an equation in $x$, $y$, and $z$ is called the ***graph*** of the equation.

Recall that the standard equation of the circle in 2-space that has center $(x_0, y_0)$ and radius $r$ is

$$(x - x_0)^2 + (y - y_0)^2 = r^2 \tag{3}$$

This follows from distance formula (1) and the fact that the circle consists of all points in 2-space whose distance from $(x_0, y_0)$ is $r$. Analogously, the ***standard equation of the sphere*** in 3-space that has center $(x_0, y_0, z_0)$ and radius $r$ is

$$(x - x_0)^2 + (y - y_0)^2 + (z - z_0)^2 = r^2 \tag{4}$$

This follows from distance formula (2) and the fact that the sphere consists of all points in 3-space whose distance from $(x_0, y_0, z_0)$ is $r$. Note that (4) has the same form as the standard equation for the circle in 2-space, but with an additional term to account for the third coordinate. Some examples of the standard equation of the sphere are given in the following table:

| EQUATION | GRAPH |
|---|---|
| $(x-3)^2 + (y-2)^2 + (z-1)^2 = 9$ | Sphere with center (3, 2, 1) and radius 3 |
| $(x+1)^2 + y^2 + (z+4)^2 = 5$ | Sphere with center (−1, 0, −4) and radius $\sqrt{5}$ |
| $x^2 + y^2 + z^2 = 1$ | Sphere with center (0, 0, 0) and radius 1 |

If the terms in (4) are expanded and like terms are collected, then the resulting equation has the form

$$x^2 + y^2 + z^2 + Gx + Hy + Iz + J = 0 \tag{5}$$

The following example shows how the center and radius of a sphere that is expressed in this form can be obtained by completing the squares.

▶ **Example 2** Find the center and radius of the sphere

$$x^2 + y^2 + z^2 - 2x - 4y + 8z + 17 = 0$$

***Solution.*** We can put the equation in the form of (4) by completing the squares:

$$(x^2 - 2x) + (y^2 - 4y) + (z^2 + 8z) = -17$$
$$(x^2 - 2x + 1) + (y^2 - 4y + 4) + (z^2 + 8z + 16) = -17 + 21$$
$$(x-1)^2 + (y-2)^2 + (z+4)^2 = 4$$

which is the equation of the sphere with center $(1, 2, -4)$ and radius 2. ◀

In general, completing the squares in (5) produces an equation of the form

$$(x - x_0)^2 + (y - y_0)^2 + (z - z_0)^2 = k$$

If $k > 0$, then the graph of this equation is a sphere with center $(x_0, y_0, z_0)$ and radius $\sqrt{k}$. If $k = 0$, then the sphere has radius zero, so the graph is the single point $(x_0, y_0, z_0)$. If $k < 0$, the equation is not satisfied by any values of $x$, $y$, and $z$ (why?), so it has no graph.

**11.1.1 THEOREM** *An equation of the form*

$$x^2 + y^2 + z^2 + Gx + Hy + Iz + J = 0$$

*represents a sphere, a point, or has no graph.*

## CYLINDRICAL SURFACES

Although it is natural to graph equations in two variables in 2-space and equations in three variables in 3-space, it is also possible to graph equations in two variables in 3-space. For example, the graph of the equation $y = x^2$ in an $xy$-coordinate system is a parabola; however, there is nothing to prevent us from inquiring about its graph in an $xyz$-coordinate system. To obtain this graph we need only observe that the equation $y = x^2$ does not impose any restrictions on $z$. Thus, if we find values of $x$ and $y$ that satisfy this equation, then the coordinates of the point $(x, y, z)$ will also satisfy the equation for *arbitrary* values of $z$. Geometrically, the point $(x, y, z)$ lies on the vertical line through the point $(x, y, 0)$ in the $xy$-plane, which means that we can obtain the graph of $y = x^2$ in an $xyz$-coordinate system by first graphing the equation in the $xy$-plane and then translating that graph parallel to the $z$-axis to generate the entire graph (Figure 11.1.6).

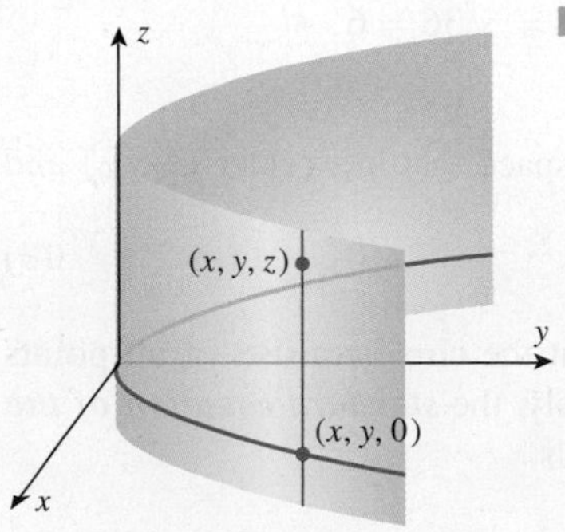

▲ **Figure 11.1.6**

The process of generating a surface by translating a plane curve parallel to some line is called ***extrusion***, and surfaces that are generated by extrusion are called ***cylindrical surfaces***. A familiar example is the surface of a right circular cylinder, which can be generated by translating a circle parallel to the axis of the cylinder. The following theorem provides basic information about graphing equations in two variables in 3-space:

**11.1.2 THEOREM** *An equation that contains only two of the variables x, y, and z represents a cylindrical surface in an xyz-coordinate system. The surface can be obtained by graphing the equation in the coordinate plane of the two variables that appear in the equation and then translating that graph parallel to the axis of the missing variable.*

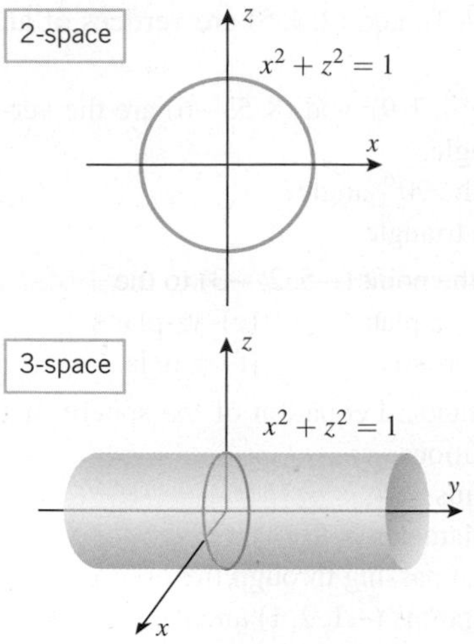

▲ **Figure 11.1.7**

► **Example 3** Sketch the graph of $x^2 + z^2 = 1$ in 3-space.

***Solution.*** Since $y$ does not appear in this equation, the graph is a cylindrical surface generated by extrusion parallel to the $y$-axis. In the $xz$-plane the graph of the equation $x^2 + z^2 = 1$ is a circle. Thus, in 3-space the graph is a right circular cylinder along the $y$-axis (Figure 11.1.7). ◄

In an $xy$-coordinate system, the graph of the equation $x = 1$ is a line parallel to the $y$-axis. What is the graph of this equation in an $xyz$-coordinate system?

► **Example 4** Sketch the graph of $z = \sin y$ in 3-space.

***Solution.*** (See Figure 11.1.8.) ◄

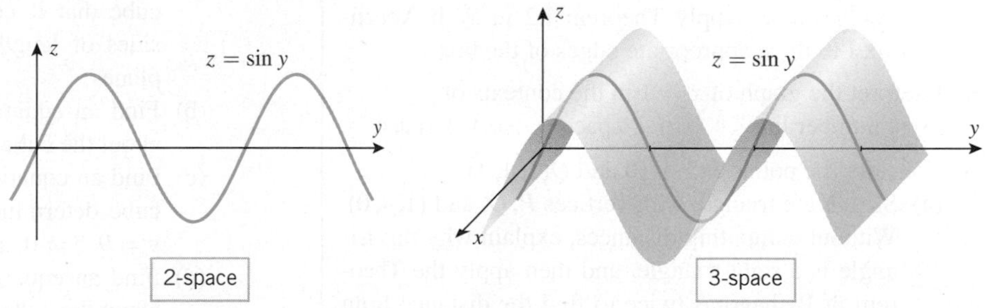

► **Figure 11.1.8**

## ✓ QUICK CHECK EXERCISES 11.1 (See page 680 for answers.)

1. The distance between the points $(1, -2, 0)$ and $(4, 0, 5)$ is ________.

2. The graph of $(x-3)^2 + (y-2)^2 + (z+1)^2 = 16$ is a ________ of radius ________ centered at ________.

3. The shortest distance from the point $(4, 0, 5)$ to the sphere $(x-1)^2 + (y+2)^2 + z^2 = 36$ is ________.

4. Let $S$ be the graph of $x^2 + z^2 + 6z = 16$ in 3-space.
   (a) The intersection of $S$ with the $xz$-plane is a circle with center ________ and radius ________.
   (b) The intersection of $S$ with the $xy$-plane is two lines, $x =$ ________ and $x =$ ________.
   (c) The intersection of $S$ with the $yz$-plane is two lines, $z =$ ________ and $z =$ ________.

## EXERCISE SET 11.1 Graphing Utility

**1.** In each part, find the coordinates of the eight corners of the box.

(a)

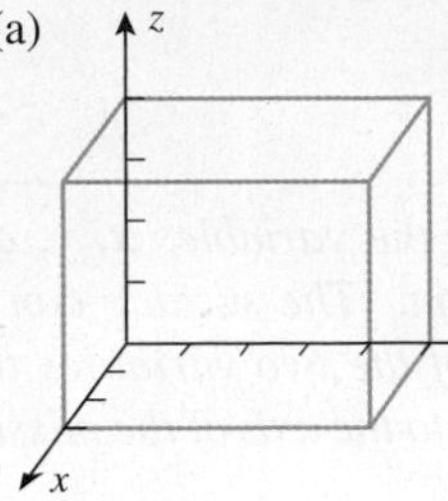


(b)

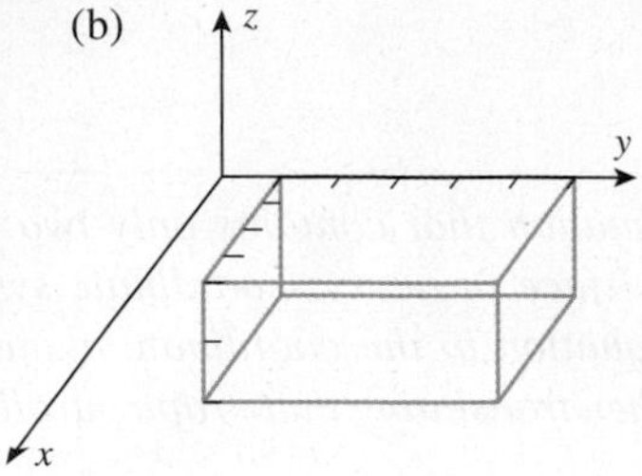


**2.** A cube of side 4 has its geometric center at the origin and its faces parallel to the coordinate planes. Sketch the cube and give the coordinates of the corners.

**FOCUS ON CONCEPTS**

**3.** Suppose that a box has its faces parallel to the coordinate planes and the points $(4, 2, -2)$ and $(-6, 1, 1)$ are endpoints of a diagonal. Sketch the box and give the coordinates of the remaining six corners.

**4.** Suppose that a box has its faces parallel to the coordinate planes and the points $(x_1, y_1, z_1)$ and $(x_2, y_2, z_2)$ are endpoints of a diagonal.
(a) Find the coordinates of the remaining six corners.
(b) Show that the midpoint of the line segment joining $(x_1, y_1, z_1)$ and $(x_2, y_2, z_2)$ is

$$\left(\tfrac{1}{2}(x_1 + x_2), \tfrac{1}{2}(y_1 + y_2), \tfrac{1}{2}(z_1 + z_2)\right)$$

[*Suggestion:* Apply Theorem I.2 in Web Appendix I to three appropriate edges of the box.]

**5.** Interpret the graph of $x = 1$ in the contexts of
(a) a number line (b) 2-space (c) 3-space.

**6.** Consider the points $P(3, 1, 0)$ and $Q(1, 4, 4)$.
(a) Sketch the triangle with vertices $P$, $Q$, and $(1, 4, 0)$. Without computing distances, explain why this triangle is a right triangle, and then apply the Theorem of Pythagoras twice to find the distance from $P$ to $Q$.
(b) Repeat part (a) using the points $P$, $Q$, and $(3, 4, 0)$.
(c) Repeat part (a) using the points $P$, $Q$, and $(1, 1, 4)$.

**7.** (a) Consider a box whose sides have lengths $a$, $b$, and $c$. Use the Theorem of Pythagoras to show that a diagonal of the box has length $d = \sqrt{a^2 + b^2 + c^2}$. [*Hint:* Use the Theorem of Pythagoras to find the length of a diagonal of the base and then again to find the length of a diagonal of the entire box.]
(b) Use the result of part (a) to derive formula (2).

**8.** (a) Make a conjecture about the set of points in 3-space that are equidistant from the origin and the point $(1, 0, 0)$.
(b) Confirm your conjecture in part (a) by using distance formula (2).

**9.** Find the center and radius of the sphere that has $(1, -2, 4)$ and $(3, 4, -12)$ as endpoints of a diameter. [See Exercise 4.]

**10.** Show that $(4, 5, 2)$, $(1, 7, 3)$, and $(2, 4, 5)$ are vertices of an equilateral triangle.

**11.** (a) Show that $(2, 1, 6)$, $(4, 7, 9)$, and $(8, 5, -6)$ are the vertices of a right triangle.
(b) Which vertex is at the $90^\circ$ angle?
(c) Find the area of the triangle.

**12.** Find the distance from the point $(-5, 2, -3)$ to the
(a) $xy$-plane (b) $xz$-plane (c) $yz$-plane
(d) $x$-axis (e) $y$-axis (f) $z$-axis.

**13.** In each part, find the standard equation of the sphere that satisfies the stated conditions.
(a) Center $(7, 1, 1)$; radius $= 4$.
(b) Center $(1, 0, -1)$; diameter $= 8$.
(c) Center $(-1, 3, 2)$ and passing through the origin.
(d) A diameter has endpoints $(-1, 2, 1)$ and $(0, 2, 3)$.

**14.** Find equations of two spheres that are centered at the origin and are tangent to the sphere of radius 1 centered at $(3, -2, 4)$.

**15.** In each part, find an equation of the sphere with center $(2, -1, -3)$ and satisfying the given condition.
(a) Tangent to the $xy$-plane
(b) Tangent to the $xz$-plane
(c) Tangent to the $yz$-plane

**16.** (a) Find an equation of the sphere that is inscribed in the cube that is centered at the point $(-2, 1, 3)$ and has sides of length 1 that are parallel to the coordinate planes.
(b) Find an equation of the sphere that is circumscribed about the cube in part (a).
(c) Find an equation of the sphere that is inscribed in the cube determined by the planes $x = 6$, $x = 2$, $y = 5$, $y = 9$, $z = 0$, and $z = 4$.
(d) Find an equation of the sphere that is circumscribed about the cube in part (c).

**17.** A sphere has center in the first octant and is tangent to each of the three coordinate planes. Show that the center of the sphere is at a point of the form $(r, r, r)$, where $r$ is the radius of the sphere.

**18.** A sphere has center in the first octant and is tangent to each of the three coordinate planes. The distance from the origin to the sphere is $3 - \sqrt{3}$ units. Find an equation for the sphere.

**19–22 True–False** Determine whether the statement is true or false. Explain your answer. ■

**19.** By definition, a "cylindrical surface" is a right circular cylinder whose axis is parallel to one of the coordinate axes.

**20.** The graph of $x^2 + y^2 = 1$ in 3-space is a circle of radius 1 centered at the origin.

**21.** If a point belongs to both the $xy$-plane and the $xz$-plane, then the point lies on the $x$-axis.

**22.** A sphere with center $P(x_0, y_0, z_0)$ and radius $r$ consists of all points $(x, y, z)$ that satisfy the inequality

$$(x - x_0)^2 + (y - y_0)^2 + (z - z_0)^2 \leq r^2$$

**23–28** Describe the surface whose equation is given. ■

**23.** $x^2 + y^2 + z^2 + 10x + 4y + 2z - 19 = 0$

**24.** $x^2 + y^2 + z^2 - y = 0$

**25.** $2x^2 + 2y^2 + 2z^2 - 2x - 3y + 5z - 2 = 0$

**26.** $x^2 + y^2 + z^2 + 2x - 2y + 2z + 3 = 0$

**27.** $x^2 + y^2 + z^2 - 3x + 4y - 8z + 25 = 0$

**28.** $x^2 + y^2 + z^2 - 2x - 6y - 8z + 1 = 0$

**29.** In each part, sketch the portion of the surface that lies in the first octant.
(a) $y = x$ (b) $y = z$ (c) $x = z$

**30.** In each part, sketch the graph of the equation in 3-space.
(a) $x = 1$ (b) $y = 1$ (c) $z = 1$

**31.** In each part, sketch the graph of the equation in 3-space.
(a) $x^2 + y^2 = 25$ (b) $y^2 + z^2 = 25$ (c) $x^2 + z^2 = 25$

**32.** In each part, sketch the graph of the equation in 3-space.
(a) $x = y^2$ (b) $z = x^2$ (c) $y = z^2$

**33.** In each part, write an equation for the surface.
(a) The plane that contains the $x$-axis and the point $(0, 1, 2)$.
(b) The plane that contains the $y$-axis and the point $(1, 0, 2)$.
(c) The right circular cylinder that has radius 1 and is centered on the line parallel to the $z$-axis that passes through the point $(1, 1, 0)$.
(d) The right circular cylinder that has radius 1 and is centered on the line parallel to the $y$-axis that passes through the point $(1, 0, 1)$.

**34.** Find equations for the following right circular cylinders. Each cylinder has radius $a$ and is tangent to two coordinate planes.

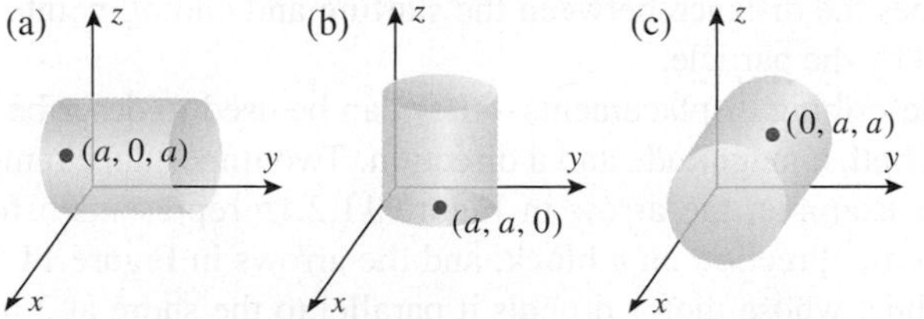


▲ **Figure Ex-34**

**35–44** Sketch the surface in 3-space. ■

**35.** $y = \sin x$

**36.** $y = e^x$

**37.** $z = 1 - y^2$

**38.** $z = \cos x$

**39.** $2x + z = 3$

**40.** $2x + 3y = 6$

**41.** $4x^2 + 9z^2 = 36$

**42.** $z = \sqrt{3 - x}$

**43.** $y^2 - 4z^2 = 4$

**44.** $yz = 1$

**45.** Generate the curve $y = x^3/(1 + x^2)$ in the $xy$-plane using a graphing utility, and then use the graph to help sketch the surface $z = y^3/(1 + y^2)$ in 3-space.

**46.** Use a graphing utility to generate the curve $y = x/(1 + x^4)$ in the $xy$-plane, and then use the graph to help sketch the surface $z = y/(1 + y^4)$ in 3-space.

**47.** If a bug walks on the sphere

$$x^2 + y^2 + z^2 + 2x - 2y - 4z - 3 = 0$$

how close and how far can it get from the origin?

**48.** Describe the set of all points in 3-space whose coordinates satisfy the inequality $x^2 + y^2 + z^2 - 2x + 8z \leq 8$.

**49.** Describe the set of all points in 3-space whose coordinates satisfy the inequality $y^2 + z^2 + 6y - 4z > 3$.

**50.** The distance between a point $P(x, y, z)$ and the point $A(1, -2, 0)$ is twice the distance between $P$ and the point $B(0, 1, 1)$. Show that the set of all such points is a sphere, and find the center and radius of the sphere.

**51.** As shown in the accompanying figure, a bowling ball of radius $R$ is placed inside a box just large enough to hold it, and it is secured for shipping by packing a Styrofoam sphere into each corner of the box. Find the radius of the largest Styrofoam sphere that can be used. [*Hint:* Take the origin of a Cartesian coordinate system at a corner of the box with the coordinate axes along the edges.]

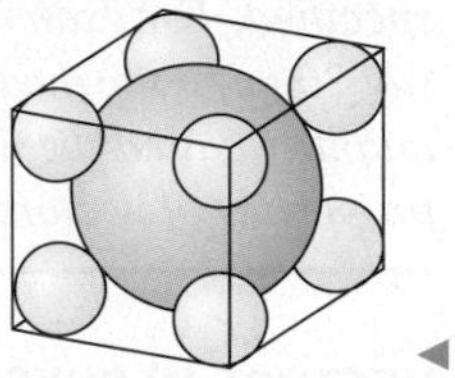

◀ **Figure Ex-51**

**52.** Consider the equation

$$x^2 + y^2 + z^2 + Gx + Hy + Iz + J = 0$$

and let $K = G^2 + H^2 + I^2 - 4J$.
(a) Prove that the equation represents a sphere if $K > 0$, a point if $K = 0$, and has no graph if $K < 0$.
(b) In the case where $K > 0$, find the center and radius of the sphere.

**53.** (a) The accompanying figure shows a surface of revolution that is generated by revolving the curve $y = f(x)$ in the $xy$-plane about the $x$-axis. Show that the equation of this surface is $y^2 + z^2 = [f(x)]^2$. [*Hint:* Each point on the curve traces a circle as it revolves about the $x$-axis.]
(b) Find an equation of the surface of revolution that is generated by revolving the curve $y = e^x$ in the $xy$-plane about the $x$-axis.
(c) Show that the ellipsoid $3x^2 + 4y^2 + 4z^2 = 16$ is a surface of revolution about the $x$-axis by finding a curve $y = f(x)$ in the $xy$-plane that generates it.

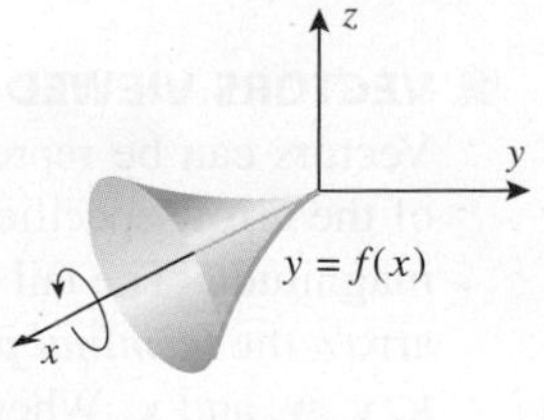


◀ **Figure Ex-53**

**54.** In each part, use the idea in Exercise 53(a) to derive a formula for the stated surface of revolution.
(a) The surface generated by revolving the curve $x = f(y)$ in the $xy$-plane about the $y$-axis.
(b) The surface generated by revolving the curve $y = f(z)$ in the $yz$-plane about the $z$-axis.
(c) The surface generated by revolving the curve $z = f(x)$ in the $xz$-plane about the $x$-axis.

**55.** Show that for all values of $\theta$ and $\phi$, the point

$$(a \sin\phi \cos\theta, a \sin\phi \sin\theta, a \cos\phi)$$

lies on the sphere $x^2 + y^2 + z^2 = a^2$.

**56. Writing** Explain how you might determine whether a set of points in 3-space is the graph of an equation involving at most two of the variables $x$, $y$, and $z$.

**57. Writing** Discuss what happens geometrically when equations in $x$, $y$, and $z$ are replaced by inequalities. For example, compare the graph of $x^2 + y^2 + z^2 = 1$ with the set of points that satisfy the inequality $x^2 + y^2 + z^2 \leq 1$.

✓ **QUICK CHECK ANSWERS 11.1** 1. $\sqrt{38}$ 2. sphere; 4; $(3, 2, -1)$ 3. $\sqrt{38} - 6$ 4. (a) $(0, 0, -3)$; 5 (b) 4; $-4$ (c) 2; $-8$

## 11.2 VECTORS

*Many physical quantities such as area, length, mass, and temperature are completely described once the magnitude of the quantity is given. Other physical quantities, called "vectors," are not completely determined until both a magnitude and a direction are specified. For example, winds are usually described by giving their speed and direction, say 20 mi/h northeast. The wind speed and wind direction together form a vector quantity called the wind velocity. In this section we will develop the basic mathematical properties of vectors.*

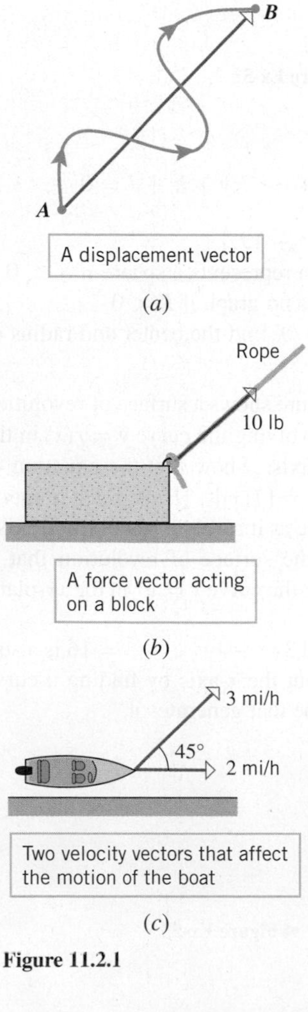


▲ **Figure 11.2.1**

### VECTORS IN PHYSICS AND ENGINEERING

If a particle moves along a number line, then a change in its position can be described by a signed real number. For example, a displacement of $-3$ describes a position change of 3 units in the negative direction along the line. However, for a particle that moves in two dimensions or in three dimensions, a signed real number is no longer sufficient to specify displacement—other methods are required. One method is to use an arrow, called a ***vector***, drawn from the starting point to the ending point; this is called the ***displacement vector*** from the first point to the second. For example, Figure 11.2.1*a* shows the displacement vector of a particle that moves from point $A$ to point $B$ along a circuitous path. Note that the length of the arrow describes the distance between the starting and ending points and not the actual distance traveled by the particle.

Arrows are not limited to describing displacements—they can be used to describe any physical quantity that involves both a magnitude and a direction. Two important examples are forces and velocities. For example, the arrow in Figure 11.2.1*b* represents a force vector of 10 lb acting in a specific direction on a block, and the arrows in Figure 11.2.1*c* show the velocity vector of a boat whose motor propels it parallel to the shore at 2 mi/h and the velocity vector of a 3 mi/h wind acting at an angle of 45° with the shoreline. Intuition suggests that the two velocity vectors will combine to produce some net velocity for the boat at an angle to the shoreline. Thus, our first objective in this section is to define mathematical operations on vectors that can be used to determine the combined effect of vectors.

### VECTORS VIEWED GEOMETRICALLY

Vectors can be represented geometrically by arrows in 2-space or 3-space; the direction of the arrow specifies the direction of the vector, and the length of the arrow describes its magnitude. The tail of the arrow is called the ***initial point*** of the vector, and the tip of the arrow the ***terminal point***. We will denote vectors with lowercase boldface type such as **a**, **k**, **v**, **w**, and **x**. When discussing vectors, we will refer to real numbers as ***scalars***. Scalars

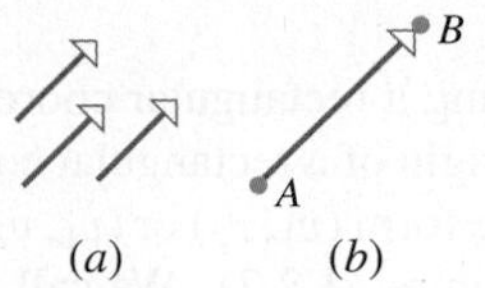


▲ **Figure 11.2.2**

will be denoted by lowercase italic type such as $a$, $k$, $v$, $w$, and $x$. Two vectors, $\mathbf{v}$ and $\mathbf{w}$, are considered to be ***equal*** (also called ***equivalent***) if they have the same length and same direction, in which case we write $\mathbf{v} = \mathbf{w}$. Thus, the three vectors in Figure 11.2.2*a* are equal, even though they are in different positions.

If the initial point of $\mathbf{v}$ is $A$ and the terminal point is $B$, then we write $\mathbf{v} = \overrightarrow{AB}$ when we want to emphasize the initial and terminal points (Figure 11.2.2*b*). If the initial and terminal points of a vector coincide, then the vector has length zero; we call this the ***zero vector*** and denote it by $\mathbf{0}$. The zero vector does not have a specific direction, so we will agree that it can be assigned any convenient direction in a specific problem.

There are various algebraic operations that are performed on vectors, all of whose definitions originated in physics. We begin with vector addition.

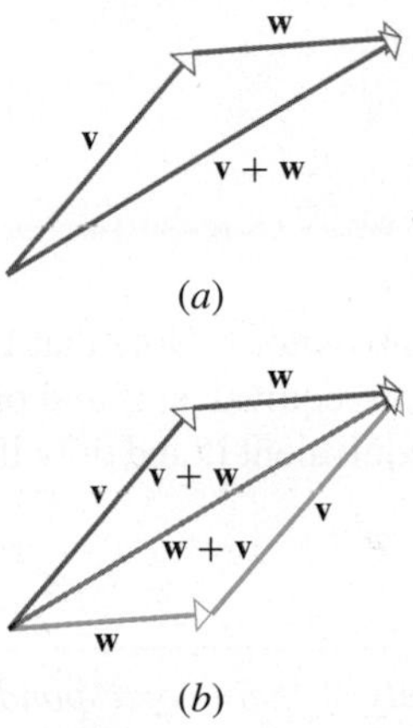


▲ **Figure 11.2.3**

> **11.2.1 DEFINITION** If $\mathbf{v}$ and $\mathbf{w}$ are vectors, then the ***sum*** $\mathbf{v} + \mathbf{w}$ is the vector from the initial point of $\mathbf{v}$ to the terminal point of $\mathbf{w}$ when the vectors are positioned so the initial point of $\mathbf{w}$ is at the terminal point of $\mathbf{v}$ (Figure 11.2.3*a*).

In Figure 11.2.3*b* we have constructed two sums, $\mathbf{v} + \mathbf{w}$ (from purple arrows) and $\mathbf{w} + \mathbf{v}$ (from green arrows). It is evident that

$$\mathbf{v} + \mathbf{w} = \mathbf{w} + \mathbf{v}$$

and that the sum (gray arrow) coincides with the diagonal of the parallelogram determined by $\mathbf{v}$ and $\mathbf{w}$ when these vectors are positioned so they have the same initial point.

Since the initial and terminal points of $\mathbf{0}$ coincide, it follows that

$$\mathbf{0} + \mathbf{v} = \mathbf{v} + \mathbf{0} = \mathbf{v}$$

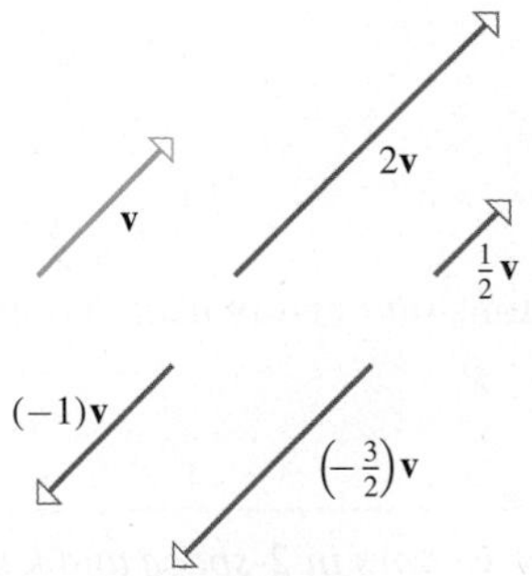


▲ **Figure 11.2.4**

> **11.2.2 DEFINITION** If $\mathbf{v}$ is a nonzero vector and $k$ is a nonzero real number (a scalar), then the ***scalar multiple*** $k\mathbf{v}$ is defined to be the vector whose length is $|k|$ times the length of $\mathbf{v}$ and whose direction is the same as that of $\mathbf{v}$ if $k > 0$ and opposite to that of $\mathbf{v}$ if $k < 0$. We define $k\mathbf{v} = \mathbf{0}$ if $k = 0$ or $\mathbf{v} = \mathbf{0}$.

Figure 11.2.4 shows the geometric relationship between a vector $\mathbf{v}$ and various scalar multiples of it. Observe that if $k$ and $\mathbf{v}$ are nonzero, then the vectors $\mathbf{v}$ and $k\mathbf{v}$ lie on the same line if their initial points coincide and lie on parallel or coincident lines if they do not. Thus, we say that $\mathbf{v}$ and $k\mathbf{v}$ are ***parallel vectors***. Observe also that the vector $(-1)\mathbf{v}$ has the same length as $\mathbf{v}$ but is oppositely directed. We call $(-1)\mathbf{v}$ the ***negative*** of $\mathbf{v}$ and denote it by $-\mathbf{v}$ (Figure 11.2.5). In particular, $-\mathbf{0} = (-1)\mathbf{0} = \mathbf{0}$.

Vector subtraction is defined in terms of addition and scalar multiplication by

$$\mathbf{v} - \mathbf{w} = \mathbf{v} + (-\mathbf{w})$$

The difference $\mathbf{v} - \mathbf{w}$ can be obtained geometrically by first constructing the vector $-\mathbf{w}$ and then adding $\mathbf{v}$ and $-\mathbf{w}$, say by the parallelogram method (Figure 11.2.6*a*). However, if $\mathbf{v}$ and $\mathbf{w}$ are positioned so their initial points coincide, then $\mathbf{v} - \mathbf{w}$ can be formed more directly, as shown in Figure 11.2.6*b*, by drawing the vector from the terminal point of $\mathbf{w}$ (the second term) to the terminal point of $\mathbf{v}$ (the first term). In the special case where $\mathbf{v} = \mathbf{w}$ the terminal points of the vectors coincide, so their difference is $\mathbf{0}$; that is,

$$\mathbf{v} + (-\mathbf{v}) = \mathbf{v} - \mathbf{v} = \mathbf{0}$$

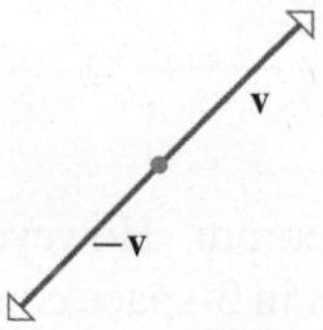


▲ **Figure 11.2.5**

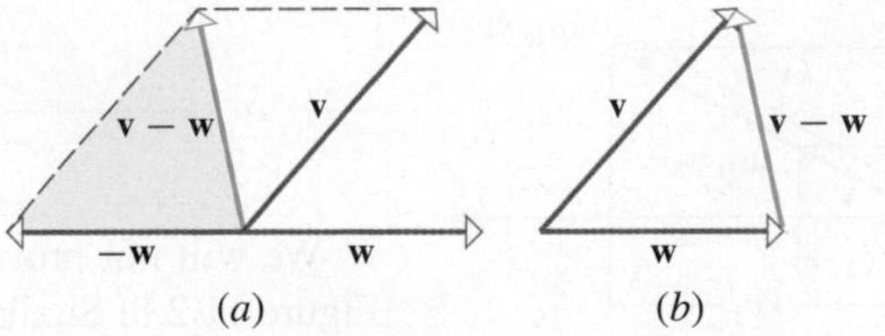


▲ **Figure 11.2.6**

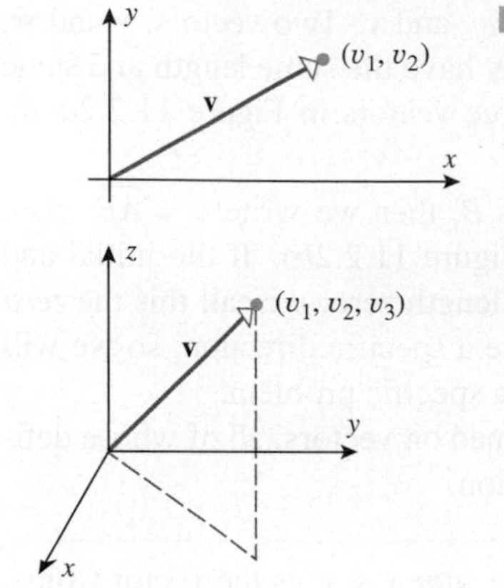


▲ Figure 11.2.7

## VECTORS IN COORDINATE SYSTEMS

Problems involving vectors are often best solved by introducing a rectangular coordinate system. If a vector **v** is positioned with its initial point at the origin of a rectangular coordinate system, then its terminal point will have coordinates of the form $(v_1, v_2)$ or $(v_1, v_2, v_3)$, depending on whether the vector is in 2-space or 3-space (Figure 11.2.7). We call these coordinates the ***components*** of **v**, and we write **v** in *component form* using the ***bracket notation***

$$\mathbf{v} = \langle v_1, v_2 \rangle \quad \text{or} \quad \mathbf{v} = \langle v_1, v_2, v_3 \rangle$$

2-space 3-space

In particular, the zero vectors in 2-space and 3-space are

$$\mathbf{0} = \langle 0, 0 \rangle \quad \text{and} \quad \mathbf{0} = \langle 0, 0, 0 \rangle$$

respectively.

Note the difference in notation between a *point* $(v_1, v_2)$ and a *vector* $\langle v_1, v_2 \rangle$.

Components provide a simple way of identifying equivalent vectors. Note that if two vectors have their initial points at the origin, then the vectors are equivalent if and only if their terminal points coincide. It follows that two vectors are equivalent if and only if they have the same components.

**11.2.3 THEOREM** *Two vectors are equivalent if and only if their corresponding components are equal.*

For example,

$$\langle a, b, c \rangle = \langle 1, -4, 2 \rangle$$

if and only if $a = 1$, $b = -4$, and $c = 2$.

## ARITHMETIC OPERATIONS ON VECTORS

The next theorem shows how to perform arithmetic operations on vectors using components.

**11.2.4 THEOREM** *If* $\mathbf{v} = \langle v_1, v_2 \rangle$ *and* $\mathbf{w} = \langle w_1, w_2 \rangle$ *are vectors in 2-space and k is any scalar, then*

$$\mathbf{v} + \mathbf{w} = \langle v_1 + w_1, v_2 + w_2 \rangle \quad (1)$$
$$\mathbf{v} - \mathbf{w} = \langle v_1 - w_1, v_2 - w_2 \rangle \quad (2)$$
$$k\mathbf{v} = \langle kv_1, kv_2 \rangle \quad (3)$$

*Similarly, if* $\mathbf{v} = \langle v_1, v_2, v_3 \rangle$ *and* $\mathbf{w} = \langle w_1, w_2, w_3 \rangle$ *are vectors in 3-space and k is any scalar, then*

$$\mathbf{v} + \mathbf{w} = \langle v_1 + w_1, v_2 + w_2, v_3 + w_3 \rangle \quad (4)$$
$$\mathbf{v} - \mathbf{w} = \langle v_1 - w_1, v_2 - w_2, v_3 - w_3 \rangle \quad (5)$$
$$k\mathbf{v} = \langle kv_1, kv_2, kv_3 \rangle \quad (6)$$

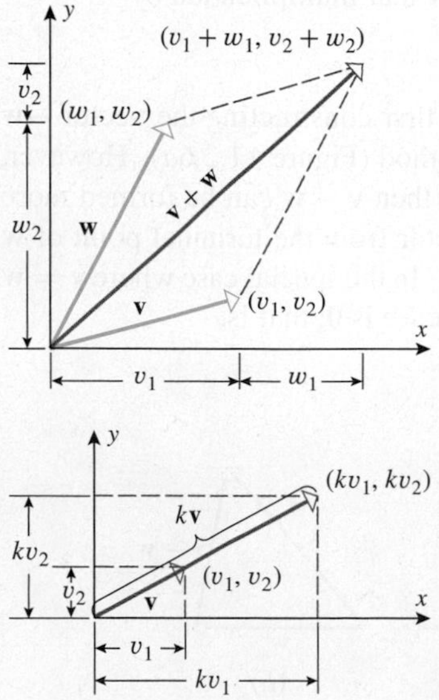


▲ Figure 11.2.8

We will not prove this theorem. However, results (1) and (3) should be evident from Figure 11.2.8. Similar figures in 3-space can be used to motivate (4) and (6). Formulas (2) and (5) can be obtained by writing $\mathbf{v} + \mathbf{w} = \mathbf{v} + (-1)\mathbf{w}$.

▶ **Example 1** If $\mathbf{v} = \langle -2, 0, 1\rangle$ and $\mathbf{w} = \langle 3, 5, -4\rangle$, then

$$\mathbf{v} + \mathbf{w} = \langle -2, 0, 1\rangle + \langle 3, 5, -4\rangle = \langle 1, 5, -3\rangle$$
$$3\mathbf{v} = \langle -6, 0, 3\rangle$$
$$-\mathbf{w} = \langle -3, -5, 4\rangle$$
$$\mathbf{w} - 2\mathbf{v} = \langle 3, 5, -4\rangle - \langle -4, 0, 2\rangle = \langle 7, 5, -6\rangle \blacktriangleleft$$

## VECTORS WITH INITIAL POINT NOT AT THE ORIGIN

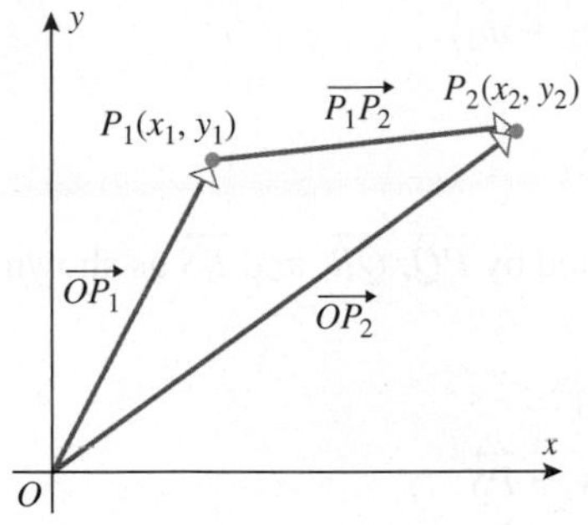

▲ **Figure 11.2.9**

Recall that we defined the components of a vector to be the coordinates of its terminal point when its initial point is at the origin. We will now consider the problem of finding the components of a vector whose initial point is not at the origin. To be specific, suppose that $P_1(x_1, y_1)$ and $P_2(x_2, y_2)$ are points in 2-space and we are interested in finding the components of the vector $\overrightarrow{P_1P_2}$. As illustrated in Figure 11.2.9, we can write this vector as

$$\overrightarrow{P_1P_2} = \overrightarrow{OP_2} - \overrightarrow{OP_1} = \langle x_2, y_2\rangle - \langle x_1, y_1\rangle = \langle x_2 - x_1, y_2 - y_1\rangle$$

Thus, we have shown that the components of the vector $\overrightarrow{P_1P_2}$ can be obtained by subtracting the coordinates of its initial point from the coordinates of its terminal point. Similar computations hold in 3-space, so we have established the following result.

> **11.2.5 THEOREM** *If $\overrightarrow{P_1P_2}$ is a vector in 2-space with initial point $P_1(x_1, y_1)$ and terminal point $P_2(x_2, y_2)$, then*
>
> $$\overrightarrow{P_1P_2} = \langle x_2 - x_1, y_2 - y_1\rangle \tag{7}$$
>
> *Similarly, if $\overrightarrow{P_1P_2}$ is a vector in 3-space with initial point $P_1(x_1, y_1, z_1)$ and terminal point $P_2(x_2, y_2, z_2)$, then*
>
> $$\overrightarrow{P_1P_2} = \langle x_2 - x_1, y_2 - y_1, z_2 - z_1\rangle \tag{8}$$

▶ **Example 2** In 2-space the vector from $P_1(1, 3)$ to $P_2(4, -2)$ is

$$\overrightarrow{P_1P_2} = \langle 4 - 1, -2 - 3\rangle = \langle 3, -5\rangle$$

and in 3-space the vector from $A(0, -2, 5)$ to $B(3, 4, -1)$ is

$$\overrightarrow{AB} = \langle 3 - 0, 4 - (-2), -1 - 5\rangle = \langle 3, 6, -6\rangle \blacktriangleleft$$

## RULES OF VECTOR ARITHMETIC

The following theorem shows that many of the familiar rules of ordinary arithmetic also hold for vector arithmetic.

> It follows from part (*b*) of Theorem 11.2.6 that the expression
>
> $$\mathbf{u} + \mathbf{v} + \mathbf{w}$$
>
> is unambiguous since the same vector results no matter how the terms are grouped.

> **11.2.6 THEOREM** *For any vectors* **u**, **v**, *and* **w** *and any scalars k and l, the following relationships hold:*
>
> (*a*) $\mathbf{u} + \mathbf{v} = \mathbf{v} + \mathbf{u}$
> (*b*) $(\mathbf{u} + \mathbf{v}) + \mathbf{w} = \mathbf{u} + (\mathbf{v} + \mathbf{w})$
> (*c*) $\mathbf{u} + \mathbf{0} = \mathbf{0} + \mathbf{u} = \mathbf{u}$
> (*d*) $\mathbf{u} + (-\mathbf{u}) = \mathbf{0}$
> (*e*) $k(l\mathbf{u}) = (kl)\mathbf{u}$
> (*f*) $k(\mathbf{u} + \mathbf{v}) = k\mathbf{u} + k\mathbf{v}$
> (*g*) $(k + l)\mathbf{u} = k\mathbf{u} + l\mathbf{u}$
> (*h*) $1\mathbf{u} = \mathbf{u}$

The results in this theorem can be proved either algebraically by using components or geometrically by treating the vectors as arrows. We will prove part (*b*) both ways and leave some of the remaining proofs as exercises.

Observe that in Figure 11.2.10 the vectors **u**, **v**, and **w** are positioned "tip to tail" and that

$$\mathbf{u}+\mathbf{v}+\mathbf{w}$$

is the vector from the initial point of **u** (the first term in the sum) to the terminal point of **w** (the last term in the sum). This "tip to tail" method of vector addition also works for four or more vectors (Figure 11.2.11).

**PROOF (*b*) (ALGEBRAIC IN 2-SPACE)** Let $\mathbf{u}=\langle u_1,u_2\rangle$, $\mathbf{v}=\langle v_1,v_2\rangle$, and $\mathbf{w}=\langle w_1,w_2\rangle$. Then

$$\begin{aligned}(\mathbf{u}+\mathbf{v})+\mathbf{w} &= (\langle u_1,u_2\rangle+\langle v_1,v_2\rangle)+\langle w_1,w_2\rangle\\ &= \langle u_1+v_1,u_2+v_2\rangle+\langle w_1,w_2\rangle\\ &= \langle (u_1+v_1)+w_1,(u_2+v_2)+w_2\rangle\\ &= \langle u_1+(v_1+w_1),u_2+(v_2+w_2)\rangle\\ &= \langle u_1,u_2\rangle+\langle v_1+w_1,v_2+w_2\rangle\\ &= \mathbf{u}+(\mathbf{v}+\mathbf{w})\end{aligned}$$

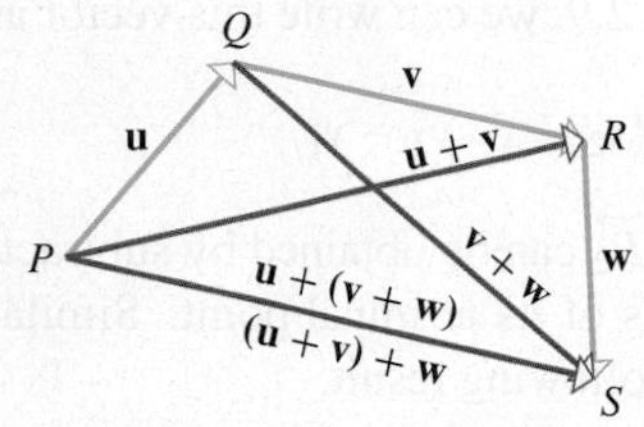

▲ **Figure 11.2.10**

**PROOF (*b*) (GEOMETRIC)** Let **u**, **v**, and **w** be represented by $\overrightarrow{PQ}$, $\overrightarrow{QR}$, and $\overrightarrow{RS}$ as shown in Figure 11.2.10. Then

$$\mathbf{v}+\mathbf{w}=\overrightarrow{QS} \quad\text{and}\quad \mathbf{u}+(\mathbf{v}+\mathbf{w})=\overrightarrow{PS}$$
$$\mathbf{u}+\mathbf{v}=\overrightarrow{PR} \quad\text{and}\quad (\mathbf{u}+\mathbf{v})+\mathbf{w}=\overrightarrow{PS}$$

Therefore,

$$(\mathbf{u}+\mathbf{v})+\mathbf{w}=\mathbf{u}+(\mathbf{v}+\mathbf{w}) \ \blacksquare$$

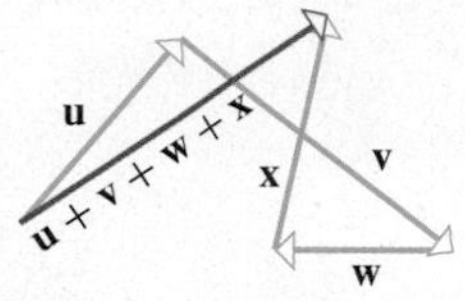

▲ **Figure 11.2.11**

## NORM OF A VECTOR

The distance between the initial and terminal points of a vector **v** is called the ***length***, the ***norm***, or the ***magnitude*** of **v** and is denoted by $\|\mathbf{v}\|$. This distance does not change if the vector is translated, so for purposes of calculating the norm we can assume that the vector is positioned with its initial point at the origin (Figure 11.2.12). This makes it evident that the norm of a vector $\mathbf{v}=\langle v_1,v_2\rangle$ in 2-space is given by

$$\|\mathbf{v}\|=\sqrt{v_1^2+v_2^2} \tag{9}$$

and the norm of a vector $\mathbf{v}=\langle v_1,v_2,v_3\rangle$ in 3-space is given by

$$\|\mathbf{v}\|=\sqrt{v_1^2+v_2^2+v_3^2} \tag{10}$$

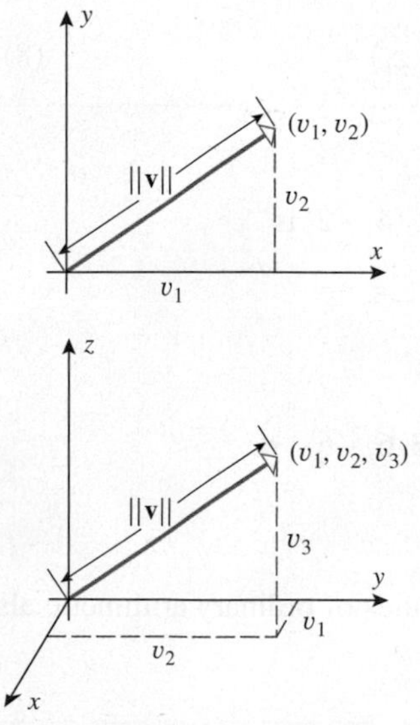

▲ **Figure 11.2.12**

▶ **Example 3** Find the norms of $\mathbf{v}=\langle -2,3\rangle$, $10\mathbf{v}=\langle -20,30\rangle$, and $\mathbf{w}=\langle 2,3,6\rangle$.

***Solution.*** From (9) and (10)

$$\begin{aligned}\|\mathbf{v}\| &= \sqrt{(-2)^2+3^2}=\sqrt{13}\\ \|10\mathbf{v}\| &= \sqrt{(-20)^2+30^2}=\sqrt{1300}=10\sqrt{13}\\ \|\mathbf{w}\| &= \sqrt{2^2+3^2+6^2}=\sqrt{49}=7 \ \blacktriangleleft\end{aligned}$$

Note that $\|10\mathbf{v}\|=10\|\mathbf{v}\|$ in Example 3. This is consistent with Definition 11.2.2, which stipulated that for any vector **v** and scalar $k$, the length of $k\mathbf{v}$ must be $|k|$ times the length of **v**; that is,

$$\|k\mathbf{v}\|=|k|\|\mathbf{v}\| \tag{11}$$

Thus, for example,

$$\begin{aligned}\|3\mathbf{v}\| &= |3|\|\mathbf{v}\|=3\|\mathbf{v}\|\\ \|-2\mathbf{v}\| &= |-2|\|\mathbf{v}\|=2\|\mathbf{v}\|\\ \|-1\mathbf{v}\| &= |-1|\|\mathbf{v}\|=\|\mathbf{v}\|\end{aligned}$$

This applies to vectors in 2-space and 3-space.

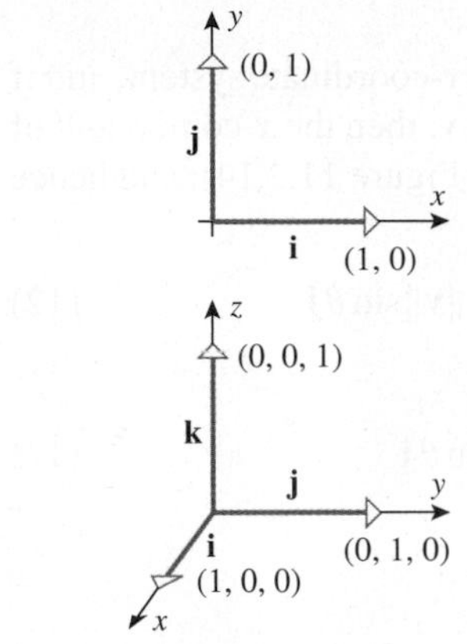


▲ Figure 11.2.13

## UNIT VECTORS

A vector of length 1 is called a ***unit vector***. In an $xy$-coordinate system the unit vectors along the $x$- and $y$-axes are denoted by **i** and **j**, respectively; and in an $xyz$-coordinate system the unit vectors along the $x$-, $y$-, and $z$-axes are denoted by **i**, **j**, and **k**, respectively (Figure 11.2.13). Thus,

$$\mathbf{i} = \langle 1, 0\rangle, \quad \mathbf{j} = \langle 0, 1\rangle \qquad \text{In 2-space}$$

$$\mathbf{i} = \langle 1, 0, 0\rangle, \quad \mathbf{j} = \langle 0, 1, 0\rangle, \quad \mathbf{k} = \langle 0, 0, 1\rangle \qquad \text{In 3-space}$$

Every vector in 2-space is expressible uniquely in terms of **i** and **j**, and every vector in 3-space is expressible uniquely in terms of **i**, **j**, and **k** as follows:

$$\mathbf{v} = \langle v_1, v_2\rangle = \langle v_1, 0\rangle + \langle 0, v_2\rangle = v_1\langle 1, 0\rangle + v_2\langle 0, 1\rangle = v_1\mathbf{i} + v_2\mathbf{j}$$

$$\mathbf{v} = \langle v_1, v_2, v_3\rangle = v_1\langle 1, 0, 0\rangle + v_2\langle 0, 1, 0\rangle + v_3\langle 0, 0, 1\rangle = v_1\mathbf{i} + v_2\mathbf{j} + v_3\mathbf{k}$$

▶ **Example 4** The following table provides some examples of vector notation in 2-space and 3-space.

| 2-SPACE | 3-SPACE |
|---|---|
| $\langle 2, 3\rangle = 2\mathbf{i} + 3\mathbf{j}$ | $\langle 2, -3, 4\rangle = 2\mathbf{i} - 3\mathbf{j} + 4\mathbf{k}$ |
| $\langle -4, 0\rangle = -4\mathbf{i} + 0\mathbf{j} = -4\mathbf{i}$ | $\langle 0, 3, 0\rangle = 3\mathbf{j}$ |
| $\langle 0, 0\rangle = 0\mathbf{i} + 0\mathbf{j} = \mathbf{0}$ | $\langle 0, 0, 0\rangle = 0\mathbf{i} + 0\mathbf{j} + 0\mathbf{k} = \mathbf{0}$ |
| $(3\mathbf{i} + 2\mathbf{j}) + (4\mathbf{i} + \mathbf{j}) = 7\mathbf{i} + 3\mathbf{j}$ | $(3\mathbf{i} + 2\mathbf{j} - \mathbf{k}) - (4\mathbf{i} - \mathbf{j} + 2\mathbf{k}) = -\mathbf{i} + 3\mathbf{j} - 3\mathbf{k}$ |
| $5(6\mathbf{i} - 2\mathbf{j}) = 30\mathbf{i} - 10\mathbf{j}$ | $2(\mathbf{i} + \mathbf{j} - \mathbf{k}) + 4(\mathbf{i} - \mathbf{j}) = 6\mathbf{i} - 2\mathbf{j} - 2\mathbf{k}$ |
| $\lVert 2\mathbf{i} - 3\mathbf{j}\rVert = \sqrt{2^2 + (-3)^2} = \sqrt{13}$ | $\lVert \mathbf{i} + 2\mathbf{j} - 3\mathbf{k}\rVert = \sqrt{1^2 + 2^2 + (-3)^2} = \sqrt{14}$ |
| $\lVert v_1\mathbf{i} + v_2\mathbf{j}\rVert = \sqrt{v_1^2 + v_2^2}$ | $\lVert\langle v_1, v_2, v_3\rangle\rVert = \sqrt{v_1^2 + v_2^2 + v_3^2}$ |

◀

The two notations for vectors illustrated in Example 4 are completely interchangeable, the choice being a matter of convenience or personal preference.

## NORMALIZING A VECTOR

A common problem in applications is to find a unit vector **u** that has the same direction as some given nonzero vector **v**. This can be done by multiplying **v** by the reciprocal of its length; that is,

$$\mathbf{u} = \frac{1}{\lVert\mathbf{v}\rVert}\mathbf{v} = \frac{\mathbf{v}}{\lVert\mathbf{v}\rVert}$$

is a unit vector with the same direction as **v**—the direction is the same because $k = 1/\lVert\mathbf{v}\rVert$ is a positive scalar, and the length is 1 because

$$\lVert\mathbf{u}\rVert = \lVert k\mathbf{v}\rVert = |k|\lVert\mathbf{v}\rVert = k\lVert\mathbf{v}\rVert = \frac{1}{\lVert\mathbf{v}\rVert}\lVert\mathbf{v}\rVert = 1$$

The process of multiplying a vector **v** by the reciprocal of its length to obtain a unit vector with the same direction is called ***normalizing*** **v**.

**TECHNOLOGY MASTERY**

Many calculating utilities can perform vector operations, and some have built-in norm and normalization operations. If your calculator has these capabilities, use it to check the computations in Examples 1, 3, and 5.

▶ **Example 5** Find the unit vector that has the same direction as $\mathbf{v} = 2\mathbf{i} + 2\mathbf{j} - \mathbf{k}$.

***Solution.*** The vector **v** has length

$$\lVert\mathbf{v}\rVert = \sqrt{2^2 + 2^2 + (-1)^2} = 3$$

so the unit vector **u** in the same direction as **v** is

$$\mathbf{u} = \tfrac{1}{3}\mathbf{v} = \tfrac{2}{3}\mathbf{i} + \tfrac{2}{3}\mathbf{j} - \tfrac{1}{3}\mathbf{k} \quad ◀$$

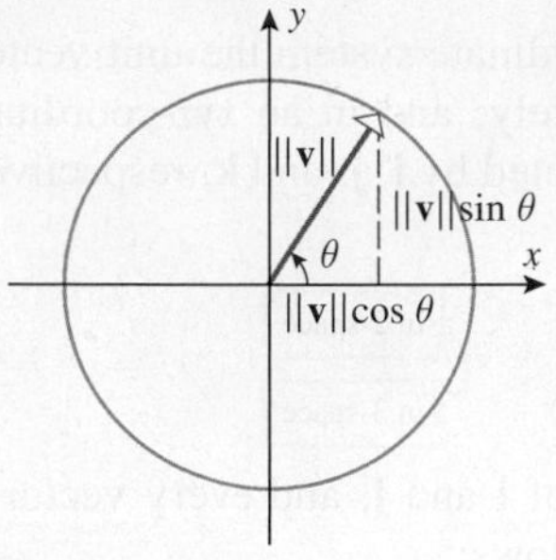


▲ Figure 11.2.14

## VECTORS DETERMINED BY LENGTH AND ANGLE

If $\mathbf{v}$ is a nonzero vector with its initial point at the origin of an $xy$-coordinate system, and if $\theta$ is the angle from the positive $x$-axis to the radial line through $\mathbf{v}$, then the $x$-component of $\mathbf{v}$ can be written as $\|\mathbf{v}\|\cos\theta$ and the $y$-component as $\|\mathbf{v}\|\sin\theta$ (Figure 11.2.14); and hence $\mathbf{v}$ can be expressed in trigonometric form as

$$\mathbf{v} = \|\mathbf{v}\|\langle\cos\theta, \sin\theta\rangle \quad \text{or} \quad \mathbf{v} = \|\mathbf{v}\|\cos\theta\mathbf{i} + \|\mathbf{v}\|\sin\theta\mathbf{j} \tag{12}$$

In the special case of a unit vector $\mathbf{u}$ this simplifies to

$$\mathbf{u} = \langle\cos\theta, \sin\theta\rangle \quad \text{or} \quad \mathbf{u} = \cos\theta\mathbf{i} + \sin\theta\mathbf{j} \tag{13}$$

### ▶ Example 6

(a) Find the vector of length 2 that makes an angle of $\pi/4$ with the positive $x$-axis.

(b) Find the angle that the vector $\mathbf{v} = -\sqrt{3}\mathbf{i} + \mathbf{j}$ makes with the positive $x$-axis.

***Solution (a).*** From (12)

$$\mathbf{v} = 2\cos\frac{\pi}{4}\mathbf{i} + 2\sin\frac{\pi}{4}\mathbf{j} = \sqrt{2}\mathbf{i} + \sqrt{2}\mathbf{j}$$

***Solution (b).*** We will normalize $\mathbf{v}$, then use (13) to find $\sin\theta$ and $\cos\theta$, and then use these values to find $\theta$. Normalizing $\mathbf{v}$ yields

$$\frac{\mathbf{v}}{\|\mathbf{v}\|} = \frac{-\sqrt{3}\mathbf{i} + \mathbf{j}}{\sqrt{(-\sqrt{3})^2 + 1^2}} = -\frac{\sqrt{3}}{2}\mathbf{i} + \frac{1}{2}\mathbf{j}$$

Thus, $\cos\theta = -\sqrt{3}/2$ and $\sin\theta = 1/2$, from which we conclude that $\theta = 5\pi/6$. ◀

## VECTORS DETERMINED BY LENGTH AND A VECTOR IN THE SAME DIRECTION

It is a common problem in many applications that a direction in 2-space or 3-space is determined by some known unit vector $\mathbf{u}$, and it is of interest to find the components of a vector $\mathbf{v}$ that has the same direction as $\mathbf{u}$ and some specified length $\|\mathbf{v}\|$. This can be done by expressing $\mathbf{v}$ as

$$\mathbf{v} = \|\mathbf{v}\|\mathbf{u}$$

v is equal to its length times a unit vector in the same direction.

and then reading off the components of $\|\mathbf{v}\|\mathbf{u}$.

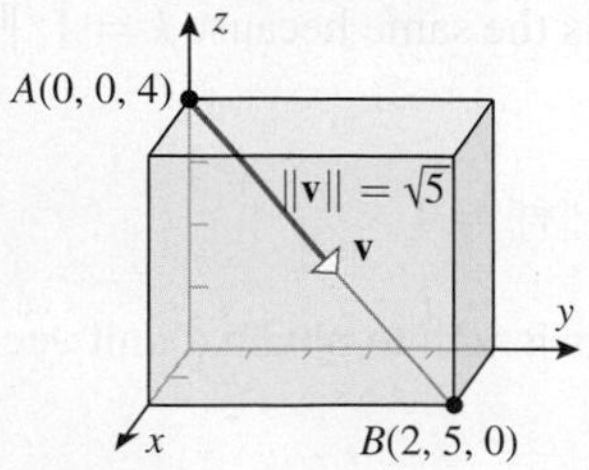


▲ Figure 11.2.15

### ▶ Example 7

Figure 11.2.15 shows a vector $\mathbf{v}$ of length $\sqrt{5}$ that extends along the line through $A$ and $B$. Find the components of $\mathbf{v}$.

***Solution.*** First we will find the components of the vector $\overrightarrow{AB}$, then we will normalize this vector to obtain a unit vector in the direction of $\mathbf{v}$, and then we will multiply this unit vector by $\|\mathbf{v}\|$ to obtain the vector $\mathbf{v}$. The computations are as follows:

$$\overrightarrow{AB} = \langle 2, 5, 0\rangle - \langle 0, 0, 4\rangle = \langle 2, 5, -4\rangle$$

$$\|\overrightarrow{AB}\| = \sqrt{2^2 + 5^2 + (-4)^2} = \sqrt{45} = 3\sqrt{5}$$

$$\frac{\overrightarrow{AB}}{\|\overrightarrow{AB}\|} = \left\langle \frac{2}{3\sqrt{5}}, \frac{5}{3\sqrt{5}}, -\frac{4}{3\sqrt{5}} \right\rangle$$

$$\mathbf{v} = \|\mathbf{v}\|\left(\frac{\overrightarrow{AB}}{\|\overrightarrow{AB}\|}\right) = \sqrt{5}\left\langle \frac{2}{3\sqrt{5}}, \frac{5}{3\sqrt{5}}, -\frac{4}{3\sqrt{5}} \right\rangle = \left\langle \frac{2}{3}, \frac{5}{3}, -\frac{4}{3} \right\rangle$$ ◀

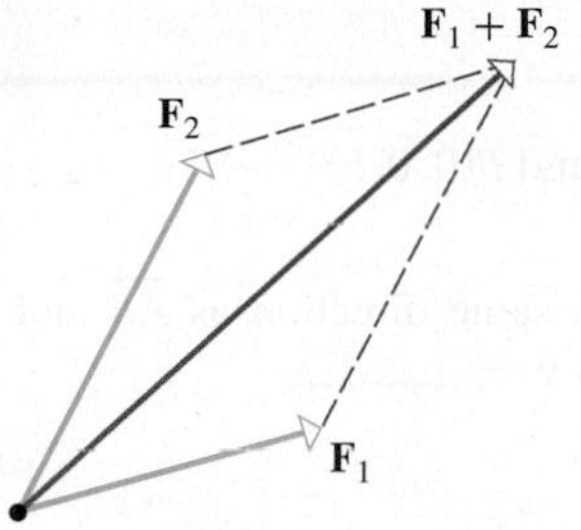


The single force $\mathbf{F}_1 + \mathbf{F}_2$ has the same effect as the two forces $\mathbf{F}_1$ and $\mathbf{F}_2$.

▲ **Figure 11.2.16**

## RESULTANT OF TWO CONCURRENT FORCES

The effect that a force has on an object depends on the magnitude and direction of the force and the point at which it is applied. Thus, forces are regarded to be vector quantities and, indeed, the algebraic operations on vectors that we have defined in this section have their origin in the study of forces. For example, it is a fact of physics that if two forces $\mathbf{F}_1$ and $\mathbf{F}_2$ are applied at the same point on an object, then the two forces have the same effect on the object as the single force $\mathbf{F}_1 + \mathbf{F}_2$ applied at the point (Figure 11.2.16). Physicists and engineers call $\mathbf{F}_1 + \mathbf{F}_2$ the ***resultant*** of $\mathbf{F}_1$ and $\mathbf{F}_2$, and they say that the forces $\mathbf{F}_1$ and $\mathbf{F}_2$ are ***concurrent*** to indicate that they are applied at the same point.

In many applications, the magnitudes of two concurrent forces and the angle between them are known, and the problem is to find the magnitude and direction of the resultant. One approach to solving this problem is to use (12) to find the components of the concurrent forces, and then use (1) to find the components of the resultant. The next example illustrates this method.

▶ **Example 8** Suppose that two forces are applied to an eye bracket, as shown in Figure 11.2.17. Find the magnitude of the resultant and the angle $\theta$ that it makes with the positive $x$-axis.

***Solution.*** Note that $\mathbf{F}_1$ makes an angle of $30°$ with the positive $x$-axis and $\mathbf{F}_2$ makes an angle of $30° + 40° = 70°$ with the positive $x$-axis. Since we are given that $\|\mathbf{F}_1\| = 200$ N and $\|\mathbf{F}_2\| = 300$ N, (12) yields

$$\mathbf{F}_1 = 200\langle \cos 30°, \sin 30° \rangle = \langle 100\sqrt{3}, 100 \rangle$$

and

$$\mathbf{F}_2 = 300\langle \cos 70°, \sin 70° \rangle = \langle 300\cos 70°, 300\sin 70° \rangle$$

Therefore, the resultant $\mathbf{F} = \mathbf{F}_1 + \mathbf{F}_2$ has component form

$$\begin{aligned}\mathbf{F} = \mathbf{F}_1 + \mathbf{F}_2 &= \langle 100\sqrt{3} + 300\cos 70°, 100 + 300\sin 70° \rangle \\ &= 100\langle \sqrt{3} + 3\cos 70°, 1 + 3\sin 70° \rangle \approx \langle 275.8, 381.9 \rangle\end{aligned}$$

The magnitude of the resultant is then

$$\|\mathbf{F}\| = 100\sqrt{\left(\sqrt{3} + 3\cos 70°\right)^2 + \left(1 + 3\sin 70°\right)^2} \approx 471 \text{ N}$$

Let $\theta$ denote the angle $\mathbf{F}$ makes with the positive $x$-axis when the initial point of $\mathbf{F}$ is at the origin. Using (12) and equating the $x$-components of $\mathbf{F}$ yield

$$\|\mathbf{F}\|\cos\theta = 100\sqrt{3} + 300\cos 70° \quad \text{or} \quad \cos\theta = \frac{100\sqrt{3} + 300\cos 70°}{\|\mathbf{F}\|}$$

Since the terminal point of $\mathbf{F}$ is in the first quadrant, we have

$$\theta = \cos^{-1}\left(\frac{100\sqrt{3} + 300\cos 70°}{\|\mathbf{F}\|}\right) \approx 54.2°$$

(Figure 11.2.18). ◀

The resultant of three or more concurrent forces can be found by working in pairs. For example, the resultant of three forces can be found by finding the resultant of any two of the forces and then finding the resultant of that resultant with the third force.

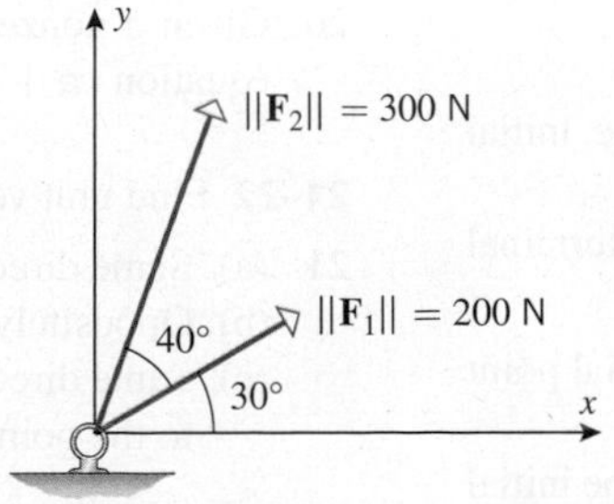


▲ **Figure 11.2.17**

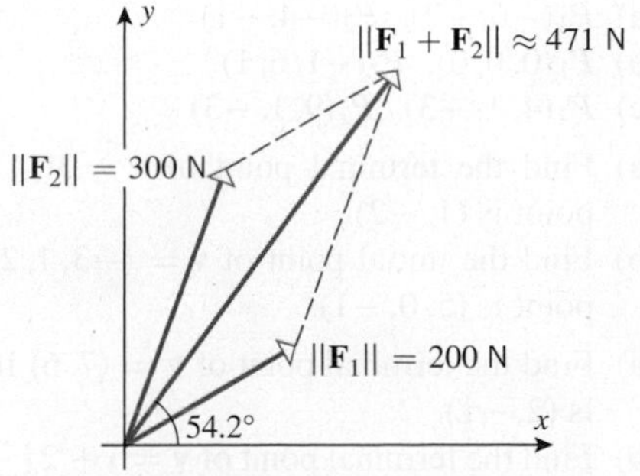


▲ **Figure 11.2.18**

## ✓ QUICK CHECK EXERCISES 11.2 *(See page 690 for answers.)*

1. If $\mathbf{v} = \langle 3, -1, 7\rangle$ and $\mathbf{w} = \langle 4, 10, -5\rangle$, then
   (a) $\|\mathbf{v}\| =$ ________ (b) $\mathbf{v} + \mathbf{w} =$ ________
   (c) $\mathbf{v} - \mathbf{w} =$ ________ (d) $2\mathbf{v} =$ ________.
2. The unit vector in the direction of $\mathbf{v} = \langle 3, -1, 7\rangle$ is ________.
3. The unit vector in 2-space that makes an angle of $\pi/3$ with the positive $x$-axis is ________.
4. Consider points $A(3, 4, 0)$ and $B(0, 0, 5)$.
   (a) $\overrightarrow{AB} =$ ________
   (b) If $\mathbf{v}$ is a vector in the same direction as $\overrightarrow{AB}$ and the length of $\mathbf{v}$ is $\sqrt{2}$, then $\mathbf{v} =$ ________.

## EXERCISE SET 11.2 Graphing Utility

**1–4** Sketch the vectors with their initial points at the origin. ■

1. (a) $\langle 2, 5\rangle$ (b) $\langle -5, -4\rangle$ (c) $\langle 2, 0\rangle$
   (d) $-5\mathbf{i} + 3\mathbf{j}$ (e) $3\mathbf{i} - 2\mathbf{j}$ (f) $-6\mathbf{j}$
2. (a) $\langle -3, 7\rangle$ (b) $\langle 6, -2\rangle$ (c) $\langle 0, -8\rangle$
   (d) $4\mathbf{i} + 2\mathbf{j}$ (e) $-2\mathbf{i} - \mathbf{j}$ (f) $4\mathbf{i}$
3. (a) $\langle 1, -2, 2\rangle$ (b) $\langle 2, 2, -1\rangle$
   (c) $-\mathbf{i} + 2\mathbf{j} + 3\mathbf{k}$ (d) $2\mathbf{i} + 3\mathbf{j} - \mathbf{k}$
4. (a) $\langle -1, 3, 2\rangle$ (b) $\langle 3, 4, 2\rangle$
   (c) $2\mathbf{j} - \mathbf{k}$ (d) $\mathbf{i} - \mathbf{j} + 2\mathbf{k}$

**5–6** Find the components of the vector, and sketch an equivalent vector with its initial point at the origin. ■

5. (a)
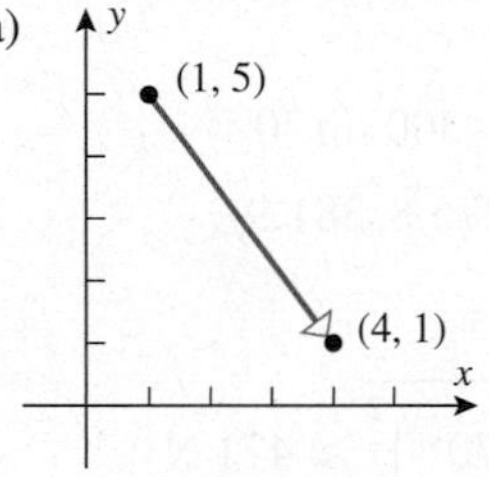

(b)
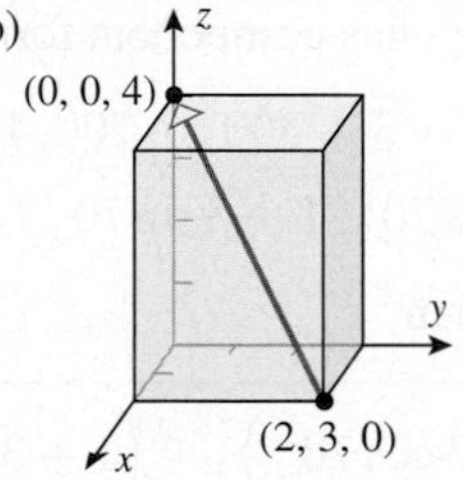


6. (a)
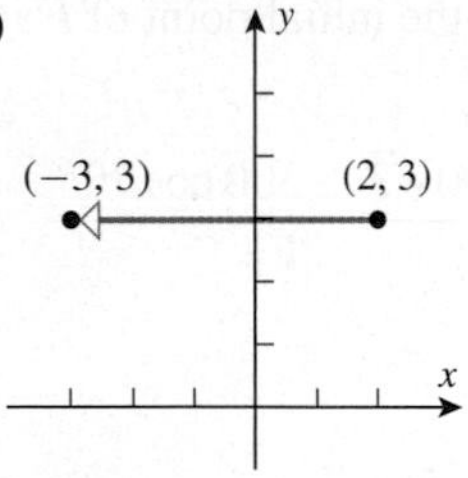

(b)
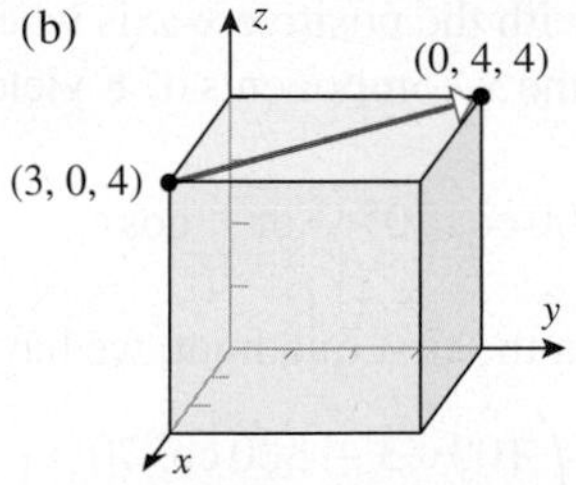


**7–8** Find the components of the vector $\overrightarrow{P_1P_2}$. ■

7. (a) $P_1(3, 5)$, $P_2(2, 8)$ (b) $P_1(7, -2)$, $P_2(0, 0)$
   (c) $P_1(5, -2, 1)$, $P_2(2, 4, 2)$
8. (a) $P_1(-6, -2)$, $P_2(-4, -1)$
   (b) $P_1(0, 0, 0)$, $P_2(-1, 6, 1)$
   (c) $P_1(4, 1, -3)$, $P_2(9, 1, -3)$
9. (a) Find the terminal point of $\mathbf{v} = 3\mathbf{i} - 2\mathbf{j}$ if the initial point is $(1, -2)$.
   (b) Find the initial point of $\mathbf{v} = \langle -3, 1, 2\rangle$ if the terminal point is $(5, 0, -1)$.
10. (a) Find the terminal point of $\mathbf{v} = \langle 7, 6\rangle$ if the initial point is $(2, -1)$.
    (b) Find the terminal point of $\mathbf{v} = \mathbf{i} + 2\mathbf{j} - 3\mathbf{k}$ if the initial point is $(-2, 1, 4)$.

**11–12** Perform the stated operations on the given vectors $\mathbf{u}$, $\mathbf{v}$, and $\mathbf{w}$. ■

11. $\mathbf{u} = 3\mathbf{i} - \mathbf{k}$, $\mathbf{v} = \mathbf{i} - \mathbf{j} + 2\mathbf{k}$, $\mathbf{w} = 3\mathbf{j}$
    (a) $\mathbf{w} - \mathbf{v}$ (b) $6\mathbf{u} + 4\mathbf{w}$
    (c) $-\mathbf{v} - 2\mathbf{w}$ (d) $4(3\mathbf{u} + \mathbf{v})$
    (e) $-8(\mathbf{v} + \mathbf{w}) + 2\mathbf{u}$ (f) $3\mathbf{w} - (\mathbf{v} - \mathbf{w})$
12. $\mathbf{u} = \langle 2, -1, 3\rangle$, $\mathbf{v} = \langle 4, 0, -2\rangle$, $\mathbf{w} = \langle 1, 1, 3\rangle$
    (a) $\mathbf{u} - \mathbf{w}$ (b) $7\mathbf{v} + 3\mathbf{w}$ (c) $-\mathbf{w} + \mathbf{v}$
    (d) $3(\mathbf{u} - 7\mathbf{v})$ (e) $-3\mathbf{v} - 8\mathbf{w}$ (f) $2\mathbf{v} - (\mathbf{u} + \mathbf{w})$

**13–14** Find the norm of $\mathbf{v}$. ■

13. (a) $\mathbf{v} = \langle 1, -1\rangle$ (b) $\mathbf{v} = -\mathbf{i} + 7\mathbf{j}$
    (c) $\mathbf{v} = \langle -1, 2, 4\rangle$ (d) $\mathbf{v} = -3\mathbf{i} + 2\mathbf{j} + \mathbf{k}$
14. (a) $\mathbf{v} = \langle 3, 4\rangle$ (b) $\mathbf{v} = \sqrt{2}\mathbf{i} - \sqrt{7}\mathbf{j}$
    (c) $\mathbf{v} = \langle 0, -3, 0\rangle$ (d) $\mathbf{v} = \mathbf{i} + \mathbf{j} + \mathbf{k}$
15. Let $\mathbf{u} = \mathbf{i} - 3\mathbf{j} + 2\mathbf{k}$, $\mathbf{v} = \mathbf{i} + \mathbf{j}$, and $\mathbf{w} = 2\mathbf{i} + 2\mathbf{j} - 4\mathbf{k}$. Find
    (a) $\|\mathbf{u} + \mathbf{v}\|$ (b) $\|\mathbf{u}\| + \|\mathbf{v}\|$
    (c) $\|-2\mathbf{u}\| + 2\|\mathbf{v}\|$ (d) $\|3\mathbf{u} - 5\mathbf{v} + \mathbf{w}\|$
    (e) $\dfrac{1}{\|\mathbf{w}\|}\mathbf{w}$ (f) $\left\|\dfrac{1}{\|\mathbf{w}\|}\mathbf{w}\right\|$.
16. Is it possible to have $\|\mathbf{u} - \mathbf{v}\| = \|\mathbf{u} + \mathbf{v}\|$ if $\mathbf{u}$ and $\mathbf{v}$ are nonzero vectors? Justify your conclusion geometrically.

**17–20 True–False** Determine whether the statement is true or false. Explain your answer. ■

17. The norm of the sum of two vectors is equal to the sum of the norms of the two vectors.
18. If two distinct vectors $\mathbf{v}$ and $\mathbf{w}$ are drawn with the same initial point, then a vector drawn between the terminal points of $\mathbf{v}$ and $\mathbf{w}$ will be either $\mathbf{v} - \mathbf{w}$ or $\mathbf{w} - \mathbf{v}$.
19. There are exactly two unit vectors that are parallel to a given nonzero vector.
20. Given a nonzero scalar $c$ and vectors $\mathbf{b}$ and $\mathbf{d}$, the vector equation $c\mathbf{a} + \mathbf{b} = \mathbf{d}$ has a unique solution $\mathbf{a}$.

**21–22** Find unit vectors that satisfy the stated conditions. ■

21. (a) Same direction as $-\mathbf{i} + 4\mathbf{j}$.
    (b) Oppositely directed to $6\mathbf{i} - 4\mathbf{j} + 2\mathbf{k}$.
    (c) Same direction as the vector from the point $A(-1, 0, 2)$ to the point $B(3, 1, 1)$.

**22.** (a) Oppositely directed to $3\mathbf{i} - 4\mathbf{j}$.
(b) Same direction as $2\mathbf{i} - \mathbf{j} - 2\mathbf{k}$.
(c) Same direction as the vector from the point $A(-3, 2)$ to the point $B(1, -1)$.

**23–24** Find the vectors that satisfy the stated conditions. ■

**23.** (a) Oppositely directed to $\mathbf{v} = \langle 3, -4\rangle$ and half the length of $\mathbf{v}$.
(b) Length $\sqrt{17}$ and same direction as $\mathbf{v} = \langle 7, 0, -6\rangle$.

**24.** (a) Same direction as $\mathbf{v} = -2\mathbf{i} + 3\mathbf{j}$ and three times the length of $\mathbf{v}$.
(b) Length 2 and oppositely directed to $\mathbf{v} = -3\mathbf{i} + 4\mathbf{j} + \mathbf{k}$.

**25.** In each part, find the component form of the vector $\mathbf{v}$ in 2-space that has the stated length and makes the stated angle $\theta$ with the positive $x$-axis.
(a) $\|\mathbf{v}\| = 3;\ \theta = \pi/4$ (b) $\|\mathbf{v}\| = 2;\ \theta = 90^\circ$
(c) $\|\mathbf{v}\| = 5;\ \theta = 120^\circ$ (d) $\|\mathbf{v}\| = 1;\ \theta = \pi$

**26.** Find the component forms of $\mathbf{v} + \mathbf{w}$ and $\mathbf{v} - \mathbf{w}$ in 2-space, given that $\|\mathbf{v}\| = 1$, $\|\mathbf{w}\| = 1$, $\mathbf{v}$ makes an angle of $\pi/6$ with the positive $x$-axis, and $\mathbf{w}$ makes an angle of $3\pi/4$ with the positive $x$-axis.

**27–28** Find the component form of $\mathbf{v} + \mathbf{w}$, given that $\mathbf{v}$ and $\mathbf{w}$ are unit vectors. ■

**27.**
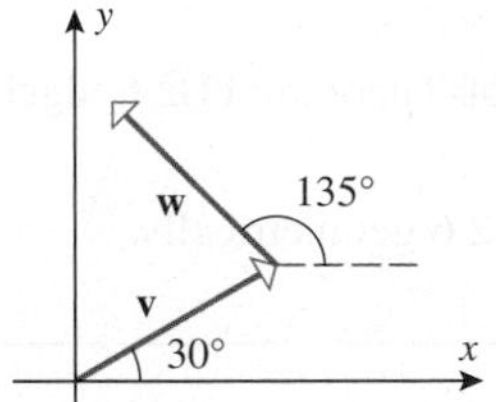


**28.**
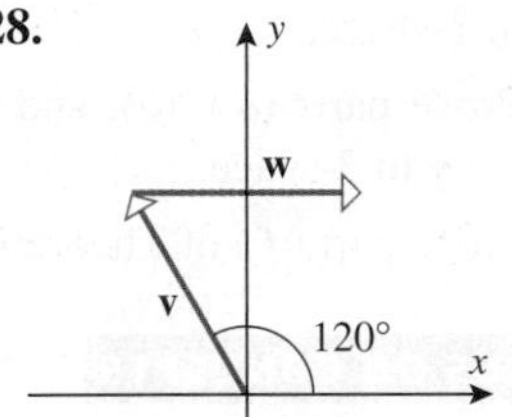


**29.** In each part, sketch the vector $\mathbf{u} + \mathbf{v} + \mathbf{w}$ and express it in component form.

(a)
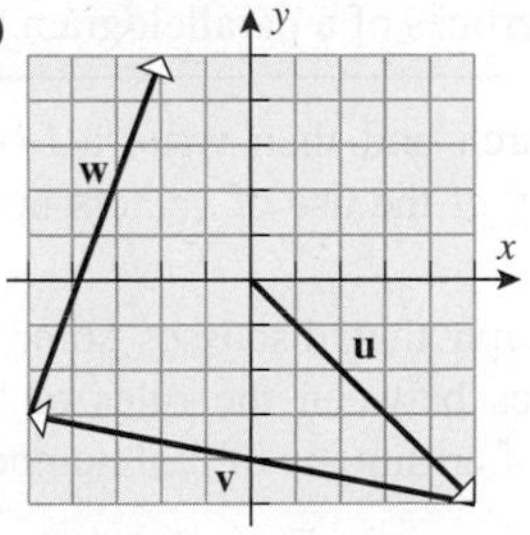


(b)
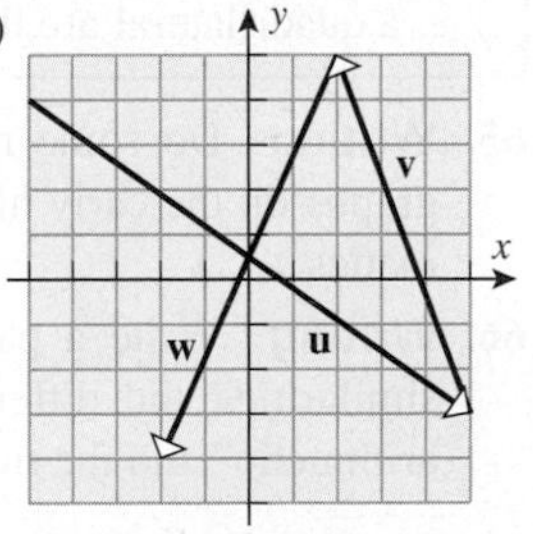


**30.** In each part of Exercise 29, sketch the vector $\mathbf{u} - \mathbf{v} + \mathbf{w}$ and express it in component form.

**31.** Let $\mathbf{u} = \langle 1, 3\rangle$, $\mathbf{v} = \langle 2, 1\rangle$, $\mathbf{w} = \langle 4, -1\rangle$. Find the vector $\mathbf{x}$ that satisfies $2\mathbf{u} - \mathbf{v} + \mathbf{x} = 7\mathbf{x} + \mathbf{w}$.

**32.** Let $\mathbf{u} = \langle -1, 1\rangle$, $\mathbf{v} = \langle 0, 1\rangle$, and $\mathbf{w} = \langle 3, 4\rangle$. Find the vector $\mathbf{x}$ that satisfies $\mathbf{u} - 2\mathbf{x} = \mathbf{x} - \mathbf{w} + 3\mathbf{v}$.

**33.** Find $\mathbf{u}$ and $\mathbf{v}$ if $\mathbf{u} + 2\mathbf{v} = 3\mathbf{i} - \mathbf{k}$ and $3\mathbf{u} - \mathbf{v} = \mathbf{i} + \mathbf{j} + \mathbf{k}$.

**34.** Find $\mathbf{u}$ and $\mathbf{v}$ if $\mathbf{u} + \mathbf{v} = \langle 2, -3\rangle$ and $3\mathbf{u} + 2\mathbf{v} = \langle -1, 2\rangle$.

**35.** Use vectors to find the lengths of the diagonals of the parallelogram that has $\mathbf{i} + \mathbf{j}$ and $\mathbf{i} - 2\mathbf{j}$ as adjacent sides.

**36.** Use vectors to find the fourth vertex of a parallelogram, three of whose vertices are $(0, 0)$, $(1, 3)$, and $(2, 4)$. [*Note:* There is more than one answer.]

**37.** (a) Given that $\|\mathbf{v}\| = 3$, find all values of $k$ such that $\|k\mathbf{v}\| = 5$.
(b) Given that $k = -2$ and $\|k\mathbf{v}\| = 6$, find $\|\mathbf{v}\|$.

**38.** What do you know about $k$ and $\mathbf{v}$ if $\|k\mathbf{v}\| = 0$?

**39.** In each part, find two unit vectors in 2-space that satisfy the stated condition.
(a) Parallel to the line $y = 3x + 2$
(b) Parallel to the line $x + y = 4$
(c) Perpendicular to the line $y = -5x + 1$

**40.** In each part, find two unit vectors in 3-space that satisfy the stated condition.
(a) Perpendicular to the $xy$-plane
(b) Perpendicular to the $xz$-plane
(c) Perpendicular to the $yz$-plane

**FOCUS ON CONCEPTS**

**41.** Let $\mathbf{r} = \langle x, y\rangle$ be an arbitrary vector. In each part, describe the set of all points $(x, y)$ in 2-space that satisfy the stated condition.
(a) $\|\mathbf{r}\| = 1$ (b) $\|\mathbf{r}\| \le 1$ (c) $\|\mathbf{r}\| > 1$

**42.** Let $\mathbf{r} = \langle x, y\rangle$ and $\mathbf{r}_0 = \langle x_0, y_0\rangle$. In each part, describe the set of all points $(x, y)$ in 2-space that satisfy the stated condition.
(a) $\|\mathbf{r} - \mathbf{r}_0\| = 1$ (b) $\|\mathbf{r} - \mathbf{r}_0\| \le 1$ (c) $\|\mathbf{r} - \mathbf{r}_0\| > 1$

**43.** Let $\mathbf{r} = \langle x, y, z\rangle$ be an arbitrary vector. In each part, describe the set of all points $(x, y, z)$ in 3-space that satisfy the stated condition.
(a) $\|\mathbf{r}\| = 1$ (b) $\|\mathbf{r}\| \le 1$ (c) $\|\mathbf{r}\| > 1$

**44.** Let $\mathbf{r}_1 = \langle x_1, y_1\rangle$, $\mathbf{r}_2 = \langle x_2, y_2\rangle$, and $\mathbf{r} = \langle x, y\rangle$. Assuming that $k > \|\mathbf{r}_2 - \mathbf{r}_1\|$, describe the set of all points $(x, y)$ for which $\|\mathbf{r} - \mathbf{r}_1\| + \|\mathbf{r} - \mathbf{r}_2\| = k$.

**45–50** Find the magnitude of the resultant force and the angle that it makes with the positive $x$-axis. ■

**45.**
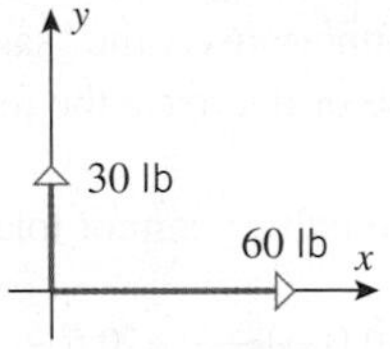


**46.**
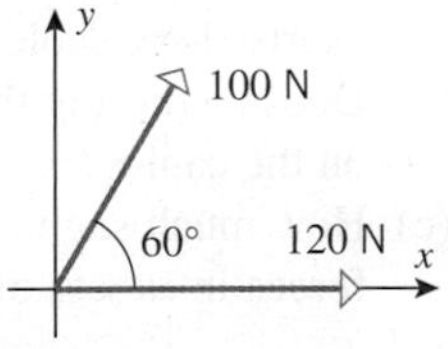


**47.**
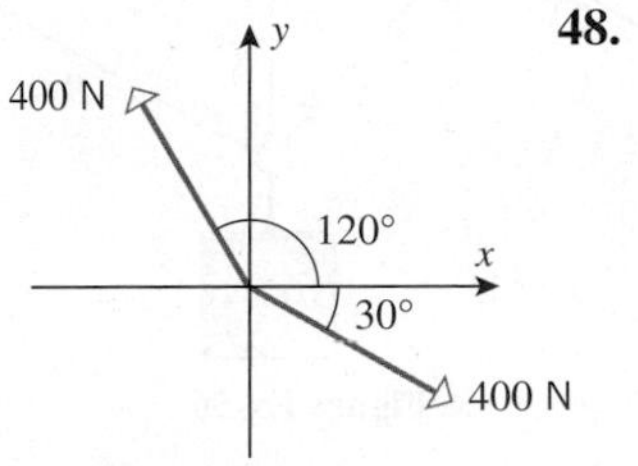


**48.**
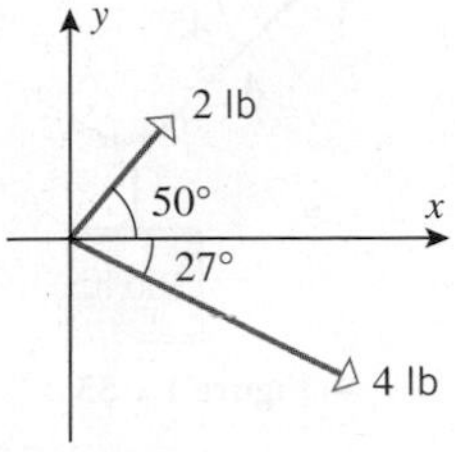


**49.**
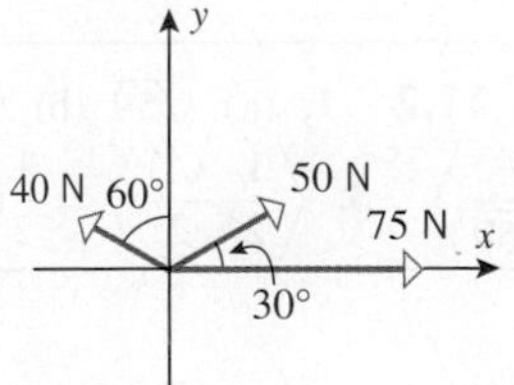


**50.**
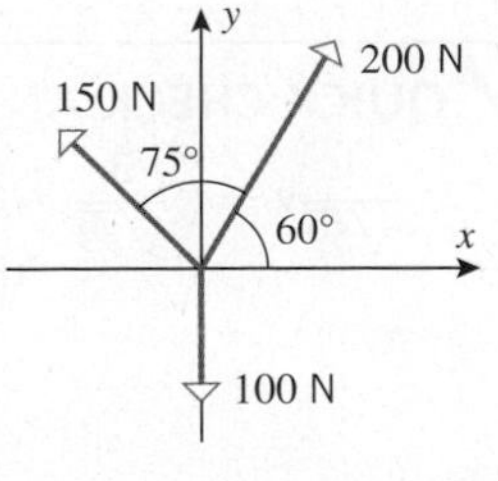

**51–52** A particle is said to be in ***static equilibrium*** if the resultant of all forces applied to it is zero. In these exercises, find the force $\mathbf{F}$ that must be applied to the point to produce static equilibrium. Describe $\mathbf{F}$ by specifying its magnitude and the angle that it makes with the positive $x$-axis. ■

**51.**

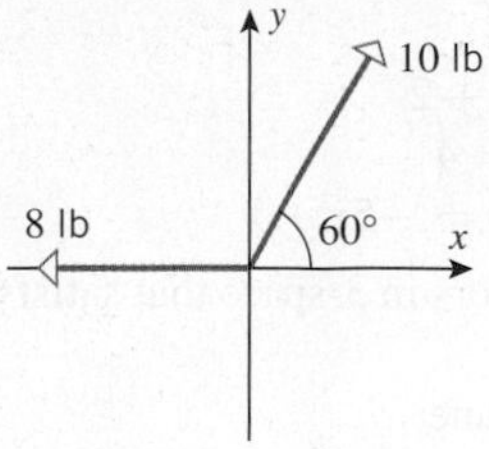


**52.**

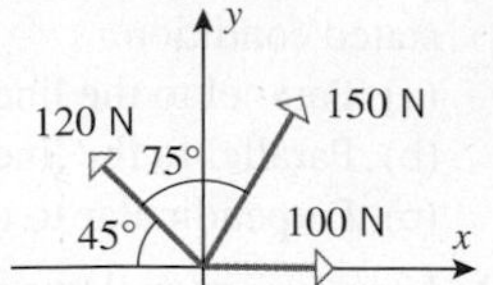


**53.** The accompanying figure shows a 250 lb traffic light supported by two flexible cables. The magnitudes of the forces that the cables apply to the eye ring are called the cable ***tensions***. Find the tensions in the cables if the traffic light is in static equilibrium (defined above Exercise 51).

**54.** Find the tensions in the cables shown in the accompanying figure if the block is in static equilibrium (see Exercise 53).

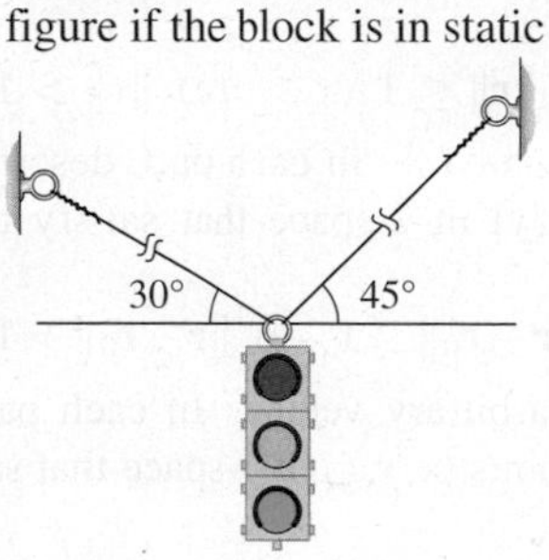


▲ **Figure Ex-53**

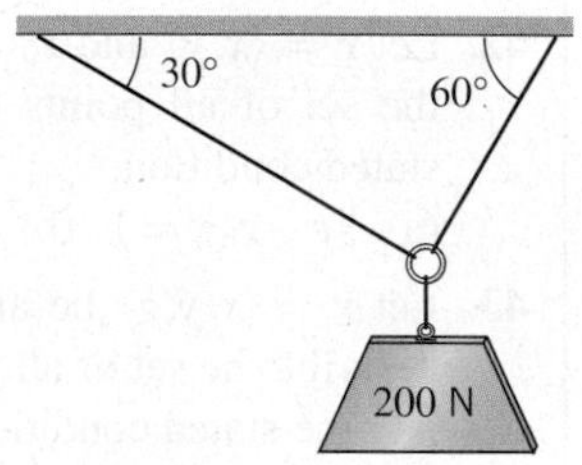


▲ **Figure Ex-54**

**55.** A block weighing 300 lb is suspended by cables $A$ and $B$, as shown in the accompanying figure. Determine the forces that the block exerts along the cables.

**56.** A block weighing 100 N is suspended by cables $A$ and $B$, as shown in the accompanying figure.
(a) Use a graphing utility to graph the forces that the block exerts along cables $A$ and $B$ as functions of the "sag" $d$.
(b) Does increasing the sag increase or decrease the forces on the cables?
(c) How much sag is required if the cables cannot tolerate forces in excess of 150 N?

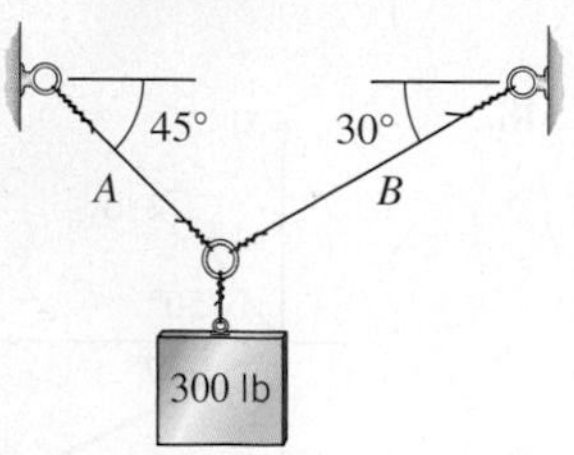


▲ **Figure Ex-55**

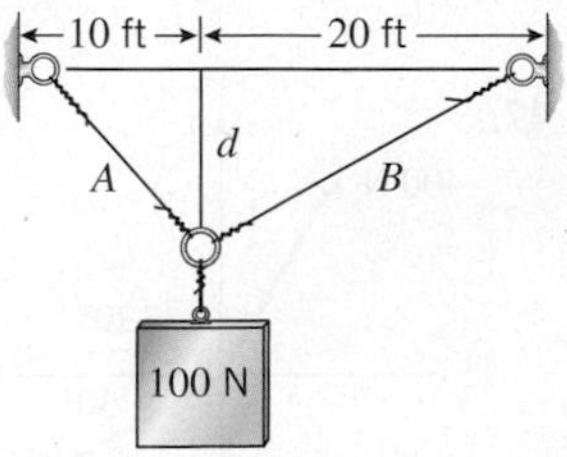


▲ **Figure Ex-56**

**57.** A vector $\mathbf{w}$ is said to be a ***linear combination*** of the vectors $\mathbf{v}_1$ and $\mathbf{v}_2$ if $\mathbf{w}$ can be expressed as $\mathbf{w} = c_1\mathbf{v}_1 + c_2\mathbf{v}_2$, where $c_1$ and $c_2$ are scalars.
(a) Find scalars $c_1$ and $c_2$ to express the vector $4\mathbf{j}$ as a linear combination of the vectors $\mathbf{v}_1 = 2\mathbf{i} - \mathbf{j}$ and $\mathbf{v}_2 = 4\mathbf{i} + 2\mathbf{j}$.
(b) Show that the vector $\langle 3, 5\rangle$ cannot be expressed as a linear combination of the vectors $\mathbf{v}_1 = \langle 1, -3\rangle$ and $\mathbf{v}_2 = \langle -2, 6\rangle$.

**58.** A vector $\mathbf{w}$ is a ***linear combination*** of the vectors $\mathbf{v}_1$, $\mathbf{v}_2$, and $\mathbf{v}_3$ if $\mathbf{w}$ can be expressed as $\mathbf{w} = c_1\mathbf{v}_1 + c_2\mathbf{v}_2 + c_3\mathbf{v}_3$, where $c_1$, $c_2$, and $c_3$ are scalars.
(a) Find scalars $c_1$, $c_2$, and $c_3$ to express $\langle -1, 1, 5\rangle$ as a linear combination of $\mathbf{v}_1 = \langle 1, 0, 1\rangle$, $\mathbf{v}_2 = \langle 3, 2, 0\rangle$, and $\mathbf{v}_3 = \langle 0, 1, 1\rangle$.
(b) Show that the vector $2\mathbf{i} + \mathbf{j} - \mathbf{k}$ cannot be expressed as a linear combination of $\mathbf{v}_1 = \mathbf{i} - \mathbf{j}$, $\mathbf{v}_2 = 3\mathbf{i} + \mathbf{k}$, and $\mathbf{v}_3 = 4\mathbf{i} - \mathbf{j} + \mathbf{k}$.

**59.** Use a theorem from plane geometry to show that if $\mathbf{u}$ and $\mathbf{v}$ are vectors in 2-space or 3-space, then

$$\|\mathbf{u} + \mathbf{v}\| \le \|\mathbf{u}\| + \|\mathbf{v}\|$$

which is called the ***triangle inequality for vectors***. Give some examples to illustrate this inequality.

**60.** Prove parts ($a$), ($c$), and ($e$) of Theorem 11.2.6 algebraically in 2-space.

**61.** Prove parts ($d$), ($g$), and ($h$) of Theorem 11.2.6 algebraically in 2-space.

**62.** Prove part ($f$) of Theorem 11.2.6 geometrically.

**FOCUS ON CONCEPTS**

**63.** Use vectors to prove that the line segment joining the midpoints of two sides of a triangle is parallel to the third side and half as long.

**64.** Use vectors to prove that the midpoints of the sides of a quadrilateral are the vertices of a parallelogram.

**65. Writing** Do some research and then write a few paragraphs on the early history of the use of vectors in mathematics.

**66. Writing** Write a paragraph that discusses some of the similarities and differences between the rules of "vector arithmetic" and the rules of arithmetic of real numbers.

✓ **QUICK CHECK ANSWERS 11.2** 1. (a) $\sqrt{59}$ (b) $\langle 7, 9, 2\rangle$ (c) $\langle -1, -11, 12\rangle$ (d) $\langle 6, -2, 14\rangle$ 2. $\dfrac{1}{\sqrt{59}}\mathbf{v} = \left\langle \dfrac{3}{\sqrt{59}}, -\dfrac{1}{\sqrt{59}}, \dfrac{7}{\sqrt{59}}\right\rangle$ 3. $\left\langle \dfrac{1}{2}, \dfrac{\sqrt{3}}{2}\right\rangle = \dfrac{1}{2}\mathbf{i} + \dfrac{\sqrt{3}}{2}\mathbf{j}$ 4. (a) $\langle -3, -4, 5\rangle$ (b) $\frac{1}{5}\overrightarrow{AB} = \langle -\frac{3}{5}, -\frac{4}{5}, 1\rangle$

# 11.3 DOT PRODUCT; PROJECTIONS

*In the last section we defined three operations on vectors—addition, subtraction, and scalar multiplication. In scalar multiplication a vector is multiplied by a scalar and the result is a vector. In this section we will define a new kind of multiplication in which two vectors are multiplied to produce a scalar. This multiplication operation has many uses, some of which we will also discuss in this section.*

## DEFINITION OF THE DOT PRODUCT

**11.3.1 DEFINITION** If $\mathbf{u} = \langle u_1, u_2\rangle$ and $\mathbf{v} = \langle v_1, v_2\rangle$ are vectors in 2-space, then the ***dot product*** of $\mathbf{u}$ and $\mathbf{v}$ is written as $\mathbf{u}\cdot\mathbf{v}$ and is defined as

$$\mathbf{u}\cdot\mathbf{v} = u_1v_1 + u_2v_2$$

Similarly, if $\mathbf{u} = \langle u_1, u_2, u_3\rangle$ and $\mathbf{v} = \langle v_1, v_2, v_3\rangle$ are vectors in 3-space, then their dot product is defined as

$$\mathbf{u}\cdot\mathbf{v} = u_1v_1 + u_2v_2 + u_3v_3$$

In words, the dot product of two vectors is formed by multiplying their corresponding components and adding the resulting products. Note that the dot product of two vectors is a scalar.

**▶ Example 1**

$$\langle 3,5\rangle\cdot\langle -1,2\rangle = 3(-1)+5(2) = 7$$
$$\langle 2,3\rangle\cdot\langle -3,2\rangle = 2(-3)+3(2) = 0$$
$$\langle 1,-3,4\rangle\cdot\langle 1,5,2\rangle = 1(1)+(-3)(5)+4(2) = -6$$

Here are the same computations expressed another way:

$$(3\mathbf{i}+5\mathbf{j})\cdot(-\mathbf{i}+2\mathbf{j}) = 3(-1)+5(2) = 7$$
$$(2\mathbf{i}+3\mathbf{j})\cdot(-3\mathbf{i}+2\mathbf{j}) = 2(-3)+3(2) = 0$$
$$(\mathbf{i}-3\mathbf{j}+4\mathbf{k})\cdot(\mathbf{i}+5\mathbf{j}+2\mathbf{k}) = 1(1)+(-3)(5)+4(2) = -6 \;◀$$

**TECHNOLOGY MASTERY**

Many calculating utilities have a built-in dot product operation. If your calculating utility has this capability, use it to check the computations in Example 1.

## ALGEBRAIC PROPERTIES OF THE DOT PRODUCT

The following theorem provides some of the basic algebraic properties of the dot product.

**11.3.2 THEOREM** *If* $\mathbf{u}$, $\mathbf{v}$, *and* $\mathbf{w}$ *are vectors in 2- or 3-space and k is a scalar, then:*

(*a*) $\mathbf{u}\cdot\mathbf{v} = \mathbf{v}\cdot\mathbf{u}$

(*b*) $\mathbf{u}\cdot(\mathbf{v}+\mathbf{w}) = \mathbf{u}\cdot\mathbf{v}+\mathbf{u}\cdot\mathbf{w}$

(*c*) $k(\mathbf{u}\cdot\mathbf{v}) = (k\mathbf{u})\cdot\mathbf{v} = \mathbf{u}\cdot(k\mathbf{v})$

(*d*) $\mathbf{v}\cdot\mathbf{v} = \|\mathbf{v}\|^2$

(*e*) $\mathbf{0}\cdot\mathbf{v} = 0$

Note the difference between the two zeros that appear in part (e) of Theorem 11.3.2—the zero on the left side is the *zero vector* (boldface), whereas the zero on the right side is the *zero scalar* (lightface).

We will prove parts (*c*) and (*d*) for vectors in 3-space and leave some of the others as exercises.

**PROOF (*c*)** Let $\mathbf{u} = \langle u_1, u_2, u_3\rangle$ and $\mathbf{v} = \langle v_1, v_2, v_3\rangle$. Then

$$k(\mathbf{u}\cdot\mathbf{v}) = k(u_1v_1+u_2v_2+u_3v_3) = (ku_1)v_1+(ku_2)v_2+(ku_3)v_3 = (k\mathbf{u})\cdot\mathbf{v}$$

Similarly, $k(\mathbf{u}\cdot\mathbf{v}) = \mathbf{u}\cdot(k\mathbf{v})$.

**PROOF (*d*)** $\mathbf{v}\cdot\mathbf{v} = v_1v_1+v_2v_2+v_3v_3 = v_1^2+v_2^2+v_3^2 = \|\mathbf{v}\|^2$. ■

The following alternative form of the formula in part (*d*) of Theorem 11.3.2 provides a useful way of expressing the norm of a vector in terms of a dot product:

$$\|\mathbf{v}\| = \sqrt{\mathbf{v} \cdot \mathbf{v}} \tag{1}$$

## ANGLE BETWEEN VECTORS

Suppose that **u** and **v** are nonzero vectors in 2-space or 3-space that are positioned so their initial points coincide. We define the ***angle between* u *and* v** to be the angle $\theta$ determined by the vectors that satisfies the condition $0 \le \theta \le \pi$ (Figure 11.3.1). In 2-space, $\theta$ is the smallest counterclockwise angle through which one of the vectors can be rotated until it aligns with the other.

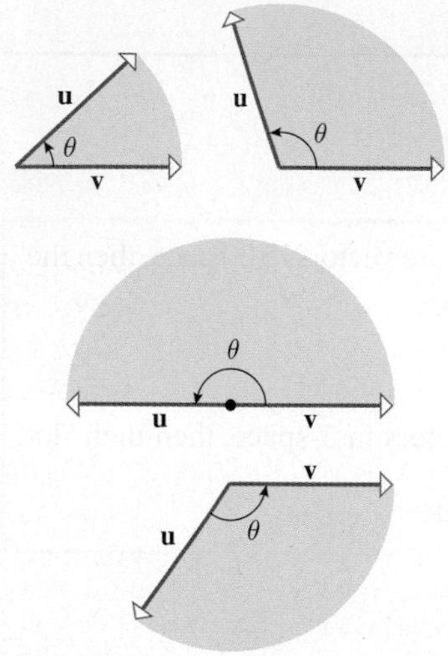


θ is the angle between **u** and **v**.

▲ **Figure 11.3.1**

The next theorem provides a way of calculating the angle between two vectors from their components.

> **11.3.3 THEOREM** *If* **u** *and* **v** *are nonzero vectors in 2-space or 3-space, and if $\theta$ is the angle between them, then*
>
> $$\cos\theta = \frac{\mathbf{u} \cdot \mathbf{v}}{\|\mathbf{u}\|\|\mathbf{v}\|} \tag{2}$$

**PROOF** Suppose that the vectors **u**, **v**, and **v** − **u** are positioned to form three sides of a triangle, as shown in Figure 11.3.2. It follows from the law of cosines that

$$\|\mathbf{v} - \mathbf{u}\|^2 = \|\mathbf{u}\|^2 + \|\mathbf{v}\|^2 - 2\|\mathbf{u}\|\|\mathbf{v}\|\cos\theta \tag{3}$$

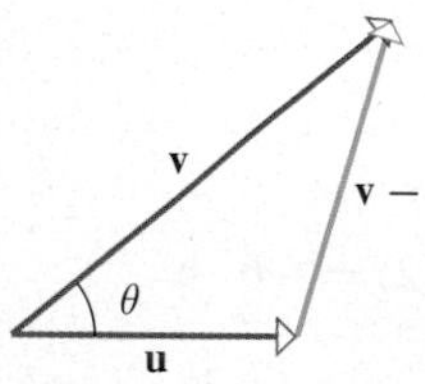


▲ **Figure 11.3.2**

Using the properties of the dot product in Theorem 11.3.2, we can rewrite the left side of this equation as

$$\begin{aligned}\|\mathbf{v} - \mathbf{u}\|^2 &= (\mathbf{v} - \mathbf{u}) \cdot (\mathbf{v} - \mathbf{u}) \\ &= (\mathbf{v} - \mathbf{u}) \cdot \mathbf{v} - (\mathbf{v} - \mathbf{u}) \cdot \mathbf{u} \\ &= \mathbf{v} \cdot \mathbf{v} - \mathbf{u} \cdot \mathbf{v} - \mathbf{v} \cdot \mathbf{u} + \mathbf{u} \cdot \mathbf{u} \\ &= \|\mathbf{v}\|^2 - 2\mathbf{u} \cdot \mathbf{v} + \|\mathbf{u}\|^2\end{aligned}$$

Substituting this back into (3) yields

$$\|\mathbf{v}\|^2 - 2\mathbf{u} \cdot \mathbf{v} + \|\mathbf{u}\|^2 = \|\mathbf{u}\|^2 + \|\mathbf{v}\|^2 - 2\|\mathbf{u}\|\|\mathbf{v}\|\cos\theta$$

which we can simplify and rewrite as

$$\mathbf{u} \cdot \mathbf{v} = \|\mathbf{u}\|\|\mathbf{v}\|\cos\theta$$

Finally, dividing both sides of this equation by $\|\mathbf{u}\|\|\mathbf{v}\|$ yields (2). ■

► **Example 2** Find the angle between the vector $\mathbf{u} = \mathbf{i} - 2\mathbf{j} + 2\mathbf{k}$ and

(a) $\mathbf{v} = -3\mathbf{i} + 6\mathbf{j} + 2\mathbf{k}$ (b) $\mathbf{w} = 2\mathbf{i} + 7\mathbf{j} + 6\mathbf{k}$ (c) $\mathbf{z} = -3\mathbf{i} + 6\mathbf{j} - 6\mathbf{k}$

***Solution (a).***

$$\cos\theta = \frac{\mathbf{u} \cdot \mathbf{v}}{\|\mathbf{u}\|\|\mathbf{v}\|} = \frac{-11}{(3)(7)} = -\frac{11}{21}$$

Thus,

$$\theta = \cos^{-1}\left(-\tfrac{11}{21}\right) \approx 2.12 \text{ radians} \approx 121.6^\circ$$

***Solution (b).***

$$\cos\theta = \frac{\mathbf{u} \cdot \mathbf{w}}{\|\mathbf{u}\|\|\mathbf{w}\|} = \frac{0}{\|\mathbf{u}\|\|\mathbf{w}\|} = 0$$

Thus, $\theta = \pi/2$, which means that the vectors are perpendicular.

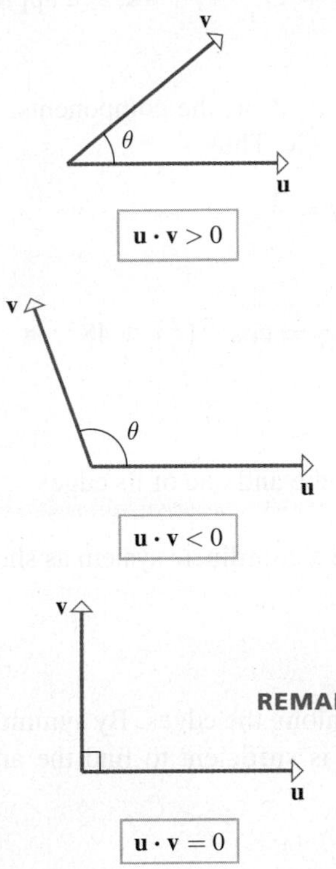

▲ Figure 11.3.3

***Solution (c).***

$$\cos\theta = \frac{\mathbf{u}\cdot\mathbf{z}}{\|\mathbf{u}\|\|\mathbf{z}\|} = \frac{-27}{(3)(9)} = -1$$

Thus, $\theta = \pi$, which means that the vectors are oppositely directed. (In retrospect, we could have seen this without computing $\theta$, since $\mathbf{z} = -3\mathbf{u}$.) ◄

## INTERPRETING THE SIGN OF THE DOT PRODUCT

It will often be convenient to express Formula (2) as

$$\mathbf{u}\cdot\mathbf{v} = \|\mathbf{u}\|\|\mathbf{v}\|\cos\theta \tag{4}$$

which expresses the dot product of **u** and **v** in terms of the lengths of these vectors and the angle between them. Since **u** and **v** are assumed to be nonzero vectors, this version of the formula makes it clear that the sign of $\mathbf{u}\cdot\mathbf{v}$ is the same as the sign of $\cos\theta$. Thus, we can tell from the dot product whether the angle between two vectors is acute or obtuse or whether the vectors are perpendicular (Figure 11.3.3).

**REMARK** The terms "perpendicular," "orthogonal," and "normal" are all commonly used to describe geometric objects that meet at right angles. For consistency, we will say that two vectors are *orthogonal*, a vector is *normal* to a plane, and two planes are *perpendicular*. Moreover, although the zero vector does not make a well-defined angle with other vectors, we will consider **0** to be orthogonal to *all* vectors. This convention allows us to say that **u** and **v** are orthogonal vectors if and only if $\mathbf{u}\cdot\mathbf{v} = 0$, and makes Formula (4) valid if **u** or **v** (or both) is zero.

## DIRECTION ANGLES

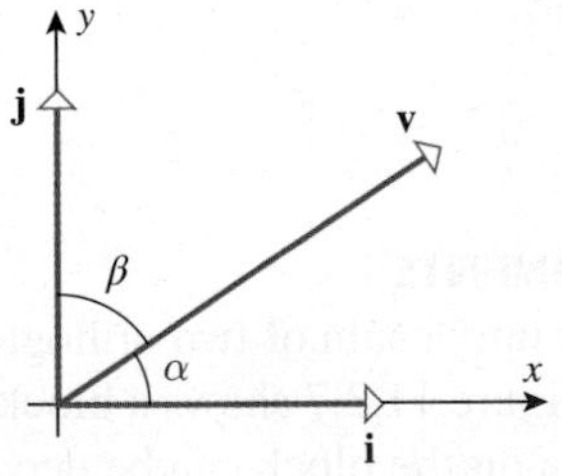

▲ Figure 11.3.4

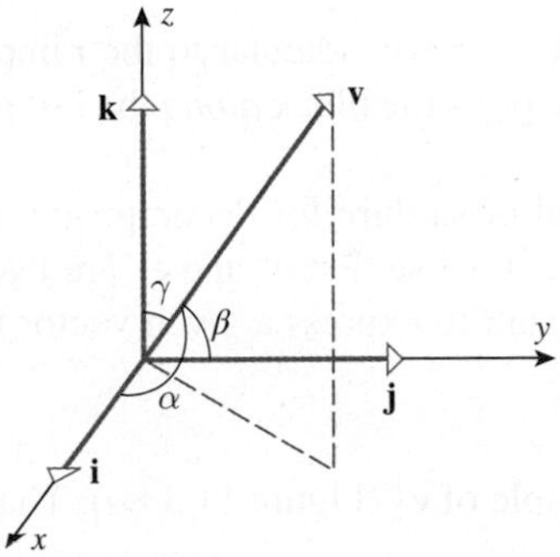

▲ Figure 11.3.5

In an $xy$-coordinate system, the direction of a nonzero vector **v** is completely determined by the angles $\alpha$ and $\beta$ between **v** and the unit vectors **i** and **j** (Figure 11.3.4), and in an $xyz$-coordinate system the direction is completely determined by the angles $\alpha$, $\beta$, and $\gamma$ between **v** and the unit vectors **i**, **j**, and **k** (Figure 11.3.5). In both 2-space and 3-space the angles between a nonzero vector **v** and the vectors **i**, **j**, and **k** are called the ***direction angles*** of **v**, and the cosines of those angles are called the ***direction cosines*** of **v**. Formulas for the direction cosines of a vector can be obtained from Formula (2). For example, if $\mathbf{v} = v_1\mathbf{i} + v_2\mathbf{j} + v_3\mathbf{k}$, then

$$\cos\alpha = \frac{\mathbf{v}\cdot\mathbf{i}}{\|\mathbf{v}\|\|\mathbf{i}\|} = \frac{v_1}{\|\mathbf{v}\|}, \quad \cos\beta = \frac{\mathbf{v}\cdot\mathbf{j}}{\|\mathbf{v}\|\|\mathbf{j}\|} = \frac{v_2}{\|\mathbf{v}\|}, \quad \cos\gamma = \frac{\mathbf{v}\cdot\mathbf{k}}{\|\mathbf{v}\|\|\mathbf{k}\|} = \frac{v_3}{\|\mathbf{v}\|}$$

Thus, we have the following theorem.

> **11.3.4 THEOREM** *The direction cosines of a nonzero vector* $\mathbf{v} = v_1\mathbf{i} + v_2\mathbf{j} + v_3\mathbf{k}$ *are*
>
> $$\cos\alpha = \frac{v_1}{\|\mathbf{v}\|}, \quad \cos\beta = \frac{v_2}{\|\mathbf{v}\|}, \quad \cos\gamma = \frac{v_3}{\|\mathbf{v}\|}$$

The direction cosines of a vector $\mathbf{v} = v_1\mathbf{i} + v_2\mathbf{j} + v_3\mathbf{k}$ can be computed by normalizing **v** and reading off the components of $\mathbf{v}/\|\mathbf{v}\|$, since

$$\frac{\mathbf{v}}{\|\mathbf{v}\|} = \frac{v_1}{\|\mathbf{v}\|}\mathbf{i} + \frac{v_2}{\|\mathbf{v}\|}\mathbf{j} + \frac{v_3}{\|\mathbf{v}\|}\mathbf{k} = (\cos\alpha)\mathbf{i} + (\cos\beta)\mathbf{j} + (\cos\gamma)\mathbf{k}$$

We leave it as an exercise for you to show that the direction cosines of a vector satisfy the equation

$$\cos^2\alpha + \cos^2\beta + \cos^2\gamma = 1 \tag{5}$$

▶ **Example 3** Find the direction cosines of the vector $\mathbf{v} = 2\mathbf{i} - 4\mathbf{j} + 4\mathbf{k}$, and approximate the direction angles to the nearest degree.

***Solution.*** First we will normalize the vector $\mathbf{v}$ and then read off the components. We have $\|\mathbf{v}\| = \sqrt{4+16+16} = 6$, so that $\mathbf{v}/\|\mathbf{v}\| = \frac{1}{3}\mathbf{i} - \frac{2}{3}\mathbf{j} + \frac{2}{3}\mathbf{k}$. Thus,

$$\cos\alpha = \tfrac{1}{3}, \quad \cos\beta = -\tfrac{2}{3}, \quad \cos\gamma = \tfrac{2}{3}$$

With the help of a calculating utility we obtain

$$\alpha = \cos^{-1}\left(\tfrac{1}{3}\right) \approx 71^\circ, \quad \beta = \cos^{-1}\left(-\tfrac{2}{3}\right) \approx 132^\circ, \quad \gamma = \cos^{-1}\left(\tfrac{2}{3}\right) \approx 48^\circ \ ◀$$

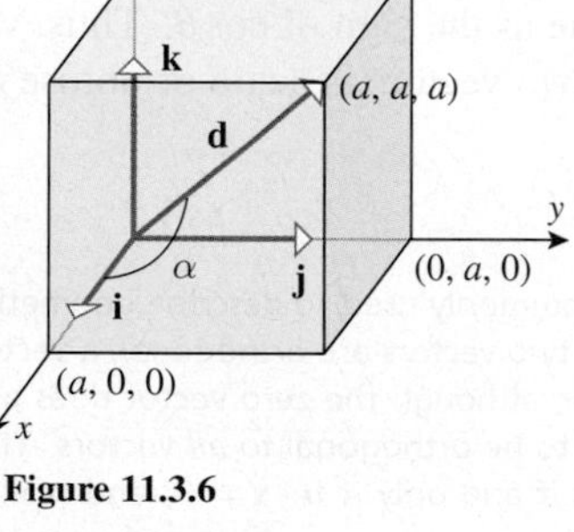

▲ **Figure 11.3.6**

▶ **Example 4** Find the angle between a diagonal of a cube and one of its edges.

***Solution.*** Assume that the cube has side $a$, and introduce a coordinate system as shown in Figure 11.3.6. In this coordinate system the vector

$$\mathbf{d} = a\mathbf{i} + a\mathbf{j} + a\mathbf{k}$$

is a diagonal of the cube and the unit vectors $\mathbf{i}$, $\mathbf{j}$, and $\mathbf{k}$ run along the edges. By symmetry, the diagonal makes the same angle with each edge, so it is sufficient to find the angle between $\mathbf{d}$ and $\mathbf{i}$ (the direction angle $\alpha$). Thus,

$$\cos\alpha = \frac{\mathbf{d}\cdot\mathbf{i}}{\|\mathbf{d}\|\|\mathbf{i}\|} = \frac{a}{\|\mathbf{d}\|} = \frac{a}{\sqrt{3a^2}} = \frac{1}{\sqrt{3}}$$

and hence

$$\alpha = \cos^{-1}\left(\frac{1}{\sqrt{3}}\right) \approx 0.955 \text{ radian} \approx 54.7^\circ \ ◀$$

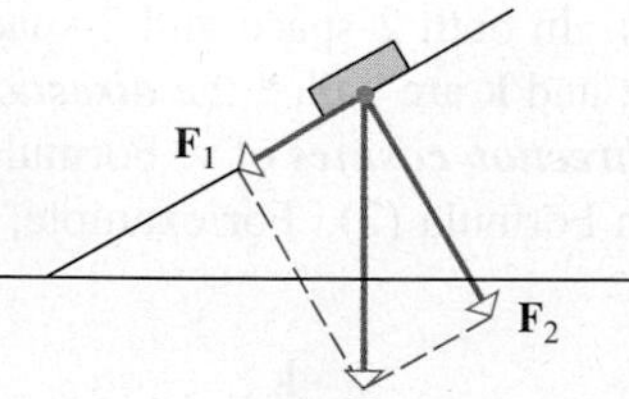

The force of gravity pulls the block against the ramp and down the ramp.

▲ **Figure 11.3.7**

## DECOMPOSING VECTORS INTO ORTHOGONAL COMPONENTS

In many applications it is desirable to "decompose" a vector into a sum of two orthogonal vectors with convenient specified directions. For example, Figure 11.3.7 shows a block on an inclined plane. The downward force $\mathbf{F}$ that gravity exerts on the block can be decomposed into the sum

$$\mathbf{F} = \mathbf{F}_1 + \mathbf{F}_2$$

where the force $\mathbf{F}_1$ is parallel to the ramp and the force $\mathbf{F}_2$ is perpendicular to the ramp. The forces $\mathbf{F}_1$ and $\mathbf{F}_2$ are useful because $\mathbf{F}_1$ is the force that pulls the block *along* the ramp, and $\mathbf{F}_2$ is the force that the block exerts *against* the ramp.

Thus, our next objective is to develop a computational procedure for decomposing a vector into a sum of orthogonal vectors. For this purpose, suppose that $\mathbf{e}_1$ and $\mathbf{e}_2$ are two orthogonal *unit* vectors in 2-space, and suppose that we want to express a given vector $\mathbf{v}$ as a sum

$$\mathbf{v} = \mathbf{w}_1 + \mathbf{w}_2$$

so that $\mathbf{w}_1$ is a scalar multiple of $\mathbf{e}_1$ and $\mathbf{w}_2$ is a scalar multiple of $\mathbf{e}_2$ (Figure 11.3.8*a*). That is, we want to find scalars $k_1$ and $k_2$ such that

$$\mathbf{v} = k_1\mathbf{e}_1 + k_2\mathbf{e}_2 \tag{6}$$

We can find $k_1$ by taking the dot product of $\mathbf{v}$ with $\mathbf{e}_1$. This yields

$$\begin{aligned}\mathbf{v}\cdot\mathbf{e}_1 &= (k_1\mathbf{e}_1 + k_2\mathbf{e}_2)\cdot\mathbf{e}_1\\ &= k_1(\mathbf{e}_1\cdot\mathbf{e}_1) + k_2(\mathbf{e}_2\cdot\mathbf{e}_1)\\ &= k_1\|\mathbf{e}_1\|^2 + 0 = k_1\end{aligned}$$

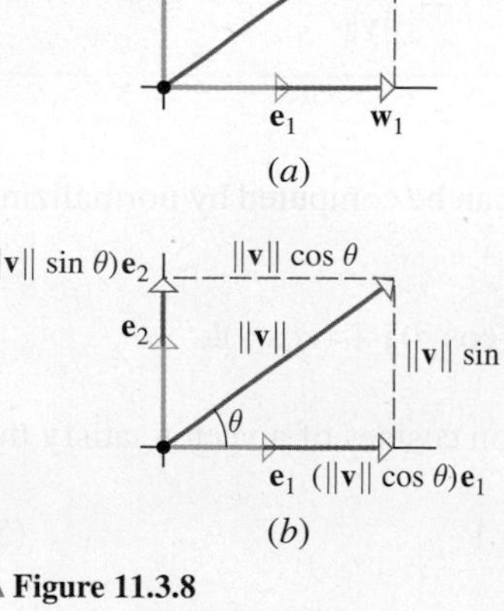

▲ **Figure 11.3.8**

Similarly,

$$\mathbf{v}\cdot\mathbf{e}_2 = (k_1\mathbf{e}_1 + k_2\mathbf{e}_2)\cdot\mathbf{e}_2 = k_1(\mathbf{e}_1\cdot\mathbf{e}_2) + k_2(\mathbf{e}_2\cdot\mathbf{e}_2) = 0 + k_2\|\mathbf{e}_2\|^2 = k_2$$

Substituting these expressions for $k_1$ and $k_2$ in (6) yields

$$\mathbf{v} = (\mathbf{v}\cdot\mathbf{e}_1)\mathbf{e}_1 + (\mathbf{v}\cdot\mathbf{e}_2)\mathbf{e}_2 \tag{7}$$

In this formula we call $(\mathbf{v}\cdot\mathbf{e}_1)\mathbf{e}_1$ and $(\mathbf{v}\cdot\mathbf{e}_2)\mathbf{e}_2$ the ***vector components*** of $\mathbf{v}$ along $\mathbf{e}_1$ and $\mathbf{e}_2$, respectively; and we call $\mathbf{v}\cdot\mathbf{e}_1$ and $\mathbf{v}\cdot\mathbf{e}_2$ the ***scalar components*** of $\mathbf{v}$ along $\mathbf{e}_1$ and $\mathbf{e}_2$, respectively. If $\theta$ denotes the angle between $\mathbf{v}$ and $\mathbf{e}_1$, and the angle between $\mathbf{v}$ and $\mathbf{e}_2$ is $\pi/2$ or less, then the scalar components of $\mathbf{v}$ can be written in trigonometric form as

$$\mathbf{v}\cdot\mathbf{e}_1 = \|\mathbf{v}\|\cos\theta \quad\text{and}\quad \mathbf{v}\cdot\mathbf{e}_2 = \|\mathbf{v}\|\sin\theta \tag{8}$$

(Figure 11.3.8*b*). Moreover, the vector components of $\mathbf{v}$ can be expressed as

$$(\mathbf{v}\cdot\mathbf{e}_1)\mathbf{e}_1 = (\|\mathbf{v}\|\cos\theta)\mathbf{e}_1 \quad\text{and}\quad (\mathbf{v}\cdot\mathbf{e}_2)\mathbf{e}_2 = (\|\mathbf{v}\|\sin\theta)\mathbf{e}_2 \tag{9}$$

and the decomposition (6) can be expressed as

$$\mathbf{v} = (\|\mathbf{v}\|\cos\theta)\mathbf{e}_1 + (\|\mathbf{v}\|\sin\theta)\mathbf{e}_2 \tag{10}$$

provided the angle between $\mathbf{v}$ and $\mathbf{e}_2$ is at most $\pi/2$.

Note that the vector components of $\mathbf{v}$ along $\mathbf{e}_1$ and $\mathbf{e}_2$ are *vectors*, whereas the scalar components of $\mathbf{v}$ along $\mathbf{e}_1$ and $\mathbf{e}_2$ are *numbers*.

▶ **Example 5** Let

$$\mathbf{v} = \langle 2, 3\rangle,\quad \mathbf{e}_1 = \left\langle \frac{1}{\sqrt{2}}, \frac{1}{\sqrt{2}}\right\rangle,\quad\text{and}\quad \mathbf{e}_2 = \left\langle -\frac{1}{\sqrt{2}}, \frac{1}{\sqrt{2}}\right\rangle$$

Find the scalar components of $\mathbf{v}$ along $\mathbf{e}_1$ and $\mathbf{e}_2$ and the vector components of $\mathbf{v}$ along $\mathbf{e}_1$ and $\mathbf{e}_2$.

***Solution.*** The scalar components of $\mathbf{v}$ along $\mathbf{e}_1$ and $\mathbf{e}_2$ are

$$\mathbf{v}\cdot\mathbf{e}_1 = 2\left(\frac{1}{\sqrt{2}}\right) + 3\left(\frac{1}{\sqrt{2}}\right) = \frac{5}{\sqrt{2}}$$

$$\mathbf{v}\cdot\mathbf{e}_2 = 2\left(-\frac{1}{\sqrt{2}}\right) + 3\left(\frac{1}{\sqrt{2}}\right) = \frac{1}{\sqrt{2}}$$

so the vector components are

$$(\mathbf{v}\cdot\mathbf{e}_1)\mathbf{e}_1 = \frac{5}{\sqrt{2}}\left\langle \frac{1}{\sqrt{2}}, \frac{1}{\sqrt{2}}\right\rangle = \left\langle \frac{5}{2}, \frac{5}{2}\right\rangle$$

$$(\mathbf{v}\cdot\mathbf{e}_2)\mathbf{e}_2 = \frac{1}{\sqrt{2}}\left\langle -\frac{1}{\sqrt{2}}, \frac{1}{\sqrt{2}}\right\rangle = \left\langle -\frac{1}{2}, \frac{1}{2}\right\rangle \blacktriangleleft$$

Notice that in Example 5

$$(\mathbf{v}\cdot\mathbf{e}_1)\mathbf{e}_1 + (\mathbf{v}\cdot\mathbf{e}_2)\mathbf{e}_2 = \langle 2, 3\rangle = \mathbf{v}$$

as guaranteed by (7).

▶ **Example 6** A rope is attached to a 100 lb block on a ramp that is inclined at an angle of 30° with the ground (Figure 11.3.9*a*). How much force does the block exert against the ramp, and how much force must be applied to the rope in a direction parallel to the ramp to prevent the block from sliding down the ramp? (Assume that the ramp is smooth, that is, exerts no frictional forces.)

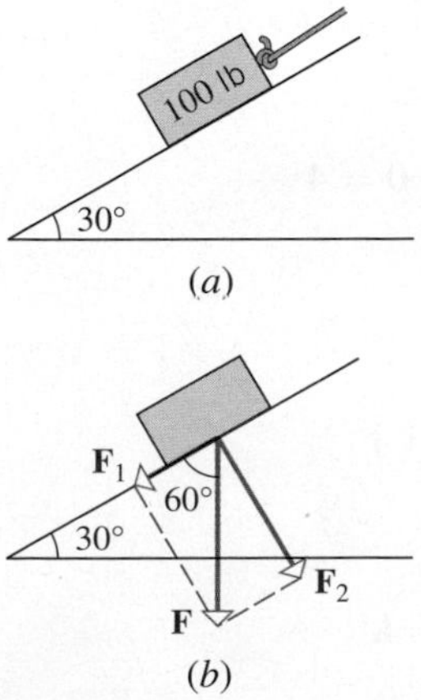

▲ **Figure 11.3.9**

***Solution.*** Let $\mathbf{F}$ denote the downward force of gravity on the block (so $\|\mathbf{F}\| = 100$ lb), and let $\mathbf{F}_1$ and $\mathbf{F}_2$ be the vector components of $\mathbf{F}$ parallel and perpendicular to the ramp (as shown in Figure 11.3.9*b*). The lengths of $\mathbf{F}_1$ and $\mathbf{F}_2$ are

$$\|\mathbf{F}_1\| = \|\mathbf{F}\|\cos 60^\circ = 100\left(\frac{1}{2}\right) = 50 \text{ lb}$$

$$\|\mathbf{F}_2\| = \|\mathbf{F}\|\sin 60^\circ = 100\left(\frac{\sqrt{3}}{2}\right) \approx 86.6 \text{ lb}$$

Thus, the block exerts a force of approximately 86.6 lb against the ramp, and it requires a force of 50 lb to prevent the block from sliding down the ramp. ◀

## ORTHOGONAL PROJECTIONS

The vector components of $\mathbf{v}$ along $\mathbf{e}_1$ and $\mathbf{e}_2$ in (7) are also called the *orthogonal projections* of $\mathbf{v}$ on $\mathbf{e}_1$ and $\mathbf{e}_2$ and are commonly denoted by

$$\text{proj}_{\mathbf{e}_1}\mathbf{v} = (\mathbf{v}\cdot\mathbf{e}_1)\mathbf{e}_1 \quad \text{and} \quad \text{proj}_{\mathbf{e}_2}\mathbf{v} = (\mathbf{v}\cdot\mathbf{e}_2)\mathbf{e}_2$$

In general, if $\mathbf{e}$ is a unit vector, then we define the ***orthogonal projection of*** $\mathbf{v}$ ***on*** $\mathbf{e}$ to be

$$\text{proj}_{\mathbf{e}}\mathbf{v} = (\mathbf{v}\cdot\mathbf{e})\mathbf{e} \tag{11}$$

The orthogonal projection of $\mathbf{v}$ on an arbitrary nonzero vector $\mathbf{b}$ can be obtained by normalizing $\mathbf{b}$ and then applying Formula (11); that is,

$$\text{proj}_{\mathbf{b}}\mathbf{v} = \left(\mathbf{v}\cdot\frac{\mathbf{b}}{\|\mathbf{b}\|}\right)\left(\frac{\mathbf{b}}{\|\mathbf{b}\|}\right)$$

which can be rewritten as

$$\text{proj}_{\mathbf{b}}\mathbf{v} = \frac{\mathbf{v}\cdot\mathbf{b}}{\|\mathbf{b}\|^2}\mathbf{b} \tag{12}$$

Geometrically, if $\mathbf{b}$ and $\mathbf{v}$ have a common initial point, then $\text{proj}_{\mathbf{b}}\mathbf{v}$ is the vector that is determined when a perpendicular is dropped from the terminal point of $\mathbf{v}$ to the line through $\mathbf{b}$ (illustrated in Figure 11.3.10 in two cases).

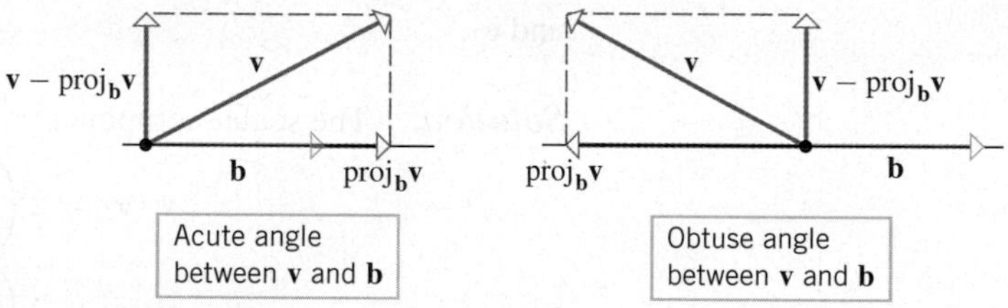


▶ **Figure 11.3.10**

Moreover, it is evident from Figure 11.3.10 that if we subtract $\text{proj}_{\mathbf{b}}\mathbf{v}$ from $\mathbf{v}$, then the resulting vector

$$\mathbf{v} - \text{proj}_{\mathbf{b}}\mathbf{v}$$

will be orthogonal to $\mathbf{b}$; we call this the ***vector component of*** $\mathbf{v}$ ***orthogonal to*** $\mathbf{b}$.

Stated informally, the orthogonal projection $\text{proj}_{\mathbf{b}}\mathbf{v}$ is the "shadow" that $\mathbf{v}$ casts on the line through $\mathbf{b}$.

▶ **Example 7** Find the orthogonal projection of $\mathbf{v} = \mathbf{i}+\mathbf{j}+\mathbf{k}$ on $\mathbf{b} = 2\mathbf{i}+2\mathbf{j}$, and then find the vector component of $\mathbf{v}$ orthogonal to $\mathbf{b}$.

***Solution.*** We have

$$\mathbf{v}\cdot\mathbf{b} = (\mathbf{i}+\mathbf{j}+\mathbf{k})\cdot(2\mathbf{i}+2\mathbf{j}) = 2+2+0 = 4$$
$$\|\mathbf{b}\|^2 = 2^2+2^2 = 8$$

Thus, the orthogonal projection of $\mathbf{v}$ on $\mathbf{b}$ is

$$\text{proj}_{\mathbf{b}}\mathbf{v} = \frac{\mathbf{v}\cdot\mathbf{b}}{\|\mathbf{b}\|^2}\mathbf{b} = \frac{4}{8}(2\mathbf{i}+2\mathbf{j}) = \mathbf{i}+\mathbf{j}$$

and the vector component of $\mathbf{v}$ orthogonal to $\mathbf{b}$ is

$$\mathbf{v} - \text{proj}_{\mathbf{b}}\mathbf{v} = (\mathbf{i}+\mathbf{j}+\mathbf{k}) - (\mathbf{i}+\mathbf{j}) = \mathbf{k}$$

These results are consistent with Figure 11.3.11. ◀

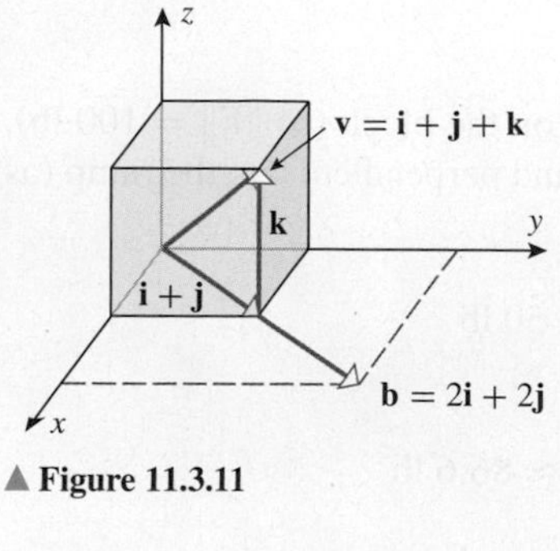


▲ **Figure 11.3.11**

## WORK

In Section 6.6 we discussed the work done by a constant force acting on an object that moves along a line. We defined the work $W$ done on the object by a constant force of magnitude $F$ acting in the direction of motion over a distance $d$ to be

$$W = Fd = \text{force} \times \text{distance} \tag{13}$$

If we let $\mathbf{F}$ denote a force vector of magnitude $\|\mathbf{F}\| = F$ *acting in the direction of motion*, then we can write (13) as

$$W = \|\mathbf{F}\|d$$

Furthermore, if we assume that the object moves along a line from point $P$ to point $Q$, then $d = \|\overrightarrow{PQ}\|$, so that the work can be expressed entirely in vector form as

$$W = \|\mathbf{F}\|\|\overrightarrow{PQ}\|$$

(Figure 11.3.12*a*). In the case where a constant force $\mathbf{F}$ is not in the direction of motion, but rather makes an angle $\theta$ with the displacement vector $\overrightarrow{PQ}$, then we *define* the work $W$ done by $\mathbf{F}$ to be

$$W = (\|\mathbf{F}\|\cos\theta)\|\overrightarrow{PQ}\| = \mathbf{F}\cdot\overrightarrow{PQ} \tag{14}$$

(Figure 11.3.12*b*).

Note that in Formula (14) the quantity $\|\mathbf{F}\|\cos\theta$ is the scalar component of force along the displacement vector. Thus, in the case where $\cos\theta > 0$, a force of magnitude $\|\mathbf{F}\|$ acting at an angle $\theta$ does the same work as a force of magnitude $\|\mathbf{F}\|\cos\theta$ acting in the direction of motion.

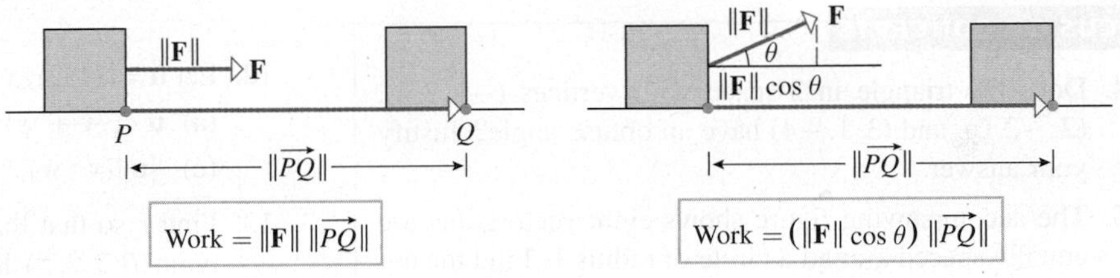

(*a*) (*b*)

▲ **Figure 11.3.12**

From Formula (14), the work $W$ can be expressed as $W = (\|\mathbf{F}\|\cos\theta)\|\overrightarrow{PQ}\|$ or as $W = \mathbf{F}\cdot\overrightarrow{PQ}$. Although these two expressions are mathematically equivalent, in practice it may be more convenient to use one of them instead of the other.

### ▶ Example 8

(a) A wagon is pulled horizontally by exerting a constant force of 10 lb on the handle at an angle of 60° with the horizontal. How much work is done in moving the wagon 50 ft?

(b) A force of $\mathbf{F} = 3\mathbf{i} - \mathbf{j} + 2\mathbf{k}$ lb is applied to a point that moves on a line from $P(-1, 1, 2)$ to $Q(3, 0, -2)$. If distance is measured in feet, how much work is done?

***Solution (a).*** With $\|\mathbf{F}\| = 10$, $\theta = 60°$, and $\|\overrightarrow{PQ}\| = 50$, it follows that the work done is

$$W = (\|\mathbf{F}\|\cos\theta)\|\overrightarrow{PQ}\| = 10\cdot\frac{1}{2}\cdot 50 = 250 \text{ ft·lb}$$

***Solution (b).*** Since $\overrightarrow{PQ} = (3-(-1))\mathbf{i} + (0-1)\mathbf{j} + (-2-2)\mathbf{k} = 4\mathbf{i} - \mathbf{j} - 4\mathbf{k}$, the work done is

$$W = \mathbf{F}\cdot\overrightarrow{PQ} = (3\mathbf{i} - \mathbf{j} + 2\mathbf{k})\cdot(4\mathbf{i} - \mathbf{j} - 4\mathbf{k}) = 12 + 1 - 8 = 5 \text{ ft·lb}$$ ◀

## ✓ QUICK CHECK EXERCISES 11.3

(See page 700 for answers.)

1. $\langle 3, 1, -2\rangle \cdot \langle 6, 0, 5\rangle =$ ______
2. Suppose that $\mathbf{u}$, $\mathbf{v}$, and $\mathbf{w}$ are vectors in 3-space such that $\|\mathbf{u}\| = 5$, $\mathbf{u}\cdot\mathbf{v} = 7$, and $\mathbf{u}\cdot\mathbf{w} = -3$.
   (a) $\mathbf{u}\cdot\mathbf{u} =$ ______ (b) $\mathbf{v}\cdot\mathbf{u} =$ ______
   (c) $\mathbf{u}\cdot(\mathbf{v} - \mathbf{w}) =$ ______ (d) $\mathbf{u}\cdot(2\mathbf{w}) =$ ______
3. For the vectors $\mathbf{u}$ and $\mathbf{v}$ in the preceding exercise, if the angle between $\mathbf{u}$ and $\mathbf{v}$ is $\pi/3$, then $\|\mathbf{v}\| =$ ______.
4. The direction cosines of $\langle 2, -1, 3\rangle$ are $\cos\alpha =$ ______, $\cos\beta =$ ______, and $\cos\gamma =$ ______.
5. The orthogonal projection of $\mathbf{v} = 10\mathbf{i}$ on $\mathbf{b} = -3\mathbf{i} + \mathbf{j}$ is ______.

## EXERCISE SET 11.3 [C] CAS

1. In each part, find the dot product of the vectors and the cosine of the angle between them.
   (a) $\mathbf{u} = \mathbf{i} + 2\mathbf{j}$, $\mathbf{v} = 6\mathbf{i} - 8\mathbf{j}$
   (b) $\mathbf{u} = \langle -7, -3 \rangle$, $\mathbf{v} = \langle 0, 1 \rangle$
   (c) $\mathbf{u} = \mathbf{i} - 3\mathbf{j} + 7\mathbf{k}$, $\mathbf{v} = 8\mathbf{i} - 2\mathbf{j} - 2\mathbf{k}$
   (d) $\mathbf{u} = \langle -3, 1, 2 \rangle$, $\mathbf{v} = \langle 4, 2, -5 \rangle$

2. In each part use the given information to find $\mathbf{u} \cdot \mathbf{v}$.
   (a) $\|\mathbf{u}\| = 1$, $\|\mathbf{v}\| = 2$, the angle between $\mathbf{u}$ and $\mathbf{v}$ is $\pi/6$.
   (b) $\|\mathbf{u}\| = 2$, $\|\mathbf{v}\| = 3$, the angle between $\mathbf{u}$ and $\mathbf{v}$ is $135°$.

3. In each part, determine whether $\mathbf{u}$ and $\mathbf{v}$ make an acute angle, an obtuse angle, or are orthogonal.
   (a) $\mathbf{u} = 7\mathbf{i} + 3\mathbf{j} + 5\mathbf{k}$, $\mathbf{v} = -8\mathbf{i} + 4\mathbf{j} + 2\mathbf{k}$
   (b) $\mathbf{u} = 6\mathbf{i} + \mathbf{j} + 3\mathbf{k}$, $\mathbf{v} = 4\mathbf{i} - 6\mathbf{k}$
   (c) $\mathbf{u} = \langle 1, 1, 1 \rangle$, $\mathbf{v} = \langle -1, 0, 0 \rangle$
   (d) $\mathbf{u} = \langle 4, 1, 6 \rangle$, $\mathbf{v} = \langle -3, 0, 2 \rangle$

### FOCUS ON CONCEPTS

4. Does the triangle in 3-space with vertices $(-1, 2, 3)$, $(2, -2, 0)$, and $(3, 1, -4)$ have an obtuse angle? Justify your answer.

5. The accompanying figure shows eight vectors that are equally spaced around a circle of radius 1. Find the dot product of $\mathbf{v}_0$ with each of the other seven vectors.

6. The accompanying figure shows six vectors that are equally spaced around a circle of radius 5. Find the dot product of $\mathbf{v}_0$ with each of the other five vectors.

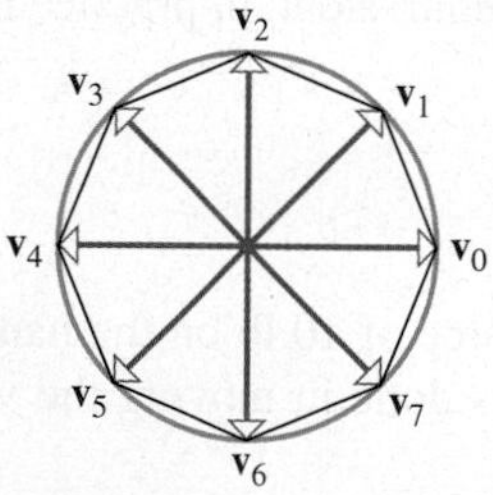

▲ Figure Ex-5

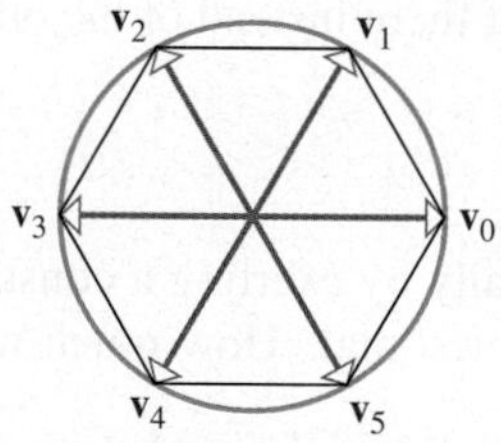

▲ Figure Ex-6

7. (a) Use vectors to show that $A(2, -1, 1)$, $B(3, 2, -1)$, and $C(7, 0, -2)$ are vertices of a right triangle. At which vertex is the right angle?
   (b) Use vectors to find the interior angles of the triangle with vertices $(-1, 0)$, $(2, -1)$, and $(1, 4)$. Express your answers to the nearest degree.

8. (a) Show that if $\mathbf{v} = a\mathbf{i} + b\mathbf{j}$ is a vector in 2-space, then the vectors
$$\mathbf{v}_1 = -b\mathbf{i} + a\mathbf{j} \quad \text{and} \quad \mathbf{v}_2 = b\mathbf{i} - a\mathbf{j}$$
   are both orthogonal to $\mathbf{v}$.
   (b) Use the result in part (a) to find two unit vectors that are orthogonal to the vector $\mathbf{v} = 3\mathbf{i} - 2\mathbf{j}$. Sketch the vectors $\mathbf{v}$, $\mathbf{v}_1$, and $\mathbf{v}_2$.

9. In each part, determine whether the given expression makes sense. Explain your answers.
   (a) $\mathbf{u} \cdot (\mathbf{v} \cdot \mathbf{w})$ (b) $(\mathbf{u} \cdot \mathbf{w})\mathbf{w}$ (c) $(\mathbf{u} \cdot \mathbf{v}) + \mathbf{w}$
   (d) $\mathbf{u} \cdot \mathbf{v} + k$ (e) $k \cdot (\mathbf{u} + \mathbf{v})$ (f) $(\mathbf{u} \cdot \mathbf{v})(\mathbf{v} \cdot \mathbf{w})$

10. The first, second, and third components of the "price vector" $\mathbf{p} = \langle \$479.99, \$799.99, \$1099.99 \rangle$ denote the respective prices of 40-, 55-, and 60-inch flatscreen televisions sold by a store. Suppose that $s_1$, $s_2$, and $s_3$ denote, respectively, the number of each type of television sold by the store in a given month and that $\mathbf{s} = \langle s_1, s_2, s_3 \rangle$. What is an economic interpretation of the dot product $\mathbf{p} \cdot \mathbf{s}$?

11. The $\mathbf{i}$, $\mathbf{j}$, and $\mathbf{k}$ components of the "race vector" $\mathbf{t} = 1.2\mathbf{i} + 56\mathbf{j} + 13.1\mathbf{k}$ denote the distances (in miles) to swim, bike, and run in a Half Ironman triathelon. Suppose that $v_1$, $v_2$, and $v_3$ denote, respectively, the speeds (in mi/h) of an athlete for each component and that $\mathbf{w} = v_1^{-1}\mathbf{i} + v_2^{-1}\mathbf{j} + v_3^{-1}\mathbf{k}$. What is an interpretation of the dot product $\mathbf{t} \cdot \mathbf{w}$?

12. Let $\mathbf{u} = \langle 1, 2 \rangle$, $\mathbf{v} = \langle 4, -2 \rangle$, and $\mathbf{w} = \langle 6, 0 \rangle$. Find
   (a) $\mathbf{u} \cdot (7\mathbf{v} + \mathbf{w})$ (b) $\|(\mathbf{u} \cdot \mathbf{w})\mathbf{w}\|$
   (c) $\|\mathbf{u}\|(\mathbf{v} \cdot \mathbf{w})$ (d) $(\|\mathbf{u}\|\mathbf{v}) \cdot \mathbf{w}$.

13. Find $r$ so that the vector from the point $A(1, -1, 3)$ to the point $B(3, 0, 5)$ is orthogonal to the vector from $A$ to the point $P(r, r, r)$.

14. Find two unit vectors in 2-space that make an angle of $45°$ with $4\mathbf{i} + 3\mathbf{j}$.

**15–16** Find the direction cosines of $\mathbf{v}$ and confirm that they satisfy Equation (5). Then use the direction cosines to approximate the direction angles to the nearest degree. ■

15. (a) $\mathbf{v} = \mathbf{i} + \mathbf{j} - \mathbf{k}$ (b) $\mathbf{v} = 2\mathbf{i} - 2\mathbf{j} + \mathbf{k}$

16. (a) $\mathbf{v} = 3\mathbf{i} - 2\mathbf{j} - 6\mathbf{k}$ (b) $\mathbf{v} = 3\mathbf{i} - 4\mathbf{k}$

### FOCUS ON CONCEPTS

17. Show that the direction cosines of a vector satisfy
$$\cos^2\alpha + \cos^2\beta + \cos^2\gamma = 1$$

18. Let $\theta$ and $\lambda$ be the angles shown in the accompanying figure. Show that the direction cosines of $\mathbf{v}$ can be expressed as
$$\cos\alpha = \cos\lambda\cos\theta$$
$$\cos\beta = \cos\lambda\sin\theta$$
$$\cos\gamma = \sin\lambda$$
   [*Hint:* Express $\mathbf{v}$ in component form and normalize.]

19. The accompanying figure shows a cube.
   (a) Find the angle between the vectors $\mathbf{d}$ and $\mathbf{u}$ to the nearest degree.
   (b) Make a conjecture about the angle between the vectors $\mathbf{d}$ and $\mathbf{v}$, and confirm your conjecture by computing the angle.

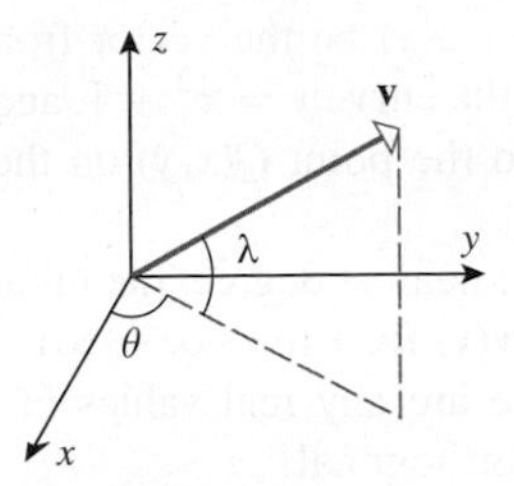

▲ Figure Ex-18

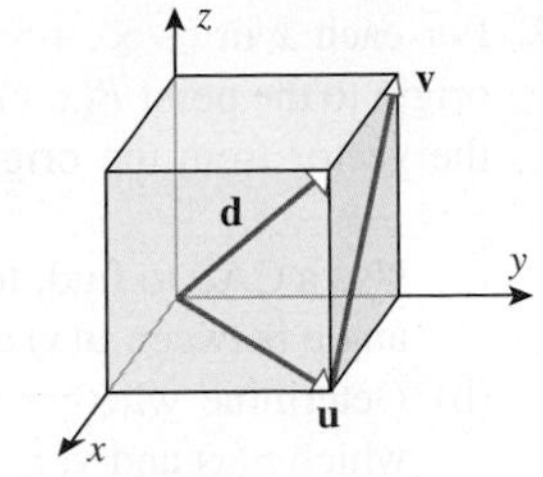

▲ Figure Ex-19

**20.** Show that two nonzero vectors $\mathbf{v}_1$ and $\mathbf{v}_2$ are orthogonal if and only if their direction cosines satisfy

$$\cos\alpha_1\cos\alpha_2 + \cos\beta_1\cos\beta_2 + \cos\gamma_1\cos\gamma_2 = 0$$

**21.** Use the result in Exercise 18 to find the direction angles of the vector shown in the accompanying figure to the nearest degree.

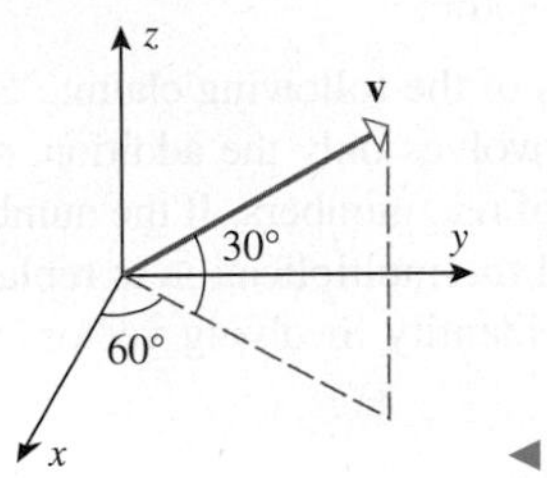

◀ Figure Ex-21

**22.** Find, to the nearest degree, the acute angle formed by two diagonals of a cube.

**23.** Find, to the nearest degree, the angles that a diagonal of a box with dimensions 10 cm by 15 cm by 25 cm makes with the edges of the box.

**24.** In each part, find the vector component of $\mathbf{v}$ along $\mathbf{b}$ and the vector component of $\mathbf{v}$ orthogonal to $\mathbf{b}$. Then sketch the vectors $\mathbf{v}$, $\text{proj}_{\mathbf{b}}\mathbf{v}$, and $\mathbf{v} - \text{proj}_{\mathbf{b}}\mathbf{v}$.

(a) $\mathbf{v} = 2\mathbf{i} - \mathbf{j}$, $\mathbf{b} = 3\mathbf{i} + 4\mathbf{j}$

(b) $\mathbf{v} = \langle 4, 5\rangle$, $\mathbf{b} = \langle 1, -2\rangle$

(c) $\mathbf{v} = -3\mathbf{i} - 2\mathbf{j}$, $\mathbf{b} = 2\mathbf{i} + \mathbf{j}$

**25.** In each part, find the vector component of $\mathbf{v}$ along $\mathbf{b}$ and the vector component of $\mathbf{v}$ orthogonal to $\mathbf{b}$.

(a) $\mathbf{v} = 2\mathbf{i} - \mathbf{j} + 3\mathbf{k}$, $\mathbf{b} = \mathbf{i} + 2\mathbf{j} + 2\mathbf{k}$

(b) $\mathbf{v} = \langle 4, -1, 7\rangle$, $\mathbf{b} = \langle 2, 3, -6\rangle$

**26–27** Express the vector $\mathbf{v}$ as the sum of a vector parallel to $\mathbf{b}$ and a vector orthogonal to $\mathbf{b}$. ■

**26.** (a) $\mathbf{v} = 2\mathbf{i} - 4\mathbf{j}$, $\mathbf{b} = \mathbf{i} + \mathbf{j}$

(b) $\mathbf{v} = 3\mathbf{i} + \mathbf{j} - 2\mathbf{k}$, $\mathbf{b} = 2\mathbf{i} - \mathbf{k}$

(c) $\mathbf{v} = 4\mathbf{i} - 2\mathbf{j} + 6\mathbf{k}$, $\mathbf{b} = -2\mathbf{i} + \mathbf{j} - 3\mathbf{k}$

**27.** (a) $\mathbf{v} = \langle -3, 5\rangle$, $\mathbf{b} = \langle 1, 1\rangle$

(b) $\mathbf{v} = \langle -2, 1, 6\rangle$, $\mathbf{b} = \langle 0, -2, 1\rangle$

(c) $\mathbf{v} = \langle 1, 4, 1\rangle$, $\mathbf{b} = \langle 3, -2, 5\rangle$

**28–31 True–False** Determine whether the statement is true or false. Explain your answer. ■

**28.** If $\mathbf{a}\cdot\mathbf{b} = \mathbf{a}\cdot\mathbf{c}$ and $\mathbf{a} \neq \mathbf{0}$, then $\mathbf{b} = \mathbf{c}$.

**29.** If $\mathbf{v}$ and $\mathbf{w}$ are nonzero orthogonal vectors, then $\mathbf{v} + \mathbf{w} \neq \mathbf{0}$.

**30.** If $\mathbf{u}$ is a unit vector that is parallel to a nonzero vector $\mathbf{v}$, then $\mathbf{u}\cdot\mathbf{v} = \pm\|\mathbf{v}\|$.

**31.** If $\mathbf{v}$ and $\mathbf{b}$ are nonzero vectors, then the orthogonal projection of $\mathbf{v}$ on $\mathbf{b}$ is a vector that is parallel to $\mathbf{b}$.

**32.** If $L$ is a line in 2-space or 3-space that passes through the points $A$ and $B$, then the distance from a point $P$ to the line $L$ is equal to the length of the component of the vector $\overrightarrow{AP}$ that is orthogonal to the vector $\overrightarrow{AB}$ (see the accompanying figure). Use this result to find the distance from the point $P(1, 0)$ to the line through $A(2, -3)$ and $B(5, 1)$.

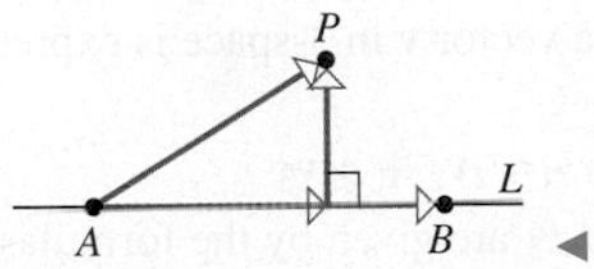

◀ Figure Ex-32

**33.** Use the method of Exercise 32 to find the distance from the point $P(-3, 1, 2)$ to the line through $A(1, 1, 0)$ and $B(-2, 3, -4)$.

**34.** As shown in the accompanying figure, a child with mass 34 kg is seated on a smooth (frictionless) playground slide that is inclined at an angle of 27° with the horizontal. Estimate the force that the child exerts on the slide, and estimate how much force must be applied in the direction of $\mathbf{P}$ to prevent the child from sliding down the slide. Take the acceleration due to gravity to be 9.8 m/s$^2$.

**35.** For the child in Exercise 34, estimate how much force must be applied in the direction of $\mathbf{Q}$ (shown in the accompanying figure) to prevent the child from sliding down the slide?

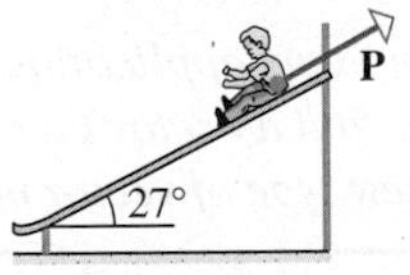

▲ Figure Ex-34

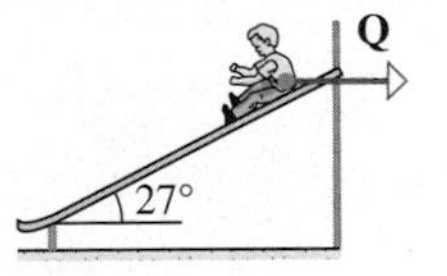

▲ Figure Ex-35

**36.** Suppose that the slide in Exercise 34 is 4 m long. Estimate the work done by gravity if the child slides from the top of the slide to the bottom.

**37.** A box is dragged along the floor by a rope that applies a force of 50 lb at an angle of 60° with the floor. How much work is done in moving the box 15 ft?

**38.** Find the work done by a force $\mathbf{F} = -3\mathbf{j}$ pounds applied to a point that moves on a line from $(1, 3)$ to $(4, 7)$. Assume that distance is measured in feet.

**39.** A force of $\mathbf{F} = 4\mathbf{i} - 6\mathbf{j} + \mathbf{k}$ newtons is applied to a point that moves a distance of 15 meters in the direction of the vector $\mathbf{i} + \mathbf{j} + \mathbf{k}$. How much work is done?

**40.** A boat travels 100 meters due north while the wind exerts a force of 500 newtons toward the northeast. How much work does the wind do?

**FOCUS ON CONCEPTS**

**41.** Let $\mathbf{u}$ and $\mathbf{v}$ be adjacent sides of a parallelogram. Use vectors to prove that the diagonals of the parallelogram are perpendicular if the sides are equal in length.

**42.** Let $\mathbf{u}$ and $\mathbf{v}$ be adjacent sides of a parallelogram. Use vectors to prove that the parallelogram is a rectangle if the diagonals are equal in length.

**43.** Prove that

$$\|\mathbf{u}+\mathbf{v}\|^2 + \|\mathbf{u}-\mathbf{v}\|^2 = 2\|\mathbf{u}\|^2 + 2\|\mathbf{v}\|^2$$

and interpret the result geometrically by translating it into a theorem about parallelograms.

**44.** Prove: $\mathbf{u}\cdot\mathbf{v} = \frac{1}{4}\|\mathbf{u}+\mathbf{v}\|^2 - \frac{1}{4}\|\mathbf{u}-\mathbf{v}\|^2$.

**45.** Show that if $\mathbf{v}_1$, $\mathbf{v}_2$, and $\mathbf{v}_3$ are mutually orthogonal nonzero vectors in 3-space, and if a vector $\mathbf{v}$ in 3-space is expressed as

$$\mathbf{v} = c_1\mathbf{v}_1 + c_2\mathbf{v}_2 + c_3\mathbf{v}_3$$

then the scalars $c_1$, $c_2$, and $c_3$ are given by the formulas

$$c_i = (\mathbf{v}\cdot\mathbf{v}_i)/\|\mathbf{v}_i\|^2, \quad i = 1, 2, 3$$

**46.** Show that the three vectors

$$\mathbf{v}_1 = 3\mathbf{i} - \mathbf{j} + 2\mathbf{k}, \quad \mathbf{v}_2 = \mathbf{i} + \mathbf{j} - \mathbf{k}, \quad \mathbf{v}_3 = \mathbf{i} - 5\mathbf{j} - 4\mathbf{k}$$

are mutually orthogonal, and then use the result of Exercise 45 to find scalars $c_1$, $c_2$, and $c_3$ so that

$$c_1\mathbf{v}_1 + c_2\mathbf{v}_2 + c_3\mathbf{v}_3 = \mathbf{i} - \mathbf{j} + \mathbf{k}$$

C **47.** For each $x$ in $(-\infty, +\infty)$, let $\mathbf{u}(x)$ be the vector from the origin to the point $P(x, y)$ on the curve $y = x^2 + 1$, and $\mathbf{v}(x)$ the vector from the origin to the point $Q(x, y)$ on the line $y = -x - 1$.

(a) Use a CAS to find, to the nearest degree, the minimum angle between $\mathbf{u}(x)$ and $\mathbf{v}(x)$ for $x$ in $(-\infty, +\infty)$.

(b) Determine whether there are any real values of $x$ for which $\mathbf{u}(x)$ and $\mathbf{v}(x)$ are orthogonal.

C **48.** Let $\mathbf{u}$ be a unit vector in the $xy$-plane of an $xyz$-coordinate system, and let $\mathbf{v}$ be a unit vector in the $yz$-plane. Let $\theta_1$ be the angle between $\mathbf{u}$ and $\mathbf{i}$, let $\theta_2$ be the angle between $\mathbf{v}$ and $\mathbf{k}$, and let $\theta$ be the angle between $\mathbf{u}$ and $\mathbf{v}$.

(a) Show that $\cos\theta = \pm\sin\theta_1\sin\theta_2$.

(b) Find $\theta$ if $\theta$ is acute and $\theta_1 = \theta_2 = 45^\circ$.

(c) Use a CAS to find, to the nearest degree, the maximum and minimum values of $\theta$ if $\theta$ is acute and $\theta_2 = 2\theta_1$.

**49.** Prove parts (*b*) and (*e*) of Theorem 11.3.2 for vectors in 3-space.

**50. Writing** Discuss some of the similarities and differences between the multiplication properties of real numbers and those of the dot product of vectors.

**51. Writing** Discuss the merits of the following claim: "Suppose an algebraic identity involves only the addition, subtraction, and multiplication of real numbers. If the numbers are replaced by vectors, and the multiplication is replaced by the dot product, then an identity involving vectors will result."

✓ **QUICK CHECK ANSWERS 11.3** 1. 8 2. (a) 25 (b) 7 (c) 10 (d) −6 3. $\frac{14}{5}$ 4. $\frac{2}{\sqrt{14}}$; $-\frac{1}{\sqrt{14}}$; $\frac{3}{\sqrt{14}}$ 5. $9\mathbf{i} - 3\mathbf{j}$

## 11.4 CROSS PRODUCT

*In many applications of vectors in mathematics, physics, and engineering, there is a need to find a vector that is orthogonal to two given vectors. In this section we will discuss a new type of vector multiplication that can be used for this purpose.*

### DETERMINANTS

Some of the concepts that we will develop in this section require basic ideas about ***determinants***, which are functions that assign numerical values to square arrays of numbers. For example, if $a_1$, $a_2$, $b_1$, and $b_2$ are real numbers, then we define a **2 × 2 *determinant*** by

$$\begin{vmatrix} a_1 & a_2 \\ b_1 & b_2 \end{vmatrix} = a_1b_2 - a_2b_1 \tag{1}$$

The purpose of the arrows is to help you remember the formula—the determinant is the product of the entries on the rightward arrow minus the product of the entries on the leftward arrow. For example,

$$\begin{vmatrix} 3 & -2 \\ 4 & 5 \end{vmatrix} = (3)(5) - (-2)(4) = 15 + 8 = 23$$

A $3 \times 3$ ***determinant*** is defined in terms of $2 \times 2$ determinants by

$$\begin{vmatrix} a_1 & a_2 & a_3 \\ b_1 & b_2 & b_3 \\ c_1 & c_2 & c_3 \end{vmatrix} = a_1 \begin{vmatrix} b_2 & b_3 \\ c_2 & c_3 \end{vmatrix} - a_2 \begin{vmatrix} b_1 & b_3 \\ c_1 & c_3 \end{vmatrix} + a_3 \begin{vmatrix} b_1 & b_2 \\ c_1 & c_2 \end{vmatrix} \tag{2}$$

The right side of this formula is easily remembered by noting that $a_1$, $a_2$, and $a_3$ are the entries in the first "row" of the left side, and the $2 \times 2$ determinants on the right side arise by deleting the first row and an appropriate column from the left side. The pattern is as follows:

$$\begin{vmatrix} a_1 & a_2 & a_3 \\ b_1 & b_2 & b_3 \\ c_1 & c_2 & c_3 \end{vmatrix} = a_1 \begin{vmatrix} a_1 & a_2 & a_3 \\ b_1 & b_2 & b_3 \\ c_1 & c_2 & c_3 \end{vmatrix} - a_2 \begin{vmatrix} a_1 & a_2 & a_3 \\ b_1 & b_2 & b_3 \\ c_1 & c_2 & c_3 \end{vmatrix} + a_3 \begin{vmatrix} a_1 & a_2 & a_3 \\ b_1 & b_2 & b_3 \\ c_1 & c_2 & c_3 \end{vmatrix}$$

For example,

$$\begin{vmatrix} 3 & -2 & -5 \\ 1 & 4 & -4 \\ 0 & 3 & 2 \end{vmatrix} = 3 \begin{vmatrix} 4 & -4 \\ 3 & 2 \end{vmatrix} - (-2) \begin{vmatrix} 1 & -4 \\ 0 & 2 \end{vmatrix} + (-5) \begin{vmatrix} 1 & 4 \\ 0 & 3 \end{vmatrix}$$

$$= 3(20) + 2(2) - 5(3) = 49$$

There are also definitions of $4 \times 4$ determinants, $5 \times 5$ determinants, and higher, but we will not need them in this text. Properties of determinants are studied in a branch of mathematics called ***linear algebra***, but we will only need the two properties stated in the following theorem.

**11.4.1 THEOREM**

(*a*) *If two rows in the array of a determinant are the same, then the value of the determinant is* 0.

(*b*) *Interchanging two rows in the array of a determinant multiplies its value by* $-1$.

We will give the proofs of parts (*a*) and (*b*) for $2 \times 2$ determinants and leave the proofs for $3 \times 3$ determinants as exercises.

**PROOF (*a*)**

$$\begin{vmatrix} a_1 & a_2 \\ a_1 & a_2 \end{vmatrix} = a_1a_2 - a_2a_1 = 0$$

**PROOF (*b*)**

$$\begin{vmatrix} b_1 & b_2 \\ a_1 & a_2 \end{vmatrix} = b_1a_2 - b_2a_1 = -(a_1b_2 - a_2b_1) = -\begin{vmatrix} a_1 & a_2 \\ b_1 & b_2 \end{vmatrix} \quad \blacksquare$$

## CROSS PRODUCT

We now turn to the main concept in this section.

**11.4.2 DEFINITION** If $\mathbf{u} = \langle u_1, u_2, u_3 \rangle$ and $\mathbf{v} = \langle v_1, v_2, v_3 \rangle$ are vectors in 3-space, then the ***cross product*** $\mathbf{u} \times \mathbf{v}$ is the vector defined by

$$\mathbf{u} \times \mathbf{v} = \begin{vmatrix} u_2 & u_3 \\ v_2 & v_3 \end{vmatrix} \mathbf{i} - \begin{vmatrix} u_1 & u_3 \\ v_1 & v_3 \end{vmatrix} \mathbf{j} + \begin{vmatrix} u_1 & u_2 \\ v_1 & v_2 \end{vmatrix} \mathbf{k} \tag{3}$$

or, equivalently,

$$\mathbf{u} \times \mathbf{v} = (u_2v_3 - u_3v_2)\mathbf{i} - (u_1v_3 - u_3v_1)\mathbf{j} + (u_1v_2 - u_2v_1)\mathbf{k} \tag{4}$$

Observe that the right side of Formula (3) has the same form as the right side of Formula (2), the difference being notation and the order of the factors in the three terms. Thus, we can rewrite (3) as

$$\mathbf{u} \times \mathbf{v} = \begin{vmatrix} \mathbf{i} & \mathbf{j} & \mathbf{k} \\ u_1 & u_2 & u_3 \\ v_1 & v_2 & v_3 \end{vmatrix} \tag{5}$$

However, this is just a mnemonic device and not a true determinant since the entries in a determinant are numbers, not vectors.

**▶ Example 1** Let $\mathbf{u} = \langle 1, 2, -2 \rangle$ and $\mathbf{v} = \langle 3, 0, 1 \rangle$. Find

(a) $\mathbf{u} \times \mathbf{v}$ (b) $\mathbf{v} \times \mathbf{u}$

***Solution (a).***

$$\mathbf{u} \times \mathbf{v} = \begin{vmatrix} \mathbf{i} & \mathbf{j} & \mathbf{k} \\ 1 & 2 & -2 \\ 3 & 0 & 1 \end{vmatrix}$$

$$= \begin{vmatrix} 2 & -2 \\ 0 & 1 \end{vmatrix} \mathbf{i} - \begin{vmatrix} 1 & -2 \\ 3 & 1 \end{vmatrix} \mathbf{j} + \begin{vmatrix} 1 & 2 \\ 3 & 0 \end{vmatrix} \mathbf{k} = 2\mathbf{i} - 7\mathbf{j} - 6\mathbf{k}$$

***Solution (b).*** We could use the method of part (a), but it is really not necessary to perform any computations. We need only observe that reversing **u** and **v** interchanges the second and third rows in (5), which in turn interchanges the rows in the arrays for the $2 \times 2$ determinants in (3). But interchanging the rows in the array of a $2 \times 2$ determinant reverses its sign, so the net effect of reversing the factors in a cross product is to reverse the signs of the components. Thus, by inspection

$$\mathbf{v} \times \mathbf{u} = -(\mathbf{u} \times \mathbf{v}) = -2\mathbf{i} + 7\mathbf{j} + 6\mathbf{k} \blacktriangleleft$$

**▶ Example 2** Show that $\mathbf{u} \times \mathbf{u} = \mathbf{0}$ for any vector **u** in 3-space.

***Solution.*** We could let $\mathbf{u} = u_1\mathbf{i} + u_2\mathbf{j} + u_3\mathbf{k}$ and apply the method in part (a) of Example 1 to show that

$$\mathbf{u} \times \mathbf{u} = \begin{vmatrix} \mathbf{i} & \mathbf{j} & \mathbf{k} \\ u_1 & u_2 & u_3 \\ u_1 & u_2 & u_3 \end{vmatrix} = 0$$

However, the actual computations are unnecessary. We need only observe that if the two factors in a cross product are the same, then each $2 \times 2$ determinant in (3) is zero because its array has identical rows. Thus, $\mathbf{u} \times \mathbf{u} = \mathbf{0}$ by inspection. ◀

## ALGEBRAIC PROPERTIES OF THE CROSS PRODUCT

Our next goal is to establish some of the basic algebraic properties of the cross product. As you read the discussion, keep in mind the essential differences between the cross product and the dot product:

- The cross product is defined only for vectors in 3-space, whereas the dot product is defined for vectors in 2-space and 3-space.
- The cross product of two vectors is a vector, whereas the dot product of two vectors is a scalar.

The main algebraic properties of the cross product are listed in the next theorem.

**11.4.3 THEOREM** *If* $\mathbf{u}$, $\mathbf{v}$, *and* $\mathbf{w}$ *are any vectors in 3-space and k is any scalar, then:*

(*a*) $\mathbf{u} \times \mathbf{v} = -(\mathbf{v} \times \mathbf{u})$

(*b*) $\mathbf{u} \times (\mathbf{v} + \mathbf{w}) = (\mathbf{u} \times \mathbf{v}) + (\mathbf{u} \times \mathbf{w})$

(*c*) $(\mathbf{u} + \mathbf{v}) \times \mathbf{w} = (\mathbf{u} \times \mathbf{w}) + (\mathbf{v} \times \mathbf{w})$

(*d*) $k(\mathbf{u} \times \mathbf{v}) = (k\mathbf{u}) \times \mathbf{v} = \mathbf{u} \times (k\mathbf{v})$

(*e*) $\mathbf{u} \times \mathbf{0} = \mathbf{0} \times \mathbf{u} = \mathbf{0}$

(*f*) $\mathbf{u} \times \mathbf{u} = \mathbf{0}$

Whereas the order of the factors does not matter for ordinary multiplication, or for dot products, it does matter for cross products. Specifically, part (*a*) of Theorem 11.4.3 shows that reversing the order of the factors in a cross product reverses the direction of the resulting vector.

Parts (*a*) and (*f*) were addressed in Examples 1 and 2. The other proofs are left as exercises.

The following cross products occur so frequently that it is helpful to be familiar with them:

$$\begin{array}{lll} \mathbf{i} \times \mathbf{j} = \mathbf{k} & \mathbf{j} \times \mathbf{k} = \mathbf{i} & \mathbf{k} \times \mathbf{i} = \mathbf{j} \\ \mathbf{j} \times \mathbf{i} = -\mathbf{k} & \mathbf{k} \times \mathbf{j} = -\mathbf{i} & \mathbf{i} \times \mathbf{k} = -\mathbf{j} \end{array} \tag{6}$$

These results are easy to obtain; for example,

$$\mathbf{i} \times \mathbf{j} = \begin{vmatrix} \mathbf{i} & \mathbf{j} & \mathbf{k} \\ 1 & 0 & 0 \\ 0 & 1 & 0 \end{vmatrix} = \begin{vmatrix} 0 & 0 \\ 1 & 0 \end{vmatrix}\mathbf{i} - \begin{vmatrix} 1 & 0 \\ 0 & 0 \end{vmatrix}\mathbf{j} + \begin{vmatrix} 1 & 0 \\ 0 & 1 \end{vmatrix}\mathbf{k} = \mathbf{k}$$

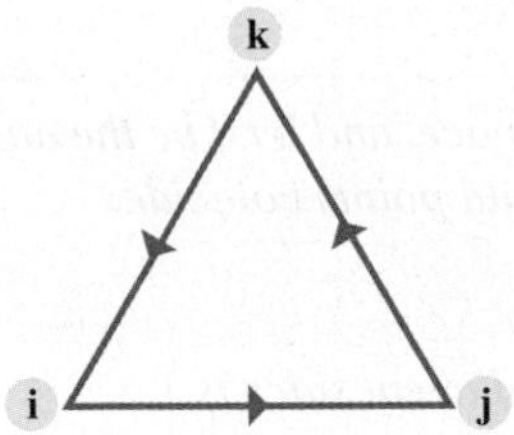

▲ **Figure 11.4.1**

However, rather than computing these cross products each time you need them, you can use the diagram in Figure 11.4.1. In this diagram, the cross product of two consecutive vectors in the counterclockwise direction is the next vector around, and the cross product of two consecutive vectors in the clockwise direction is the negative of the next vector around.

**WARNING** We can write a product of three real numbers as $uvw$ since the associative law $u(vw) = (uv)w$ ensures that the same value for the product results no matter how the factors are grouped. However, the associative law *does not* hold for cross products. For example,

$$\mathbf{i} \times (\mathbf{j} \times \mathbf{j}) = \mathbf{i} \times \mathbf{0} = \mathbf{0} \quad \text{and} \quad (\mathbf{i} \times \mathbf{j}) \times \mathbf{j} = \mathbf{k} \times \mathbf{j} = -\mathbf{i}$$

so that $\mathbf{i} \times (\mathbf{j} \times \mathbf{j}) \neq (\mathbf{i} \times \mathbf{j}) \times \mathbf{j}$. Thus, we cannot write a cross product with three vectors as $\mathbf{u} \times \mathbf{v} \times \mathbf{w}$, since this expression is ambiguous without parentheses.

## GEOMETRIC PROPERTIES OF THE CROSS PRODUCT

The following theorem shows that the cross product of two vectors is orthogonal to both factors. This property of the cross product will be used many times in the following sections.

**11.4.4 THEOREM** *If* $\mathbf{u}$ *and* $\mathbf{v}$ *are vectors in 3-space, then:*

(*a*) $\mathbf{u} \cdot (\mathbf{u} \times \mathbf{v}) = 0$ ($\mathbf{u} \times \mathbf{v}$ *is orthogonal to* $\mathbf{u}$)

(*b*) $\mathbf{v} \cdot (\mathbf{u} \times \mathbf{v}) = 0$ ($\mathbf{u} \times \mathbf{v}$ *is orthogonal to* $\mathbf{v}$)

We will prove part (*a*). The proof of part (*b*) is similar.

**PROOF (*a*)** Let $\mathbf{u} = \langle u_1, u_2, u_3 \rangle$ and $\mathbf{v} = \langle v_1, v_2, v_3 \rangle$. Then from (4)

$$\mathbf{u} \times \mathbf{v} = \langle u_2v_3 - u_3v_2, u_3v_1 - u_1v_3, u_1v_2 - u_2v_1 \rangle \tag{7}$$

so that

$$\mathbf{u} \cdot (\mathbf{u} \times \mathbf{v}) = u_1(u_2v_3 - u_3v_2) + u_2(u_3v_1 - u_1v_3) + u_3(u_1v_2 - u_2v_1) = 0 \;\blacksquare$$

▶ **Example 3** Find a vector that is orthogonal to both of the vectors $\mathbf{u} = \langle 2, -1, 3\rangle$ and $\mathbf{v} = \langle -7, 2, -1\rangle$.

Confirm that $\mathbf{u} \times \mathbf{v}$ in Example 3 is orthogonal to both $\mathbf{u}$ and $\mathbf{v}$ by computing $\mathbf{u} \cdot (\mathbf{u} \times \mathbf{v})$ and $\mathbf{v} \cdot (\mathbf{u} \times \mathbf{v})$.

***Solution.*** By Theorem 11.4.4, the vector $\mathbf{u} \times \mathbf{v}$ will be orthogonal to both $\mathbf{u}$ and $\mathbf{v}$. We compute that

$$\mathbf{u} \times \mathbf{v} = \begin{vmatrix} \mathbf{i} & \mathbf{j} & \mathbf{k} \\ 2 & -1 & 3 \\ -7 & 2 & -1 \end{vmatrix}$$

$$= \begin{vmatrix} -1 & 3 \\ 2 & -1 \end{vmatrix}\mathbf{i} - \begin{vmatrix} 2 & 3 \\ -7 & -1 \end{vmatrix}\mathbf{j} + \begin{vmatrix} 2 & -1 \\ -7 & 2 \end{vmatrix}\mathbf{k} = -5\mathbf{i} - 19\mathbf{j} - 3\mathbf{k} \quad ◀$$

It can be proved that if $\mathbf{u}$ and $\mathbf{v}$ are nonzero and nonparallel vectors, then the direction of $\mathbf{u} \times \mathbf{v}$ relative to $\mathbf{u}$ and $\mathbf{v}$ is determined by a right-hand rule;* that is, if the fingers of the right hand are cupped so they curl from $\mathbf{u}$ toward $\mathbf{v}$ in the direction of rotation that takes $\mathbf{u}$ into $\mathbf{v}$ in less than 180°, then the thumb will point (roughly) in the direction of $\mathbf{u} \times \mathbf{v}$ (Figure 11.4.2). For example, we stated in (6) that

$$\mathbf{i} \times \mathbf{j} = \mathbf{k}, \quad \mathbf{j} \times \mathbf{k} = \mathbf{i}, \quad \mathbf{k} \times \mathbf{i} = \mathbf{j}$$

all of which are consistent with the right-hand rule (verify).

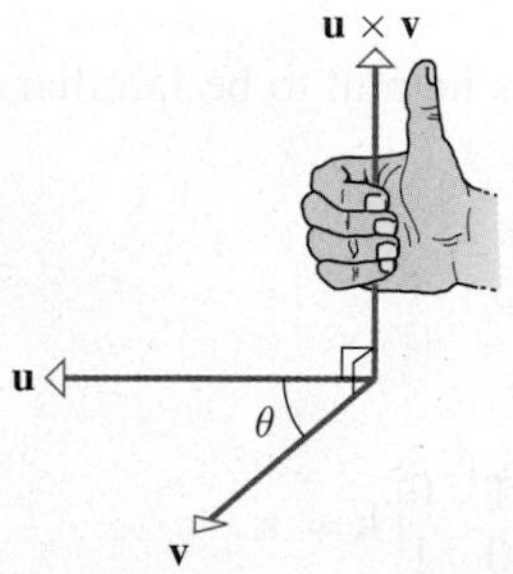

▲ Figure 11.4.2

The next theorem lists some more important geometric properties of the cross product.

**11.4.5 THEOREM** *Let $\mathbf{u}$ and $\mathbf{v}$ be nonzero vectors in 3-space, and let $\theta$ be the angle between these vectors when they are positioned so their initial points coincide.*

(*a*) $\|\mathbf{u} \times \mathbf{v}\| = \|\mathbf{u}\|\|\mathbf{v}\|\sin\theta$

(*b*) *The area A of the parallelogram that has $\mathbf{u}$ and $\mathbf{v}$ as adjacent sides is*

$$A = \|\mathbf{u} \times \mathbf{v}\| \tag{8}$$

(*c*) $\mathbf{u} \times \mathbf{v} = \mathbf{0}$ *if and only if $\mathbf{u}$ and $\mathbf{v}$ are parallel vectors, that is, if and only if they are scalar multiples of one another.*

**PROOF** (*a*)

$$\begin{aligned}
\|\mathbf{u}\|\|\mathbf{v}\|\sin\theta &= \|\mathbf{u}\|\|\mathbf{v}\|\sqrt{1-\cos^2\theta} \\
&= \|\mathbf{u}\|\|\mathbf{v}\|\sqrt{1-\frac{(\mathbf{u}\cdot\mathbf{v})^2}{\|\mathbf{u}\|^2\|\mathbf{v}\|^2}} \qquad \boxed{\text{Theorem 11.3.3}} \\
&= \sqrt{\|\mathbf{u}\|^2\|\mathbf{v}\|^2 - (\mathbf{u}\cdot\mathbf{v})^2} \\
&= \sqrt{(u_1^2+u_2^2+u_3^2)(v_1^2+v_2^2+v_3^2) - (u_1v_1+u_2v_2+u_3v_3)^2} \\
&= \sqrt{(u_2v_3-u_3v_2)^2 + (u_1v_3-u_3v_1)^2 + (u_1v_2-u_2v_1)^2} \\
&= \|\mathbf{u} \times \mathbf{v}\| \qquad \boxed{\text{See Formula (4).}}
\end{aligned}$$

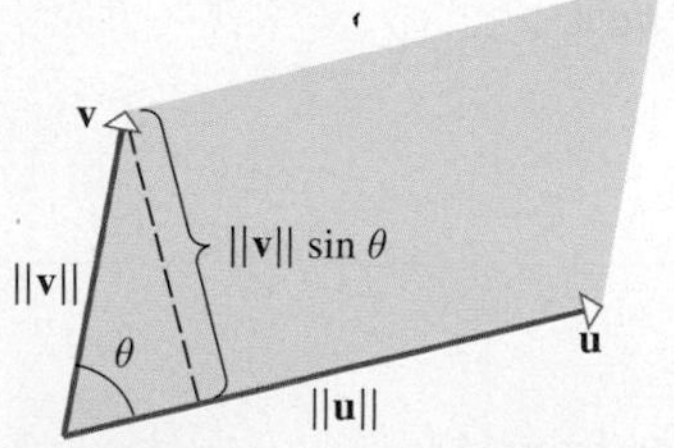

▲ Figure 11.4.3

**PROOF** (*b*) Referring to Figure 11.4.3, the parallelogram that has $\mathbf{u}$ and $\mathbf{v}$ as adjacent sides can be viewed as having base $\|\mathbf{u}\|$ and altitude $\|\mathbf{v}\|\sin\theta$. Thus, its area $A$ is

$$A = (\text{base})(\text{altitude}) = \|\mathbf{u}\|\|\mathbf{v}\|\sin\theta = \|\mathbf{u} \times \mathbf{v}\|$$

* Recall that we agreed to consider only right-handed coordinate systems in this text. Had we used left-handed systems instead, a "left-hand rule" would apply here.

**PROOF** (*c*) Since $\mathbf{u}$ and $\mathbf{v}$ are assumed to be nonzero vectors, it follows from part (*a*) that $\mathbf{u} \times \mathbf{v} = \mathbf{0}$ if and only if $\sin\theta = 0$; this is true if and only if $\theta = 0$ or $\theta = \pi$ (since $0 \le \theta \le \pi$). Geometrically, this means that $\mathbf{u} \times \mathbf{v} = \mathbf{0}$ if and only if $\mathbf{u}$ and $\mathbf{v}$ are parallel vectors. ■

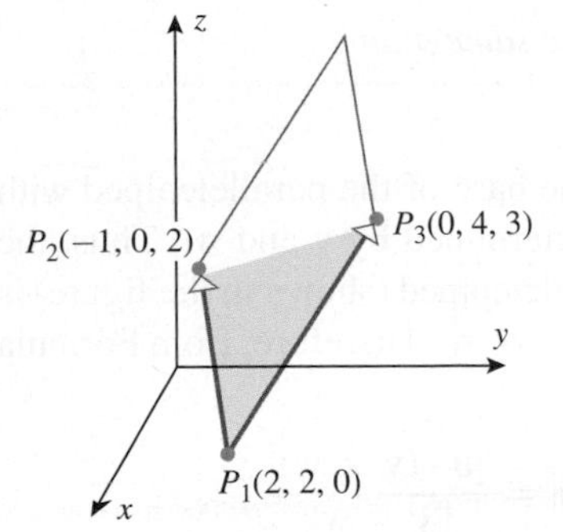

▲ **Figure 11.4.4**

▶ **Example 4** Find the area of the triangle that is determined by the points $P_1(2,2,0)$, $P_2(-1,0,2)$, and $P_3(0,4,3)$.

***Solution.*** The area $A$ of the triangle is half the area of the parallelogram determined by the vectors $\overrightarrow{P_1P_2}$ and $\overrightarrow{P_1P_3}$ (Figure 11.4.4). But $\overrightarrow{P_1P_2} = \langle -3,-2,2\rangle$ and $\overrightarrow{P_1P_3} = \langle -2,2,3\rangle$, so

$$\overrightarrow{P_1P_2} \times \overrightarrow{P_1P_3} = \langle -10, 5, -10\rangle$$

(verify), and consequently

$$A = \tfrac{1}{2}\|\overrightarrow{P_1P_2} \times \overrightarrow{P_1P_3}\| = \tfrac{15}{2} \blacktriangleleft$$

## SCALAR TRIPLE PRODUCTS

If $\mathbf{u} = \langle u_1, u_2, u_3\rangle$, $\mathbf{v} = \langle v_1, v_2, v_3\rangle$, and $\mathbf{w} = \langle w_1, w_2, w_3\rangle$ are vectors in 3-space, then the number

$$\mathbf{u} \cdot (\mathbf{v} \times \mathbf{w})$$

is called the ***scalar triple product*** of $\mathbf{u}$, $\mathbf{v}$, and $\mathbf{w}$. It is not necessary to compute the dot product and cross product to evaluate a scalar triple product—the value can be obtained directly from the formula

$$\mathbf{u} \cdot (\mathbf{v} \times \mathbf{w}) = \begin{vmatrix} u_1 & u_2 & u_3 \\ v_1 & v_2 & v_3 \\ w_1 & w_2 & w_3 \end{vmatrix} \tag{9}$$

the validity of which can be seen by writing

$$\begin{aligned} \mathbf{u} \cdot (\mathbf{v} \times \mathbf{w}) &= \mathbf{u} \cdot \left( \begin{vmatrix} v_2 & v_3 \\ w_2 & w_3 \end{vmatrix} \mathbf{i} - \begin{vmatrix} v_1 & v_3 \\ w_1 & w_3 \end{vmatrix} \mathbf{j} + \begin{vmatrix} v_1 & v_2 \\ w_1 & w_2 \end{vmatrix} \mathbf{k} \right) \\ &= u_1 \begin{vmatrix} v_2 & v_3 \\ w_2 & w_3 \end{vmatrix} - u_2 \begin{vmatrix} v_1 & v_3 \\ w_1 & w_3 \end{vmatrix} + u_3 \begin{vmatrix} v_1 & v_2 \\ w_1 & w_2 \end{vmatrix} \\ &= \begin{vmatrix} u_1 & u_2 & u_3 \\ v_1 & v_2 & v_3 \\ w_1 & w_2 & w_3 \end{vmatrix} \end{aligned}$$

**TECHNOLOGY MASTERY**

Many calculating utilities have built-in cross product and determinant operations. If your calculating utility has these capabilities, use it to check the computations in Examples 1 and 5.

▶ **Example 5** Calculate the scalar triple product $\mathbf{u} \cdot (\mathbf{v} \times \mathbf{w})$ of the vectors

$$\mathbf{u} = 3\mathbf{i} - 2\mathbf{j} - 5\mathbf{k}, \quad \mathbf{v} = \mathbf{i} + 4\mathbf{j} - 4\mathbf{k}, \quad \mathbf{w} = 3\mathbf{j} + 2\mathbf{k}$$

***Solution.***

$$\mathbf{u} \cdot (\mathbf{v} \times \mathbf{w}) = \begin{vmatrix} 3 & -2 & -5 \\ 1 & 4 & -4 \\ 0 & 3 & 2 \end{vmatrix} = 49 \blacktriangleleft$$

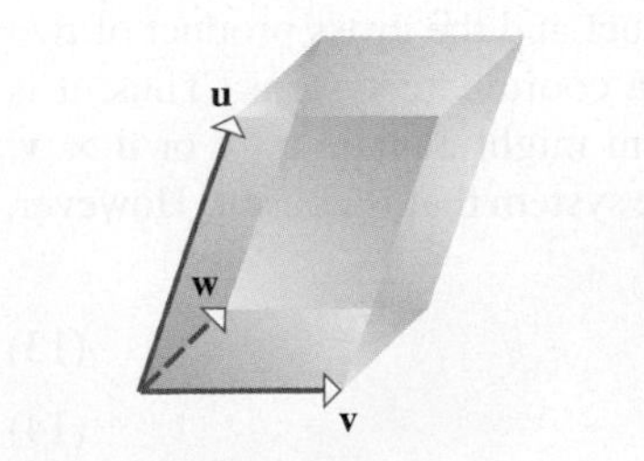

▲ **Figure 11.4.5**

## GEOMETRIC PROPERTIES OF THE SCALAR TRIPLE PRODUCT

If $\mathbf{u}$, $\mathbf{v}$, and $\mathbf{w}$ are nonzero vectors in 3-space that are positioned so their initial points coincide, then these vectors form the adjacent sides of a parallelepiped (Figure 11.4.5). The following theorem establishes a relationship between the volume of this parallelepiped and the scalar triple product of the sides.

It follows from Formula (10) that

$$\mathbf{u}\cdot(\mathbf{v}\times\mathbf{w}) = \pm V$$

The $+$ occurs when $\mathbf{u}$ makes an acute angle with $\mathbf{v}\times\mathbf{w}$ and the $-$ occurs when it makes an obtuse angle.

**11.4.6 THEOREM** *Let* $\mathbf{u}$, $\mathbf{v}$, *and* $\mathbf{w}$ *be nonzero vectors in 3-space.*

(*a*) *The volume V of the parallelepiped that has* $\mathbf{u}$, $\mathbf{v}$, *and* $\mathbf{w}$ *as adjacent edges is*

$$V = |\mathbf{u}\cdot(\mathbf{v}\times\mathbf{w})| \tag{10}$$

(*b*) $\mathbf{u}\cdot(\mathbf{v}\times\mathbf{w}) = 0$ *if and only if* $\mathbf{u}$, $\mathbf{v}$, *and* $\mathbf{w}$ *lie in the same plane.*

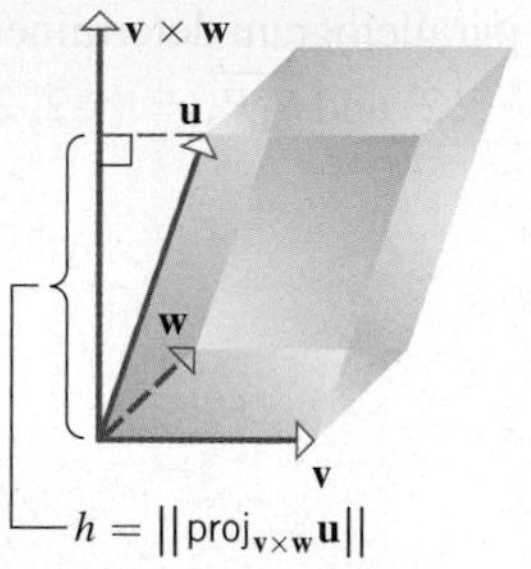


▲ **Figure 11.4.6**

**PROOF (*a*)** Referring to Figure 11.4.6, let us regard the base of the parallelepiped with $\mathbf{u}$, $\mathbf{v}$, and $\mathbf{w}$ as adjacent sides to be the parallelogram determined by $\mathbf{v}$ and $\mathbf{w}$. Thus, the area of the base is $\|\mathbf{v}\times\mathbf{w}\|$, and the altitude $h$ of the parallelepiped (shown in the figure) is the length of the orthogonal projection of $\mathbf{u}$ on the vector $\mathbf{v}\times\mathbf{w}$. Therefore, from Formula (12) of Section 11.3 we have

$$h = \|\text{proj}_{\mathbf{v}\times\mathbf{w}}\mathbf{u}\| = \frac{|\mathbf{u}\cdot(\mathbf{v}\times\mathbf{w})|}{\|\mathbf{v}\times\mathbf{w}\|^2}\|\mathbf{v}\times\mathbf{w}\| = \frac{|\mathbf{u}\cdot(\mathbf{v}\times\mathbf{w})|}{\|\mathbf{v}\times\mathbf{w}\|}$$

It now follows that the volume of the parallelepiped is

$$V = (\text{area of base})(\text{height}) = \|\mathbf{v}\times\mathbf{w}\|h = |\mathbf{u}\cdot(\mathbf{v}\times\mathbf{w})|$$

**PROOF (*b*)** The vectors $\mathbf{u}$, $\mathbf{v}$, and $\mathbf{w}$ lie in the same plane if and only if the parallelepiped with these vectors as adjacent sides has volume zero (why?). Thus, from part (*a*) the vectors lie in the same plane if and only if $\mathbf{u}\cdot(\mathbf{v}\times\mathbf{w}) = 0$. ■

## ALGEBRAIC PROPERTIES OF THE SCALAR TRIPLE PRODUCT

We observed earlier in this section that the expression $\mathbf{u}\times\mathbf{v}\times\mathbf{w}$ must be avoided because it is ambiguous without parentheses. However, the expression $\mathbf{u}\cdot\mathbf{v}\times\mathbf{w}$ is not ambiguous—it has to mean $\mathbf{u}\cdot(\mathbf{v}\times\mathbf{w})$ and not $(\mathbf{u}\cdot\mathbf{v})\times\mathbf{w}$ because we cannot form the cross product of a scalar and a vector. Similarly, the expression $\mathbf{u}\times\mathbf{v}\cdot\mathbf{w}$ must mean $(\mathbf{u}\times\mathbf{v})\cdot\mathbf{w}$ and not $\mathbf{u}\times(\mathbf{v}\cdot\mathbf{w})$. Thus, when you see an expression of the form $\mathbf{u}\cdot\mathbf{v}\times\mathbf{w}$ or $\mathbf{u}\times\mathbf{v}\cdot\mathbf{w}$, the cross product is formed first and the dot product second.

Since interchanging two rows of a determinant multiplies its value by $-1$, making two row interchanges in a determinant has no effect on its value. This being the case, it follows that

$$\mathbf{u}\cdot(\mathbf{v}\times\mathbf{w}) = \mathbf{w}\cdot(\mathbf{u}\times\mathbf{v}) = \mathbf{v}\cdot(\mathbf{w}\times\mathbf{u}) \tag{11}$$

A good way to remember Formula (11) is to observe that the second expression in the formula can be obtained from the first by leaving the dot, cross, and parentheses fixed, moving the first two vectors to the right, and bringing the third vector to the first position. The same procedure produces the third expression from the second and the first expression from the third (verify).

since the $3\times 3$ determinants that are used to compute these scalar triple products can be obtained from one another by two row interchanges (verify).

Another useful formula can be obtained by rewriting the first equality in (11) as

$$\mathbf{u}\cdot(\mathbf{v}\times\mathbf{w}) = (\mathbf{u}\times\mathbf{v})\cdot\mathbf{w}$$

and then omitting the superfluous parentheses to obtain

$$\mathbf{u}\cdot\mathbf{v}\times\mathbf{w} = \mathbf{u}\times\mathbf{v}\cdot\mathbf{w} \tag{12}$$

In words, this formula states that the dot and cross in a scalar triple product can be interchanged (provided the factors are grouped appropriately).

## DOT AND CROSS PRODUCTS ARE COORDINATE INDEPENDENT

In Definitions 11.3.1 and 11.4.2 we defined the dot product and the cross product of two vectors in terms of the components of those vectors in a coordinate system. Thus, it is theoretically possible that changing the coordinate system might change $\mathbf{u}\cdot\mathbf{v}$ or $\mathbf{u}\times\mathbf{v}$, since the components of a vector depend on the coordinate system that is chosen. However, the relationships

This independence of a coordinate system is important in applications because it allows us to choose any convenient coordinate system for solving a problem with full confidence that the choice will not affect computations that involve dot products or cross products.

$$\mathbf{u}\cdot\mathbf{v} = \|\mathbf{u}\|\|\mathbf{v}\|\cos\theta \tag{13}$$

$$\|\mathbf{u}\times\mathbf{v}\| = \|\mathbf{u}\|\|\mathbf{v}\|\sin\theta \tag{14}$$

that were obtained in Theorems 11.3.3 and 11.4.5 show that this is not the case. Formula (13) shows that the value of $\mathbf{u} \cdot \mathbf{v}$ depends only on the lengths of the vectors and the angle between them—not on the coordinate system. Similarly, Formula (14), in combination with the right-hand rule and Theorem 11.4.4, shows that $\mathbf{u} \times \mathbf{v}$ does not depend on the coordinate system (as long as it is right-handed).

## MOMENTS AND ROTATIONAL MOTION IN 3-SPACE

NASA Johnson

*Astronauts use tools that are designed to limit forces that would impart unintended rotational motion to a satellite.*

Cross products play an important role in describing rotational motion in 3-space. For example, suppose that an astronaut on a satellite repair mission in space applies a force $\mathbf{F}$ at a point $Q$ on the surface of a spherical satellite. If the force is directed along a line that passes through the center $P$ of the satellite, then Newton's Second Law of Motion implies that the force will accelerate the satellite in the direction of $\mathbf{F}$. However, if the astronaut applies the same force at an angle $\theta$ with the vector $\overrightarrow{PQ}$, then $\mathbf{F}$ will tend to cause a rotation, as well as an acceleration in the direction of $\mathbf{F}$. To see why this is so, let us resolve $\mathbf{F}$ into a sum of orthogonal components $\mathbf{F} = \mathbf{F}_1 + \mathbf{F}_2$, where $\mathbf{F}_1$ is the orthogonal projection of $\mathbf{F}$ on the vector $\overrightarrow{PQ}$ and $\mathbf{F}_2$ is the component of $\mathbf{F}$ orthogonal to $\overrightarrow{PQ}$ (Figure 11.4.7). Since the force $\mathbf{F}_1$ acts along the line through the center of the satellite, it contributes to the linear acceleration of the satellite but does not cause any rotation. However, the force $\mathbf{F}_2$ is tangent to the circle around the satellite in the plane of $\mathbf{F}$ and $\overrightarrow{PQ}$, so it causes the satellite to rotate about an axis that is perpendicular to that plane.

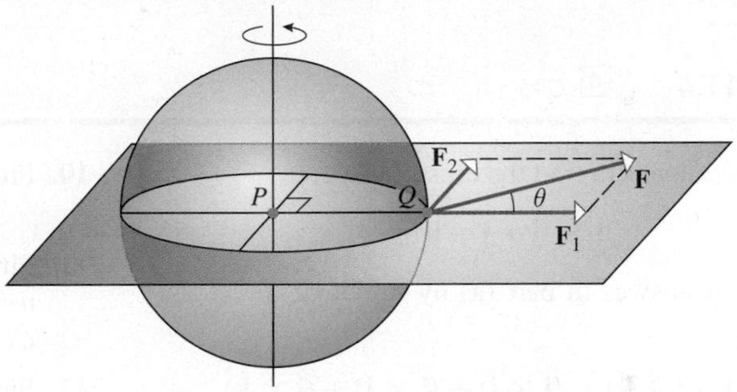


▶ **Figure 11.4.7**

You know from your own experience that the "tendency" for rotation about an axis depends on both the amount of force and how far from the axis it is applied. For example, it is easier to close a door by pushing on its outer edge than applying the same force close to the hinges. In fact, the tendency of rotation of the satellite can be measured by

$$\|\overrightarrow{PQ}\|\|\mathbf{F}_2\| \qquad \text{distance from the center} \times \text{magnitude of the force} \tag{15}$$

However, $\|\mathbf{F}_2\| = \|\mathbf{F}\|\sin\theta$, so we can rewrite (15) as

$$\|\overrightarrow{PQ}\|\|\mathbf{F}\|\sin\theta = \|\overrightarrow{PQ} \times \mathbf{F}\|$$

This is called the ***scalar moment*** or ***torque*** of $\mathbf{F}$ about the point $P$. Scalar moments have units of force times distance—pound-feet or newton-meters, for example. The vector $\overrightarrow{PQ} \times \mathbf{F}$ is called the ***vector moment*** or ***torque vector*** of $\mathbf{F}$ about $P$.

Recalling that the direction of $\overrightarrow{PQ} \times \mathbf{F}$ is determined by the right-hand rule, it follows that the direction of rotation about $P$ that results by applying the force $\mathbf{F}$ at the point $Q$ is counterclockwise looking down the axis of $\overrightarrow{PQ} \times \mathbf{F}$ (Figure 11.4.7). Thus, the vector moment $\overrightarrow{PQ} \times \mathbf{F}$ captures the essential information about the rotational effect of the force—the magnitude of the cross product provides the scalar moment of the force, and the cross product vector itself provides the axis and direction of rotation.

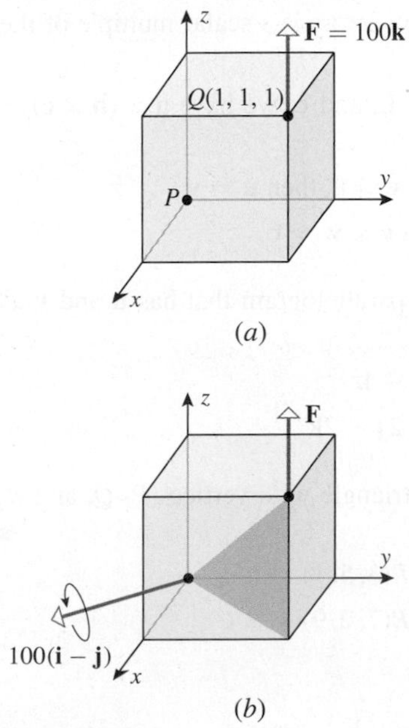


▲ **Figure 11.4.8**

▶ **Example 6** Figure 11.4.8$a$ shows a force $\mathbf{F}$ of 100 N applied in the positive $z$-direction at the point $Q(1, 1, 1)$ of a cube whose sides have a length of 1 m. Assuming that the cube is free to rotate about the point $P(0, 0, 0)$ (the origin), find the scalar moment of the force about $P$, and describe the direction of rotation.

***Solution.*** The force vector is $\mathbf{F} = 100\mathbf{k}$, and the vector from $P$ to $Q$ is $\overrightarrow{PQ} = \mathbf{i} + \mathbf{j} + \mathbf{k}$, so the vector moment of $\mathbf{F}$ about $P$ is

$$\overrightarrow{PQ} \times \mathbf{F} = \begin{vmatrix} \mathbf{i} & \mathbf{j} & \mathbf{k} \\ 1 & 1 & 1 \\ 0 & 0 & 100 \end{vmatrix} = 100\mathbf{i} - 100\mathbf{j}$$

Thus, the scalar moment of $\mathbf{F}$ about $P$ is $\|100\mathbf{i} - 100\mathbf{j}\| = 100\sqrt{2} \approx 141$ N·m, and the direction of rotation is counterclockwise looking along the vector $100\mathbf{i} - 100\mathbf{j} = 100(\mathbf{i} - \mathbf{j})$ toward its initial point (Figure 11.4.8*b*). ◀

## ✓ QUICK CHECK EXERCISES 11.4 *(See page 710 for answers.)*

1. (a) $\begin{vmatrix} 3 & 2 \\ 4 & 5 \end{vmatrix} =$ ______ (b) $\begin{vmatrix} 3 & 2 & 1 \\ 3 & 2 & 1 \\ 5 & 5 & 5 \end{vmatrix} =$ ______

2. $\langle 1, 2, 0\rangle \times \langle 3, 0, 4\rangle =$ ______

3. Suppose that $\mathbf{u}$, $\mathbf{v}$, and $\mathbf{w}$ are vectors in 3-space such that $\mathbf{u} \times \mathbf{v} = \langle 2, 7, 3\rangle$ and $\mathbf{u} \times \mathbf{w} = \langle -5, 4, 0\rangle$.
(a) $\mathbf{u} \times \mathbf{u} =$ ______ (b) $\mathbf{v} \times \mathbf{u} =$ ______
(c) $\mathbf{u} \times (\mathbf{v} + \mathbf{w}) =$ ______
(d) $\mathbf{u} \times (2\mathbf{w}) =$ ______

4. Let $\mathbf{u} = \mathbf{i} - 5\mathbf{k}$, $\mathbf{v} = 2\mathbf{i} - 4\mathbf{j} + \mathbf{k}$, and $\mathbf{w} = 3\mathbf{i} - 2\mathbf{j} + 5\mathbf{k}$.
(a) $\mathbf{u} \cdot (\mathbf{v} \times \mathbf{w}) =$ ______
(b) The volume of the parallelepiped that has $\mathbf{u}$, $\mathbf{v}$, and $\mathbf{w}$ as adjacent edges is $V =$ ______.

## EXERCISE SET 11.4 [C] CAS

1. (a) Use a determinant to find the cross product
$$\mathbf{i} \times (\mathbf{i} + \mathbf{j} + \mathbf{k})$$
(b) Check your answer in part (a) by rewriting the cross product as
$$\mathbf{i} \times (\mathbf{i} + \mathbf{j} + \mathbf{k}) = (\mathbf{i} \times \mathbf{i}) + (\mathbf{i} \times \mathbf{j}) + (\mathbf{i} \times \mathbf{k})$$
and evaluating each term.

2. In each part, use the two methods in Exercise 1 to find
(a) $\mathbf{j} \times (\mathbf{i} + \mathbf{j} + \mathbf{k})$ (b) $\mathbf{k} \times (\mathbf{i} + \mathbf{j} + \mathbf{k})$.

**3–6** Find $\mathbf{u} \times \mathbf{v}$ and check that it is orthogonal to both $\mathbf{u}$ and $\mathbf{v}$. ■

3. $\mathbf{u} = \langle 1, 2, -3\rangle$, $\mathbf{v} = \langle -4, 1, 2\rangle$

4. $\mathbf{u} = 3\mathbf{i} + 2\mathbf{j} - \mathbf{k}$, $\mathbf{v} = -\mathbf{i} - 3\mathbf{j} + \mathbf{k}$

5. $\mathbf{u} = \langle 0, 1, -2\rangle$, $\mathbf{v} = \langle 3, 0, -4\rangle$

6. $\mathbf{u} = 4\mathbf{i} + \mathbf{k}$, $\mathbf{v} = 2\mathbf{i} - \mathbf{j}$

7. Let $\mathbf{u} = \langle 2, -1, 3\rangle$, $\mathbf{v} = \langle 0, 1, 7\rangle$, and $\mathbf{w} = \langle 1, 4, 5\rangle$. Find
(a) $\mathbf{u} \times (\mathbf{v} \times \mathbf{w})$ (b) $(\mathbf{u} \times \mathbf{v}) \times \mathbf{w}$
(c) $(\mathbf{u} \times \mathbf{v}) \times (\mathbf{v} \times \mathbf{w})$ (d) $(\mathbf{v} \times \mathbf{w}) \times (\mathbf{u} \times \mathbf{v})$.

[C] 8. Use a CAS or a calculating utility that can compute determinants or cross products to solve Exercise 7.

9. Find the direction cosines of $\mathbf{u} \times \mathbf{v}$ for the vectors $\mathbf{u}$ and $\mathbf{v}$ in the accompanying figure.

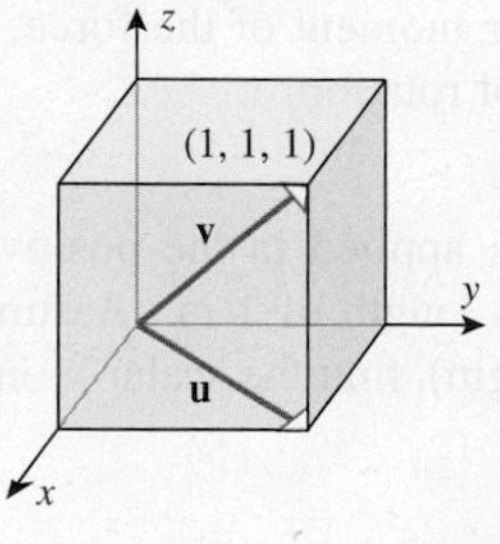


◀ **Figure Ex-9**

10. Find two unit vectors that are orthogonal to both
$$\mathbf{u} = -7\mathbf{i} + 3\mathbf{j} + \mathbf{k}, \quad \mathbf{v} = 2\mathbf{i} + 4\mathbf{k}$$

11. Find two unit vectors that are normal to the plane determined by the points $A(0, -2, 1)$, $B(1, -1, -2)$, and $C(-1, 1, 0)$.

12. Find two unit vectors that are parallel to the $yz$-plane and are orthogonal to the vector $3\mathbf{i} - \mathbf{j} + 2\mathbf{k}$.

**13–16 True–False** Determine whether the statement is true or false. Explain your answer. ■

13. If the cross product of two nonzero vectors is the zero vector, then each of the two vectors is a scalar multiple of the other.

14. For any three vectors $\mathbf{a}$, $\mathbf{b}$, and $\mathbf{c}$, we have $\mathbf{a} \times (\mathbf{b} \times \mathbf{c}) = (\mathbf{a} \times \mathbf{b}) \times \mathbf{c}$.

15. If $\mathbf{v} \times \mathbf{u} = \mathbf{v} \times \mathbf{w}$ and if $\mathbf{v} \neq \mathbf{0}$, then $\mathbf{u} = \mathbf{w}$.

16. If $\mathbf{u} = a\mathbf{v} + b\mathbf{w}$, then $\mathbf{u} \cdot \mathbf{v} \times \mathbf{w} = 0$.

**17–18** Find the area of the parallelogram that has $\mathbf{u}$ and $\mathbf{v}$ as adjacent sides. ■

17. $\mathbf{u} = \mathbf{i} - \mathbf{j} + 2\mathbf{k}$, $\mathbf{v} = 3\mathbf{j} + \mathbf{k}$

18. $\mathbf{u} = 2\mathbf{i} + 3\mathbf{j}$, $\mathbf{v} = -\mathbf{i} + 2\mathbf{j} - 2\mathbf{k}$

**19–20** Find the area of the triangle with vertices $P$, $Q$, and $R$. ■

19. $P(1, 5, -2)$, $Q(0, 0, 0)$, $R(3, 5, 1)$

20. $P(2, 0, -3)$, $Q(1, 4, 5)$, $R(7, 2, 9)$

**21–24** Find $\mathbf{u} \cdot (\mathbf{v} \times \mathbf{w})$. ■

21. $\mathbf{u} = 2\mathbf{i} - 3\mathbf{j} + \mathbf{k}$, $\mathbf{v} = 4\mathbf{i} + \mathbf{j} - 3\mathbf{k}$, $\mathbf{w} = \mathbf{j} + 5\mathbf{k}$

22. $\mathbf{u} = \langle 1, -2, 2\rangle$, $\mathbf{v} = \langle 0, 3, 2\rangle$, $\mathbf{w} = \langle -4, 1, -3\rangle$

**23.** $\mathbf{u} = \langle 2, 1, 0 \rangle$, $\mathbf{v} = \langle 1, -3, 1 \rangle$, $\mathbf{w} = \langle 4, 0, 1 \rangle$

**24.** $\mathbf{u} = \mathbf{i}$, $\mathbf{v} = \mathbf{i} + \mathbf{j}$, $\mathbf{w} = \mathbf{i} + \mathbf{j} + \mathbf{k}$

**25–26** Use a scalar triple product to find the volume of the parallelepiped that has **u**, **v**, and **w** as adjacent edges. ■

**25.** $\mathbf{u} = \langle 2, -6, 2 \rangle$, $\mathbf{v} = \langle 0, 4, -2 \rangle$, $\mathbf{w} = \langle 2, 2, -4 \rangle$

**26.** $\mathbf{u} = 3\mathbf{i} + \mathbf{j} + 2\mathbf{k}$, $\mathbf{v} = 4\mathbf{i} + 5\mathbf{j} + \mathbf{k}$, $\mathbf{w} = \mathbf{i} + 2\mathbf{j} + 4\mathbf{k}$

**27.** In each part, use a scalar triple product to determine whether the vectors lie in the same plane.
(a) $\mathbf{u} = \langle 1, -2, 1 \rangle$, $\mathbf{v} = \langle 3, 0, -2 \rangle$, $\mathbf{w} = \langle 5, -4, 0 \rangle$
(b) $\mathbf{u} = 5\mathbf{i} - 2\mathbf{j} + \mathbf{k}$, $\mathbf{v} = 4\mathbf{i} - \mathbf{j} + \mathbf{k}$, $\mathbf{w} = \mathbf{i} - \mathbf{j}$
(c) $\mathbf{u} = \langle 4, -8, 1 \rangle$, $\mathbf{v} = \langle 2, 1, -2 \rangle$, $\mathbf{w} = \langle 3, -4, 12 \rangle$

**28.** Suppose that $\mathbf{u} \cdot (\mathbf{v} \times \mathbf{w}) = 3$. Find
(a) $\mathbf{u} \cdot (\mathbf{w} \times \mathbf{v})$ (b) $(\mathbf{v} \times \mathbf{w}) \cdot \mathbf{u}$
(c) $\mathbf{w} \cdot (\mathbf{u} \times \mathbf{v})$ (d) $\mathbf{v} \cdot (\mathbf{u} \times \mathbf{w})$
(e) $(\mathbf{u} \times \mathbf{w}) \cdot \mathbf{v}$ (f) $\mathbf{v} \cdot (\mathbf{w} \times \mathbf{w})$.

**29.** Consider the parallelepiped with adjacent edges

$$\mathbf{u} = 3\mathbf{i} + 2\mathbf{j} + \mathbf{k}$$
$$\mathbf{v} = \mathbf{i} + \mathbf{j} + 2\mathbf{k}$$
$$\mathbf{w} = \mathbf{i} + 3\mathbf{j} + 3\mathbf{k}$$

(a) Find the volume.
(b) Find the area of the face determined by **u** and **w**.
(c) Find the angle between **u** and the plane containing the face determined by **v** and **w**.

**30.** Show that in 3-space the distance $d$ from a point $P$ to the line $L$ through points $A$ and $B$ can be expressed as

$$d = \frac{\|\overrightarrow{AP} \times \overrightarrow{AB}\|}{\|\overrightarrow{AB}\|}$$

**31.** Use the result in Exercise 30 to find the distance between the point $P$ and the line through the points $A$ and $B$.
(a) $P(-3, 1, 2)$, $A(1, 1, 0)$, $B(-2, 3, -4)$
(b) $P(4, 3)$, $A(2, 1)$, $B(0, 2)$

**32.** It is a theorem of solid geometry that the volume of a tetrahedron is $\frac{1}{3}$(area of base) · (height). Use this result to prove that the volume of a tetrahedron with adjacent edges given by the vectors **u**, **v**, and **w** is $\frac{1}{6}|\mathbf{u} \cdot (\mathbf{v} \times \mathbf{w})|$.

**33.** Use the result of Exercise 32 to find the volume of the tetrahedron with vertices

$$P(-1, 2, 0),\ Q(2, 1, -3),\ R(1, 0, 1),\ S(3, -2, 3)$$

**34.** Let $\theta$ be the angle between the vectors $\mathbf{u} = 2\mathbf{i} + 3\mathbf{j} - 6\mathbf{k}$ and $\mathbf{v} = 2\mathbf{i} + 3\mathbf{j} + 6\mathbf{k}$.
(a) Use the dot product to find $\cos\theta$.
(b) Use the cross product to find $\sin\theta$.
(c) Confirm that $\sin^2\theta + \cos^2\theta = 1$.

**FOCUS ON CONCEPTS**

**35.** Let $A$, $B$, $C$, and $D$ be four distinct points in 3-space. If $\overrightarrow{AB} \times \overrightarrow{CD} \neq \mathbf{0}$ and $\overrightarrow{AC} \cdot (\overrightarrow{AB} \times \overrightarrow{CD}) = 0$, explain why the line through $A$ and $B$ must intersect the line through $C$ and $D$.

**36.** Let $A$, $B$, and $C$ be three distinct noncollinear points in 3-space. Describe the set of all points $P$ that satisfy the vector equation $\overrightarrow{AP} \cdot (\overrightarrow{AB} \times \overrightarrow{AC}) = 0$.

**37.** What can you say about the angle between nonzero vectors **u** and **v** if $\mathbf{u} \cdot \mathbf{v} = \|\mathbf{u} \times \mathbf{v}\|$?

**38.** Show that if **u** and **v** are vectors in 3-space, then

$$\|\mathbf{u} \times \mathbf{v}\|^2 = \|\mathbf{u}\|^2\|\mathbf{v}\|^2 - (\mathbf{u} \cdot \mathbf{v})^2$$

[*Note:* This result is sometimes called ***Lagrange's identity***.]

**39.** The accompanying figure shows a force **F** of 10 lb applied in the positive $y$-direction to the point $Q(1, 1, 1)$ of a cube whose sides have a length of 1 ft. In each part, find the scalar moment of **F** about the point $P$, and describe the direction of rotation, if any, if the cube is free to rotate about $P$.
(a) $P$ is the point $(0, 0, 0)$. (b) $P$ is the point $(1, 0, 0)$.
(c) $P$ is the point $(1, 0, 1)$.

**40.** The accompanying figure shows a force **F** of 1000 N applied to the corner of a box.
(a) Find the scalar moment of **F** about the point $P$.
(b) Find the direction angles of the vector moment of **F** about the point $P$ to the nearest degree.

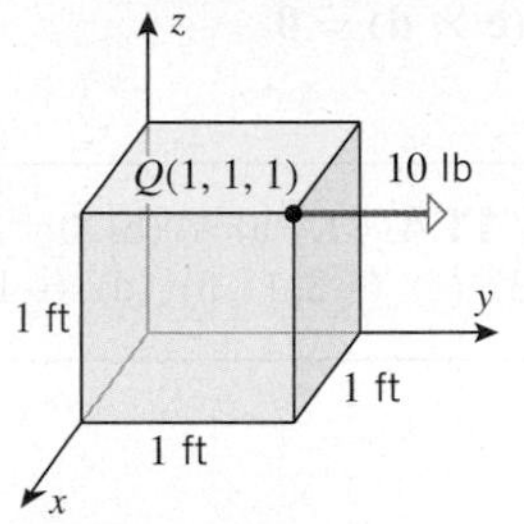


▲ **Figure Ex-39**

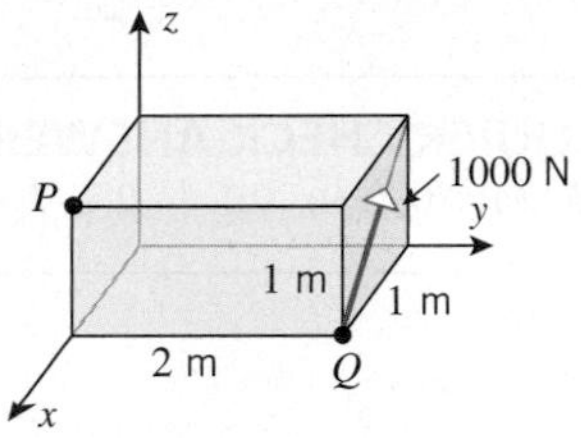


▲ **Figure Ex-40**

**41.** As shown in the accompanying figure, a force of 200 N is applied at an angle of 18° to a point near the end of a monkey wrench. Find the scalar moment of the force about the center of the bolt. [*Note:* Treat this as a problem in two dimensions.]

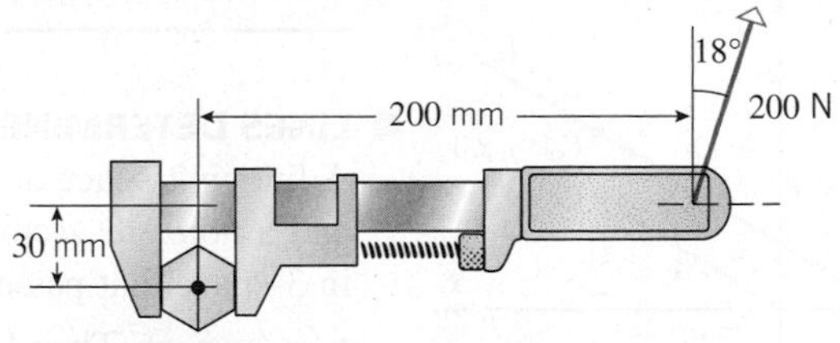


▲ **Figure Ex-41**

**42.** Prove parts ($b$) and ($c$) of Theorem 11.4.3.

**43.** Prove parts ($d$) and ($e$) of Theorem 11.4.3.

**44.** Prove part ($b$) of Theorem 11.4.1 for $3 \times 3$ determinants. [*Note:* Just give the proof for the first two rows.] Then use ($b$) to prove ($a$).

**FOCUS ON CONCEPTS**

**45.** Expressions of the form

$$\mathbf{u} \times (\mathbf{v} \times \mathbf{w}) \quad \text{and} \quad (\mathbf{u} \times \mathbf{v}) \times \mathbf{w}$$

are called ***vector triple products***. It can be proved with some effort that

$$\mathbf{u} \times (\mathbf{v} \times \mathbf{w}) = (\mathbf{u} \cdot \mathbf{w})\mathbf{v} - (\mathbf{u} \cdot \mathbf{v})\mathbf{w}$$
$$(\mathbf{u} \times \mathbf{v}) \times \mathbf{w} = (\mathbf{w} \cdot \mathbf{u})\mathbf{v} - (\mathbf{w} \cdot \mathbf{v})\mathbf{u}$$

These expressions can be summarized with the following mnemonic rule:

vector triple product = (outer · remote)adjacent
− (outer · adjacent)remote

See if you can figure out what the expressions "outer," "remote," and "adjacent" mean in this rule, and then use the rule to find the two vector triple products of the vectors

$$\mathbf{u} = \mathbf{i} + 3\mathbf{j} - \mathbf{k}, \quad \mathbf{v} = \mathbf{i} + \mathbf{j} + 2\mathbf{k}, \quad \mathbf{w} = 3\mathbf{i} - \mathbf{j} + 2\mathbf{k}$$

**46.** (a) Use the result in Exercise 45 to show that $\mathbf{u} \times (\mathbf{v} \times \mathbf{w})$ lies in the same plane as $\mathbf{v}$ and $\mathbf{w}$, and $(\mathbf{u} \times \mathbf{v}) \times \mathbf{w}$ lies in the same plane as $\mathbf{u}$ and $\mathbf{v}$.
(b) Use a geometrical argument to justify the results in part (a).

**47.** In each part, use the result in Exercise 45 to prove the vector identity.
(a) $(\mathbf{a} \times \mathbf{b}) \times (\mathbf{c} \times \mathbf{d}) = (\mathbf{a} \times \mathbf{b} \cdot \mathbf{d})\mathbf{c} - (\mathbf{a} \times \mathbf{b} \cdot \mathbf{c})\mathbf{d}$
(b) $(\mathbf{a} \times \mathbf{b}) \times \mathbf{c} + (\mathbf{b} \times \mathbf{c}) \times \mathbf{a} + (\mathbf{c} \times \mathbf{a}) \times \mathbf{b} = 0$

**48.** Prove: If $\mathbf{a}$, $\mathbf{b}$, $\mathbf{c}$, and $\mathbf{d}$ lie in the same plane when positioned with a common initial point, then

$$(\mathbf{a} \times \mathbf{b}) \times (\mathbf{c} \times \mathbf{d}) = \mathbf{0}$$

C **49.** Use a CAS to approximate the minimum area of a triangle if two of its vertices are $(2, -1, 0)$ and $(3, 2, 2)$ and its third vertex is on the curve $y = \ln x$ in the $xy$-plane.

**50.** If a force $\mathbf{F}$ is applied to an object at a point $Q$, then the line through $Q$ parallel to $\mathbf{F}$ is called the ***line of action*** of the force. We defined the vector moment of $\mathbf{F}$ about a point $P$ to be $\overrightarrow{PQ} \times \mathbf{F}$. Show that if $Q'$ is any point on the line of action of $\mathbf{F}$, then $\overrightarrow{PQ} \times \mathbf{F} = \overrightarrow{PQ'} \times \mathbf{F}$; that is, it is not essential to use the point of application to compute the vector moment—any point on the line of action will do. [*Hint:* Write $\overrightarrow{PQ'} = \overrightarrow{PQ} + \overrightarrow{QQ'}$ and use properties of the cross product.]

**51. Writing** Discuss some of the similarities and differences between the multiplication of real numbers and the cross product of vectors.

**52. Writing** In your own words, describe what it means to say that the cross-product operation is "coordinate independent," and state why this fact is significant.

✓ **QUICK CHECK ANSWERS 11.4** 1. (a) 7 (b) 0 2. $8\mathbf{i} - 4\mathbf{j} - 6\mathbf{k}$ 3. (a) $\langle 0, 0, 0\rangle$ (b) $\langle -2, -7, -3\rangle$ (c) $\langle -3, 11, 3\rangle$ (d) $\langle -10, 8, 0\rangle$ 4. (a) $-58$ (b) 58

## 11.5 PARAMETRIC EQUATIONS OF LINES

*In this section we will discuss parametric equations of lines in 2-space and 3-space. In 3-space, parametric equations of lines are especially important because they generally provide the most convenient form for representing lines algebraically.*

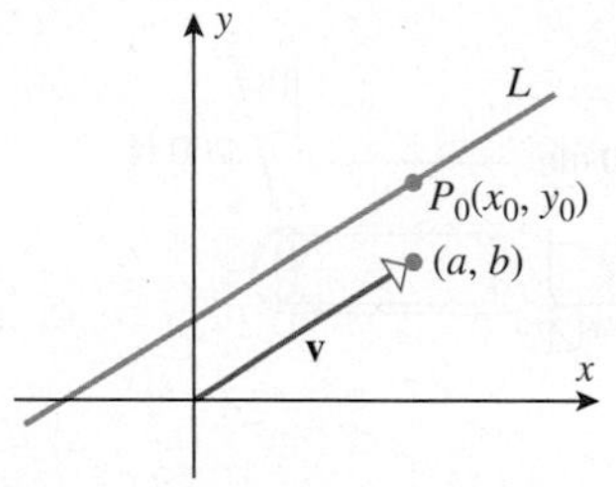


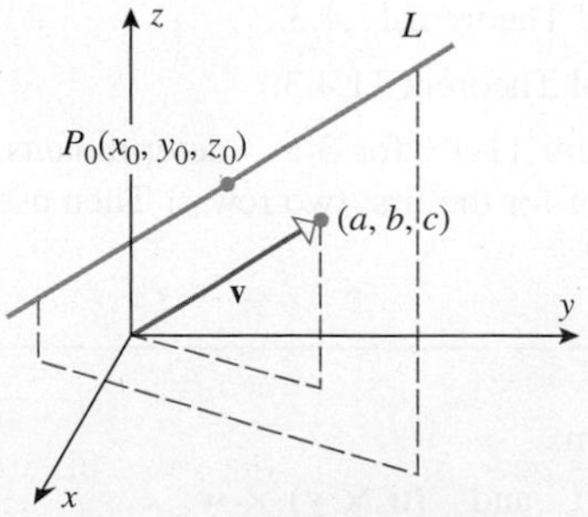


A unique line $L$ passes through $P_0$ and is parallel to $\mathbf{v}$.

▲ **Figure 11.5.1**

### LINES DETERMINED BY A POINT AND A VECTOR

A line in 2-space or 3-space can be determined uniquely by specifying a point on the line and a nonzero vector parallel to the line (Figure 11.5.1). For example, consider a line $L$ in 3-space that passes through the point $P_0(x_0, y_0, z_0)$ and is parallel to the nonzero vector $\mathbf{v} = \langle a, b, c\rangle$. Then $L$ consists precisely of those points $P(x, y, z)$ for which the vector $\overrightarrow{P_0P}$ is parallel to $\mathbf{v}$ (Figure 11.5.2). In other words, the point $P(x, y, z)$ is on $L$ if and only if $\overrightarrow{P_0P}$ is a scalar multiple of $\mathbf{v}$, say

$$\overrightarrow{P_0P} = t\mathbf{v}$$

This equation can be written as

$$\langle x - x_0, y - y_0, z - z_0\rangle = \langle ta, tb, tc\rangle$$

which implies that

$$x - x_0 = ta, \quad y - y_0 = tb, \quad z - z_0 = tc$$

Thus, $L$ can be described by the parametric equations

$$x = x_0 + at, \quad y = y_0 + bt, \quad z = z_0 + ct$$

A similar description applies to lines in 2-space. We summarize these descriptions in the following theorem.

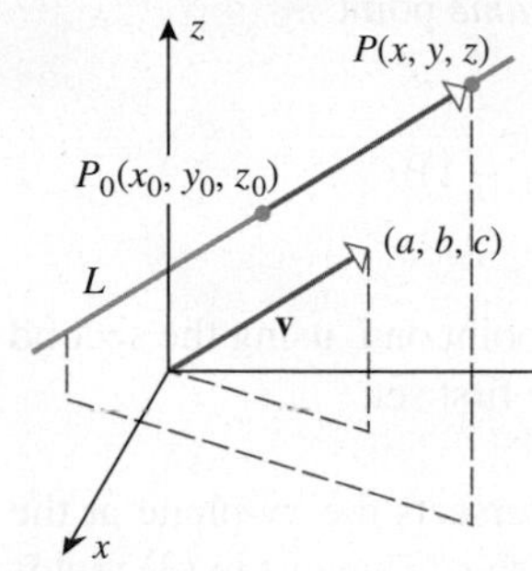


▲ Figure 11.5.2

**11.5.1 THEOREM**

(a) *The line in 2-space that passes through the point $P_0(x_0, y_0)$ and is parallel to the nonzero vector $\mathbf{v} = \langle a, b\rangle = a\mathbf{i} + b\mathbf{j}$ has parametric equations*

$$x = x_0 + at, \quad y = y_0 + bt \tag{1}$$

(b) *The line in 3-space that passes through the point $P_0(x_0, y_0, z_0)$ and is parallel to the nonzero vector $\mathbf{v} = \langle a, b, c\rangle = a\mathbf{i} + b\mathbf{j} + c\mathbf{k}$ has parametric equations*

$$x = x_0 + at, \quad y = y_0 + bt, \quad z = z_0 + ct \tag{2}$$

**REMARK** Although it is not stated explicitly, it is understood in Equations (1) and (2) that $-\infty < t < +\infty$, which reflects the fact that lines extend indefinitely.

**▶ Example 1** Find parametric equations of the line

(a) passing through (4, 2) and parallel to $\mathbf{v} = \langle -1, 5\rangle$;
(b) passing through $(1, 2, -3)$ and parallel to $\mathbf{v} = 4\mathbf{i} + 5\mathbf{j} - 7\mathbf{k}$;
(c) passing through the origin in 3-space and parallel to $\mathbf{v} = \langle 1, 1, 1\rangle$.

***Solution (a).*** From (1) with $x_0 = 4$, $y_0 = 2$, $a = -1$, and $b = 5$ we obtain

$$x = 4 - t, \quad y = 2 + 5t$$

***Solution (b).*** From (2) we obtain

$$x = 1 + 4t, \quad y = 2 + 5t, \quad z = -3 - 7t$$

***Solution (c).*** From (2) with $x_0 = 0$, $y_0 = 0$, $z_0 = 0$, $a = 1$, $b = 1$, and $c = 1$ we obtain

$$x = t, \quad y = t, \quad z = t$$ ◀

**▶ Example 2**

(a) Find parametric equations of the line $L$ passing through the points $P_1(2, 4, -1)$ and $P_2(5, 0, 7)$.
(b) Where does the line intersect the $xy$-plane?

***Solution (a).*** The vector $\overrightarrow{P_1P_2} = \langle 3, -4, 8\rangle$ is parallel to $L$ and the point $P_1(2, 4, -1)$ lies on $L$, so it follows from (2) that $L$ has parametric equations

$$x = 2 + 3t, \quad y = 4 - 4t, \quad z = -1 + 8t \tag{3}$$

Had we used $P_2$ as the point on $L$ rather than $P_1$, we would have obtained the equations

$$x = 5 + 3t, \quad y = -4t, \quad z = 7 + 8t$$

Although these equations look different from those obtained using $P_1$, the two sets of equations are actually equivalent in that both generate $L$ as $t$ varies from $-\infty$ to $+\infty$. To see this, note that if $t_1$ gives a point

$$(x, y, z) = (2 + 3t_1, 4 - 4t_1, -1 + 8t_1)$$

on $L$ using the first set of equations, then $t_2 = t_1 - 1$ gives the *same* point

$$\begin{aligned}(x, y, z) &= (5 + 3t_2, -4t_2, 7 + 8t_2)\\ &= (5 + 3(t_1 - 1), -4(t_1 - 1), 7 + 8(t_1 - 1))\\ &= (2 + 3t_1, 4 - 4t_1, -1 + 8t_1)\end{aligned}$$

on $L$ using the second set of equations. Conversely, if $t_2$ gives a point on $L$ using the second set of equations, then $t_1 = t_2 + 1$ gives the same point using the first set.

***Solution (b).*** It follows from (3) in part (a) that the line intersects the $xy$-plane at the point where $z = -1 + 8t = 0$, that is, when $t = \frac{1}{8}$. Substituting this value of $t$ in (3) yields the point of intersection $(x, y, z) = \left(\frac{19}{8}, \frac{7}{2}, 0\right)$. ◄

▶ **Example 3** Let $L_1$ and $L_2$ be the lines

$$L_1\colon x = 1 + 4t, \quad y = 5 - 4t, \quad z = -1 + 5t$$
$$L_2\colon x = 2 + 8t, \quad y = 4 - 3t, \quad z = 5 + t$$

(a) Are the lines parallel?
(b) Do the lines intersect?

***Solution (a).*** The line $L_1$ is parallel to the vector $4\mathbf{i} - 4\mathbf{j} + 5\mathbf{k}$, and the line $L_2$ is parallel to the vector $8\mathbf{i} - 3\mathbf{j} + \mathbf{k}$. These vectors are not parallel since neither is a scalar multiple of the other. Thus, the lines are not parallel.

***Solution (b).*** For $L_1$ and $L_2$ to intersect at some point $(x_0, y_0, z_0)$ these coordinates would have to satisfy the equations of both lines. In other words, there would have to exist values $t_1$ and $t_2$ for the parameters such that

$$x_0 = 1 + 4t_1, \quad y_0 = 5 - 4t_1, \quad z_0 = -1 + 5t_1$$

and

$$x_0 = 2 + 8t_2, \quad y_0 = 4 - 3t_2, \quad z_0 = 5 + t_2$$

This leads to three conditions on $t_1$ and $t_2$,

$$\begin{aligned}1 + 4t_1 &= 2 + 8t_2\\ 5 - 4t_1 &= 4 - 3t_2\\ -1 + 5t_1 &= 5 + t_2\end{aligned} \tag{4}$$

Thus, the lines intersect if there are values of $t_1$ and $t_2$ that satisfy all three equations, and the lines do not intersect if there are no such values. You should be familiar with methods for solving systems of two linear equations in two unknowns; however, this is a system of three linear equations in two unknowns. To determine whether this system has a solution we will solve the first two equations for $t_1$ and $t_2$ and then check whether these values satisfy the third equation.

We will solve the first two equations by the method of elimination. We can eliminate the unknown $t_1$ by adding the equations. This yields the equation

$$6 = 6 + 5t_2$$

from which we obtain $t_2 = 0$. We can now find $t_1$ by substituting this value of $t_2$ in either the first or second equation. This yields $t_1 = \frac{1}{4}$. However, the values $t_1 = \frac{1}{4}$ and $t_2 = 0$ do not satisfy the third equation in (4), so the lines do not intersect. ◄

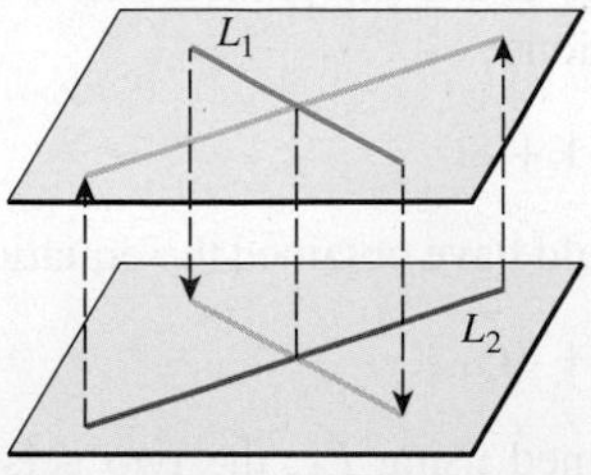


Parallel planes containing skew lines $L_1$ and $L_2$ can be determined by translating each line until it intersects the other.

▲ **Figure 11.5.3**

Two lines in 3-space that are not parallel and do not intersect (such as those in Example 3) are called ***skew*** lines. As illustrated in Figure 11.5.3, any two skew lines lie in parallel planes.

## LINE SEGMENTS

Sometimes one is not interested in an entire line, but rather some *segment* of a line. Parametric equations of a line segment can be obtained by finding parametric equations for the entire line, and then restricting the parameter appropriately so that only the desired segment is generated.

**▶ Example 4** Find parametric equations describing the line segment joining the points $P_1(2, 4, -1)$ and $P_2(5, 0, 7)$.

***Solution.*** From Example 2, the line through the points $P_1$ and $P_2$ has parametric equations $x = 2 + 3t$, $y = 4 - 4t$, $z = -1 + 8t$. With these equations, the point $P_1$ corresponds to $t = 0$ and $P_2$ to $t = 1$. Thus, the line segment that joins $P_1$ and $P_2$ is given by

$$x = 2 + 3t, \quad y = 4 - 4t, \quad z = -1 + 8t \qquad (0 \le t \le 1)$$ ◀

## VECTOR EQUATIONS OF LINES

We will now show how vector notation can be used to express the parametric equations of a line more compactly. Because two vectors are equal if and only if their components are equal, (1) and (2) can be written in vector form as

$$\langle x, y \rangle = \langle x_0 + at, y_0 + bt \rangle$$

$$\langle x, y, z \rangle = \langle x_0 + at, y_0 + bt, z_0 + ct \rangle$$

or, equivalently, as

$$\langle x, y \rangle = \langle x_0, y_0 \rangle + t\langle a, b \rangle \tag{5}$$

$$\langle x, y, z \rangle = \langle x_0, y_0, z_0 \rangle + t\langle a, b, c \rangle \tag{6}$$

For the equation in 2-space we define the vectors $\mathbf{r}$, $\mathbf{r}_0$, and $\mathbf{v}$ as

$$\mathbf{r} = \langle x, y \rangle, \quad \mathbf{r}_0 = \langle x_0, y_0 \rangle, \quad \mathbf{v} = \langle a, b \rangle \tag{7}$$

and for the equation in 3-space we define them as

$$\mathbf{r} = \langle x, y, z \rangle, \quad \mathbf{r}_0 = \langle x_0, y_0, z_0 \rangle, \quad \mathbf{v} = \langle a, b, c \rangle \tag{8}$$

Substituting (7) and (8) in (5) and (6), respectively, yields the equation

$$\mathbf{r} = \mathbf{r}_0 + t\mathbf{v} \tag{9}$$

in both cases. We call this the ***vector equation of a line*** in 2-space or 3-space. In this equation, $\mathbf{v}$ is a nonzero vector parallel to the line, and $\mathbf{r}_0$ is a vector whose components are the coordinates of a point on the line.

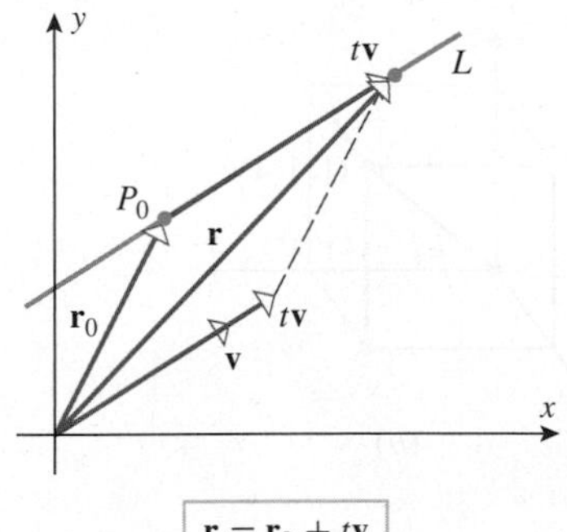


▲ **Figure 11.5.4**

We can interpret Equation (9) geometrically by positioning the vectors $\mathbf{r}_0$ and $\mathbf{v}$ with their initial points at the origin and the vector $t\mathbf{v}$ with its initial point at $P_0$ (Figure 11.5.4). The vector $t\mathbf{v}$ is a scalar multiple of $\mathbf{v}$ and hence is parallel to $\mathbf{v}$ and $L$. Moreover, since the initial point of $t\mathbf{v}$ is at the point $P_0$ on $L$, this vector actually runs along $L$; hence, the vector $\mathbf{r} = \mathbf{r}_0 + t\mathbf{v}$ can be interpreted as the vector from the origin to a point on $L$. As the parameter $t$ varies from 0 to $+\infty$, the terminal point of $\mathbf{r}$ traces out the portion of $L$ that extends from $P_0$ in the direction of $\mathbf{v}$, and as $t$ varies from 0 to $-\infty$, the terminal point of $\mathbf{r}$ traces out the portion of $L$ that extends from $P_0$ in the direction that is opposite to $\mathbf{v}$. Thus, the entire line is traced as $t$ varies over the interval $(-\infty, +\infty)$, and it is traced in the direction of $\mathbf{v}$ as $t$ increases.

**▶ Example 5** The equation

$$\langle x, y, z \rangle = \langle -1, 0, 2 \rangle + t\langle 1, 5, -4 \rangle$$

is of form (9) with

$$\mathbf{r}_0 = \langle -1, 0, 2 \rangle \quad \text{and} \quad \mathbf{v} = \langle 1, 5, -4 \rangle$$

Thus, the equation represents the line in 3-space that passes through the point $(-1, 0, 2)$ and is parallel to the vector $\langle 1, 5, -4 \rangle$. ◀

► **Example 6** Find an equation of the line in 3-space that passes through the points $P_1(2, 4, -1)$ and $P_2(5, 0, 7)$.

***Solution.*** The vector

$$\overrightarrow{P_1P_2} = \langle 3, -4, 8 \rangle$$

is parallel to the line, so it can be used as $\mathbf{v}$ in (9). For $\mathbf{r}_0$ we can use either the vector from the origin to $P_1$ or the vector from the origin to $P_2$. Using the former yields

$$\mathbf{r}_0 = \langle 2, 4, -1 \rangle$$

Thus, a vector equation of the line through $P_1$ and $P_2$ is

$$\langle x, y, z \rangle = \langle 2, 4, -1 \rangle + t\langle 3, -4, 8 \rangle$$

If needed, we can express the line parametrically by equating corresponding components on the two sides of this vector equation, in which case we obtain the parametric equations in Example 2 (verify). ◄

## ✓ QUICK CHECK EXERCISES 11.5 *(See page 717 for answers.)*

1. Let $L$ be the line through (2, 5) and parallel to $\mathbf{v} = \langle 3, -1 \rangle$.
   (a) Parametric equations of $L$ are

   $x =$ ________ $y =$ ________

   (b) A vector equation of $L$ is $\langle x, y \rangle =$ ________.
2. Parametric equations for the line through (5, 3, 7) and parallel to the line $x = 3 - t, y = 2, z = 8 + 4t$ are

   $x =$ ________, $y =$ ________, $z =$ ________
3. Parametric equations for the line segment joining the points (3, 0, 11) and (2, 6, 7) are

   $x =$ ________, $y =$ ________, $z =$ ________ (________)
4. The line through the points $(-3, 8, -4)$ and $(1, 0, 8)$ intersects the $yz$-plane at ________.

## EXERCISE SET 11.5 Graphing Utility C CAS

1. (a) Find parametric equations for the lines through the corner of the unit square shown in part (*a*) of the accompanying figure.
   (b) Find parametric equations for the lines through the corner of the unit cube shown in part (*b*) of the accompanying figure.

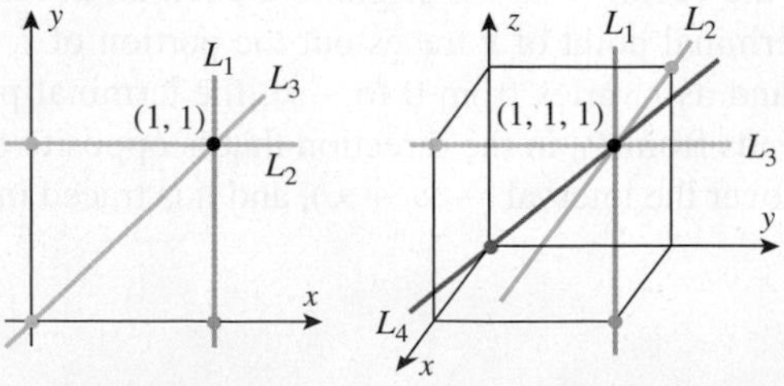


(*a*) (*b*)

▲ **Figure Ex-1**

2. (a) Find parametric equations for the line segments in the unit square in part (*a*) of the accompanying figure.
   (b) Find parametric equations for the line segments in the unit cube shown in part (*b*) of the accompanying figure.

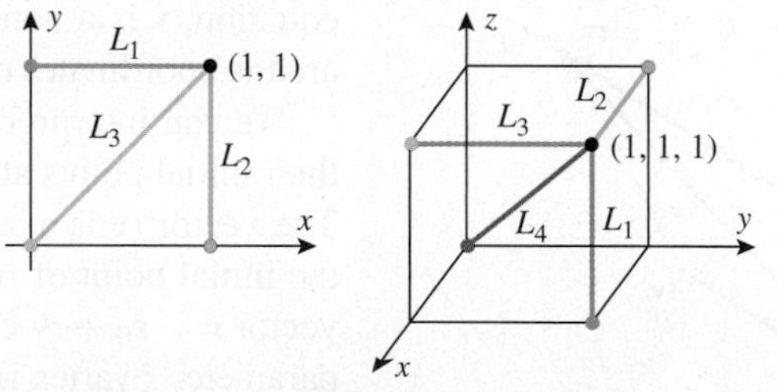


(*a*) (*b*)

▲ **Figure Ex-2**

**3–4** Find parametric equations for the line through $P_1$ and $P_2$ and also for the line segment joining those points. ■

3. (a) $P_1(3, -2)$, $P_2(5, 1)$ (b) $P_1(5, -2, 1)$, $P_2(2, 4, 2)$
4. (a) $P_1(0, 1)$, $P_2(-3, -4)$
   (b) $P_1(-1, 3, 5)$, $P_2(-1, 3, 2)$

**5–6** Find parametric equations for the line whose vector equation is given. ■

5. (a) $\langle x, y \rangle = \langle 2, -3 \rangle + t\langle 1, -4 \rangle$
   (b) $x\mathbf{i} + y\mathbf{j} + z\mathbf{k} = \mathbf{k} + t(\mathbf{i} - \mathbf{j} + \mathbf{k})$

6. (a) $x\mathbf{i} + y\mathbf{j} = (3\mathbf{i} - 4\mathbf{j}) + t(2\mathbf{i} + \mathbf{j})$
(b) $\langle x, y, z\rangle = \langle -1, 0, 2\rangle + t\langle -1, 3, 0\rangle$

**7–8** Find a point $P$ on the line and a vector $\mathbf{v}$ parallel to the line by inspection. ■

7. (a) $x\mathbf{i} + y\mathbf{j} = (2\mathbf{i} - \mathbf{j}) + t(4\mathbf{i} - \mathbf{j})$
(b) $\langle x, y, z\rangle = \langle -1, 2, 4\rangle + t\langle 5, 7, -8\rangle$

8. (a) $\langle x, y\rangle = \langle -1, 5\rangle + t\langle 2, 3\rangle$
(b) $x\mathbf{i} + y\mathbf{j} + z\mathbf{k} = (\mathbf{i} + \mathbf{j} - 2\mathbf{k}) + t\mathbf{j}$

**9–10** Express the given parametric equations of a line using bracket notation and also using **i**, **j**, **k** notation. ■

9. (a) $x = -3 + t,\ y = 4 + 5t$
(b) $x = 2 - t,\ y = -3 + 5t,\ z = t$

10. (a) $x = t,\ y = -2 + t$
(b) $x = 1 + t,\ y = -7 + 3t,\ z = 4 - 5t$

**11–14 True–False** Determine whether the statement is true or false. Explain your answer. In these exercises $L_0$ and $L_1$ are lines in 3-space whose parametric equations are

$$L_0: x = x_0 + a_0t, \quad y = y_0 + b_0t, \quad z = z_0 + c_0t$$
$$L_1: x = x_1 + a_1t, \quad y = y_1 + b_1t, \quad z = z_1 + c_1t$$ ■

11. By definition, if $L_1$ and $L_2$ do not intersect, then $L_1$ and $L_2$ are parallel.

12. If $L_1$ and $L_2$ are parallel, then $\mathbf{v}_0 = \langle a_0, b_0, c_0\rangle$ is a scalar multiple of $\mathbf{v}_1 = \langle a_1, b_1, c_1\rangle$.

13. If $L_1$ and $L_2$ intersect at a point $(x, y, z)$, then there exists a single value of $t$ such that

$$L_0: x = x_0 + a_0t, \quad y = y_0 + b_0t, \quad z = z_0 + c_0t$$
$$L_1: x = x_1 + a_1t, \quad y = y_1 + b_1t, \quad z = z_1 + c_1t$$

are satisfied.

14. If $L_0$ passes through the origin, then the vectors $\langle a_0, b_0, c_0\rangle$ and $\langle x_0, y_0, z_0\rangle$ are parallel.

**15–22** Find parametric equations of the line that satisfies the stated conditions. ■

15. The line through $(-5, 2)$ that is parallel to $2\mathbf{i} - 3\mathbf{j}$.

16. The line through $(0, 3)$ that is parallel to the line $x = -5 + t, y = 1 - 2t$.

17. The line that is tangent to the circle $x^2 + y^2 = 25$ at the point $(3, -4)$.

18. The line that is tangent to the parabola $y = x^2$ at the point $(-2, 4)$.

19. The line through $(-1, 2, 4)$ that is parallel to $3\mathbf{i} - 4\mathbf{j} + \mathbf{k}$.

20. The line through $(2, -1, 5)$ that is parallel to $\langle -1, 2, 7\rangle$.

21. The line through $(-2, 0, 5)$ that is parallel to the line given by $x = 1 + 2t, y = 4 - t, z = 6 + 2t$.

22. The line through the origin that is parallel to the line given by $x = t, y = -1 + t, z = 2$.

23. Where does the line $x = 1 + 3t, y = 2 - t$ intersect
(a) the $x$-axis (b) the $y$-axis
(c) the parabola $y = x^2$?

24. Where does the line $\langle x, y\rangle = \langle 4t, 3t\rangle$ intersect the circle $x^2 + y^2 = 25$?

**25–26** Find the intersections of the lines with the $xy$-plane, the $xz$-plane, and the $yz$-plane. ■

25. $x = -2,\ y = 4 + 2t,\ z = -3 + t$

26. $x = -1 + 2t,\ y = 3 + t,\ z = 4 - t$

27. Where does the line $x = 1 + t, y = 3 - t, z = 2t$ intersect the cylinder $x^2 + y^2 = 16$?

28. Where does the line $x = 2 - t, y = 3t, z = -1 + 2t$ intersect the plane $2y + 3z = 6$?

**29–30** Show that the lines $L_1$ and $L_2$ intersect, and find their point of intersection. ■

29. $L_1: x = 2 + t,\ y = 2 + 3t,\ z = 3 + t$
$L_2: x = 2 + t,\ y = 3 + 4t,\ z = 4 + 2t$

30. $L_1: x + 1 = 4t,\ y - 3 = t,\ z - 1 = 0$
$L_2: x + 13 = 12t,\ y - 1 = 6t,\ z - 2 = 3t$

**31–32** Show that the lines $L_1$ and $L_2$ are skew. ■

31. $L_1: x = 1 + 7t,\ y = 3 + t,\ z = 5 - 3t$
$L_2: x = 4 - t,\ y = 6,\ z = 7 + 2t$

32. $L_1: x = 2 + 8t,\ y = 6 - 8t,\ z = 10t$
$L_2: x = 3 + 8t,\ y = 5 - 3t,\ z = 6 + t$

**33–34** Determine whether the lines $L_1$ and $L_2$ are parallel. ■

33. $L_1: x = 3 - 2t,\ y = 4 + t,\ z = 6 - t$
$L_2: x = 5 - 4t,\ y = -2 + 2t,\ z = 7 - 2t$

34. $L_1: x = 5 + 3t,\ y = 4 - 2t,\ z = -2 + 3t$
$L_2: x = -1 + 9t,\ y = 5 - 6t,\ z = 3 + 8t$

**35–36** Determine whether the points $P_1$, $P_2$, and $P_3$ lie on the same line. ■

35. $P_1(6, 9, 7),\ P_2(9, 2, 0),\ P_3(0, -5, -3)$

36. $P_1(1, 0, 1),\ P_2(3, -4, -3),\ P_3(4, -6, -5)$

**37–38** Show that the lines $L_1$ and $L_2$ are the same. ■

37. $L_1: x = 3 - t,\ y = 1 + 2t$
$L_2: x = -1 + 3t,\ y = 9 - 6t$

38. $L_1: x = 1 + 3t,\ y = -2 + t,\ z = 2t$
$L_2: x = 4 - 6t,\ y = -1 - 2t,\ z = 2 - 4t$

**FOCUS ON CONCEPTS**

39. Sketch the vectors $\mathbf{r}_0 = \langle -1, 2\rangle$ and $\mathbf{v} = \langle 1, 1\rangle$, and then sketch the six vectors $\mathbf{r}_0 \pm \mathbf{v}$, $\mathbf{r}_0 \pm 2\mathbf{v}$, $\mathbf{r}_0 \pm 3\mathbf{v}$. Draw the line $L: x = -1 + t,\ y = 2 + t$, and describe the relationship between $L$ and the vectors you sketched. What is the vector equation of $L$?

40. Sketch the vectors $\mathbf{r}_0 = \langle 0, 2, 1\rangle$ and $\mathbf{v} = \langle 1, 0, 1\rangle$, and then sketch the vectors $\mathbf{r}_0 + \mathbf{v}$, $\mathbf{r}_0 + 2\mathbf{v}$, and $\mathbf{r}_0 + 3\mathbf{v}$. Draw the line $L: x = t,\ y = 2,\ z = 1 + t$, and describe the relationship between $L$ and the vectors you sketched. What is the vector equation of $L$?

41. Sketch the vectors $\mathbf{r}_0 = \langle -2, 0\rangle$ and $\mathbf{r}_1 = \langle 1, 3\rangle$, and then sketch the vectors

$$\tfrac{1}{3}\mathbf{r}_0 + \tfrac{2}{3}\mathbf{r}_1, \quad \tfrac{1}{2}\mathbf{r}_0 + \tfrac{1}{2}\mathbf{r}_1, \quad \tfrac{2}{3}\mathbf{r}_0 + \tfrac{1}{3}\mathbf{r}_1$$

Draw the line segment $(1-t)\mathbf{r}_0 + t\mathbf{r}_1$ $(0 \le t \le 1)$. If $n$ is a positive integer, what is the position of the point on this line segment corresponding to $t = 1/n$, relative to the points $(-2, 0)$ and $(1, 3)$?

**42.** Sketch the vectors $\mathbf{r}_0 = \langle 2, 0, 4\rangle$ and $\mathbf{r}_1 = \langle 0, 4, 0\rangle$, and then sketch the vectors

$$\tfrac{1}{4}\mathbf{r}_0 + \tfrac{3}{4}\mathbf{r}_1, \quad \tfrac{1}{2}\mathbf{r}_0 + \tfrac{1}{2}\mathbf{r}_1, \quad \tfrac{3}{4}\mathbf{r}_0 + \tfrac{1}{4}\mathbf{r}_1$$

Draw the line segment $(1-t)\mathbf{r}_0 + t\mathbf{r}_1$ $(0 \le t \le 1)$. If $n$ is a positive integer, what is the position of the point on this line segment corresponding to $t = 1/n$, relative to the points $(2, 0, 4)$ and $(0, 4, 0)$?

**43–44** Describe the line segment represented by the vector equation. ■

**43.** $\langle x, y\rangle = \langle 1, 0\rangle + t\langle -2, 3\rangle \quad (0 \le t \le 2)$

**44.** $\langle x, y, z\rangle = \langle -2, 1, 4\rangle + t\langle 3, 0, -1\rangle \quad (0 \le t \le 3)$

**45.** Find the point on the line segment joining $P_1(3, 6)$ and $P_2(8, -4)$ that is $\frac{2}{5}$ of the way from $P_1$ to $P_2$.

**46.** Find the point on the line segment joining $P_1(1, 4, -3)$ and $P_2(1, 5, -1)$ that is $\frac{2}{3}$ of the way from $P_1$ to $P_2$.

**47–48** Use the method in Exercise 32 of Section 11.3 to find the distance from the point $P$ to the line $L$, and then check your answer using the method in Exercise 30 of Section 11.4. ■

**47.** $P(-2, 1, 1)$
$L$: $x = 3 - t,\ y = t,\ z = 1 + 2t$

**48.** $P(1, 4, -3)$
$L$: $x = 2 + t,\ y = -1 - t,\ z = 3t$

**49–50** Show that the lines $L_1$ and $L_2$ are parallel, and find the distance between them. ■

**49.** $L_1$: $x = 2 - t,\ y = 2t,\ z = 1 + t$
$L_2$: $x = 1 + 2t,\ y = 3 - 4t,\ z = 5 - 2t$

**50.** $L_1$: $x = 2t,\ y = 3 + 4t,\ z = 2 - 6t$
$L_2$: $x = 1 + 3t,\ y = 6t,\ z = -9t$

**51.** (a) Find parametric equations for the line through the points $(x_0, y_0, z_0)$ and $(x_1, y_1, z_1)$.
(b) Find parametric equations for the line through the point $(x_1, y_1, z_1)$ and parallel to the line

$$x = x_0 + at, \quad y = y_0 + bt, \quad z = z_0 + ct$$

**52.** Let $L$ be the line that passes through the point $(x_0, y_0, z_0)$ and is parallel to the vector $\mathbf{v} = \langle a, b, c\rangle$, where $a$, $b$, and $c$ are nonzero. Show that a point $(x, y, z)$ lies on the line $L$ if and only if

$$\frac{x - x_0}{a} = \frac{y - y_0}{b} = \frac{z - z_0}{c}$$

These equations, which are called the ***symmetric equations*** of $L$, provide a nonparametric representation of $L$.

**53.** (a) Describe the line whose symmetric equations are

$$\frac{x-1}{2} = \frac{y+3}{4} = z - 5$$

(see Exercise 52).
(b) Find parametric equations for the line in part (a).

**54.** Consider the lines $L_1$ and $L_2$ whose symmetric equations are

$$L_1\colon \frac{x-1}{2} = \frac{y+\frac{3}{2}}{1} = \frac{z+1}{2}$$

$$L_2\colon \frac{x-4}{-1} = \frac{y-3}{-2} = \frac{z+4}{2}$$

(see Exercise 52).
(a) Are $L_1$ and $L_2$ parallel? Perpendicular?
(b) Find parametric equations for $L_1$ and $L_2$.
(c) Do $L_1$ and $L_2$ intersect? If so, where?

**55.** Let $L_1$ and $L_2$ be the lines whose parametric equations are

$$L_1\colon x = 1 + 2t, \quad y = 2 - t, \quad z = 4 - 2t$$
$$L_2\colon x = 9 + t, \quad y = 5 + 3t, \quad z = -4 - t$$

(a) Show that $L_1$ and $L_2$ intersect at the point $(7, -1, -2)$.
(b) Find, to the nearest degree, the acute angle between $L_1$ and $L_2$ at their intersection.
(c) Find parametric equations for the line that is perpendicular to $L_1$ and $L_2$ and passes through their point of intersection.

**56.** Let $L_1$ and $L_2$ be the lines whose parametric equations are

$$L_1\colon x = 4t, \quad y = 1 - 2t, \quad z = 2 + 2t$$
$$L_2\colon x = 1 + t, \quad y = 1 - t, \quad z = -1 + 4t$$

(a) Show that $L_1$ and $L_2$ intersect at the point $(2, 0, 3)$.
(b) Find, to the nearest degree, the acute angle between $L_1$ and $L_2$ at their intersection.
(c) Find parametric equations for the line that is perpendicular to $L_1$ and $L_2$ and passes through their point of intersection.

**57–58** Find parametric equations of the line that contains the point $P$ and intersects the line $L$ at a right angle, and find the distance between $P$ and $L$. ■

**57.** $P(0, 2, 1)$
$L$: $x = 2t,\ y = 1 - t,\ z = 2 + t$

**58.** $P(3, 1, -2)$
$L$: $x = -2 + 2t,\ y = 4 + 2t,\ z = 2 + t$

**59.** Two bugs are walking along lines in 3-space. At time $t$ bug 1 is at the point $(x, y, z)$ on the line

$$x = 4 - t, \quad y = 1 + 2t, \quad z = 2 + t$$

and at the same time $t$ bug 2 is at the point $(x, y, z)$ on the line

$$x = t, \quad y = 1 + t, \quad z = 1 + 2t$$

Assume that distance is in centimeters and that time is in minutes.
(a) Find the distance between the bugs at time $t = 0$.
(b) Use a graphing utility to graph the distance between the bugs as a function of time from $t = 0$ to $t = 5$.
(c) What does the graph tell you about the distance between the bugs?
(d) How close do the bugs get?

**60.** Suppose that the temperature $T$ at a point $(x, y, z)$ on the line $x = t, y = 1 + t, z = 3 - 2t$ is $T = 25x^2yz$. Use a CAS or a calculating utility with a root-finding capability to approximate the maximum temperature on that portion of the line that extends from the $xz$-plane to the $xy$-plane.

**61. Writing** Give some examples of geometric problems that can be solved using the parametric equations of a line, and describe their solution. For example, how would you find the points of intersection of a line and a sphere?

**62. Writing** Discuss how the vector equation of a line can be used to model the motion of a point that is moving with constant velocity in 3-space.

✓ QUICK CHECK ANSWERS 11.5 1. (a) $2+3t;\ 5-t$ (b) $\langle 2,5\rangle + t\langle 3,-1\rangle$ 2. $5-t;\ 3;\ 7+4t$ 3. $3-t;\ 6t;\ 11-4t;\ 0\le t\le 1$ 4. $(0,2,5)$

## 11.6 PLANES IN 3-SPACE

*In this section we will use vectors to derive equations of planes in 3-space, and then we will use these equations to solve various geometric problems.*

### PLANES PARALLEL TO THE COORDINATE PLANES

The graph of the equation $x=a$ in an $xyz$-coordinate system consists of all points of the form $(a,y,z)$, where $y$ and $z$ are arbitrary. One such point is $(a,0,0)$, and all others are in the plane that passes through this point and is parallel to the $yz$-plane (Figure 11.6.1). Similarly, the graph of $y=b$ is the plane through $(0,b,0)$ that is parallel to the $xz$-plane, and the graph of $z=c$ is the plane through $(0,0,c)$ that is parallel to the $xy$-plane.

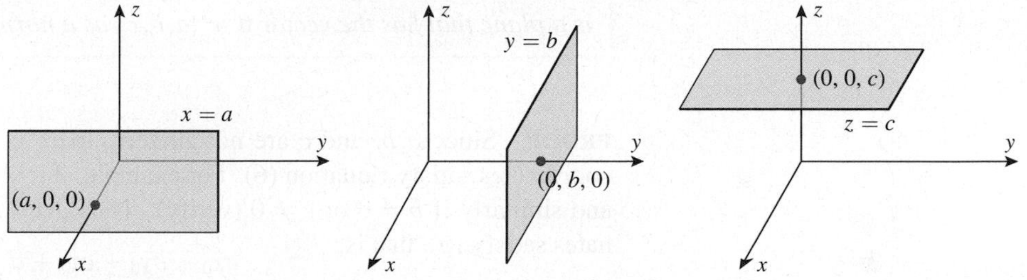

▲ Figure 11.6.1

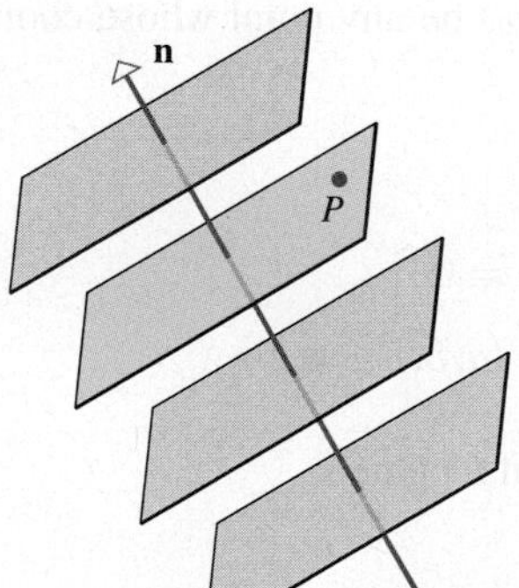

The colored plane is determined uniquely by the point $P$ and the vector **n** perpendicular to the plane.

▲ Figure 11.6.2

### PLANES DETERMINED BY A POINT AND A NORMAL VECTOR

A plane in 3-space can be determined uniquely by specifying a point in the plane and a vector perpendicular to the plane (Figure 11.6.2). A vector perpendicular to a plane is called a ***normal*** to the plane.

Suppose that we want to find an equation of the plane passing through $P_0(x_0,y_0,z_0)$ and perpendicular to the vector $\mathbf{n}=\langle a,b,c\rangle$. Define the vectors $\mathbf{r}_0$ and $\mathbf{r}$ as

$$\mathbf{r}_0=\langle x_0,y_0,z_0\rangle \quad\text{and}\quad \mathbf{r}=\langle x,y,z\rangle$$

It should be evident from Figure 11.6.3 that the plane consists precisely of those points $P(x,y,z)$ for which the vector $\mathbf{r}-\mathbf{r}_0$ is orthogonal to $\mathbf{n}$; or, expressed as an equation,

$$\mathbf{n}\cdot(\mathbf{r}-\mathbf{r}_0)=0 \tag{1}$$

If preferred, we can express this vector equation in terms of components as

$$\langle a,b,c\rangle\cdot\langle x-x_0,y-y_0,z-z_0\rangle=0 \tag{2}$$

from which we obtain

$$a(x-x_0)+b(y-y_0)+c(z-z_0)=0 \tag{3}$$

This is called the ***point-normal form*** of the equation of a plane. Formulas (1) and (2) are vector versions of this formula.

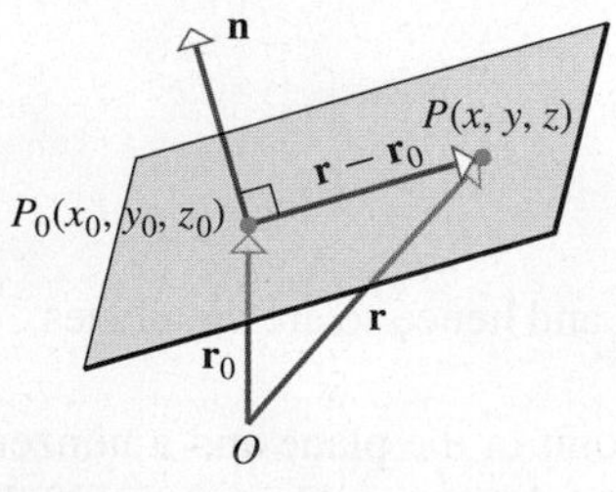

▲ Figure 11.6.3

What does Equation (1) represent if

$$\mathbf{n} = \langle a, b \rangle, \ \mathbf{r}_0 = \langle x_0, y_0 \rangle, \ \mathbf{r} = \langle x, y \rangle$$

are vectors in an $xy$-plane in 2-space? Draw a picture.

▶ **Example 1** Find an equation of the plane passing through the point $(3, -1, 7)$ and perpendicular to the vector $\mathbf{n} = \langle 4, 2, -5 \rangle$.

***Solution.*** From (3), a point-normal form of the equation is

$$4(x-3) + 2(y+1) - 5(z-7) = 0 \tag{4}$$

If preferred, this equation can be written in vector form as

$$\langle 4, 2, -5 \rangle \cdot \langle x-3, y+1, z-7 \rangle = 0 \ ◀$$

Observe that if we multiply out the terms in (3) and simplify, we obtain an equation of the form

$$ax + by + cz + d = 0 \tag{5}$$

For example, Equation (4) in Example 1 can be rewritten as

$$4x + 2y - 5z + 25 = 0$$

The following theorem shows that every equation of form (5) represents a plane in 3-space.

**11.6.1 THEOREM** *If $a$, $b$, $c$, and $d$ are constants, and $a$, $b$, and $c$ are not all zero, then the graph of the equation*

$$ax + by + cz + d = 0 \tag{6}$$

*is a plane that has the vector $\mathbf{n} = \langle a, b, c \rangle$ as a normal.*

PROOF Since $a, b$, and $c$ are not all zero, there is at least one point $(x_0, y_0, z_0)$ whose coordinates satisfy Equation (6). For example, if $a \neq 0$, then such a point is $(-d/a, 0, 0)$, and similarly if $b \neq 0$ or $c \neq 0$ (verify). Thus, let $(x_0, y_0, z_0)$ be any point whose coordinates satisfy (6); that is,

$$ax_0 + by_0 + cz_0 + d = 0$$

Subtracting this equation from (6) yields

$$a(x - x_0) + b(y - y_0) + c(z - z_0) = 0$$

which is the point-normal form of a plane with normal $\mathbf{n} = \langle a, b, c \rangle$. ■

Equation (6) is called the ***general form*** of the equation of a plane.

▶ **Example 2** Determine whether the planes

$$3x - 4y + 5z = 0 \quad \text{and} \quad -6x + 8y - 10z - 4 = 0$$

are parallel.

***Solution.*** It is clear geometrically that two planes are parallel if and only if their normals are parallel vectors. A normal to the first plane is

$$\mathbf{n}_1 = \langle 3, -4, 5 \rangle$$

and a normal to the second plane is

$$\mathbf{n}_2 = \langle -6, 8, -10 \rangle$$

Since $\mathbf{n}_2$ is a scalar multiple of $\mathbf{n}_1$, the normals are parallel, and hence so are the planes. ◀

We have seen that a unique plane is determined by a point in the plane and a nonzero vector normal to the plane. In contrast, a unique plane is not determined by a point in the plane and a nonzero vector *parallel* to the plane (Figure 11.6.4). However, a unique plane is determined by a point in the plane and two nonparallel vectors that are parallel to the plane (Figure 11.6.5). A unique plane is also determined by three noncollinear points that lie in the plane (Figure 11.6.6).

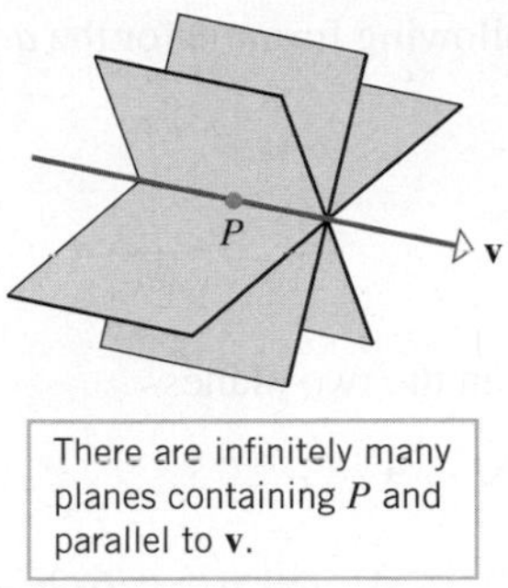


▲ **Figure 11.6.4**

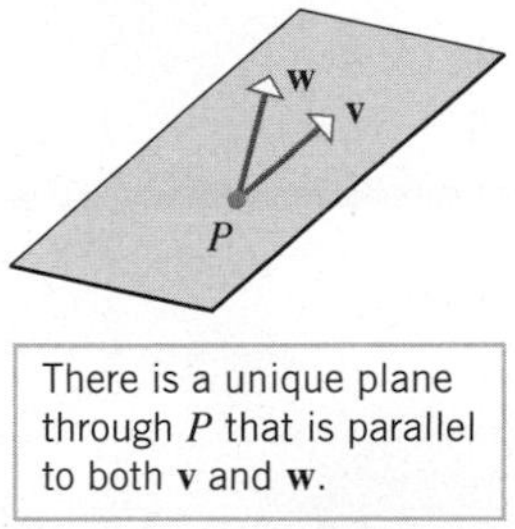


▲ **Figure 11.6.5**

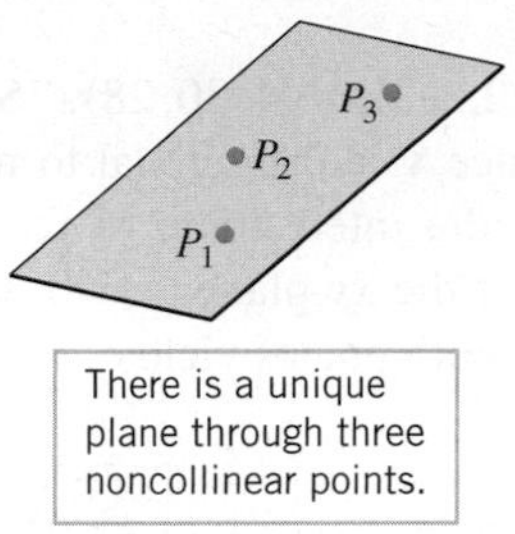


▲ **Figure 11.6.6**

▶ **Example 3** Find an equation of the plane through the points $P_1(1, 2, -1)$, $P_2(2, 3, 1)$, and $P_3(3, -1, 2)$.

***Solution.*** Since the points $P_1$, $P_2$, and $P_3$ lie in the plane, the vectors $\overrightarrow{P_1P_2} = \langle 1, 1, 2\rangle$ and $\overrightarrow{P_1P_3} = \langle 2, -3, 3\rangle$ are parallel to the plane. Therefore,

$$\overrightarrow{P_1P_2} \times \overrightarrow{P_1P_3} = \begin{vmatrix} \mathbf{i} & \mathbf{j} & \mathbf{k} \\ 1 & 1 & 2 \\ 2 & -3 & 3 \end{vmatrix} = 9\mathbf{i} + \mathbf{j} - 5\mathbf{k}$$

is normal to the plane, since it is orthogonal to both $\overrightarrow{P_1P_2}$ and $\overrightarrow{P_1P_3}$. By using this normal and the point $P_1(1, 2, -1)$ in the plane, we obtain the point-normal form

$$9(x - 1) + (y - 2) - 5(z + 1) = 0$$

which can be rewritten as

$$9x + y - 5z - 16 = 0 \blacktriangleleft$$

▶ **Example 4** Determine whether the line

$$x = 3 + 8t, \quad y = 4 + 5t, \quad z = -3 - t$$

is parallel to the plane $x - 3y + 5z = 12$.

***Solution.*** The vector $\mathbf{v} = \langle 8, 5, -1\rangle$ is parallel to the line and the vector $\mathbf{n} = \langle 1, -3, 5\rangle$ is normal to the plane. For the line and plane to be parallel, the vectors $\mathbf{v}$ and $\mathbf{n}$ must be orthogonal. But this is not so, since the dot product

$$\mathbf{v} \cdot \mathbf{n} = (8)(1) + (5)(-3) + (-1)(5) = -12$$

is nonzero. Thus, the line and plane are not parallel. ◀

▶ **Example 5** Find the intersection of the line and plane in Example 4.

***Solution.*** If we let $(x_0, y_0, z_0)$ be the point of intersection, then the coordinates of this point satisfy both the equation of the plane and the parametric equations of the line. Thus,

$$x_0 - 3y_0 + 5z_0 = 12 \tag{7}$$

and for some value of $t$, say $t = t_0$,

$$x_0 = 3 + 8t_0, \quad y_0 = 4 + 5t_0, \quad z_0 = -3 - t_0 \tag{8}$$

Substituting (8) in (7) yields

$$(3 + 8t_0) - 3(4 + 5t_0) + 5(-3 - t_0) = 12$$

Solving for $t_0$ yields $t_0 = -3$ and on substituting this value in (8), we obtain

$$(x_0, y_0, z_0) = (-21, -11, 0) \blacktriangleleft$$

## ■ INTERSECTING PLANES

Two distinct intersecting planes determine two positive angles of intersection—an (acute) angle $\theta$ that satisfies the condition $0 \le \theta \le \pi/2$ and the supplement of that angle (Figure 11.6.7*a*). If $\mathbf{n}_1$ and $\mathbf{n}_2$ are normals to the planes, then depending on the directions of $\mathbf{n}_1$ and $\mathbf{n}_2$, the angle $\theta$ is either the angle between $\mathbf{n}_1$ and $\mathbf{n}_2$ or the angle between $\mathbf{n}_1$ and $-\mathbf{n}_2$

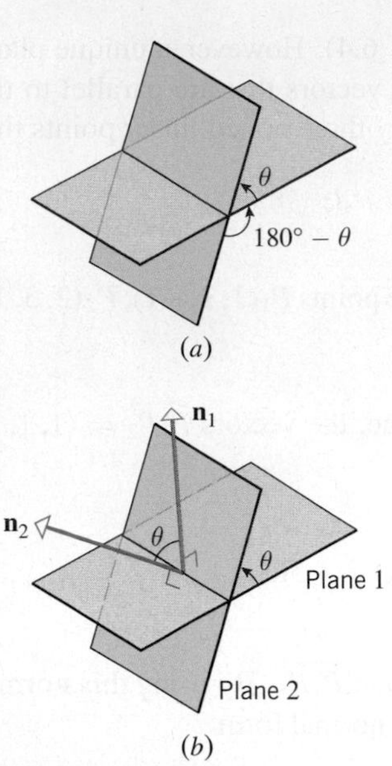


▲ Figure 11.6.7

(Figure 11.6.7*b*). In both cases, Theorem 11.3.3 yields the following formula for the *acute angle θ between the planes*:

$$\cos\theta = \frac{|\mathbf{n}_1 \cdot \mathbf{n}_2|}{\|\mathbf{n}_1\|\|\mathbf{n}_2\|} \tag{9}$$

**▶ Example 6** Find the acute angle of intersection between the two planes

$$2x - 4y + 4z = 6 \quad \text{and} \quad 6x + 2y - 3z = 4$$

***Solution.*** The given equations yield the normals $\mathbf{n}_1 = \langle 2, -4, 4\rangle$ and $\mathbf{n}_2 = \langle 6, 2, -3\rangle$. Thus, Formula (9) yields

$$\cos\theta = \frac{|\mathbf{n}_1 \cdot \mathbf{n}_2|}{\|\mathbf{n}_1\|\,\|\mathbf{n}_2\|} = \frac{|-8|}{\sqrt{36}\sqrt{49}} = \frac{4}{21}$$

from which we obtain

$$\theta = \cos^{-1}\left(\frac{4}{21}\right) \approx 79^\circ \blacktriangleleft$$

**▶ Example 7** Find an equation for the line $L$ of intersection of the planes in Example 6.

***Solution.*** First compute $\mathbf{v} = \mathbf{n}_1 \times \mathbf{n}_2 = \langle 2, -4, 4\rangle \times \langle 6, 2, -3\rangle = \langle 4, 30, 28\rangle$. Since $\mathbf{v}$ is orthogonal to $\mathbf{n}_1$, it is parallel to the first plane, and since $\mathbf{v}$ is orthogonal to $\mathbf{n}_2$, it is parallel to the second plane. That is, $\mathbf{v}$ is parallel to $L$, the intersection of the two planes. To find a point on $L$ we observe that $L$ must intersect the $xy$-plane, $z = 0$, since $\mathbf{v} \cdot \langle 0, 0, 1\rangle = 28 \neq 0$. Substituting $z = 0$ in the equations of both planes yields

$$\begin{aligned} 2x - 4y &= 6 \\ 6x + 2y &= 4 \end{aligned}$$

with solution $x = 1, y = -1$. Thus, $P(1, -1, 0)$ is a point on $L$. A vector equation for $L$ is

$$\langle x, y, z\rangle = \langle 1, -1, 0\rangle + t\langle 4, 30, 28\rangle \blacktriangleleft$$

## DISTANCE PROBLEMS INVOLVING PLANES

Next we will consider three basic distance problems in 3-space:

- Find the distance between a point and a plane.
- Find the distance between two parallel planes.
- Find the distance between two skew lines.

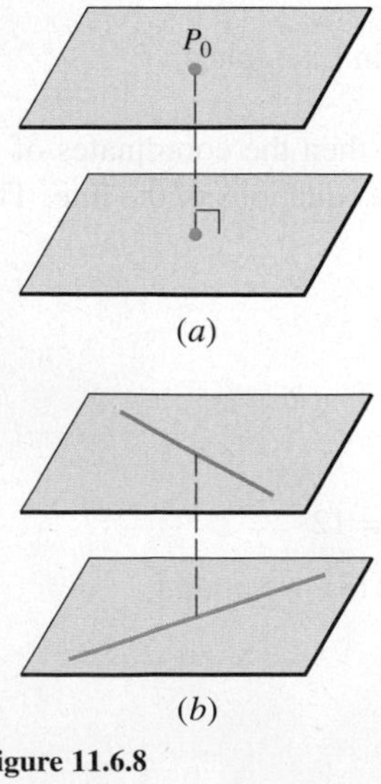


▲ Figure 11.6.8

The three problems are related. If we can find the distance between a point and a plane, then we can find the distance between parallel planes by computing the distance between one of the planes and an arbitrary point $P_0$ in the other plane (Figure 11.6.8*a*). Moreover, we can find the distance between two skew lines by computing the distance between parallel planes containing them (Figure 11.6.8*b*).

**11.6.2 THEOREM** *The distance $D$ between a point $P_0(x_0, y_0, z_0)$ and the plane $ax + by + cz + d = 0$ is*

$$D = \frac{|ax_0 + by_0 + cz_0 + d|}{\sqrt{a^2 + b^2 + c^2}} \tag{10}$$

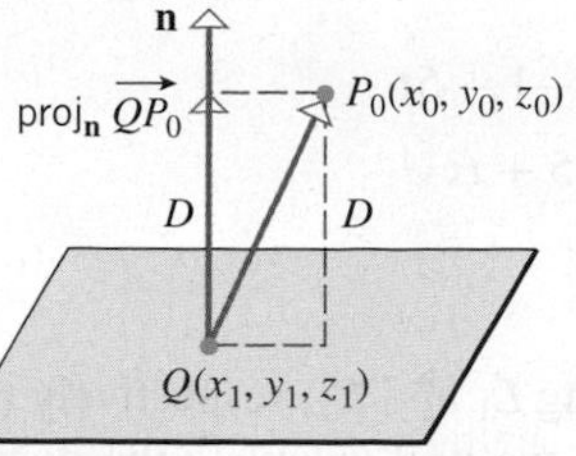

▲ **Figure 11.6.9**

**PROOF** Let $Q(x_1, y_1, z_1)$ be any point in the plane, and position the normal $\mathbf{n} = \langle a, b, c\rangle$ so that its initial point is at $Q$. As illustrated in Figure 11.6.9, the distance $D$ is equal to the length of the orthogonal projection of $\overrightarrow{QP_0}$ on $\mathbf{n}$. Thus, from (12) of Section 11.3,

$$D = \|\text{proj}_{\mathbf{n}}\overrightarrow{QP_0}\| = \left\|\frac{\overrightarrow{QP_0}\cdot\mathbf{n}}{\|\mathbf{n}\|^2}\mathbf{n}\right\| = \frac{|\overrightarrow{QP_0}\cdot\mathbf{n}|}{\|\mathbf{n}\|^2}\|\mathbf{n}\| = \frac{|\overrightarrow{QP_0}\cdot\mathbf{n}|}{\|\mathbf{n}\|}$$

But

$$\overrightarrow{QP_0} = \langle x_0 - x_1, y_0 - y_1, z_0 - z_1\rangle$$
$$\overrightarrow{QP_0}\cdot\mathbf{n} = a(x_0 - x_1) + b(y_0 - y_1) + c(z_0 - z_1)$$
$$\|\mathbf{n}\| = \sqrt{a^2 + b^2 + c^2}$$

Thus,

$$D = \frac{|a(x_0 - x_1) + b(y_0 - y_1) + c(z_0 - z_1)|}{\sqrt{a^2 + b^2 + c^2}} \tag{11}$$

Since the point $Q(x_1, y_1, z_1)$ lies in the plane, its coordinates satisfy the equation of the plane; that is,

$$ax_1 + by_1 + cz_1 + d = 0$$

or

$$d = -ax_1 - by_1 - cz_1$$

Combining this expression with (11) yields (10). ■

There is an analog of Formula (10) in 2-space that can be used to compute the distance between a point and a line (see Exercise 52).

▶ **Example 8** Find the distance $D$ between the point $(1, -4, -3)$ and the plane

$$2x - 3y + 6z = -1$$

***Solution.*** Formula (10) requires the plane be rewritten in the form $ax + by + cz + d = 0$. Thus, we rewrite the equation of the given plane as

$$2x - 3y + 6z + 1 = 0$$

from which we obtain $a = 2, b = -3, c = 6$, and $d = 1$. Substituting these values and the coordinates of the given point in (10), we obtain

$$D = \frac{|(2)(1) + (-3)(-4) + 6(-3) + 1|}{\sqrt{2^2 + (-3)^2 + 6^2}} = \frac{|-3|}{7} = \frac{3}{7} \blacktriangleleft$$

▶ **Example 9** The planes

$$x + 2y - 2z = 3 \quad \text{and} \quad 2x + 4y - 4z = 7$$

are parallel since their normals, $\langle 1, 2, -2\rangle$ and $\langle 2, 4, -4\rangle$, are parallel vectors. Find the distance between these planes.

***Solution.*** To find the distance $D$ between the planes, we can select an *arbitrary* point in one of the planes and compute its distance to the other plane. By setting $y = z = 0$ in the equation $x + 2y - 2z = 3$, we obtain the point $P_0(3, 0, 0)$ in this plane. From (10), the distance from $P_0$ to the plane $2x + 4y - 4z = 7$ is

$$D = \frac{|(2)(3) + 4(0) + (-4)(0) - 7|}{\sqrt{2^2 + 4^2 + (-4)^2}} = \frac{1}{6} \blacktriangleleft$$

▶ **Example 10** It was shown in Example 3 of Section 11.5 that the lines

$$L_1\colon x = 1 + 4t, \quad y = 5 - 4t, \quad z = -1 + 5t$$
$$L_2\colon x = 2 + 8t, \quad y = 4 - 3t, \quad z = 5 + t$$

are skew. Find the distance between them.

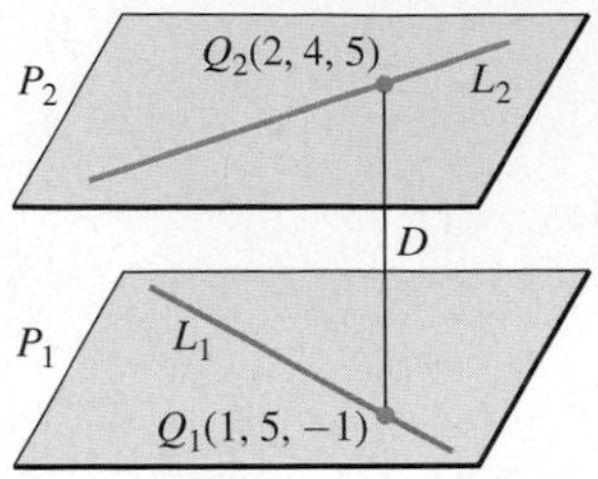

▲ **Figure 11.6.10**

***Solution.*** Let $P_1$ and $P_2$ denote parallel planes containing $L_1$ and $L_2$, respectively (Figure 11.6.10). To find the distance $D$ between $L_1$ and $L_2$, we will calculate the distance from a point in $P_1$ to the plane $P_2$. Since $L_1$ lies in plane $P_1$, we can find a point in $P_1$ by finding a point on the line $L_1$; we can do this by substituting any convenient value of $t$ in the parametric equations of $L_1$. The simplest choice is $t = 0$, which yields the point $Q_1(1, 5, -1)$.

The next step is to find an equation for the plane $P_2$. For this purpose, observe that the vector $\mathbf{u}_1 = \langle 4, -4, 5\rangle$ is parallel to line $L_1$, and therefore also parallel to planes $P_1$ and $P_2$. Similarly, $\mathbf{u}_2 = \langle 8, -3, 1\rangle$ is parallel to $L_2$ and hence parallel to $P_1$ and $P_2$. Therefore, the cross product

$$\mathbf{n} = \mathbf{u}_1 \times \mathbf{u}_2 = \begin{vmatrix} \mathbf{i} & \mathbf{j} & \mathbf{k} \\ 4 & -4 & 5 \\ 8 & -3 & 1 \end{vmatrix} = 11\mathbf{i} + 36\mathbf{j} + 20\mathbf{k}$$

is normal to both $P_1$ and $P_2$. Using this normal and the point $Q_2(2, 4, 5)$ found by setting $t = 0$ in the equations of $L_2$, we obtain an equation for $P_2$:

$$11(x - 2) + 36(y - 4) + 20(z - 5) = 0$$

or

$$11x + 36y + 20z - 266 = 0$$

The distance between $Q_1(1, 5, -1)$ and this plane is

$$D = \frac{|(11)(1) + (36)(5) + (20)(-1) - 266|}{\sqrt{11^2 + 36^2 + 20^2}} = \frac{95}{\sqrt{1817}}$$

which is also the distance between $L_1$ and $L_2$. ◀

## ✓QUICK CHECK EXERCISES 11.6 (See page 724 for answers.)

1. The point-normal form of the equation of the plane through $(0, 3, 5)$ and perpendicular to $\langle -4, 1, 7\rangle$ is ______.
2. A normal vector for the plane $4x - 2y + 7z - 11 = 0$ is ______.
3. A normal vector for the plane through the points $(2, 5, 1)$, $(3, 7, 0)$, and $(2, 5, 2)$ is ______.
4. The acute angle of intersection of the planes $x + y - 2z = 5$ and $3y - 4z = 6$ is ______.
5. The distance between the point $(9, 8, 3)$ and the plane $x + y - 2z = 5$ is ______.

## EXERCISE SET 11.6

1. Find equations of the planes $P_1$, $P_2$, and $P_3$ that are parallel to the coordinate planes and pass through the corner $(3, 4, 5)$ of the box shown in the accompanying figure.
2. Find equations of the planes $P_1$, $P_2$, and $P_3$ that are parallel to the coordinate planes and pass through the corner $(x_0, y_0, z_0)$ of the box shown in the accompanying figure.

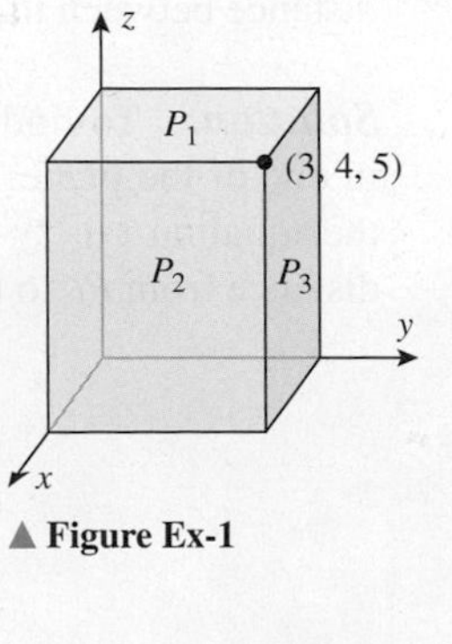

▲ **Figure Ex-1**

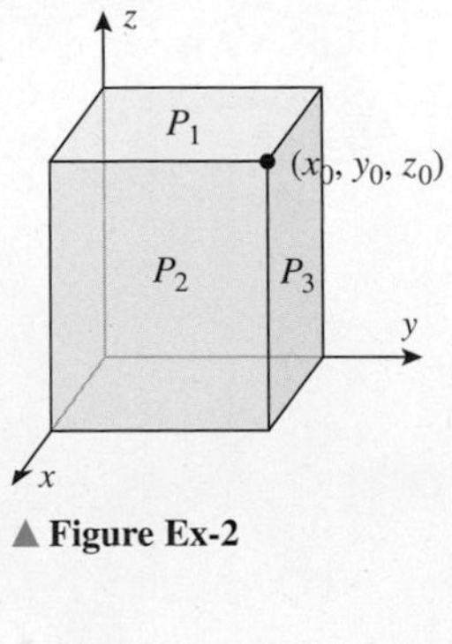

▲ **Figure Ex-2**

**3–6** Find an equation of the plane that passes through the point $P$ and has the vector $\mathbf{n}$ as a normal. ■

**3.** $P(2, 6, 1)$; $\mathbf{n} = \langle 1, 4, 2 \rangle$

**4.** $P(-1, -1, 2)$; $\mathbf{n} = \langle -1, 7, 6 \rangle$

**5.** $P(1, 0, 0)$; $\mathbf{n} = \langle 0, 0, 1 \rangle$

**6.** $P(0, 0, 0)$; $\mathbf{n} = \langle 2, -3, -4 \rangle$

**7–10** Find an equation of the plane indicated in the figure. ■

**7.**

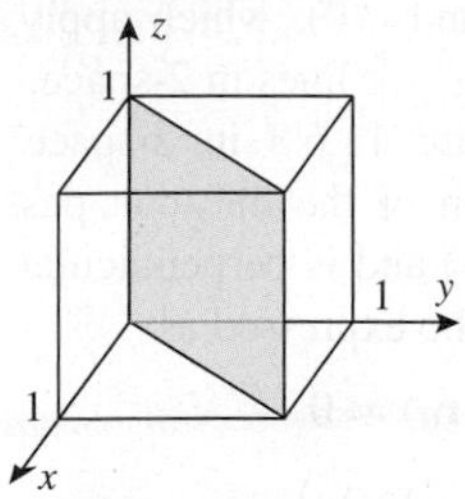


**8.**

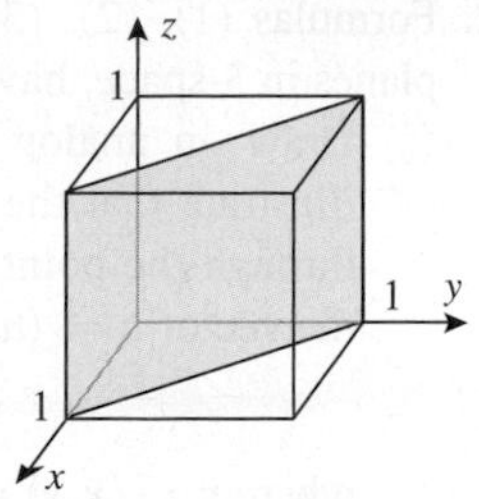


**9.**

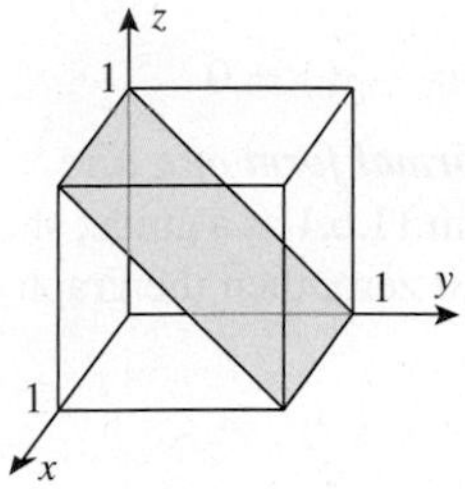


**10.**

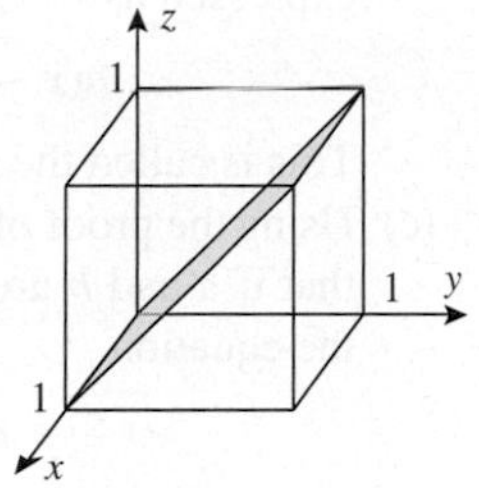


**11–12** Find an equation of the plane that passes through the given points. ■

**11.** $(-2, 1, 1)$, $(0, 2, 3)$, and $(1, 0, -1)$

**12.** $(3, 2, 1)$, $(2, 1, -1)$, and $(-1, 3, 2)$

**13–14** Determine whether the planes are parallel, perpendicular, or neither. ■

**13.** (a) $2x - 8y - 6z - 2 = 0$; $-x + 4y + 3z - 5 = 0$
(b) $3x - 2y + z = 1$; $4x + 5y - 2z = 4$
(c) $x - y + 3z - 2 = 0$; $2x + z = 1$

**14.** (a) $3x - 2y + z = 4$; $6x - 4y + 3z = 7$
(b) $y = 4x - 2z + 3$; $x = \frac{1}{4}y + \frac{1}{2}z$
(c) $x + 4y + 7z = 3$; $5x - 3y + z = 0$

**15–16** Determine whether the line and plane are parallel, perpendicular, or neither. ■

**15.** (a) $x = 4 + 2t,\ y = -t,\ z = -1 - 4t$; $3x + 2y + z - 7 = 0$
(b) $x = t,\ y = 2t,\ z = 3t$; $x - y + 2z = 5$
(c) $x = -1 + 2t,\ y = 4 + t,\ z = 1 - t$; $4x + 2y - 2z = 7$

**16.** (a) $x = 3 - t,\ y = 2 + t,\ z = 1 - 3t$; $2x + 2y - 5 = 0$
(b) $x = 1 - 2t,\ y = t,\ z = -t$; $6x - 3y + 3z = 1$
(c) $x = t,\ y = 1 - t,\ z = 2 + t$; $x + y + z = 1$

**17–18** Determine whether the line and plane intersect; if so, find the coordinates of the intersection. ■

**17.** (a) $x = t,\ y = t,\ z = t$; $3x - 2y + z - 5 = 0$
(b) $x = 2 - t,\ y = 3 + t,\ z = t$; $2x + y + z = 1$

**18.** (a) $x = 3t,\ y = 5t,\ z = -t$; $2x - y + z + 1 = 0$
(b) $x = 1 + t,\ y = -1 + 3t,\ z = 2 + 4t$; $x - y + 4z = 7$

**19–20** Find the acute angle of intersection of the planes to the nearest degree. ■

**19.** $x = 0$ and $2x - y + z - 4 = 0$

**20.** $x + 2y - 2z = 5$ and $6x - 3y + 2z = 8$

**21–24 True–False** Determine whether the statement is true or false. Explain your answer. ■

**21.** Every plane has exactly two unit normal vectors.

**22.** If a plane is parallel to one of the coordinate planes, then its normal vector is parallel to one of the three vectors $\mathbf{i}$, $\mathbf{j}$, or $\mathbf{k}$.

**23.** If two planes intersect in a line $L$, then $L$ is parallel to the cross product of the normals to the two planes.

**24.** If $a^2 + b^2 + c^2 = 1$, then the distance from $P(x_0, y_0, z_0)$ to the plane $ax + by + cz = 0$ is $|\langle a, b, c \rangle \cdot \langle x_0, y_0, z_0 \rangle|$.

**25–34** Find an equation of the plane that satisfies the stated conditions. ■

**25.** The plane through the origin that is parallel to the plane $4x - 2y + 7z + 12 = 0$.

**26.** The plane that contains the line $x = -2 + 3t$, $y = 4 + 2t$, $z = 3 - t$ and is perpendicular to the plane $x - 2y + z = 5$.

**27.** The plane through the point $(-1, 4, 2)$ that contains the line of intersection of the planes $4x - y + z - 2 = 0$ and $2x + y - 2z - 3 = 0$.

**28.** The plane through $(-1, 4, -3)$ that is perpendicular to the line $x - 2 = t$, $y + 3 = 2t$, $z = -t$.

**29.** The plane through $(1, 2, -1)$ that is perpendicular to the line of intersection of the planes $2x + y + z = 2$ and $x + 2y + z = 3$.

**30.** The plane through the points $P_1(-2, 1, 4)$, $P_2(1, 0, 3)$ that is perpendicular to the plane $4x - y + 3z = 2$.

**31.** The plane through $(-1, 2, -5)$ that is perpendicular to the planes $2x - y + z = 1$ and $x + y - 2z = 3$.

**32.** The plane that contains the point $(2, 0, 3)$ and the line $x = -1 + t$, $y = t$, $z = -4 + 2t$.

**33.** The plane whose points are equidistant from $(2, -1, 1)$ and $(3, 1, 5)$.

**34.** The plane that contains the line $x = 3t$, $y = 1 + t$, $z = 2t$ and is parallel to the intersection of the planes $y + z = -1$ and $2x - y + z = 0$.

**35.** Find parametric equations of the line through the point $(5, 0, -2)$ that is parallel to the planes $x - 4y + 2z = 0$ and $2x + 3y - z + 1 = 0$.

**36.** Let $L$ be the line $x = 3t + 1$, $y = -5t$, $z = t$.
(a) Show that $L$ lies in the plane $2x + y - z = 2$.
(b) Show that $L$ is parallel to the plane $x + y + 2z = 0$. Is the line above, below, or on this plane?

**37.** Show that the lines
$$x = -2 + t, \quad y = 3 + 2t, \quad z = 4 - t$$
$$x = 3 - t, \quad y = 4 - 2t, \quad z = t$$
are parallel and find an equation of the plane they determine.

**38.** Show that the lines
$$L_1: x + 1 = 4t, \quad y - 3 = t, \quad z - 1 = 0$$
$$L_2: x + 13 = 12t, \quad y - 1 = 6t, \quad z - 2 = 3t$$
intersect and find an equation of the plane they determine.

**FOCUS ON CONCEPTS**

**39.** Do the points $(1, 0, -1)$, $(0, 2, 3)$, $(-2, 1, 1)$, and $(4, 2, 3)$ lie in the same plane? Justify your answer two different ways.

**40.** Show that if $a$, $b$, and $c$ are nonzero, then the plane whose intercepts with the coordinate axes are $x = a$, $y = b$, and $z = c$ is given by the equation
$$\frac{x}{a} + \frac{y}{b} + \frac{z}{c} = 1$$

**41–42** Find parametric equations of the line of intersection of the planes. ■

**41.** $-2x + 3y + 7z + 2 = 0$, $x + 2y - 3z + 5 = 0$

**42.** $3x - 5y + 2z = 0$, $z = 0$

**43–44** Find the distance between the point and the plane. ■

**43.** $(1, -2, 3)$; $2x - 2y + z = 4$

**44.** $(0, 1, 5)$; $3x + 6y - 2z - 5 = 0$

**45–46** Find the distance between the given parallel planes. ■

**45.** $-2x + y + z = 0$, $6x - 3y - 3z - 5 = 0$

**46.** $x + y + z = 1$, $x + y + z = -1$

**47–48** Find the distance between the given skew lines. ■

**47.** $x = 1 + 7t$, $y = 3 + t$, $z = 5 - 3t$
$x = 4 - t$, $y = 6$, $z = 7 + 2t$

**48.** $x = 3 - t$, $y = 4 + 4t$, $z = 1 + 2t$
$x = t$, $y = 3$, $z = 2t$

**49.** Find an equation of the sphere with center $(2, 1, -3)$ that is tangent to the plane $x - 3y + 2z = 4$.

**50.** Locate the point of intersection of the plane $2x + y - z = 0$ and the line through $(3, 1, 0)$ that is perpendicular to the plane.

**51.** Show that the line $x = -1 + t$, $y = 3 + 2t$, $z = -t$ and the plane $2x - 2y - 2z + 3 = 0$ are parallel, and find the distance between them.

**FOCUS ON CONCEPTS**

**52.** Formulas (1), (2), (3), (5), and (10), which apply to planes in 3-space, have analogs for lines in 2-space.
(a) Draw an analog of Figure 11.6.3 in 2-space to illustrate that the equation of the line that passes through the point $P(x_0, y_0)$ and is perpendicular to the vector $\mathbf{n} = \langle a, b\rangle$ can be expressed as
$$\mathbf{n} \cdot (\mathbf{r} - \mathbf{r}_0) = 0$$
where $\mathbf{r} = \langle x, y\rangle$ and $\mathbf{r}_0 = \langle x_0, y_0\rangle$.
(b) Show that the vector equation in part (a) can be expressed as
$$a(x - x_0) + b(y - y_0) = 0$$
This is called the ***point-normal form of a line***.
(c) Using the proof of Theorem 11.6.1 as a guide, show that if $a$ and $b$ are not both zero, then the graph of the equation
$$ax + by + c = 0$$
is a line that has $\mathbf{n} = \langle a, b\rangle$ as a normal.
(d) Using the proof of Theorem 11.6.2 as a guide, show that the distance $D$ between a point $P(x_0, y_0)$ and the line $ax + by + c = 0$ is
$$D = \frac{|ax_0 + by_0 + c|}{\sqrt{a^2 + b^2}}$$
(e) Use the formula in part (d) to find the distance between the point $P(-3, 5)$ and the line $y = -2x + 1$.

**53.** (a) Show that the distance $D$ between parallel planes
$$ax + by + cz + d_1 = 0$$
$$ax + by + cz + d_2 = 0$$
is
$$D = \frac{|d_1 - d_2|}{\sqrt{a^2 + b^2 + c^2}}$$
(b) Use the formula in part (a) to solve Exercise 45.

**54. Writing** Explain why any line in 3-space must lie in some vertical plane. Must any line in 3-space also lie in some horizontal plane?

**55. Writing** Given two planes, discuss the various possibilities for the set of points they have in common. Then consider the set of points that three planes can have in common.

✓ **QUICK CHECK ANSWERS 11.6** 1. $-4x + (y - 3) + 7(z - 5) = 0$ 2. $\langle 4, -2, 7\rangle$ 3. $\langle 2, -1, 0\rangle$ 4. $\cos^{-1}\frac{11}{5\sqrt{6}} \approx 26^\circ$ 5. $\sqrt{6}$

# 11.7 QUADRIC SURFACES

*In this section we will study an important class of surfaces that are the three-dimensional analogs of the conic sections.*

## TRACES OF SURFACES

Although the general shape of a curve in 2-space can be obtained by plotting points, this method is not usually helpful for surfaces in 3-space because too many points are required. It is more common to build up the shape of a surface with a network of ***mesh lines***, which are curves obtained by cutting the surface with well-chosen planes. For example, Figure 11.7.1, which was generated by a CAS, shows the graph of $z = x^3 - 3xy^2$ rendered with a combination of mesh lines and colorization to produce the surface detail. This surface is called a "monkey saddle" because a monkey sitting astride the surface has a place for its two legs and tail.

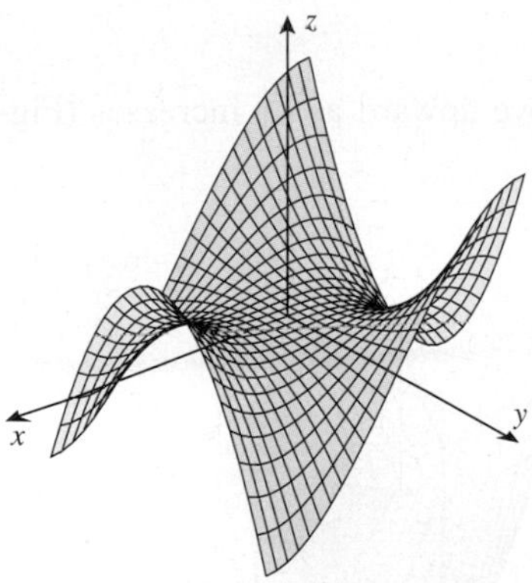


▲ **Figure 11.7.1**

The mesh line that results when a surface is cut by a plane is called the ***trace*** of the surface in the plane (Figure 11.7.2). One way to deduce the shape of a surface is by examining its traces in planes parallel to the coordinate planes. For example, consider the surface

$$z = x^2 + y^2 \tag{1}$$

To find its trace in the plane $z = k$, we substitute this value of $z$ into (1), which yields

$$x^2 + y^2 = k \quad (z = k) \tag{2}$$

The parenthetical part of Equation (2) is a reminder that the $z$-coordinate of each point in the trace is $z = k$. This needs to be stated explicitly because the variable $z$ does not appear in the equation $x^2 + y^2 = k$.

If $k < 0$, this equation has no real solutions, so there is no trace. However, if $k \geq 0$, then the graph of (2) is a circle of radius $\sqrt{k}$ centered at the point $(0, 0, k)$ on the $z$-axis (Figure 11.7.3*a*). Thus, for nonnegative values of $k$ the traces parallel to the $xy$-plane form a family of circles, centered on the $z$-axis, whose radii start at zero and increase with $k$. This suggests that the surface has the form shown in Figure 11.7.3*b*.

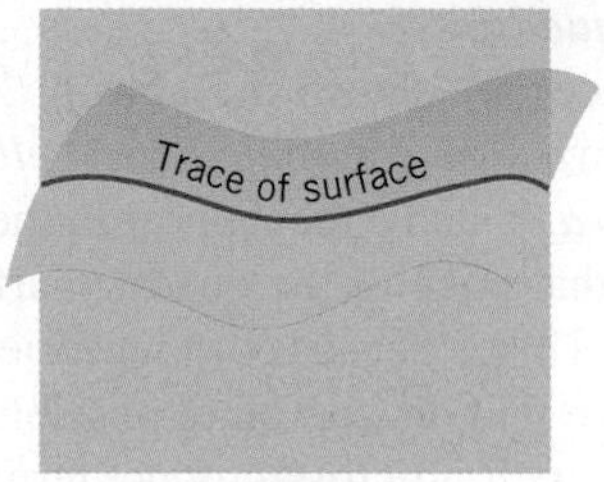


▲ **Figure 11.7.2**

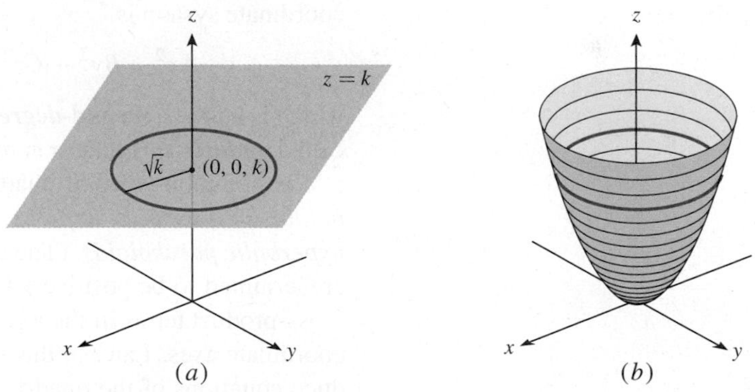


▲ **Figure 11.7.3**

To obtain more detailed information about the shape of this surface, we can examine the traces of (1) in planes parallel to the $yz$-plane. Such planes have equations of the form $x = k$, so we substitute this in (1) to obtain

$$z = k^2 + y^2 \quad (x = k)$$

which we can rewrite as

$$z - k^2 = y^2 \quad (x = k) \tag{3}$$

For simplicity, let us start with the case where $k = 0$ (the trace in the $yz$-plane), in which case the trace has the equation

$$z = y^2 \quad (x = 0)$$

You should be able to recognize that this is a parabola in the plane $x = 0$ that has its vertex at the origin, opens in the positive $z$-direction, and is symmetric about the $z$-axis (the blue parabola in Figure 11.7.4*a*). You should also be able to recognize that the $-k^2$ term in (3) has the effect of translating the parabola $z = y^2$ in the positive $z$-direction, so its new vertex in the plane $x = k$ is at the point $(k, 0, k^2)$. This is the red parabola in Figure 11.7.4*a*. Thus, the traces in planes parallel to the $yz$-plane form a family of parabolas whose vertices move upward as $k^2$ increases (Figure 11.7.4*b*). Similarly, the traces in planes parallel to the $xz$-plane have equations of the form

$$z - k^2 = x^2 \qquad (y = k)$$

which again is a family of parabolas whose vertices move upward as $k^2$ increases (Figure 11.7.4*c*).

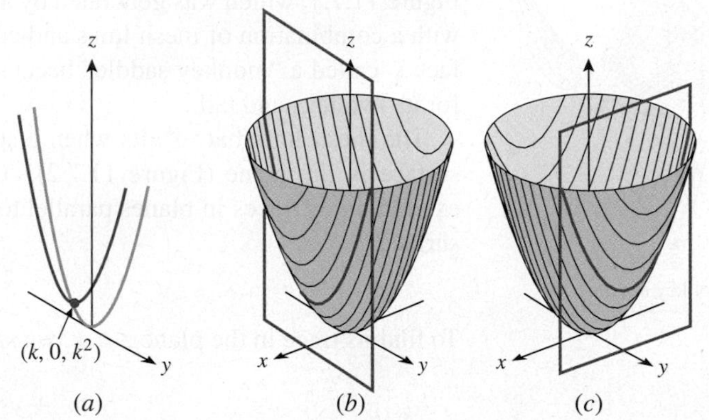


▶ **Figure 11.7.4**

## THE QUADRIC SURFACES

In the discussion of Formula (2) in Section 10.5 we noted that a second-degree equation

$$Ax^2 + Bxy + Cy^2 + Dx + Ey + F = 0$$

represents a conic section (possibly degenerate). The analog of this equation in an $xyz$-coordinate system is

$$Ax^2 + By^2 + Cz^2 + Dxy + Exz + Fyz + Gx + Hy + Iz + J = 0 \qquad (4)$$

which is called a ***second-degree equation in x, y, and z***. The graphs of such equations are called ***quadric surfaces*** or sometimes ***quadrics***.

Six common types of quadric surfaces are shown in Table 11.7.1—*ellipsoids, hyperboloids of one sheet, hyperboloids of two sheets, elliptic cones, elliptic paraboloids,* and *hyperbolic paraboloids*. (The constants $a$, $b$, and $c$ that appear in the equations in the table are assumed to be positive.) Observe that none of the quadric surfaces in the table have cross-product terms in their equations. This is because of their orientations relative to the coordinate axes. Later in this section we will discuss other possible orientations that produce equations of the quadric surfaces with no cross-product terms. In the special case where the elliptic cross sections of an elliptic cone or an elliptic paraboloid are circles, the terms *circular cone* and *circular paraboloid* are used.

## TECHNIQUES FOR GRAPHING QUADRIC SURFACES

Accurate graphs of quadric surfaces are best left for graphing utilities. However, the techniques that we will now discuss can be used to generate rough sketches of these surfaces that are useful for various purposes.

A rough sketch of an ellipsoid

$$\frac{x^2}{a^2} + \frac{y^2}{b^2} + \frac{z^2}{c^2} = 1 \qquad (a > 0, b > 0, c > 0) \qquad (5)$$

can be obtained by first plotting the intersections with the coordinate axes, and then sketching the elliptical traces in the coordinate planes. Example 1 illustrates this technique.

**Table 11.7.1**

| SURFACE | EQUATION | SURFACE | EQUATION |
|---|---|---|---|
| ELLIPSOID 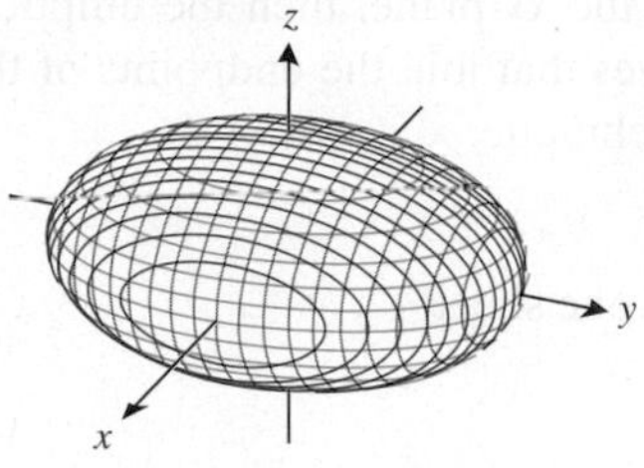  | $\dfrac{x^2}{a^2}+\dfrac{y^2}{b^2}+\dfrac{z^2}{c^2}=1$<br>The traces in the coordinate planes are ellipses, as are the traces in those planes that are parallel to the coordinate planes and intersect the surface in more than one point. | ELLIPTIC CONE 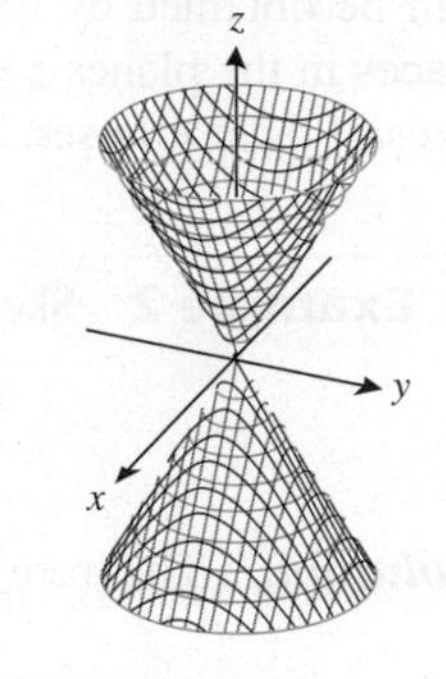  | $z^2=\dfrac{x^2}{a^2}+\dfrac{y^2}{b^2}$<br>The trace in the $xy$-plane is a point (the origin), and the traces in planes parallel to the $xy$-plane are ellipses. The traces in the $yz$- and $xz$-planes are pairs of lines intersecting at the origin. The traces in planes parallel to these are hyperbolas. |
| HYPERBOLOID OF ONE SHEET 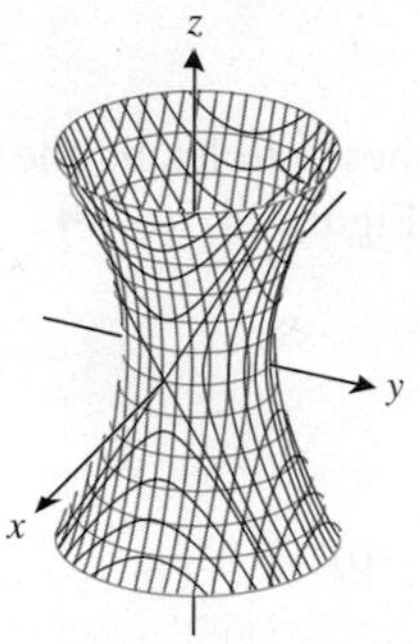  | $\dfrac{x^2}{a^2}+\dfrac{y^2}{b^2}-\dfrac{z^2}{c^2}=1$<br>The trace in the $xy$-plane is an ellipse, as are the traces in planes parallel to the $xy$-plane. The traces in the $yz$-plane and $xz$-plane are hyperbolas, as are the traces in those planes that are parallel to these and do not pass through the $x$- or $y$-intercepts. At these intercepts the traces are pairs of intersecting lines. | ELLIPTIC PARABOLOID 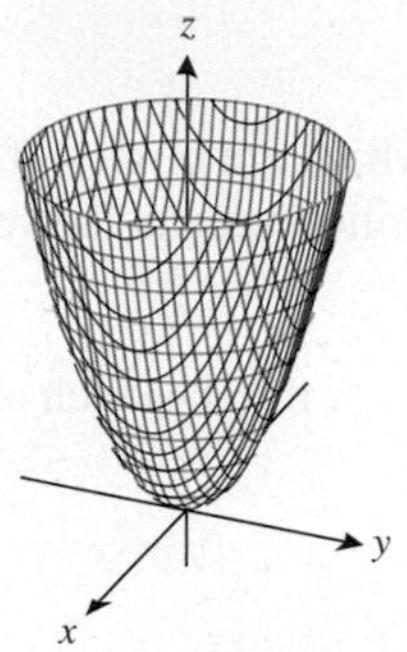  | $z=\dfrac{x^2}{a^2}+\dfrac{y^2}{b^2}$<br>The trace in the $xy$-plane is a point (the origin), and the traces in planes parallel to and above the $xy$-plane are ellipses. The traces in the $yz$- and $xz$-planes are parabolas, as are the traces in planes parallel to these. |
| HYPERBOLOID OF TWO SHEETS 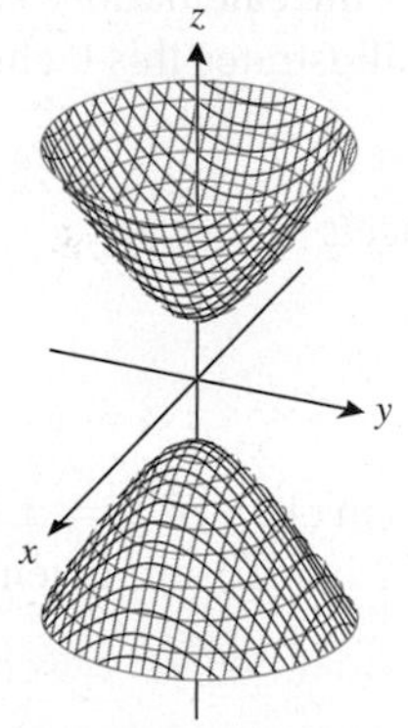  | $\dfrac{z^2}{c^2}-\dfrac{x^2}{a^2}-\dfrac{y^2}{b^2}=1$<br>There is no trace in the $xy$-plane. In planes parallel to the $xy$-plane that intersect the surface in more than one point the traces are ellipses. In the $yz$- and $xz$-planes, the traces are hyperbolas, as are the traces in those planes that are parallel to these. | HYPERBOLIC PARABOLOID 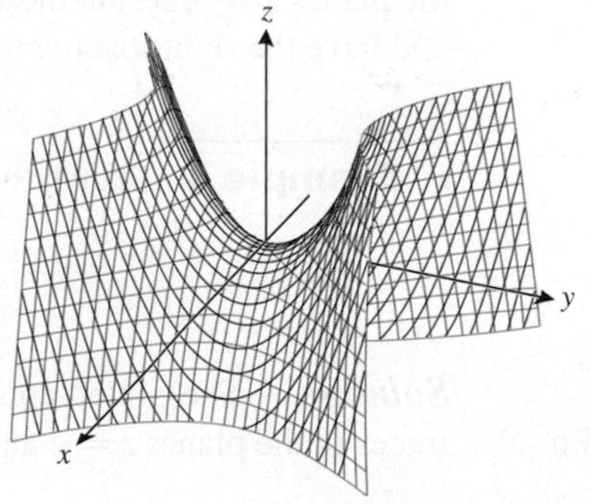  | $z=\dfrac{y^2}{b^2}-\dfrac{x^2}{a^2}$<br>The trace in the $xy$-plane is a pair of lines intersecting at the origin. The traces in planes parallel to the $xy$-plane are hyperbolas. The hyperbolas above the $xy$-plane open in the $y$-direction, and those below in the $x$-direction. The traces in the $yz$- and $xz$-planes are parabolas, as are the traces in planes parallel to these. |

**▶ Example 1** Sketch the ellipsoid

$$\frac{x^2}{4}+\frac{y^2}{16}+\frac{z^2}{9}=1 \tag{6}$$

***Solution.*** The $x$-intercepts can be obtained by setting $y=0$ and $z=0$ in (6). This yields $x=\pm 2$. Similarly, the $y$-intercepts are $y=\pm 4$, and the $z$-intercepts are $z=\pm 3$. Sketching the elliptical traces in the coordinate planes yields the graph in Figure 11.7.5. ◀

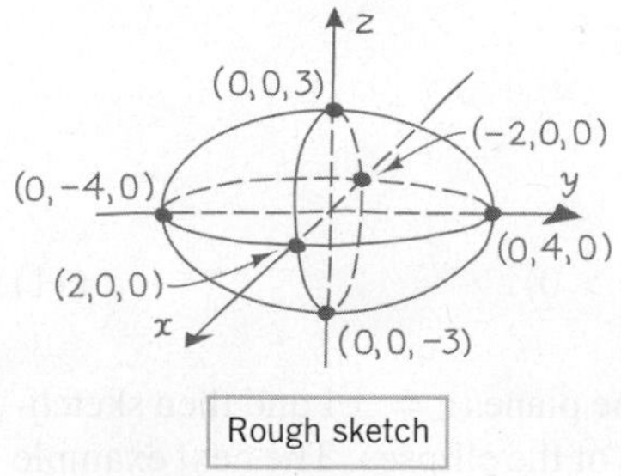


▲ **Figure 11.7.5**

A rough sketch of a hyperboloid of one sheet

$$\frac{x^2}{a^2}+\frac{y^2}{b^2}-\frac{z^2}{c^2}=1 \qquad (a>0, b>0, c>0) \tag{7}$$

can be obtained by first sketching the elliptical trace in the $xy$-plane, then the elliptical traces in the planes $z=\pm c$, and then the hyperbolic curves that join the endpoints of the axes of these ellipses. The next example illustrates this technique.

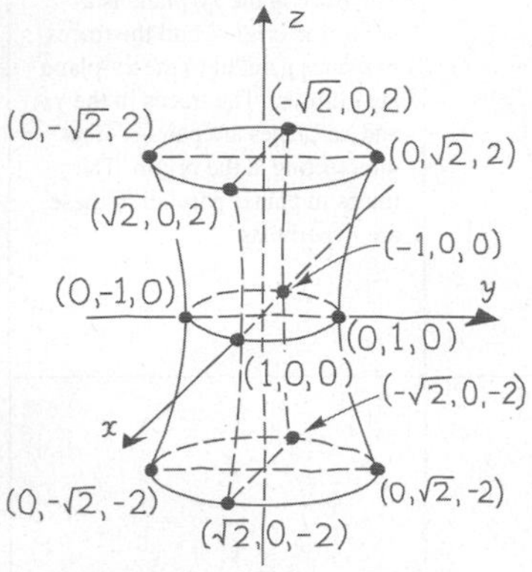


Rough sketch

▲ **Figure 11.7.6**

► **Example 2** Sketch the graph of the hyperboloid of one sheet

$$x^2+y^2-\frac{z^2}{4}=1 \tag{8}$$

***Solution.*** The trace in the $xy$-plane, obtained by setting $z=0$ in (8), is

$$x^2+y^2=1 \qquad (z=0)$$

which is a circle of radius 1 centered on the $z$-axis. The traces in the planes $z=2$ and $z=-2$, obtained by setting $z=\pm 2$ in (8), are given by

$$x^2+y^2=2 \qquad (z=\pm 2)$$

which are circles of radius $\sqrt{2}$ centered on the $z$-axis. Joining these circles by the hyperbolic traces in the vertical coordinate planes yields the graph in Figure 11.7.6. ◄

A rough sketch of the hyperboloid of two sheets

$$\frac{z^2}{c^2}-\frac{x^2}{a^2}-\frac{y^2}{b^2}=1 \qquad (a>0, b>0, c>0) \tag{9}$$

can be obtained by first plotting the intersections with the $z$-axis, then sketching the elliptical traces in the planes $z=\pm 2c$, and then sketching the hyperbolic traces that connect the $z$-axis intersections and the endpoints of the axes of the ellipses. (It is not essential to use the planes $z=\pm 2c$, but these are good choices since they simplify the calculations slightly and have the right spacing for a good sketch.) The next example illustrates this technique.

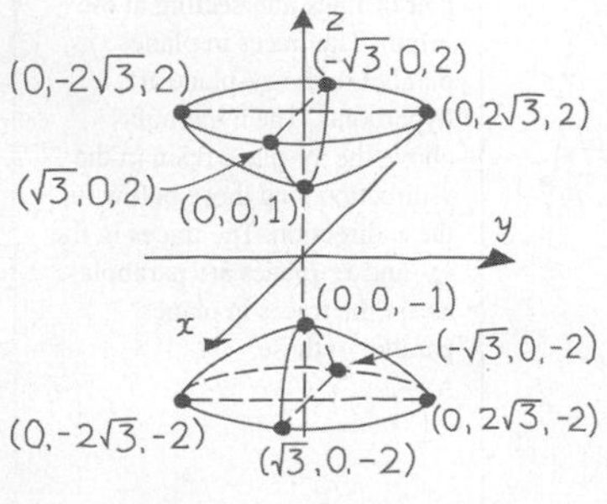


Rough sketch

▲ **Figure 11.7.7**

► **Example 3** Sketch the graph of the hyperboloid of two sheets

$$z^2-x^2-\frac{y^2}{4}=1 \tag{10}$$

***Solution.*** The $z$-intercepts, obtained by setting $x=0$ and $y=0$ in (10), are $z=\pm 1$. The traces in the planes $z=2$ and $z=-2$, obtained by setting $z=\pm 2$ in (10), are given by

$$\frac{x^2}{3}+\frac{y^2}{12}=1 \qquad (z=\pm 2)$$

Sketching these ellipses and the hyperbolic traces in the vertical coordinate planes yields Figure 11.7.7. ◄

A rough sketch of the elliptic cone

$$z^2=\frac{x^2}{a^2}+\frac{y^2}{b^2} \qquad (a>0, b>0) \tag{11}$$

can be obtained by first sketching the elliptical traces in the planes $z=\pm 1$ and then sketching the linear traces that connect the endpoints of the axes of the ellipses. The next example illustrates this technique.

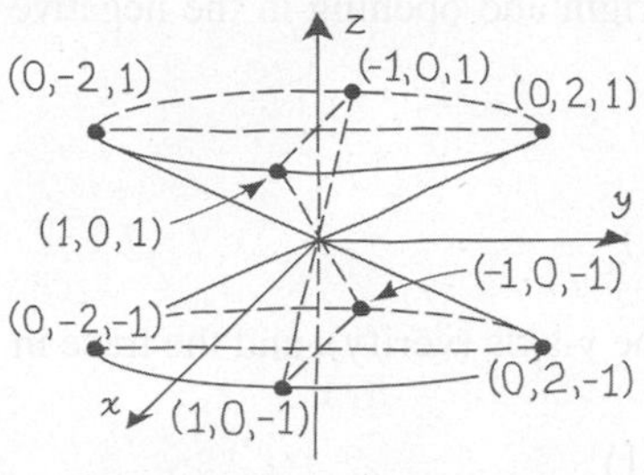


▲ Figure 11.7.8

**▶ Example 4** Sketch the graph of the elliptic cone

$$z^2 = x^2 + \frac{y^2}{4} \tag{12}$$

***Solution.*** The traces of (12) in the planes $z = \pm 1$ are given by

$$x^2 + \frac{y^2}{4} = 1 \quad (z = \pm 1)$$

Sketching these ellipses and the linear traces in the vertical coordinate planes yields the graph in Figure 11.7.8. ◀

In the special cases of (11) and (13) where $a = b$, the traces parallel to the $xy$-plane are circles. In these cases, we call (11) a ***circular cone*** and (13) a ***circular paraboloid.***

A rough sketch of the elliptic paraboloid

$$z = \frac{x^2}{a^2} + \frac{y^2}{b^2} \quad (a > 0, b > 0) \tag{13}$$

can be obtained by first sketching the elliptical trace in the plane $z = 1$ and then sketching the parabolic traces in the vertical coordinate planes to connect the origin to the ends of the axes of the ellipse. The next example illustrates this technique.

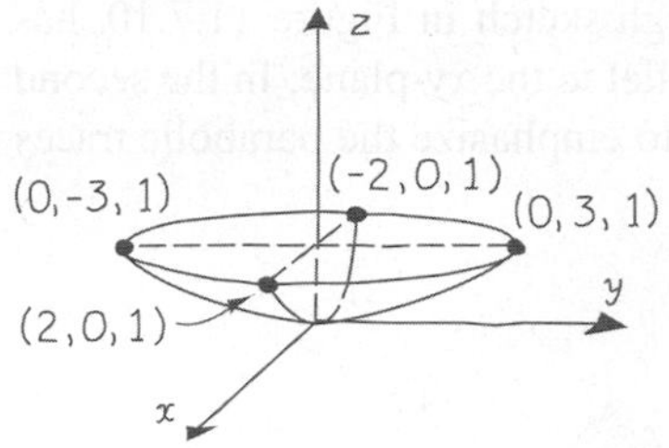


▲ Figure 11.7.9

**▶ Example 5** Sketch the graph of the elliptic paraboloid

$$z = \frac{x^2}{4} + \frac{y^2}{9} \tag{14}$$

***Solution.*** The trace of (14) in the plane $z = 1$ is

$$\frac{x^2}{4} + \frac{y^2}{9} = 1 \quad (z = 1)$$

Sketching this ellipse and the parabolic traces in the vertical coordinate planes yields the graph in Figure 11.7.9. ◀

A rough sketch of the hyperbolic paraboloid

$$z = \frac{y^2}{b^2} - \frac{x^2}{a^2} \quad (a > 0, b > 0) \tag{15}$$

can be obtained by first sketching the two parabolic traces that pass through the origin (one in the plane $x = 0$ and the other in the plane $y = 0$). After the parabolic traces are drawn, sketch the hyperbolic traces in the planes $z = \pm 1$ and then fill in any missing edges. The next example illustrates this technique.

**▶ Example 6** Sketch the graph of the hyperbolic paraboloid

$$z = \frac{y^2}{4} - \frac{x^2}{9} \tag{16}$$

***Solution.*** Setting $x = 0$ in (16) yields

$$z = \frac{y^2}{4} \quad (x = 0)$$

which is a parabola in the $yz$-plane with vertex at the origin and opening in the positive $z$-direction (since $z \geq 0$), and setting $y = 0$ yields

$$z = -\frac{x^2}{9} \quad (y = 0)$$

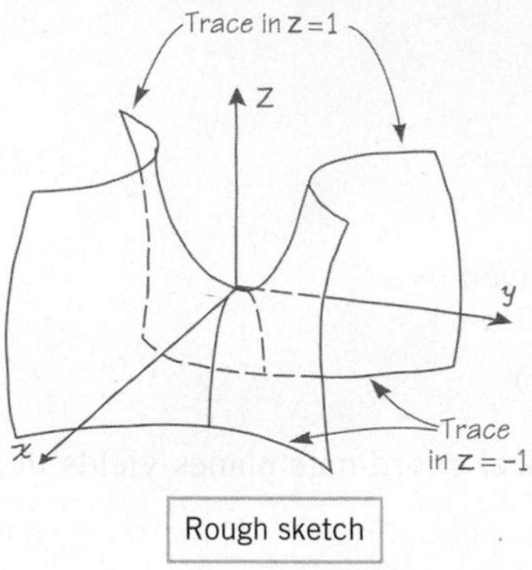


▲ Figure 11.7.10

which is a parabola in the $xz$-plane with vertex at the origin and opening in the negative $z$-direction.

The trace in the plane $z = 1$ is

$$\frac{y^2}{4} - \frac{x^2}{9} = 1 \qquad (z = 1)$$

which is a hyperbola that opens along a line parallel to the $y$-axis (verify), and the trace in the plane $z = -1$ is

$$\frac{x^2}{9} - \frac{y^2}{4} = 1 \qquad (z = -1)$$

which is a hyperbola that opens along a line parallel to the $x$-axis. Combining all of the above information leads to the sketch in Figure 11.7.10. ◄

**REMARK** The hyperbolic paraboloid in Figure 11.7.10 has an interesting behavior at the origin—the trace in the $xz$-plane has a relative maximum at $(0, 0, 0)$, and the trace in the $yz$-plane has a relative minimum at $(0, 0, 0)$. Thus, a bug walking on the surface may view the origin as a highest point if traveling along one path, or may view the origin as a lowest point if traveling along a different path. A point with this property is commonly called a ***saddle point*** or a ***minimax point***.

Figure 11.7.11 shows two computer-generated views of the hyperbolic paraboloid in Example 6. The first view, which is much like our rough sketch in Figure 11.7.10, has cuts at the top and bottom that are hyperbolic traces parallel to the $xy$-plane. In the second view the top horizontal cut has been omitted; this helps to emphasize the parabolic traces parallel to the $xz$-plane.

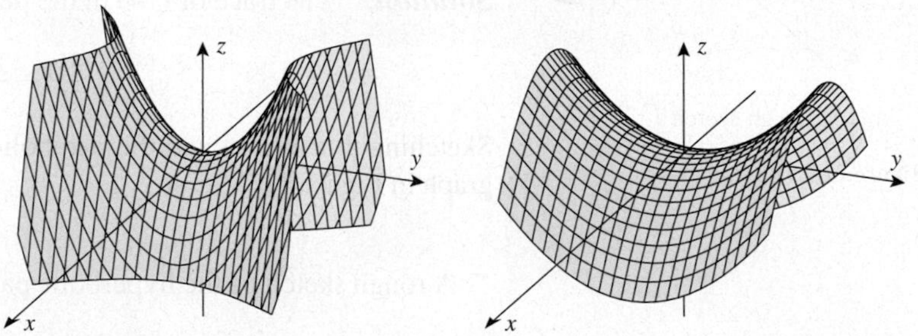


► Figure 11.7.11

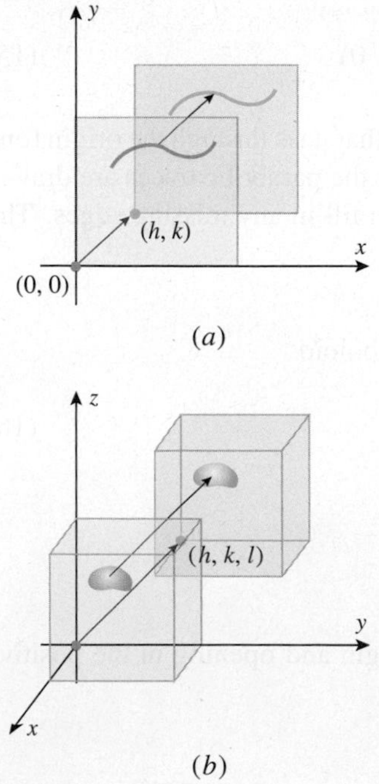


▲ Figure 11.7.12

## TRANSLATIONS OF QUADRIC SURFACES

In Section 10.4 we saw that a conic in an $xy$-coordinate system can be translated by substituting $x - h$ for $x$ and $y - k$ for $y$ in its equation. To understand why this works, think of the $xy$-axes as fixed and think of the plane as a transparent sheet of plastic on which all graphs are drawn. When the coordinates of points are modified by substituting $(x - h, y - k)$ for $(x, y)$, the geometric effect is to translate the sheet of plastic (and hence all curves) so that the point on the plastic that was initially at $(0, 0)$ is moved to the point $(h, k)$ (see Figure 11.7.12$a$).

For the analog in three dimensions, think of the $xyz$-axes as fixed and think of 3-space as a transparent block of plastic in which all surfaces are embedded. When the coordinates of points are modified by substituting $(x - h, y - k, z - l)$ for $(x, y, z)$, the geometric effect is to translate the block of plastic (and hence all surfaces) so that the point in the plastic block that was initially at $(0, 0, 0)$ is moved to the point $(h, k, l)$ (see Figure 11.7.12$b$).

► **Example 7** Describe the surface $z = (x - 1)^2 + (y + 2)^2 + 3$.

***Solution.*** The equation can be rewritten as

$$z - 3 = (x - 1)^2 + (y + 2)^2$$

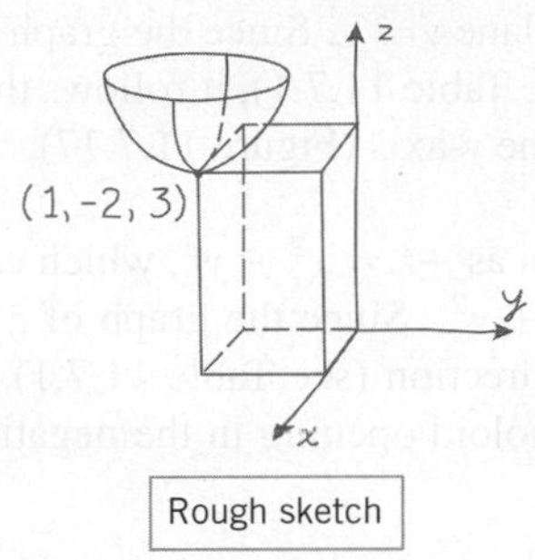


▲ **Figure 11.7.13**

This surface is the paraboloid that results by translating the paraboloid

$$z = x^2 + y^2$$

in Figure 11.7.3 so that the new "vertex" is at the point $(1, -2, 3)$. A rough sketch of this paraboloid is shown in Figure 11.7.13. ◄

▶ **Example 8** Describe the surface

$$4x^2 + 4y^2 + z^2 + 8y - 4z = -4$$

***Solution.*** Completing the squares yields

$$4x^2 + 4(y + 1)^2 + (z - 2)^2 = -4 + 4 + 4$$

or

$$x^2 + (y + 1)^2 + \frac{(z - 2)^2}{4} = 1$$

Thus, the surface is the ellipsoid that results when the ellipsoid

$$x^2 + y^2 + \frac{z^2}{4} = 1$$

is translated so that the new "center" is at the point $(0, -1, 2)$. A rough sketch of this ellipsoid is shown in Figure 11.7.14. ◄

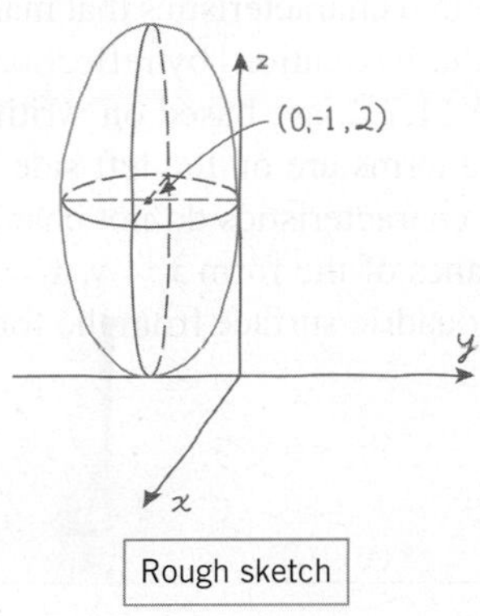


▲ **Figure 11.7.14**

In Figure 11.7.14, the cross section in the $yz$-plane is shown tangent to both the $y$- and $z$-axes. Confirm that this is correct.

## REFLECTIONS OF SURFACES IN 3-SPACE

Recall that in an $xy$-coordinate system a point $(x, y)$ is reflected about the $x$-axis if $y$ is replaced by $-y$, and it is reflected about the $y$-axis if $x$ is replaced by $-x$. In an $xyz$-coordinate system, a point $(x, y, z)$ is reflected about the $xy$-plane if $z$ is replaced by $-z$, it is reflected about the $yz$-plane if $x$ is replaced by $-x$, and it is reflected about the $xz$-plane if $y$ is replaced by $-y$ (Figure 11.7.15). It follows that *replacing a variable by its negative in the equation of a surface causes that surface to be reflected about a coordinate plane.*

Recall also that in an $xy$-coordinate system a point $(x, y)$ is reflected about the line $y = x$ if $x$ and $y$ are interchanged. However, in an $xyz$-coordinate system, interchanging $x$ and $y$ reflects the point $(x, y, z)$ about the plane $y = x$ (Figure 11.7.16). Similarly, interchanging $x$ and $z$ reflects the point about the plane $x = z$, and interchanging $y$ and $z$ reflects it about the plane $y = z$. Thus, it follows that *interchanging two variables in the equation of a surface reflects that surface about a plane that makes a* 45° *angle with two of the coordinate planes.*

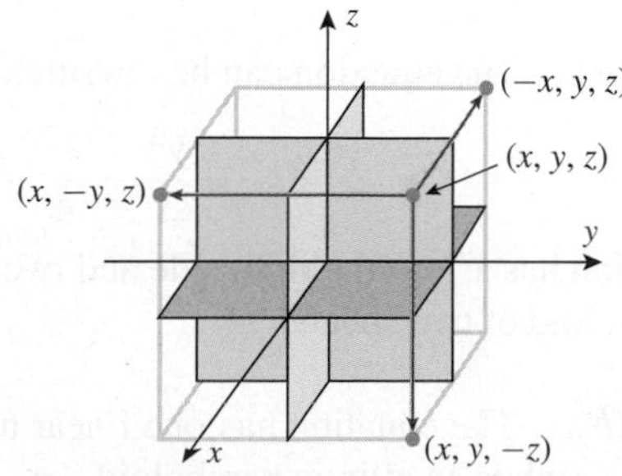


▲ **Figure 11.7.15**

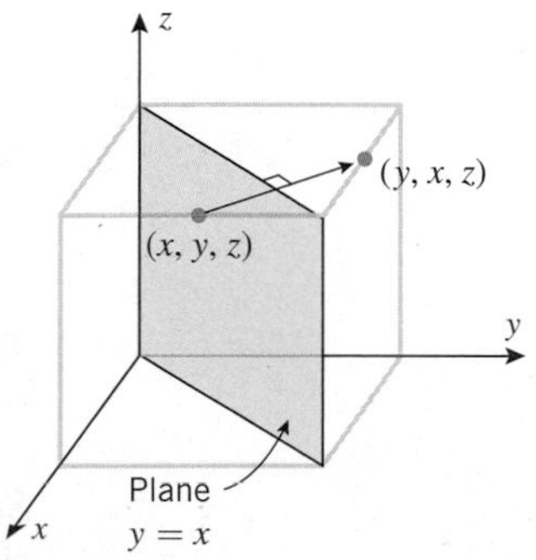


▲ **Figure 11.7.16**

▶ **Example 9** Describe the surfaces

(a) $y^2 = x^2 + z^2$ (b) $z = -(x^2 + y^2)$

***Solution (a).*** The graph of the equation $y^2 = x^2 + z^2$ results from interchanging $y$ and $z$ in the equation $z^2 = x^2 + y^2$. Thus, the graph of the equation $y^2 = x^2 + z^2$ can be

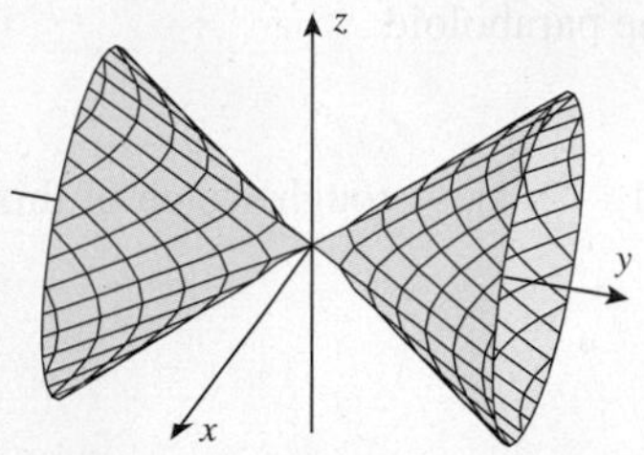
▲ Figure 11.7.17

obtained by reflecting the graph of $z^2 = x^2 + y^2$ about the plane $y = z$. Since the graph of $z^2 = x^2 + y^2$ is a circular cone opening along the $z$-axis (see Table 11.7.1), it follows that the graph of $y^2 = x^2 + z^2$ is a circular cone opening along the $y$-axis (Figure 11.7.17).

***Solution (b).*** The equation $z = -(x^2 + y^2)$ can be written as $-z = x^2 + y^2$, which can be obtained by replacing $z$ with $-z$ in the equation $z = x^2 + y^2$. Since the graph of $z = x^2 + y^2$ is a circular paraboloid opening in the positive $z$-direction (see Table 11.7.1), it follows that the graph of $z = -(x^2 + y^2)$ is a circular paraboloid opening in the negative $z$-direction (Figure 11.7.18). ◀

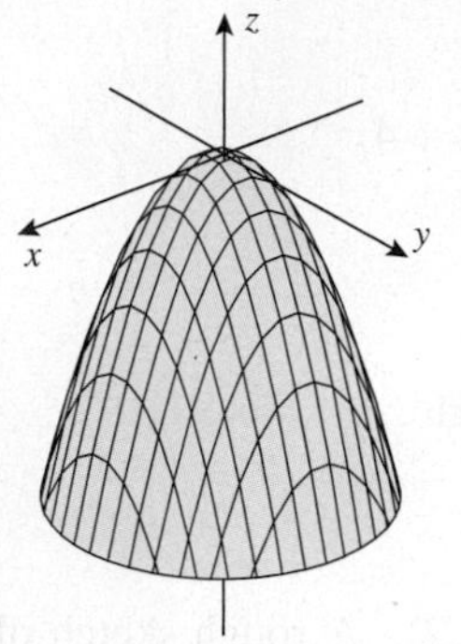
▲ Figure 11.7.18

## A TECHNIQUE FOR IDENTIFYING QUADRIC SURFACES

The equations of the quadric surfaces in Table 11.7.1 have certain characteristics that make it possible to identify quadric surfaces that are derived from these equations by reflections. These identifying characteristics, which are shown in Table 11.7.2, are based on writing the equation of the quadric surface so that all of the variable terms are on the left side of the equation and there is a 1 or a 0 on the right side. These characteristics do not change when the surface is reflected about a coordinate plane or planes of the form $x = y$, $x = z$, or $y = z$, thereby making it possible to identify the reflected quadric surface from the form of its equation.

**Table 11.7.2**

IDENTIFYING A QUADRIC SURFACE FROM THE FORM OF ITS EQUATION

| | | | | | | |
|---|---|---|---|---|---|---|
| EQUATION | $\frac{x^2}{a^2}+\frac{y^2}{b^2}+\frac{z^2}{c^2}=1$ | $\frac{x^2}{a^2}+\frac{y^2}{b^2}-\frac{z^2}{c^2}=1$ | $\frac{z^2}{c^2}-\frac{x^2}{a^2}-\frac{y^2}{b^2}=1$ | $z^2-\frac{x^2}{a^2}-\frac{y^2}{b^2}=0$ | $z-\frac{x^2}{a^2}-\frac{y^2}{b^2}=0$ | $z-\frac{y^2}{b^2}+\frac{x^2}{a^2}=0$ |
| CHARACTERISTIC | No minus signs | One minus sign | Two minus signs | No linear terms | One linear term; two quadratic terms with the same sign | One linear term; two quadratic terms with opposite signs |
| CLASSIFICATION | Ellipsoid | Hyperboloid of one sheet | Hyperboloid of two sheets | Elliptic cone | Elliptic paraboloid | Hyperbolic paraboloid |

▶ **Example 10** Identify the surfaces

(a) $3x^2 - 4y^2 + 12z^2 + 12 = 0$ (b) $4x^2 - 4y + z^2 = 0$

***Solution (a).*** The equation can be rewritten as

$$\frac{y^2}{3} - \frac{x^2}{4} - z^2 = 1$$

This equation has a 1 on the right side and two negative terms on the left side, so its graph is a hyperboloid of two sheets.

***Solution (b).*** The equation has one linear term and two quadratic terms with the same sign, so its graph is an elliptic paraboloid. ◀

## ✓ QUICK CHECK EXERCISES 11.7 

(See page 735 for answers.)

1. For the surface $4x^2 + y^2 + z^2 = 9$, classify the indicated trace as an ellipse, hyperbola, or parabola.
(a) $x = 0$ (b) $y = 0$ (c) $z = 1$

2. For the surface $4x^2 + z^2 - y^2 = 9$, classify the indicated trace as an ellipse, hyperbola, or parabola.
(a) $x = 0$ (b) $y = 0$ (c) $z = 1$

3. For the surface $4x^2 + y^2 - z = 0$, classify the indicated trace as an ellipse, hyperbola, or parabola.
(a) $x = 0$ (b) $y = 0$ (c) $z = 1$

4. Classify each surface as an ellipsoid, hyperboloid of one sheet, hyperboloid of two sheets, elliptic cone, elliptic paraboloid, or hyperbolic paraboloid.
(a) $\frac{x^2}{36} + \frac{y^2}{25} - z = 0$ (b) $\frac{x^2}{36} + \frac{y^2}{25} + z^2 = 1$
(c) $\frac{x^2}{36} - \frac{y^2}{25} + z = 0$ (d) $\frac{x^2}{36} + \frac{y^2}{25} - z^2 = 1$
(e) $\frac{x^2}{36} + \frac{y^2}{25} - z^2 = 0$ (f) $z^2 - \frac{x^2}{36} - \frac{y^2}{25} = 1$

## EXERCISE SET 11.7

**1–2** Identify the quadric surface as an ellipsoid, hyperboloid of one sheet, hyperboloid of two sheets, elliptic cone, elliptic paraboloid, or hyperbolic paraboloid by matching the equation with one of the forms given in Table 11.7.1. State the values of $a$, $b$, and $c$ in each case. ■

**1.** (a) $z = \frac{x^2}{4} + \frac{y^2}{9}$ (b) $z = \frac{y^2}{25} - x^2$
(c) $x^2 + y^2 - z^2 = 16$ (d) $x^2 + y^2 - z^2 = 0$
(e) $4z = x^2 + 4y^2$ (f) $z^2 - x^2 - y^2 = 1$

**2.** (a) $6x^2 + 3y^2 + 4z^2 = 12$ (b) $y^2 - x^2 - z = 0$
(c) $9x^2 + y^2 - 9z^2 = 9$ (d) $4x^2 + y^2 - 4z^2 = -4$
(e) $2z - x^2 - 4y^2 = 0$ (f) $12z^2 - 3x^2 = 4y^2$

**3.** Find an equation for and sketch the surface that results when the circular paraboloid $z = x^2 + y^2$ is reflected about the plane
(a) $z = 0$ (b) $x = 0$ (c) $y = 0$
(d) $y = x$ (e) $x = z$ (f) $y = z$.

**4.** Find an equation for and sketch the surface that results when the hyperboloid of one sheet $x^2 + y^2 - z^2 = 1$ is reflected about the plane
(a) $z = 0$ (b) $x = 0$ (c) $y = 0$
(d) $y = x$ (e) $x = z$ (f) $y = z$.

**FOCUS ON CONCEPTS**

**5.** The given equations represent quadric surfaces whose orientations are different from those in Table 11.7.1. In each part, identify the quadric surface, and give a verbal description of its orientation (e.g., an elliptic cone opening along the $z$-axis or a hyperbolic paraboloid straddling the $y$-axis).
(a) $\frac{z^2}{c^2} - \frac{y^2}{b^2} + \frac{x^2}{a^2} = 1$ (b) $\frac{x^2}{a^2} - \frac{y^2}{b^2} - \frac{z^2}{c^2} = 1$
(c) $x = \frac{y^2}{b^2} + \frac{z^2}{c^2}$ (d) $x^2 = \frac{y^2}{b^2} + \frac{z^2}{c^2}$
(e) $y = \frac{z^2}{c^2} - \frac{x^2}{a^2}$ (f) $y = -\left(\frac{x^2}{a^2} + \frac{z^2}{c^2}\right)$

**6.** For each of the surfaces in Exercise 5, find the equation of the surface that results if the given surface is reflected about the $xz$-plane and that surface is then reflected about the plane $z = 0$.

**7–8** Find equations of the traces in the coordinate planes and sketch the traces in an $xyz$-coordinate system. [*Suggestion:* If you have trouble sketching a trace directly in three dimensions, start with a sketch in two dimensions by placing the coordinate plane in the plane of the paper, then transfer the sketch to three dimensions.] ■

**7.** (a) $\frac{x^2}{9} + \frac{y^2}{25} + \frac{z^2}{4} = 1$ (b) $z = x^2 + 4y^2$
(c) $\frac{x^2}{9} + \frac{y^2}{16} - \frac{z^2}{4} = 1$

**8.** (a) $y^2 + 9z^2 = x$ (b) $4x^2 - y^2 + 4z^2 = 4$
(c) $z^2 = x^2 + \frac{y^2}{4}$

**9–10** In these exercises, traces of the surfaces in the planes are conic sections. In each part, find an equation of the trace, and state whether it is an ellipse, a parabola, or a hyperbola. ■

**9.** (a) $4x^2 + y^2 + z^2 = 4;\ y = 1$
(b) $4x^2 + y^2 + z^2 = 4;\ x = \frac{1}{2}$
(c) $9x^2 - y^2 - z^2 = 16;\ x = 2$
(d) $9x^2 - y^2 - z^2 = 16;\ z = 2$
(e) $z = 9x^2 + 4y^2;\ y = 2$
(f) $z = 9x^2 + 4y^2;\ z = 4$

**10.** (a) $9x^2 - y^2 + 4z^2 = 9;\ x = 2$
(b) $9x^2 - y^2 + 4z^2 = 9;\ y = 4$
(c) $x^2 + 4y^2 - 9z^2 = 0;\ y = 1$
(d) $x^2 + 4y^2 - 9z^2 = 0;\ z = 1$
(e) $z = x^2 - 4y^2;\ x = 1$
(f) $z = x^2 - 4y^2;\ z = 4$

**11–14 True–False** Determine whether the statement is true or false. Explain your answer. ■

**11.** A quadric surface is the graph of a fourth-degree polynomial in $x$, $y$, and $z$.

**12.** Every ellipsoid will intersect the $z$-axis in exactly two points.

**13.** Every ellipsoid is a surface of revolution.

**14.** The hyperbolic paraboloid
$$z = \frac{y^2}{b^2} - \frac{x^2}{a^2}$$
intersects the $xy$-plane in a pair of intersecting lines.

**15–26** Identify and sketch the quadric surface. ■

**15.** $x^2 + \frac{y^2}{4} + \frac{z^2}{9} = 1$ **16.** $x^2 + 4y^2 + 9z^2 = 36$

**17.** $\frac{x^2}{4} + \frac{y^2}{9} - \frac{z^2}{16} = 1$ **18.** $x^2 + y^2 - z^2 = 9$

**19.** $4z^2 = x^2 + 4y^2$ **20.** $9x^2 + 4y^2 - 36z^2 = 0$

**21.** $9z^2 - 4y^2 - 9x^2 = 36$ **22.** $y^2 - \frac{x^2}{4} - \frac{z^2}{9} = 1$

**23.** $z = y^2 - x^2$ **24.** $16z = y^2 - x^2$

**25.** $4z = x^2 + 2y^2$ **26.** $z - 3x^2 - 3y^2 = 0$

**27–32** The given equation represents a quadric surface whose orientation is different from that in Table 11.7.1. Identify and sketch the surface. ■

**27.** $x^2 - 3y^2 - 3z^2 = 0$

**28.** $x - y^2 - 4z^2 = 0$

**29.** $2y^2 - x^2 + 2z^2 = 8$

**30.** $x^2 - 3y^2 - 3z^2 = 9$

**31.** $z = \dfrac{x^2}{4} - \dfrac{y^2}{9}$

**32.** $4x^2 - y^2 + 4z^2 = 16$

**33–36** Sketch the surface. ■

**33.** $z = \sqrt{x^2 + y^2}$

**34.** $z = \sqrt{1 - x^2 - y^2}$

**35.** $z = \sqrt{x^2 + y^2 - 1}$

**36.** $z = \sqrt{1 + x^2 + y^2}$

**37–40** Identify the surface and make a rough sketch that shows its position and orientation. ■

**37.** $z = (x + 2)^2 + (y - 3)^2 - 9$

**38.** $4x^2 - y^2 + 16(z - 2)^2 = 100$

**39.** $9x^2 + y^2 + 4z^2 - 18x + 2y + 16z = 10$

**40.** $z^2 = 4x^2 + y^2 + 8x - 2y + 4z$

**41–42** Use the ellipsoid $4x^2 + 9y^2 + 18z^2 = 72$ in these exercises. ■

**41.** (a) Find an equation of the elliptical trace in the plane $z = \sqrt{2}$.
(b) Find the lengths of the major and minor axes of the ellipse in part (a).
(c) Find the coordinates of the foci of the ellipse in part (a).
(d) Describe the orientation of the focal axis of the ellipse in part (a) relative to the coordinate axes.

**42.** (a) Find an equation of the elliptical trace in the plane $x = 3$.
(b) Find the lengths of the major and minor axes of the ellipse in part (a).
(c) Find the coordinates of the foci of the ellipse in part (a).
(d) Describe the orientation of the focal axis of the ellipse in part (a) relative to the coordinate axes.

**43–46** These exercises refer to the hyperbolic paraboloid $z = y^2 - x^2$. ■

**43.** (a) Find an equation of the hyperbolic trace in the plane $z = 4$.
(b) Find the vertices of the hyperbola in part (a).
(c) Find the foci of the hyperbola in part (a).
(d) Describe the orientation of the focal axis of the hyperbola in part (a) relative to the coordinate axes.

**44.** (a) Find an equation of the hyperbolic trace in the plane $z = -4$.
(b) Find the vertices of the hyperbola in part (a).
(c) Find the foci of the hyperbola in part (a).
(d) Describe the orientation of the focal axis of the hyperbola in part (a) relative to the coordinate axes.

**45.** (a) Find an equation of the parabolic trace in the plane $x = 2$.
(b) Find the vertex of the parabola in part (a).
(c) Find the focus of the parabola in part (a).
(d) Describe the orientation of the focal axis of the parabola in part (a) relative to the coordinate axes.

**46.** (a) Find an equation of the parabolic trace in the plane $y = 2$.
(b) Find the vertex of the parabola in part (a).
(c) Find the focus of the parabola in part (a).
(d) Describe the orientation of the focal axis of the parabola in part (a) relative to the coordinate axes.

**47–48** Sketch the region enclosed between the surfaces and describe their curve of intersection. ■

**47.** The paraboloids $z = x^2 + y^2$ and $z = 4 - x^2 - y^2$

**48.** The ellipsoid $2x^2 + 2y^2 + z^2 = 3$ and the paraboloid $z = x^2 + y^2$.

**49–50** Find an equation for the surface generated by revolving the curve about the $y$-axis. ■

**49.** $y = 4x^2$ $(z = 0)$

**50.** $y = 2x$ $(z = 0)$

**51.** Find an equation of the surface consisting of all points $P(x, y, z)$ that are equidistant from the point $(0, 0, 1)$ and the plane $z = -1$. Identify the surface.

**52.** Find an equation of the surface consisting of all points $P(x, y, z)$ that are twice as far from the plane $z = -1$ as from the point $(0, 0, 1)$. Identify the surface.

**53.** If a sphere

$$\frac{x^2}{a^2} + \frac{y^2}{a^2} + \frac{z^2}{a^2} = 1$$

of radius $a$ is compressed in the $z$-direction, then the resulting surface, called an ***oblate spheroid***, has an equation of the form

$$\frac{x^2}{a^2} + \frac{y^2}{a^2} + \frac{z^2}{c^2} = 1$$

where $c < a$. Show that the oblate spheroid has a circular trace of radius $a$ in the $xy$-plane and an elliptical trace in the $xz$-plane with major axis of length $2a$ along the $x$-axis and minor axis of length $2c$ along the $z$-axis.

**54.** The Earth's rotation causes a flattening at the poles, so its shape is often modeled as an oblate spheroid rather than a sphere (see Exercise 53 for terminology). One of the models used by global positioning satellites is the ***World Geodetic System of 1984*** (WGS-84), which treats the Earth as an oblate spheroid whose equatorial radius is 6378.1370 km and whose polar radius (the distance from the Earth's center to the poles) is 6356.5231 km. Use the WGS-84 model to find an equation for the surface of the Earth relative to the coordinate system shown in the accompanying figure.

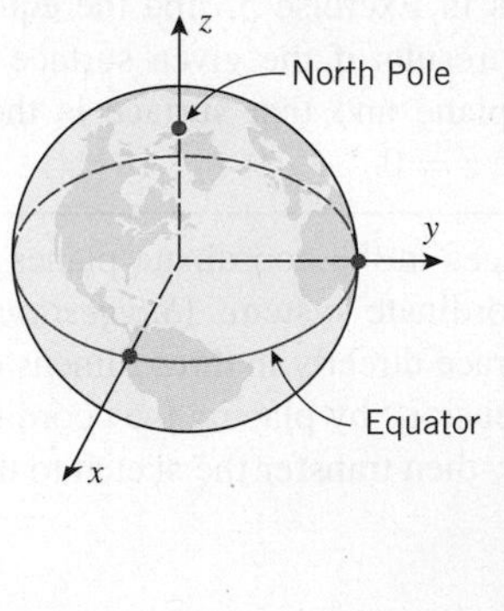


◀ **Figure Ex-54**

55. Use the method of slicing to show that the volume of the ellipsoid

$$\frac{x^2}{a^2} + \frac{y^2}{b^2} + \frac{z^2}{c^2} = 1$$

is $\frac{4}{3}\pi abc$.

56. **Writing** Discuss some of the connections between conic sections and traces of quadric surfaces.

57. **Writing** Give a sequence of steps for determining the type of quadric surface that is associated with a quadratic equation in $x$, $y$, and $z$.

✓ QUICK CHECK ANSWERS 11.7 1. (a) ellipse (b) ellipse (c) ellipse 2. (a) hyperbola (b) ellipse (c) hyperbola 3. (a) parabola (b) parabola (c) ellipse 4. (a) elliptic paraboloid (b) ellipsoid (c) hyperbolic paraboloid (d) hyperboloid of one sheet (e) elliptic cone (f) hyperboloid of two sheets

## 11.8 CYLINDRICAL AND SPHERICAL COORDINATES

*In this section we will discuss two new types of coordinate systems in 3-space that are often more useful than rectangular coordinate systems for studying surfaces with symmetries. These new coordinate systems also have important applications in navigation, astronomy, and the study of rotational motion about an axis.*

### CYLINDRICAL AND SPHERICAL COORDINATE SYSTEMS

Three coordinates are required to establish the location of a point in 3-space. We have already done this using rectangular coordinates. However, Figure 11.8.1 shows two other possibilities: part (*a*) of the figure shows the ***rectangular coordinates*** $(x, y, z)$ of a point $P$, part (*b*) shows the ***cylindrical coordinates*** $(r, \theta, z)$ of $P$, and part (*c*) shows the ***spherical coordinates*** $(\rho, \theta, \phi)$ of $P$. In a rectangular coordinate system the coordinates can be any real numbers, but in cylindrical and spherical coordinate systems there are restrictions on the allowable values of the coordinates (as indicated in Figure 11.8.1).

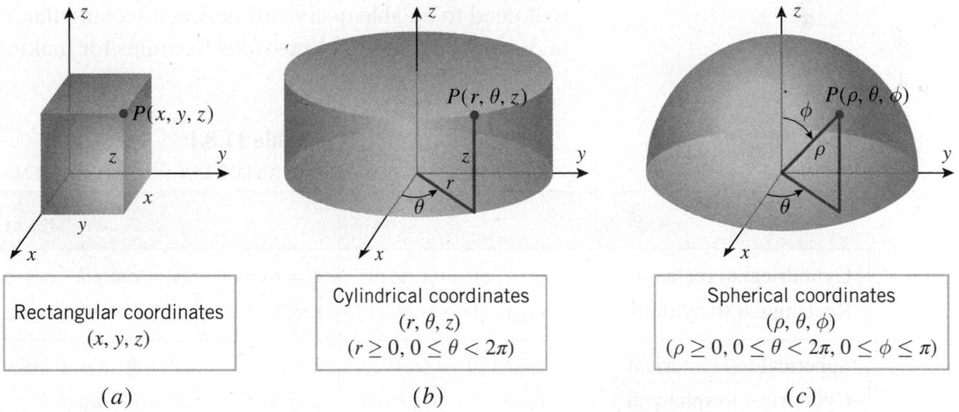


▲ Figure 11.8.1

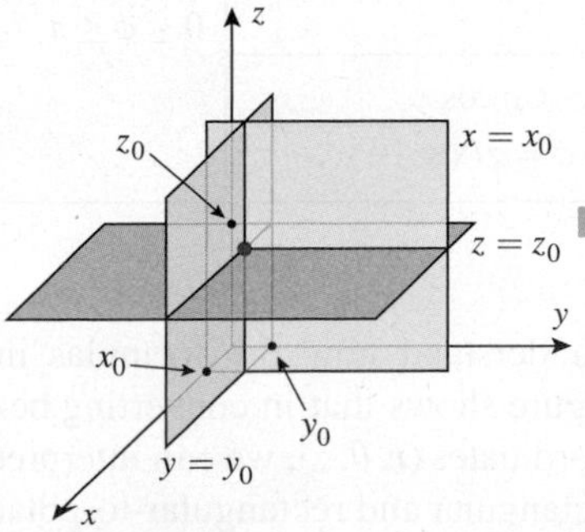


▲ Figure 11.8.2

### CONSTANT SURFACES

In rectangular coordinates the surfaces represented by equations of the form

$$x = x_0, \quad y = y_0, \quad \text{and} \quad z = z_0$$

where $x_0$, $y_0$, and $z_0$ are constants, are planes parallel to the $yz$-plane, $xz$-plane, and $xy$-plane, respectively (Figure 11.8.2). In cylindrical coordinates the surfaces represented by equations of the form

$$r = r_0, \quad \theta = \theta_0, \quad \text{and} \quad z = z_0$$

where $r_0$, $\theta_0$, and $z_0$ are constants, are shown in Figure 11.8.3:

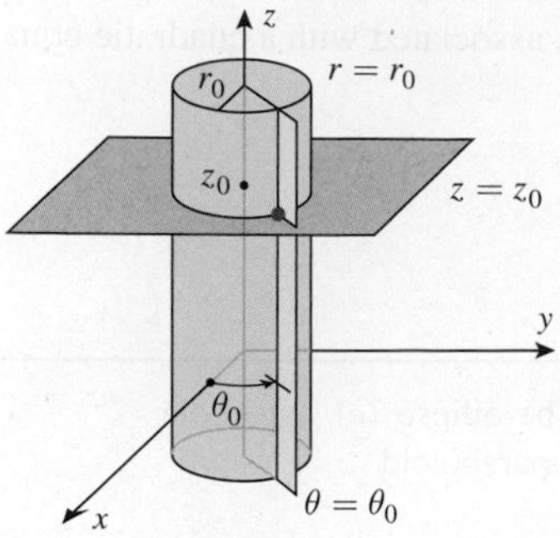

▲ **Figure 11.8.3**

- The surface $r = r_0$ is a right circular cylinder of radius $r_0$ centered on the $z$-axis.
- The surface $\theta = \theta_0$ is a half-plane attached along the $z$-axis and making an angle $\theta_0$ with the positive $x$-axis.
- The surface $z = z_0$ is a horizontal plane.

In spherical coordinates the surfaces represented by equations of the form

$$\rho = \rho_0, \quad \theta = \theta_0, \quad \text{and} \quad \phi = \phi_0$$

where $\rho_0$, $\theta_0$, and $\phi_0$ are constants, are shown in Figure 11.8.4:

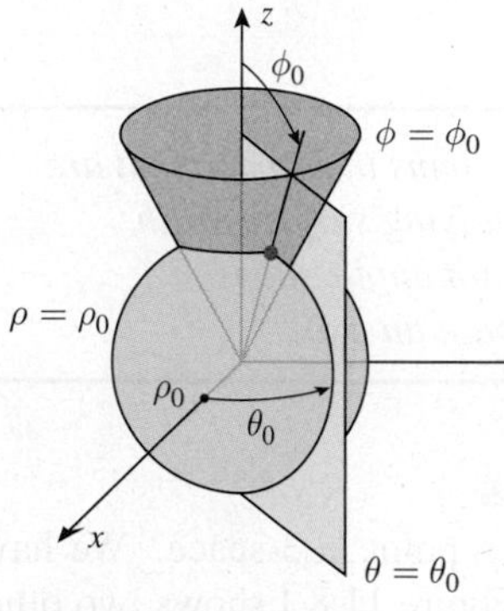

▲ **Figure 11.8.4**

- The surface $\rho = \rho_0$ consists of all points whose distance $\rho$ from the origin is $\rho_0$. Assuming $\rho_0$ to be nonnegative, this is a sphere of radius $\rho_0$ centered at the origin.
- As in cylindrical coordinates, the surface $\theta = \theta_0$ is a half-plane attached along the $z$-axis, making an angle of $\theta_0$ with the positive $x$-axis.
- The surface $\phi = \phi_0$ consists of all points from which a line segment to the origin makes an angle of $\phi_0$ with the positive $z$-axis. If $0 < \phi_0 < \pi/2$, this will be the nappe of a cone opening up, while if $\pi/2 < \phi_0 < \pi$, this will be the nappe of a cone opening down. (If $\phi_0 = \pi/2$, then the cone is flat, and the surface is the $xy$-plane.)

## CONVERTING COORDINATES

Just as we needed to convert between rectangular and polar coordinates in 2-space, so we will need to be able to convert between rectangular, cylindrical, and spherical coordinates in 3-space. Table 11.8.1 provides formulas for making these conversions.

**Table 11.8.1**

CONVERSION FORMULAS FOR COORDINATE SYSTEMS

| CONVERSION | | FORMULAS | RESTRICTIONS |
|---|---|---|---|
| Cylindrical to rectangular | $(r, \theta, z) \to (x, y, z)$ | $x = r\cos\theta, \quad y = r\sin\theta, \quad z = z$ | |
| Rectangular to cylindrical | $(x, y, z) \to (r, \theta, z)$ | $r = \sqrt{x^2 + y^2}, \tan\theta = y/x, z = z$ | |
| Spherical to cylindrical | $(\rho, \theta, \phi) \to (r, \theta, z)$ | $r = \rho\sin\phi, \quad \theta = \theta, \quad z = \rho\cos\phi$ | $r \ge 0, \rho \ge 0$ <br> $0 \le \theta < 2\pi$ <br> $0 \le \phi \le \pi$ |
| Cylindrical to spherical | $(r, \theta, z) \to (\rho, \theta, \phi)$ | $\rho = \sqrt{r^2 + z^2}, \theta = \theta, \quad \tan\phi = r/z$ | |
| Spherical to rectangular | $(\rho, \theta, \phi) \to (x, y, z)$ | $x = \rho\sin\phi\cos\theta, y = \rho\sin\phi\sin\theta, z = \rho\cos\phi$ | |
| Rectangular to spherical | $(x, y, z) \to (\rho, \theta, \phi)$ | $\rho = \sqrt{x^2 + y^2 + z^2}, \tan\theta = y/x, \cos\phi = z/\sqrt{x^2 + y^2 + z^2}$ | |

The diagrams in Figure 11.8.5 will help you to understand how the formulas in Table 11.8.1 are derived. For example, part (*a*) of the figure shows that in converting between rectangular coordinates $(x, y, z)$ and cylindrical coordinates $(r, \theta, z)$, we can interpret $(r, \theta)$ as polar coordinates of $(x, y)$. Thus, the polar-to-rectangular and rectangular-to-polar conversion formulas (1) and (2) of Section 10.2 provide the conversion formulas between rectangular and cylindrical coordinates in the table.

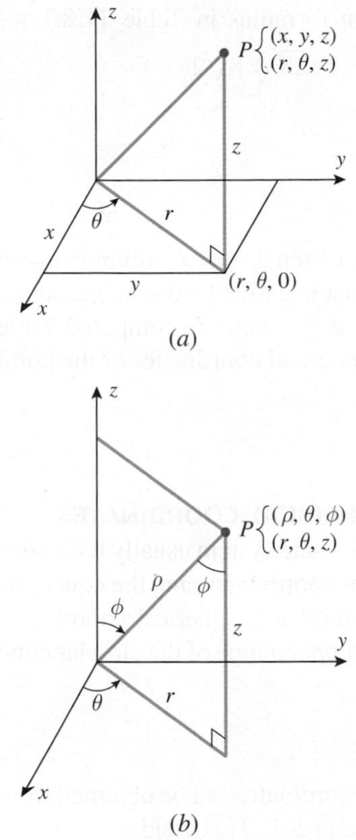

Comparison of coordinate systems

▲ **Figure 11.8.5**

Part (*b*) of Figure 11.8.5 suggests that the spherical coordinates $(\rho, \theta, \phi)$ of a point $P$ can be converted to cylindrical coordinates $(r, \theta, z)$ by the conversion formulas

$$r = \rho \sin \phi, \quad \theta = \theta, \quad z = \rho \cos \phi \tag{1}$$

Moreover, since the cylindrical coordinates $(r, \theta, z)$ of $P$ can be converted to rectangular coordinates $(x, y, z)$ by the conversion formulas

$$x = r \cos \theta, \quad y = r \sin \theta, \quad z = z \tag{2}$$

we can obtain direct conversion formulas from spherical coordinates to rectangular coordinates by substituting (1) in (2). This yields

$$x = \rho \sin \phi \cos \theta, \quad y = \rho \sin \phi \sin \theta, \quad z = \rho \cos \phi \tag{3}$$

The other conversion formulas in Table 11.8.1 are left as exercises.

### ▸ Example 1

(a) Find the rectangular coordinates of the point with cylindrical coordinates

$$(r, \theta, z) = (4, \pi/3, -3)$$

(b) Find the rectangular coordinates of the point with spherical coordinates

$$(\rho, \theta, \phi) = (4, \pi/3, \pi/4)$$

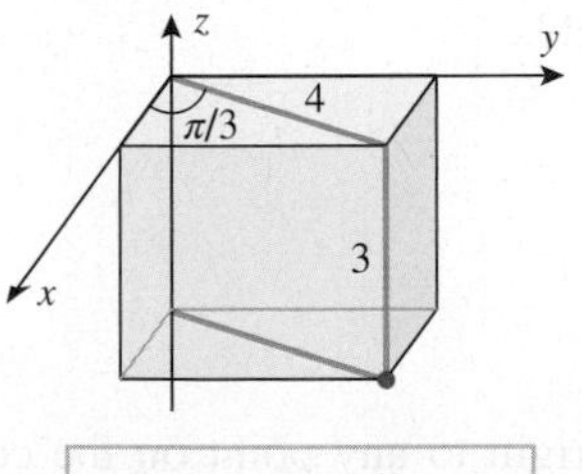

cylindrical: $(4, \pi/3, -3)$
rectangular: $(2, 2\sqrt{3}, -3)$

▲ **Figure 11.8.6**

***Solution (a).*** Applying the cylindrical-to-rectangular conversion formulas in Table 11.8.1 yields

$$x = r \cos \theta = 4 \cos \frac{\pi}{3} = 2, \quad y = r \sin \theta = 4 \sin \frac{\pi}{3} = 2\sqrt{3}, \quad z = -3$$

Thus, the rectangular coordinates of the point are $(x, y, z) = (2, 2\sqrt{3}, -3)$ (Figure 11.8.6).

***Solution (b).*** Applying the spherical-to-rectangular conversion formulas in Table 11.8.1 yields

$$x = \rho \sin \phi \cos \theta = 4 \sin \frac{\pi}{4} \cos \frac{\pi}{3} = \sqrt{2}$$

$$y = \rho \sin \phi \sin \theta = 4 \sin \frac{\pi}{4} \sin \frac{\pi}{3} = \sqrt{6}$$

$$z = \rho \cos \phi = 4 \cos \frac{\pi}{4} = 2\sqrt{2}$$

The rectangular coordinates of the point are $(x, y, z) = (\sqrt{2}, \sqrt{6}, 2\sqrt{2})$ (Figure 11.8.7). ◂

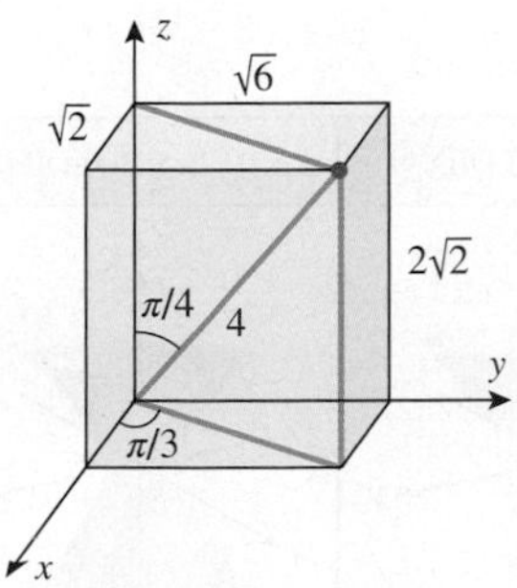

spherical: $(4, \pi/3, \pi/4)$
rectangular: $(\sqrt{2}, \sqrt{6}, 2\sqrt{2})$

▲ **Figure 11.8.7**

Since the interval $0 \le \theta < 2\pi$ covers two periods of the tangent function, the conversion formula $\tan \theta = y/x$ does not completely determine $\theta$. The following example shows how to deal with this ambiguity.

**▸ Example 2** Find the spherical coordinates of the point that has rectangular coordinates

$$(x, y, z) = (4, -4, 4\sqrt{6})$$

How should $\theta$ be chosen if $x = 0$? How should $\theta$ be chosen if $y = 0$?

*Solution.* From the rectangular-to-spherical conversion formulas in Table 11.8.1 we obtain

$$\rho = \sqrt{x^2 + y^2 + z^2} = \sqrt{16 + 16 + 96} = \sqrt{128} = 8\sqrt{2}$$

$$\tan\theta = \frac{y}{x} = -1$$

$$\cos\phi = \frac{z}{\sqrt{x^2 + y^2 + z^2}} = \frac{4\sqrt{6}}{8\sqrt{2}} = \frac{\sqrt{3}}{2}$$

From the restriction $0 \le \theta < 2\pi$ and the computed value of $\tan\theta$, the possibilities for $\theta$ are $\theta = 3\pi/4$ and $\theta = 7\pi/4$. However, the given point has a negative $y$-coordinate, so we must have $\theta = 7\pi/4$. Moreover, from the restriction $0 \le \phi \le \pi$ and the computed value of $\cos\phi$, the only possibility for $\phi$ is $\phi = \pi/6$. Thus, the spherical coordinates of the point are $(\rho, \theta, \phi) = (8\sqrt{2}, 7\pi/4, \pi/6)$ (Figure 11.8.8). ◄

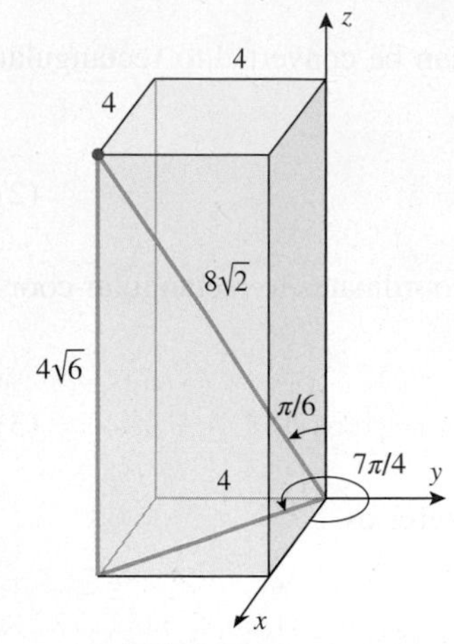


rectangular: $(4, -4, 4\sqrt{6})$
spherical: $(8\sqrt{2}, 7\pi/4, \pi/6)$

▲ **Figure 11.8.8**

## EQUATIONS OF SURFACES IN CYLINDRICAL AND SPHERICAL COORDINATES

Surfaces of revolution about the $z$-axis of a rectangular coordinate system usually have simpler equations in cylindrical coordinates than in rectangular coordinates, and the equations of surfaces with symmetry about the origin are usually simpler in spherical coordinates than in rectangular coordinates. For example, consider the upper nappe of the circular cone whose equation in rectangular coordinates is

$$z = \sqrt{x^2 + y^2}$$

(Table 11.8.2). The corresponding equation in cylindrical coordinates can be obtained from the cylindrical-to-rectangular conversion formulas in Table 11.8.1. This yields

$$z = \sqrt{(r\cos\theta)^2 + (r\sin\theta)^2} = \sqrt{r^2} = |r| = r$$

so the equation of the cone in cylindrical coordinates is $z = r$. Going a step further, the equation of the cone in spherical coordinates can be obtained from the spherical-to-cylindrical conversion formulas from Table 11.8.1. This yields

$$\rho\cos\phi = \rho\sin\phi$$

which, if $\rho \ne 0$, can be rewritten as

$$\tan\phi = 1 \quad \text{or} \quad \phi = \frac{\pi}{4}$$

Geometrically, this tells us that the radial line from the origin to any point on the cone makes an angle of $\pi/4$ with the $z$-axis.

**Table 11.8.2**

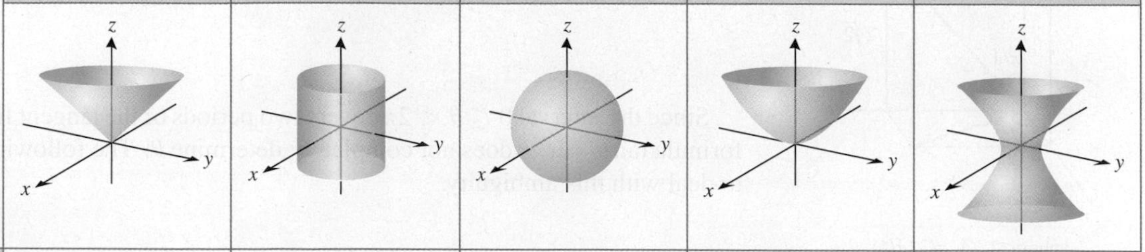


| | CONE | CYLINDER | SPHERE | PARABOLOID | HYPERBOLOID |
|---|---|---|---|---|---|
| RECTANGULAR | $z = \sqrt{x^2 + y^2}$ | $x^2 + y^2 = 1$ | $x^2 + y^2 + z^2 = 1$ | $z = x^2 + y^2$ | $x^2 + y^2 - z^2 = 1$ |
| CYLINDRICAL | $z = r$ | $r = 1$ | $z^2 = 1 - r^2$ | $z = r^2$ | $z^2 = r^2 - 1$ |
| SPHERICAL | $\phi = \pi/4$ | $\rho = \csc\phi$ | $\rho = 1$ | $\rho = \cos\phi\csc^2\phi$ | $\rho^2 = -\sec 2\phi$ |

▶ **Example 3** Find equations of the paraboloid $z = x^2 + y^2$ in cylindrical and spherical coordinates.

*Solution.* The rectangular-to-cylindrical conversion formulas in Table 11.8.1 yield

$$z = r^2 \tag{4}$$

which is the equation in cylindrical coordinates. Now applying the spherical-to-cylindrical conversion formulas to (4) yields

$$\rho\cos\phi = \rho^2\sin^2\phi$$

which we can rewrite as

$$\rho = \cos\phi\csc^2\phi$$

Alternatively, we could have obtained this equation directly from the equation in rectangular coordinates by applying the spherical-to-rectangular conversion formulas (verify). ◀

Verify the equations given in Table 11.8.2 for the cylinder and hyperboloid in cylindrical and spherical coordinates.

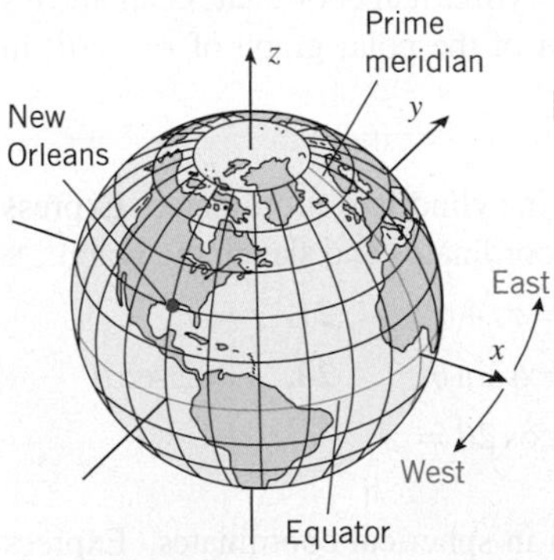

▲ **Figure 11.8.9**

## SPHERICAL COORDINATES IN NAVIGATION

Spherical coordinates are related to longitude and latitude coordinates used in navigation. To see why this is so, let us construct a right-hand rectangular coordinate system with its origin at the center of the Earth, its positive $z$-axis passing through the North Pole, and its positive $x$-axis passing through the prime meridian (Figure 11.8.9). If we assume the Earth to be a sphere of radius $\rho = 4000$ miles, then each point on the Earth has spherical coordinates of the form $(4000, \theta, \phi)$, where $\phi$ and $\theta$ determine the latitude and longitude of the point. It is common to specify longitudes in degrees east or west of the prime meridian and latitudes in degrees north or south of the equator. However, the next example shows that it is a simple matter to determine $\phi$ and $\theta$ from such data.

© Jon Arnold/DanitaDelimont.com

*Modern navigation systems use multiple coordinate representations to calculate position.*

▶ **Example 4** The city of New Orleans is located at 90° west longitude and 30° north latitude. Find its spherical and rectangular coordinates relative to the coordinate axes of Figure 11.8.9. (Assume that distance is in miles.)

*Solution.* A longitude of 90° west corresponds to $\theta = 360° - 90° = 270°$ or $\theta = 3\pi/2$ radians; and a latitude of 30° north corresponds to $\phi = 90° - 30° = 60°$ or $\phi = \pi/3$ radians. Thus, the spherical coordinates $(\rho, \theta, \phi)$ of New Orleans are $(4000, 3\pi/2, \pi/3)$.

To find the rectangular coordinates we apply the spherical-to-rectangular conversion formulas in Table 11.8.1. This yields

$$x = 4000\sin\frac{\pi}{3}\cos\frac{3\pi}{2} = 4000\frac{\sqrt{3}}{2}(0) = 0 \text{ mi}$$

$$y = 4000\sin\frac{\pi}{3}\sin\frac{3\pi}{2} = 4000\frac{\sqrt{3}}{2}(-1) = -2000\sqrt{3} \text{ mi}$$

$$z = 4000\cos\frac{\pi}{3} = 4000\left(\frac{1}{2}\right) = 2000 \text{ mi} \blacktriangleleft$$

## ✓QUICK CHECK EXERCISES 11.8

*(See page 741 for answers.)*

1. The conversion formulas from cylindrical coordinates $(r, \theta, z)$ to rectangular coordinates $(x, y, z)$ are

   $x =$ ______, $y =$ ______, $z =$ ______

2. The conversion formulas from spherical coordinates $(\rho, \theta, \phi)$ to rectangular coordinates $(x, y, z)$ are

   $x =$ ______, $y =$ ______, $z =$ ______

3. The conversion formulas from spherical coordinates $(\rho, \theta, \phi)$ to cylindrical coordinates $(r, \theta, z)$ are

   $r =$ ______, $\theta =$ ______, $z =$ ______

4. Let $P$ be the point in 3-space with rectangular coordinates $(\sqrt{2}, -\sqrt{2}, 2\sqrt{3})$.
   (a) Cylindrical coordinates for $P$ are $(r, \theta, z) =$ ______.
   (b) Spherical coordinates for $P$ are $(\rho, \theta, \phi) =$ ______.

5. Give an equation of a sphere of radius 5, centered at the origin, in
(a) rectangular coordinates
(b) cylindrical coordinates
(c) spherical coordinates.

## EXERCISE SET 11.8 Graphing Utility C CAS

**1–2** Convert from rectangular to cylindrical coordinates. ■

**1.** (a) $(4\sqrt{3}, 4, -4)$ (b) $(-5, 5, 6)$
(c) $(0, 2, 0)$ (d) $(4, -4\sqrt{3}, 6)$

**2.** (a) $(\sqrt{2}, -\sqrt{2}, 1)$ (b) $(0, 1, 1)$
(c) $(-4, 4, -7)$ (d) $(2, -2, -2)$

**3–4** Convert from cylindrical to rectangular coordinates. ■

**3.** (a) $(4, \pi/6, 3)$ (b) $(8, 3\pi/4, -2)$
(c) $(5, 0, 4)$ (d) $(7, \pi, -9)$

**4.** (a) $(6, 5\pi/3, 7)$ (b) $(1, \pi/2, 0)$
(c) $(3, \pi/2, 5)$ (d) $(4, \pi/2, -1)$

**5–6** Convert from rectangular to spherical coordinates. ■

**5.** (a) $(1, \sqrt{3}, -2)$ (b) $(1, -1, \sqrt{2})$
(c) $(0, 3\sqrt{3}, 3)$ (d) $(-5\sqrt{3}, 5, 0)$

**6.** (a) $(4, 4, 4\sqrt{6})$ (b) $(1, -\sqrt{3}, -2)$
(c) $(2, 0, 0)$ (d) $(\sqrt{3}, 1, 2\sqrt{3})$

**7–8** Convert from spherical to rectangular coordinates. ■

**7.** (a) $(5, \pi/6, \pi/4)$ (b) $(7, 0, \pi/2)$
(c) $(1, \pi, 0)$ (d) $(2, 3\pi/2, \pi/2)$

**8.** (a) $(1, 2\pi/3, 3\pi/4)$ (b) $(3, 7\pi/4, 5\pi/6)$
(c) $(8, \pi/6, \pi/4)$ (d) $(4, \pi/2, \pi/3)$

**9–10** Convert from cylindrical to spherical coordinates. ■

**9.** (a) $(\sqrt{3}, \pi/6, 3)$ (b) $(1, \pi/4, -1)$
(c) $(2, 3\pi/4, 0)$ (d) $(6, 1, -2\sqrt{3})$

**10.** (a) $(4, 5\pi/6, 4)$ (b) $(2, 0, -2)$
(c) $(4, \pi/2, 3)$ (d) $(6, \pi, 2)$

**11–12** Convert from spherical to cylindrical coordinates. ■

**11.** (a) $(5, \pi/4, 2\pi/3)$ (b) $(1, 7\pi/6, \pi)$
(c) $(3, 0, 0)$ (d) $(4, \pi/6, \pi/2)$

**12.** (a) $(5, \pi/2, 0)$ (b) $(6, 0, 3\pi/4)$
(c) $(\sqrt{2}, 3\pi/4, \pi)$ (d) $(5, 2\pi/3, 5\pi/6)$

C **13.** Use a CAS or a programmable calculating utility to set up the conversion formulas in Table 11.8.1, and then use the CAS or calculating utility to solve the problems in Exercises 1, 3, 5, 7, 9, and 11.

C **14.** Use a CAS or a programmable calculating utility to set up the conversion formulas in Table 11.8.1, and then use the CAS or calculating utility to solve the problems in Exercises 2, 4, 6, 8, 10, and 12.

**15–18 True–False** Determine whether the statement is true or false. Explain your answer. ■

**15.** In cylindrical coordinates for a point, $r$ is the distance from the point to the $z$-axis.

**16.** In spherical coordinates for a point, $\rho$ is the distance from the point to the origin.

**17.** The graph of $\theta = \theta_0$ in cylindrical coordinates is the same as the graph of $\theta = \theta_0$ in spherical coordinates.

**18.** The graph of $r = f(\theta)$ in cylindrical coordinates can always be obtained by extrusion of the polar graph of $r = f(\theta)$ in the $xy$-plane.

**19–26** An equation is given in cylindrical coordinates. Express the equation in rectangular coordinates and sketch the graph. ■

**19.** $r = 3$ **20.** $\theta = \pi/4$ **21.** $z = r^2$
**22.** $z = r\cos\theta$ **23.** $r = 4\sin\theta$ **24.** $r = 2\sec\theta$
**25.** $r^2 + z^2 = 1$ **26.** $r^2\cos 2\theta = z$

**27–34** An equation is given in spherical coordinates. Express the equation in rectangular coordinates and sketch the graph. ■

**27.** $\rho = 3$ **28.** $\theta = \pi/3$ **29.** $\phi = \pi/4$
**30.** $\rho = 2\sec\phi$ **31.** $\rho = 4\cos\phi$ **32.** $\rho\sin\phi = 1$
**33.** $\rho\sin\phi = 2\cos\theta$ **34.** $\rho - 2\sin\phi\cos\theta = 0$

**35–46** An equation of a surface is given in rectangular coordinates. Find an equation of the surface in (a) cylindrical coordinates and (b) spherical coordinates. ■

**35.** $z = 3$ **36.** $y = 2$
**37.** $z = 3x^2 + 3y^2$ **38.** $z = \sqrt{3x^2 + 3y^2}$
**39.** $x^2 + y^2 = 4$ **40.** $x^2 + y^2 - 6y = 0$
**41.** $x^2 + y^2 + z^2 = 9$ **42.** $z^2 = x^2 - y^2$
**43.** $2x + 3y + 4z = 1$ **44.** $x^2 + y^2 - z^2 = 1$
**45.** $x^2 = 16 - z^2$ **46.** $x^2 + y^2 + z^2 = 2z$

### FOCUS ON CONCEPTS

**47–50** Describe the region in 3-space that satisfies the given inequalities. ■

**47.** $r^2 \le z \le 4$ **48.** $0 \le r \le 2\sin\theta,\ \ 0 \le z \le 3$
**49.** $1 \le \rho \le 3$ **50.** $0 \le \phi \le \pi/6,\ \ 0 \le \rho \le 2$

**51.** St. Petersburg (Leningrad), Russia, is located at 30° east longitude and 60° north latitude. Find its spherical and rectangular coordinates relative to the coordinate axes of Figure 11.8.9. Take miles as the unit of distance and assume the Earth to be a sphere of radius 4000 miles.

**52.** (a) Show that the curve of intersection of the surfaces $z = \sin\theta$ and $r = a$ (cylindrical coordinates) is an ellipse.
(b) Sketch the surface $z = \sin\theta$ for $0 \le \theta \le \pi/2$.

**53.** The accompanying figure shows a right circular cylinder of radius 10 cm spinning at 3 revolutions per minute about the $z$-axis. At time $t = 0$ s, a bug at the point $(0, 10, 0)$ begins walking straight up the face of the cylinder at the rate of 0.5 cm/min.
(a) Find the cylindrical coordinates of the bug after 2 min.
(b) Find the rectangular coordinates of the bug after 2 min.
(c) Find the spherical coordinates of the bug after 2 min.

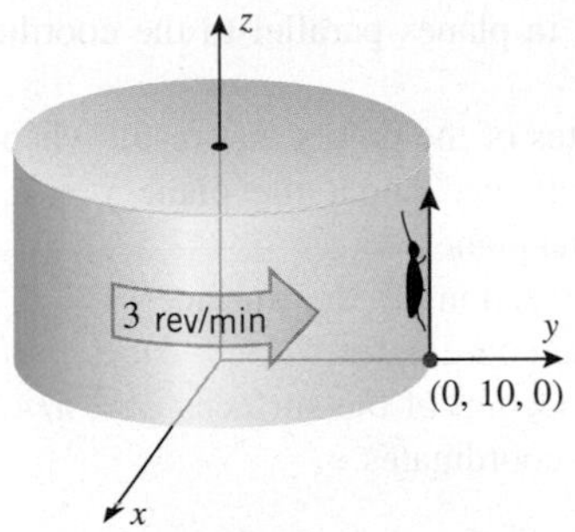

◀ Figure Ex-53

**54.** Referring to Exercise 53, use a graphing utility to graph the bug's distance from the origin as a function of time.

**C** **55.** The shape of a natural draft cooling tower for a power plant is given by the graph of

$$\frac{x^2}{540} + \frac{y^2}{540} - \frac{(z-70)^2}{1350} = 1$$

where $0 \le z \le 100$ denotes height above the ground in meters. Estimate the exterior surface area (top and side) of the tower.

**56.** Assuming it to be hollow, estimate the volume of the cooling tower in the preceding exercise.

**57. Writing** Discuss some practical applications in which nonrectangular coordinate systems are useful.

**58. Writing** The terms "zenith" and "azimuth" are used in celestial navigation. How do these terms relate to spherical coordinates?

✓ **QUICK CHECK ANSWERS 11.8** 1. $r\cos\theta$; $r\sin\theta$; $z$ 2. $\rho\sin\phi\cos\theta$; $\rho\sin\phi\sin\theta$; $\rho\cos\phi$ 3. $\rho\sin\phi$; $\theta$; $\rho\cos\theta$ 4. (a) $(2, 7\pi/4, 2\sqrt{3})$ (b) $(4, 7\pi/4, \pi/6)$ 5. (a) $x^2+y^2+z^2 = 25$ (b) $r^2+z^2 = 25$ (c) $\rho = 5$

## CHAPTER 11 REVIEW EXERCISES

**1.** (a) What is the difference between a vector and a scalar? Give a physical example of each.
(b) How can you determine whether or not two vectors are orthogonal?
(c) How can you determine whether or not two vectors are parallel?
(d) How can you determine whether or not three vectors with a common initial point lie in the same plane in 3-space?

**2.** (a) Sketch vectors **u** and **v** for which **u** + **v** and **u** − **v** are orthogonal.
(b) How can you use vectors to determine whether four points in 3-space lie in the same plane?
(c) If forces $\mathbf{F}_1 = \mathbf{i}$ and $\mathbf{F}_2 = \mathbf{j}$ are applied at a point in 2-space, what force would you apply at that point to cancel the combined effect of $\mathbf{F}_1$ and $\mathbf{F}_2$?
(d) Write an equation of the sphere with center $(1, -2, 2)$ that passes through the origin.

**3.** (a) Draw a picture that shows the direction angles $\alpha$, $\beta$, and $\gamma$ of a vector.
(b) What are the components of a unit vector in 2-space that makes an angle of 120° with the vector **i** (two answers)?
(c) How can you use vectors to determine whether a triangle with known vertices $P_1$, $P_2$, and $P_3$ has an obtuse angle?
(d) True or false: The cross product of orthogonal unit vectors is a unit vector. Explain your reasoning.

**4.** (a) Make a table that shows all possible cross products of the vectors **i**, **j**, and **k**.
(b) Give a geometric interpretation of $\|\mathbf{u} \times \mathbf{v}\|$.
(c) Give a geometric interpretation of $|\mathbf{u} \cdot (\mathbf{v} \times \mathbf{w})|$.
(d) Write an equation of the plane that passes through the origin and is perpendicular to the line $x = t$, $y = 2t$, $z = -t$.

**5.** In each part, find an equation of the sphere with center $(-3, 5, -4)$ and satisfying the given condition.
(a) Tangent to the $xy$-plane
(b) Tangent to the $xz$-plane
(c) Tangent to the $yz$-plane

**6.** Find the largest and smallest distances between the point $P(1, 1, 1)$ and the sphere

$$x^2 + y^2 + z^2 - 2y + 6z - 6 = 0$$

**7.** Given the points $P(3, 4)$, $Q(1, 1)$, and $R(5, 2)$, use vector methods to find the coordinates of the fourth vertex of the parallelogram whose adjacent sides are $\overrightarrow{PQ}$ and $\overrightarrow{QR}$.

**8.** Let $\mathbf{u} = \langle 3, 5, -1\rangle$ and $\mathbf{v} = \langle 2, -2, 3\rangle$. Find
(a) $2\mathbf{u} + 5\mathbf{v}$ (b) $\dfrac{1}{\|\mathbf{v}\|}\mathbf{v}$
(c) $\|\mathbf{u}\|$ (d) $\|\mathbf{u} - \mathbf{v}\|$.

**9.** Let $\mathbf{a} = c\mathbf{i} + \mathbf{j}$ and $\mathbf{b} = 4\mathbf{i} + 3\mathbf{j}$. Find $c$ so that
(a) $\mathbf{a}$ and $\mathbf{b}$ are orthogonal
(b) the angle between $\mathbf{a}$ and $\mathbf{b}$ is $\pi/4$
(c) the angle between $\mathbf{a}$ and $\mathbf{b}$ is $\pi/6$
(d) $\mathbf{a}$ and $\mathbf{b}$ are parallel.

**10.** Let $\mathbf{r}_0 = \langle x_0, y_0, z_0 \rangle$ and $\mathbf{r} = \langle x, y, z \rangle$. Describe the set of all points $(x, y, z)$ for which
(a) $\mathbf{r} \cdot \mathbf{r}_0 = 0$ (b) $(\mathbf{r} - \mathbf{r}_0) \cdot \mathbf{r}_0 = 0$.

**11.** Show that if $\mathbf{u}$ and $\mathbf{v}$ are unit vectors and $\theta$ is the angle between them, then $\|\mathbf{u} - \mathbf{v}\| = 2 \sin \frac{1}{2}\theta$.

**12.** Find the vector with length 5 and direction angles $\alpha = 60°$, $\beta = 120°$, $\gamma = 135°$.

**13.** Assuming that force is in pounds and distance is in feet, find the work done by a constant force $\mathbf{F} = 3\mathbf{i} - 4\mathbf{j} + \mathbf{k}$ acting on a particle that moves on a straight line from $P(5, 7, 0)$ to $Q(6, 6, 6)$.

**14.** Assuming that force is in newtons and distance is in meters, find the work done by the resultant of the constant forces $\mathbf{F}_1 = \mathbf{i} - 3\mathbf{j} + \mathbf{k}$ and $\mathbf{F}_2 = \mathbf{i} + 2\mathbf{j} + 2\mathbf{k}$ acting on a particle that moves on a straight line from $P(-1, -2, 3)$ to $Q(0, 2, 0)$.

**15.** (a) Find the area of the triangle with vertices $A(1, 0, 1)$, $B(0, 2, 3)$, and $C(2, 1, 0)$.
(b) Use the result in part (a) to find the length of the altitude from vertex $C$ to side $AB$.

**16.** True or false? Explain your reasoning.
(a) If $\mathbf{u} \cdot \mathbf{v} = 0$, then $\mathbf{u} = \mathbf{0}$ or $\mathbf{v} = \mathbf{0}$.
(b) If $\mathbf{u} \times \mathbf{v} = \mathbf{0}$, then $\mathbf{u} = \mathbf{0}$ or $\mathbf{v} = \mathbf{0}$.
(c) If $\mathbf{u} \cdot \mathbf{v} = 0$ and $\mathbf{u} \times \mathbf{v} = \mathbf{0}$, then $\mathbf{u} = \mathbf{0}$ or $\mathbf{v} = \mathbf{0}$.

**17.** Consider the points

$$A(1, -1, 2),\ B(2, -3, 0),\ C(-1, -2, 0),\ D(2, 1, -1)$$

(a) Find the volume of the parallelepiped that has the vectors $\overrightarrow{AB}, \overrightarrow{AC}, \overrightarrow{AD}$ as adjacent edges.
(b) Find the distance from $D$ to the plane containing $A$, $B$, and $C$.

**18.** Suppose that a force $\mathbf{F}$ with a magnitude of 9 lb is applied to the lever–shaft assembly shown in the accompanying figure.
(a) Express the force $\mathbf{F}$ in component form.
(b) Find the vector moment of $\mathbf{F}$ about the origin.

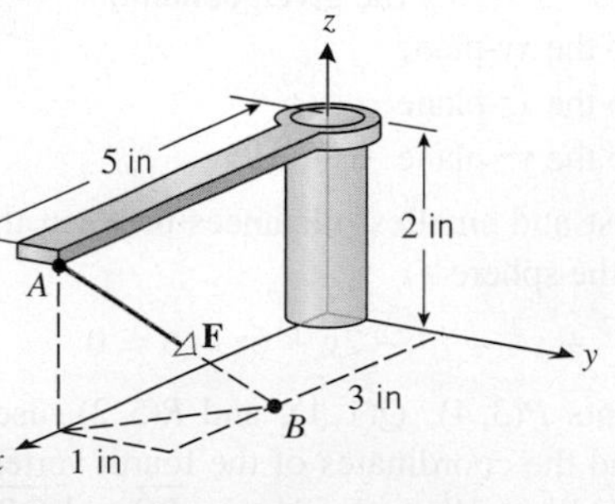

**Figure Ex-18**

**19.** Let $P$ be the point $(4, 1, 2)$. Find parametric equations for the line through $P$ and parallel to the vector $\langle 1, -1, 0 \rangle$.

**20.** (a) Find parametric equations for the intersection of the planes $2x + y - z = 3$ and $x + 2y + z = 3$.
(b) Find the acute angle between the two planes.

**21.** Find an equation of the plane that is parallel to the plane $x + 5y - z + 8 = 0$ and contains the point $(1, 1, 4)$.

**22.** Find an equation of the plane through the point $(4, 3, 0)$ and parallel to the vectors $\mathbf{i} + \mathbf{k}$ and $2\mathbf{j} - \mathbf{k}$.

**23.** What condition must the constants satisfy for the planes

$$a_1x + b_1y + c_1z = d_1 \quad \text{and} \quad a_2x + b_2y + c_2z = d_2$$

to be perpendicular?

**24.** (a) List six common types of quadric surfaces, and describe their traces in planes parallel to the coordinate planes.
(b) Give the coordinates of the points that result when the point $(x, y, z)$ is reflected about the plane $y = x$, the plane $y = z$, and the plane $x = z$.
(c) Describe the intersection of the surfaces $r = 5$ and $z = 1$ in cylindrical coordinates.
(d) Describe the intersection of the surfaces $\phi = \pi/4$ and $\theta = 0$ in spherical coordinates.

**25.** In each part, identify the surface by completing the squares.
(a) $x^2 + 4y^2 - z^2 - 6x + 8y + 4z = 0$
(b) $x^2 + y^2 + z^2 + 6x - 4y + 12z = 0$
(c) $x^2 + y^2 - z^2 - 2x + 4y + 5 = 0$

**26.** In each part, express the equation in cylindrical and spherical coordinates.
(a) $x^2 + y^2 = z$ (b) $x^2 - y^2 - z^2 = 0$

**27.** In each part, express the equation in rectangular coordinates.
(a) $z = r^2 \cos 2\theta$ (b) $\rho^2 \sin\phi \cos\phi \cos\theta = 1$

**28–29** Sketch the solid in 3-space that is described in cylindrical coordinates by the stated inequalities. ■

**28.** (a) $1 \le r \le 2$ (b) $2 \le z \le 3$ (c) $\pi/6 \le \theta \le \pi/3$
(d) $1 \le r \le 2$, $2 \le z \le 3$, and $\pi/6 \le \theta \le \pi/3$

**29.** (a) $r^2 + z^2 \le 4$ (b) $r \le 1$
(c) $r^2 + z^2 \le 4$ and $r > 1$

**30–31** Sketch the solid in 3-space that is described in spherical coordinates by the stated inequalities. ■

**30.** (a) $0 \le \rho \le 2$ (b) $0 \le \phi \le \pi/6$
(c) $0 \le \rho \le 2$ and $0 \le \phi \le \pi/6$

**31.** (a) $0 \le \rho \le 5$, $0 \le \phi \le \pi/2$, and $0 \le \theta \le \pi/2$
(b) $0 \le \phi \le \pi/3$ and $0 \le \rho \le 2 \sec\phi$
(c) $0 \le \rho \le 2$ and $\pi/6 \le \phi \le \pi/3$

**32.** Sketch the surface whose equation in spherical coordinates is $\rho = a(1 - \cos\phi)$. [*Hint:* The surface is shaped like a familiar fruit.]

## CHAPTER 11 MAKING CONNECTIONS

**1.** Define a "rotation operator" $R$ on vectors in the $xy$-plane by the formula
$$R(x\mathbf{i} + y\mathbf{j}) = -y\mathbf{i} + x\mathbf{j}$$
(a) Verify that $R$ rotates vectors $90^\circ$ counterclockwise.
(b) Prove that $R$ has the following linearity properties:
$$R(c\mathbf{v}) = cR(\mathbf{v}) \quad \text{and} \quad R(\mathbf{v} + \mathbf{w}) = R(\mathbf{v}) + R(\mathbf{w})$$

**2.** (a) Given a triangle in the $xy$-plane, assign to each side of the triangle an outward normal vector whose length is the same as that of the corresponding side. Prove that the sum of the resulting three normal vectors is the zero vector.
(b) Extend the result of part (a) to a polygon of $n$ sides in the $xy$-plane. [*Hint:* Use the results of the preceding exercise.]

**3.** (a) Given a tetrahedron in 3-space, assign to each face of the tetrahedron an outward normal vector whose length is numerically the same as the area of the corresponding face. Prove that the sum of the resulting four normal vectors is the zero vector. [*Hint:* Use cross products.]
(b) Extend your result from part (a) to a pyramid with a four-sided base. [*Hint:* Divide the base into two triangles and use the result from part (a) on each of the two resulting tetrahedra.]
(c) Can you extend the results of parts (a) and (b) to other polyhedra?

**4.** Given a tetrahedron in 3-space, pick a vertex and label the three faces that meet at that vertex as $A$, $B$, and $C$. Let $a$, $b$, and $c$ denote the respective areas of those faces, and let $d$ denote the area of the fourth face of the tetrahedron. Let $\alpha$ denote the (internal) angle between faces $A$ and $B$, $\beta$ the angle between $B$ and $C$, and $\gamma$ the angle between $A$ and $C$.
(a) Prove that
$$d^2 = a^2 + b^2 + c^2 - 2ab\cos\alpha - 2bc\cos\beta - 2ac\cos\gamma$$
This result is sometimes referred to as the ***law of cosines for a tetrahedron***. [*Hint:* Use the result in part (a) of the preceding exercise.]
(b) With the result in part (a) as motivation, state and prove a "Theorem of Pythagoras for a Tetrahedron."

**5.** Any circle that lies on a sphere can be realized as the intersection of the sphere and a plane. If the plane passes through the center of the sphere, then the circle is referred to as a ***great circle***. Given two points on a sphere, the ***great circle distance*** between the two points is the length of the smallest arc of a great circle that contains both points. Assume that $\Sigma$ is a sphere of radius $\rho$ centered at the origin in 3-space. If points $P$ and $Q$ lie on $\Sigma$ and have spherical coordinates $(\rho, \theta_1, \phi_1)$ and $(\rho, \theta_2, \phi_2)$, respectively, prove that the great circle distance between $P$ and $Q$ is
$$\rho\cos^{-1}(\cos\phi_1\cos\phi_2 + \cos(\theta_1 - \theta_2)\sin\phi_1\sin\phi_2)$$

**6.** A ship at sea is at point $A$ that is $60^\circ$ west longitude and $40^\circ$ north latitude. The ship travels to point $B$ that is $40^\circ$ west longitude and $20^\circ$ north latitude. Assuming that the Earth is a sphere with radius 6370 kilometers, find the shortest distance the ship can travel in going from $A$ to $B$, given that the shortest distance between two points on a sphere is along the arc of the great circle joining the points. [*Suggestion:* Introduce an $xyz$-coordinate system as in Figure 11.8.9, and use the result of the preceding exercise.]

Krystian Janczyński/iStockphoto

*The design of a roller coaster requires an understanding of the mathematical principles governing the motion of objects that move with varying speed and direction.*

# 12

# VECTOR-VALUED FUNCTIONS

In this chapter we will consider functions whose values are vectors. Such functions provide a unified way of studying parametric curves in 2-space and 3-space and are a basic tool for analyzing the motion of particles along curved paths. We will begin by developing the calculus of vector-valued functions—we will show how to differentiate and integrate such functions, and we will develop some of the basic properties of these operations. We will then apply these calculus tools to define three fundamental vectors that can be used to describe such basic characteristics of curves as curvature and twisting tendencies. Once this is done, we will develop the concepts of velocity and acceleration for such motion, and we will apply these concepts to explain various physical phenomena. Finally, we will use the calculus of vector-valued functions to develop basic principles of gravitational attraction and to derive Kepler's laws of planetary motion.

## 12.1 INTRODUCTION TO VECTOR-VALUED FUNCTIONS

*In Section 11.5 we discussed parametric equations of lines in 3-space. In this section we will discuss more general parametric curves in 3-space, and we will show how vector notation can be used to express parametric equations in 2-space and 3-space in a more compact form. This will lead us to consider a new kind of function—namely, functions that associate vectors with real numbers. Such functions have many important applications in physics and engineering.*

### PARAMETRIC CURVES IN 3-SPACE

Recall from Section 10.1 that if $f$ and $g$ are well-behaved functions, then the pair of parametric equations

$$x = f(t), \quad y = g(t) \tag{1}$$

generates a curve in 2-space that is traced in a specific direction as the parameter $t$ increases. We defined this direction to be the *orientation* of the curve or the *direction of increasing parameter*, and we called the curve together with its orientation the *graph* of the parametric equations or the *parametric curve* represented by the equations. Analogously, if $f$, $g$, and $h$ are three well-behaved functions, then the parametric equations

$$x = f(t), \quad y = g(t), \quad z = h(t) \tag{2}$$

generate a curve in 3-space that is traced in a specific direction as $t$ increases. As in 2-space, this direction is called the ***orientation*** or ***direction of increasing parameter***, and the curve together with its orientation is called the ***graph*** of the parametric equations or the ***parametric curve*** represented by the equations. If no restrictions are stated explicitly or are implied by the equations, then it will be understood that $t$ varies over the interval $(-\infty, +\infty)$.

▶ **Example 1** The parametric equations

$$x = 1 - t, \quad y = 3t, \quad z = 2t$$

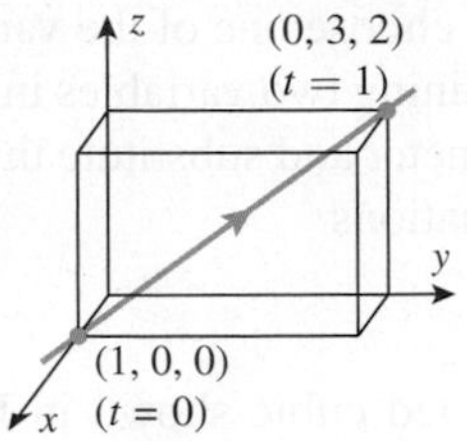


$x = 1 - t,\ y = 3t,\ z = 2t$

▲ Figure 12.1.1

represent a line in 3-space that passes through the point $(1, 0, 0)$ and is parallel to the vector $\langle -1, 3, 2\rangle$. Since $x$ decreases as $t$ increases, the line has the orientation shown in Figure 12.1.1. ◀

▶ **Example 2** Describe the parametric curve represented by the equations

$$x = a\cos t, \quad y = a\sin t, \quad z = ct$$

where $a$ and $c$ are positive constants.

***Solution.*** As the parameter $t$ increases, the value of $z = ct$ also increases, so the point $(x, y, z)$ moves upward. However, as $t$ increases, the point $(x, y, z)$ also moves in a path directly over the circle

$$x = a\cos t, \quad y = a\sin t$$

in the $xy$-plane. The combination of these upward and circular motions produces a corkscrew-shaped curve that wraps around a right circular cylinder of radius $a$ centered on the $z$-axis (Figure 12.1.2). This curve is called a ***circular helix***. ◀

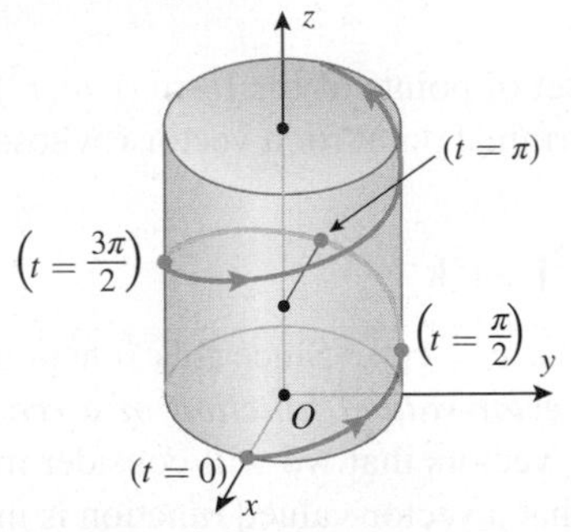


$x = a\cos t,\ y = a\sin t,\ z = ct$

▲ Figure 12.1.2

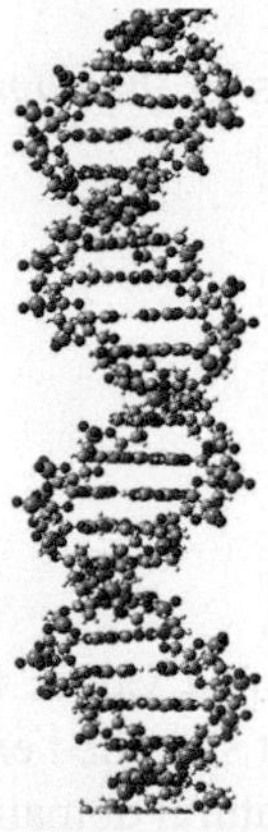

logos2012/Depositphotos

The circular helix described in Example 2 occurs in nature. Above is a computer representation of the twin helix DNA molecule (deoxyribonucleic acid). This structure contains all the inherited instructions necessary for the development of a living organism.

## PARAMETRIC CURVES GENERATED WITH TECHNOLOGY

Except in the simplest cases, parametric curves can be difficult to visualize and draw without the help of a graphing utility. For example, the ***tricuspoid*** is the graph of the parametric equations

$$x = 2\cos t + \cos 2t, \quad y = 2\sin t - \sin 2t$$

Although it would be tedious to plot the tricuspoid by hand, a computer rendering is easy to obtain and reveals the significance of the name of the curve (Figure 12.1.3). However, note that the depiction of the tricuspoid in Figure 12.1.3 is incomplete, since the orientation of the curve is not indicated. This is often the case for curves that are generated with a graphing utility. (Some graphing utilities plot parametric curves slowly enough for the orientation to be discerned, or provide a feature for tracing the points along the curve in the direction of increasing parameter.)

Parametric curves in 3-space can be difficult to visualize correctly even with the help of a graphing utility. For example, Figure 12.1.4$a$ shows a parametric curve called a *torus knot* that was produced with a CAS. However, it is unclear from this computer-generated figure whether the points of overlap are intersections or whether one portion of the curve is in front of the other. To resolve the visualization problem, some graphing utilities provide the capability of enclosing the curve within a thin tube, as in Figure 12.1.4$b$. Such graphs are called ***tube plots***.

**TECHNOLOGY MASTERY**

If you have a CAS, use it to generate the tricuspoid in Figure 12.1.3, and show that this parametric curve is oriented counterclockwise.

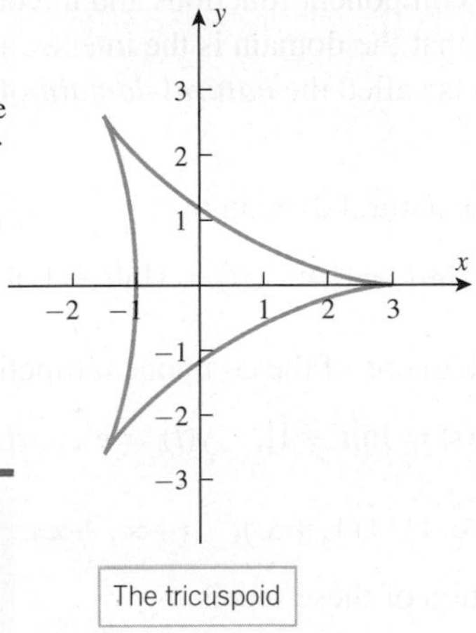


▲ Figure 12.1.3

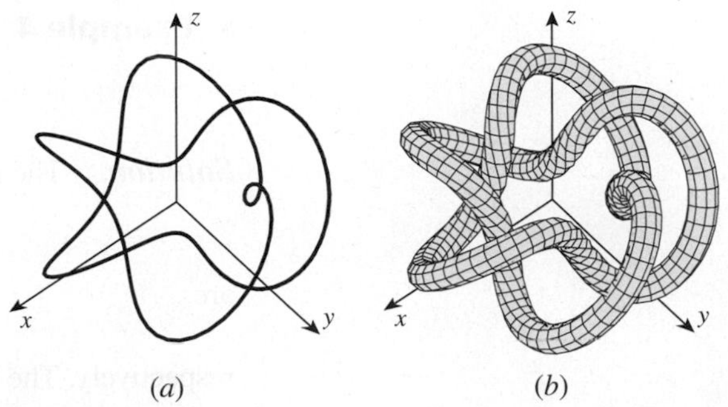


▲ Figure 12.1.4

## PARAMETRIC EQUATIONS FOR INTERSECTIONS OF SURFACES

Curves in 3-space often arise as intersections of surfaces. For example, Figure 12.1.5$a$ shows a portion of the intersection of the cylinders $z = x^3$ and $y = x^2$. One method for

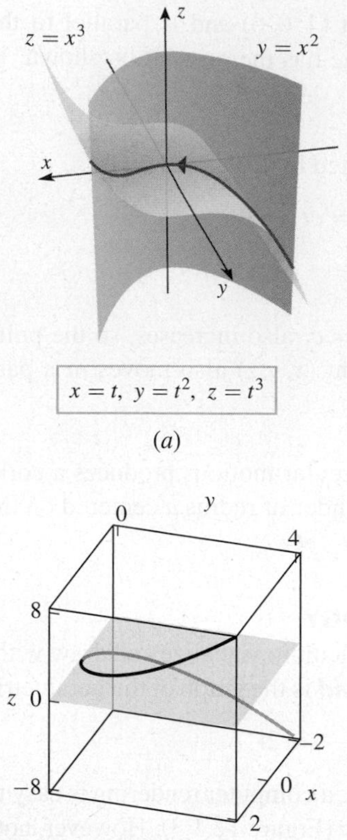


▲ **Figure 12.1.5**

Whereas a vector-valued function in 3-space, such as (4), has three components, a vector-valued function in 2-space has only two components and hence has the form

$$r(t) = \langle x(t), y(t)\rangle$$
$$= x(t)\mathbf{i} + y(t)\mathbf{j}$$

Find the vector-valued function in 2-space whose component functions are $x(t) = t$ and $y(t) = t^2$.

finding parametric equations for the curve of intersection is to choose one of the variables as the parameter and use the two equations to express the remaining two variables in terms of that parameter. In particular, if we choose $x = t$ as the parameter and substitute this into the equations $z = x^3$ and $y = x^2$, we obtain the parametric equations

$$x = t, \quad y = t^2, \quad z = t^3 \tag{3}$$

This curve is called a ***twisted cubic***. The portion of the twisted cubic shown in Figure 12.1.5*a* corresponds to $t \geq 0$; a computer-generated graph of the twisted cubic for positive and negative values of $t$ is shown in Figure 12.1.5*b*. Some other examples and techniques for finding intersections of surfaces are discussed in the exercises.

## VECTOR-VALUED FUNCTIONS

The twisted cubic defined by the equations in (3) is the set of points of the form $(t, t^2, t^3)$ for real values of $t$. If we view each of these points as a terminal point for a vector $\mathbf{r}$ whose initial point is at the origin,

$$\mathbf{r} = \langle x, y, z\rangle = \langle t, t^2, t^3\rangle = t\mathbf{i} + t^2\mathbf{j} + t^3\mathbf{k}$$

then we obtain $\mathbf{r}$ as a function of the parameter $t$, that is, $\mathbf{r} = \mathbf{r}(t)$. Since this function produces a *vector*, we say that $\mathbf{r} = \mathbf{r}(t)$ defines $\mathbf{r}$ as a ***vector-valued function of a real variable***, or more simply, a ***vector-valued function***. The vectors that we will consider in this text are either in 2-space or 3-space, so we will say that a vector-valued function is in 2-space or in 3-space according to the kind of vectors that it produces.

If $\mathbf{r}(t)$ is a vector-valued function in 3-space, then for each allowable value of $t$ the vector $\mathbf{r} = \mathbf{r}(t)$ can be represented in terms of components as

$$\mathbf{r} = \mathbf{r}(t) = \langle x(t), y(t), z(t)\rangle = x(t)\mathbf{i} + y(t)\mathbf{j} + z(t)\mathbf{k} \tag{4}$$

The functions $x(t)$, $y(t)$, and $z(t)$ are called the ***component functions*** or the ***components*** of $\mathbf{r}(t)$.

**▶ Example 3** The component functions of

$$\mathbf{r}(t) = \langle t, t^2, t^3\rangle = t\mathbf{i} + t^2\mathbf{j} + t^3\mathbf{k}$$

are

$$x(t) = t, \quad y(t) = t^2, \quad z(t) = t^3 \ ◀$$

The ***domain*** of a vector-valued function $\mathbf{r}(t)$ is the set of allowable values for $t$. If $\mathbf{r}(t)$ is defined in terms of component functions and the domain is not specified explicitly, then it will be understood that the domain is the intersection of the natural domains of the component functions; this is called the ***natural domain*** of $\mathbf{r}(t)$.

**▶ Example 4** Find the natural domain of

$$\mathbf{r}(t) = \langle \ln|t-1|, e^t, \sqrt{t}\rangle = (\ln|t-1|)\mathbf{i} + e^t\mathbf{j} + \sqrt{t}\mathbf{k}$$

***Solution.*** The natural domains of the component functions

$$x(t) = \ln|t-1|, \quad y(t) = e^t, \quad z(t) = \sqrt{t}$$

are

$$(-\infty, 1) \cup (1, +\infty), \quad (-\infty, +\infty), \quad [0, +\infty)$$

respectively. The intersection of these sets is

$$[0, 1) \cup (1, +\infty)$$

(verify), so the natural domain of $\mathbf{r}(t)$ consists of all values of $t$ such that

$$0 \leq t < 1 \quad \text{or} \quad t > 1 \ ◀$$

## GRAPHS OF VECTOR-VALUED FUNCTIONS

If $\mathbf{r}(t)$ is a vector-valued function in 2-space or 3-space, then we define the ***graph*** of $\mathbf{r}(t)$ to be the parametric curve described by the component functions for $\mathbf{r}(t)$. For example, if

$$\mathbf{r}(t) = \langle 1-t, 3t, 2t \rangle = (1-t)\mathbf{i} + 3t\mathbf{j} + 2t\mathbf{k} \tag{5}$$

then the graph of $\mathbf{r} = \mathbf{r}(t)$ is the graph of the parametric equations

$$x = 1 - t, \quad y = 3t, \quad z = 2t$$

Thus, the graph of (5) is the line in Figure 12.1.1.

Strictly speaking, we should write $(\cos t)\mathbf{i}$ and $(\sin t)\mathbf{j}$ rather than $\cos t\mathbf{i}$ and $\sin t\mathbf{j}$ for clarity. However, it is a common practice to omit the parentheses in such cases, since no misinterpretation is possible. Why?

**▶ Example 5** Describe the graph of the vector-valued function

$$\mathbf{r}(t) = \langle \cos t, \sin t, t \rangle = \cos t\mathbf{i} + \sin t\mathbf{j} + t\mathbf{k}$$

***Solution.*** The corresponding parametric equations are

$$x = \cos t, \quad y = \sin t, \quad z = t$$

Thus, as we saw in Example 2, the graph is a circular helix wrapped around a cylinder of radius 1. ◀

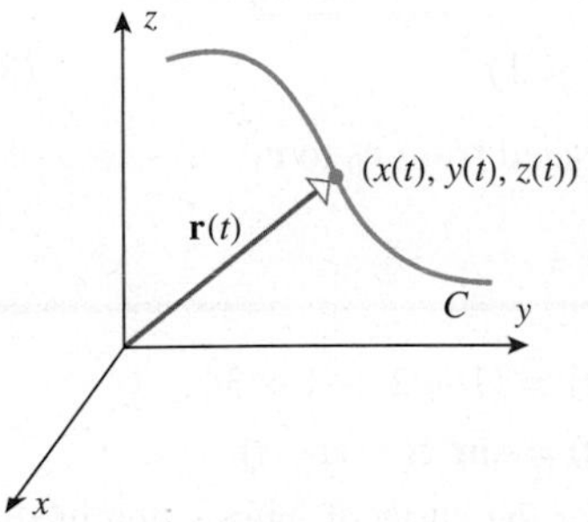


As $t$ varies, the tip of the radius vector $\mathbf{r}(t)$ traces out the curve $C$.

▲ **Figure 12.1.6**

Up to now we have considered parametric curves to be paths traced by moving points. However, if a parametric curve is viewed as the graph of a vector-valued function, then we can also imagine the graph to be traced by the tip of a moving vector. For example, if the curve $C$ in 3-space is the graph of

$$\mathbf{r}(t) = x(t)\mathbf{i} + y(t)\mathbf{j} + z(t)\mathbf{k}$$

and if we position $\mathbf{r}(t)$ so its initial point is at the origin, then its terminal point will fall on the curve $C$ (as shown in Figure 12.1.6). Thus, when $\mathbf{r}(t)$ is positioned with its initial point at the origin, its terminal point will trace out the curve $C$ as the parameter $t$ varies, in which case we call $\mathbf{r}(t)$ the ***radius vector*** or the ***position vector*** for $C$. For simplicity, we will sometimes let the dependence on $t$ be understood and write $\mathbf{r}$ rather than $\mathbf{r}(t)$ for a radius vector.

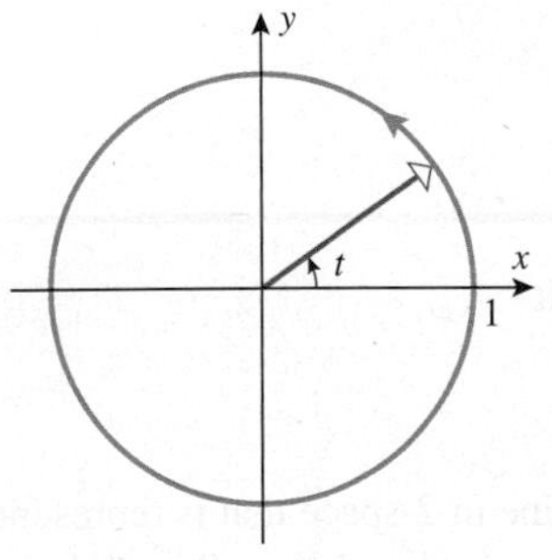


$\mathbf{r} = \cos t\mathbf{i} + \sin t\mathbf{j}$

▲ **Figure 12.1.7**

**▶ Example 6** Sketch the graph and a radius vector of

(a) $\mathbf{r}(t) = \cos t\mathbf{i} + \sin t\mathbf{j}, \quad 0 \le t \le 2\pi$

(b) $\mathbf{r}(t) = \cos t\mathbf{i} + \sin t\mathbf{j} + 2\mathbf{k}, \quad 0 \le t \le 2\pi$

***Solution (a).*** The corresponding parametric equations are

$$x = \cos t, \quad y = \sin t \qquad (0 \le t \le 2\pi)$$

so the graph is a circle of radius 1, centered at the origin, and oriented counterclockwise. The graph and a radius vector are shown in Figure 12.1.7.

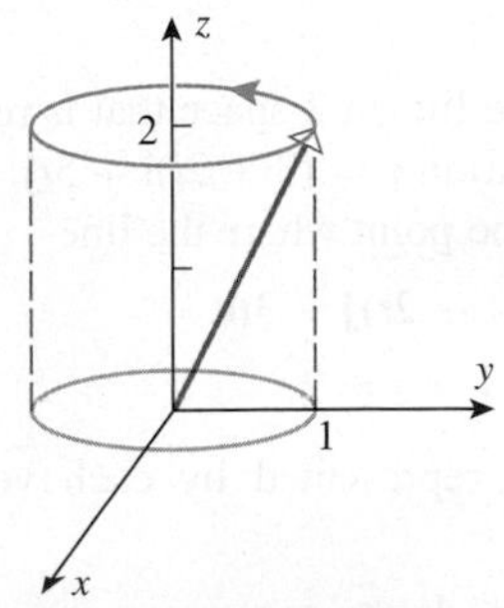


$\mathbf{r} = \cos t\mathbf{i} + \sin t\mathbf{j} + 2\mathbf{k}$

▲ **Figure 12.1.8**

***Solution (b).*** The corresponding parametric equations are

$$x = \cos t, \quad y = \sin t, \quad z = 2 \qquad (0 \le t \le 2\pi)$$

From the third equation, the tip of the radius vector traces a curve in the plane $z = 2$, and from the first two equations, the curve is a circle of radius 1 centered at the point $(0, 0, 2)$ and traced counterclockwise looking down the $z$-axis. The graph and a radius vector are shown in Figure 12.1.8. ◀

## VECTOR FORM OF A LINE SEGMENT

Recall from Formula (9) of Section 11.5 that if $\mathbf{r}_0$ is a vector in 2-space or 3-space with its initial point at the origin, then the line that passes through the terminal point of $\mathbf{r}_0$ and is parallel to the vector $\mathbf{v}$ can be expressed in vector form as

$$\mathbf{r} = \mathbf{r}_0 + t\mathbf{v}$$

In particular, if $\mathbf{r}_0$ and $\mathbf{r}_1$ are vectors in 2-space or 3-space with their initial points at the origin, then the line that passes through the terminal points of these vectors can be expressed in vector form as

$$\mathbf{r} = \mathbf{r}_0 + t(\mathbf{r}_1 - \mathbf{r}_0) \quad \text{or} \quad \mathbf{r} = (1-t)\mathbf{r}_0 + t\mathbf{r}_1 \qquad (6\text{–}7)$$

as indicated in Figure 12.1.9.

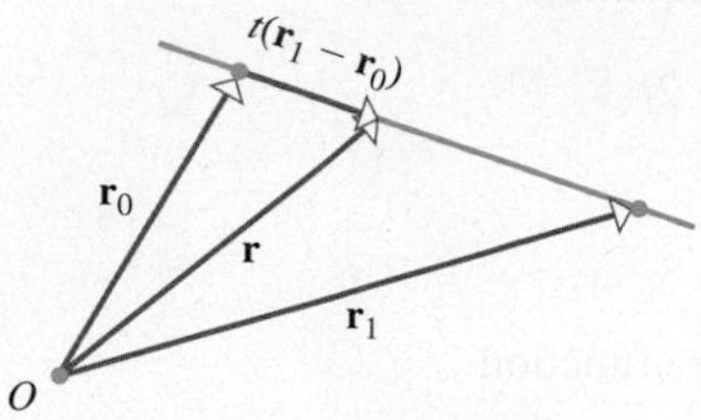


▲ Figure 12.1.9

It is common to call either (6) or (7) the ***two-point vector form of a line*** and to say, for simplicity, that the line passes through the *points* $\mathbf{r}_0$ and $\mathbf{r}_1$ (as opposed to saying that it passes through the *terminal points* of $\mathbf{r}_0$ and $\mathbf{r}_1$).

It is understood in (6) and (7) that $t$ varies from $-\infty$ to $+\infty$. However, if we restrict $t$ to vary over the interval $0 \le t \le 1$, then $\mathbf{r}$ will vary from $\mathbf{r}_0$ to $\mathbf{r}_1$. Thus, the equation

$$\mathbf{r} = (1-t)\mathbf{r}_0 + t\mathbf{r}_1 \qquad (0 \le t \le 1) \qquad (8)$$

represents the line segment in 2-space or 3-space that is traced from $\mathbf{r}_0$ to $\mathbf{r}_1$.

## ✓ QUICK CHECK EXERCISES 12.1 *(See page 750 for answers.)*

1. (a) Express the parametric equations
$$x = \frac{1}{t}, \quad y = \sqrt{t}, \quad z = \sin^{-1} t$$
as a single vector equation of the form
$$\mathbf{r} = x(t)\mathbf{i} + y(t)\mathbf{j} + z(t)\mathbf{k}$$
(b) The vector equation in part (a) defines $\mathbf{r} = \mathbf{r}(t)$ as a vector-valued function. The domain of $\mathbf{r}(t)$ is ______ and $\mathbf{r}\left(\frac{1}{2}\right) =$ ______.

2. Describe the graph of $\mathbf{r}(t) = \langle 1+2t, -1+3t \rangle$.

3. Describe the graph of $\mathbf{r}(t) = \sin^2 t\mathbf{i} + \cos^2 t\mathbf{j}$.

4. Find a vector equation for the curve of intersection of the surfaces $y = x^2$ and $z = y$ in terms of the parameter $x = t$.

## EXERCISE SET 12.1 ▭ Graphing Utility

**1–4** Find the domain of $\mathbf{r}(t)$ and the value of $\mathbf{r}(t_0)$. ■

1. $\mathbf{r}(t) = \cos t\mathbf{i} - 3t\mathbf{j}$; $t_0 = \pi$
2. $\mathbf{r}(t) = \langle \sqrt{3t+1}, t^2 \rangle$; $t_0 = 1$
3. $\mathbf{r}(t) = \cos \pi t\mathbf{i} - \ln t\mathbf{j} + \sqrt{t-2}\,\mathbf{k}$; $t_0 = 3$
4. $\mathbf{r}(t) = \langle 2e^{-t}, \sin^{-1} t, \ln(1-t) \rangle$; $t_0 = 0$

**5–6** Express the parametric equations as a single vector equation of the form

$$\mathbf{r} = x(t)\mathbf{i} + y(t)\mathbf{j} \quad \text{or} \quad \mathbf{r} = x(t)\mathbf{i} + y(t)\mathbf{j} + z(t)\mathbf{k} \ ■$$

5. $x = 3\cos t$, $y = t + \sin t$
6. $x = 2t$, $y = 2\sin 3t$, $z = 5\cos 3t$

**7–8** Find the parametric equations that correspond to the given vector equation. ■

7. $\mathbf{r} = 3t^2\mathbf{i} - 2\mathbf{j}$
8. $\mathbf{r} = (2t-1)\mathbf{i} - 3\sqrt{t}\,\mathbf{j} + \sin 3t\mathbf{k}$

**9–14** Describe the graph of the equation. ■

9. $\mathbf{r} = (3-2t)\mathbf{i} + 5t\mathbf{j}$
10. $\mathbf{r} = 2\sin 3t\mathbf{i} - 2\cos 3t\mathbf{j}$
11. $\mathbf{r} = 2t\mathbf{i} - 3\mathbf{j} + (1+3t)\mathbf{k}$
12. $\mathbf{r} = 3\mathbf{i} + 2\cos t\mathbf{j} + 2\sin t\mathbf{k}$
13. $\mathbf{r} = 2\cos t\mathbf{i} - 3\sin t\mathbf{j} + \mathbf{k}$
14. $\mathbf{r} = -3\mathbf{i} + (1-t^2)\mathbf{j} + t\mathbf{k}$

15. (a) Find the slope of the line in 2-space that is represented by the vector equation $\mathbf{r} = (1-2t)\mathbf{i} - (2-3t)\mathbf{j}$.
(b) Find the coordinates of the point where the line
$$\mathbf{r} = (2+t)\mathbf{i} + (1-2t)\mathbf{j} + 3t\mathbf{k}$$
intersects the $xz$-plane.

16. (a) Find the $y$-intercept of the line in 2-space that is represented by the vector equation $\mathbf{r} = (3+2t)\mathbf{i} + 5t\mathbf{j}$.
(b) Find the coordinates of the point where the line
$$\mathbf{r} = t\mathbf{i} + (1+2t)\mathbf{j} - 3t\mathbf{k}$$
intersects the plane $3x - y - z = 2$.

**17–18** Sketch the line segment represented by each vector equation. ■

17. (a) $\mathbf{r} = (1-t)\mathbf{i} + t\mathbf{j}$; $0 \le t \le 1$
(b) $\mathbf{r} = (1-t)(\mathbf{i}+\mathbf{j}) + t(\mathbf{i}-\mathbf{j})$; $0 \le t \le 1$

18. (a) $\mathbf{r} = (1-t)(\mathbf{i}+\mathbf{j}) + t\mathbf{k}$; $0 \le t \le 1$
(b) $\mathbf{r} = (1-t)(\mathbf{i}+\mathbf{j}+\mathbf{k}) + t(\mathbf{i}+\mathbf{j})$; $0 \le t \le 1$

**19–20** Write a vector equation for the line segment from $P$ to $Q$. ■

**19.**

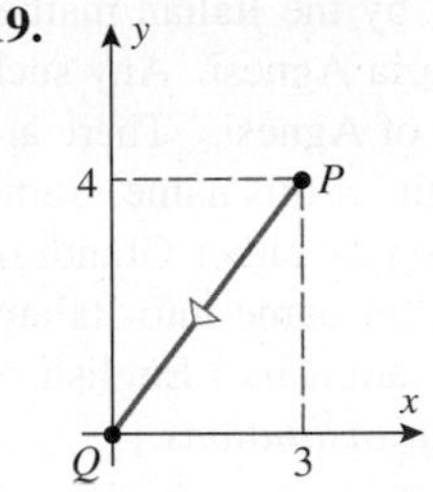


**20.**

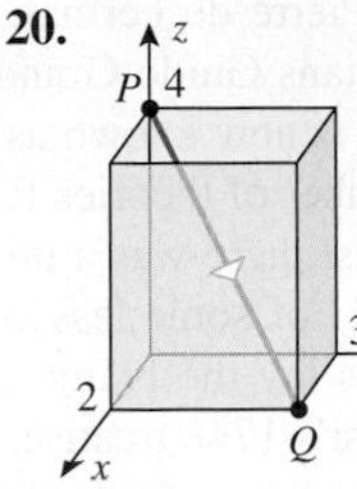


**21–30** Sketch the graph of $\mathbf{r}(t)$ and show the direction of increasing $t$. ■

**21.** $\mathbf{r}(t) = 2\mathbf{i} + t\mathbf{j}$

**22.** $\mathbf{r}(t) = \langle 3t - 4, 6t + 2 \rangle$

**23.** $\mathbf{r}(t) = (1 + \cos t)\mathbf{i} + (3 - \sin t)\mathbf{j};\ 0 \le t \le 2\pi$

**24.** $\mathbf{r}(t) = \langle 2\cos t, 5\sin t \rangle;\ 0 \le t \le 2\pi$

**25.** $\mathbf{r}(t) = \cosh t\mathbf{i} + \sinh t\mathbf{j}$

**26.** $\mathbf{r}(t) = \sqrt{t}\mathbf{i} + (2t + 4)\mathbf{j}$

**27.** $\mathbf{r}(t) = 2\cos t\mathbf{i} + 2\sin t\mathbf{j} + t\mathbf{k}$

**28.** $\mathbf{r}(t) = 9\cos t\mathbf{i} + 4\sin t\mathbf{j} + t\mathbf{k}$

**29.** $\mathbf{r}(t) = t\mathbf{i} + t^2\mathbf{j} + 2\mathbf{k}$

**30.** $\mathbf{r}(t) = t\mathbf{i} + t\mathbf{j} + \sin t\mathbf{k};\ 0 \le t \le 2\pi$

**31–34 True–False** Determine whether the statement is true or false. Explain your answer. ■

**31.** The natural domain of a vector-valued function is the union of the domains of its component functions.

**32.** If $\mathbf{r}(t) = \langle x(t), y(t) \rangle$ is a vector-valued function in 2-space, then the graph of $\mathbf{r}(t)$ is a surface in 3-space.

**33.** If $\mathbf{r}_0$ and $\mathbf{r}_1$ are vectors in 3-space, then the graph of the vector-valued function

$$\mathbf{r}(t) = (1 - t)\mathbf{r}_0 + t\mathbf{r}_1 \quad (0 \le t \le 1)$$

is the straight line segment joining the terminal points of $\mathbf{r}_0$ and $\mathbf{r}_1$.

**34.** The graph of $\mathbf{r}(t) = \langle 2\cos t, 2\sin t, t \rangle$ is a circular helix.

**35–36** Sketch the curve of intersection of the surfaces, and find parametric equations for the intersection in terms of parameter $x = t$. Check your work with a graphing utility by generating the parametric curve over the interval $-1 \le t \le 1$. ■

**35.** $z = x^2 + y^2,\ x - y = 0$

**36.** $y + x = 0,\ z = \sqrt{2 - x^2 - y^2}$

**37–38** Sketch the curve of intersection of the surfaces, and find a vector equation for the curve in terms of the parameter $x = t$. ■

**37.** $9x^2 + y^2 + 9z^2 = 81,\ y = x^2 \quad (z > 0)$

**38.** $y = x,\ x + y + z = 1$

**39.** Show that the graph of

$$\mathbf{r} = t\sin t\mathbf{i} + t\cos t\mathbf{j} + t^2\mathbf{k}$$

lies on the paraboloid $z = x^2 + y^2$.

**40.** Show that the graph of

$$\mathbf{r} = t\mathbf{i} + \frac{1+t}{t}\mathbf{j} + \frac{1-t^2}{t}\mathbf{k}, \quad t > 0$$

lies in the plane $x - y + z + 1 = 0$.

**FOCUS ON CONCEPTS**

**41.** Show that the graph of

$$\mathbf{r} = \sin t\mathbf{i} + 2\cos t\mathbf{j} + \sqrt{3}\sin t\mathbf{k}$$

is a circle, and find its center and radius. [*Hint:* Show that the curve lies on both a sphere and a plane.]

**42.** Show that the graph of

$$\mathbf{r} = 3\cos t\mathbf{i} + 3\sin t\mathbf{j} + 3\sin t\mathbf{k}$$

is an ellipse, and find the lengths of the major and minor axes. [*Hint:* Show that the graph lies on both a circular cylinder and a plane and use the result in Exercise 44 of Section 10.4.]

**43.** For the helix $\mathbf{r} = a\cos t\mathbf{i} + a\sin t\mathbf{j} + ct\mathbf{k}$, find the value of $c$ $(c > 0)$ so that the helix will make one complete turn in a distance of 3 units measured along the $z$-axis.

**44.** How many revolutions will the circular helix

$$\mathbf{r} = a\cos t\mathbf{i} + a\sin t\mathbf{j} + 0.2t\mathbf{k}$$

make in a distance of 10 units measured along the $z$-axis?

**45.** Show that the curve $\mathbf{r} = t\cos t\mathbf{i} + t\sin t\mathbf{j} + t\mathbf{k},\ t \ge 0$, lies on the cone $z = \sqrt{x^2 + y^2}$. Describe the curve.

**46.** Describe the curve $\mathbf{r} = a\cos t\mathbf{i} + b\sin t\mathbf{j} + ct\mathbf{k}$, where $a$, $b$, and $c$ are positive constants such that $a \ne b$.

**47.** In each part, match the vector equation with one of the accompanying graphs, and explain your reasoning.

(a) $\mathbf{r} = t\mathbf{i} - t\mathbf{j} + \sqrt{2 - t^2}\mathbf{k}$
(b) $\mathbf{r} = \sin \pi t\mathbf{i} - t\mathbf{j} + t\mathbf{k}$
(c) $\mathbf{r} = \sin t\mathbf{i} + \cos t\mathbf{j} + \sin 2t\mathbf{k}$
(d) $\mathbf{r} = \frac{1}{2}t\mathbf{i} + \cos 3t\mathbf{j} + \sin 3t\mathbf{k}$

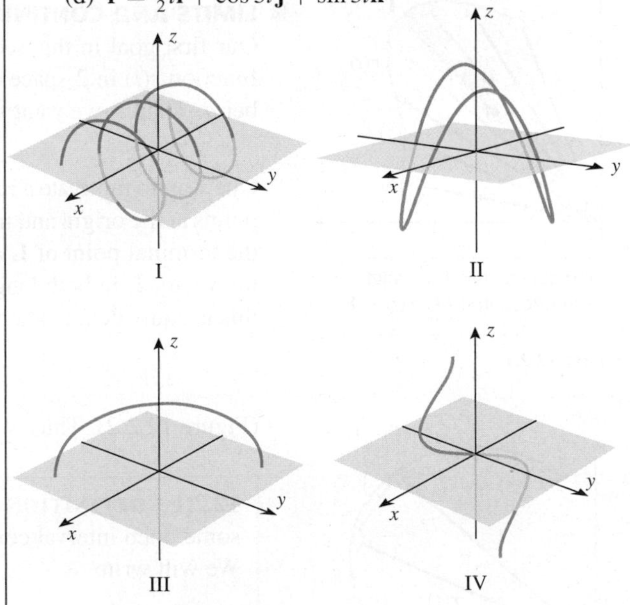


**48.** Check your conclusions in Exercise 47 by generating the curves with a graphing utility. [*Note:* Your graphing utility may look at the curve from a different viewpoint. Read the documentation for your graphing utility to determine how to control the viewpoint, and see if you can generate a reasonable facsimile of the graphs shown in the figure by adjusting the viewpoint and choosing the interval of $t$-values appropriately.]

**49.** (a) Find parametric equations for the curve of intersection of the circular cylinder $x^2 + y^2 = 9$ and the parabolic cylinder $z = x^2$ in terms of a parameter $t$ for which $x = 3\cos t$.
(b) Use a graphing utility to generate the curve of intersection in part (a).

**50.** (a) Sketch the graph of
$$\mathbf{r}(t) = \left\langle 2t, \frac{2}{1+t^2} \right\rangle$$
(b) Prove that the curve in part (a) is also the graph of the function
$$y = \frac{8}{4+x^2}$$
[The graphs of $y = a^3/(a^2 + x^2)$, where $a$ denotes a constant, were first studied by the French mathematician Pierre de Fermat, and later by the Italian mathematicians Guido Grandi and Maria Agnesi. Any such curve is now known as a "witch of Agnesi." There are a number of theories for the origin of this name. Some suggest there was a mistranslation by either Grandi or Agnesi of some less colorful Latin name into Italian. Others lay the blame on a translation into English of Agnesi's 1748 treatise, *Analytical Institutions*.]

**51. Writing** Consider the curve $C$ of intersection of the cone $z = \sqrt{x^2 + y^2}$ and the plane $z = y + 2$. Sketch and identify the curve $C$, and describe a procedure for finding a vector-valued function $\mathbf{r}(t)$ whose graph is $C$.

**52. Writing** Suppose that $\mathbf{r}_1(t)$ and $\mathbf{r}_2(t)$ are vector-valued functions in 2-space. Explain why solving the equation $\mathbf{r}_1(t) = \mathbf{r}_2(t)$ may not produce all of the points where the graphs of these functions intersect.

✓ **QUICK CHECK ANSWERS 12.1** 1. (a) $\mathbf{r} = \frac{1}{t}\mathbf{i} + \sqrt{t}\mathbf{j} + \sin^{-1} t\mathbf{k}$ (b) $0 < t \le 1$; $2\mathbf{i} + \frac{\sqrt{2}}{2}\mathbf{j} + \frac{\pi}{6}\mathbf{k}$ 2. The graph is a line through $(1, -1)$ with direction vector $2\mathbf{i} + 3\mathbf{j}$. 3. The graph is the line segment in the $xy$-plane from $(0, 1)$ to $(1, 0)$. 4. $\mathbf{r} = \langle t, t^2, t^2 \rangle$

## 12.2 CALCULUS OF VECTOR-VALUED FUNCTIONS

*In this section we will define limits, derivatives, and integrals of vector-valued functions and discuss their properties.*

### LIMITS AND CONTINUITY

Our first goal in this section is to develop a notion of what it means for a vector-valued function $\mathbf{r}(t)$ in 2-space or 3-space to approach a limiting vector $\mathbf{L}$ as $t$ approaches a number $a$. That is, we want to define
$$\lim_{t \to a} \mathbf{r}(t) = \mathbf{L} \tag{1}$$
One way to motivate a reasonable definition of (1) is to position $\mathbf{r}(t)$ and $\mathbf{L}$ with their initial points at the origin and interpret this limit to mean that the terminal point of $\mathbf{r}(t)$ approaches the terminal point of $\mathbf{L}$ as $t$ approaches $a$ or, equivalently, that the vector $\mathbf{r}(t)$ approaches the vector $\mathbf{L}$ in both length and direction at $t$ approaches $a$ (Figure 12.2.1). Algebraically, this is equivalent to stating that
$$\lim_{t \to a} \|\mathbf{r}(t) - \mathbf{L}\| = 0 \tag{2}$$
(Figure 12.2.2). Thus, we make the following definition.

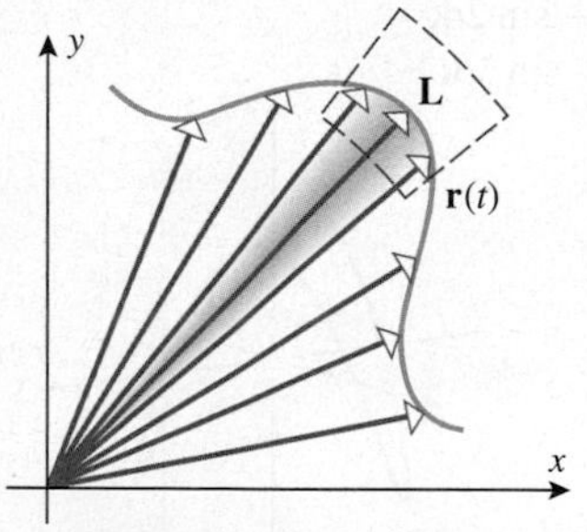

$\mathbf{r}(t)$ approaches $\mathbf{L}$ in length and direction if $\lim_{t \to a} \mathbf{r}(t) = \mathbf{L}$.

▲ **Figure 12.2.1**

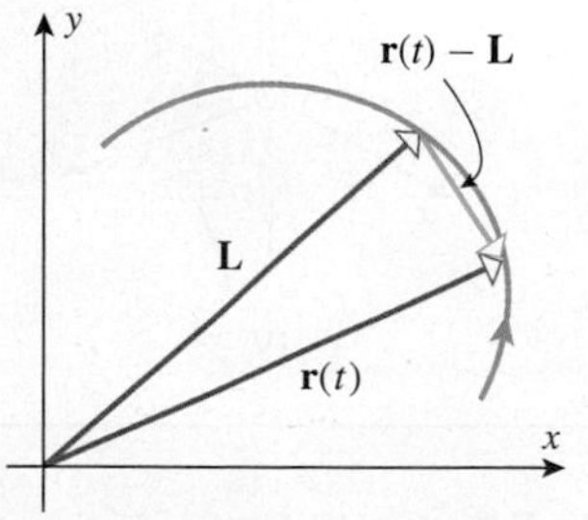

$\|\mathbf{r}(t) - \mathbf{L}\|$ is the distance between terminal points for vectors $\mathbf{r}(t)$ and $\mathbf{L}$ when positioned with the same initial points.

▲ **Figure 12.2.2**

> **12.2.1 DEFINITION** Let $\mathbf{r}(t)$ be a vector-valued function that is defined for all $t$ in some open interval containing the number $a$, except that $\mathbf{r}(t)$ need not be defined at $a$. We will write
> $$\lim_{t \to a} \mathbf{r}(t) = \mathbf{L}$$
> if and only if
> $$\lim_{t \to a} \|\mathbf{r}(t) - \mathbf{L}\| = 0$$

It is clear intuitively that $\mathbf{r}(t)$ will approach a limiting vector $\mathbf{L}$ as $t$ approaches $a$ if and only if the component functions of $\mathbf{r}(t)$ approach the corresponding components of $\mathbf{L}$. This suggests the following theorem, whose formal proof is omitted.

Note that $\|\mathbf{r}(t) - \mathbf{L}\|$ is a real number for each value of $t$, so even though this expression involves a vector-valued function, the limit

$$\lim_{t \to a} \|\mathbf{r}(t) - \mathbf{L}\|$$

is an ordinary limit of a real-valued function.

**12.2.2 THEOREM**

(a) *If* $\mathbf{r}(t) = \langle x(t), y(t)\rangle = x(t)\mathbf{i} + y(t)\mathbf{j}$, *then*

$$\lim_{t\to a} \mathbf{r}(t) = \left\langle \lim_{t\to a} x(t), \lim_{t\to a} y(t)\right\rangle = \lim_{t\to a} x(t)\mathbf{i} + \lim_{t\to a} y(t)\mathbf{j}$$

*provided the limits of the component functions exist. Conversely, the limits of the component functions exist provided* $\mathbf{r}(t)$ *approaches a limiting vector as* $t$ *approaches* $a$.

(b) *If* $\mathbf{r}(t) = \langle x(t), y(t), z(t)\rangle = x(t)\mathbf{i} + y(t)\mathbf{j} + z(t)\mathbf{k}$, *then*

$$\lim_{t\to a} \mathbf{r}(t) = \left\langle \lim_{t\to a} x(t), \lim_{t\to a} y(t), \lim_{t\to a} z(t)\right\rangle$$

$$= \lim_{t\to a} x(t)\mathbf{i} + \lim_{t\to a} y(t)\mathbf{j} + \lim_{t\to a} z(t)\mathbf{k}$$

*provided the limits of the component functions exist. Conversely, the limits of the component functions exist provided* $\mathbf{r}(t)$ *approaches a limiting vector as* $t$ *approaches* $a$.

How would you define the one-sided limits

$$\lim_{t\to a^+} \mathbf{r}(t) \quad \text{and} \quad \lim_{t\to a^-} \mathbf{r}(t)?$$

▶ **Example 1** Let $\mathbf{r}(t) = t^2\mathbf{i} + e^t\mathbf{j} - (2\cos \pi t)\mathbf{k}$. Then

$$\lim_{t\to 0} \mathbf{r}(t) = \left(\lim_{t\to 0} t^2\right)\mathbf{i} + \left(\lim_{t\to 0} e^t\right)\mathbf{j} - \left(\lim_{t\to 0} 2\cos \pi t\right)\mathbf{k} = \mathbf{j} - 2\mathbf{k}$$

Alternatively, using the angle bracket notation for vectors,

$$\lim_{t\to 0} \mathbf{r}(t) = \lim_{t\to 0} \langle t^2, e^t, -2\cos \pi t\rangle = \left\langle \lim_{t\to 0} t^2, \lim_{t\to 0} e^t, \lim_{t\to 0} (-2\cos \pi t)\right\rangle = \langle 0, 1, -2\rangle$$ ◀

Limits of vector-valued functions have many of the same properties as limits of real-valued functions. For example, assuming that the limits exist, the limit of a sum is the sum of the limits, the limit of a difference is the difference of the limits, and a constant scalar factor can be moved through a limit symbol.

Motivated by the definition of continuity for real-valued functions, we define a vector-valued function $\mathbf{r}(t)$ to be ***continuous*** at $t = a$ if

$$\lim_{t\to a} \mathbf{r}(t) = \mathbf{r}(a) \tag{3}$$

That is, $\mathbf{r}(a)$ is defined, the limit of $\mathbf{r}(t)$ as $t \to a$ exists, and the two are equal. As in the case for real-valued functions, we say that $\mathbf{r}(t)$ is ***continuous on an interval*** $I$ if it is continuous at each point of $I$ [with the understanding that at an endpoint in $I$ the two-sided limit in (3) is replaced by the appropriate one-sided limit]. It follows from Theorem 12.2.2 that a vector-valued function is continuous at $t = a$ if and only if its component functions are continuous at $t = a$.

## DERIVATIVES

The derivative of a vector-valued function is defined by a limit similar to that for the derivative of a real-valued function.

**12.2.3 DEFINITION** If $\mathbf{r}(t)$ is a vector-valued function, we define the ***derivative of*** $\mathbf{r}$ ***with respect to*** $t$ to be the vector-valued function $\mathbf{r}'$ given by

$$\mathbf{r}'(t) = \lim_{h\to 0} \frac{\mathbf{r}(t+h) - \mathbf{r}(t)}{h} \tag{4}$$

The domain of $\mathbf{r}'$ consists of all values of $t$ in the domain of $\mathbf{r}(t)$ for which the limit exists.

The function $\mathbf{r}(t)$ is ***differentiable*** at $t$ if the limit in (4) exists. All of the standard notations for derivatives continue to apply. For example, the derivative of $\mathbf{r}(t)$ can be expressed as

$$\frac{d}{dt}[\mathbf{r}(t)], \quad \frac{d\mathbf{r}}{dt}, \quad \mathbf{r}'(t), \quad \text{or} \quad \mathbf{r}'$$

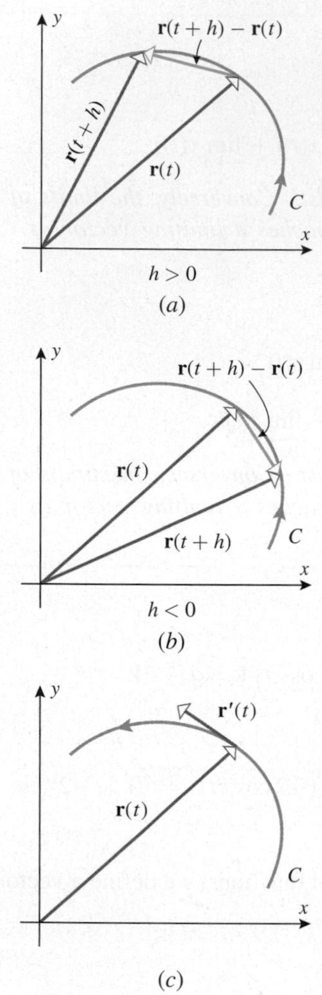

▲ **Figure 12.2.3**

It is important to keep in mind that $\mathbf{r}'(t)$ is a vector, not a number, and hence has a magnitude and a direction for each value of $t$ [except if $\mathbf{r}'(t) = \mathbf{0}$, in which case $\mathbf{r}'(t)$ has magnitude zero but no specific direction]. In the next section we will consider the significance of the magnitude of $\mathbf{r}'(t)$, but for now our goal is to obtain a geometric interpretation of the direction of $\mathbf{r}'(t)$. For this purpose, consider parts (*a*) and (*b*) of Figure 12.2.3. These illustrations show the graph $C$ of $\mathbf{r}(t)$ (with its orientation) and the vectors $\mathbf{r}(t)$, $\mathbf{r}(t+h)$, and $\mathbf{r}(t+h) - \mathbf{r}(t)$ for positive $h$ and for negative $h$. In both cases, the vector $\mathbf{r}(t+h) - \mathbf{r}(t)$ runs along the secant line joining the terminal points of $\mathbf{r}(t+h)$ and $\mathbf{r}(t)$, but with opposite directions in the two cases. In the case where $h$ is positive the vector $\mathbf{r}(t+h) - \mathbf{r}(t)$ points in the direction of increasing parameter, and in the case where $h$ is negative it points in the opposite direction. However, in the case where $h$ is negative the direction gets reversed when we multiply by $1/h$, so in both cases the vector

$$\frac{1}{h}[\mathbf{r}(t+h) - \mathbf{r}(t)] = \frac{\mathbf{r}(t+h) - \mathbf{r}(t)}{h}$$

points in the direction of increasing parameter and runs along the secant line. As $h \to 0$, the secant line approaches the tangent line at the terminal point of $\mathbf{r}(t)$, so we can conclude that the limit

$$\mathbf{r}'(t) = \lim_{h \to 0} \frac{\mathbf{r}(t+h) - \mathbf{r}(t)}{h}$$

(if it exists and is nonzero) is a vector that is tangent to the curve $C$ at the tip of $\mathbf{r}(t)$ and points in the direction of increasing parameter (Figure 12.2.3*c*).

We can summarize all of this as follows.

**12.2.4 GEOMETRIC INTERPRETATION OF THE DERIVATIVE** Suppose that $C$ is the graph of a vector-valued function $\mathbf{r}(t)$ in 2-space or 3-space and that $\mathbf{r}'(t)$ exists and is nonzero for a given value of $t$. If the vector $\mathbf{r}'(t)$ is positioned with its initial point at the terminal point of the radius vector $\mathbf{r}(t)$, then $\mathbf{r}'(t)$ is tangent to $C$ and points in the direction of increasing parameter.

Since limits of vector-valued functions can be computed componentwise, it seems reasonable that we should be able to compute derivatives in terms of component functions as well. This is the result of the next theorem.

**12.2.5 THEOREM** *If $\mathbf{r}(t)$ is a vector-valued function, then $\mathbf{r}$ is differentiable at $t$ if and only if each of its component functions is differentiable at $t$, in which case the component functions of $\mathbf{r}'(t)$ are the derivatives of the corresponding component functions of $\mathbf{r}(t)$.*

**PROOF** For simplicity, we give the proof in 2-space; the proof in 3-space is identical, except for the additional component. Assume that $\mathbf{r}(t) = x(t)\mathbf{i} + y(t)\mathbf{j}$. Then

$$\begin{aligned}
\mathbf{r}'(t) &= \lim_{h \to 0} \frac{\mathbf{r}(t+h) - \mathbf{r}(t)}{h} \\
&= \lim_{h \to 0} \frac{[x(t+h)\mathbf{i} + y(t+h)\mathbf{j}] - [x(t)\mathbf{i} + y(t)\mathbf{j}]}{h} \\
&= \left(\lim_{h \to 0} \frac{x(t+h) - x(t)}{h}\right)\mathbf{i} + \left(\lim_{h \to 0} \frac{y(t+h) - y(t)}{h}\right)\mathbf{j} \\
&= x'(t)\mathbf{i} + y'(t)\mathbf{j} \quad \blacksquare
\end{aligned}$$

► **Example 2** Let $\mathbf{r}(t) = t^2\mathbf{i} + e^t\mathbf{j} - (2\cos \pi t)\mathbf{k}$. Then

$$\begin{aligned}
\mathbf{r}'(t) &= \frac{d}{dt}(t^2)\mathbf{i} + \frac{d}{dt}(e^t)\mathbf{j} - \frac{d}{dt}(2\cos \pi t)\mathbf{k} \\
&= 2t\mathbf{i} + e^t\mathbf{j} + (2\pi \sin \pi t)\mathbf{k} \quad ◄
\end{aligned}$$

## DERIVATIVE RULES

Many of the rules for differentiating real-valued functions have analogs in the context of differentiating vector-valued functions. We state some of these in the following theorem.

**12.2.6 THEOREM** ***(Rules of Differentiation)*** *Let* $\mathbf{r}(t)$, $\mathbf{r}_1(t)$, *and* $\mathbf{r}_2(t)$ *be differentiable vector-valued functions that are all in 2-space or all in 3-space, and let* $f(t)$ *be a differentiable real-valued function, k a scalar, and* $\mathbf{c}$ *a constant vector (that is, a vector whose value does not depend on t). Then the following rules of differentiation hold:*

(a) $\dfrac{d}{dt}[\mathbf{c}] = \mathbf{0}$

(b) $\dfrac{d}{dt}[k\mathbf{r}(t)] = k\dfrac{d}{dt}[\mathbf{r}(t)]$

(c) $\dfrac{d}{dt}[\mathbf{r}_1(t) + \mathbf{r}_2(t)] = \dfrac{d}{dt}[\mathbf{r}_1(t)] + \dfrac{d}{dt}[\mathbf{r}_2(t)]$

(d) $\dfrac{d}{dt}[\mathbf{r}_1(t) - \mathbf{r}_2(t)] = \dfrac{d}{dt}[\mathbf{r}_1(t)] - \dfrac{d}{dt}[\mathbf{r}_2(t)]$

(e) $\dfrac{d}{dt}[f(t)\mathbf{r}(t)] = f(t)\dfrac{d}{dt}[\mathbf{r}(t)] + \dfrac{d}{dt}[f(t)]\mathbf{r}(t)$

The proofs of most of these rules are immediate consequences of Definition 12.2.3, although the last rule can be seen more easily by application of the product rule for real-valued functions to the component functions. The proof of Theorem 12.2.6 is left as an exercise.

## TANGENT LINES TO GRAPHS OF VECTOR-VALUED FUNCTIONS

Motivated by the discussion of the geometric interpretation of the derivative of a vector-valued function, we make the following definition.

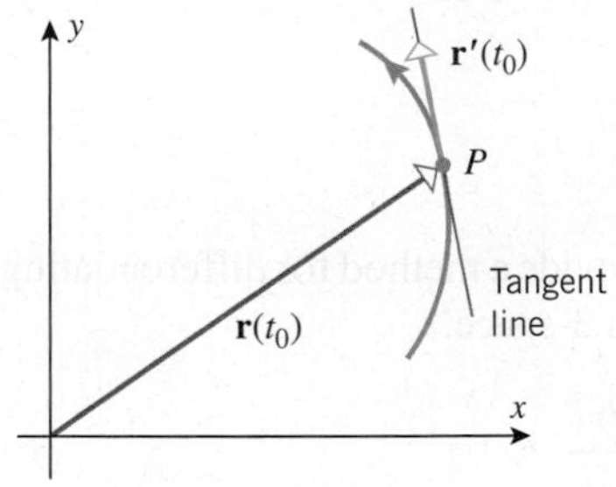


▲ **Figure 12.2.4**

**12.2.7 DEFINITION** Let $P$ be a point on the graph of a vector-valued function $\mathbf{r}(t)$, and let $\mathbf{r}(t_0)$ be the radius vector from the origin to $P$ (Figure 12.2.4). If $\mathbf{r}'(t_0)$ exists and $\mathbf{r}'(t_0) \neq \mathbf{0}$, then we call $\mathbf{r}'(t_0)$ a ***tangent vector*** to the graph of $\mathbf{r}(t)$ at $\mathbf{r}(t_0)$, and we call the line through $P$ that is parallel to the tangent vector the ***tangent line*** to the graph of $\mathbf{r}(t)$ at $\mathbf{r}(t_0)$.

Let $\mathbf{r}_0 = \mathbf{r}(t_0)$ and $\mathbf{v}_0 = \mathbf{r}'(t_0)$. It follows from Formula (9) of Section 11.5 that the tangent line to the graph of $\mathbf{r}(t)$ at $\mathbf{r}_0$ is given by the vector equation

$$\mathbf{r} = \mathbf{r}_0 + t\mathbf{v}_0 \tag{5}$$

▶ **Example 3** Find parametric equations of the tangent line to the circular helix

$$x = \cos t, \quad y = \sin t, \quad z = t$$

where $t = t_0$, and use that result to find parametric equations for the tangent line at the point where $t = \pi$.

***Solution.*** The vector equation of the helix is

$$\mathbf{r}(t) = \cos t\mathbf{i} + \sin t\mathbf{j} + t\mathbf{k}$$

so we have

$$\mathbf{r}_0 = \mathbf{r}(t_0) = \cos t_0\mathbf{i} + \sin t_0\mathbf{j} + t_0\mathbf{k}$$

$$\mathbf{v}_0 = \mathbf{r}'(t_0) = (-\sin t_0)\mathbf{i} + \cos t_0\mathbf{j} + \mathbf{k}$$

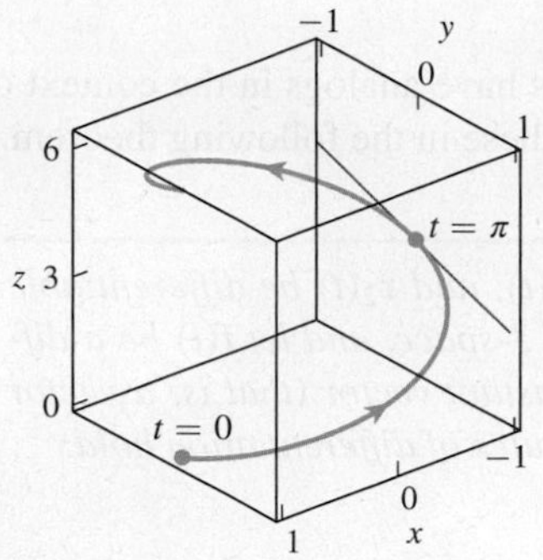


▲ Figure 12.2.5

It follows from (5) that the vector equation of the tangent line at $t = t_0$ is

$$\mathbf{r} = \cos t_0 \mathbf{i} + \sin t_0 \mathbf{j} + t_0 \mathbf{k} + t[(-\sin t_0)\mathbf{i} + \cos t_0 \mathbf{j} + \mathbf{k}]$$
$$= (\cos t_0 - t \sin t_0)\mathbf{i} + (\sin t_0 + t\cos t_0)\mathbf{j} + (t_0 + t)\mathbf{k}$$

Thus, the parametric equations of the tangent line at $t = t_0$ are

$$x = \cos t_0 - t\sin t_0, \quad y = \sin t_0 + t\cos t_0, \quad z = t_0 + t$$

In particular, the tangent line at $t = \pi$ has parametric equations

$$x = -1, \quad y = -t, \quad z = \pi + t$$

The graph of the helix and this tangent line are shown in Figure 12.2.5. ◀

▶ **Example 4** Let

$$\mathbf{r}_1(t) = (\tan^{-1} t)\mathbf{i} + (\sin t)\mathbf{j} + t^2\mathbf{k}$$

and

$$\mathbf{r}_2(t) = (t^2 - t)\mathbf{i} + (2t - 2)\mathbf{j} + (\ln t)\mathbf{k}$$

The graphs of $\mathbf{r}_1(t)$ and $\mathbf{r}_2(t)$ intersect at the origin. Find the degree measure of the acute angle between the tangent lines to the graphs of $\mathbf{r}_1(t)$ and $\mathbf{r}_2(t)$ at the origin.

***Solution.*** The graph of $\mathbf{r}_1(t)$ passes through the origin at $t = 0$, where its tangent vector is

$$\mathbf{r}_1'(0) = \left\langle \frac{1}{1+t^2}, \cos t, 2t \right\rangle \bigg|_{t=0} = \langle 1, 1, 0 \rangle$$

The graph of $\mathbf{r}_2(t)$ passes through the origin at $t = 1$ (verify), where its tangent vector is

$$\mathbf{r}_2'(1) = \left\langle 2t - 1, 2, \frac{1}{t} \right\rangle \bigg|_{t=1} = \langle 1, 2, 1 \rangle$$

By Theorem 11.3.3, the angle $\theta$ between these two tangent vectors satisfies

$$\cos\theta = \frac{\langle 1,1,0\rangle \cdot \langle 1,2,1\rangle}{\|\langle 1,1,0\rangle\|\,\|\langle 1,2,1\rangle\|} = \frac{1+2+0}{\sqrt{2}\sqrt{6}} = \frac{3}{\sqrt{12}} = \frac{\sqrt{3}}{2}$$

It follows that $\theta = \pi/6$ radians, or 30°. ◀

## DERIVATIVES OF DOT AND CROSS PRODUCTS

The following rules, which are derived in the exercises, provide a method for differentiating dot products in 2-space and 3-space and cross products in 3-space.

> Note that in (6) the order of the factors in each term on the right does not matter, but in (7) it does.

$$\frac{d}{dt}[\mathbf{r}_1(t) \cdot \mathbf{r}_2(t)] = \mathbf{r}_1(t) \cdot \frac{d\mathbf{r}_2}{dt} + \frac{d\mathbf{r}_1}{dt} \cdot \mathbf{r}_2(t) \tag{6}$$

$$\frac{d}{dt}[\mathbf{r}_1(t) \times \mathbf{r}_2(t)] = \mathbf{r}_1(t) \times \frac{d\mathbf{r}_2}{dt} + \frac{d\mathbf{r}_1}{dt} \times \mathbf{r}_2(t) \tag{7}$$

In plane geometry one learns that a tangent line to a circle is perpendicular to the radius at the point of tangency. Consequently, if a point moves along a circle in 2-space that is centered at the origin, then one would expect the radius vector and the tangent vector at any point on the circle to be orthogonal. This is the motivation for the following useful theorem, which is applicable in both 2-space and 3-space.

**12.2.8 THEOREM** *If $\mathbf{r}(t)$ is a differentiable vector-valued function in 2-space or 3-space and $\|\mathbf{r}(t)\|$ is constant for all t, then*

$$\mathbf{r}(t) \cdot \mathbf{r}'(t) = 0 \tag{8}$$

*that is, $\mathbf{r}(t)$ and $\mathbf{r}'(t)$ are orthogonal vectors for all t.*

**PROOF** It follows from (6) with $\mathbf{r}_1(t) = \mathbf{r}_2(t) = \mathbf{r}(t)$ that

$$\frac{d}{dt}[\mathbf{r}(t)\cdot\mathbf{r}(t)] = \mathbf{r}(t)\cdot\frac{d\mathbf{r}}{dt} + \frac{d\mathbf{r}}{dt}\cdot\mathbf{r}(t)$$

or, equivalently,

$$\frac{d}{dt}[\|\mathbf{r}(t)\|^2] = 2\mathbf{r}(t)\cdot\frac{d\mathbf{r}}{dt} \tag{9}$$

But $\|\mathbf{r}(t)\|^2$ is constant, so its derivative is zero. Thus

$$2\mathbf{r}(t)\cdot\frac{d\mathbf{r}}{dt} = 0$$

from which (8) follows. ■

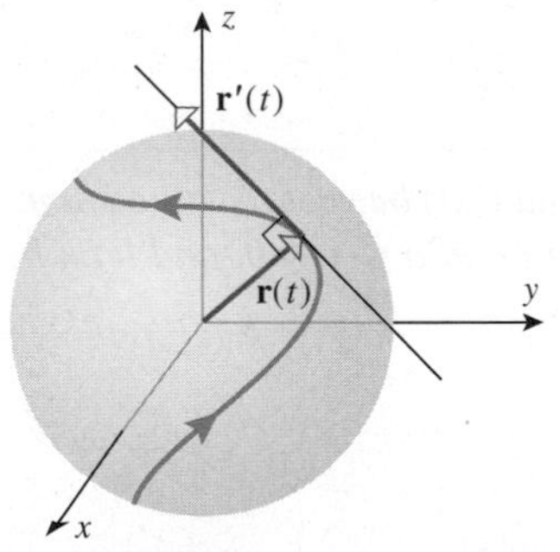


▲ **Figure 12.2.6**

▶ **Example 5** Just as a tangent line to a circle in 2-space is perpendicular to the radius at the point of tangency, so a tangent vector to a curve on the surface of a sphere in 3-space that is centered at the origin is orthogonal to the radius vector at the point of tangency (Figure 12.2.6). To see that this is so, suppose that the graph of $\mathbf{r}(t)$ lies on the surface of a sphere of positive radius $k$ centered at the origin. For each value of $t$ we have $\|\mathbf{r}(t)\| = k$, so by Theorem 12.2.8

$$\mathbf{r}(t)\cdot\mathbf{r}'(t) = 0$$

and hence the radius vector $\mathbf{r}(t)$ and the tangent vector $\mathbf{r}'(t)$ are orthogonal. ◀

## DEFINITE INTEGRALS OF VECTOR-VALUED FUNCTIONS

If $\mathbf{r}(t)$ is a vector-valued function that is continuous on the interval $a \le t \le b$, then we define the ***definite integral*** of $\mathbf{r}(t)$ over this interval as a limit of Riemann sums, just as in Definition 5.5.1, except here the integrand is a vector-valued function. Specifically, we define

$$\int_a^b \mathbf{r}(t)\,dt = \lim_{\max \Delta t_k \to 0} \sum_{k=1}^{n} \mathbf{r}(t_k^*)\Delta t_k \tag{10}$$

It follows from (10) that the definite integral of $\mathbf{r}(t)$ over the interval $a \le t \le b$ can be expressed as a vector whose components are the definite integrals of the component functions of $\mathbf{r}(t)$. For example, if $\mathbf{r}(t) = x(t)\mathbf{i} + y(t)\mathbf{j}$, then

$$\begin{aligned}
\int_a^b \mathbf{r}(t)\,dt &= \lim_{\max \Delta t_k \to 0} \sum_{k=1}^{n} \mathbf{r}(t_k^*)\Delta t_k \\
&= \lim_{\max \Delta t_k \to 0} \left[\left(\sum_{k=1}^{n} x(t_k^*)\Delta t_k\right)\mathbf{i} + \left(\sum_{k=1}^{n} y(t_k^*)\Delta t_k\right)\mathbf{j}\right] \\
&= \left(\lim_{\max \Delta t_k \to 0} \sum_{k=1}^{n} x(t_k^*)\Delta t_k\right)\mathbf{i} + \left(\lim_{\max \Delta t_k \to 0} \sum_{k=1}^{n} y(t_k^*)\Delta t_k\right)\mathbf{j} \\
&= \left(\int_a^b x(t)\,dt\right)\mathbf{i} + \left(\int_a^b y(t)\,dt\right)\mathbf{j}
\end{aligned}$$

In general, we have

$$\int_a^b \mathbf{r}(t)\,dt = \left(\int_a^b x(t)\,dt\right)\mathbf{i} + \left(\int_a^b y(t)\,dt\right)\mathbf{j} \qquad \boxed{\text{2-space}} \tag{11}$$

$$\int_a^b \mathbf{r}(t)\,dt = \left(\int_a^b x(t)\,dt\right)\mathbf{i} + \left(\int_a^b y(t)\,dt\right)\mathbf{j} + \left(\int_a^b z(t)\,dt\right)\mathbf{k} \qquad \boxed{\text{3-space}} \tag{12}$$

Rewrite Formulas (11) and (12) in bracket notation with

$$\mathbf{r}(t) = \langle x(t), y(t)\rangle$$

and

$$\mathbf{r}(t) = \langle x(t), y(t), z(t)\rangle$$

respectively.

► **Example 6** Let $\mathbf{r}(t) = t^2\mathbf{i} + e^t\mathbf{j} - (2\cos \pi t)\mathbf{k}$. Then

$$\int_0^1 \mathbf{r}(t)\,dt = \left(\int_0^1 t^2\,dt\right)\mathbf{i} + \left(\int_0^1 e^t\,dt\right)\mathbf{j} - \left(\int_0^1 2\cos \pi t\,dt\right)\mathbf{k}$$

$$= \frac{t^3}{3}\bigg]_0^1 \mathbf{i} + e^t\bigg]_0^1 \mathbf{j} - \frac{2}{\pi}\sin \pi t\bigg]_0^1 \mathbf{k} = \frac{1}{3}\mathbf{i} + (e-1)\mathbf{j} \blacktriangleleft$$

## RULES OF INTEGRATION

As with differentiation, many of the rules for integrating real-valued functions have analogs for vector-valued functions.

**12.2.9 THEOREM** *(Rules of Integration)* *Let $\mathbf{r}(t)$, $\mathbf{r}_1(t)$, and $\mathbf{r}_2(t)$ be vector-valued functions in 2-space or 3-space that are continuous on the interval $a \le t \le b$, and let $k$ be a scalar. Then the following rules of integration hold:*

(a) $$\int_a^b k\mathbf{r}(t)\,dt = k\int_a^b \mathbf{r}(t)\,dt$$

(b) $$\int_a^b [\mathbf{r}_1(t) + \mathbf{r}_2(t)]\,dt = \int_a^b \mathbf{r}_1(t)\,dt + \int_a^b \mathbf{r}_2(t)\,dt$$

(c) $$\int_a^b [\mathbf{r}_1(t) - \mathbf{r}_2(t)]\,dt = \int_a^b \mathbf{r}_1(t)\,dt - \int_a^b \mathbf{r}_2(t)\,dt$$

We omit the proof.

## ANTIDERIVATIVES OF VECTOR-VALUED FUNCTIONS

An ***antiderivative*** for a vector-valued function $\mathbf{r}(t)$ is a vector-valued function $\mathbf{R}(t)$ such that

$$\mathbf{R}'(t) = \mathbf{r}(t) \tag{13}$$

As in Chapter 4, we express Equation (13) using integral notation as

$$\int \mathbf{r}(t)\,dt = \mathbf{R}(t) + \mathbf{C} \tag{14}$$

where $\mathbf{C}$ represents an arbitrary constant *vector*.

Since differentiation of vector-valued functions can be performed componentwise, it follows that antidifferentiation can be done this way as well. This is illustrated in the next example.

► **Example 7**

$$\int (2t\mathbf{i} + 3t^2\mathbf{j})\,dt = \left(\int 2t\,dt\right)\mathbf{i} + \left(\int 3t^2\,dt\right)\mathbf{j}$$

$$= (t^2 + C_1)\mathbf{i} + (t^3 + C_2)\mathbf{j}$$

$$= (t^2\mathbf{i} + t^3\mathbf{j}) + (C_1\mathbf{i} + C_2\mathbf{j}) = (t^2\mathbf{i} + t^3\mathbf{j}) + \mathbf{C}$$

where $\mathbf{C} = C_1\mathbf{i} + C_2\mathbf{j}$ is an arbitrary vector constant of integration. ◄

Most of the familiar integration properties have vector counterparts. For example, vector differentiation and integration are inverse operations in the sense that

$$\frac{d}{dt}\left[\int \mathbf{r}(t)\,dt\right] = \mathbf{r}(t) \quad \text{and} \quad \int \mathbf{r}'(t)\,dt = \mathbf{r}(t) + \mathbf{C} \tag{15–16}$$

Moreover, if $\mathbf{R}(t)$ is an antiderivative of $\mathbf{r}(t)$ on an interval containing $t = a$ and $t = b$, then we have the following vector form of the Fundamental Theorem of Calculus:

$$\int_a^b \mathbf{r}(t)\,dt = \mathbf{R}(t)\Big]_a^b = \mathbf{R}(b) - \mathbf{R}(a) \tag{17}$$

▶ **Example 8** Evaluate the definite integral $\int_0^2 (2t\mathbf{i} + 3t^2\mathbf{j})\,dt$.

***Solution.*** Integrating the components yields

$$\int_0^2 (2t\mathbf{i} + 3t^2\mathbf{j})\,dt = t^2\Big]_0^2\mathbf{i} + t^3\Big]_0^2\mathbf{j} = 4\mathbf{i} + 8\mathbf{j}$$

***Alternative Solution.*** The function $\mathbf{R}(t) = t^2\mathbf{i} + t^3\mathbf{j}$ is an antiderivative of the integrand since $\mathbf{R}'(t) = 2t\mathbf{i} + 3t^2\mathbf{j}$. Thus, it follows from (17) that

$$\int_0^2 (2t\mathbf{i} + 3t^2\mathbf{j})\,dt = \mathbf{R}(t)\Big]_0^2 = t^2\mathbf{i} + t^3\mathbf{j}\Big]_0^2 = (4\mathbf{i} + 8\mathbf{j}) - (0\mathbf{i} + 0\mathbf{j}) = 4\mathbf{i} + 8\mathbf{j} \blacktriangleleft$$

▶ **Example 9** Find $\mathbf{r}(t)$ given that $\mathbf{r}'(t) = \langle 3, 2t\rangle$ and $\mathbf{r}(1) = \langle 2, 5\rangle$.

***Solution.*** Integrating $\mathbf{r}'(t)$ to obtain $\mathbf{r}(t)$ yields

$$\mathbf{r}(t) = \int \mathbf{r}'(t)\,dt = \int \langle 3, 2t\rangle\,dt = \langle 3t, t^2\rangle + \mathbf{C}$$

where $\mathbf{C}$ is a vector constant of integration. To find the value of $\mathbf{C}$ we substitute $t = 1$ and use the given value of $\mathbf{r}(1)$ to obtain

$$\mathbf{r}(1) = \langle 3, 1\rangle + \mathbf{C} = \langle 2, 5\rangle$$

so that $\mathbf{C} = \langle -1, 4\rangle$. Thus,

$$\mathbf{r}(t) = \langle 3t, t^2\rangle + \langle -1, 4\rangle = \langle 3t - 1, t^2 + 4\rangle \blacktriangleleft$$

## ✓ QUICK CHECK EXERCISES 12.2 

(See page 759 for answers.)

1. (a) $\lim_{t\to 3} (t^2\mathbf{i} + 2t\mathbf{j}) =$ ______
   (b) $\lim_{t\to \pi/4} \langle \cos t, \sin t\rangle =$ ______
2. Find $\mathbf{r}'(t)$.
   (a) $\mathbf{r}(t) = (4 + 5t)\mathbf{i} + (t - t^2)\mathbf{j}$
   (b) $\mathbf{r}(t) = \left\langle \frac{1}{t}, \tan t, e^{2t}\right\rangle$
3. Suppose that $\mathbf{r}_1(0) = \langle 3, 2, 1\rangle, \mathbf{r}_2(0) = \langle 1, 2, 3\rangle$, $\mathbf{r}_1'(0) = \langle 0, 0, 0\rangle$, and $\mathbf{r}_2'(0) = \langle -6, -4, -2\rangle$. Use this information to evaluate the derivative of each function at $t = 0$.
   (a) $\mathbf{r}(t) = 2\mathbf{r}_1(t) - \mathbf{r}_2(t)$
   (b) $\mathbf{r}(t) = \cos t\mathbf{r}_1(t) + e^{2t}\mathbf{r}_2(t)$
   (c) $\mathbf{r}(t) = \mathbf{r}_1(t) \times \mathbf{r}_2(t)$
   (d) $f(t) = \mathbf{r}_1(t) \cdot \mathbf{r}_2(t)$
4. (a) $\int_0^1 \langle 2t, t^2, \sin \pi t\rangle\,dt =$ ______
   (b) $\int (t\mathbf{i} - 3t^2\mathbf{j} + e^t\mathbf{k})\,dt =$ ______

## EXERCISE SET 12.2 

Graphing Utility

**1–4** Find the limit. ■

1. $\lim_{t\to +\infty} \left\langle \frac{t^2+1}{3t^2+2}, \frac{1}{t}\right\rangle$
2. $\lim_{t\to 0+} \left(\sqrt{t}\mathbf{i} + \frac{\sin t}{t}\mathbf{j}\right)$
3. $\lim_{t\to 2} (t\mathbf{i} - 3\mathbf{j} + t^2\mathbf{k})$
4. $\lim_{t\to 1} \left\langle \frac{3}{t^2}, \frac{\ln t}{t^2-1}, \sin 2t\right\rangle$

**5–6** Determine whether $\mathbf{r}(t)$ is continuous at $t = 0$. Explain your reasoning. ■

5. (a) $\mathbf{r}(t) = 3\sin t\mathbf{i} - 2t\mathbf{j}$  (b) $\mathbf{r}(t) = t^2\mathbf{i} + \frac{1}{t}\mathbf{j} + t\mathbf{k}$
6. (a) $\mathbf{r}(t) = e^t\mathbf{i} + \mathbf{j} + \csc t\mathbf{k}$
   (b) $\mathbf{r}(t) = 5\mathbf{i} - \sqrt{3t+1}\,\mathbf{j} + e^{2t}\mathbf{k}$

**7.** Sketch the circle $\mathbf{r}(t) = \cos t\mathbf{i} + \sin t\mathbf{j}$, and in each part draw the vector with its correct length.
(a) $\mathbf{r}'(\pi/4)$ (b) $\mathbf{r}''(\pi)$ (c) $\mathbf{r}(2\pi) - \mathbf{r}(3\pi/2)$

**8.** Sketch the circle $\mathbf{r}(t) = \cos t\mathbf{i} - \sin t\mathbf{j}$, and in each part draw the vector with its correct length.
(a) $\mathbf{r}'(\pi/4)$ (b) $\mathbf{r}''(\pi)$ (c) $\mathbf{r}(2\pi) - \mathbf{r}(3\pi/2)$

**9–10** Find $\mathbf{r}'(t)$. ■

**9.** $\mathbf{r}(t) = 4\mathbf{i} - \cos t\mathbf{j}$

**10.** $\mathbf{r}(t) = (\tan^{-1} t)\mathbf{i} + t\cos t\mathbf{j} - \sqrt{t}\mathbf{k}$

**11–14** Find the vector $\mathbf{r}'(t_0)$; then sketch the graph of $\mathbf{r}(t)$ in 2-space and draw the tangent vector $\mathbf{r}'(t_0)$. ■

**11.** $\mathbf{r}(t) = \langle t, t^2\rangle;\ t_0 = 2$ **12.** $\mathbf{r}(t) = t^3\mathbf{i} + t^2\mathbf{j};\ t_0 = 1$

**13.** $\mathbf{r}(t) = \sec t\mathbf{i} + \tan t\mathbf{j};\ t_0 = 0$

**14.** $\mathbf{r}(t) = 2\sin t\mathbf{i} + 3\cos t\mathbf{j};\ t_0 = \pi/6$

**15–16** Find the vector $\mathbf{r}'(t_0)$; then sketch the graph of $\mathbf{r}(t)$ in 3-space and draw the tangent vector $\mathbf{r}'(t_0)$. ■

**15.** $\mathbf{r}(t) = 2\sin t\mathbf{i} + \mathbf{j} + 2\cos t\mathbf{k};\ t_0 = \pi/2$

**16.** $\mathbf{r}(t) = \cos t\mathbf{i} + \sin t\mathbf{j} + t\mathbf{k};\ t_0 = \pi/4$

**17–18** Use a graphing utility to generate the graph of $\mathbf{r}(t)$ and the graph of the tangent line at $t_0$ on the same screen. ■

**17.** $\mathbf{r}(t) = \sin \pi t\mathbf{i} + t^2\mathbf{j};\ t_0 = \frac{1}{2}$

**18.** $\mathbf{r}(t) = 3\sin t\mathbf{i} + 4\cos t\mathbf{j};\ t_0 = \pi/4$

**19–22** Find parametric equations of the line tangent to the graph of $\mathbf{r}(t)$ at the point where $t = t_0$. ■

**19.** $\mathbf{r}(t) = t^2\mathbf{i} + (2 - \ln t)\mathbf{j};\ t_0 = 1$

**20.** $\mathbf{r}(t) = e^{2t}\mathbf{i} - 2\cos 3t\mathbf{j};\ t_0 = 0$

**21.** $\mathbf{r}(t) = 2\cos \pi t\mathbf{i} + 2\sin \pi t\mathbf{j} + 3t\mathbf{k};\ t_0 = \frac{1}{3}$

**22.** $\mathbf{r}(t) = \ln t\mathbf{i} + e^{-t}\mathbf{j} + t^3\mathbf{k};\ t_0 = 2$

**23–26** Find a vector equation of the line tangent to the graph of $\mathbf{r}(t)$ at the point $P_0$ on the curve. ■

**23.** $\mathbf{r}(t) = (2t - 1)\mathbf{i} + \sqrt{3t + 4}\mathbf{j};\ P_0(-1, 2)$

**24.** $\mathbf{r}(t) = 4\cos t\mathbf{i} - 3t\mathbf{j};\ P_0(2, -\pi)$

**25.** $\mathbf{r}(t) = t^2\mathbf{i} - \dfrac{1}{t+1}\mathbf{j} + (4 - t^2)\mathbf{k};\ P_0(4, 1, 0)$

**26.** $\mathbf{r}(t) = \sin t\mathbf{i} + \cosh t\mathbf{j} + (\tan^{-1} t)\mathbf{k};\ P_0(0, 1, 0)$

**27.** Let $\mathbf{r}(t) = \cos t\mathbf{i} + \sin t\mathbf{j} + \mathbf{k}$. Find
(a) $\lim_{t\to 0} (\mathbf{r}(t) - \mathbf{r}'(t))$ (b) $\lim_{t\to 0} (\mathbf{r}(t) \times \mathbf{r}'(t))$
(c) $\lim_{t\to 0} (\mathbf{r}(t) \cdot \mathbf{r}'(t))$.

**28.** Let $\mathbf{r}(t) = t\mathbf{i} + t^2\mathbf{j} + t^3\mathbf{k}$. Find

$$\lim_{t\to 1} \mathbf{r}(t) \cdot (\mathbf{r}'(t) \times \mathbf{r}''(t))$$

**29–30** Calculate

$$\frac{d}{dt}[\mathbf{r}_1(t) \cdot \mathbf{r}_2(t)] \quad \text{and} \quad \frac{d}{dt}[\mathbf{r}_1(t) \times \mathbf{r}_2(t)]$$

first by differentiating the product directly and then by applying Formulas (6) and (7). ■

**29.** $\mathbf{r}_1(t) = 2t\mathbf{i} + 3t^2\mathbf{j} + t^3\mathbf{k},\ \mathbf{r}_2(t) = t^4\mathbf{k}$

**30.** $\mathbf{r}_1(t) = \cos t\mathbf{i} + \sin t\mathbf{j} + t\mathbf{k},\ \mathbf{r}_2(t) = \mathbf{i} + t\mathbf{k}$

**31–34** Evaluate the indefinite integral. ■

**31.** $\displaystyle\int (3\mathbf{i} + 4t\mathbf{j})\,dt$ **32.** $\displaystyle\int \left(t^2\mathbf{i} - 2t\mathbf{j} + \frac{1}{t}\mathbf{k}\right) dt$

**33.** $\displaystyle\int \langle te^t, \ln t\rangle\,dt$ **34.** $\displaystyle\int \langle e^{-t}, e^t, 3t^2\rangle\,dt$

**35–40** Evaluate the definite integral. ■

**35.** $\displaystyle\int_0^{\pi/2} \langle \cos 2t, \sin 2t\rangle\,dt$ **36.** $\displaystyle\int_0^1 (t^2\mathbf{i} + t^3\mathbf{j})\,dt$

**37.** $\displaystyle\int_0^2 \|t\mathbf{i} + t^2\mathbf{j}\|\,dt$

**38.** $\displaystyle\int_{-3}^3 \langle (3 - t)^{3/2}, (3 + t)^{3/2}, 1\rangle\,dt$

**39.** $\displaystyle\int_1^9 (t^{1/2}\mathbf{i} + t^{-1/2}\mathbf{j})\,dt$ **40.** $\displaystyle\int_0^1 (e^{2t}\mathbf{i} + e^{-t}\mathbf{j} + t\mathbf{k})\,dt$

**41–44 True–False** Determine whether the statement is true or false. Explain your answer. ■

**41.** If a vector-valued function $\mathbf{r}(t)$ is continuous at $t = a$, then the limit

$$\lim_{h\to 0} \frac{\mathbf{r}(a + h) - \mathbf{r}(a)}{h}$$

exists.

**42.** If $\mathbf{r}(t)$ is a vector-valued function in 2-space and $\|\mathbf{r}(t)\|$ is constant, then $\mathbf{r}(t)$ and $\mathbf{r}'(t)$ are parallel vectors for all $t$.

**43.** If $\mathbf{r}(t)$ is a vector-valued function that is continuous on the interval $a \le t \le b$, then

$$\int_a^b \mathbf{r}(t)\,dt$$

is a vector.

**44.** If $\mathbf{r}(t)$ is a vector-valued function that is continuous on the interval $[a, b]$, then for $a < t < b$,

$$\frac{d}{dt}\left[\int_a^t \mathbf{r}(u)\,du\right] = \mathbf{r}(t)$$

**45–48** Solve the vector initial-value problem for $\mathbf{y}(t)$ by integrating and using the initial conditions to find the constants of integration. ■

**45.** $\mathbf{y}'(t) = 2t\mathbf{i} + 3t^2\mathbf{j},\ \mathbf{y}(0) = \mathbf{i} - \mathbf{j}$

**46.** $\mathbf{y}'(t) = \cos t\mathbf{i} + \sin t\mathbf{j},\ \mathbf{y}(0) = \mathbf{i} - \mathbf{j}$

**47.** $\mathbf{y}''(t) = \mathbf{i} + e^t\mathbf{j},\ \mathbf{y}(0) = 2\mathbf{i},\ \mathbf{y}'(0) = \mathbf{j}$

**48.** $\mathbf{y}''(t) = 12t^2\mathbf{i} - 2t\mathbf{j},\ \mathbf{y}(0) = 2\mathbf{i} - 4\mathbf{j},\ \mathbf{y}'(0) = \mathbf{0}$

**49.** (a) Find the points where the curve

$$\mathbf{r} = t\mathbf{i} + t^2\mathbf{j} - 3t\mathbf{k}$$

intersects the plane $2x - y + z = -2$.

(b) For the curve and plane in part (a), find, to the nearest degree, the acute angle that the tangent line to the curve makes with a line normal to the plane at each point of intersection.

**50.** Find where the tangent line to the curve

$$\mathbf{r} = e^{-2t}\mathbf{i} + \cos t\mathbf{j} + 3\sin t\mathbf{k}$$

at the point (1, 1, 0) intersects the $yz$-plane.

**51–52** Show that the graphs of $\mathbf{r}_1(t)$ and $\mathbf{r}_2(t)$ intersect at the point $P$. Find, to the nearest degree, the acute angle between the tangent lines to the graphs of $\mathbf{r}_1(t)$ and $\mathbf{r}_2(t)$ at the point $P$. ■

**51.** $\mathbf{r}_1(t) = t^2\mathbf{i} + t\mathbf{j} + 3t^3\mathbf{k}$
$\mathbf{r}_2(t) = (t-1)\mathbf{i} + \frac{1}{4}t^2\mathbf{j} + (5-t)\mathbf{k}$; $P(1, 1, 3)$

**52.** $\mathbf{r}_1(t) = 2e^{-t}\mathbf{i} + \cos t\mathbf{j} + (t^2+3)\mathbf{k}$
$\mathbf{r}_2(t) = (1-t)\mathbf{i} + t^2\mathbf{j} + (t^3+4)\mathbf{k}$; $P(2, 1, 3)$

**FOCUS ON CONCEPTS**

**53.** Use Formula (7) to derive the differentiation formula

$$\frac{d}{dt}[\mathbf{r}(t) \times \mathbf{r}'(t)] = \mathbf{r}(t) \times \mathbf{r}''(t)$$

**54.** Let $\mathbf{u} = \mathbf{u}(t)$, $\mathbf{v} = \mathbf{v}(t)$, and $\mathbf{w} = \mathbf{w}(t)$ be differentiable vector-valued functions. Use Formulas (6) and (7) to show that

$$\frac{d}{dt}[\mathbf{u} \cdot (\mathbf{v} \times \mathbf{w})]$$
$$= \frac{d\mathbf{u}}{dt} \cdot [\mathbf{v} \times \mathbf{w}] + \mathbf{u} \cdot \left[\frac{d\mathbf{v}}{dt} \times \mathbf{w}\right] + \mathbf{u} \cdot \left[\mathbf{v} \times \frac{d\mathbf{w}}{dt}\right]$$

**55.** Let $u_1$, $u_2$, $u_3$, $v_1$, $v_2$, $v_3$, $w_1$, $w_2$, and $w_3$ be differentiable functions of $t$. Use Exercise 54 to show that

$$\frac{d}{dt}\begin{vmatrix} u_1 & u_2 & u_3 \\ v_1 & v_2 & v_3 \\ w_1 & w_2 & w_3 \end{vmatrix}$$
$$= \begin{vmatrix} u_1' & u_2' & u_3' \\ v_1 & v_2 & v_3 \\ w_1 & w_2 & w_3 \end{vmatrix} + \begin{vmatrix} u_1 & u_2 & u_3 \\ v_1' & v_2' & v_3' \\ w_1 & w_2 & w_3 \end{vmatrix} + \begin{vmatrix} u_1 & u_2 & u_3 \\ v_1 & v_2 & v_3 \\ w_1' & w_2' & w_3' \end{vmatrix}$$

**56.** Prove Theorem 12.2.6 for 2-space.

**57.** Derive Formulas (6) and (7) for 3-space.

**58.** Prove Theorem 12.2.9 for 2-space.

**59. Writing** Explain what it means for a vector-valued function $\mathbf{r}(t)$ to be differentiable, and discuss geometric interpretations of $\mathbf{r}'(t)$.

**60. Writing** Let $\mathbf{r}(t) = \langle t^2, t^3 + 1\rangle$ and define $\theta(t)$ to be the angle between $\mathbf{r}(t)$ and $\mathbf{r}'(t)$. The graph of $\theta = \theta(t)$ is shown in the accompanying figure. Interpret important features of this graph in terms of information about $\mathbf{r}(t)$ and $\mathbf{r}'(t)$. Accompany your discussion with a graph of $\mathbf{r}(t)$, highlighting particular instances of the vectors $\mathbf{r}(t)$ and $\mathbf{r}'(t)$.

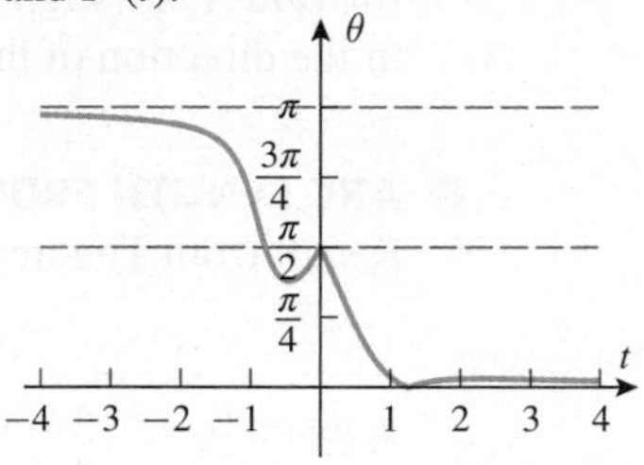


◀ **Figure Ex-60**

✓ **QUICK CHECK ANSWERS 12.2** 1. (a) $9\mathbf{i} + 6\mathbf{j}$ (b) $\left\langle \frac{\sqrt{2}}{2}, \frac{\sqrt{2}}{2} \right\rangle$ 2. (a) $\mathbf{r}'(t) = 5\mathbf{i} + (1-2t)\mathbf{j}$ (b) $\mathbf{r}'(t) = \left\langle -\frac{1}{t^2}, \sec^2 t, 2e^{2t} \right\rangle$ 3. (a) $\langle 6, 4, 2\rangle$ (b) $\langle -4, 0, 4\rangle$ (c) $\mathbf{0}$ (d) $-28$ 4. (a) $\left\langle 1, \frac{1}{3}, \frac{2}{\pi} \right\rangle$ (b) $\frac{t^2}{2}\mathbf{i} - t^3\mathbf{j} + e^t\mathbf{k} + \mathbf{C}$

## 12.3 CHANGE OF PARAMETER; ARC LENGTH

*We observed in earlier sections that a curve in 2-space or 3-space can be represented parametrically in more than one way. For example, in Section 10.1 we gave two parametric representations of a circle—one in which the circle was traced clockwise and the other in which it was traced counterclockwise. Sometimes it will be desirable to change the parameter for a parametric curve to a different parameter that is better suited for the problem at hand. In this section we will investigate issues associated with changes of parameter, and we will show that arc length plays a special role in parametric representations of curves.*

### ■ SMOOTH PARAMETRIZATIONS

Graphs of vector-valued functions range from continuous and smooth to discontinuous and wildly erratic. In this text we will not be concerned with graphs of the latter type, so we will need to impose restrictions to eliminate the unwanted behavior. We will say that a curve represented by $\mathbf{r}(t)$ is ***smoothly parametrized*** by $\mathbf{r}(t)$, or that $\mathbf{r}(t)$ is a ***smooth function*** of $t$ if $\mathbf{r}'(t)$ is continuous and $\mathbf{r}'(t) \neq \mathbf{0}$ for any allowable value of $t$. Geometrically, this

Mathematically, "smoothness" is a property of the *parametrization* and not of the curve itself. Exercise 38 gives an example of a curve that is well-behaved geometrically and has one parametrization that is smooth and another that is not.

means that a smoothly parametrized curve can have no abrupt changes in direction as the parameter increases.

▶ **Example 1** Determine whether the following vector-valued functions are smooth.

(a) $\mathbf{r}(t) = a\cos t\mathbf{i} + a\sin t\mathbf{j} + ct\mathbf{k} \quad (a > 0, c > 0)$

(b) $\mathbf{r}(t) = t^2\mathbf{i} + t^3\mathbf{j}$

***Solution (a).*** We have

$$\mathbf{r}'(t) = -a\sin t\mathbf{i} + a\cos t\mathbf{j} + c\mathbf{k}$$

The components are continuous functions, and there is no value of $t$ for which all three of them are zero (verify), so $\mathbf{r}(t)$ is a smooth function. The graph of $\mathbf{r}(t)$ is the circular helix in Figure 12.1.2.

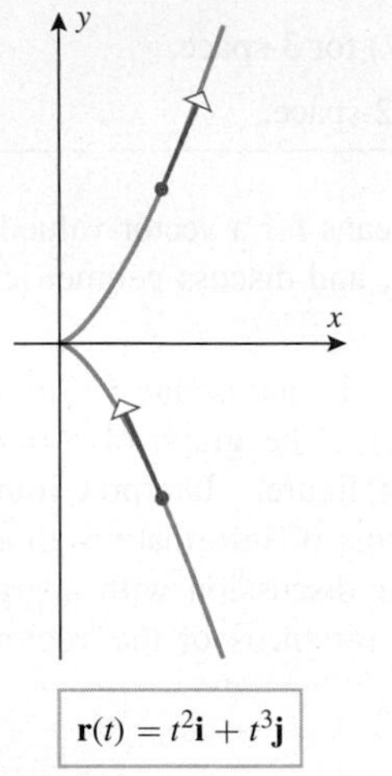


▲ **Figure 12.3.1**

***Solution (b).*** We have

$$\mathbf{r}'(t) = 2t\mathbf{i} + 3t^2\mathbf{j}$$

Although the components are continuous functions, they are both equal to zero if $t = 0$, so $\mathbf{r}(t)$ is not a smooth function. The graph of $\mathbf{r}(t)$, which is shown in Figure 12.3.1, is a semicubical parabola traced in the upward direction (see Example 6 of Section 10.1). Observe that for values of $t$ slightly less than zero the angle between $\mathbf{r}'(t)$ and $\mathbf{i}$ is near $\pi$, and for values of $t$ slightly larger than zero the angle is near 0; hence there is a sudden reversal in the direction of the tangent vector as $t$ increases through $t = 0$ (see Exercise 44). ◀

## ARC LENGTH FROM THE VECTOR VIEWPOINT

Recall from Theorem 10.1.1 that the arc length $L$ of a parametric curve

$$x = x(t), \quad y = y(t) \qquad (a \le t \le b) \tag{1}$$

is given by the formula

$$L = \int_a^b \sqrt{\left(\frac{dx}{dt}\right)^2 + \left(\frac{dy}{dt}\right)^2}\, dt \tag{2}$$

Analogously, the arc length $L$ of a parametric curve

$$x = x(t), \quad y = y(t), \quad z = z(t) \qquad (a \le t \le b) \tag{3}$$

in 3-space is given by the formula

$$L = \int_a^b \sqrt{\left(\frac{dx}{dt}\right)^2 + \left(\frac{dy}{dt}\right)^2 + \left(\frac{dz}{dt}\right)^2}\, dt \tag{4}$$

Formulas (2) and (4) have vector forms that we can obtain by letting

$$\underbrace{\mathbf{r}(t) = x(t)\mathbf{i} + y(t)\mathbf{j}}_{\text{2-space}} \quad \text{or} \quad \underbrace{\mathbf{r}(t) = x(t)\mathbf{i} + y(t)\mathbf{j} + z(t)\mathbf{k}}_{\text{3-space}}$$

It follows that

$$\underbrace{\frac{d\mathbf{r}}{dt} = \frac{dx}{dt}\mathbf{i} + \frac{dy}{dt}\mathbf{j}}_{\text{2-space}} \quad \text{or} \quad \underbrace{\frac{d\mathbf{r}}{dt} = \frac{dx}{dt}\mathbf{i} + \frac{dy}{dt}\mathbf{j} + \frac{dz}{dt}\mathbf{k}}_{\text{3-space}}$$

and hence

$$\underbrace{\left\|\frac{d\mathbf{r}}{dt}\right\| = \sqrt{\left(\frac{dx}{dt}\right)^2 + \left(\frac{dy}{dt}\right)^2}}_{\text{2-space}} \quad \text{or} \quad \underbrace{\left\|\frac{d\mathbf{r}}{dt}\right\| = \sqrt{\left(\frac{dx}{dt}\right)^2 + \left(\frac{dy}{dt}\right)^2 + \left(\frac{dz}{dt}\right)^2}}_{\text{3-space}}$$

Substituting these expressions in (2) and (4) leads us to the following theorem.

**12.3.1 THEOREM** *If C is the graph in 2-space or 3-space of a smooth vector-valued function* $\mathbf{r}(t)$, *then its arc length L from* $t = a$ *to* $t = b$ *is*

$$L = \int_a^b \left\| \frac{d\mathbf{r}}{dt} \right\| dt \tag{5}$$

▶ **Example 2** Find the arc length of that portion of the circular helix

$$x = \cos t, \quad y = \sin t, \quad z = t$$

from $t = 0$ to $t = \pi$.

***Solution.*** Set $\mathbf{r}(t) = (\cos t)\mathbf{i} + (\sin t)\mathbf{j} + t\mathbf{k} = \langle \cos t, \sin t, t \rangle$. Then

$$\mathbf{r}'(t) = \langle -\sin t, \cos t, 1 \rangle \quad \text{and} \quad \|\mathbf{r}'(t)\| = \sqrt{(-\sin t)^2 + (\cos t)^2 + 1} = \sqrt{2}$$

From Theorem 12.3.1 the arc length of the helix is

$$L = \int_0^\pi \left\| \frac{d\mathbf{r}}{dt} \right\| dt = \int_0^\pi \sqrt{2}\, dt = \sqrt{2}\pi \blacktriangleleft$$

## ARC LENGTH AS A PARAMETER

For many purposes the best parameter to use for representing a curve in 2-space or 3-space parametrically is the length of arc measured along the curve from some fixed reference point. This can be done as follows:

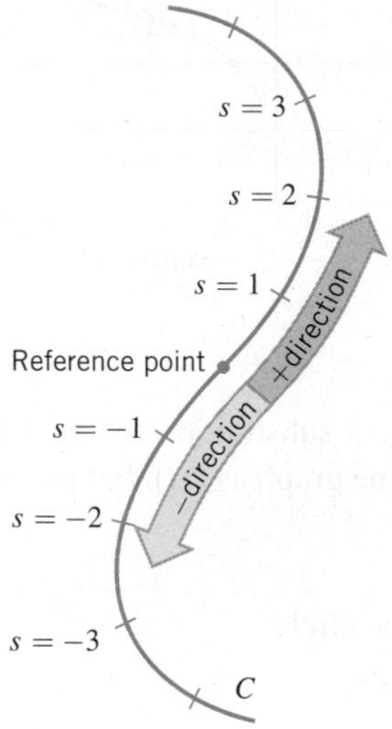


▲ **Figure 12.3.2**

***Using Arc Length as a Parameter***

**Step 1.** Select an arbitrary point on the curve $C$ to serve as a ***reference point***.

**Step 2.** Starting from the reference point, choose one direction along the curve to be the ***positive direction*** and the other to be the ***negative direction***.

**Step 3.** If $P$ is a point on the curve, let $s$ be the "signed" arc length along $C$ from the reference point to $P$, where $s$ is positive if $P$ is in the positive direction from the reference point and $s$ is negative if $P$ is in the negative direction. Figure 12.3.2 illustrates this idea.

By this procedure, a unique point $P$ on the curve is determined when a value for $s$ is given. For example, $s = 2$ determines the point that is 2 units along the curve in the positive direction from the reference point, and $s = -\frac{3}{2}$ determines the point that is $\frac{3}{2}$ units along the curve in the negative direction from the reference point.

Let us now treat $s$ as a variable. As the value of $s$ changes, the corresponding point $P$ moves along $C$ and the coordinates of $P$ become functions of $s$. Thus, in 2-space the coordinates of $P$ are $(x(s), y(s))$, and in 3-space they are $(x(s), y(s), z(s))$. Therefore, in 2-space or 3-space the curve $C$ is given by the parametric equations

$$x = x(s), \quad y = y(s) \quad \text{or} \quad x = x(s), \quad y = y(s), \quad z = z(s)$$

A parametric representation of a curve with arc length as the parameter is called an ***arc length parametrization*** of the curve. Note that a given curve will generally have infinitely many different arc length paramctrizations, since the reference point and orientation can be chosen arbitrarily.

▶ **Example 3** Find the arc length parametrization of the circle $x^2 + y^2 = a^2$ with counterclockwise orientation and $(a, 0)$ as the reference point.

***Solution.*** The circle with counterclockwise orientation can be represented by the parametric equations

$$x = a\cos t, \quad y = a\sin t \quad (0 \le t \le 2\pi) \tag{6}$$

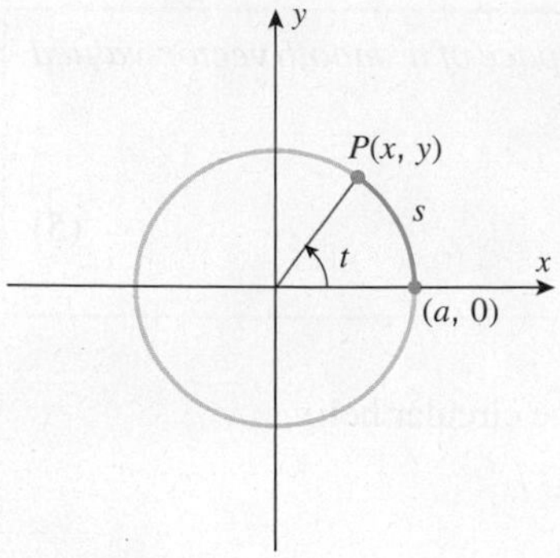


▲ Figure 12.3.3

in which $t$ can be interpreted as the angle in radian measure from the positive $x$-axis to the radius from the origin to the point $P(x, y)$ (Figure 12.3.3). If we take the positive direction for measuring the arc length to be counterclockwise, and we take $(a, 0)$ to be the reference point, then $s$ and $t$ are related by

$$s = at \quad \text{or} \quad t = s/a$$

Making this change of variable in (6) and noting that $s$ increases from 0 to $2\pi a$ as $t$ increases from 0 to $2\pi$ yields the following arc length parametrization of the circle:

$$x = a\cos(s/a), \quad y = a\sin(s/a) \qquad (0 \le s \le 2\pi a) \blacktriangleleft$$

## CHANGE OF PARAMETER

In many situations the solution of a problem can be simplified by choosing the parameter in a vector-valued function or a parametric curve in the right way. The two most common parameters for curves in 2-space or 3-space are time and arc length. However, there are other useful possibilities as well. For example, in analyzing the motion of a particle in 2-space, it is often desirable to parametrize its trajectory in terms of the angle $\phi$ between the tangent vector and the positive $x$-axis (Figure 12.3.4). Thus, our next objective is to develop methods for changing the parameter in a vector-valued function or parametric curve. This will allow us to move freely between different possible parametrizations.

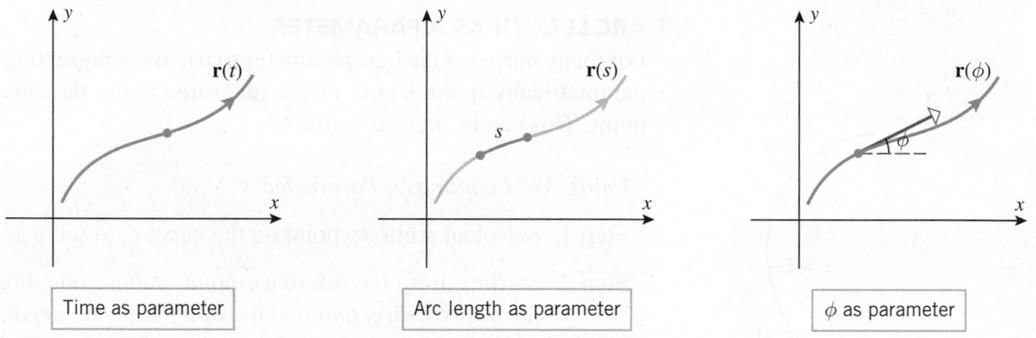


▲ Figure 12.3.4

A ***change of parameter*** in a vector-valued function $\mathbf{r}(t)$ is a substitution $t = g(\tau)$ that produces a new vector-valued function $\mathbf{r}(g(\tau))$ having the same graph as $\mathbf{r}(t)$, but possibly traced differently as the parameter $\tau$ increases.

**▶ Example 4** Find a change of parameter $t = g(\tau)$ for the circle

$$\mathbf{r}(t) = \cos t\mathbf{i} + \sin t\mathbf{j} \qquad (0 \le t \le 2\pi)$$

such that

(a) the circle is traced counterclockwise as $\tau$ increases over the interval $[0, 1]$;

(b) the circle is traced clockwise as $\tau$ increases over the interval $[0, 1]$.

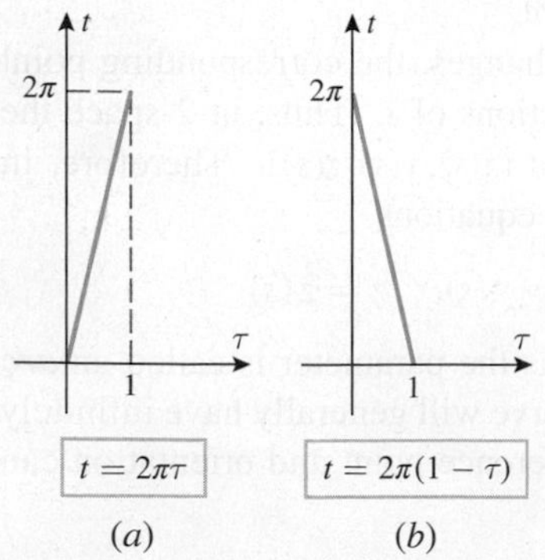


▲ Figure 12.3.5

***Solution (a).*** The given circle is traced counterclockwise as $t$ increases. Thus, if we choose $g$ to be an increasing function, then it will follow from the relationship $t = g(\tau)$ that $t$ increases when $\tau$ increases, thereby ensuring that the circle will be traced counterclockwise as $\tau$ increases. We also want to choose $g$ so that $t$ increases from 0 to $2\pi$ as $\tau$ increases from 0 to 1. A simple choice of $g$ that satisfies all of the required criteria is the linear function graphed in Figure 12.3.5$a$. The equation of this line is

$$t = g(\tau) = 2\pi\tau \tag{7}$$

which is the desired change of parameter. The resulting representation of the circle in terms of the parameter $\tau$ is

$$\mathbf{r}(g(\tau)) = \cos 2\pi\tau\mathbf{i} + \sin 2\pi\tau\mathbf{j} \qquad (0 \le \tau \le 1)$$

***Solution (b).*** To ensure that the circle is traced clockwise, we will choose $g$ to be a decreasing function such that $t$ decreases from $2\pi$ to 0 as $\tau$ increases from 0 to 1. A simple choice of $g$ that achieves this is the linear function

$$t = g(\tau) = 2\pi(1-\tau) \tag{8}$$

graphed in Figure 12.3.5*b*. The resulting representation of the circle in terms of the parameter $\tau$ is

$$\mathbf{r}(g(\tau)) = \cos(2\pi(1-\tau))\mathbf{i} + \sin(2\pi(1-\tau))\mathbf{j} \qquad (0 \le \tau \le 1)$$

which simplifies to (verify)

$$\mathbf{r}(g(\tau)) = \cos 2\pi\tau\mathbf{i} - \sin 2\pi\tau\mathbf{j} \qquad (0 \le \tau \le 1) \blacktriangleleft$$

When making a change of parameter $t = g(\tau)$ in a vector-valued function $\mathbf{r}(t)$, it will be important to ensure that the new vector-valued function $\mathbf{r}(g(\tau))$ is smooth if $\mathbf{r}(t)$ is smooth. To establish conditions under which this happens, we will need the following version of the chain rule for vector-valued functions. The proof is left as an exercise.

Strictly speaking, since $d\mathbf{r}/dt$ is a vector and $dt/d\tau$ is a scalar, Formula (9) should be written in the form

$$\frac{d\mathbf{r}}{d\tau} = \frac{dt}{d\tau}\frac{d\mathbf{r}}{dt}$$

(scalar first). However, reversing the order of the factors makes the formula easier to remember, and we will continue to do so.

**12.3.2 THEOREM (*Chain Rule*)** *Let $\mathbf{r}(t)$ be a vector-valued function in 2-space or 3-space that is differentiable with respect to $t$. If $t = g(\tau)$ is a change of parameter in which $g$ is differentiable with respect to $\tau$, then $\mathbf{r}(g(\tau))$ is differentiable with respect to $\tau$ and*

$$\frac{d\mathbf{r}}{d\tau} = \frac{d\mathbf{r}}{dt}\frac{dt}{d\tau} \tag{9}$$

A change of parameter $t = g(\tau)$ in which $\mathbf{r}(g(\tau))$ is smooth if $\mathbf{r}(t)$ is smooth is called a ***smooth change of parameter***. It follows from (9) that $t = g(\tau)$ will be a smooth change of parameter if $dt/d\tau$ is continuous and $dt/d\tau \ne 0$ for all values of $\tau$, since these conditions imply that $d\mathbf{r}/d\tau$ is continuous and nonzero if $d\mathbf{r}/dt$ is continuous and nonzero. Smooth changes of parameter fall into two categories—those for which $dt/d\tau > 0$ for all $\tau$ (called ***positive changes of parameter***) and those for which $dt/d\tau < 0$ for all $\tau$ (called ***negative changes of parameter***). A positive change of parameter preserves the orientation of a parametric curve, and a negative change of parameter reverses it.

► **Example 5** In Example 4 the change of parameter in Formula (7) is positive since $dt/d\tau = 2\pi > 0$, and the change of parameter given by Formula (8) is negative since $dt/d\tau = -2\pi < 0$. The positive change of parameter preserved the orientation of the circle, and the negative change of parameter reversed it. ◄

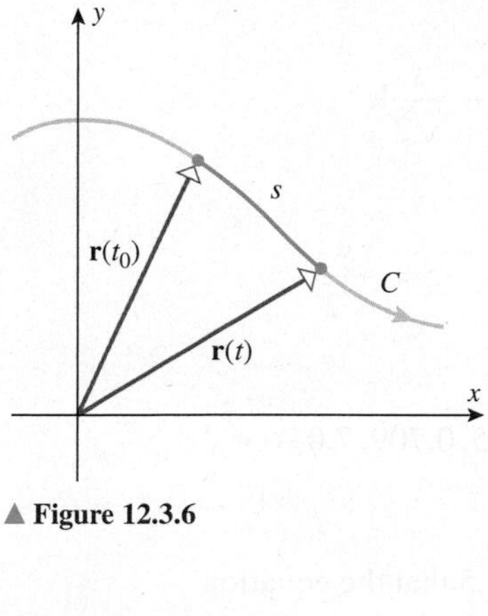

▲ **Figure 12.3.6**

## FINDING ARC LENGTH PARAMETRIZATIONS

Next we will consider the problem of finding an arc length parametrization of a vector-valued function that is expressed initially in terms of some other parameter $t$. The following theorem will provide a general method for doing this.

**12.3.3 THEOREM** *Let $C$ be the graph of a smooth vector-valued function $\mathbf{r}(t)$ in 2-space or 3-space, and let $\mathbf{r}(t_0)$ be any point on $C$. Then the following formula defines a positive change of parameter from $t$ to $s$, where $s$ is an arc length parameter having $\mathbf{r}(t_0)$ as its reference point (Figure 12.3.6):*

$$s = \int_{t_0}^{t} \left\| \frac{d\mathbf{r}}{du} \right\| du \tag{10}$$

**PROOF** From (5) with $u$ as the variable of integration instead of $t$, the integral represents the arc length of that portion of $C$ between $\mathbf{r}(t_0)$ and $\mathbf{r}(t)$ if $t > t_0$ and the negative of that arc length if $t < t_0$. Thus, $s$ is the arc length parameter with $\mathbf{r}(t_0)$ as its reference point and its positive direction in the direction of increasing $t$. ■

When needed, Formula (10) can be expressed in component form as

$$s = \int_{t_0}^{t} \sqrt{\left(\frac{dx}{du}\right)^2 + \left(\frac{dy}{du}\right)^2}\, du \qquad \boxed{\text{2-space}} \tag{11}$$

$$s = \int_{t_0}^{t} \sqrt{\left(\frac{dx}{du}\right)^2 + \left(\frac{dy}{du}\right)^2 + \left(\frac{dz}{du}\right)^2}\, du \qquad \boxed{\text{3-space}} \tag{12}$$

▶ **Example 6** Find the arc length parametrization of the circular helix

$$\mathbf{r} = \cos t\mathbf{i} + \sin t\mathbf{j} + t\mathbf{k} \tag{13}$$

that has reference point $\mathbf{r}(0) = (1, 0, 0)$ and the same orientation as the given helix.

***Solution.*** Replacing $t$ by $u$ in $\mathbf{r}$ for integration purposes and taking $t_0 = 0$ in Formula (10), we obtain

$$\mathbf{r} = \cos u\mathbf{i} + \sin u\mathbf{j} + u\mathbf{k}$$

$$\frac{d\mathbf{r}}{du} = (-\sin u)\mathbf{i} + \cos u\mathbf{j} + \mathbf{k}$$

$$\left\|\frac{d\mathbf{r}}{du}\right\| = \sqrt{(-\sin u)^2 + \cos^2 u + 1} = \sqrt{2}$$

$$s = \int_0^t \left\|\frac{d\mathbf{r}}{du}\right\| du = \int_0^t \sqrt{2}\, du = \sqrt{2}u\Big]_0^t = \sqrt{2}t$$

Thus, $t = s/\sqrt{2}$, so (13) can be reparametrized in terms of $s$ as

$$\mathbf{r} = \cos\left(\frac{s}{\sqrt{2}}\right)\mathbf{i} + \sin\left(\frac{s}{\sqrt{2}}\right)\mathbf{j} + \frac{s}{\sqrt{2}}\mathbf{k}$$

We are guaranteed that this reparametrization preserves the orientation of the helix since Formula (10) produces a positive change of parameter. ◀

▶ **Example 7** A bug walks along the trunk of a tree following a path modeled by the circular helix in Example 6. The bug starts at the reference point $(1, 0, 0)$ and walks up the helix for a distance of 10 units. What are the bug's final coordinates?

***Solution.*** From Example 6, the arc length parametrization of the helix relative to the reference point $(1, 0, 0)$ is

$$\mathbf{r} = \cos\left(\frac{s}{\sqrt{2}}\right)\mathbf{i} + \sin\left(\frac{s}{\sqrt{2}}\right)\mathbf{j} + \frac{s}{\sqrt{2}}\mathbf{k}$$

or, expressed parametrically,

$$x = \cos\left(\frac{s}{\sqrt{2}}\right), \quad y = \sin\left(\frac{s}{\sqrt{2}}\right), \quad z = \frac{s}{\sqrt{2}}$$

Thus, at $s = 10$ the coordinates are

$$\left(\cos\left(\frac{10}{\sqrt{2}}\right), \sin\left(\frac{10}{\sqrt{2}}\right), \frac{10}{\sqrt{2}}\right) \approx (0.705, 0.709, 7.07) \blacktriangleleft$$

▶ **Example 8** Recall from Formula (9) of Section 11.5 that the equation

$$\mathbf{r} = \mathbf{r}_0 + t\mathbf{v} \tag{14}$$

is the vector form of the line that passes through the terminal point of $\mathbf{r}_0$ and is parallel to the vector $\mathbf{v}$. Find the arc length parametrization of the line that has reference point $\mathbf{r}_0$ and the same orientation as the given line.

***Solution.*** Replacing $t$ by $u$ in (14) for integration purposes and taking $t_0 = 0$ in Formula (10), we obtain

$$\mathbf{r} = \mathbf{r}_0 + u\mathbf{v} \quad \text{and} \quad \frac{d\mathbf{r}}{du} = \mathbf{v} \qquad \boxed{\text{Since } \mathbf{r}_0 \text{ is constant}}$$

It follows from this that

$$s = \int_0^t \left\| \frac{d\mathbf{r}}{du} \right\| du = \int_0^t \|\mathbf{v}\|\, du = \|\mathbf{v}\|u \Big]_0^t = t\|\mathbf{v}\|$$

This implies that $t = s/\|\mathbf{v}\|$, so (14) can be reparametrized in terms of $s$ as

In words, Formula (15) tells us that the line represented by Equation (14) can be reparametrized in terms of arc length with $\mathbf{r}_0$ as the reference point by normalizing $\mathbf{v}$ and then replacing $t$ by $s$.

$$\mathbf{r} = \mathbf{r}_0 + s\left(\frac{\mathbf{v}}{\|\mathbf{v}\|}\right) \blacktriangleleft \tag{15}$$

**▶ Example 9** Find the arc length parametrization of the line

$$x = 2t + 1, \quad y = 3t - 2$$

that has the same orientation as the given line and uses $(1, -2)$ as the reference point.

***Solution.*** The line passes through the point $(1, -2)$ and is parallel to $\mathbf{v} = 2\mathbf{i} + 3\mathbf{j}$. To find the arc length parametrization of the line, we need only rewrite the given equations using $\mathbf{v}/\|\mathbf{v}\|$ rather than $\mathbf{v}$ to determine the direction and replace $t$ by $s$. Since

$$\frac{\mathbf{v}}{\|\mathbf{v}\|} = \frac{2\mathbf{i} + 3\mathbf{j}}{\sqrt{13}} = \frac{2}{\sqrt{13}}\mathbf{i} + \frac{3}{\sqrt{13}}\mathbf{j}$$

it follows that the parametric equations for the line in terms of $s$ are

$$x = \frac{2}{\sqrt{13}}s + 1, \quad y = \frac{3}{\sqrt{13}}s - 2 \blacktriangleleft$$

## PROPERTIES OF ARC LENGTH PARAMETRIZATIONS

Because arc length parameters for a curve $C$ are intimately related to the geometric characteristics of $C$, arc length parametrizations have properties that are not enjoyed by other parametrizations. For example, the following theorem shows that if a smooth curve is represented parametrically using an arc length parameter, then the tangent vectors all have length 1.

**12.3.4 THEOREM**

(*a*) *If $C$ is the graph of a smooth vector-valued function $\mathbf{r}(t)$ in 2-space or 3-space, where $t$ is a general parameter, and if $s$ is the arc length parameter for $C$ defined by Formula (10), then for every value of $t$ the tangent vector has length*

$$\left\| \frac{d\mathbf{r}}{dt} \right\| = \frac{ds}{dt} \tag{16}$$

(*b*) *If $C$ is the graph of a smooth vector-valued function $\mathbf{r}(s)$ in 2-space or 3-space, where $s$ is an arc length parameter, then for every value of $s$ the tangent vector to $C$ has length*

$$\left\| \frac{d\mathbf{r}}{ds} \right\| = 1 \tag{17}$$

(*c*) *If $C$ is the graph of a smooth vector-valued function $\mathbf{r}(t)$ in 2-space or 3-space, and if $\|d\mathbf{r}/dt\| = 1$ for every value of $t$, then for any value of $t_0$ in the domain of $\mathbf{r}$, the parameter $s = t - t_0$ is an arc length parameter that has its reference point at the point on $C$ where $t = t_0$.*

**PROOF (*a*)** This result follows by applying the Fundamental Theorem of Calculus (Theorem 4.6.3) to Formula (10).

**PROOF (*b*)** Let $t = s$ in part (*a*).

**PROOF (*c*)** It follows from Theorem 12.3.3 that the formula

$$s = \int_{t_0}^{t} \left\| \frac{d\mathbf{r}}{du} \right\| du$$

defines an arc length parameter for $C$ with reference point $\mathbf{r}(0)$. However, $\|d\mathbf{r}/du\| = 1$ by hypothesis, so we can rewrite the formula for $s$ as

$$s = \int_{t_0}^{t} du = u \Big]_{t_0}^{t} = t - t_0 \quad \blacksquare$$

The component forms of Formulas (16) and (17) will be of sufficient interest in later sections that we provide them here for reference:

$$\frac{ds}{dt} = \left\| \frac{d\mathbf{r}}{dt} \right\| = \sqrt{\left(\frac{dx}{dt}\right)^2 + \left(\frac{dy}{dt}\right)^2} \qquad \text{2-space} \qquad (18)$$

$$\frac{ds}{dt} = \left\| \frac{d\mathbf{r}}{dt} \right\| = \sqrt{\left(\frac{dx}{dt}\right)^2 + \left(\frac{dy}{dt}\right)^2 + \left(\frac{dz}{dt}\right)^2} \qquad \text{3-space} \qquad (19)$$

$$\left\| \frac{d\mathbf{r}}{ds} \right\| = \sqrt{\left(\frac{dx}{ds}\right)^2 + \left(\frac{dy}{ds}\right)^2} = 1 \qquad \text{2-space} \qquad (20)$$

$$\left\| \frac{d\mathbf{r}}{ds} \right\| = \sqrt{\left(\frac{dx}{ds}\right)^2 + \left(\frac{dy}{ds}\right)^2 + \left(\frac{dz}{ds}\right)^2} = 1 \qquad \text{3-space} \qquad (21)$$

Note that Formulas (18) and (19) do not involve $t_0$, and hence do not depend on where the reference point for $s$ is chosen. This is to be expected since changing the reference point shifts $s$ by a constant (the arc length between the two reference points), and this constant drops out on differentiating.

## ✓ QUICK CHECK EXERCISES 12.3

*(See page 768 for answers.)*

**1.** If $\mathbf{r}(t)$ is a smooth vector-valued function, then the integral

$$\int_a^b \left\| \frac{d\mathbf{r}}{dt} \right\| dt$$

may be interpreted geometrically as the ________.

**2.** If $\mathbf{r}(s)$ is a smooth vector-valued function parametrized by arc length $s$, then

$$\left\| \frac{d\mathbf{r}}{ds} \right\| = \underline{\qquad\qquad}$$

and the arc length of the graph of $\mathbf{r}$ over the interval $a \le s \le b$ is ________.

**3.** If $\mathbf{r}(t)$ is a smooth vector-valued function, then the arc length parameter $s$ having $\mathbf{r}(t_0)$ as the reference point may be defined by the integral

$$s = \int_{t_0}^{t} \underline{\qquad\qquad} du$$

**4.** Suppose that $\mathbf{r}(t)$ is a smooth vector-valued function of $t$ with $\mathbf{r}'(1) = \langle \sqrt{3}, -\sqrt{3}, -1 \rangle$, and let $\mathbf{r}_1(t)$ be defined by the equation $\mathbf{r}_1(t) = \mathbf{r}(2\cos t)$. Then $\mathbf{r}_1'(\pi/3) =$ ________.

## EXERCISE SET 12.3

**1–4** Determine whether $\mathbf{r}(t)$ is a smooth function of the parameter $t$. ■

**1.** $\mathbf{r}(t) = t^3\mathbf{i} + (3t^2 - 2t)\mathbf{j} + t^2\mathbf{k}$

**2.** $\mathbf{r}(t) = \cos t^2\mathbf{i} + \sin t^2\mathbf{j} + e^{-t}\mathbf{k}$

**3.** $\mathbf{r}(t) = te^{-t}\mathbf{i} + (t^2 - 2t)\mathbf{j} + \cos \pi t\mathbf{k}$

**4.** $\mathbf{r}(t) = \sin \pi t\mathbf{i} + (2t - \ln t)\mathbf{j} + (t^2 - t)\mathbf{k}$

**5–8** Find the arc length of the parametric curve. ■

**5.** $x = \cos^3 t, y = \sin^3 t, z = 2;\ 0 \le t \le \pi/2$

**6.** $x = 3\cos t, y = 3\sin t, z = 4t;\ 0 \le t \le \pi$

**7.** $x = e^t, y = e^{-t}, z = \sqrt{2}t;\ 0 \le t \le 1$

**8.** $x = \frac{1}{2}t, y = \frac{1}{3}(1-t)^{3/2}, z = \frac{1}{3}(1+t)^{3/2};\ -1 \le t \le 1$

**9–12** Find the arc length of the graph of $\mathbf{r}(t)$. ■

**9.** $\mathbf{r}(t) = t^3\mathbf{i} + t\mathbf{j} + \frac{1}{2}\sqrt{6}t^2\mathbf{k};\ 1 \le t \le 3$

**10.** $\mathbf{r}(t) = (4+3t)\mathbf{i} + (2-2t)\mathbf{j} + (5+t)\mathbf{k};\ 3 \le t \le 4$

**11.** $\mathbf{r}(t) = 3\cos t\mathbf{i} + 3\sin t\mathbf{j} + t\mathbf{k};\ 0 \le t \le 2\pi$

**12.** $\mathbf{r}(t) = t^2\mathbf{i} + (\cos t + t\sin t)\mathbf{j} + (\sin t - t\cos t)\mathbf{k};$ $0 \le t \le \pi$

**13–16** Calculate $d\mathbf{r}/d\tau$ by the chain rule, and then check your result by expressing $\mathbf{r}$ in terms of $\tau$ and differentiating. ■

**13.** $\mathbf{r} = t\mathbf{i} + t^2\mathbf{j};\ t = 4\tau + 1$

**14.** $\mathbf{r} = \langle 3\cos t, 3\sin t\rangle;\ t = \pi\tau$

**15.** $\mathbf{r} = e^t\mathbf{i} + 4e^{-t}\mathbf{j};\ t = \tau^2$

**16.** $\mathbf{r} = \mathbf{i} + 3t^{3/2}\mathbf{j} + t\mathbf{k};\ t = 1/\tau$

**17–20 True–False** Determine whether the statement is true or false. Explain your answer. ■

**17.** If $\mathbf{r}(t)$ is a smooth vector-valued function in 2-space, then
$$\int_a^b \|\mathbf{r}'(t)\|\,dt$$
is a vector.

**18.** If the line $y = x$ is parametrized by the vector-valued function $\mathbf{r}(t)$, then $\mathbf{r}(t)$ is smooth.

**19.** If $\mathbf{r}(s)$ parametrizes the graph of $y = |x|$ in 2-space by arc length, then $\mathbf{r}(s)$ is smooth.

**20.** If a curve $C$ in the plane is parametrized by the smooth vector-valued function $\mathbf{r}(s)$, where $s$ is an arc length parameter, then
$$\int_{-1}^{3} \|\mathbf{r}'(s)\|\,ds = 4$$

**21.** (a) Find the arc length parametrization of the line
$$x = t, \quad y = t$$
that has the same orientation as the given line and has reference point $(0, 0)$.
(b) Find the arc length parametrization of the line
$$x = t, \quad y = t, \quad z = t$$
that has the same orientation as the given line and has reference point $(0, 0, 0)$.

**22.** Find arc length parametrizations of the lines in Exercise 21 that have the stated reference points but are oriented opposite to the given lines.

**23.** (a) Find the arc length parametrization of the line
$$x = 1+t, \quad y = 3-2t, \quad z = 4+2t$$
that has the same direction as the given line and has reference point $(1, 3, 4)$.
(b) Use the parametric equations obtained in part (a) to find the point on the line that is 25 units from the reference point in the direction of increasing parameter.

**24.** (a) Find the arc length parametrization of the line
$$x = -5+3t, \quad y = 2t, \quad z = 5+t$$
that has the same direction as the given line and has reference point $(-5, 0, 5)$.
(b) Use the parametric equations obtained in part (a) to find the point on the line that is 10 units from the reference point in the direction of increasing parameter.

**25–30** Find an arc length parametrization of the curve that has the same orientation as the given curve and for which the reference point corresponds to $t = 0$. ■

**25.** $\mathbf{r}(t) = (3+\cos t)\mathbf{i} + (2+\sin t)\mathbf{j};\ 0 \le t \le 2\pi$

**26.** $\mathbf{r}(t) = \cos^3 t\mathbf{i} + \sin^3 t\mathbf{j};\ 0 \le t \le \pi/2$

**27.** $\mathbf{r}(t) = \frac{1}{3}t^3\mathbf{i} + \frac{1}{2}t^2\mathbf{j};\ t \ge 0$

**28.** $\mathbf{r}(t) = (1+t)^2\mathbf{i} + (1+t)^3\mathbf{j};\ 0 \le t \le 1$

**29.** $\mathbf{r}(t) = e^t\cos t\mathbf{i} + e^t\sin t\mathbf{j};\ 0 \le t \le \pi/2$

**30.** $\mathbf{r}(t) = \sin e^t\mathbf{i} + \cos e^t\mathbf{j} + \sqrt{3}e^t\mathbf{k};\ t \ge 0$

**31.** Show that the arc length of the circular helix $x = a\cos t$, $y = a\sin t$, $z = ct$ for $0 \le t \le t_0$ is $t_0\sqrt{a^2+c^2}$.

**32.** Use the result in Exercise 31 to show the circular helix
$$\mathbf{r} = a\cos t\mathbf{i} + a\sin t\mathbf{j} + ct\mathbf{k}$$
can be expressed as
$$\mathbf{r} = \left(a\cos\frac{s}{w}\right)\mathbf{i} + \left(a\sin\frac{s}{w}\right)\mathbf{j} + \frac{cs}{w}\mathbf{k}$$
where $w = \sqrt{a^2+c^2}$ and $s$ is an arc length parameter with reference point at $(a, 0, 0)$.

**33.** Find an arc length parametrization of the cycloid
$$\begin{aligned} x &= at - a\sin t \\ y &= a - a\cos t \end{aligned} \qquad (0 \le t \le 2\pi)$$
with $(0, 0)$ as the reference point.

**34.** Show that in cylindrical coordinates a curve given by the parametric equations $r = r(t)$, $\theta = \theta(t)$, $z = z(t)$ for $a \le t \le b$ has arc length
$$L = \int_a^b \sqrt{\left(\frac{dr}{dt}\right)^2 + r^2\left(\frac{d\theta}{dt}\right)^2 + \left(\frac{dz}{dt}\right)^2}\,dt$$
[*Hint:* Use the relationships $x = r\cos\theta, y = r\sin\theta$.]

**35.** In each part, use the formula in Exercise 34 to find the arc length of the curve.
(a) $r = e^{2t}, \theta = t, z = e^{2t};\ 0 \le t \le \ln 2$
(b) $r = t^2, \theta = \ln t, z = \frac{1}{3}t^3;\ 1 \le t \le 2$

**36.** Show that in spherical coordinates a curve given by the parametric equations $\rho = \rho(t)$, $\theta = \theta(t)$, $\phi = \phi(t)$ for $a \le t \le b$ has arc length
$$L = \int_a^b \sqrt{\left(\frac{d\rho}{dt}\right)^2 + \rho^2\sin^2\phi\left(\frac{d\theta}{dt}\right)^2 + \rho^2\left(\frac{d\phi}{dt}\right)^2}\,dt$$
[*Hint:* $x = \rho\sin\phi\cos\theta$, $y = \rho\sin\phi\sin\theta$, $z = \rho\cos\phi$.]

**37.** In each part, use the formula in Exercise 36 to find the arc length of the curve.
(a) $\rho = e^{-t}, \theta = 2t, \phi = \pi/4;\ 0 \le t \le 2$
(b) $\rho = 2t, \theta = \ln t, \phi = \pi/6;\ 1 \le t \le 5$

**FOCUS ON CONCEPTS**

**38.** (a) Sketch the graph of $\mathbf{r}(t) = t\mathbf{i} + t^2\mathbf{j}$. Show that $\mathbf{r}(t)$ is a smooth vector-valued function but the change of parameter $t = \tau^3$ produces a vector-valued function that is not smooth, yet has the same graph as $\mathbf{r}(t)$.

(cont.)

(b) Examine how the two vector-valued functions are traced, and see if you can explain what causes the problem.

**39.** Find a change of parameter $t = g(\tau)$ for the semicircle

$$\mathbf{r}(t) = \cos t\mathbf{i} + \sin t\mathbf{j} \quad (0 \le t \le \pi)$$

such that

(a) the semicircle is traced counterclockwise as $\tau$ varies over the interval [0, 1]

(b) the semicircle is traced clockwise as $\tau$ varies over the interval [0, 1].

**40.** What change of parameter $t = g(\tau)$ would you make if you wanted to trace the graph of $\mathbf{r}(t)$ $(0 \le t \le 1)$ in the opposite direction with $\tau$ varying from 0 to 1?

**41.** As illustrated in the accompanying figure, copper cable with a diameter of $\frac{1}{2}$ inch is to be wrapped in a circular helix around a cylinder that has a 12-inch diameter. What length of cable (measured along its centerline) will make one complete turn around the cylinder in a distance of 20 inches (between centerlines) measured parallel to the axis of the cylinder?

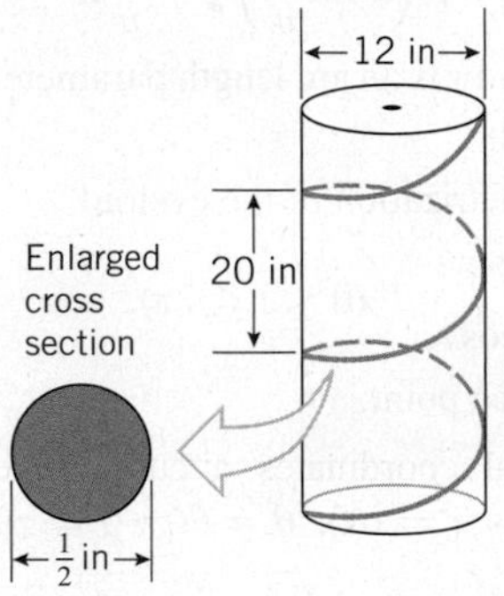


◀ **Figure Ex-41**

**42.** Let $\mathbf{r}(t) = \langle \cos t, \sin t, t^{3/2} \rangle$. Find

(a) $\|\mathbf{r}'(t)\|$ (b) $\dfrac{ds}{dt}$ (c) $\displaystyle\int_0^2 \|\mathbf{r}'(t)\|\,dt$.

**43.** Let $\mathbf{r}(t) = \ln t\mathbf{i} + 2t\mathbf{j} + t^2\mathbf{k}$. Find

(a) $\|\mathbf{r}'(t)\|$ (b) $\dfrac{ds}{dt}$ (c) $\displaystyle\int_1^3 \|\mathbf{r}'(t)\|\,dt$.

**44.** Let $\mathbf{r}(t) = t^2\mathbf{i} + t^3\mathbf{j}$ (see Figure 12.3.1). Let $\theta(t)$ be the angle between $\mathbf{r}'(t)$ and $\mathbf{i}$. Show that

$$\theta(t) \to \pi \text{ as } t \to 0^- \quad \text{and} \quad \theta(t) \to 0 \text{ as } t \to 0^+$$

**45.** Prove: If $\mathbf{r}(t)$ is a smoothly parametrized function, then the angles between $\mathbf{r}'(t)$ and the vectors $\mathbf{i}$, $\mathbf{j}$, and $\mathbf{k}$ are continuous functions of $t$.

**46.** Prove the vector form of the chain rule for 2-space (Theorem 12.3.2) by expressing $\mathbf{r}(t)$ in terms of components.

**47. Writing** The triangle with vertices (0, 0), (1, 0), and (0, 1) has three "corners." Discuss whether it is possible to have a smooth vector-valued function whose graph is this triangle. Also discuss whether it is possible to have a differentiable vector-valued function whose graph is this triangle.

✓ **QUICK CHECK ANSWERS 12.3** 1. arc length of the graph of $\mathbf{r}(t)$ from $t = a$ to $t = b$ 2. 1; $b - a$ 3. $\left\|\dfrac{d\mathbf{r}}{du}\right\|$ 4. $\langle -3, 3, \sqrt{3} \rangle$

## 12.4 UNIT TANGENT, NORMAL, AND BINORMAL VECTORS

*In this section we will discuss some of the fundamental geometric properties of vector-valued functions. Our work here will have important applications to the study of motion along a curved path in 2-space or 3-space and to the study of the geometric properties of curves and surfaces.*

### UNIT TANGENT VECTORS

Recall that if $C$ is the graph of a *smooth* vector-valued function $\mathbf{r}(t)$ in 2-space or 3-space, then the vector $\mathbf{r}'(t)$ is nonzero, tangent to $C$, and points in the direction of increasing parameter. Thus, by normalizing $\mathbf{r}'(t)$ we obtain a unit vector

$$\mathbf{T}(t) = \frac{\mathbf{r}'(t)}{\|\mathbf{r}'(t)\|} \tag{1}$$

that is tangent to $C$ and points in the direction of increasing parameter. We call $\mathbf{T}(t)$ the ***unit tangent vector*** to $C$ at $t$.

As a general rule, we will position $\mathbf{T}(t)$ with its initial point at the terminal point of $\mathbf{r}(t)$, as in Figure 12.4.1. This will ensure that $\mathbf{T}(t)$ is actually tangent to the graph of $\mathbf{r}(t)$ and not simply parallel to the tangent line.

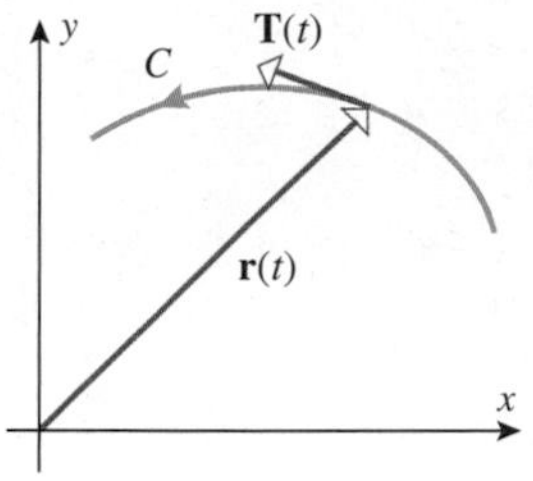


▲ Figure 12.4.1

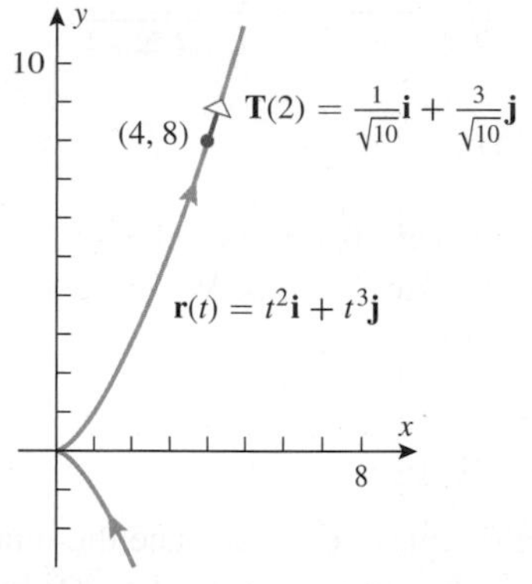


▲ Figure 12.4.2

► **Example 1** Find the unit tangent vector to the graph of $\mathbf{r}(t) = t^2\mathbf{i} + t^3\mathbf{j}$ at the point where $t = 2$.

***Solution.*** Since

$$\mathbf{r}'(t) = 2t\mathbf{i} + 3t^2\mathbf{j}$$

we obtain

$$\mathbf{T}(2) = \frac{\mathbf{r}'(2)}{\|\mathbf{r}'(2)\|} = \frac{4\mathbf{i} + 12\mathbf{j}}{\sqrt{160}} = \frac{4\mathbf{i} + 12\mathbf{j}}{4\sqrt{10}} = \frac{1}{\sqrt{10}}\mathbf{i} + \frac{3}{\sqrt{10}}\mathbf{j}$$

The graph of $\mathbf{r}(t)$ and the vector $\mathbf{T}(2)$ are shown in Figure 12.4.2. ◄

## UNIT NORMAL VECTORS

Recall from Theorem 12.2.8 that if a vector-valued function $\mathbf{r}(t)$ has constant norm, then $\mathbf{r}(t)$ and $\mathbf{r}'(t)$ are orthogonal vectors. In particular, $\mathbf{T}(t)$ has constant norm 1, so $\mathbf{T}(t)$ and $\mathbf{T}'(t)$ are orthogonal vectors. This implies that $\mathbf{T}'(t)$ is perpendicular to the tangent line to $C$ at $t$, so we say that $\mathbf{T}'(t)$ is ***normal*** to $C$ at $t$. It follows that if $\mathbf{T}'(t) \neq \mathbf{0}$, and if we normalize $\mathbf{T}'(t)$, then we obtain a unit vector

$$\mathbf{N}(t) = \frac{\mathbf{T}'(t)}{\|\mathbf{T}'(t)\|} \tag{2}$$

that is normal to $C$ and points in the same direction as $\mathbf{T}'(t)$. We call $\mathbf{N}(t)$ the ***principal unit normal vector*** to $C$ at $t$, or more simply, the ***unit normal vector***. Observe that the unit normal vector is defined only at points where $\mathbf{T}'(t) \neq \mathbf{0}$. Unless stated otherwise, we will assume that this condition is satisfied. In particular, this *excludes* straight lines.

**REMARK** In 2-space there are two unit vectors that are orthogonal to $\mathbf{T}(t)$, and in 3-space there are infinitely many such vectors (Figure 12.4.3). In both cases the principal unit normal is that particular normal that points in the direction of $\mathbf{T}'(t)$. After the next example we will show that for a nonlinear parametric curve in 2-space the principal unit normal is the one that points "inward" toward the concave side of the curve.

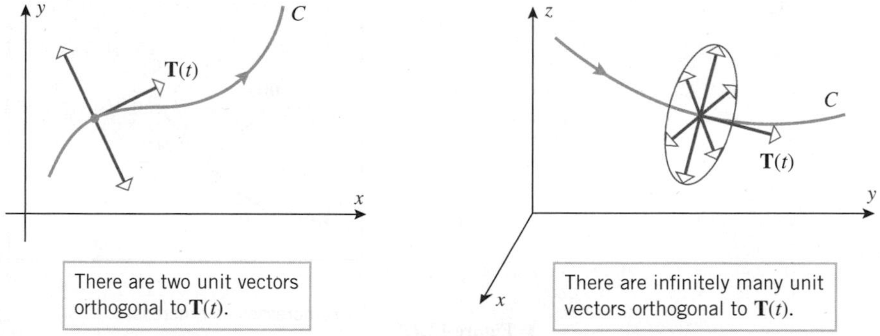


▲ Figure 12.4.3

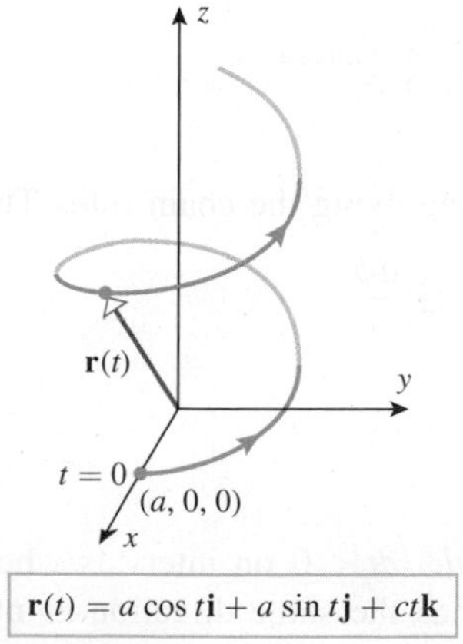


▲ Figure 12.4.4

► **Example 2** Find $\mathbf{T}(t)$ and $\mathbf{N}(t)$ for the circular helix

$$x = a\cos t, \quad y = a\sin t, \quad z = ct$$

where $a > 0$.

***Solution.*** The radius vector for the helix is

$$\mathbf{r}(t) = a\cos t\,\mathbf{i} + a\sin t\,\mathbf{j} + ct\mathbf{k}$$

(Figure 12.4.4). Thus,

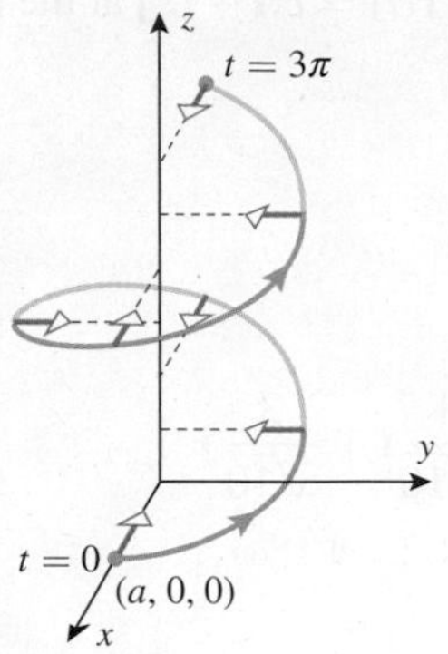

▲ Figure 12.4.5

$$\mathbf{r}'(t) = (-a\sin t)\mathbf{i} + a\cos t\,\mathbf{j} + c\mathbf{k}$$
$$\|\mathbf{r}'(t)\| = \sqrt{(-a\sin t)^2 + (a\cos t)^2 + c^2} = \sqrt{a^2 + c^2}$$
$$\mathbf{T}(t) = \frac{\mathbf{r}'(t)}{\|\mathbf{r}'(t)\|} = -\frac{a\sin t}{\sqrt{a^2+c^2}}\mathbf{i} + \frac{a\cos t}{\sqrt{a^2+c^2}}\mathbf{j} + \frac{c}{\sqrt{a^2+c^2}}\mathbf{k}$$
$$\mathbf{T}'(t) = -\frac{a\cos t}{\sqrt{a^2+c^2}}\mathbf{i} - \frac{a\sin t}{\sqrt{a^2+c^2}}\mathbf{j}$$
$$\|\mathbf{T}'(t)\| = \sqrt{\left(-\frac{a\cos t}{\sqrt{a^2+c^2}}\right)^2 + \left(-\frac{a\sin t}{\sqrt{a^2+c^2}}\right)^2} = \sqrt{\frac{a^2}{a^2+c^2}} = \frac{a}{\sqrt{a^2+c^2}}$$
$$\mathbf{N}(t) = \frac{\mathbf{T}'(t)}{\|\mathbf{T}'(t)\|} = (-\cos t)\mathbf{i} - (\sin t)\mathbf{j} = -(\cos t\mathbf{i} + \sin t\mathbf{j})$$

Note that the **k** component of the principal unit normal $\mathbf{N}(t)$ is zero for every value of $t$, so this vector always lies in a horizontal plane, as illustrated in Figure 12.4.5. We leave it as an exercise to show that this vector actually always points toward the $z$-axis. ◄

## INWARD UNIT NORMAL VECTORS IN 2-SPACE

Our next objective is to show that for a nonlinear parametric curve $C$ in 2-space the unit normal vector always points toward the concave side of $C$. For this purpose, let $\phi(t)$ be the angle from the positive $x$-axis to $\mathbf{T}(t)$, and let $\mathbf{n}(t)$ be the unit vector that results when $\mathbf{T}(t)$ is rotated counterclockwise through an angle of $\pi/2$ (Figure 12.4.6). Since $\mathbf{T}(t)$ and $\mathbf{n}(t)$ are unit vectors, it follows from Formula (13) of Section 11.2 that these vectors can be expressed as

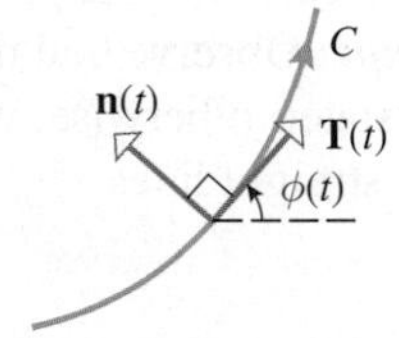

▲ Figure 12.4.6

$$\mathbf{T}(t) = \cos\phi(t)\mathbf{i} + \sin\phi(t)\mathbf{j} \tag{3}$$

and

$$\mathbf{n}(t) = \cos[\phi(t) + \pi/2]\mathbf{i} + \sin[\phi(t) + \pi/2]\mathbf{j} = -\sin\phi(t)\mathbf{i} + \cos\phi(t)\mathbf{j} \tag{4}$$

Observe that on intervals where $\phi(t)$ is increasing the vector $\mathbf{n}(t)$ points *toward* the concave side of $C$, and on intervals where $\phi(t)$ is decreasing it points *away* from the concave side (Figure 12.4.7).

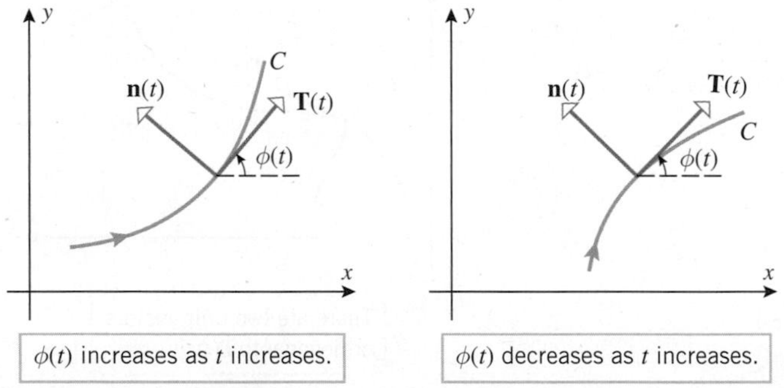

► Figure 12.4.7

Now let us differentiate $\mathbf{T}(t)$ by using Formula (3) and applying the chain rule. This yields

$$\frac{d\mathbf{T}}{dt} = \frac{d\mathbf{T}}{d\phi}\frac{d\phi}{dt} = [(-\sin\phi)\mathbf{i} + (\cos\phi)\mathbf{j}]\frac{d\phi}{dt}$$

and thus from (4)

$$\frac{d\mathbf{T}}{dt} = \mathbf{n}(t)\frac{d\phi}{dt} \tag{5}$$

But $d\phi/dt > 0$ on intervals where $\phi(t)$ is increasing and $d\phi/dt < 0$ on intervals where $\phi(t)$ is decreasing. Thus, it follows from (5) that $d\mathbf{T}/dt$ has the same direction as $\mathbf{n}(t)$ on intervals where $\phi(t)$ is increasing and the opposite direction on intervals where $\phi(t)$

is decreasing. Therefore, $\mathbf{T}'(t) = d\mathbf{T}/dt$ points "inward" toward the concave side of the curve in all cases, and hence so does $\mathbf{N}(t)$. For this reason, $\mathbf{N}(t)$ is also called the ***inward unit normal*** when applied to curves in 2-space.

## COMPUTING T AND N FOR CURVES PARAMETRIZED BY ARC LENGTH

In the case where $\mathbf{r}(s)$ is parametrized by arc length, the procedures for computing the unit tangent vector $\mathbf{T}(s)$ and the unit normal vector $\mathbf{N}(s)$ are simpler than in the general case. For example, we showed in Theorem 12.3.4 that if $s$ is an arc length parameter, then $\|\mathbf{r}'(s)\| = 1$. Thus, Formula (1) for the unit tangent vector simplifies to

$$\mathbf{T}(s) = \mathbf{r}'(s) \tag{6}$$

and consequently Formula (2) for the unit normal vector simplifies to

$$\mathbf{N}(s) = \frac{\mathbf{r}''(s)}{\|\mathbf{r}''(s)\|} \tag{7}$$

**WARNING**

Formulas (6) and (7) are only applicable when the curve is parametrized by an arc length parameter $s$. For other parametrizations Formulas (1) and (2) can be used.

**Example 3** The circle of radius $a$ with counterclockwise orientation and centered at the origin can be represented by the vector-valued function

$$\mathbf{r} = a\cos t\,\mathbf{i} + a\sin t\,\mathbf{j} \qquad (0 \le t \le 2\pi) \tag{8}$$

Parametrize this circle by arc length and find $\mathbf{T}(s)$ and $\mathbf{N}(s)$.

***Solution.*** In (8) we can interpret $t$ as the angle in radian measure from the positive $x$-axis to the radius vector (Figure 12.4.8). This angle subtends an arc of length $s = at$ on the circle, so we can reparametrize the circle in terms of $s$ by substituting $s/a$ for $t$ in (8). This yields

$$\mathbf{r}(s) = a\cos(s/a)\mathbf{i} + a\sin(s/a)\mathbf{j} \qquad (0 \le s \le 2\pi a)$$

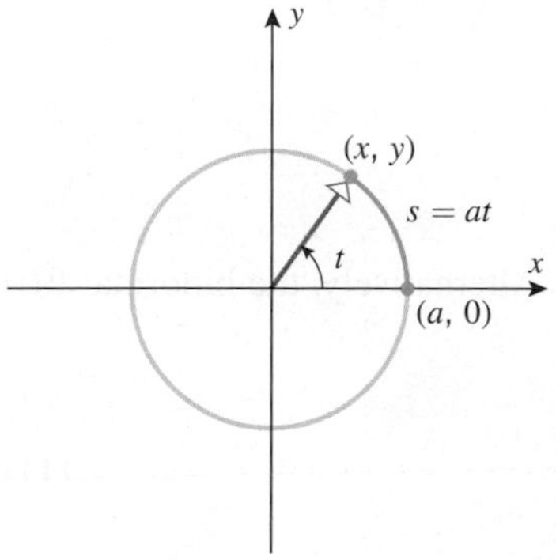


▲ Figure 12.4.8

To find $\mathbf{T}(s)$ and $\mathbf{N}(s)$ from Formulas (6) and (7), we must compute $\mathbf{r}'(s)$, $\mathbf{r}''(s)$, and $\|\mathbf{r}''(s)\|$. Doing so, we obtain

$$\mathbf{r}'(s) = -\sin(s/a)\mathbf{i} + \cos(s/a)\mathbf{j}$$

$$\mathbf{r}''(s) = -(1/a)\cos(s/a)\mathbf{i} - (1/a)\sin(s/a)\mathbf{j}$$

$$\|\mathbf{r}''(s)\| = \sqrt{(-1/a)^2\cos^2(s/a) + (-1/a)^2\sin^2(s/a)} = 1/a$$

Thus,

$$\mathbf{T}(s) = \mathbf{r}'(s) = -\sin(s/a)\mathbf{i} + \cos(s/a)\mathbf{j}$$

$$\mathbf{N}(s) = \mathbf{r}''(s)/\|\mathbf{r}''(s)\| = -\cos(s/a)\mathbf{i} - \sin(s/a)\mathbf{j}$$

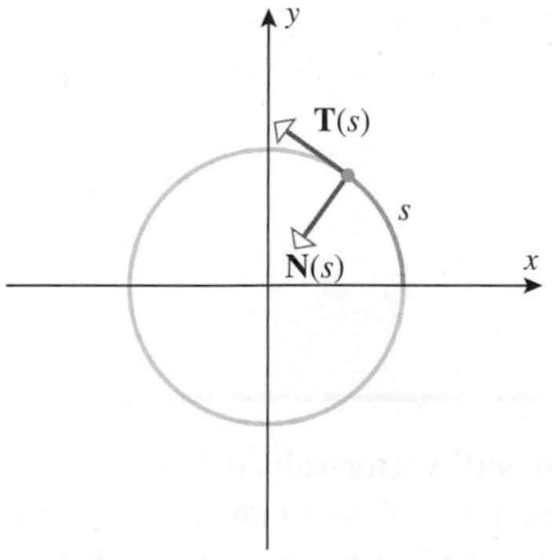


▲ Figure 12.4.9

so $\mathbf{N}(s)$ points toward the center of the circle for all $s$ (Figure 12.4.9). This makes sense geometrically and is also consistent with our earlier observation that in 2-space the unit normal vector is the inward normal. ◄

## BINORMAL VECTORS IN 3-SPACE

If $C$ is the graph of a vector-valued function $\mathbf{r}(t)$ in 3-space, then we define the ***binormal vector*** to $C$ at $t$ to be

$$\mathbf{B}(t) = \mathbf{T}(t) \times \mathbf{N}(t) \tag{9}$$

It follows from properties of the cross product that $\mathbf{B}(t)$ is orthogonal to both $\mathbf{T}(t)$ and $\mathbf{N}(t)$ and is oriented relative to $\mathbf{T}(t)$ and $\mathbf{N}(t)$ by the right-hand rule. Moreover, $\mathbf{T}(t) \times \mathbf{N}(t)$ is a unit vector since

$$\|\mathbf{T}(t) \times \mathbf{N}(t)\| = \|\mathbf{T}(t)\|\|\mathbf{N}(t)\| \sin(\pi/2) = 1$$

Thus, $\{\mathbf{T}(t), \mathbf{N}(t), \mathbf{B}(t)\}$ is a set of three mutually orthogonal unit vectors.

Just as the vectors $\mathbf{i}$, $\mathbf{j}$, and $\mathbf{k}$ determine a right-handed coordinate system in 3-space, so do the vectors $\mathbf{T}(t)$, $\mathbf{N}(t)$, and $\mathbf{B}(t)$. At each point on a smooth parametric curve $C$ in

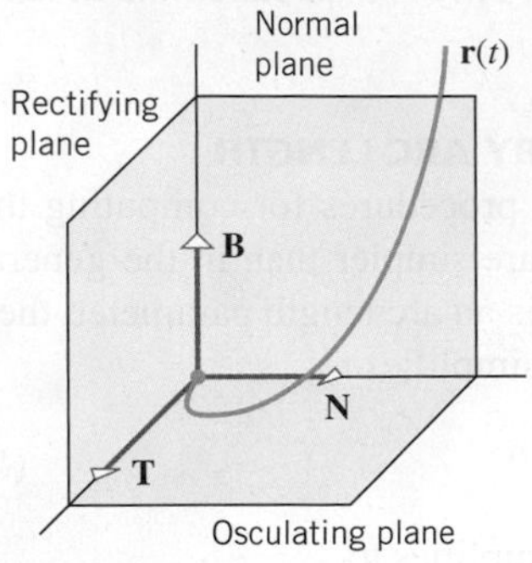


▲ Figure 12.4.10

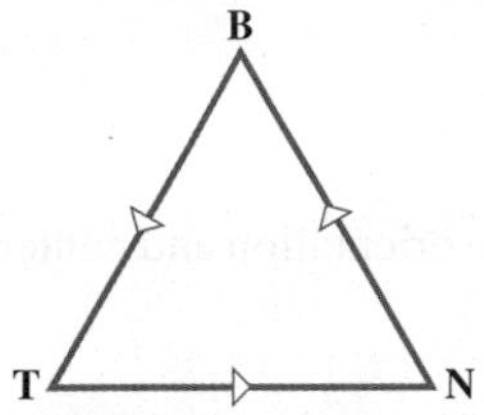


In (10), the vectors **B**, **N**, and **T** are each expressed as the cross product of the other two taken in the counterclockwise direction around the above triangle.

▲ Figure 12.4.11

3-space, these vectors determine three mutually perpendicular planes that pass through the point—the **TB**-plane (called the ***rectifying plane***), the **TN**-plane (called the ***osculating plane***), and the **NB**-plane (called the ***normal plane***) (Figure 12.4.10). Moreover, one can show that a coordinate system determined by $\mathbf{T}(t)$, $\mathbf{N}(t)$, and $\mathbf{B}(t)$ is right-handed in the sense that each of these vectors is related to the other two by the right-hand rule (Figure 12.4.11):

$$\mathbf{B}(t) = \mathbf{T}(t) \times \mathbf{N}(t), \quad \mathbf{N}(t) = \mathbf{B}(t) \times \mathbf{T}(t), \quad \mathbf{T}(t) = \mathbf{N}(t) \times \mathbf{B}(t) \tag{10}$$

The coordinate system determined by $\mathbf{T}(t)$, $\mathbf{N}(t)$, and $\mathbf{B}(t)$ is called the **TNB*-frame*** or sometimes the ***Frenet frame*** in honor of the French mathematician Jean Frédéric Frenet (1816–1900) who pioneered its application to the study of space curves. Typically, the $xyz$-coordinate system determined by the unit vectors **i**, **j**, and **k** remains fixed, whereas the **TNB**-frame changes as its origin moves along the curve $C$ (Figure 12.4.12).

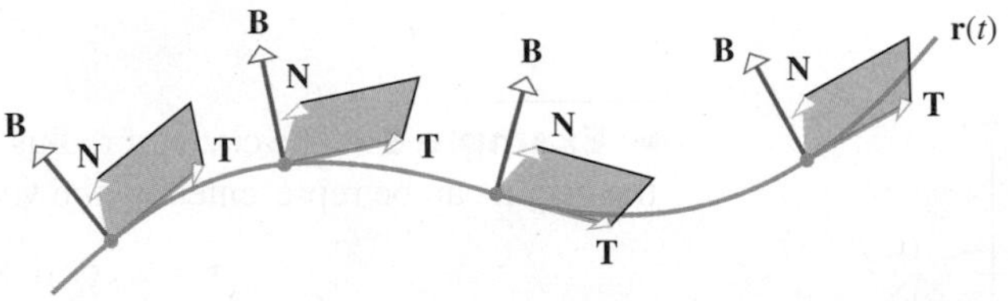


▶ Figure 12.4.12

Formula (9) expresses $\mathbf{B}(t)$ in terms of $\mathbf{T}(t)$ and $\mathbf{N}(t)$. Alternatively, the binormal $\mathbf{B}(t)$ can be expressed directly in terms of $\mathbf{r}(t)$ as

$$\mathbf{B}(t) = \frac{\mathbf{r}'(t) \times \mathbf{r}''(t)}{\|\mathbf{r}'(t) \times \mathbf{r}''(t)\|} \tag{11}$$

and in the case where the parameter is arc length it can be expressed in terms of $\mathbf{r}(s)$ as

$$\mathbf{B}(s) = \frac{\mathbf{r}'(s) \times \mathbf{r}''(s)}{\|\mathbf{r}''(s)\|} \tag{12}$$

We omit the proof.

## ✓ QUICK CHECK EXERCISES 12.4 (See page 773 for answers.)

1. If $C$ is the graph of a smooth vector-valued function $\mathbf{r}(t)$, then the unit tangent, unit normal, and binormal to $C$ at $t$ are defined, respectively, by

   $\mathbf{T}(t) =$ ______, $\mathbf{N}(t) =$ ______, $\mathbf{B}(t) =$ ______

2. If $C$ is the graph of a smooth vector-valued function $\mathbf{r}(s)$ parametrized by arc length, then the definitions of the unit tangent and unit normal to $C$ at $s$ simplify, respectively, to

   $\mathbf{T}(s) =$ ______ and $\mathbf{N}(s) =$ ______

3. If $C$ is the graph of a smooth vector-valued function $\mathbf{r}(t)$, then the unit binormal vector to $C$ at $t$ may be computed directly in terms of $\mathbf{r}'(t)$ and $\mathbf{r}''(t)$ by the formula $\mathbf{B}(t) =$ ______. When $t = s$ is the arc length parameter, this formula simplifies to $\mathbf{B}(s) =$ ______.

4. Suppose that $C$ is the graph of a smooth vector-valued function $\mathbf{r}(s)$ parametrized by arc length with $\mathbf{r}'(0) = \left\langle \frac{2}{3}, \frac{1}{3}, \frac{2}{3} \right\rangle$ and $\mathbf{r}''(0) = \langle -3, 12, -3 \rangle$. Then

   $\mathbf{T}(0) =$ ______, $\mathbf{N}(0) =$ ______, $\mathbf{B}(0) =$ ______

## EXERCISE SET 12.4

**FOCUS ON CONCEPTS**

1. In each part, sketch the unit tangent and normal vectors at the points $P$, $Q$, and $R$, taking into account the orientation of the curve $C$.

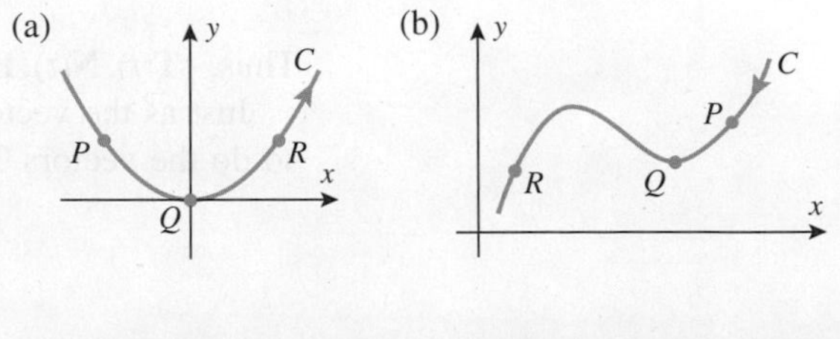

2. Make a rough sketch that shows the ellipse
$$\mathbf{r}(t) = 3\cos t\mathbf{i} + 2\sin t\mathbf{j}$$
for $0 \le t \le 2\pi$ and the unit tangent and normal vectors at the points $t = 0$, $t = \pi/4$, $t = \pi/2$, and $t = \pi$.

3. In the marginal note associated with Example 8 of Section 12.3, we observed that a line $\mathbf{r} = \mathbf{r}_0 + t\mathbf{v}$ can be parametrized in terms of an arc length parameter $s$ with reference point $\mathbf{r}_0$ by normalizing $\mathbf{v}$. Use this result to show that the tangent line to the graph of $\mathbf{r}(t)$ at the point $t_0$ can be expressed as
$$\mathbf{r} = \mathbf{r}(t_0) + s\mathbf{T}(t_0)$$
where $s$ is an arc length parameter with reference point $\mathbf{r}(t_0)$.

4. Use the result in Exercise 3 to show that the tangent line to the parabola
$$x = t, \quad y = t^2$$
at the point $(1, 1)$ can be expressed parametrically as
$$x = 1 + \frac{s}{\sqrt{5}}, \quad y = 1 + \frac{2s}{\sqrt{5}}$$

**5–12** Find $\mathbf{T}(t)$ and $\mathbf{N}(t)$ at the given point. ■

5. $\mathbf{r}(t) = (t^2 - 1)\mathbf{i} + t\mathbf{j};\ t = 1$

6. $\mathbf{r}(t) = \frac{1}{2}t^2\mathbf{i} + \frac{1}{3}t^3\mathbf{j};\ t = 1$

7. $\mathbf{r}(t) = 5\cos t\mathbf{i} + 5\sin t\mathbf{j};\ t = \pi/3$

8. $\mathbf{r}(t) = \ln t\mathbf{i} + t\mathbf{j};\ t = e$

9. $\mathbf{r}(t) = 4\cos t\mathbf{i} + 4\sin t\mathbf{j} + t\mathbf{k};\ t = \pi/2$

10. $\mathbf{r}(t) = t\mathbf{i} + \frac{1}{2}t^2\mathbf{j} + \frac{1}{3}t^3\mathbf{k};\ t = 0$

11. $x = e^t\cos t, y = e^t\sin t, z = e^t;\ t = 0$

12. $x = \cosh t, y = \sinh t, z = t;\ t = \ln 2$

**13–14** Use the result in Exercise 3 to find parametric equations for the tangent line to the graph of $\mathbf{r}(t)$ at $t_0$ in terms of an arc length parameter $s$. ■

13. $\mathbf{r}(t) = \sin t\mathbf{i} + \cos t\mathbf{j} + \frac{1}{2}t^2\mathbf{k};\ t_0 = 0$

14. $\mathbf{r}(t) = t\mathbf{i} + t\mathbf{j} + \sqrt{9 - t^2}\mathbf{k};\ t_0 = 1$

**15–18** Use the formula $\mathbf{B}(t) = \mathbf{T}(t) \times \mathbf{N}(t)$ to find $\mathbf{B}(t)$, and then check your answer by using Formula (11) to find $\mathbf{B}(t)$ directly from $\mathbf{r}(t)$. ■

15. $\mathbf{r}(t) = 3\sin t\mathbf{i} + 3\cos t\mathbf{j} + 4t\mathbf{k}$

16. $\mathbf{r}(t) = e^t\sin t\mathbf{i} + e^t\cos t\mathbf{j} + 3\mathbf{k}$

17. $\mathbf{r}(t) = (\sin t - t\cos t)\mathbf{i} + (\cos t + t\sin t)\mathbf{j} + \mathbf{k}$

18. $\mathbf{r}(t) = a\cos t\mathbf{i} + a\sin t\mathbf{j} + ct\mathbf{k} \quad (a \ne 0, c \ne 0)$

**19–20** Find $\mathbf{T}(t)$, $\mathbf{N}(t)$, and $\mathbf{B}(t)$ for the given value of $t$. Then find equations for the osculating, normal, and rectifying planes at the point that corresponds to that value of $t$. ■

19. $\mathbf{r}(t) = \cos t\mathbf{i} + \sin t\mathbf{j} + \mathbf{k};\ t = \pi/4$

20. $\mathbf{r}(t) = e^t\mathbf{i} + e^t\cos t\mathbf{j} + e^t\sin t\mathbf{k};\ t = 0$

**21–24 True–False** Determine whether the statement is true or false. Explain your answer. ■

21. If $C$ is the graph of a smooth vector-valued function $\mathbf{r}(t)$ in 2-space, then the unit tangent vector $\mathbf{T}(t)$ to $C$ is orthogonal to $\mathbf{r}(t)$ and points in the direction of increasing parameter.

22. If $C$ is the graph of a smooth vector-valued function $\mathbf{r}(t)$ in 2-space, then the angle measured in the counterclockwise direction from the unit tangent vector $\mathbf{T}(t)$ to the unit normal vector $\mathbf{N}(t)$ is $\pi/2$.

23. If the smooth vector-valued function $\mathbf{r}(s)$ is parametrized by arc length and $\mathbf{r}''(s)$ is defined, then $\mathbf{r}'(s)$ and $\mathbf{r}''(s)$ are orthogonal vectors.

24. The binormal vector $\mathbf{B}(t)$ to the graph of a vector-valued function $\mathbf{r}(t)$ in 3-space is the dot product of unit tangent and unit normal vectors, $\mathbf{T}(t)$ and $\mathbf{N}(t)$.

25. **Writing** Look up the definition of "osculating" in a dictionary and discuss why "osculating plane" is an appropriate term for the **TN**-plane.

26. **Writing** Discuss some of the advantages of parametrizing a curve by arc length.

✓ **QUICK CHECK ANSWERS 12.4** 1. $\dfrac{\mathbf{r}'(t)}{\|\mathbf{r}'(t)\|}$; $\dfrac{\mathbf{T}'(t)}{\|\mathbf{T}'(t)\|}$; $\mathbf{T}(t) \times \mathbf{N}(t)$ 2. $\mathbf{r}'(s)$; $\dfrac{\mathbf{r}''(s)}{\|\mathbf{r}''(s)\|}$ 3. $\dfrac{\mathbf{r}'(t) \times \mathbf{r}''(t)}{\|\mathbf{r}'(t) \times \mathbf{r}''(t)\|}$; $\dfrac{\mathbf{r}'(s) \times \mathbf{r}''(s)}{\|\mathbf{r}''(s)\|}$ 4. $\left\langle \frac{2}{3}, \frac{1}{3}, \frac{2}{3} \right\rangle$; $\left\langle -\frac{1}{3\sqrt{2}}, \frac{4}{3\sqrt{2}}, -\frac{1}{3\sqrt{2}} \right\rangle$; $\left\langle -\frac{1}{\sqrt{2}}, 0, \frac{1}{\sqrt{2}} \right\rangle$

## 12.5 CURVATURE

*In this section we will consider the problem of obtaining a numerical measure of how sharply a curve in 2-space or 3-space bends. Our results will have applications in geometry and in the study of motion along a curved path.*

### ■ DEFINITION OF CURVATURE

Suppose that $C$ is the graph of a smooth vector-valued function in 2-space or 3-space that is parametrized in terms of arc length. Figure 12.5.1 suggests that for a curve in 2-space the "sharpness" of the bend in $C$ is closely related to $d\mathbf{T}/ds$, which is the rate of change of the unit tangent vector **T** with respect to $s$. (Keep in mind that **T** has constant length, so only its direction changes.) If $C$ is a straight line (no bend), then the direction of **T** remains constant (Figure 12.5.1*a*); if $C$ bends slightly, then **T** undergoes a gradual change of direction (Figure 12.5.1*b*); and if $C$ bends sharply, then **T** undergoes a rapid change of direction (Figure 12.5.1*c*).

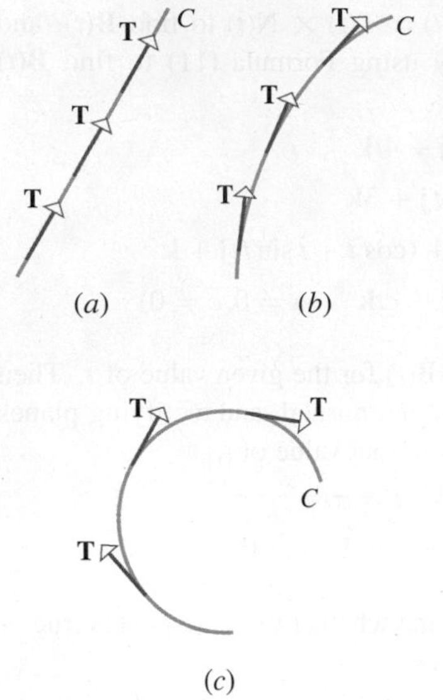

▲ Figure 12.5.1

The situation in 3-space is more complicated because bends in a curve are not limited to a single plane—they can occur in all directions, as illustrated by the complicated tube plot in Figure 12.1.4. To describe the bending characteristics of a curve in 3-space completely, one must take into account $d\mathbf{T}/ds$, $d\mathbf{N}/ds$, and $d\mathbf{B}/ds$. A complete study of this topic would take us too far afield, so we will limit our discussion to $d\mathbf{T}/ds$, which is the most important of these derivatives in applications.

**12.5.1 DEFINITION** If $C$ is a smooth curve in 2-space or 3-space that is parametrized by arc length, then the ***curvature*** of $C$, denoted by $\kappa = \kappa(s)$ ($\kappa$ = Greek "kappa"), is defined by

$$\kappa(s) = \left\| \frac{d\mathbf{T}}{ds} \right\| = \|\mathbf{r}''(s)\| \qquad (1)$$

Observe that $\kappa(s)$ is a real-valued function of $s$, since it is the *length* of $d\mathbf{T}/ds$ that measures the curvature. In general, the curvature will vary from point to point along a curve; however, the following example shows that the curvature is constant for circles in 2-space, as you might expect.

▶ **Example 1** In Example 3 of Section 12.4 we showed that the circle of radius $a$, centered at the origin, can be parametrized in terms of arc length as

$$\mathbf{r}(s) = a\cos\left(\frac{s}{a}\right)\mathbf{i} + a\sin\left(\frac{s}{a}\right)\mathbf{j} \qquad (0 \le s \le 2\pi a)$$

Thus,

$$\mathbf{r}''(s) = -\frac{1}{a}\cos\left(\frac{s}{a}\right)\mathbf{i} - \frac{1}{a}\sin\left(\frac{s}{a}\right)\mathbf{j}$$

and hence from (1)

$$\kappa(s) = \|\mathbf{r}''(s)\| = \sqrt{\left[-\frac{1}{a}\cos\left(\frac{s}{a}\right)\right]^2 + \left[-\frac{1}{a}\sin\left(\frac{s}{a}\right)\right]^2} = \frac{1}{a}$$

so the circle has constant curvature $1/a$. ◀

The next example shows that lines have zero curvature, which is consistent with the fact that they do not bend.

▶ **Example 2** Recall from Formula (15) of Section 12.3 that a line in 2-space or 3-space can be parametrized in terms of arc length as

$$\mathbf{r} = \mathbf{r}_0 + s\mathbf{u}$$

where the terminal point of $\mathbf{r}_0$ is a point on the line and $\mathbf{u}$ is a unit vector parallel to the line. Since $\mathbf{u}$ and $\mathbf{r}_0$ are constant, their derivatives with respect to $s$ are zero, and hence

$$\mathbf{r}'(s) = \frac{d\mathbf{r}}{ds} = \frac{d}{ds}[\mathbf{r}_0 + s\mathbf{u}] = \mathbf{0} + \mathbf{u} = \mathbf{u}$$

$$\mathbf{r}''(s) = \frac{d\mathbf{r}'}{ds} = \frac{d}{ds}[\mathbf{u}] = \mathbf{0}$$

Thus,

$$\kappa(s) = \|\mathbf{r}''(s)\| = 0 \;◀$$

## FORMULAS FOR CURVATURE

Formula (1) is only applicable if the curve is parametrized in terms of arc length. The following theorem provides two formulas for curvature in terms of a general parameter $t$.

**12.5.2 THEOREM** *If $\mathbf{r}(t)$ is a smooth vector-valued function in 2-space or 3-space, then for each value of $t$ at which $\mathbf{T}'(t)$ and $\mathbf{r}''(t)$ exist, the curvature $\kappa$ can be expressed as*

(a) $$\kappa(t) = \frac{\|\mathbf{T}'(t)\|}{\|\mathbf{r}'(t)\|} \tag{2}$$

(b) $$\kappa(t) = \frac{\|\mathbf{r}'(t) \times \mathbf{r}''(t)\|}{\|\mathbf{r}'(t)\|^3} \tag{3}$$

**PROOF (a)** It follows from Formula (1) and Formula (16) of Section 12.3 that

$$\kappa(t) = \left\|\frac{d\mathbf{T}}{ds}\right\| = \left\|\frac{d\mathbf{T}/dt}{ds/dt}\right\| = \left\|\frac{d\mathbf{T}/dt}{\|d\mathbf{r}/dt\|}\right\| = \frac{\|\mathbf{T}'(t)\|}{\|\mathbf{r}'(t)\|}$$

**PROOF (b)** It follows from Formula (1) of Section 12.4 that

$$\mathbf{r}'(t) = \|\mathbf{r}'(t)\|\mathbf{T}(t) \tag{4}$$

$$\mathbf{r}''(t) = \|\mathbf{r}'(t)\|'\mathbf{T}(t) + \|\mathbf{r}'(t)\|\mathbf{T}'(t) \tag{5}$$

But from Formula (2) of Section 12.4 and part (a) of this theorem we have

$$\mathbf{T}'(t) = \|\mathbf{T}'(t)\|\mathbf{N}(t) \quad \text{and} \quad \|\mathbf{T}'(t)\| = \kappa(t)\|\mathbf{r}'(t)\|$$

so

$$\mathbf{T}'(t) = \kappa(t)\|\mathbf{r}'(t)\|\mathbf{N}(t)$$

Substituting this into (5) yields

$$\mathbf{r}''(t) = \|\mathbf{r}'(t)\|'\mathbf{T}(t) + \kappa(t)\|\mathbf{r}'(t)\|^2\mathbf{N}(t) \tag{6}$$

Thus, from (4) and (6)

$$\mathbf{r}'(t) \times \mathbf{r}''(t) = \|\mathbf{r}'(t)\|\,\|\mathbf{r}'(t)\|'(\mathbf{T}(t) \times \mathbf{T}(t)) + \kappa(t)\|\mathbf{r}'(t)\|^3(\mathbf{T}(t) \times \mathbf{N}(t))$$

But the cross product of a vector with itself is zero, so this equation simplifies to

$$\mathbf{r}'(t) \times \mathbf{r}''(t) = \kappa(t)\|\mathbf{r}'(t)\|^3(\mathbf{T}(t) \times \mathbf{N}(t)) = \kappa(t)\|\mathbf{r}'(t)\|^3\mathbf{B}(t)$$

It follows from this equation and the fact that $\mathbf{B}(t)$ is a unit vector that

$$\|\mathbf{r}'(t) \times \mathbf{r}''(t)\| = \kappa(t)\|\mathbf{r}'(t)\|^3$$

Formula (3) now follows. ∎

**REMARK** Formula (2) is useful if $\mathbf{T}(t)$ is known or is easy to obtain; however, Formula (3) will usually be easier to apply, since it involves only $\mathbf{r}(t)$ and its derivatives. We also note that cross products were defined only for vectors in 3-space, so to use Formula (3) in 2-space we must first write the 2-space function $\mathbf{r}(t) = x(t)\mathbf{i} + y(t)\mathbf{j}$ as the 3-space function $\mathbf{r}(t) = x(t)\mathbf{i} + y(t)\mathbf{j} + 0\mathbf{k}$ with a zero $\mathbf{k}$ component.

**▶ Example 3** Find $\kappa(t)$ for the circular helix

$$x = a\cos t, \quad y = a\sin t, \quad z = ct$$

where $a > 0$.

***Solution.*** The radius vector for the helix is

$$\mathbf{r}(t) = a\cos t\mathbf{i} + a\sin t\mathbf{j} + ct\mathbf{k}$$

Thus,

$$\mathbf{r}'(t) = (-a \sin t)\mathbf{i} + a \cos t\,\mathbf{j} + c\mathbf{k}$$
$$\mathbf{r}''(t) = (-a \cos t)\mathbf{i} + (-a \sin t)\mathbf{j}$$

$$\mathbf{r}'(t) \times \mathbf{r}''(t) = \begin{vmatrix} \mathbf{i} & \mathbf{j} & \mathbf{k} \\ -a \sin t & a \cos t & c \\ -a \cos t & -a \sin t & 0 \end{vmatrix} = (ac \sin t)\mathbf{i} - (ac \cos t)\mathbf{j} + a^2\mathbf{k}$$

Therefore,

$$\|\mathbf{r}'(t)\| = \sqrt{(-a \sin t)^2 + (a \cos t)^2 + c^2} = \sqrt{a^2 + c^2}$$

and

$$\|\mathbf{r}'(t) \times \mathbf{r}''(t)\| = \sqrt{(ac \sin t)^2 + (-ac \cos t)^2 + a^4}$$
$$= \sqrt{a^2c^2 + a^4} = a\sqrt{a^2 + c^2}$$

so

$$\kappa(t) = \frac{\|\mathbf{r}'(t) \times \mathbf{r}''(t)\|}{\|\mathbf{r}'(t)\|^3} = \frac{a\sqrt{a^2 + c^2}}{\left(\sqrt{a^2 + c^2}\right)^3} = \frac{a}{a^2 + c^2}$$

Note that $\kappa$ does not depend on $t$, which tells us that the helix has constant curvature. ◀

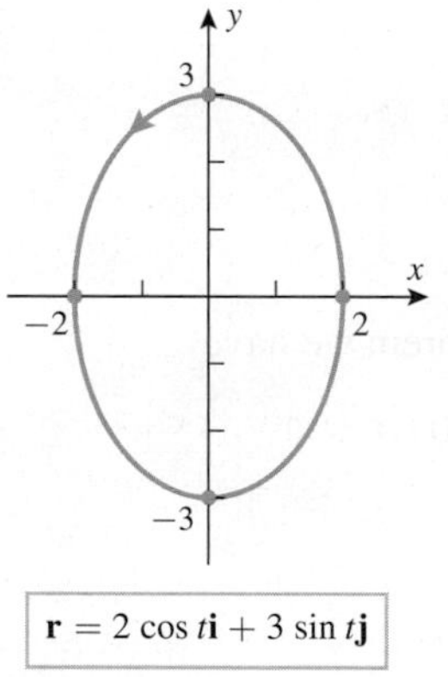


▲ Figure 12.5.2

▶ **Example 4** The graph of the vector equation

$$\mathbf{r} = 2 \cos t\mathbf{i} + 3 \sin t\mathbf{j} \quad (0 \le t \le 2\pi)$$

is the ellipse in Figure 12.5.2. Find the curvature of the ellipse at the endpoints of the major and minor axes, and use a graphing utility to generate the graph of $\kappa(t)$.

***Solution.*** To apply Formula (3), we must treat the ellipse as a curve in the $xy$-plane of an $xyz$-coordinate system by adding a zero **k** component and writing its equation as

$$\mathbf{r} = 2 \cos t\mathbf{i} + 3 \sin t\mathbf{j} + 0\mathbf{k}$$

It is not essential to write the zero **k** component explicitly as long as you assume it to be there when you calculate a cross product. Thus,

$$\mathbf{r}'(t) = (-2 \sin t)\mathbf{i} + 3 \cos t\mathbf{j}$$
$$\mathbf{r}''(t) = (-2 \cos t)\mathbf{i} + (-3 \sin t)\mathbf{j}$$

$$\mathbf{r}'(t) \times \mathbf{r}''(t) = \begin{vmatrix} \mathbf{i} & \mathbf{j} & \mathbf{k} \\ -2 \sin t & 3 \cos t & 0 \\ -2 \cos t & -3 \sin t & 0 \end{vmatrix} = [(6 \sin^2 t) + (6 \cos^2 t)]\mathbf{k} = 6\mathbf{k}$$

Therefore,

$$\|\mathbf{r}'(t)\| = \sqrt{(-2 \sin t)^2 + (3 \cos t)^2} = \sqrt{4 \sin^2 t + 9 \cos^2 t}$$
$$\|\mathbf{r}'(t) \times \mathbf{r}''(t)\| = 6$$

so

$$\kappa(t) = \frac{\|\mathbf{r}'(t) \times \mathbf{r}''(t)\|}{\|\mathbf{r}'(t)\|^3} = \frac{6}{[4 \sin^2 t + 9 \cos^2 t]^{3/2}} \tag{7}$$

The endpoints of the minor axis are $(2, 0)$ and $(-2, 0)$, which correspond to $t = 0$ and $t = \pi$, respectively. Substituting these values in (7) yields the same curvature at both points, namely,

$$\kappa = \kappa(0) = \kappa(\pi) = \frac{6}{9^{3/2}} = \frac{6}{27} = \frac{2}{9}$$

The endpoints of the major axis are $(0, 3)$ and $(0, -3)$, which correspond to $t = \pi/2$ and $t = 3\pi/2$, respectively; from (7) the curvature at these points is

$$\kappa = \kappa\left(\frac{\pi}{2}\right) = \kappa\left(\frac{3\pi}{2}\right) = \frac{6}{4^{3/2}} = \frac{3}{4}$$

Observe that the curvature is greater at the ends of the major axis than at the ends of the minor axis, as you might expect. Figure 12.5.3 shows the graph of $\kappa$ versus $t$. This graph illustrates clearly that the curvature is minimum at $t = 0$ (the right end of the minor axis), increases to a maximum at $t = \pi/2$ (the top of the major axis), decreases to a minimum again at $t = \pi$ (the left end of the minor axis), and continues cyclically in this manner. Figure 12.5.4 provides another way of picturing the curvature. ◄

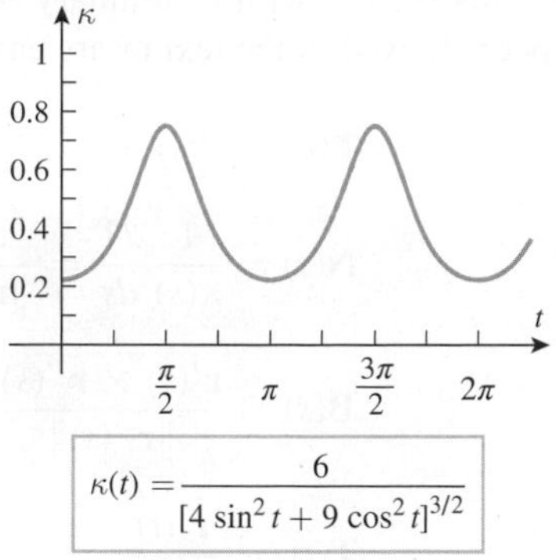


▲ Figure 12.5.3

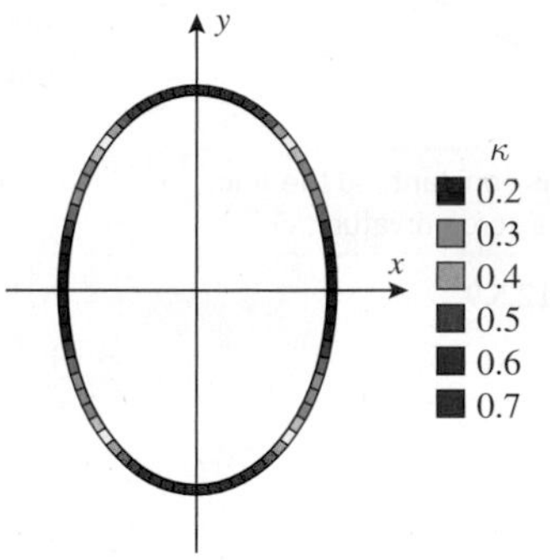


▲ Figure 12.5.4

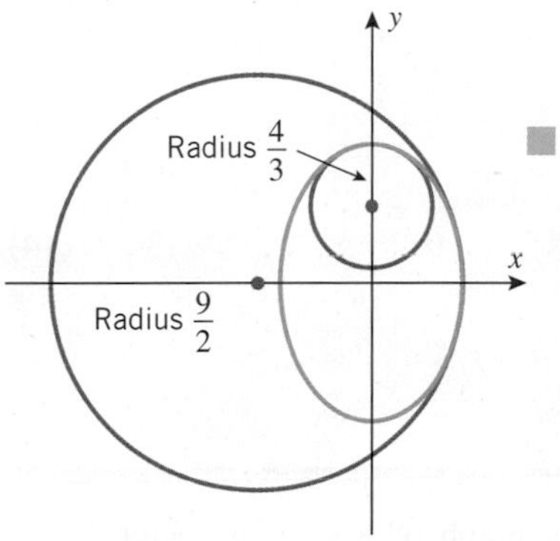


▲ Figure 12.5.5

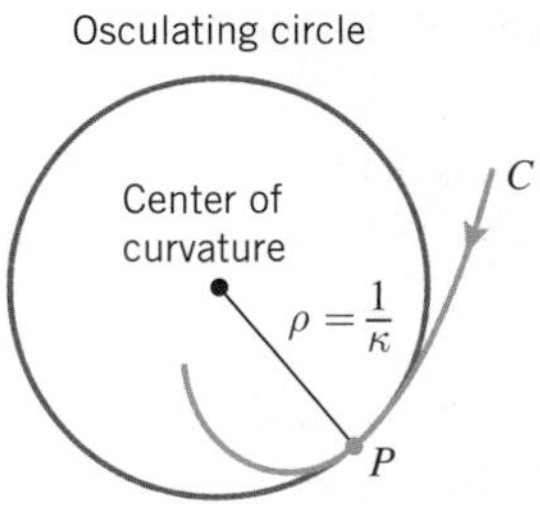


▲ Figure 12.5.6

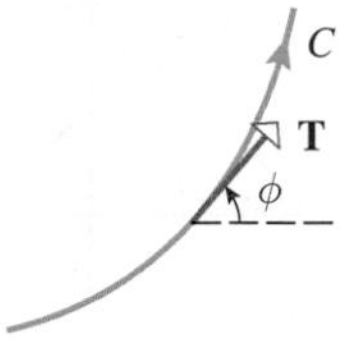


▲ Figure 12.5.7

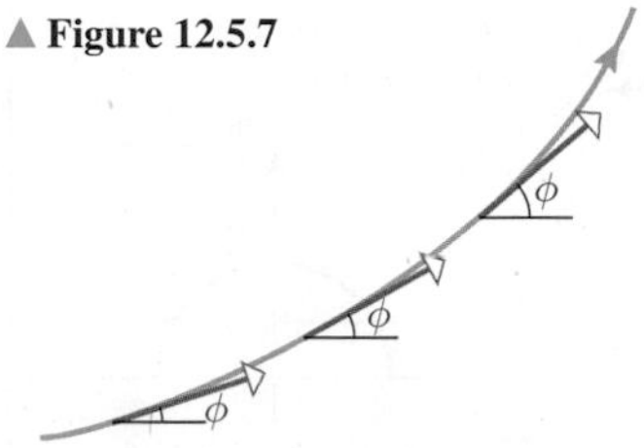

In 2-space, $\kappa(s)$ is the magnitude of the rate of change of $\phi$ with respect to $s$.

▲ Figure 12.5.8

## RADIUS OF CURVATURE

In the last example we found the curvature at the ends of the minor axis to be $\frac{2}{9}$ and the curvature at the ends of the major axis to be $\frac{3}{4}$. To obtain a better understanding of the meaning of these numbers, recall from Example 1 that a circle of radius $a$ has a constant curvature of $1/a$; thus, the curvature of the ellipse at the ends of the minor axis is the same as that of a circle of radius $\frac{9}{2}$, and the curvature at the ends of the major axis is the same as that of a circle of radius $\frac{4}{3}$ (Figure 12.5.5).

In general, if a curve $C$ in 2-space has nonzero curvature $\kappa$ at a point $P$, then the circle of radius $\rho = 1/\kappa$ sharing a common tangent with $C$ at $P$, and centered on the concave side of the curve at $P$, is called the ***osculating circle*** or ***circle of curvature*** at $P$ (Figure 12.5.6). The osculating circle and the curve $C$ not only touch at $P$ but they have equal curvatures at that point. In this sense, the osculating circle is the circle that best approximates the curve $C$ near $P$. The radius $\rho$ of the osculating circle at $P$ is called the ***radius of curvature*** at $P$, and the center of the circle is called the ***center of curvature*** at $P$ (Figure 12.5.6).

## AN INTERPRETATION OF CURVATURE IN 2-SPACE

A useful geometric interpretation of curvature in 2-space can be obtained by considering the angle $\phi$ measured counterclockwise from the direction of the positive $x$-axis to the unit tangent vector $\mathbf{T}$ (Figure 12.5.7). By Formula (13) of Section 11.2, we can express $\mathbf{T}$ in terms of $\phi$ as

$$\mathbf{T}(\phi) = \cos\phi\,\mathbf{i} + \sin\phi\,\mathbf{j}$$

Thus,

$$\frac{d\mathbf{T}}{d\phi} = (-\sin\phi)\mathbf{i} + \cos\phi\,\mathbf{j}$$

$$\frac{d\mathbf{T}}{ds} = \frac{d\mathbf{T}}{d\phi}\frac{d\phi}{ds}$$

from which we obtain

$$\kappa(s) = \left\|\frac{d\mathbf{T}}{ds}\right\| = \left|\frac{d\phi}{ds}\right| \left\|\frac{d\mathbf{T}}{d\phi}\right\| = \left|\frac{d\phi}{ds}\right| \sqrt{(-\sin\phi)^2 + \cos^2\phi} = \left|\frac{d\phi}{ds}\right|$$

In summary, we have shown that

$$\kappa(s) = \left|\frac{d\phi}{ds}\right| \qquad (8)$$

which tells us that curvature in 2-space can be interpreted as the magnitude of the rate of change of $\phi$ with respect to $s$—the greater the curvature, the more rapidly $\phi$ changes with $s$ (Figure 12.5.8). In the case of a straight line, the angle $\phi$ is constant (Figure 12.5.9) and consequently $\kappa(s) = |d\phi/ds| = 0$, which is consistent with the fact that a straight line has zero curvature at every point.

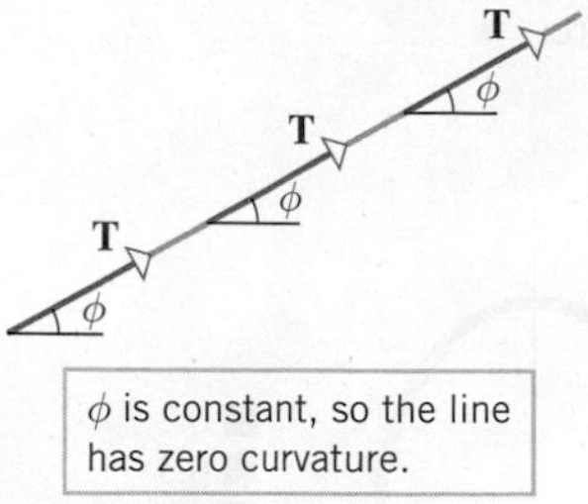


▲ **Figure 12.5.9**

## FORMULA SUMMARY

We conclude this section with a summary of formulas for **T**, **N**, and **B**. These formulas have either been derived in the text or are easily derivable from formulas we have already established.

$$\mathbf{T}(s) = \mathbf{r}'(s) \tag{9}$$

$$\mathbf{N}(s) = \frac{1}{\kappa(s)}\frac{d\mathbf{T}}{ds} = \frac{\mathbf{r}''(s)}{\|\mathbf{r}''(s)\|} = \frac{\mathbf{r}''(s)}{\kappa(s)} \tag{10}$$

$$\mathbf{B}(s) = \frac{\mathbf{r}'(s) \times \mathbf{r}''(s)}{\|\mathbf{r}''(s)\|} = \frac{\mathbf{r}'(s) \times \mathbf{r}''(s)}{\kappa(s)} \tag{11}$$

$$\mathbf{T}(t) = \frac{\mathbf{r}'(t)}{\|\mathbf{r}'(t)\|} \tag{12}$$

$$\mathbf{B}(t) = \frac{\mathbf{r}'(t) \times \mathbf{r}''(t)}{\|\mathbf{r}'(t) \times \mathbf{r}''(t)\|} \tag{13}$$

$$\mathbf{N}(t) = \mathbf{B}(t) \times \mathbf{T}(t) \tag{14}$$

## ✓QUICK CHECK EXERCISES 12.5 (See page 781 for answers.)

1. If $C$ is a smooth curve parametrized by arc length, then the curvature is defined by $\kappa(s) =$ ______.
2. Let $\mathbf{r}(t)$ be a smooth vector-valued function with curvature $\kappa(t)$.
   (a) The curvature may be expressed in terms of $\mathbf{T}'(t)$ and $\mathbf{r}'(t)$ as $\kappa(t) =$ ______.
   (b) The curvature may be expressed directly in terms of $\mathbf{r}'(t)$ and $\mathbf{r}''(t)$ as $\kappa(t) =$ ______.
3. Suppose that $C$ is the graph of a smooth vector-valued function $\mathbf{r}(s) = \langle x(s), y(s)\rangle$ parametrized by arc length and that the unit tangent $\mathbf{T}(s) = \langle \cos\phi(s), \sin\phi(s)\rangle$. Then the curvature can be expressed in terms of $\phi(s)$ as $\kappa(s) =$ ______.
4. Suppose that $C$ is a smooth curve and that $x^2 + y^2 = 4$ is the osculating circle to $C$ at $P(1, \sqrt{3})$. Then the curvature of $C$ at $P$ is ______.

## EXERCISE SET 12.5 Graphing Utility C CAS

**FOCUS ON CONCEPTS**

**1–2** Use the osculating circle shown in the figure to estimate the curvature at the indicated point. ■

**1.**

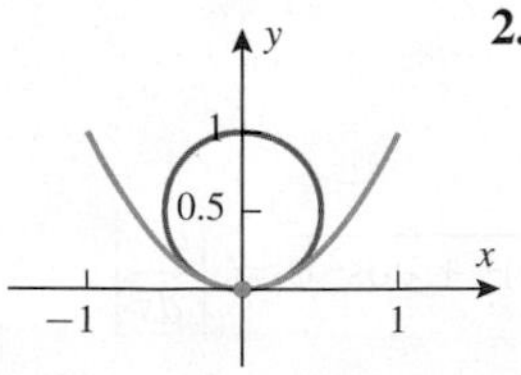


**2.**

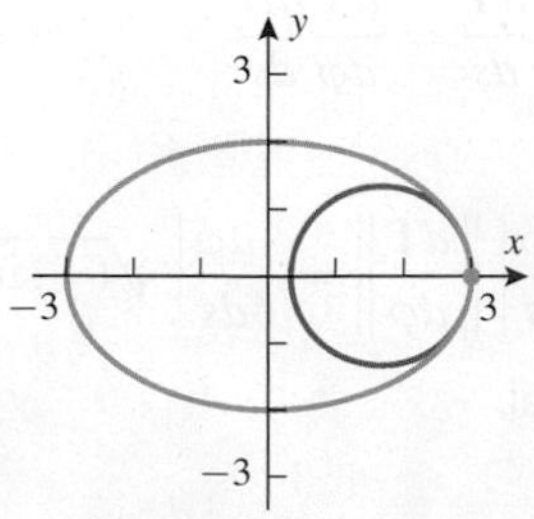


**3–4** For a plane curve $y = f(x)$ the curvature at $(x, f(x))$ is a function $\kappa(x)$. In these exercises the graphs of $f(x)$ and $\kappa(x)$ are shown. Determine which is which and explain your reasoning. ■

**3.** (a) (b)

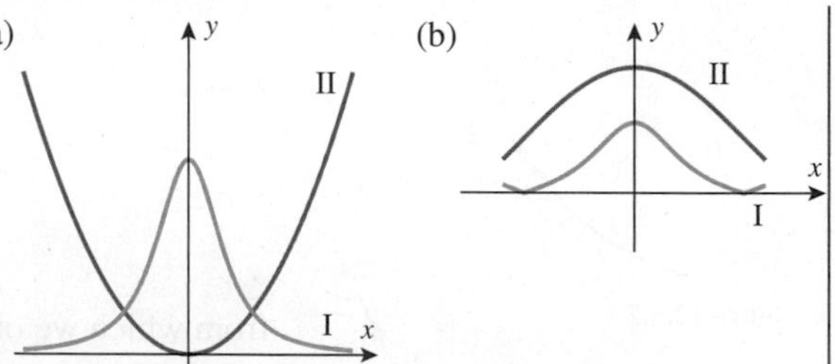


**4.** (a) (b)

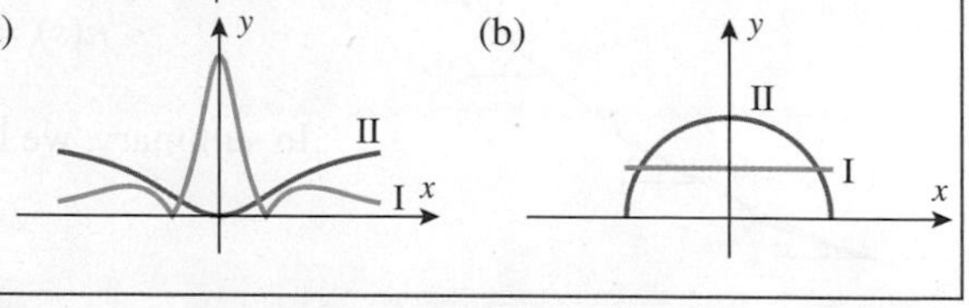


**5–12** Use Formula (3) to find $\kappa(t)$. ■

**5.** $\mathbf{r}(t) = t^2\mathbf{i} + t^3\mathbf{j}$

**6.** $\mathbf{r}(t) = 4\cos t\mathbf{i} + \sin t\mathbf{j}$

**7.** $\mathbf{r}(t) = e^{3t}\mathbf{i} + e^{-t}\mathbf{j}$

**8.** $x = 1 - t^3,\ y = t - t^2$

**9.** $\mathbf{r}(t) = 4\cos t\mathbf{i} + 4\sin t\mathbf{j} + t\mathbf{k}$

**10.** $\mathbf{r}(t) = t\mathbf{i} + \frac{1}{2}t^2\mathbf{j} + \frac{1}{3}t^3\mathbf{k}$

**11.** $x = \cosh t,\ y = \sinh t,\ z = t$

**12.** $\mathbf{r}(t) = \mathbf{i} + t\mathbf{j} + t^2\mathbf{k}$

**13–16** Find the curvature and the radius of curvature at the stated point. ■

**13.** $\mathbf{r}(t) = 3\cos t\mathbf{i} + 4\sin t\mathbf{j} + t\mathbf{k};\ t = \pi/2$

**14.** $\mathbf{r}(t) = e^t\mathbf{i} + e^{-t}\mathbf{j} + t\mathbf{k};\ t = 0$

**15.** $x = e^t\cos t,\ y = e^t\sin t,\ z = e^t;\ t = 0$

**16.** $x = \sin t,\ y = \cos t,\ z = \frac{1}{2}t^2;\ t = 0$

**17–18** Confirm that $s$ is an arc length parameter by showing that $\|d\mathbf{r}/ds\| = 1$, and then apply Formula (1) to find $\kappa(s)$. ■

**17.** $\mathbf{r} = \sin\left(1 + \dfrac{s}{2}\right)\mathbf{i} + \cos\left(1 + \dfrac{s}{2}\right)\mathbf{j} + \sqrt{3}\left(1 + \dfrac{s}{2}\right)\mathbf{k}$

**18.** $\mathbf{r} = \left(1 - \frac{2}{3}s\right)^{3/2}\mathbf{i} + \left(\frac{2}{3}s\right)^{3/2}\mathbf{j} \quad \left(0 \le s \le \frac{3}{2}\right)$

**19–22 True–False** Determine whether the statement is true or false. Explain your answer. ■

**19.** A circle of radius 2 has constant curvature $\frac{1}{2}$.

**20.** A vertical line in 2-space has undefined curvature.

**21.** If $\mathbf{r}(s)$ is parametrized by arc length, then the curvature of the graph of $\mathbf{r}(s)$ is the length of $\mathbf{r}'(s)$.

**22.** If $C$ is a curve in 2-space, then the osculating circle to $C$ at a point $P$ has radius equal to the curvature of $C$ at $P$.

**23.** (a) Use Formula (3) to show that in 2-space the curvature of a smooth parametric curve

$$x = x(t), \quad y = y(t)$$

is

$$\kappa(t) = \frac{|x'y'' - y'x''|}{(x'^2 + y'^2)^{3/2}}$$

where primes denote differentiation with respect to $t$.

(b) Use the result in part (a) to show that in 2-space the curvature of the plane curve given by $y = f(x)$ is

$$\kappa(x) = \frac{|d^2y/dx^2|}{[1 + (dy/dx)^2]^{3/2}}$$

[*Hint:* Express $y = f(x)$ parametrically with $x = t$ as the parameter.]

**24.** Use part (b) of Exercise 23 to show that the curvature of $y = f(x)$ can be expressed in terms of the angle of inclination of the tangent line as

$$\kappa(\phi) = \left|\frac{d^2y}{dx^2}\cos^3\phi\right|$$

[*Hint:* $\tan\phi = dy/dx$.]

**25–28** Use the result in Exercise 23(b) to find the curvature at the stated point. ■

**25.** $y = \sin x;\ x = \pi/2$

**26.** $y = \tan x;\ x = \pi/4$

**27.** $y = e^{-x};\ x = 1$

**28.** $y^2 - 4x^2 = 9;\ (2, 5)$

**29–32** Use the result in Exercise 23(a) to find the curvature at the stated point. ■

**29.** $x = t^2,\ y = t^3;\ t = \frac{1}{2}$

**30.** $x = e^{3t},\ y = e^{-t};\ t = 0$

**31.** $x = t,\ y = 1/t;\ t = 1$

**32.** $x = 2\sin 2t,\ y = 3\sin t;\ t = \pi/2$

**33.** In each part, use the formulas in Exercise 23 to help find the radius of curvature at the stated points. Then sketch the graph together with the osculating circles at those points.

(a) $y = \cos x$ at $x = 0$ and $x = \pi$

(b) $x = 2\cos t,\ y = \sin t\ (0 \le t \le 2\pi)$ at $t = 0$ and $t = \pi/2$

**34.** Use the formula in Exercise 23(a) to find $\kappa(t)$ for the curve $x = e^{-t}\cos t,\ y = e^{-t}\sin t$. Then sketch the graph of $\kappa(t)$.

**35–36** Generate the graph of $y = f(x)$ using a graphing utility, and then make a conjecture about the shape of the graph of $y = \kappa(x)$. Check your conjecture by generating the graph of $y = \kappa(x)$. ■

**35.** $f(x) = xe^{-x}$ for $0 \le x \le 5$

**36.** $f(x) = x^3 - x$ for $-1 \le x \le 1$

C **37.** (a) If you have a CAS, read the documentation on calculating higher-order derivatives. Then use the CAS and part (b) of Exercise 23 to find $\kappa(x)$ for $f(x) = x^4 - 2x^2$.

(b) Use the CAS to generate the graphs of $f(x) = x^4 - 2x^2$ and $\kappa(x)$ on the same screen for $-2 \le x \le 2$.

(c) Find the radius of curvature at each relative extremum.

(d) Make a reasonably accurate hand-drawn sketch that shows the graph of $f(x) = x^4 - 2x^2$ and the osculating circles in their correct proportions at the relative extrema.

C **38.** (a) Use a CAS to graph the parametric curve $x = t\cos t$, $y = t\sin t$ for $t \ge 0$.

(b) Make a conjecture about the behavior of the curvature $\kappa(t)$ as $t \to +\infty$.

(c) Use the CAS and part (a) of Exercise 23 to find $\kappa(t)$.

(d) Check your conjecture by finding the limit of $\kappa(t)$ as $t \to +\infty$.

**39.** Use the formula in Exercise 23(a) to show that for a curve in polar coordinates described by $r = f(\theta)$ the curvature is

$$\kappa(\theta) = \frac{\left|r^2 + 2\left(\dfrac{dr}{d\theta}\right)^2 - r\dfrac{d^2r}{d\theta^2}\right|}{\left[r^2 + \left(\dfrac{dr}{d\theta}\right)^2\right]^{3/2}}$$

[*Hint:* Let $\theta$ be the parameter and use the relationships $x = r\cos\theta,\ y = r\sin\theta$.]

**40.** Use the result in Exercise 39 to show that a circle has constant curvature.

**41–44** Use the formula in Exercise 39 to find the curvature at the indicated point. ■

**41.** $r = 1 + \cos\theta;\ \theta = \pi/2$

**42.** $r = e^{2\theta};\ \theta = 1$

**43.** $r = \sin 3\theta;\ \theta = 0$

**44.** $r = \theta;\ \theta = 1$

**45.** Find the radius of curvature of the parabola $y^2 = 4px$ at $(0, 0)$.

**46.** At what point(s) does $y = e^x$ have maximum curvature?

**47.** At what point(s) does $4x^2 + 9y^2 = 36$ have a minimum radius of curvature?

**48.** Find the maximum and minimum values of the radius of curvature for the curve $x = \cos t$, $y = \sin t$, $z = \cos t$.

**49.** Use the formula in Exercise 39 to show that the curvature of the polar curve $r = e^{a\theta}$ is inversely proportional to $r$.

C **50.** Use the formula in Exercise 39 and a CAS to show that the curvature of the lemniscate $r = \sqrt{a \cos 2\theta}$ is directly proportional to $r$.

**51.** (a) Use the result in Exercise 24 to show that for the parabola $y = x^2$ the curvature $\kappa(\phi)$ at points where the tangent line has an angle of inclination of $\phi$ is

$$\kappa(\phi) = |2\cos^3\phi|$$

(b) Use the result in part (a) to find the radius of curvature of the parabola at the point on the parabola where the tangent line has slope 1.

(c) Make a sketch with reasonably accurate proportions that shows the osculating circle at the point on the parabola where the tangent line has slope 1.

**52.** The ***evolute*** of a smooth parametric curve $C$ in 2-space is the curve formed from the centers of curvature of $C$. The accompanying figure shows the ellipse $x = 3\cos t$, $y = 2\sin t$ $(0 \le t \le 2\pi)$ and its evolute graphed together.

(a) Which points on the evolute correspond to $t = 0$ and $t = \pi/2$?

(b) In what direction is the evolute traced as $t$ increases from 0 to $2\pi$?

(c) What does the evolute of a circle look like? Explain your reasoning.

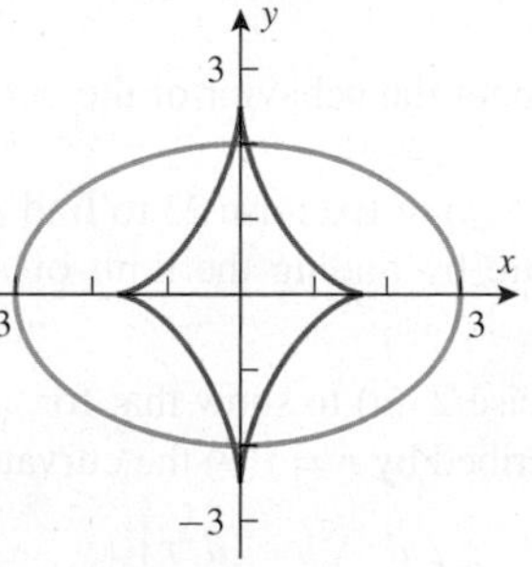


Figure Ex-52

**FOCUS ON CONCEPTS**

**53–57** These exercises are concerned with the problem of creating a single smooth curve by piecing together two separate smooth curves. If two smooth curves $C_1$ and $C_2$ are joined at a point $P$ to form a curve $C$, then we will say that $C_1$ and $C_2$ make a ***smooth transition*** at $P$ if the curvature of $C$ is continuous at $P$. ■

**53.** Show that the transition at $x = 0$ from the horizontal line $y = 0$ for $x \le 0$ to the parabola $y = x^2$ for $x > 0$ is not smooth, whereas the transition to $y = x^3$ for $x > 0$ is smooth.

**54.** (a) Sketch the graph of the curve defined piecewise by $y = x^2$ for $x < 0$, $y = x^4$ for $x \ge 0$.

(b) Show that for the curve in part (a) the transition at $x = 0$ is not smooth.

**55.** The accompanying figure shows the arc of a circle of radius $r$ with center at $(0, r)$. Find the value of $a$ so that there is a smooth transition from the circle to the parabola $y = ax^2$ at the point where $x = 0$.

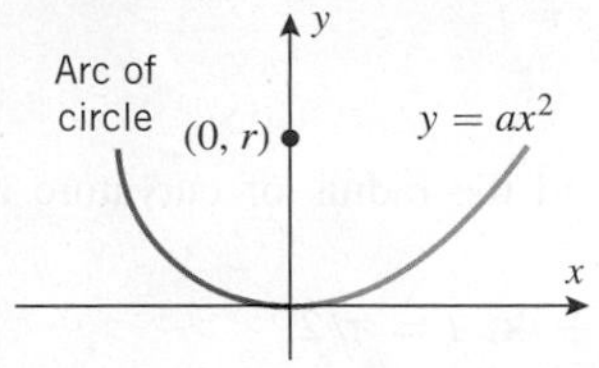


Figure Ex-55

**56.** Find $a$, $b$, and $c$ so that there is a smooth transition at $x = 0$ from the curve $y = e^x$ for $x \le 0$ to the parabola $y = ax^2 + bx + c$ for $x > 0$. [*Hint:* The curvature is continuous at those points where $y''$ is continuous.]

**57.** Assume that $f$ is a function for which $f'''(x)$ is defined for all $x \le 0$. Explain why it is always possible to find numbers $a$, $b$, and $c$ such that there is a smooth transition at $x = 0$ from the curve $y = f(x)$, $x \le 0$, to the parabola $y = ax^2 + bx + c$.

**58–61** Assume that $s$ is an arc length parameter for a smooth vector-valued function $\mathbf{r}(s)$ in 3-space and that $d\mathbf{T}/ds$ and $d\mathbf{N}/ds$ exist at each point on the curve. (This implies that $d\mathbf{B}/ds$ exists as well, since $\mathbf{B} = \mathbf{T} \times \mathbf{N}$.) ■

**58.** Show that

$$\frac{d\mathbf{T}}{ds} = \kappa(s)\mathbf{N}(s)$$

and use this result to obtain the formulas in (10).

**59.** (a) Show that $d\mathbf{B}/ds$ is perpendicular to $\mathbf{B}(s)$.

(b) Show that $d\mathbf{B}/ds$ is perpendicular to $\mathbf{T}(s)$. [*Hint:* Use the fact that $\mathbf{B}(s)$ is perpendicular to both $\mathbf{T}(s)$ and $\mathbf{N}(s)$, and differentiate $\mathbf{B} \cdot \mathbf{T}$ with respect to $s$.]

(c) Use the results in parts (a) and (b) to show that $d\mathbf{B}/ds$ is a scalar multiple of $\mathbf{N}(s)$. The *negative* of this scalar is called the ***torsion*** of $\mathbf{r}(s)$ and is denoted by $\tau(s)$. Thus,

$$\frac{d\mathbf{B}}{ds} = -\tau(s)\mathbf{N}(s)$$

(d) Show that $\tau(s) = 0$ for all $s$ if the graph of $\mathbf{r}(s)$ lies in a plane. [*Note:* For reasons that we cannot discuss here, the torsion is related to the "twisting" properties of the curve, and $\tau(s)$ is regarded as a numerical measure of the tendency for the curve to twist out of the osculating plane.]

**60.** Let $\kappa$ be the curvature of $C$ and $\tau$ the torsion (defined in Exercise 59). By differentiating $\mathbf{N} = \mathbf{B} \times \mathbf{T}$ with respect to $s$, show that $d\mathbf{N}/ds = -\kappa\mathbf{T} + \tau\mathbf{B}$.

**61.** The following derivatives, known as the ***Frenet–Serret formulas***, are fundamental in the theory of curves in 3-space:

$$d\mathbf{T}/ds = \kappa\mathbf{N} \quad \text{[Exercise 58]}$$
$$d\mathbf{N}/ds = -\kappa\mathbf{T} + \tau\mathbf{B} \quad \text{[Exercise 60]}$$
$$d\mathbf{B}/ds = -\tau\mathbf{N} \quad \text{[Exercise 59(c)]}$$

Use the first two Frenet–Serret formulas and the fact that $\mathbf{r}'(s) = \mathbf{T}$ if $\mathbf{r} = \mathbf{r}(s)$ to show that

$$\tau = \frac{[\mathbf{r}'(s) \times \mathbf{r}''(s)] \cdot \mathbf{r}'''(s)}{\|\mathbf{r}''(s)\|^2} \quad \text{and} \quad \mathbf{B} = \frac{\mathbf{r}'(s) \times \mathbf{r}''(s)}{\|\mathbf{r}''(s)\|}$$

**62.** (a) Use the chain rule and the first two Frenet–Serret formulas in Exercise 61 to show that
$$\mathbf{T}' = \kappa s'\mathbf{N} \quad\text{and}\quad \mathbf{N}' = -\kappa s'\mathbf{T} + \tau s'\mathbf{B}$$
where primes denote differentiation with respect to $t$.

(b) Show that Formulas (4) and (6) can be written in the form
$$\mathbf{r}'(t) = s'\mathbf{T} \quad\text{and}\quad \mathbf{r}''(t) = s''\mathbf{T} + \kappa(s')^2\mathbf{N}$$

(c) Use the results in parts (a) and (b) to show that
$$\mathbf{r}'''(t) = [s''' - \kappa^2(s')^3]\mathbf{T} + [3\kappa s's'' + \kappa'(s')^2]\mathbf{N} + \kappa\tau(s')^3\mathbf{B}$$

(d) Use the results in parts (b) and (c) to show that
$$\tau(t) = \frac{[\mathbf{r}'(t) \times \mathbf{r}''(t)] \cdot \mathbf{r}'''(t)}{\|\mathbf{r}'(t) \times \mathbf{r}''(t)\|^2}$$

**63–66** Use the formula in Exercise 62(d) to find the torsion $\tau = \tau(t)$. ■

**63.** The twisted cubic $\mathbf{r}(t) = 2t\mathbf{i} + t^2\mathbf{j} + \frac{1}{3}t^3\mathbf{k}$

**64.** The circular helix $\mathbf{r}(t) = a\cos t\mathbf{i} + a\sin t\mathbf{j} + ct\mathbf{k}$

**65.** $\mathbf{r}(t) = e^t\mathbf{i} + e^{-t}\mathbf{j} + \sqrt{2}t\mathbf{k}$

**66.** $\mathbf{r}(t) = (t - \sin t)\mathbf{i} + (1 - \cos t)\mathbf{j} + t\mathbf{k}$

**67. Writing** One property of a twice-differentiable function $f(x)$ is that an inflection point on the graph is a point at which the tangent line crosses the graph of $f$. Consider the analogous issue in 2-space for an osculating circle to a curve $C$ at a point $P$: What does it mean for the osculating circle to cross (or not to cross) $C$ at $P$? Investigate this issue through some examples of your own and write a brief essay, with illustrations, supporting your conclusions.

**68. Writing** The accompanying figure is the graph of the radius of curvature versus $\theta$ in rectangular coordinates for the cardioid $r = 1 + \cos\theta$. In words, explain what the graph tells you about the cardioid.

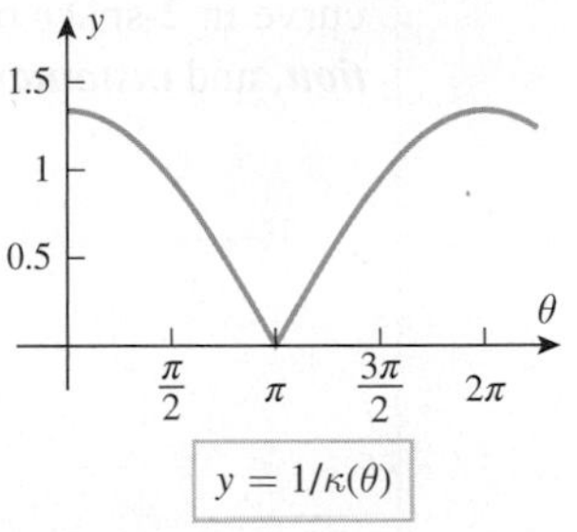


◀ **Figure Ex-68**

✓ QUICK CHECK ANSWERS 12.5 1. $\left\|\dfrac{d\mathbf{T}}{ds}\right\| = \|\mathbf{r}''(s)\|$ 2. (a) $\dfrac{\|\mathbf{T}'(t)\|}{\|\mathbf{r}'(t)\|}$ (b) $\dfrac{\|\mathbf{r}'(t) \times \mathbf{r}''(t)\|}{\|\mathbf{r}'(t)\|^3}$ 3. $\left|\dfrac{d\phi}{ds}\right|$ 4. $\dfrac{1}{2}$

# 12.6 MOTION ALONG A CURVE

*In earlier sections we considered the motion of a particle along a line. In that situation there are only two directions in which the particle can move—the positive direction or the negative direction. Motion in 2-space or 3-space is more complicated because there are infinitely many directions in which a particle can move. In this section we will show how vectors can be used to analyze motion along curves in 2-space or 3-space.*

## VELOCITY, ACCELERATION, AND SPEED

Let us assume that the motion of a particle in 2-space or 3-space is described by a smooth vector-valued function $\mathbf{r}(t)$ in which the parameter $t$ denotes time; we will call this the ***position function*** or ***trajectory*** of the particle. As the particle moves along its trajectory, its direction of motion and its speed can vary from instant to instant. Thus, before we can undertake any analysis of such motion, we must have clear answers to the following questions:

- What is the direction of motion of the particle at an instant of time?
- What is the speed of the particle at an instant of time?

We will define the direction of motion at time $t$ to be the direction of the unit tangent vector $\mathbf{T}(t)$, and we will define the speed to be $ds/dt$—the instantaneous rate of change of the arc length traveled by the particle from an arbitrary reference point. Taking this a step further, we will combine the speed and the direction of motion to form the vector

$$\mathbf{v}(t) = \frac{ds}{dt}\mathbf{T}(t) \qquad (1)$$

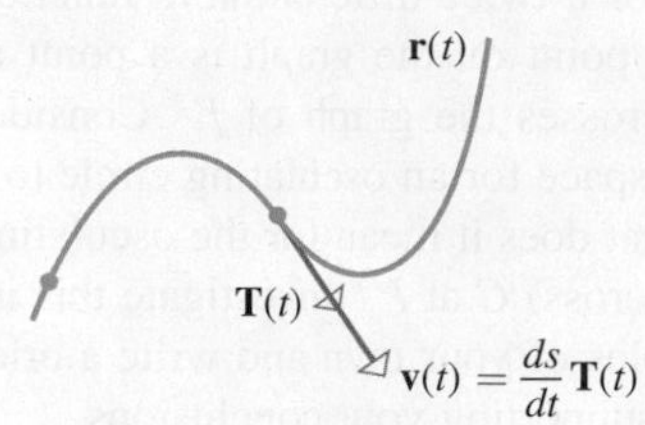


The length of the velocity vector is the speed of the particle, and the direction of the velocity vector is the direction of motion.

▲ Figure 12.6.1

which we call the ***velocity*** of the particle at time $t$. Thus, at each instant of time the velocity vector $\mathbf{v}(t)$ points in the direction of motion and has a magnitude that is equal to the speed of the particle (Figure 12.6.1).

Recall that for motion along a coordinate line the velocity function is the derivative of the position function. The same is true for motion along a curve, since

$$\frac{d\mathbf{r}}{dt} = \frac{d\mathbf{r}}{ds}\frac{ds}{dt} = \frac{ds}{dt}\mathbf{T}(t) = \mathbf{v}(t)$$

For motion along a coordinate line, the acceleration function was defined to be the derivative of the velocity function. The definition is the same for motion along a curve.

**12.6.1 DEFINITION** If $\mathbf{r}(t)$ is the position function of a particle moving along a curve in 2-space or 3-space, then the ***instantaneous velocity***, ***instantaneous acceleration***, and ***instantaneous speed*** of the particle at time $t$ are defined by

$$\text{velocity} = \mathbf{v}(t) = \frac{d\mathbf{r}}{dt} \tag{2}$$

$$\text{acceleration} = \mathbf{a}(t) = \frac{d\mathbf{v}}{dt} = \frac{d^2\mathbf{r}}{dt^2} \tag{3}$$

$$\text{speed} = \|\mathbf{v}(t)\| = \frac{ds}{dt} \tag{4}$$

As shown in Table 12.6.1, the position, velocity, acceleration, and speed can also be expressed in component form.

**Table 12.6.1**

FORMULAS FOR POSITION, VELOCITY, ACCELERATION, AND SPEED

| | 2-SPACE | 3-SPACE |
|---|---|---|
| POSITION | $\mathbf{r}(t) = x(t)\mathbf{i} + y(t)\mathbf{j}$ | $\mathbf{r}(t) = x(t)\mathbf{i} + y(t)\mathbf{j} + z(t)\mathbf{k}$ |
| VELOCITY | $\mathbf{v}(t) = \frac{dx}{dt}\mathbf{i} + \frac{dy}{dt}\mathbf{j}$ | $\mathbf{v}(t) = \frac{dx}{dt}\mathbf{i} + \frac{dy}{dt}\mathbf{j} + \frac{dz}{dt}\mathbf{k}$ |
| ACCELERATION | $\mathbf{a}(t) = \frac{d^2x}{dt^2}\mathbf{i} + \frac{d^2y}{dt^2}\mathbf{j}$ | $\mathbf{a}(t) = \frac{d^2x}{dt^2}\mathbf{i} + \frac{d^2y}{dt^2}\mathbf{j} + \frac{d^2z}{dt^2}\mathbf{k}$ |
| SPEED | $\|\mathbf{v}(t)\| = \sqrt{\left(\frac{dx}{dt}\right)^2 + \left(\frac{dy}{dt}\right)^2}$ | $\|\mathbf{v}(t)\| = \sqrt{\left(\frac{dx}{dt}\right)^2 + \left(\frac{dy}{dt}\right)^2 + \left(\frac{dz}{dt}\right)^2}$ |

▶ **Example 1** A particle moves along a circular path in such a way that its $x$- and $y$-coordinates at time $t$ are

$$x = 2\cos t, \quad y = 2\sin t$$

(a) Find the instantaneous velocity and speed of the particle at time $t$.

(b) Sketch the path of the particle, and show the position and velocity vectors at time $t = \pi/4$ with the velocity vector drawn so that its initial point is at the tip of the position vector.

(c) Show that at each instant the acceleration vector is perpendicular to the velocity vector.

***Solution (a).*** At time $t$, the position vector is

$$\mathbf{r}(t) = 2\cos t\mathbf{i} + 2\sin t\mathbf{j}$$

so the instantaneous velocity and speed are

$$\mathbf{v}(t) = \frac{d\mathbf{r}}{dt} = -2\sin t\mathbf{i} + 2\cos t\mathbf{j}$$

$$\|\mathbf{v}(t)\| = \sqrt{(-2\sin t)^2 + (2\cos t)^2} = 2$$

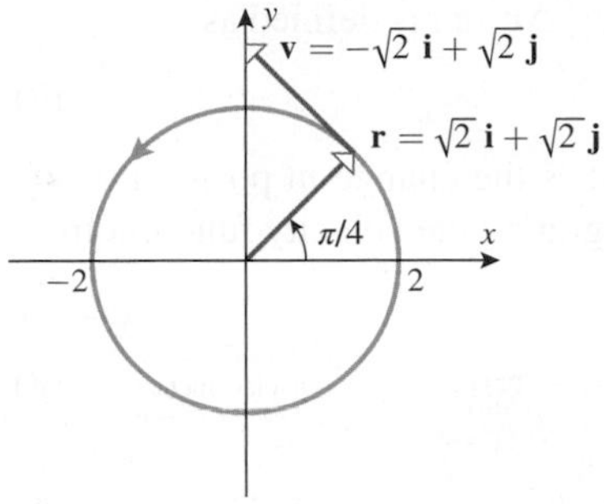


▲ Figure 12.6.2

***Solution (b).*** The graph of the parametric equations is a circle of radius 2 centered at the origin. At time $t = \pi/4$ the position and velocity vectors of the particle are

$$\mathbf{r}(\pi/4) = 2\cos(\pi/4)\mathbf{i} + 2\sin(\pi/4)\mathbf{j} = \sqrt{2}\mathbf{i} + \sqrt{2}\mathbf{j}$$

$$\mathbf{v}(\pi/4) = -2\sin(\pi/4)\mathbf{i} + 2\cos(\pi/4)\mathbf{j} = -\sqrt{2}\mathbf{i} + \sqrt{2}\mathbf{j}$$

These vectors and the circle are shown in Figure 12.6.2.

***Solution (c).*** At time $t$, the acceleration vector is

$$\mathbf{a}(t) = \frac{d\mathbf{v}}{dt} = -2\cos t\mathbf{i} - 2\sin t\mathbf{j}$$

How could you apply Theorem 12.2.8 to answer part (c) of Example 1?

One way of showing that $\mathbf{v}(t)$ and $\mathbf{a}(t)$ are perpendicular is to show that their dot product is zero (try it). However, it is easier to observe that $\mathbf{a}(t)$ is the negative of $\mathbf{r}(t)$, which implies that $\mathbf{v}(t)$ and $\mathbf{a}(t)$ are perpendicular, since at each point on a circle the radius and tangent lines are perpendicular. ◀

Since $\mathbf{v}(t)$ can be obtained by differentiating $\mathbf{r}(t)$, and since $\mathbf{a}(t)$ can be obtained by differentiating $\mathbf{v}(t)$, it follows that $\mathbf{r}(t)$ can be obtained by integrating $\mathbf{v}(t)$, and $\mathbf{v}(t)$ can be obtained by integrating $\mathbf{a}(t)$. However, such integrations do not produce unique functions because constants of integration occur. Typically, initial conditions are required to determine these constants.

▶ **Example 2** A particle moves through 3-space in such a way that its velocity is

$$\mathbf{v}(t) = \mathbf{i} + t\mathbf{j} + t^2\mathbf{k}$$

Find the coordinates of the particle at time $t = 1$ given that the particle is at the point $(-1, 2, 4)$ at time $t = 0$.

***Solution.*** Integrating the velocity function to obtain the position function yields

$$\mathbf{r}(t) = \int \mathbf{v}(t)\,dt = \int (\mathbf{i} + t\mathbf{j} + t^2\mathbf{k})\,dt = t\mathbf{i} + \frac{t^2}{2}\mathbf{j} + \frac{t^3}{3}\mathbf{k} + \mathbf{C} \tag{5}$$

where $\mathbf{C}$ is a vector constant of integration. Since the coordinates of the particle at time $t = 0$ are $(-1, 2, 4)$, the position vector at time $t = 0$ is

$$\mathbf{r}(0) = -\mathbf{i} + 2\mathbf{j} + 4\mathbf{k} \tag{6}$$

It follows on substituting $t = 0$ in (5) and equating the result with (6) that

$$\mathbf{C} = -\mathbf{i} + 2\mathbf{j} + 4\mathbf{k}$$

Substituting this value of $\mathbf{C}$ in (5) and simplifying yields

$$\mathbf{r}(t) = (t-1)\mathbf{i} + \left(\frac{t^2}{2} + 2\right)\mathbf{j} + \left(\frac{t^3}{3} + 4\right)\mathbf{k}$$

Thus, at time $t = 1$ the position vector of the particle is

$$\mathbf{r}(1) = 0\mathbf{i} + \frac{5}{2}\mathbf{j} + \frac{13}{3}\mathbf{k}$$

so its coordinates at that instant are $\left(0, \frac{5}{2}, \frac{13}{3}\right)$. ◀

## DISPLACEMENT AND DISTANCE TRAVELED

If a particle travels along a curve $C$ in 2-space or 3-space, the ***displacement*** of the particle over the time interval $t_1 \leq t \leq t_2$ is commonly denoted by $\Delta\mathbf{r}$ and is defined as

$$\Delta\mathbf{r} = \mathbf{r}(t_2) - \mathbf{r}(t_1) \tag{7}$$

(Figure 12.6.3). The displacement vector, which describes the change in position of the particle during the time interval, can be obtained by integrating the velocity function from $t_1$ to $t_2$:

$$\Delta\mathbf{r} = \int_{t_1}^{t_2} \mathbf{v}(t)\,dt = \int_{t_1}^{t_2} \frac{d\mathbf{r}}{dt}\,dt = \mathbf{r}(t)\Big]_{t_1}^{t_2} = \mathbf{r}(t_2) - \mathbf{r}(t_1) \qquad \text{Displacement} \tag{8}$$

It follows from Theorem 12.3.1 that we can find the distance $s$ traveled by a particle over a time interval $t_1 \leq t \leq t_2$ by integrating the speed over that interval, since

$$s = \int_{t_1}^{t_2} \left\|\frac{d\mathbf{r}}{dt}\right\| dt = \int_{t_1}^{t_2} \|\mathbf{v}(t)\|\,dt \qquad \text{Distance traveled} \tag{9}$$

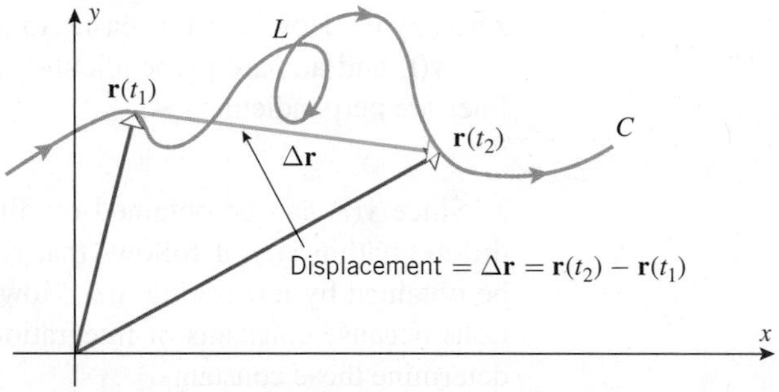


▶ Figure 12.6.3

---

▶ **Example 3** Suppose that a particle moves along a circular helix in 3-space so that its position vector at time $t$ is

$$\mathbf{r}(t) = (4\cos\pi t)\mathbf{i} + (4\sin\pi t)\mathbf{j} + t\mathbf{k}$$

Find the distance traveled and the displacement of the particle during the time interval $1 \leq t \leq 5$.

***Solution.*** We have

$$\mathbf{v}(t) = \frac{d\mathbf{r}}{dt} = (-4\pi\sin\pi t)\mathbf{i} + (4\pi\cos\pi t)\mathbf{j} + \mathbf{k}$$

$$\|\mathbf{v}(t)\| = \sqrt{(-4\pi\sin\pi t)^2 + (4\pi\cos\pi t)^2 + 1} = \sqrt{16\pi^2 + 1}$$

Thus, it follows from (9) that the distance traveled by the particle from time $t = 1$ to $t = 5$ is

$$s = \int_1^5 \sqrt{16\pi^2 + 1}\,dt = 4\sqrt{16\pi^2 + 1}$$

Moreover, it follows from (8) that the displacement over the time interval is

$$\begin{aligned}\Delta\mathbf{r} &= \mathbf{r}(5) - \mathbf{r}(1)\\ &= (4\cos 5\pi\mathbf{i} + 4\sin 5\pi\mathbf{j} + 5\mathbf{k}) - (4\cos\pi\mathbf{i} + 4\sin\pi\mathbf{j} + \mathbf{k})\\ &= (-4\mathbf{i} + 5\mathbf{k}) - (-4\mathbf{i} + \mathbf{k}) = 4\mathbf{k}\end{aligned}$$

which tells us that the change in the position of the particle over the time interval was 4 units straight up. ◀

## NORMAL AND TANGENTIAL COMPONENTS OF ACCELERATION

You know from your experience as an automobile passenger that if a car speeds up rapidly, then your body is thrown back against the backrest of the seat. You also know that if the car rounds a turn in the road, then your body is thrown toward the outside of the curve—the greater the curvature in the road, the greater this effect. The explanation of these effects can be understood by resolving the velocity and acceleration components of the motion into vector components that are parallel to the unit tangent and unit normal vectors. The following theorem explains how to do this.

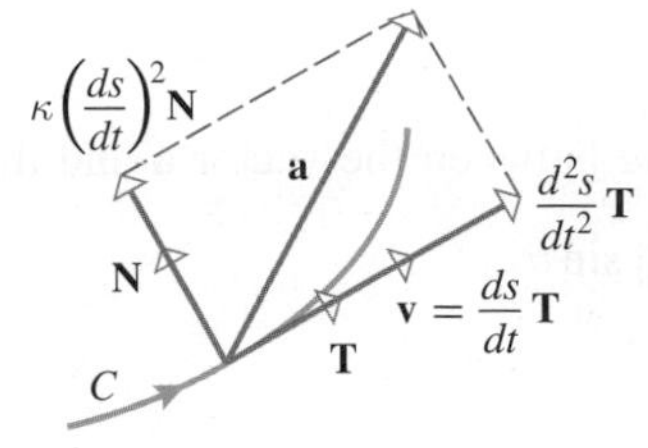


▲ **Figure 12.6.4**

**12.6.2 THEOREM** *If a particle moves along a smooth curve C in 2-space or 3-space, then at each point on the curve velocity and acceleration vectors can be written as*

$$\mathbf{v} = \frac{ds}{dt}\mathbf{T} \qquad \mathbf{a} = \frac{d^2s}{dt^2}\mathbf{T} + \kappa\left(\frac{ds}{dt}\right)^2\mathbf{N} \tag{10–11}$$

*where s is an arc length parameter for the curve, and* **T**, **N**, *and* $\kappa$ *denote the unit tangent vector, unit normal vector, and curvature at the point (Figure 12.6.4).*

PROOF Formula (10) is just a restatement of (1). To obtain (11), we differentiate both sides of (10) with respect to $t$; this yields

$$\begin{aligned}\mathbf{a} = \frac{d}{dt}\left(\frac{ds}{dt}\mathbf{T}\right) &= \frac{d^2s}{dt^2}\mathbf{T} + \frac{ds}{dt}\frac{d\mathbf{T}}{dt}\\ &= \frac{d^2s}{dt^2}\mathbf{T} + \frac{ds}{dt}\frac{d\mathbf{T}}{ds}\frac{ds}{dt}\\ &= \frac{d^2s}{dt^2}\mathbf{T} + \left(\frac{ds}{dt}\right)^2\frac{d\mathbf{T}}{ds}\\ &= \frac{d^2s}{dt^2}\mathbf{T} + \left(\frac{ds}{dt}\right)^2\kappa\mathbf{N}\end{aligned}$$

Formula (10) of Section 12.5

from which (11) follows. ■

The coefficients of **T** and **N** in (11) are commonly denoted by

$$a_T = \frac{d^2s}{dt^2} \qquad a_N = \kappa\left(\frac{ds}{dt}\right)^2 \tag{12–13}$$

in which case Formula (11) is expressed as

$$\mathbf{a} = a_T\mathbf{T} + a_N\mathbf{N} \tag{14}$$

Formula (14) applies to motion in both 2-space and 3-space. What is interesting is that the 3-space formula does not involve the binormal vector **B**, so the acceleration vector always lies in the plane of **T** and **N** (the osculating plane), even for highly twisting paths of motion (Figure 12.6.5).

In this formula the scalars $a_T$ and $a_N$ are called the ***tangential scalar component of acceleration*** and the ***normal scalar component of acceleration***, and the vectors $a_T\mathbf{T}$ and $a_N\mathbf{N}$ are called the ***tangential vector component of acceleration*** and the ***normal vector component of acceleration***.

The scalar components of acceleration explain the effect that you experience when a car speeds up rapidly or rounds a turn. The rapid increase in speed produces a large value for $d^2s/dt^2$, which results in a large tangential scalar component of acceleration; and by Newton's second law this corresponds to a large tangential force on the car in the direction of motion. To understand the effect of rounding a turn, observe that the normal scalar component of acceleration has the curvature $\kappa$ and the square of the speed $ds/dt$ as factors. Thus, sharp turns or turns taken at high speed both correspond to large normal forces on the car.

Although Formulas (12) and (13) provide useful insight into the behavior of particles moving along curved paths, they are not always the best formulas for computations. The following theorem provides some more useful formulas that relate $a_T$, $a_N$, and $\kappa$ to the velocity **v** and acceleration **a**.

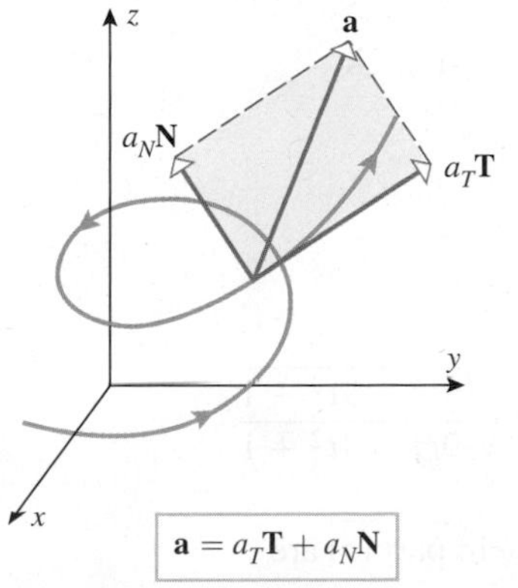


▲ **Figure 12.6.5**

Theorem 12.6.3 applies to motion in 2-space and 3-space, but for motion in 2-space you will have to add a zero **k** component to **v** to calculate the cross product.

**12.6.3 THEOREM** *If a particle moves along a smooth curve C in 2-space or 3-space, then at each point on the curve the velocity* **v** *and the acceleration* **a** *are related to* $a_T$, $a_N$, *and* $\kappa$ *by the formulas*

$$a_T = \frac{\mathbf{v}\cdot\mathbf{a}}{\|\mathbf{v}\|} \qquad a_N = \frac{\|\mathbf{v}\times\mathbf{a}\|}{\|\mathbf{v}\|} \qquad \kappa = \frac{\|\mathbf{v}\times\mathbf{a}\|}{\|\mathbf{v}\|^3} \tag{15–17}$$

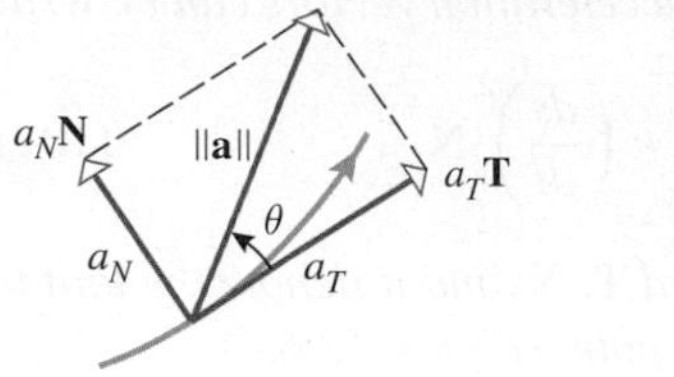


$a_T = \|\mathbf{a}\| \cos\theta$
$a_N = \|\mathbf{a}\| \sin\theta$

▲ **Figure 12.6.6**

PROOF As illustrated in Figure 12.6.6, let $\theta$ be the angle between the vector **a** and the vector $a_T\mathbf{T}$. Thus,

$$a_T = \|\mathbf{a}\|\cos\theta \quad \text{and} \quad a_N = \|\mathbf{a}\|\sin\theta$$

from which we obtain

$$a_T = \|\mathbf{a}\|\cos\theta = \frac{\|\mathbf{v}\|\|\mathbf{a}\|\cos\theta}{\|\mathbf{v}\|} = \frac{\mathbf{v}\cdot\mathbf{a}}{\|\mathbf{v}\|}$$

$$a_N = \|\mathbf{a}\|\sin\theta = \frac{\|\mathbf{v}\|\|\mathbf{a}\|\sin\theta}{\|\mathbf{v}\|} = \frac{\|\mathbf{v}\times\mathbf{a}\|}{\|\mathbf{v}\|}$$

$$\kappa = \frac{a_N}{(ds/dt)^2} = \frac{a_N}{\|\mathbf{v}\|^2} = \frac{1}{\|\mathbf{v}\|^2}\frac{\|\mathbf{v}\times\mathbf{a}\|}{\|\mathbf{v}\|} = \frac{\|\mathbf{v}\times\mathbf{a}\|}{\|\mathbf{v}\|^3} \quad \blacksquare$$

Recall that for nonlinear smooth curves in 2-space the unit normal vector **N** is the inward normal (points toward the concave side of the curve). Explain why the same is true for $a_N\mathbf{N}$.

▶ **Example 4** Suppose that a particle moves through 3-space so that its position vector at time $t$ is

$$\mathbf{r}(t) = t\mathbf{i} + t^2\mathbf{j} + t^3\mathbf{k}$$

(The path is the twisted cubic shown in Figure 12.1.5.)

(a) Find the scalar tangential and normal components of acceleration at time $t$.

(b) Find the scalar tangential and normal components of acceleration at time $t = 1$.

(c) Find the vector tangential and normal components of acceleration at time $t = 1$.

(d) Find the curvature of the path at the point where the particle is located at time $t = 1$.

***Solution (a).*** We have

$$\mathbf{v}(t) = \mathbf{r}'(t) = \mathbf{i} + 2t\mathbf{j} + 3t^2\mathbf{k}$$
$$\mathbf{a}(t) = \mathbf{v}'(t) = 2\mathbf{j} + 6t\mathbf{k}$$
$$\|\mathbf{v}(t)\| = \sqrt{1 + 4t^2 + 9t^4}$$
$$\mathbf{v}(t)\cdot\mathbf{a}(t) = 4t + 18t^3$$
$$\mathbf{v}(t)\times\mathbf{a}(t) = \begin{vmatrix} \mathbf{i} & \mathbf{j} & \mathbf{k} \\ 1 & 2t & 3t^2 \\ 0 & 2 & 6t \end{vmatrix} = 6t^2\mathbf{i} - 6t\mathbf{j} + 2\mathbf{k}$$

Thus, from (15) and (16)

$$a_T = \frac{\mathbf{v}\cdot\mathbf{a}}{\|\mathbf{v}\|} = \frac{4t + 18t^3}{\sqrt{1 + 4t^2 + 9t^4}}$$

$$a_N = \frac{\|\mathbf{v}\times\mathbf{a}\|}{\|\mathbf{v}\|} = \frac{\sqrt{36t^4 + 36t^2 + 4}}{\sqrt{1 + 4t^2 + 9t^4}} = 2\sqrt{\frac{9t^4 + 9t^2 + 1}{9t^4 + 4t^2 + 1}}$$

***Solution (b).*** At time $t = 1$, the components $a_T$ and $a_N$ in part (a) are

$$a_T = \frac{22}{\sqrt{14}} \approx 5.88 \quad \text{and} \quad a_N = 2\sqrt{\frac{19}{14}} \approx 2.33$$

***Solution (c).*** Since **T** and **v** have the same direction, **T** can be obtained by normalizing **v**, that is,

$$\mathbf{T}(t) = \frac{\mathbf{v}(t)}{\|\mathbf{v}(t)\|}$$

At time $t = 1$ we have

$$\mathbf{T}(1) = \frac{\mathbf{v}(1)}{\|\mathbf{v}(1)\|} = \frac{\mathbf{i} + 2\mathbf{j} + 3\mathbf{k}}{\|\mathbf{i} + 2\mathbf{j} + 3\mathbf{k}\|} = \frac{1}{\sqrt{14}}(\mathbf{i} + 2\mathbf{j} + 3\mathbf{k})$$

From this and part (b) we obtain the vector tangential component of acceleration:

$$a_T(1)\mathbf{T}(1) = \frac{22}{\sqrt{14}}\mathbf{T}(1) = \frac{11}{7}(\mathbf{i} + 2\mathbf{j} + 3\mathbf{k}) = \frac{11}{7}\mathbf{i} + \frac{22}{7}\mathbf{j} + \frac{33}{7}\mathbf{k}$$

To find the normal vector component of acceleration, we rewrite $\mathbf{a} = a_T\mathbf{T} + a_N\mathbf{N}$ as

$$a_N\mathbf{N} = \mathbf{a} - a_T\mathbf{T}$$

Thus, at time $t = 1$ the normal vector component of acceleration is

$$\begin{aligned} a_N(1)\mathbf{N}(1) &= \mathbf{a}(1) - a_T(1)\mathbf{T}(1) \\ &= (2\mathbf{j} + 6\mathbf{k}) - \left(\frac{11}{7}\mathbf{i} + \frac{22}{7}\mathbf{j} + \frac{33}{7}\mathbf{k}\right) \\ &= -\frac{11}{7}\mathbf{i} - \frac{8}{7}\mathbf{j} + \frac{9}{7}\mathbf{k} \end{aligned}$$

***Solution (d).*** We will apply Formula (17) with $t = 1$. From part (a)

$$\|\mathbf{v}(1)\| = \sqrt{14} \quad \text{and} \quad \mathbf{v}(1) \times \mathbf{a}(1) = 6\mathbf{i} - 6\mathbf{j} + 2\mathbf{k}$$

Thus, at time $t = 1$

$$\kappa = \frac{\|\mathbf{v} \times \mathbf{a}\|}{\|\mathbf{v}\|^3} = \frac{\sqrt{76}}{(\sqrt{14})^3} = \frac{1}{14}\sqrt{\frac{38}{7}} \approx 0.17 \blacktriangleleft$$

In the case where $\|\mathbf{a}\|$ and $a_T$ are known, there is a useful alternative to Formula (16) for $a_N$ that does not require the calculation of a cross product. It follows algebraically from Formula (14) (see Exercise 51) or geometrically from Figure 12.6.6 and the Theorem of Pythagoras that

$$a_N = \sqrt{\|\mathbf{a}\|^2 - a_T^2} \tag{18}$$

Confirm that the value of $a_N$ computed in Example 4 agrees with the value that results by applying Formula (18).

## A MODEL OF PROJECTILE MOTION

Earlier in this text we examined various problems concerned with objects moving *vertically* in the Earth's gravitational field (see the subsection of Section 5.7 entitled Free-Fall Model and the subsection of Section 8.4 entitled A Model of Free-Fall Motion Retarded by Air Resistance). Now we will consider the motion of a projectile launched along a *curved* path in the Earth's gravitational field. For this purpose we will need the following *vector version* of Newton's Second Law of Motion (6.6.4)

$$\mathbf{F} = m\mathbf{a} \tag{19}$$

and we will need to make three modeling assumptions:

- The mass $m$ of the object is constant.
- The only force acting on the object after it is launched is the force of the Earth's gravity. (Thus, air resistance and the gravitational effect of other planets and celestial objects are ignored.)
- The object remains sufficiently close to the Earth that we can assume the force of gravity to be constant.

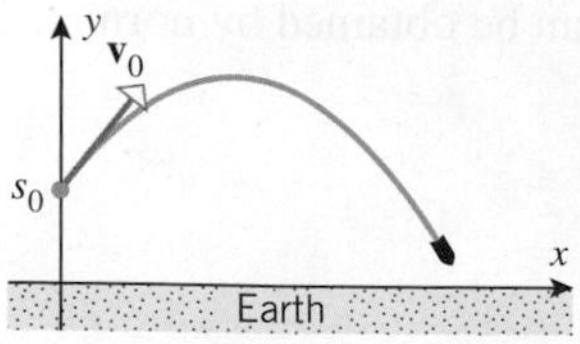


▲ **Figure 12.6.7**

Let us assume that at time $t = 0$ an object of mass $m$ is launched from a height of $s_0$ above the Earth with an initial velocity vector of $\mathbf{v}_0$. Furthermore, let us introduce an $xy$-coordinate system as shown in Figure 12.6.7. In this coordinate system the positive $y$-direction is up, the origin is at the surface of the Earth, and the initial location of the object is $(0, s_0)$. Our objective is to use basic principles of physics to derive the velocity function $\mathbf{v}(t)$ and the position function $\mathbf{r}(t)$ from the acceleration function $\mathbf{a}(t)$ of the object. Our starting point is the physical observation that the downward force $\mathbf{F}$ of the Earth's gravity on an object of mass $m$ is

$$\mathbf{F} = -mg\mathbf{j}$$

where $g$ is the acceleration due to gravity. It follows from this fact and Newton's second law (19) that

$$m\mathbf{a} = -mg\mathbf{j}$$

or on canceling $m$ from both sides

$$\mathbf{a} = -g\mathbf{j} \tag{20}$$

Observe that this acceleration function does not involve $t$ and hence is constant. We can now obtain the velocity function $\mathbf{v}(t)$ by integrating this acceleration function and using the initial condition $\mathbf{v}(0) = \mathbf{v}_0$ to find the constant of integration. Integrating (20) with respect to $t$ and keeping in mind that $-g\mathbf{j}$ is constant yields

$$\mathbf{v}(t) = \int -g\mathbf{j}\,dt = -gt\mathbf{j} + \mathbf{c}_1$$

where $\mathbf{c}_1$ is a vector constant of integration. Substituting $t = 0$ in this equation and using the initial condition $\mathbf{v}(0) = \mathbf{v}_0$ yields $\mathbf{v}_0 = \mathbf{c}_1$. Thus, the velocity function of the object is

$$\mathbf{v}(t) = -gt\mathbf{j} + \mathbf{v}_0 \tag{21}$$

To obtain the position function $\mathbf{r}(t)$ of the object, we will integrate the velocity function and use the known initial position of the object to find the constant of integration. For this purpose observe that the object has coordinates $(0, s_0)$ at time $t = 0$, so the position vector at that time is

$$\mathbf{r}(0) = 0\mathbf{i} + s_0\mathbf{j} = s_0\mathbf{j} \tag{22}$$

This is the initial condition that we will need to find the constant of integration. Integrating (21) with respect to $t$ yields

$$\mathbf{r}(t) = \int (-gt\mathbf{j} + \mathbf{v}_0)\,dt = -\tfrac{1}{2}gt^2\mathbf{j} + t\mathbf{v}_0 + \mathbf{c}_2 \tag{23}$$

where $\mathbf{c}_2$ is another vector constant of integration. Substituting $t = 0$ in (23) and using initial condition (22) yields

$$s_0\mathbf{j} = \mathbf{c}_2$$

so that (23) can be written as

$$\mathbf{r}(t) = \left(-\tfrac{1}{2}gt^2 + s_0\right)\mathbf{j} + t\mathbf{v}_0 \tag{24}$$

This formula expresses the position function of the object in terms of its known initial position and velocity.

Observe that the mass $m$ does not appear in Formulas (21) and (24) and hence has no influence on the velocity or the trajectory of the object. This explains the famous observation of Galileo that two objects of different mass that are released from the same height reach the ground at the same time if air resistance is neglected.

## ■ PARAMETRIC EQUATIONS OF PROJECTILE MOTION

Formulas (21) and (24) can be used to obtain parametric equations for the position and velocity in terms of the initial speed of the object and the angle that the initial velocity vector makes with the positive $x$-axis. For this purpose, let $v_0 = \|\mathbf{v}_0\|$ be the initial speed, let $\alpha$ be the angle that the initial velocity vector $\mathbf{v}_0$ makes with the positive $x$-axis, let $v_x$ and $v_y$ be the horizontal and vertical scalar components of $\mathbf{v}(t)$ at time $t$, and let $x$ and $y$ be the horizontal and vertical components of $\mathbf{r}(t)$ at time $t$. As illustrated in Figure 12.6.8, the initial velocity vector can be expressed as

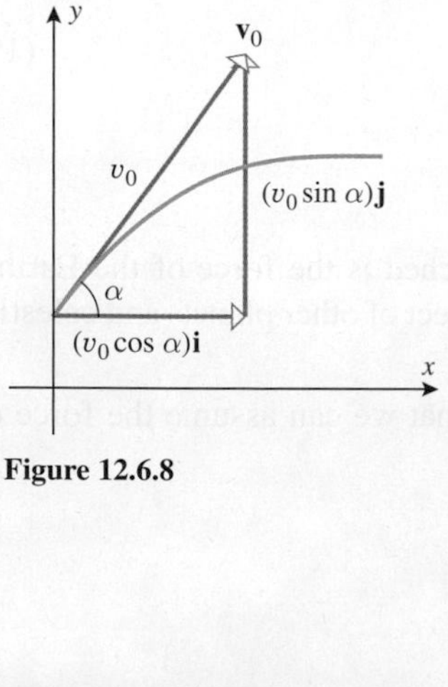


▲ **Figure 12.6.8**

$$\mathbf{v}_0 = (v_0\cos\alpha)\mathbf{i} + (v_0\sin\alpha)\mathbf{j} \tag{25}$$

Substituting this expression in (24) and combining like components yields (verify)

$$\mathbf{r}(t) = (v_0 \cos\alpha)t\mathbf{i} + \left(s_0 + (v_0 \sin\alpha)t - \tfrac{1}{2}gt^2\right)\mathbf{j} \tag{26}$$

which is equivalent to the parametric equations

$$x = (v_0 \cos\alpha)t, \quad y = s_0 + (v_0 \sin\alpha)t - \tfrac{1}{2}gt^2 \tag{27}$$

Similarly, substituting (25) in (21) and combining like components yields

$$\mathbf{v}(t) = (v_0 \cos\alpha)\mathbf{i} + (v_0 \sin\alpha - gt)\mathbf{j}$$

which is equivalent to the parametric equations

$$v_x = v_0 \cos\alpha, \quad v_y = v_0 \sin\alpha - gt \tag{28}$$

The parameter $t$ can be eliminated in (27) by solving the first equation for $t$ and substituting in the second equation. We leave it for you to show that this yields

$$y = s_0 + (\tan\alpha)x - \left(\frac{g}{2v_0^2 \cos^2\alpha}\right)x^2 \tag{29}$$

which is the equation of a parabola, since the right side is a quadratic polynomial in $x$. Thus, we have shown that the trajectory of the projectile is a parabolic arc.

▶ **Example 5** A shell, fired from a cannon, has a muzzle speed (the speed as it leaves the barrel) of 800 ft/s. The barrel makes an angle of 45° with the horizontal and, for simplicity, the barrel opening is assumed to be at ground level.

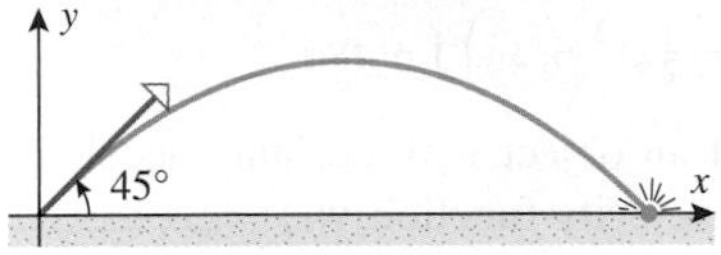

▲ Figure 12.6.9

(a) Find parametric equations for the shell's trajectory relative to the coordinate system in Figure 12.6.9.

(b) How high does the shell rise?

(c) How far does the shell travel horizontally?

(d) What is the speed of the shell at its point of impact with the ground?

***Solution (a).*** From (27) with $v_0 = 800$ ft/s, $\alpha = 45°$, $s_0 = 0$ ft (since the shell starts at ground level), and $g = 32$ ft/s$^2$, we obtain the parametric equations

$$x = (800 \cos 45°)t, \quad y = (800 \sin 45°)t - 16t^2 \quad (t \geq 0)$$

which simplify to

$$x = 400\sqrt{2}t, \quad y = 400\sqrt{2}t - 16t^2 \quad (t \geq 0) \tag{30}$$

***Solution (b).*** The maximum height of the shell is the maximum value of $y$ in (30), which occurs when $dy/dt = 0$, that is, when

$$400\sqrt{2} - 32t = 0 \quad \text{or} \quad t = \frac{25\sqrt{2}}{2}$$

Substituting this value of $t$ in (30) yields

$$y = 5000 \text{ ft}$$

as the maximum height of the shell.

***Solution (c).*** The shell will hit the ground when $y = 0$. From (30), this occurs when

$$400\sqrt{2}t - 16t^2 = 0 \quad \text{or} \quad t(400\sqrt{2} - 16t) = 0$$

The solution $t = 0$ corresponds to the initial position of the shell and the solution $t = 25\sqrt{2}$ to the time of impact. Substituting the latter value in the equation for $x$ in (30) yields

$$x = 20{,}000 \text{ ft}$$

as the horizontal distance traveled by the shell.

***Solution (d).*** From (30), the position function of the shell is

$$\mathbf{r}(t) = 400\sqrt{2}t\mathbf{i} + (400\sqrt{2}t - 16t^2)\mathbf{j}$$

so that the velocity function is

$$\mathbf{v}(t) = \mathbf{r}'(t) = 400\sqrt{2}\mathbf{i} + (400\sqrt{2} - 32t)\mathbf{j}$$

From part (c), impact occurs when $t = 25\sqrt{2}$, so the velocity vector at this point is

$$\mathbf{v}(25\sqrt{2}) = 400\sqrt{2}\mathbf{i} + [400\sqrt{2} - 32(25\sqrt{2})]\mathbf{j} = 400\sqrt{2}\mathbf{i} - 400\sqrt{2}\mathbf{j}$$

Thus, the speed at impact is

$$\|\mathbf{v}(25\sqrt{2})\| = \sqrt{(400\sqrt{2})^2 + (-400\sqrt{2})^2} = 800 \text{ ft/s} \blacktriangleleft$$

The speed at impact and the muzzle speed of the shell in Example 5 are the same. Is this an expected result? Explain.

## ✓ QUICK CHECK EXERCISES 12.6 (See page 793 for answers.)

**1.** If $\mathbf{r}(t)$ is the position function of a particle, then the velocity, acceleration, and speed of the particle at time $t$ are given, respectively, by

$$\mathbf{v}(t) = \_\_\_\_\_\_, \quad \mathbf{a}(t) = \_\_\_\_\_\_, \quad \frac{ds}{dt} = \_\_\_\_\_\_$$

**2.** If $\mathbf{r}(t)$ is the position function of a particle, then the displacement of the particle over the time interval $t_1 \le t \le t_2$ is ______, and the distance $s$ traveled by the particle during this time interval is given by the integral ______.

**3.** The tangential scalar component of acceleration is given by the formula ______, and the normal scalar component of acceleration is given by the formula ______.

**4.** The projectile motion model

$$\mathbf{r}(t) = \left(-\tfrac{1}{2}gt^2 + s_0\right)\mathbf{j} + t\mathbf{v}_0$$

describes the motion of an object with constant acceleration $\mathbf{a} =$ ______ and velocity function $\mathbf{v}(t) =$ ______. The initial position of the object is ______ and its initial velocity is ______.

## EXERCISE SET 12.6 Graphing Utility C CAS

**1–4** In these exercises $\mathbf{r}(t)$ is the position vector of a particle moving in the plane. Find the velocity, acceleration, and speed at an arbitrary time $t$. Then sketch the path of the particle together with the velocity and acceleration vectors at the indicated time $t$. ■

**1.** $\mathbf{r}(t) = 3\cos t\mathbf{i} + 3\sin t\mathbf{j};\ t = \pi/3$

**2.** $\mathbf{r}(t) = t\mathbf{i} + t^2\mathbf{j};\ t = 2$

**3.** $\mathbf{r}(t) = e^t\mathbf{i} + e^{-t}\mathbf{j};\ t = 0$

**4.** $\mathbf{r}(t) = (2 + 4t)\mathbf{i} + (1 - t)\mathbf{j};\ t = 1$

**5–8** Find the velocity, speed, and acceleration at the given time $t$ of a particle moving along the given curve. ■

**5.** $\mathbf{r}(t) = t\mathbf{i} + \frac{1}{2}t^2\mathbf{j} + \frac{1}{3}t^3\mathbf{k};\ t = 1$

**6.** $x = 1 + 3t, y = 2 - 4t, z = 7 + t;\ t = 2$

**7.** $x = 2\cos t, y = 2\sin t, z = t;\ t = \pi/4$

**8.** $\mathbf{r}(t) = e^t \sin t\mathbf{i} + e^t \cos t\mathbf{j} + t\mathbf{k};\ t = \pi/2$

**FOCUS ON CONCEPTS**

**9.** As illustrated in the accompanying figure, suppose that the equations of motion of a particle moving along an elliptic path are $x = a\cos\omega t$, $y = b\sin\omega t$.

(a) Show that the acceleration is directed toward the origin.

(b) Show that the magnitude of the acceleration is proportional to the distance from the particle to the origin.

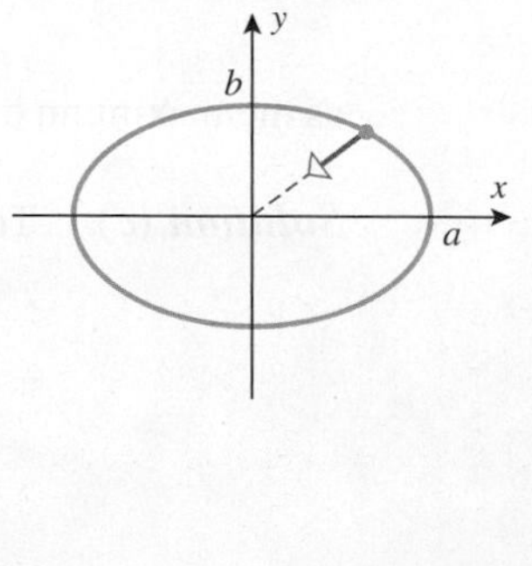


◀ **Figure Ex-9**

**10.** Suppose that a particle vibrates in such a way that its position function is $\mathbf{r}(t) = 16 \sin \pi t\mathbf{i} + 4 \cos 2\pi t\mathbf{j}$, where distance is in millimeters and $t$ is in seconds.
(a) Find the velocity and acceleration at time $t = 1$ s.
(b) Show that the particle moves along a parabolic curve.
(c) Show that the particle moves back and forth along the curve.

**11.** What can you say about the trajectory of a particle that moves in 2-space or 3-space with zero acceleration? Justify your answer.

**12.** Recall from Theorem 12.2.8 that if $\mathbf{r}(t)$ is a vector-valued function in 2-space or 3-space, and if $\|\mathbf{r}(t)\|$ is constant for all $t$, then $\mathbf{r}(t) \cdot \mathbf{r}'(t) = 0$.
(a) Translate this theorem into a statement about the motion of a particle in 2-space or 3-space.
(b) Replace $\mathbf{r}(t)$ by $\mathbf{r}'(t)$ in the theorem, and translate the result into a statement about the motion of a particle in 2-space or 3-space.

**13.** Suppose that the position vector of a particle moving in the plane is $\mathbf{r} = 12\sqrt{t}\mathbf{i} + t^{3/2}\mathbf{j}, t > 0$. Find the minimum speed of the particle and its location when it has this speed.

**14.** Suppose that the motion of a particle is described by the position vector $\mathbf{r} = (t - t^2)\mathbf{i} - t^2\mathbf{j}$. Find the minimum speed of the particle and its location when it has this speed.

**15.** Suppose that the position function of a particle moving in 2-space is $\mathbf{r} = \sin 3t\mathbf{i} - 2 \cos 3t\mathbf{j}, 0 \le t \le 2\pi/3$.
(a) Use a graphing utility to graph the speed of the particle versus time from $t = 0$ to $t = 2\pi/3$.
(b) What are the maximum and minimum speeds of the particle?
(c) Use the graph to estimate the time at which the maximum speed first occurs.
(d) Find the exact time at which the maximum speed first occurs.

**16.** Suppose that the position function of a particle moving in 3-space is $\mathbf{r} = 3 \cos 2t\mathbf{i} + \sin 2t\mathbf{j} + 4t\mathbf{k}$.
(a) Use a graphing utility to graph the speed of the particle versus time from $t = 0$ to $t = \pi$.
(b) Use the graph to estimate the maximum and minimum speeds of the particle.
(c) Use the graph to estimate the time at which the maximum speed first occurs.
(d) Find the exact values of the maximum and minimum speeds and the exact time at which the maximum speed first occurs.

**17–20** Use the given information to find the position and velocity vectors of the particle. ■

**17.** $\mathbf{a}(t) = -\cos t\mathbf{i} - \sin t\mathbf{j};\ \mathbf{v}(0) = \mathbf{i};\ \mathbf{r}(0) = \mathbf{j}$

**18.** $\mathbf{a}(t) = \mathbf{i} + e^{-t}\mathbf{j};\ \mathbf{v}(0) = 2\mathbf{i} + \mathbf{j};\ \mathbf{r}(0) = \mathbf{i} - \mathbf{j}$

**19.** $\mathbf{a}(t) = \sin t\mathbf{i} + \cos t\mathbf{j} + e^t\mathbf{k};\ \mathbf{v}(0) = \mathbf{k};\ \mathbf{r}(0) = -\mathbf{i} + \mathbf{k}$

**20.** $\mathbf{a}(t) = (t+1)^{-2}\mathbf{j} - e^{-2t}\mathbf{k};\ \mathbf{v}(0) = 3\mathbf{i} - \mathbf{j};\ \mathbf{r}(0) = 2\mathbf{k}$

**21.** Find, to the nearest degree, the angle between $\mathbf{v}$ and $\mathbf{a}$ for $\mathbf{r} = t^3\mathbf{i} + t^2\mathbf{j}$ when $t = 1$.

**22.** Show that the angle between $\mathbf{v}$ and $\mathbf{a}$ is constant for the position vector $\mathbf{r} = e^t \cos t\mathbf{i} + e^t \sin t\mathbf{j}$. Find the angle.

**23.** (a) Suppose that at time $t = t_0$ an electron has a position vector of $\mathbf{r} = 3.5\mathbf{i} - 1.7\mathbf{j} + \mathbf{k}$, and at a later time $t = t_1$ it has a position vector of $\mathbf{r} = 4.2\mathbf{i} + \mathbf{j} - 2.4\mathbf{k}$. What is the displacement of the electron during the time interval from $t_0$ to $t_1$?
(b) Suppose that during a certain time interval a proton has a displacement of $\Delta\mathbf{r} = 0.7\mathbf{i} + 2.9\mathbf{j} - 1.2\mathbf{k}$ and its final position vector is known to be $\mathbf{r} = 3.6\mathbf{k}$. What was the initial position vector of the proton?

**24.** Suppose that the position function of a particle moving along a circle in the $xy$-plane is $\mathbf{r} = 5 \cos 2\pi t\mathbf{i} + 5 \sin 2\pi t\mathbf{j}$.
(a) Sketch some typical displacement vectors over the time interval from $t = 0$ to $t = 1$.
(b) What is the distance traveled by the particle during the time interval?

**25–28** Find the displacement and the distance traveled over the indicated time interval. ■

**25.** $\mathbf{r} = t^2\mathbf{i} + \frac{1}{3}t^3\mathbf{j};\ 1 \le t \le 3$

**26.** $\mathbf{r} = (1 - 3\sin t)\mathbf{i} + 3\cos t\mathbf{j};\ 0 \le t \le 3\pi/2$

**27.** $\mathbf{r} = e^t\mathbf{i} + e^{-t}\mathbf{j} + \sqrt{2}t\mathbf{k};\ 0 \le t \le \ln 3$

**28.** $\mathbf{r} = \cos 2t\mathbf{i} + (1 - \cos 2t)\mathbf{j} + \left(3 + \frac{1}{2}\cos 2t\right)\mathbf{k};\ 0 \le t \le \pi$

**29–30** The position vectors $\mathbf{r}_1$ and $\mathbf{r}_2$ of two particles are given. Show that the particles move along the same path but the speed of the first is constant and the speed of the second is not. ■

**29.** $\mathbf{r}_1 = 2\cos 3t\mathbf{i} + 2\sin 3t\mathbf{j}$
$\mathbf{r}_2 = 2\cos(t^2)\mathbf{i} + 2\sin(t^2)\mathbf{j} \quad (t \ge 0)$

**30.** $\mathbf{r}_1 = (3 + 2t)\mathbf{i} + t\mathbf{j} + (1 - t)\mathbf{k}$
$\mathbf{r}_2 = (5 - 2t^3)\mathbf{i} + (1 - t^3)\mathbf{j} + t^3\mathbf{k}$

**31–36** The position function of a particle is given. Use Theorem 12.6.3 to find
(a) the scalar tangential and normal components of acceleration at the stated time $t$;
(b) the vector tangential and normal components of acceleration at the stated time $t$;
(c) the curvature of the path at the point where the particle is located at the stated time $t$. ■

**31.** $\mathbf{r} = e^{-t}\mathbf{i} + e^t\mathbf{j};\ t = 0$

**32.** $\mathbf{r} = \cos(t^2)\mathbf{i} + \sin(t^2)\mathbf{j};\ t = \sqrt{\pi}/2$

**33.** $\mathbf{r} = (t^3 - 2t)\mathbf{i} + (t^2 - 4)\mathbf{j};\ t = 1$

**34.** $\mathbf{r} = e^t\cos t\mathbf{i} + e^t\sin t\mathbf{j};\ t = \pi/4$

**35.** $\mathbf{r} = e^t\mathbf{i} + e^{-2t}\mathbf{j} + t\mathbf{k};\ t = 0$

**36.** $\mathbf{r} = 3\sin t\mathbf{i} + 2\cos t\mathbf{j} - \sin 2t\mathbf{k};\ t = \pi/2$

**37–38** In these exercises $\mathbf{v}$ and $\mathbf{a}$ are given at a certain instant of time. Find $a_T$, $a_N$, $\mathbf{T}$, and $\mathbf{N}$ at this instant. ■

**37.** $\mathbf{v} = -4\mathbf{j},\ \mathbf{a} = 2\mathbf{i} + 3\mathbf{j}$

**38.** $\mathbf{v} = 2\mathbf{i} + 2\mathbf{j} + \mathbf{k},\ \mathbf{a} = \mathbf{i} + 2\mathbf{k}$

**39–40** The speed $\|\mathbf{v}\|$ of a particle at an arbitrary time $t$ is given. Find the scalar tangential component of acceleration at the indicated time. ■

**39.** $\|\mathbf{v}\| = \sqrt{t^2 + e^{-3t}}$; $t = 0$

**40.** $\|\mathbf{v}\| = \sqrt{(4t-1)^2 + \cos^2 \pi t}$; $t = \frac{1}{4}$

**41.** The nuclear accelerator at the Enrico Fermi Laboratory is circular with a radius of 1 km. Find the scalar normal component of acceleration of a proton moving around the accelerator with a constant speed of $2.9 \times 10^5$ km/s.

**42.** Suppose that a particle moves with nonzero acceleration along the curve $y = f(x)$. Use part (b) of Exercise 23 in Section 12.5 to show that the acceleration vector is tangent to the curve at each point where $f''(x) = 0$.

**43–44** Use the given information and Exercise 23 of Section 12.5 to find the normal scalar component of acceleration as a function of $x$. ■

**43.** A particle moves along the parabola $y = x^2$ with a constant speed of 3 units per second.

**44.** A particle moves along the curve $x = \ln y$ with a constant speed of 2 units per second.

**45–46** Use the given information to find the normal scalar component of acceleration at time $t = 1$. ■

**45.** $\mathbf{a}(1) = \mathbf{i} + 2\mathbf{j} - 2\mathbf{k}$; $a_T(1) = 3$

**46.** $\|\mathbf{a}(1)\| = 9$; $a_T(1)\mathbf{T}(1) = 2\mathbf{i} - 2\mathbf{j} + \mathbf{k}$

**47–50 True–False** Determine whether the statement is true or false. Explain your answer. ■

**47.** The velocity and unit tangent vectors for a moving particle are parallel.

**48.** If a particle moves along a smooth curve $C$ in 3-space, then at each point on $C$ the normal scalar component of acceleration for the particle is the product of the curvature of $C$ and speed of the particle at the point.

**49.** If a particle is moving along a smooth curve $C$ and passes through a point at which the curvature is zero, then the velocity and acceleration vectors have the same direction at that point.

**50.** The distance traveled by a particle over a time interval is the magnitude of the displacement vector for the particle during that time interval.

**51.** Derive Formula (18) from Formula (14).

**52.** An automobile travels at a constant speed around a curve whose radius of curvature is 1000 m. What is the maximum allowable speed if the maximum acceptable value for the normal scalar component of acceleration is 1.5 m/s$^2$?

**53.** If an automobile of mass $m$ rounds a curve, then its inward vector component of acceleration $a_N\mathbf{N}$ is caused by the frictional force $\mathbf{F}$ of the road. Thus, it follows from the vector form of Newton's second law [Equation (19)] that the frictional force and the normal scalar component of acceleration are related by the equation $\mathbf{F} = ma_N\mathbf{N}$. Thus,

$$\|\mathbf{F}\| = m\kappa\left(\frac{ds}{dt}\right)^2$$

Use this result to find the magnitude of the frictional force in newtons exerted by the road on a 500 kg go-cart driven at a speed of 10 km/h around a circular track of radius 15 m. [*Note:* 1 N = 1 kg·m/s$^2$.]

**54.** A shell is fired from ground level with a muzzle speed of 320 ft/s and elevation angle of 60°. Find
(a) parametric equations for the shell's trajectory
(b) the maximum height reached by the shell
(c) the horizontal distance traveled by the shell
(d) the speed of the shell at impact.

**55.** A rock is thrown downward from the top of a building, 168 ft high, at an angle of 60° with the horizontal. How far from the base of the building will the rock land if its initial speed is 80 ft/s?

**56.** Solve Exercise 55 assuming that the rock is thrown horizontally at a speed of 80 ft/s.

**57.** A shell is to be fired from ground level at an elevation angle of 30°. What should the muzzle speed be in order for the maximum height of the shell to be 2500 ft?

**58.** A shell, fired from ground level at an elevation angle of 45°, hits the ground 24,500 m away. Calculate the muzzle speed of the shell.

**59.** Find two elevation angles that will enable a shell, fired from ground level with a muzzle speed of 800 ft/s, to hit a ground-level target 10,000 ft away.

**60.** A ball rolls off a table 4 ft high while moving at a constant speed of 5 ft/s.
(a) How long does it take for the ball to hit the floor after it leaves the table?
(b) At what speed does the ball hit the floor?
(c) If a ball were dropped from rest at table height just as the rolling ball leaves the table, which ball would hit the ground first? Justify your answer.

**61.** As illustrated in the accompanying figure, a fire hose sprays water with an initial velocity of 40 ft/s at an angle of 60° with the horizontal.
(a) Confirm that the water will clear corner point $A$.
(b) Confirm that the water will hit the roof.
(c) How far from corner point $A$ will the water hit the roof?

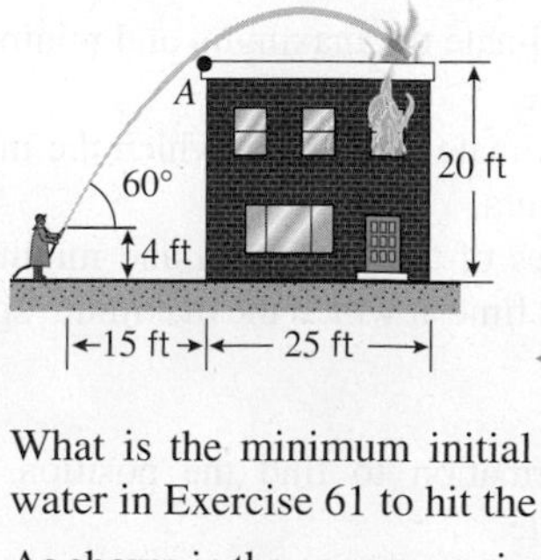


◀ **Figure Ex-61**

**62.** What is the minimum initial velocity that will allow the water in Exercise 61 to hit the roof?

**63.** As shown in the accompanying figure on the next page, water is sprayed from a hose with an initial velocity of 35 m/s at an angle of 45° with the horizontal.
(a) What is the radius of curvature of the stream at the point where it leaves the hose?

*(cont.)*

(b) What is the maximum height of the stream above the nozzle of the hose?

**64.** As illustrated in the accompanying figure, a train is traveling on a curved track. At a point where the train is traveling at a speed of 132 ft/s and the radius of curvature of the track is 3000 ft, the engineer hits the brakes to make the train slow down at a constant rate of 7.5 ft/s$^2$.
(a) Find the magnitude of the acceleration vector at the instant the engineer hits the brakes.
(b) Approximate the angle between the acceleration vector and the unit tangent vector **T** at the instant the engineer hits the brakes.

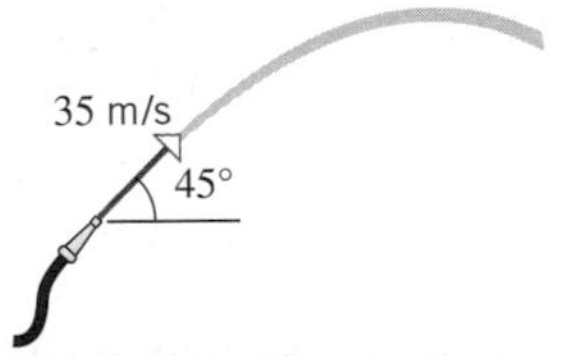

▲ **Figure Ex-63**

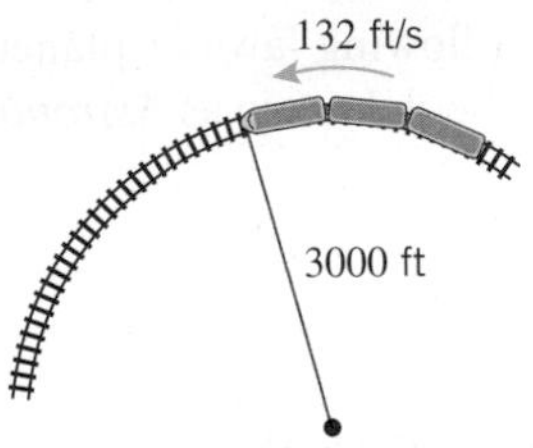

▲ **Figure Ex-64**

**65.** A shell is fired from ground level at an elevation angle of $\alpha$ and a muzzle speed of $v_0$.
(a) Show that the maximum height reached by the shell is
$$\text{maximum height} = \frac{(v_0 \sin \alpha)^2}{2g}$$
(b) The ***horizontal range*** $R$ of the shell is the horizontal distance traveled when the shell returns to ground level. Show that $R = (v_0^2 \sin 2\alpha)/g$. For what elevation angle will the range be maximum? What is the maximum range?

**66.** A shell is fired from ground level with an elevation angle $\alpha$ and a muzzle speed of $v_0$. Find two angles that can be used to hit a target at ground level that is a distance of three-fourths the maximum range of the shell. Express your answer to the nearest tenth of a degree. [*Hint:* See Exercise 65(b).]

**67.** At time $t = 0$ a baseball that is 5 ft above the ground is hit with a bat. The ball leaves the bat with a speed of 80 ft/s at an angle of 30° above the horizontal.
(a) How long will it take for the baseball to hit the ground? Express your answer to the nearest hundredth of a second.
(b) Use the result in part (a) to find the horizontal distance traveled by the ball. Express your answer to the nearest tenth of a foot.

**68.** Repeat Exercise 67, assuming that the ball leaves the bat with a speed of 70 ft/s at an angle of 60° above the horizontal.

C **69.** At time $t = 0$ a skier leaves the end of a ski jump with a speed of $v_0$ ft/s at an angle $\alpha$ with the horizontal (see the accompanying figure). The skier lands 259 ft down the incline 2.9 s later.
(a) Approximate $v_0$ to the nearest ft/s and $\alpha$ to the nearest degree. [*Note:* Use $g = 32$ ft/s$^2$ as the acceleration due to gravity.]
(b) Use a CAS or a calculating utility with a numerical integration capability to approximate the distance traveled by the skier.

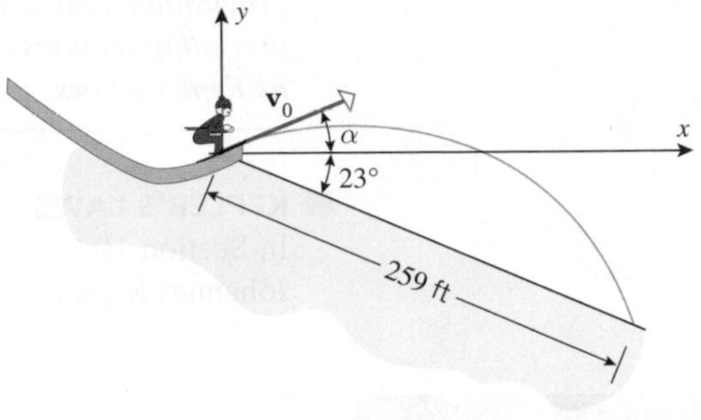

▲ **Figure Ex-69**

**70.** At time $t = 0$ a projectile is fired from a height $h$ above level ground at an elevation angle of $\alpha$ with a speed $v$. Let $R$ be the horizontal distance to the point where the projectile hits the ground.
(a) Show that $\alpha$ and $R$ must satisfy the equation
$$g(\sec^2 \alpha)R^2 - 2v^2(\tan \alpha)R - 2v^2 h = 0$$
(b) If $g, h,$ and $v$ are constant, then the equation in part (a) defines $R$ implicitly as a function of $\alpha$. Let $R_0$ be the maximum value of $R$ and $\alpha_0$ the value of $\alpha$ when $R = R_0$. Use implicit differentiation to find $dR/d\alpha$ and show that
$$\tan \alpha_0 = \frac{v^2}{gR_0}$$
[*Hint:* Assume that $dR/d\alpha = 0$ when $R$ attains a maximum.]
(c) Use the results in parts (a) and (b) to show that
$$R_0 = \frac{v}{g}\sqrt{v^2 + 2gh}$$
and
$$\alpha_0 = \tan^{-1} \frac{v}{\sqrt{v^2 + 2gh}}$$

**71. Writing** Consider the various forces that a passenger in a car would sense while traveling over the crest of a hill or around a curve. Relate these sensations to the tangential and normal vector components of the acceleration vector for the car's motion. Discuss how speeding up or slowing down (e.g., doubling or halving the car's speed) affects these components.

**72. Writing** The formula
$$\mathbf{r}(t) = (v_0 \cos \alpha)t\mathbf{i} + (s_0 + (v_0 \sin \alpha)t - \tfrac{1}{2}gt^2)\mathbf{j}$$
models a position function for projectile motion [Formula (26)]. Identify the various quantities ($v_0, \alpha, s_0,$ and $g$) in this formula and discuss how the formula is derived, including any assumptions that are made.

✓ **QUICK CHECK ANSWERS 12.6** 1. $\dfrac{d\mathbf{r}}{dt}$; $\dfrac{d\mathbf{v}}{dt} = \dfrac{d^2\mathbf{r}}{dt^2}$; $\|\mathbf{v}(t)\|$ 2. $\mathbf{r}(t_2) - \mathbf{r}(t_1)$; $\displaystyle\int_{t_1}^{t_2} \|\mathbf{v}(t)\|\, dt$ 3. $\dfrac{d^2 s}{dt^2}$; $\kappa(ds/dt)^2$ 4. $-g\mathbf{j}$; $-gt\mathbf{j} + \mathbf{v}_0$; $s_0\mathbf{j}$; $\mathbf{v}_0$

# 12.7 KEPLER'S LAWS OF PLANETARY MOTION

*One of the great advances in the history of astronomy occurred in the early 1600s when Johannes Kepler* deduced from empirical data that all planets in our solar system move in elliptical orbits with the Sun at a focus. Subsequently, Isaac Newton showed mathematically that such planetary motion is the consequence of an inverse-square law of gravitational attraction. In this section we will use the concepts developed in the preceding sections of this chapter to derive three basic laws of planetary motion, known as **Kepler's laws**.*

## KEPLER'S LAWS

In Section 10.6 we stated the following laws of planetary motion that were published by Johannes Kepler in 1609 in his book known as *Astronomia Nova*.

cigdem/Shutterstock

*The planets in our solar system move in accordance with Kepler's three laws.*

**12.7.1 KEPLER'S LAWS**

- First law (***Law of Orbits***). Each planet moves in an elliptical orbit with the Sun at a focus.
- Second law (***Law of Areas***). Equal areas are swept out in equal times by the line from the Sun to a planet.
- Third law (***Law of Periods***). The square of a planet's period (the time it takes the planet to complete one orbit about the Sun) is proportional to the cube of the semimajor axis of its orbit.

## CENTRAL FORCES

If a particle moves under the influence of a *single* force that is always directed toward a fixed point $O$, then the particle is said to be moving in a ***central force field***. The force is called a ***central force***, and the point $O$ is called the ***center of force***. For example, in the simplest model of planetary motion, it is assumed that the only force acting on a planet is the force of the Sun's gravity, directed toward the center of the Sun. This model, which produces Kepler's laws, ignores the forces that other celestial objects exert on the planet as well as the minor effect that the planet's gravity has on the Sun. Central force models are also used to study the motion of comets, asteroids, planetary moons, and artificial satellites. They also have important applications in electromagnetics. Our objective in this section is to develop some basic principles about central force fields and then use those results to derive Kepler's laws.

Suppose that a particle $P$ of mass $m$ moves in a central force field due to a force $\mathbf{F}$ that is directed toward a fixed point $O$, and let $\mathbf{r} = \mathbf{r}(t)$ be the position vector from $O$ to $P$ (Figure 12.7.1). Let $\mathbf{v} = \mathbf{v}(t)$ and $\mathbf{a} = \mathbf{a}(t)$ be the velocity and acceleration functions of the particle, and assume that $\mathbf{F}$ and $\mathbf{a}$ are related by Newton's second law ($\mathbf{F} = m\mathbf{a}$).

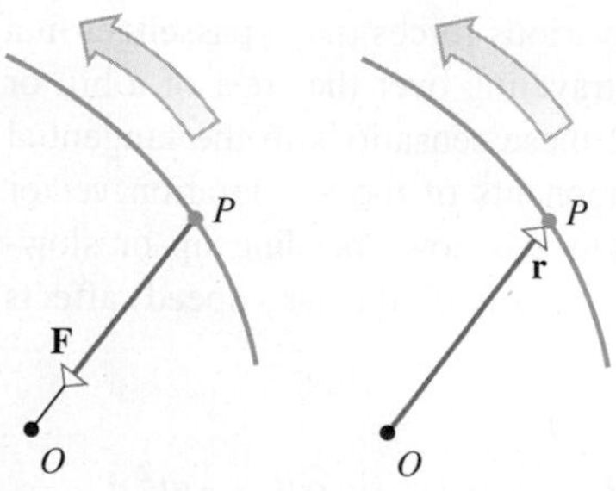


▲ Figure 12.7.1

Our first objective is to show that the particle $P$ moves in a plane containing the point $O$. For this purpose observe that $\mathbf{a}$ has the same direction as $\mathbf{F}$ by Newton's second law, and this implies that $\mathbf{a}$ and $\mathbf{r}$ are oppositely directed vectors. Thus, it follows from part (*c*) of Theorem 11.4.5 that

$$\mathbf{r} \times \mathbf{a} = \mathbf{0}$$

Since the velocity and acceleration of the particle are given by $\mathbf{v} = d\mathbf{r}/dt$ and $\mathbf{a} = d\mathbf{v}/dt$, respectively, we have

$$\frac{d}{dt}(\mathbf{r} \times \mathbf{v}) = \mathbf{r} \times \frac{d\mathbf{v}}{dt} + \frac{d\mathbf{r}}{dt} \times \mathbf{v} = (\mathbf{r} \times \mathbf{a}) + (\mathbf{v} \times \mathbf{v}) = \mathbf{0} + \mathbf{0} = \mathbf{0} \tag{1}$$

* See biography on p. 666.

Astronomers call the plane containing the orbit of a planet the ***ecliptic*** of the planet.

Integrating the left and right sides of this equation with respect to $t$ yields

$$\mathbf{r} \times \mathbf{v} = \mathbf{b} \tag{2}$$

where $\mathbf{b}$ is a constant (independent of $t$). However, $\mathbf{b}$ is orthogonal to both $\mathbf{r}$ and $\mathbf{v}$, so we can conclude that $\mathbf{r} = \mathbf{r}(t)$ and $\mathbf{v} = \mathbf{v}(t)$ lie in a fixed plane containing the point $O$.

## NEWTON'S LAW OF UNIVERSAL GRAVITATION

Our next objective is to derive the position function of a particle moving under a central force in a polar coordinate system. For this purpose we will need the following result, known as ***Newton's Law of Universal Gravitation***.

**12.7.2 NEWTON'S LAW OF UNIVERSAL GRAVITATION** Every particle of matter in the Universe attracts every other particle of matter in the Universe with a force that is proportional to the product of their masses and inversely proportional to the square of the distance between them. Specifically, if a particle of mass $M$ and a particle of mass $m$ are at a distance $r$ from each other, then they attract each other with equal and opposite forces, $\mathbf{F}$ and $-\mathbf{F}$, of magnitude

$$\|\mathbf{F}\| = \frac{GMm}{r^2} \tag{3}$$

where $G$ is a constant called the ***universal gravitational constant***.

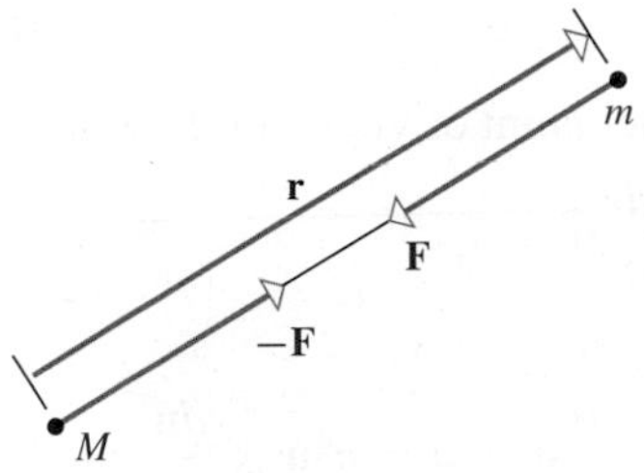


$M$ exerts force $\mathbf{F}$ on $m$, and $m$ exerts force $-\mathbf{F}$ on $M$.

▲ **Figure 12.7.2**

To obtain a formula for the vector force $\mathbf{F}$ that mass $M$ exerts on mass $m$, we will let $\mathbf{r}$ be the radius vector from mass $M$ to mass $m$ (Figure 12.7.2). Thus, the distance $r$ between the masses is $\|\mathbf{r}\|$, and the force $\mathbf{F}$ can be expressed in terms of $\mathbf{r}$ as

$$\mathbf{F} = \|\mathbf{F}\|\left(-\frac{\mathbf{r}}{\|\mathbf{r}\|}\right) = \|\mathbf{F}\|\left(-\frac{\mathbf{r}}{r}\right)$$

which from (3) can be expressed as

$$\mathbf{F} = -\frac{GMm}{r^3}\mathbf{r} \tag{4}$$

We start by finding a formula for the acceleration function. To do this we use Formula (4) and Newton's second law to obtain

$$m\mathbf{a} = -\frac{GMm}{r^3}\mathbf{r}$$

from which we obtain

$$\mathbf{a} = -\frac{GM}{r^3}\mathbf{r} \tag{5}$$

Observe in Formula (5) that the acceleration $\mathbf{a}$ does not involve $m$. Thus, the mass of a planet has no effect on its acceleration.

To obtain a formula for the position function of the mass $m$, we will need to introduce a coordinate system and make some assumptions about the initial conditions:

- The distance $r$ from $m$ to $M$ is minimum at time $t = 0$.
- The mass $m$ has nonzero position and velocity vectors $\mathbf{r}_0$ and $\mathbf{v}_0$ at time $t = 0$.
- A polar coordinate system is introduced with its pole at mass $M$ and oriented so $\theta = 0$ at time $t = 0$.
- The vector $\mathbf{v}_0$ is perpendicular to the polar axis at time $t = 0$.

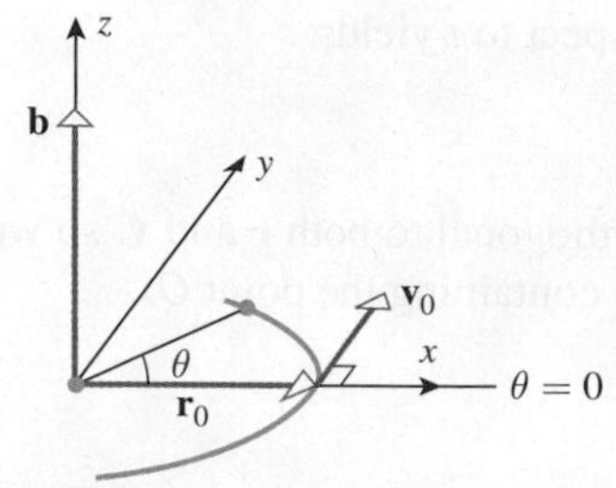

▲ Figure 12.7.3

Moreover, to ensure that the polar angle $\theta$ increases with $t$, let us agree to observe this polar coordinate system looking toward the pole from the terminal point of the vector $\mathbf{b} = \mathbf{r}_0 \times \mathbf{v}_0$. We will also find it useful to superimpose an $xyz$-coordinate system on the polar coordinate system with the positive $z$-axis in the direction of $\mathbf{b}$ (Figure 12.7.3).

For computational purposes, it will be helpful to denote $\|\mathbf{r}_0\|$ by $r_0$ and $\|\mathbf{v}_0\|$ by $v_0$, in which case we can express the vectors $\mathbf{r}_0$ and $\mathbf{v}_0$ in $xyz$-coordinates as

$$\mathbf{r}_0 = r_0\mathbf{i} \quad \text{and} \quad \mathbf{v}_0 = v_0\mathbf{j}$$

and the vector $\mathbf{b}$ as

$$\mathbf{b} = \mathbf{r}_0 \times \mathbf{v}_0 = r_0\mathbf{i} \times v_0\mathbf{j} = r_0 v_0 \mathbf{k} \tag{6}$$

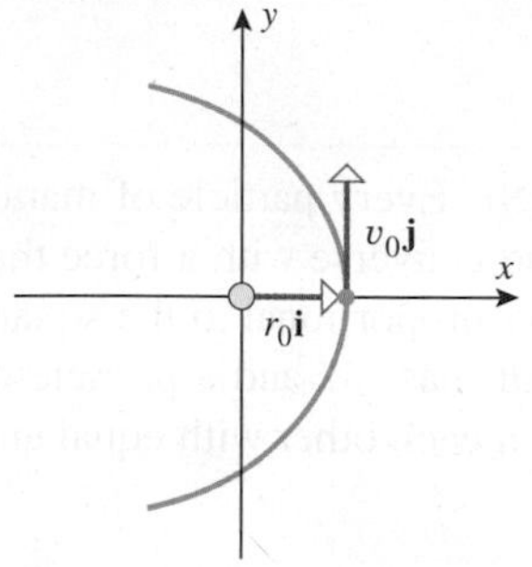

▲ Figure 12.7.4

(Figure 12.7.4). It will also be useful to introduce the unit vector

$$\mathbf{u} = \cos\theta\mathbf{i} + \sin\theta\mathbf{j} \tag{7}$$

which will allow us to express the polar form of the position vector $\mathbf{r}$ as

$$\mathbf{r} = r\cos\theta\mathbf{i} + r\sin\theta\mathbf{j} = r(\cos\theta\mathbf{i} + \sin\theta\mathbf{j}) = r\mathbf{u} \tag{8}$$

and to express the acceleration vector $\mathbf{a}$ in terms of $\mathbf{u}$ by rewriting (5) as

$$\mathbf{a} = -\frac{GM}{r^2}\mathbf{u} \tag{9}$$

We are now ready to derive the position function of the mass $m$ in polar coordinates. For this purpose, recall from (2) that the vector $\mathbf{b} = \mathbf{r} \times \mathbf{v}$ is constant, so it follows from (6) that the relationship

$$\mathbf{b} = \mathbf{r} \times \mathbf{v} = r_0 v_0 \mathbf{k} \tag{10}$$

holds for *all* values of $t$. Now let us examine $\mathbf{b}$ from another point of view. It follows from (8) that

$$\mathbf{v} = \frac{d\mathbf{r}}{dt} = \frac{d}{dt}(r\mathbf{u}) = r\frac{d\mathbf{u}}{dt} + \frac{dr}{dt}\mathbf{u}$$

and hence

$$\mathbf{b} = \mathbf{r} \times \mathbf{v} = (r\mathbf{u}) \times \left(r\frac{d\mathbf{u}}{dt} + \frac{dr}{dt}\mathbf{u}\right) = r^2\mathbf{u} \times \frac{d\mathbf{u}}{dt} + r\frac{dr}{dt}\mathbf{u} \times \mathbf{u} = r^2\mathbf{u} \times \frac{d\mathbf{u}}{dt} \tag{11}$$

But (7) implies that

$$\frac{d\mathbf{u}}{dt} = \frac{d\mathbf{u}}{d\theta}\frac{d\theta}{dt} = (-\sin\theta\mathbf{i} + \cos\theta\mathbf{j})\frac{d\theta}{dt}$$

so

$$\mathbf{u} \times \frac{d\mathbf{u}}{dt} = \frac{d\theta}{dt}\mathbf{k} \tag{12}$$

Substituting (12) in (11) yields

$$\mathbf{b} = r^2\frac{d\theta}{dt}\mathbf{k} \tag{13}$$

Thus, it follows from (7), (9), and (13) that

$$\begin{aligned} \mathbf{a} \times \mathbf{b} &= -\frac{GM}{r^2}(\cos\theta\mathbf{i} + \sin\theta\mathbf{j}) \times \left(r^2\frac{d\theta}{dt}\mathbf{k}\right) \\ &= GM(-\sin\theta\mathbf{i} + \cos\theta\mathbf{j})\frac{d\theta}{dt} = GM\frac{d\mathbf{u}}{dt} \end{aligned} \tag{14}$$

From this formula and the fact that $d\mathbf{b}/dt = \mathbf{0}$ (since $\mathbf{b}$ is constant), we obtain

$$\frac{d}{dt}(\mathbf{v} \times \mathbf{b}) = \mathbf{v} \times \frac{d\mathbf{b}}{dt} + \frac{d\mathbf{v}}{dt} \times \mathbf{b} = \mathbf{a} \times \mathbf{b} = GM\frac{d\mathbf{u}}{dt}$$

Integrating both sides of this equation with respect to $t$ yields

$$\mathbf{v} \times \mathbf{b} = GM\mathbf{u} + \mathbf{C} \tag{15}$$

where $\mathbf{C}$ is a vector constant of integration. This constant can be obtained by evaluating both sides of the equation at $t = 0$. We leave it as an exercise to show that

$$\mathbf{C} = (r_0 v_0^2 - GM)\mathbf{i} \tag{16}$$

from which it follows that

$$\mathbf{v} \times \mathbf{b} = GM\mathbf{u} + (r_0v_0^2 - GM)\mathbf{i} \tag{17}$$

We can now obtain the position function by computing the scalar triple product $\mathbf{r} \cdot (\mathbf{v} \times \mathbf{b})$ in two ways. First we use (10) and property (11) of Section 11.4 to obtain

$$\mathbf{r} \cdot (\mathbf{v} \times \mathbf{b}) = (\mathbf{r} \times \mathbf{v}) \cdot \mathbf{b} = \mathbf{b} \cdot \mathbf{b} = r_0^2v_0^2 \tag{18}$$

and next we use (17) to obtain

$$\begin{aligned}\mathbf{r} \cdot (\mathbf{v} \times \mathbf{b}) &= \mathbf{r} \cdot (GM\mathbf{u}) + \mathbf{r} \cdot (r_0v_0^2 - GM)\mathbf{i}\\ &= \mathbf{r} \cdot \left(GM\frac{\mathbf{r}}{r}\right) + r\mathbf{u} \cdot (r_0v_0^2 - GM)\mathbf{i}\\ &= GMr + r(r_0v_0^2 - GM)\cos\theta\end{aligned}$$

If we now equate this to (18), we obtain

$$r_0^2v_0^2 = GMr + r(r_0v_0^2 - GM)\cos\theta$$

which when solved for $r$ gives

$$r = \frac{r_0^2v_0^2}{GM + (r_0v_0^2 - GM)\cos\theta} = \frac{\dfrac{r_0^2v_0^2}{GM}}{1 + \left(\dfrac{r_0v_0^2}{GM} - 1\right)\cos\theta} \tag{19}$$

or more simply

$$r = \frac{k}{1 + e\cos\theta} \tag{20}$$

where

$$k = \frac{r_0^2v_0^2}{GM} \quad \text{and} \quad e = \frac{r_0v_0^2}{GM} - 1 \tag{21–22}$$

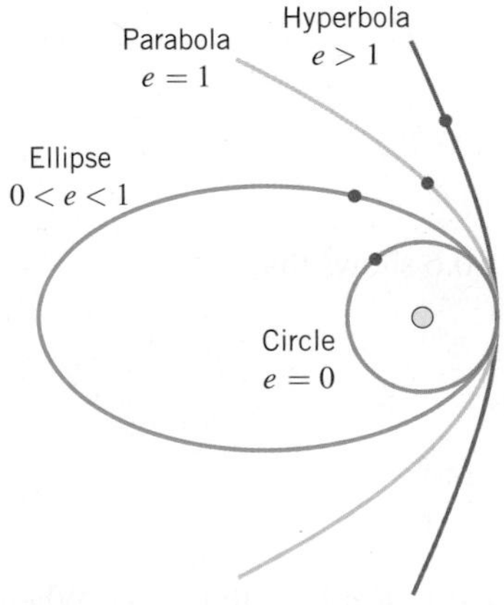

▲ **Figure 12.7.5**

We will leave it as an exercise to show that $e \geq 0$. Accepting this to be so, it follows by comparing (20) to Formula (3) of Section 10.6 that the trajectory is a conic section with eccentricity $e$, the focus at the pole, and $d = k/e$. Thus, depending on whether $e < 1$, $e = 1$, or $e > 1$, the trajectory will be, respectively, an ellipse, a parabola, or a hyperbola (Figure 12.7.5).

Note from Formula (22) that $e$ depends on $r_0$ and $v_0$, so the exact form of the trajectory is determined by the mass $M$ and the initial conditions. If the initial conditions are such that $e < 1$, then the mass $m$ becomes trapped in an elliptical orbit; otherwise the mass $m$ "escapes" and never returns to its initial position. Accordingly, the initial velocity that produces an eccentricity of $e = 1$ is called the ***escape speed*** and is denoted by $v_{\text{esc}}$. Thus, it follows from (22) that

$$v_{\text{esc}} = \sqrt{\frac{2GM}{r_0}} \tag{23}$$

(verify).

## KEPLER'S FIRST AND SECOND LAWS

It follows from our general discussion of central force fields that the planets have elliptical orbits with the Sun at the focus, which is Kepler's first law. To derive Kepler's second law, we begin by equating (10) and (13) to obtain

$$r^2\frac{d\theta}{dt} = r_0v_0 \tag{24}$$

To prove that the radial line from the center of the Sun to the center of a planet sweeps out equal areas in equal times, let $r = f(\theta)$ denote the polar equation of the planet, and let

$A$ denote the area swept out by the radial line as it varies from any fixed angle $\theta_0$ to an angle $\theta$. It follows from the area formula in 10.3.4 that $A$ can be expressed as

$$A = \int_{\theta_0}^{\theta} \frac{1}{2}[f(\phi)]^2\, d\phi$$

where the dummy variable $\phi$ is introduced for the integration to reserve $\theta$ for the upper limit. It now follows from Part 2 of the Fundamental Theorem of Calculus and the chain rule that

$$\frac{dA}{dt} = \frac{dA}{d\theta}\frac{d\theta}{dt} = \frac{1}{2}[f(\theta)]^2\frac{d\theta}{dt} = \frac{1}{2}r^2\frac{d\theta}{dt}$$

Thus, it follows from (24) that

$$\frac{dA}{dt} = \frac{1}{2}r_0v_0 \tag{25}$$

which shows that $A$ changes at a constant rate. This implies that equal areas are swept out in equal times.

## KEPLER'S THIRD LAW

To derive Kepler's third law, we let $a$ and $b$ be the semimajor and semiminor axes of the elliptical orbit, and we recall that the area of this ellipse is $\pi ab$. It follows by integrating (25) that in $t$ units of time the radial line will sweep out an area of $A = \frac{1}{2}r_0v_0t$. Thus, if $T$ denotes the time required for the planet to make one revolution around the Sun (the period), then the radial line will sweep out the area of the entire ellipse during that time and hence

$$\pi ab = \frac{1}{2}r_0v_0T$$

from which we obtain

$$T^2 = \frac{4\pi^2a^2b^2}{r_0^2v_0^2} \tag{26}$$

However, it follows from Formula (1) of Section 10.6 and the relationship $c^2 = a^2 - b^2$ for an ellipse that

$$e = \frac{c}{a} = \frac{\sqrt{a^2-b^2}}{a}$$

Thus, $b^2 = a^2(1-e^2)$ and hence (26) can be written as

$$T^2 = \frac{4\pi^2a^4(1-e^2)}{r_0^2v_0^2} \tag{27}$$

But comparing Equation (20) to Equation (17) of Section 10.6 shows that

$$k = a(1-e^2)$$

Finally, substituting this expression and (21) in (27) yields

$$T^2 = \frac{4\pi^2a^3}{r_0^2v_0^2}k = \frac{4\pi^2a^3}{r_0^2v_0^2}\frac{r_0^2v_0^2}{GM} = \frac{4\pi^2}{GM}a^3 \tag{28}$$

Thus, we have proved that $T^2$ is proportional to $a^3$, which is Kepler's third law. When convenient, Formula (28) can also be expressed as

$$T = \frac{2\pi}{\sqrt{GM}}a^{3/2} \tag{29}$$

## ARTIFICIAL SATELLITES

Kepler's second and third laws and Formula (23) also apply to satellites that orbit a celestial body; we need only interpret $M$ to be the mass of the body exerting the force and $m$ to be the mass of the satellite. Values of $GM$ that are required in many of the formulas in this section have been determined experimentally for various attracting bodies (Table 12.7.1).

Recall that for orbits of planets around the Sun, the point at which the distance between the center of the planet and the center of the Sun is maximum is called the *aphelion* and

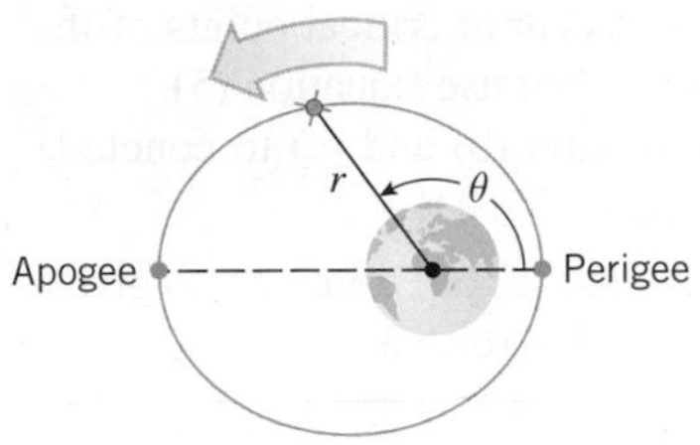

▲ Figure 12.7.6

the point at which it is minimum the *perihelion*. For satellites orbiting the Earth, the point at which the maximum distance occurs is called the ***apogee***, and the point at which the minimum distance occurs is called the ***perigee*** (Figure 12.7.6). The actual distances between the centers at apogee and perigee are called the ***apogee distance*** and the ***perigee distance***.

**Table 12.7.1**

| ATTRACTING BODY | INTERNATIONAL SYSTEM | BRITISH ENGINEERING SYSTEM |
|---|---|---|
| Earth | $GM = 3.99 \times 10^{14}$ m³/s² <br> $GM = 3.99 \times 10^{5}$ km³/s² | $GM = 1.41 \times 10^{16}$ ft³/s² <br> $GM = 1.24 \times 10^{12}$ mi³/h² |
| Sun | $GM = 1.33 \times 10^{20}$ m³/s² <br> $GM = 1.33 \times 10^{11}$ km³/s² | $GM = 4.69 \times 10^{21}$ ft³/s² <br> $GM = 4.13 \times 10^{17}$ mi³/h² |
| Moon | $GM = 4.90 \times 10^{12}$ m³/s² <br> $GM = 4.90 \times 10^{3}$ km³/s² | $GM = 1.73 \times 10^{14}$ ft³/s² <br> $GM = 1.53 \times 10^{10}$ mi³/h² |

► **Example 1** A geosynchronous orbit for a satellite is a circular orbit about the equator of the Earth in which the satellite stays fixed over a point on the equator. Use the fact that the Earth makes one revolution about its axis every 24 hours to find the altitude in miles of a communications satellite in geosynchronous orbit. Assume the Earth to be a sphere of radius 4000 mi.

***Solution.*** To remain fixed over a point on the equator, the satellite must have a period of $T = 24$ h. It follows from (28) or (29) and the Earth value of $GM = 1.24 \times 10^{12}$ mi³/h² from Table 12.7.1 that

$$a = \sqrt[3]{\frac{GMT^2}{4\pi^2}} = \sqrt[3]{\frac{(1.24 \times 10^{12})(24)^2}{4\pi^2}} \approx 26{,}250 \text{ mi}$$

and hence the altitude $h$ of the satellite is

$$h \approx 26{,}250 - 4000 = 22{,}250 \text{ mi} \blacktriangleleft$$

## ✓QUICK CHECK EXERCISES 12.7 (See page 800 for answers.)

1. Let $G$ denote the universal gravitational constant and let $M$ and $m$ denote masses a distance $r$ apart.
   (a) According to Newton's Law of Universal Gravitation, $M$ and $m$ attract each other with a force of magnitude ________.
   (b) If $\mathbf{r}$ is the radius vector from $M$ to $m$, then the force of attraction that mass $M$ exerts on mass $m$ is ________.
2. Suppose that a mass $m$ is in an orbit about a mass $M$ and that $r_0$ is the minimum distance from $m$ to $M$. If $G$ is the universal gravitational constant, then the "escape" speed of $m$ is ________.
3. For a planet in an elliptical orbit about the Sun, the square of the planet's period is proportional to what power of the semimajor axis of its orbit?
4. Suppose that a mass $m$ is in an orbit about a mass $M$ and that $r_0$ is the minimum distance from $m$ to $M$. If $v_0$ is the speed of mass $m$ when it is a distance $r_0$ from $M$, and if $G$ denotes the universal gravitational constant, then the eccentricity of the orbit is ________.

## EXERCISE SET 12.7

**1–14** In exercises that require numerical values, use Table 12.7.1 and the following values, where needed:

radius of Earth = 4000 mi = 6440 km
radius of Moon = 1080 mi = 1740 km
1 year (Earth year) = 365 days ■

**FOCUS ON CONCEPTS**

1. (a) Obtain the value of $\mathbf{C}$ given in Formula (16) by setting $t = 0$ in (15).
   (b) Use Formulas (7), (17), and (22) to show that
   $$\mathbf{v} \times \mathbf{b} = GM[(e + \cos\theta)\mathbf{i} + \sin\theta\,\mathbf{j}]$$

*(cont.)*

(c) Show that $\|\mathbf{v} \times \mathbf{b}\| = \|\mathbf{v}\|\|\mathbf{b}\|$.

(d) Use the results in parts (b) and (c) to show that the speed of a particle in an elliptical orbit is

$$v = \frac{v_0}{1+e}\sqrt{e^2 + 2e\cos\theta + 1}$$

(e) Suppose that a particle is in an elliptical orbit. Use part (d) to conclude that the distance from the particle to the center of force is a minimum if and only if the speed of the particle is a maximum. Similarly, argue that the distance from the particle to the center of force is a maximum if and only if the speed of the particle is a minimum.

**2.** Use the result in Exercise 1(d) to show that when a particle in an elliptical orbit with eccentricity $e$ reaches an end of the minor axis, its speed is

$$v = v_0\sqrt{\frac{1-e}{1+e}}$$

**3.** Use the result in Exercise 1(d) to show that for a particle in an elliptical orbit with eccentricity $e$, the maximum and minimum speeds are related by

$$v_{\max} = v_{\min}\frac{1+e}{1-e}$$

**4.** Use Formula (22) and the result in Exercise 1(d) to show that the speed $v$ of a particle in a circular orbit of radius $r_0$ is constant and is given by

$$v = \sqrt{\frac{GM}{r_0}}$$

**5.** Suppose that a particle is in an elliptical orbit in a central force field in which the center of force is at a focus, and let $\mathbf{r} = \mathbf{r}(t)$ and $\mathbf{v} = \mathbf{v}(t)$ be the position and velocity functions of the particle, respectively. Let $r_{\min}$ and $r_{\max}$ denote the minimum and maximum distances from the particle to the center of force, and let $v_{\min}$ and $v_{\max}$ denote the minimum and maximum speeds of the particle.

(a) Review the discussion of ellipses in polar coordinates in Section 10.6, and show that if the ellipse has eccentricity $e$ and semimajor axis $a$, then $r_{\min} = a(1-e)$ and $r_{\max} = a(1+e)$.

(b) Explain why $r_{\min}$ and $r_{\max}$ occur at points at which $\mathbf{r}$ and $\mathbf{v}$ are orthogonal. [*Hint:* First argue that the extreme values of $\|\mathbf{r}\|$ occur at critical points of the function $\|\mathbf{r}\|^2 = \mathbf{r}\cdot\mathbf{r}$.]

(c) Explain why $v_{\min}$ and $v_{\max}$ occur at points at which $\mathbf{r}$ and $\mathbf{v}$ are orthogonal. [*Hint:* First argue that the extreme values of $\|\mathbf{v}\|$ occur at critical points of the function $\|\mathbf{v}\|^2 = \mathbf{v}\cdot\mathbf{v}$. Then use Equation (5).]

(d) Use Equation (2) and parts (b) and (c) to conclude that $r_{\max}v_{\min} = r_{\min}v_{\max}$.

**6.** Use the results in parts (a) and (d) of Exercise 5 to give a derivation of the equation in Exercise 3.

**7.** Use the result in Exercise 4 to find the speed in km/s of a satellite in a circular orbit that is 200 km above the surface of the Earth.

**8.** Use the result in Exercise 4 to find the speed in mi/h of a communications satellite that is in geosynchronous orbit around the Earth (see Example 1).

**9.** Find the escape speed in km/s for a space probe in a circular orbit that is 300 km above the surface of the Earth.

**10.** The universal gravitational constant is approximately

$$G = 6.67 \times 10^{-11}\ \text{m}^3/\text{kg}\cdot\text{s}^2$$

and the semimajor axis of the Earth's orbit is approximately

$$a = 149.6 \times 10^6\ \text{km}$$

Estimate the mass of the Sun in kg.

**11.** (a) The eccentricity of the Moon's orbit around the Earth is 0.055, and its semimajor axis is $a = 238{,}900$ mi. Find the maximum and minimum distances between the surface of the Earth and the surface of the Moon.

(b) Find the period of the Moon's orbit in days.

**12.** (a) *Vanguard 1* was launched in March 1958 with perigee and apogee altitudes above the Earth of 649 km and 4340 km, respectively. Find the length of the semimajor axis of its orbit.

(b) Use the result in part (a) of Exercise 16 in Section 10.6 to find the eccentricity of its orbit.

(c) Find the period of *Vanguard 1* in minutes.

**13.** (a) Suppose that a space probe is in a circular orbit at an altitude of 180 mi above the surface of the Earth. Use the result in Exercise 4 to find its speed.

(b) During a very short period of time, a thruster rocket on the space probe is fired to increase the speed of the probe by 600 mi/h in its direction of motion. Find the eccentricity of the resulting elliptical orbit, and use the result in part (a) of Exercise 5 to find the apogee altitude.

**14.** Show that the quantity $e$ defined by Formula (22) is nonnegative. [*Hint:* The polar axis was chosen so that $r$ is minimum when $\theta = 0$.]

**✓ QUICK CHECK ANSWERS 12.7** 1. (a) $\dfrac{GMm}{r^2}$ (b) $-\dfrac{GMm}{r^3}\mathbf{r}$ 2. $\sqrt{\dfrac{2GM}{r_0}}$ 3. 3 4. $e = \dfrac{r_0v_0^2}{GM} - 1$

## CHAPTER 12 REVIEW EXERCISES

**1.** In words, what is meant by the graph of a vector-valued function?

**2–5** Describe the graph of the equation. ■

**2.** $\mathbf{r} = (2 - 3t)\mathbf{i} - 4t\mathbf{j}$ **3.** $\mathbf{r} = 3\sin 2t\mathbf{i} + 3\cos 2t\mathbf{j}$

**4.** $\mathbf{r} = 3\cos t\mathbf{i} + 2\sin t\mathbf{j} - \mathbf{k}$ **5.** $\mathbf{r} = -2\mathbf{i} + t\mathbf{j} + (t^2 - 1)\mathbf{k}$

**6.** Describe the graph of the vector-valued function.
(a) $\mathbf{r} = \mathbf{r}_0 + t(\mathbf{r}_1 - \mathbf{r}_0)$
(b) $\mathbf{r} = \mathbf{r}_0 + t(\mathbf{r}_1 - \mathbf{r}_0) \quad (0 \le t \le 1)$
(c) $\mathbf{r} = \mathbf{r}_0 + t\mathbf{r}'(t_0)$

**7.** Show that the graph of $\mathbf{r}(t) = t\sin \pi t\mathbf{i} + t\mathbf{j} + t\cos \pi t\mathbf{k}$ lies on the surface of a cone, and sketch the cone.

**8.** Find parametric equations for the intersection of the surfaces

$$y = x^2 \quad \text{and} \quad 2x^2 + y^2 + 6z^2 = 24$$

and sketch the intersection.

**9.** In words, give a geometric description of the statement $\lim_{t\to a} \mathbf{r}(t) = \mathbf{L}$.

**10.** Evaluate $\lim_{t\to 0}\left(e^{-t}\mathbf{i} + \dfrac{1-\cos t}{t}\mathbf{j} + t^2\mathbf{k}\right)$.

**11.** Find parametric equations of the line tangent to the graph of

$$\mathbf{r}(t) = (t + \cos 2t)\mathbf{i} - (t^2 + t)\mathbf{j} + \sin t\mathbf{k}$$

at the point where $t = 0$.

**12.** Suppose that $\mathbf{r}_1(t)$ and $\mathbf{r}_2(t)$ are smooth vector-valued functions such that $\mathbf{r}_1(0) = \langle -1, 1, 2\rangle$, $\mathbf{r}_2(0) = \langle 1, 2, 1\rangle$, $\mathbf{r}_1'(0) = \langle 1, 0, 1\rangle$, and $\mathbf{r}_2'(0) = \langle 4, 0, 2\rangle$. Use this information to evaluate the derivative at $t = 0$ of each function.
(a) $\mathbf{r}(t) = 3\mathbf{r}_1(t) + 2\mathbf{r}_2(t)$ (b) $\mathbf{r}(t) = [\ln(t+1)]\mathbf{r}_1(t)$
(c) $\mathbf{r}(t) = \mathbf{r}_1(t) \times \mathbf{r}_2(t)$ (d) $f(t) = \mathbf{r}_1(t) \cdot \mathbf{r}_2(t)$

**13.** Evaluate $\displaystyle\int (\cos t\mathbf{i} + \sin t\mathbf{j})\, dt$.

**14.** Evaluate $\displaystyle\int_0^{\pi/3} \langle \cos 3t, -\sin 3t\rangle\, dt$.

**15.** Solve the vector initial-value problem

$$\mathbf{y}'(t) = t^2\mathbf{i} + 2t\mathbf{j}, \quad \mathbf{y}(0) = \mathbf{i} + \mathbf{j}$$

**16.** Solve the vector initial-value problem

$$\frac{d\mathbf{r}}{dt} = \mathbf{r}, \quad \mathbf{r}(0) = \mathbf{r}_0$$

for the unknown vector-valued function $\mathbf{r}(t)$.

**17.** Find the arc length of the graph of

$$\mathbf{r}(t) = e^{\sqrt{2}t}\mathbf{i} + e^{-\sqrt{2}t}\mathbf{j} + 2t\mathbf{k} \quad (0 \le t \le \sqrt{2}\ln 2)$$

**18.** Suppose that $\mathbf{r}(t)$ is a smooth vector-valued function of $t$ with $\mathbf{r}'(0) = 3\mathbf{i} - \mathbf{j} + \mathbf{k}$ and that $\mathbf{r}_1(t) = \mathbf{r}(2 - e^{t\ln 2})$. Find $\mathbf{r}_1'(1)$.

**19.** Find the arc length parametrization of the line through $P(-1, 4, 3)$ and $Q(0, 2, 5)$ that has reference point $P$ and orients the line in the direction from $P$ to $Q$.

**20.** Find an arc length parametrization of the curve

$$\mathbf{r}(t) = \langle e^t\cos t, -e^t\sin t\rangle \quad (0 \le t \le \pi/2)$$

which has the same orientation and has $\mathbf{r}(0)$ as the reference point.

**21.** Suppose that $\mathbf{r}(t)$ is a smooth vector-valued function. State the definitions of $\mathbf{T}(t)$, $\mathbf{N}(t)$, and $\mathbf{B}(t)$.

**22.** Find $\mathbf{T}(0)$, $\mathbf{N}(0)$, and $\mathbf{B}(0)$ for the curve

$$\mathbf{r}(t) = \left\langle 2\cos t, 2\cos t + \frac{3}{\sqrt{5}}\sin t, \cos t - \frac{6}{\sqrt{5}}\sin t\right\rangle$$

**23.** State the definition of "curvature" and explain what it means geometrically.

**24.** Suppose that $\mathbf{r}(t)$ is a smooth curve with $\mathbf{r}'(0) = \mathbf{i}$ and $\mathbf{r}''(0) = \mathbf{i} + 2\mathbf{j}$. Find the curvature at $t = 0$.

**25–28** Find the curvature of the curve at the stated point. ■

**25.** $\mathbf{r}(t) = 2\cos t\mathbf{i} + 3\sin t\mathbf{j} - t\mathbf{k};\ t = \pi/2$

**26.** $\mathbf{r}(t) = \langle 2t, e^{2t}, e^{-2t}\rangle;\ t = 0$

**27.** $y = \cos x;\ x = \pi/2$ **28.** $y = \ln x;\ x = 1$

**29.** Suppose that $\mathbf{r}(t)$ is the position function of a particle moving in 2-space or 3-space. In each part, explain what the given quantity represents physically.
(a) $\left\|\dfrac{d\mathbf{r}}{dt}\right\|$ (b) $\displaystyle\int_{t_0}^{t_1}\left\|\frac{d\mathbf{r}}{dt}\right\| dt$ (c) $\|\mathbf{r}(t)\|$

**30.** (a) What does Theorem 12.2.8 tell you about the velocity vector of a particle that moves over a sphere?
(b) What does Theorem 12.2.8 tell you about the acceleration vector of a particle that moves with constant speed?
(c) Show that the particle with position function

$$\mathbf{r}(t) = \sqrt{1 - \tfrac{1}{4}\cos^2 t}\cos t\mathbf{i} + \sqrt{1 - \tfrac{1}{4}\cos^2 t}\sin t\mathbf{j} + \tfrac{1}{2}\cos t\mathbf{k}$$

moves over a sphere.

**31.** As illustrated in the accompanying figure on the next page, suppose that a particle moves counterclockwise around a circle of radius $R$ centered at the origin at a constant rate of $\omega$ radians per second. This is called ***uniform circular motion***. If we assume that the particle is at the point $(R, 0)$ at time $t = 0$, then its position function will be

$$\mathbf{r}(t) = R\cos \omega t\mathbf{i} + R\sin \omega t\mathbf{j}$$

(a) Show that the velocity vector $\mathbf{v}(t)$ is always tangent to the circle and that the particle has constant speed $v$ given by

$$v = R\omega$$

(b) Show that the acceleration vector $\mathbf{a}(t)$ is always directed toward the center of the circle and has constant magnitude $a$ given by

$$a = R\omega^2$$

*(cont.)*

(c) Show that the time $T$ required for the particle to make one complete revolution is

$$T = \frac{2\pi}{\omega} = \frac{2\pi R}{v}$$

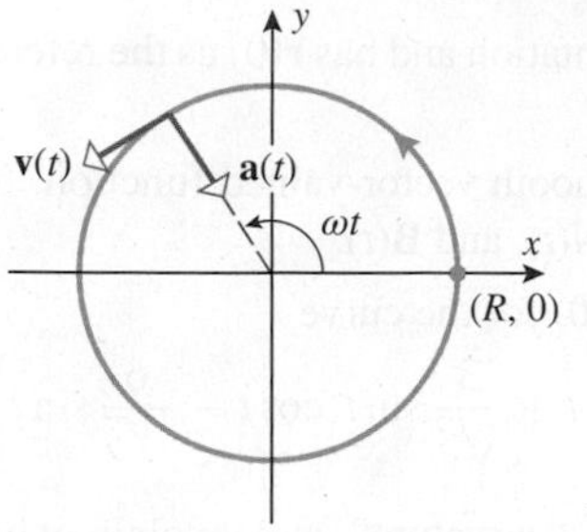


◀ Figure Ex-31

**32.** If a particle of mass $m$ has uniform circular motion (see Exercise 31), then the acceleration vector $\mathbf{a}(t)$ is called the ***centripetal acceleration***. According to Newton's second law, this acceleration must be produced by some force $\mathbf{F}(t)$, called the ***centripetal force***, that is related to $\mathbf{a}(t)$ by the equation $\mathbf{F}(t) = m\mathbf{a}(t)$. If this force is not present, then the particle cannot undergo uniform circular motion.

(a) Show that the direction of the centripetal force varies with time but that it has constant magnitude $F$ given by

$$F = \frac{mv^2}{R}$$

(b) An astronaut with a mass of $m = 60$ kg orbits the Earth at an altitude of $h = 3200$ km with a constant speed of $v = 6.43$ km/s. Find her centripetal acceleration assuming that the radius of the Earth is 6440 km.

(c) What centripetal gravitational force in newtons does the Earth exert on the astronaut?

**33.** At time $t = 0$ a particle at the origin of an $xyz$-coordinate system has a velocity vector of $\mathbf{v}_0 = \mathbf{i} + 2\mathbf{j} - \mathbf{k}$. The acceleration function of the particle is $\mathbf{a}(t) = 2t^2\mathbf{i} + \mathbf{j} + \cos 2t\mathbf{k}$.

(a) Find the position function of the particle.

(b) Find the speed of the particle at time $t = 1$.

**34.** Let $\mathbf{v} = \mathbf{v}(t)$ and $\mathbf{a} = \mathbf{a}(t)$ be the velocity and acceleration vectors for a particle moving in 2-space or 3-space. Show that the rate of change of its speed can be expressed as

$$\frac{d}{dt}(\|\mathbf{v}\|) = \frac{1}{\|\mathbf{v}\|}(\mathbf{v} \cdot \mathbf{a})$$

**35.** Use Formula (23) in Section 12.7 and refer to Table 12.7.1 to find the escape speed (in km/s) for a space probe 600 km above the surface of the Earth.

**36.** As illustrated in the accompanying figure, the polar coordinates of a rocket are tracked by radar from a point that is $b$ units from the launching pad. Show that the speed $v$ of the rocket can be expressed in terms $b$, $\theta$, and $d\theta/dt$ as

$$v = b\sec^2\theta\frac{d\theta}{dt}$$

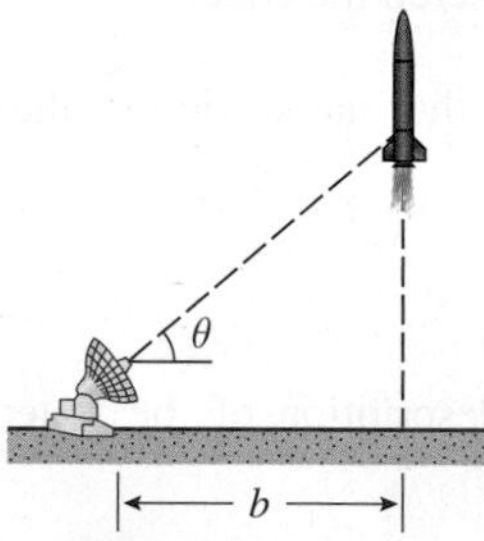


◀ Figure Ex-36

**37.** A player throws a ball with an initial speed of 60 ft/s at an unknown angle $\alpha$ with the horizontal from a point that is 4 ft above the floor of a gymnasium. Given that the ceiling of the gymnasium is 25 ft high, determine the maximum height $h$ at which the ball can hit a wall that is 60 ft away (see the accompanying figure).

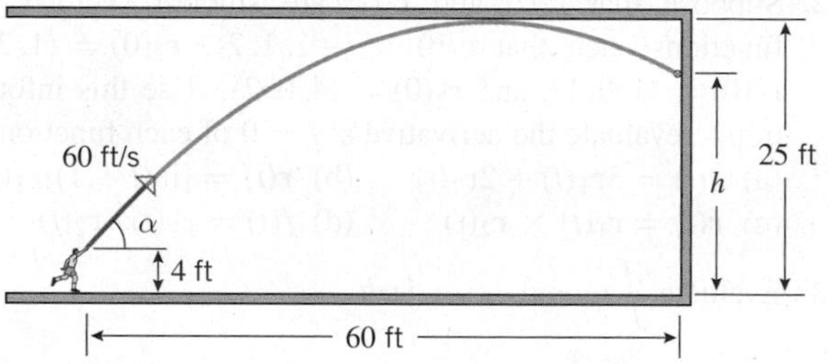


▲ Figure Ex-37

## CHAPTER 12 MAKING CONNECTIONS

C CAS

**1.** (a) Use the formulas

$$\mathbf{N}(t) = \mathbf{B}(t) \times \mathbf{T}(t)$$

$$\mathbf{T}(t) = \mathbf{r}'(t)/\|\mathbf{r}'(t)\|$$

and

$$\mathbf{B}(t) = \frac{\mathbf{r}'(t) \times \mathbf{r}''(t)}{\|\mathbf{r}'(t) \times \mathbf{r}''(t)\|}$$

to show that $\mathbf{N}(t)$ can be expressed in terms of $\mathbf{r}(t)$ as

$$\mathbf{N}(t) = \frac{\mathbf{r}'(t) \times \mathbf{r}''(t)}{\|\mathbf{r}'(t) \times \mathbf{r}''(t)\|} \times \frac{\mathbf{r}'(t)}{\|\mathbf{r}'(t)\|}$$

(b) Use properties of cross products to show that the formula in part (a) can be expressed as

$$\mathbf{N}(t) = \frac{(\mathbf{r}'(t) \times \mathbf{r}''(t)) \times \mathbf{r}'(t)}{\|(\mathbf{r}'(t) \times \mathbf{r}''(t)) \times \mathbf{r}'(t)\|}$$

(c) Use the result in part (b) to find $\mathbf{N}(t)$ at the given point.

(i) $\mathbf{r}(t) = (t^2 - 1)\mathbf{i} + t\mathbf{j}$; $t = 1$

(ii) $\mathbf{r}(t) = 4\cos t\mathbf{i} + 4\sin t\mathbf{j} + t\mathbf{k}$; $t = \pi/2$

**2.** (a) Use the result in Exercise 1(b) and Exercise 45 of Section 11.4 to show that $\mathbf{N}(t)$ can be expressed directly in terms of $\mathbf{r}(t)$ as

$$\mathbf{N}(t) = \frac{\mathbf{u}(t)}{\|\mathbf{u}(t)\|}$$

where

$$\mathbf{u}(t) = \|\mathbf{r}'(t)\|^2\mathbf{r}''(t) - (\mathbf{r}'(t) \cdot \mathbf{r}''(t))\mathbf{r}'(t)$$

(cont.)

(b) Use the result in part (a) to find $\mathbf{N}(t)$.
(i) $\mathbf{r}(t) = \sin t\mathbf{i} + \cos t\mathbf{j} + t\mathbf{k}$
(ii) $\mathbf{r}(t) = t\mathbf{i} + t^2\mathbf{j} + t^3\mathbf{k}$

**3.** In Making Connections Exercise 1 of Chapter 10 we defined the Cornu spiral parametrically as

$$x = \int_0^t \cos\left(\frac{\pi u^2}{2}\right) du, \quad y = \int_0^t \sin\left(\frac{\pi u^2}{2}\right) du$$

This curve, which is graphed in the accompanying figure, is used in highway design to create a gradual transition from a straight road (zero curvature) to an exit ramp with positive curvature.

(a) Express the Cornu spiral as a vector-valued function $\mathbf{r}(t)$, and then use Theorem 12.3.4 to show that $s = t$ is the arc length parameter with reference point $(0, 0)$.
(b) Replace $t$ by $s$ and use Formula (1) of Section 12.5 to show that $\kappa(s) = \pi|s|$. [*Note:* If $s \geq 0$, then the curvature $\kappa(s) = \pi s$ increases from 0 at a constant rate with respect to $s$. This makes the spiral ideal for joining a curved road to a straight road.]
(c) What happens to the curvature of the Cornu spiral as $s \to +\infty$? In words, explain why this is consistent with the graph.

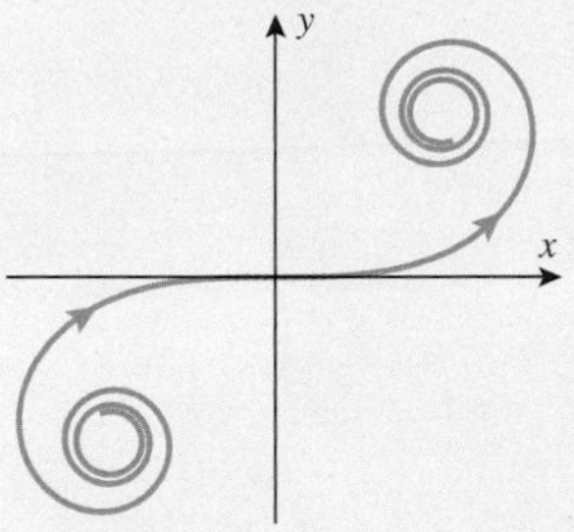

◀ **Figure Ex-3**

C **4.** In 1975, German engineer Werner Stengel pioneered the use of Cornu spirals (see Exercise 3) in the design of loops for roller coasters with the *Revolution* at Six Flags Magic Mountain in California. For this design, the top of the loop is a circular arc, joined at either end to Cornu spirals that ease the transitions to horizontal track. The accompanying figure illustrates this design when the circular arc (in red) is a semicircle, quarter-circle, or a single point, respectively. Suppose that a roller-coaster loop is designed to be 45 feet across at its widest point. For each case in Figure Ex-4, find the vertical distance between the level of the horizontal track and the top of the loop. Use the numerical integration capability of your CAS to estimate integrals, as necessary.

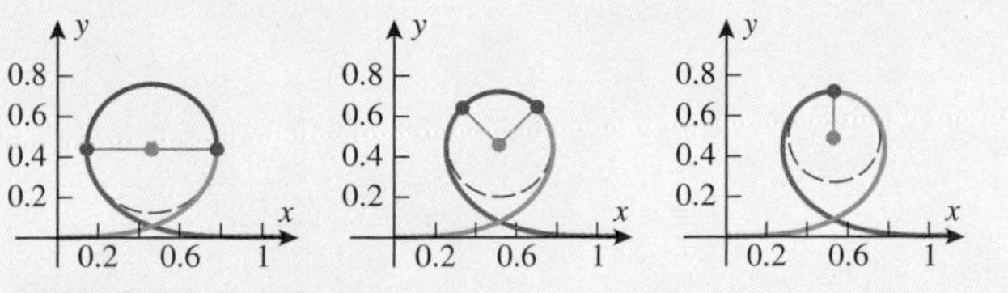

▲ **Figure Ex-4**

**5.** Use the results in Exercise 61 of Section 12.5 and the results in Exercise 32 of Section 12.3 to show that for the circular helix

$$\mathbf{r} = a\cos t\mathbf{i} + a\sin t\mathbf{j} + ct\mathbf{k}$$

with $a > 0$, the torsion and the binormal vector are

$$\tau = \frac{c}{w^2}$$

and

$$\mathbf{B} = \left(\frac{c}{w}\sin\frac{s}{w}\right)\mathbf{i} - \left(\frac{c}{w}\cos\frac{s}{w}\right)\mathbf{j} + \left(\frac{a}{w}\right)\mathbf{k}$$

where $w = \sqrt{a^2 + c^2}$ and $s$ has reference point $(a, 0, 0)$.

**6.** Suppose that the position function of a point moving in the $xy$-plane is

$$\mathbf{r} = x(t)\mathbf{i} + y(t)\mathbf{j}$$

This equation can be expressed in polar coordinates by making the substitution

$$x(t) = r(t)\cos\theta(t), \quad y(t) = r(t)\sin\theta(t)$$

This yields

$$\mathbf{r} = r(t)\cos\theta(t)\mathbf{i} + r(t)\sin\theta(t)\mathbf{j}$$

which can be expressed as

$$\mathbf{r} = r(t)\mathbf{e}_r(t)$$

where $\mathbf{e}_r(t) = \cos\theta(t)\mathbf{i} + \sin\theta(t)\mathbf{j}$.

(a) Show that $\mathbf{e}_r(t)$ is a unit vector in the same direction as the radius vector $\mathbf{r}$ if $r(t) > 0$. Also, show that $\mathbf{e}_\theta(t) = -\sin\theta(t)\mathbf{i} + \cos\theta(t)\mathbf{j}$ is the unit vector that results when $\mathbf{e}_r(t)$ is rotated counterclockwise through an angle of $\pi/2$. The vector $\mathbf{e}_r(t)$ is called the ***radial unit vector*** and the vector $\mathbf{e}_\theta(t)$ is called the ***transverse unit vector*** (see the accompanying figure).
(b) Show that the velocity function $\mathbf{v} = \mathbf{v}(t)$ can be expressed in terms of radial and transverse components as

$$\mathbf{v} = \frac{dr}{dt}\mathbf{e}_r + r\frac{d\theta}{dt}\mathbf{e}_\theta$$

(c) Show that the acceleration function $\mathbf{a} = \mathbf{a}(t)$ can be expressed in terms of radial and transverse components as

$$\mathbf{a} = \left[\frac{d^2r}{dt^2} - r\left(\frac{d\theta}{dt}\right)^2\right]\mathbf{e}_r + \left[r\frac{d^2\theta}{dt^2} + 2\frac{dr}{dt}\frac{d\theta}{dt}\right]\mathbf{e}_\theta$$

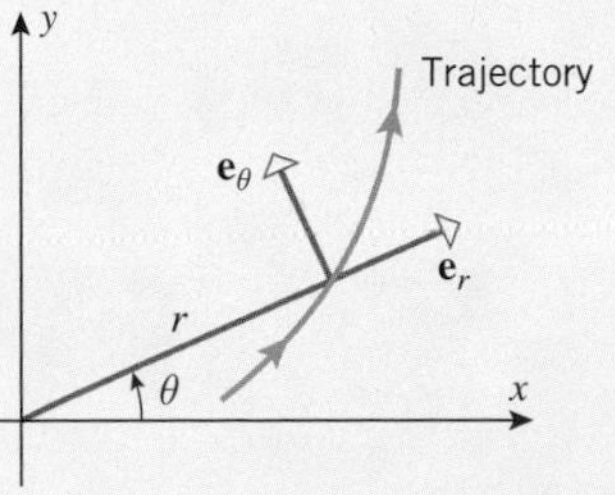

◀ **Figure Ex-6**

## EXPANDING THE CALCULUS HORIZON

For a practical application of projectile motion in a whimsical setting, see the module entitled **Blammo the Human Cannonball** at:

www.wiley.com/college/anton

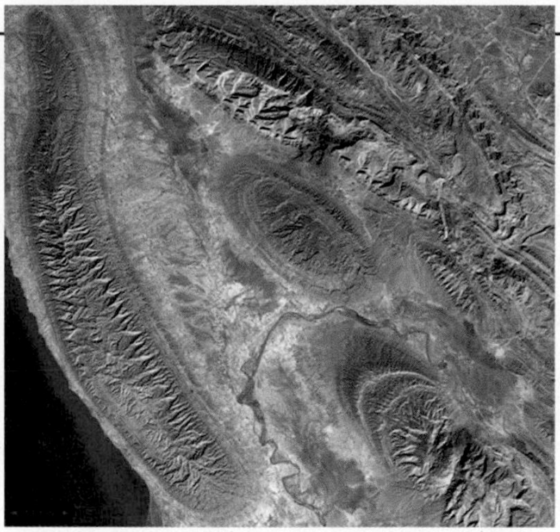

Library of Congress, Geography and Map Division

*Three-dimensional surfaces have high points and low points that are analogous to the peaks and valleys of a mountain range. In this chapter we will use derivatives to locate these points and to study other features of such surfaces.*

# 13 PARTIAL DERIVATIVES

In this chapter we will extend many of the basic concepts of calculus to functions of two or more variables, commonly called functions of several variables. These concepts include limits and continuity, differentiability, tangents, rates of change, and extreme values. Although many of these ideas extend in a natural way to functions of several variables, such functions also possess unique features that will suggest the development of some new mathematical concepts and tools.

## 13.1 FUNCTIONS OF TWO OR MORE VARIABLES

*In previous sections we studied real-valued functions of a real variable and vector-valued functions of a real variable. In this section we will consider real-valued functions of two or more real variables.*

### NOTATION AND TERMINOLOGY

There are many familiar formulas in which a given variable depends on two or more other variables. For example, the area $A$ of a triangle depends on the base length $b$ and height $h$ by the formula $A = \frac{1}{2}bh$; the volume $V$ of a rectangular box depends on the length $l$, the width $w$, and the height $h$ by the formula $V = lwh$; and the arithmetic average $\bar{x}$ of $n$ real numbers, $x_1, x_2, \ldots, x_n$, depends on those numbers by the formula

$$\bar{x} = \frac{1}{n}(x_1 + x_2 + \cdots + x_n)$$

Thus, we say that

$A$ is a function of the two variables $b$ and $h$;
$V$ is a function of the three variables $l$, $w$, and $h$;
$\bar{x}$ is a function of the $n$ variables $x_1, x_2, \ldots, x_n$.

The terminology and notation for functions of two or more variables is similar to that for functions of one variable. For example, the expression

$$z = f(x, y)$$

means that $z$ is a function of $x$ and $y$ in the sense that a unique value of the dependent variable $z$ is determined by specifying values for the independent variables $x$ and $y$. Similarly,

$$w = f(x, y, z)$$

expresses $w$ as a function of $x$, $y$, and $z$, and

$$u = f(x_1, x_2, \ldots, x_n)$$

expresses $u$ as a function of $x_1, x_2, \ldots, x_n$.

As with functions of one variable, the independent variables of a function of two or more variables may be restricted to lie in some set $D$, which we call the ***domain*** of $f$. Sometimes the domain will be determined by physical restrictions on the variables. If the function is defined by a formula and if there are no physical restrictions or other restrictions stated explicitly, then it is understood that the domain consists of all points for which the formula yields a real value for the dependent variable. We call this the ***natural domain*** of the function. The following definitions summarize this discussion.

By extension, one can define the notion of "$n$-dimensional space" in which a "point" is a sequence of $n$ real numbers $(x_1, x_2, \ldots, x_n)$, and a function of $n$ real variables is a rule that assigns a unique real number $f(x_1, x_2, \ldots, x_n)$ to each point in some set in this space.

**13.1.1 DEFINITION** A ***function f of two variables***, $x$ and $y$, is a rule that assigns a unique real number $f(x, y)$ to each point $(x, y)$ in some set $D$ in the $xy$-plane.

**13.1.2 DEFINITION** A ***function f of three variables***, $x$, $y$, and $z$, is a rule that assigns a unique real number $f(x, y, z)$ to each point $(x, y, z)$ in some set $D$ in three-dimensional space.

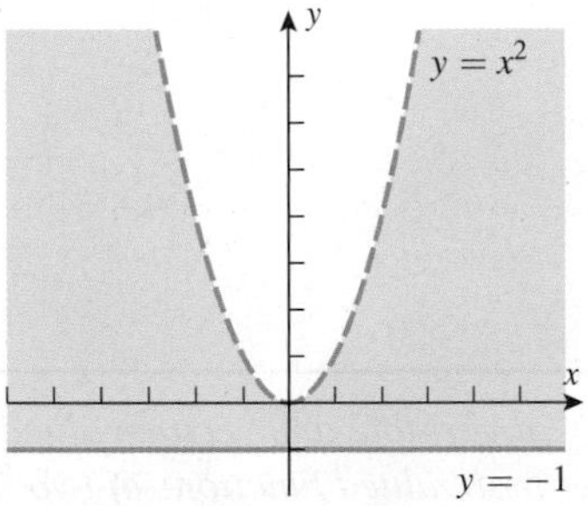


▲ **Figure 13.1.1**

▶ **Example 1** Let $f(x, y) = \sqrt{y+1} + \ln(x^2 - y)$. Find $f(e, 0)$ and sketch the natural domain of $f$.

***Solution.*** By substitution,

$$f(e, 0) = \sqrt{0+1} + \ln(e^2 - 0) = \sqrt{1} + \ln(e^2) = 1 + 2 = 3$$

To find the natural domain of $f$, we note that $\sqrt{y+1}$ is defined only when $y \geq -1$, while $\ln(x^2 - y)$ is defined only when $0 < x^2 - y$ or $y < x^2$. Thus, the natural domain of $f$ consists of all points in the $xy$-plane for which $-1 \leq y < x^2$. To sketch the natural domain, we first sketch the parabola $y = x^2$ as a "dashed" curve and the line $y = -1$ as a solid curve. The natural domain of $f$ is then the region lying above or on the line $y = -1$ and below the parabola $y = x^2$ (Figure 13.1.1). ◀

▶ **Example 2** Let

$$f(x, y, z) = \sqrt{1 - x^2 - y^2 - z^2}$$

Find $f\left(0, \frac{1}{2}, -\frac{1}{2}\right)$ and the natural domain of $f$.

***Solution.*** By substitution,

$$f\left(0, \tfrac{1}{2}, -\tfrac{1}{2}\right) = \sqrt{1 - (0)^2 - \left(\tfrac{1}{2}\right)^2 - \left(-\tfrac{1}{2}\right)^2} = \sqrt{\tfrac{1}{2}}$$

Because of the square root sign, we must have $0 \leq 1 - x^2 - y^2 - z^2$ in order to have a real value for $f(x, y, z)$. Rewriting this inequality in the form

$$x^2 + y^2 + z^2 \leq 1$$

we see that the natural domain of $f$ consists of all points on or within the sphere

$$x^2 + y^2 + z^2 = 1 \text{ ◀}$$

## FUNCTIONS DESCRIBED BY TABLES

The wind chill index is that temperature (in °F) which would produce the same sensation on exposed skin at a wind speed of 3 mi/h as the temperature and wind speed combination in current weather conditions.

Sometimes it is useful to represent a function of two variables in table form, rather than as an explicit formula. For example, the U.S. National Weather Service uses the formula

$$W = 35.74 + 0.6215T + (0.4275T - 35.75)v^{0.16} \tag{1}$$

to model the wind chill index $W$ (in °F) as a function of the temperature $T$ (in °F) and the wind speed $v$ (in mi/h) for wind speeds greater than 3 mi/h. This formula is sufficiently complex that it is difficult to get an intuitive feel for the relationship between the variables.

**Table 13.1.1**

| WIND SPEED $v$ (mi/h) \ TEMPERATURE $T$ (°F) | 20 | 25 | 30 | 35 |
|---|---|---|---|---|
| 5 | 13 | 19 | 25 | 31 |
| 15 | 6 | 13 | 19 | 25 |
| 25 | 3 | 9 | 16 | 23 |
| 35 | 0 | 7 | 14 | 21 |
| 45 | −2 | 5 | 12 | 19 |

One can get a clearer sense of the relationship by selecting sample values of $T$ and $v$ and constructing a table, such as Table 13.1.1, in which we have rounded the values of $W$ to the nearest integer. For example, if the temperature is 30°F and the wind speed is 5 mi/h, it feels as if the temperature is 25°F. If the wind speed increases to 15 mi/h, the temperature then feels as if it has dropped to 19°F. Note that in this case, an increase in wind speed of 10 mi/h causes a 6°F decrease in the wind chill index. To estimate wind chill values not displayed in the table, we can use ***linear interpolation***. For example, suppose that the temperature is 30°F and the wind speed is 7 mi/h. A reasonable estimate for the drop in the wind chill index from its value when the wind speed is 5 mi/h would be $\frac{2}{10} \cdot 6°\text{F} = 1.2°\text{F}$. (Why?) The resulting estimate in wind chill would then be $25° - 1.2° = 23.8°\text{F}$.

In some cases, tables for functions of two variables arise directly from experimental data, in which case one must either work directly with the table or else use some technique to construct a formula that models the data in the table. Such modeling techniques are developed in statistics and numerical analysis texts.

## GRAPHS OF FUNCTIONS OF TWO VARIABLES

Recall that for a function $f$ of one variable, the graph of $f(x)$ in the $xy$-plane was defined to be the graph of the equation $y = f(x)$. Similarly, if $f$ is a function of two variables, we define the ***graph*** of $f(x, y)$ in $xyz$-space to be the graph of the equation $z = f(x, y)$. In general, such a graph will be a surface in 3-space.

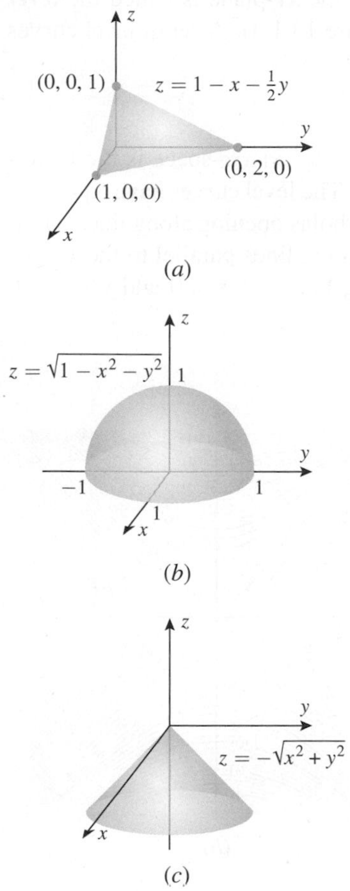


▲ **Figure 13.1.2**

▶ **Example 3** In each part, describe the graph of the function in an $xyz$-coordinate system.

(a) $f(x, y) = 1 - x - \frac{1}{2}y$ (b) $f(x, y) = \sqrt{1 - x^2 - y^2}$

(c) $f(x, y) = -\sqrt{x^2 + y^2}$

***Solution (a).*** By definition, the graph of the given function is the graph of the equation

$$z = 1 - x - \tfrac{1}{2}y$$

which is a plane. A triangular portion of the plane can be sketched by plotting the intersections with the coordinate axes and joining them with line segments (Figure 13.1.2*a*).

***Solution (b).*** By definition, the graph of the given function is the graph of the equation

$$z = \sqrt{1 - x^2 - y^2} \tag{2}$$

After squaring both sides, this can be rewritten as

$$x^2 + y^2 + z^2 = 1$$

which represents a sphere of radius 1, centered at the origin. Since (2) imposes the added condition that $z \geq 0$, the graph is just the upper hemisphere (Figure 13.1.2*b*).

***Solution (c).*** The graph of the given function is the graph of the equation

$$z = -\sqrt{x^2 + y^2} \tag{3}$$

After squaring, we obtain

$$z^2 = x^2 + y^2$$

which is the equation of a circular cone (see Table 11.7.1). Since (3) imposes the condition that $z \leq 0$, the graph is just the lower nappe of the cone (Figure 13.1.2*c*). ◀

## LEVEL CURVES

A topographic (or contour) map represents a three-dimensional landscape, such as a mountain range, by two-dimensional contour lines or curves of constant elevation. Consider, for example, the model hill and its contour map shown in Figure 13.1.3. The contour map is constructed by passing planes of constant elevation through the hill, projecting the resulting contours onto a flat surface, and labeling the contours with their elevations. In Figure 13.1.3, note how the two gullies appear as indentations in the contour lines and how the curves are close together on the contour map where the hill has a steep slope and become more widely spaced where the slope is gradual.

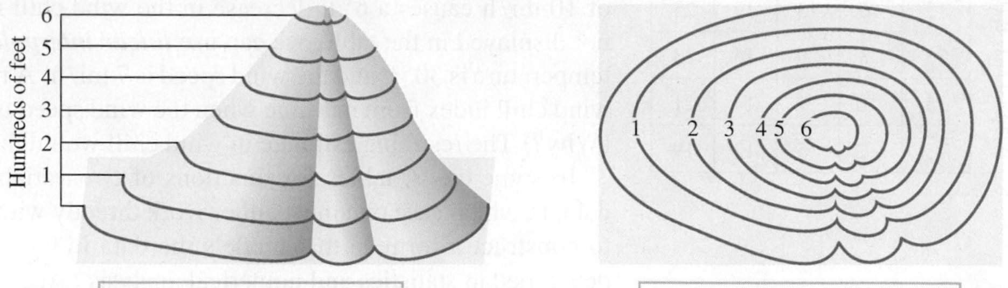


A perspective view of a model hill with two gullies

A contour map of the model hill

▲ Figure 13.1.3

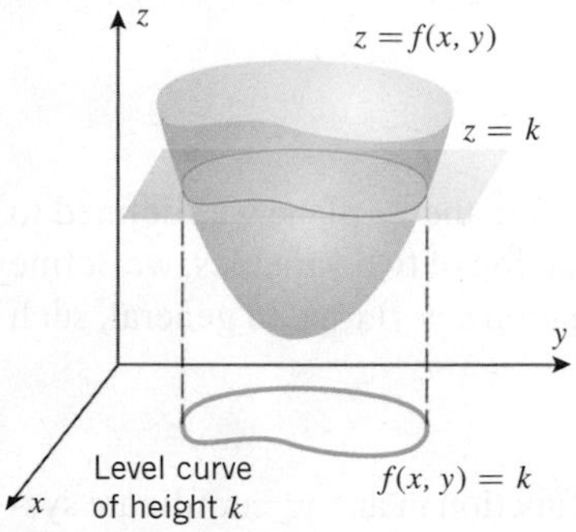


▲ Figure 13.1.4

Contour maps are also useful for studying functions of two variables. If the surface $z = f(x, y)$ is cut by the horizontal plane $z = k$, then at all points on the intersection we have $f(x, y) = k$. The projection of this intersection onto the $xy$-plane is called the ***level curve of height k*** or the ***level curve with constant k*** (Figure 13.1.4). A set of level curves for $z = f(x, y)$ is called a ***contour plot*** or ***contour map*** of $f$.

▶ **Example 4** The graph of the function $f(x, y) = y^2 - x^2$ in $xyz$-space is the hyperbolic paraboloid (saddle surface) shown in Figure 13.1.5$a$. The level curves have equations of the form $y^2 - x^2 = k$. For $k > 0$ these curves are hyperbolas opening along lines parallel to the $y$-axis; for $k < 0$ they are hyperbolas opening along lines parallel to the $x$-axis; and for $k = 0$ the level curve consists of the intersecting lines $y + x = 0$ and $y - x = 0$ (Figure 13.1.5$b$). ◀

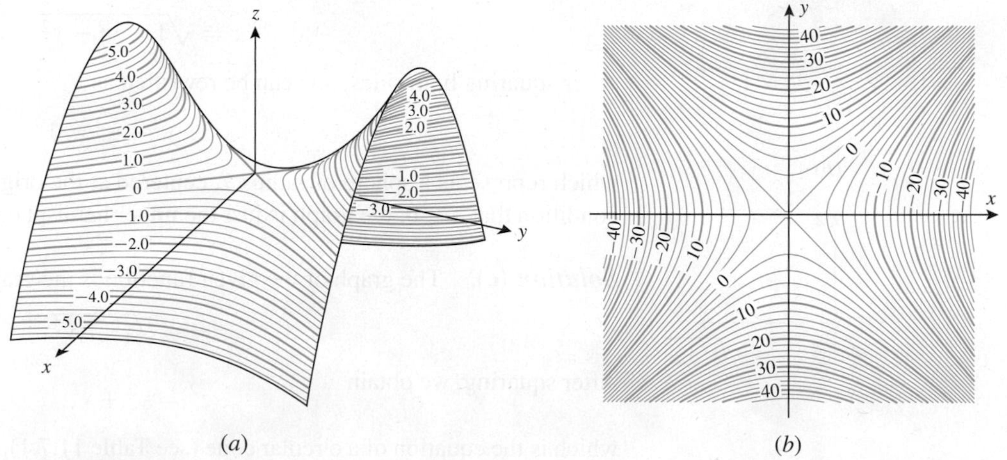


▲ Figure 13.1.5

▶ **Example 5** Sketch the contour plot of $f(x, y) = 4x^2 + y^2$ using level curves of height $k = 0, 1, 2, 3, 4, 5$.

***Solution.*** The graph of the surface $z = 4x^2 + y^2$ is the paraboloid shown in the left part of Figure 13.1.6, so we can reasonably expect the contour plot to be a family of ellipses centered at the origin. The level curve of height $k$ has the equation $4x^2 + y^2 = k$. If $k = 0$, then the graph is the single point $(0, 0)$. For $k > 0$ we can rewrite the equation as

$$\frac{x^2}{k/4} + \frac{y^2}{k} = 1$$

which represents a family of ellipses with $x$-intercepts $\pm\sqrt{k}/2$ and $y$-intercepts $\pm\sqrt{k}$. The contour plot for the specified values of $k$ is shown in the right part of Figure 13.1.6. ◄

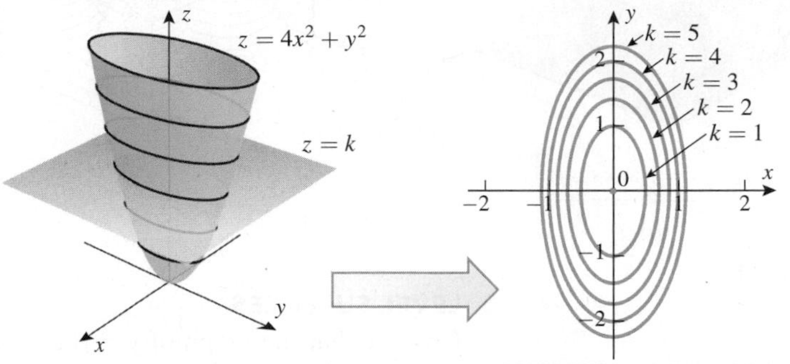


► **Figure 13.1.6**

In the last two examples we used a formula for $f(x, y)$ to find the contour plot of $f$. Conversely, if we are given a contour plot of some function, then we can use the plot to estimate values of the function.

► **Example 6** Let $f(r, L)$ be the monthly payment on a 5-year car loan as a function of the interest rate $r$ and the loan amount $L$. Figure 13.1.7 is a contour plot of $f(r, L)$. Use this plot in each part.

(a) Estimate the monthly payment on a loan of \$3000 at an interest rate of 7%.

(b) Estimate the monthly payment on a loan of \$5000 at an interest rate of 3%.

(c) Estimate the loan amount if the monthly payment is \$80 and the interest rate is 3%.

***Solution (a).*** Since the point $(7, 3000)$ appears to lie on the contour labeled 60, we estimate the monthly payment to be \$60.

***Solution (b).*** Since the point $(3, 5000)$ appears to be midway between the contours labeled 80 and 100, we estimate the monthly payment to be \$90.

***Solution (c).*** The vertical line $x = 3$ intersects the contour labeled 80 at a point whose $L$ coordinate appears to be 4500. Hence, we estimate the loan amount to be \$4500. ◄

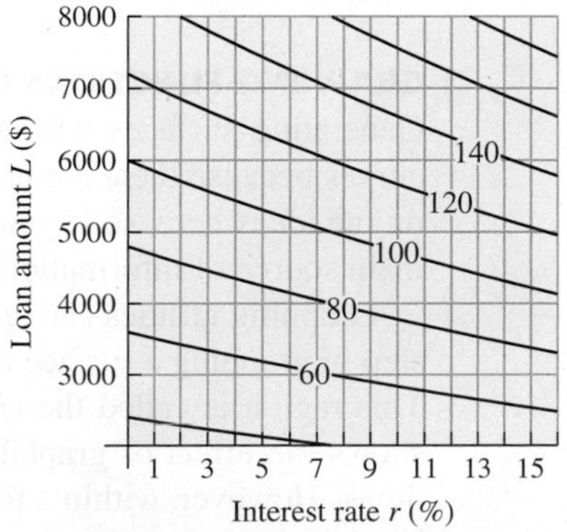


► **Figure 13.1.7**

## CONTOUR PLOTS USING TECHNOLOGY

Except in the simplest cases, contour plots can be difficult to produce without the help of a graphing utility. Figure 13.1.8 illustrates how graphing technology can be used to display level curves. Figure 13.1.8*a* shows the graph of $f(x, y) = |\sin x \sin y|$ plotted over the domain $0 \le x \le 2\pi$, $0 \le y \le 2\pi$, and Figure 13.1.8*b* displays curves of constant elevation on the graph of $f$. The projections of these curves into the $xy$-plane are contours of $f$. Figure 13.1.8$c$ illustrates how the use of color can enhance the display of these contours.

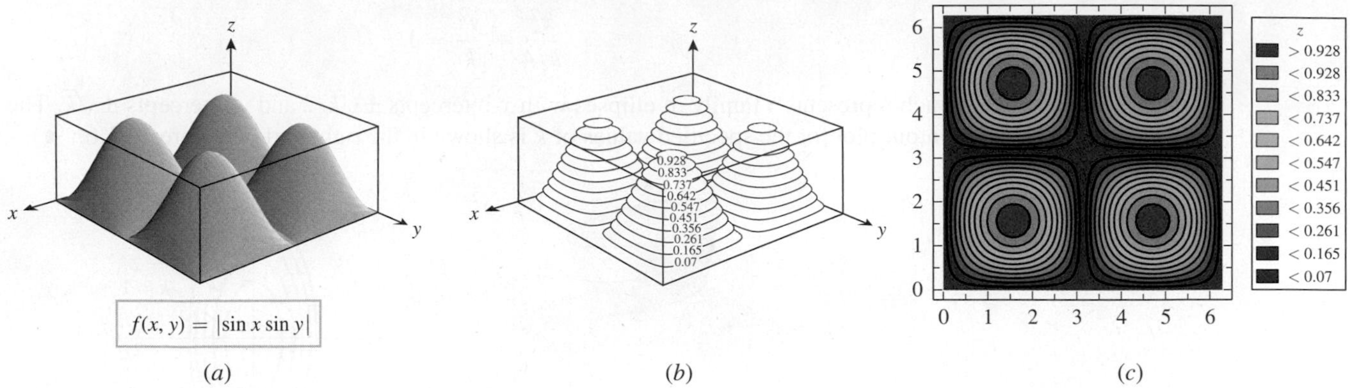


▲ Figure 13.1.8

## LEVEL SURFACES

Observe that the graph of $y = f(x)$ is a curve in 2-space, and the graph of $z = f(x, y)$ is a surface in 3-space, so the number of dimensions required for these graphs is one greater than the number of independent variables. Accordingly, there is no "direct" way to graph a function of three variables since four dimensions are required. However, if $k$ is a constant, then the graph of the equation $f(x, y, z) = k$ will generally be a surface in 3-space (e.g., the graph of $x^2 + y^2 + z^2 = 1$ is a sphere), which we call the ***level surface with constant k***. Some geometric insight into the behavior of the function $f$ can sometimes be obtained by graphing these level surfaces for various values of $k$.

**WARNING**

A level surface need *not* be level in the sense of being horizontal—it is simply a surface on which all values of $f$ are the same.

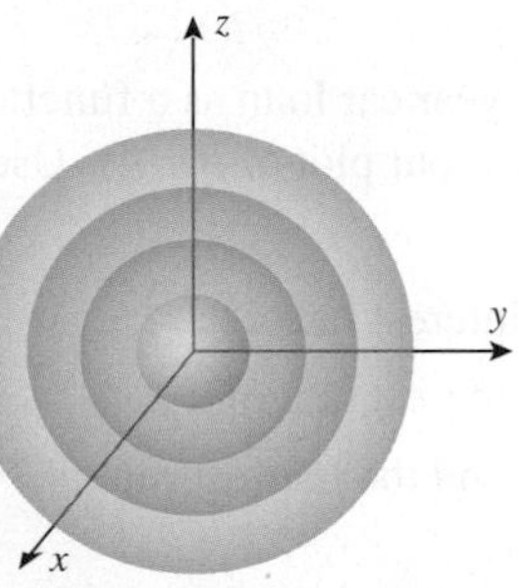


Level surfaces of $f(x, y, z) = x^2 + y^2 + z^2$

▲ Figure 13.1.9

▶ **Example 7** Describe the level surfaces of

(a) $f(x, y, z) = x^2 + y^2 + z^2$ (b) $f(x, y, z) = z^2 - x^2 - y^2$

***Solution (a).*** The level surfaces have equations of the form

$$x^2 + y^2 + z^2 = k$$

For $k > 0$ the graph of this equation is a sphere of radius $\sqrt{k}$, centered at the origin; for $k = 0$ the graph is the single point $(0, 0, 0)$; and for $k < 0$ there is no level surface (Figure 13.1.9).

***Solution (b).*** The level surfaces have equations of the form

$$z^2 - x^2 - y^2 = k$$

As discussed in Section 11.7, this equation represents a cone if $k = 0$, a hyperboloid of two sheets if $k > 0$, and a hyperboloid of one sheet if $k < 0$ (Figure 13.1.10). ◀

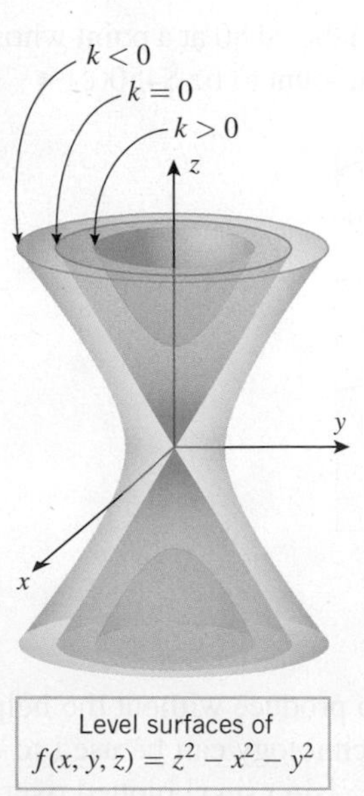


Level surfaces of $f(x, y, z) = z^2 - x^2 - y^2$

▲ Figure 13.1.10

## GRAPHING FUNCTIONS OF TWO VARIABLES USING TECHNOLOGY

Generating surfaces with a graphing utility is more complicated than generating plane curves because there are more factors that must be taken into account. We can only touch on the ideas here, so if you want to use a graphing utility, its documentation will be your main source of information.

Graphing utilities can only show a portion of $xyz$-space in a viewing screen, so the first step in graphing a surface is to determine which portion of $xyz$-space you want to display. This region is called the ***viewing box*** or ***viewing window***. For example, Figure 13.1.11 shows the effect of graphing the paraboloid $z = x^2 + y^2$ in three different viewing windows. However, within a fixed viewing box, the appearance of the surface is also affected by the ***viewpoint***, that is, the direction from which the surface is viewed, and the distance from the viewer to the surface. For example, Figure 13.1.12 shows the graph of the paraboloid $z = x^2 + y^2$ from three different viewpoints using the first viewing box in Figure 13.1.11.

Table 13.1.2 shows six surfaces in 3-space along with their associated contour plots. Note that the level curves correspond to traces on the surface in horizontal planes.

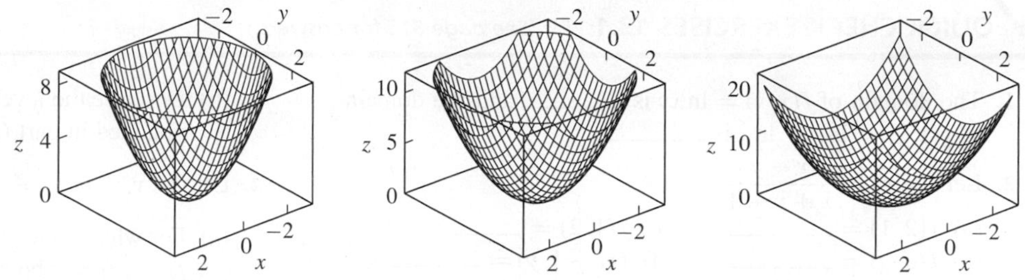

▲ **Figure 13.1.11** Varying the viewing box.

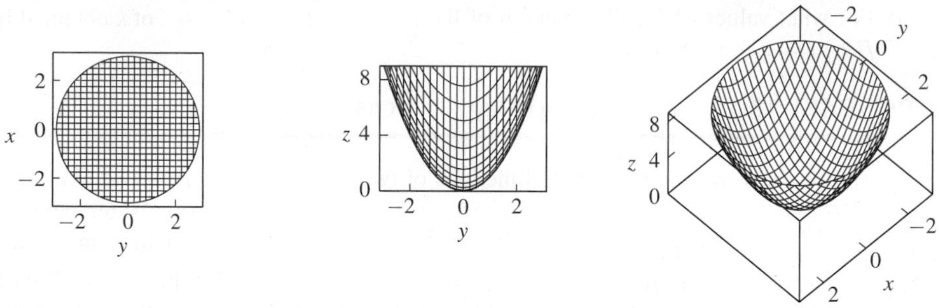

▲ **Figure 13.1.12** Varying the viewpoint.

**TECHNOLOGY MASTERY**

If you have a graphing utility that can generate surfaces in 3-space, read the documentation and try to duplicate some of the surfaces in Figures 13.1.11 and 13.1.12 and Table 13.1.2.

**Table 13.1.2**

| SURFACE | CONTOUR PLOT | SURFACE | CONTOUR PLOT |
|---|---|---|---|
| $z = \cos y$ 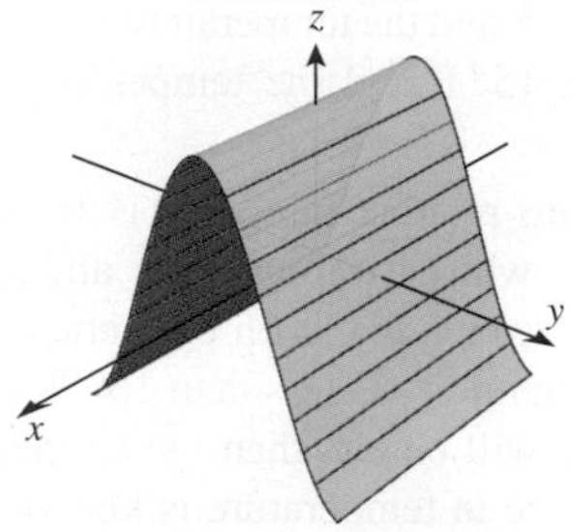 | 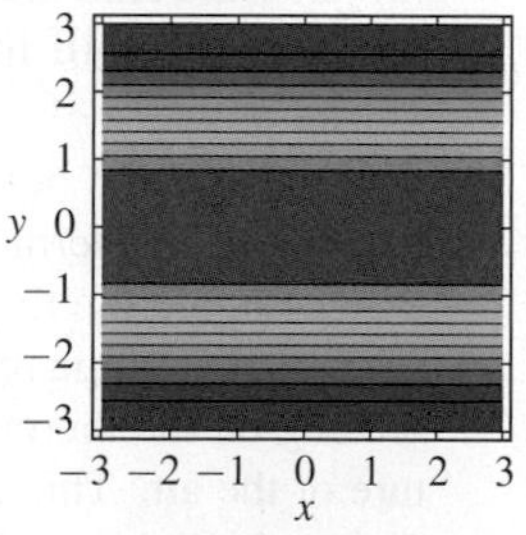 | $z = 5e^x \sin y$ 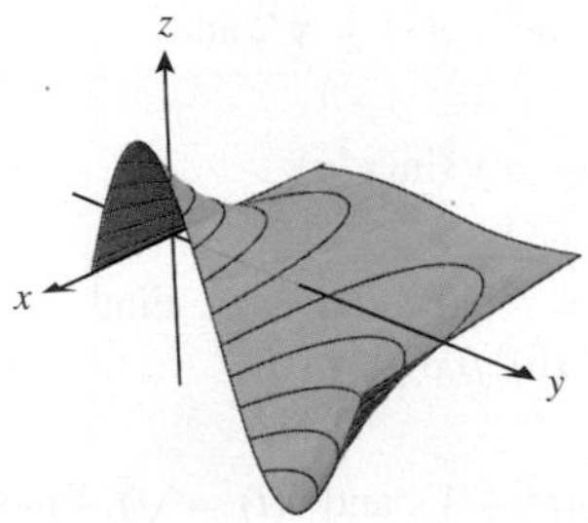 | 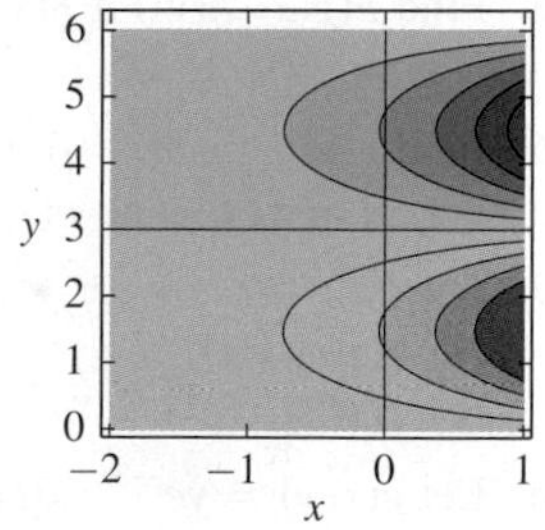 |
| $z = \sin\left(\sqrt{x^2 + y^2}\right)$ 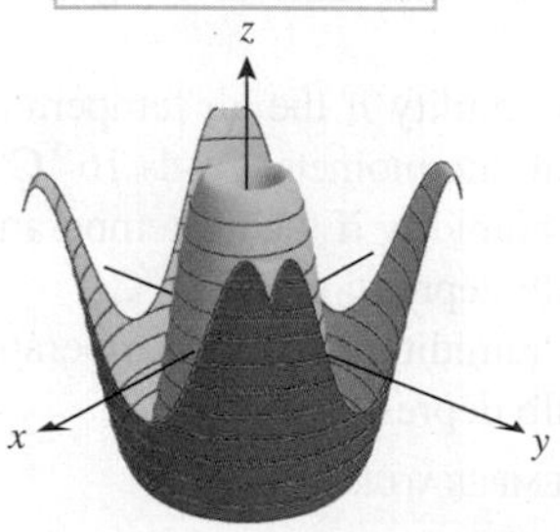 | 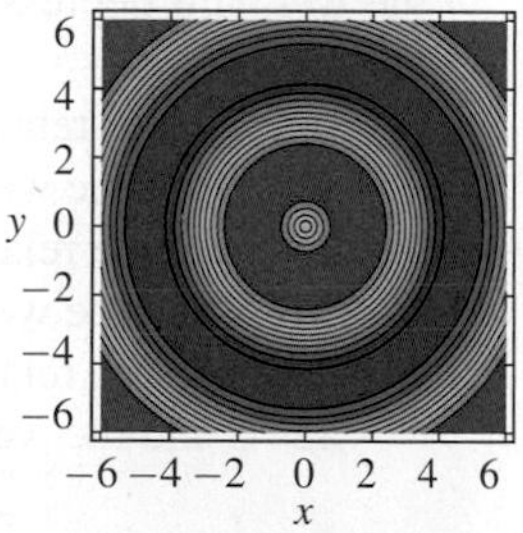 | $z = xye^{-\frac{1}{2}(x^2 + y^2)}$ 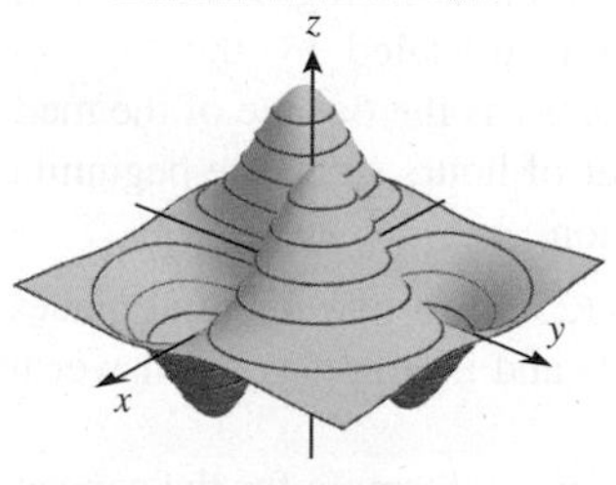 | 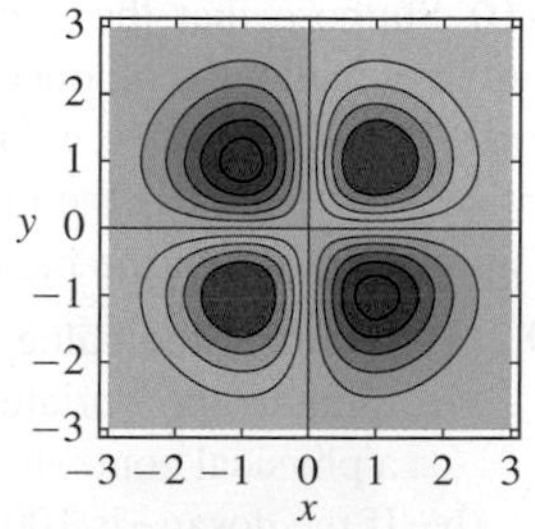 |
| $z = \cos(xy)$ 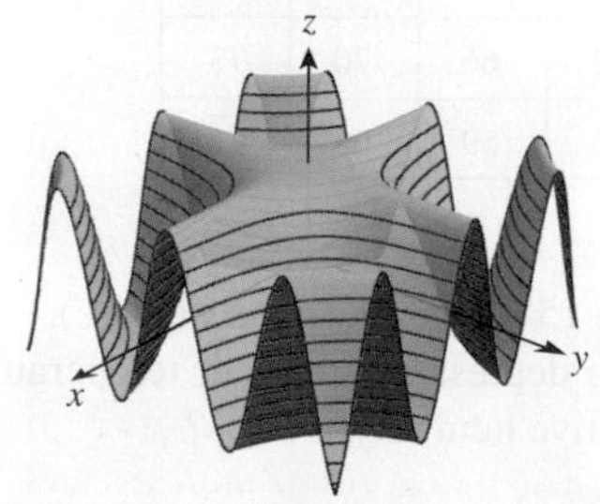 | 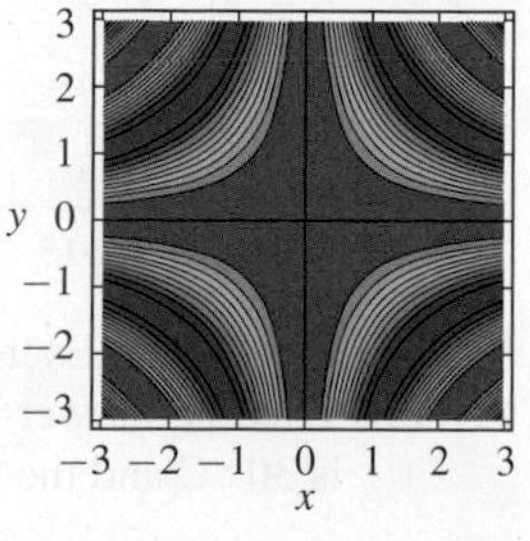 | $z = xy$ 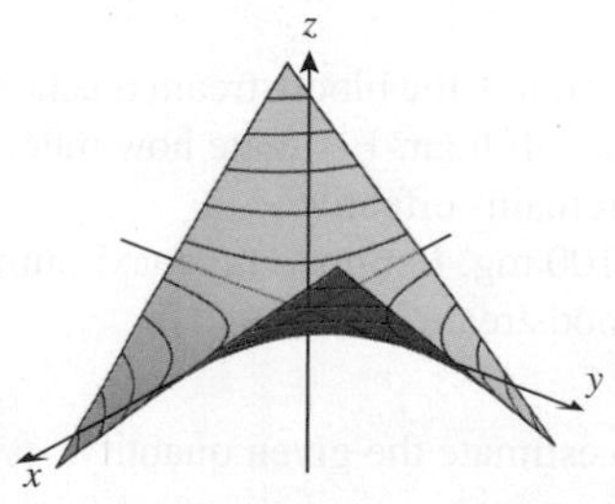 | 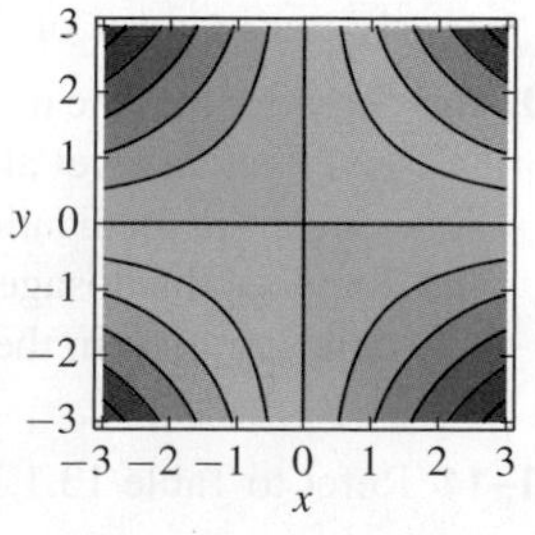 |

## ✓QUICK CHECK EXERCISES 13.1 *(See page 815 for answers.)*

1. The domain of $f(x, y) = \ln xy$ is ________ and the domain of $g(x, y) = \ln x + \ln y$ is ________.

2. Let $f(x, y) = \dfrac{x - y}{x + y + 1}$.
   (a) $f(2, 1) =$ ________ (b) $f(1, 2) =$ ________
   (c) $f(a, a) =$ ________ (d) $f(y + 1, y) =$ ________

3. Let $f(x, y) = e^{x+y}$.
   (a) For what values of $k$ will the graph of the level curve $f(x, y) = k$ be nonempty?
   (b) Describe the level curves $f(x, y) = k$ for the values of $k$ obtained in part (a).

4. Let $f(x, y, z) = \dfrac{1}{x^2 + y^2 + z^2 + 1}$.
   (a) For what values of $k$ will the graph of the level surface $f(x, y, z) = k$ be nonempty?
   (b) Describe the level surfaces $f(x, y, z) = k$ for the values of $k$ obtained in part (a).

## EXERCISE SET 13.1 Graphing Utility C CAS

**1–8** These exercises are concerned with functions of two variables.

1. Let $f(x, y) = x^2y + 1$. Find
   (a) $f(2, 1)$ (b) $f(1, 2)$ (c) $f(0, 0)$
   (d) $f(1, -3)$ (e) $f(3a, a)$ (f) $f(ab, a - b)$.

2. Let $f(x, y) = x + \sqrt[3]{xy}$. Find
   (a) $f(t, t^2)$ (b) $f(x, x^2)$ (c) $f(2y^2, 4y)$.

3. Let $f(x, y) = xy + 3$. Find
   (a) $f(x + y, x - y)$ (b) $f(xy, 3x^2y^3)$.

4. Let $g(x) = x \sin x$. Find
   (a) $g(x/y)$ (b) $g(xy)$ (c) $g(x - y)$.

5. Find $F(g(x), h(y))$ if $F(x, y) = xe^{xy}$, $g(x) = x^3$, and $h(y) = 3y + 1$.

6. Find $g(u(x, y), v(x, y))$ if $g(x, y) = y \sin(x^2y)$, $u(x, y) = x^2y^3$, and $v(x, y) = \pi xy$.

7. Let $f(x, y) = x + 3x^2y^2$, $x(t) = t^2$, and $y(t) = t^3$. Find
   (a) $f(x(t), y(t))$ (b) $f(x(0), y(0))$
   (c) $f(x(2), y(2))$.

8. Let $g(x, y) = ye^{-3x}$, $x(t) = \ln(t^2 + 1)$, and $y(t) = \sqrt{t}$. Find $g(x(t), y(t))$.

**9–10** Suppose that the concentration $C$ in mg/L of medication in a patient's bloodstream is modeled by the function $C(x, t) = 0.2x(e^{-0.2t} - e^{-t})$, where $x$ is the dosage of the medication in mg and $t$ is the number of hours since the beginning of administration of the medication.

9. (a) Estimate the value of $C(25, 3)$ to two decimal places. Include appropriate units and interpret your answer in a physical context.
   (b) If the dosage is 100 mg, give a formula for the concentration as a function of time $t$.
   (c) Give a formula that describes the concentration after 1 hour in terms of the dosage $x$.

10. (a) Suppose that the medication in the bloodstream reaches an effective level after a half hour. Estimate how much longer the medication remains effective.
    (b) Suppose the dosage is 100 mg. Estimate the maximum concentration in the bloodstream.

**11–14** Refer to Table 13.1.1 to estimate the given quantity.

11. The wind chill index when
    (a) the temperature is 25°F and the wind speed is 7 mi/h
    (b) the temperature is 28°F and the wind speed is 5 mi/h.

12. The wind chill index when
    (a) the temperature is 35°F and the wind speed is 14 mi/h
    (b) the temperature is 32°F and the wind speed is 15 mi/h.

13. The temperature when
    (a) the wind chill index is 16°F and the wind speed is 25 mi/h
    (b) the wind chill index is 6°F and the wind speed is 25 mi/h.

14. The wind speed when
    (a) the wind chill index is 7°F and the temperature is 25°F
    (b) the wind chill index is 15°F and the temperature is 30°F.

15. One method for determining relative humidity is to wet the bulb of a thermometer, whirl it through the air, and then compare the thermometer reading with the actual air temperature. If the relative humidity is less than 100%, the reading on the thermometer will be less than the temperature of the air. This difference in temperature is known as the *wet-bulb depression*. The accompanying table gives the relative humidity as a function of the air temperature and the wet-bulb depression. Use the table to complete parts (a)–(c).
    (a) What is the relative humidity if the air temperature is 20°C and the wet-bulb thermometer reads 16°C?
    (b) Estimate the relative humidity if the air temperature is 25°C and the wet-bulb depression is 3.5°C.
    (c) Estimate the relative humidity if the air temperature is 22°C and the wet-bulb depression is 5°C.

| WET-BULB DEPRESSION (°C) \ AIR TEMPERATURE (°C) | 15 | 20 | 25 | 30 |
|---|---|---|---|---|
| 3 | 71 | 74 | 77 | 79 |
| 4 | 62 | 66 | 70 | 73 |
| 5 | 53 | 59 | 63 | 67 |

▲ **Table Ex-15**

16. Use the table in Exercise 15 to complete parts (a)–(c).
    (a) What is the wet-bulb depression if the air temperature is 30°C and the relative humidity is 73%?

(b) Estimate the relative humidity if the air temperature is 15°C and the wet-bulb depression is 4.25°C.
(c) Estimate the relative humidity if the air temperature is 26°C and the wet-bulb depression is 3°C.

**17–20** These exercises involve functions of three variables. ■

**17.** Let $f(x, y, z) = xy^2z^3 + 3$. Find
(a) $f(2, 1, 2)$ (b) $f(-3, 2, 1)$
(c) $f(0, 0, 0)$ (d) $f(a, a, a)$
(e) $f(t, t^2, -t)$ (f) $f(a + b, a - b, b)$.

**18.** Let $f(x, y, z) = zxy + x$. Find
(a) $f(x + y, x - y, x^2)$ (b) $f(xy, y/x, xz)$.

**19.** Find $F(f(x), g(y), h(z))$ if $F(x, y, z) = ye^{xyz}$, $f(x) = x^2$, $g(y) = y + 1$, and $h(z) = z^2$.

**20.** Find $g(u(x, y, z), v(x, y, z), w(x, y, z))$ if $g(x, y, z) = z \sin xy$, $u(x, y, z) = x^2z^3$, $v(x, y, z) = \pi xyz$, and $w(x, y, z) = xy/z$.

**21–22** These exercises are concerned with functions of four or more variables. ■

**21.** (a) Let $f(x, y, z, t) = x^2y^3\sqrt{z + t}$. Find $f(\sqrt{5}, 2, \pi, 3\pi)$.
(b) Let $f(x_1, x_2, \ldots, x_n) = \sum_{k=1}^{n} kx_k$. Find $f(1, 1, \ldots, 1)$.

**22.** (a) Let $f(u, v, \lambda, \phi) = e^{u+v} \cos \lambda \tan \phi$. Find $f(-2, 2, 0, \pi/4)$.
(b) Let $f(x_1, x_2, \ldots, x_n) = x_1^2 + x_2^2 + \cdots + x_n^2$. Find $f(1, 2, \ldots, n)$.

**23–26** Sketch the domain of $f$. Use solid lines for portions of the boundary included in the domain and dashed lines for portions not included. ■

**23.** $f(x, y) = \ln(1 - x^2 - y^2)$ **24.** $f(x, y) = \sqrt{x^2 + y^2 - 4}$

**25.** $f(x, y) = \dfrac{1}{x - y^2}$ **26.** $f(x, y) = \ln xy$

**27–28** Describe the domain of $f$ in words. ■

**27.** (a) $f(x, y) = xe^{-\sqrt{y+2}}$
(b) $f(x, y, z) = \sqrt{25 - x^2 - y^2 - z^2}$
(c) $f(x, y, z) = e^{xyz}$

**28.** (a) $f(x, y) = \dfrac{\sqrt{4 - x^2}}{y^2 + 3}$ (b) $f(x, y) = \ln(y - 2x)$
(c) $f(x, y, z) = \dfrac{xyz}{x + y + z}$

**29–32 True–False** Determine whether the statement is true or false. Explain your answer. ■

**29.** If the domain of $f(x, y)$ is the $xy$-plane, then the domain of $f(\sin^{-1}t, \sqrt{t})$ is the interval $[0, 1]$.

**30.** If $f(x, y) = y/x$, then a contour $f(x, y) = m$ is the straight line $y = mx$.

**31.** The natural domain of $f(x, y, z) = \sqrt{1 - x^2 - y^2}$ is a disk of radius 1 centered at the origin in the $xy$-plane.

**32.** Every level surface of $f(x, y, z) = x + 2y + 3z$ is a plane.

**33–42** Sketch the graph of $f$. ■

**33.** $f(x, y) = 3$ **34.** $f(x, y) = \sqrt{9 - x^2 - y^2}$

**35.** $f(x, y) = \sqrt{x^2 + y^2}$ **36.** $f(x, y) = x^2 + y^2$

**37.** $f(x, y) = x^2 - y^2$ **38.** $f(x, y) = 4 - x^2 - y^2$

**39.** $f(x, y) = \sqrt{x^2 + y^2 + 1}$ **40.** $f(x, y) = \sqrt{x^2 + y^2 - 1}$

**41.** $f(x, y) = y + 1$ **42.** $f(x, y) = x^2$

**43–44** In each part, select the term that best describes the level curves of the function $f$. Choose from the terms lines, circles, noncircular ellipses, parabolas, or hyperbolas. ■

**43.** (a) $f(x, y) = 5x^2 - 5y^2$ (b) $f(x, y) = y - 4x^2$
(c) $f(x, y) = x^2 + 3y^2$ (d) $f(x, y) = 3x^2$

**44.** (a) $f(x, y) = x^2 - 2xy + y^2$ (b) $f(x, y) = 2x^2 + 2y^2$
(c) $f(x, y) = x^2 - 2x - y^2$ (d) $f(x, y) = 2y^2 - x$

**45–46** Refer to Figure 13.1.7 in each part. ■

**45.** Suppose that \$6000 is borrowed at an interest rate of 11%.
(a) Estimate the monthly payment on the loan.
(b) If the interest rate drops to 9%, estimate how much more can be borrowed without increasing the monthly payment.

**46.** Suppose that \$3000 is borrowed at an interest rate of 4%.
(a) Estimate the monthly payment on the loan.
(b) If the interest rate increases to 7%, estimate how much less would need to be borrowed so as not to increase the monthly payment.

**FOCUS ON CONCEPTS**

**47.** In each part, match the contour plot with one of the functions

$$f(x, y) = \sqrt{x^2 + y^2}, \quad f(x, y) = x^2 + y^2, \quad f(x, y) = 1 - x^2 - y^2$$

by inspection, and explain your reasoning. Larger values of $z$ are indicated by lighter colors in the contour plot, and the concentric contours correspond to equally spaced values of $z$.

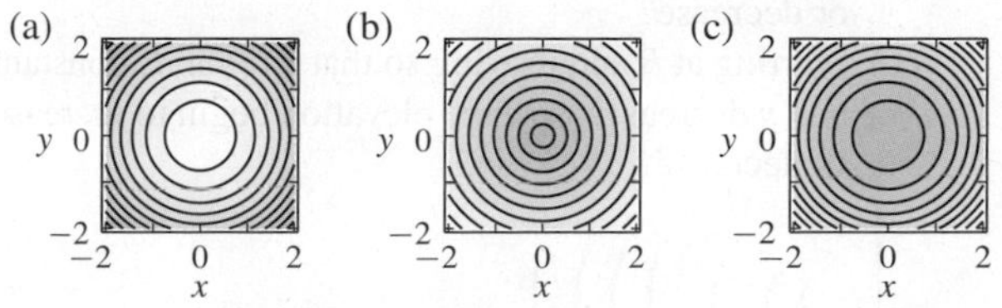


**48.** In each part, match the contour plot with one of the surfaces in the accompanying figure on the next page by inspection, and explain your reasoning. The larger the value of $z$, the lighter the color in the contour plot.

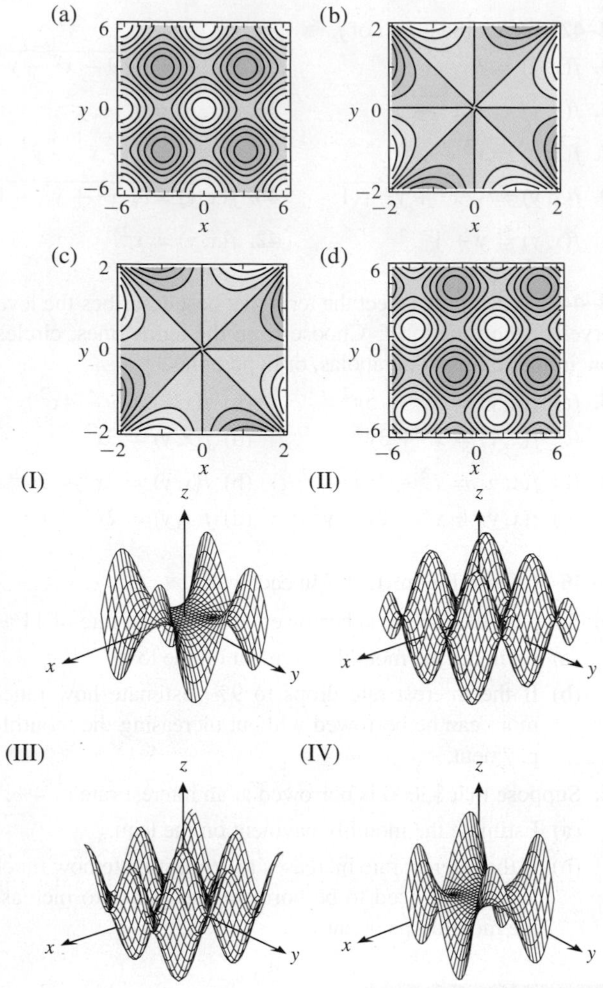


▲ Figure Ex-48

**49.** In each part, the questions refer to the contour map in the accompanying figure.
(a) Is $A$ or $B$ the higher point? Explain your reasoning.
(b) Is the slope steeper at point $A$ or at point $B$? Explain your reasoning.
(c) Starting at $A$ and moving so that $y$ remains constant and $x$ increases, will the elevation begin to increase or decrease?
(d) Starting at $B$ and moving so that $y$ remains constant and $x$ increases, will the elevation begin to increase or decrease?
(e) Starting at $A$ and moving so that $x$ remains constant and $y$ decreases, will the elevation begin to increase or decrease?
(f) Starting at $B$ and moving so that $x$ remains constant and $y$ decreases, will the elevation begin to increase or decrease?

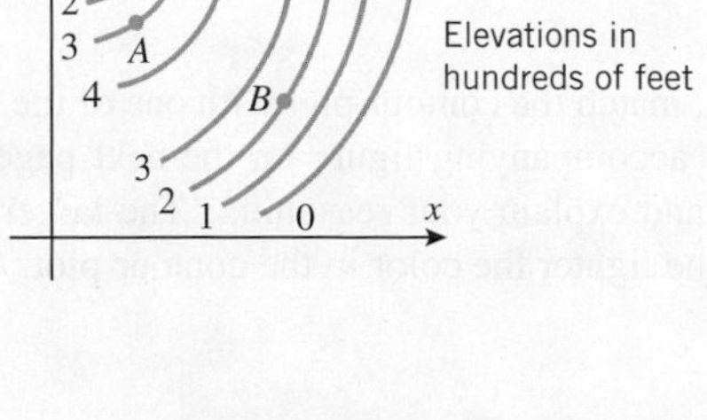


◀ Figure Ex-49

**50.** A curve connecting points of equal atmospheric pressure on a weather map is called an ***isobar***. On a typical weather map the isobars refer to pressure at mean sea level and are given in units of ***millibars*** (mb). Mathematically, isobars are level curves for the pressure function $p(x, y)$ defined at the geographic points $(x, y)$ represented on the map. Tightly packed isobars correspond to steep slopes on the graph of the pressure function, and these are usually associated with strong winds—the steeper the slope, the greater the speed of the wind.
(a) Referring to the accompanying weather map, is the wind speed greater in Medicine Hat, Alberta or in Chicago? Explain your reasoning.
(b) Estimate the average rate of change in atmospheric pressure (in mb/mi) from Medicine Hat to Chicago, given that the distance between the two cities is approximately 1400 mi.

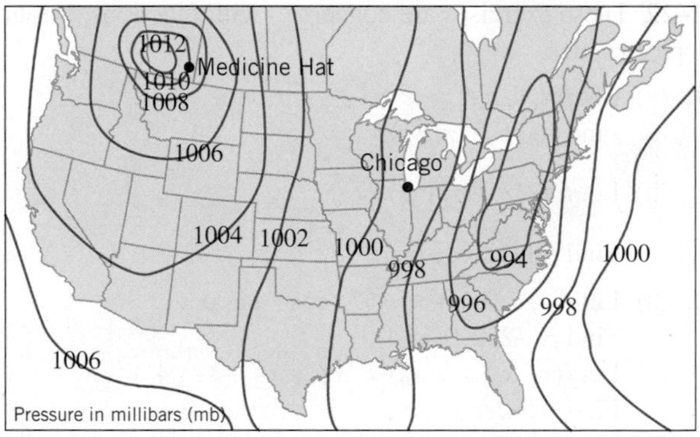


▲ Figure Ex-50

**51–56** Sketch the level curve $z = k$ for the specified values of $k$. ■

**51.** $z = x^2 + y^2$; $k = 0, 1, 2, 3, 4$

**52.** $z = y/x$; $k = -2, -1, 0, 1, 2$

**53.** $z = x^2 + y$; $k = -2, -1, 0, 1, 2$

**54.** $z = x^2 + 9y^2$; $k = 0, 1, 2, 3, 4$

**55.** $z = x^2 - y^2$; $k = -2, -1, 0, 1, 2$

**56.** $z = y \csc x$; $k = -2, -1, 0, 1, 2$

**57–60** Sketch the level surface $f(x, y, z) = k$. ■

**57.** $f(x, y, z) = 4x^2 + y^2 + 4z^2$; $k = 16$

**58.** $f(x, y, z) = x^2 + y^2 - z^2$; $k = 0$

**59.** $f(x, y, z) = z - x^2 - y^2 + 4$; $k = 7$

**60.** $f(x, y, z) = 4x - 2y + z$; $k = 1$

**61–64** Describe the level surfaces in words. ■

**61.** $f(x, y, z) = (x - 2)^2 + y^2 + z^2$

**62.** $f(x, y, z) = 3x - y + 2z$

**63.** $f(x, y, z) = x^2 + z^2$

**64.** $f(x, y, z) = z - x^2 - y^2$

**65.** Let $f(x, y) = x^2 - 2x^3 + 3xy$. Find an equation of the level curve that passes through the point
(a) $(-1, 1)$ (b) $(0, 0)$ (c) $(2, -1)$.

**66.** Let $f(x, y) = ye^x$. Find an equation of the level curve that passes through the point
(a) $(\ln 2, 1)$ (b) $(0, 3)$ (c) $(1, -2)$.

**67.** Let $f(x, y, z) = x^2 + y^2 - z$. Find an equation of the level surface that passes through the point
(a) $(1, -2, 0)$ (b) $(1, 0, 3)$ (c) $(0, 0, 0)$.

**68.** Let $f(x, y, z) = xyz + 3$. Find an equation of the level surface that passes through the point
(a) $(1, 0, 2)$ (b) $(-2, 4, 1)$ (c) $(0, 0, 0)$.

**69.** If $T(x, y)$ is the temperature at a point $(x, y)$ on a thin metal plate in the $xy$-plane, then the level curves of $T$ are called ***isothermal curves***. All points on such a curve are at the same temperature. Suppose that a plate occupies the first quadrant and $T(x, y) = xy$.
(a) Sketch the isothermal curves on which $T = 1$, $T = 2$, and $T = 3$.
(b) An ant, initially at $(1, 4)$, wants to walk on the plate so that the temperature along its path remains constant. What path should the ant take and what is the temperature along that path?

**70.** If $V(x, y)$ is the voltage or potential at a point $(x, y)$ in the $xy$-plane, then the level curves of $V$ are called ***equipotential curves***. Along such a curve, the voltage remains constant. Given that

$$V(x, y) = \frac{8}{\sqrt{16 + x^2 + y^2}}$$

sketch the equipotential curves at which $V = 2.0$, $V = 1.0$, and $V = 0.5$.

**71.** Let $f(x, y) = x^2 + y^3$.
(a) Use a graphing utility to generate the level curve that passes through the point $(2, -1)$.
(b) Generate the level curve of height 1.

**72.** Let $f(x, y) = 2\sqrt{xy}$.
(a) Use a graphing utility to generate the level curve that passes through the point $(2, 2)$.
(b) Generate the level curve of height 8.

C **73.** Let $f(x, y) = xe^{-(x^2+y^2)}$.
(a) Use a CAS to generate the graph of $f$ for $-2 \le x \le 2$ and $-2 \le y \le 2$.
(b) Generate a contour plot for the surface, and confirm visually that it is consistent with the surface obtained in part (a).
(c) Read the appropriate documentation and explore the effect of generating the graph of $f$ from various viewpoints.

C **74.** Let $f(x, y) = \frac{1}{10}e^x \sin y$.
(a) Use a CAS to generate the graph of $f$ for $0 \le x \le 4$ and $0 \le y \le 2\pi$.
(b) Generate a contour plot for the surface, and confirm visually that it is consistent with the surface obtained in part (a).
(c) Read the appropriate documentation and explore the effect of generating the graph of $f$ from various viewpoints.

**75.** In each part, describe in words how the graph of $g$ is related to the graph of $f$.
(a) $g(x, y) = f(x - 1, y)$ (b) $g(x, y) = 1 + f(x, y)$
(c) $g(x, y) = -f(x, y + 1)$

**76.** (a) Sketch the graph of $f(x, y) = e^{-(x^2+y^2)}$.
(b) Describe in words how the graph of the function $g(x, y) = e^{-a(x^2+y^2)}$ is related to the graph of $f$ for positive values of $a$.

**77. Writing** Find a few practical examples of functions of two and three variables, and discuss how physical considerations affect their domains.

**78. Writing** Describe two different ways in which a function $f(x, y)$ can be represented geometrically. Discuss some of the advantages and disadvantages of each representation.

---

✓ **QUICK CHECK ANSWERS 13.1** 1. points $(x, y)$ in the first or third quadrants; points $(x, y)$ in the first quadrant 2. (a) $\frac{1}{4}$ (b) $-\frac{1}{4}$ (c) 0 (d) $1/(2y + 2)$ 3. (a) $k > 0$ (b) the lines $x + y = \ln k$ 4. (a) $0 < k \le 1$ (b) spheres of radius $\sqrt{(1 - k)/k}$ for $0 < k < 1$, the single point $(0, 0, 0)$ for $k = 1$

---

## 13.2 LIMITS AND CONTINUITY

*In this section we will introduce the notions of limit and continuity for functions of two or more variables. We will not go into great detail—our objective is to develop the basic concepts accurately and to obtain results needed in later sections. A more extensive study of these topics is usually given in advanced calculus.*

### LIMITS ALONG CURVES

For a function of one variable there are two one-sided limits at a point $x_0$, namely,

$$\lim_{x \to x_0^+} f(x) \quad \text{and} \quad \lim_{x \to x_0^-} f(x)$$

reflecting the fact that there are only two directions from which $x$ can approach $x_0$, the right or the left. For functions of two or three variables there are infinitely many different

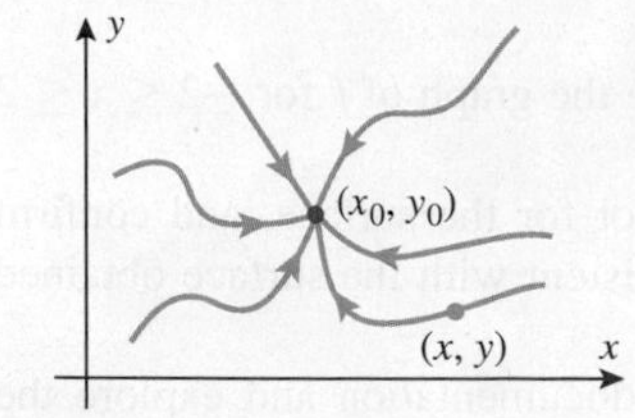

▲ Figure 13.2.1

curves along which one point can approach another (Figure 13.2.1). Our first objective in this section is to define the limit of $f(x, y)$ as $(x, y)$ approaches a point $(x_0, y_0)$ along a curve $C$ (and similarly for functions of three variables).

If $C$ is a smooth parametric curve in 2-space or 3-space that is represented by the equations

$$x = x(t), \quad y = y(t) \qquad \text{or} \qquad x = x(t), \quad y = y(t), \quad z = z(t)$$

and if $x_0 = x(t_0)$, $y_0 = y(t_0)$, and $z_0 = z(t_0)$, then the limits

$$\lim_{\substack{(x,y)\to(x_0,y_0)\\ \text{(along } C)}} f(x, y) \quad \text{and} \quad \lim_{\substack{(x,y,z)\to(x_0,y_0,z_0)\\ \text{(along } C)}} f(x, y, z)$$

are defined by

$$\lim_{\substack{(x,y)\to(x_0,y_0)\\ \text{(along } C)}} f(x, y) = \lim_{t\to t_0} f(x(t), y(t)) \tag{1}$$

$$\lim_{\substack{(x,y,z)\to(x_0,y_0,z_0)\\ \text{(along } C)}} f(x, y, z) = \lim_{t\to t_0} f(x(t), y(t), z(t)) \tag{2}$$

In words, Formulas (1) and (2) state that a limit of a function $f$ along a parametric curve can be obtained by substituting the parametric equations for the curve into the formula for the function and then computing the limit of the resulting function of one variable at the appropriate point.

In these formulas the limit of the function of $t$ must be treated as a one-sided limit if $(x_0, y_0)$ or $(x_0, y_0, z_0)$ is an endpoint of $C$.

A geometric interpretation of the limit along a curve for a function of two variables is shown in Figure 13.2.2: As the point $(x(t), y(t))$ moves along the curve $C$ in the $xy$-plane toward $(x_0, y_0)$, the point $(x(t), y(t), f(x(t), y(t)))$ moves directly above it along the graph of $z = f(x, y)$ with $f(x(t), y(t))$ approaching the limiting value $L$. In the figure we followed a common practice of omitting the zero $z$-coordinate for points in the $xy$-plane.

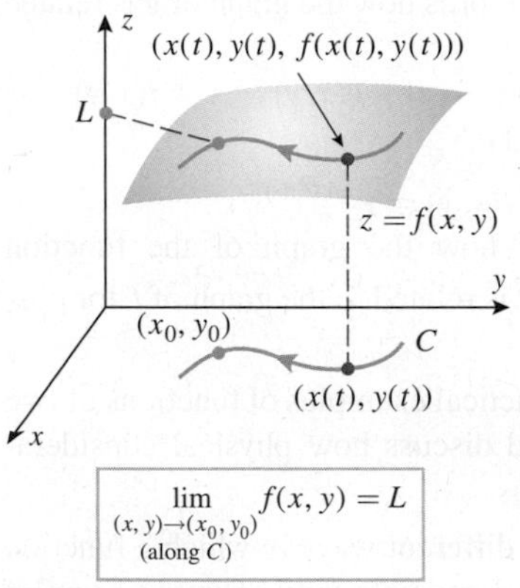

▲ Figure 13.2.2

**▶ Example 1** Figure 13.2.3*a* shows a computer-generated graph of the function

$$f(x, y) = -\frac{xy}{x^2 + y^2}$$

The graph reveals that the surface has a ridge above the line $y = -x$, which is to be expected since $f(x, y)$ has a constant value of $\frac{1}{2}$ for $y = -x$, except at $(0, 0)$ where $f$ is undefined (verify). Moreover, the graph suggests that the limit of $f(x, y)$ as $(x, y) \to (0, 0)$ along a line through the origin varies with the direction of the line. Find this limit along

(a) the $x$-axis (b) the $y$-axis (c) the line $y = x$
(d) the line $y = -x$ (e) the parabola $y = x^2$

***Solution (a).*** The $x$-axis has parametric equations $x = t$, $y = 0$, with $(0, 0)$ corresponding to $t = 0$, so

$$\lim_{\substack{(x,y)\to(0,0)\\ \text{(along } y=0)}} f(x, y) = \lim_{t\to 0} f(t, 0) = \lim_{t\to 0}\left(-\frac{0}{t^2}\right) = \lim_{t\to 0} 0 = 0$$

which is consistent with Figure 13.2.3*b*.

***Solution (b).*** The $y$-axis has parametric equations $x = 0$, $y = t$, with $(0, 0)$ corresponding to $t = 0$, so

$$\lim_{\substack{(x,y)\to(0,0)\\ \text{(along } x=0)}} f(x, y) = \lim_{t\to 0} f(0, t) = \lim_{t\to 0}\left(-\frac{0}{t^2}\right) = \lim_{t\to 0} 0 = 0$$

which is consistent with Figure 13.2.3*b*.

***Solution (c).*** The line $y = x$ has parametric equations $x = t$, $y = t$, with $(0, 0)$ corresponding to $t = 0$, so

$$\lim_{\substack{(x,y)\to(0,0)\\ \text{(along } y=x)}} f(x, y) = \lim_{t\to 0} f(t, t) = \lim_{t\to 0}\left(-\frac{t^2}{2t^2}\right) = \lim_{t\to 0}\left(-\frac{1}{2}\right) = -\frac{1}{2}$$

which is consistent with Figure 13.2.3*b*.

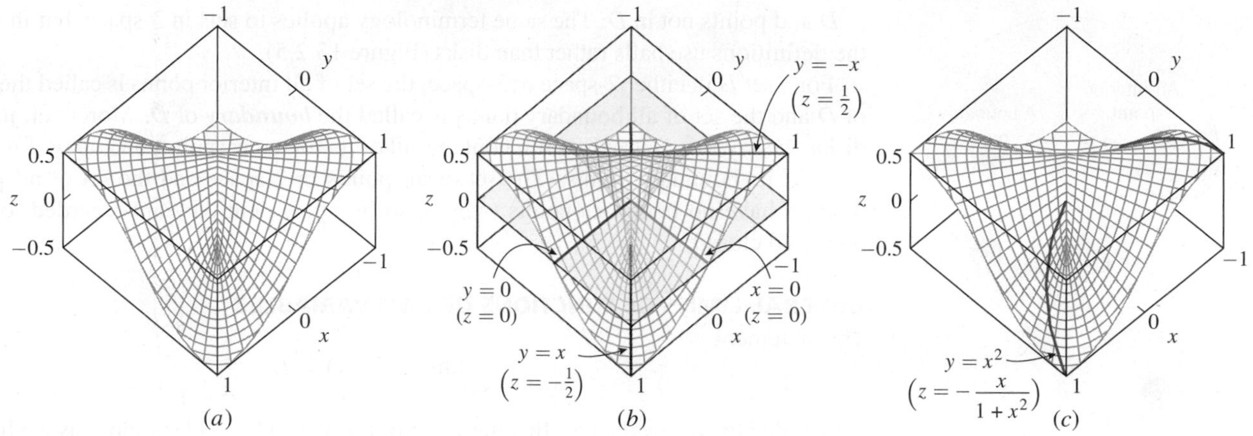


▲ **Figure 13.2.3**

***Solution (d).*** The line $y = -x$ has parametric equations $x = t, y = -t$, with $(0, 0)$ corresponding to $t = 0$, so

$$\lim_{\substack{(x,y)\to(0,0)\\(\text{along } y=-x)}} f(x, y) = \lim_{t\to 0} f(t, -t) = \lim_{t\to 0} \frac{t^2}{2t^2} = \lim_{t\to 0} \frac{1}{2} = \frac{1}{2}$$

which is consistent with Figure 13.2.3*b*.

For uniformity, we have chosen the same parameter $t$ in each part of Example 1. We could have used $x$ or $y$ as the parameter, according to the context. For example, part (b) could be computed using

$$\lim_{y\to 0} f(0, y)$$

and part (e) could be computed using

$$\lim_{x\to 0} f(x, x^2)$$

***Solution (e).*** The parabola $y = x^2$ has parametric equations $x = t, y = t^2$, with $(0, 0)$ corresponding to $t = 0$, so

$$\lim_{\substack{(x,y)\to(0,0)\\(\text{along } y=x^2)}} f(x, y) = \lim_{t\to 0} f(t, t^2) = \lim_{t\to 0} \left(-\frac{t^3}{t^2 + t^4}\right) = \lim_{t\to 0} \left(-\frac{t}{1 + t^2}\right) = 0$$

This is consistent with Figure 13.2.3*c*, which shows the parametric curve

$$x = t, \quad y = t^2, \quad z = -\frac{t}{1 + t^2}$$

superimposed on the surface. ◀

## OPEN AND CLOSED SETS

Although limits along specific curves are useful for many purposes, they do not tell the complete story about the limiting behavior of a function at a point; what is required is a limit concept that accounts for the behavior of the function in an *entire vicinity* of a point, not just along smooth curves passing through the point. For this purpose, we start by introducing some terminology.

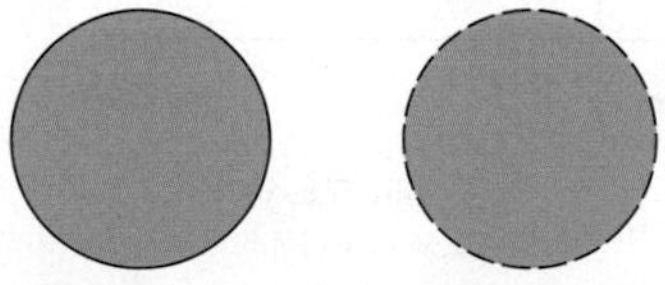

A closed disk includes all of the points on its bounding circle.

An open disk contains none of the points on its bounding circle.

▲ **Figure 13.2.4**

Let $C$ be a circle in 2-space that is centered at $(x_0, y_0)$ and has positive radius $\delta$. The set of points that are enclosed by the circle, but do not lie on the circle, is called the ***open disk*** of radius $\delta$ centered at $(x_0, y_0)$, and the set of points that lie on the circle together with those enclosed by the circle is called the ***closed disk*** of radius $\delta$ centered at $(x_0, y_0)$ (Figure 13.2.4). Analogously, if $S$ is a sphere in 3-space that is centered at $(x_0, y_0, z_0)$ and has positive radius $\delta$, then the set of points that are enclosed by the sphere, but do not lie on the sphere, is called the ***open ball*** of radius $\delta$ centered at $(x_0, y_0, z_0)$, and the set of points that lie on the sphere together with those enclosed by the sphere is called the ***closed ball*** of radius $\delta$ centered at $(x_0, y_0, z_0)$. Disks and balls are the two-dimensional and three-dimensional analogs of intervals on a line.

The notions of "open" and "closed" can be extended to more general sets in 2-space and 3-space. If $D$ is a set of points in 2-space, then a point $(x_0, y_0)$ is called an ***interior point*** of $D$ if there is *some* open disk centered at $(x_0, y_0)$ that contains only points of $D$, and $(x_0, y_0)$ is called a ***boundary point*** of $D$ if *every* open disk centered at $(x_0, y_0)$ contains both points in $D$ and points not in $D$. The same terminology applies to sets in 3-space, but in that case the definitions use balls rather than disks (Figure 13.2.5).

For a set $D$ in either 2-space or 3-space, the set of all interior points is called the ***interior*** of $D$ and the set of all boundary points is called the ***boundary*** of $D$. Moreover, just as for disks, we say that $D$ is ***closed*** if it contains all of its boundary points and ***open*** if it contains *none* of its boundary points. The set of all points in 2-space and the set of all points in 3-space have no boundary points (why?), so by agreement they are regarded to be both open and closed.

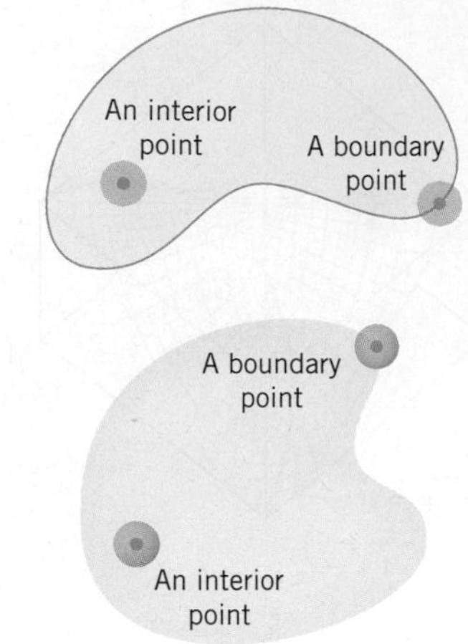

▲ **Figure 13.2.5**

## GENERAL LIMITS OF FUNCTIONS OF TWO VARIABLES

The statement

$$\lim_{(x,y)\to(x_0,y_0)} f(x,y) = L$$

is intended to convey the idea that the value of $f(x, y)$ can be made as close as we like to the number $L$ by restricting the point $(x, y)$ to be sufficiently close to (but different from) the point $(x_0, y_0)$. This idea has a formal expression in the following definition and is illustrated in Figure 13.2.6.

**13.2.1 DEFINITION** Let $f$ be a function of two variables, and assume that $f$ is defined at all points of some open disk centered at $(x_0, y_0)$, except possibly at $(x_0, y_0)$. We will write

$$\lim_{(x,y)\to(x_0,y_0)} f(x,y) = L \tag{3}$$

if given any number $\epsilon > 0$, we can find a number $\delta > 0$ such that $f(x, y)$ satisfies

$$|f(x,y) - L| < \epsilon$$

whenever the distance between $(x, y)$ and $(x_0, y_0)$ satisfies

$$0 < \sqrt{(x-x_0)^2 + (y-y_0)^2} < \delta$$

When convenient, (3) can also be written as

$$\lim_{\substack{x\to x_0 \\ y\to y_0}} f(x,y) = L$$

or as

$$f(x,y)\to L \quad \text{as} \quad (x,y)\to(x_0,y_0)$$

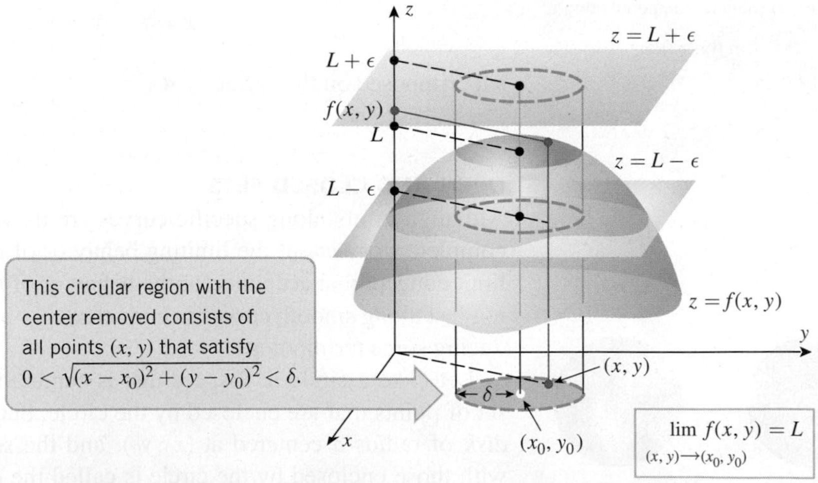

▲ **Figure 13.2.6**

In Figure 13.2.6, the condition

$$|f(x,y) - L| < \epsilon$$

is satisfied at each point $(x, y)$ within the circular region. However, the fact that this condition is satisfied at the center of the circular region is not relevant to the limit.

Another illustration of Definition 13.2.1 is shown in the "arrow diagram" of Figure 13.2.7. As in Figure 13.2.6, this figure is intended to convey the idea that the values of $f(x, y)$ can be forced within $\epsilon$ units of $L$ on the $z$-axis by restricting $(x, y)$ to lie within $\delta$ units of $(x_0, y_0)$ in the $xy$-plane. We used a white dot at $(x_0, y_0)$ to suggest that the epsilon condition need not hold at this point.

We note without proof that the standard properties of limits hold for limits along curves and for general limits of functions of two variables, so that computations involving such limits can be performed in the usual way.

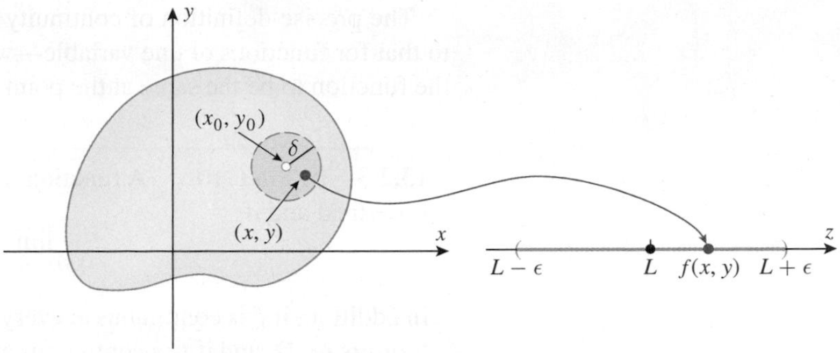


▶ Figure 13.2.7

### ▶ Example 2

$$\begin{aligned}\lim_{(x,y)\to(1,4)} [5x^3y^2 - 9] &= \lim_{(x,y)\to(1,4)} [5x^3y^2] - \lim_{(x,y)\to(1,4)} 9 \\ &= 5\left[\lim_{(x,y)\to(1,4)} x\right]^3 \left[\lim_{(x,y)\to(1,4)} y\right]^2 - 9 \\ &= 5(1)^3(4)^2 - 9 = 71 \blacktriangleleft\end{aligned}$$

## RELATIONSHIPS BETWEEN GENERAL LIMITS AND LIMITS ALONG SMOOTH CURVES

Stated informally, if $f(x, y)$ has limit $L$ as $(x, y)$ approaches $(x_0, y_0)$, then the value of $f(x, y)$ gets closer and closer to $L$ as the distance between $(x, y)$ and $(x_0, y_0)$ approaches zero. Since this statement imposes no restrictions on the direction in which $(x, y)$ approaches $(x_0, y_0)$, it is plausible that the function $f(x, y)$ will also have the limit $L$ as $(x, y)$ approaches $(x_0, y_0)$ along *any* smooth curve $C$. This is the implication of the following theorem, which we state without proof.

**WARNING**

In general, one cannot show that

$$\lim_{(x,y)\to(x_0,y_0)} f(x, y) = L$$

by showing that this limit holds along a specific curve, or even some specific family of curves. The problem is there may be some other curve along which the limit does not exist or has a value different from $L$ (see Exercise 34, for example).

**13.2.2 THEOREM**

(*a*) *If $f(x, y) \to L$ as $(x, y) \to (x_0, y_0)$, then $f(x, y) \to L$ as $(x, y) \to (x_0, y_0)$ along any smooth curve.*

(*b*) *If the limit of $f(x, y)$ fails to exist as $(x, y) \to (x_0, y_0)$ along some smooth curve, or if $f(x, y)$ has different limits as $(x, y) \to (x_0, y_0)$ along two different smooth curves, then the limit of $f(x, y)$ does not exist as $(x, y) \to (x_0, y_0)$.*

### ▶ Example 3

The limit

$$\lim_{(x,y)\to(0,0)} -\frac{xy}{x^2 + y^2}$$

does not exist because in Example 1 we found two different smooth curves along which this limit had different values. Specifically,

$$\lim_{\substack{(x,y)\to(0,0)\\(\text{along } x=0)}} -\frac{xy}{x^2+y^2} = 0 \quad\text{and}\quad \lim_{\substack{(x,y)\to(0,0)\\(\text{along } y=x)}} -\frac{xy}{x^2+y^2} = -\frac{1}{2} \blacktriangleleft$$

## CONTINUITY

Stated informally, a function of one variable is continuous if its graph is an unbroken curve without jumps or holes. To extend this idea to functions of two variables, imagine that the graph of $z = f(x, y)$ is formed from a thin sheet of clay that has been molded into peaks and valleys. We will regard $f$ as being continuous if the clay surface has no jumps, tears, or holes. For example, the function graphed in Figure 13.2.8 fails to be continuous because its graph exhibits a vertical jump at the origin.

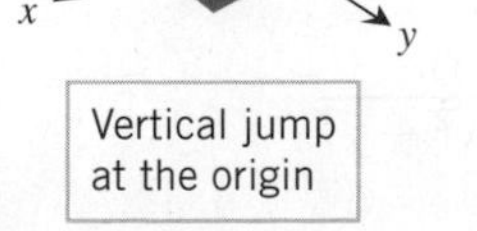


▲ Figure 13.2.8

The precise definition of continuity at a point for functions of two variables is similar to that for functions of one variable—we require the limit of the function and the value of the function to be the same at the point.

**13.2.3 DEFINITION** A function $f(x, y)$ is said to be ***continuous at*** $(x_0, y_0)$ if $f(x_0, y_0)$ is defined and if

$$\lim_{(x,y)\to(x_0,y_0)} f(x, y) = f(x_0, y_0)$$

In addition, if $f$ is continuous at every point in an open set $D$, then we say that $f$ is ***continuous on D***, and if $f$ is continuous at every point in the $xy$-plane, then we say that $f$ is ***continuous everywhere***.

The following theorem, which we state without proof, illustrates some of the ways in which continuous functions can be combined to produce new continuous functions.

**13.2.4 THEOREM**

(*a*) *If $g(x)$ is continuous at $x_0$ and $h(y)$ is continuous at $y_0$, then $f(x, y) = g(x)h(y)$ is continuous at $(x_0, y_0)$.*

(*b*) *If $h(x, y)$ is continuous at $(x_0, y_0)$ and $g(u)$ is continuous at $u = h(x_0, y_0)$, then the composition $f(x, y) = g(h(x, y))$ is continuous at $(x_0, y_0)$.*

(*c*) *If $f(x, y)$ is continuous at $(x_0, y_0)$, and if $x(t)$ and $y(t)$ are continuous at $t_0$ with $x(t_0) = x_0$ and $y(t_0) = y_0$, then the composition $f(x(t), y(t))$ is continuous at $t_0$.*

► **Example 4** Use Theorem 13.2.4 to show that the functions $f(x, y) = 3x^2y^5$ and $f(x, y) = \sin(3x^2y^5)$ are continuous everywhere.

***Solution.*** The polynomials $g(x) = 3x^2$ and $h(y) = y^5$ are continuous at every real number, and therefore by part (*a*) of Theorem 13.2.4, the function $f(x, y) = 3x^2y^5$ is continuous at every point $(x, y)$ in the $xy$-plane. Since $3x^2y^5$ is continuous at every point in the $xy$-plane and $\sin u$ is continuous at every real number $u$, it follows from part (*b*) of Theorem 13.2.4 that the composition $f(x, y) = \sin(3x^2y^5)$ is continuous everywhere. ◄

Theorem 13.2.4 is one of a whole class of theorems about continuity of functions in two or more variables. The content of these theorems can be summarized informally with three basic principles:

***Recognizing Continuous Functions***

- A composition of continuous functions is continuous.
- A sum, difference, or product of continuous functions is continuous.
- A quotient of continuous functions is continuous, except where the denominator is zero.

By using these principles and Theorem 13.2.4, you should be able to confirm that the following functions are all continuous everywhere:

$$xe^{xy} + y^{2/3}, \quad \cosh(xy^3) - |xy|, \quad \frac{xy}{1 + x^2 + y^2}$$

**▶ Example 5** Evaluate $\lim_{(x,y)\to(-1,2)} \dfrac{xy}{x^2+y^2}$.

***Solution.*** Since $f(x, y) = xy/(x^2 + y^2)$ is continuous at $(-1, 2)$ (why?), it follows from the definition of continuity for functions of two variables that

$$\lim_{(x,y)\to(-1,2)} \frac{xy}{x^2+y^2} = \frac{(-1)(2)}{(-1)^2+(2)^2} = -\frac{2}{5} \blacktriangleleft$$

**▶ Example 6** Since the function

$$f(x, y) = \frac{x^3y^2}{1-xy}$$

is a quotient of continuous functions, it is continuous except where $1 - xy = 0$. Thus, $f(x, y)$ is continuous everywhere except on the hyperbola $xy = 1$. ◀

## LIMITS AT DISCONTINUITIES

Sometimes it is easy to recognize when a limit does not exist. For example, it is evident that

$$\lim_{(x,y)\to(0,0)} \frac{1}{x^2+y^2} = +\infty$$

which implies that the values of the function approach $+\infty$ as $(x, y)\to(0, 0)$ along any smooth curve (Figure 13.2.9). However, it is not evident whether the limit

$$\lim_{(x,y)\to(0,0)} (x^2 + y^2)\ln(x^2 + y^2)$$

exists because it is an indeterminate form of type $0 \cdot \infty$. Although L'Hôpital's rule cannot be applied directly, the following example illustrates a method for finding this limit by converting to polar coordinates.

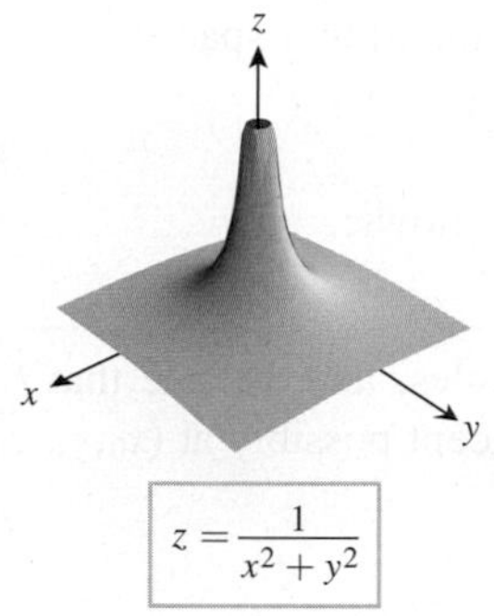

▲ Figure 13.2.9

**▶ Example 7** Find $\lim_{(x,y)\to(0,0)} (x^2 + y^2)\ln(x^2 + y^2)$.

***Solution.*** Let $(r, \theta)$ be polar coordinates of the point $(x, y)$ with $r \geq 0$. Then we have

$$x = r\cos\theta, \quad y = r\sin\theta, \quad r^2 = x^2 + y^2$$

Moreover, since $r \geq 0$ we have $r = \sqrt{x^2+y^2}$, so that $r\to0^+$ if and only if $(x, y)\to(0, 0)$. Thus, we can rewrite the given limit as

$$\begin{aligned}\lim_{(x,y)\to(0,0)} (x^2 + y^2)\ln(x^2 + y^2) &= \lim_{r\to0^+} r^2\ln r^2 \\ &= \lim_{r\to0^+} \frac{2\ln r}{1/r^2} && \text{This converts the limit to an indeterminate form of type } \infty/\infty. \\ &= \lim_{r\to0^+} \frac{2/r}{-2/r^3} && \text{L'Hôpital's rule} \\ &= \lim_{r\to0^+} (-r^2) = 0 \blacktriangleleft\end{aligned}$$

**REMARK** The graph of $f(x, y) = (x^2 + y^2)\ln(x^2 + y^2)$ in Example 7 is a surface with a hole (sometimes called a *puncture*) at the origin (Figure 13.2.10). We can remove this discontinuity by *defining* $f(0, 0)$ to be 0. (See Exercises 39 and 40, which also deal with the notion of a "removable" discontinuity.)

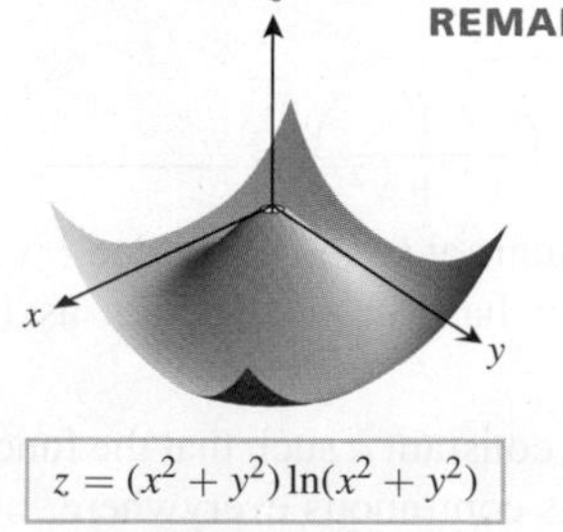

▲ Figure 13.2.10

## CONTINUITY AT BOUNDARY POINTS

Recall that in our study of continuity for functions of one variable, we first defined continuity at a point, then continuity on an open interval, and then, by using one-sided limits, we extended the notion of continuity to include endpoints of the interval. Similarly, for functions of two variables one can extend the notion of continuity of $f(x, y)$ to the boundary of its domain by modifying Definition 13.2.1 appropriately so that $(x, y)$ is restricted to approach $(x_0, y_0)$ through points lying wholly in the domain of $f$. We will omit the details.

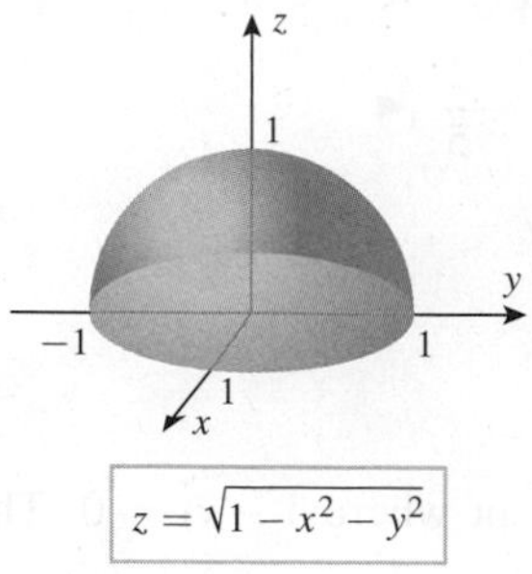

▲ Figure 13.2.11

▶ **Example 8** The graph of the function $f(x, y) = \sqrt{1 - x^2 - y^2}$ is the upper hemisphere shown in Figure 13.2.11, and the natural domain of $f$ is the closed unit disk

$$x^2 + y^2 \leq 1$$

The graph of $f$ has no jumps, tears or holes, so it passes our "intuitive test" of continuity. In this case the continuity at a point $(x_0, y_0)$ on the boundary reflects the fact that

$$\lim_{(x,y)\to(x_0,y_0)} \sqrt{1 - x^2 - y^2} = \sqrt{1 - x_0^2 - y_0^2} = 0$$

when $(x, y)$ is restricted to points on the closed unit disk $x^2 + y^2 \leq 1$. It follows that $f$ is continuous on its domain. ◀

## EXTENSIONS TO THREE VARIABLES

All of the results in this section can be extended to functions of three or more variables. For example, the distance between the points $(x, y, z)$ and $(x_0, y_0, z_0)$ in 3-space is

$$\sqrt{(x - x_0)^2 + (y - y_0)^2 + (z - z_0)^2}$$

so the natural extension of Definition 13.2.1 to 3-space is as follows:

**13.2.5 DEFINITION** Let $f$ be a function of three variables, and assume that $f$ is defined at all points within a ball centered at $(x_0, y_0, z_0)$, except possibly at $(x_0, y_0, z_0)$. We will write

$$\lim_{(x,y,z)\to(x_0,y_0,z_0)} f(x, y, z) = L \tag{4}$$

if given any number $\epsilon > 0$, we can find a number $\delta > 0$ such that $f(x, y, z)$ satisfies

$$|f(x, y, z) - L| < \epsilon$$

whenever the distance between $(x, y, z)$ and $(x_0, y_0, z_0)$ satisfies

$$0 < \sqrt{(x - x_0)^2 + (y - y_0)^2 + (z - z_0)^2} < \delta$$

As with functions of one and two variables, we define a function $f(x, y, z)$ of three variables to be continuous at a point $(x_0, y_0, z_0)$ if the limit of the function and the value of the function are the same at this point; that is,

$$\lim_{(x,y,z)\to(x_0,y_0,z_0)} f(x, y, z) = f(x_0, y_0, z_0)$$

Although we will omit the details, the properties of limits and continuity that we discussed for functions of two variables, including the notion of continuity at boundary points, carry over to functions of three variables.

## ✓QUICK CHECK EXERCISES 13.2 (See page 824 for answers.)

1. Let
$$f(x, y) = \frac{x^2 - y^2}{x^2 + y^2}$$
Determine the limit of $f(x, y)$ as $(x, y)$ approaches $(0, 0)$ along the curve $C$.
(a) $C: x = 0$ (b) $C: y = 0$
(c) $C: y = x$ (d) $C: y = x^2$

2. (a) $\lim_{(x,y)\to(3,2)} x \cos \pi y =$ ______
(b) $\lim_{(x,y)\to(0,1)} e^{xy^2} =$ ______
(c) $\lim_{(x,y)\to(0,0)} (x^2 + y^2) \sin\left(\frac{1}{x^2 + y^2}\right) =$ ______

3. A function $f(x, y)$ is continuous at $(x_0, y_0)$ provided $f(x_0, y_0)$ exists and provided $f(x, y)$ has limit ______ as $(x, y)$ approaches ______.

4. Determine all values of the constant $a$ such that the function $f(x, y) = \sqrt{x^2 - ay^2 + 1}$ is continuous everywhere.

## EXERCISE SET 13.2

**1–6** Use limit laws and continuity properties to evaluate the limit. ■

**1.** $\displaystyle\lim_{(x,y)\to(1,3)} (4xy^2 - x)$

**2.** $\displaystyle\lim_{(x,y)\to(0,0)} \frac{4x - y}{\sin y - 1}$

**3.** $\displaystyle\lim_{(x,y)\to(-1,2)} \frac{xy^3}{x + y}$

**4.** $\displaystyle\lim_{(x,y)\to(1,-3)} e^{2x-y^2}$

**5.** $\displaystyle\lim_{(x,y)\to(0,0)} \ln(1 + x^2y^3)$

**6.** $\displaystyle\lim_{(x,y)\to(4,-2)} x\sqrt[3]{y^3 + 2x}$

**7–8** Show that the limit does not exist by considering the limits as $(x, y)\to(0, 0)$ along the coordinate axes. ■

**7.** (a) $\displaystyle\lim_{(x,y)\to(0,0)} \frac{3}{x^2 + 2y^2}$ (b) $\displaystyle\lim_{(x,y)\to(0,0)} \frac{x + y}{2x^2 + y^2}$

**8.** (a) $\displaystyle\lim_{(x,y)\to(0,0)} \frac{x - y}{x^2 + y^2}$ (b) $\displaystyle\lim_{(x,y)\to(0,0)} \frac{\cos xy}{x^2 + y^2}$

**9–12** Evaluate the limit using the substitution $z = x^2 + y^2$ and observing that $z\to 0^+$ if and only if $(x, y)\to(0, 0)$. ■

**9.** $\displaystyle\lim_{(x,y)\to(0,0)} \frac{\sin(x^2 + y^2)}{x^2 + y^2}$

**10.** $\displaystyle\lim_{(x,y)\to(0,0)} \frac{1 - \cos(x^2 + y^2)}{x^2 + y^2}$

**11.** $\displaystyle\lim_{(x,y)\to(0,0)} e^{-1/(x^2+y^2)}$

**12.** $\displaystyle\lim_{(x,y)\to(0,0)} \frac{e^{-1/\sqrt{x^2+y^2}}}{\sqrt{x^2 + y^2}}$

**13–22** Determine whether the limit exists. If so, find its value. ■

**13.** $\displaystyle\lim_{(x,y)\to(0,0)} \frac{x^4 - y^4}{x^2 + y^2}$

**14.** $\displaystyle\lim_{(x,y)\to(0,0)} \frac{x^4 - 16y^4}{x^2 + 4y^2}$

**15.** $\displaystyle\lim_{(x,y)\to(0,0)} \frac{xy}{3x^2 + 2y^2}$

**16.** $\displaystyle\lim_{(x,y)\to(0,0)} \frac{1 - x^2 - y^2}{x^2 + y^2}$

**17.** $\displaystyle\lim_{(x,y,z)\to(2,-1,2)} \frac{xz^2}{\sqrt{x^2 + y^2 + z^2}}$

**18.** $\displaystyle\lim_{(x,y,z)\to(2,0,-1)} \ln(2x + y - z)$

**19.** $\displaystyle\lim_{(x,y,z)\to(0,0,0)} \frac{\sin(x^2 + y^2 + z^2)}{\sqrt{x^2 + y^2 + z^2}}$

**20.** $\displaystyle\lim_{(x,y,z)\to(0,0,0)} \frac{\sin\sqrt{x^2 + y^2 + z^2}}{x^2 + y^2 + z^2}$

**21.** $\displaystyle\lim_{(x,y,z)\to(0,0,0)} \frac{e^{\sqrt{x^2+y^2+z^2}}}{\sqrt{x^2 + y^2 + z^2}}$

**22.** $\displaystyle\lim_{(x,y,z)\to(0,0,0)} \tan^{-1}\left[\frac{1}{x^2 + y^2 + z^2}\right]$

**23–26** Evaluate the limits by converting to polar coordinates, as in Example 7. ■

**23.** $\displaystyle\lim_{(x,y)\to(0,0)} \sqrt{x^2 + y^2}\ln(x^2 + y^2)$

**24.** $\displaystyle\lim_{(x,y)\to(0,0)} y\ln(x^2 + y^2)$

**25.** $\displaystyle\lim_{(x,y)\to(0,0)} \frac{x^2y^2}{\sqrt{x^2 + y^2}}$

**26.** $\displaystyle\lim_{(x,y)\to(0,0)} \frac{xy}{\sqrt{x^2 + 2y^2}}$

**27–28** Evaluate the limits by converting to spherical coordinates $(\rho, \theta, \phi)$ and by observing that $\rho\to 0^+$ if and only if $(x, y, z)\to(0, 0, 0)$. ■

**27.** $\displaystyle\lim_{(x,y,z)\to(0,0,0)} \frac{xyz}{x^2 + y^2 + z^2}$

**28.** $\displaystyle\lim_{(x,y,z)\to(0,0,0)} \frac{\sin x \sin y}{\sqrt{x^2 + 2y^2 + 3z^2}}$

**29–32 True–False** Determine whether the statement is true or false. Explain your answer. ■

**29.** If $D$ is an open set in 2-space or in 3-space, then every point in $D$ is an interior point of $D$.

**30.** If $f(x, y)\to L$ as $(x, y)$ approaches $(0, 0)$ along the $x$-axis, and if $f(x, y)\to L$ as $(x, y)$ approaches $(0, 0)$ along the $y$-axis, then $\lim_{(x,y)\to(0,0)} f(x, y) = L$.

**31.** If $f$ and $g$ are functions of two variables such that $f + g$ and $fg$ are both continuous, then $f$ and $g$ are themselves continuous.

**32.** If $\lim_{x\to 0^+} f(x) = L \neq 0$, then

$$\lim_{(x,y)\to(0,0)} \frac{x^2 + y^2}{f(x^2 + y^2)} = 0$$

**FOCUS ON CONCEPTS**

**33.** The accompanying figure shows a portion of the graph of

$$f(x, y) = \frac{x^2y}{x^4 + y^2}$$

(a) Based on the graph in the figure, does $f(x, y)$ have a limit as $(x, y)\to(0, 0)$? Explain your reasoning.

(b) Show that $f(x, y)\to 0$ as $(x, y)\to(0, 0)$ along any line $y = mx$. Does this imply that $f(x, y)\to 0$ as $(x, y)\to(0, 0)$? Explain.

(c) Show that $f(x, y)\to \frac{1}{2}$ as $(x, y)\to(0, 0)$ along the parabola $y = x^2$, and confirm visually that this is consistent with the graph of $f(x, y)$.

(d) Based on parts (b) and (c), does $f(x, y)$ have a limit as $(x, y)\to(0, 0)$? Is this consistent with your answer to part (a)?

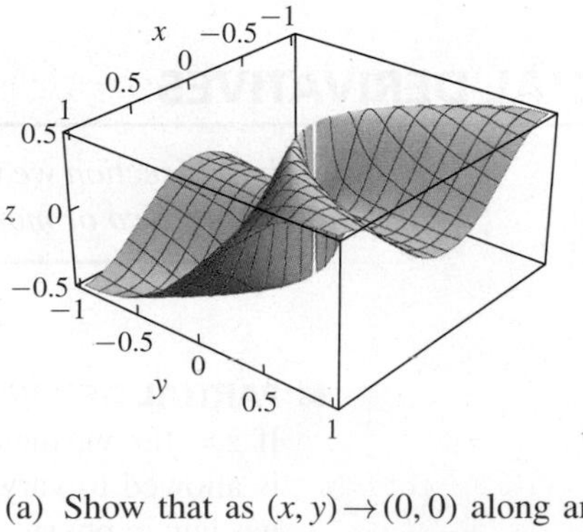


◀ **Figure Ex-33**

**34.** (a) Show that as $(x, y)\to(0, 0)$ along any straight line $y = mx$, or along any parabola $y = kx^2$, the value of

$$\frac{x^3y}{2x^6 + y^2}$$

approaches 0.

*(cont.)*

(b) Show that
$$\lim_{(x,y)\to(0,0)} \frac{x^3y}{2x^6+y^2}$$
does not exist by letting $(x, y)\to(0, 0)$ along the curve $y = x^3$.

**35.** (a) Show that the value of
$$\frac{xyz}{x^2+y^4+z^4}$$
approaches 0 as $(x, y, z)\to(0, 0, 0)$ along any line $x = at$, $y = bt$, $z = ct$.

(b) Show that the limit
$$\lim_{(x,y,z)\to(0,0,0)} \frac{xyz}{x^2+y^4+z^4}$$
does not exist by letting $(x, y, z)\to(0, 0, 0)$ along the curve $x = t^2$, $y = t$, $z = t$.

**36.** Find $\displaystyle\lim_{(x,y)\to(0,1)} \tan^{-1}\left[\frac{x^2+1}{x^2+(y-1)^2}\right]$.

**37.** Find $\displaystyle\lim_{(x,y)\to(0,1)} \tan^{-1}\left[\frac{x^2-1}{x^2+(y-1)^2}\right]$.

**38.** Let $f(x,y) = \begin{cases} \dfrac{\sin(x^2+y^2)}{x^2+y^2}, & (x,y)\neq(0,0) \\ 1, & (x,y)=(0,0). \end{cases}$

Show that $f$ is continuous at $(0, 0)$.

**39–40** A function $f(x, y)$ is said to have a ***removable discontinuity*** at $(x_0, y_0)$ if $\lim_{(x,y)\to(x_0,y_0)} f(x, y)$ exists but $f$ is not continuous at $(x_0, y_0)$, either because $f$ is not defined at $(x_0, y_0)$ or because $f(x_0, y_0)$ differs from the value of the limit. Determine whether $f(x, y)$ has a removable discontinuity at $(0, 0)$. ■

**39.** $f(x,y) = \dfrac{x^2}{x^2+y^2}$

**40.** $f(x) = \begin{cases} x^2+7y^2, & \text{if } (x,y)\neq(0,0) \\ -4, & \text{if } (x,y)=(0,0) \end{cases}$

**41–48** Sketch the largest region on which the function $f$ is continuous. ■

**41.** $f(x, y) = y\ln(1 + x)$

**42.** $f(x,y) = \sqrt{x-y}$

**43.** $f(x,y) = \dfrac{x^2y}{\sqrt{25-x^2-y^2}}$

**44.** $f(x, y) = \ln(2x - y + 1)$

**45.** $f(x,y) = \dfrac{y}{11x^2+3}$

**46.** $f(x,y) = e^{1-xy}$

**47.** $f(x,y) = \sin^{-1}(xy)$

**48.** $f(x,y) = \tan^{-1}(y-x)$

**49–52** Describe the largest region on which the function $f$ is continuous. ■

**49.** $f(x,y,z) = 3x^2e^{yz}\cos(xyz)$

**50.** $f(x,y,z) = \ln(4-x^2-y^2-z^2)$

**51.** $f(x,y,z) = \dfrac{y+1}{x^2+z^2-1}$

**52.** $f(x,y,z) = \sin\sqrt{x^2+y^2+3z^2}$

**53. Writing** Describe the procedure you would use to determine whether or not the limit
$$\lim_{(x,y)\to(x_0,y_0)} f(x,y)$$
exists.

**54. Writing** In your own words, state the geometric interpretations of $\epsilon$ and $\delta$ in the definition of
$$\lim_{(x,y)\to(x_0,y_0)} f(x,y) = L$$
given in Definition 13.2.1.

✓**QUICK CHECK ANSWERS 13.2** 1. (a) −1 (b) 1 (c) 0 (d) 1 2. (a) 3 (b) 1 (c) 0 3. $f(x_0, y_0)$; $(x_0, y_0)$ 4. $a \leq 0$

## 13.3 PARTIAL DERIVATIVES

*In this section we will develop the mathematical tools for studying rates of change that involve two or more independent variables.*

### ■ PARTIAL DERIVATIVES OF FUNCTIONS OF TWO VARIABLES

If $z = f(x, y)$, then one can inquire how the value of $z$ changes if $y$ is held fixed and $x$ is allowed to vary, or if $x$ is held fixed and $y$ is allowed to vary. For example, the ideal gas law in physics states that under appropriate conditions the pressure exerted by a gas is a function of the volume of the gas and its temperature. Thus, a physicist studying gases might be interested in the rate of change of the pressure if the volume is held fixed and the temperature is allowed to vary, or if the temperature is held fixed and the volume is allowed to vary. We now define a derivative that describes such rates of change.

Suppose that $(x_0, y_0)$ is a point in the domain of a function $f(x, y)$. If we fix $y = y_0$, then $f(x, y_0)$ is a function of the variable $x$ alone. The value of the derivative

$$\frac{d}{dx}[f(x, y_0)]$$

at $x_0$ then gives us a measure of the instantaneous rate of change of $f$ with respect to $x$ at the point $(x_0, y_0)$. Similarly, the value of the derivative

$$\frac{d}{dy}[f(x_0, y)]$$

at $y_0$ gives us a measure of the instantaneous rate of change of $f$ with respect to $y$ at the point $(x_0, y_0)$. These derivatives are so basic to the study of differential calculus of multivariable functions that they have their own name and notation.

**13.3.1 DEFINITION** If $z = f(x, y)$ and $(x_0, y_0)$ is a point in the domain of $f$, then the ***partial derivative of f with respect to x*** at $(x_0, y_0)$ [also called the ***partial derivative of z with respect to x*** at $(x_0, y_0)$] is the derivative at $x_0$ of the function that results when $y = y_0$ is held fixed and $x$ is allowed to vary. This partial derivative is denoted by $f_x(x_0, y_0)$ and is given by

$$f_x(x_0, y_0) = \frac{d}{dx}[f(x, y_0)]\bigg|_{x=x_0} = \lim_{\Delta x \to 0} \frac{f(x_0 + \Delta x, y_0) - f(x_0, y_0)}{\Delta x} \tag{1}$$

Similarly, the ***partial derivative of f with respect to y*** at $(x_0, y_0)$ [also called the ***partial derivative of z with respect to y*** at $(x_0, y_0)$] is the derivative at $y_0$ of the function that results when $x = x_0$ is held fixed and $y$ is allowed to vary. This partial derivative is denoted by $f_y(x_0, y_0)$ and is given by

$$f_y(x_0, y_0) = \frac{d}{dy}[f(x_0, y)]\bigg|_{y=y_0} = \lim_{\Delta y \to 0} \frac{f(x_0, y_0 + \Delta y) - f(x_0, y_0)}{\Delta y} \tag{2}$$

The limits in (1) and (2) show the relationship between partial derivatives and derivatives of functions of one variable. In practice, our usual method for computing partial derivatives is to hold one variable fixed and then differentiate the resulting function using the derivative rules for functions of one variable.

▶ **Example 1** Find $f_x(1, 3)$ and $f_y(1, 3)$ for the function $f(x, y) = 2x^3y^2 + 2y + 4x$.

***Solution.*** Since

$$f_x(x, 3) = \frac{d}{dx}[f(x, 3)] = \frac{d}{dx}[18x^3 + 4x + 6] = 54x^2 + 4$$

we have $f_x(1, 3) = 54 + 4 = 58$. Also, since

$$f_y(1, y) = \frac{d}{dy}[f(1, y)] = \frac{d}{dy}[2y^2 + 2y + 4] = 4y + 2$$

we have $f_y(1, 3) = 4(3) + 2 = 14$. ◀

## THE PARTIAL DERIVATIVE FUNCTIONS

Formulas (1) and (2) define the partial derivatives of a function at a specific point $(x_0, y_0)$. However, often it will be desirable to omit the subscripts and think of the partial derivatives as functions of the variables $x$ and $y$. These functions are

$$f_x(x, y) = \lim_{\Delta x \to 0} \frac{f(x + \Delta x, y) - f(x, y)}{\Delta x} \qquad f_y(x, y) = \lim_{\Delta y \to 0} \frac{f(x, y + \Delta y) - f(x, y)}{\Delta y}$$

The following example gives an alternative way of performing the computations in Example 1.

▶ **Example 2** Find $f_x(x, y)$ and $f_y(x, y)$ for $f(x, y) = 2x^3y^2 + 2y + 4x$, and use those partial derivatives to compute $f_x(1, 3)$ and $f_y(1, 3)$.

***Solution.*** Keeping $y$ fixed and differentiating with respect to $x$ yields

$$f_x(x, y) = \frac{d}{dx}[2x^3y^2 + 2y + 4x] = 6x^2y^2 + 4$$

and keeping $x$ fixed and differentiating with respect to $y$ yields

$$f_y(x, y) = \frac{d}{dy}[2x^3y^2 + 2y + 4x] = 4x^3y + 2$$

Thus,

$$f_x(1, 3) = 6(1^2)(3^2) + 4 = 58 \quad \text{and} \quad f_y(1, 3) = 4(1^3)3 + 2 = 14$$

which agree with the results in Example 1. ◀

**TECHNOLOGY MASTERY**

Computer algebra systems have specific commands for calculating partial derivatives. If you have a CAS, use it to find the partial derivatives $f_x(x, y)$ and $f_y(x, y)$ in Example 2.

## PARTIAL DERIVATIVE NOTATION

If $z = f(x, y)$, then the partial derivatives $f_x$ and $f_y$ are also denoted by the symbols

$$\frac{\partial f}{\partial x}, \quad \frac{\partial z}{\partial x} \quad \text{and} \quad \frac{\partial f}{\partial y}, \quad \frac{\partial z}{\partial y}$$

The symbol $\partial$ is called a partial derivative sign. It is derived from the Cyrillic alphabet.

Some typical notations for the partial derivatives of $z = f(x, y)$ at a point $(x_0, y_0)$ are

$$\left.\frac{\partial f}{\partial x}\right|_{x=x_0, y=y_0}, \quad \left.\frac{\partial z}{\partial x}\right|_{(x_0,y_0)}, \quad \left.\frac{\partial f}{\partial x}\right|_{(x_0,y_0)}, \quad \frac{\partial f}{\partial x}(x_0, y_0), \quad \frac{\partial z}{\partial x}(x_0, y_0)$$

▶ **Example 3** Find $\partial z/\partial x$ and $\partial z/\partial y$ if $z = x^4 \sin(xy^3)$.

***Solution.***

$$\begin{aligned}\frac{\partial z}{\partial x} &= \frac{\partial}{\partial x}[x^4 \sin(xy^3)] = x^4 \frac{\partial}{\partial x}[\sin(xy^3)] + \sin(xy^3) \cdot \frac{\partial}{\partial x}(x^4)\\ &= x^4 \cos(xy^3) \cdot y^3 + \sin(xy^3) \cdot 4x^3 = x^4y^3 \cos(xy^3) + 4x^3 \sin(xy^3)\\ \frac{\partial z}{\partial y} &= \frac{\partial}{\partial y}[x^4 \sin(xy^3)] = x^4 \frac{\partial}{\partial y}[\sin(xy^3)] + \sin(xy^3) \cdot \frac{\partial}{\partial y}(x^4)\\ &= x^4 \cos(xy^3) \cdot 3xy^2 + \sin(xy^3) \cdot 0 = 3x^5y^2 \cos(xy^3)\end{aligned}$$ ◀

## PARTIAL DERIVATIVES VIEWED AS RATES OF CHANGE AND SLOPES

Recall that if $y = f(x)$, then the value of $f'(x_0)$ can be interpreted either as the rate of change of $y$ with respect to $x$ at $x_0$ or as the slope of the tangent line to the graph of $f$ at $x_0$. Partial derivatives have analogous interpretations. To see that this is so, suppose that $C_1$ is the intersection of the surface $z = f(x, y)$ with the plane $y = y_0$ and that $C_2$ is its intersection with the plane $x = x_0$ (Figure 13.3.1). Thus, $f_x(x, y_0)$ can be interpreted as the rate of change of $z$ with respect to $x$ along the curve $C_1$, and $f_y(x_0, y)$ can be interpreted as the rate of change of $z$ with respect to $y$ along the curve $C_2$. In particular, $f_x(x_0, y_0)$ is the rate of change of $z$ with respect to $x$ along the curve $C_1$ at the point $(x_0, y_0)$, and $f_y(x_0, y_0)$ is the rate of change of $z$ with respect to $y$ along the curve $C_2$ at the point $(x_0, y_0)$.

▶ **Example 4** Recall that the wind chill temperature index is given by the formula

$$W = 35.74 + 0.6215T + (0.4275T - 35.75)v^{0.16}$$

Compute the partial derivative of $W$ with respect to $v$ at the point $(T, v) = (25, 10)$ and interpret this partial derivative as a rate of change.

In an applied problem, the interpretations of $f_x(x_0, y_0)$ and $f_y(x_0, y_0)$ must be accompanied by the proper units. See Example 4.

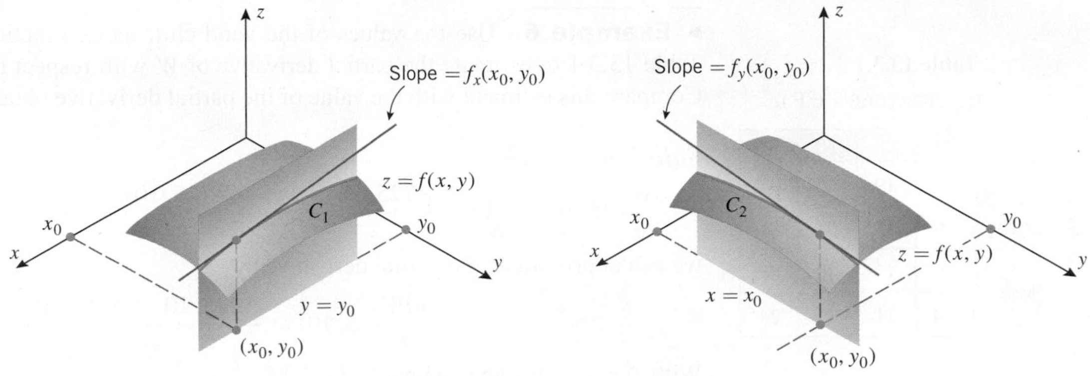


▲ **Figure 13.3.1**

***Solution.*** Holding $T$ fixed and differentiating with respect to $v$ yields

$$\frac{\partial W}{\partial v}(T, v) = 0 + 0 + (0.4275T - 35.75)(0.16)v^{0.16-1} = (0.4275T - 35.75)(0.16)v^{-0.84}$$

Since $W$ is in degrees Fahrenheit and $v$ is in miles per hour, a rate of change of $W$ with respect to $v$ will have units $^\circ\mathrm{F}/(\mathrm{mi/h})$ (which may also be written as $^\circ\mathrm{F{\cdot}h/mi}$). Substituting $T = 25$ and $v = 10$ gives

$$\frac{\partial W}{\partial v}(25, 10) = (-4.01)10^{-0.84} \approx -0.58\ \frac{^\circ\mathrm{F}}{\mathrm{mi/h}}$$

as the instantaneous rate of change of $W$ with respect to $v$ at $(T, v) = (25, 10)$. We conclude that if the air temperature is a constant $25^\circ$F and the wind speed changes by a small amount from an initial speed of 10 mi/h, then the ratio of the change in the wind chill index to the change in wind speed should be about $-0.58^\circ\mathrm{F}/(\mathrm{mi/h})$. ◀

> Confirm the conclusion of Example 4 by calculating
>
> $$\frac{W(25, 10 + \Delta v) - W(25, 10)}{\Delta v}$$
>
> for values of $\Delta v$ near 0.

Geometrically, $f_x(x_0, y_0)$ can be viewed as the slope of the tangent line to the curve $C_1$ at the point $(x_0, y_0)$, and $f_y(x_0, y_0)$ can be viewed as the slope of the tangent line to the curve $C_2$ at the point $(x_0, y_0)$ (Figure 13.3.1). We will call $f_x(x_0, y_0)$ the ***slope of the surface in the x-direction*** at $(x_0, y_0)$ and $f_y(x_0, y_0)$ the ***slope of the surface in the y-direction*** at $(x_0, y_0)$.

▶ **Example 5** Let $f(x, y) = x^2y + 5y^3$.

(a) Find the slope of the surface $z = f(x, y)$ in the $x$-direction at the point $(1, -2)$.

(b) Find the slope of the surface $z = f(x, y)$ in the $y$-direction at the point $(1, -2)$.

***Solution (a).*** Differentiating $f$ with respect to $x$ with $y$ held fixed yields

$$f_x(x, y) = 2xy$$

Thus, the slope in the $x$-direction is $f_x(1, -2) = -4$; that is, $z$ is decreasing at the rate of 4 units per unit increase in $x$.

***Solution (b).*** Differentiating $f$ with respect to $y$ with $x$ held fixed yields

$$f_y(x, y) = x^2 + 15y^2$$

Thus, the slope in the $y$-direction is $f_y(1, -2) = 61$; that is, $z$ is increasing at the rate of 61 units per unit increase in $y$. ◀

## ESTIMATING PARTIAL DERIVATIVES FROM TABULAR DATA

For functions that are presented in tabular form, we can estimate partial derivatives by using adjacent entries within the table.

**Table 13.3.1**

TEMPERATURE $T$ (°F)

| WIND SPEED $v$ (mi/h) | 20 | 25 | 30 | 35 |
|---|---|---|---|---|
| 5 | 13 | 19 | 25 | 31 |
| 10 | 9 | 15 | 21 | 27 |
| 15 | 6 | 13 | 19 | 25 |
| 20 | 4 | 11 | 17 | 24 |

▶ **Example 6** Use the values of the wind chill index function $W(T, v)$ displayed in Table 13.3.1 to estimate the partial derivative of $W$ with respect to $v$ at $(T, v) = (25, 10)$. Compare this estimate with the value of the partial derivative obtained in Example 4.

***Solution.*** Since

$$\frac{\partial W}{\partial v}(25, 10) = \lim_{\Delta v \to 0} \frac{W(25, 10 + \Delta v) - W(25, 10)}{\Delta v} = \lim_{\Delta v \to 0} \frac{W(25, 10 + \Delta v) - 15}{\Delta v}$$

we can approximate the partial derivative by

$$\frac{\partial W}{\partial v}(25, 10) \approx \frac{W(25, 10 + \Delta v) - 15}{\Delta v}$$

With $\Delta v = 5$ this approximation is

$$\frac{\partial W}{\partial v}(25, 10) \approx \frac{W(25, 10 + 5) - 15}{5} = \frac{W(25, 15) - 15}{5} = \frac{13 - 15}{5} = -\frac{2}{5} \frac{°\mathrm{F}}{\mathrm{mi/h}}$$

and with $\Delta v = -5$ this approximation is

$$\frac{\partial W}{\partial v}(25, 10) \approx \frac{W(25, 10 - 5) - 15}{-5} = \frac{W(25, 5) - 15}{-5} = \frac{19 - 15}{-5} = -\frac{4}{5} \frac{°\mathrm{F}}{\mathrm{mi/h}}$$

We will take the average, $-\frac{3}{5} = -0.6°\mathrm{F/(mi/h)}$, of these two approximations as our estimate of $(\partial W/\partial v)(25, 10)$. This is close to the value

$$\frac{\partial W}{\partial v}(25, 10) = (-4.01)10^{-0.84} \approx -0.58 \frac{°\mathrm{F}}{\mathrm{mi/h}}$$

found in Example 4. ◀

## IMPLICIT PARTIAL DIFFERENTIATION

▶ **Example 7** Find the slope of the sphere $x^2 + y^2 + z^2 = 1$ in the $y$-direction at the points $\left(\frac{2}{3}, \frac{1}{3}, \frac{2}{3}\right)$ and $\left(\frac{2}{3}, \frac{1}{3}, -\frac{2}{3}\right)$ (Figure 13.3.2).

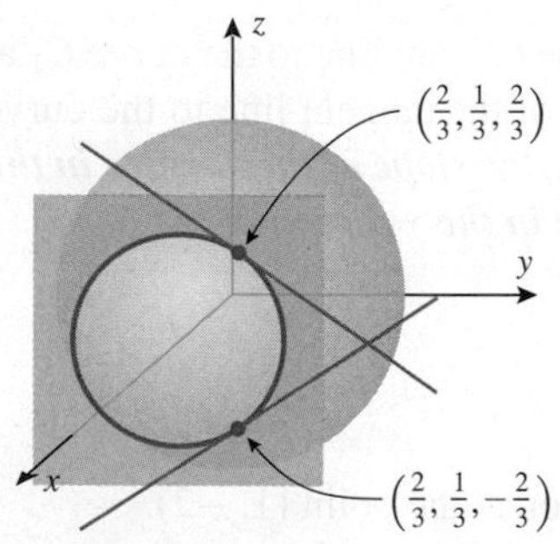


▲ **Figure 13.3.2**

***Solution.*** The point $\left(\frac{2}{3}, \frac{1}{3}, \frac{2}{3}\right)$ lies on the upper hemisphere $z = \sqrt{1 - x^2 - y^2}$, and the point $\left(\frac{2}{3}, \frac{1}{3}, -\frac{2}{3}\right)$ lies on the lower hemisphere $z = -\sqrt{1 - x^2 - y^2}$. We could find the slopes by differentiating each expression for $z$ separately with respect to $y$ and then evaluating the derivatives at $x = \frac{2}{3}$ and $y = \frac{1}{3}$. However, it is more efficient to differentiate the given equation

$$x^2 + y^2 + z^2 = 1$$

implicitly with respect to $y$, since this will give us both slopes with one differentiation. To perform the implicit differentiation, we view $z$ as a function of $x$ and $y$ and differentiate both sides with respect to $y$, taking $x$ to be fixed. The computations are as follows:

$$\frac{\partial}{\partial y}[x^2 + y^2 + z^2] = \frac{\partial}{\partial y}[1]$$

$$0 + 2y + 2z\frac{\partial z}{\partial y} = 0$$

$$\frac{\partial z}{\partial y} = -\frac{y}{z}$$

Substituting the $y$- and $z$-coordinates of the points $\left(\frac{2}{3}, \frac{1}{3}, \frac{2}{3}\right)$ and $\left(\frac{2}{3}, \frac{1}{3}, -\frac{2}{3}\right)$ in this expression, we find that the slope at the point $\left(\frac{2}{3}, \frac{1}{3}, \frac{2}{3}\right)$ is $-\frac{1}{2}$ and the slope at $\left(\frac{2}{3}, \frac{1}{3}, -\frac{2}{3}\right)$ is $\frac{1}{2}$. ◀

Check the results in Example 7 by differentiating the functions

$$z = \sqrt{1 - x^2 - y^2}$$

and

$$z = -\sqrt{1 - x^2 - y^2}$$

directly.

▶ **Example 8** Suppose that $D = \sqrt{x^2 + y^2}$ is the length of the diagonal of a rectangle whose sides have lengths $x$ and $y$ that are allowed to vary. Find a formula for the rate of change of $D$ with respect to $x$ if $x$ varies with $y$ held constant, and use this formula to find the rate of change of $D$ with respect to $x$ at the point where $x = 3$ and $y = 4$.

***Solution.*** Differentiating both sides of the equation $D^2 = x^2 + y^2$ with respect to $x$ yields

$$2D\frac{\partial D}{\partial x} = 2x \quad \text{and thus} \quad D\frac{\partial D}{\partial x} = x$$

Since $D = 5$ when $x = 3$ and $y = 4$, it follows that

$$5\left.\frac{\partial D}{\partial x}\right|_{x=3,y=4} = 3 \quad \text{or} \quad \left.\frac{\partial D}{\partial x}\right|_{x=3,y=4} = \frac{3}{5}$$

Thus, $D$ is increasing at a rate of $\frac{3}{5}$ unit per unit increase in $x$ at the point $(3, 4)$. ◄

## PARTIAL DERIVATIVES AND CONTINUITY

In contrast to the case of functions of a single variable, the existence of partial derivatives for a multivariable function does not guarantee the continuity of the function. This fact is shown in the following example.

► **Example 9** Let

$$f(x, y) = \begin{cases} -\dfrac{xy}{x^2 + y^2}, & (x, y) \neq (0, 0) \\ 0, & (x, y) = (0, 0) \end{cases} \tag{3}$$

(a) Show that $f_x(x, y)$ and $f_y(x, y)$ exist at all points $(x, y)$.

(b) Explain why $f$ is not continuous at $(0, 0)$.

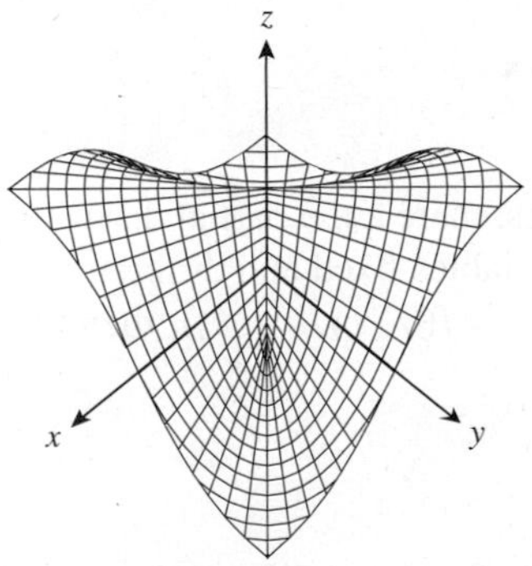


▲ **Figure 13.3.3**

***Solution (a).*** Figure 13.3.3 shows the graph of $f$. Note that $f$ is similar to the function considered in Example 1 of Section 13.2, except that here we have assigned $f$ a value of 0 at $(0, 0)$. Except at this point, the partial derivatives of $f$ are

$$f_x(x, y) = -\frac{(x^2 + y^2)y - xy(2x)}{(x^2 + y^2)^2} = \frac{x^2y - y^3}{(x^2 + y^2)^2} \tag{4}$$

$$f_y(x, y) = -\frac{(x^2 + y^2)x - xy(2y)}{(x^2 + y^2)^2} = \frac{xy^2 - x^3}{(x^2 + y^2)^2} \tag{5}$$

It is not evident from Formula (3) whether $f$ has partial derivatives at $(0, 0)$, and if so, what the values of those derivatives are. To answer that question we will have to use the definitions of the partial derivatives (Definition 13.3.1). Applying Formulas (1) and (2) to (3) we obtain

$$f_x(0, 0) = \lim_{\Delta x \to 0} \frac{f(\Delta x, 0) - f(0, 0)}{\Delta x} = \lim_{\Delta x \to 0} \frac{0 - 0}{\Delta x} = 0$$

$$f_y(0, 0) = \lim_{\Delta y \to 0} \frac{f(0, \Delta y) - f(0, 0)}{\Delta y} = \lim_{\Delta y \to 0} \frac{0 - 0}{\Delta y} = 0$$

This shows that $f$ has partial derivatives at $(0, 0)$ and the values of both partial derivatives are 0 at that point.

***Solution (b).*** We saw in Example 3 of Section 13.2 that

$$\lim_{(x,y)\to(0,0)} -\frac{xy}{x^2 + y^2}$$

does not exist. Thus, $f$ is not continuous at $(0, 0)$. ◄

We will study the relationship between the continuity of a function and the properties of its partial derivatives in the next section.

## PARTIAL DERIVATIVES OF FUNCTIONS WITH MORE THAN TWO VARIABLES

For a function $f(x, y, z)$ of three variables, there are three ***partial derivatives***:

$$f_x(x, y, z), \quad f_y(x, y, z), \quad f_z(x, y, z)$$

The partial derivative $f_x$ is calculated by holding $y$ and $z$ constant and differentiating with respect to $x$. For $f_y$ the variables $x$ and $z$ are held constant, and for $f_z$ the variables $x$ and $y$ are held constant. If a dependent variable

$$w = f(x, y, z)$$

is used, then the three partial derivatives of $f$ can be denoted by

$$\frac{\partial w}{\partial x}, \quad \frac{\partial w}{\partial y}, \quad \text{and} \quad \frac{\partial w}{\partial z}$$

▶ **Example 10** If $f(x, y, z) = x^3y^2z^4 + 2xy + z$, then

$$f_x(x, y, z) = 3x^2y^2z^4 + 2y$$
$$f_y(x, y, z) = 2x^3yz^4 + 2x$$
$$f_z(x, y, z) = 4x^3y^2z^3 + 1$$
$$f_z(-1, 1, 2) = 4(-1)^3(1)^2(2)^3 + 1 = -31 \blacktriangleleft$$

▶ **Example 11** If $f(\rho, \theta, \phi) = \rho^2 \cos\phi \sin\theta$, then

$$f_\rho(\rho, \theta, \phi) = 2\rho \cos\phi \sin\theta$$
$$f_\theta(\rho, \theta, \phi) = \rho^2 \cos\phi \cos\theta$$
$$f_\phi(\rho, \theta, \phi) = -\rho^2 \sin\phi \sin\theta \blacktriangleleft$$

In general, if $f(v_1, v_2, \ldots, v_n)$ is a function of $n$ variables, there are $n$ partial derivatives of $f$, each of which is obtained by holding $n - 1$ of the variables fixed and differentiating the function $f$ with respect to the remaining variable. If $w = f(v_1, v_2, \ldots, v_n)$, then these partial derivatives are denoted by

$$\frac{\partial w}{\partial v_1}, \frac{\partial w}{\partial v_2}, \ldots, \frac{\partial w}{\partial v_n}$$

where $\partial w/\partial v_i$ is obtained by holding all variables except $v_i$ fixed and differentiating with respect to $v_i$.

## HIGHER-ORDER PARTIAL DERIVATIVES

Suppose that $f$ is a function of two variables $x$ and $y$. Since the partial derivatives $\partial f/\partial x$ and $\partial f/\partial y$ are also functions of $x$ and $y$, these functions may themselves have partial derivatives. This gives rise to four possible ***second-order*** partial derivatives of $f$, which are defined by

$$\frac{\partial^2 f}{\partial x^2} = \frac{\partial}{\partial x}\left(\frac{\partial f}{\partial x}\right) = f_{xx} \qquad \frac{\partial^2 f}{\partial y^2} = \frac{\partial}{\partial y}\left(\frac{\partial f}{\partial y}\right) = f_{yy}$$

Differentiate twice with respect to $x$. | Differentiate twice with respect to $y$.

$$\frac{\partial^2 f}{\partial y \partial x} = \frac{\partial}{\partial y}\left(\frac{\partial f}{\partial x}\right) = f_{xy} \qquad \frac{\partial^2 f}{\partial x \partial y} = \frac{\partial}{\partial x}\left(\frac{\partial f}{\partial y}\right) = f_{yx}$$

Differentiate first with respect to $x$ and then with respect to $y$. | Differentiate first with respect to $y$ and then with respect to $x$.

The last two cases are called the ***mixed second-order partial derivatives*** or the ***mixed second partials***. Also, the derivatives $\partial f/\partial x$ and $\partial f/\partial y$ are often called the ***first-order partial derivatives*** when it is necessary to distinguish them from higher-order partial derivatives. Similar conventions apply to the second-order partial derivatives of a function of three variables.

**WARNING** Observe that the two notations for the mixed second partials have opposite conventions for the order of differentiation. In the "$\partial$" notation the derivatives are taken right to left, and in the "subscript" notation they are taken left to right. The conventions are logical if you insert parentheses:

$$\frac{\partial^2 f}{\partial y \partial x} = \frac{\partial}{\partial y}\left(\frac{\partial f}{\partial x}\right)$$ Right to left. Differentiate inside the parentheses first.

$$f_{xy} = (f_x)_y$$ Left to right. Differentiate inside the parentheses first.

▶ **Example 12** Find the second-order partial derivatives of $f(x, y) = x^2y^3 + x^4y$.

***Solution.*** We have

$$\frac{\partial f}{\partial x} = 2xy^3 + 4x^3y \quad \text{and} \quad \frac{\partial f}{\partial y} = 3x^2y^2 + x^4$$

so that

$$\frac{\partial^2 f}{\partial x^2} = \frac{\partial}{\partial x}\left(\frac{\partial f}{\partial x}\right) = \frac{\partial}{\partial x}(2xy^3 + 4x^3y) = 2y^3 + 12x^2y$$

$$\frac{\partial^2 f}{\partial y^2} = \frac{\partial}{\partial y}\left(\frac{\partial f}{\partial y}\right) = \frac{\partial}{\partial y}(3x^2y^2 + x^4) = 6x^2y$$

$$\frac{\partial^2 f}{\partial x \partial y} = \frac{\partial}{\partial x}\left(\frac{\partial f}{\partial y}\right) = \frac{\partial}{\partial x}(3x^2y^2 + x^4) = 6xy^2 + 4x^3$$

$$\frac{\partial^2 f}{\partial y \partial x} = \frac{\partial}{\partial y}\left(\frac{\partial f}{\partial x}\right) = \frac{\partial}{\partial y}(2xy^3 + 4x^3y) = 6xy^2 + 4x^3 \blacktriangleleft$$

Third-order, fourth-order, and higher-order partial derivatives can be obtained by successive differentiation. Some possibilities are

$$\frac{\partial^3 f}{\partial x^3} = \frac{\partial}{\partial x}\left(\frac{\partial^2 f}{\partial x^2}\right) = f_{xxx} \qquad \frac{\partial^4 f}{\partial y^4} = \frac{\partial}{\partial y}\left(\frac{\partial^3 f}{\partial y^3}\right) = f_{yyyy}$$

$$\frac{\partial^3 f}{\partial y^2 \partial x} = \frac{\partial}{\partial y}\left(\frac{\partial^2 f}{\partial y \partial x}\right) = f_{xyy} \qquad \frac{\partial^4 f}{\partial y^2 \partial x^2} = \frac{\partial}{\partial y}\left(\frac{\partial^3 f}{\partial y \partial x^2}\right) = f_{xxyy}$$

▶ **Example 13** Let $f(x, y) = y^2e^x + y$. Find $f_{xyy}$.

***Solution.***

$$f_{xyy} = \frac{\partial^3 f}{\partial y^2 \partial x} = \frac{\partial^2}{\partial y^2}\left(\frac{\partial f}{\partial x}\right) = \frac{\partial^2}{\partial y^2}(y^2e^x) = \frac{\partial}{\partial y}(2ye^x) = 2e^x \blacktriangleleft$$

## EQUALITY OF MIXED PARTIALS

For a function $f(x, y)$ it might be expected that there would be four distinct second-order partial derivatives: $f_{xx}, f_{xy}, f_{yx}$, and $f_{yy}$. However, observe that the mixed second-order partial derivatives in Example 12 are equal. The following theorem (proved in Web Appendix L) explains why this is so.

If $f$ is a function of three variables, then the analog of Theorem 13.3.2 holds for each pair of mixed second-order partials if we replace "open disk" by "open ball." How many second-order partials does $f(x, y, z)$ have?

**13.3.2 THEOREM** *Let $f$ be a function of two variables. If $f_{xy}$ and $f_{yx}$ are continuous on some open disk, then $f_{xy} = f_{yx}$ on that disk.*

It follows from this theorem that if $f_{xy}(x, y)$ and $f_{yx}(x, y)$ are continuous everywhere, then $f_{xy}(x, y) = f_{yx}(x, y)$ for all values of $x$ and $y$. Since polynomials are continuous everywhere, this explains why the mixed second-order partials in Example 12 are equal.

## THE WAVE EQUATION

Consider a string of length $L$ that is stretched taut between $x = 0$ and $x = L$ on an $x$-axis, and suppose that the string is set into vibratory motion by "plucking" it at time $t = 0$ (Figure 13.3.4*a*). The displacement of a point on the string depends on both its coordinate $x$ and the elapsed time $t$, and hence is described by a function $u(x, t)$ of two variables. For a fixed value $t$, the function $u(x, t)$ depends on $x$ alone, and the graph of $u$ versus $x$ describes the shape of the string—think of it as a "snapshot" of the string at time $t$ (Figure 13.3.4*b*). It follows that at a fixed time $t$, the partial derivative $\partial u/\partial x$ represents the slope of the string at $x$, and the sign of the second partial derivative $\partial^2 u/\partial x^2$ tells us whether the string is concave up or concave down at $x$ (Figure 13.3.4*c*).

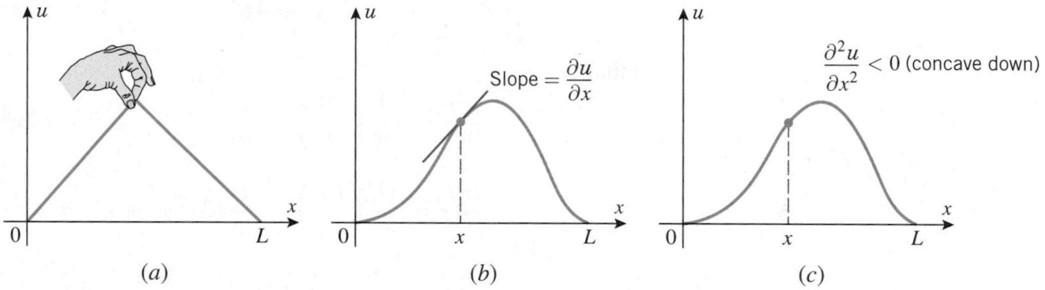


▲ **Figure 13.3.4**

Ken Vander Putten/iStockphoto
*The vibration of a plucked string is governed by the wave equation.*

For a fixed value of $x$, the function $u(x, t)$ depends on $t$ alone, and the graph of $u$ versus $t$ is the position versus time curve of the point on the string with coordinate $x$. Thus, for a fixed value of $x$, the partial derivative $\partial u/\partial t$ is the velocity of the point with coordinate $x$, and $\partial^2 u/\partial t^2$ is the acceleration of that point.

It can be proved that under appropriate conditions the function $u(x, t)$ satisfies an equation of the form

$$\frac{\partial^2 u}{\partial t^2} = c^2 \frac{\partial^2 u}{\partial x^2} \tag{6}$$

where $c$ is a positive constant that depends on the physical characteristics of the string. This equation, which is called the ***one-dimensional wave equation***, involves partial derivatives of the unknown function $u(x, t)$ and hence is classified as a ***partial differential equation***. Techniques for solving partial differential equations are studied in advanced courses and will not be discussed in this text.

▶ **Example 14** Show that the function $u(x, t) = \sin(x - ct)$ is a solution of Equation (6).

***Solution.*** We have

$$\frac{\partial u}{\partial x} = \cos(x - ct), \qquad \frac{\partial^2 u}{\partial x^2} = -\sin(x - ct)$$

$$\frac{\partial u}{\partial t} = -c\cos(x - ct), \qquad \frac{\partial^2 u}{\partial t^2} = -c^2\sin(x - ct)$$

Thus, $u(x, t)$ satisfies (6). ◀

## ✓ QUICK CHECK EXERCISES 13.3 (See page 837 for answers.)

1. Let $f(x, y) = x \sin xy$. Then $f_x(x, y) =$ ______ and $f_y(x, y) =$ ______.
2. The slope of the surface $z = xy^2$ in the $x$-direction at the point (2, 3) is ______, and the slope of this surface in the $y$-direction at the point (2, 3) is ______.
3. The volume $V$ of a right circular cone of radius $r$ and height $h$ is given by $V = \frac{1}{3}\pi r^2 h$.
   (a) Find a formula for the instantaneous rate of change of $V$ with respect to $r$ if $r$ changes and $h$ remains constant.
   (b) Find a formula for the instantaneous rate of change of $V$ with respect to $h$ if $h$ changes and $r$ remains constant.
4. Find all second-order partial derivatives for the function $f(x, y) = x^2y^3$.

## EXERCISE SET 13.3 Graphing Utility

1. Let $f(x, y) = 3x^3y^2$. Find
   (a) $f_x(x, y)$ (b) $f_y(x, y)$ (c) $f_x(1, y)$
   (d) $f_x(x, 1)$ (e) $f_y(1, y)$ (f) $f_y(x, 1)$
   (g) $f_x(1, 2)$ (h) $f_y(1, 2)$.
2. Let $z = e^{2x} \sin y$. Find
   (a) $\partial z/\partial x$ (b) $\partial z/\partial y$ (c) $\partial z/\partial x|_{(0,y)}$
   (d) $\partial z/\partial x|_{(x,0)}$ (e) $\partial z/\partial y|_{(0,y)}$ (f) $\partial z/\partial y|_{(x,0)}$
   (g) $\partial z/\partial x|_{(\ln 2,0)}$ (h) $\partial z/\partial y|_{(\ln 2,0)}$.

**3–10** Evaluate the indicated partial derivatives. ■

3. $z = 9x^2y - 3x^5y$; $\dfrac{\partial z}{\partial x}, \dfrac{\partial z}{\partial y}$
4. $f(x, y) = 10x^2y^4 - 6xy^2 + 10x^2$; $f_x(x, y)$, $f_y(x, y)$
5. $z = (x^2 + 5x - 2y)^8$; $\dfrac{\partial z}{\partial x}, \dfrac{\partial z}{\partial y}$
6. $f(x, y) = \dfrac{1}{xy^2 - x^2y}$; $f_x(x, y)$, $f_y(x, y)$
7. $\dfrac{\partial}{\partial p}(e^{-7p/q})$, $\dfrac{\partial}{\partial q}(e^{-7p/q})$
8. $\dfrac{\partial}{\partial x}(xe^{\sqrt{15xy}})$, $\dfrac{\partial}{\partial y}(xe^{\sqrt{15xy}})$
9. $z = \sin(5x^3y + 7xy^2)$; $\dfrac{\partial z}{\partial x}, \dfrac{\partial z}{\partial y}$
10. $f(x, y) = \cos(2xy^2 - 3x^2y^2)$; $f_x(x, y)$, $f_y(x, y)$
11. Let $f(x, y) = \sqrt{3x + 2y}$.
    (a) Find the slope of the surface $z = f(x, y)$ in the $x$-direction at the point (4, 2).
    (b) Find the slope of the surface $z = f(x, y)$ in the $y$-direction at the point (4, 2).
12. Let $f(x, y) = xe^{-y} + 5y$.
    (a) Find the slope of the surface $z = f(x, y)$ in the $x$-direction at the point (3, 0).
    (b) Find the slope of the surface $z = f(x, y)$ in the $y$-direction at the point (3, 0).
13. Let $z = \sin(y^2 - 4x)$.
    (a) Find the rate of change of $z$ with respect to $x$ at the point (2, 1) with $y$ held fixed.
    (b) Find the rate of change of $z$ with respect to $y$ at the point (2, 1) with $x$ held fixed.
14. Let $z = (x + y)^{-1}$.
    (a) Find the rate of change of $z$ with respect to $x$ at the point $(-2, 4)$ with $y$ held fixed.
    (b) Find the rate of change of $z$ with respect to $y$ at the point $(-2, 4)$ with $x$ held fixed.

### FOCUS ON CONCEPTS

15. Use the information in the accompanying figure to find the values of the first-order partial derivatives of $f$ at the point (1, 2).

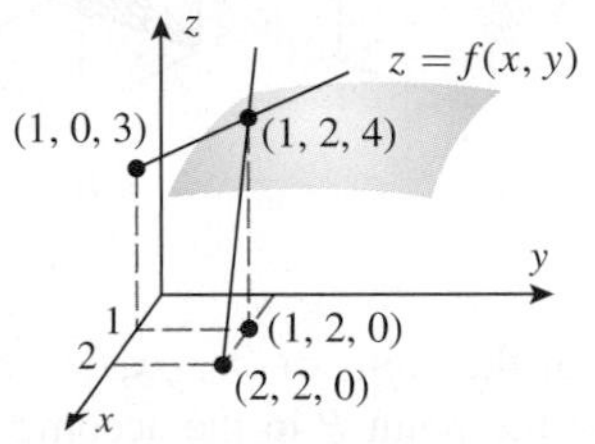


◀ **Figure Ex-15**

16. The accompanying figure shows a contour plot for an unspecified function $f(x, y)$. Make a conjecture about the signs of the partial derivatives $f_x(x_0, y_0)$ and $f_y(x_0, y_0)$, and explain your reasoning.

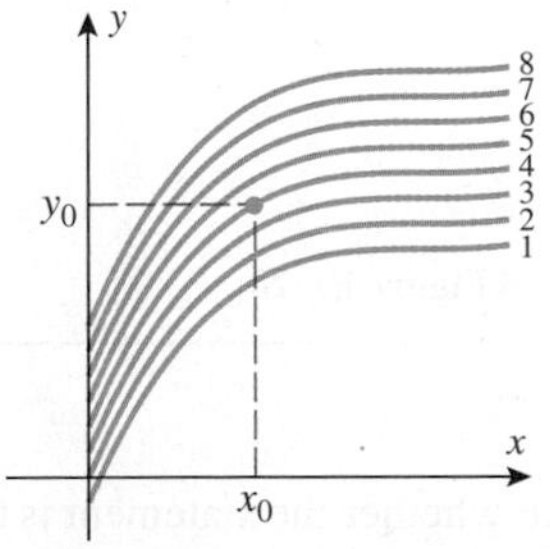


◀ **Figure Ex-16**

17. Suppose that Nolan throws a baseball to Ryan and that the baseball leaves Nolan's hand at the same height at which it is caught by Ryan. It we ignore air resistance, the horizontal range $r$ of the baseball is a function of the initial speed $v$ of the ball when it leaves Nolan's hand and the angle $\theta$ above the horizontal at which it is thrown. Use the accompanying table and the method of Example 6 to estimate
    (a) the partial derivative of $r$ with respect to $v$ when $v = 80$ ft/s and $\theta = 40°$

(b) the partial derivative of $r$ with respect to $\theta$ when $v = 80$ ft/s and $\theta = 40°$.

| ANGLE $\theta$ (degrees) \ SPEED $v$ (ft/s) | 75 | 80 | 85 | 90 |
|---|---|---|---|---|
| 35 | 165 | 188 | 212 | 238 |
| 40 | 173 | 197 | 222 | 249 |
| 45 | 176 | 200 | 226 | 253 |
| 50 | 173 | 197 | 222 | 249 |

◀ Table Ex-17

**18.** Use the table in Exercise 17 and the method of Example 6 to estimate
(a) the partial derivative of $r$ with respect to $v$ when $v = 85$ ft/s and $\theta = 45°$
(b) the partial derivative of $r$ with respect to $\theta$ when $v = 85$ ft/s and $\theta = 45°$.

**19.** The accompanying figure shows the graphs of an unspecified function $f(x, y)$ and its partial derivatives $f_x(x, y)$ and $f_y(x, y)$. Determine which is which, and explain your reasoning.

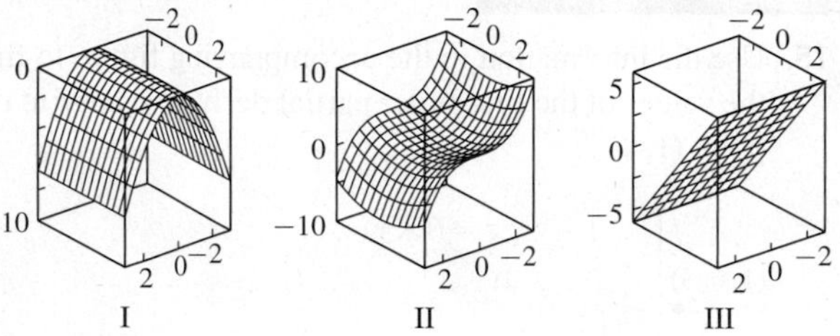


▲ Figure Ex-19

**20.** What can you say about the signs of $\partial z/\partial x$, $\partial^2 z/\partial x^2$, $\partial z/\partial y$, and $\partial^2 z/\partial y^2$ at the point $P$ in the accompanying figure? Explain your reasoning.

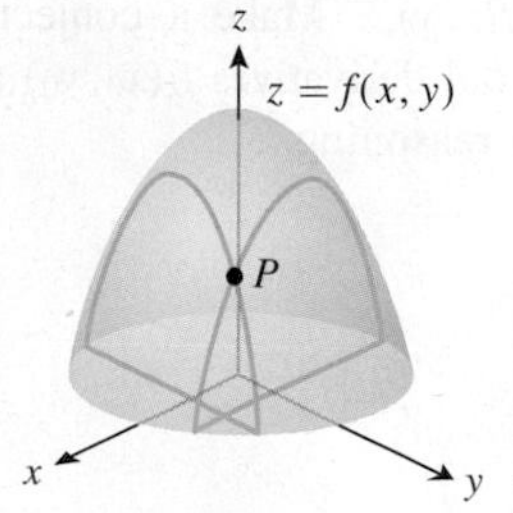


◀ Figure Ex-20

**21–24 True–False** Determine whether the statement is true or false. Explain your answer. ■

**21.** If the line $y = 2$ is a contour of $f(x, y)$ through $(4, 2)$, then $f_x(4, 2) = 0$.

**22.** If the plane $x = 3$ intersects the surface $z = f(x, y)$ in a curve that passes through $(3, 4, 16)$ and satisfies $z = y^2$, then $f_y(3, 4) = 8$.

**23.** If the graph of $z = f(x, y)$ is a plane in 3-space, then both $f_x$ and $f_y$ are constant functions.

**24.** There exists a polynomial $f(x, y)$ that satisfies the equations $f_x(x, y) = 3x^2 + y^2 + 2y$ and $f_y(x, y) = 2xy + 2y$.

**25–30** Find $\partial z/\partial x$ and $\partial z/\partial y$. ■

**25.** $z = 4e^{x^2y^3}$ **26.** $z = \cos(x^5y^4)$

**27.** $z = x^3 \ln(1 + xy^{-3/5})$ **28.** $z = e^{xy} \sin 4y^2$

**29.** $z = \dfrac{xy}{x^2 + y^2}$ **30.** $z = \dfrac{x^2y^3}{\sqrt{x + y}}$

**31–36** Find $f_x(x, y)$ and $f_y(x, y)$. ■

**31.** $f(x, y) = \sqrt{3x^5y - 7x^3y}$ **32.** $f(x, y) = \dfrac{x + y}{x - y}$

**33.** $f(x, y) = y^{-3/2} \tan^{-1}(x/y)$

**34.** $f(x, y) = x^3e^{-y} + y^3 \sec\sqrt{x}$

**35.** $f(x, y) = (y^2 \tan x)^{-4/3}$

**36.** $f(x, y) = \cosh(\sqrt{x}) \sinh^2(xy^2)$

**37–40** Evaluate the indicated partial derivatives. ■

**37.** $f(x, y) = 9 - x^2 - 7y^3$; $f_x(3, 1)$, $f_y(3, 1)$

**38.** $f(x, y) = x^2ye^{xy}$; $\partial f/\partial x(1, 1)$, $\partial f/\partial y(1, 1)$

**39.** $z = \sqrt{x^2 + 4y^2}$; $\partial z/\partial x(1, 2)$, $\partial z/\partial y(1, 2)$

**40.** $w = x^2 \cos xy$; $\partial w/\partial x\left(\frac{1}{2}, \pi\right)$, $\partial w/\partial y\left(\frac{1}{2}, \pi\right)$

**41.** Let $f(x, y, z) = x^2y^4z^3 + xy + z^2 + 1$. Find
(a) $f_x(x, y, z)$ (b) $f_y(x, y, z)$ (c) $f_z(x, y, z)$
(d) $f_x(1, y, z)$ (e) $f_y(1, 2, z)$ (f) $f_z(1, 2, 3)$.

**42.** Let $w = x^2y \cos z$. Find
(a) $\partial w/\partial x(x, y, z)$ (b) $\partial w/\partial y(x, y, z)$
(c) $\partial w/\partial z(x, y, z)$ (d) $\partial w/\partial x(2, y, z)$
(e) $\partial w/\partial y(2, 1, z)$ (f) $\partial w/\partial z(2, 1, 0)$.

**43–46** Find $f_x$, $f_y$, and $f_z$. ■

**43.** $f(x, y, z) = z \ln(x^2y \cos z)$

**44.** $f(x, y, z) = y^{-3/2} \sec\left(\dfrac{xz}{y}\right)$

**45.** $f(x, y, z) = \tan^{-1}\left(\dfrac{1}{xy^2z^3}\right)$

**46.** $f(x, y, z) = \cosh(\sqrt{z}) \sinh^2(x^2yz)$

**47–50** Find $\partial w/\partial x$, $\partial w/\partial y$, and $\partial w/\partial z$. ■

**47.** $w = ye^z \sin xz$ **48.** $w = \dfrac{x^2 - y^2}{y^2 + z^2}$

**49.** $w = \sqrt{x^2 + y^2 + z^2}$ **50.** $w = y^3e^{2x+3z}$

**51.** Let $f(x, y, z) = y^2e^{xz}$. Find
(a) $\partial f/\partial x|_{(1,1,1)}$ (b) $\partial f/\partial y|_{(1,1,1)}$ (c) $\partial f/\partial z|_{(1,1,1)}$.

**52.** Let $w = \sqrt{x^2 + 4y^2 - z^2}$. Find
(a) $\partial w/\partial x|_{(2,1,-1)}$ (b) $\partial w/\partial y|_{(2,1,-1)}$
(c) $\partial w/\partial z|_{(2,1,-1)}$.

**53.** Let $f(x, y) = e^x \cos y$. Use a graphing utility to graph the functions $f_x(0, y)$ and $f_y(x, \pi/2)$.

**54.** Let $f(x, y) = e^x \sin y$. Use a graphing utility to graph the functions $f_x(0, y)$ and $f_y(x, 0)$.

**55.** A point moves along the intersection of the elliptic paraboloid $z = x^2 + 3y^2$ and the plane $y = 1$. At what rate is $z$ changing with respect to $x$ when the point is at $(2, 1, 7)$?

**56.** A point moves along the intersection of the elliptic paraboloid $z = x^2 + 3y^2$ and the plane $x = 2$. At what rate is $z$ changing with respect to $y$ when the point is at $(2, 1, 7)$?

**57.** A point moves along the intersection of the plane $y = 3$ and the surface $z = \sqrt{29 - x^2 - y^2}$. At what rate is $z$ changing with respect to $x$ when the point is at $(4, 3, 2)$?

**58.** Find the slope of the tangent line at $(-1, 1, 5)$ to the curve of intersection of the surface $z = x^2 + 4y^2$ and
(a) the plane $x = -1$ (b) the plane $y = 1$.

**59.** The volume $V$ of a right circular cylinder is given by the formula $V = \pi r^2 h$, where $r$ is the radius and $h$ is the height.
(a) Find a formula for the instantaneous rate of change of $V$ with respect to $r$ if $r$ changes and $h$ remains constant.
(b) Find a formula for the instantaneous rate of change of $V$ with respect to $h$ if $h$ changes and $r$ remains constant.
(c) Suppose that $h$ has a constant value of 4 in, but $r$ varies. Find the rate of change of $V$ with respect to $r$ at the point where $r = 6$ in.
(d) Suppose that $r$ has a constant value of 8 in, but $h$ varies. Find the instantaneous rate of change of $V$ with respect to $h$ at the point where $h = 10$ in.

**60.** The volume $V$ of a right circular cone is given by

$$V = \frac{\pi}{24} d^2 \sqrt{4s^2 - d^2}$$

where $s$ is the slant height and $d$ is the diameter of the base.
(a) Find a formula for the instantaneous rate of change of $V$ with respect to $s$ if $d$ remains constant.
(b) Find a formula for the instantaneous rate of change of $V$ with respect to $d$ if $s$ remains constant.
(c) Suppose that $d$ has a constant value of 16 cm, but $s$ varies. Find the rate of change of $V$ with respect to $s$ when $s = 10$ cm.
(d) Suppose that $s$ has a constant value of 10 cm, but $d$ varies. Find the rate of change of $V$ with respect to $d$ when $d = 16$ cm.

**61.** According to the ideal gas law, the pressure, temperature, and volume of a gas are related by $P = kT/V$, where $k$ is a constant of proportionality. Suppose that $V$ is measured in cubic inches ($\text{in}^3$), $T$ is measured in kelvins (K), and that for a certain gas the constant of proportionality is $k = 10$ in·lb/K.
(a) Find the instantaneous rate of change of pressure with respect to temperature if the temperature is 80 K and the volume remains fixed at 50 $\text{in}^3$.
(b) Find the instantaneous rate of change of volume with respect to pressure if the volume is 50 $\text{in}^3$ and the temperature remains fixed at 80 K.

**62.** The temperature at a point $(x, y)$ on a metal plate in the $xy$-plane is $T(x, y) = x^3 + 2y^2 + x$ degrees Celsius. Assume that distance is measured in centimeters and find the rate at which temperature changes with respect to distance if we start at the point $(1, 2)$ and move
(a) to the right and parallel to the $x$-axis
(b) upward and parallel to the $y$-axis.

**63.** The length, width, and height of a rectangular box are $l = 5$, $w = 2$, and $h = 3$, respectively.
(a) Find the instantaneous rate of change of the volume of the box with respect to the length if $w$ and $h$ are held constant.
(b) Find the instantaneous rate of change of the volume of the box with respect to the width if $l$ and $h$ are held constant.
(c) Find the instantaneous rate of change of the volume of the box with respect to the height if $l$ and $w$ are held constant.

**64.** The area $A$ of a triangle is given by $A = \frac{1}{2}ab\sin\theta$, where $a$ and $b$ are the lengths of two sides and $\theta$ is the angle between these sides. Suppose that $a = 5$, $b = 10$, and $\theta = \pi/3$.
(a) Find the rate at which $A$ changes with respect to $a$ if $b$ and $\theta$ are held constant.
(b) Find the rate at which $A$ changes with respect to $\theta$ if $a$ and $b$ are held constant.
(c) Find the rate at which $b$ changes with respect to $a$ if $A$ and $\theta$ are held constant.

**65.** The volume of a right circular cone of radius $r$ and height $h$ is $V = \frac{1}{3}\pi r^2 h$. Show that if the height remains constant while the radius changes, then the volume satisfies

$$\frac{\partial V}{\partial r} = \frac{2V}{r}$$

**66.** Find parametric equations for the tangent line at $(1, 3, 3)$ to the curve of intersection of the surface $z = x^2 y$ and
(a) the plane $x = 1$ (b) the plane $y = 3$.

**67.** (a) By differentiating implicitly, find the slope of the hyperboloid $x^2 + y^2 - z^2 = 1$ in the $x$-direction at the points $(3, 4, 2\sqrt{6})$ and $(3, 4, -2\sqrt{6})$.
(b) Check the results in part (a) by solving for $z$ and differentiating the resulting functions directly.

**68.** (a) By differentiating implicitly, find the slope of the hyperboloid $x^2 + y^2 - z^2 = 1$ in the $y$-direction at the points $(3, 4, 2\sqrt{6})$ and $(3, 4, -2\sqrt{6})$.
(b) Check the results in part (a) by solving for $z$ and differentiating the resulting functions directly.

**69–72** Calculate $\partial z/\partial x$ and $\partial z/\partial y$ using implicit differentiation. Leave your answers in terms of $x$, $y$, and $z$. ■

**69.** $(x^2 + y^2 + z^2)^{3/2} = 1$ **70.** $\ln(2x^2 + y - z^3) = x$

**71.** $x^2 + z\sin xyz = 0$ **72.** $e^{xy}\sinh z - z^2 x + 1 = 0$

**73–76** Find $\partial w/\partial x$, $\partial w/\partial y$, and $\partial w/\partial z$ using implicit differentiation. Leave your answers in terms of $x$, $y$, $z$, and $w$. ■

**73.** $(x^2 + y^2 + z^2 + w^2)^{3/2} = 4$

**74.** $\ln(2x^2 + y - z^3 + 3w) = z$

**75.** $w^2 + w\sin xyz = 1$

**76.** $e^{xy}\sinh w - z^2 w + 1 = 0$

**77–80** Find $f_x$ and $f_y$. ■

**77.** $f(x, y) = \int_y^x e^{t^2}\,dt$ **78.** $f(x, y) = \int_1^{xy} e^{t^2}\,dt$

**79.** $f(x, y) = \int_0^{x^2y^3} \sin t^3 \, dt$ **80.** $f(x, y) = \int_{x+y}^{x-y} \sin t^3 \, dt$

**81.** Let $z = \sqrt{x} \cos y$. Find
(a) $\partial^2 z/\partial x^2$ (b) $\partial^2 z/\partial y^2$
(c) $\partial^2 z/\partial x \partial y$ (d) $\partial^2 z/\partial y \partial x$.

**82.** Let $f(x, y) = 4x^2 - 2y + 7x^4y^5$. Find
(a) $f_{xx}$ (b) $f_{yy}$ (c) $f_{xy}$ (d) $f_{yx}$.

**83.** Let $f(x, y) = \sin(3x^2 + 6y^2)$. Find
(a) $f_{xx}$ (b) $f_{yy}$ (c) $f_{xy}$ (d) $f_{yx}$.

**84.** Let $f(x, y) = xe^{2y}$. Find
(a) $f_{xx}$ (b) $f_{yy}$ (c) $f_{xy}$ (d) $f_{yx}$.

**85–92** Confirm that the mixed second-order partial derivatives of $f$ are the same. ■

**85.** $f(x, y) = 4x^2 - 8xy^4 + 7y^5 - 3$

**86.** $f(x, y) = \sqrt{x^2 + y^2}$ **87.** $f(x, y) = e^x \cos y$

**88.** $f(x, y) = e^{x-y^2}$ **89.** $f(x, y) = \ln(4x - 5y)$

**90.** $f(x, y) = \ln(x^2 + y^2)$

**91.** $f(x, y) = (x - y)/(x + y)$

**92.** $f(x, y) = (x^2 - y^2)/(x^2 + y^2)$

**93.** Express the following derivatives in "$\partial$" notation.
(a) $f_{xxx}$ (b) $f_{xyy}$ (c) $f_{yyxx}$ (d) $f_{xyyy}$

**94.** Express the derivatives in "subscript" notation.
(a) $\dfrac{\partial^3 f}{\partial y^2 \partial x}$ (b) $\dfrac{\partial^4 f}{\partial x^4}$ (c) $\dfrac{\partial^4 f}{\partial y^2 \partial x^2}$ (d) $\dfrac{\partial^5 f}{\partial x^2 \partial y^3}$

**95.** Given $f(x, y) = x^3y^5 - 2x^2y + x$, find
(a) $f_{xxy}$ (b) $f_{yxy}$ (c) $f_{yyy}$.

**96.** Given $z = (2x - y)^5$, find
(a) $\dfrac{\partial^3 z}{\partial y \partial x \partial y}$ (b) $\dfrac{\partial^3 z}{\partial x^2 \partial y}$ (c) $\dfrac{\partial^4 z}{\partial x^2 \partial y^2}$.

**97.** Given $f(x, y) = y^3e^{-5x}$, find
(a) $f_{xyy}(0, 1)$ (b) $f_{xxx}(0, 1)$ (c) $f_{yyxx}(0, 1)$.

**98.** Given $w = e^y \cos x$, find
(a) $\left.\dfrac{\partial^3 w}{\partial y^2 \partial x}\right|_{(\pi/4,0)}$ (b) $\left.\dfrac{\partial^3 w}{\partial x^2 \partial y}\right|_{(\pi/4,0)}$

**99.** Let $f(x, y, z) = x^3y^5z^7 + xy^2 + y^3z$. Find
(a) $f_{xy}$ (b) $f_{yz}$ (c) $f_{xz}$ (d) $f_{zz}$
(e) $f_{zyy}$ (f) $f_{xxy}$ (g) $f_{zyx}$ (h) $f_{xxyz}$.

**100.** Let $w = (4x - 3y + 2z)^5$. Find
(a) $\dfrac{\partial^2 w}{\partial x \partial z}$ (b) $\dfrac{\partial^3 w}{\partial x \partial y \partial z}$ (c) $\dfrac{\partial^4 w}{\partial z^2 \partial y \partial x}$.

**101.** Show that the function satisfies ***Laplace's equation***

$$\frac{\partial^2 z}{\partial x^2} + \frac{\partial^2 z}{\partial y^2} = 0$$

(a) $z = x^2 - y^2 + 2xy$
(b) $z = e^x \sin y + e^y \cos x$
(c) $z = \ln(x^2 + y^2) + 2\tan^{-1}(y/x)$

**102.** Show that the function satisfies the ***heat equation***

$$\frac{\partial z}{\partial t} = c^2 \frac{\partial^2 z}{\partial x^2} \quad (c > 0, \text{ constant})$$

(a) $z = e^{-t}\sin(x/c)$ (b) $z = e^{-t}\cos(x/c)$

**103.** Show that the function $u(x, t) = \sin c\omega t \sin \omega x$ satisfies the wave equation [Equation (6)] for all real values of $\omega$.

**104.** In each part, show that $u(x, y)$ and $v(x, y)$ satisfy the ***Cauchy–Riemann equations***

$$\frac{\partial u}{\partial x} = \frac{\partial v}{\partial y} \quad \text{and} \quad \frac{\partial u}{\partial y} = -\frac{\partial v}{\partial x}$$

(a) $u = x^2 - y^2$, $v = 2xy$
(b) $u = e^x \cos y$, $v = e^x \sin y$
(c) $u = \ln(x^2 + y^2)$, $v = 2\tan^{-1}(y/x)$

**105.** Show that if $u(x, y)$ and $v(x, y)$ each have equal mixed second partials, and if $u$ and $v$ satisfy the Cauchy–Riemann equations (Exercise 104), then $u$, $v$, and $u + v$ satisfy Laplace's equation (Exercise 101).

**106.** When two resistors having resistances $R_1$ ohms and $R_2$ ohms are connected in parallel, their combined resistance $R$ in ohms is $R = R_1R_2/(R_1 + R_2)$. Show that

$$\frac{\partial^2 R}{\partial R_1^2}\frac{\partial^2 R}{\partial R_2^2} = \frac{4R^2}{(R_1 + R_2)^4}$$

**107–110** Find the indicated partial derivatives. ■

**107.** $f(v, w, x, y) = 4v^2w^3x^4y^5$;
$\partial f/\partial v$, $\partial f/\partial w$, $\partial f/\partial x$, $\partial f/\partial y$

**108.** $w = r\cos st + e^u \sin ur$;
$\partial w/\partial r$, $\partial w/\partial s$, $\partial w/\partial t$, $\partial w/\partial u$

**109.** $f(v_1, v_2, v_3, v_4) = \dfrac{v_1^2 - v_2^2}{v_3^2 + v_4^2}$;
$\partial f/\partial v_1$, $\partial f/\partial v_2$, $\partial f/\partial v_3$, $\partial f/\partial v_4$

**110.** $V = xe^{2x-y} + we^{zw} + yw$;
$\partial V/\partial x$, $\partial V/\partial y$, $\partial V/\partial z$, $\partial V/\partial w$

**111.** Let $u(w, x, y, z) = xe^{yw}\sin^2 z$. Find
(a) $\dfrac{\partial u}{\partial x}(0, 0, 1, \pi)$ (b) $\dfrac{\partial u}{\partial y}(0, 0, 1, \pi)$
(c) $\dfrac{\partial u}{\partial w}(0, 0, 1, \pi)$ (d) $\dfrac{\partial u}{\partial z}(0, 0, 1, \pi)$
(e) $\dfrac{\partial^4 u}{\partial x \partial y \partial w \partial z}$ (f) $\dfrac{\partial^4 u}{\partial w \partial z \partial y^2}$.

**112.** Let $f(v, w, x, y) = 2v^{1/2}w^4x^{1/2}y^{2/3}$. Find $f_v(1, -2, 4, 8)$, $f_w(1, -2, 4, 8)$, $f_x(1, -2, 4, 8)$, and $f_y(1, -2, 4, 8)$.

**113–114** Find $\partial w/\partial x_i$ for $i = 1, 2, \ldots, n$. ■

**113.** $w = \cos(x_1 + 2x_2 + \cdots + nx_n)$

**114.** $w = \left(\displaystyle\sum_{k=1}^{n} x_k\right)^{1/n}$

**115–116** Describe the largest set on which Theorem 13.3.2 can be used to prove that $f_{xy}$ and $f_{yx}$ are equal on that set. Then confirm by direct computation that $f_{xy} = f_{yx}$ on the given set. ■

**115.** (a) $f(x, y) = 4x^3y + 3x^2y$ (b) $f(x, y) = x^3/y$

**116.** (a) $f(x, y) = \sqrt{x^2 + y^2 - 1}$
(b) $f(x, y) = \sin(x^2 + y^3)$

**117.** Let $f(x, y) = 2x^2 - 3xy + y^2$. Find $f_x(2, -1)$ and $f_y(2, -1)$ by evaluating the limits in Definition 13.3.1. Then check your work by calculating the derivative in the usual way.

**118.** Let $f(x, y) = (x^2 + y^2)^{2/3}$. Show that

$$f_x(x, y) = \begin{cases} \dfrac{4x}{3(x^2 + y^2)^{1/3}}, & (x, y) \neq (0, 0) \\ 0, & (x, y) = (0, 0) \end{cases}$$

***Source:*** This problem, due to Don Cohen, appeared in *Mathematics and Computer Education*, Vol. 25, No. 2, 1991, p. 179.

**119.** Let $f(x, y) = (x^3 + y^3)^{1/3}$.
(a) Show that $f_y(0, 0) = 1$.
(b) At what points, if any, does $f_y(x, y)$ fail to exist?

**120. Writing** Explain how one might use the graph of the equation $z = f(x, y)$ to determine the signs of $f_x(x_0, y_0)$ and $f_y(x_0, y_0)$ by inspection.

**121. Writing** Explain how one might use the graphs of some appropriate contours of $z = f(x, y)$ to determine the signs of $f_x(x_0, y_0)$ and $f_y(x_0, y_0)$ by inspection.

✓ QUICK CHECK ANSWERS 13.3 1. $\sin xy + xy\cos xy$; $x^2\cos xy$ 2. 9; 12 3. (a) $\frac{2}{3}\pi rh$ (b) $\frac{1}{3}\pi r^2$ 4. $f_{xx}(x, y) = 2y^3$, $f_{yy}(x, y) = 6x^2y$, $f_{xy}(x, y) = f_{yx}(x, y) = 6xy^2$

## 13.4 DIFFERENTIABILITY, DIFFERENTIALS, AND LOCAL LINEARITY

*In this section we will extend the notion of differentiability to functions of two or three variables. Our definition of differentiability will be based on the idea that a function is differentiable at a point provided it can be very closely approximated by a linear function near that point. In the process, we will expand the concept of a "differential" to functions of more than one variable and define the "local linear approximation" of a function.*

### DIFFERENTIABILITY

Recall that a function $f$ of one variable is called differentiable at $x_0$ if it has a derivative at $x_0$, that is, if the limit

$$f'(x_0) = \lim_{\Delta x \to 0} \frac{f(x_0 + \Delta x) - f(x_0)}{\Delta x} \tag{1}$$

exists. As a consequence of (1) a differentiable function enjoys a number of other important properties:

- The graph of $y = f(x)$ has a nonvertical tangent line at the point $(x_0, f(x_0))$;
- $f$ may be closely approximated by a linear function near $x_0$ (Section 3.5);
- $f$ is continuous at $x_0$.

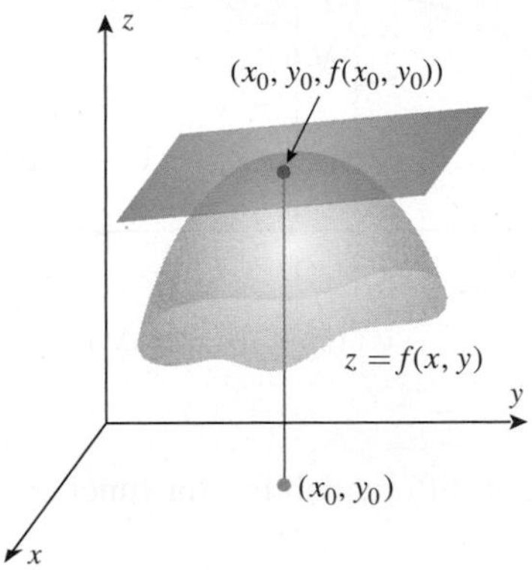

▲ **Figure 13.4.1**

Our primary objective in this section is to extend the notion of differentiability to functions of two or three variables in such a way that the natural analogs of these properties hold. For example, if a function $f(x, y)$ of two variables is differentiable at a point $(x_0, y_0)$, we want it to be the case that

- the surface $z = f(x, y)$ has a nonvertical tangent plane at the point $(x_0, y_0, f(x_0, y_0))$ (Figure 13.4.1);
- the values of $f$ at points near $(x_0, y_0)$ can be very closely approximated by the values of a linear function;
- $f$ is continuous at $(x_0, y_0)$.

One could reasonably conjecture that a function $f$ of two or three variables should be called differentiable at a point if all the first-order partial derivatives of the function exist at that point. However, this condition alone is not strong enough to guarantee that the properties above hold. For instance, we saw in Example 9 of Section 13.3 that the mere existence of both first-order partial derivatives for a function is not sufficient to guarantee the continuity of the function. To determine what else we should include in our definition, it will be helpful to reexamine one of the consequences of differentiability for a *single-variable* function $f(x)$. Suppose that $f(x)$ is differentiable at $x = x_0$ and let

$$\Delta f = f(x_0 + \Delta x) - f(x_0)$$

denote the change in $f$ that corresponds to the change $\Delta x$ in $x$ from $x_0$ to $x_0 + \Delta x$. We saw in Section 3.5 that

$$\Delta f \approx f'(x_0)\Delta x$$

provided $\Delta x$ is close to 0. In fact, for $\Delta x$ close to 0 the error $\Delta f - f'(x_0)\Delta x$ in this approximation will have magnitude much smaller than that of $\Delta x$ because

$$\lim_{\Delta x \to 0} \frac{\Delta f - f'(x_0)\Delta x}{\Delta x} = \lim_{\Delta x \to 0} \left( \frac{f(x_0 + \Delta x) - f(x_0)}{\Delta x} - f'(x_0) \right) = f'(x_0) - f'(x_0) = 0$$

Since the magnitude of $\Delta x$ is just the distance between the points $x_0$ and $x_0 + \Delta x$, we see that when the two points are close together, the magnitude of the error in the approximation will be much smaller than the distance between the two points (Figure 13.4.2). The extension of this idea to functions of two or three variables is the "extra ingredient" needed in our definition of differentiability for multivariable functions.

For a function $f(x, y)$, the symbol $\Delta f$, called the ***increment*** of $f$, denotes the change in the value of $f(x, y)$ that results when $(x, y)$ varies from some initial position $(x_0, y_0)$ to some new position $(x_0 + \Delta x, y_0 + \Delta y)$; thus

$$\Delta f = f(x_0 + \Delta x, y_0 + \Delta y) - f(x_0, y_0) \tag{2}$$

(see Figure 13.4.3). [If a dependent variable $z = f(x, y)$ is used, then we will sometimes write $\Delta z$ rather than $\Delta f$.] Let us assume that both $f_x(x_0, y_0)$ and $f_y(x_0, y_0)$ exist and (by analogy with the one-variable case) make the approximation

Show that if $f(x, y)$ is a linear function, then (3) becomes an equality.

$$\Delta f \approx f_x(x_0, y_0)\Delta x + f_y(x_0, y_0)\Delta y \tag{3}$$

For $\Delta x$ and $\Delta y$ close to 0, we would like the error

$$\Delta f - f_x(x_0, y_0)\Delta x - f_y(x_0, y_0)\Delta y$$

in this approximation to be much smaller than the distance $\sqrt{(\Delta x)^2 + (\Delta y)^2}$ between $(x_0, y_0)$ and $(x_0 + \Delta x, y_0 + \Delta y)$. We can guarantee this by requiring that

$$\lim_{(\Delta x, \Delta y) \to (0,0)} \frac{\Delta f - f_x(x_0, y_0)\Delta x - f_y(x_0, y_0)\Delta y}{\sqrt{(\Delta x)^2 + (\Delta y)^2}} = 0$$

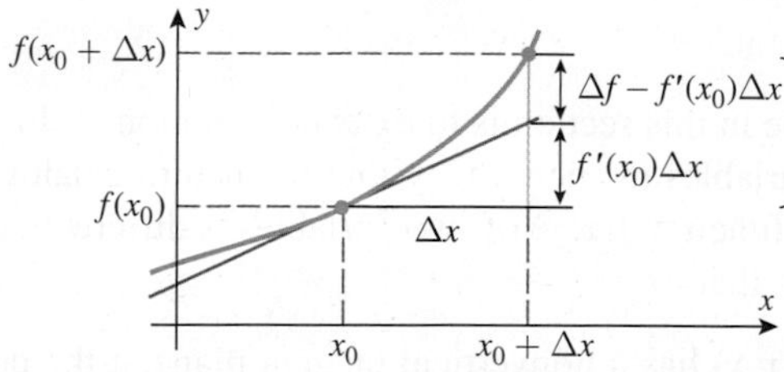


▲ **Figure 13.4.2**

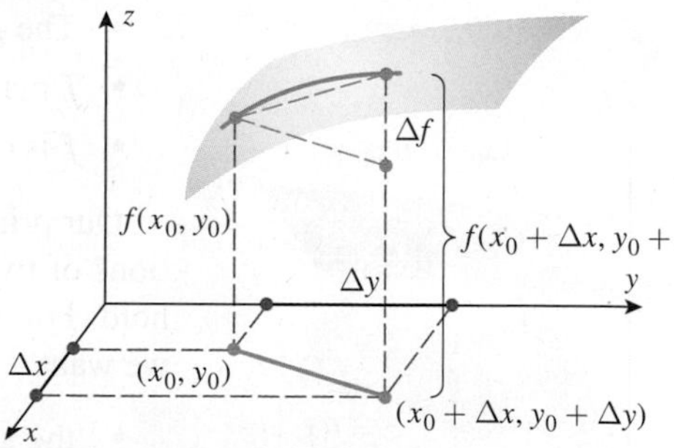


▲ **Figure 13.4.3**

Based on these ideas, we can now give our definition of differentiability for functions of two variables.

**13.4.1 DEFINITION** A function $f$ of two variables is said to be ***differentiable*** at $(x_0, y_0)$ provided $f_x(x_0, y_0)$ and $f_y(x_0, y_0)$ both exist and

$$\lim_{(\Delta x, \Delta y) \to (0,0)} \frac{\Delta f - f_x(x_0, y_0)\Delta x - f_y(x_0, y_0)\Delta y}{\sqrt{(\Delta x)^2 + (\Delta y)^2}} = 0 \tag{4}$$

As with the one-variable case, verification of differentiability using this definition involves the computation of a limit.

**Example 1** Use Definition 13.4.1 to prove that $f(x, y) = x^2 + y^2$ is differentiable at $(0, 0)$.

***Solution.*** The increment is

$$\Delta f = f(0 + \Delta x, 0 + \Delta y) - f(0, 0) = (\Delta x)^2 + (\Delta y)^2$$

Since $f_x(x, y) = 2x$ and $f_y(x, y) = 2y$, we have $f_x(0, 0) = f_y(0, 0) = 0$, and (4) becomes

$$\lim_{(\Delta x,\Delta y)\to(0,0)} \frac{(\Delta x)^2 + (\Delta y)^2}{\sqrt{(\Delta x)^2 + (\Delta y)^2}} = \lim_{(\Delta x,\Delta y)\to(0,0)} \sqrt{(\Delta x)^2 + (\Delta y)^2} = 0$$

Therefore, $f$ is differentiable at $(0, 0)$. ◀

We now derive an important consequence of limit (4). Define a function

$$\epsilon = \epsilon(\Delta x, \Delta y) = \frac{\Delta f - f_x(x_0, y_0)\Delta x - f_y(x_0, y_0)\Delta y}{\sqrt{(\Delta x)^2 + (\Delta y)^2}} \quad \text{for } (\Delta x, \Delta y) \neq (0, 0)$$

and define $\epsilon(0, 0)$ to be 0. Equation (4) then implies that

$$\lim_{(\Delta x,\Delta y)\to(0,0)} \epsilon(\Delta x, \Delta y) = 0$$

Furthermore, it immediately follows from the definition of $\epsilon$ that

$$\Delta f = f_x(x_0, y_0)\Delta x + f_y(x_0, y_0)\Delta y + \epsilon(\Delta x, \Delta y)\sqrt{(\Delta x)^2 + (\Delta y)^2} \tag{5}$$

In other words, if $f$ is differentiable at $(x_0, y_0)$, then $\Delta f$ may be expressed as shown in (5), where $\epsilon \to 0$ as $(\Delta x, \Delta y) \to (0, 0)$ and where $\epsilon = 0$ if $(\Delta x, \Delta y) = (0, 0)$.

For functions of three variables we have an analogous definition of differentiability in terms of the increment

$$\Delta f = f(x_0 + \Delta x, y_0 + \Delta y, z_0 + \Delta z) - f(x_0, y_0, z_0)$$

**13.4.2 DEFINITION** A function $f$ of three variables is said to be ***differentiable*** at $(x_0, y_0, z_0)$ provided $f_x(x_0, y_0, z_0)$, $f_y(x_0, y_0, z_0)$, and $f_z(x_0, y_0, z_0)$ exist and

$$\lim_{(\Delta x,\Delta y,\Delta z)\to(0,0,0)} \frac{\Delta f - f_x(x_0, y_0, z_0)\Delta x - f_y(x_0, y_0, z_0)\Delta y - f_z(x_0, y_0, z_0)\Delta z}{\sqrt{(\Delta x)^2 + (\Delta y)^2 + (\Delta z)^2}} = 0 \tag{6}$$

In a manner similar to the two-variable case, we can express the limit (6) in terms of a function $\epsilon(\Delta x, \Delta y, \Delta z)$ that vanishes at $(\Delta x, \Delta y, \Delta z) = (0, 0, 0)$ and is continuous there. The details are left as an exercise for the reader.

If a function $f$ of two variables is differentiable at each point of a region $R$ in the $xy$-plane, then we say that $f$ is ***differentiable on R***; and if $f$ is differentiable at every point in the $xy$-plane, then we say that $f$ is ***differentiable everywhere***. For a function $f$ of three variables we have corresponding conventions.

## DIFFERENTIABILITY AND CONTINUITY

Recall that we want a function to be continuous at every point at which it is differentiable. The next result shows this to be the case.

**13.4.3 THEOREM** *If a function is differentiable at a point, then it is continuous at that point.*

**PROOF** We will give the proof for $f(x, y)$, a function of two variables, since that will reveal the essential ideas. Assume that $f$ is differentiable at $(x_0, y_0)$. To prove that $f$ is continuous at $(x_0, y_0)$ we must show that

$$\lim_{(x,y)\to(x_0,y_0)} f(x, y) = f(x_0, y_0)$$

which, on letting $x = x_0 + \Delta x$ and $y = y_0 + \Delta y$, is equivalent to

$$\lim_{(\Delta x,\Delta y)\to(0,0)} f(x_0 + \Delta x, y_0 + \Delta y) = f(x_0, y_0)$$

By Equation (2) this is equivalent to

$$\lim_{(\Delta x,\Delta y)\to(0,0)} \Delta f = 0$$

However, from Equation (5)

$$\begin{aligned}\lim_{(\Delta x,\Delta y)\to(0,0)} \Delta f &= \lim_{(\Delta x,\Delta y)\to(0,0)} \Big[f_x(x_0, y_0)\Delta x + f_y(x_0, y_0)\Delta y \\ &\qquad + \epsilon(\Delta x, \Delta y)\sqrt{(\Delta x)^2 + (\Delta y)^2}\,\Big] \\ &= 0 + 0 + 0 \cdot 0 = 0 \;\blacksquare\end{aligned}$$

The converse of Theorem 13.4.3 is false. For example, the function

$$f(x, y) = \sqrt{x^2 + y^2}$$

is continuous at $(0, 0)$ but is not differentiable at $(0, 0)$. Why not?

It can be difficult to verify that a function is differentiable at a point directly from the definition. The next theorem, whose proof is usually studied in more advanced courses, provides simple conditions for a function to be differentiable at a point.

**13.4.4 THEOREM** *If all first-order partial derivatives of $f$ exist and are continuous at a point, then $f$ is differentiable at that point.*

For example, consider the function

$$f(x, y, z) = x + yz$$

Since $f_x(x, y, z) = 1$, $f_y(x, y, z) = z$, and $f_z(x, y, z) = y$ are defined and continuous everywhere, we conclude from Theorem 13.4.4 that $f$ is differentiable everywhere.

## DIFFERENTIALS

As with the one-variable case, the approximation

$$\Delta f \approx f_x(x_0, y_0)\Delta x + f_y(x_0, y_0)\Delta y$$

for a function of two variables and the approximation

$$\Delta f \approx f_x(x_0, y_0, z_0)\Delta x + f_y(x_0, y_0, z_0)\Delta y + f_z(x_0, y_0, z_0)\Delta z \tag{7}$$

for a function of three variables have a convenient formulation in the language of differentials. If $z = f(x, y)$ is differentiable at a point $(x_0, y_0)$, we let

$$dz = f_x(x_0, y_0)\,dx + f_y(x_0, y_0)\,dy \tag{8}$$

denote a new function with dependent variable $dz$ and independent variables $dx$ and $dy$. We refer to this function (also denoted $df$) as the ***total differential of*** $z$ at $(x_0, y_0)$ or as the ***total differential of f*** at $(x_0, y_0)$. Similarly, for a function $w = f(x, y, z)$ of three variables we have the ***total differential of w*** at $(x_0, y_0, z_0)$,

$$dw = f_x(x_0, y_0, z_0)\,dx + f_y(x_0, y_0, z_0)\,dy + f_z(x_0, y_0, z_0)\,dz \tag{9}$$

which is also referred to as the ***total differential of f*** at $(x_0, y_0, z_0)$. It is common practice to omit the subscripts and write Equations (8) and (9) as

$$dz = f_x(x, y)\,dx + f_y(x, y)\,dy \tag{10}$$

and

$$dw = f_x(x, y, z)\,dx + f_y(x, y, z)\,dy + f_z(x, y, z)\,dz \tag{11}$$

In the two-variable case, the approximation

$$\Delta f \approx f_x(x_0, y_0)\Delta x + f_y(x_0, y_0)\Delta y$$

can be written in the form

$$\Delta f \approx df \tag{12}$$

for $dx = \Delta x$ and $dy = \Delta y$. Equivalently, we can write approximation (12) as

$$\Delta z \approx dz \tag{13}$$

In other words, we can estimate the change $\Delta z$ in $z$ by the value of the differential $dz$ where $dx$ is the change in $x$ and $dy$ is the change in $y$. Furthermore, it follows from (4) that if $\Delta x$ and $\Delta y$ are close to 0, then the magnitude of the error in approximation (13) will be much smaller than the distance $\sqrt{(\Delta x)^2 + (\Delta y)^2}$ between $(x_0, y_0)$ and $(x_0 + \Delta x, y_0 + \Delta y)$.

▶ **Example 2** Use (13) to approximate the change in $z = xy^2$ from its value at $(0.5, 1.0)$ to its value at $(0.503, 1.004)$. Compare the magnitude of the error in this approximation with the distance between the points $(0.5, 1.0)$ and $(0.503, 1.004)$.

***Solution.*** For $z = xy^2$ we have $dz = y^2\,dx + 2xy\,dy$. Evaluating this differential at $(x, y) = (0.5, 1.0)$, $dx = \Delta x = 0.503 - 0.5 = 0.003$, and $dy = \Delta y = 1.004 - 1.0 = 0.004$ yields

$$dz = 1.0^2(0.003) + 2(0.5)(1.0)(0.004) = 0.007$$

Since $z = 0.5$ at $(x, y) = (0.5, 1.0)$ and $z = 0.507032048$ at $(x, y) = (0.503, 1.004)$, we have

$$\Delta z = 0.507032048 - 0.5 = 0.007032048$$

and the error in approximating $\Delta z$ by $dz$ has magnitude

$$|dz - \Delta z| = |0.007 - 0.007032048| = 0.000032048$$

Since the distance between $(0.5, 1.0)$ and $(0.503, 1.004) = (0.5 + \Delta x, 1.0 + \Delta y)$ is

$$\sqrt{(\Delta x)^2 + (\Delta y)^2} = \sqrt{(0.003)^2 + (0.004)^2} = \sqrt{0.000025} = 0.005$$

we have

$$\frac{|dz - \Delta z|}{\sqrt{(\Delta x)^2 + (\Delta y)^2}} = \frac{0.000032048}{0.005} = 0.0064096 < \frac{1}{150}$$

Thus, the magnitude of the error in our approximation is less than $\frac{1}{150}$ of the distance between the two points. ◀

With the appropriate changes in notation, the preceding analysis can be extended to functions of three or more variables.

▶ **Example 3** The length, width, and height of a rectangular box are measured with an error of at most 5%. Use a total differential to estimate the maximum percentage error that results if these quantities are used to calculate the diagonal of the box.

***Solution.*** The diagonal $D$ of a box with length $x$, width $y$, and height $z$ is given by

$$D = \sqrt{x^2 + y^2 + z^2}$$

Let $x_0$, $y_0$, $z_0$, and $D_0 = \sqrt{x_0^2 + y_0^2 + z_0^2}$ denote the actual values of the length, width, height, and diagonal of the box. The total differential $dD$ of $D$ at $(x_0, y_0, z_0)$ is given by

$$dD = \frac{x_0}{\sqrt{x_0^2 + y_0^2 + z_0^2}}\,dx + \frac{y_0}{\sqrt{x_0^2 + y_0^2 + z_0^2}}\,dy + \frac{z_0}{\sqrt{x_0^2 + y_0^2 + z_0^2}}\,dz$$

If $x$, $y$, $z$, and $D = \sqrt{x^2 + y^2 + z^2}$ are the measured and computed values of the length, width, height, and diagonal, respectively, then

$$\Delta x = x - x_0, \quad \Delta y = y - y_0, \quad \Delta z = z - z_0$$

and

$$\left|\frac{\Delta x}{x_0}\right| \le 0.05, \quad \left|\frac{\Delta y}{y_0}\right| \le 0.05, \quad \left|\frac{\Delta z}{z_0}\right| \le 0.05$$

We are seeking an estimate for the maximum size of $\Delta D/D_0$. With the aid of Equation (11) we have

$$\begin{aligned}\frac{\Delta D}{D_0} \approx \frac{dD}{D_0} &= \frac{1}{x_0^2 + y_0^2 + z_0^2}[x_0\Delta x + y_0\Delta y + z_0\Delta z] \\ &= \frac{1}{x_0^2 + y_0^2 + z_0^2}\left[x_0^2\frac{\Delta x}{x_0} + y_0^2\frac{\Delta y}{y_0} + z_0^2\frac{\Delta z}{z_0}\right]\end{aligned}$$

Since

$$\begin{aligned}\left|\frac{dD}{D_0}\right| &= \frac{1}{x_0^2 + y_0^2 + z_0^2}\left|x_0^2\frac{\Delta x}{x_0} + y_0^2\frac{\Delta y}{y_0} + z_0^2\frac{\Delta z}{z_0}\right| \\ &\le \frac{1}{x_0^2 + y_0^2 + z_0^2}\left(x_0^2\left|\frac{\Delta x}{x_0}\right| + y_0^2\left|\frac{\Delta y}{y_0}\right| + z_0^2\left|\frac{\Delta z}{z_0}\right|\right) \\ &\le \frac{1}{x_0^2 + y_0^2 + z_0^2}\left(x_0^2(0.05) + y_0^2(0.05) + z_0^2(0.05)\right) = 0.05\end{aligned}$$

we estimate the maximum percentage error in $D$ to be 5%. ◀

## LOCAL LINEAR APPROXIMATIONS

We now show that if a function $f$ is differentiable at a point, then it can be very closely approximated by a linear function near that point. For example, suppose that $f(x, y)$ is differentiable at the point $(x_0, y_0)$. Then approximation (3) can be written in the form

$$f(x_0 + \Delta x, y_0 + \Delta y) \approx f(x_0, y_0) + f_x(x_0, y_0)\Delta x + f_y(x_0, y_0)\Delta y$$

If we let $x = x_0 + \Delta x$ and $y = x_0 + \Delta y$, this approximation becomes

$$f(x, y) \approx f(x_0, y_0) + f_x(x_0, y_0)(x - x_0) + f_y(x_0, y_0)(y - y_0) \tag{14}$$

Show that if $f(x, y)$ is a linear function, then (14) becomes an equality.

which yields a linear approximation of $f(x, y)$. Since the error in this approximation is equal to the error in approximation (3), we conclude that for $(x, y)$ close to $(x_0, y_0)$, the error in (14) will be much smaller than the distance between these two points. When $f(x, y)$ is differentiable at $(x_0, y_0)$ we let

Explain why the error in approximation (14) is the same as the error in approximation (3).

$$L(x, y) = f(x_0, y_0) + f_x(x_0, y_0)(x - x_0) + f_y(x_0, y_0)(y - y_0) \tag{15}$$

and refer to $L(x, y)$ as the ***local linear approximation to $f$ at $(x_0, y_0)$***.

▶ **Example 4** Let $L(x, y)$ denote the local linear approximation to $f(x, y) = \sqrt{x^2 + y^2}$ at the point $(3, 4)$. Compare the error in approximating

$$f(3.04, 3.98) = \sqrt{(3.04)^2 + (3.98)^2}$$

by $L(3.04, 3.98)$ with the distance between the points $(3, 4)$ and $(3.04, 3.98)$.

***Solution.*** We have

$$f_x(x, y) = \frac{x}{\sqrt{x^2 + y^2}} \quad \text{and} \quad f_y(x, y) = \frac{y}{\sqrt{x^2 + y^2}}$$

with $f_x(3, 4) = \frac{3}{5}$ and $f_y(3, 4) = \frac{4}{5}$. Therefore, the local linear approximation to $f$ at $(3, 4)$ is given by

$$L(x, y) = 5 + \tfrac{3}{5}(x - 3) + \tfrac{4}{5}(y - 4)$$

Consequently,

$$f(3.04, 3.98) \approx L(3.04, 3.98) = 5 + \tfrac{3}{5}(0.04) + \tfrac{4}{5}(-0.02) = 5.008$$

Since

$$f(3.04, 3.98) = \sqrt{(3.04)^2 + (3.98)^2} \approx 5.00819$$

the error in the approximation is about $5.00819 - 5.008 = 0.00019$. This is less than $\frac{1}{200}$ of the distance

$$\sqrt{(3.04-3)^2 + (3.98-4)^2} \approx 0.045$$

between the points $(3, 4)$ and $(3.04, 3.98)$. ◀

For a function $f(x, y, z)$ that is differentiable at $(x_0, y_0, z_0)$, the local linear approximation is

$$\begin{aligned} L(x, y, z) = f(x_0, y_0, z_0) &+ f_x(x_0, y_0, z_0)(x - x_0) \\ &+ f_y(x_0, y_0, z_0)(y - y_0) + f_z(x_0, y_0, z_0)(z - z_0) \end{aligned} \tag{16}$$

We have formulated our definitions in this section in such a way that continuity and local linearity are consequences of differentiability. In Section 13.7 we will show that if a function $f(x, y)$ is differentiable at a point $(x_0, y_0)$, then the graph of $L(x, y)$ is a nonvertical tangent plane to the graph of $f$ at the point $(x_0, y_0, f(x_0, y_0))$.

## ✓ QUICK CHECK EXERCISES 13.4

(See page 845 for answers.)

1. Assume that $f(x, y)$ is differentiable at $(x_0, y_0)$ and let $\Delta f$ denote the change in $f$ from its value at $(x_0, y_0)$ to its value at $(x_0 + \Delta x, y_0 + \Delta y)$.
   (a) $\Delta f \approx$ ______
   (b) The limit that guarantees the error in the approximation in part (a) is very small when both $\Delta x$ and $\Delta y$ are close to 0 is ______.
2. Compute the differential of each function.
   (a) $z = xe^{y^2}$ (b) $w = x \sin(yz)$
3. If $f$ is differentiable at $(x_0, y_0)$, then the local linear approximation to $f$ at $(x_0, y_0)$ is $L(x) =$ ______.
4. Assume that $f(1, -2) = 4$ and $f(x, y)$ is differentiable at $(1, -2)$ with $f_x(1, -2) = 2$ and $f_y(1, -2) = -3$. Estimate the value of $f(0.9, -1.950)$.

## EXERCISE SET 13.4

**FOCUS ON CONCEPTS**

1. Suppose that a function $f(x, y)$ is differentiable at the point $(3, 4)$ with $f_x(3, 4) = 2$ and $f_y(3, 4) = -1$. If $f(3, 4) = 5$, estimate the value of $f(3.01, 3.98)$.
2. Suppose that a function $f(x, y)$ is differentiable at the point $(-1, 2)$ with $f_x(-1, 2) = 1$ and $f_y(-1, 2) = 3$. If $f(-1, 2) = 2$, estimate the value of $f(-0.99, 2.02)$.
3. Suppose that a function $f(x, y, z)$ is differentiable at the point $(1, 2, 3)$ with $f_x(1, 2, 3) = 1$, $f_y(1, 2, 3) = 2$, and $f_z(1, 2, 3) = 3$. If $f(1, 2, 3) = 4$, estimate the value of $f(1.01, 2.02, 3.03)$.
4. Suppose that a function $f(x, y, z)$ is differentiable at the point $(2, 1, -2)$, $f_x(2, 1, -2) = -1$, $f_y(2, 1, -2) = 1$, and $f_z(2, 1, -2) = -2$. If $f(2, 1, -2) = 0$, estimate the value of $f(1.98, 0.99, -1.97)$.
5. Use Definitions 13.4.1 and 13.4.2 to prove that a constant function of two or three variables is differentiable everywhere.
6. Use Definitions 13.4.1 and 13.4.2 to prove that a linear function of two or three variables is differentiable everywhere.
7. Use Definition 13.4.2 to prove that
$$f(x, y, z) = x^2 + y^2 + z^2$$
is differentiable at $(0, 0, 0)$.
8. Use Definition 13.4.2 to determine all values of $r$ such that $f(x, y, z) = (x^2 + y^2 + z^2)^r$ is differentiable at $(0, 0, 0)$.

**9–20** Compute the differential $dz$ or $dw$ of the function. ■

9. $z = 7x - 2y$
10. $z = e^{xy}$
11. $z = x^3y^2$
12. $z = 5x^2y^5 - 2x + 4y + 7$
13. $z = \tan^{-1} xy$
14. $z = e^{-3x} \cos 6y$
15. $w = 8x - 3y + 4z$
16. $w = e^{xyz}$
17. $w = x^3y^2z$
18. $w = 4x^2y^3z^7 - 3xy + z + 5$
19. $w = \tan^{-1}(xyz)$
20. $w = \sqrt{x} + \sqrt{y} + \sqrt{z}$

**21–26** Use a total differential to approximate the change in the values of $f$ from $P$ to $Q$. Compare your estimate with the actual change in $f$. ■

**21.** $f(x, y) = x^2 + 2xy - 4x$; $P(1, 2)$, $Q(1.01, 2.04)$

**22.** $f(x, y) = x^{1/3}y^{1/2}$; $P(8, 9)$, $Q(7.78, 9.03)$

**23.** $f(x, y) = \dfrac{x+y}{xy}$; $P(-1, -2)$, $Q(-1.02, -2.04)$

**24.** $f(x, y) = \ln\sqrt{1+xy}$; $P(0, 2)$, $Q(-0.09, 1.98)$

**25.** $f(x, y, z) = 2xy^2z^3$; $P(1, -1, 2)$, $Q(0.99, -1.02, 2.02)$

**26.** $f(x, y, z) = \dfrac{xyz}{x+y+z}$; $P(-1, -2, 4)$, $Q(-1.04, -1.98, 3.97)$

**27–30 True–False** Determine whether the statement is true or false. Explain your answer. ■

**27.** By definition, a function $f(x, y)$ is differentiable at $(x_0, y_0)$ provided both $f_x(x_0, y_0)$ and $f_y(x_0, y_0)$ are defined.

**28.** For any point $(x_0, y_0)$ in the domain of a function $f(x, y)$, we have

$$\lim_{(\Delta x, \Delta y)\to(0,0)} \Delta f = 0$$

where

$$\Delta f = f(x_0 + \Delta x, y_0 + \Delta y) - f(x_0, y_0)$$

**29.** If $f_x$ and $f_y$ are both continuous at $(x_0, y_0)$, then so is $f$.

**30.** The graph of a local linear approximation to a function $f(x, y)$ is a plane.

**31.** In the accompanying figure a rectangle with initial length $x_0$ and initial width $y_0$ has been enlarged, resulting in a rectangle with length $x_0 + \Delta x$ and width $y_0 + \Delta y$. What portion of the figure represents the increase in the area of the rectangle? What portion of the figure represents an approximation of the increase in area by a total differential?

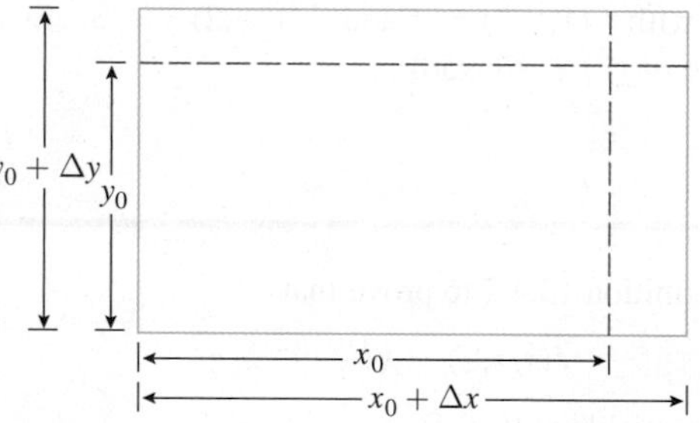


▲ **Figure Ex-31**

**32.** The volume $V$ of a right circular cone of radius $r$ and height $h$ is given by $V = \frac{1}{3}\pi r^2 h$. Suppose that the height decreases from 20 in to 19.95 in and the radius increases from 4 in to 4.05 in. Compare the change in volume of the cone with an approximation of this change using a total differential.

**33–40** (a) Find the local linear approximation $L$ to the specified function $f$ at the designated point $P$. (b) Compare the error in approximating $f$ by $L$ at the specified point $Q$ with the distance between $P$ and $Q$. ■

**33.** $f(x, y) = \dfrac{1}{\sqrt{x^2+y^2}}$; $P(4, 3)$, $Q(3.92, 3.01)$

**34.** $f(x, y) = x^{0.5}y^{0.3}$; $P(1, 1)$, $Q(1.05, 0.97)$

**35.** $f(x, y) = x \sin y$; $P(0, 0)$, $Q(0.003, 0.004)$

**36.** $f(x, y) = \ln xy$; $P(1, 2)$, $Q(1.01, 2.02)$

**37.** $f(x, y, z) = xyz$; $P(1, 2, 3)$, $Q(1.001, 2.002, 3.003)$

**38.** $f(x, y, z) = \dfrac{x+y}{y+z}$; $P(-1, 1, 1)$, $Q(-0.99, 0.99, 1.01)$

**39.** $f(x, y, z) = xe^{yz}$; $P(1, -1, -1)$, $Q(0.99, -1.01, -0.99)$

**40.** $f(x, y, z) = \ln(x + yz)$; $P(2, 1, -1)$, $Q(2.02, 0.97, -1.01)$

**41.** In each part, confirm that the stated formula is the local linear approximation at $(0, 0)$.

(a) $e^x \sin y \approx y$ (b) $\dfrac{2x+1}{y+1} \approx 1 + 2x - y$

**42.** Show that the local linear approximation of the function $f(x, y) = x^\alpha y^\beta$ at $(1, 1)$ is

$$x^\alpha y^\beta \approx 1 + \alpha(x-1) + \beta(y-1)$$

**43.** In each part, confirm that the stated formula is the local linear approximation at $(1, 1, 1)$.

(a) $xyz + 2 \approx x + y + z$ (b) $\dfrac{4x}{y+z} \approx 2x - y - z + 2$

**44.** Based on Exercise 42, what would you conjecture is the local linear approximation to $x^\alpha y^\beta z^\gamma$ at $(1, 1, 1)$? Verify your conjecture by finding this local linear approximation.

**45.** Suppose that a function $f(x, y)$ is differentiable at the point $(1, 1)$ with $f_x(1, 1) = 2$ and $f(1, 1) = 3$. Let $L(x, y)$ denote the local linear approximation of $f$ at $(1, 1)$. If $L(1.1, 0.9) = 3.15$, find the value of $f_y(1, 1)$.

**46.** Suppose that a function $f(x, y)$ is differentiable at the point $(0, -1)$ with $f_y(0, -1) = -2$ and $f(0, -1) = 3$. Let $L(x, y)$ denote the local linear approximation of $f$ at $(0, -1)$. If $L(0.1, -1.1) = 3.3$, find the value of $f_x(0, -1)$.

**47.** Suppose that a function $f(x, y, z)$ is differentiable at the point $(3, 2, 1)$ and $L(x, y, z) = x - y + 2z - 2$ is the local linear approximation to $f$ at $(3, 2, 1)$. Find $f(3, 2, 1)$, $f_x(3, 2, 1)$, $f_y(3, 2, 1)$, and $f_z(3, 2, 1)$.

**48.** Suppose that a function $f(x, y, z)$ is differentiable at the point $(0, -1, -2)$ and $L(x, y, z) = x + 2y + 3z + 4$ is the local linear approximation to $f$ at $(0, -1, -2)$. Find $f(0, -1, -2)$, $f_x(0, -1, -2)$, $f_y(0, -1, -2)$, and $f_z(0, -1, -2)$.

**49–52** A function $f$ is given along with a local linear approximation $L$ to $f$ at a point $P$. Use the information given to determine point $P$. ■

**49.** $f(x, y) = x^2 + y^2$; $L(x, y) = 2y - 2x - 2$

**50.** $f(x, y) = x^2y$; $L(x, y) = 4y - 4x + 8$

**51.** $f(x, y, z) = xy + z^2$; $L(x, y, z) = y + 2z - 1$

**52.** $f(x, y, z) = xyz$; $L(x, y, z) = x - y - z - 2$

**53.** The length and width of a rectangle are measured with errors of at most 3% and 5%, respectively. Use differentials to approximate the maximum percentage error in the calculated area.

**54.** The radius and height of a right circular cone are measured with errors of at most 1% and 4%, respectively. Use differentials to approximate the maximum percentage error in the calculated volume.

**55.** The period $T$ of a simple pendulum with small oscillations is calculated from the formula $T = 2\pi\sqrt{L/g}$, where $L$ is the length of the pendulum and $g$ is the acceleration due to gravity. Suppose that measured values of $L$ and $g$ have errors of at most 0.5% and 0.1%, respectively. Use differentials to approximate the maximum percentage error in the calculated value of $T$.

**56.** The speed of sound $\nu$ in a medium of bulk modulus $B$ and density $\rho$ is
$$\nu = \sqrt{\frac{B}{\rho}}$$
Use a differential to estimate the maximum percentage change in $\nu$ produced by percentage changes in $B$ and $\rho$ of 0.7% and 0.3%, respectively.

**57.** The magnitude $E$ of an electric field at a point outside a charged spherical shell is proportional to the total charge $q$ of the shell and is inversely proportional to the square of the distance $r$ from the point to the center of the shell. Suppose that measured values of $q$ and $r$ have errors of at most 0.2% and 0.5%, respectively. Use differentials to approximate the maximum percentage error in the calculated value of $E$.

**58.** According to the ideal gas law, the pressure, temperature, and volume of a confined gas are related by $P = kT/V$, where $k$ is a constant. Use differentials to approximate the percentage change in pressure if the temperature of a gas is increased 3% and the volume is increased 5%.

**59.** Suppose that certain measured quantities $x$ and $y$ have errors of at most $r$% and $s$%, respectively. For each of the following formulas in $x$ and $y$, use differentials to approximate the maximum possible error in the calculated result.
(a) $xy$ (b) $x/y$ (c) $x^2y^3$ (d) $x^3\sqrt{y}$

**60.** The total resistance $R$ of three resistances $R_1$, $R_2$, and $R_3$, connected in parallel, is given by
$$\frac{1}{R} = \frac{1}{R_1} + \frac{1}{R_2} + \frac{1}{R_3}$$
Suppose that $R_1$, $R_2$, and $R_3$ are measured to be 100 ohms, 200 ohms, and 500 ohms, respectively, with a maximum error of 10% in each. Use differentials to approximate the maximum percentage error in the calculated value of $R$.

**61.** The area of a triangle is to be computed from the formula $A = \frac{1}{2}ab\sin\theta$, where $a$ and $b$ are the lengths of two sides and $\theta$ is the included angle. Suppose that $a$, $b$, and $\theta$ are measured to be 40 ft, 50 ft, and 30°, respectively. Use differentials to approximate the maximum error in the calculated value of $A$ if the maximum errors in $a$, $b$, and $\theta$ are $\frac{1}{2}$ ft, $\frac{1}{4}$ ft, and 2°, respectively.

**62.** The length, width, and height of a rectangular box are measured with errors of at most $r$% (where $r$ is small). Use differentials to approximate the maximum percentage error in the computed value of the volume.

**63.** Use Theorem 13.4.4 to prove that $f(x, y) = x^2 \sin y$ is differentiable everywhere.

**64.** Use Theorem 13.4.4 to prove that $f(x, y, z) = xy \sin z$ is differentiable everywhere.

**65.** Suppose that $f(x, y)$ is differentiable at the point $(x_0, y_0)$ and let $z_0 = f(x_0, y_0)$. Prove that $g(x, y, z) = z - f(x, y)$ is differentiable at $(x_0, y_0, z_0)$.

**66.** Suppose that $\Delta f$ satisfies an equation in the form of (5), where $\epsilon(\Delta x, \Delta y)$ is continuous at $(\Delta x, \Delta y) = (0, 0)$ with $\epsilon(0, 0) = 0$. Prove that $f$ is differentiable at $(x_0, y_0)$.

**67. Writing** Discuss the similarities and differences between the definition of "differentiability" for a function of a single variable and the definition of "differentiability" for a function of two variables.

**68. Writing** Discuss the use of differentials in the approximation of increments and in the estimation of errors.

✓ **QUICK CHECK ANSWERS 13.4** 1. (a) $f_x(x_0, y_0)\Delta x + f_y(x_0, y_0)\Delta y$ (b) $\lim_{(\Delta x,\Delta y)\to(0,0)} \dfrac{\Delta f - f_x(x_0, y_0)\Delta x - f_y(x_0, y_0)\Delta y}{\sqrt{(\Delta x)^2 + (\Delta y)^2}} = 0$
2. (a) $dz = e^{y^2}dx + 2xye^{y^2}dy$ (b) $dw = \sin(yz)\,dx + xz\cos(yz)\,dy + xy\cos(yz)\,dz$ 3. $f(x_0, y_0) + f_x(x_0, y_0)(x - x_0) + f_y(x_0, y_0)(y - y_0)$
4. 3.65

## 13.5 THE CHAIN RULE

*In this section we will derive versions of the chain rule for functions of two or three variables. These new versions will allow us to generate useful relationships among the derivatives and partial derivatives of various functions.*

### CHAIN RULES FOR DERIVATIVES

If $y$ is a differentiable function of $x$ and $x$ is a differentiable function of $t$, then the chain rule for functions of one variable states that, under composition, $y$ becomes a differentiable function of $t$ with
$$\frac{dy}{dt} = \frac{dy}{dx}\frac{dx}{dt}$$

We will now derive a version of the chain rule for functions of two variables.

Assume that $z = f(x, y)$ is a function of $x$ and $y$, and suppose that $x$ and $y$ are in turn functions of a single variable $t$, say

$$x = x(t), \quad y = y(t)$$

The composition $z = f(x(t), y(t))$ then expresses $z$ as a function of the single variable $t$. Thus, we can ask for the derivative $dz/dt$ and we can inquire about its relationship to the derivatives $\partial z/\partial x$, $\partial z/\partial y$, $dx/dt$, and $dy/dt$. Letting $\Delta x$, $\Delta y$, and $\Delta z$ denote the changes in $x, y$, and $z$, respectively, that correspond to a change of $\Delta t$ in $t$, we have

$$\frac{dz}{dt} = \lim_{\Delta t \to 0} \frac{\Delta z}{\Delta t}, \quad \frac{dx}{dt} = \lim_{\Delta t \to 0} \frac{\Delta x}{\Delta t}, \quad \text{and} \quad \frac{dy}{dt} = \lim_{\Delta t \to 0} \frac{\Delta y}{\Delta t}$$

It follows from (3) of Section 13.4 that

$$\Delta z \approx \frac{\partial z}{\partial x}\Delta x + \frac{\partial z}{\partial y}\Delta y \tag{1}$$

where the partial derivatives are evaluated at $(x(t), y(t))$. Dividing both sides of (1) by $\Delta t$ yields

$$\frac{\Delta z}{\Delta t} \approx \frac{\partial z}{\partial x}\frac{\Delta x}{\Delta t} + \frac{\partial z}{\partial y}\frac{\Delta y}{\Delta t} \tag{2}$$

Similarly, we can produce the analog of (2) for functions of three variables as follows: assume that $w = f(x, y, z)$ is a function of $x$, $y$, and $z$, and suppose that $x$, $y$, and $z$ are functions of a single variable $t$. As above we define $\Delta w$, $\Delta x$, $\Delta y$, and $\Delta z$ to be the changes in $w$, $x$, $y$, and $z$ that correspond to a change of $\Delta t$ in $t$. Then (7) in Section 13.4 implies that

$$\Delta w \approx \frac{\partial w}{\partial x}\Delta x + \frac{\partial w}{\partial y}\Delta y + \frac{\partial w}{\partial z}\Delta z \tag{3}$$

and dividing both sides of (3) by $\Delta t$ yields

$$\frac{\Delta w}{\Delta t} \approx \frac{\partial w}{\partial x}\frac{\Delta x}{\Delta t} + \frac{\partial w}{\partial y}\frac{\Delta y}{\Delta t} + \frac{\partial w}{\partial z}\frac{\Delta z}{\Delta t} \tag{4}$$

Taking the limit as $\Delta t \to 0$ of both sides of (2) and (4) suggests the following results. (A complete proof of the two-variable case can be found in Web Appendix L.)

**13.5.1 THEOREM** (***Chain Rules for Derivatives***) *If $x = x(t)$ and $y = y(t)$ are differentiable at $t$, and if $z = f(x, y)$ is differentiable at the point $(x, y) = (x(t), y(t))$, then $z = f(x(t), y(t))$ is differentiable at $t$ and*

$$\frac{dz}{dt} = \frac{\partial z}{\partial x}\frac{dx}{dt} + \frac{\partial z}{\partial y}\frac{dy}{dt} \tag{5}$$

*where the ordinary derivatives are evaluated at $t$ and the partial derivatives are evaluated at $(x, y)$.*

*If each of the functions $x = x(t)$, $y = y(t)$, and $z = z(t)$ is differentiable at $t$, and if $w = f(x, y, z)$ is differentiable at the point $(x, y, z) = (x(t), y(t), z(t))$, then the function $w = f(x(t), y(t), z(t))$ is differentiable at $t$ and*

$$\frac{dw}{dt} = \frac{\partial w}{\partial x}\frac{dx}{dt} + \frac{\partial w}{\partial y}\frac{dy}{dt} + \frac{\partial w}{\partial z}\frac{dz}{dt} \tag{6}$$

*where the ordinary derivatives are evaluated at $t$ and the partial derivatives are evaluated at $(x, y, z)$.*

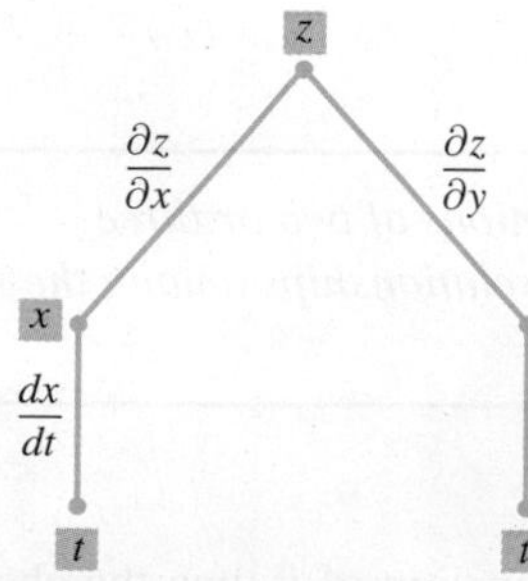


▲ **Figure 13.5.1**

Formula (5) can be represented schematically by a "tree diagram" that is constructed as follows (Figure 13.5.1). Starting with $z$ at the top of the tree and moving downward, join each variable by lines (or branches) to those variables on which it depends *directly*. Thus,

$z$ is joined to $x$ and $y$ and these in turn are joined to $t$. Next, label each branch with a derivative whose "numerator" contains the variable at the top end of that branch and whose "denominator" contains the variable at the bottom end of that branch. This completes the "tree." To find the formula for $dz/dt$, follow the two paths through the tree that start with $z$ and end with $t$. Each such path corresponds to a term in Formula (5).

Create a tree diagram for Formula (6).

**▶ Example 1** Suppose that

$$z = x^2 y, \quad x = t^2, \quad y = t^3$$

Use the chain rule to find $dz/dt$, and check the result by expressing $z$ as a function of $t$ and differentiating directly.

***Solution.*** By the chain rule [Formula (5)],

$$\begin{aligned}\frac{dz}{dt} &= \frac{\partial z}{\partial x}\frac{dx}{dt} + \frac{\partial z}{\partial y}\frac{dy}{dt} = (2xy)(2t) + (x^2)(3t^2)\\ &= (2t^5)(2t) + (t^4)(3t^2) = 7t^6\end{aligned}$$

Alternatively, we can express $z$ directly as a function of $t$,

$$z = x^2 y = (t^2)^2(t^3) = t^7$$

and then differentiate to obtain $dz/dt = 7t^6$. However, this procedure may not always be convenient. ◀

**▶ Example 2** Suppose that

$$w = \sqrt{x^2 + y^2 + z^2}, \quad x = \cos\theta, \quad y = \sin\theta, \quad z = \tan\theta$$

Use the chain rule to find $dw/d\theta$ when $\theta = \pi/4$.

***Solution.*** From Formula (6) with $\theta$ in the place of $t$, we obtain

$$\begin{aligned}\frac{dw}{d\theta} &= \frac{\partial w}{\partial x}\frac{dx}{d\theta} + \frac{\partial w}{\partial y}\frac{dy}{d\theta} + \frac{\partial w}{\partial z}\frac{dz}{d\theta}\\ &= \frac{1}{2}(x^2 + y^2 + z^2)^{-1/2}(2x)(-\sin\theta) + \frac{1}{2}(x^2 + y^2 + z^2)^{-1/2}(2y)(\cos\theta)\\ &\quad + \frac{1}{2}(x^2 + y^2 + z^2)^{-1/2}(2z)(\sec^2\theta)\end{aligned}$$

When $\theta = \pi/4$, we have

$$x = \cos\frac{\pi}{4} = \frac{1}{\sqrt{2}}, \quad y = \sin\frac{\pi}{4} = \frac{1}{\sqrt{2}}, \quad z = \tan\frac{\pi}{4} = 1$$

Confirm the result of Example 2 by expressing $w$ directly as a function of $\theta$.

Substituting $x = 1/\sqrt{2}$, $y = 1/\sqrt{2}$, $z = 1$, $\theta = \pi/4$ in the formula for $dw/d\theta$ yields

$$\begin{aligned}\left.\frac{dw}{d\theta}\right|_{\theta=\pi/4} &= \frac{1}{2}\left(\frac{1}{\sqrt{2}}\right)(\sqrt{2})\left(-\frac{1}{\sqrt{2}}\right) + \frac{1}{2}\left(\frac{1}{\sqrt{2}}\right)(\sqrt{2})\left(\frac{1}{\sqrt{2}}\right) + \frac{1}{2}\left(\frac{1}{\sqrt{2}}\right)(2)(2)\\ &= \sqrt{2} \; ◀\end{aligned}$$

**REMARK** There are many variations in derivative notations, each of which gives the chain rule a different look. If $z = f(x, y)$, where $x$ and $y$ are functions of $t$, then some possibilities are

$$\frac{dz}{dt} = f_x\frac{dx}{dt} + f_y\frac{dy}{dt}$$

$$\frac{df}{dt} = \frac{\partial f}{\partial x}\frac{dx}{dt} + \frac{\partial f}{\partial y}\frac{dy}{dt}$$

$$\frac{df}{dt} = f_x x'(t) + f_y y'(t)$$

## CHAIN RULES FOR PARTIAL DERIVATIVES

In Formula (5) the variables $x$ and $y$ are each functions of a single variable $t$. We now consider the case where $x$ and $y$ are each functions of two variables. Let $z = f(x, y)$ and suppose that $x$ and $y$ are functions of $u$ and $v$, say

$$x = x(u, v), \quad y = y(u, v)$$

The composition $z = f(x(u, v), y(u, v))$ expresses $z$ as a function of the two variables $u$ and $v$. Thus, we can ask for the partial derivatives $\partial z/\partial u$ and $\partial z/\partial v$; and we can inquire about the relationship between these derivatives and the derivatives $\partial z/\partial x$, $\partial z/\partial y$, $\partial x/\partial u$, $\partial x/\partial v$, $\partial y/\partial u$, and $\partial y/\partial v$.

Similarly, if $w = f(x, y, z)$ and $x$, $y$, and $z$ are each functions of $u$ and $v$, then the composition $w = f(x(u, v), y(u, v), z(u, v))$ expresses $w$ as a function of $u$ and $v$. Thus we can also ask for the derivatives $\partial w/\partial u$ and $\partial w/\partial v$; and we can investigate the relationship between these derivatives, the partial derivatives $\partial w/\partial x$, $\partial w/\partial y$, and $\partial w/\partial z$, and the partial derivatives of $x$, $y$, and $z$ with respect to $u$ and $v$.

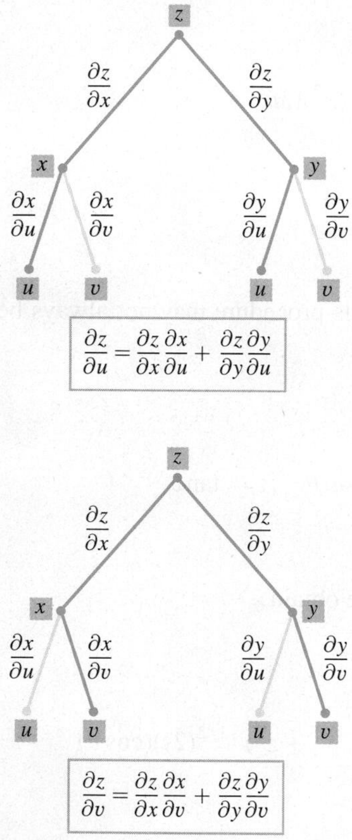


▲ Figure 13.5.2

**13.5.2 THEOREM (*Chain Rules for Partial Derivatives*)** *If $x = x(u, v)$ and $y = y(u, v)$ have first-order partial derivatives at the point $(u, v)$, and if $z = f(x, y)$ is differentiable at the point $(x, y) = (x(u, v), y(u, v))$, then $z = f(x(u, v), y(u, v))$ has first-order partial derivatives at the point $(u, v)$ given by*

$$\frac{\partial z}{\partial u} = \frac{\partial z}{\partial x}\frac{\partial x}{\partial u} + \frac{\partial z}{\partial y}\frac{\partial y}{\partial u} \quad \text{and} \quad \frac{\partial z}{\partial v} = \frac{\partial z}{\partial x}\frac{\partial x}{\partial v} + \frac{\partial z}{\partial y}\frac{\partial y}{\partial v} \tag{7–8}$$

*If each function $x = x(u, v)$, $y = y(u, v)$, and $z = z(u, v)$ has first-order partial derivatives at the point $(u, v)$, and if the function $w = f(x, y, z)$ is differentiable at the point $(x, y, z) = (x(u, v), y(u, v), z(u, v))$, then $w = f(x(u, v), y(u, v), z(u, v))$ has first-order partial derivatives at the point $(u, v)$ given by*

$$\frac{\partial w}{\partial u} = \frac{\partial w}{\partial x}\frac{\partial x}{\partial u} + \frac{\partial w}{\partial y}\frac{\partial y}{\partial u} + \frac{\partial w}{\partial z}\frac{\partial z}{\partial u} \quad \text{and} \quad \frac{\partial w}{\partial v} = \frac{\partial w}{\partial x}\frac{\partial x}{\partial v} + \frac{\partial w}{\partial y}\frac{\partial y}{\partial v} + \frac{\partial w}{\partial z}\frac{\partial z}{\partial v} \tag{9–10}$$

**PROOF** We will prove Formula (7); the other formulas are derived similarly. If $v$ is held fixed, then $x = x(u, v)$ and $y = y(u, v)$ become functions of $u$ alone. Thus, we are back to the case of Theorem 13.5.1. If we apply that theorem with $u$ in place of $t$, and if we use $\partial$ rather than $d$ to indicate that the variable $v$ is fixed, we obtain

$$\frac{\partial z}{\partial u} = \frac{\partial z}{\partial x}\frac{\partial x}{\partial u} + \frac{\partial z}{\partial y}\frac{\partial y}{\partial u} \quad \blacksquare$$

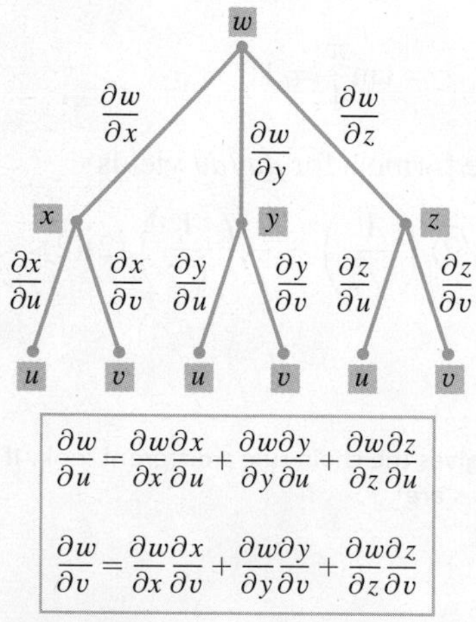


▲ Figure 13.5.3

Figures 13.5.2 and 13.5.3 show tree diagrams for the formulas in Theorem 13.5.2. As illustrated in Figure 13.5.2, the formula for $\partial z/\partial u$ can be obtained by tracing all paths through the tree that start with $z$ and end with $u$, and the formula for $\partial z/\partial v$ can be obtained by tracing all paths through the tree that start with $z$ and end with $v$. Figure 13.5.3 displays analogous results for $\partial w/\partial u$ and $\partial w/\partial v$.

► **Example 3** Given that

$$z = e^{xy}, \quad x = 2u + v, \quad y = u/v$$

find $\partial z/\partial u$ and $\partial z/\partial v$ using the chain rule.

***Solution.***

$$\frac{\partial z}{\partial u} = \frac{\partial z}{\partial x}\frac{\partial x}{\partial u} + \frac{\partial z}{\partial y}\frac{\partial y}{\partial u} = (ye^{xy})(2) + (xe^{xy})\left(\frac{1}{v}\right) = \left[2y + \frac{x}{v}\right]e^{xy}$$

$$= \left[\frac{2u}{v} + \frac{2u+v}{v}\right]e^{(2u+v)(u/v)} = \left[\frac{4u}{v} + 1\right]e^{(2u+v)(u/v)}$$

$$\frac{\partial z}{\partial v} = \frac{\partial z}{\partial x}\frac{\partial x}{\partial v} + \frac{\partial z}{\partial y}\frac{\partial y}{\partial v} = (ye^{xy})(1) + (xe^{xy})\left(-\frac{u}{v^2}\right)$$

$$= \left[y - x\left(\frac{u}{v^2}\right)\right]e^{xy} = \left[\frac{u}{v} - (2u+v)\left(\frac{u}{v^2}\right)\right]e^{(2u+v)(u/v)}$$

$$= -\frac{2u^2}{v^2}e^{(2u+v)(u/v)} \blacktriangleleft$$

▶ **Example 4** Suppose that

$$w = e^{xyz}, \quad x = 3u + v, \quad y = 3u - v, \quad z = u^2 v$$

Use appropriate forms of the chain rule to find $\partial w/\partial u$ and $\partial w/\partial v$.

***Solution.*** From the tree diagram and corresponding formulas in Figure 13.5.3 we obtain

$$\frac{\partial w}{\partial u} = yze^{xyz}(3) + xze^{xyz}(3) + xye^{xyz}(2uv) = e^{xyz}(3yz + 3xz + 2xyuv)$$

and

$$\frac{\partial w}{\partial v} = yze^{xyz}(1) + xze^{xyz}(-1) + xye^{xyz}(u^2) = e^{xyz}(yz - xz + xyu^2)$$

If desired, we can express $\partial w/\partial u$ and $\partial w/\partial v$ in terms of $u$ and $v$ alone by replacing $x, y,$ and $z$ by their expressions in terms of $u$ and $v$. ◀

## OTHER VERSIONS OF THE CHAIN RULE

Although we will not prove it, the chain rule extends to functions $w = f(v_1, v_2, \ldots, v_n)$ of $n$ variables. For example, if each $v_i$ is a function of $t$, $i = 1, 2, \ldots, n$, the relevant formula is

$$\frac{dw}{dt} = \frac{\partial w}{\partial v_1}\frac{dv_1}{dt} + \frac{\partial w}{\partial v_2}\frac{dv_2}{dt} + \cdots + \frac{\partial w}{\partial v_n}\frac{dv_n}{dt} \tag{11}$$

Note that (11) is a natural extension of Formulas (5) and (6) in Theorem 13.5.1.

There are infinitely many variations of the chain rule, depending on the number of variables and the choice of independent and dependent variables. A good working procedure is to use tree diagrams to derive new versions of the chain rule as needed.

▶ **Example 5** Suppose that $w = x^2 + y^2 - z^2$ and

$$x = \rho\sin\phi\cos\theta, \quad y = \rho\sin\phi\sin\theta, \quad z = \rho\cos\phi$$

Use appropriate forms of the chain rule to find $\partial w/\partial \rho$ and $\partial w/\partial \theta$.

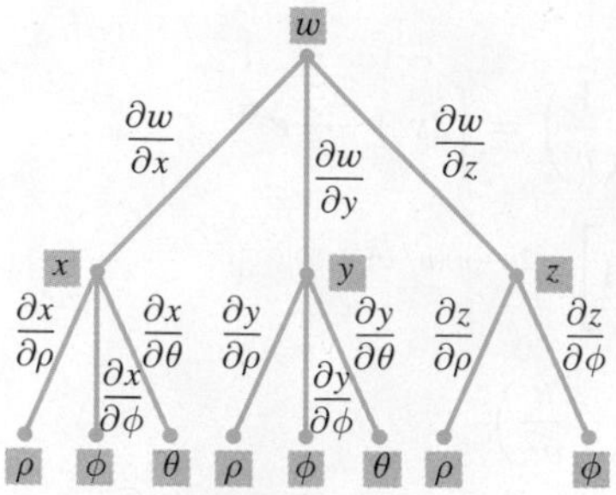


$$\frac{\partial w}{\partial \rho} = \frac{\partial w}{\partial x}\frac{\partial x}{\partial \rho} + \frac{\partial w}{\partial y}\frac{\partial y}{\partial \rho} + \frac{\partial w}{\partial z}\frac{\partial z}{\partial \rho}$$

$$\frac{\partial w}{\partial \theta} = \frac{\partial w}{\partial x}\frac{\partial x}{\partial \theta} + \frac{\partial w}{\partial y}\frac{\partial y}{\partial \theta}$$

▲ **Figure 13.5.4**

***Solution.*** From the tree diagram and corresponding formulas in Figure 13.5.4 we obtain

$$\begin{aligned}
\frac{\partial w}{\partial \rho} &= 2x\sin\phi\cos\theta + 2y\sin\phi\sin\theta - 2z\cos\phi \\
&= 2\rho\sin^2\phi\cos^2\theta + 2\rho\sin^2\phi\sin^2\theta - 2\rho\cos^2\phi \\
&= 2\rho\sin^2\phi(\cos^2\theta + \sin^2\theta) - 2\rho\cos^2\phi \\
&= 2\rho(\sin^2\phi - \cos^2\phi) \\
&= -2\rho\cos 2\phi \\
\frac{\partial w}{\partial \theta} &= (2x)(-\rho\sin\phi\sin\theta) + (2y)\rho\sin\phi\cos\theta \\
&= -2\rho^2\sin^2\phi\sin\theta\cos\theta + 2\rho^2\sin^2\phi\sin\theta\cos\theta \\
&= 0
\end{aligned}$$

This result is explained by the fact that $w$ does not vary with $\theta$. You can see this directly by expressing the variables $x$, $y$, and $z$ in terms of $\rho$, $\phi$, and $\theta$ in the formula for $w$. (Verify that $w = -\rho^2\cos 2\phi$.) ◄

---

► **Example 6** Suppose that

$$w = xy + yz, \quad y = \sin x, \quad z = e^x$$

Use an appropriate form of the chain rule to find $dw/dx$.

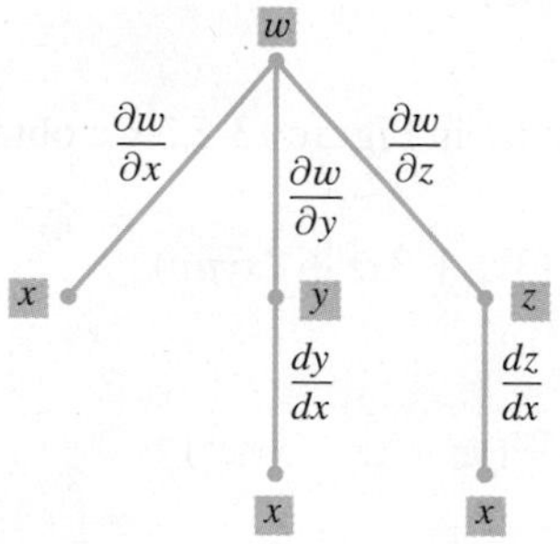


$$\frac{dw}{dx} = \frac{\partial w}{\partial x} + \frac{\partial w}{\partial y}\frac{dy}{dx} + \frac{\partial w}{\partial z}\frac{dz}{dx}$$

▲ **Figure 13.5.5**

***Solution.*** From the tree diagram and corresponding formulas in Figure 13.5.5 we obtain

$$\begin{aligned}
\frac{dw}{dx} &= y + (x+z)\cos x + ye^x \\
&= \sin x + (x + e^x)\cos x + e^x\sin x
\end{aligned}$$

This result can also be obtained by first expressing $w$ explicitly in terms of $x$ as

$$w = x\sin x + e^x\sin x$$

and then differentiating with respect to $x$; however, such direct substitution is not always possible. ◄

**WARNING** The symbol $\partial z$, unlike the differential $dz$, has no meaning of its own. For example, if we were to "cancel" partial symbols in the chain-rule formula

$$\frac{\partial z}{\partial u} = \frac{\partial z}{\partial x}\frac{\partial x}{\partial u} + \frac{\partial z}{\partial y}\frac{\partial y}{\partial u}$$

we would obtain

$$\frac{\partial z}{\partial u} = \frac{\partial z}{\partial u} + \frac{\partial z}{\partial u}$$

which is false in cases where $\partial z/\partial u \neq 0$.

One of the principal uses of the chain rule for functions of a *single* variable was to compute formulas for the derivatives of compositions of functions. Theorems 13.5.1 and 13.5.2 are important not so much for the computation of formulas but because they allow us to express *relationships* among various derivatives. As an illustration, we revisit the topic of implicit differentiation.

## IMPLICIT DIFFERENTIATION

Consider the special case where $z = f(x, y)$ is a function of $x$ and $y$ and $y$ is a differentiable function of $x$. Equation (5) then becomes

$$\frac{dz}{dx} = \frac{\partial f}{\partial x}\frac{dx}{dx} + \frac{\partial f}{\partial y}\frac{dy}{dx} = \frac{\partial f}{\partial x} + \frac{\partial f}{\partial y}\frac{dy}{dx} \tag{12}$$

This result can be used to find derivatives of functions that are defined implicitly. For example, suppose that the equation

$$f(x, y) = c \tag{13}$$

defines $y$ implicitly as a differentiable function of $x$ and we are interested in finding $dy/dx$. Differentiating both sides of (13) with respect to $x$ and applying (12) yields

$$\frac{\partial f}{\partial x} + \frac{\partial f}{\partial y}\frac{dy}{dx} = 0$$

Thus, if $\partial f/\partial y \neq 0$, we obtain

$$\frac{dy}{dx} = -\frac{\partial f/\partial x}{\partial f/\partial y}$$

In summary, we have the following result.

Show that the function $y = x$ is defined implicitly by the equation

$$x^2 - 2xy + y^2 = 0$$

but that Theorem 13.5.3 is not applicable for finding $dy/dx$.

**13.5.3 THEOREM** *If the equation $f(x, y) = c$ defines $y$ implicitly as a differentiable function of $x$, and if $\partial f/\partial y \neq 0$, then*

$$\frac{dy}{dx} = -\frac{\partial f/\partial x}{\partial f/\partial y} \tag{14}$$

▶ **Example 7** Given that

$$x^3 + y^2x - 3 = 0$$

find $dy/dx$ using (14), and check the result using implicit differentiation.

***Solution.*** By (14) with $f(x, y) = x^3 + y^2x - 3$,

$$\frac{dy}{dx} = -\frac{\partial f/\partial x}{\partial f/\partial y} = -\frac{3x^2 + y^2}{2yx}$$

Alternatively, differentiating implicitly yields

$$3x^2 + y^2 + x\left(2y\frac{dy}{dx}\right) - 0 = 0 \quad \text{or} \quad \frac{dy}{dx} = -\frac{3x^2 + y^2}{2yx}$$

which agrees with the result obtained by (14). ◀

The chain rule also applies to implicit partial differentiation. Consider the case where $w = f(x, y, z)$ is a function of $x$, $y$, and $z$ and $z$ is a differentiable function of $x$ and $y$. It follows from Theorem 13.5.2 that

$$\frac{\partial w}{\partial x} = \frac{\partial f}{\partial x} + \frac{\partial f}{\partial z}\frac{\partial z}{\partial x} \tag{15}$$

If the equation

$$f(x, y, z) = c \tag{16}$$

defines $z$ implicitly as a differentiable function of $x$ and $y$, then taking the partial derivative of each side of (16) with respect to $x$ and applying (15) gives

$$\frac{\partial f}{\partial x} + \frac{\partial f}{\partial z}\frac{\partial z}{\partial x} = 0$$

If $\partial f/\partial z \neq 0$, then

$$\frac{\partial z}{\partial x} = -\frac{\partial f/\partial x}{\partial f/\partial z}$$

A similar result holds for $\partial z/\partial y$.

**13.5.4 THEOREM** *If the equation $f(x, y, z) = c$ defines $z$ implicitly as a differentiable function of $x$ and $y$, and if $\partial f/\partial z \neq 0$, then*

$$\frac{\partial z}{\partial x} = -\frac{\partial f/\partial x}{\partial f/\partial z} \quad \textit{and} \quad \frac{\partial z}{\partial y} = -\frac{\partial f/\partial y}{\partial f/\partial z}$$

**▶ Example 8** Consider the sphere $x^2 + y^2 + z^2 = 1$. Find $\partial z/\partial x$ and $\partial z/\partial y$ at the point $\left(\frac{2}{3}, \frac{1}{3}, \frac{2}{3}\right)$.

Note the similarity between the expression for $\partial z/\partial y$ found in Example 8 and that found in Example 7 of Section 13.3.

***Solution.*** By Theorem 13.5.4 with $f(x, y, z) = x^2 + y^2 + z^2$,

$$\frac{\partial z}{\partial x} = -\frac{\partial f/\partial x}{\partial f/\partial z} = -\frac{2x}{2z} = -\frac{x}{z} \quad \text{and} \quad \frac{\partial z}{\partial y} = -\frac{\partial f/\partial y}{\partial f/\partial z} = -\frac{2y}{2z} = -\frac{y}{z}$$

At the point $\left(\frac{2}{3}, \frac{1}{3}, \frac{2}{3}\right)$, evaluating these derivatives gives $\partial z/\partial x = -1$ and $\partial z/\partial y = -\frac{1}{2}$. ◀

## ✓ QUICK CHECK EXERCISES 13.5 *(See page 855 for answers.)*

**1.** Suppose that $z = xy^2$ and $x$ and $y$ are differentiable functions of $t$ with $x = 1$, $y = -1$, $dx/dt = -2$, and $dy/dt = 3$ when $t = -1$. Then $dz/dt =$ ______ when $t = -1$.

**2.** Suppose that $C$ is the graph of the equation $f(x, y) = 1$ and that this equation defines $y$ implicitly as a differentiable function of $x$. If the point $(2, 1)$ belongs to $C$ with $f_x(2, 1) = 3$ and $f_y(2, 1) = -1$, then the tangent line to $C$ at the point $(2, 1)$ has slope ______.

**3.** A rectangle is growing in such a way that when its length is 5 ft and its width is 2 ft, the length is increasing at a rate of 3 ft/s and its width is increasing at a rate of 4 ft/s. At this instant the area of the rectangle is growing at a rate of ______.

**4.** Suppose that $z = x/y$, where $x$ and $y$ are differentiable functions of $u$ and $v$ such that $x = 3$, $y = 1$, $\partial x/\partial u = 4$, $\partial x/\partial v = -2$, $\partial y/\partial u = 1$, and $\partial y/\partial v = -1$ when $u = 2$ and $v = 1$. When $u = 2$ and $v = 1$, $\partial z/\partial u =$ ______ and $\partial z/\partial v =$ ______.

## EXERCISE SET 13.5

**1–6** Use an appropriate form of the chain rule to find $dz/dt$. ■

**1.** $z = 3x^2y^3$; $x = t^4$, $y = t^2$

**2.** $z = \ln(2x^2 + y)$; $x = \sqrt{t}$, $y = t^{2/3}$

**3.** $z = 3\cos x - \sin xy$; $x = 1/t$, $y = 3t$

**4.** $z = \sqrt{1 + x - 2xy^4}$; $x = \ln t$, $y = t$

**5.** $z = e^{1-xy}$; $x = t^{1/3}$, $y = t^3$

**6.** $z = \cosh^2 xy$; $x = t/2$, $y = e^t$

**7–10** Use an appropriate form of the chain rule to find $dw/dt$. ■

**7.** $w = 5x^2y^3z^4$; $x = t^2$, $y = t^3$, $z = t^5$

**8.** $w = \ln(3x^2 - 2y + 4z^3)$; $x = t^{1/2}$, $y = t^{2/3}$, $z = t^{-2}$

**9.** $w = 5\cos xy - \sin xz$; $x = 1/t$, $y = t$, $z = t^3$

**10.** $w = \sqrt{1 + x - 2yz^4x}$; $x = \ln t$, $y = t$, $z = 4t$

**FOCUS ON CONCEPTS**

**11.** Suppose that

$$w = x^3y^2z^4; \quad x = t^2, \quad y = t + 2, \quad z = 2t^4$$

Find the rate of change of $w$ with respect to $t$ at $t = 1$ by using the chain rule, and then check your work by expressing $w$ as a function of $t$ and differentiating.

**12.** Suppose that

$$w = x\sin yz^2; \quad x = \cos t, \quad y = t^2, \quad z = e^t$$

Find the rate of change of $w$ with respect to $t$ at $t = 0$ by using the chain rule, and then check your work by expressing $w$ as a function of $t$ and differentiating.

**13.** Suppose that $z = f(x, y)$ is differentiable at the point $(4, 8)$ with $f_x(4, 8) = 3$ and $f_y(4, 8) = -1$. If $x = t^2$ and $y = t^3$, find $dz/dt$ when $t = 2$.

14. Suppose that $w = f(x, y, z)$ is differentiable at the point $(1, 0, 2)$ with $f_x(1, 0, 2) = 1$, $f_y(1, 0, 2) = 2$, and $f_z(1, 0, 2) = 3$. If $x = t$, $y = \sin(\pi t)$, and $z = t^2 + 1$, find $dw/dt$ when $t = 1$.

15. Explain how the product rule for functions of a single variable may be viewed as a consequence of the chain rule applied to a particular function of two variables.

16. A student attempts to differentiate the function $x^x$ using the power rule, mistakenly getting $x \cdot x^{x-1}$. A second student attempts to differentiate $x^x$ by treating it as an exponential function, mistakenly getting $(\ln x)x^x$. Use the chain rule to explain why the correct derivative is the sum of these two incorrect results.

**17–22** Use appropriate forms of the chain rule to find $\partial z/\partial u$ and $\partial z/\partial v$. ■

17. $z = 8x^2y - 2x + 3y$; $x = uv$, $y = u - v$

18. $z = x^2 - y \tan x$; $x = u/v$, $y = u^2v^2$

19. $z = x/y$; $x = 2 \cos u$, $y = 3 \sin v$

20. $z = 3x - 2y$; $x = u + v \ln u$, $y = u^2 - v \ln v$

21. $z = e^{x^2 y}$; $x = \sqrt{uv}$, $y = 1/v$

22. $z = \cos x \sin y$; $x = u - v$, $y = u^2 + v^2$

**23–30** Use appropriate forms of the chain rule to find the derivatives. ■

23. Let $T = x^2y - xy^3 + 2$; $x = r \cos \theta$, $y = r \sin \theta$. Find $\partial T/\partial r$ and $\partial T/\partial \theta$.

24. Let $R = e^{2s - t^2}$; $s = 3\phi$, $t = \phi^{1/2}$. Find $dR/d\phi$.

25. Let $t = u/v$; $u = x^2 - y^2$, $v = 4xy^3$. Find $\partial t/\partial x$ and $\partial t/\partial y$.

26. Let $w = rs/(r^2 + s^2)$; $r = uv$, $s = u - 2v$. Find $\partial w/\partial u$ and $\partial w/\partial v$.

27. Let $z = \ln(x^2 + 1)$, where $x = r \cos \theta$. Find $\partial z/\partial r$ and $\partial z/\partial \theta$.

28. Let $u = rs^2 \ln t$, $r = x^2$, $s = 4y + 1$, $t = xy^3$. Find $\partial u/\partial x$ and $\partial u/\partial y$.

29. Let $w = 4x^2 + 4y^2 + z^2$, $x = \rho \sin \phi \cos \theta$, $y = \rho \sin \phi \sin \theta$, $z = \rho \cos \phi$. Find $\partial w/\partial \rho$, $\partial w/\partial \phi$, and $\partial w/\partial \theta$.

30. Let $w = 3xy^2z^3$, $y = 3x^2 + 2$, $z = \sqrt{x - 1}$. Find $dw/dx$.

31. Use a chain rule to find the value of $\left.\dfrac{dw}{ds}\right|_{s=1/4}$ if

$w = r^2 - r \tan \theta$; $r = \sqrt{s}$, $\theta = \pi s$.

32. Use a chain rule to find the values of

$$\left.\frac{\partial f}{\partial u}\right|_{u=1, v=-2} \quad \text{and} \quad \left.\frac{\partial f}{\partial v}\right|_{u=1, v=-2}$$

if $f(x, y) = x^2y^2 - x + 2y$; $x = \sqrt{u}$, $y = uv^3$.

33. Use a chain rule to find the values of

$$\left.\frac{\partial z}{\partial r}\right|_{r=2, \theta=\pi/6} \quad \text{and} \quad \left.\frac{\partial z}{\partial \theta}\right|_{r=2, \theta=\pi/6}$$

if $z = xye^{x/y}$; $x = r \cos \theta$, $y = r \sin \theta$.

34. Use a chain rule to find $\left.\dfrac{dz}{dt}\right|_{t=3}$ if $z = x^2y$; $x = t^2$, $y = t + 7$.

35. Let $a$ and $b$ denote two sides of a triangle and let $\theta$ denote the included angle. Suppose that $a$, $b$, and $\theta$ vary with time in such a way that the area of the triangle remains constant. At a certain instant $a = 5$ cm, $b = 4$ cm, and $\theta = \pi/6$ radians, and at that instant both $a$ and $b$ are increasing at a rate of 3 cm/s. Estimate the rate at which $\theta$ is changing at that instant.

36. The voltage, $V$ (in volts), across a circuit is given by Ohm's law: $V = IR$, where $I$ is the current (in amperes) flowing through the circuit and $R$ is the resistance (in ohms). If two circuits with resistances $R_1$ and $R_2$ are connected in parallel, then their combined resistance, $R$, is given by

$$\frac{1}{R} = \frac{1}{R_1} + \frac{1}{R_2}$$

Suppose that the current is 3 amperes and is increasing at $10^{-2}$ ampere/s, $R_1$ is 2 ohms and is increasing at 0.4 ohm/s, and $R_2$ is 5 ohms and is decreasing at 0.7 ohm/s. Estimate the rate at which the voltage is changing.

**37–40 True–False** Determine whether the statement is true or false. Explain your answer. ■

37. The symbols $\partial z$ and $\partial x$ are defined in such a way that the partial derivative $\partial z/\partial x$ can be interpreted as a ratio.

38. If $z$ is a differentiable function of $x_1, x_2$, and $x_3$, and if $x_i$ is a differentiable function of $t$ for $i = 1, 2, 3$, then $z$ is a differentiable function of $t$ and

$$\frac{dz}{dt} = \sum_{i=1}^{3} \frac{\partial z}{\partial x_i}\frac{dx_i}{dt}$$

39. If $z$ is a differentiable function of $x$ and $y$, and if $x$ and $y$ are twice differentiable functions of $t$, then $z$ is a twice differentiable function of $t$ and

$$\frac{d^2z}{dt^2} = \frac{\partial z}{\partial x}\frac{d^2x}{dt^2} + \frac{\partial z}{\partial y}\frac{d^2y}{dt^2}$$

40. If $f(x, y)$ is a differentiable function of $x$ and $y$, and if the line $y = x$ is a contour of $f$, then $f_y(t, t) = -f_x(t, t)$ for all real numbers $t$.

**41–44** Use Theorem 13.5.3 to find $dy/dx$ and check your result using implicit differentiation. ■

41. $x^2y^3 + \cos y = 0$

42. $x^3 - 3xy^2 + y^3 = 5$

43. $e^{xy} + ye^y = 1$

44. $x - \sqrt{xy} + 3y = 4$

**45–48** Find $\partial z/\partial x$ and $\partial z/\partial y$ by implicit differentiation, and confirm that the results obtained agree with those predicted by the formulas in Theorem 13.5.4. ■

45. $x^2 - 3yz^2 + xyz - 2 = 0$

46. $\ln(1 + z) + xy^2 + z = 1$

47. $ye^x - 5 \sin 3z = 3z$

48. $e^{xy} \cos yz - e^{yz} \sin xz + 2 = 0$

49. (a) Suppose that $z = f(u)$ and $u = g(x, y)$. Draw a tree diagram, and use it to construct chain rules that express $\partial z/\partial x$ and $\partial z/\partial y$ in terms of $dz/du$, $\partial u/\partial x$, and $\partial u/\partial y$.

(b) Show that

$$\frac{\partial^2 z}{\partial x^2} = \frac{dz}{du}\frac{\partial^2 u}{\partial x^2} + \frac{d^2 z}{du^2}\left(\frac{\partial u}{\partial x}\right)^2$$

$$\frac{\partial^2 z}{\partial y^2} = \frac{dz}{du}\frac{\partial^2 u}{\partial y^2} + \frac{d^2 z}{du^2}\left(\frac{\partial u}{\partial y}\right)^2$$

$$\frac{\partial^2 z}{\partial y \partial x} = \frac{dz}{du}\frac{\partial^2 u}{\partial y \partial x} + \frac{d^2 z}{du^2}\frac{\partial u}{\partial x}\frac{\partial u}{\partial y}$$

**50.** (a) Let $z = f(x^2 - y^2)$. Use the result in Exercise 49(a) to show that

$$y\frac{\partial z}{\partial x} + x\frac{\partial z}{\partial y} = 0$$

(b) Let $z = f(xy)$. Use the result in Exercise 49(a) to show that

$$x\frac{\partial z}{\partial x} - y\frac{\partial z}{\partial y} = 0$$

(c) Confirm the result in part (a) in the case where $z = \sin(x^2 - y^2)$.

(d) Confirm the result in part (b) in the case where $z = e^{xy}$.

**51.** Let $f$ be a differentiable function of one variable, and let $z = f(x + 2y)$. Show that

$$2\frac{\partial z}{\partial x} - \frac{\partial z}{\partial y} = 0$$

**52.** Let $f$ be a differentiable function of one variable, and let $z = f(x^2 + y^2)$. Show that

$$y\frac{\partial z}{\partial x} - x\frac{\partial z}{\partial y} = 0$$

**53.** Let $f$ be a differentiable function of one variable, and let $w = f(u)$, where $u = x + 2y + 3z$. Show that

$$\frac{\partial w}{\partial x} + \frac{\partial w}{\partial y} + \frac{\partial w}{\partial z} = 6\frac{dw}{du}$$

**54.** Let $f$ be a differentiable function of one variable, and let $w = f(\rho)$, where $\rho = (x^2 + y^2 + z^2)^{1/2}$. Show that

$$\left(\frac{\partial w}{\partial x}\right)^2 + \left(\frac{\partial w}{\partial y}\right)^2 + \left(\frac{\partial w}{\partial z}\right)^2 = \left(\frac{dw}{d\rho}\right)^2$$

**55.** Let $z = f(x - y, y - x)$. Show that $\partial z/\partial x + \partial z/\partial y = 0$.

**56.** Let $f$ be a differentiable function of three variables and suppose that $w = f(x - y, y - z, z - x)$. Show that

$$\frac{\partial w}{\partial x} + \frac{\partial w}{\partial y} + \frac{\partial w}{\partial z} = 0$$

**57.** Suppose that the equation $z = f(x, y)$ is expressed in the polar form $z = g(r, \theta)$ by making the substitution $x = r\cos\theta$ and $y = r\sin\theta$.

(a) View $r$ and $\theta$ as functions of $x$ and $y$ and use implicit differentiation to show that

$$\frac{\partial r}{\partial x} = \cos\theta \quad \text{and} \quad \frac{\partial \theta}{\partial x} = -\frac{\sin\theta}{r}$$

(b) View $r$ and $\theta$ as functions of $x$ and $y$ and use implicit differentiation to show that

$$\frac{\partial r}{\partial y} = \sin\theta \quad \text{and} \quad \frac{\partial \theta}{\partial y} = \frac{\cos\theta}{r}$$

(c) Use the results in parts (a) and (b) to show that

$$\frac{\partial z}{\partial x} = \frac{\partial z}{\partial r}\cos\theta - \frac{1}{r}\frac{\partial z}{\partial \theta}\sin\theta$$

$$\frac{\partial z}{\partial y} = \frac{\partial z}{\partial r}\sin\theta + \frac{1}{r}\frac{\partial z}{\partial \theta}\cos\theta$$

(d) Use the result in part (c) to show that

$$\left(\frac{\partial z}{\partial x}\right)^2 + \left(\frac{\partial z}{\partial y}\right)^2 = \left(\frac{\partial z}{\partial r}\right)^2 + \frac{1}{r^2}\left(\frac{\partial z}{\partial \theta}\right)^2$$

(e) Use the result in part (c) to show that if $z = f(x, y)$ satisfies Laplace's equation

$$\frac{\partial^2 z}{\partial x^2} + \frac{\partial^2 z}{\partial y^2} = 0$$

then $z = g(r, \theta)$ satisfies the equation

$$\frac{\partial^2 z}{\partial r^2} + \frac{1}{r^2}\frac{\partial^2 z}{\partial \theta^2} + \frac{1}{r}\frac{\partial z}{\partial r} = 0$$

and conversely. The latter equation is called the ***polar form of Laplace's equation***.

**58.** Show that the function

$$z = \tan^{-1}\frac{2xy}{x^2 - y^2}$$

satisfies Laplace's equation; then make the substitution $x = r\cos\theta$, $y = r\sin\theta$, and show that the resulting function of $r$ and $\theta$ satisfies the polar form of Laplace's equation given in part (e) of Exercise 57.

**59.** (a) Show that if $u(x, y)$ and $v(x, y)$ satisfy the Cauchy–Riemann equations (Exercise 104, Section 13.3), and if $x = r\cos\theta$ and $y = r\sin\theta$, then

$$\frac{\partial u}{\partial r} = \frac{1}{r}\frac{\partial v}{\partial \theta} \quad \text{and} \quad \frac{\partial v}{\partial r} = -\frac{1}{r}\frac{\partial u}{\partial \theta}$$

This is called the ***polar form of the Cauchy–Riemann equations***.

(b) Show that the functions

$$u = \ln(x^2 + y^2), \quad v = 2\tan^{-1}(y/x)$$

satisfy the Cauchy–Riemann equations; then make the substitution $x = r\cos\theta$, $y = r\sin\theta$, and show that the resulting functions of $r$ and $\theta$ satisfy the polar form of the Cauchy–Riemann equations.

**60.** Recall from Formula (6) of Section 13.3 that under appropriate conditions a plucked string satisfies the wave equation

$$\frac{\partial^2 u}{\partial t^2} = c^2\frac{\partial^2 u}{\partial x^2}$$

where $c$ is a positive constant.

(a) Show that a function of the form $u(x, t) = f(x + ct)$ satisfies the wave equation.

(b) Show that a function of the form $u(x, t) = g(x - ct)$ satisfies the wave equation.

(c) Show that a function of the form

$$u(x, t) = f(x + ct) + g(x - ct)$$

satisfies the wave equation.

(d) It can be proved that every solution of the wave equation is expressible in the form stated in part (c). Confirm that $u(x, t) = \sin t \sin x$ satisfies the wave equation in which $c = 1$, and then use appropriate trigonometric identities to express this function in the form $f(x + t) + g(x - t)$.

**61.** Let $f$ be a differentiable function of three variables, and let $w = f(x, y, z)$, $x = \rho\sin\phi\cos\theta$, $y = \rho\sin\phi\sin\theta$, and $z = \rho\cos\phi$. Express $\partial w/\partial \rho$, $\partial w/\partial \phi$, and $\partial w/\partial \theta$ in terms of $\partial w/\partial x$, $\partial w/\partial y$, and $\partial w/\partial z$.

**62.** Let $w = f(x, y, z)$ be differentiable, where $z = g(x, y)$. Taking $x$ and $y$ as the independent variables, express each of the following in terms of $\partial f/\partial x$, $\partial f/\partial y$, $\partial f/\partial z$, $\partial z/\partial x$, and $\partial z/\partial y$.
(a) $\partial w/\partial x$ (b) $\partial w/\partial y$

**63.** Let $w = \ln(e^r + e^s + e^t + e^u)$. Show that
$$w_{rstu} = -6e^{r+s+t+u-4w}$$
[*Hint:* Take advantage of the relationship $e^w = e^r + e^s + e^t + e^u$.]

**64.** Suppose that $w$ is a differentiable function of $x_1$, $x_2$, and $x_3$, and
$$x_1 = a_1y_1 + b_1y_2$$
$$x_2 = a_2y_1 + b_2y_2$$
$$x_3 = a_3y_1 + b_3y_2$$
where the $a$'s and $b$'s are constants. Express $\partial w/\partial y_1$ and $\partial w/\partial y_2$ in terms of $\partial w/\partial x_1$, $\partial w/\partial x_2$, and $\partial w/\partial x_3$.

**65.** (a) Let $w$ be a differentiable function of $x_1$, $x_2$, $x_3$, and $x_4$, and let each $x_i$ be a differentiable function of $t$. Find a chain-rule formula for $dw/dt$.
(b) Let $w$ be a differentiable function of $x_1$, $x_2$, $x_3$, and $x_4$, and let each $x_i$ be a differentiable function of $v_1$, $v_2$, and $v_3$. Find chain-rule formulas for $\partial w/\partial v_1$, $\partial w/\partial v_2$, and $\partial w/\partial v_3$.

**66.** Let $w = (x_1^2 + x_2^2 + \cdots + x_n^2)^k$, where $n \geq 2$. For what values of $k$ does
$$\frac{\partial^2 w}{\partial x_1^2} + \frac{\partial^2 w}{\partial x_2^2} + \cdots + \frac{\partial^2 w}{\partial x_n^2} = 0$$
hold?

**67.** Derive the identity
$$\frac{d}{dx}\int_{h(x)}^{g(x)} f(t)\,dt = f(g(x))g'(x) - f(h(x))h'(x)$$
by letting $u = g(x)$ and $v = h(x)$ and then differentiating the function
$$F(u, v) = \int_v^u f(t)\,dt$$
with respect to $x$.

**68.** Prove: If $f$, $f_x$, and $f_y$ are continuous on a circular region containing $A(x_0, y_0)$ and $B(x_1, y_1)$, then there is a point $(x^*, y^*)$ on the line segment joining $A$ and $B$ such that
$$f(x_1, y_1) - f(x_0, y_0) = f_x(x^*, y^*)(x_1 - x_0) + f_y(x^*, y^*)(y_1 - y_0)$$
This result is the two-dimensional version of the Mean-Value Theorem. [*Hint:* Express the line segment joining $A$ and $B$ in parametric form and use the Mean-Value Theorem for functions of one variable.]

**69.** Prove: If $f_x(x, y) = 0$ and $f_y(x, y) = 0$ throughout a circular region, then $f(x, y)$ is constant on that region. [*Hint:* Use the result of Exercise 68.]

**70. Writing** Use differentials to give an informal justification for the chain rules for derivatives.

**71. Writing** Compare the use of the formula
$$\frac{dy}{dx} = -\frac{\partial f/\partial x}{\partial f/\partial y}$$
with the process of implicit differentiation.

✓ **QUICK CHECK ANSWERS 13.5** 1. −8 2. 3 3. 26 ft²/s 4. 1; 1

## 13.6 DIRECTIONAL DERIVATIVES AND GRADIENTS

*The partial derivatives $f_x(x, y)$ and $f_y(x, y)$ represent the rates of change of $f(x, y)$ in directions parallel to the x- and y-axes. In this section we will investigate rates of change of $f(x, y)$ in other directions.*

### DIRECTIONAL DERIVATIVES

In this section we extend the concept of a *partial* derivative to the more general notion of a *directional* derivative. We have seen that the partial derivatives of a function give the instantaneous rates of change of that function in directions parallel to the coordinate axes. Directional derivatives allow us to compute the rates of change of a function with respect to distance in *any* direction.

Suppose that we wish to compute the instantaneous rate of change of a function $f(x, y)$ with respect to distance from a point $(x_0, y_0)$ in some direction. Since there are infinitely many different directions from $(x_0, y_0)$ in which we could move, we need a convenient method for describing a specific direction starting at $(x_0, y_0)$. One way to do this is to use a unit vector
$$\mathbf{u} = u_1\mathbf{i} + u_2\mathbf{j}$$
that has its initial point at $(x_0, y_0)$ and points in the desired direction (Figure 13.6.1). This vector determines a line $l$ in the $xy$-plane that can be expressed parametrically as
$$x = x_0 + su_1, \quad y = y_0 + su_2 \tag{1}$$

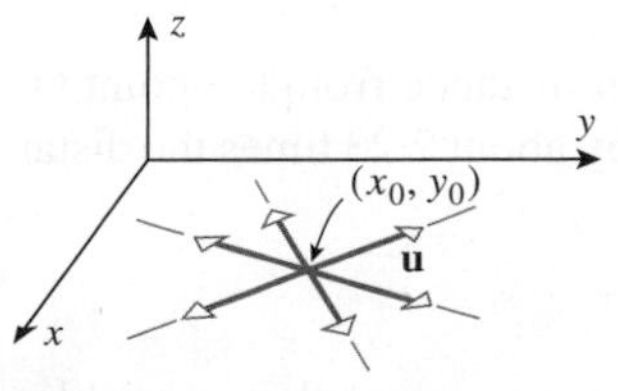

▲ **Figure 13.6.1**

Since $u$ is a unit vector, $s$ is the arc length parameter that has its reference point at $(x_0, y_0)$ and has positive values in the direction of $\mathbf{u}$. For $s = 0$, the point $(x, y)$ is at the reference point $(x_0, y_0)$, and as $s$ increases, the point $(x, y)$ moves along $l$ in the direction of $\mathbf{u}$. On the line $l$ the variable $z = f(x_0 + su_1, y_0 + su_2)$ is a function of the parameter $s$. The value of the derivative $dz/ds$ at $s = 0$ then gives an instantaneous rate of change of $f(x, y)$ with respect to distance from $(x_0, y_0)$ in the direction of $\mathbf{u}$.

**13.6.1 DEFINITION** If $f(x, y)$ is a function of $x$ and $y$, and if $\mathbf{u} = u_1\mathbf{i} + u_2\mathbf{j}$ is a unit vector, then the ***directional derivative of f in the direction of*** $\mathbf{u}$ at $(x_0, y_0)$ is denoted by $D_{\mathbf{u}}f(x_0, y_0)$ and is defined by

$$D_{\mathbf{u}}f(x_0, y_0) = \frac{d}{ds}\left[f(x_0 + su_1, y_0 + su_2)\right]_{s=0} \tag{2}$$

provided this derivative exists.

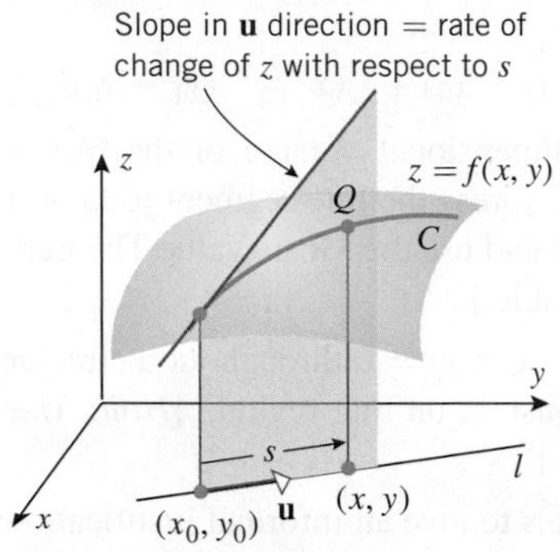


▲ Figure 13.6.2

Geometrically, $D_{\mathbf{u}}f(x_0, y_0)$ can be interpreted as the ***slope of the surface*** $z = f(x, y)$ ***in the direction of*** $\mathbf{u}$ at the point $(x_0, y_0, f(x_0, y_0))$ (Figure 13.6.2). Usually the value of $D_{\mathbf{u}}f(x_0, y_0)$ will depend on both the point $(x_0, y_0)$ and the direction $\mathbf{u}$. Thus, at a fixed point the slope of the surface may vary with the direction (Figure 13.6.3). Analytically, the directional derivative represents the ***instantaneous rate of change of f(x, y) with respect to distance in the direction of*** $\mathbf{u}$ at the point $(x_0, y_0)$.

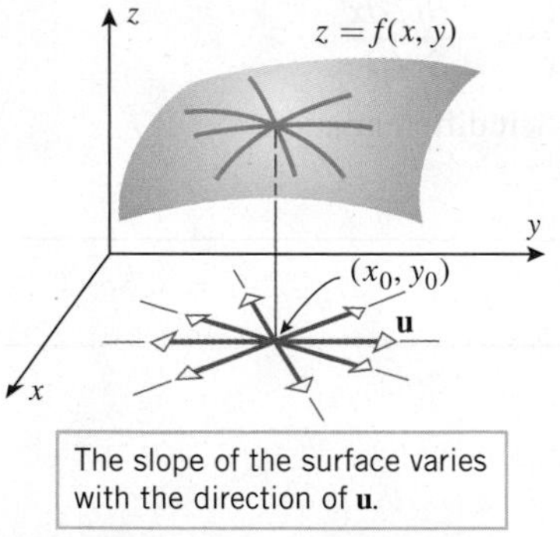


▲ Figure 13.6.3

► **Example 1** Let $f(x, y) = xy$. Find and interpret $D_{\mathbf{u}}f(1, 2)$ for the unit vector

$$\mathbf{u} = \frac{\sqrt{3}}{2}\mathbf{i} + \frac{1}{2}\mathbf{j}$$

***Solution.*** It follows from Equation (2) that

$$D_{\mathbf{u}}f(1, 2) = \frac{d}{ds}\left[f\left(1 + \frac{\sqrt{3}s}{2}, 2 + \frac{s}{2}\right)\right]_{s=0}$$

Since

$$f\left(1 + \frac{\sqrt{3}s}{2}, 2 + \frac{s}{2}\right) = \left(1 + \frac{\sqrt{3}s}{2}\right)\left(2 + \frac{s}{2}\right) = \frac{\sqrt{3}}{4}s^2 + \left(\frac{1}{2} + \sqrt{3}\right)s + 2$$

we have

$$D_{\mathbf{u}}f(1, 2) = \frac{d}{ds}\left[\frac{\sqrt{3}}{4}s^2 + \left(\frac{1}{2} + \sqrt{3}\right)s + 2\right]_{s=0}$$

$$= \left[\frac{\sqrt{3}}{2}s + \frac{1}{2} + \sqrt{3}\right]_{s=0} = \frac{1}{2} + \sqrt{3}$$

Since $\frac{1}{2} + \sqrt{3} \approx 2.23$, we conclude that if we move a small distance from the point $(1, 2)$ in the direction of $\mathbf{u}$, the function $f(x, y) = xy$ will increase by about 2.23 times the distance moved. ◄

The definition of a directional derivative for a function $f(x, y, z)$ of three variables is similar to Definition 13.6.1.

**13.6.2 DEFINITION** If $\mathbf{u} = u_1\mathbf{i} + u_2\mathbf{j} + u_3\mathbf{k}$ is a unit vector, and if $f(x, y, z)$ is a function of $x$, $y$, and $z$, then the ***directional derivative of f in the direction of*** $\mathbf{u}$ at $(x_0, y_0, z_0)$ is denoted by $D_{\mathbf{u}}f(x_0, y_0, z_0)$ and is defined by

$$D_{\mathbf{u}}f(x_0, y_0, z_0) = \frac{d}{ds}\left[f(x_0 + su_1, y_0 + su_2, z_0 + su_3)\right]_{s=0} \tag{3}$$

provided this derivative exists.

Although Equation (3) does not have a convenient geometric interpretation, we can still interpret directional derivatives for functions of three variables in terms of instantaneous rates of change in a specified direction.

For a function that is differentiable at a point, directional derivatives exist in every direction from the point and can be computed directly in terms of the first-order partial derivatives of the function.

**13.6.3 THEOREM**

(*a*) *If $f(x, y)$ is differentiable at $(x_0, y_0)$, and if $\mathbf{u} = u_1\mathbf{i} + u_2\mathbf{j}$ is a unit vector, then the directional derivative $D_{\mathbf{u}}f(x_0, y_0)$ exists and is given by*

$$D_{\mathbf{u}}f(x_0, y_0) = f_x(x_0, y_0)u_1 + f_y(x_0, y_0)u_2 \tag{4}$$

(*b*) *If $f(x, y, z)$ is differentiable at $(x_0, y_0, z_0)$, and if $\mathbf{u} = u_1\mathbf{i} + u_2\mathbf{j} + u_3\mathbf{k}$ is a unit vector, then the directional derivative $D_{\mathbf{u}}f(x_0, y_0, z_0)$ exists and is given by*

$$D_{\mathbf{u}}f(x_0, y_0, z_0) = f_x(x_0, y_0, z_0)u_1 + f_y(x_0, y_0, z_0)u_2 + f_z(x_0, y_0, z_0)u_3 \tag{5}$$

**PROOF** We will give the proof of part (*a*); the proof of part (*b*) is similar and will be omitted. The function $z = f(x_0 + su_1, y_0 + su_2)$ is the composition of the function $z = f(x, y)$ with the functions

$$x = x(s) = x_0 + su_1 \quad \text{and} \quad y = y(s) = y_0 + su_2$$

As such, the chain rule in Formula (5) of Section 13.5 immediately gives

$$\begin{aligned} D_{\mathbf{u}}f(x_0, y_0) &= \frac{d}{ds}\left[f(x_0 + su_1, y_0 + su_2)\right]_{s=0} \\ &= \left.\frac{dz}{ds}\right|_{s=0} = f_x(x_0, y_0)u_1 + f_y(x_0, y_0)u_2 \quad \blacksquare \end{aligned}$$

We can use Theorem 13.6.3 to confirm the result of Example 1. For $f(x, y) = xy$ we have $f_x(1, 2) = 2$ and $f_y(1, 2) = 1$ (verify). With

$$\mathbf{u} = \frac{\sqrt{3}}{2}\mathbf{i} + \frac{1}{2}\mathbf{j}$$

Equation (4) becomes

$$D_{\mathbf{u}}f(1, 2) = 2\left(\frac{\sqrt{3}}{2}\right) + \frac{1}{2} = \sqrt{3} + \frac{1}{2}$$

which agrees with our solution in Example 1.

Recall from Formula (13) of Section 11.2 that a unit vector $\mathbf{u}$ in the $xy$-plane can be expressed as

$$\mathbf{u} = \cos\phi\,\mathbf{i} + \sin\phi\,\mathbf{j} \tag{6}$$

where $\phi$ is the angle from the positive $x$-axis to $\mathbf{u}$. Thus, Formula (4) can also be expressed as

$$D_{\mathbf{u}}f(x_0, y_0) = f_x(x_0, y_0)\cos\phi + f_y(x_0, y_0)\sin\phi \tag{7}$$

▶ **Example 2** Find the directional derivative of $f(x, y) = e^{xy}$ at $(-2, 0)$ in the direction of the unit vector that makes an angle of $\pi/3$ with the positive $x$-axis.

***Solution.*** The partial derivatives of $f$ are

$$f_x(x, y) = ye^{xy}, \quad f_y(x, y) = xe^{xy}$$
$$f_x(-2, 0) = 0, \quad f_y(-2, 0) = -2$$

The unit vector $\mathbf{u}$ that makes an angle of $\pi/3$ with the positive $x$-axis is

$$\mathbf{u} = \cos(\pi/3)\mathbf{i} + \sin(\pi/3)\mathbf{j} = \frac{1}{2}\mathbf{i} + \frac{\sqrt{3}}{2}\mathbf{j}$$

Thus, from (7)

$$\begin{aligned} D_{\mathbf{u}}f(-2, 0) &= f_x(-2, 0)\cos(\pi/3) + f_y(-2, 0)\sin(\pi/3) \\ &= 0(1/2) + (-2)(\sqrt{3}/2) = -\sqrt{3} \end{aligned}$$ ◀

Note that in Example 3 we used a ***unit vector*** to specify the direction of the directional derivative. This is required in order to apply either Formula (4) or Formula (5).

▶ **Example 3** Find the directional derivative of $f(x, y, z) = x^2y - yz^3 + z$ at the point $(1, -2, 0)$ in the direction of the vector $\mathbf{a} = 2\mathbf{i} + \mathbf{j} - 2\mathbf{k}$.

***Solution.*** The partial derivatives of $f$ are

$$f_x(x, y, z) = 2xy, \quad f_y(x, y, z) = x^2 - z^3, \quad f_z(x, y, z) = -3yz^2 + 1$$
$$f_x(1, -2, 0) = -4, \quad f_y(1, -2, 0) = 1, \quad f_z(1, -2, 0) = 1$$

Since $\mathbf{a}$ is not a unit vector, we normalize it, getting

$$\mathbf{u} = \frac{\mathbf{a}}{\|\mathbf{a}\|} = \frac{1}{\sqrt{9}}(2\mathbf{i} + \mathbf{j} - 2\mathbf{k}) = \frac{2}{3}\mathbf{i} + \frac{1}{3}\mathbf{j} - \frac{2}{3}\mathbf{k}$$

Formula (5) then yields

$$D_{\mathbf{u}}f(1, -2, 0) = (-4)\left(\frac{2}{3}\right) + \frac{1}{3} - \frac{2}{3} = -3$$ ◀

## THE GRADIENT

Formula (4) can be expressed in the form of a dot product as

$$\begin{aligned} D_{\mathbf{u}}f(x_0, y_0) &= (f_x(x_0, y_0)\mathbf{i} + f_y(x_0, y_0)\mathbf{j}) \cdot (u_1\mathbf{i} + u_2\mathbf{j}) \\ &= (f_x(x_0, y_0)\mathbf{i} + f_y(x_0, y_0)\mathbf{j}) \cdot \mathbf{u} \end{aligned}$$

Similarly, Formula (5) can be expressed as

$$D_{\mathbf{u}}f(x_0, y_0, z_0) = (f_x(x_0, y_0, z_0)\mathbf{i} + f_y(x_0, y_0, z_0)\mathbf{j} + f_z(x_0, y_0, z_0)\mathbf{k}) \cdot \mathbf{u}$$

In both cases the directional derivative is obtained by dotting the direction vector $\mathbf{u}$ with a new vector constructed from the first-order partial derivatives of $f$.

Remember that $\nabla f$ is not a product of $\nabla$ and $f$. Think of $\nabla$ as an "operator" that acts on a function $f$ to produce the gradient $\nabla f$.

**13.6.4 DEFINITION**

(a) If $f$ is a function of $x$ and $y$, then the ***gradient of f*** is defined by

$$\nabla f(x, y) = f_x(x, y)\mathbf{i} + f_y(x, y)\mathbf{j} \tag{8}$$

(b) If $f$ is a function of $x$, $y$, and $z$, then the ***gradient of f*** is defined by

$$\nabla f(x, y, z) = f_x(x, y, z)\mathbf{i} + f_y(x, y, z)\mathbf{j} + f_z(x, y, z)\mathbf{k} \tag{9}$$

The symbol $\nabla$ (read "del") is an inverted delta. (It is sometimes called a "nabla" because of its similarity in form to an ancient Hebrew ten-stringed harp of that name.)

Formulas (4) and (5) can now be written as

$$D_{\mathbf{u}}f(x_0, y_0) = \nabla f(x_0, y_0) \cdot \mathbf{u} \tag{10}$$

and

$$D_{\mathbf{u}}f(x_0, y_0, z_0) = \nabla f(x_0, y_0, z_0) \cdot \mathbf{u} \tag{11}$$

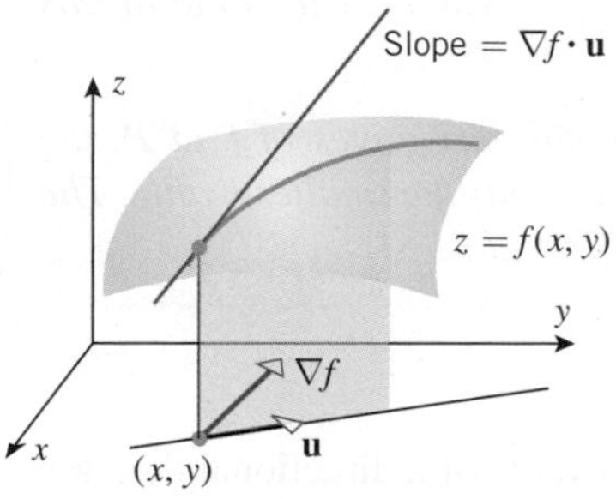

▲ **Figure 13.6.4**

respectively. For example, using Formula (11) our solution to Example 3 would take the form

$$\begin{aligned} D_{\mathbf{u}}f(1,-2,0) &= \nabla f(1,-2,0) \cdot \mathbf{u} = (-4\mathbf{i}+\mathbf{j}+\mathbf{k}) \cdot \left(\tfrac{2}{3}\mathbf{i}+\tfrac{1}{3}\mathbf{j}-\tfrac{2}{3}\mathbf{k}\right) \\ &= (-4)\left(\tfrac{2}{3}\right) + \tfrac{1}{3} - \tfrac{2}{3} = -3 \end{aligned}$$

Formula (10) can be interpreted to mean that the slope of the surface $z = f(x, y)$ at the point $(x_0, y_0)$ in the direction of $\mathbf{u}$ is the dot product of the gradient with $\mathbf{u}$ (Figure 13.6.4).

## PROPERTIES OF THE GRADIENT

The gradient is not merely a notational device to simplify the formula for the directional derivative; we will see that the length and direction of the gradient $\nabla f$ provide important information about the function $f$ and the surface $z = f(x, y)$. For example, suppose that $\nabla f(x, y) \neq \mathbf{0}$, and let us use Formula (4) of Section 11.3 to rewrite (10) as

$$D_{\mathbf{u}}\, f(x, y) = \nabla f(x, y) \cdot \mathbf{u} = \|\nabla f(x, y)\|\|\mathbf{u}\|\cos\theta = \|\nabla f(x, y)\|\cos\theta \tag{12}$$

where $\theta$ is the angle between $\nabla f(x, y)$ and $\mathbf{u}$. Equation (12) tells us that the maximum value of $D_{\mathbf{u}}f$ at the point $(x, y)$ is $\|\nabla f(x, y)\|$, and this maximum occurs when $\theta = 0$, that is, when $\mathbf{u}$ is in the direction of $\nabla f(x, y)$. Geometrically, this means:

*At $(x, y)$, the surface $z = f(x, y)$ has its maximum slope in the direction of the gradient, and the maximum slope is $\|\nabla f(x, y)\|$.*

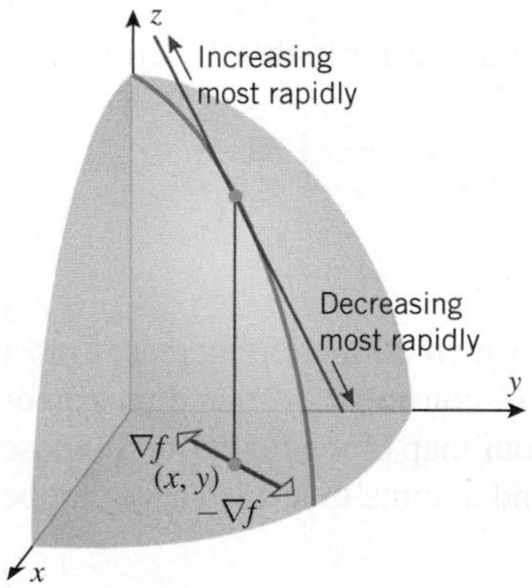

▲ **Figure 13.6.5**

That is, the function $f(x, y)$ increases most rapidly in the direction of its gradient (Figure 13.6.5).

Similarly, (12) tells us that the minimum value of $D_{\mathbf{u}}f$ at the point $(x, y)$ is $-\|\nabla f(x, y)\|$, and this minimum occurs when $\theta = \pi$, that is, when $\mathbf{u}$ is oppositely directed to $\nabla f(x, y)$. Geometrically, this means:

*At $(x, y)$, the surface $z = f(x, y)$ has its minimum slope in the direction that is opposite to the gradient, and the minimum slope is $-\|\nabla f(x, y)\|$.*

That is, the function $f(x, y)$ decreases most rapidly in the direction opposite to its gradient (Figure 13.6.5).

Finally, in the case where $\nabla f(x, y) = \mathbf{0}$, it follows from (12) that $D_{\mathbf{u}}f(x, y) = 0$ in all directions at the point $(x, y)$. This typically occurs where the surface $z = f(x, y)$ has a "relative maximum," a "relative minimum," or a saddle point.

A similar analysis applies to functions of three variables. As a consequence, we have the following result.

**13.6.5 THEOREM** *Let $f$ be a function of either two variables or three variables, and let $P$ denote the point $P(x_0, y_0)$ or $P(x_0, y_0, z_0)$, respectively. Assume that $f$ is differentiable at $P$.*

(a) *If $\nabla f = \mathbf{0}$ at $P$, then all directional derivatives of $f$ at $P$ are zero.*

(b) *If $\nabla f \neq \mathbf{0}$ at $P$, then among all possible directional derivatives of $f$ at $P$, the derivative in the direction of $\nabla f$ at $P$ has the largest value. The value of this largest directional derivative is $\|\nabla f\|$ at $P$.*

(c) *If $\nabla f \neq \mathbf{0}$ at $P$, then among all possible directional derivatives of $f$ at $P$, the derivative in the direction opposite to that of $\nabla f$ at $P$ has the smallest value. The value of this smallest directional derivative is $-\|\nabla f\|$ at $P$.*

▶ **Example 4** Let $f(x, y) = x^2 e^y$. Find the maximum value of a directional derivative at $(-2, 0)$, and find the unit vector in the direction in which the maximum value occurs.

***Solution.*** Since

$$\nabla f(x, y) = f_x(x, y)\mathbf{i} + f_y(x, y)\mathbf{j} = 2xe^y\mathbf{i} + x^2 e^y\mathbf{j}$$

the gradient of $f$ at $(-2, 0)$ is

$$\nabla f(-2, 0) = -4\mathbf{i} + 4\mathbf{j}$$

By Theorem 13.6.5, the maximum value of the directional derivative is

$$\|\nabla f(-2, 0)\| = \sqrt{(-4)^2 + 4^2} = \sqrt{32} = 4\sqrt{2}$$

This maximum occurs in the direction of $\nabla f(-2, 0)$. The unit vector in this direction is

$$\mathbf{u} = \frac{\nabla f(-2, 0)}{\|\nabla f(-2, 0)\|} = \frac{1}{4\sqrt{2}}(-4\mathbf{i} + 4\mathbf{j}) = -\frac{1}{\sqrt{2}}\mathbf{i} + \frac{1}{\sqrt{2}}\mathbf{j} \blacktriangleleft$$

What would be the minimum value of a directional derivative of

$$f(x, y) = x^2 e^y$$

at $(-2, 0)$?

## GRADIENTS ARE NORMAL TO LEVEL CURVES

We have seen that the gradient points in the direction in which a function increases most rapidly. For a function $f(x, y)$ of two variables, we will now consider how this direction of maximum rate of increase can be determined from a contour map of the function. Suppose that $(x_0, y_0)$ is a point on a level curve $f(x, y) = c$ of $f$, and assume that this curve can be smoothly parametrized as

$$x = x(s), \quad y = y(s) \tag{13}$$

where $s$ is an arc length parameter. Recall from Formula (6) of Section 12.4 that the unit tangent vector to (13) is

$$\mathbf{T} = \mathbf{T}(s) = \left(\frac{dx}{ds}\right)\mathbf{i} + \left(\frac{dy}{ds}\right)\mathbf{j}$$

Since $\mathbf{T}$ gives a direction along which $f$ is nearly constant, we would expect the instantaneous rate of change of $f$ with respect to distance in the direction of $\mathbf{T}$ to be 0. That is, we would expect that

$$D_{\mathbf{T}} f(x, y) = \nabla f(x, y) \cdot \mathbf{T}(s) = 0$$

To show this to be the case, we differentiate both sides of the equation $f(x, y) = c$ with respect to $s$. Assuming that $f$ is differentiable at $(x, y)$, we can use the chain rule to obtain

$$\frac{\partial f}{\partial x}\frac{dx}{ds} + \frac{\partial f}{\partial y}\frac{dy}{ds} = 0$$

which we can rewrite as

$$\left(\frac{\partial f}{\partial x}\mathbf{i} + \frac{\partial f}{\partial y}\mathbf{j}\right) \cdot \left(\frac{dx}{ds}\mathbf{i} + \frac{dy}{ds}\mathbf{j}\right) = 0$$

or, alternatively, as

$$\nabla f(x, y) \cdot \mathbf{T} = 0$$

Therefore, if $\nabla f(x, y) \neq \mathbf{0}$, then $\nabla f(x, y)$ should be normal to the level curve $f(x, y) = c$ at any point $(x, y)$ on the curve.

It is proved in advanced courses that if $f(x, y)$ has continuous first-order partial derivatives, and if $\nabla f(x_0, y_0) \neq \mathbf{0}$, then near $(x_0, y_0)$ the graph of $f(x, y) = c$ is indeed a smooth curve through $(x_0, y_0)$. Furthermore, we also know from Theorem 13.4.4 that $f$ will be differentiable at $(x_0, y_0)$. We therefore have the following result.

Show that the level curves for

$$f(x, y) = x^2 + y^2$$

are circles and verify Theorem 13.6.6 at $(x_0, y_0) = (3, 4)$.

**13.6.6 THEOREM** *Assume that $f(x, y)$ has continuous first-order partial derivatives in an open disk centered at $(x_0, y_0)$ and that $\nabla f(x_0, y_0) \neq \mathbf{0}$. Then $\nabla f(x_0, y_0)$ is normal to the level curve of $f$ through $(x_0, y_0)$.*

When we examine a contour map, we instinctively regard the distance between adjacent contours to be measured in a normal direction. If the contours correspond to equally spaced values of $f$, then the closer together the contours appear to be, the more rapidly the values of $f$ will be changing in that normal direction. It follows from Theorems 13.6.5 and 13.6.6 that this rate of change of $f$ is given by $\|\nabla f(x, y)\|$. Thus, the closer together the contours appear to be, the greater the length of the gradient of $f$.

► **Example 5** A contour plot of a function $f$ is given in Figure 13.6.6*a*. Sketch the directions of the gradient of $f$ at the points $P$, $Q$, and $R$. At which of these three points does the gradient vector have maximum length? Minimum length?

***Solution.*** It follows from Theorems 13.6.5 and 13.6.6 that the directions of the gradient vectors will be as given in Figure 13.6.6*b*. Based on the density of the contour lines, we would guess that the gradient of $f$ has maximum length at $R$ and minimum length at $P$, with the length at $Q$ somewhere in between. ◄

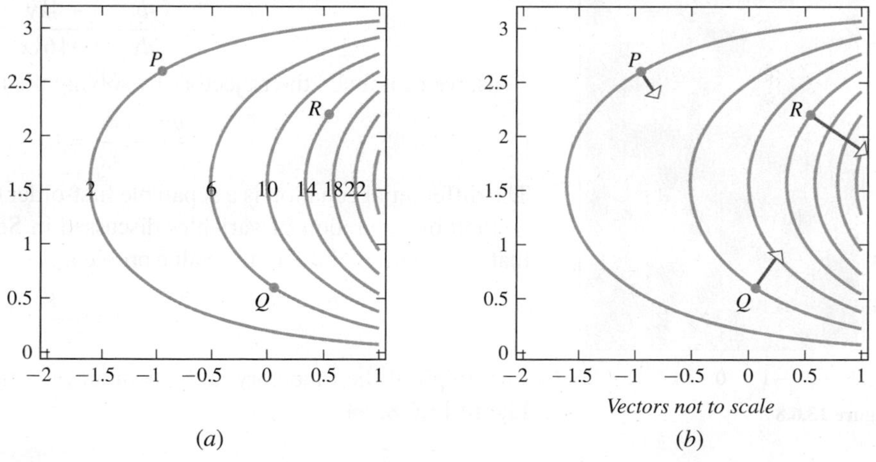


▲ **Figure 13.6.6**

**REMARK** If $(x_0, y_0)$ is a point on the level curve $f(x, y) = c$, then the slope of the surface $z = f(x, y)$ at that point in the direction of $\mathbf{u}$ is

$$D_{\mathbf{u}} f(x_0, y_0) = \nabla f(x_0, y_0) \cdot \mathbf{u}$$

If $\mathbf{u}$ is tangent to the level curve at $(x_0, y_0)$, then $f(x, y)$ is neither increasing nor decreasing in that direction, so $D_{\mathbf{u}} f(x_0, y_0) = 0$. Thus, $\nabla f(x_0, y_0)$, $-\nabla f(x_0, y_0)$, and the tangent vector $\mathbf{u}$ mark the directions of maximum slope, minimum slope, and zero slope at a point $(x_0, y_0)$ on a level curve (Figure 13.6.7). Good skiers use these facts intuitively to control their speed by zigzagging down ski slopes—they ski across the slope with their skis tangential to a level curve to stop their downhill motion, and they point their skis down the slope and normal to the level curve to obtain the most rapid descent.

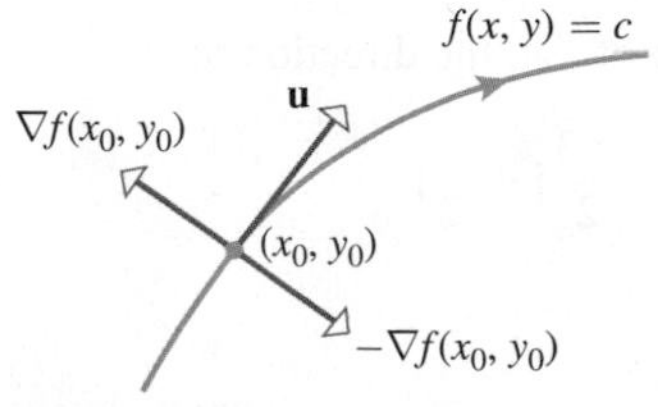


▲ **Figure 13.6.7**

U. S. Air Force photo by Master Sgt. Michael Ammons

*Heat-seeking missiles such as "Stinger" and "Sidewinder" use infrared sensors to measure gradients.*

## AN APPLICATION OF GRADIENTS

There are numerous applications in which the motion of an object must be controlled so that it moves toward a heat source. For example, in medical applications the operation of certain diagnostic equipment is designed to locate heat sources generated by tumors or infections, and in military applications the trajectories of heat-seeking missiles are controlled to seek and destroy enemy aircraft. The following example illustrates how gradients are used to solve such problems.

▶ **Example 6** A heat-seeking particle is located at the point (2, 3) on a flat metal plate whose temperature at a point $(x, y)$ is

$$T(x, y) = 10 - 8x^2 - 2y^2$$

Find an equation for the trajectory of the particle if it moves continuously in the direction of maximum temperature increase.

***Solution.*** Assume that the trajectory is represented parametrically by the equations

$$x = x(t), \quad y = y(t)$$

where the particle is at the point (2, 3) at time $t = 0$. Because the particle moves in the direction of maximum temperature increase, its direction of motion at time $t$ is in the direction of the gradient of $T(x, y)$, and hence its velocity vector $\mathbf{v}(t)$ at time $t$ points in the direction of the gradient. Thus, there is a scalar $k$ that depends on $t$ such that

$$\mathbf{v}(t) = k\nabla T(x, y)$$

from which we obtain

$$\frac{dx}{dt}\mathbf{i} + \frac{dy}{dt}\mathbf{j} = k(-16x\mathbf{i} - 4y\mathbf{j})$$

Equating components yields

$$\frac{dx}{dt} = -16kx, \quad \frac{dy}{dt} = -4ky$$

and dividing to eliminate $k$ yields

$$\frac{dy}{dx} = \frac{-4ky}{-16kx} = \frac{y}{4x}$$

Thus, we can obtain the trajectory by solving the initial-value problem

$$\frac{dy}{dx} - \frac{y}{4x} = 0, \quad y(2) = 3$$

The differential equation is a separable first-order equation and hence can be solved by the method of separation of variables discussed in Section 8.2. We leave it for you to show that the solution of the initial-value problem is

$$y = \frac{3}{\sqrt[4]{2}}x^{1/4}$$

The graph of the trajectory and a contour plot of the temperature function are shown in Figure 13.6.8. ◀

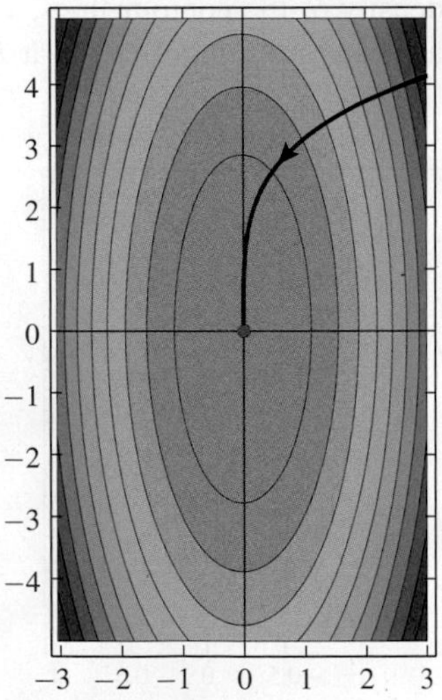


▲ **Figure 13.6.8**

## ✓QUICK CHECK EXERCISES 13.6 *(See page 866 for answers.)*

**1.** The gradient of $f(x, y, z) = xy^2z^3$ at the point (1, 1, 1) is ________.

**2.** Suppose that the differentiable function $f(x, y)$ has the property that

$$f\left(2 + \frac{s\sqrt{3}}{2}, 1 + \frac{s}{2}\right) = 3se^s$$

The directional derivative of $f$ in the direction of

$$\mathbf{u} = \frac{\sqrt{3}}{2}\mathbf{i} + \frac{1}{2}\mathbf{j}$$

at (2, 1) is ________.

3. If the gradient of $f(x, y)$ at the origin is $6\mathbf{i} + 8\mathbf{j}$, then the directional derivative of $f$ in the direction of $\mathbf{a} = 3\mathbf{i} + 4\mathbf{j}$ at the origin is ______. The slope of the tangent line to the level curve of $f$ through the origin at $(0, 0)$ is ______.

4. If the gradient of $f(x, y, z)$ at $(1, 2, 3)$ is $2\mathbf{i} - 2\mathbf{j} + \mathbf{k}$, then the maximum value for a directional derivative of $f$ at $(1, 2, 3)$ is ______ and the minimum value for a directional derivative at this point is ______.

## EXERCISE SET 13.6 Graphing Utility C CAS

**1–8** Find $D_{\mathbf{u}}f$ at $P$. ■

1. $f(x, y) = (1 + xy)^{3/2}$; $P(3, 1)$; $\mathbf{u} = \frac{1}{\sqrt{2}}\mathbf{i} + \frac{1}{\sqrt{2}}\mathbf{j}$
2. $f(x, y) = \sin(5x - 3y)$; $P(3, 5)$; $\mathbf{u} = \frac{3}{5}\mathbf{i} - \frac{4}{5}\mathbf{j}$
3. $f(x, y) = \ln(1 + x^2 + y)$; $P(0, 0)$; $\mathbf{u} = -\frac{1}{\sqrt{10}}\mathbf{i} - \frac{3}{\sqrt{10}}\mathbf{j}$
4. $f(x, y) = \dfrac{cx + dy}{x - y}$; $P(3, 4)$; $\mathbf{u} = \frac{4}{5}\mathbf{i} + \frac{3}{5}\mathbf{j}$
5. $f(x, y, z) = 4x^5y^2z^3$; $P(2, -1, 1)$; $\mathbf{u} = \frac{1}{3}\mathbf{i} + \frac{2}{3}\mathbf{j} - \frac{2}{3}\mathbf{k}$
6. $f(x, y, z) = ye^{xz} + z^2$; $P(0, 2, 3)$; $\mathbf{u} = \frac{2}{7}\mathbf{i} - \frac{3}{7}\mathbf{j} + \frac{6}{7}\mathbf{k}$
7. $f(x, y, z) = \ln(x^2 + 2y^2 + 3z^2)$; $P(-1, 2, 4)$; $\mathbf{u} = -\frac{3}{13}\mathbf{i} - \frac{4}{13}\mathbf{j} - \frac{12}{13}\mathbf{k}$
8. $f(x, y, z) = \sin xyz$; $P\left(\frac{1}{2}, \frac{1}{3}, \pi\right)$; $\mathbf{u} = \frac{1}{\sqrt{3}}\mathbf{i} - \frac{1}{\sqrt{3}}\mathbf{j} + \frac{1}{\sqrt{3}}\mathbf{k}$

**9–18** Find the directional derivative of $f$ at $P$ in the direction of $\mathbf{a}$. ■

9. $f(x, y) = 4x^3y^2$; $P(2, 1)$; $\mathbf{a} = 4\mathbf{i} - 3\mathbf{j}$
10. $f(x, y) = 9x^3 - 2y^3$; $P(1, 0)$; $\mathbf{a} = \mathbf{i} - \mathbf{j}$
11. $f(x, y) = y^2 \ln x$; $P(1, 4)$; $\mathbf{a} = -3\mathbf{i} + 3\mathbf{j}$
12. $f(x, y) = e^x \cos y$; $P(0, \pi/4)$; $\mathbf{a} = 5\mathbf{i} - 2\mathbf{j}$
13. $f(x, y) = \tan^{-1}(y/x)$; $P(-2, 2)$; $\mathbf{a} = -\mathbf{i} - \mathbf{j}$
14. $f(x, y) = xe^y - ye^x$; $P(0, 0)$; $\mathbf{a} = 5\mathbf{i} - 2\mathbf{j}$
15. $f(x, y, z) = xy + z^2$; $P(-3, 0, 4)$; $\mathbf{a} = \mathbf{i} + \mathbf{j} + \mathbf{k}$
16. $f(x, y, z) = y - \sqrt{x^2 + z^2}$; $P(-3, 1, 4)$; $\mathbf{a} = 2\mathbf{i} - 2\mathbf{j} - \mathbf{k}$
17. $f(x, y, z) = \dfrac{z - x}{z + y}$; $P(1, 0, -3)$; $\mathbf{a} = -6\mathbf{i} + 3\mathbf{j} - 2\mathbf{k}$
18. $f(x, y, z) = e^{x+y+3z}$; $P(-2, 2, -1)$; $\mathbf{a} = 20\mathbf{i} - 4\mathbf{j} + 5\mathbf{k}$

**19–22** Find the directional derivative of $f$ at $P$ in the direction of a vector making the counterclockwise angle $\theta$ with the positive $x$-axis. ■

19. $f(x, y) = \sqrt{xy}$; $P(1, 4)$; $\theta = \pi/3$
20. $f(x, y) = \dfrac{x - y}{x + y}$; $P(-1, -2)$; $\theta = \pi/2$
21. $f(x, y) = \tan(2x + y)$; $P(\pi/6, \pi/3)$; $\theta = 7\pi/4$
22. $f(x, y) = \sinh x \cosh y$; $P(0, 0)$; $\theta = \pi$
23. Find the directional derivative of
$$f(x, y) = \frac{x}{x + y}$$
at $P(1, 0)$ in the direction of $Q(-1, -1)$.
24. Find the directional derivative of $f(x, y) = e^{-x} \sec y$ at $P(0, \pi/4)$ in the direction of the origin.
25. Find the directional derivative of $f(x, y) = \sqrt{xy}e^y$ at $P(1, 1)$ in the direction of the negative $y$-axis.
26. Let
$$f(x, y) = \frac{y}{x + y}$$
Find a unit vector $\mathbf{u}$ for which $D_{\mathbf{u}}f(2, 3) = 0$.
27. Find the directional derivative of
$$f(x, y, z) = \frac{y}{x + z}$$
at $P(2, 1, -1)$ in the direction from $P$ to $Q(-1, 2, 0)$.
28. Find the directional derivative of the function
$$f(x, y, z) = x^3y^2z^5 - 2xz + yz + 3x$$
at $P(-1, -2, 1)$ in the direction of the negative $z$-axis.

### FOCUS ON CONCEPTS

29. Suppose that $D_{\mathbf{u}}f(1, 2) = -5$ and $D_{\mathbf{v}}f(1, 2) = 10$, where $\mathbf{u} = \frac{3}{5}\mathbf{i} - \frac{4}{5}\mathbf{j}$ and $\mathbf{v} = \frac{4}{5}\mathbf{i} + \frac{3}{5}\mathbf{j}$. Find
(a) $f_x(1, 2)$ (b) $f_y(1, 2)$
(c) the directional derivative of $f$ at $(1, 2)$ in the direction of the origin.
30. Given that $f_x(-5, 1) = -3$ and $f_y(-5, 1) = 2$, find the directional derivative of $f$ at $P(-5, 1)$ in the direction of the vector from $P$ to $Q(-4, 3)$.
31. The accompanying figure shows some level curves of an unspecified function $f(x, y)$. Which of the three vectors shown in the figure is most likely to be $\nabla f$? Explain.
32. The accompanying figure shows some level curves of an unspecified function $f(x, y)$. Of the gradients at $P$ and $Q$, which probably has the greater length? Explain.

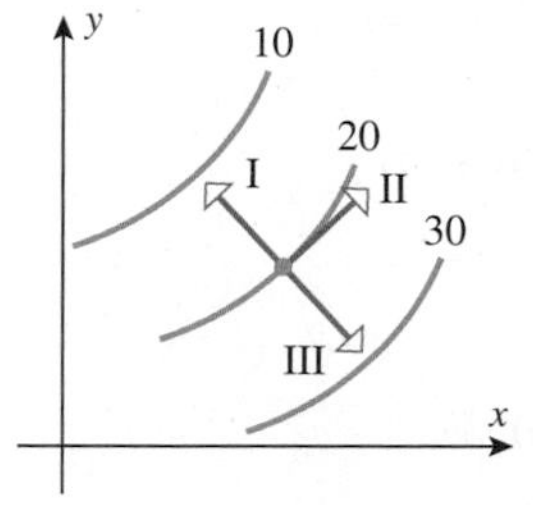

▲ Figure Ex-31

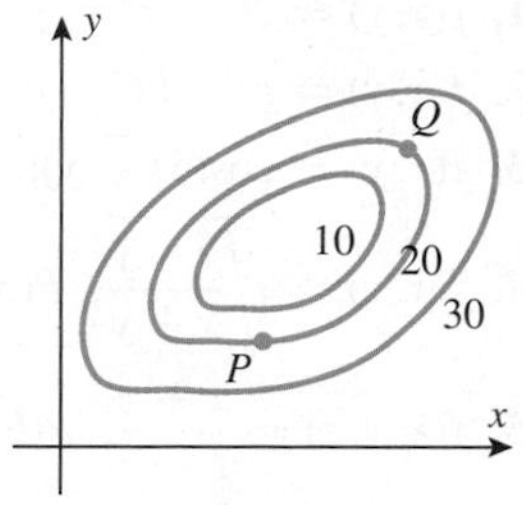

▲ Figure Ex-32

**33–40** Find $\nabla z$ or $\nabla w$. ■

33. $z = \sin(7y^2 - 7xy)$
34. $z = 7\sin(6x/y)$
35. $z = \dfrac{6x + 7y}{6x - 7y}$
36. $z = \dfrac{6xe^{3y}}{x + 8y}$
37. $w = -x^9 - y^3 + z^{12}$
38. $w = xe^{8y} \sin 6z$
39. $w = \ln\sqrt{x^2 + y^2 + z^2}$
40. $w = e^{-5x} \sec x^2yz$

**41–46** Find the gradient of $f$ at the indicated point. ■

**41.** $f(x, y) = 5x^2 + y^4$; $(4, 2)$

**42.** $f(x, y) = 5\sin x^2 + \cos 3y$; $(\sqrt{\pi}/2, 0)$

**43.** $f(x, y) = (x^2 + xy)^3$; $(-1, -1)$

**44.** $f(x, y) = (x^2 + y^2)^{-1/2}$; $(3, 4)$

**45.** $f(x, y, z) = y\ln(x + y + z)$; $(-3, 4, 0)$

**46.** $f(x, y, z) = y^2 z\tan^3 x$; $(\pi/4, -3, 1)$

**47–50** Sketch the level curve of $f(x, y)$ that passes through $P$ and draw the gradient vector at $P$. ■

**47.** $f(x, y) = 4x - 2y + 3$; $P(1, 2)$

**48.** $f(x, y) = y/x^2$; $P(-2, 2)$

**49.** $f(x, y) = x^2 + 4y^2$; $P(-2, 0)$

**50.** $f(x, y) = x^2 - y^2$; $P(2, -1)$

**51.** Find a unit vector $\mathbf{u}$ that is normal at $P(1, -2)$ to the level curve of $f(x, y) = 4x^2y$ through $P$.

**52.** Find a unit vector $\mathbf{u}$ that is normal at $P(2, -3)$ to the level curve of $f(x, y) = 3x^2y - xy$ through $P$.

**53–60** Find a unit vector in the direction in which $f$ increases most rapidly at $P$, and find the rate of change of $f$ at $P$ in that direction. ■

**53.** $f(x, y) = 4x^3y^2$; $P(-1, 1)$

**54.** $f(x, y) = 3x - \ln y$; $P(2, 4)$

**55.** $f(x, y) = \sqrt{x^2 + y^2}$; $P(4, -3)$

**56.** $f(x, y) = \dfrac{x}{x + y}$; $P(0, 2)$

**57.** $f(x, y, z) = x^3z^2 + y^3z + z - 1$; $P(1, 1, -1)$

**58.** $f(x, y, z) = \sqrt{x - 3y + 4z}$; $P(0, -3, 0)$

**59.** $f(x, y, z) = \dfrac{x}{z} + \dfrac{z}{y^2}$; $P(1, 2, -2)$

**60.** $f(x, y, z) = \tan^{-1}\left(\dfrac{x}{y + z}\right)$; $P(4, 2, 2)$

**61–66** Find a unit vector in the direction in which $f$ decreases most rapidly at $P$, and find the rate of change of $f$ at $P$ in that direction. ■

**61.** $f(x, y) = 20 - x^2 - y^2$; $P(-1, -3)$

**62.** $f(x, y) = e^{xy}$; $P(2, 3)$

**63.** $f(x, y) = \cos(3x - y)$; $P(\pi/6, \pi/4)$

**64.** $f(x, y) = \sqrt{\dfrac{x - y}{x + y}}$; $P(3, 1)$

**65.** $f(x, y, z) = \dfrac{x + z}{z - y}$; $P(5, 7, 6)$

**66.** $f(x, y, z) = 4e^{xy}\cos z$; $P(0, 1, \pi/4)$

**67–70 True–False** Determine whether the statement is true or false. Explain your answer. In each exercise, assume that $f$ denotes a differentiable function of two variables whose domain is the $xy$-plane. ■

**67.** If $\mathbf{v} = 2\mathbf{u}$, then the directional derivative of $f$ in the direction of $\mathbf{v}$ at a point $(x_0, y_0)$ is twice the directional derivative of $f$ in the direction of $\mathbf{u}$ at the point $(x_0, y_0)$.

**68.** If $y = x^2$ is a contour of $f$, then $f_x(0, 0) = 0$.

**69.** If $\mathbf{u}$ is a fixed unit vector and $D_{\mathbf{u}}f(x, y) = 0$ for all points $(x, y)$, then $f$ is a constant function.

**70.** If the displacement vector from $(x_0, y_0)$ to $(x_1, y_1)$ is a positive multiple of $\nabla f(x_0, y_0)$, then $f(x_0, y_0) \le f(x_1, y_1)$.

**FOCUS ON CONCEPTS**

**71.** Given that $\nabla f(4, -5) = 2\mathbf{i} - \mathbf{j}$, find the directional derivative of the function $f$ at the point $(4, -5)$ in the direction of $\mathbf{a} = 5\mathbf{i} + 2\mathbf{j}$.

**72.** Given that $\nabla f(x_0, y_0) = \mathbf{i} - 2\mathbf{j}$ and $D_{\mathbf{u}}f(x_0, y_0) = -2$, find $\mathbf{u}$ (two answers).

**73.** The accompanying figure shows some level curves of an unspecified function $f(x, y)$.

(a) Use the available information to approximate the length of the vector $\nabla f(1, 2)$, and sketch the approximation. Explain how you approximated the length and determined the direction of the vector.

(b) Sketch an approximation of the vector $-\nabla f(4, 4)$.

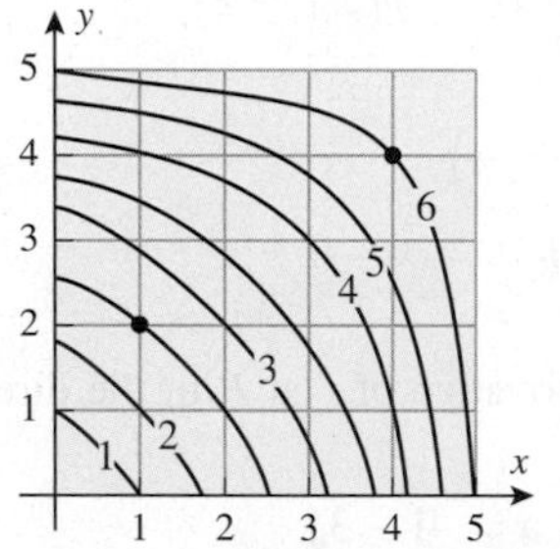


◀ **Figure Ex-73**

**74.** The accompanying figure shows a topographic map of a hill and a point $P$ at the bottom of the hill. Suppose that you want to climb from the point $P$ toward the top of the hill in such a way that you are always ascending in the direction of steepest slope. Sketch the projection of your path on the contour map. This is called the ***path of steepest ascent***. Explain how you determined the path.

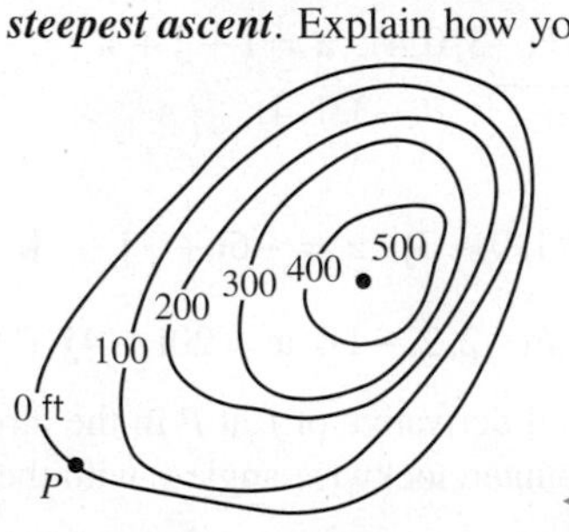


◀ **Figure Ex-74**

**75.** Let $z = 3x^2 - y^2$. Find all points at which $\|\nabla z\| = 6$.

**76.** Given that $z = 3x + y^2$, find $\nabla\|\nabla z\|$ at the point $(5, 2)$.

**77.** A particle moves along a path $C$ given by the equations $x = t$ and $y = -t^2$. If $z = x^2 + y^2$, find $dz/ds$ along $C$ at the instant when the particle is at the point $(2, -4)$.

**78.** The temperature (in degrees Celsius) at a point $(x, y)$ on a metal plate in the $xy$-plane is

$$T(x, y) = \frac{xy}{1 + x^2 + y^2}$$

*(cont.)*

(a) Find the rate of change of temperature at $(1, 1)$ in the direction of $\mathbf{a} = 2\mathbf{i} - \mathbf{j}$.
(b) An ant at $(1, 1)$ wants to walk in the direction in which the temperature drops most rapidly. Find a unit vector in that direction.

**79.** If the electric potential at a point $(x, y)$ in the $xy$-plane is $V(x, y)$, then the ***electric intensity vector*** at the point $(x, y)$ is $\mathbf{E} = -\nabla V(x, y)$. Suppose that $V(x, y) = e^{-2x}\cos 2y$.
(a) Find the electric intensity vector at $(\pi/4, 0)$.
(b) Show that at each point in the plane, the electric potential decreases most rapidly in the direction of the vector $\mathbf{E}$.

**80.** On a certain mountain, the elevation $z$ above a point $(x, y)$ in an $xy$-plane at sea level is $z = 2000 - 0.02x^2 - 0.04y^2$, where $x$, $y$, and $z$ are in meters. The positive $x$-axis points east, and the positive $y$-axis north. A climber is at the point $(-20, 5, 1991)$.
(a) If the climber uses a compass reading to walk due west, will she begin to ascend or descend?
(b) If the climber uses a compass reading to walk northeast, will she ascend or descend? At what rate?
(c) In what compass direction should the climber begin walking to travel a level path (two answers)?

**81.** Given that the directional derivative of $f(x, y, z)$ at the point $(3, -2, 1)$ in the direction of $\mathbf{a} = 2\mathbf{i} - \mathbf{j} - 2\mathbf{k}$ is $-5$ and that $\|\nabla f(3, -2, 1)\| = 5$, find $\nabla f(3, -2, 1)$.

**82.** The temperature (in degrees Celsius) at a point $(x, y, z)$ in a metal solid is

$$T(x, y, z) = \frac{xyz}{1 + x^2 + y^2 + z^2}$$

(a) Find the rate of change of temperature with respect to distance at $(1, 1, 1)$ in the direction of the origin.
(b) Find the direction in which the temperature rises most rapidly at the point $(1, 1, 1)$. (Express your answer as a unit vector.)
(c) Find the rate at which the temperature rises moving from $(1, 1, 1)$ in the direction obtained in part (b).

**83.** Let $r = \sqrt{x^2 + y^2}$.
(a) Show that $\nabla r = \dfrac{\mathbf{r}}{r}$, where $\mathbf{r} = x\mathbf{i} + y\mathbf{j}$.
(b) Show that $\nabla f(r) = f'(r)\nabla r = \dfrac{f'(r)}{r}\mathbf{r}$.

**84.** Use the formula in part (b) of Exercise 83 to find
(a) $\nabla f(r)$ if $f(r) = re^{-3r}$
(b) $f(r)$ if $\nabla f(r) = 3r^2\mathbf{r}$ and $f(2) = 1$.

**85.** Let $\mathbf{u}_r$ be a unit vector whose counterclockwise angle from the positive $x$-axis is $\theta$, and let $\mathbf{u}_\theta$ be a unit vector $90°$ counterclockwise from $\mathbf{u}_r$. Show that if $z = f(x, y)$, $x = r\cos\theta$, and $y = r\sin\theta$, then

$$\nabla z = \frac{\partial z}{\partial r}\mathbf{u}_r + \frac{1}{r}\frac{\partial z}{\partial \theta}\mathbf{u}_\theta$$

[*Hint:* Use part (c) of Exercise 57, Section 13.5.]

**86.** Prove: If $f$ and $g$ are differentiable, then
(a) $\nabla(f + g) = \nabla f + \nabla g$
(b) $\nabla(cf) = c\nabla f$ ($c$ constant)
(c) $\nabla(fg) = f\nabla g + g\nabla f$
(d) $\nabla\left(\dfrac{f}{g}\right) = \dfrac{g\nabla f - f\nabla g}{g^2}$
(e) $\nabla(f^n) = nf^{n-1}\nabla f$.

**87–88** A heat-seeking particle is located at the point $P$ on a flat metal plate whose temperature at a point $(x, y)$ is $T(x, y)$. Find parametric equations for the trajectory of the particle if it moves continuously in the direction of maximum temperature increase. ■

**87.** $T(x, y) = 5 - 4x^2 - y^2$; $P(1, 4)$

**88.** $T(x, y) = 100 - x^2 - 2y^2$; $P(5, 3)$

**89.** Use a graphing utility to generate the trajectory of the particle together with some representative level curves of the temperature function in Exercise 87.

**90.** Use a graphing utility to generate the trajectory of the particle together with some representative level curves of the temperature function in Exercise 88.

C **91.** (a) Use a CAS to graph $f(x, y) = (x^2 + 3y^2)e^{-(x^2+y^2)}$.
(b) At how many points do you think it is true that $D_{\mathbf{u}}f(x, y) = 0$ for all unit vectors $\mathbf{u}$?
(c) Use a CAS to find $\nabla f$.
(d) Use a CAS to solve the equation $\nabla f(x, y) = \mathbf{0}$ for $x$ and $y$.
(e) Use the result in part (d) together with Theorem 13.6.5 to check your conjecture in part (b).

**92.** Prove: If $x = x(t)$ and $y = y(t)$ are differentiable at $t$, and if $z = f(x, y)$ is differentiable at the point $(x(t), y(t))$, then

$$\frac{dz}{dt} = \nabla z \cdot \mathbf{r}'(t)$$

where $\mathbf{r}(t) = x(t)\mathbf{i} + y(t)\mathbf{j}$.

**93.** Prove: If $f$, $f_x$, and $f_y$ are continuous on a circular region, and if $\nabla f(x, y) = \mathbf{0}$ throughout the region, then $f(x, y)$ is constant on the region. [*Hint:* See Exercise 69, Section 13.5.]

**94.** Prove: If the function $f$ is differentiable at the point $(x, y)$ and if $D_{\mathbf{u}}f(x, y) = 0$ in two nonparallel directions, then $D_{\mathbf{u}}f(x, y) = 0$ in all directions.

**95.** Given that the functions $u = u(x, y, z)$, $v = v(x, y, z)$, $w = w(x, y, z)$, and $f(u, v, w)$ are all differentiable, show that

$$\nabla f(u, v, w) = \frac{\partial f}{\partial u}\nabla u + \frac{\partial f}{\partial v}\nabla v + \frac{\partial f}{\partial w}\nabla w$$

**96. Writing** Let $f$ denote a differentiable function of two variables. Write a short paragraph that discusses the connections between directional derivatives of $f$ and slopes of lines to the graph of $f$.

**97. Writing** Let $f$ denote a differentiable function of two variables. Although we have defined what it means to say that $f$ is differentiable, we have not defined the "derivative" of $f$. Write a short paragraph that discusses the merits of defining the derivative of $f$ to be the gradient $\nabla f$.

**✓ QUICK CHECK ANSWERS 13.6** 1. $\langle 1, 2, 3\rangle$ 2. 3 3. 10; $-\frac{3}{4}$ 4. 3; $-3$

## 13.7 TANGENT PLANES AND NORMAL VECTORS

*In this section we will discuss tangent planes to surfaces in three-dimensional space. We will be concerned with three main questions: What is a tangent plane? When do tangent planes exist? How do we find equations of tangent planes?*

### TANGENT PLANES AND NORMAL VECTORS TO LEVEL SURFACES $F(x, y, z) = c$

We begin by considering the problem of finding tangent planes to level surfaces of a function $F(x, y, z)$. These surfaces are represented by equations of the form $F(x, y, z) = c$. We will assume that $F$ has continuous first-order partial derivatives, since this has an important geometric consequence. Fix $c$, and suppose that $P_0(x_0, y_0, z_0)$ satisfies the equation $F(x, y, z) = c$. In advanced courses it is proved that if $F$ has continuous first-order partial derivatives, and if $\nabla F(x_0, y_0, z_0) \neq \mathbf{0}$, then near $P_0$ the graph of $F(x, y, z) = c$ is indeed a "surface" rather than some possibly exotic-looking set of points in 3-space.

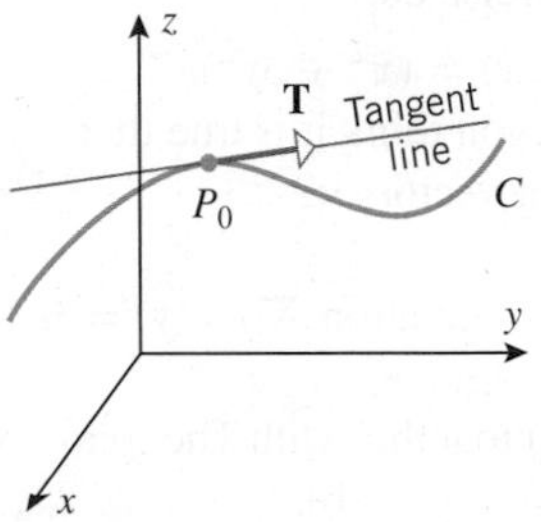

▲ **Figure 13.7.1**

We will base our concept of a tangent plane to a level surface $S$: $F(x, y, z) = c$ on the more elementary notion of a tangent line to a curve $C$ in 3-space (Figure 13.7.1). Intuitively, we would expect a tangent plane to $S$ at a point $P_0$ to be composed of the tangent lines at $P_0$ of all curves on $S$ that pass through $P_0$ (Figure 13.7.2). Suppose $C$ is a curve on $S$ through $P_0$ that is parametrized by $x = x(t)$, $y = y(t)$, $z = z(t)$ with $x_0 = x(t_0)$, $y_0 = y(t_0)$, and $z_0 = z(t_0)$. The tangent line $l$ to $C$ through $P_0$ is then parallel to the vector

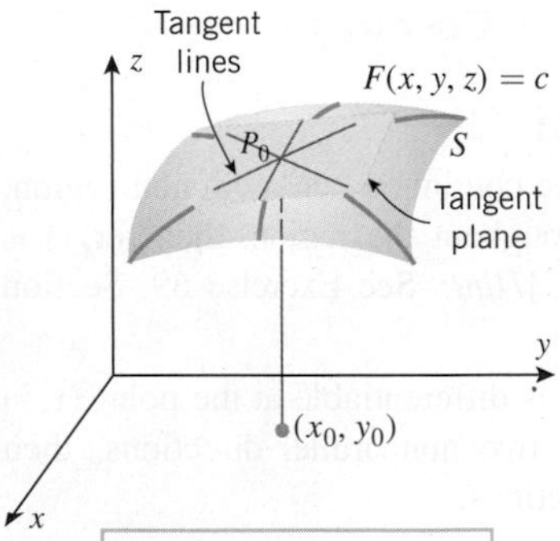

▲ **Figure 13.7.2**

$$\mathbf{r}' = x'(t_0)\mathbf{i} + y'(t_0)\mathbf{j} + z'(t_0)\mathbf{k}$$

where we assume that $\mathbf{r}' \neq \mathbf{0}$ (Definition 12.2.7). Since $C$ is on the surface $F(x, y, z) = c$, we have

$$c = F(x(t), y(t), z(t)) \tag{1}$$

Computing the derivative at $t_0$ of both sides of (1), we have by the chain rule that

$$0 = F_x(x_0, y_0, z_0)x'(t_0) + F_y(x_0, y_0, z_0)y'(t_0) + F_z(x_0, y_0, z_0)z'(t_0)$$

We can write this equation in vector form as

$$0 = (F_x(x_0, y_0, z_0)\mathbf{i} + F_y(x_0, y_0, z_0)\mathbf{j} + F_z(x_0, y_0, z_0)\mathbf{k}) \cdot (x'(t_0)\mathbf{i} + y'(t_0)\mathbf{j} + z'(t_0)\mathbf{k})$$

or

$$0 = \nabla F(x_0, y_0, z_0) \cdot \mathbf{r}' \tag{2}$$

It follows that if $\nabla F(x_0, y_0, z_0) \neq \mathbf{0}$, then $\nabla F(x_0, y_0, z_0)$ is normal to line $l$. Therefore, the tangent line $l$ to $C$ at $P_0$ is contained in the plane through $P_0$ with normal vector $\nabla F(x_0, y_0, z_0)$. Since $C$ was *arbitrary*, we conclude that the same is true for any curve on $S$ through $P_0$ (Figure 13.7.3). Thus, it makes sense to define the tangent plane to $S$ at $P_0$ to be the plane through $P_0$ whose normal vector is

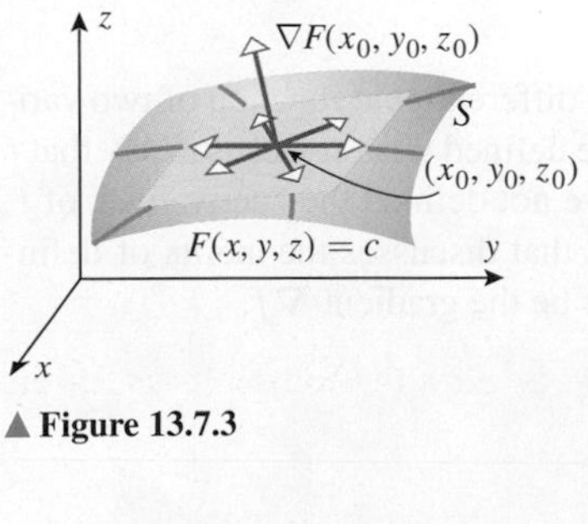

▲ **Figure 13.7.3**

$$\mathbf{n} = \nabla F(x_0, y_0, z_0) = \langle F_x(x_0, y_0, z_0), F_y(x_0, y_0, z_0), F_z(x_0, y_0, z_0)\rangle$$

Using the point-normal form [see Formula (3) in Section 11.6], we have the following definition.

Definition 13.7.1 can be viewed as an extension of Theorem 13.6.6 from curves to surfaces.

**13.7.1 DEFINITION** Assume that $F(x, y, z)$ has continuous first-order partial derivatives and that $P_0(x_0, y_0, z_0)$ is a point on the level surface $S$: $F(x, y, z) = c$. If $\nabla F(x_0, y_0, z_0) \neq \mathbf{0}$, then $\mathbf{n} = \nabla F(x_0, y_0, z_0)$ is a ***normal vector*** to $S$ at $P_0$ and the ***tangent plane*** to $S$ at $P_0$ is the plane with equation

$$F_x(x_0, y_0, z_0)(x - x_0) + F_y(x_0, y_0, z_0)(y - y_0) + F_z(x_0, y_0, z_0)(z - z_0) = 0 \quad (3)$$

The line through the point $P_0$ parallel to the normal vector $\mathbf{n}$ is perpendicular to the tangent plane (3). We will call this the ***normal line***, or sometimes more simply the ***normal*** to the surface $F(x, y, z) = c$ at $P_0$. It follows that this line can be expressed parametrically as

$$x = x_0 + F_x(x_0, y_0, z_0)t, \quad y = y_0 + F_y(x_0, y_0, z_0)t, \quad z = z_0 + F_z(x_0, y_0, z_0)t \quad (4)$$

▶ **Example 1** Consider the ellipsoid $x^2 + 4y^2 + z^2 = 18$.

(a) Find an equation of the tangent plane to the ellipsoid at the point $(1, 2, 1)$.

(b) Find parametric equations of the line that is normal to the ellipsoid at the point $(1, 2, 1)$.

(c) Find the acute angle that the tangent plane at the point $(1, 2, 1)$ makes with the $xy$-plane.

***Solution (a).*** We apply Definition 13.7.1 with $F(x, y, z) = x^2 + 4y^2 + z^2$ and $(x_0, y_0, z_0) = (1, 2, 1)$. Since

$$\nabla F(x, y, z) = \langle F_x(x, y, z), F_y(x, y, z), F_z(x, y, z)\rangle = \langle 2x, 8y, 2z\rangle$$

we have

$$\mathbf{n} = \nabla F(1, 2, 1) = \langle 2, 16, 2\rangle$$

Hence, from (3) the equation of the tangent plane is

$$2(x - 1) + 16(y - 2) + 2(z - 1) = 0 \quad \text{or} \quad x + 8y + z = 18$$

***Solution (b).*** Since $\mathbf{n} = \langle 2, 16, 2\rangle$ at the point $(1, 2, 1)$, it follows from (4) that parametric equations for the normal line to the ellipsoid at the point $(1, 2, 1)$ are

$$x = 1 + 2t, \quad y = 2 + 16t, \quad z = 1 + 2t$$

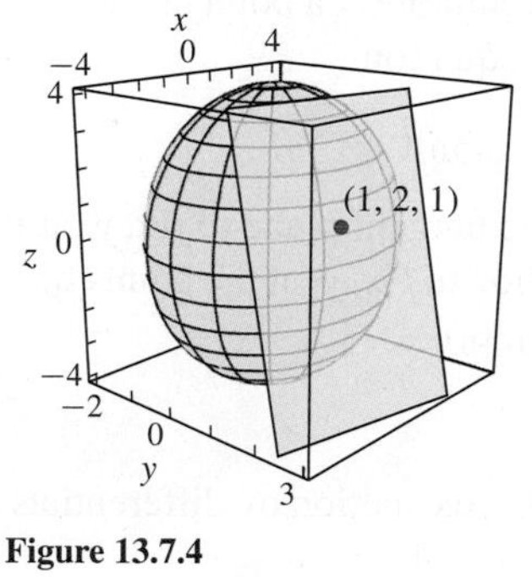


▲ **Figure 13.7.4**

***Solution (c).*** To find the acute angle $\theta$ between the tangent plane and the $xy$-plane, we will apply Formula (9) of Section 11.6 with $\mathbf{n}_1 = \mathbf{n} = \langle 2, 16, 2\rangle$ and $\mathbf{n}_2 = \langle 0, 0, 1\rangle$. This yields

$$\cos\theta = \frac{|\langle 2, 16, 2\rangle \cdot \langle 0, 0, 1\rangle|}{\|\langle 2, 16, 2\rangle\| \, \|\langle 0, 0, 1\rangle\|} = \frac{2}{(2\sqrt{66})(1)} = \frac{1}{\sqrt{66}}$$

Thus,

$$\theta = \cos^{-1}\left(\frac{1}{\sqrt{66}}\right) \approx 83^\circ$$

(Figure 13.7.4). ◀

## TANGENT PLANES TO SURFACES OF THE FORM $z = f(x, y)$

To find a tangent plane to a surface of the form $z = f(x, y)$, we can use Equation (3) with the function $F(x, y, z) = z - f(x, y)$.

▶ **Example 2** Find an equation for the tangent plane and parametric equations for the normal line to the surface $z = x^2y$ at the point $(2, 1, 4)$.

***Solution.*** Let $F(x, y, z) = z - x^2y$. Then $F(x, y, z) = 0$ on the surface, so we can find the find the gradient of $F$ at the point $(2, 1, 4)$:

$$\nabla F(x, y, z) = -2xy\mathbf{i} - x^2\mathbf{j} + \mathbf{k}$$
$$\nabla F(2, 1, 4) = -4\mathbf{i} - 4\mathbf{j} + \mathbf{k}$$

From (3) the tangent plane has equation

$$-4(x-2) - 4(y-1) + 1(z-4) = 0 \quad \text{or} \quad -4x - 4y + z = -8$$

and the normal line has equations

$$x = 2 - 4t, \qquad y = 1 - 4t, \qquad z = 4 + t \blacktriangleleft$$

Suppose that $f(x, y)$ is differentiable at a point $(x_0, y_0)$ and that $z_0 = f(x_0, y_0)$. It can be shown that the procedure of Example 2 can be used to find the tangent plane to the surface $z = f(x, y)$ at the point $(x_0, y_0, z_0)$. This yields an alternative equation for a tangent plane to the graph of a differentiable function.

**13.7.2 THEOREM** *If $f(x, y)$ is differentiable at the point $(x_0, y_0)$, then the tangent plane to the surface $z = f(x, y)$ at the point $P_0(x_0, y_0, f(x_0, y_0))$ [or $(x_0, y_0)$] is the plane*

$$z = f(x_0, y_0) + f_x(x_0, y_0)(x - x_0) + f_y(x_0, y_0)(y - y_0) \tag{5}$$

**PROOF** Consider the function $F(x, y, z) = z - f(x, y)$. Since $F(x, y, z) = 0$ on the surface, we will apply (3) to this function. The partial derivatives of $F$ are

$$F_x(x, y, z) = -f_x(x, y), \quad F_y(x, y, z) = -f_y(x, y), \quad F_z(x, y, z) = 1$$

Since the point at which we evaluate these derivatives lies on the surface, it will have the form $(x_0, y_0, f(x_0, y_0))$. Thus, (3) gives

$$\begin{aligned} 0 &= F_x(x_0, y_0, z_0)(x - x_0) + F_y(x_0, y_0, z_0)(y - y_0) + F_z(x_0, y_0, z_0)(z - f(x_0, y_0)) \\ &= -f_x(x_0, y_0)(x - x_0) - f_y(x_0, y_0)(y - y_0) + 1(z - f(x_0, y_0)) \end{aligned}$$

which is equivalent to (5). ■

Recall from Section 13.4 that if a function $f(x, y)$ is differentiable at a point $(x_0, y_0)$, then the local linear approximation $L(x, y)$ to $f$ at $(x_0, y_0)$ has the equation

$$L(x, y) = f(x_0, y_0) + f_x(x_0, y_0)(x - x_0) + f_y(x_0, y_0)(y - y_0)$$

Notice that the equation $z = L(x, y)$ is identical to that of the tangent plane to $f(x, y)$ at the point $(x_0, y_0)$. Thus, the graph of the local linear approximation to $f(x, y)$ at the point $(x_0, y_0)$ is the tangent plane to the surface $z = f(x, y)$ at the point $(x_0, y_0)$.

## TANGENT PLANES AND TOTAL DIFFERENTIALS

Recall that for a function $z = f(x, y)$ of two variables, the approximation by differentials is

$$\Delta z = \Delta f = f(x, y) - f(x_0, y_0) \approx dz = f_x(x_0, y_0)(x - x_0) + f_y(x_0, y_0)(y - y_0)$$

Note that the tangent plane in Figure 13.7.5 is analogous to the tangent line in Figure 13.4.2.

The tangent plane provides a geometric interpretation of this approximation. We see in Figure 13.7.5 that $\Delta z$ is the change in $z$ *along the surface* $z = f(x, y)$ from the point $P_0(x_0, y_0, f(x_0, y_0))$ to the point $P(x, y, f(x, y))$, and $dz$ is the change in $z$ *along the tangent plane* from $P_0$ to $Q(x, y, L(x, y))$. The small vertical displacement at $(x, y)$ between the surface and the plane represents the error in the local linear approximation to $f$ at $(x_0, y_0)$. We have seen that near $(x_0, y_0)$ this error term has magnitude much smaller than the distance between $(x, y)$ and $(x_0, y_0)$.

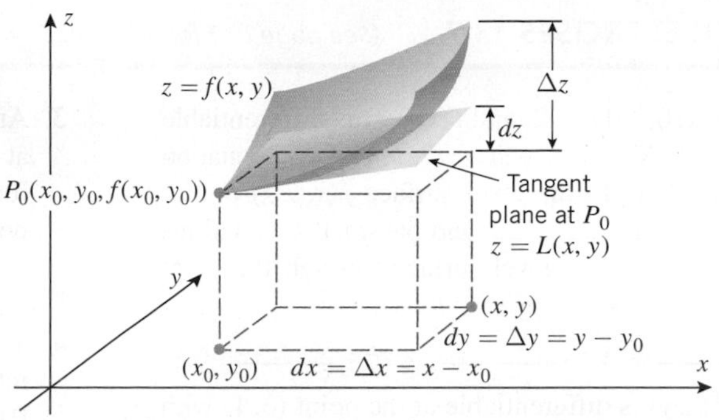


▶ Figure 13.7.5

## USING GRADIENTS TO FIND TANGENT LINES TO INTERSECTIONS OF SURFACES

In general, the intersection of two surfaces $F(x, y, z) = 0$ and $G(x, y, z) = 0$ will be a curve in 3-space. If $(x_0, y_0, z_0)$ is a point on this curve, then $\nabla F(x_0, y_0, z_0)$ will be normal to the surface $F(x, y, z) = 0$ at $(x_0, y_0, z_0)$ and $\nabla G(x_0, y_0, z_0)$ will be normal to the surface $G(x, y, z) = 0$ at $(x_0, y_0, z_0)$. Thus, if the curve of intersection can be smoothly parametrized, then its unit tangent vector $\mathbf{T}$ at $(x_0, y_0, z_0)$ will be orthogonal to both $\nabla F(x_0, y_0, z_0)$ and $\nabla G(x_0, y_0, z_0)$ (Figure 13.7.6). Consequently, if

$$\nabla F(x_0, y_0, z_0) \times \nabla G(x_0, y_0, z_0) \neq \mathbf{0}$$

then this cross product will be parallel to $\mathbf{T}$ and hence will be tangent to the curve of intersection. This tangent vector can be used to determine the direction of the tangent line to the curve of intersection at the point $(x_0, y_0, z_0)$.

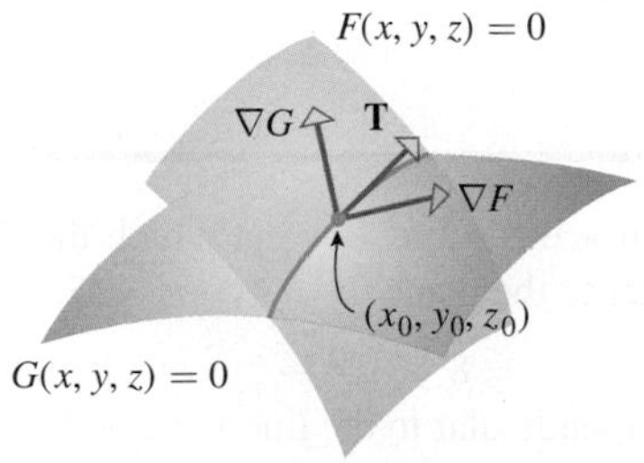


▲ Figure 13.7.6

▶ **Example 3** Find parametric equations of the tangent line to the curve of intersection of the paraboloid $z = x^2 + y^2$ and the ellipsoid $3x^2 + 2y^2 + z^2 = 9$ at the point $(1, 1, 2)$ (Figure 13.7.7).

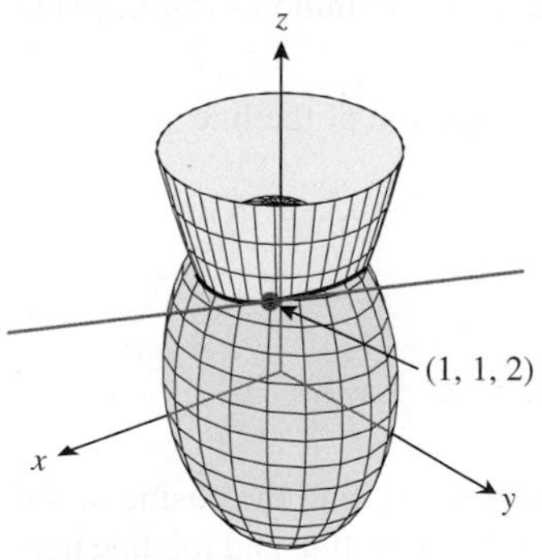


▲ Figure 13.7.7

***Solution.*** We begin by rewriting the equations of the surfaces as

$$x^2 + y^2 - z = 0 \quad \text{and} \quad 3x^2 + 2y^2 + z^2 - 9 = 0$$

and we take

$$F(x, y, z) = x^2 + y^2 - z \quad \text{and} \quad G(x, y, z) = 3x^2 + 2y^2 + z^2 - 9$$

We will need the gradients of these functions at the point $(1, 1, 2)$. The computations are

$$\nabla F(x, y, z) = 2x\mathbf{i} + 2y\mathbf{j} - \mathbf{k}, \quad \nabla G(x, y, z) = 6x\mathbf{i} + 4y\mathbf{j} + 2z\mathbf{k}$$
$$\nabla F(1, 1, 2) = 2\mathbf{i} + 2\mathbf{j} - \mathbf{k}, \quad \nabla G(1, 1, 2) = 6\mathbf{i} + 4\mathbf{j} + 4\mathbf{k}$$

Thus, a tangent vector at $(1, 1, 2)$ to the curve of intersection is

$$\nabla F(1, 1, 2) \times \nabla G(1, 1, 2) = \begin{vmatrix} \mathbf{i} & \mathbf{j} & \mathbf{k} \\ 2 & 2 & -1 \\ 6 & 4 & 4 \end{vmatrix} = 12\mathbf{i} - 14\mathbf{j} - 4\mathbf{k}$$

Since any scalar multiple of this vector will do just as well, we can multiply by $\frac{1}{2}$ to reduce the size of the coefficients and use the vector of $6\mathbf{i} - 7\mathbf{j} - 2\mathbf{k}$ to determine the direction of the tangent line. This vector and the point $(1, 1, 2)$ yield the parametric equations

$$x = 1 + 6t, \quad y = 1 - 7t, \quad z = 2 - 2t \blacktriangleleft$$

## ✓ QUICK CHECK EXERCISES 13.7

(See page 872 for answers.)

1. Suppose that $f(1, 0, -1) = 2$, and $f(x, y, z)$ is differentiable at $(1, 0, -1)$ with $\nabla f(1, 0, -1) = \langle 2, 1, 1\rangle$. An equation for the tangent plane to the level surface $f(x, y, z) = 2$ at the point $(1, 0, -1)$ is ______, and parametric equations for the normal line to the level surface through the point $(1, 0, -1)$ are

$x =$ ______, $y =$ ______, $z =$ ______

2. Suppose that $f(x, y)$ is differentiable at the point $(3, 1)$ with $f(3, 1) = 4$, $f_x(3, 1) = 2$, and $f_y(3, 1) = -3$. An equation for the tangent plane to the graph of $f$ at the point $(3, 1, 4)$ is ______, and parametric equations for the normal line to the graph of $f$ through the point $(3, 1, 4)$ are

$x =$ ______, $y =$ ______, $z =$ ______

3. An equation for the tangent plane to the graph of $z = x^2\sqrt{y}$ at the point $(2, 4, 8)$ is ______, and parametric equations for the normal line to the graph of $z = x^2\sqrt{y}$ through the point $(2, 4, 8)$ are

$x =$ ______, $y =$ ______, $z =$ ______

4. The sphere $x^2 + y^2 + z^2 = 9$ and the plane $x + y + z = 5$ intersect in a circle that passes through the point $(2, 1, 2)$. Parametric equations for the tangent line to this circle at $(2, 1, 2)$ are

$x =$ ______, $y =$ ______, $z =$ ______

## EXERCISE SET 13.7 [C] CAS

1. Consider the ellipsoid $x^2 + y^2 + 4z^2 = 12$.
   (a) Find an equation of the tangent plane to the ellipsoid at the point $(2, 2, 1)$.
   (b) Find parametric equations of the line that is normal to the ellipsoid at the point $(2, 2, 1)$.
   (c) Find the acute angle that the tangent plane at the point $(2, 2, 1)$ makes with the $xy$-plane.

2. Consider the surface $xz - yz^3 + yz^2 = 2$.
   (a) Find an equation of the tangent plane to the surface at the point $(2, -1, 1)$.
   (b) Find parametric equations of the line that is normal to the surface at the point $(2, -1, 1)$.
   (c) Find the acute angle that the tangent plane at the point $(2, -1, 1)$ makes with the $xy$-plane.

**3–12** Find an equation for the tangent plane and parametric equations for the normal line to the surface at the point $P$. ■

3. $x^2 + y^2 + z^2 = 25$; $P(-3, 0, 4)$
4. $x^2y - 4z^2 = -7$; $P(-3, 1, -2)$
5. $x^2 - xyz = 56$; $P(-4, 5, 2)$
6. $z = x^2 + y^2$; $P(2, -3, 13)$
7. $z = 4x^3y^2 + 2y$; $P(1, -2, 12)$
8. $z = \frac{1}{2}x^7y^{-2}$; $P(2, 4, 4)$
9. $z = xe^{-y}$; $P(1, 0, 1)$
10. $z = \ln\sqrt{x^2 + y^2}$; $P(-1, 0, 0)$
11. $z = e^{3y}\sin 3x$; $P(\pi/6, 0, 1)$
12. $z = x^{1/2} + y^{1/2}$; $P(4, 9, 5)$

**FOCUS ON CONCEPTS**

13. Find all points on the surface at which the tangent plane is horizontal.
   (a) $z = x^3y^2$
   (b) $z = x^2 - xy + y^2 - 2x + 4y$

14. Find a point on the surface $z = 3x^2 - y^2$ at which the tangent plane is parallel to the plane $6x + 4y - z = 5$.

15. Find a point on the surface $z = 8 - 3x^2 - 2y^2$ at which the tangent plane is perpendicular to the line $x = 2 - 3t$, $y = 7 + 8t$, $z = 5 - t$.

16. Show that the surfaces

$$z = \sqrt{x^2 + y^2} \quad \text{and} \quad z = \tfrac{1}{10}(x^2 + y^2) + \tfrac{5}{2}$$

intersect at $(3, 4, 5)$ and have a common tangent plane at that point.

17. (a) Find all points of intersection of the line

$$x = -1 + t, \quad y = 2 + t, \quad z = 2t + 7$$

and the surface

$$z = x^2 + y^2$$

   (b) At each point of intersection, find the cosine of the acute angle between the given line and the line normal to the surface.

18. Show that if $f$ is differentiable and $z = xf(x/y)$, then all tangent planes to the graph of this equation pass through the origin.

**19–22 True–False** Determine whether the statement is true or false. Explain your answer. ■

19. If the tangent plane to the level surface of $F(x, y, z)$ at the point $P_0(x_0, y_0, z_0)$ is also tangent to a level surface of $G(x, y, z)$ at $P_0$, then $\nabla F(x_0, y_0, z_0) = \nabla G(x_0, y_0, z_0)$.

20. If the tangent plane to the graph of $z = f(x, y)$ at the point $(1, 1, 2)$ has equation $x - y + 2z = 4$, then $f_x(1, 1) = 1$ and $f_y(1, 1) = -1$.

**21.** If the tangent plane to the graph of $z = f(x, y)$ at the point $(1, 2, 1)$ has equation $2x + y - z = 3$, then the local linear approximation to $f$ at $(1, 2)$ is given by the function $L(x, y) = 1 + 2(x - 1) + (y - 2)$.

**22.** The normal line to the surface $z = f(x, y)$ at the point $P_0(x_0, y_0, f(x_0, y_0))$ has a direction vector given by $f_x(x_0, y_0)\mathbf{i} + f_y(x_0, y_0)\mathbf{j} - \mathbf{k}$.

**23–24** Find two unit vectors that are normal to the given surface at the point $P$. ■

**23.** $\sqrt{\dfrac{z+x}{y-1}} = z^2$; $P(3, 5, 1)$

**24.** $\sin xz - 4\cos yz = 4$; $P(\pi, \pi, 1)$

**25.** Show that every line that is normal to the sphere

$$x^2 + y^2 + z^2 = 1$$

passes through the origin.

**26.** Find all points on the ellipsoid $2x^2 + 3y^2 + 4z^2 = 9$ at which the plane tangent to the ellipsoid is parallel to the plane $x - 2y + 3z = 5$.

**27.** Find all points on the surface $x^2 + y^2 - z^2 = 1$ at which the normal line is parallel to the line through $P(1, -2, 1)$ and $Q(4, 0, -1)$.

**28.** Show that the ellipsoid $2x^2 + 3y^2 + z^2 = 9$ and the sphere

$$x^2 + y^2 + z^2 - 6x - 8y - 8z + 24 = 0$$

have a common tangent plane at the point $(1, 1, 2)$.

**29.** Find parametric equations for the tangent line to the curve of intersection of the paraboloid $z = x^2 + y^2$ and the ellipsoid $x^2 + 4y^2 + z^2 = 9$ at the point $(1, -1, 2)$.

**30.** Find parametric equations for the tangent line to the curve of intersection of the cone $z = \sqrt{x^2 + y^2}$ and the plane $x + 2y + 2z = 20$ at the point $(4, 3, 5)$.

**31.** Find parametric equations for the tangent line to the curve of intersection of the cylinders $x^2 + z^2 = 25$ and $y^2 + z^2 = 25$ at the point $(3, -3, 4)$.

C **32.** The accompanying figure shows the intersection of the surfaces $z = 8 - x^2 - y^2$ and $4x + 2y - z = 0$.
(a) Find parametric equations for the tangent line to the curve of intersection at the point $(0, 2, 4)$.
(b) Use a CAS to generate a reasonable facsimile of the figure. You need not generate the colors, but try to obtain a similar viewpoint.

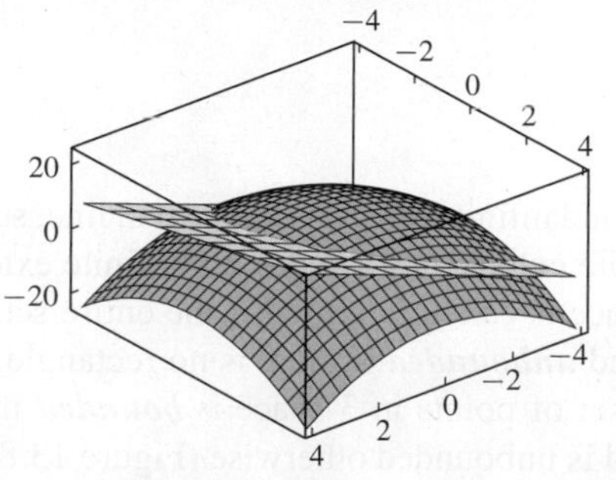

◀ **Figure Ex-32**

**33.** Show that the equation of the plane that is tangent to the ellipsoid

$$\frac{x^2}{a^2} + \frac{y^2}{b^2} + \frac{z^2}{c^2} = 1$$

at $(x_0, y_0, z_0)$ can be written in the form

$$\frac{x_0x}{a^2} + \frac{y_0y}{b^2} + \frac{z_0z}{c^2} = 1$$

**34.** Show that the equation of the plane that is tangent to the paraboloid

$$z = \frac{x^2}{a^2} + \frac{y^2}{b^2}$$

at $(x_0, y_0, z_0)$ can be written in the form

$$z + z_0 = \frac{2x_0x}{a^2} + \frac{2y_0y}{b^2}$$

**35.** Prove: If the surfaces $z = f(x, y)$ and $z = g(x, y)$ intersect at $P(x_0, y_0, z_0)$, and if $f$ and $g$ are differentiable at $(x_0, y_0)$, then the normal lines at $P$ are perpendicular if and only if

$$f_x(x_0, y_0)g_x(x_0, y_0) + f_y(x_0, y_0)g_y(x_0, y_0) = -1$$

**36.** Use the result in Exercise 35 to show that the normal lines to the cones $z = \sqrt{x^2 + y^2}$ and $z = -\sqrt{x^2 + y^2}$ are perpendicular to the normal lines to the sphere $x^2 + y^2 + z^2 = a^2$ at every point of intersection (see Figure Ex-38).

**37.** Two surfaces $f(x, y, z) = 0$ and $g(x, y, z) = 0$ are said to be ***orthogonal*** at a point $P$ of intersection if $\nabla f$ and $\nabla g$ are nonzero at $P$ and the normal lines to the surfaces are perpendicular at $P$. Show that if $\nabla f(x_0, y_0, z_0) \neq \mathbf{0}$ and $\nabla g(x_0, y_0, z_0) \neq \mathbf{0}$, then the surfaces $f(x, y, z) = 0$ and $g(x, y, z) = 0$ are orthogonal at the point $(x_0, y_0, z_0)$ if and only if

$$f_xg_x + f_yg_y + f_zg_z = 0$$

at this point. [*Note:* This is a more general version of the result in Exercise 35.]

**38.** Use the result of Exercise 37 to show that the sphere $x^2 + y^2 + z^2 = a^2$ and the cone $z^2 = x^2 + y^2$ are orthogonal at every point of intersection (see the accompanying figure).

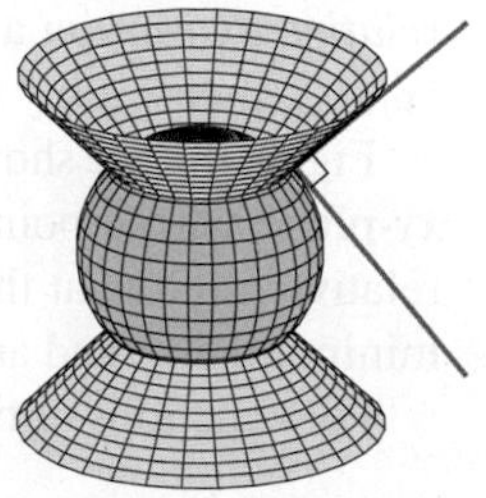
◀ **Figure Ex-38**

**39.** Show that the volume of the solid bounded by the coordinate planes and a plane tangent to the portion of the surface $xyz = k$, $k > 0$, in the first octant does not depend on the point of tangency.

**40. Writing** Discuss the role of the chain rule in defining a tangent plane to a level surface.

**41. Writing** Discuss the relationship between tangent planes and local linear approximations for functions of two variables.

✓ **QUICK CHECK ANSWERS 13.7** 1. $2(x-1)+y+(z+1)=0$; $x=1+2t$; $y=t$; $z=-1+t$
2. $z=4+2(x-3)-3(y-1)$; $x=3+2t$; $y=1-3t$; $z=4-t$
3. $z=8+8(x-2)+(y-4)$; $x=2+8t$; $y=4+t$; $z=8-t$ 4. $x=2+t$; $y=1$; $z=2-t$

# 13.8 MAXIMA AND MINIMA OF FUNCTIONS OF TWO VARIABLES

*Earlier in this text we learned how to find maximum and minimum values of a function of one variable. In this section we will develop similar techniques for functions of two variables.*

## EXTREMA

If we imagine the graph of a function $f$ of two variables to be a mountain range (Figure 13.8.1), then the mountaintops, which are the high points in their immediate vicinity, are called *relative maxima* of $f$, and the valley bottoms, which are the low points in their immediate vicinity, are called *relative minima* of $f$.

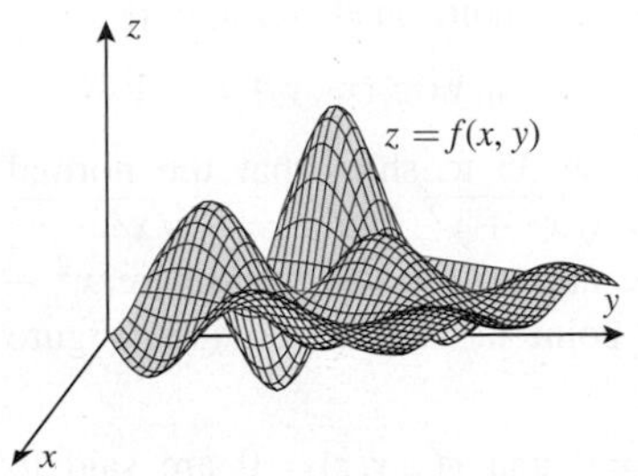

▲ **Figure 13.8.1**

Just as a geologist might be interested in finding the highest mountain and deepest valley in an entire mountain range, so a mathematician might be interested in finding the largest and smallest values of $f(x, y)$ over the *entire* domain of $f$. These are called the *absolute maximum* and *absolute minimum values* of $f$. The following definitions make these informal ideas precise.

**13.8.1 DEFINITION** A function $f$ of two variables is said to have a ***relative maximum*** at a point $(x_0, y_0)$ if there is a disk centered at $(x_0, y_0)$ such that $f(x_0, y_0) \geq f(x, y)$ for all points $(x, y)$ that lie inside the disk, and $f$ is said to have an ***absolute maximum*** at $(x_0, y_0)$ if $f(x_0, y_0) \geq f(x, y)$ for all points $(x, y)$ in the domain of $f$.

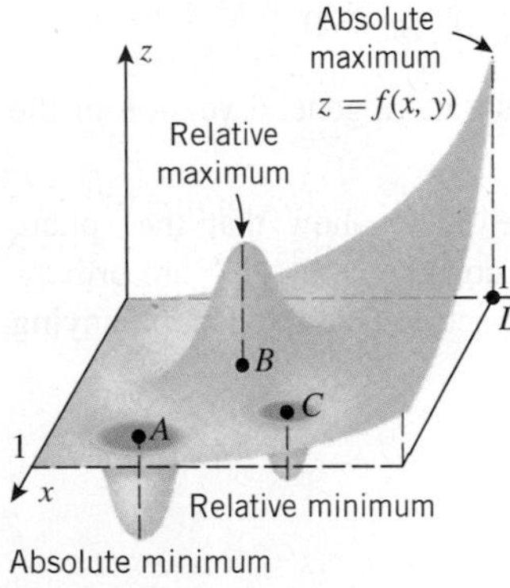

▲ **Figure 13.8.2**

**13.8.2 DEFINITION** A function $f$ of two variables is said to have a ***relative minimum*** at a point $(x_0, y_0)$ if there is a disk centered at $(x_0, y_0)$ such that $f(x_0, y_0) \leq f(x, y)$ for all points $(x, y)$ that lie inside the disk, and $f$ is said to have an ***absolute minimum*** at $(x_0, y_0)$ if $f(x_0, y_0) \leq f(x, y)$ for all points $(x, y)$ in the domain of $f$.

If $f$ has a relative maximum or a relative minimum at $(x_0, y_0)$, then we say that $f$ has a ***relative extremum*** at $(x_0, y_0)$, and if $f$ has an absolute maximum or absolute minimum at $(x_0, y_0)$, then we say that $f$ has an ***absolute extremum*** at $(x_0, y_0)$.

Figure 13.8.2 shows the graph of a function $f$ whose domain is the square region in the $xy$-plane whose points satisfy the inequalities $0 \leq x \leq 1, 0 \leq y \leq 1$. The function $f$ has relative minima at the points $A$ and $C$ and a relative maximum at $B$. There is an absolute minimum at $A$ and an absolute maximum at $D$.

For functions of two variables we will be concerned with two important questions:

- Are there any relative or absolute extrema?
- If so, where are they located?

## BOUNDED SETS

Just as we distinguished between finite intervals and infinite intervals on the real line, so we will want to distinguish between regions of "finite extent" and regions of "infinite extent" in 2-space and 3-space. A set of points in 2-space is called ***bounded*** if the entire set can be contained within some rectangle, and is called ***unbounded*** if there is no rectangle that contains all the points of the set. Similarly, a set of points in 3-space is ***bounded*** if the entire set can be contained within some box, and is unbounded otherwise (Figure 13.8.3).

Explain why any subset of a bounded set is also bounded.

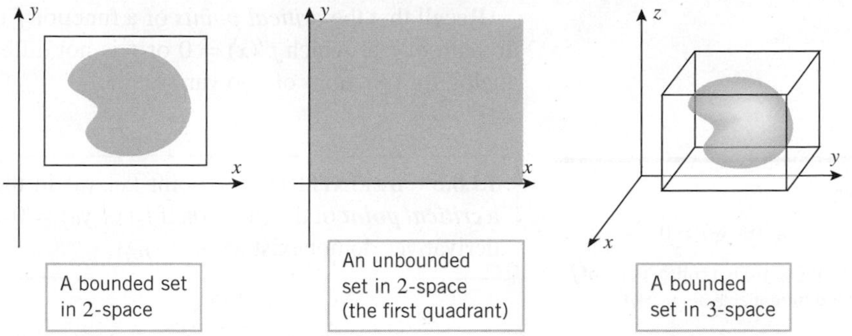


▶ Figure 13.8.3

## THE EXTREME-VALUE THEOREM

For functions of one variable that are continuous on a closed interval, the Extreme-Value Theorem (Theorem 4.4.2) answered the existence question for absolute extrema. The following theorem, which we state without proof, is the corresponding result for functions of two variables.

> **13.8.3 THEOREM** (*Extreme-Value Theorem*) *If $f(x, y)$ is continuous on a closed and bounded set $R$, then $f$ has both an absolute maximum and an absolute minimum on $R$.*

▶ **Example 1** The square region $R$ whose points satisfy the inequalities

$$0 \leq x \leq 1 \quad \text{and} \quad 0 \leq y \leq 1$$

is a closed and bounded set in the $xy$-plane. The function $f$ whose graph is shown in Figure 13.8.2 is continuous on $R$; thus, it is guaranteed to have an absolute maximum and minimum on $R$ by the last theorem. These occur at points $D$ and $A$ that are shown in the figure. ◀

**REMARK** If any of the conditions in the Extreme-Value Theorem fail to hold, then there is no guarantee that an absolute maximum or absolute minimum exists on the region $R$. Thus, a discontinuous function on a closed and bounded set need not have any absolute extrema, and a continuous function on a set that is not closed and bounded also need not have any absolute extrema.

## FINDING RELATIVE EXTREMA

Recall that if a function $g$ of one variable has a relative extremum at a point $x_0$ where $g$ is differentiable, then $g'(x_0) = 0$. To obtain the analog of this result for functions of two variables, suppose that $f(x, y)$ has a relative maximum at a point $(x_0, y_0)$ and that the partial derivatives of $f$ exist at $(x_0, y_0)$. It seems plausible geometrically that the traces of the surface $z = f(x, y)$ on the planes $x = x_0$ and $y = y_0$ have horizontal tangent lines at $(x_0, y_0)$ (Figure 13.8.4), so

$$f_x(x_0, y_0) = 0 \quad \text{and} \quad f_y(x_0, y_0) = 0$$

The same conclusion holds if $f$ has a relative minimum at $(x_0, y_0)$, all of which suggests the following result, which we state without formal proof.

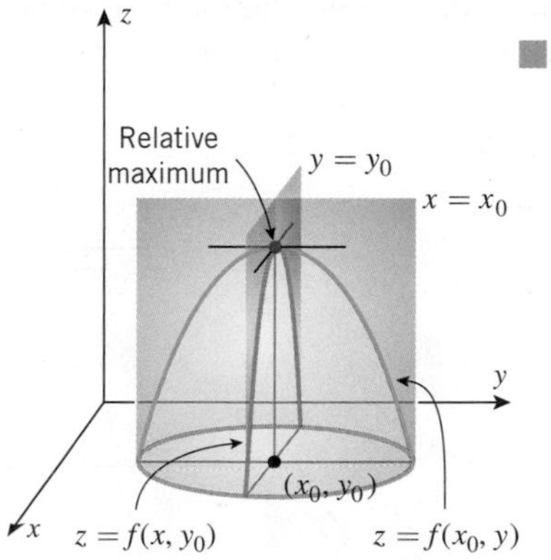


▲ Figure 13.8.4

> **13.8.4 THEOREM** *If $f$ has a relative extremum at a point $(x_0, y_0)$, and if the first-order partial derivatives of $f$ exist at this point, then*
>
> $$f_x(x_0, y_0) = 0 \quad \textit{and} \quad f_y(x_0, y_0) = 0$$

Recall that the *critical points* of a function $f$ of one variable are those values of $x$ in the domain of $f$ at which $f'(x) = 0$ or $f$ is not differentiable. The following definition is the analog for functions of two variables.

Explain why

$$D_{\mathbf{u}}f(x_0, y_0) = 0$$

for all **u** if $(x_0, y_0)$ is a critical point of $f$ and $f$ is differentiable at $(x_0, y_0)$.

**13.8.5 DEFINITION** A point $(x_0, y_0)$ in the domain of a function $f(x, y)$ is called a ***critical point*** of the function if $f_x(x_0, y_0) = 0$ and $f_y(x_0, y_0) = 0$ or if one or both partial derivatives do not exist at $(x_0, y_0)$.

It follows from this definition and Theorem 13.8.4 that relative extrema occur at critical points, just as for a function of one variable. However, recall that for a function of one variable a relative extremum need not occur at *every* critical point. For example, the function might have an inflection point with a horizontal tangent line at the critical point (see Figure 4.2.6). Similarly, a function of two variables need not have a relative extremum at every critical point. For example, consider the function

$$f(x, y) = y^2 - x^2$$

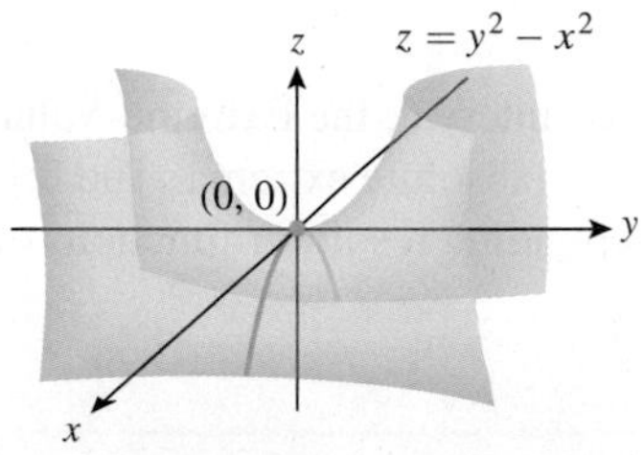

The function $f(x, y) = y^2 - x^2$ has neither a relative maximum nor a relative minimum at the critical point (0, 0).

▲ **Figure 13.8.5**

This function, whose graph is the hyperbolic paraboloid shown in Figure 13.8.5, has a critical point at (0, 0), since

$$f_x(x, y) = -2x \quad \text{and} \quad f_y(x, y) = 2y$$

from which it follows that

$$f_x(0, 0) = 0 \quad \text{and} \quad f_y(0, 0) = 0$$

However, the function $f$ has neither a relative maximum nor a relative minimum at (0, 0). For obvious reasons, the point (0, 0) is called a *saddle point* of $f$. In general, we will say that a surface $z = f(x, y)$ has a ***saddle point*** at $(x_0, y_0)$ if there are two distinct vertical planes through this point such that the trace of the surface in one of the planes has a relative maximum at $(x_0, y_0)$ and the trace in the other has a relative minimum at $(x_0, y_0)$.

► **Example 2** The three functions graphed in Figure 13.8.6 all have critical points at (0, 0). For the paraboloids, the partial derivatives at the origin are zero. You can check this algebraically by evaluating the partial derivatives at (0, 0), but you can see it geometrically by observing that the traces in the $xz$-plane and $yz$-plane have horizontal tangent lines at (0, 0). For the cone neither partial derivative exists at the origin because the traces in the $xz$-plane and the $yz$-plane have corners there. The paraboloid in part (*a*) and the cone in part (*c*) have a relative minimum and absolute minimum at the origin, and the paraboloid in part (*b*) has a relative maximum and an absolute maximum at the origin. ◄

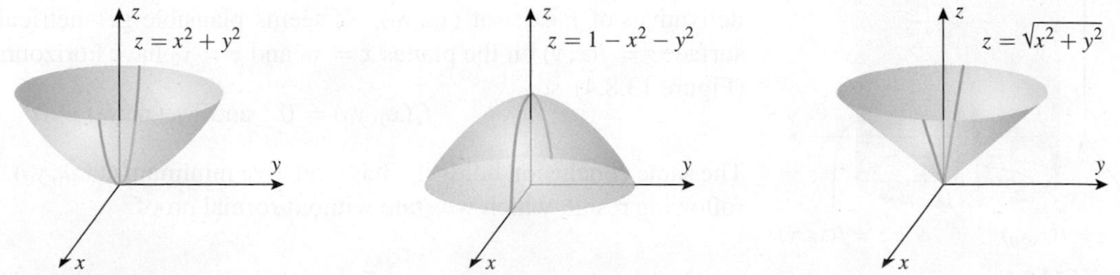

$f_x(0, 0) = f_y(0, 0) = 0$
relative and absolute min at (0, 0)
(*a*)

$f_x(0, 0) = f_y(0, 0) = 0$
relative and absolute max at (0, 0)
(*b*)

$f_x(0, 0)$ and $f_y(0, 0)$ do not exist
relative and absolute min at (0, 0)
(*c*)

▲ **Figure 13.8.6**

## THE SECOND PARTIALS TEST

For functions of one variable the second derivative test (Theorem 4.4.2) was used to determine the behavior of a function at a critical point. The following theorem, which is usually proved in advanced calculus, is the analog of that theorem for functions of two variables.

**13.8.6 THEOREM (*The Second Partials Test*)** *Let $f$ be a function of two variables with continuous second-order partial derivatives in some disk centered at a critical point $(x_0, y_0)$, and let*

$$D = f_{xx}(x_0, y_0)f_{yy}(x_0, y_0) - f_{xy}^2(x_0, y_0)$$

*(a) If $D > 0$ and $f_{xx}(x_0, y_0) > 0$, then $f$ has a relative minimum at $(x_0, y_0)$.*

*(b) If $D > 0$ and $f_{xx}(x_0, y_0) < 0$, then $f$ has a relative maximum at $(x_0, y_0)$.*

*(c) If $D < 0$, then $f$ has a saddle point at $(x_0, y_0)$.*

*(d) If $D = 0$, then no conclusion can be drawn.*

With the notation of Theorem 13.8.6, show that if $D > 0$, then $f_{xx}(x_0, y_0)$ and $f_{yy}(x_0, y_0)$ have the same sign. Thus, we can replace $f_{xx}(x_0, y_0)$ by $f_{yy}(x_0, y_0)$ in parts (*a*) and (*b*) of the theorem.

▶ **Example 3** Locate all relative extrema and saddle points of

$$f(x, y) = 3x^2 - 2xy + y^2 - 8y$$

***Solution.*** Since $f_x(x, y) = 6x - 2y$ and $f_y(x, y) = -2x + 2y - 8$, the critical points of $f$ satisfy the equations

$$6x - 2y = 0$$
$$-2x + 2y - 8 = 0$$

Solving these for $x$ and $y$ yields $x = 2, y = 6$ (verify), so $(2, 6)$ is the only critical point. To apply Theorem 13.8.6 we need the second-order partial derivatives

$$f_{xx}(x, y) = 6, \quad f_{yy}(x, y) = 2, \quad f_{xy}(x, y) = -2$$

At the point $(2, 6)$ we have

$$D = f_{xx}(2, 6)f_{yy}(2, 6) - f_{xy}^2(2, 6) = (6)(2) - (-2)^2 = 8 > 0$$

and

$$f_{xx}(2, 6) = 6 > 0$$

so $f$ has a relative minimum at $(2, 6)$ by part (*a*) of the second partials test. Figure 13.8.7 shows a graph of $f$ in the vicinity of the relative minimum. ◀

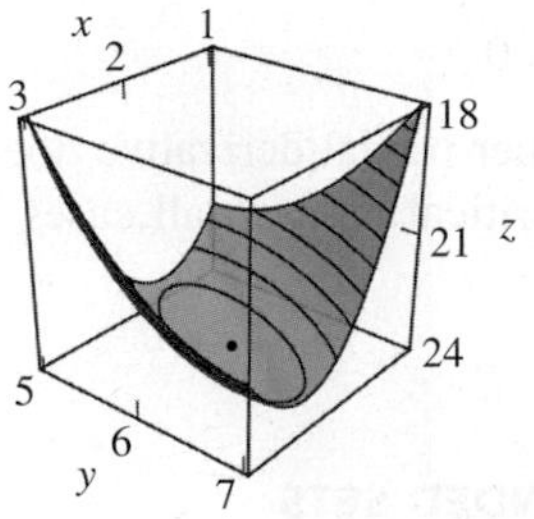


$f(x, y) = 3x^2 - 2xy + y^2 - 8y$

▲ **Figure 13.8.7**

▶ **Example 4** Locate all relative extrema and saddle points of

$$f(x, y) = 4xy - x^4 - y^4$$

***Solution.*** Since

$$f_x(x, y) = 4y - 4x^3$$
$$f_y(x, y) = 4x - 4y^3 \quad (1)$$

the critical points of $f$ have coordinates satisfying the equations

$$4y - 4x^3 = 0 \qquad y = x^3$$
$$\text{or} \qquad\qquad\qquad\qquad (2)$$
$$4x - 4y^3 = 0 \qquad x = y^3$$

Substituting the top equation in the bottom yields $x = (x^3)^3$ or, equivalently, $x^9 - x = 0$ or $x(x^8 - 1) = 0$, which has solutions $x = 0, x = 1, x = -1$. Substituting these values in the top equation of (2), we obtain the corresponding $y$-values $y = 0, y = 1, y = -1$. Thus, the critical points of $f$ are $(0, 0)$, $(1, 1)$, and $(-1, -1)$.

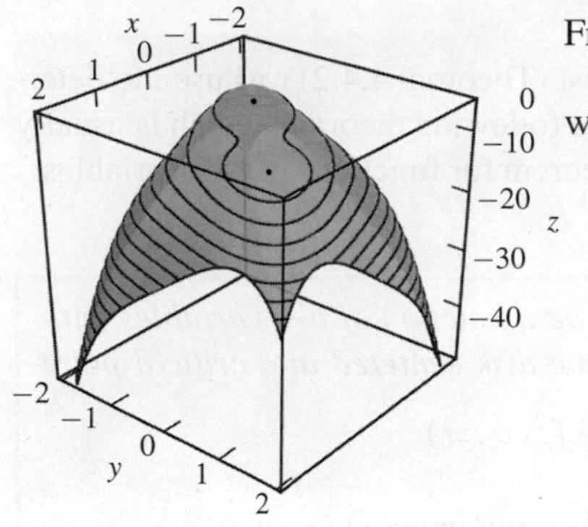


$f(x, y) = 4xy - x^4 - y^4$

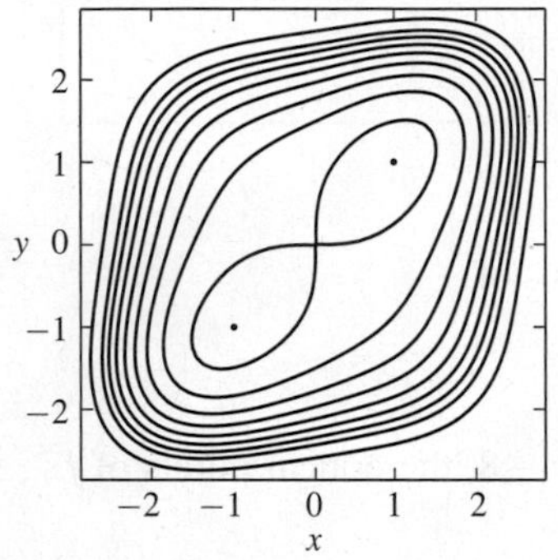


▲ **Figure 13.8.8**

The "figure eight" pattern at $(0, 0)$ in the contour plot for the surface in Figure 13.8.8 is typical for level curves that pass through a saddle point. If a bug starts at the point $(0, 0, 0)$ on the surface, in how many directions can it walk and remain in the $xy$-plane?

From (1),

$$f_{xx}(x, y) = -12x^2, \quad f_{yy}(x, y) = -12y^2, \quad f_{xy}(x, y) = 4$$

which yields the following table:

| CRITICAL POINT $(x_0, y_0)$ | $f_{xx}(x_0, y_0)$ | $f_{yy}(x_0, y_0)$ | $f_{xy}(x_0, y_0)$ | $D = f_{xx}f_{yy} - f_{xy}^2$ |
|---|---|---|---|---|
| (0, 0) | 0 | 0 | 4 | −16 |
| (1, 1) | −12 | −12 | 4 | 128 |
| (−1, −1) | −12 | −12 | 4 | 128 |

At the points $(1, 1)$ and $(-1, -1)$, we have $D > 0$ and $f_{xx} < 0$, so relative maxima occur at these critical points. At $(0, 0)$ there is a saddle point since $D < 0$. The surface and a contour plot are shown in Figure 13.8.8. ◄

The following theorem, which is the analog for functions of two variables of Theorem 4.4.3, will lead to an important method for finding absolute extrema.

**13.8.7 THEOREM** *If a function $f$ of two variables has an absolute extremum (either an absolute maximum or an absolute minimum) at an interior point of its domain, then this extremum occurs at a critical point.*

PROOF If $f$ has an absolute maximum at the point $(x_0, y_0)$ in the interior of the domain of $f$, then $f$ has a relative maximum at $(x_0, y_0)$. If both partial derivatives exist at $(x_0, y_0)$, then

$$f_x(x_0, y_0) = 0 \quad \text{and} \quad f_y(x_0, y_0) = 0$$

by Theorem 13.8.4, so $(x_0, y_0)$ is a critical point of $f$. If either partial derivative does not exist, then again $(x_0, y_0)$ is a critical point, so $(x_0, y_0)$ is a critical point in all cases. The proof for an absolute minimum is similar. ■

## FINDING ABSOLUTE EXTREMA ON CLOSED AND BOUNDED SETS

If $f(x, y)$ is continuous on a closed and bounded set $R$, then the Extreme-Value Theorem (Theorem 13.8.3) guarantees the existence of an absolute maximum and an absolute minimum of $f$ on $R$. These absolute extrema can occur either on the boundary of $R$ or in the interior of $R$, but if an absolute extremum occurs in the interior, then it occurs at a critical point by Theorem 13.8.7. Thus, we are led to the following procedure for finding absolute extrema:

Compare this procedure with that in Section 4.4 for finding the extreme values of $f(x)$ on a closed interval.

***How to Find the Absolute Extrema of a Continuous Function f of Two Variables on a Closed and Bounded Set R***

**Step 1.** Find the critical points of $f$ that lie in the interior of $R$.

**Step 2.** Find all boundary points at which the absolute extrema can occur.

**Step 3.** Evaluate $f(x, y)$ at the points obtained in the preceding steps. The largest of these values is the absolute maximum and the smallest the absolute minimum.

► **Example 5** Find the absolute maximum and minimum values of

$$f(x, y) = 3xy - 6x - 3y + 7 \tag{3}$$

on the closed triangular region $R$ with vertices $(0, 0)$, $(3, 0)$, and $(0, 5)$.

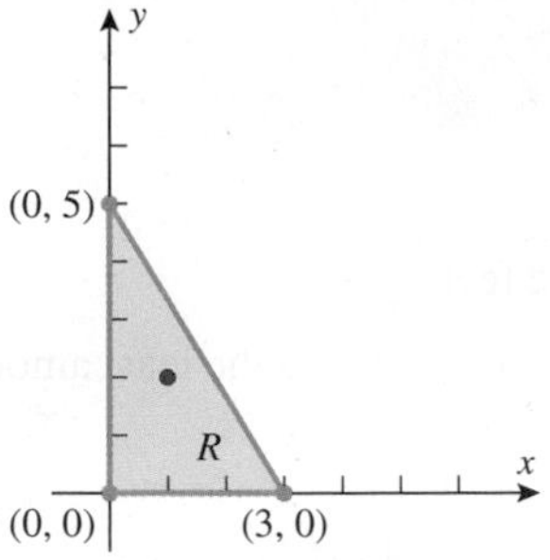


▲ **Figure 13.8.9**

***Solution.*** The region $R$ is shown in Figure 13.8.9. We have

$$\frac{\partial f}{\partial x} = 3y - 6 \quad \text{and} \quad \frac{\partial f}{\partial y} = 3x - 3$$

so all critical points occur where

$$3y - 6 = 0 \quad \text{and} \quad 3x - 3 = 0$$

Solving these equations yields $x = 1$ and $y = 2$, so $(1, 2)$ is the only critical point. As shown in Figure 13.8.9, this critical point is in the interior of $R$.

Next we want to determine the locations of the points on the boundary of $R$ at which the absolute extrema might occur. The boundary of $R$ consists of three line segments, each of which we will treat separately:

*The line segment between* $(0, 0)$ *and* $(3, 0)$: On this line segment we have $y = 0$, so (3) simplifies to a function of the single variable $x$,

$$u(x) = f(x, 0) = -6x + 7, \quad 0 \le x \le 3$$

This function has no critical points because $u'(x) = -6$ is nonzero for all $x$. Thus the extreme values of $u(x)$ occur at the endpoints $x = 0$ and $x = 3$, which correspond to the points $(0, 0)$ and $(3, 0)$ of $R$.

*The line segment between* $(0, 0)$ *and* $(0, 5)$: On this line segment we have $x = 0$, so (3) simplifies to a function of the single variable $y$,

$$v(y) = f(0, y) = -3y + 7, \quad 0 \le y \le 5$$

This function has no critical points because $v'(y) = -3$ is nonzero for all $y$. Thus, the extreme values of $v(y)$ occur at the endpoints $y = 0$ and $y = 5$, which correspond to the points $(0, 0)$ and $(0, 5)$ of $R$.

*The line segment between* $(3, 0)$ *and* $(0, 5)$: In the $xy$-plane, an equation for this line segment is

$$y = -\tfrac{5}{3}x + 5, \quad 0 \le x \le 3 \tag{4}$$

so (3) simplifies to a function of the single variable $x$,

$$\begin{aligned} w(x) &= f\left(x, -\tfrac{5}{3}x + 5\right) = 3x\left(-\tfrac{5}{3}x + 5\right) - 6x - 3\left(-\tfrac{5}{3}x + 5\right) + 7 \\ &= -5x^2 + 14x - 8, \quad 0 \le x \le 3 \end{aligned}$$

Since $w'(x) = -10x + 14$, the equation $w'(x) = 0$ yields $x = \frac{7}{5}$ as the only critical point of $w$. Thus, the extreme values of $w$ occur either at the critical point $x = \frac{7}{5}$ or at the endpoints $x = 0$ and $x = 3$. The endpoints correspond to the points $(0, 5)$ and $(3, 0)$ of $R$, and from (4) the critical point corresponds to $\left(\frac{7}{5}, \frac{8}{3}\right)$.

Finally, Table 13.8.1 lists the values of $f(x, y)$ at the interior critical point and at the points on the boundary where an absolute extremum can occur. From the table we conclude that the absolute maximum value of $f$ is $f(0, 0) = 7$ and the absolute minimum value is $f(3, 0) = -11$. ◄

**Table 13.8.1**

| $(x, y)$ | $(0, 0)$ | $(3, 0)$ | $(0, 5)$ | $\left(\frac{7}{5}, \frac{8}{3}\right)$ | $(1, 2)$ |
|---|---|---|---|---|---|
| $f(x, y)$ | 7 | −11 | −8 | $\frac{9}{5}$ | 1 |

► **Example 6** Determine the dimensions of a rectangular box, open at the top, having a volume of 32 ft$^3$, and requiring the least amount of material for its construction.

***Solution.*** Let

$x$ = length of the box (in feet)
$y$ = width of the box (in feet)
$z$ = height of the box (in feet)
$S$ = surface area of the box (in square feet)

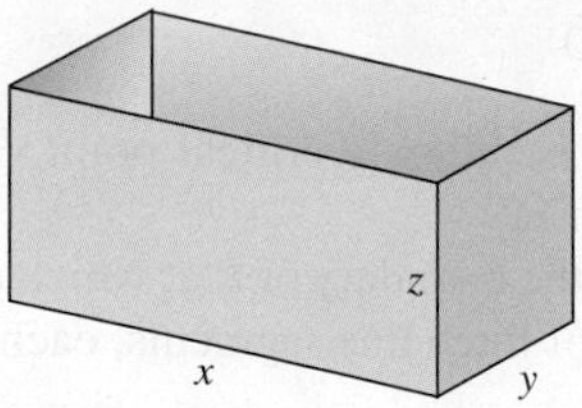


Two sides each have area $xz$.
Two sides each have area $yz$.
The base has area $xy$.

▲ **Figure 13.8.10**

We may reasonably assume that the box with least surface area requires the least amount of material, so our objective is to minimize the surface area

$$S = xy + 2xz + 2yz \tag{5}$$

(Figure 13.8.10) subject to the volume requirement

$$xyz = 32 \tag{6}$$

From (6) we obtain $z = 32/xy$, so (5) can be rewritten as

$$S = xy + \frac{64}{y} + \frac{64}{x} \tag{7}$$

which expresses $S$ as a function of two variables. The dimensions $x$ and $y$ in this formula must be positive, but otherwise have no limitation, so our problem reduces to finding the absolute minimum value of $S$ over the open first quadrant: $x > 0$, $y > 0$. Because this region is neither closed nor bounded, we have no mathematical guarantee at this stage that an absolute minimum exists. However, if $S$ has an absolute minimum value in the open first quadrant, then it must occur at a critical point of $S$. Thus, our next step is to find the critical points of $S$.

Differentiating (7) we obtain

$$\frac{\partial S}{\partial x} = y - \frac{64}{x^2}, \quad \frac{\partial S}{\partial y} = x - \frac{64}{y^2} \tag{8}$$

so the coordinates of the critical points of $S$ satisfy

$$y - \frac{64}{x^2} = 0, \quad x - \frac{64}{y^2} = 0$$

Solving the first equation for $y$ yields

$$y = \frac{64}{x^2} \tag{9}$$

and substituting this expression in the second equation yields

$$x - \frac{64}{(64/x^2)^2} = 0$$

which can be rewritten as

$$x\left(1 - \frac{x^3}{64}\right) = 0$$

The solutions of this equation are $x = 0$ and $x = 4$. Since we require $x > 0$, the only solution of significance is $x = 4$. Substituting this value into (9) yields $y = 4$. We conclude that the point $(x, y) = (4, 4)$ is the only critical point of $S$ in the first quadrant. Since $S = 48$ if $x = y = 4$, this suggests we try to show that the minimum value of $S$ on the open first quadrant is 48.

It immediately follows from Equation (7) that $48 < S$ at any point in the first quadrant for which at least one of the inequalities

$$xy > 48, \quad \frac{64}{y} > 48, \quad \frac{64}{x} > 48$$

is satisfied. Therefore, to prove that $48 \leq S$, we can restrict attention to the set of points in the first quadrant that satisfy the three inequalities

$$xy \leq 48, \quad \frac{64}{y} \leq 48, \quad \frac{64}{x} \leq 48$$

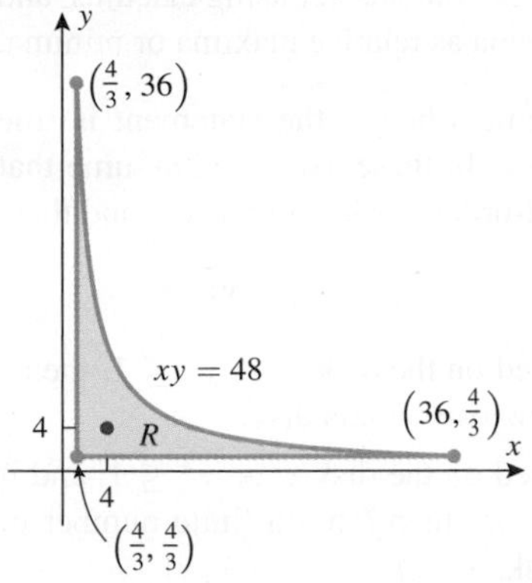

▲ **Figure 13.8.11**

These inequalities can be rewritten as

$$xy \leq 48, \quad y \geq \frac{4}{3}, \quad x \geq \frac{4}{3}$$

and they define a closed and bounded region $R$ within the first quadrant (Figure 13.8.11). The function $S$ is continuous on $R$, so Theorem 13.8.3 guarantees that $S$ has an absolute minimum value somewhere on $R$. Since the point $(4, 4)$ lies within $R$, and $48 < S$ on the boundary of $R$ (why?), the minimum value of $S$ on $R$ must occur at an interior point. It then follows from Theorem 13.8.7 that the mimimum value of $S$ on $R$ must occur at a critical point of $S$. Hence, the absolute minimum of $S$ on $R$ (and therefore on the entire open first quadrant) is $S = 48$ at the point $(4, 4)$. Substituting $x = 4$ and $y = 4$ into (6) yields $z = 2$, so the box using the least material has a height of 2 ft and a square base whose edges are 4 ft long. ◂

**REMARK** Fortunately, in our solution to Example 6 we were able to prove the existence of an absolute minimum of $S$ in the first quadrant. The general problem of finding the absolute extrema of a function on an unbounded region, or on a region that is not closed, can be difficult and will not be considered in this text. However, in applied problems we can sometimes use physical considerations to deduce that an absolute extremum has been found. For example, the graph of Equation (7) in Figure 13.8.12 strongly suggests that the relative minimum at $x = 4$ and $y = 4$ is also an absolute minimum.

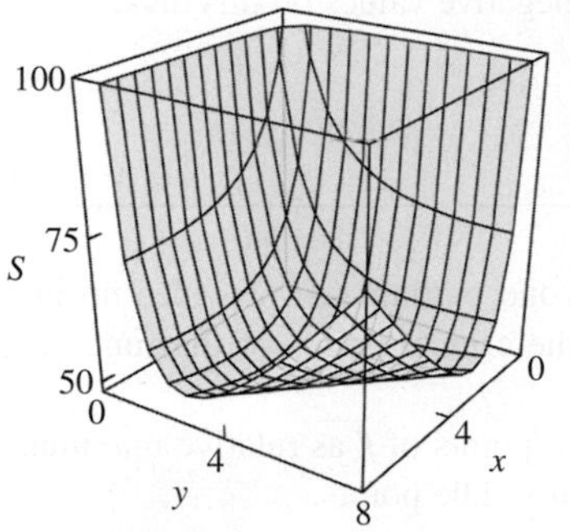

▲ **Figure 13.8.12**

## ✓QUICK CHECK EXERCISES 13.8 (See page 883 for answers.)

1. The critical points of the function $f(x, y) = x^3 + xy + y^2$ are ______.
2. Suppose that $f(x, y)$ has continuous second-order partial derivatives everywhere and that the origin is a critical point for $f$. State what information (if any) is provided by the second partials test if
   (a) $f_{xx}(0,0) = 2,\ f_{xy}(0,0) = 2,\ f_{yy}(0,0) = 2$
   (b) $f_{xx}(0,0) = -2,\ f_{xy}(0,0) = 2,\ f_{yy}(0,0) = 2$
   (c) $f_{xx}(0,0) = 3,\ f_{xy}(0,0) = 2,\ f_{yy}(0,0) = 2$
   (d) $f_{xx}(0,0) = -3,\ f_{xy}(0,0) = 2,\ f_{yy}(0,0) = -2$.
3. For the function $f(x, y) = x^3 - 3xy + y^3$, state what information (if any) is provided by the second partials test at the point
   (a) $(0, 0)$ (b) $(-1, -1)$ (c) $(1, 1)$.
4. A rectangular box has total surface area of 2 ft$^2$. Express the volume of the box as a function of the dimensions $x$ and $y$ of the base of the box.

## EXERCISE SET 13.8 Graphing Utility C CAS

**1–2** Locate all absolute maxima and minima, if any, by inspection. Then check your answers using calculus. ■

1. (a) $f(x, y) = (x - 2)^2 + (y + 1)^2$
   (b) $f(x, y) = 1 - x^2 - y^2$
   (c) $f(x, y) = x + 2y - 5$
2. (a) $f(x, y) = 1 - (x + 1)^2 - (y - 5)^2$
   (b) $f(x, y) = e^{xy}$
   (c) $f(x, y) = x^2 - y^2$

**3–4** Complete the squares and locate all absolute maxima and minima, if any, by inspection. Then check your answers using calculus. ■

3. $f(x, y) = 13 - 6x + x^2 + 4y + y^2$
4. $f(x, y) = 1 - 2x - x^2 + 4y - 2y^2$

**FOCUS ON CONCEPTS**

**5–8** The contour plots show all significant features of the function. Make a conjecture about the number and the location of all relative extrema and saddle points, and then use calculus to check your conjecture. ■

**5.**

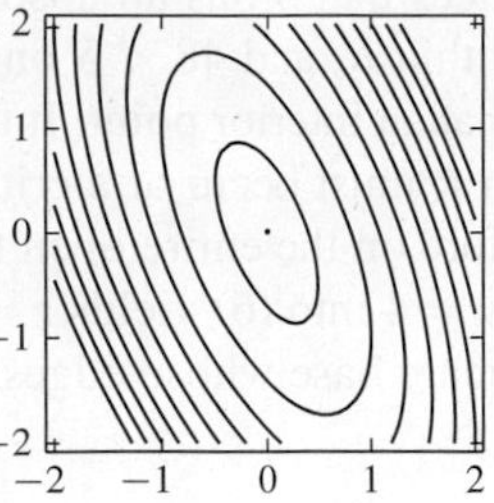


$f(x, y) = 3x^2 + 2xy + y^2$

**6.**

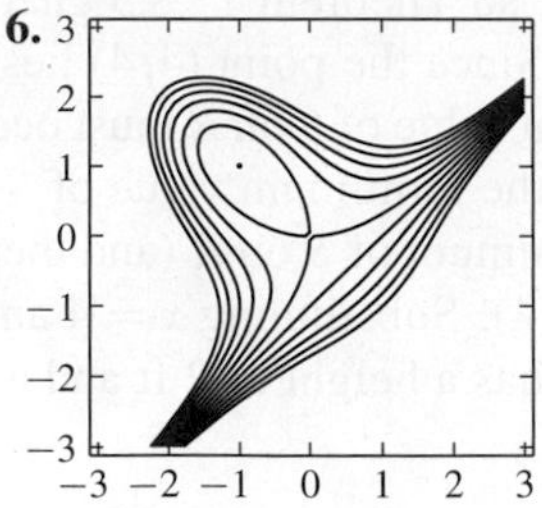


$f(x, y) = x^3 - 3xy - y^3$

**7.**

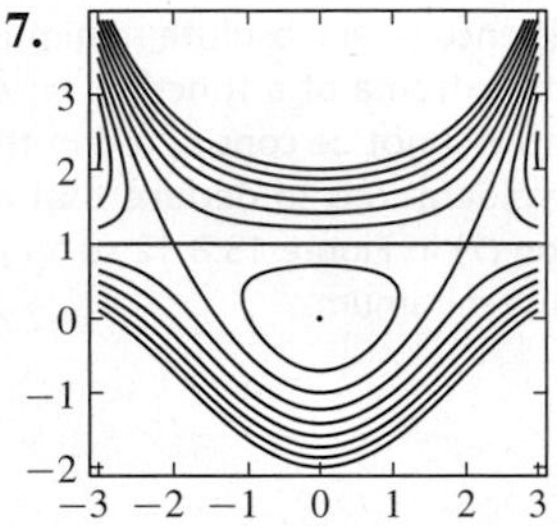


$f(x, y) = x^2 + 2y^2 - x^2y$

**8.**

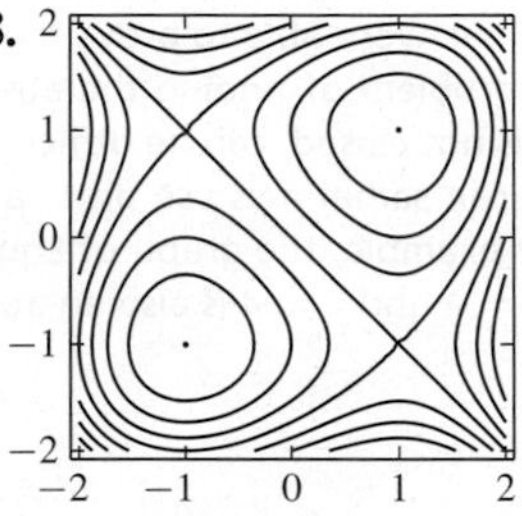


$f(x, y) = x^3 + y^3 - 3x - 3y$

**9–20** Locate all relative maxima, relative minima, and saddle points, if any. ■

**9.** $f(x, y) = y^2 + xy + 3y + 2x + 3$

**10.** $f(x, y) = x^2 + xy - 2y - 2x + 1$

**11.** $f(x, y) = x^2 + xy + y^2 - 3x$

**12.** $f(x, y) = xy - x^3 - y^2$

**13.** $f(x, y) = x^2 + y^2 + \dfrac{2}{xy}$

**14.** $f(x, y) = xe^y$

**15.** $f(x, y) = x^2 + y - e^y$

**16.** $f(x, y) = xy + \dfrac{2}{x} + \dfrac{4}{y}$

**17.** $f(x, y) = e^x \sin y$

**18.** $f(x, y) = y \sin x$

**19.** $f(x, y) = e^{-(x^2+y^2+2x)}$

**20.** $f(x, y) = xy + \dfrac{a^3}{x} + \dfrac{b^3}{y} \quad (a \neq 0, b \neq 0)$

C **21.** Use a CAS to generate a contour plot of

$$f(x, y) = 2x^2 - 4xy + y^4 + 2$$

for $-2 \leq x \leq 2$ and $-2 \leq y \leq 2$, and use the plot to approximate the locations of all relative extrema and saddle points in the region. Check your answer using calculus, and identify the relative extrema as relative maxima or minima.

C **22.** Use a CAS to generate a contour plot of

$$f(x, y) = 2y^2x - yx^2 + 4xy$$

for $-5 \leq x \leq 5$ and $-5 \leq y \leq 5$, and use the plot to approximate the locations of all relative extrema and saddle points in the region. Check your answer using calculus, and identify the relative extrema as relative maxima or minima.

**23–26 True–False** Determine whether the statement is true or false. Explain your answer. In these exercises, assume that $f(x, y)$ has continuous second-order partial derivatives and that

$$D(x, y) = f_{xx}(x, y)f_{yy}(x, y) - f_{xy}^2(x, y) \quad ■$$

**23.** If the function $f$ is defined on the disk $x^2 + y^2 \leq 1$, then $f$ has a critical point somewhere on this disk.

**24.** If the function $f$ is defined on the disk $x^2 + y^2 \leq 1$, and if $f$ is not a constant function, then $f$ has a finite number of critical points on this disk.

**25.** If $P(x_0, y_0)$ is a critical point of $f$, and if $f$ is defined on a disk centered at $P$ with $D(x_0, y_0) > 0$, then $f$ has a relative extremum at $P$.

**26.** If $P(x_0, y_0)$ is a critical point of $f$ with $f(x_0, y_0) = 0$, and if $f$ is defined on a disk centered at $P$ with $D(x_0, y_0) < 0$, then $f$ has both positive and negative values on this disk.

**FOCUS ON CONCEPTS**

**27.** (a) Show that the second partials test provides no information about the critical points of the function $f(x, y) = x^4 + y^4$.
(b) Classify all critical points of $f$ as relative maxima, relative minima, or saddle points.

**28.** (a) Show that the second partials test provides no information about the critical points of the function $f(x, y) = x^4 - y^4$.
(b) Classify all critical points of $f$ as relative maxima, relative minima, or saddle points.

**29.** Recall from Theorem 4.4.4 that if a continuous function of one variable has exactly one relative extremum on an interval, then that relative extremum is an absolute extremum on the interval. This exercise shows that this result does not extend to functions of two variables.
(a) Show that $f(x, y) = 3xe^y - x^3 - e^{3y}$ has only one critical point and that a relative maximum occurs there. (See the accompanying figure.)
(b) Show that $f$ does not have an absolute maximum.

***Source:*** This exercise is based on the article "The Only Critical Point in Town Test" by Ira Rosenholtz and Lowell Smylie, *Mathematics Magazine*, Vol. 58, No. 3, May 1985, pp. 149–150.

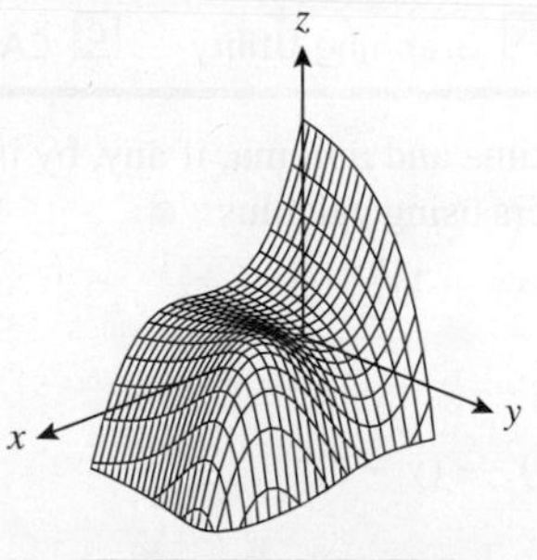


$z = 3xe^y - x^3 - e^{3y}$

◄ **Figure Ex-29**

**30.** If $f$ is a continuous function of one variable with two relative maxima on an interval, then there must be a relative minimum between the relative maxima. (Convince yourself of this by drawing some pictures.) The purpose of this exercise is to show that this result does not extend to functions of two variables. Show that $f(x, y) = 4x^2e^y - 2x^4 - e^{4y}$ has two relative maxima but no other critical points (see Figure Ex-30).

***Source:*** This exercise is based on the problem "Two Mountains Without a Valley" proposed and solved by Ira Rosenholtz, *Mathematics Magazine*, Vol. 60, No. 1, February 1987, p. 48.

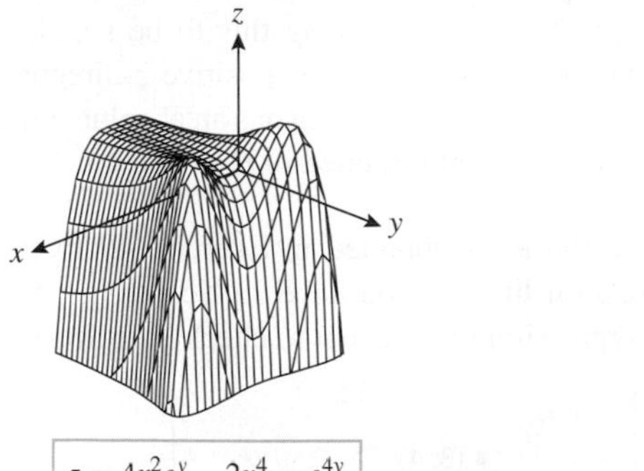


◀ **Figure Ex-30**

**31–36** Find the absolute extrema of the given function on the indicated closed and bounded set $R$. ■

**31.** $f(x, y) = xy - x - 3y$; $R$ is the triangular region with vertices $(0, 0)$, $(0, 4)$, and $(5, 0)$.

**32.** $f(x, y) = xy - 2x$; $R$ is the triangular region with vertices $(0, 0)$, $(0, 4)$, and $(4, 0)$.

**33.** $f(x, y) = x^2 - 3y^2 - 2x + 6y$; $R$ is the region bounded by the square with vertices $(0, 0)$, $(0, 2)$, $(2, 2)$, and $(2, 0)$.

**34.** $f(x, y) = xe^y - x^2 - e^y$; $R$ is the rectangular region with vertices $(0, 0)$, $(0, 1)$, $(2, 1)$, and $(2, 0)$.

**35.** $f(x, y) = x^2 + 2y^2 - x$; $R$ is the disk $x^2 + y^2 \leq 4$.

**36.** $f(x, y) = xy^2$; $R$ is the region that satisfies the inequalities $x \geq 0$, $y \geq 0$, and $x^2 + y^2 \leq 1$.

**37.** Find three positive numbers whose sum is 48 and such that their product is as large as possible.

**38.** Find three positive numbers whose sum is 27 and such that the sum of their squares is as small as possible.

**39.** Find all points on the portion of the plane $x + y + z = 5$ in the first octant at which $f(x, y, z) = xy^2z^2$ has a maximum value.

**40.** Find the points on the surface $x^2 - yz = 5$ that are closest to the origin.

**41.** Find the dimensions of the rectangular box of maximum volume that can be inscribed in a sphere of radius $a$.

**42.** An international airline has a regulation that each passenger can carry a suitcase having the sum of its width, length, and height less than or equal to 129 cm. Find the dimensions of the suitcase of maximum volume that a passenger can carry under this regulation.

**43.** A closed rectangular box with a volume of 16 ft$^3$ is made from two kinds of materials. The top and bottom are made of material costing 10¢ per square foot and the sides from material costing 5¢ per square foot. Find the dimensions of the box so that the cost of materials is minimized.

**44.** A manufacturer makes two models of an item, standard and deluxe. It costs \$40 to manufacture the standard model and \$60 for the deluxe. A market research firm estimates that if the standard model is priced at $x$ dollars and the deluxe at $y$ dollars, then the manufacturer will sell $500(y - x)$ of the standard items and $45{,}000 + 500(x - 2y)$ of the deluxe each year. How should the items be priced to maximize the profit?

**45.** Consider the function

$$f(x, y) = 4x^2 - 3y^2 + 2xy$$

over the unit square $0 \leq x \leq 1, 0 \leq y \leq 1$.
(a) Find the maximum and minimum values of $f$ on each edge of the square.
(b) Find the maximum and minimum values of $f$ on each diagonal of the square.
(c) Find the maximum and minimum values of $f$ on the entire square.

**46.** Show that among all parallelograms with perimeter $l$, a square with sides of length $l/4$ has maximum area. [*Hint:* The area of a parallelogram is given by the formula $A = ab \sin \alpha$, where $a$ and $b$ are the lengths of two adjacent sides and $\alpha$ is the angle between them.]

**47.** Determine the dimensions of a rectangular box, open at the top, having volume $V$, and requiring the least amount of material for its construction.

**48.** A length of sheet metal 27 inches wide is to be made into a water trough by bending up two sides as shown in the accompanying figure. Find $x$ and $\phi$ so that the trapezoid-shaped cross section has a maximum area.

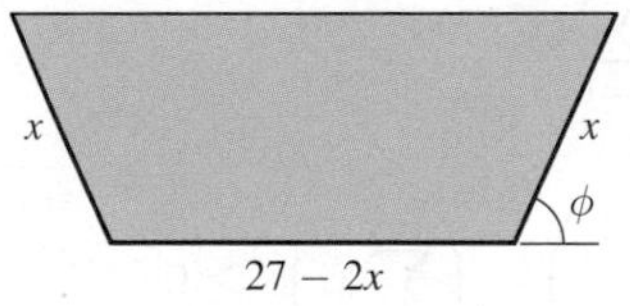


◀ **Figure Ex-48**

**49–50** A common problem in experimental work is to obtain a mathematical relationship $y = f(x)$ between two variables $x$ and $y$ by "fitting" a curve to points in the plane that correspond to experimentally determined values of $x$ and $y$, say

$$(x_1, y_1), (x_2, y_2), \ldots, (x_n, y_n)$$

The curve $y = f(x)$ is called a ***mathematical model*** of the data. The general form of the function $f$ is commonly determined by some underlying physical principle, but sometimes it is just determined by the pattern of the data. We are concerned with fitting a straight line $y = mx + b$ to data. Usually, the data will not lie on a line (possibly due to experimental error or variations in experimental conditions), so the problem is to find a line that fits the data "best" according to some criterion. One criterion for selecting the line of best fit is to choose $m$ and $b$ to minimize the function

$$g(m, b) = \sum_{i=1}^{n} (mx_i + b - y_i)^2$$

This is called the ***method of least squares***, and the resulting line is called the ***regression line*** or the ***least squares line of best fit***. Geometrically, $|mx_i + b - y_i|$ is the vertical distance between the data point $(x_i, y_i)$ and the line $y = mx + b$.

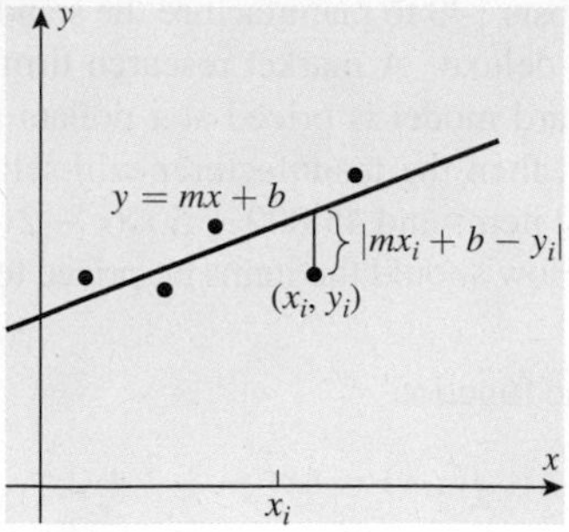


These vertical distances are called the ***residuals*** of the data points, so the effect of minimizing $g(m, b)$ is to minimize the sum of the squares of the residuals. In these exercises, we will derive a formula for the regression line. ■

**49.** The purpose of this exercise is to find the values of $m$ and $b$ that produce the regression line.

(a) To minimize $g(m, b)$, we start by finding values of $m$ and $b$ such that $\partial g/\partial m = 0$ and $\partial g/\partial b = 0$. Show that these equations are satisfied if $m$ and $b$ satisfy the conditions

$$\left(\sum_{i=1}^{n} x_i^2\right) m + \left(\sum_{i=1}^{n} x_i\right) b = \sum_{i=1}^{n} x_i y_i$$

$$\left(\sum_{i=1}^{n} x_i\right) m + nb = \sum_{i=1}^{n} y_i$$

(b) Let $\bar{x} = (x_1 + x_2 + \cdots + x_n)/n$ denote the arithmetic average of $x_1, x_2, \ldots, x_n$. Use the fact that

$$\sum_{i=1}^{n} (x_i - \bar{x})^2 \geq 0$$

to show that

$$n\left(\sum_{i=1}^{n} x_i^2\right) - \left(\sum_{i=1}^{n} x_i\right)^2 \geq 0$$

with equality if and only if all the $x_i$'s are the same.

(c) Assuming that not all the $x_i$'s are the same, prove that the equations in part (a) have the unique solution

$$m = \frac{n\sum_{i=1}^{n} x_i y_i - \sum_{i=1}^{n} x_i \sum_{i=1}^{n} y_i}{n\sum_{i=1}^{n} x_i^2 - \left(\sum_{i=1}^{n} x_i\right)^2}$$

$$b = \frac{1}{n}\left(\sum_{i=1}^{n} y_i - m\sum_{i=1}^{n} x_i\right)$$

[*Note:* We have shown that $g$ has a critical point at these values of $m$ and $b$. In the next exercise we will show that $g$ has an absolute minimum at this critical point. Accepting this to be so, we have shown that the line $y = mx + b$ is the regression line for these values of $m$ and $b$.]

**50.** Assume that not all the $x_i$'s are the same, so that $g(m, b)$ has a unique critical point at the values of $m$ and $b$ obtained in Exercise 49(c). The purpose of this exercise is to show that $g$ has an absolute minimum value at this point.

(a) Find the partial derivatives $g_{mm}(m, b)$, $g_{bb}(m, b)$, and $g_{mb}(m, b)$, and then apply the second partials test to show that $g$ has a relative minimum at the critical point obtained in Exercise 49.

(b) Show that the graph of the equation $z = g(m, b)$ is a quadric surface. [*Hint:* See Formula (4) of Section 11.7.]

(c) It can be proved that the graph of $z = g(m, b)$ is an elliptic paraboloid. Accepting this to be so, show that this paraboloid opens in the positive $z$-direction, and explain how this shows that $g$ has an absolute minimum at the critical point obtained in Exercise 49.

**51–54** Use the formulas obtained in Exercise 49 to find and draw the regression line. If you have a calculating utility that can calculate regression lines, use it to check your work. ■

**51.**

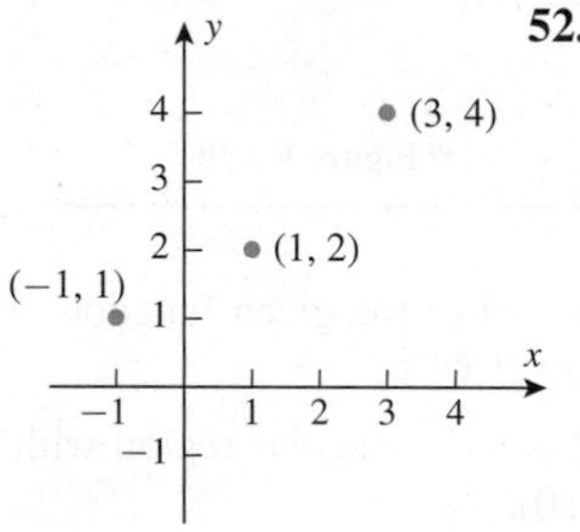


**52.**

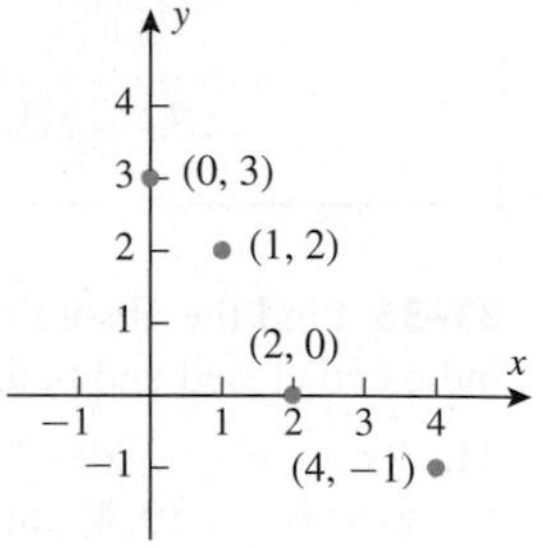


**53.**

| $x$ | 1 | 2 | 3 | 4 |
|---|---|---|---|---|
| $y$ | 1.5 | 1.6 | 2.1 | 3.0 |

**54.**

| $x$ | 1 | 2 | 3 | 4 | 5 |
|---|---|---|---|---|---|
| $y$ | 4.2 | 3.5 | 3.0 | 2.4 | 2.0 |

**55.** The following table shows the life expectancy by year of birth of females in the United States:

| YEAR OF BIRTH | 2000 | 2001 | 2002 | 2003 | 2004 | 2005 | 2006 | 2007 |
|---|---|---|---|---|---|---|---|---|
| LIFE EXPECTANCY | 79.3 | 79.4 | 79.5 | 79.6 | 79.9 | 79.9 | 80.2 | 80.4 |

***Source:*** Data from *The 2011 Statistical Abstract*, the U.S. Census Bureau.

(a) Take $t = 0$ to be the year 1930, and let $y$ be the life expectancy for birth year $t$. Use the regression capability of a calculating utility to find the regression line of $y$ as a function of $t$.

(b) Use a graphing utility to make a graph that shows the data points and the regression line.

(c) Use the regression line to make a conjecture about the life expectancy of females born in the year 2015.

**56.** A company manager wants to establish a relationship between the sales of a certain product and the price. The company research department provides the following data:

| PRICE ($x$) IN DOLLARS | \$35.00 | \$40.00 | \$45.00 | \$48.00 | \$50.00 |
|---|---|---|---|---|---|
| DAILY SALES VOLUME ($y$) IN UNITS | 80 | 75 | 68 | 66 | 63 |

(a) Use a calculating utility to find the regression line of $y$ as a function of $x$.
(b) Use a graphing utility to make a graph that shows the data points and the regression line.
(c) Use the regression line to make a conjecture about the number of units that would be sold at a price of \$60.00.

**57.** If a gas is cooled with its volume held constant, then it follows from the ***ideal gas law*** in physics that its pressure drops proportionally to the drop in temperature. The temperature that, in theory, corresponds to a pressure of zero is called ***absolute zero***. Suppose that an experiment produces the following data for pressure $P$ versus temperature $T$ with the volume held constant:

| $P$ (KILOPASCALS) | 134 | 142 | 155 | 160 | 171 | 184 |
|---|---|---|---|---|---|---|
| $T$ (°CELSIUS) | 0 | 20 | 40 | 60 | 80 | 100 |

(a) Use a calculating utility to find the regression line of $P$ as a function of $T$.
(b) Use a graphing utility to make a graph that shows the data points and the regression line.
(c) Use the regression line to estimate the value of absolute zero in degrees Celsius.

**58.** Find
(a) a continuous function $f(x, y)$ that is defined on the entire $xy$-plane and has no absolute extrema on the $xy$-plane;
(b) a function $f(x, y)$ that is defined everywhere on the rectangle $0 \le x \le 1, 0 \le y \le 1$ and has no absolute extrema on the rectangle.

**59.** Show that if $f$ has a relative maximum at $(x_0, y_0)$, then $G(x) = f(x, y_0)$ has a relative maximum at $x = x_0$ and $H(y) = f(x_0, y)$ has a relative maximum at $y = y_0$.

**60. Writing** Explain how to determine the location of relative extrema or saddle points of $f(x, y)$ by examining the contours of $f$.

**61. Writing** Suppose that the second partials test gives no information about a certain critical point $(x_0, y_0)$ because $D(x_0, y_0) = 0$. Discuss what other steps you might take to determine whether there is a relative extremum at that critical point.

---

✓ **QUICK CHECK ANSWERS 13.8** 1. $(0, 0)$ and $\left(\frac{1}{6}, -\frac{1}{12}\right)$ 2. (a) no information (b) a saddle point at $(0, 0)$ (c) a relative minimum at $(0, 0)$ (d) a relative maximum at $(0, 0)$ 3. (a) a saddle point at $(0, 0)$ (b) no information, since $(-1, -1)$ is not a critical point (c) a relative minimum at $(1, 1)$ 4. $V = \dfrac{xy(1 - xy)}{x + y}$

---

## 13.9 LAGRANGE MULTIPLIERS

*In this section we will study a powerful new method for maximizing or minimizing a function subject to constraints on the variables. This method will help us to solve certain optimization problems that are difficult or impossible to solve using the methods studied in the last section.*

### EXTREMUM PROBLEMS WITH CONSTRAINTS

In Example 6 of the last section, we solved the problem of minimizing

$$S = xy + 2xz + 2yz \tag{1}$$

subject to the constraint

$$xyz - 32 = 0 \tag{2}$$

This is a special case of the following general problem:

**13.9.1** ***Three-Variable Extremum Problem with One Constraint***
Maximize or minimize the function $f(x, y, z)$ subject to the constraint $g(x, y, z) = 0$.

We will also be interested in the following two-variable version of this problem:

**13.9.2** ***Two-Variable Extremum Problem with One Constraint***
Maximize or minimize the function $f(x, y)$ subject to the constraint $g(x, y) = 0$.

## LAGRANGE MULTIPLIERS

One way to attack problems of these types is to solve the constraint equation for one of the variables in terms of the others and substitute the result into $f$. This produces a new function of one or two variables that incorporates the constraint and can be maximized or minimized by applying standard methods. For example, to solve the problem in Example 6 of the last section we substituted (2) into (1) to obtain

$$S = xy + \frac{64}{y} + \frac{64}{x}$$

which we then minimized by finding the critical points and applying the second partials test. However, this approach hinges on our ability to solve the constraint equation for one of the variables in terms of the others. If this cannot be done, then other methods must be used. One such method, called the *method of Lagrange multipliers*, will be discussed in this section.

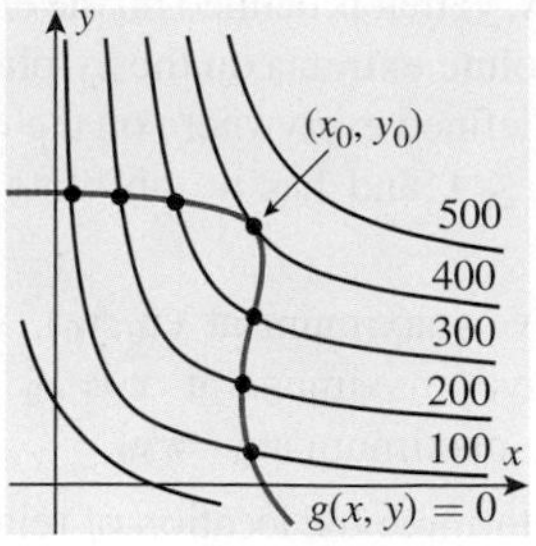


Maximum of $f(x, y)$ is 400

(*a*)

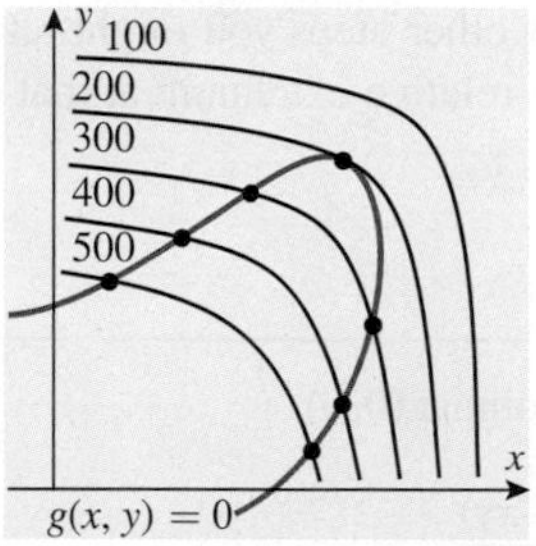


Minimum of $f(x, y)$ is 200

(*b*)

▲ **Figure 13.9.1**

To motivate the method of Lagrange multipliers, suppose that we are trying to maximize a function $f(x, y)$ subject to the constraint $g(x, y) = 0$. Geometrically, this means that we are looking for a point $(x_0, y_0)$ on the graph of the constraint curve at which $f(x, y)$ is as large as possible. To help locate such a point, let us construct a contour plot of $f(x, y)$ in the same coordinate system as the graph of $g(x, y) = 0$. For example, Figure 13.9.1*a* shows some typical level curves of $f(x, y) = c$, which we have labeled $c = 100, 200, 300, 400$, and 500 for purposes of illustration. In this figure, each point of intersection of $g(x, y) = 0$ with a level curve is a candidate for a solution, since these points lie on the constraint curve. Among the seven such intersections shown in the figure, the maximum value of $f(x, y)$ occurs at the intersection $(x_0, y_0)$ where $f(x, y)$ has a value of 400. Note that at $(x_0, y_0)$ the constraint curve and the level curve just touch and thus have a *common* tangent line at this point. Since $\nabla f(x_0, y_0)$ is normal to the level curve $f(x, y) = 400$ at $(x_0, y_0)$, and since $\nabla g(x_0, y_0)$ is normal to the constraint curve $g(x, y) = 0$ at $(x_0, y_0)$, we conclude that the vectors $\nabla f(x_0, y_0)$ and $\nabla g(x_0, y_0)$ must be parallel. That is,

$$\nabla f(x_0, y_0) = \lambda \nabla g(x_0, y_0) \tag{3}$$

for some scalar $\lambda$. The same condition holds at points on the constraint curve where $f(x, y)$ has a minimum. For example, if the level curves are as shown in Figure 13.9.1*b*, then the minimum value of $f(x, y)$ occurs where the constraint curve just touches a level curve. Thus, to find the maximum or minimum of $f(x, y)$ subject to the constraint $g(x, y) = 0$, we look for points at which (3) holds—this is the method of Lagrange multipliers.

Our next objective in this section is to make the preceding intuitive argument more precise. For this purpose it will help to begin with some terminology about the problem

**Joseph Louis Lagrange (1736–1813)** French–Italian mathematician and astronomer. Lagrange, the son of a public official, was born in Turin, Italy. (Baptismal records list his name as Giuseppe Lodovico Lagrangia.) Although his father wanted him to be a lawyer, Lagrange was attracted to mathematics and astronomy after reading a memoir by the astronomer Halley. At age 16 he began to study mathematics on his own and by age 19 was appointed to a professorship at the Royal Artillery School in Turin. The following year Lagrange sent Euler solutions to some famous problems using new methods that eventually blossomed into a branch of mathematics called calculus of variations. These methods and Lagrange's applications of them to problems in celestial mechanics were so monumental that by age 25 he was regarded by many of his contemporaries as the greatest living mathematician.

In 1776, on the recommendations of Euler, he was chosen to succeed Euler as the director of the Berlin Academy. During his stay in Berlin, Lagrange distinguished himself not only in celestial mechanics, but also in algebraic equations and the theory of numbers. After twenty years in Berlin, he moved to Paris at the invitation of Louis XVI. He was given apartments in the Louvre and treated with great honor, even during the revolution.

Napoleon was a great admirer of Lagrange and showered him with honors—count, senator, and Legion of Honor. The years Lagrange spent in Paris were devoted primarily to didactic treatises summarizing his mathematical conceptions. One of Lagrange's most famous works is a memoir, *Mécanique Analytique*, in which he reduced the theory of mechanics to a few general formulas from which all other necessary equations could be derived.

It is an interesting historical fact that Lagrange's father speculated unsuccessfully in several financial ventures, so his family was forced to live quite modestly. Lagrange himself stated that if his family had money, he would not have made mathematics his vocation. In spite of his fame, Lagrange was always a shy and modest man. On his death, he was buried with honor in the Pantheon.

*[Image: traveler1116/iStockphoto]*

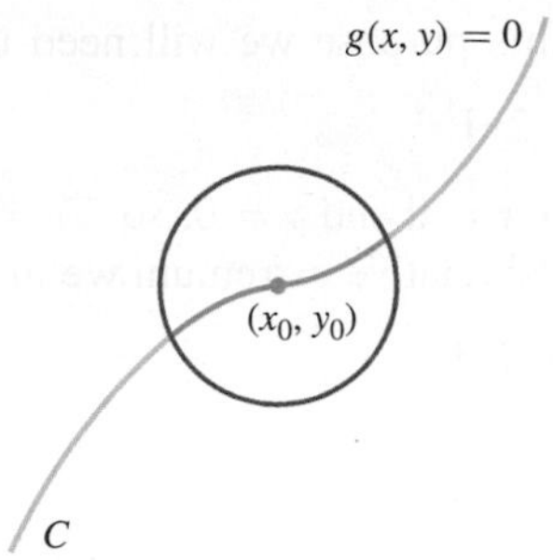


A constrained relative maximum occurs at $(x_0, y_0)$ if $f(x_0, y_0) \geq f(x, y)$ on some segment of $C$ that extends on both sides of $(x_0, y_0)$.

▲ **Figure 13.9.2**

of maximizing or minimizing a function $f(x, y)$ subject to a constraint $g(x, y) = 0$. As with other kinds of maximization and minimization problems, we need to distinguish between relative and absolute extrema. We will say that $f$ has a ***constrained absolute maximum (minimum)*** at $(x_0, y_0)$ if $f(x_0, y_0)$ is the largest (smallest) value of $f$ on the constraint curve, and we will say that $f$ has a ***constrained relative maximum (minimum)*** at $(x_0, y_0)$ if $f(x_0, y_0)$ is the largest (smallest) value of $f$ on some segment of the constraint curve that extends on both sides of the point $(x_0, y_0)$ (Figure 13.9.2).

Let us assume that a constrained relative maximum or minimum occurs at the point $(x_0, y_0)$, and for simplicity let us further assume that the equation $g(x, y) = 0$ can be smoothly parametrized as

$$x = x(s), \quad y = y(s)$$

where $s$ is an arc length parameter with reference point $(x_0, y_0)$ at $s = 0$. Thus, the quantity

$$z = f(x(s), y(s))$$

has a relative maximum or minimum at $s = 0$, and this implies that $dz/ds = 0$ at that point. From the chain rule, this equation can be expressed as

$$\frac{dz}{ds} = \frac{\partial f}{\partial x}\frac{dx}{ds} + \frac{\partial f}{\partial y}\frac{dy}{ds} = \left(\frac{\partial f}{\partial x}\mathbf{i} + \frac{\partial f}{\partial y}\mathbf{j}\right) \cdot \left(\frac{dx}{ds}\mathbf{i} + \frac{dy}{ds}\mathbf{j}\right) = 0$$

where the derivatives are all evaluated at $s = 0$. However, the first factor in the dot product is the gradient of $f$, and the second factor is the unit tangent vector to the constraint curve. Since the point $(x_0, y_0)$ corresponds to $s = 0$, it follows from this equation that

$$\nabla f(x_0, y_0) \cdot \mathbf{T}(0) = 0$$

which implies that the gradient is either $\mathbf{0}$ or is normal to the constraint curve at a constrained relative extremum. However, the constraint curve $g(x, y) = 0$ is a level curve for the function $g(x, y)$, so that if $\nabla g(x_0, y_0) \neq \mathbf{0}$, then $\nabla g(x_0, y_0)$ is normal to this curve at $(x_0, y_0)$. It then follows that there is some scalar $\lambda$ such that

$$\nabla f(x_0, y_0) = \lambda \nabla g(x_0, y_0) \tag{4}$$

This scalar is called a ***Lagrange multiplier***. Thus, the ***method of Lagrange multipliers*** for finding constrained relative extrema is to look for points on the constraint curve $g(x, y) = 0$ at which Equation (4) is satisfied for some scalar $\lambda$.

**13.9.3 THEOREM** ***(Constrained-Extremum Principle for Two Variables and One Constraint)*** *Let $f$ and $g$ be functions of two variables with continuous first partial derivatives on some open set containing the constraint curve $g(x, y) = 0$, and assume that $\nabla g \neq \mathbf{0}$ at any point on this curve. If $f$ has a constrained relative extremum, then this extremum occurs at a point $(x_0, y_0)$ on the constraint curve at which the gradient vectors $\nabla f(x_0, y_0)$ and $\nabla g(x_0, y_0)$ are parallel; that is, there is some number $\lambda$ such that*

$$\nabla f(x_0, y_0) = \lambda \nabla g(x_0, y_0)$$

► **Example 1** At what point or points on the circle $x^2 + y^2 = 1$ does $f(x, y) = xy$ have an absolute maximum, and what is that maximum?

***Solution.*** The circle $x^2 + y^2 = 1$ is a closed and bounded set and $f(x, y) = xy$ is a continuous function, so it follows from the Extreme-Value Theorem (Theorem 13.8.3) that $f$ has an absolute maximum and an absolute minimum on the circle. To find these extrema, we will use Lagrange multipliers to find the constrained relative extrema, and then we will evaluate $f$ at those relative extrema to find the absolute extrema.

We want to maximize $f(x, y) = xy$ subject to the constraint

$$g(x, y) = x^2 + y^2 - 1 = 0 \tag{5}$$

First we will look for constrained *relative* extrema. For this purpose we will need the gradients

$$\nabla f = y\mathbf{i} + x\mathbf{j} \quad \text{and} \quad \nabla g = 2x\mathbf{i} + 2y\mathbf{j}$$

From the formula for $\nabla g$ we see that $\nabla g = \mathbf{0}$ if and only if $x = 0$ and $y = 0$, so $\nabla g \neq \mathbf{0}$ at any point on the circle $x^2 + y^2 = 1$. Thus, at a constrained relative extremum we must have

$$\nabla f = \lambda \nabla g \quad \text{or} \quad y\mathbf{i} + x\mathbf{j} = \lambda(2x\mathbf{i} + 2y\mathbf{j})$$

which is equivalent to the pair of equations

$$y = 2x\lambda \quad \text{and} \quad x = 2y\lambda$$

It follows from these equations that if $x = 0$, then $y = 0$, and if $y = 0$, then $x = 0$. In either case we have $x^2 + y^2 = 0$, so the constraint equation $x^2 + y^2 = 1$ is not satisfied. Thus, we can assume that $x$ and $y$ are nonzero, and we can rewrite the equations as

$$\lambda = \frac{y}{2x} \quad \text{and} \quad \lambda = \frac{x}{2y}$$

from which we obtain

$$\frac{y}{2x} = \frac{x}{2y}$$

or

$$y^2 = x^2 \tag{6}$$

Substituting this in (5) yields

$$2x^2 - 1 = 0$$

from which we obtain $x = \pm 1/\sqrt{2}$. Each of these values, when substituted in Equation (6), produces $y$-values of $y = \pm 1/\sqrt{2}$. Thus, constrained relative extrema occur at the points $(1/\sqrt{2}, 1/\sqrt{2})$, $(1/\sqrt{2}, -1/\sqrt{2})$, $(-1/\sqrt{2}, 1/\sqrt{2})$, and $(-1/\sqrt{2}, -1/\sqrt{2})$. The values of $xy$ at these points are as follows:

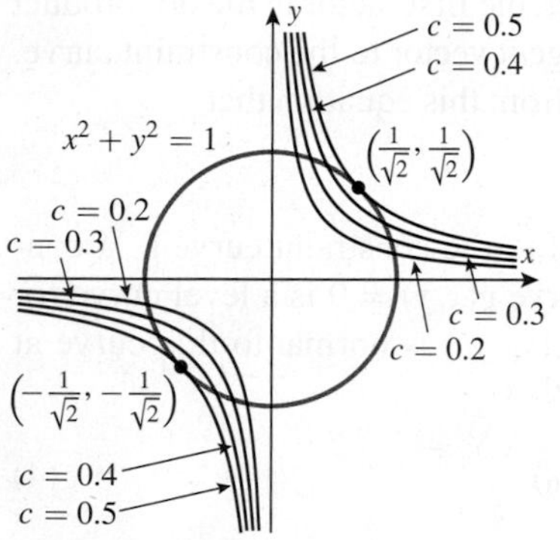

▲ **Figure 13.9.3**

| $(x, y)$ | $(1/\sqrt{2}, 1/\sqrt{2})$ | $(1/\sqrt{2}, -1/\sqrt{2})$ | $(-1/\sqrt{2}, 1/\sqrt{2})$ | $(-1/\sqrt{2}, -1/\sqrt{2})$ |
|---|---|---|---|---|
| $xy$ | 1/2 | −1/2 | −1/2 | 1/2 |

Give another solution to Example 1 using the parametrization

$$x = \cos\theta, \quad y = \sin\theta$$

and the identity

$$\sin 2\theta = 2\sin\theta\cos\theta$$

Thus, the function $f(x, y) = xy$ has an absolute maximum of $\frac{1}{2}$ occurring at the two points $(1/\sqrt{2}, 1/\sqrt{2})$ and $(-1/\sqrt{2}, -1/\sqrt{2})$. Although it was not asked for, we can also see that $f$ has an absolute minimum of $-\frac{1}{2}$ occurring at the points $(1/\sqrt{2}, -1/\sqrt{2})$ and $(-1/\sqrt{2}, 1/\sqrt{2})$. Figure 13.9.3 shows some level curves $xy = c$ and the constraint curve in the vicinity of the maxima. A similar figure for the minima can be obtained using negative values of $c$ for the level curves $xy = c$. ◀

**REMARK** If $c$ is a constant, then the functions $g(x, y)$ and $g(x, y) - c$ have the same gradient since the constant $c$ drops out when we differentiate. Consequently, it is *not* essential to rewrite a constraint of the form $g(x, y) = c$ as $g(x, y) - c = 0$ in order to apply the constrained-extremum principle. Thus, in the last example, we could have kept the constraint in the form $x^2 + y^2 = 1$ and then taken $g(x, y) = x^2 + y^2$ rather than $g(x, y) = x^2 + y^2 - 1$.

► **Example 2** Use the method of Lagrange multipliers to find the dimensions of a rectangle with perimeter $p$ and maximum area.

***Solution.*** Let

$x$ = length of the rectangle, $y$ = width of the rectangle, $A$ = area of the rectangle

We want to maximize $A = xy$ on the line segment

$$2x + 2y = p, \quad 0 \leq x, y \tag{7}$$

that corresponds to the perimeter constraint. This segment is a closed and bounded set, and since $f(x, y) = xy$ is a continuous function, it follows from the Extreme-Value Theorem (Theorem 13.8.3) that $f$ has an absolute maximum on this segment. This absolute maximum must also be a constrained relative maximum since $f$ is 0 at the endpoints of the segment and positive elsewhere on the segment. If $g(x, y) = 2x + 2y$, then we have

$$\nabla f = y\mathbf{i} + x\mathbf{j} \quad \text{and} \quad \nabla g = 2\mathbf{i} + 2\mathbf{j}$$

Noting that $\nabla g \neq \mathbf{0}$, it follows from (4) that

$$y\mathbf{i} + x\mathbf{j} = \lambda(2\mathbf{i} + 2\mathbf{j})$$

at a constrained relative maximum. This is equivalent to the two equations

$$y = 2\lambda \quad \text{and} \quad x = 2\lambda$$

Eliminating $\lambda$ from these equations we obtain $x = y$, which shows that the rectangle is actually a square. Using this condition and constraint (7), we obtain $x = p/4$, $y = p/4$. ◀

## THREE VARIABLES AND ONE CONSTRAINT

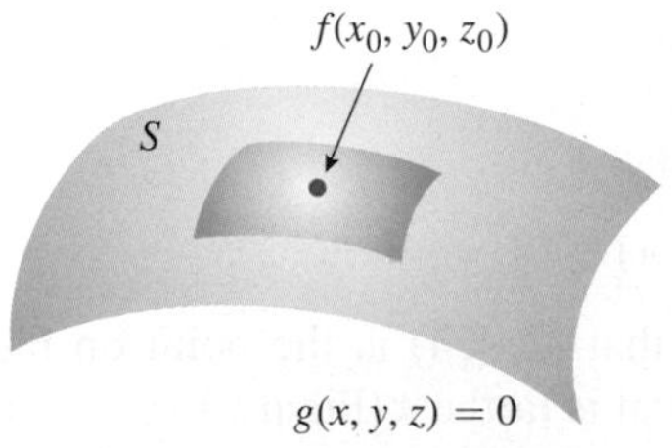


A constrained relative maximum occurs at $(x_0, y_0, z_0)$ if $f(x_0, y_0, z_0) \geq f(x, y, z)$ at all points of $S$ near $(x_0, y_0, z_0)$.

▲ **Figure 13.9.4**

The method of Lagrange multipliers can also be used to maximize or minimize a function of three variables $f(x, y, z)$ subject to a constraint $g(x, y, z) = 0$. As a rule, the graph of $g(x, y, z) = 0$ will be some surface $S$ in 3-space. Thus, from a geometric viewpoint, the problem is to maximize or minimize $f(x, y, z)$ as $(x, y, z)$ varies over the surface $S$ (Figure 13.9.4). As usual, we distinguish between relative and absolute extrema. We will say that $f$ has a ***constrained absolute maximum (minimum)*** at $(x_0, y_0, z_0)$ if $f(x_0, y_0, z_0)$ is the largest (smallest) value of $f(x, y, z)$ on $S$, and we will say that $f$ has a ***constrained relative maximum (minimum)*** at $(x_0, y_0, z_0)$ if $f(x_0, y_0, z_0)$ is the largest (smallest) value of $f(x, y, z)$ at all points of $S$ "near" $(x_0, y_0, z_0)$.

The following theorem, which we state without proof, is the three-variable analog of Theorem 13.9.3.

**13.9.4 THEOREM** ***(Constrained-Extremum Principle for Three Variables and One Constraint)*** *Let $f$ and $g$ be functions of three variables with continuous first partial derivatives on some open set containing the constraint surface $g(x, y, z) = 0$, and assume that $\nabla g \neq \mathbf{0}$ at any point on this surface. If $f$ has a constrained relative extremum, then this extremum occurs at a point $(x_0, y_0, z_0)$ on the constraint surface at which the gradient vectors $\nabla f(x_0, y_0, z_0)$ and $\nabla g(x_0, y_0, z_0)$ are parallel; that is, there is some number $\lambda$ such that*

$$\nabla f(x_0, y_0, z_0) = \lambda \nabla g(x_0, y_0, z_0)$$

▶ **Example 3** Find the points on the sphere $x^2 + y^2 + z^2 = 36$ that are closest to and farthest from the point (1, 2, 2).

***Solution.*** To avoid radicals, we will find points on the sphere that minimize and maximize the *square* of the distance to (1, 2, 2). Thus, we want to find the relative extrema of

$$f(x, y, z) = (x - 1)^2 + (y - 2)^2 + (z - 2)^2$$

subject to the constraint

$$x^2 + y^2 + z^2 = 36 \tag{8}$$

If we let $g(x, y, z) = x^2 + y^2 + z^2$, then $\nabla g = 2x\mathbf{i} + 2y\mathbf{j} + 2z\mathbf{k}$. Thus, $\nabla g = \mathbf{0}$ if and only if $x = y = z = 0$. It follows that $\nabla g \neq \mathbf{0}$ at any point of the sphere (8), and hence the constrained relative extrema must occur at points where

$$\nabla f(x, y, z) = \lambda \nabla g(x, y, z)$$

That is,

$$2(x - 1)\mathbf{i} + 2(y - 2)\mathbf{j} + 2(z - 2)\mathbf{k} = \lambda(2x\mathbf{i} + 2y\mathbf{j} + 2z\mathbf{k})$$

which leads to the equations

$$2(x-1) = 2x\lambda, \quad 2(y-2) = 2y\lambda, \quad 2(z-2) = 2z\lambda \tag{9}$$

We may assume that $x$, $y$, and $z$ are nonzero since $x = 0$ does not satisfy the first equation, $y = 0$ does not satisfy the second, and $z = 0$ does not satisfy the third. Thus, we can rewrite (9) as

$$\frac{x-1}{x} = \lambda, \quad \frac{y-2}{y} = \lambda, \quad \frac{z-2}{z} = \lambda$$

The first two equations imply that

$$\frac{x-1}{x} = \frac{y-2}{y}$$

from which it follows that

$$y = 2x \tag{10}$$

Similarly, the first and third equations imply that

$$z = 2x \tag{11}$$

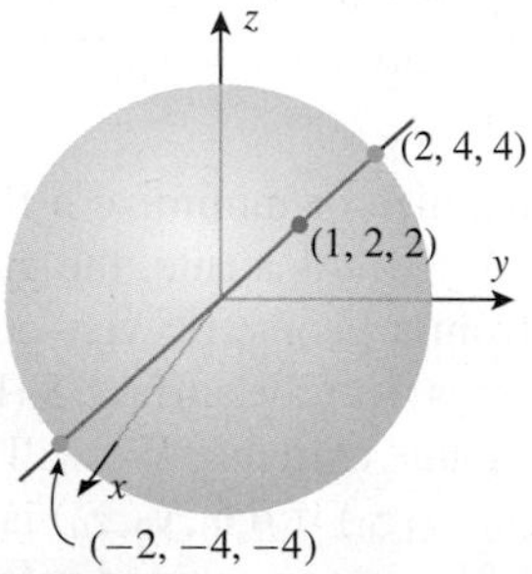

▲ **Figure 13.9.5**

Substituting (10) and (11) in the constraint equation (8), we obtain

$$9x^2 = 36 \quad \text{or} \quad x = \pm 2$$

Substituting these values in (10) and (11) yields two points:

$$(2, 4, 4) \quad \text{and} \quad (-2, -4, -4)$$

Since $f(2, 4, 4) = 9$ and $f(-2, -4, -4) = 81$, it follows that $(2, 4, 4)$ is the point on the sphere closest to $(1, 2, 2)$, and $(-2, -4, -4)$ is the point that is farthest (Figure 13.9.5). ◀

**REMARK** Solving nonlinear systems such as (9) usually involves trial and error. A technique that sometimes works is demonstrated in Example 3. In that example the equations were solved for a common variable ($\lambda$), and we then derived relationships between the remaining variables ($x$, $y$, and $z$). Substituting those relationships in the constraint equation led to the value of one of the variables, and the values of the other variables were then computed.

Next we will use Lagrange multipliers to solve the problem of Example 6 in the last section.

▶ **Example 4** Use Lagrange multipliers to determine the dimensions of a rectangular box, open at the top, having a volume of 32 ft$^3$, and requiring the least amount of material for its construction.

***Solution.*** With the notation introduced in Example 6 of the last section, the problem is to minimize the surface area

$$S = xy + 2xz + 2yz$$

subject to the volume constraint

$$xyz = 32 \tag{12}$$

If we let $f(x, y, z) = xy + 2xz + 2yz$ and $g(x, y, z) = xyz$, then

$$\nabla f = (y + 2z)\mathbf{i} + (x + 2z)\mathbf{j} + (2x + 2y)\mathbf{k} \quad \text{and} \quad \nabla g = yz\mathbf{i} + xz\mathbf{j} + xy\mathbf{k}$$

It follows that $\nabla g \neq \mathbf{0}$ at any point on the surface $xyz = 32$, since $x$, $y$, and $z$ are all nonzero on this surface. Thus, at a constrained relative extremum we must have $\nabla f = \lambda \nabla g$, that is,

$$(y + 2z)\mathbf{i} + (x + 2z)\mathbf{j} + (2x + 2y)\mathbf{k} = \lambda(yz\mathbf{i} + xz\mathbf{j} + xy\mathbf{k})$$

This condition yields the three equations

$$y + 2z = \lambda yz, \quad x + 2z = \lambda xz, \quad 2x + 2y = \lambda xy$$

Because $x$, $y$, and $z$ are nonzero, these equations can be rewritten as

$$\frac{1}{z} + \frac{2}{y} = \lambda, \quad \frac{1}{z} + \frac{2}{x} = \lambda, \quad \frac{2}{y} + \frac{2}{x} = \lambda$$

From the first two equations,

$$y = x \tag{13}$$

and from the first and third equations,

$$z = \tfrac{1}{2}x \tag{14}$$

Substituting (13) and (14) in the volume constraint (12) yields

$$\tfrac{1}{2}x^3 = 32$$

This equation, together with (13) and (14), yields

$$x = 4, \quad y = 4, \quad z = 2$$

which agrees with the result that was obtained in Example 6 of the last section. ◀

There are variations in the method of Lagrange multipliers that can be used to solve problems with two or more constraints. However, we will not discuss that topic here.

## ✓ QUICK CHECK EXERCISES 13.9 *(See page 890 for answers.)*

**1.** (a) Suppose that $f(x, y)$ and $g(x, y)$ are differentiable at the origin and have nonzero gradients there, and that $g(0, 0) = 0$. If the maximum value of $f(x, y)$ subject to the constraint $g(x, y) = 0$ occurs at the origin, how is the tangent line to the graph of $g(x, y) = 0$ related to the tangent line at the origin to the level curve of $f$ through $(0, 0)$?

(b) Suppose that $f(x, y, z)$ and $g(x, y, z)$ are differentiable at the origin and have nonzero gradients there, and that $g(0, 0, 0) = 0$. If the maximum value of $f(x, y, z)$ subject to the constraint $g(x, y, z) = 0$ occurs at the origin, how is the tangent plane to the graph of the constraint $g(x, y, z) = 0$ related to the tangent plane at the origin to the level surface of $f$ through $(0, 0, 0)$?

**2.** The maximum value of $x + y$ subject to the constraint $x^2 + y^2 = 1$ is ______.

**3.** The maximum value of $x + y + z$ subject to the constraint $x^2 + y^2 + z^2 = 1$ is ______.

**4.** The maximum and minimum values of $2x + 3y$ subject to the constraint $x + y = 1$, where $0 \le x, 0 \le y$, are ______ and ______, respectively.

## EXERCISE SET 13.9 [Graphing Utility] Graphing Utility [C] CAS

**FOCUS ON CONCEPTS**

**1.** The accompanying figure shows graphs of the line $x + y = 4$ and the level curves of height $c = 2$, 4, 6, and 8 for the function $f(x, y) = xy$.

(a) Use the figure to find the maximum value of the function $f(x, y) = xy$ subject to $x + y = 4$, and explain your reasoning.

(b) How can you tell from the figure that your answer to part (a) is not the minimum value of $f$ subject to the constraint?

(c) Use Lagrange multipliers to check your work.

**2.** The accompanying figure shows the graphs of the line $3x + 4y = 25$ and the level curves of height $c = 9$, 16, 25, 36, and 49 for the function $f(x, y) = x^2 + y^2$.

(a) Use the accompanying figure to find the minimum value of the function $f(x, y) = x^2 + y^2$ subject to $3x + 4y = 25$, and explain your reasoning.

(b) How can you tell from the accompanying figure that your answer to part (a) is not the maximum value of $f$ subject to the constraint?

(c) Use Lagrange multipliers to check your work.

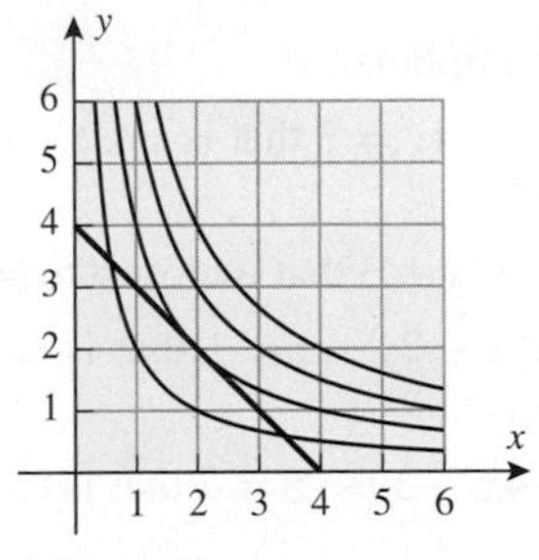

▲ **Figure Ex-1**

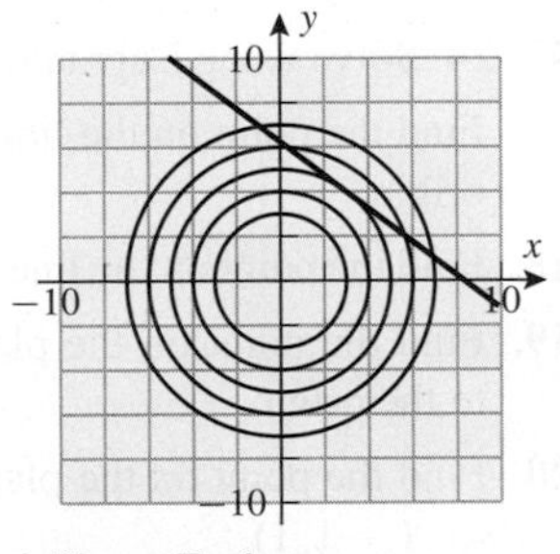

▲ **Figure Ex-2**

[Graphing Utility] **3.** (a) On a graphing utility, graph the circle $x^2 + y^2 = 25$ and two distinct level curves of $f(x, y) = x^2 - y$ that just touch the circle in a single point.

(b) Use the results you obtained in part (a) to approximate the maximum and minimum values of $f$ subject to the constraint $x^2 + y^2 = 25$.

(c) Check your approximations in part (b) using Lagrange multipliers.

C **4.** (a) If you have a CAS with implicit plotting capability, use it to graph the circle $(x-4)^2+(y-4)^2=4$ and two level curves of $f(x,y)=x^3+y^3-3xy$ that just touch the circle.
(b) Use the result you obtained in part (a) to approximate the minimum value of $f$ subject to the constraint $(x-4)^2+(y-4)^2=4$.
(c) Confirm graphically that you have found a minimum and not a maximum.
(d) Check your approximation using Lagrange multipliers and solving the required equations numerically.

**5–12** Use Lagrange multipliers to find the maximum and minimum values of $f$ subject to the given constraint. Also, find the points at which these extreme values occur. ■

**5.** $f(x,y)=xy;\ 4x^2+8y^2=16$

**6.** $f(x,y)=x^2-y^2;\ x^2+y^2=25$

**7.** $f(x,y)=4x^3+y^2;\ 2x^2+y^2=1$

**8.** $f(x,y)=x-3y-1;\ x^2+3y^2=16$

**9.** $f(x,y,z)=2x+y-2z;\ x^2+y^2+z^2=4$

**10.** $f(x,y,z)=3x+6y+2z;\ 2x^2+4y^2+z^2=70$

**11.** $f(x,y,z)=xyz;\ x^2+y^2+z^2=1$

**12.** $f(x,y,z)=x^4+y^4+z^4;\ x^2+y^2+z^2=1$

**13–16 True–False** Determine whether the statement is true or false. Explain your answer. ■

**13.** A "Lagrange multiplier" is a special type of gradient vector.

**14.** The extrema of $f(x,y)$ subject to the constraint $g(x,y)=0$ occur at those points for which $\nabla f=\nabla g$.

**15.** In the method of Lagrange mutlipliers it is necessary to solve a constraint equation $g(x,y)=0$ for $y$ in terms of $x$.

**16.** The extrema of $f(x,y)$ subject to the constraint $g(x,y)=0$ occur at those points at which a contour of $f$ is tangent to the constraint curve $g(x,y)=0$.

**17–24** Solve using Lagrange multipliers. ■

**17.** Find the point on the line $2x-4y=3$ that is closest to the origin.

**18.** Find the point on the line $y=2x+3$ that is closest to $(4,2)$.

**19.** Find the point on the plane $x+2y+z=1$ that is closest to the origin.

**20.** Find the point on the plane $4x+3y+z=2$ that is closest to $(1,-1,1)$.

**21.** Find the points on the circle $x^2+y^2=45$ that are closest to and farthest from $(1,2)$.

**22.** Find the points on the surface $xy-z^2=1$ that are closest to the origin.

**23.** Find a vector in 3-space whose length is 5 and whose components have the largest possible sum.

**24.** Suppose that the temperature at a point $(x,y)$ on a metal plate is $T(x,y)=4x^2-4xy+y^2$. An ant, walking on the plate, traverses a circle of radius 5 centered at the origin. What are the highest and lowest temperatures encountered by the ant?

**25–32** Use Lagrange multipliers to solve the indicated exercises from Section 13.8. ■

**25.** Exercise 38

**26.** Exercise 39

**27.** Exercise 40

**28.** Exercise 41

**29.** Exercise 43

**30.** Exercises 45(a) and (b)

**31.** Exercise 46

**32.** Exercise 47

C **33.** Let $\alpha$, $\beta$, and $\gamma$ be the angles of a triangle.
(a) Use Lagrange multipliers to find the maximum value of $f(\alpha,\beta,\gamma)=\cos\alpha\cos\beta\cos\gamma$, and determine the angles for which the maximum occurs.
(b) Express $f(\alpha,\beta,\gamma)$ as a function of $\alpha$ and $\beta$ alone, and use a CAS to graph this function of two variables. Confirm that the result obtained in part (a) is consistent with the graph.

**34.** The accompanying figure shows the intersection of the elliptic paraboloid $z=x^2+4y^2$ and the right circular cylinder $x^2+y^2=1$. Use Lagrange multipliers to find the highest and lowest points on the curve of intersection.

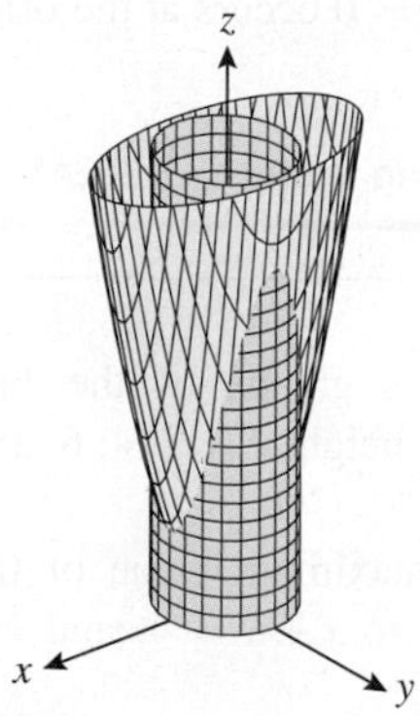

◀ **Figure Ex-34**

**35. Writing** List a sequence of steps for solving a two-variable extremum problem with one constraint using the method of Lagrange multipliers. Interpret each step geometrically.

**36. Writing** Redo Example 2 using the methods of Section 4.5, and compare your solution with that of Example 2. For example, how is the perimeter constraint used in each approach?

✓ **QUICK CHECK ANSWERS 13.9** 1. (a) They are the same line. (b) They are the same plane. 2. $\sqrt{2}$ 3. $\sqrt{3}$ 4. 3; 2

## CHAPTER 13 REVIEW EXERCISES

Graphing Utility

1. Let $f(x, y) = e^x \ln y$. Find
(a) $f(\ln y, e^x)$ (b) $f(r + s, rs)$.

2. Sketch the domain of $f$ using solid lines for portions of the boundary included in the domain and dashed lines for portions not included.
(a) $f(x, y) = \ln(xy - 1)$ (b) $f(x, y) = (\sin^{-1} x)/e^y$

3. Show that the level curves of the cone $z = \sqrt{x^2 + y^2}$ and the paraboloid $z = x^2 + y^2$ are circles, and make a sketch that illustrates the difference between the contour plots of the two functions.

4. (a) In words, describe the level surfaces of the function $f(x, y, z) = a^2x^2 + a^2y^2 + z^2$, where $a > 0$.
(b) Find a function $f(x, y, z)$ whose level surfaces form a family of circular paraboloids that open in the positive $z$-direction.

**5–6** (a) Find the limit of $f(x, y)$ as $(x, y) \to (0, 0)$ if it exists, and (b) determine whether $f$ is continuous at $(0, 0)$. ■

5. $f(x, y) = \dfrac{x^4 - x + y - x^3y}{x - y}$

6. $f(x, y) = \begin{cases} \dfrac{x^4 - y^4}{x^2 + y^2} & \text{if } (x, y) \neq (0, 0) \\ 0 & \text{if } (x, y) = (0, 0) \end{cases}$

7. (a) A company manufactures two types of computer monitors: standard monitors and high resolution monitors. Suppose that $P(x, y)$ is the profit that results from producing and selling $x$ standard monitors and $y$ high-resolution monitors. What do the two partial derivatives $\partial P/\partial x$ and $\partial P/\partial y$ represent?
(b) Suppose that the temperature at time $t$ at a point $(x, y)$ on the surface of a lake is $T(x, y, t)$. What do the partial derivatives $\partial T/\partial x$, $\partial T/\partial y$, and $\partial T/\partial t$ represent?

8. Let $z = f(x, y)$.
(a) Express $\partial z/\partial x$ and $\partial z/\partial y$ as limits.
(b) In words, what do the derivatives $f_x(x_0, y_0)$ and $f_y(x_0, y_0)$ tell you about the surface $z = f(x, y)$?
(c) In words, what do the derivatives $\partial z/\partial x(x_0, y_0)$ and $\partial z/\partial y(x_0, y_0)$ tell you about the rates of change of $z$ with respect to $x$ and $y$?

9. The pressure in newtons per square meter (N/m$^2$) of a gas in a cylinder is given by $P = 10T/V$ with $T$ in kelvins (K) and $V$ in cubic meters (m$^3$).
(a) If $T$ is increasing at a rate of 3 K/min with $V$ held fixed at 2.5 m$^3$, find the rate at which the pressure is changing when $T = 50$ K.
(b) If $T$ is held fixed at 50 K while $V$ is decreasing at the rate of 3 m$^3$/min, find the rate at which the pressure is changing when $V = 2.5$ m$^3$.

10. Find the slope of the tangent line at the point $(1, -2, -3)$ on the curve of intersection of the surface $z = 5 - 4x^2 - y^2$ with
(a) the plane $x = 1$ (b) the plane $y = -2$.

**11–14** Verify the assertion. ■

11. If $w = \tan(x^2 + y^2) + x\sqrt{y}$, then $w_{xy} = w_{yx}$.

12. If $w = \ln(3x - 3y) + \cos(x + y)$, then $\partial^2 w/\partial x^2 = \partial^2 w/\partial y^2$.

13. If $F(x, y, z) = 2z^3 - 3(x^2 + y^2)z$, then $F$ satisfies the equation $F_{xx} + F_{yy} + F_{zz} = 0$.

14. If $f(x, y, z) = xyz + x^2 + \ln(y/z)$, then $f_{xyzx} = f_{zxxy}$.

15. What do $\Delta f$ and $df$ represent, and how are they related?

16. If $w = x^2y - 2xy + y^2x$, find the increment $\Delta w$ and the differential $dw$ if $(x, y)$ varies from $(1, 0)$ to $(1.1, -0.1)$.

17. Use differentials to estimate the change in the volume $V = \frac{1}{3}x^2h$ of a pyramid with a square base when its height $h$ is increased from 2 to 2.2 m and its base dimension $x$ is decreased from 1 to 0.9 m. Compare this to $\Delta V$.

18. Find the local linear approximation of $f(x, y) = \sin(xy)$ at $\left(\frac{1}{3}, \pi\right)$.

19. Suppose that $z$ is a differentiable function of $x$ and $y$ with

$$\frac{\partial z}{\partial x}(1, 2) = 4 \quad \text{and} \quad \frac{\partial z}{\partial y}(1, 2) = 2$$

If $x = x(t)$ and $y = y(t)$ are differentiable functions of $t$ with $x(0) = 1$, $y(0) = 2$, $x'(0) = -\frac{1}{2}$, and (under composition) $z'(0) = 2$, find $y'(0)$.

20. In each part, use Theorem 13.5.3 to find $dy/dx$.
(a) $3x^2 - 5xy + \tan xy = 0$
(b) $x \ln y + \sin(x - y) = \pi$

21. Given that $f(x, y) = 0$, use Theorem 13.5.3 to express $d^2y/dx^2$ in terms of partial derivatives of $f$.

22. Let $z = f(x, y)$, where $x = g(t)$ and $y = h(t)$.
(a) Show that

$$\frac{d}{dt}\left(\frac{\partial z}{\partial x}\right) = \frac{\partial^2 z}{\partial x^2}\frac{dx}{dt} + \frac{\partial^2 z}{\partial y \partial x}\frac{dy}{dt}$$

and

$$\frac{d}{dt}\left(\frac{\partial z}{\partial y}\right) = \frac{\partial^2 z}{\partial x \partial y}\frac{dx}{dt} + \frac{\partial^2 z}{\partial y^2}\frac{dy}{dt}$$

(b) Use the formulas in part (a) to help find a formula for $d^2z/dt^2$.

23. (a) How are the directional derivative and the gradient of a function related?
(b) Under what conditions is the directional derivative of a differentiable function 0?
(c) In what direction does the directional derivative of a differentiable function have its maximum value? Its minimum value?

24. In words, what does the derivative $D_{\mathbf{u}}f(x_0, y_0)$ tell you about the surface $z = f(x, y)$?

25. Find $D_{\mathbf{u}}f(-3, 5)$ for $f(x, y) = y \ln(x + y)$ if $\mathbf{u} = \frac{3}{5}\mathbf{i} + \frac{4}{5}\mathbf{j}$.

26. Suppose that $\nabla f(0, 0) = 2\mathbf{i} + \frac{3}{2}\mathbf{j}$.
(a) Find a unit vector $\mathbf{u}$ such that $D_{\mathbf{u}}f(0, 0)$ is a maximum. What is this maximum value?
(b) Find a unit vector $\mathbf{u}$ such that $D_{\mathbf{u}}f(0, 0)$ is a minimum. What is this minimum value?

27. At the point $(1, 2)$, the directional derivative $D_{\mathbf{u}}f$ is $2\sqrt{2}$ toward $P_1(2, 3)$ and $-3$ toward $P_2(1, 0)$. Find $D_{\mathbf{u}}f(1, 2)$ toward the origin.

28. Find equations for the tangent plane and normal line to the given surface at $P_0$.
(a) $z = x^2 e^{2y}$; $P_0(1, \ln 2, 4)$
(b) $x^2y^3z^4 + xyz = 2$; $P_0(2, 1, -1)$

29. Find all points $P_0$ on the surface $z = 2 - xy$ at which the normal line passes through the origin.

30. Show that for all tangent planes to the surface

$$x^{2/3} + y^{2/3} + z^{2/3} = 1$$

the sum of the squares of the $x$-, $y$-, and $z$-intercepts is 1.

31. Find all points on the paraboloid $z = 9x^2 + 4y^2$ at which the normal line is parallel to the line through the points $P(4, -2, 5)$ and $Q(-2, -6, 4)$.

32. Suppose the equations of motion of a particle are $x = t - 1$, $y = 4e^{-t}$, $z = 2 - \sqrt{t}$, where $t > 0$. Find, to the nearest tenth of a degree, the acute angle between the velocity vector and the normal line to the surface $(x^2/4) + y^2 + z^2 = 1$ at the points where the particle collides with the surface. Use a calculating utility with a root-finding capability where needed.

**33–36** Locate all relative minima, relative maxima, and saddle points. ■

33. $f(x, y) = x^2 + 3xy + 3y^2 - 6x + 3y$

34. $f(x, y) = x^2y - 6y^2 - 3x^2$

35. $f(x, y) = x^3 - 3xy + \frac{1}{2}y^2$

36. $f(x, y) = 4x^2 - 12xy + 9y^2$

**37–39** Solve these exercises two ways:
(a) Use the constraint to eliminate a variable.
(b) Use Lagrange multipliers. ■

37. Find all relative extrema of $x^2y^2$ subject to the constraint $4x^2 + y^2 = 8$.

38. Find the dimensions of the rectangular box of maximum volume that can be inscribed in the ellipsoid

$$(x/a)^2 + (y/b)^2 + (z/c)^2 = 1$$

39. As illustrated in the accompanying figure, suppose that a current $I$ branches into currents $I_1$, $I_2$, and $I_3$ through resistors $R_1$, $R_2$, and $R_3$ in such a way that the total power dissipated in the three resistors is a minimum. Find the ratios $I_1 : I_2 : I_3$ if the power dissipated in $R_i$ is $I_i^2 R_i (i = 1, 2, 3)$ and $I_1 + I_2 + I_3 = I$.

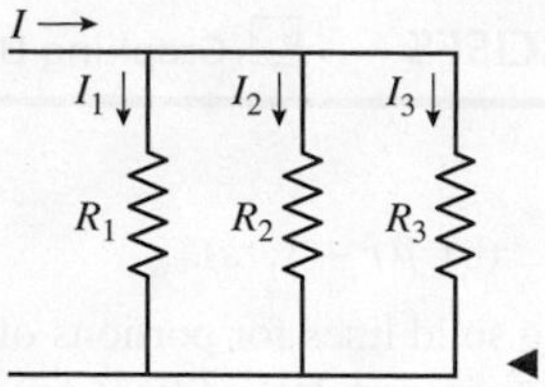


◀ Figure Ex-39

**40–42** In economics, a ***production model*** is a mathematical relationship between the output of a company or a country and the labor and capital equipment required to produce that output. Much of the pioneering work in the field of production models occurred in the 1920s when Paul Douglas of the University of Chicago and his collaborator Charles Cobb proposed that the output $P$ can be expressed in terms of the labor $L$ and the capital equipment $K$ by an equation of the form

$$P = cL^{\alpha}K^{\beta}$$

where $c$ is a constant of proportionality and $\alpha$ and $\beta$ are constants such that $0 < \alpha < 1$ and $0 < \beta < 1$. This is called the ***Cobb–Douglas production model***. Typically, $P$, $L$, and $K$ are all expressed in terms of their equivalent monetary values. These exercises explore properties of this model. ■

40. (a) Consider the Cobb–Douglas production model given by the formula $P = L^{0.75}K^{0.25}$. Sketch the level curves $P(L, K) = 1$, $P(L, K) = 2$, and $P(L, K) = 3$ in an $LK$-coordinate system ($L$ horizontal and $K$ vertical). Your sketch need not be accurate numerically, but it should show the general shape of the curves and their relative positions.
(b) Use a graphing utility to make a more extensive contour plot of the model.

41. (a) Find $\partial P/\partial L$ and $\partial P/\partial K$ for the Cobb–Douglas production model $P = cL^{\alpha}K^{\beta}$.
(b) The derivative $\partial P/\partial L$ is called the ***marginal productivity of labor***, and the derivative $\partial P/\partial K$ is called the ***marginal productivity of capital***. Explain what these quantities mean in practical terms.
(c) Show that if $\beta = 1 - \alpha$, then $P$ satisfies the partial differential equation

$$K\frac{\partial P}{\partial K} + L\frac{\partial P}{\partial L} = P$$

42. Consider the Cobb–Douglas production model

$$P = 1000L^{0.6}K^{0.4}$$

(a) Find the maximum output value of $P$ if labor costs \$50.00 per unit, capital costs \$100.00 per unit, and the total cost of labor and capital is set at \$200,000.
(b) How should the \$200,000 be allocated between labor and capital to achieve the maximum?

## CHAPTER 13 MAKING CONNECTIONS

1. Suppose that a function $z = f(x, y)$ is expressed in polar form by making the substitutions $x = r\cos\theta$ and $y = r\sin\theta$. Show that

$$r\frac{\partial z}{\partial r} = x\frac{\partial z}{\partial x} + y\frac{\partial z}{\partial y}$$

$$\frac{\partial z}{\partial \theta} = -y\frac{\partial z}{\partial x} + x\frac{\partial z}{\partial y}$$

2. A function $f(x, y)$ is said to be ***homogeneous of degree n*** if $f(tx, ty) = t^n f(x, y)$ for $t > 0$. In each part, show that the function is homogeneous, and find its degree.
(a) $f(x, y) = 3x^2 + y^2$ (b) $f(x, y) = \sqrt{x^2 + y^2}$
(c) $f(x, y) = x^2y - 2y^3$ (d) $f(x, y) = \dfrac{5}{(x^2 + 2y^2)^2}$

3. Suppose that a function $f(x, y)$ is defined for all points $(x, y) \neq (0, 0)$. Prove that $f$ is homogeneous of degree $n$ if and only if there exists a function $g(\theta)$ that is $2\pi$ periodic such that in polar form the equation $z = f(x, y)$ becomes

$$z = r^n g(\theta)$$

for $r > 0$ and $-\infty < \theta < +\infty$.

4. (a) Use the chain rule to show that if $f(x, y)$ is a homogeneous function of degree $n$, then

$$x\frac{\partial f}{\partial x} + y\frac{\partial f}{\partial y} = nf$$

[*Hint:* Let $u = tx$ and $v = ty$ in $f(tx, ty)$, and differentiate both sides of $f(u, v) = t^n f(x, y)$ with respect to $t$.]
(b) Use the results of Exercises 1 and 3 to give another derivation of the equation in part (a).
(c) Confirm that the functions in Exercise 2 satisfy the equation in part (a).

5. Suppose that a function $f(x, y)$ is defined for all points $(x, y) \neq (0, 0)$ and satisfies

$$x\frac{\partial f}{\partial x} + y\frac{\partial f}{\partial y} = nf$$

Prove that $f$ is homogeneous of degree $n$. [*Hint:* Express the function $z = f(x, y)$ in polar form and use Exercise 1 to conclude that

$$r\frac{\partial z}{\partial r} - nz = 0$$

Divide both sides of this equation by $r^{n+1}$ and interpret the left-hand side of the resulting equation as the partial derivative with respect to $r$ of a product of two functions.]

14

# MULTIPLE INTEGRALS

urban_light/Depositphotos

*Finding the areas of complex surfaces such as those used in the design of the Denver International Airport require integration methods studied in this chapter.*

In this chapter we will extend the concept of a definite integral to functions of two and three variables. Whereas functions of one variable are usually integrated over intervals, functions of two variables are usually integrated over regions in 2-space and functions of three variables over regions in 3-space. Calculating such integrals will require some new techniques that will be a central focus in this chapter. Once we have developed the basic methods for integrating functions of two and three variables, we will show how such integrals can be used to calculate surface areas and volumes of solids; and we will also show how they can be used to find masses and centers of gravity of flat plates and three-dimensional solids. In addition to our study of integration, we will generalize the concept of a parametric curve in 2-space to a parametric surface in 3-space. This will allow us to work with a wider variety of surfaces than previously possible and will provide a powerful tool for generating surfaces using computers and other graphing utilities.

## 14.1 DOUBLE INTEGRALS

*The notion of a definite integral can be extended to functions of two or more variables. In this section we will discuss the double integral, which is the extension to functions of two variables.*

### VOLUME

Recall that the definite integral of a function of one variable

$$\int_a^b f(x)\,dx = \lim_{\max \Delta x_k \to 0} \sum_{k=1}^{n} f(x_k^*)\Delta x_k = \lim_{n\to+\infty} \sum_{k=1}^{n} f(x_k^*)\Delta x_k \tag{1}$$

arose from the problem of finding areas under curves. [In the rightmost expression in (1), we use the "limit as $n \to +\infty$" to encapsulate the process by which we increase the number of subintervals of $[a, b]$ in such a way that the lengths of the subintervals approach zero.] Integrals of functions of two variables arise from the problem of finding volumes under surfaces.

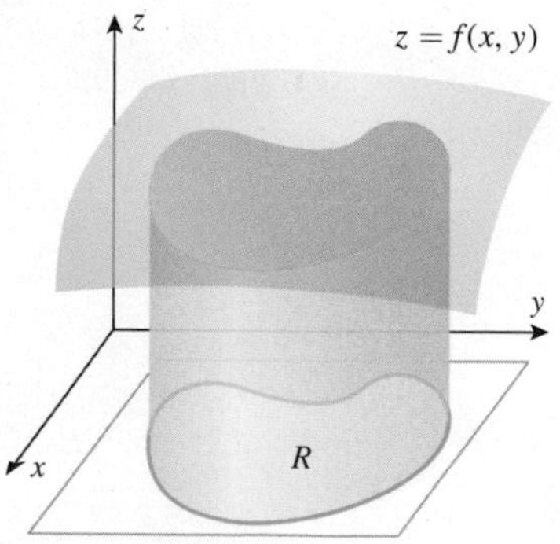


▲ **Figure 14.1.1**

**14.1.1 THE VOLUME PROBLEM** Given a function $f$ of two variables that is continuous and nonnegative on a region $R$ in the $xy$-plane, find the volume of the solid enclosed between the surface $z = f(x, y)$ and the region $R$ (Figure 14.1.1).

Later, we will place more restrictions on the region $R$, but for now we will just assume that the entire region can be enclosed within some suitably large rectangle with sides parallel to the coordinate axes. This ensures that $R$ does not extend indefinitely in any direction.

The procedure for finding the volume $V$ of the solid in Figure 14.1.1 will be similar to the limiting process used for finding areas, except that now the approximating elements will be rectangular parallelepipeds rather than rectangles. We proceed as follows:

- Using lines parallel to the coordinate axes, divide the rectangle enclosing the region $R$ into subrectangles, and exclude from consideration all those subrectangles that contain any points outside of $R$. This leaves only rectangles that are subsets of $R$

(Figure 14.1.2). Assume that there are $n$ such rectangles, and denote the area of the $k$th such rectangle by $\Delta A_k$.

- Choose any arbitrary point in each subrectangle, and denote the point in the $k$th subrectangle by $(x_k^*, y_k^*)$. As shown in Figure 14.1.3, the product $f(x_k^*, y_k^*)\Delta A_k$ is the volume of a rectangular parallelepiped with base area $\Delta A_k$ and height $f(x_k^*, y_k^*)$, so the sum
$$\sum_{k=1}^{n} f(x_k^*, y_k^*)\Delta A_k$$
can be viewed as an approximation to the volume $V$ of the entire solid.
- There are two sources of error in the approximation: first, the parallelepipeds have flat tops, whereas the surface $z = f(x, y)$ may be curved; second, the rectangles that form the bases of the parallelepipeds may not completely cover the region $R$. However, if we repeat the above process with more and more subdivisions in such a way that both the lengths and the widths of the subrectangles approach zero, then it is plausible that the errors of both types approach zero, and the exact volume of the solid will be
$$V = \lim_{n\to+\infty} \sum_{k=1}^{n} f(x_k^*, y_k^*)\Delta A_k$$

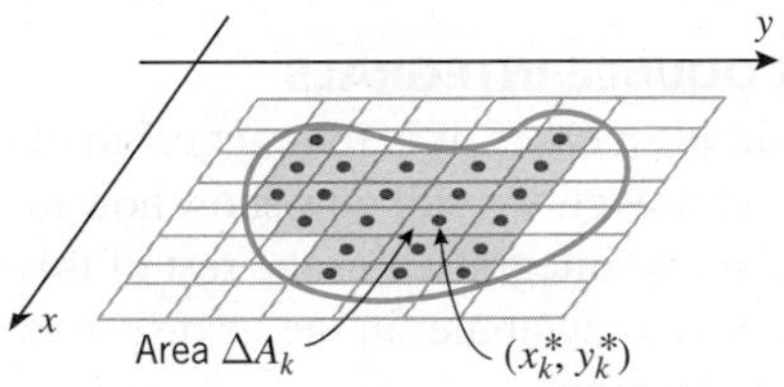

▲ **Figure 14.1.2**

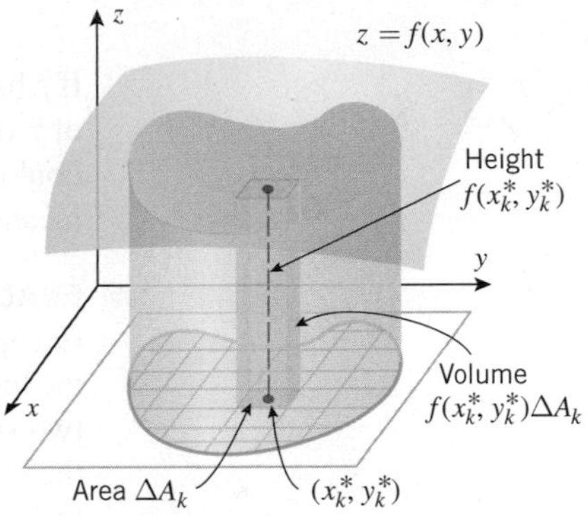

▲ **Figure 14.1.3**

This suggests the following definition.

Definition 14.1.2 is satisfactory for our present purposes, but some issues would have to be resolved before it could be regarded as rigorous. For example, we would have to prove that the limit actually exists and that its value does not depend on how the points $(x_1^*, y_1^*), (x_2^*, y_2^*), \ldots, (x_n^*, y_n^*)$ are chosen. These facts are true if the region $R$ is not too "complicated" and if $f$ is continuous on $R$. The details are beyond the scope of this text.

**14.1.2 DEFINITION** (*Volume Under a Surface*) If $f$ is a function of two variables that is continuous and nonnegative on a region $R$ in the $xy$-plane, then the volume of the solid enclosed between the surface $z = f(x, y)$ and the region $R$ is defined by
$$V = \lim_{n\to+\infty} \sum_{k=1}^{n} f(x_k^*, y_k^*)\Delta A_k \tag{2}$$
Here, $n\to+\infty$ indicates the process of increasing the number of subrectangles of the rectangle enclosing $R$ in such a way that both the lengths and the widths of the subrectangles approach zero.

It is assumed in Definition 14.1.2 that $f$ is nonnegative on the region $R$. If $f$ is continuous on $R$ and has both positive and negative values, then the limit
$$\lim_{n\to+\infty} \sum_{k=1}^{n} f(x_k^*, y_k^*)\Delta A_k \tag{3}$$
no longer represents the volume between $R$ and the surface $z = f(x, y)$; rather, it represents a *difference* of volumes—the volume between $R$ and the portion of the surface that is above

the $xy$-plane minus the volume between $R$ and the portion of the surface below the $xy$-plane. We call this the ***net signed volume*** between the region $R$ and the surface $z = f(x, y)$.

## DEFINITION OF A DOUBLE INTEGRAL

As in Definition 14.1.2, the notation $n \to +\infty$ in (3) encapsulates a process in which the enclosing rectangle for $R$ is repeatedly subdivided in such a way that both the lengths and the widths of the subrectangles approach zero. Thus, we have extended the notion conveyed by Formula (1) where the definite integral of a one-variable function is expressed as a limit of Riemann sums. By extension, the sums in (3) are also called ***Riemann sums***, and the limit of the Riemann sums is denoted by

$$\iint_R f(x, y)\, dA = \lim_{n \to +\infty} \sum_{k=1}^{n} f(x_k^*, y_k^*)\Delta A_k \tag{4}$$

which is called the ***double integral*** of $f(x, y)$ over $R$.

If $f$ is continuous and nonnegative on the region $R$, then the volume formula in (2) can be expressed as

$$V = \iint_R f(x, y)\, dA \tag{5}$$

If $f$ has both positive and negative values on $R$, then a positive value for the double integral of $f$ over $R$ means that there is more volume above $R$ than below, a negative value for the double integral means that there is more volume below $R$ than above, and a value of zero means that the volume above $R$ is the same as the volume below $R$.

## EVALUATING DOUBLE INTEGRALS

Except in the simplest cases, it is impractical to obtain the value of a double integral from the limit in (4). However, we will now show how to evaluate double integrals by calculating two successive single integrals. For the rest of this section we will limit our discussion to the case where $R$ is a rectangle; in the next section we will consider double integrals over more complicated regions.

The partial derivatives of a function $f(x, y)$ are calculated by holding one of the variables fixed and differentiating with respect to the other variable. Let us consider the reverse of this process, ***partial integration***. The symbols

$$\int_a^b f(x, y)\, dx \quad \text{and} \quad \int_c^d f(x, y)\, dy$$

denote ***partial definite integrals***; the first integral, called the ***partial definite integral with respect to x***, is evaluated by holding $y$ fixed and integrating with respect to $x$, and the second integral, called the ***partial definite integral with respect to y***, is evaluated by holding $x$ fixed and integrating with respect to $y$. As the following example shows, the partial definite integral with respect to $x$ is a function of $y$, and the partial definite integral with respect to $y$ is a function of $x$.

### ▶ Example 1

$$\int_0^1 xy^2\, dx = y^2 \int_0^1 x\, dx = \left.\frac{y^2x^2}{2}\right]_{x=0}^{1} = \frac{y^2}{2}$$

$$\int_0^1 xy^2\, dy = x \int_0^1 y^2\, dy = \left.\frac{xy^3}{3}\right]_{y=0}^{1} = \frac{x}{3} \quad ◀$$

A partial definite integral with respect to $x$ is a function of $y$ and hence can be integrated with respect to $y$; similarly, a partial definite integral with respect to $y$ can be integrated with respect to $x$. This two-stage integration process is called ***iterated*** (or ***repeated***) ***integration***. We introduce the following notation:

$$\int_c^d \int_a^b f(x,y)\,dx\,dy = \int_c^d \left[\int_a^b f(x,y)\,dx\right] dy \tag{6}$$

$$\int_a^b \int_c^d f(x,y)\,dy\,dx = \int_a^b \left[\int_c^d f(x,y)\,dy\right] dx \tag{7}$$

These integrals are called ***iterated integrals***.

▶ **Example 2** Evaluate

(a) $\displaystyle\int_1^3 \int_2^4 (40-2xy)\,dy\,dx$ (b) $\displaystyle\int_2^4 \int_1^3 (40-2xy)\,dx\,dy$

***Solution (a).***

$$\begin{aligned}\int_1^3 \int_2^4 (40-2xy)\,dy\,dx &= \int_1^3 \left[\int_2^4 (40-2xy)\,dy\right] dx\\ &= \int_1^3 (40y - xy^2)\Big]_{y=2}^{4}\,dx\\ &= \int_1^3 [(160-16x)-(80-4x)]\,dx\\ &= \int_1^3 (80-12x)\,dx\\ &= (80x-6x^2)\Big]_1^3 = 112\end{aligned}$$

***Solution (b).***

$$\begin{aligned}\int_2^4 \int_1^3 (40-2xy)\,dx\,dy &= \int_2^4 \left[\int_1^3 (40-2xy)\,dx\right] dy\\ &= \int_2^4 (40x - x^2y)\Big]_{x=1}^{3}\,dy\\ &= \int_2^4 [(120-9y)-(40-y)]\,dy\\ &= \int_2^4 (80-8y)\,dy\\ &= (80y-4y^2)\Big]_2^4 = 112 \blacktriangleleft\end{aligned}$$

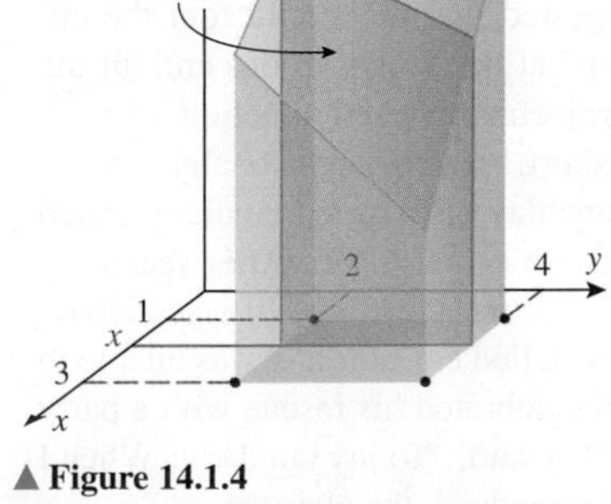

▲ **Figure 14.1.4**

It is no accident that both parts of Example 2 produced the same answer. Consider the solid $S$ bounded above by the surface $z = 40 - 2xy$ and below by the rectangle $R$ defined by $1 \le x \le 3$ and $2 \le y \le 4$. By the method of slicing discussed in Section 6.2, the volume of $S$ is given by

$$V = \int_1^3 A(x)\,dx$$

where $A(x)$ is the area of a vertical cross section of $S$ taken perpendicular to the $x$-axis (Figure 14.1.4). For a fixed value of $x$, $1 \le x \le 3$, $z = 40 - 2xy$ is a function of $y$, so the integral

$$A(x) = \int_2^4 (40-2xy)\,dy$$

represents the area under the graph of this function of $y$. Thus,

$$V = \int_1^3 \left[\int_2^4 (40-2xy)\,dy\right] dx = \int_1^3 \int_2^4 (40-2xy)\,dy\,dx$$

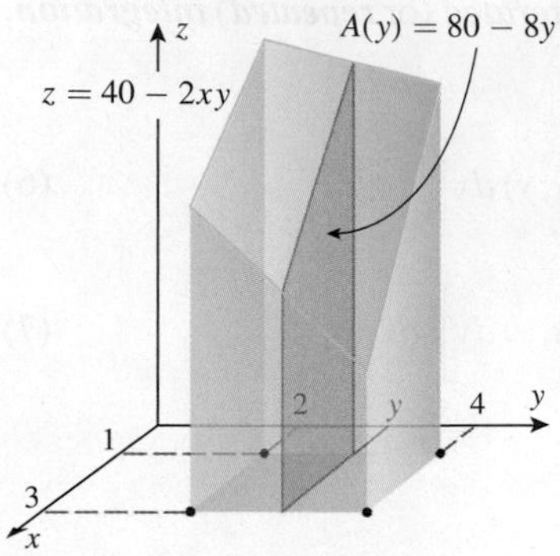


▲ Figure 14.1.5

We will often denote the rectangle

$$\{(x, y) : a \le x \le b, c \le y \le d\}$$

as $[a, b] \times [c, d]$ for simplicity.

is the volume of $S$. Similarly, by the method of slicing with cross sections of $S$ taken perpendicular to the $y$-axis, the volume of $S$ is given by

$$V = \int_2^4 A(y)\,dy = \int_2^4 \left[\int_1^3 (40 - 2xy)\,dx\right] dy = \int_2^4 \int_1^3 (40 - 2xy)\,dx\,dy$$

(Figure 14.1.5). Thus, the iterated integrals in parts (a) and (b) of Example 2 both measure the volume of $S$, which by Formula (5) is the double integral of $z = 40 - 2xy$ over $R$. That is,

$$\int_1^3 \int_2^4 (40 - 2xy)\,dy\,dx = \iint_R (40 - 2xy)\,dA = \int_2^4 \int_1^3 (40 - 2xy)\,dx\,dy$$

The geometric argument above applies to any continuous function $f(x, y)$ that is nonnegative on a rectangle $R = [a, b] \times [c, d]$, as is the case for $f(x, y) = 40 - 2xy$ on $[1, 3] \times [2, 4]$. The conclusion that the double integral of $f(x, y)$ over $R$ has the same value as either of the two possible iterated integrals is true even when $f$ is negative at some points in $R$. We state this result in the following theorem and omit a formal proof.

**14.1.3 THEOREM (*Fubini's Theorem*)** *Let $R$ be the rectangle defined by the inequalities*

$$a \le x \le b, \quad c \le y \le d$$

*If $f(x, y)$ is continuous on this rectangle, then*

$$\iint_R f(x, y)\,dA = \int_c^d \int_a^b f(x, y)\,dx\,dy = \int_a^b \int_c^d f(x, y)\,dy\,dx$$

Theorem 14.1.3 allows us to evaluate a double integral over a rectangle by converting it to an iterated integral. This can be done in two ways, both of which produce the value of the double integral.

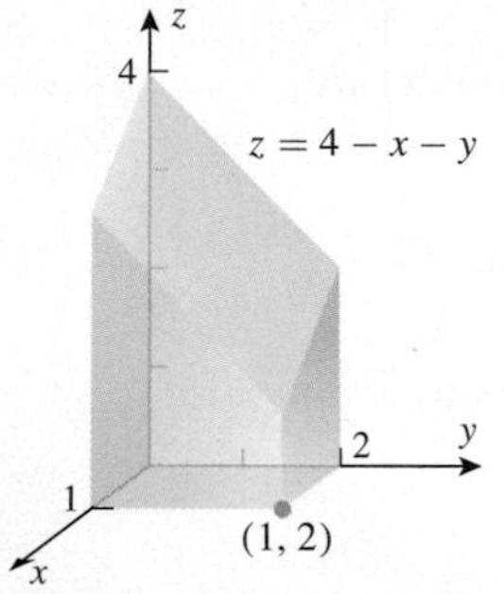


▲ Figure 14.1.6

**▶ Example 3** Use a double integral to find the volume of the solid that is bounded above by the plane $z = 4 - x - y$ and below by the rectangle $R = [0, 1] \times [0, 2]$ (Figure 14.1.6).

***Solution.*** The volume is the double integral of $z = 4 - x - y$ over $R$. Using Theorem 14.1.3, this can be obtained from either of the iterated integrals

$$\int_0^2 \int_0^1 (4 - x - y)\,dx\,dy \quad \text{or} \quad \int_0^1 \int_0^2 (4 - x - y)\,dy\,dx \tag{8}$$

**Guido Fubini (1879–1943)** Italian mathematician. Fubini, the son of a mathematician, showed brilliance in mathematics as a young pupil in Venice. He entered college at the Scuola Normale Superiore di Pisa in 1896 and presented his doctoral thesis on the subject of elliptic geometry in 1900 at the young age of 20. He subsequently had teaching positions at various universities, finally settling at the University of Turin where he remained for several decades. His mathematical work was diverse, and he made major contributions to many branches of mathematics. At the outbreak of World War I he shifted his attention to the accuracy of artillery fire, and following the war he worked on other applied subjects such as electrical circuits and acoustics. In 1939, as he neared age 60 and retirement, Benito Mussolini's Fascists adopted Hitler's anti-Jewish policies, so Fubini, who was Jewish, accepted a position at Princeton University, where he stayed until his death four years later. Fubini was well liked by his colleagues at Princeton and stories about him abound. He once gave a lecture on ballistics in which he showed that if you fired a projectile of a certain shape, then under the right conditions it could double back on itself and hit your own troops. Then, tongue in cheek, he suggested that one could fool the enemy by aiming this "Fubini Gun" at one's own troops and hit the unsuspecting enemy after the projectile reversed direction.

Fubini was exceptionally short, which occasionally caused problems. The story goes that one day his worried landlady called his friends to report that he had not come home. After searching everywhere, including the area near the local lake, it was discovered that Fubini was trapped in a stalled elevator and was unable to reach any of the buttons. Fubini celebrated his rescue with a party and later left a sign in his room that said, "To my landlady: When I am not home at 6:30 at night, please check the elevator. . . ."

Using the first of these, we obtain

$$V = \iint_R (4-x-y)\,dA = \int_0^2 \int_0^1 (4-x-y)\,dx\,dy$$
$$= \int_0^2 \left[4x - \frac{x^2}{2} - xy\right]_{x=0}^{1} dy = \int_0^2 \left(\frac{7}{2} - y\right) dy$$
$$= \left[\frac{7}{2}y - \frac{y^2}{2}\right]_0^2 = 5$$

You can check this result by evaluating the second integral in (8). ◀

**TECHNOLOGY MASTERY**

If you have a CAS with a built-in capability for computing iterated double integrals, use it to check Example 3.

Theorem 14.1.3 guarantees that the double integral in Example 4 can also be evaluated by integrating first with respect to $y$ and then with respect to $x$. Verify this.

▶ **Example 4** Evaluate the double integral

$$\iint_R y^2 x\,dA$$

over the rectangle $R = \{(x, y) : -3 \le x \le 2, 0 \le y \le 1\}$.

***Solution.*** In view of Theorem 14.1.3, the value of the double integral can be obtained by evaluating one of two possible iterated double integrals. We choose to integrate first with respect to $x$ and then with respect to $y$.

$$\iint_R y^2 x\,dA = \int_0^1 \int_{-3}^2 y^2 x\,dx\,dy = \int_0^1 \left[\frac{1}{2}y^2x^2\right]_{x=-3}^{2} dy$$
$$= \int_0^1 \left(-\frac{5}{2}y^2\right) dy = -\frac{5}{6}y^3\Big]_0^1 = -\frac{5}{6} \quad ◀$$

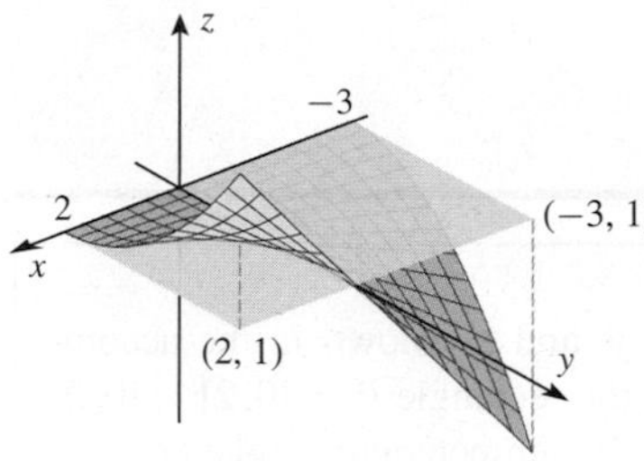


$z = y^2x$ on $[-3, 2] \times [0, 1]$

▲ **Figure 14.1.7**

The integral in Example 4 can be interpreted as the net signed volume between the rectangle $[-3, 2] \times [0, 1]$ and the surface $z = y^2x$. That is, it is the volume below $z = y^2x$ and above $[0, 2] \times [0, 1]$ minus the volume above $z = y^2x$ and below $[-3, 0] \times [0, 1]$ (Figure 14.1.7).

## PROPERTIES OF DOUBLE INTEGRALS

To distinguish between double integrals of functions of two variables and definite integrals of functions of one variable, we will refer to the latter as ***single integrals***. Because double integrals, like single integrals, are defined as limits, they inherit many of the properties of limits. The following results, which we state without proof, are analogs of those in Theorem 5.5.4.

$$\iint_R cf(x, y)\,dA = c\iint_R f(x, y)\,dA \quad (c \text{ a constant}) \tag{9}$$

$$\iint_R [f(x, y) + g(x, y)]\,dA = \iint_R f(x, y)\,dA + \iint_R g(x, y)\,dA \tag{10}$$

$$\iint_R [f(x, y) - g(x, y)]\,dA = \iint_R f(x, y)\,dA - \iint_R g(x, y)\,dA \tag{11}$$

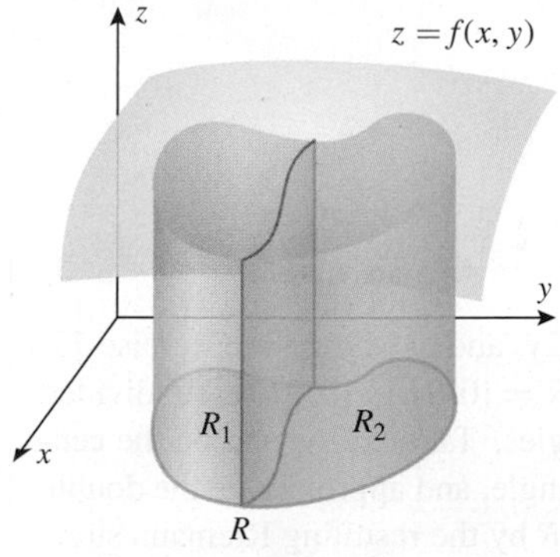


The volume of the entire solid is the sum of the volumes of the solids above $R_1$ and $R_2$.

▲ **Figure 14.1.8**

Figure 14.1.8 illustrates the result that if $f(x, y)$ is nonnegative on a region $R$, then subdividing $R$ into two regions $R_1$ and $R_2$ has the effect of subdividing the solid between $R$

and $z = f(x, y)$ into two solids, the sum of whose volumes is the volume of the entire solid. This suggests the following result, which holds even if $f$ has negative values:

$$\iint_R f(x,y)\,dA = \iint_{R_1} f(x,y)\,dA + \iint_{R_2} f(x,y)\,dA \tag{12}$$

The proof of this result will be omitted.

## ✓ QUICK CHECK EXERCISES 14.1 *(See page 902 for answers.)*

1. The double integral is defined as a limit of Riemann sums by
$$\iint_R f(x,y)\,dA = \underline{\hspace{2cm}}$$

2. The iterated integral
$$\int_1^5 \int_2^4 f(x,y)\,dx\,dy$$
integrates $f$ over the rectangle defined by
$\underline{\hspace{1.5cm}} \le x \le \underline{\hspace{1.5cm}}$, $\underline{\hspace{1.5cm}} \le y \le \underline{\hspace{1.5cm}}$

3. Supply the missing integrand and limits of integration.
$$\int_1^5 \int_2^4 (3x^2 - 2xy + y^2)\,dx\,dy = \int_{\square}^{\square} \underline{\hspace{2cm}}\,dy$$

4. The volume of the solid enclosed by the surface $z = x/y$ and the rectangle $0 \le x \le 4$, $1 \le y \le e^2$ in the $xy$-plane is $\underline{\hspace{1.5cm}}$.

## EXERCISE SET 14.1 [C] CAS

**1–12** Evaluate the iterated integrals. ■

1. $\displaystyle\int_0^1 \int_0^2 (x+3)\,dy\,dx$

2. $\displaystyle\int_1^3 \int_{-1}^1 (2x-4y)\,dy\,dx$

3. $\displaystyle\int_2^4 \int_0^1 x^2y\,dx\,dy$

4. $\displaystyle\int_{-2}^0 \int_{-1}^2 (x^2+y^2)\,dx\,dy$

5. $\displaystyle\int_0^{\ln 3} \int_0^{\ln 2} e^{x+y}\,dy\,dx$

6. $\displaystyle\int_0^2 \int_0^1 y\sin x\,dy\,dx$

7. $\displaystyle\int_{-1}^0 \int_2^5 dx\,dy$

8. $\displaystyle\int_4^6 \int_{-3}^7 dy\,dx$

9. $\displaystyle\int_0^1 \int_0^1 \frac{x}{(xy+1)^2}\,dy\,dx$

10. $\displaystyle\int_{\pi/2}^{\pi} \int_1^2 x\cos xy\,dy\,dx$

11. $\displaystyle\int_0^{\ln 2} \int_0^1 xye^{y^2x}\,dy\,dx$

12. $\displaystyle\int_3^4 \int_1^2 \frac{1}{(x+y)^2}\,dy\,dx$

**13–16** Evaluate the double integral over the rectangular region $R$. ■

13. $\displaystyle\iint_R 4xy^3\,dA$; $R = \{(x,y): -1 \le x \le 1, -2 \le y \le 2\}$

14. $\displaystyle\iint_R \frac{xy}{\sqrt{x^2+y^2+1}}\,dA$;
$R = \{(x,y): 0 \le x \le 1, 0 \le y \le 1\}$

15. $\displaystyle\iint_R x\sqrt{1-x^2}\,dA$; $R = \{(x,y): 0 \le x \le 1, 2 \le y \le 3\}$

16. $\displaystyle\iint_R (x\sin y - y\sin x)\,dA$;
$R = \{(x,y): 0 \le x \le \pi/2, 0 \le y \le \pi/3\}$

**FOCUS ON CONCEPTS**

17. (a) Let $f(x,y) = x^2 + y$, and as shown in the accompanying figure, let the rectangle $R = [0,2] \times [0,2]$ be subdivided into 16 subrectangles. Take $(x_k^*, y_k^*)$ to be the center of the $k$th rectangle, and approximate the double integral of $f$ over $R$ by the resulting Riemann sum.
(b) Compare the result in part (a) to the exact value of the integral.

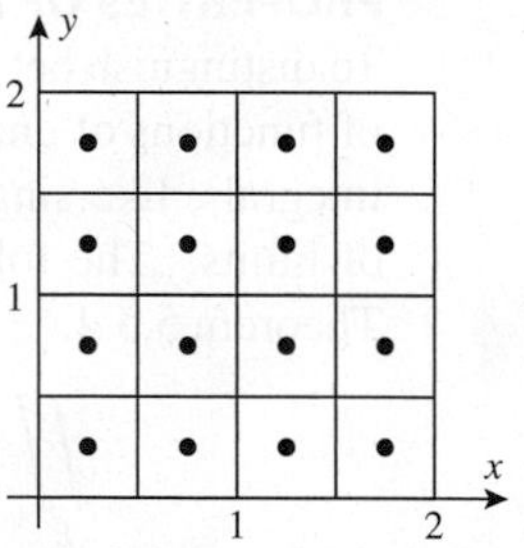

◀ Figure Ex-17

18. (a) Let $f(x,y) = x - 2y$, and as shown in Exercise 17, let the rectangle $R = [0,2] \times [0,2]$ be subdivided into 16 subrectangles. Take $(x_k^*, y_k^*)$ to be the center of the $k$th rectangle, and approximate the double integral of $f$ over $R$ by the resulting Riemann sum.
(b) Compare the result in part (a) to the exact value of the integral.

**19–20** Each iterated integral represents the volume of a solid. Make a sketch of the solid. Use geometry to find the volume of the solid, and then evaluate the iterated integral. ■

19. $\displaystyle\int_0^5 \int_1^2 4\,dx\,dy$

20. $\displaystyle\int_0^1 \int_0^1 (2-x-y)\,dx\,dy$

**21–22** Each iterated integral represents the volume of a solid. Make a sketch of the solid. (You do *not* have to find the volume.) ■

**21.** $\int_0^3 \int_0^4 \sqrt{25 - x^2 - y^2}\, dy\, dx$

**22.** $\int_{-2}^2 \int_{-2}^2 (x^2 + y^2)\, dx\, dy$

**23–26 True–False** Determine whether the statement is true or false. Explain your answer. ■

**23.** In the definition of a double integral

$$\iint_R f(x, y)\, dA = \lim_{n \to +\infty} \sum_{k=1}^n f(x_k^*, y_k^*) \Delta A_k$$

the symbol $\Delta A_k$ represents a rectangular region within $R$ from which the point $(x_k^*, y_k^*)$ is taken.

**24.** If $R$ is the rectangle $\{(x, y) : 1 \le x \le 4, 0 \le y \le 3\}$ and $\int_0^3 f(x, y)\, dy = 2x$, then

$$\iint_R f(x, y)\, dA = 15$$

**25.** If $R$ is the rectangle $\{(x, y) : 1 \le x \le 5, 2 \le y \le 4\}$, then

$$\iint_R f(x, y)\, dA = \int_1^5 \int_2^4 f(x, y)\, dx\, dy$$

**26.** Suppose that for some region $R$ in the $xy$-plane

$$\iint_R f(x, y)\, dA = 0$$

If $R$ is subdivided into two regions $R_1$ and $R_2$, then

$$\iint_{R_1} f(x, y)\, dA = -\iint_{R_2} f(x, y)\, dA$$

**27.** In this exercise, suppose that $f(x, y) = g(x)h(y)$ and $R = \{(x, y) : a \le x \le b, c \le y \le d\}$. Show that

$$\iint_R f(x, y)\, dA = \left[\int_a^b g(x)\, dx\right]\left[\int_c^d h(y)\, dy\right]$$

**28.** Use the result in Exercise 27 to evaluate the integral

$$\int_0^{\ln 2} \int_{-1}^1 \sqrt{e^y + 1} \tan x\, dx\, dy$$

by inspection. Explain your reasoning.

**29–32** Use a double integral to find the volume. ■

**29.** The volume under the plane $z = 2x + y$ and over the rectangle $R = \{(x, y) : 3 \le x \le 5, 1 \le y \le 2\}$.

**30.** The volume under the surface $z = 3x^3 + 3x^2 y$ and over the rectangle $R = \{(x, y) : 1 \le x \le 3, 0 \le y \le 2\}$.

**31.** The volume of the solid enclosed by the surface $z = x^2$ and the planes $x = 0$, $x = 2$, $y = 3$, $y = 0$, and $z = 0$.

**32.** The volume in the first octant bounded by the coordinate planes, the plane $y = 4$, and the plane $(x/3) + (z/5) = 1$.

**33.** Evaluate the integral by choosing a convenient order of integration:

$$\iint_R x \cos(xy) \cos^2 \pi x\, dA;\ R = \left[0, \tfrac{1}{2}\right] \times [0, \pi]$$

**34.** (a) Sketch the solid in the first octant that is enclosed by the planes $x = 0$, $z = 0$, $x = 5$, $z - y = 0$, and $z = -2y + 6$.

(b) Find the volume of the solid by breaking it into two parts.

**35–40** The ***average value*** or ***mean value*** of a continuous function $f(x, y)$ over a rectangle $R = [a, b] \times [c, d]$ is defined as

$$f_{\text{ave}} = \frac{1}{A(R)} \iint_R f(x, y)\, dA$$

where $A(R) = (b - a)(d - c)$ is the area of the rectangle $R$ (compare to Definition 5.8.1). Use this definition in these exercises. ■

**35.** Find the average value of $f(x, y) = xy^2$ over the rectangle $[0, 8] \times [0, 6]$.

**36.** Find the average value of $f(x, y) = x^2 + 7y$ over the rectangle $[0, 3] \times [0, 6]$.

**37.** Find the average value of $f(x, y) = y \sin xy$ over the rectangle $[0, 1] \times [0, \pi/2]$.

**38.** Find the average value of $f(x, y) = x(x^2 + y)^{1/2}$ over the rectangle $[0, 1] \times [0, 3]$.

**39.** Suppose that the temperature in degrees Celsius at a point $(x, y)$ on a flat metal plate is $T(x, y) = 10 - 8x^2 - 2y^2$, where $x$ and $y$ are in meters. Find the average temperature of the rectangular portion of the plate for which $0 \le x \le 1$ and $0 \le y \le 2$.

**40.** Show that if $f(x, y)$ is constant on the rectangle $R = [a, b] \times [c, d]$, say $f(x, y) = k$, then $f_{\text{ave}} = k$ over $R$.

**41–42** Most computer algebra systems have commands for approximating double integrals numerically. Read the relevant documentation and use a CAS to find a numerical approximation of the double integral in these exercises. ■

C **41.** $\int_0^2 \int_0^1 \sin \sqrt{x^3 + y^3}\, dx\, dy$

C **42.** $\int_{-1}^1 \int_{-1}^1 e^{-(x^2+y^2)}\, dx\, dy$

C **43.** Use a CAS to evaluate the iterated integrals

$$\int_0^1 \int_0^1 \frac{y - x}{(x + y)^3}\, dx\, dy \quad \text{and} \quad \int_0^1 \int_0^1 \frac{y - x}{(x + y)^3}\, dy\, dx$$

Does this contradict Theorem 14.1.3? Explain.

C **44.** Use a CAS to show that the volume $V$ under the surface $z = xy^3 \sin xy$ over the rectangle shown in the accompanying figure is $V = 3/\pi$.

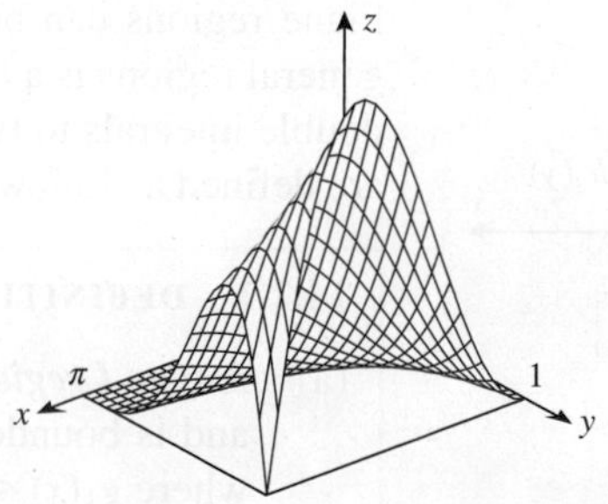


◀ **Figure Ex-44**

**45. Writing** Discuss how computing a volume using an iterated double integral corresponds to the method of computing a volume by slicing (Section 6.2).

**46. Writing** Discuss how the double integral property given in Formula (12) generalizes the single integral property in Theorem 5.5.5.

✓ QUICK CHECK ANSWERS 14.1 1. $\lim_{n\to+\infty}\sum_{k=1}^{n} f(x_k^*, y_k^*)\Delta A_k$ 2. $2 \le x \le 4,\ 1 \le y \le 5$ 3. $\int_1^5 (56 - 12y + 2y^2)\,dy$ 4. 16

## 14.2 DOUBLE INTEGRALS OVER NONRECTANGULAR REGIONS

*In this section we will show how to evaluate double integrals over regions other than rectangles.*

### ITERATED INTEGRALS WITH NONCONSTANT LIMITS OF INTEGRATION

Later in this section we will see that double integrals over nonrectangular regions can often be evaluated as iterated integrals of the following types:

Note that in (1) and (2) the limits of integration in the outer integral are constants. This is consistent with the fact that the value of each iterated integral is a number that represents a net signed volume.

$$\int_a^b \int_{g_1(x)}^{g_2(x)} f(x,y)\,dy\,dx = \int_a^b \left[\int_{g_1(x)}^{g_2(x)} f(x,y)\,dy\right] dx \tag{1}$$

$$\int_c^d \int_{h_1(y)}^{h_2(y)} f(x,y)\,dx\,dy = \int_c^d \left[\int_{h_1(y)}^{h_2(y)} f(x,y)\,dx\right] dy \tag{2}$$

We begin with an example that illustrates how to evaluate such integrals.

► **Example 1** Evaluate

$$\text{(a)}\ \int_0^1 \int_{-x}^{x^2} y^2 x\,dy\,dx \qquad \text{(b)}\ \int_0^{\pi/3} \int_0^{\cos y} x \sin y\,dx\,dy$$

***Solution (a).***

$$\int_0^1 \int_{-x}^{x^2} y^2 x\,dy\,dx = \int_0^1 \left[\int_{-x}^{x^2} y^2 x\,dy\right] dx = \int_0^1 \left.\frac{y^3 x}{3}\right]_{y=-x}^{x^2} dx$$

$$= \int_0^1 \left[\frac{x^7}{3} + \frac{x^4}{3}\right] dx = \left(\frac{x^8}{24} + \frac{x^5}{15}\right)\bigg]_0^1 = \frac{13}{120}$$

***Solution (b).***

$$\int_0^{\pi/3} \int_0^{\cos y} x \sin y\,dx\,dy = \int_0^{\pi/3} \left[\int_0^{\cos y} x \sin y\,dx\right] dy = \int_0^{\pi/3} \left.\frac{x^2}{2}\sin y\right]_{x=0}^{\cos y} dy$$

$$= \int_0^{\pi/3} \left[\frac{1}{2}\cos^2 y \sin y\right] dy = -\frac{1}{6}\cos^3 y\bigg]_0^{\pi/3} = \frac{7}{48} \ ◄$$

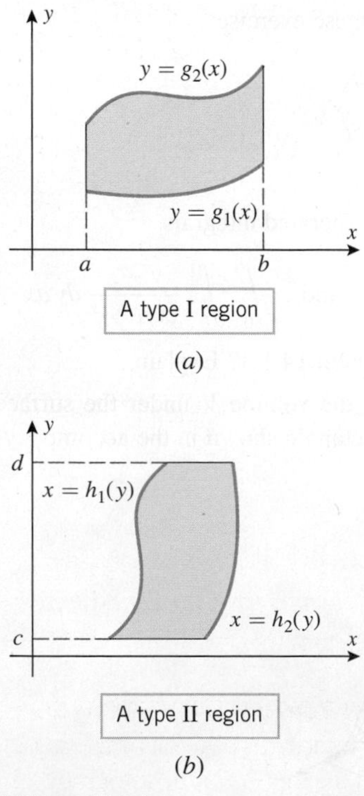

▲ **Figure 14.2.1**

### DOUBLE INTEGRALS OVER NONRECTANGULAR REGIONS

Plane regions can be extremely complex, and the theory of double integrals over very general regions is a topic for advanced courses in mathematics. We will limit our study of double integrals to two basic types of regions, which we will call *type I* and *type II*; they are defined as follows.

**14.2.1 DEFINITION**

(a) A ***type I region*** is bounded on the left and right by vertical lines $x = a$ and $x = b$ and is bounded below and above by continuous curves $y = g_1(x)$ and $y = g_2(x)$, where $g_1(x) \le g_2(x)$ for $a \le x \le b$ (Figure 14.2.1*a*).

(b) A ***type II region*** is bounded below and above by horizontal lines $y = c$ and $y = d$ and is bounded on the left and right by continuous curves $x = h_1(y)$ and $x = h_2(y)$ satisfying $h_1(y) \le h_2(y)$ for $c \le y \le d$ (Figure 14.2.1*b*).

The following theorem will enable us to evaluate double integrals over type I and type II regions using iterated integrals.

**14.2.2 THEOREM**

(*a*) *If R is a type I region on which f(x, y) is continuous, then*

$$\iint_R f(x, y)\, dA = \int_a^b \int_{g_1(x)}^{g_2(x)} f(x, y)\, dy\, dx \tag{3}$$

(*b*) *If R is a type II region on which f(x, y) is continuous, then*

$$\iint_R f(x, y)\, dA = \int_c^d \int_{h_1(y)}^{h_2(y)} f(x, y)\, dx\, dy \tag{4}$$

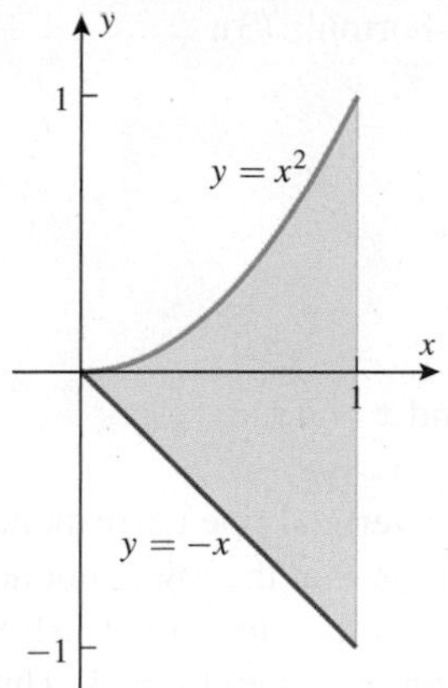

▲ Figure 14.2.2

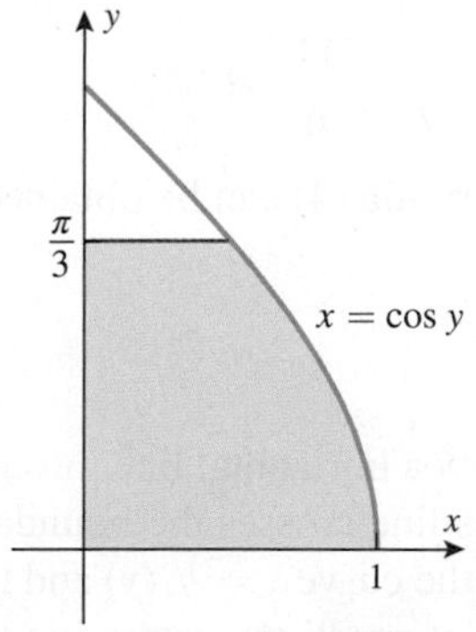

▲ Figure 14.2.3

► **Example 2** Each of the iterated integrals in Example 1 is equal to a double integral over a region $R$. Identify the region $R$ in each case.

***Solution.*** Using Theorem 14.2.2, the integral in Example 1(a) is the double integral of the function $f(x, y) = y^2x$ over the type I region $R$ bounded on the left and right by the vertical lines $x = 0$ and $x = 1$ and bounded below and above by the curves $y = -x$ and $y = x^2$ (Figure 14.2.2). The integral in Example 1(b) is the double integral of the function $f(x, y) = x \sin y$ over the type II region $R$ bounded below and above by the horizontal lines $y = 0$ and $y = \pi/3$ and bounded on the left and right by the curves $x = 0$ and $x = \cos y$ (Figure 14.2.3). ◄

We will not prove Theorem 14.2.2, but for the case where $f(x, y)$ is nonnegative on the region $R$, it can be made plausible by a geometric argument that is similar to that given for Theorem 14.1.3. Since $f(x, y)$ is nonnegative, the double integral can be interpreted as the volume of the solid $S$ that is bounded above by the surface $z = f(x, y)$ and below by the region $R$, so it suffices to show that the iterated integrals also represent this volume. Consider the iterated integral in (3), for example. For a fixed value of $x$, the function $f(x, y)$ is a function of $y$, and hence the integral

$$A(x) = \int_{g_1(x)}^{g_2(x)} f(x, y)\, dy$$

represents the area under the graph of this function of $y$ between $y = g_1(x)$ and $y = g_2(x)$. This area, shown in yellow in Figure 14.2.4, is the cross-sectional area at $x$ of the solid $S$, and hence by the method of slicing, the volume $V$ of the solid $S$ is

$$V = \int_a^b \int_{g_1(x)}^{g_2(x)} f(x, y)\, dy\, dx$$

which shows that in (3) the iterated integral is equal to the double integral. Similarly, the iterated integral in (4) is equal to the corresponding double integral.

## SETTING UP LIMITS OF INTEGRATION FOR EVALUATING DOUBLE INTEGRALS

To apply Theorem 14.2.2, it is helpful to start with a two-dimensional sketch of the region $R$. [It is not necessary to graph $f(x, y)$.] For a type I region, the limits of integration in Formula (3) can be obtained as follows:

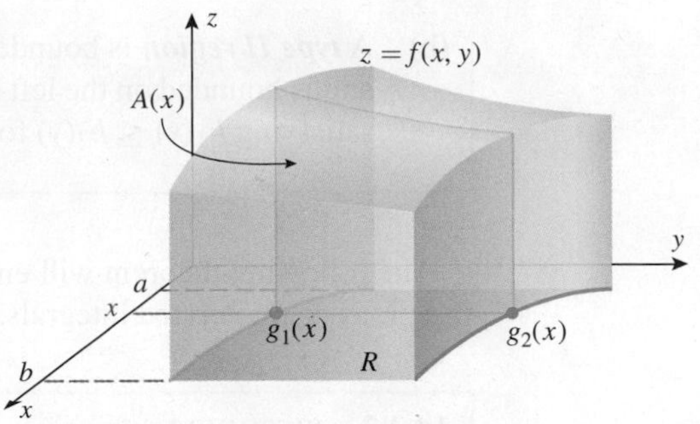


▶ Figure 14.2.4

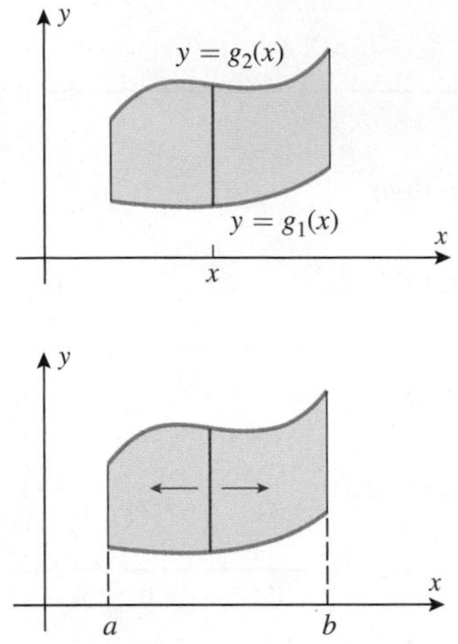


▲ Figure 14.2.5

> ***Determining Limits of Integration: Type I Region***
>
> **Step 1.** Since $x$ is held fixed for the first integration, we draw a vertical line through the region $R$ at an arbitrary fixed value $x$ (Figure 14.2.5). This line crosses the boundary of $R$ twice. The lower point of intersection is on the curve $y = g_1(x)$ and the higher point is on the curve $y = g_2(x)$. These two intersections determine the lower and upper $y$-limits of integration in Formula (3).
>
> **Step 2.** Imagine moving the line drawn in Step 1 first to the left and then to the right (Figure 14.2.5). The leftmost position where the line intersects the region $R$ is $x = a$, and the rightmost position where the line intersects the region $R$ is $x = b$. This yields the limits for the $x$-integration in Formula (3).

▶ **Example 3** Evaluate

$$\iint_R xy\, dA$$

over the region $R$ enclosed between $y = \frac{1}{2}x$, $y = \sqrt{x}$, $x = 2$, and $x = 4$.

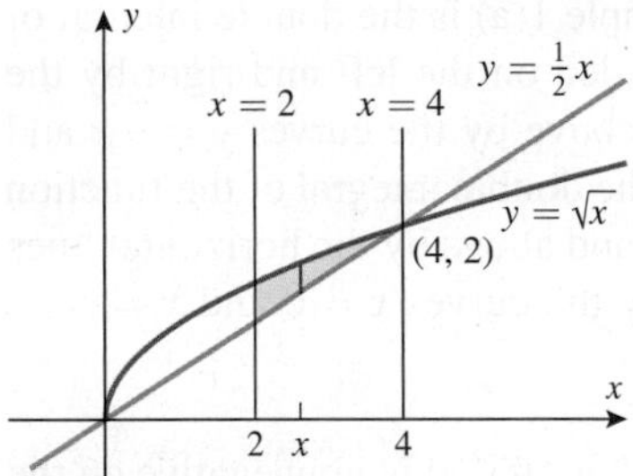


▲ Figure 14.2.6

***Solution.*** We view $R$ as a type I region. The region $R$ and a vertical line corresponding to a fixed $x$ are shown in Figure 14.2.6. This line meets the region $R$ at the lower boundary $y = \frac{1}{2}x$ and the upper boundary $y = \sqrt{x}$. These are the $y$-limits of integration. Moving this line first left and then right yields the $x$-limits of integration, $x = 2$ and $x = 4$. Thus,

$$\iint_R xy\, dA = \int_2^4 \int_{x/2}^{\sqrt{x}} xy\, dy\, dx = \int_2^4 \left[\frac{xy^2}{2}\right]_{y=x/2}^{\sqrt{x}} dx = \int_2^4 \left(\frac{x^2}{2} - \frac{x^3}{8}\right) dx$$

$$= \left[\frac{x^3}{6} - \frac{x^4}{32}\right]_2^4 = \left(\frac{64}{6} - \frac{256}{32}\right) - \left(\frac{8}{6} - \frac{16}{32}\right) = \frac{11}{6} \blacktriangleleft$$

If $R$ is a type II region, then the limits of integration in Formula (4) can be obtained as follows:

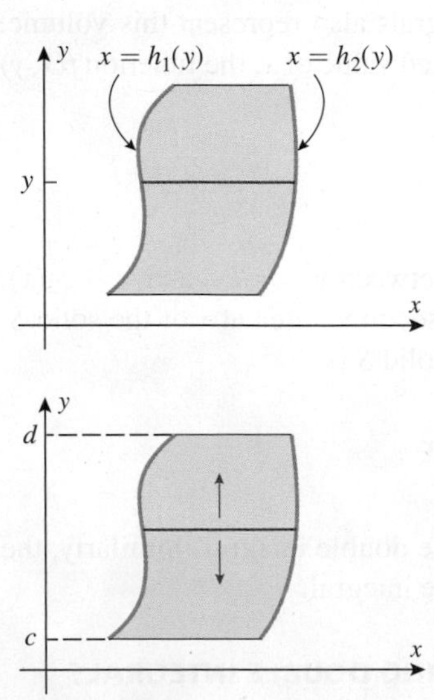


▲ Figure 14.2.7

> ***Determining Limits of Integration: Type II Region***
>
> **Step 1.** Since $y$ is held fixed for the first integration, we draw a horizontal line through the region $R$ at a fixed value $y$ (Figure 14.2.7). This line crosses the boundary of $R$ twice. The leftmost point of intersection is on the curve $x = h_1(y)$ and the rightmost point is on the curve $x = h_2(y)$. These intersections determine the $x$-limits of integration in (4).
>
> **Step 2.** Imagine moving the line drawn in Step 1 first down and then up (Figure 14.2.7). The lowest position where the line intersects the region $R$ is $y = c$, and the highest position where the line intersects the region $R$ is $y = d$. This yields the $y$-limits of integration in (4).

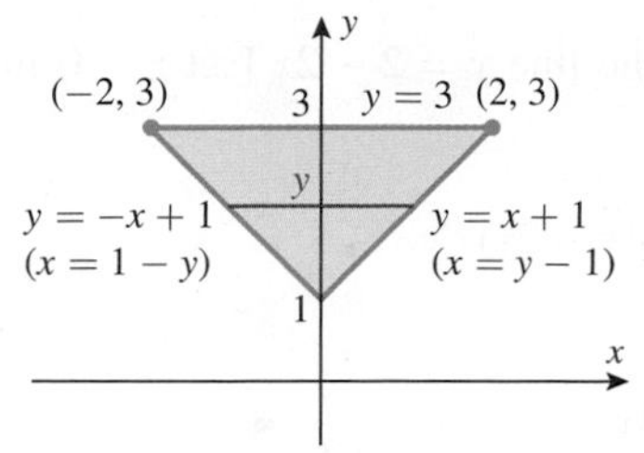


▲ Figure 14.2.8

To integrate over a type II region, the left- and right-hand boundaries must be expressed in the form $x = h_1(y)$ and $x = h_2(y)$. This is why we rewrote the boundary equations

$$y = -x + 1 \quad \text{and} \quad y = x + 1$$

as

$$x = 1 - y \quad \text{and} \quad x = y - 1$$

in Example 4.

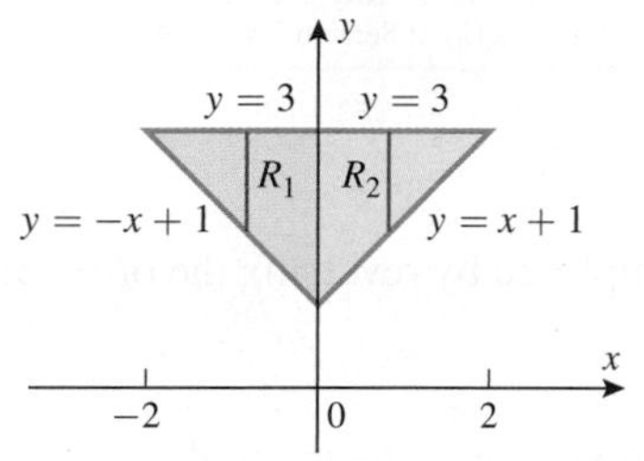


▲ Figure 14.2.9

► **Example 4** Evaluate

$$\iint_R (2x - y^2)\, dA$$

over the triangular region $R$ enclosed between the lines $y = -x + 1$, $y = x + 1$, and $y = 3$.

***Solution.*** We view $R$ as a type II region. The region $R$ and a horizontal line corresponding to a fixed $y$ are shown in Figure 14.2.8. This line meets the region $R$ at its left-hand boundary $x = 1 - y$ and its right-hand boundary $x = y - 1$. These are the $x$-limits of integration. Moving this line first down and then up yields the $y$-limits, $y = 1$ and $y = 3$. Thus,

$$\iint_R (2x - y^2)\, dA = \int_1^3 \int_{1-y}^{y-1} (2x - y^2)\, dx\, dy = \int_1^3 \left[x^2 - y^2 x\right]_{x=1-y}^{y-1} dy$$

$$= \int_1^3 [(1 - 2y + 2y^2 - y^3) - (1 - 2y + y^3)]\, dy$$

$$= \int_1^3 (2y^2 - 2y^3)\, dy = \left[\frac{2y^3}{3} - \frac{y^4}{2}\right]_1^3 = -\frac{68}{3} \blacktriangleleft$$

In Example 4 we could have treated $R$ as a type I region, but with an added complication. Viewed as a type I region, the upper boundary of $R$ is the line $y = 3$ (Figure 14.2.9) and the lower boundary consists of two parts, the line $y = -x + 1$ to the left of the $y$-axis and the line $y = x + 1$ to the right of the $y$-axis. To carry out the integration it is necessary to decompose the region $R$ into two parts, $R_1$ and $R_2$, as shown in Figure 14.2.9, and write

$$\iint_R (2x - y^2)\, dA = \iint_{R_1} (2x - y^2)\, dA + \iint_{R_2} (2x - y^2)\, dA$$

$$= \int_{-2}^{0} \int_{-x+1}^{3} (2x - y^2)\, dy\, dx + \int_0^2 \int_{x+1}^{3} (2x - y^2)\, dy\, dx$$

This will yield the same result that was obtained in Example 4. (Verify.)

► **Example 5** Use a double integral to find the volume of the tetrahedron bounded by the coordinate planes and the plane $z = 4 - 4x - 2y$.

***Solution.*** The tetrahedron in question is bounded above by the plane

$$z = 4 - 4x - 2y \tag{5}$$

and below by the triangular region $R$ shown in Figure 14.2.10. Thus, the volume is given by

$$V = \iint_R (4 - 4x - 2y)\, dA$$

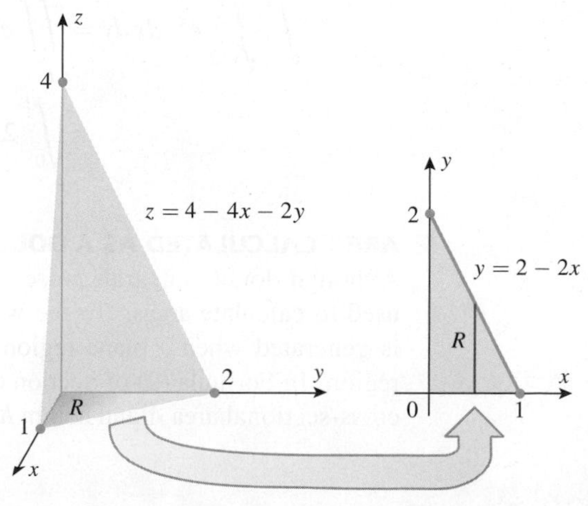


► Figure 14.2.10

The region $R$ is bounded by the $x$-axis, the $y$-axis, and the line $y = 2 - 2x$ [set $z = 0$ in (5)], so that treating $R$ as a type I region yields

$$V = \iint_R (4 - 4x - 2y)\, dA = \int_0^1 \int_0^{2-2x} (4 - 4x - 2y)\, dy\, dx$$

$$= \int_0^1 \left[4y - 4xy - y^2\right]_{y=0}^{2-2x} dx = \int_0^1 (4 - 8x + 4x^2)\, dx = \frac{4}{3} \blacktriangleleft$$

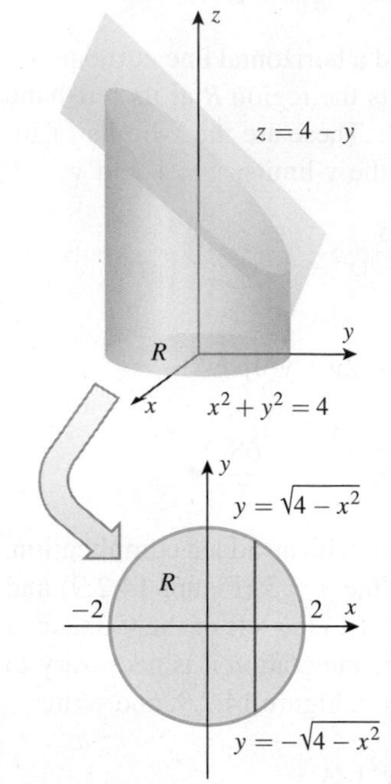


▲ **Figure 14.2.11**

► **Example 6** Find the volume of the solid bounded by the cylinder $x^2 + y^2 = 4$ and the planes $y + z = 4$ and $z = 0$.

***Solution.*** The solid shown in Figure 14.2.11 is bounded above by the plane $z = 4 - y$ and below by the region $R$ within the circle $x^2 + y^2 = 4$. The volume is given by

$$V = \iint_R (4 - y)\, dA$$

Treating $R$ as a type I region we obtain

$$V = \int_{-2}^{2} \int_{-\sqrt{4-x^2}}^{\sqrt{4-x^2}} (4 - y)\, dy\, dx = \int_{-2}^{2} \left[4y - \frac{1}{2}y^2\right]_{y=-\sqrt{4-x^2}}^{\sqrt{4-x^2}} dx$$

$$= \int_{-2}^{2} 8\sqrt{4 - x^2}\, dx = 8(2\pi) = 16\pi$$ 

See Formula (3) of Section 7.4. ◄

## REVERSING THE ORDER OF INTEGRATION

Sometimes the evaluation of an iterated integral can be simplified by reversing the order of integration. The next example illustrates how this is done.

► **Example 7** Since there is no elementary antiderivative of $e^{x^2}$, the integral

$$\int_0^2 \int_{y/2}^1 e^{x^2}\, dx\, dy$$

cannot be evaluated by performing the $x$-integration first. Evaluate this integral by expressing it as an equivalent iterated integral with the order of integration reversed.

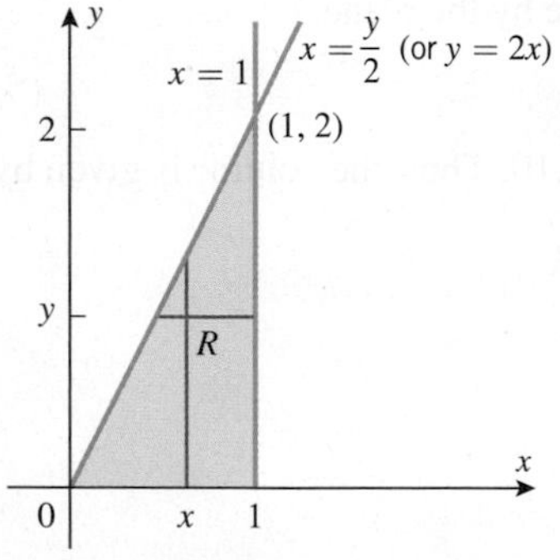


▲ **Figure 14.2.12**

***Solution.*** For the inside integration, $y$ is fixed and $x$ varies from the line $x = y/2$ to the line $x = 1$ (Figure 14.2.12). For the outside integration, $y$ varies from 0 to 2, so the given iterated integral is equal to a double integral over the triangular region $R$ in Figure 14.2.12.

To reverse the order of integration, we treat $R$ as a type I region, which enables us to write the given integral as

$$\int_0^2 \int_{y/2}^1 e^{x^2}\, dx\, dy = \iint_R e^{x^2}\, dA = \int_0^1 \int_0^{2x} e^{x^2}\, dy\, dx = \int_0^1 \left[e^{x^2} y\right]_{y=0}^{2x} dx$$

$$= \int_0^1 2xe^{x^2}\, dx = e^{x^2}\Big]_0^1 = e - 1 \blacktriangleleft$$

## AREA CALCULATED AS A DOUBLE INTEGRAL

Although double integrals arose in the context of calculating volumes, they can also be used to calculate areas. To see why this is so, recall that a *right cylinder* is a solid that is generated when a plane region is translated along a line that is perpendicular to the region. In Formula (2) of Section 6.2 we stated that the volume $V$ of a right cylinder with cross-sectional area $A$ and height $h$ is

$$V = A \cdot h \tag{6}$$

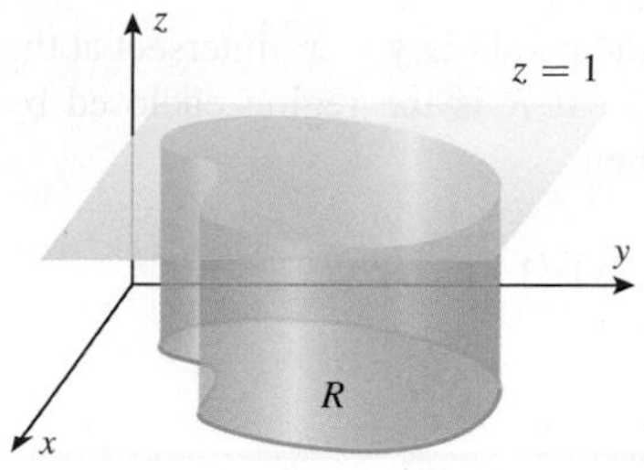


Cylinder with base $R$ and height 1

▲ **Figure 14.2.13**

Formula (7) can be confusing because it equates an area and a volume; the formula is intended to equate only the *numerical values* of the area and volume and not the units, which must, of course, be different.

Now suppose that we are interested in finding the area $A$ of a region $R$ in the $xy$-plane. If we translate the region $R$ upward 1 unit, then the resulting solid will be a right cylinder that has cross-sectional area $A$, base $R$, and the plane $z = 1$ as its top (Figure 14.2.13). Thus, it follows from (6) that

$$\iint_R 1\, dA = (\text{area of } R) \cdot 1$$

which we can rewrite as

$$\text{area of } R = \iint_R 1\, dA = \iint_R dA \tag{7}$$

▶ **Example 8** Use a double integral to find the area of the region $R$ enclosed between the parabola $y = \frac{1}{2}x^2$ and the line $y = 2x$.

***Solution.*** The region $R$ may be treated equally well as type I (Figure 14.2.14*a*) or type II (Figure 14.2.14*b*). Treating $R$ as type I yields

$$\begin{aligned}\text{area of } R &= \iint_R dA = \int_0^4 \int_{x^2/2}^{2x} dy\, dx = \int_0^4 [y]_{y=x^2/2}^{2x}\, dx \\ &= \int_0^4 \left(2x - \frac{1}{2}x^2\right) dx = \left[x^2 - \frac{x^3}{6}\right]_0^4 = \frac{16}{3}\end{aligned}$$

Treating $R$ as type II yields

$$\begin{aligned}\text{area of } R &= \iint_R dA = \int_0^8 \int_{y/2}^{\sqrt{2y}} dx\, dy = \int_0^8 [x]_{x=y/2}^{\sqrt{2y}}\, dy \\ &= \int_0^8 \left(\sqrt{2y} - \frac{1}{2}y\right) dy = \left[\frac{2\sqrt{2}}{3}y^{3/2} - \frac{y^2}{4}\right]_0^8 = \frac{16}{3}\end{aligned}$$ ◀

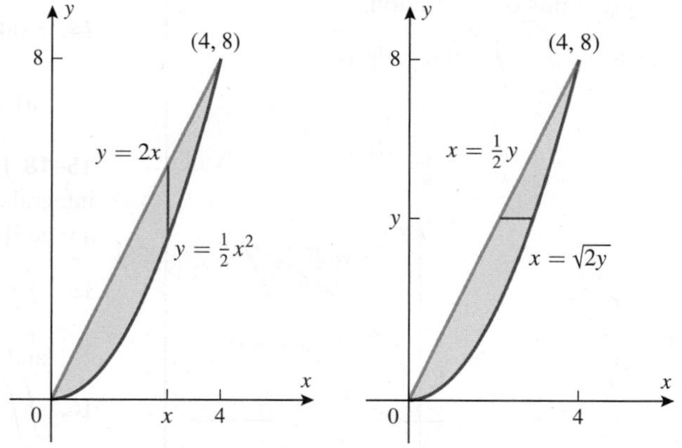


▶ **Figure 14.2.14** (*a*) (*b*)

## ✓ QUICK CHECK EXERCISES 14.2

(*See page 910 for answers.*)

**1.** Supply the missing integrand and limits of integration.

(a) $\displaystyle\int_1^5 \int_2^{y/2} 6x^2y\, dx\, dy = \int_{\square}^{\square} \underline{\qquad\quad}\, dy$

(b) $\displaystyle\int_1^5 \int_2^{x/2} 6x^2y\, dy\, dx = \int_{\square}^{\square} \underline{\qquad\quad}\, dx$

**2.** Let $R$ be the triangular region in the $xy$-plane with vertices $(0, 0)$, $(3, 0)$, and $(0, 4)$. Supply the missing portions of the integrals.

(a) Treating $R$ as a type I region,

$$\iint_R f(x, y)\, dA = \int_{\square}^{\square} \int_{\square}^{\square} f(x, y) \underline{\qquad\quad}$$

(b) Treating $R$ as a type II region,

$$\iint_R f(x, y)\, dA = \int_{\square}^{\square} \int_{\square}^{\square} f(x, y) \underline{\qquad\quad}$$

**3.** Let $R$ be the triangular region in the $xy$-plane with vertices $(0, 0)$, $(3, 3)$, and $(0, 4)$. Expressed as an iterated double integral, the area of $R$ is $A(R) = $ ______.

**4.** The line $y = 2 - x$ and the parabola $y = x^2$ intersect at the points $(-2, 4)$ and $(1, 1)$. If $R$ is the region enclosed by $y = 2 - x$ and $y = x^2$, then

$$\iint_R (1 + 2y)\, dA = \underline{\qquad\qquad}$$

## EXERCISE SET 14.2 Graphing Utility  C CAS

**1–8** Evaluate the iterated integral. ■

**1.** $\displaystyle\int_0^1 \int_{x^2}^{x} xy^2\, dy\, dx$ **2.** $\displaystyle\int_1^{3/2} \int_y^{3-y} y\, dx\, dy$

**3.** $\displaystyle\int_0^3 \int_0^{\sqrt{9-y^2}} y\, dx\, dy$ **4.** $\displaystyle\int_{1/4}^1 \int_{x^2}^{x} \sqrt{\frac{x}{y}}\, dy\, dx$

**5.** $\displaystyle\int_{\sqrt{\pi}}^{\sqrt{2\pi}} \int_0^{x^3} \sin\frac{y}{x}\, dy\, dx$ **6.** $\displaystyle\int_{-1}^1 \int_{-x^2}^{x^2} (x^2 - y)\, dy\, dx$

**7.** $\displaystyle\int_0^1 \int_0^{x} y\sqrt{x^2 - y^2}\, dy\, dx$ **8.** $\displaystyle\int_1^2 \int_0^{y^2} e^{x/y^2}\, dx\, dy$

**FOCUS ON CONCEPTS**

**9.** Let $R$ be the region shown in the accompanying figure. Fill in the missing limits of integration.

(a) $\displaystyle\iint_R f(x, y)\, dA = \int_\square^\square \int_\square^\square f(x, y)\, dy\, dx$

(b) $\displaystyle\iint_R f(x, y)\, dA = \int_\square^\square \int_\square^\square f(x, y)\, dx\, dy$

**10.** Let $R$ be the region shown in the accompanying figure. Fill in the missing limits of integration.

(a) $\displaystyle\iint_R f(x, y)\, dA = \int_\square^\square \int_\square^\square f(x, y)\, dy\, dx$

(b) $\displaystyle\iint_R f(x, y)\, dA = \int_\square^\square \int_\square^\square f(x, y)\, dx\, dy$

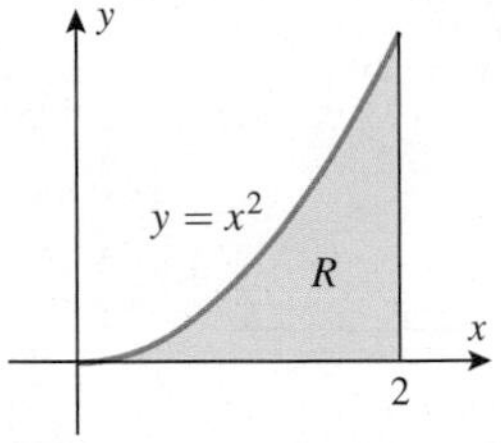


▲ Figure Ex-9

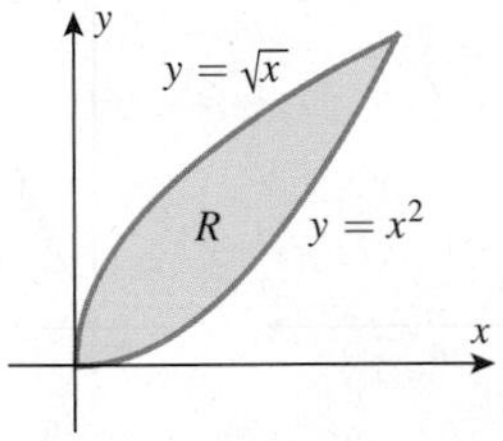


▲ Figure Ex-10

**11.** Let $R$ be the region shown in the accompanying figure. Fill in the missing limits of integration.

(a) $\displaystyle\iint_R f(x, y)\, dA = \int_1^2 \int_\square^\square f(x, y)\, dy\, dx + \int_2^4 \int_\square^\square f(x, y)\, dy\, dx + \int_4^5 \int_\square^\square f(x, y)\, dy\, dx$

(b) $\displaystyle\iint_R f(x, y)\, dA = \int_\square^\square \int_\square^\square f(x, y)\, dx\, dy$

**12.** Let $R$ be the region shown in the accompanying figure. Fill in the missing limits of integration.

(a) $\displaystyle\iint_R f(x, y)\, dA = \int_\square^\square \int_\square^\square f(x, y)\, dy\, dx$

(b) $\displaystyle\iint_R f(x, y)\, dA = \int_\square^\square \int_\square^\square f(x, y)\, dx\, dy$

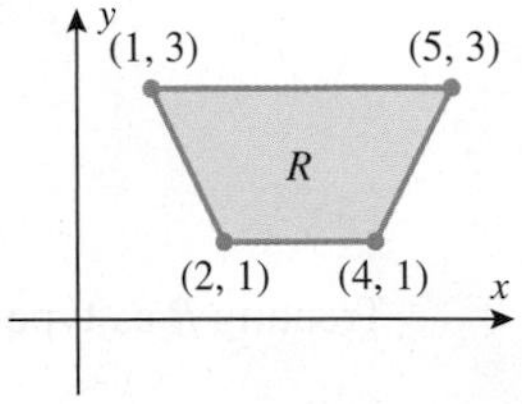


▲ Figure Ex-11

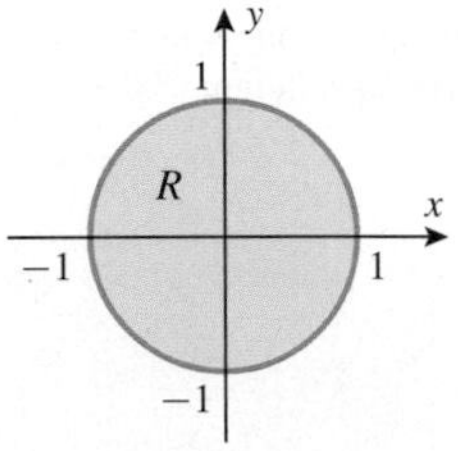


▲ Figure Ex-12

**13.** Evaluate $\displaystyle\iint_R xy\, dA$, where $R$ is the region in

(a) Exercise 9 (b) Exercise 11.

**14.** Evaluate $\displaystyle\iint_R (x + y)\, dA$, where $R$ is the region in

(a) Exercise 10 (b) Exercise 12.

**15–18** Evaluate the double integral in two ways using iterated integrals: (a) viewing $R$ as a type I region, and (b) viewing $R$ as a type II region. ■

**15.** $\displaystyle\iint_R x^2\, dA$; $R$ is the region bounded by $y = 16/x$, $y = x$, and $x = 8$.

**16.** $\displaystyle\iint_R xy^2\, dA$; $R$ is the region enclosed by $y = 1$, $y = 2$, $x = 0$, and $y = x$.

**17.** $\displaystyle\iint_R (3x - 2y)\, dA$; $R$ is the region enclosed by the circle $x^2 + y^2 = 1$.

**18.** $\displaystyle\iint_R y\, dA$; $R$ is the region in the first quadrant enclosed between the circle $x^2 + y^2 = 25$ and the line $x + y = 5$.

**19–24** Evaluate the double integral. ■

**19.** $\displaystyle\iint_R x(1 + y^2)^{-1/2}\, dA$; $R$ is the region in the first quadrant enclosed by $y = x^2$, $y = 4$, and $x = 0$.

**20.** $\iint_R x\cos y\,dA$; $R$ is the triangular region bounded by the lines $y = x$, $y = 0$, and $x = \pi$.

**21.** $\iint_R xy\,dA$; $R$ is the region enclosed by $y = \sqrt{x}$, $y = 6 - x$, and $y = 0$.

**22.** $\iint_R x\,dA$; $R$ is the region enclosed by $y = \sin^{-1} x$, $x = 1/\sqrt{2}$, and $y = 0$.

**23.** $\iint_R (x - 1)\,dA$; $R$ is the region in the first quadrant enclosed between $y = x$ and $y = x^3$.

**24.** $\iint_R x^2\,dA$; $R$ is the region in the first quadrant enclosed by $xy = 1$, $y = x$, and $y = 2x$.

**25.** Evaluate $\iint_R \sin(y^3)\,dA$, where $R$ is the region bounded by $y = \sqrt{x}$, $y = 2$, and $x = 0$. [*Hint:* Choose the order of integration carefully.]

**26.** Evaluate $\iint_R x\,dA$, where $R$ is the region bounded by $x = \ln y$, $x = 0$, and $y = e$.

**27.** (a) By hand or with the help of a graphing utility, make a sketch of the region $R$ enclosed between the curves $y = x + 2$ and $y = e^x$.
(b) Estimate the intersections of the curves in part (a).
(c) Viewing $R$ as a type I region, estimate $\iint_R x\,dA$.
(d) Viewing $R$ as a type II region, estimate $\iint_R x\,dA$.

**28.** (a) By hand or with the help of a graphing utility, make a sketch of the region $R$ enclosed between the curves $y = 4x^3 - x^4$ and $y = 3 - 4x + 4x^2$.
(b) Find the intersections of the curves in part (a).
(c) Find $\iint_R x\,dA$.

**29–32** Use double integration to find the area of the plane region enclosed by the given curves. ■

**29.** $y = \sin x$ and $y = \cos x$, for $0 \le x \le \pi/4$.

**30.** $y^2 = -x$ and $3y - x = 4$.

**31.** $y^2 = 9 - x$ and $y^2 = 9 - 9x$.

**32.** $y = \cosh x$, $y = \sinh x$, $x = 0$, and $x = 1$.

**33–36 True–False** Determine whether the statement is true or false. Explain your answer. ■

**33.** $\int_0^1 \int_{x^2}^{2x} f(x, y)\,dy\,dx = \int_{x^2}^{2x} \int_0^1 f(x, y)\,dx\,dy$

**34.** If a region $R$ is bounded below by $y = g_1(x)$ and above by $y = g_2(x)$ for $a \le x \le b$, then

$$\iint_R f(x, y)\,dA = \int_a^b \int_{g_1(x)}^{g_2(x)} f(x, y)\,dy\,dx$$

**35.** If $R$ is the region in the $xy$-plane enclosed by $y = x^2$ and $y = 1$, then

$$\iint_R f(x, y)\,dA = 2\int_0^1 \int_{x^2}^1 f(x, y)\,dy\,dx$$

**36.** The area of a region $R$ in the $xy$-plane is given by $\iint_R xy\,dA$.

**37–38** Use double integration to find the volume of the solid. ■

**37.**

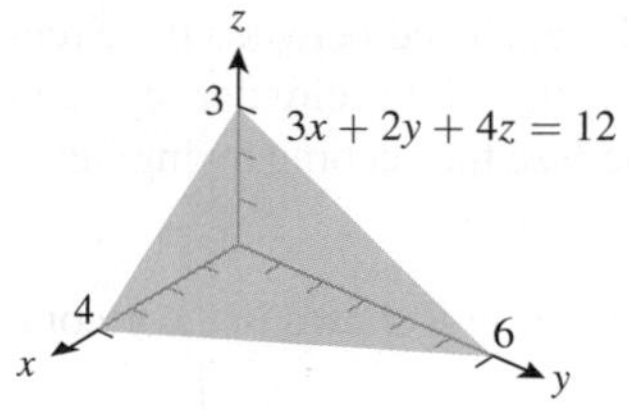


**38.**

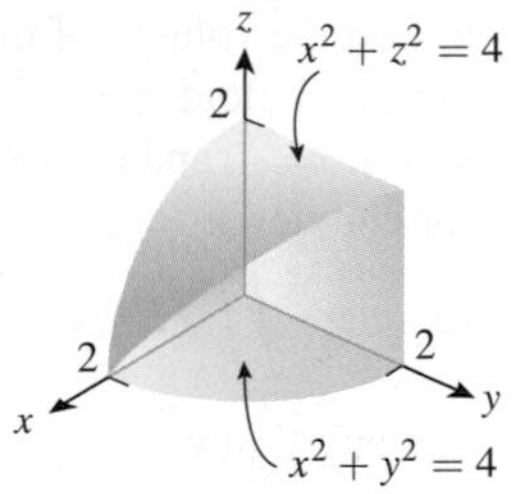


**39–44** Use double integration to find the volume of each solid. ■

**39.** The solid bounded by the cylinder $x^2 + y^2 = 9$ and the planes $z = 0$ and $z = 3 - x$.

**40.** The solid in the first octant bounded above by the paraboloid $z = x^2 + 3y^2$, below by the plane $z = 0$, and laterally by $y = x^2$ and $y = x$.

**41.** The solid bounded above by the paraboloid $z = 9x^2 + y^2$, below by the plane $z = 0$, and laterally by the planes $x = 0$, $y = 0$, $x = 3$, and $y = 2$.

**42.** The solid enclosed by $y^2 = x$, $z = 0$, and $x + z = 1$.

**43.** The wedge cut from the cylinder $4x^2 + y^2 = 9$ by the planes $z = 0$ and $z = y + 3$.

**44.** The solid in the first octant bounded above by $z = 9 - x^2$, below by $z = 0$, and laterally by $y^2 = 3x$.

C **45–46** Use a double integral and a CAS to find the volume of the solid. ■

**45.** The solid bounded above by the paraboloid $z = 1 - x^2 - y^2$ and below by the $xy$-plane.

**46.** The solid in the first octant that is bounded by the paraboloid $z = x^2 + y^2$, the cylinder $x^2 + y^2 = 4$, and the coordinate planes.

**47–52** Express the integral as an equivalent integral with the order of integration reversed. ■

**47.** $\int_0^2 \int_0^{\sqrt{x}} f(x, y)\,dy\,dx$

**48.** $\int_0^4 \int_{2y}^8 f(x, y)\,dx\,dy$

**49.** $\int_0^2 \int_1^{e^y} f(x, y)\,dx\,dy$

**50.** $\int_1^e \int_0^{\ln x} f(x, y)\,dy\,dx$

**51.** $\int_0^1 \int_{\sin^{-1} y}^{\pi/2} f(x, y)\,dx\,dy$

**52.** $\int_0^1 \int_{y^2}^{\sqrt{y}} f(x, y)\,dx\,dy$

**53–56** Evaluate the integral by first reversing the order of integration. ■

**53.** $\int_0^1 \int_{4x}^4 e^{-y^2}\,dy\,dx$

**54.** $\int_0^2 \int_{y/2}^1 \cos(x^2)\,dx\,dy$

**55.** $\int_0^4 \int_{\sqrt{y}}^2 e^{x^3}\,dx\,dy$ **56.** $\int_1^3 \int_0^{\ln x} x\,dy\,dx$

C **57.** Try to evaluate the integral with a CAS using the stated order of integration, and then by reversing the order of integration.

(a) $\int_0^4 \int_{\sqrt{x}}^2 \sin \pi y^3\,dy\,dx$

(b) $\int_0^1 \int_{\sin^{-1} y}^{\pi/2} \sec^2 (\cos x)\,dx\,dy$

**58.** Use the appropriate Wallis formula (see Exercise Set 7.3) to find the volume of the solid enclosed between the circular paraboloid $z = x^2 + y^2$, the right circular cylinder $x^2 + y^2 = 4$, and the $xy$-plane (see the accompanying figure for cut view).

**59.** Evaluate $\iint_R xy^2\,dA$ over the region $R$ shown in the accompanying figure.

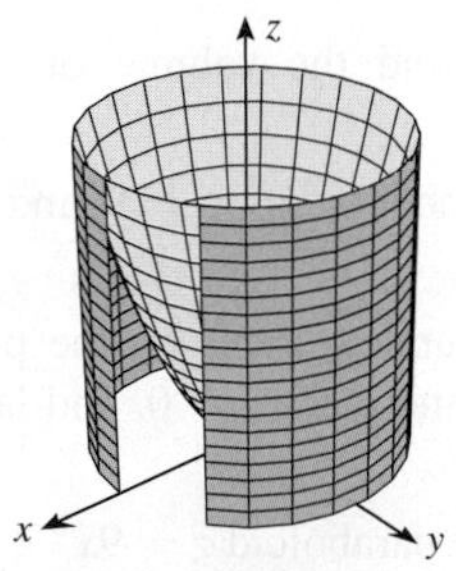

▲ Figure Ex-58

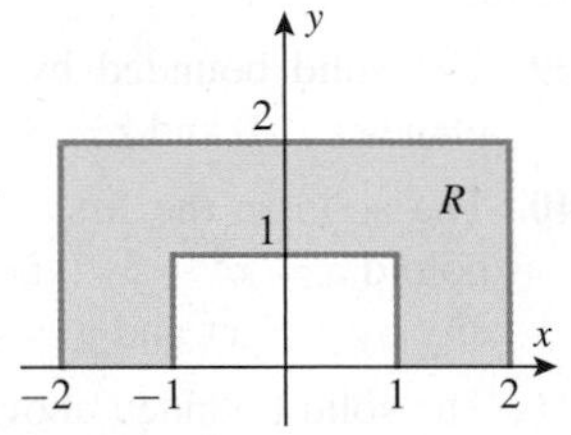

▲ Figure Ex-59

**60.** Give a geometric argument to show that

$$\int_0^1 \int_0^{\sqrt{1-y^2}} \sqrt{1 - x^2 - y^2}\,dx\,dy = \frac{\pi}{6}$$

**61–62** The ***average value*** or ***mean value*** of a continuous function $f(x, y)$ over a region $R$ in the $xy$-plane is defined as

$$f_{\text{ave}} = \frac{1}{A(R)} \iint_R f(x, y)\,dA$$

where $A(R)$ is the area of the region $R$ (compare to the definition preceding Exercise 35 in Section 14.1). Use this definition in these exercises. ■

**61.** Find the average value of $1/(1 + x^2)$ over the triangular region with vertices (0, 0), (1, 1), and (0, 1).

**62.** Find the average value of $f(x, y) = x^2 - xy$ over the region enclosed by $y = x$ and $y = 3x - x^2$.

**63.** Suppose that the temperature in degrees Celsius at a point $(x, y)$ on a flat metal plate is $T(x, y) = 5xy + x^2$, where $x$ and $y$ are in meters. Find the average temperature of the diamond-shaped portion of the plate described by the inequalities $|2x + y| \le 4$ and $|2x - y| \le 4$.

**64.** A circular lens of radius 2 inches has thickness $1 - (r^2/4)$ inches at all points $r$ inches from the center of the lens. Find the average thickness of the lens.

C **65.** Use a CAS to approximate the intersections of the curves $y = \sin x$ and $y = x/2$, and then approximate the volume of the solid in the first octant that is below the surface $z = \sqrt{1 + x + y}$ and above the region in the $xy$-plane that is enclosed by the curves.

**66. Writing** Describe the steps you would follow to find the limits of integration that express a double integral over a nonrectangular region as an iterated double integral. Illustrate your discussion with an example.

**67. Writing** Describe the steps you would follow to reverse the order of integration in an iterated double integral. Illustrate your discussion with an example.

✓ **QUICK CHECK ANSWERS 14.2** 1. (a) $\int_1^5 \left(\frac{1}{4}y^4 - 16y\right) dy$ (b) $\int_1^5 \left(\frac{3}{4}x^4 - 12x^2\right) dx$ 2. (a) $\int_0^3 \int_0^{-\frac{4}{3}x+4} f(x, y)\,dy\,dx$ (b) $\int_0^4 \int_0^{-\frac{3}{4}y+3} f(x, y)\,dx\,dy$ 3. $\int_0^3 \int_x^{-\frac{1}{3}x+4} dy\,dx$ 4. $\int_{-2}^1 \int_{x^2}^{2-x} (1 + 2y)\,dy\,dx = 18.9$

## 14.3 DOUBLE INTEGRALS IN POLAR COORDINATES

*In this section we will study double integrals in which the integrand and the region of integration are expressed in polar coordinates. Such integrals are important for two reasons: first, they arise naturally in many applications, and second, many double integrals in rectangular coordinates can be evaluated more easily if they are converted to polar coordinates.*

### ■ SIMPLE POLAR REGIONS

Some double integrals are easier to evaluate if the region of integration is expressed in polar coordinates. This is usually true if the region is bounded by a cardioid, a rose curve, a spiral, or, more generally, by any curve whose equation is simpler in polar coordinates than in rectangular coordinates. For example, the quarter-disk in Figure 14.3.1 is described in rectangular coordinates by

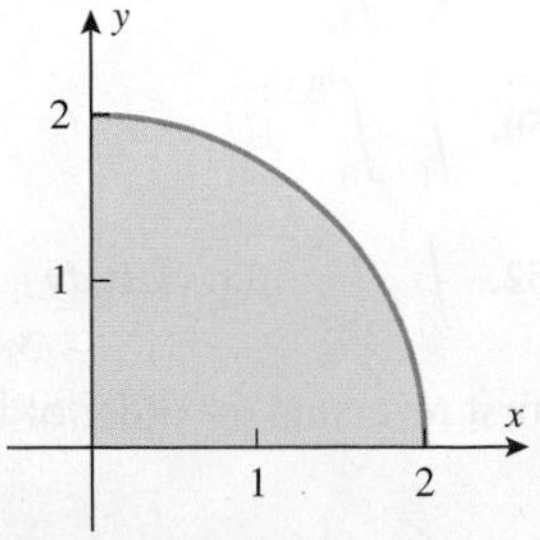

▲ Figure 14.3.1

$$0 \le y \le \sqrt{4 - x^2}, \quad 0 \le x \le 2$$

However, in polar coordinates the region is described more simply by

$$0 \le r \le 2, \quad 0 \le \theta \le \pi/2$$

Moreover, double integrals whose integrands involve $x^2 + y^2$ also tend to be easier to evaluate in polar coordinates because this sum simplifies to $r^2$ when the conversion formulas $x = r\cos\theta$ and $y = r\sin\theta$ are applied.

An overview of polar coordinates can be found in Section 10.2.

Figure 14.3.2$a$ shows a region $R$ in a polar coordinate system that is enclosed between two rays, $\theta = \alpha$ and $\theta = \beta$, and two polar curves, $r = r_1(\theta)$ and $r = r_2(\theta)$. If, as shown in the figure, the functions $r_1(\theta)$ and $r_2(\theta)$ are continuous and their graphs do not cross, then the region $R$ is called a *simple polar region*. If $r_1(\theta)$ is identically zero, then the boundary $r = r_1(\theta)$ reduces to a point (the origin), and the region has the general shape shown in Figure 14.3.2$b$. If, in addition, $\beta = \alpha + 2\pi$, then the rays coincide, and the region has the general shape shown in Figure 14.3.2$c$. The following definition expresses these geometric ideas algebraically.

**14.3.1 DEFINITION** A ***simple polar region*** in a polar coordinate system is a region that is enclosed between two rays, $\theta = \alpha$ and $\theta = \beta$, and two continuous polar curves, $r = r_1(\theta)$ and $r = r_2(\theta)$, where the equations of the rays and the polar curves satisfy the following conditions:

(i) $\alpha \le \beta$ (ii) $\beta - \alpha \le 2\pi$ (iii) $0 \le r_1(\theta) \le r_2(\theta)$

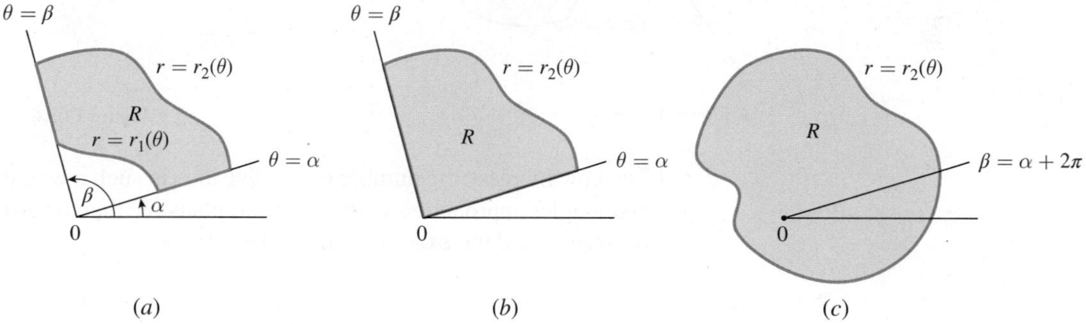


▲ **Figure 14.3.2**

**REMARK** Conditions (i) and (ii) together imply that the ray $\theta = \beta$ can be obtained by rotating the ray $\theta = \alpha$ counterclockwise through an angle that is at most $2\pi$ radians. This is consistent with Figure 14.3.2. Condition (iii) implies that the boundary curves $r = r_1(\theta)$ and $r = r_2(\theta)$ can touch but cannot actually cross over one another (why?). Thus, in keeping with Figure 14.3.2, it is appropriate to describe $r = r_1(\theta)$ as the ***inner boundary*** of the region and $r = r_2(\theta)$ as the ***outer boundary***.

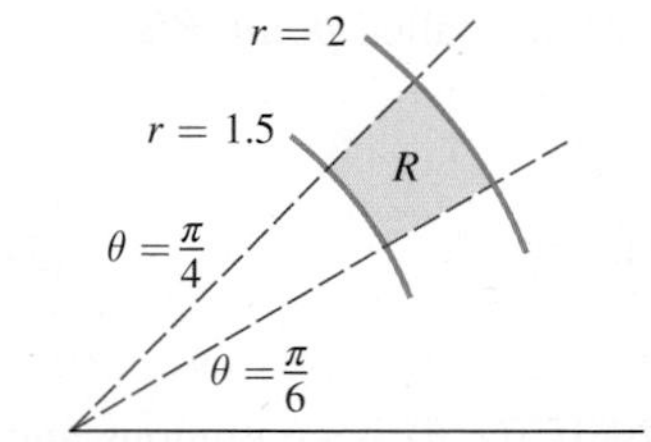


▲ **Figure 14.3.3**

A ***polar rectangle*** is a simple polar region for which the bounding polar curves are circular arcs. For example, Figure 14.3.3 shows the polar rectangle $R$ given by

$$1.5 \le r \le 2, \quad \frac{\pi}{6} \le \theta \le \frac{\pi}{4}$$

## DOUBLE INTEGRALS IN POLAR COORDINATES

Next we will consider the polar version of Problem 14.1.1.

**14.3.2 THE VOLUME PROBLEM IN POLAR COORDINATES** Given a function $f(r, \theta)$ that is continuous and nonnegative on a simple polar region $R$, find the volume of the solid that is enclosed between the region $R$ and the surface whose equation in cylindrical coordinates is $z = f(r, \theta)$ (Figure 14.3.4).

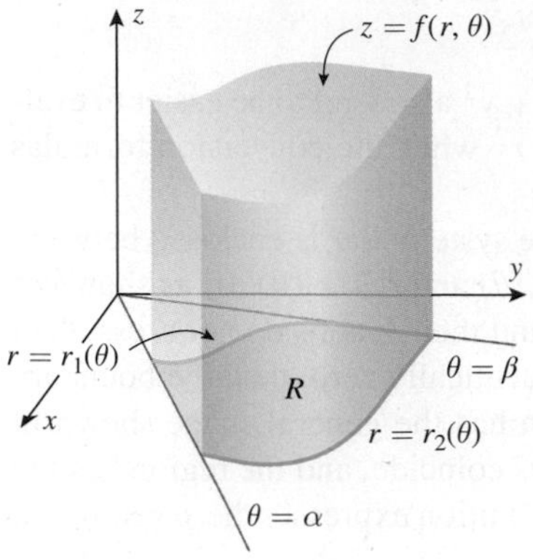


▲ Figure 14.3.4

To motivate a formula for the volume $V$ of the solid in Figure 14.3.4, we will use a limit process similar to that used to obtain Formula (2) of Section 14.1, except that here we will use circular arcs and rays to subdivide the region $R$ into polar rectangles. As shown in Figure 14.3.5, we will exclude from consideration all polar rectangles that contain any points outside of $R$, leaving only polar rectangles that are subsets of $R$. Assume that there are $n$ such polar rectangles, and denote the area of the $k$th polar rectangle by $\Delta A_k$. Let $(r_k^*, \theta_k^*)$ be any point in this polar rectangle. As shown in Figure 14.3.6, the product $f(r_k^*, \theta_k^*)\Delta A_k$ is the volume of a solid with base area $\Delta A_k$ and height $f(r_k^*, \theta_k^*)$, so the sum

$$\sum_{k=1}^{n} f(r_k^*, \theta_k^*)\Delta A_k$$

can be viewed as an approximation to the volume $V$ of the entire solid.

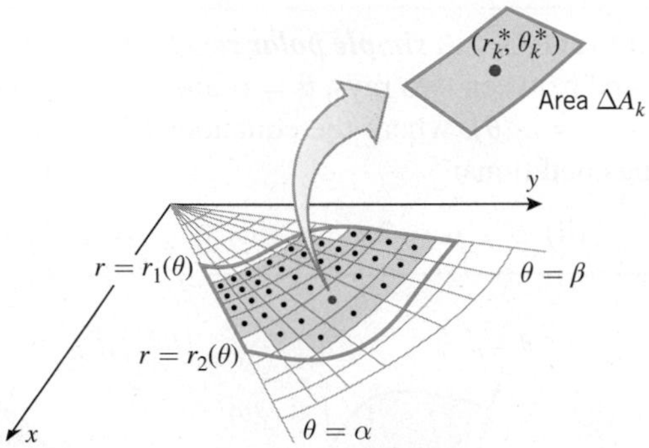


▲ Figure 14.3.5

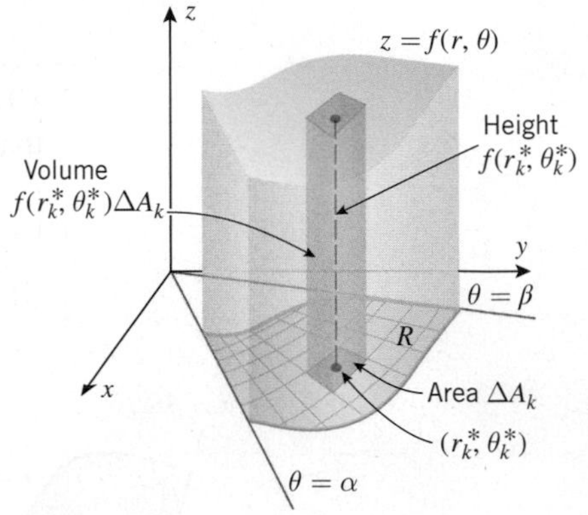


▲ Figure 14.3.6

If we now increase the number of subdivisions in such a way that the dimensions of the polar rectangles approach zero, then it seems plausible that the errors in the approximations approach zero, and the exact volume of the solid is

$$V = \lim_{n\to+\infty} \sum_{k=1}^{n} f(r_k^*, \theta_k^*)\Delta A_k \tag{1}$$

If $f(r, \theta)$ is continuous on $R$ and has both positive and negative values, then the limit

$$\lim_{n\to+\infty} \sum_{k=1}^{n} f(r_k^*, \theta_k^*)\Delta A_k \tag{2}$$

represents the net signed volume between the region $R$ and the surface $z = f(r, \theta)$ (as with double integrals in rectangular coordinates). The sums in (2) are called ***polar Riemann sums***, and the limit of the polar Riemann sums is denoted by

$$\iint_R f(r, \theta)\, dA = \lim_{n\to+\infty} \sum_{k=1}^{n} f(r_k^*, \theta_k^*)\Delta A_k \tag{3}$$

which is called the ***polar double integral*** of $f(r, \theta)$ over $R$. If $f(r, \theta)$ is continuous and nonnegative on $R$, then the volume formula (1) can be expressed as

$$V = \iint_R f(r, \theta)\, dA \tag{4}$$

Polar double integrals are also called ***double integrals in polar coordinates*** to distinguish them from double integrals over regions in the $xy$-plane; the latter are called ***double integrals in rectangular coordinates***. Double integrals in polar coordinates have the usual integral properties, such as those stated in Formulas (9), (10), and (11) of Section 14.1.

## EVALUATING POLAR DOUBLE INTEGRALS

In Sections 14.1 and 14.2 we evaluated double integrals in rectangular coordinates by expressing them as iterated integrals. Polar double integrals are evaluated the same way. To motivate the formula that expresses a double polar integral as an iterated integral, we

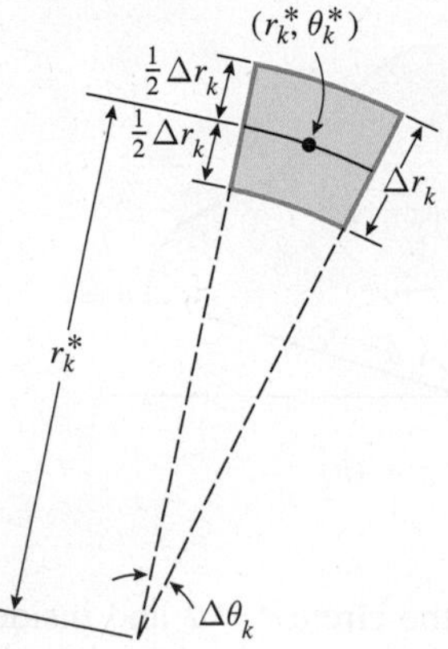

▲ Figure 14.3.7

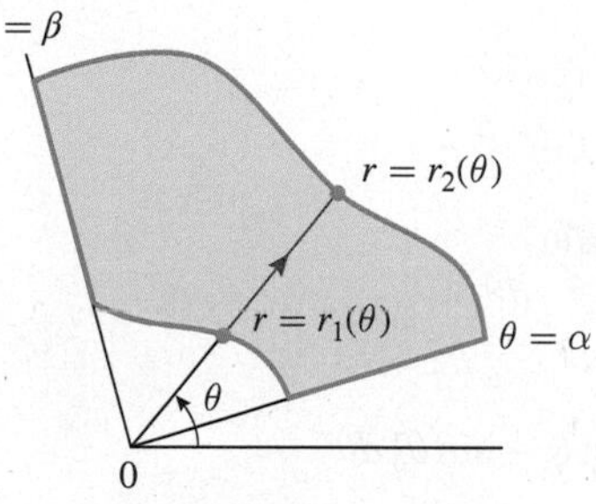

▲ Figure 14.3.8

Note the extra factor of $r$ that appears in the integrand when expressing a polar double integral as an iterated integral in polar coordinates.

will assume that $f(r, \theta)$ is nonnegative so that we can interpret (3) as a volume. To begin, let us choose the arbitrary point $(r_k^*, \theta_k^*)$ in (3) to be at the "center" of the $k$th polar rectangle as shown in Figure 14.3.7. Suppose also that this polar rectangle has a central angle $\Delta\theta_k$ and a "radial thickness" $\Delta r_k$. Thus, the inner radius of this polar rectangle is $r_k^* - \frac{1}{2}\Delta r_k$ and the outer radius is $r_k^* + \frac{1}{2}\Delta r_k$. Treating the area $\Delta A_k$ of this polar rectangle as the difference in area of two sectors, we obtain

$$\Delta A_k = \tfrac{1}{2}\left(r_k^* + \tfrac{1}{2}\Delta r_k\right)^2 \Delta\theta_k - \tfrac{1}{2}\left(r_k^* - \tfrac{1}{2}\Delta r_k\right)^2 \Delta\theta_k$$

which simplifies to

$$\Delta A_k = r_k^* \Delta r_k \Delta\theta_k \tag{5}$$

Thus, from (3) and (4)

$$V = \iint_R f(r, \theta)\, dA = \lim_{n \to +\infty} \sum_{k=1}^{n} f(r_k^*, \theta_k^*) r_k^* \Delta r_k \Delta\theta_k$$

which suggests that the volume $V$ can be expressed as the iterated integral

$$V = \iint_R f(r, \theta)\, dA = \int_\alpha^\beta \int_{r_1(\theta)}^{r_2(\theta)} f(r, \theta) r\, dr\, d\theta \tag{6}$$

in which the limits of integration are chosen to cover the region $R$; that is, with $\theta$ fixed between $\alpha$ and $\beta$, the value of $r$ varies from $r_1(\theta)$ to $r_2(\theta)$ (Figure 14.3.8).

Although we assumed $f(r, \theta)$ to be nonnegative in deriving Formula (6), it can be proved that the relationship between the polar double integral and the iterated integral in this formula also holds if $f$ has negative values. Accepting this to be so, we obtain the following theorem, which we state without formal proof.

**14.3.3 THEOREM** *If $R$ is a simple polar region whose boundaries are the rays $\theta = \alpha$ and $\theta = \beta$ and the curves $r = r_1(\theta)$ and $r = r_2(\theta)$ shown in Figure 14.3.8, and if $f(r, \theta)$ is continuous on $R$, then*

$$\iint_R f(r, \theta)\, dA = \int_\alpha^\beta \int_{r_1(\theta)}^{r_2(\theta)} f(r, \theta) r\, dr\, d\theta \tag{7}$$

To apply this theorem you will need to be able to find the rays and the curves that form the boundary of the region $R$, since these determine the limits of integration in the iterated integral. This can be done as follows:

***Determining Limits of Integration for a Polar Double Integral: Simple Polar Region***

**Step 1.** Since $\theta$ is held fixed for the first integration, draw a radial line from the origin through the region $R$ at a fixed angle $\theta$ (Figure 14.3.9*a*). This line crosses the boundary of $R$ at most twice. The innermost point of intersection is on the inner boundary curve $r = r_1(\theta)$ and the outermost point is on the outer boundary curve $r = r_2(\theta)$. These intersections determine the $r$-limits of integration in (7).

**Step 2.** Imagine rotating the radial line from Step 1 about the origin, thus sweeping out the region $R$. The least angle at which the radial line intersects the region $R$ is $\theta = \alpha$ and the greatest angle is $\theta = \beta$ (Figure 14.3.9*b*). This determines the $\theta$-limits of integration.

▶ **Example 1** Evaluate

$$\iint_R \sin\theta\, dA$$

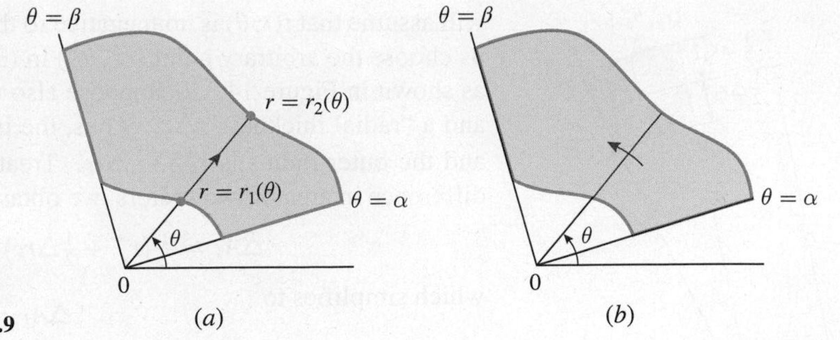


▶ Figure 14.3.9

where $R$ is the region in the first quadrant that is outside the circle $r = 2$ and inside the cardioid $r = 2(1 + \cos\theta)$.

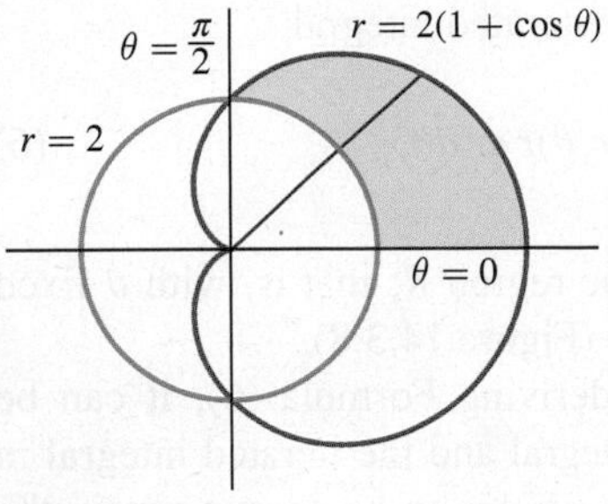


▲ Figure 14.3.10

***Solution.*** The region $R$ is sketched in Figure 14.3.10. Following the two steps outlined above we obtain

$$\begin{aligned}
\iint_R \sin\theta\, dA &= \int_0^{\pi/2} \int_2^{2(1+\cos\theta)} (\sin\theta) r\, dr\, d\theta \\
&= \int_0^{\pi/2} \left[\frac{1}{2} r^2 \sin\theta\right]_{r=2}^{2(1+\cos\theta)} d\theta \\
&= 2 \int_0^{\pi/2} [(1+\cos\theta)^2 \sin\theta - \sin\theta]\, d\theta \\
&= 2\left[-\frac{1}{3}(1+\cos\theta)^3 + \cos\theta\right]_0^{\pi/2} \\
&= 2\left[-\frac{1}{3} - \left(-\frac{5}{3}\right)\right] = \frac{8}{3} \blacktriangleleft
\end{aligned}$$

---

▶ **Example 2** The sphere of radius $a$ centered at the origin is expressed in rectangular coordinates as $x^2 + y^2 + z^2 = a^2$, and hence its equation in cylindrical coordinates is $r^2 + z^2 = a^2$. Use this equation and a polar double integral to find the volume of the sphere.

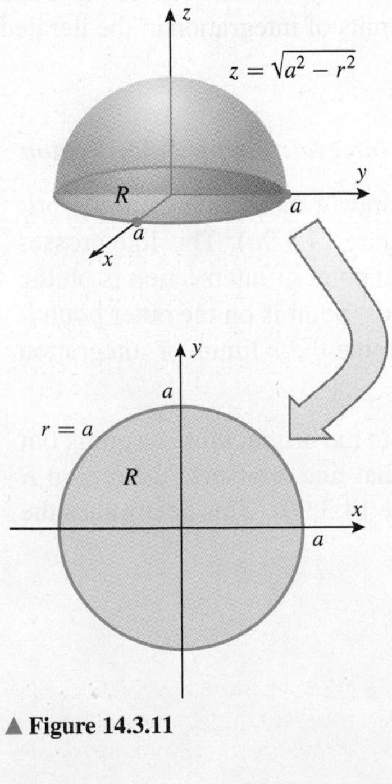


▲ Figure 14.3.11

***Solution.*** In cylindrical coordinates the upper hemisphere is given by the equation

$$z = \sqrt{a^2 - r^2}$$

so the volume enclosed by the entire sphere is

$$V = 2 \iint_R \sqrt{a^2 - r^2}\, dA$$

where $R$ is the circular region shown in Figure 14.3.11. Thus,

$$\begin{aligned}
V = 2 \iint_R \sqrt{a^2 - r^2}\, dA &= \int_0^{2\pi} \int_0^a \sqrt{a^2 - r^2}(2r)\, dr\, d\theta \\
&= \int_0^{2\pi} \left[-\frac{2}{3}(a^2 - r^2)^{3/2}\right]_{r=0}^{a} d\theta = \int_0^{2\pi} \frac{2}{3} a^3\, d\theta \\
&= \left[\frac{2}{3} a^3 \theta\right]_0^{2\pi} = \frac{4}{3}\pi a^3 \blacktriangleleft
\end{aligned}$$

## FINDING AREAS USING POLAR DOUBLE INTEGRALS

Recall from Formula (7) of Section 14.2 that the area of a region $R$ in the $xy$-plane can be expressed as

$$\text{area of } R = \iint_R 1\, dA = \iint_R dA \tag{8}$$

The argument used to derive this result can also be used to show that the formula applies to polar double integrals over regions in polar coordinates.

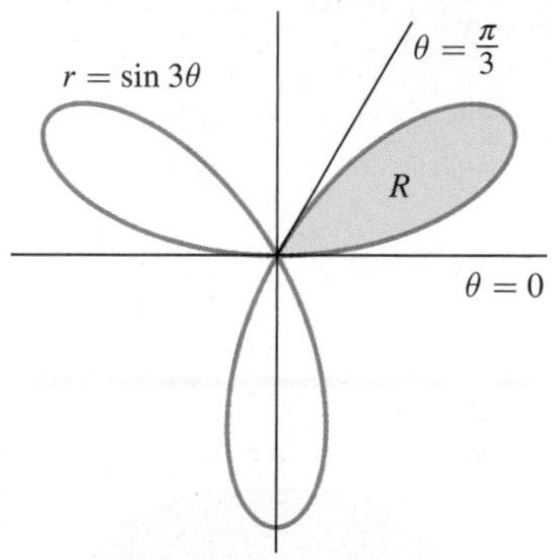

▲ Figure 14.3.12

► **Example 3** Use a polar double integral to find the area enclosed by the three-petaled rose $r = \sin 3\theta$.

***Solution.*** The rose is sketched in Figure 14.3.12. We will use Formula (8) to calculate the area of the petal $R$ in the first quadrant and multiply by 3.

$$\begin{aligned} A = 3\iint_R dA &= 3\int_0^{\pi/3}\int_0^{\sin 3\theta} r\, dr\, d\theta \\ &= \frac{3}{2}\int_0^{\pi/3} \sin^2 3\theta\, d\theta = \frac{3}{4}\int_0^{\pi/3} (1 - \cos 6\theta)\, d\theta \\ &= \frac{3}{4}\left[\theta - \frac{\sin 6\theta}{6}\right]_0^{\pi/3} = \frac{1}{4}\pi \end{aligned}$$ ◄

## CONVERTING DOUBLE INTEGRALS FROM RECTANGULAR TO POLAR COORDINATES

Sometimes a double integral that is difficult to evaluate in rectangular coordinates can be evaluated more easily in polar coordinates by making the substitution $x = r\cos\theta$, $y = r\sin\theta$ and expressing the region of integration in polar form; that is, we rewrite the double integral in rectangular coordinates as

$$\iint_R f(x, y)\, dA = \iint_R f(r\cos\theta, r\sin\theta)\, dA = \iint_{\substack{\text{appropriate}\\\text{limits}}} f(r\cos\theta, r\sin\theta) r\, dr\, d\theta \tag{9}$$

► **Example 4** Use polar coordinates to evaluate $\displaystyle\int_{-1}^{1}\int_0^{\sqrt{1-x^2}} (x^2 + y^2)^{3/2}\, dy\, dx$.

***Solution.*** In this problem we are starting with an iterated integral in rectangular coordinates rather than a double integral, so before we can make the conversion to polar coordinates we will have to identify the region of integration. Observe that for fixed $x$ the $y$-integration runs from $y = 0$ to $y = \sqrt{1 - x^2}$, which tells us that the lower boundary of the region is the $x$-axis and the upper boundary is a semicircle of radius 1 centered at the origin. From the $x$-integration we see that $x$ varies from $-1$ to 1, so we conclude that the region of integration is as shown in Figure 14.3.13. In polar coordinates, this is the region swept out as $r$ varies between 0 and 1 and $\theta$ varies between 0 and $\pi$. Thus,

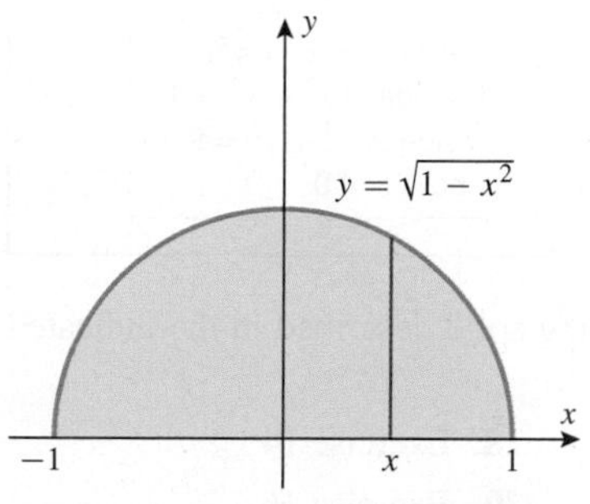

▲ Figure 14.3.13

$$\begin{aligned} \int_{-1}^{1}\int_0^{\sqrt{1-x^2}} (x^2 + y^2)^{3/2}\, dy\, dx &= \iint_R (x^2 + y^2)^{3/2}\, dA \\ &= \int_0^{\pi}\int_0^1 (r^3) r\, dr\, d\theta = \int_0^{\pi} \frac{1}{5}\, d\theta = \frac{\pi}{5} \end{aligned}$$ ◄

**REMARK** The reason the conversion to polar coordinates worked so nicely in Example 4 is that the substitution $x = r\cos\theta$, $y = r\sin\theta$ collapsed the sum $x^2 + y^2$ into the single term $r^2$, thereby simplifying the integrand. Whenever you see an expression involving $x^2 + y^2$ in the integrand, you should consider the possibility of converting to polar coordinates.

## ✓ QUICK CHECK EXERCISES 14.3 *(See page 917 for answers.)*

1. The polar region inside the circle $r = 2\sin\theta$ and outside the circle $r = 1$ is a simple polar region given by the inequalities

$$\_\_\_\_ \le r \le \_\_\_\_, \quad \_\_\_\_ \le \theta \le \_\_\_\_$$

2. Let $R$ be the region in the first quadrant enclosed between the circles $x^2 + y^2 = 9$ and $x^2 + y^2 = 100$. Supply the missing limits of integration.

$$\iint_R f(r,\theta)\,dA = \int_{\square}^{\square}\int_{\square}^{\square} f(r,\theta)r\,dr\,d\theta$$

3. Let $V$ be the volume of the solid bounded above by the hemisphere $z = \sqrt{1 - r^2}$ and bounded below by the disk enclosed within the circle $r = \sin\theta$. Expressed as a double integral in polar coordinates, $V =$ _______.

4. Express the iterated integral as a double integral in polar coordinates.

$$\int_{1/\sqrt{2}}^{1}\int_{\sqrt{1-x^2}}^{x}\left(\frac{1}{x^2+y^2}\right)dy\,dx = \_\_\_\_\_\_\_$$

## EXERCISE SET 14.3

**1–6** Evaluate the iterated integral. ■

1. $\displaystyle\int_0^{\pi/2}\int_0^{\sin\theta} r\cos\theta\,dr\,d\theta$

2. $\displaystyle\int_0^{\pi}\int_0^{1+\cos\theta} r\,dr\,d\theta$

3. $\displaystyle\int_0^{\pi/2}\int_0^{a\sin\theta} r^2\,dr\,d\theta$

4. $\displaystyle\int_0^{\pi/6}\int_0^{\cos 3\theta} r\,dr\,d\theta$

5. $\displaystyle\int_0^{\pi}\int_0^{1-\sin\theta} r^2\cos\theta\,dr\,d\theta$

6. $\displaystyle\int_0^{\pi/2}\int_0^{\cos\theta} r^3\,dr\,d\theta$

**7–10** Use a double integral in polar coordinates to find the area of the region described. ■

7. The region enclosed by the cardioid $r = 1 - \cos\theta$.
8. The region enclosed by the rose $r = \sin 2\theta$.
9. The region in the first quadrant bounded by $r = 1$ and $r = \sin 2\theta$, with $\pi/4 \le \theta \le \pi/2$.
10. The region inside the circle $x^2 + y^2 = 4$ and to the right of the line $x = 1$.

**FOCUS ON CONCEPTS**

**11–12** Let $R$ be the region described. Sketch the region $R$ and fill in the missing limits of integration.

$$\iint_R f(r,\theta)\,dA = \int_{\square}^{\square}\int_{\square}^{\square} f(r,\theta)r\,dr\,d\theta \quad ■$$

11. The region inside the circle $r = 4\sin\theta$ and outside the circle $r = 2$.
12. The region inside the circle $r = 1$ and outside the cardioid $r = 1 + \cos\theta$.

**13–16** Express the volume of the solid described as a double integral in polar coordinates. ■

**13.**

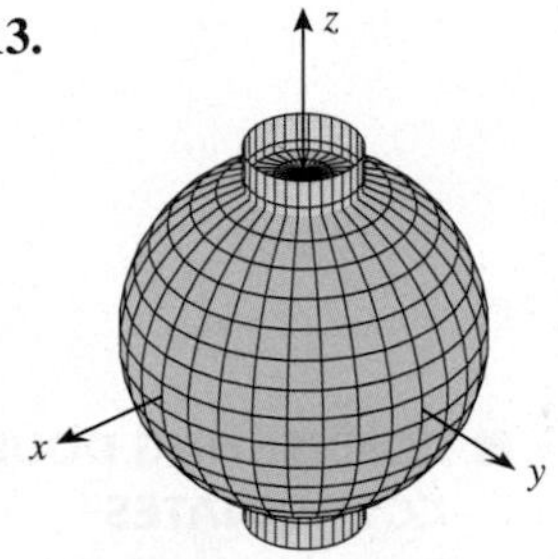


Inside of $x^2 + y^2 + z^2 = 9$
Outside of $x^2 + y^2 = 1$

**14.**

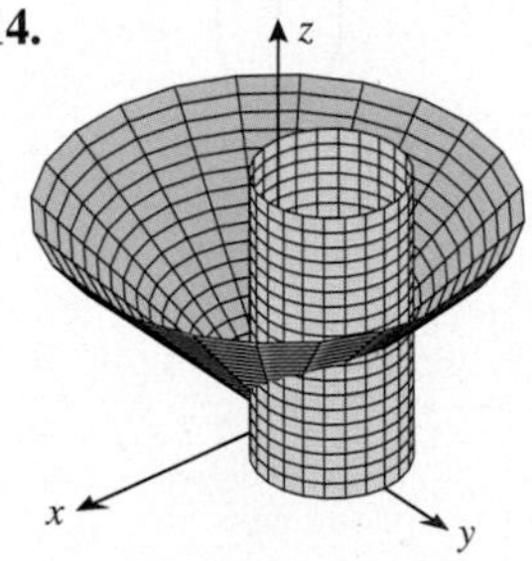


Below $z = \sqrt{x^2 + y^2}$
Inside of $x^2 + y^2 = 2y$
Above $z = 0$

**15.**

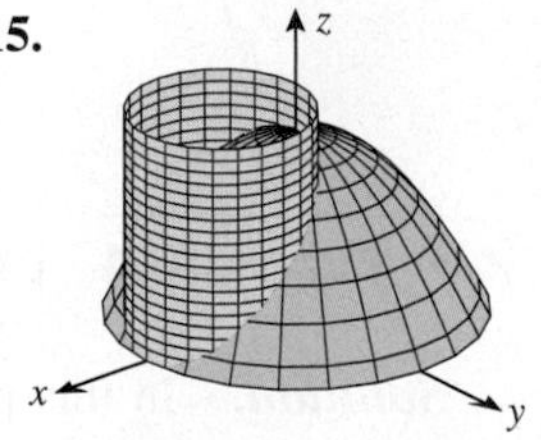


Below $z = 1 - x^2 - y^2$
Inside of $x^2 + y^2 - x = 0$
Above $z = 0$

**16.**

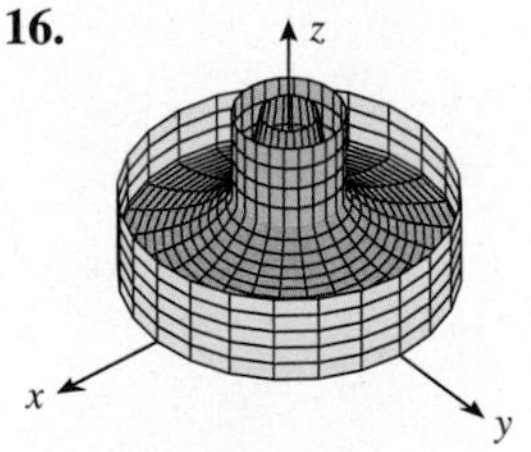


Below $z = (x^2 + y^2)^{-1/2}$
Outside of $x^2 + y^2 = 1$
Inside of $x^2 + y^2 = 9$
Above $z = 0$

**17–20** Find the volume of the solid described in the indicated exercise. ■

17. Exercise 13
18. Exercise 14
19. Exercise 15
20. Exercise 16

21. Find the volume of the solid in the first octant bounded above by the surface $z = r\sin\theta$, below by the $xy$-plane, and laterally by the plane $x = 0$ and the surface $r = 3\sin\theta$.

22. Find the volume of the solid inside the surface $r^2 + z^2 = 4$ and outside the surface $r = 2\cos\theta$.

**23–26** Use polar coordinates to evaluate the double integral. ■

**23.** $\iint_R \sin(x^2+y^2)\,dA$, where $R$ is the region enclosed by the circle $x^2+y^2=9$.

**24.** $\iint_R \sqrt{9-x^2-y^2}\,dA$, where $R$ is the region in the first quadrant within the circle $x^2+y^2=9$.

**25.** $\iint_R \frac{1}{1+x^2+y^2}\,dA$, where $R$ is the sector in the first quadrant bounded by $y=0$, $y=x$, and $x^2+y^2=4$.

**26.** $\iint_R 2y\,dA$, where $R$ is the region in the first quadrant bounded above by the circle $(x-1)^2+y^2=1$ and below by the line $y=x$.

**27–34** Evaluate the iterated integral by converting to polar coordinates. ■

**27.** $\int_0^1 \int_0^{\sqrt{1-x^2}} (x^2+y^2)\,dy\,dx$

**28.** $\int_{-2}^2 \int_{-\sqrt{4-y^2}}^{\sqrt{4-y^2}} e^{-(x^2+y^2)}\,dx\,dy$

**29.** $\int_0^2 \int_0^{\sqrt{2x-x^2}} \sqrt{x^2+y^2}\,dy\,dx$

**30.** $\int_0^1 \int_0^{\sqrt{1-y^2}} \cos(x^2+y^2)\,dx\,dy$

**31.** $\int_0^a \int_0^{\sqrt{a^2-x^2}} \frac{dy\,dx}{(1+x^2+y^2)^{3/2}} \quad (a>0)$

**32.** $\int_0^1 \int_y^{\sqrt{y}} \sqrt{x^2+y^2}\,dx\,dy$

**33.** $\int_0^{\sqrt{2}} \int_y^{\sqrt{4-y^2}} \frac{1}{\sqrt{1+x^2+y^2}}\,dx\,dy$

**34.** $\int_{-4}^0 \int_{-\sqrt{16-x^2}}^{\sqrt{16-x^2}} 3x\,dy\,dx$

**35–38 True–False** Determine whether the statement is true or false. Explain your answer. ■

**35.** The disk of radius 2 that is centered at the origin is a polar rectangle.

**36.** If $f$ is continuous and nonnegative on a simple polar region $R$, then the volume of the solid enclosed between $R$ and the surface $z=f(r,\theta)$ is expressed as

$$\iint_R f(r,\theta)r\,dA$$

**37.** If $R$ is the region in the first quadrant between the circles $r=1$ and $r=2$, and if $f$ is continuous on $R$, then

$$\iint_R f(r,\theta)\,dA = \int_0^{\pi/2}\int_1^2 f(r,\theta)\,dr\,d\theta$$

**38.** The area enclosed by the circle $r=\sin\theta$ is given by

$$A=\int_0^{2\pi}\int_0^{\sin\theta} r\,dr\,d\theta$$

**39.** Evaluate $\iint_R x^2\,dA$ over the region $R$ shown in the accompanying figure.

**40.** Show that the shaded area in the accompanying figure is $a^2\phi - \frac{1}{2}a^2\sin 2\phi$.

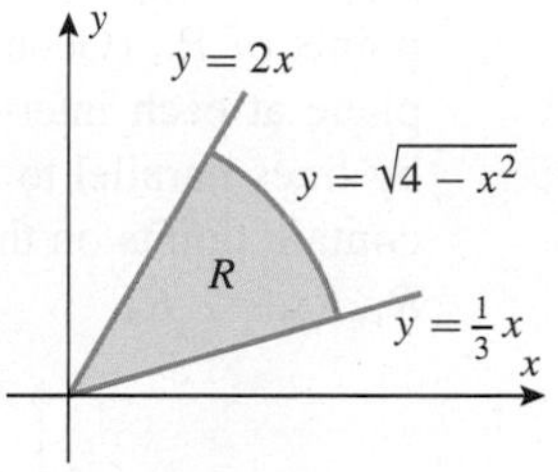


▲ **Figure Ex-39**

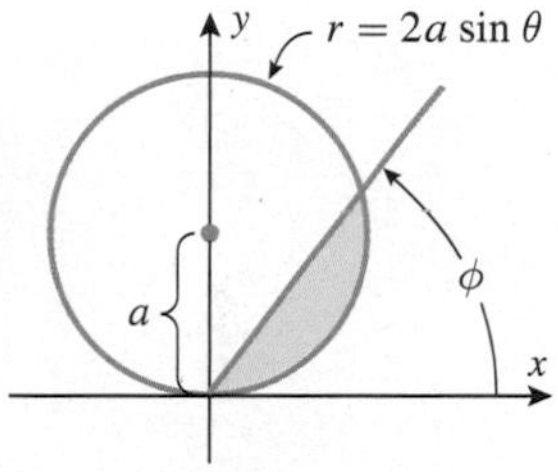


▲ **Figure Ex-40**

**41.** (a) Use a double integral in polar coordinates to find the volume of the oblate spheroid

$$\frac{x^2}{a^2}+\frac{y^2}{a^2}+\frac{z^2}{c^2}=1 \quad (0<c<a)$$

(b) Use the result in part (a) and the World Geodetic System of 1984 (WGS-84) discussed in Exercise 54 of Section 11.7 to find the volume of the Earth in cubic meters.

**42.** Use polar coordinates to find the volume of the solid that is above the $xy$-plane, inside the cylinder $x^2+y^2-ay=0$, and inside the ellipsoid

$$\frac{x^2}{a^2}+\frac{y^2}{a^2}+\frac{z^2}{c^2}=1$$

**43.** Find the area of the region enclosed by the lemniscate $r^2=2a^2\cos 2\theta$.

**44.** Find the area in the first quadrant that is inside the circle $r=4\sin\theta$ and outside the lemniscate $r^2=8\cos 2\theta$.

**45. Writing** Discuss how computing a volume of revolution using a polar double integral corresponds to the method of cylindrical shells (Section 6.3).

✓ **QUICK CHECK ANSWERS 14.3** 1. $1\le r\le 2\sin\theta$, $\pi/6\le\theta\le 5\pi/6$ 2. $\int_0^{\pi/2}\int_3^{10} f(r,\theta)r\,dr\,d\theta$ 3. $\int_0^{\pi}\int_0^{\sin\theta} r\sqrt{1-r^2}\,dr\,d\theta$ 4. $\int_0^{\pi/4}\int_1^{\sec\theta} \frac{1}{r}\,dr\,d\theta$

## 14.4 SURFACE AREA; PARAMETRIC SURFACES

*Earlier we showed how to find the surface area of a surface of revolution. In this section we will derive area formulas for surfaces with equations of the form $z = f(x, y)$ and for surfaces that are represented by parametric equations.*

### SURFACE AREA FOR SURFACES OF THE FORM $z = f(x, y)$

In Section 6.5 we showed that the expression

$$\int_a^b 2\pi f(x)\sqrt{1 + [f'(x)]^2}\, dx$$

gives the area of the surface that is generated by revolving the portion of the curve $y = f(x)$ over the interval $[a, b]$ about the $x$-axis, assuming that $f$ is smooth and nonnegative on the interval. We now obtain a formula for the surface area $S$ of a surface of the form $z = f(x, y)$.

Consider a surface $\sigma$ of the form $z = f(x, y)$ defined over a region $R$ in the $xy$-plane (Figure 14.4.1$a$). We will assume that $f$ has continuous first partial derivatives at the interior points of $R$. (Geometrically, this means that the surface will have a nonvertical tangent plane at each interior point of $R$.) We begin by subdividing $R$ into rectangular regions by lines parallel to the $x$- and $y$-axes and by discarding any nonrectangular portions that contain points on the boundary of $R$. Assume that what remains are $n$ rectangles labeled $R_1, R_2, \ldots, R_n$.

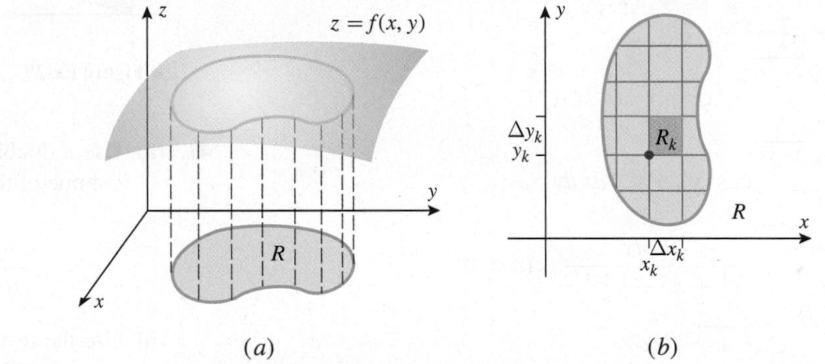


► Figure 14.4.1

Let $(x_k, y_k)$ be the lower left corner of the $k$th rectangle $R_k$, and assume that $R_k$ has area $\Delta A_k = \Delta x_k \Delta y_k$, where $\Delta x_k$ and $\Delta y_k$ are the dimensions of $R_k$ (Figure 14.4.1$b$). The portion of $\sigma$ that lies over $R_k$ will be some *curvilinear patch* on the surface that has a corner at $P_k(x_k, y_k, f(x_k, y_k))$; denote the area of this patch by $\Delta S_k$ (Figure 14.4.2$a$). To obtain an approximation of $\Delta S_k$, we will replace $\sigma$ by the tangent plane to $\sigma$ at $P_k$. The equation of this tangent plane is

$$z = f(x_k, y_k) + f_x(x_k, y_k)(x - x_k) + f_y(x_k, y_k)(y - y_k)$$

(see Theorem 13.7.2). The portion of the tangent plane that lies over $R_k$ will be a parallelogram $\tau_k$. This parallelogram will have a vertex at $P_k$ and adjacent sides determined by the vectors

$$\mathbf{q}_k = \left\langle \Delta x_k, 0, \frac{\partial z}{\partial x}\Delta x_k \right\rangle \quad \text{and} \quad \mathbf{r}_k = \left\langle 0, \Delta y_k, \frac{\partial z}{\partial y}\Delta y_k \right\rangle$$

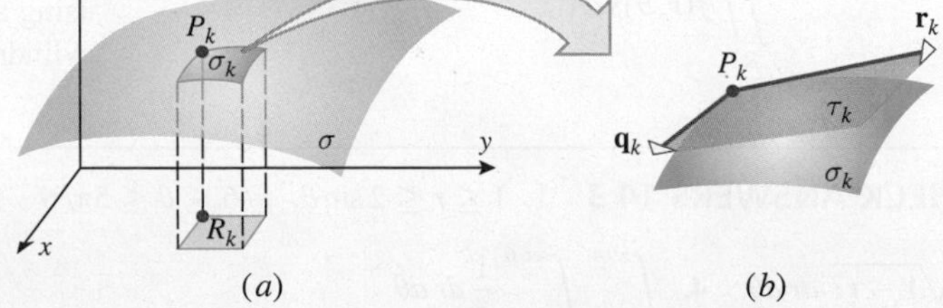


► Figure 14.4.2

as illustrated in Figure 14.4.2*b*. [Here we use $\partial z/\partial x$ to represent $f_x(x_k, y_k)$ and $\partial z/\partial y$ to represent $f_y(x_k, y_k)$.]

If the dimensions of $R_k$ are small, then $\tau_k$ should provide a good approximation to the curvilinear patch $\sigma_k$. By Theorem 11.4.5(*b*), the area of the parallelogram $\tau_k$ is the length of the cross product of $\mathbf{q}_k$ and $\mathbf{r}_k$. Thus, we expect the approximation

$$\Delta S_k \approx \text{area } \tau_k = \|\mathbf{q}_k \times \mathbf{r}_k\|$$

to be good when $\Delta x_k$ and $\Delta y_k$ are close to 0. Computing the cross product yields

$$\|\mathbf{q}_k \times \mathbf{r}_k\| = \left\| \begin{matrix} \mathbf{i} & \mathbf{j} & \mathbf{k} \\ \Delta x_k & 0 & \dfrac{\partial z}{\partial x}\Delta x_k \\ 0 & \Delta y_k & \dfrac{\partial z}{\partial y}\Delta y_k \end{matrix} \right\| = \left(-\frac{\partial z}{\partial x}\mathbf{i} - \frac{\partial z}{\partial y}\mathbf{j} + \mathbf{k}\right)\Delta x_k \Delta y_k$$

so

$$\Delta S_k \approx \left\| \left(-\frac{\partial z}{\partial x}\mathbf{i} - \frac{\partial z}{\partial y}\mathbf{j} + \mathbf{k}\right)\Delta x_k \Delta y_k \right\| = \left\| -\frac{\partial z}{\partial x}\mathbf{i} - \frac{\partial z}{\partial y}\mathbf{j} + \mathbf{k} \right\| \Delta x_k \Delta y_k$$
$$= \sqrt{\left(\frac{\partial z}{\partial x}\right)^2 + \left(\frac{\partial z}{\partial y}\right)^2 + 1}\, \Delta A_k \tag{1}$$

It follows that the surface area of the entire surface can be approximated as

$$S \approx \sum_{k=1}^{n} \sqrt{\left(\frac{\partial z}{\partial x}\right)^2 + \left(\frac{\partial z}{\partial y}\right)^2 + 1}\, \Delta A_k$$

If we assume that the errors in the approximations approach zero as $n$ increases in such a way that the dimensions of the rectangles approach zero, then it is plausible that the exact value of $S$ is

$$S = \lim_{n \to +\infty} \sum_{k=1}^{n} \sqrt{\left(\frac{\partial z}{\partial x}\right)^2 + \left(\frac{\partial z}{\partial y}\right)^2 + 1}\, \Delta A_k$$

or, equivalently,

$$S = \iint_R \sqrt{\left(\frac{\partial z}{\partial x}\right)^2 + \left(\frac{\partial z}{\partial y}\right)^2 + 1}\, dA \tag{2}$$

► **Example 1** Find the surface area of that portion of the surface $z = \sqrt{4 - x^2}$ that lies above the rectangle $R$ in the $xy$-plane whose coordinates satisfy $0 \le x \le 1$ and $0 \le y \le 4$.

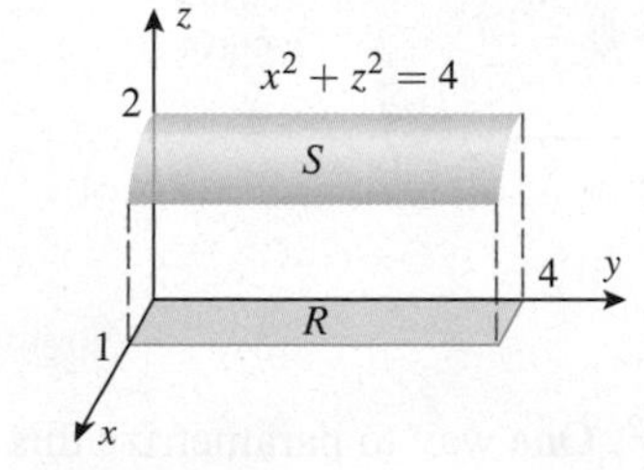


▲ **Figure 14.4.3**

***Solution.*** As shown in Figure 14.4.3, the surface is a portion of the right circular cylinder $x^2 + z^2 = 4$. It follows from (2) that the surface area is

$$S = \iint_R \sqrt{\left(\frac{\partial z}{\partial x}\right)^2 + \left(\frac{\partial z}{\partial y}\right)^2 + 1}\, dA$$
$$= \iint_R \sqrt{\left(-\frac{x}{\sqrt{4 - x^2}}\right)^2 + 0 + 1}\, dA = \int_0^4 \int_0^1 \frac{2}{\sqrt{4 - x^2}}\, dx\, dy$$
$$= 2\int_0^4 \left[\sin^{-1}\left(\frac{1}{2}x\right)\right]_{x=0}^{1} dy = 2\int_0^4 \frac{\pi}{6}\, dy = \frac{4}{3}\pi \blacktriangleleft$$

Formula 21 of Section 7.1

► **Example 2** Find the surface area of the portion of the paraboloid $z = x^2 + y^2$ below the plane $z = 1$.

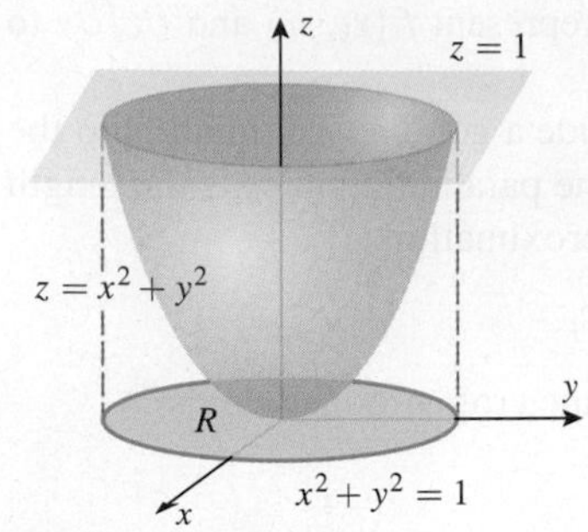


▲ Figure 14.4.4

***Solution.*** The surface $z = x^2 + y^2$ is the circular paraboloid shown in Figure 14.4.4. The trace of the paraboloid in the plane $z = 1$ projects onto the circle $x^2 + y^2 = 1$ in the $xy$-plane, and the portion of the paraboloid that lies below the plane $z = 1$ projects onto the region $R$ that is enclosed by this circle. Thus, it follows from (2) that the surface area is

$$S = \iint_R \sqrt{4x^2 + 4y^2 + 1}\, dA$$

The expression $4x^2 + 4y^2 + 1 = 4(x^2 + y^2) + 1$ in the integrand suggests that we evaluate the integral in polar coordinates. In accordance with Formula (9) of Section 14.3, we substitute $x = r\cos\theta$ and $y = r\sin\theta$ in the integrand, replace $dA$ by $r\,dr\,d\theta$, and find the limits of integration by expressing the region $R$ in polar coordinates. This yields

$$S = \int_0^{2\pi}\int_0^1 \sqrt{4r^2+1}\, r\,dr\,d\theta = \int_0^{2\pi}\left[\frac{1}{12}(4r^2+1)^{3/2}\right]_{r=0}^{1} d\theta$$
$$= \int_0^{2\pi} \frac{1}{12}(5\sqrt{5}-1)\,d\theta = \frac{1}{6}\pi(5\sqrt{5}-1) \blacktriangleleft$$

Some surfaces can't be described conveniently in terms of a function $z = f(x, y)$. For such surfaces, a parametric description may provide a simpler approach. We pause for a discussion of surfaces represented parametrically, with the ultimate goal of deriving a formula for the area of a parametric surface.

## PARAMETRIC REPRESENTATION OF SURFACES

We have seen that curves in 3-space can be represented by three equations involving one parameter, say

$$x = x(t), \quad y = y(t), \quad z = z(t)$$

Surfaces in 3-space can be represented parametrically by three equations involving two parameters, say

$$x = x(u, v), \quad y = y(u, v), \quad z = z(u, v) \tag{3}$$

To visualize why such equations represent a surface, think of $(u, v)$ as a point that varies over some region in a $uv$-plane. If $u$ is held constant, then $v$ is the only varying parameter in (3), and hence these equations represent a curve in 3-space. We call this a ***constant u-curve*** (Figure 14.4.5). Similarly, if $v$ is held constant, then $u$ is the only varying parameter in (3), so again these equations represent a curve in 3-space. We call this a ***constant v-curve***. By varying the constants we generate a family of $u$-curves and a family of $v$-curves that together form a surface.

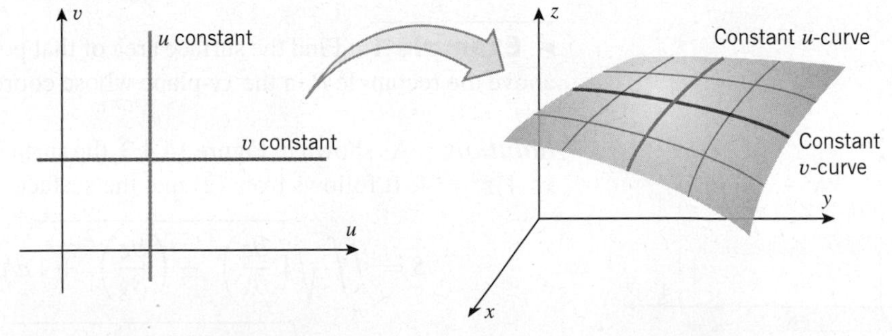


► Figure 14.4.5

► **Example 3** Consider the paraboloid $z = 4 - x^2 - y^2$. One way to parametrize this surface is to take $x = u$ and $y = v$ as the parameters, in which case the surface is represented by the parametric equations

$$x = u, \quad y = v, \quad z = 4 - u^2 - v^2 \tag{4}$$

Figure 14.4.6*a* shows a computer-generated graph of this surface. The constant $u$-curves correspond to constant $x$-values and hence appear on the surface as traces parallel to the $yz$-plane. Similarly, the constant $v$-curves correspond to constant $y$-values and hence appear on the surface as traces parallel to the $xz$-plane. ◄

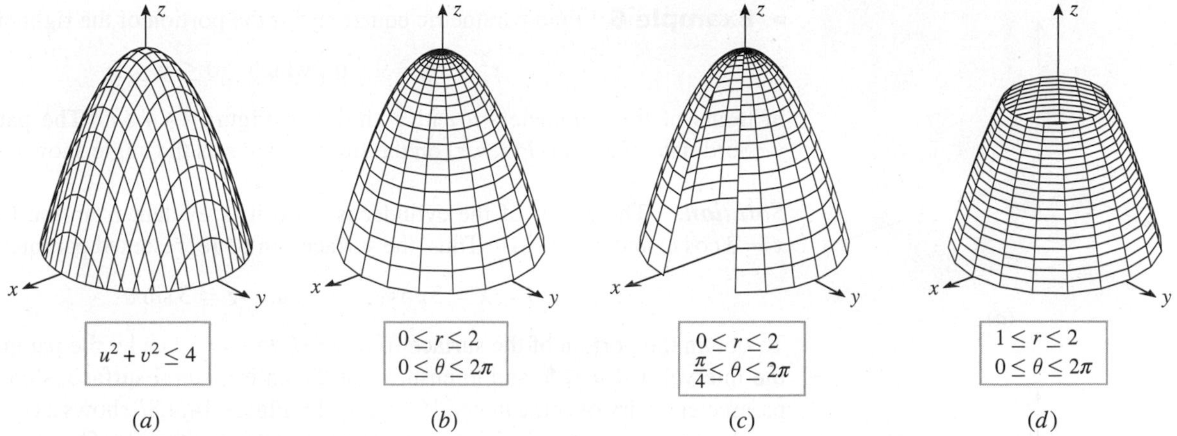


▲ **Figure 14.4.6**

**TECHNOLOGY MASTERY**

If you have a graphing utility that can generate parametric surfaces, consult the relevant documentation and then try to generate the surfaces in Figure 14.4.6.

▶ **Example 4** The paraboloid $z = 4 - x^2 - y^2$ that was considered in Example 3 can also be parametrized by first expressing the equation in cylindrical coordinates. For this purpose, we make the substitution $x = r\cos\theta$, $y = r\sin\theta$, which yields $z = 4 - r^2$. Thus, the paraboloid can be represented parametrically in terms of $r$ and $\theta$ as

$$x = r\cos\theta, \quad y = r\sin\theta, \quad z = 4 - r^2 \tag{5}$$

A computer-generated graph of this surface for $0 \leq r \leq 2$ and $0 \leq \theta \leq 2\pi$ is shown in Figure 14.4.6*b*. The constant $r$-curves correspond to constant $z$-values and hence appear on the surface as traces parallel to the $xy$-plane. The constant $\theta$-curves appear on the surface as traces from vertical planes through the origin at varying angles with the $x$-axis. Parts (*c*) and (*d*) of Figure 14.4.6 show the effect of restrictions on the parameters $r$ and $\theta$. ◀

▶ **Example 5** One way to generate the sphere $x^2 + y^2 + z^2 = 1$ with a graphing utility is to graph the upper and lower hemispheres

$$z = \sqrt{1 - x^2 - y^2} \quad \text{and} \quad z = -\sqrt{1 - x^2 - y^2}$$

on the same screen. However, this sometimes produces a fragmented sphere (Figure 14.4.7*a*) because roundoff error sporadically produces negative values inside the radical when $1 - x^2 - y^2$ is near zero. A better graph can be generated by first expressing the sphere in spherical coordinates as $\rho = 1$ and then using the spherical-to-rectangular conversion formulas in Table 11.8.1 to obtain the parametric equations

$$x = \sin\phi\cos\theta, \quad y = \sin\phi\sin\theta, \quad z = \cos\phi$$

with parameters $\theta$ and $\phi$. Figure 14.4.7*b* shows the graph of this parametric surface for $0 \leq \theta \leq 2\pi$ and $0 \leq \phi \leq \pi$. In the language of cartographers, the constant $\phi$-curves are the ***lines of latitude*** and the constant $\theta$-curves are the ***lines of longitude***. ◀

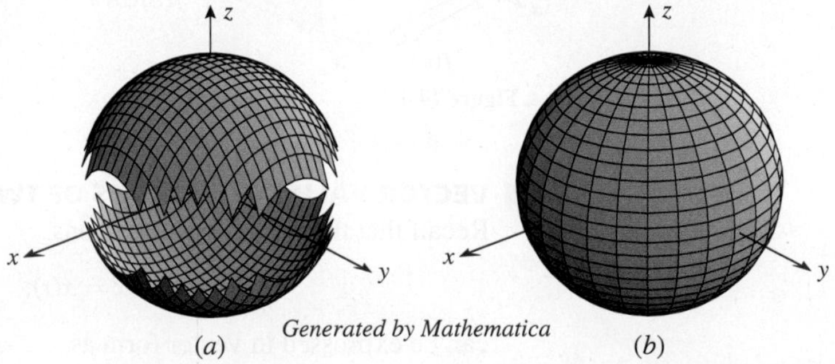


▶ **Figure 14.4.7**

**▸ Example 6** Find parametric equations for the portion of the right circular cylinder

$$x^2 + z^2 = 9 \quad \text{for which} \quad 0 \le y \le 5$$

in terms of the parameters $u$ and $v$ shown in Figure 14.4.8*a*. The parameter $u$ is the $y$-coordinate of a point $P(x, y, z)$ on the surface, and $v$ is the angle shown in the figure.

***Solution.*** The radius of the cylinder is 3, so it is evident from the figure that $y = u$, $x = 3\cos v$, and $z = 3\sin v$. Thus, the surface can be represented parametrically as

$$x = 3\cos v, \quad y = u, \quad z = 3\sin v$$

To obtain the portion of the surface from $y = 0$ to $y = 5$, we let the parameter $u$ vary over the interval $0 \le u \le 5$, and to ensure that the entire lateral surface is covered, we let the parameter $v$ vary over the interval $0 \le v \le 2\pi$. Figure 14.4.8*b* shows a computer-generated graph of the surface in which $u$ and $v$ vary over these intervals. Constant $u$-curves appear as circular traces parallel to the $xz$-plane, and constant $v$-curves appear as lines parallel to the $y$-axis. ◂

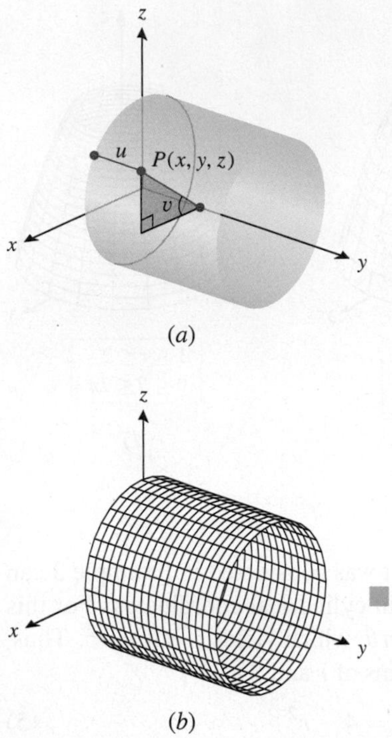

▲ Figure 14.4.8

## REPRESENTING SURFACES OF REVOLUTION PARAMETRICALLY

The basic idea of Example 6 can be adapted to obtain parametric equations for surfaces of revolution. For example, suppose that we want to find parametric equations for the surface generated by revolving the plane curve $y = f(x)$ about the $x$-axis. Figure 14.4.9 suggests that the surface can be represented parametrically as

$$x = u, \quad y = f(u)\cos v, \quad z = f(u)\sin v \tag{6}$$

where $v$ is the angle shown.

In the exercises we will discuss formulas analogous to (6) for surfaces of revolution about other axes.

**▸ Example 7** Find parametric equations for the surface generated by revolving the curve $y = 1/x$ about the $x$-axis.

***Solution.*** From (6) this surface can be represented parametrically as

$$x = u, \quad y = \frac{1}{u}\cos v, \quad z = \frac{1}{u}\sin v$$

Figure 14.4.10 shows a computer-generated graph of the surface in which $0.7 \le u \le 5$ and $0 \le v \le 2\pi$. This surface is a portion of Gabriel's horn, which was discussed in Exercise 55 of Section 7.8. ◂

A general principle for representing surfaces of revolution parametrically is to let the variable about whose axis the curve is revolving be equal to $u$ and let the other variables be $f(u)\cos v$ and $f(u)\sin v$.

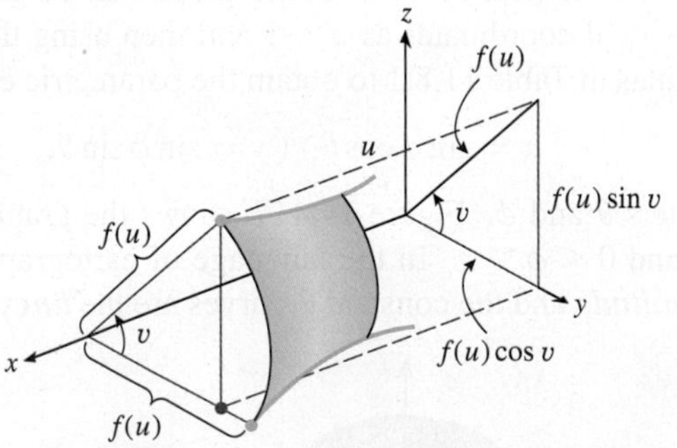

▲ Figure 14.4.9

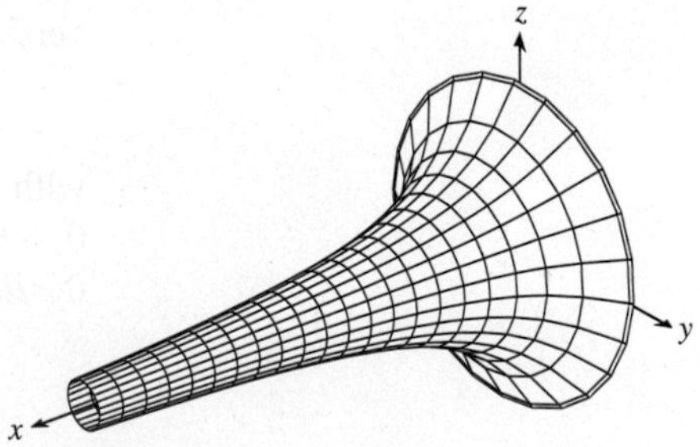

▲ Figure 14.4.10

## VECTOR-VALUED FUNCTIONS OF TWO VARIABLES

Recall that the parametric equations

$$x = x(t), \quad y = y(t), \quad z = z(t)$$

can be expressed in vector form as

$$\mathbf{r} = x(t)\mathbf{i} + y(t)\mathbf{j} + z(t)\mathbf{k}$$

where $\mathbf{r} = x\mathbf{i} + y\mathbf{j} + z\mathbf{k}$ is the radius vector and $\mathbf{r}(t) = x(t)\mathbf{i} + y(t)\mathbf{j} + z(t)\mathbf{k}$ is a vector-valued function of one variable. Similarly, the parametric equations

$$x = x(u, v), \quad y = y(u, v), \quad z = z(u, v)$$

can be expressed in vector form as

$$\mathbf{r} = x(u, v)\mathbf{i} + y(u, v)\mathbf{j} + z(u, v)\mathbf{k}$$

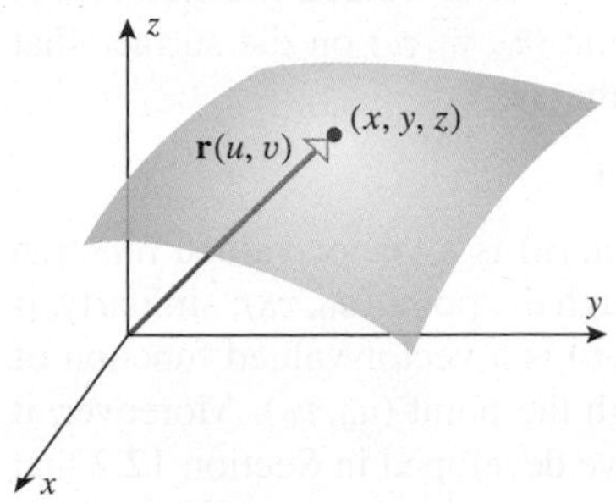

▲ Figure 14.4.11

Here the function $\mathbf{r}(u, v) = x(u, v)\mathbf{i} + y(u, v)\mathbf{j} + z(u, v)\mathbf{k}$ is a ***vector-valued function of two variables***. We define the ***graph*** of $\mathbf{r}(u, v)$ to be the graph of the corresponding parametric equations. Geometrically, we can view $\mathbf{r}$ as a vector from the origin to a point $(x, y, z)$ that moves over the surface $\mathbf{r} = \mathbf{r}(u, v)$ as $u$ and $v$ vary (Figure 14.4.11). As with vector-valued functions of one variable, we say that $\mathbf{r}(u, v)$ is ***continuous*** if each component is continuous.

**▶ Example 8** The paraboloid in Example 3 was expressed parametrically as

$$x = u, \quad y = v, \quad z = 4 - u^2 - v^2$$

These equations can be expressed in vector form as

$$\mathbf{r} = u\mathbf{i} + v\mathbf{j} + (4 - u^2 - v^2)\mathbf{k} \blacktriangleleft$$

## PARTIAL DERIVATIVES OF VECTOR-VALUED FUNCTIONS

Partial derivatives of vector-valued functions of two variables are obtained by taking partial derivatives of the components. For example, if

$$\mathbf{r}(u, v) = x(u, v)\mathbf{i} + y(u, v)\mathbf{j} + z(u, v)\mathbf{k}$$

then

$$\frac{\partial \mathbf{r}}{\partial u} = \frac{\partial x}{\partial u}\mathbf{i} + \frac{\partial y}{\partial u}\mathbf{j} + \frac{\partial z}{\partial u}\mathbf{k}$$

$$\frac{\partial \mathbf{r}}{\partial v} = \frac{\partial x}{\partial v}\mathbf{i} + \frac{\partial y}{\partial v}\mathbf{j} + \frac{\partial z}{\partial v}\mathbf{k}$$

These derivatives can also be written as $\mathbf{r}_u$ and $\mathbf{r}_v$ or $\mathbf{r}_u(u, v)$ and $\mathbf{r}_v(u, v)$ and can be expressed as the limits

$$\frac{\partial \mathbf{r}}{\partial u} = \lim_{\Delta u \to 0} \frac{\mathbf{r}(u + \Delta u, v) - \mathbf{r}(u, v)}{\Delta u} = \lim_{w \to u} \frac{\mathbf{r}(w, v) - \mathbf{r}(u, v)}{w - u} \tag{7}$$

$$\frac{\partial \mathbf{r}}{\partial v} = \lim_{\Delta v \to 0} \frac{\mathbf{r}(u, v + \Delta v) - \mathbf{r}(u, v)}{\Delta v} = \lim_{w \to v} \frac{\mathbf{r}(u, w) - \mathbf{r}(u, v)}{w - v} \tag{8}$$

**▶ Example 9** Find the partial derivatives of the vector-valued function $\mathbf{r}$ in Example 8.

***Solution.***

$$\frac{\partial \mathbf{r}}{\partial u} = \frac{\partial}{\partial u}[u\mathbf{i} + v\mathbf{j} + (4 - u^2 - v^2)\mathbf{k}] = \mathbf{i} - 2u\mathbf{k}$$

$$\frac{\partial \mathbf{r}}{\partial v} = \frac{\partial}{\partial v}[u\mathbf{i} + v\mathbf{j} + (4 - u^2 - v^2)\mathbf{k}] = \mathbf{j} - 2v\mathbf{k} \blacktriangleleft$$

## TANGENT PLANES TO PARAMETRIC SURFACES

Our next objective is to show how to find tangent planes to parametric surfaces. Let $\sigma$ denote a parametric surface in 3-space, with $P_0$ a point on $\sigma$. We will say that a plane is ***tangent*** to $\sigma$ at $P_0$ provided a line through $P_0$ lies in the plane if and only if it is a tangent line at $P_0$ to a curve on $\sigma$. We showed in Section 13.7 that if $z = f(x, y)$, then the graph of $f$ has a tangent plane at a point if $f$ is differentiable at that point. It is beyond the scope of this text to obtain precise conditions under which a parametric surface has a tangent plane at a point, so we will simply assume the existence of tangent planes at points of interest and focus on finding their equations.

Suppose that the parametric surface $\sigma$ is the graph of the vector-valued function $\mathbf{r}(u, v)$ and that we are interested in the tangent plane at the point $(x_0, y_0, z_0)$ on the surface that corresponds to the parameter values $u = u_0$ and $v = v_0$; that is,

$$\mathbf{r}(u_0, v_0) = x_0\mathbf{i} + y_0\mathbf{j} + z_0\mathbf{k}$$

If $v = v_0$ is kept fixed and $u$ is allowed to vary, then $\mathbf{r}(u, v_0)$ is a vector-valued function of one variable whose graph is the constant $v$-curve through the point $(u_0, v_0)$; similarly, if $u = u_0$ is kept fixed and $v$ is allowed to vary, then $\mathbf{r}(u_0, v)$ is a vector-valued function of one variable whose graph is the constant $u$-curve through the point $(u_0, v_0)$. Moreover, it follows from the geometric interpretation of the derivative developed in Section 12.2 that if $\partial\mathbf{r}/\partial u \neq \mathbf{0}$ at $(u_0, v_0)$, then this vector is tangent to the constant $v$-curve through $(u_0, v_0)$; and if $\partial\mathbf{r}/\partial v \neq \mathbf{0}$ at $(u_0, v_0)$, then this vector is tangent to the constant $u$-curve through $(u_0, v_0)$ (Figure 14.4.12). Thus, if $\partial\mathbf{r}/\partial u \times \partial\mathbf{r}/\partial v \neq \mathbf{0}$ at $(u_0, v_0)$, then the vector

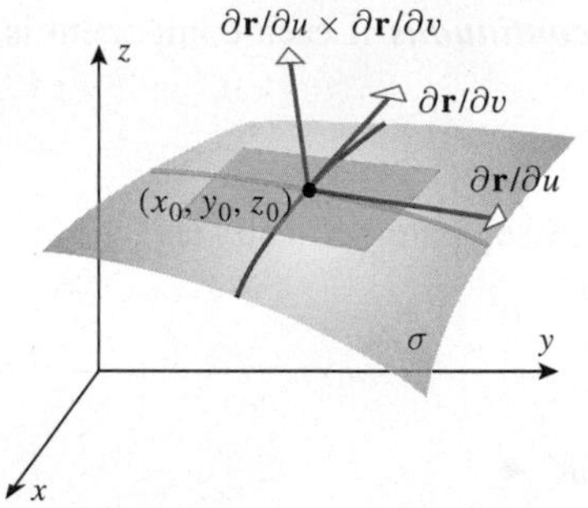

▲ Figure 14.4.12

$$\frac{\partial\mathbf{r}}{\partial u} \times \frac{\partial\mathbf{r}}{\partial v} = \begin{vmatrix} \mathbf{i} & \mathbf{j} & \mathbf{k} \\ \dfrac{\partial x}{\partial u} & \dfrac{\partial y}{\partial u} & \dfrac{\partial z}{\partial u} \\ \dfrac{\partial x}{\partial v} & \dfrac{\partial y}{\partial v} & \dfrac{\partial z}{\partial v} \end{vmatrix} \tag{9}$$

is orthogonal to both tangent vectors at the point $(u_0, v_0)$ and hence is normal to the tangent plane and the surface at this point (Figure 14.4.12). Accordingly, we make the following definition.

**14.4.1 DEFINITION** If a parametric surface $\sigma$ is the graph of $\mathbf{r} = \mathbf{r}(u, v)$, and if $\partial\mathbf{r}/\partial u \times \partial\mathbf{r}/\partial v \neq \mathbf{0}$ at a point on the surface, then the ***principal unit normal vector*** to the surface at that point is denoted by $\mathbf{n}$ or $\mathbf{n}(u, v)$ and is defined as

$$\mathbf{n} = \frac{\dfrac{\partial\mathbf{r}}{\partial u} \times \dfrac{\partial\mathbf{r}}{\partial v}}{\left\| \dfrac{\partial\mathbf{r}}{\partial u} \times \dfrac{\partial\mathbf{r}}{\partial v} \right\|} \tag{10}$$

▶ **Example 10** Find an equation of the tangent plane to the parametric surface

$$x = uv, \quad y = u, \quad z = v^2$$

at the point where $u = 2$ and $v = -1$. This surface, called ***Whitney's umbrella***, is an example of a self-intersecting parametric surface (Figure 14.4.13).

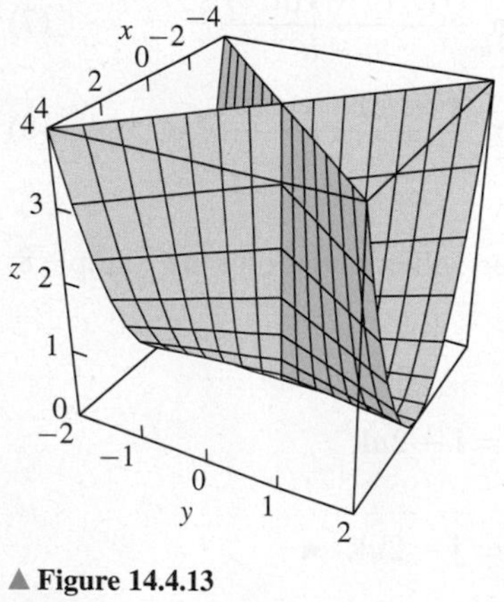

▲ Figure 14.4.13

***Solution.*** We start by writing the equations in the vector form

$$\mathbf{r} = uv\mathbf{i} + u\mathbf{j} + v^2\mathbf{k}$$

The partial derivatives of $\mathbf{r}$ are

$$\frac{\partial\mathbf{r}}{\partial u}(u, v) = v\mathbf{i} + \mathbf{j}$$

$$\frac{\partial\mathbf{r}}{\partial v}(u, v) = u\mathbf{i} + 2v\mathbf{k}$$

and at $u = 2$ and $v = -1$ these partial derivatives are

$$\frac{\partial\mathbf{r}}{\partial u}(2, -1) = -\mathbf{i} + \mathbf{j}$$

$$\frac{\partial\mathbf{r}}{\partial v}(2, -1) = 2\mathbf{i} - 2\mathbf{k}$$

Thus, from (9) and (10) a normal to the surface at this point is

$$\frac{\partial \mathbf{r}}{\partial u}(2,-1) \times \frac{\partial \mathbf{r}}{\partial v}(2,-1) = \begin{vmatrix} \mathbf{i} & \mathbf{j} & \mathbf{k} \\ -1 & 1 & 0 \\ 2 & 0 & -2 \end{vmatrix} = -2\mathbf{i} - 2\mathbf{j} - 2\mathbf{k}$$

Since any normal will suffice to find the tangent plane, it makes sense to multiply this vector by $-\frac{1}{2}$ and use the simpler normal $\mathbf{i}+\mathbf{j}+\mathbf{k}$. It follows from the given parametric equations that the point on the surface corresponding to $u = 2$ and $v = -1$ is $(-2, 2, 1)$, so the tangent plane at this point can be expressed in point-normal form as

$$(x+2) + (y-2) + (z-1) = 0 \quad \text{or} \quad x+y+z = 1 \blacktriangleleft$$

▶ **Example 11** The sphere $x^2+y^2+z^2 = a^2$ can be expressed in spherical coordinates as $\rho = a$, and the spherical-to-rectangular conversion formulas in Table 11.8.1 can then be used to express the sphere as the graph of the vector-valued function

$$\mathbf{r}(\phi, \theta) = a\sin\phi\cos\theta\mathbf{i} + a\sin\phi\sin\theta\mathbf{j} + a\cos\phi\mathbf{k}$$

where $0 \le \phi \le \pi$ and $0 \le \theta \le 2\pi$ (verify). Use this function to show that the radius vector is normal to the tangent plane at each point on the sphere.

***Solution.*** We will show that at each point of the sphere the unit normal vector $\mathbf{n}$ is a scalar multiple of $\mathbf{r}$ (and hence is parallel to $\mathbf{r}$). We have

$$\frac{\partial \mathbf{r}}{\partial \phi} \times \frac{\partial \mathbf{r}}{\partial \theta} = \begin{vmatrix} \mathbf{i} & \mathbf{j} & \mathbf{k} \\ \dfrac{\partial x}{\partial \phi} & \dfrac{\partial y}{\partial \phi} & \dfrac{\partial z}{\partial \phi} \\ \dfrac{\partial x}{\partial \theta} & \dfrac{\partial y}{\partial \theta} & \dfrac{\partial z}{\partial \theta} \end{vmatrix} = \begin{vmatrix} \mathbf{i} & \mathbf{j} & \mathbf{k} \\ a\cos\phi\cos\theta & a\cos\phi\sin\theta & -a\sin\phi \\ -a\sin\phi\sin\theta & a\sin\phi\cos\theta & 0 \end{vmatrix}$$
$$= a^2\sin^2\phi\cos\theta\mathbf{i} + a^2\sin^2\phi\sin\theta\mathbf{j} + a^2\sin\phi\cos\phi\mathbf{k}$$

and hence

$$\left\|\frac{\partial \mathbf{r}}{\partial \phi} \times \frac{\partial \mathbf{r}}{\partial \theta}\right\| = \sqrt{a^4\sin^4\phi\cos^2\theta + a^4\sin^4\phi\sin^2\theta + a^4\sin^2\phi\cos^2\phi}$$
$$= \sqrt{a^4\sin^4\phi + a^4\sin^2\phi\cos^2\phi}$$
$$= a^2\sqrt{\sin^2\phi} = a^2|\sin\phi| = a^2\sin\phi$$

For $\phi \ne 0$ or $\pi$, it follows from (10) that

$$\mathbf{n} = \sin\phi\cos\theta\mathbf{i} + \sin\phi\sin\theta\mathbf{j} + \cos\phi\mathbf{k} = \frac{1}{a}\mathbf{r}$$

Furthermore, the tangent planes at $\phi = 0$ or $\pi$ are horizontal, to which $\mathbf{r} = \pm a\mathbf{k}$ is clearly normal. ◀

## SURFACE AREA OF PARAMETRIC SURFACES

We now obtain a formula for the surface area $S$ of a parametric surface $\sigma$. Let $\sigma$ be a parametric surface whose vector equation is

$$\mathbf{r} = x(u,v)\mathbf{i} + y(u,v)\mathbf{j} + z(u,v)\mathbf{k}$$

Our discussion will be analogous to the case for surfaces of the form $z = f(x, y)$. Here, $R$ will be a region in the $uv$-plane that we subdivide into $n$ rectangular regions as shown in Figure 14.4.14*a*. Let $R_k$ be the $k$th rectangular region, and denote its area by $\Delta A_k$. The patch $\sigma_k$ is the image of $R_k$ on $\sigma$. The patch will have a corner at $\mathbf{r}(u_k, v_k)$; denote the area of $\sigma_k$ by $\Delta S_k$ (Figure 14.4.14*b*).

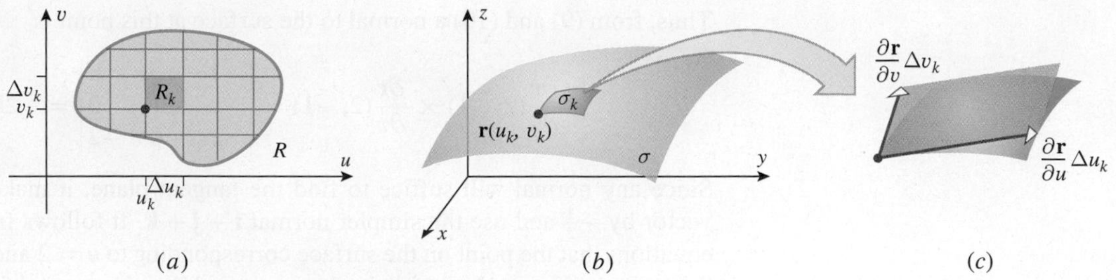

▲ **Figure 14.4.14**

Recall that in the case of $z = f(x, y)$ we used the area of a parallelogram in a tangent plane to the surface to approximate the area of the patch. In the parametric case, the desired parallelogram is spanned by the tangent vectors

$$\frac{\partial \mathbf{r}}{\partial u}\Delta u_k \quad \text{and} \quad \frac{\partial \mathbf{r}}{\partial v}\Delta v_k$$

where the partial derivatives are evaluated at $(u_k, v_k)$ (Figure 14.4.14$c$). Thus,

$$\Delta S_k \approx \left\| \frac{\partial \mathbf{r}}{\partial u}\Delta u_k \times \frac{\partial \mathbf{r}}{\partial v}\Delta v_k \right\| = \left\| \frac{\partial \mathbf{r}}{\partial u} \times \frac{\partial \mathbf{r}}{\partial v} \right\| \Delta u_k \Delta v_k = \left\| \frac{\partial \mathbf{r}}{\partial u} \times \frac{\partial \mathbf{r}}{\partial v} \right\| \Delta A_k \tag{11}$$

The surface area of the entire surface is the sum of the areas $\Delta S_k$. If we assume that the errors in the approximations in (11) approach zero as $n$ increases in such a way that the dimensions of the rectangles $R_k$ approach zero, then it is plausible that the exact value of $S$ is

$$S = \lim_{n \to +\infty} \sum_{k=1}^{n} \left\| \frac{\partial \mathbf{r}}{\partial u} \times \frac{\partial \mathbf{r}}{\partial v} \right\| \Delta A_k$$

or, equivalently,

$$S = \iint_R \left\| \frac{\partial \mathbf{r}}{\partial u} \times \frac{\partial \mathbf{r}}{\partial v} \right\| dA \tag{12}$$

▶ **Example 12** It follows from (6) that the parametric equations

$$x = u, \quad y = u\cos v, \quad z = u\sin v$$

represent the cone that results when the line $y = x$ in the $xy$-plane is revolved about the $x$-axis. Use Formula (12) to find the surface area of that portion of the cone for which $0 \le u \le 2$ and $0 \le v \le 2\pi$ (Figure 14.4.15).

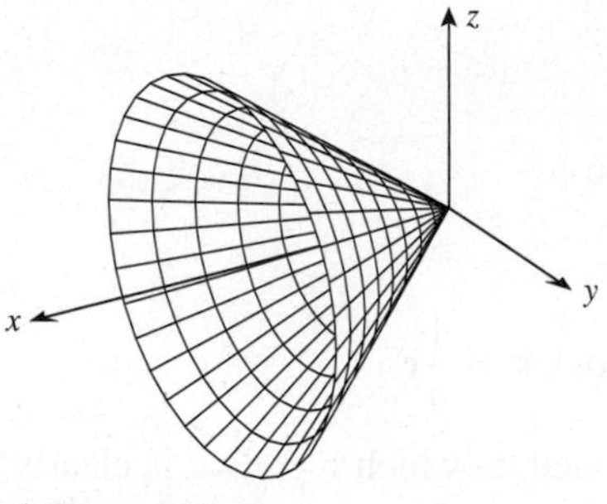

▲ **Figure 14.4.15**

***Solution.*** The surface can be expressed in vector form as

$$\mathbf{r} = u\mathbf{i} + u\cos v\mathbf{j} + u\sin v\mathbf{k} \quad (0 \le u \le 2,\ 0 \le v \le 2\pi)$$

Thus,

$$\frac{\partial \mathbf{r}}{\partial u} = \mathbf{i} + \cos v\mathbf{j} + \sin v\mathbf{k}$$

$$\frac{\partial \mathbf{r}}{\partial v} = -u\sin v\mathbf{j} + u\cos v\mathbf{k}$$

$$\frac{\partial \mathbf{r}}{\partial u} \times \frac{\partial \mathbf{r}}{\partial v} = \begin{vmatrix} \mathbf{i} & \mathbf{j} & \mathbf{k} \\ 1 & \cos v & \sin v \\ 0 & -u\sin v & u\cos v \end{vmatrix} = u\mathbf{i} - u\cos v\mathbf{j} - u\sin v\mathbf{k}$$

$$\left\| \frac{\partial \mathbf{r}}{\partial u} \times \frac{\partial \mathbf{r}}{\partial v} \right\| = \sqrt{u^2 + (-u\cos v)^2 + (-u\sin v)^2} = |u|\sqrt{2} = u\sqrt{2}$$

Thus, from (12)

$$S = \iint_R \left\| \frac{\partial \mathbf{r}}{\partial u} \times \frac{\partial \mathbf{r}}{\partial v} \right\| dA = \int_0^{2\pi} \int_0^2 \sqrt{2}u\,du\,dv = 2\sqrt{2} \int_0^{2\pi} dv = 4\pi\sqrt{2} \blacktriangleleft$$

## ✓QUICK CHECK EXERCISES 14.4 *(See page 930 for answers.)*

1. The surface area of a surface of the form $z = f(x, y)$ over a region $R$ in the $xy$-plane is given by
$$S = \iint_R \underline{\qquad\qquad} \, dA$$
2. Consider the surface represented parametrically by
$$x = 1 - u, \quad y = (1 - u)\cos v, \quad z = (1 - u)\sin v \qquad (0 \le u \le 1, 0 \le v \le 2\pi)$$
   (a) Describe the constant $u$-curves.
   (b) Describe the constant $v$-curves.
3. If
$$\mathbf{r}(u, v) = (1 - u)\mathbf{i} + [(1 - u)\cos v]\mathbf{j} + [(1 - u)\sin v]\mathbf{k}$$
then
$$\frac{\partial \mathbf{r}}{\partial u} = \underline{\qquad\qquad} \quad \text{and} \quad \frac{\partial \mathbf{r}}{\partial v} = \underline{\qquad\qquad}$$
4. If
$$\mathbf{r}(u, v) = (1 - u)\mathbf{i} + [(1 - u)\cos v]\mathbf{j} + [(1 - u)\sin v]\mathbf{k}$$
the principal unit normal to the graph of $\mathbf{r}$ at the point where $u = 1/2$ and $v = \pi/6$ is given by ________.
5. Suppose $\sigma$ is a parametric surface with vector equation
$$\mathbf{r}(u, v) = x(u, v)\mathbf{i} + y(u, v)\mathbf{j} + z(u, v)\mathbf{k}$$
If $\sigma$ has no self-intersections and $\sigma$ is smooth on a region $R$ in the $uv$-plane, then the surface area of $\sigma$ is given by
$$S = \iint_R \underline{\qquad\qquad} \, dA$$

## EXERCISE SET 14.4 Graphing Utility C CAS

**1–4** Express the area of the given surface as an iterated double integral, and then find the surface area. ■

1. The portion of the cylinder $y^2 + z^2 = 9$ that is above the rectangle $R = \{(x, y) : 0 \le x \le 2, -3 \le y \le 3\}$.
2. The portion of the plane $2x + 2y + z = 8$ in the first octant.
3. The portion of the cone $z^2 = 4x^2 + 4y^2$ that is above the region in the first quadrant bounded by the line $y = x$ and the parabola $y = x^2$.
4. The portion of the surface $z = 2x + y^2$ that is above the triangular region with vertices (0, 0), (0, 1), and (1, 1).

**5–10** Express the area of the given surface as an iterated double integral in polar coordinates, and then find the surface area. ■

5. The portion of the cone $z = \sqrt{x^2 + y^2}$ that lies inside the cylinder $x^2 + y^2 = 2x$.
6. The portion of the paraboloid $z = 1 - x^2 - y^2$ that is above the $xy$-plane.
7. The portion of the surface $z = xy$ that is above the sector in the first quadrant bounded by the lines $y = x/\sqrt{3}$, $y = 0$, and the circle $x^2 + y^2 = 9$.
8. The portion of the paraboloid $2z = x^2 + y^2$ that is inside the cylinder $x^2 + y^2 = 8$.
9. The portion of the sphere $x^2 + y^2 + z^2 = 16$ between the planes $z = 1$ and $z = 2$.
10. The portion of the sphere $x^2 + y^2 + z^2 = 8$ that is inside the cone $z = \sqrt{x^2 + y^2}$.

**11–12** Sketch the parametric surface. ■

11. (a) $x = u,\ y = v,\ z = \sqrt{u^2 + v^2}$
    (b) $x = u,\ y = \sqrt{u^2 + v^2},\ z = v$
    (c) $x = \sqrt{u^2 + v^2},\ y = u,\ z = v$
12. (a) $x = u,\ y = v,\ z = u^2 + v^2$
    (b) $x = u,\ y = u^2 + v^2,\ z = v$
    (c) $x = u^2 + v^2,\ y = u,\ z = v$

**13–14** Find a parametric representation of the surface in terms of the parameters $u = x$ and $v = y$. ■

13. (a) $2z - 3x + 4y = 5$ (b) $z = x^2$
14. (a) $z + zx^2 - y = 0$ (b) $y^2 - 3z = 5$
15. (a) Find parametric equations for the portion of the cylinder $x^2 + y^2 = 5$ that extends between the planes $z = 0$ and $z = 1$.
    (b) Find parametric equations for the portion of the cylinder $x^2 + z^2 = 4$ that extends between the planes $y = 1$ and $y = 3$.
16. (a) Find parametric equations for the portion of the plane $x + y = 1$ that extends between the planes $z = -1$ and $z = 1$.
    (b) Find parametric equations for the portion of the plane $y - 2z = 5$ that extends between the planes $x = 0$ and $x = 3$.
17. Find parametric equations for the surface generated by revolving the curve $y = \sin x$ about the $x$-axis.

**18.** Find parametric equations for the surface generated by revolving the curve $y - e^x = 0$ about the $x$-axis.

**19–24** Find a parametric representation of the surface in terms of the parameters $r$ and $\theta$, where $(r, \theta, z)$ are the cylindrical coordinates of a point on the surface. ■

**19.** $z = \dfrac{1}{1 + x^2 + y^2}$  **20.** $z = e^{-(x^2+y^2)}$

**21.** $z = 2xy$  **22.** $z = x^2 - y^2$

**23.** The portion of the sphere $x^2 + y^2 + z^2 = 9$ on or above the plane $z = 2$.

**24.** The portion of the cone $z = \sqrt{x^2 + y^2}$ on or below the plane $z = 3$.

**25.** Find a parametric representation of the cone

$$z = \sqrt{3x^2 + 3y^2}$$

in terms of parameters $\rho$ and $\theta$, where $(\rho, \theta, \phi)$ are spherical coordinates of a point on the surface.

**26.** Describe the cylinder $x^2 + y^2 = 9$ in terms of parameters $\theta$ and $\phi$, where $(\rho, \theta, \phi)$ are spherical coordinates of a point on the surface.

**FOCUS ON CONCEPTS**

**27–32** Eliminate the parameters to obtain an equation in rectangular coordinates, and describe the surface. ■

**27.** $x = 2u + v,\ y = u - v,\ z = 3v$ for $-\infty < u < +\infty$ and $-\infty < v < +\infty$.

**28.** $x = u\cos v,\ y = u^2,\ z = u\sin v$ for $0 \le u \le 2$ and $0 \le v < 2\pi$.

**29.** $x = 3\sin u,\ y = 2\cos u,\ z = 2v$ for $0 \le u < 2\pi$ and $1 \le v \le 2$.

**30.** $x = \sqrt{u}\cos v,\ y = \sqrt{u}\sin v,\ z = u$ for $0 \le u \le 4$ and $0 \le v < 2\pi$.

**31.** $\mathbf{r}(u, v) = 3u\cos v\mathbf{i} + 4u\sin v\mathbf{j} + u\mathbf{k}$ for $0 \le u \le 1$ and $0 \le v < 2\pi$.

**32.** $\mathbf{r}(u, v) = \sin u\cos v\mathbf{i} + 2\sin u\sin v\mathbf{j} + 3\cos u\mathbf{k}$ for $0 \le u \le \pi$ and $0 \le v < 2\pi$.

**33.** The accompanying figure shows the graphs of two parametric representations of the cone $z = \sqrt{x^2 + y^2}$ for $0 \le z \le 2$.

(a) Find parametric equations that produce reasonable facsimiles of these surfaces.

(b) Use a graphing utility to check your answer in part (a).

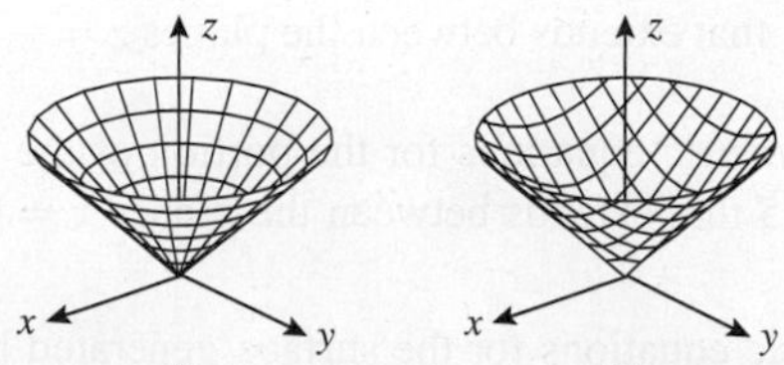

I  II

◀ **Figure Ex-33**

**34.** The accompanying figure shows the graphs of two parametric representations of the paraboloid $z = x^2 + y^2$ for $0 \le z \le 2$.

(a) Find parametric equations that produce reasonable facsimiles of these surfaces.

(b) Use a graphing utility to check your answer in part (a).

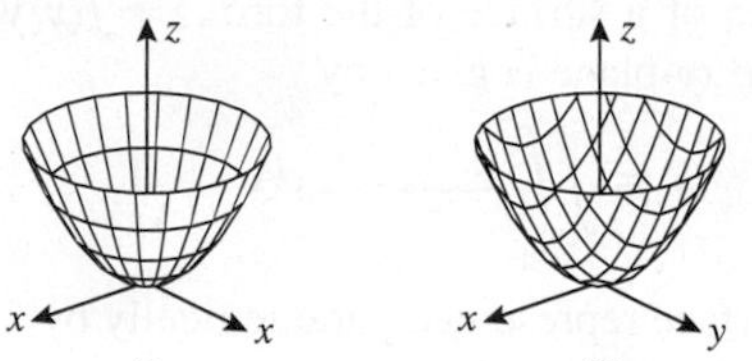

I  II

◀ **Figure Ex-34**

**35.** In each part, the figure shows a portion of the parametric surface $x = 3\cos v,\ y = u,\ z = 3\sin v$. Find restrictions on $u$ and $v$ that produce the surface, and check your answer with a graphing utility.

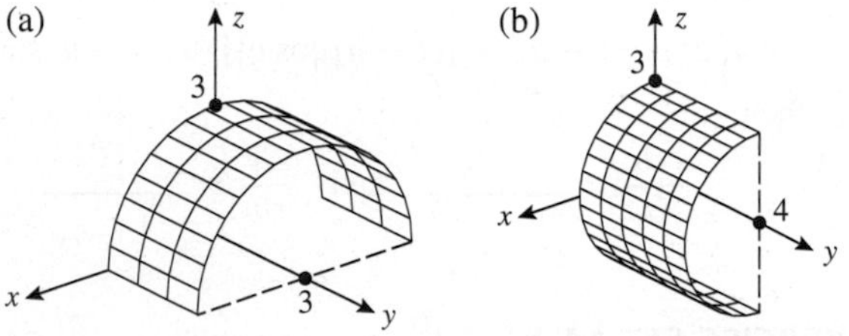


**36.** In each part, the figure shows a portion of the parametric surface $x = 3\cos v,\ y = 3\sin v,\ z = u$. Find restrictions on $u$ and $v$ that produce the surface, and check your answer with a graphing utility.

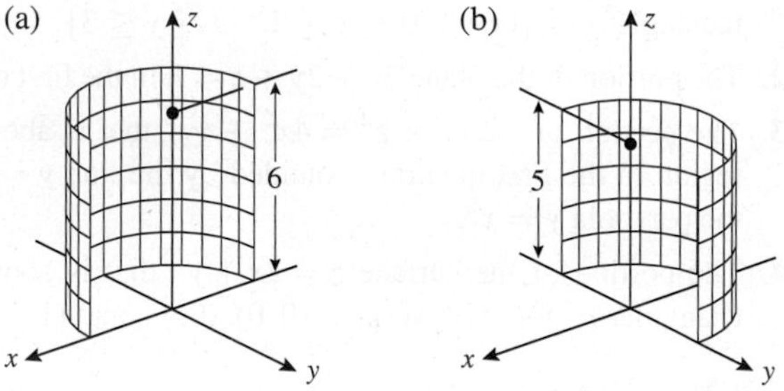


**37.** In each part, the figure shows a hemisphere that is a portion of the sphere $x = \sin\phi\cos\theta,\ y = \sin\phi\sin\theta,\ z = \cos\phi$. Find restrictions on $\phi$ and $\theta$ that produce the hemisphere, and check your answer with a graphing utility.

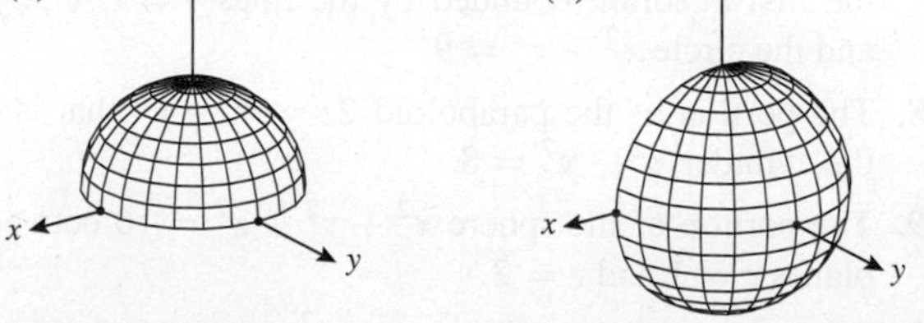


**38.** In each part, the figure shows a portion of the sphere $x = \sin\phi\cos\theta,\ y = \sin\phi\sin\theta,\ z = \cos\phi$. Find

restrictions on $\phi$ and $\theta$ that produce the surface, and check your answer with a graphing utility.

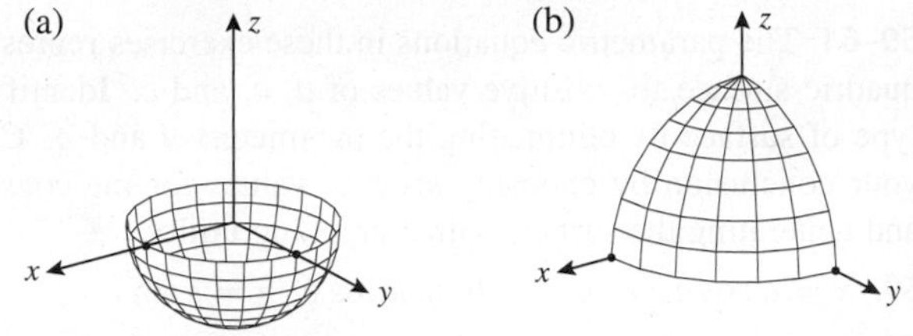


**39–44** Find an equation of the tangent plane to the parametric surface at the stated point. ■

**39.** $x = u, y = v, z = u^2 + v^2$; $(1, 2, 5)$

**40.** $x = u^2, y = v^2, z = u + v$; $(1, 4, 3)$

**41.** $x = 3v \sin u, y = 2v \cos u, z = u^2$; $(0, 2, 0)$

**42.** $\mathbf{r} = uv\mathbf{i} + (u - v)\mathbf{j} + (u + v)\mathbf{k}$; $u = 1, v = 2$

**43.** $\mathbf{r} = u \cos v\mathbf{i} + u \sin v\mathbf{j} + v\mathbf{k}$; $u = 1/2, v = \pi/4$

**44.** $\mathbf{r} = uv\mathbf{i} + ue^v\mathbf{j} + ve^u\mathbf{k}$; $u = \ln 2, v = 0$

**45–46** Find the area of the given surface. ■

**45.** The portion of the paraboloid

$$\mathbf{r}(u, v) = u \cos v\mathbf{i} + u \sin v\mathbf{j} + u^2\mathbf{k}$$

for which $1 \le u \le 2, 0 \le v \le 2\pi$.

**46.** The portion of the cone

$$\mathbf{r}(u, v) = u \cos v\mathbf{i} + u \sin v\mathbf{j} + u\mathbf{k}$$

for which $0 \le u \le 2v, 0 \le v \le \pi/2$.

**47–50 True–False** Determine whether the statement is true or false. Explain your answer. ■

**47.** If $f$ has continuous first partial derivatives in the interior of a region $R$ in the $xy$-plane, then the surface area of the surface $z = f(x, y)$ over $R$ is

$$\iint_R \sqrt{[f(x, y)]^2 + 1}\, dA$$

**48.** Suppose that $z = f(x, y)$ has continuous first partial derivatives in the interior of a region $R$ in the $xy$-plane, and set $\mathbf{q} = \langle 1, 0, \partial z/\partial x\rangle$ and $\mathbf{r} = \langle 0, 1, \partial z/\partial y\rangle$. Then the surface area of the surface $z = f(x, y)$ over $R$ is

$$\iint_R \|\mathbf{q} \times \mathbf{r}\|\, dA$$

**49.** If $\mathbf{r}(u, v) = x(u, v)\mathbf{i} + y(u, v)\mathbf{j} + z(u, v)\mathbf{k}$ such that $\partial\mathbf{r}/\partial u$ and $\partial\mathbf{r}/\partial v$ are nonzero vectors at $(u_0, v_0)$, then

$$\frac{\partial\mathbf{r}}{\partial u} \times \frac{\partial\mathbf{r}}{\partial v}$$

is normal to the graph of $\mathbf{r} = \mathbf{r}(u, v)$ at $(u_0, v_0)$.

**50.** For the function $f(x, y) = ax + by$, the area of the surface $z = f(x, y)$ over a rectangle $R$ in the $xy$-plane is the product of $\|\langle 1, 0, a\rangle \times \langle 0, 1, b\rangle\|$ and the area of $R$.

**51.** Use parametric equations to derive the formula for the surface area of a sphere of radius $a$.

**52.** Use parametric equations to derive the formula for the lateral surface area of a right circular cylinder of radius $r$ and height $h$.

**53.** The portion of the surface

$$z = \frac{h}{a}\sqrt{x^2 + y^2} \quad (a, h > 0)$$

between the $xy$-plane and the plane $z = h$ is a right circular cone of height $h$ and radius $a$. Use a double integral to show that the lateral surface area of this cone is $S = \pi a\sqrt{a^2 + h^2}$.

**54.** The accompanying figure shows the ***torus*** that is generated by revolving the circle

$$(x - a)^2 + z^2 = b^2 \quad (0 < b < a)$$

in the $xz$-plane about the $z$-axis.

(a) Show that this torus can be expressed parametrically as

$$x = (a + b \cos v) \cos u$$
$$y = (a + b \cos v) \sin u$$
$$z = b \sin v$$

where $u$ and $v$ are the parameters shown in the figure and $0 \le u \le 2\pi, 0 \le v \le 2\pi$.

(b) Use a graphing utility to generate a torus.

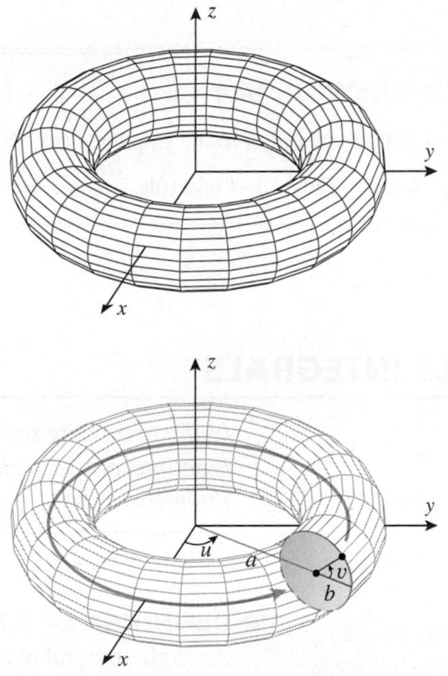


◀ **Figure Ex-54**

**55.** Find the surface area of the torus in Exercise 54(a).

**C** **56.** Use a CAS to graph the ***helicoid***

$$x = u \cos v, \quad y = u \sin v, \quad z = v$$

for $0 \le u \le 5$ and $0 \le v \le 4\pi$ (see the accompanying figure on the next page), and then use the numerical double integration operation of the CAS to approximate the surface area.

**C** **57.** Use a CAS to graph the ***pseudosphere***

$$x = \cos u \sin v$$
$$y = \sin u \sin v$$
$$z = \cos v + \ln\left(\tan \frac{v}{2}\right)$$

for $0 \le u \le 2\pi$, $0 < v < \pi$ (see the accompanying figure), and then use the numerical double integration operation of the CAS to approximate the surface area between the planes $z = -1$ and $z = 1$.

▲ Figure Ex-56

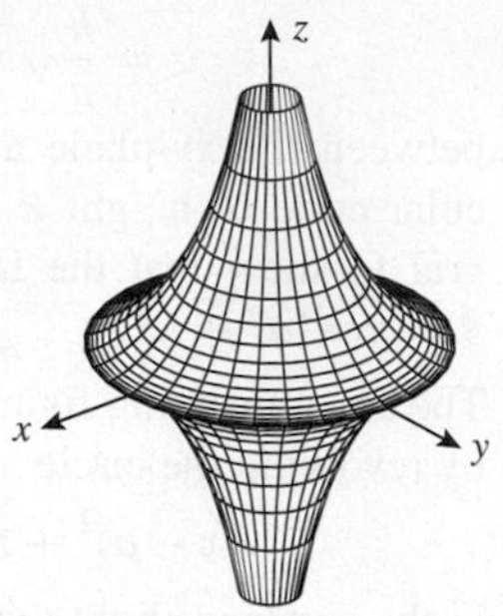

▲ Figure Ex-57

**58.** (a) Find parametric equations for the surface of revolution that is generated by revolving the curve $z = f(x)$ in the $xz$-plane about the $z$-axis.
(b) Use the result obtained in part (a) to find parametric equations for the surface of revolution that is generated by revolving the curve $z = 1/x^2$ in the $xz$-plane about the $z$-axis.
(c) Use a graphing utility to check your work by graphing the parametric surface.

**59–61** The parametric equations in these exercises represent a quadric surface for positive values of $a$, $b$, and $c$. Identify the type of surface by eliminating the parameters $u$ and $v$. Check your conclusion by choosing specific values for the constants and generating the surface with a graphing utility. ■

**59.** $x = a\cos u\cos v,\ y = b\sin u\cos v,\ z = c\sin v$

**60.** $x = a\cos u\cosh v,\ y = b\sin u\cosh v,\ z = c\sinh v$

**61.** $x = a\sinh v,\ y = b\sinh u\cosh v,\ z = c\cosh u\cosh v$

**62. Writing** An early popular approach to defining surface area was to take a limit of surface areas of inscribed polyhedra, but an example in which this approach fails was published in 1890 by H. A. Schwartz. Frieda Zames discusses Schwartz's example in her article "Surface Area and the Cylinder Area Paradox," *The Two-Year College Mathematics Journal*, Vol. 8, No. 4, September 1977, pp. 207–211. Read the article and write a short summary.

---

✓ **QUICK CHECK ANSWERS 14.4** 1. $\sqrt{\left(\dfrac{\partial z}{\partial x}\right)^2 + \left(\dfrac{\partial z}{\partial y}\right)^2 + 1}$ 2. (a) The constant $u$-curves are circles of radius $1-u$ centered at $(1-u, 0, 0)$ and parallel to the $yz$-plane. (b) The constant $v$-curves are line segments joining the points $(1, \cos v, \sin v)$ and $(0, 0, 0)$. 3. $\dfrac{\partial \mathbf{r}}{\partial u} = -\mathbf{i} - (\cos v)\mathbf{j} - (\sin v)\mathbf{k}$; $\dfrac{\partial \mathbf{r}}{\partial v} = -[(1-u)\sin v]\mathbf{j} + [(1-u)\cos v]\mathbf{k}$ 4. $\dfrac{1}{\sqrt{8}}(-2\mathbf{i} + \sqrt{3}\mathbf{j} + \mathbf{k})$ 5. $\left\|\dfrac{\partial \mathbf{r}}{\partial u} \times \dfrac{\partial \mathbf{r}}{\partial v}\right\|$

---

## 14.5 TRIPLE INTEGRALS

*In the preceding sections we defined and discussed properties of double integrals for functions of two variables. In this section we will define triple integrals for functions of three variables.*

### ■ DEFINITION OF A TRIPLE INTEGRAL

A single integral of a function $f(x)$ is defined over a finite closed interval on the $x$-axis, and a double integral of a function $f(x, y)$ is defined over a finite closed region $R$ in the $xy$-plane. Our first goal in this section is to define what is meant by a *triple integral* of $f(x, y, z)$ over a closed solid region $G$ in an $xyz$-coordinate system. To ensure that $G$ does not extend indefinitely in some direction, we will assume that it can be enclosed in a suitably large box whose sides are parallel to the coordinate planes (Figure 14.5.1). In this case we say that $G$ is a ***finite solid***.

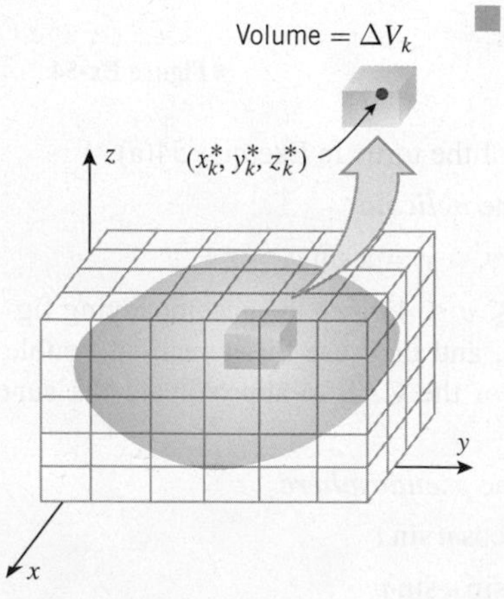

▲ Figure 14.5.1

To define the triple integral of $f(x, y, z)$ over $G$, we first divide the box into $n$ "subboxes" by planes parallel to the coordinate planes. We then discard those subboxes that contain any points outside of $G$ and choose an arbitrary point in each of the remaining subboxes. As shown in Figure 14.5.1, we denote the volume of the $k$th remaining subbox by $\Delta V_k$ and the point selected in the $k$th subbox by $(x_k^*, y_k^*, z_k^*)$. Next we form the product

$$f(x_k^*, y_k^*, z_k^*)\Delta V_k$$

for each subbox, then add the products for all of the subboxes to obtain the ***Riemann sum***

$$\sum_{k=1}^{n} f(x_k^*, y_k^*, z_k^*)\Delta V_k$$

Finally, we repeat this process with more and more subdivisions in such a way that the length, width, and height of each subbox approach zero, and $n$ approaches $+\infty$. The limit

$$\iiint_G f(x, y, z)\, dV = \lim_{n\to+\infty} \sum_{k=1}^{n} f(x_k^*, y_k^*, z_k^*)\Delta V_k \tag{1}$$

is called the ***triple integral*** of $f(x, y, z)$ over the region $G$. Conditions under which the triple integral exists are studied in advanced calculus. However, for our purposes it suffices to say that existence is ensured when $f$ is continuous on $G$ and the region $G$ is not too "complicated."

## PROPERTIES OF TRIPLE INTEGRALS

Triple integrals enjoy many properties of single and double integrals:

$$\iiint_G cf(x, y, z)\, dV = c\iiint_G f(x, y, z)\, dV \quad (c \text{ a constant})$$

$$\iiint_G [f(x, y, z) + g(x, y, z)]\, dV = \iiint_G f(x, y, z)\, dV + \iiint_G g(x, y, z)\, dV$$

$$\iiint_G [f(x, y, z) - g(x, y, z)]\, dV = \iiint_G f(x, y, z)\, dV - \iiint_G g(x, y, z)\, dV$$

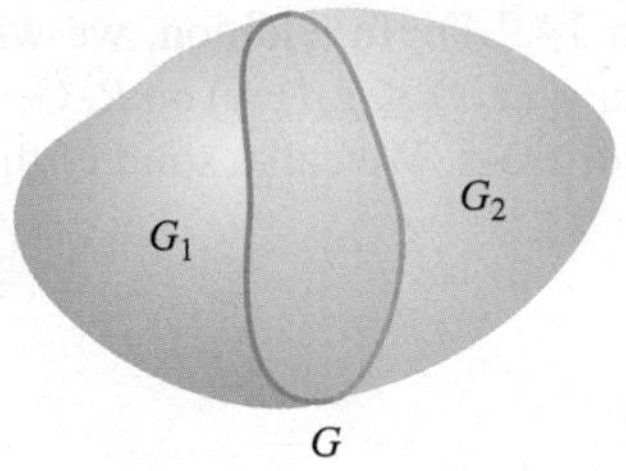


▲ **Figure 14.5.2**

Moreover, if the region $G$ is subdivided into two subregions $G_1$ and $G_2$ (Figure 14.5.2), then

$$\iiint_G f(x, y, z)\, dV = \iiint_{G_1} f(x, y, z)\, dV + \iiint_{G_2} f(x, y, z)\, dV$$

We omit the proofs.

## EVALUATING TRIPLE INTEGRALS OVER RECTANGULAR BOXES

Just as a double integral can be evaluated by two successive single integrations, so a triple integral can be evaluated by three successive integrations. The following theorem, which we state without proof, is the analog of Theorem 14.1.3.

There are two possible orders of integration for the iterated integrals in Theorem 14.1.3:

$$dx\,dy, \quad dy\,dx$$

Six orders of integration are possible for the iterated integral in Theorem 14.5.1:

$$dx\,dy\,dz, \quad dy\,dz\,dx, \quad dz\,dx\,dy$$
$$dx\,dz\,dy, \quad dz\,dy\,dx, \quad dy\,dx\,dz$$

**14.5.1 THEOREM (*Fubini's Theorem**)** *Let $G$ be the rectangular box defined by the inequalities*

$$a \le x \le b, \quad c \le y \le d, \quad k \le z \le l$$

*If $f$ is continuous on the region $G$, then*

$$\iiint_G f(x, y, z)\, dV = \int_a^b \int_c^d \int_k^l f(x, y, z)\, dz\, dy\, dx \tag{2}$$

*Moreover, the iterated integral on the right can be replaced with any of the five other iterated integrals that result by altering the order of integration.*

* See the Fubini biography on p. 898.

▶ **Example 1** Evaluate the triple integral

$$\iiint\limits_G 12xy^2z^3\, dV$$

over the rectangular box $G$ defined by the inequalities $-1 \le x \le 2, 0 \le y \le 3, 0 \le z \le 2$.

***Solution.*** Of the six possible iterated integrals we might use, we will choose the one in (2). Thus, we will first integrate with respect to $z$, holding $x$ and $y$ fixed, then with respect to $y$, holding $x$ fixed, and finally with respect to $x$.

$$\begin{aligned}\iiint\limits_G 12xy^2z^3\, dV &= \int_{-1}^{2}\int_{0}^{3}\int_{0}^{2} 12xy^2z^3\, dz\, dy\, dx\\ &= \int_{-1}^{2}\int_{0}^{3}\left[3xy^2z^4\right]_{z=0}^{2} dy\, dx = \int_{-1}^{2}\int_{0}^{3} 48xy^2\, dy\, dx\\ &= \int_{-1}^{2}\left[16xy^3\right]_{y=0}^{3} dx = \int_{-1}^{2} 432x\, dx\\ &= 216x^2\Big]_{-1}^{2} = 648 \blacktriangleleft\end{aligned}$$

## EVALUATING TRIPLE INTEGRALS OVER MORE GENERAL REGIONS

Next we will consider how to evaluate triple integrals over solids that are not rectangular boxes. For the moment we will limit our discussion to solids of the type shown in Figure 14.5.3. Specifically, we will assume that the solid $G$ is bounded above by a surface $z = g_2(x, y)$ and below by a surface $z = g_1(x, y)$ and that the projection of the solid on the $xy$-plane is a type I or type II region $R$ (see Definition 14.2.1). In addition, we will assume that $g_1(x, y)$ and $g_2(x, y)$ are continuous on $R$ and that $g_1(x, y) \le g_2(x, y)$ on $R$. Geometrically, this means that the surfaces may touch but cannot cross. We call a solid of this type a ***simple xy-solid***.

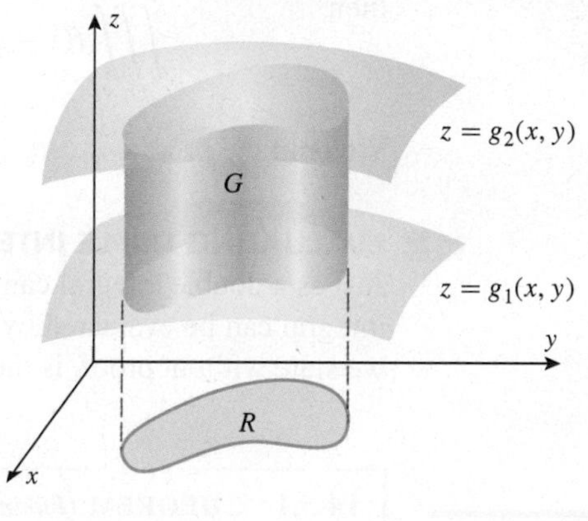


▶ **Figure 14.5.3**

The following theorem, which we state without proof, will enable us to evaluate triple integrals over simple $xy$-solids.

**14.5.2 THEOREM** *Let $G$ be a simple xy-solid with upper surface $z = g_2(x, y)$ and lower surface $z = g_1(x, y)$, and let $R$ be the projection of $G$ on the xy-plane. If $f(x, y, z)$ is continuous on $G$, then*

$$\iiint\limits_G f(x, y, z)\, dV = \iint\limits_R \left[\int_{g_1(x,y)}^{g_2(x,y)} f(x, y, z)\, dz\right] dA \qquad (3)$$

In (3), the first integration is with respect to $z$, after which a function of $x$ and $y$ remains. This function of $x$ and $y$ is then integrated over the region $R$ in the $xy$-plane. To apply (3), it is helpful to begin with a three-dimensional sketch of the solid $G$. The limits of integration can be obtained from the sketch as follows:

***Determining Limits of Integration: Simple xy-Solid***

**Step 1.** Find an equation $z = g_2(x, y)$ for the upper surface and an equation $z = g_1(x, y)$ for the lower surface of $G$. The functions $g_1(x, y)$ and $g_2(x, y)$ determine the lower and upper $z$-limits of integration.

**Step 2.** Make a two-dimensional sketch of the projection $R$ of the solid on the $xy$-plane. From this sketch determine the limits of integration for the double integral over $R$ in (3).

► **Example 2** Let $G$ be the wedge in the first octant that is cut from the cylindrical solid $y^2 + z^2 \leq 1$ by the planes $y = x$ and $x = 0$. Evaluate

$$\iiint_G z\,dV$$

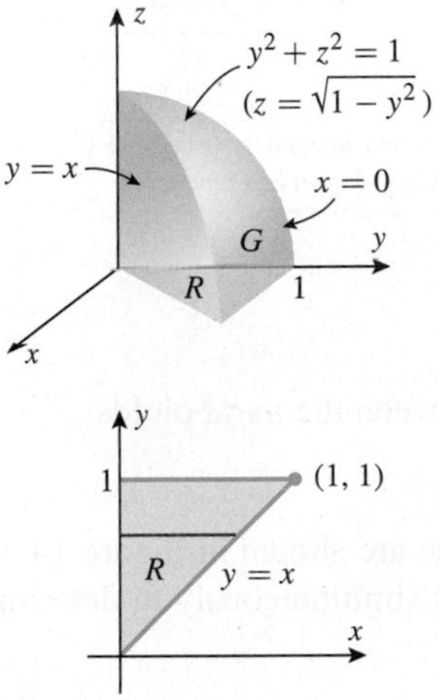


▲ **Figure 14.5.4**

*Solution.* The solid $G$ and its projection $R$ on the $xy$-plane are shown in Figure 14.5.4. The upper surface of the solid is formed by the cylinder and the lower surface by the $xy$-plane. Since the portion of the cylinder $y^2 + z^2 = 1$ that lies above the $xy$-plane has the equation $z = \sqrt{1 - y^2}$, and the $xy$-plane has the equation $z = 0$, it follows from (3) that

$$\iiint_G z\,dV = \iint_R \left[ \int_0^{\sqrt{1-y^2}} z\,dz \right] dA \tag{4}$$

For the double integral over $R$, the $x$- and $y$-integrations can be performed in either order, since $R$ is both a type I and type II region. We will integrate with respect to $x$ first. With this choice, (4) yields

$$\iiint_G z\,dV = \int_0^1 \int_0^y \int_0^{\sqrt{1-y^2}} z\,dz\,dx\,dy = \int_0^1 \int_0^y \frac{1}{2} z^2 \bigg]_{z=0}^{\sqrt{1-y^2}} dx\,dy$$

$$= \int_0^1 \int_0^y \frac{1}{2}(1 - y^2)\,dx\,dy = \frac{1}{2} \int_0^1 (1 - y^2)x \bigg]_{x=0}^{y} dy$$

$$= \frac{1}{2} \int_0^1 (y - y^3)\,dy = \frac{1}{2} \left[ \frac{1}{2} y^2 - \frac{1}{4} y^4 \right]_0^1 = \frac{1}{8} \blacktriangleleft$$

**TECHNOLOGY MASTERY**

Most computer algebra systems have a built-in capability for computing iterated triple integrals. If you have a CAS, consult the relevant documentation and use the CAS to check Examples 1 and 2.

## VOLUME CALCULATED AS A TRIPLE INTEGRAL

Triple integrals have many physical interpretations, some of which we will consider in Section 14.8. However, in the special case where $f(x, y, z) = 1$, Formula (1) yields

$$\iiint_G dV = \lim_{n \to +\infty} \sum_{k=1}^{n} \Delta V_k$$

which Figure 14.5.1 suggests is the volume of $G$; that is,

$$\text{volume of } G = \iiint_G dV \tag{5}$$

► **Example 3** Use a triple integral to find the volume of the solid within the cylinder $x^2 + y^2 = 9$ and between the planes $z = 1$ and $x + z = 5$.

***Solution.*** The solid $G$ and its projection $R$ on the $xy$-plane are shown in Figure 14.5.5. The lower surface of the solid is the plane $z = 1$ and the upper surface is the plane $x + z = 5$ or, equivalently, $z = 5 - x$. Thus, from (3) and (5)

$$\text{volume of } G = \iiint_G dV = \iint_R \left[ \int_1^{5-x} dz \right] dA \tag{6}$$

For the double integral over $R$, we will integrate with respect to $y$ first. Thus, (6) yields

$$\text{volume of } G = \int_{-3}^{3} \int_{-\sqrt{9-x^2}}^{\sqrt{9-x^2}} \int_1^{5-x} dz\, dy\, dx = \int_{-3}^{3} \int_{-\sqrt{9-x^2}}^{\sqrt{9-x^2}} z \bigg]_{z=1}^{5-x} dy\, dx$$

$$= \int_{-3}^{3} \int_{-\sqrt{9-x^2}}^{\sqrt{9-x^2}} (4 - x)\, dy\, dx = \int_{-3}^{3} (8 - 2x)\sqrt{9 - x^2}\, dx$$

$$= 8 \int_{-3}^{3} \sqrt{9 - x^2}\, dx - \int_{-3}^{3} 2x\sqrt{9 - x^2}\, dx$$

For the first integral, see Formula (3) of Section 7.4.

$$= 8\left(\frac{9}{2}\pi\right) - \int_{-3}^{3} 2x\sqrt{9 - x^2}\, dx$$

The second integral is 0 because the integrand is an odd function.

$$= 8\left(\frac{9}{2}\pi\right) - 0 = 36\pi \blacktriangleleft$$

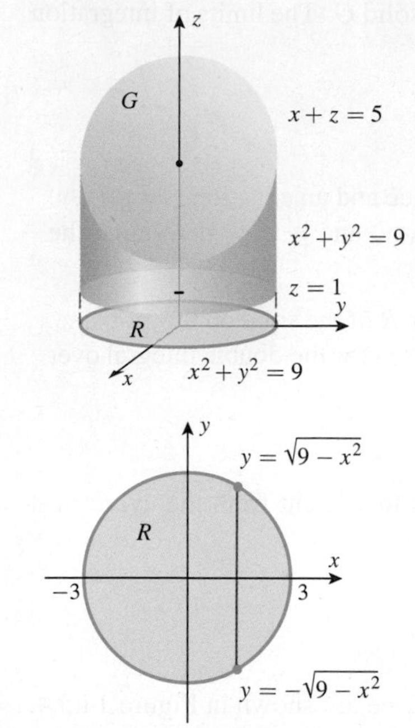

▲ Figure 14.5.5

**▶ Example 4** Find the volume of the solid enclosed between the paraboloids

$$z = 5x^2 + 5y^2 \quad \text{and} \quad z = 6 - 7x^2 - y^2$$

***Solution.*** The solid $G$ and its projection $R$ on the $xy$-plane are shown in Figure 14.5.6. The projection $R$ is obtained by solving the given equations simultaneously to determine where the paraboloids intersect. We obtain

$$5x^2 + 5y^2 = 6 - 7x^2 - y^2$$

or

$$2x^2 + y^2 = 1 \tag{7}$$

which tells us that the paraboloids intersect in a curve on the elliptic cylinder given by (7). The projection of this intersection on the $xy$-plane is an ellipse with this same equation. Therefore,

$$\text{volume of } G = \iiint_G dV = \iint_R \left[ \int_{5x^2+5y^2}^{6-7x^2-y^2} dz \right] dA$$

$$= \int_{-1/\sqrt{2}}^{1/\sqrt{2}} \int_{-\sqrt{1-2x^2}}^{\sqrt{1-2x^2}} \int_{5x^2+5y^2}^{6-7x^2-y^2} dz\, dy\, dx$$

$$= \int_{-1/\sqrt{2}}^{1/\sqrt{2}} \int_{-\sqrt{1-2x^2}}^{\sqrt{1-2x^2}} (6 - 12x^2 - 6y^2)\, dy\, dx$$

$$= \int_{-1/\sqrt{2}}^{1/\sqrt{2}} \left[ 6(1 - 2x^2)y - 2y^3 \right]_{y=-\sqrt{1-2x^2}}^{\sqrt{1-2x^2}} dx$$

$$= 8 \int_{-1/\sqrt{2}}^{1/\sqrt{2}} (1 - 2x^2)^{3/2}\, dx = \frac{8}{\sqrt{2}} \int_{-\pi/2}^{\pi/2} \cos^4\theta\, d\theta = \frac{3\pi}{\sqrt{2}} \blacktriangleleft$$

Let $x = \frac{1}{\sqrt{2}} \sin\theta$.

Use the Wallis cosine formula in Exercise 70 of Section 7.3.

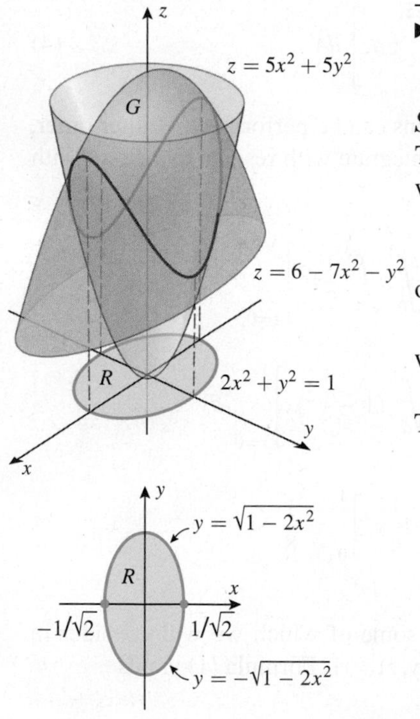

▲ Figure 14.5.6

## INTEGRATION IN OTHER ORDERS

In Formula (3) for integrating over a simple $xy$-solid, the $z$-integration was performed first. However, there are situations in which it is preferable to integrate in a different order. For example, Figure 14.5.7$a$ shows a ***simple xz-solid***, and Figure 14.5.7$b$ shows a ***simple yz-solid***. For a simple $xz$-solid it is usually best to integrate with respect to $y$ first, and for a simple $yz$-solid it is usually best to integrate with respect to $x$ first:

$$\underset{\substack{G\\ \text{simple } xz\text{-solid}}}{\iiint} f(x,y,z)\,dV = \iint_R \left[\int_{g_1(x,z)}^{g_2(x,z)} f(x,y,z)\,dy\right] dA \tag{8}$$

$$\underset{\substack{G\\ \text{simple } yz\text{-solid}}}{\iiint} f(x,y,z)\,dV = \iint_R \left[\int_{g_1(y,z)}^{g_2(y,z)} f(x,y,z)\,dx\right] dA \tag{9}$$

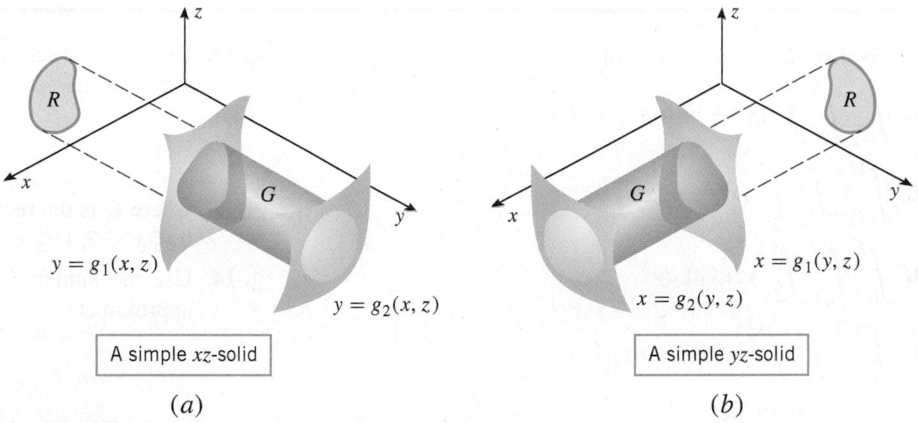


▶ **Figure 14.5.7**

Sometimes a solid $G$ can be viewed as a simple $xy$-solid, a simple $xz$-solid, and a simple $yz$-solid, in which case the order of integration can be chosen to simplify the computations.

▶ **Example 5** In Example 2 we evaluated

$$\iiint_G z\,dV$$

over the wedge in Figure 14.5.4 by integrating first with respect to $z$. Evaluate this integral by integrating first with respect to $x$.

***Solution.*** The solid is bounded in the back by the plane $x = 0$ and in the front by the plane $x = y$, so

$$\iiint_G z\,dV = \iint_R \left[\int_0^y z\,dx\right] dA$$

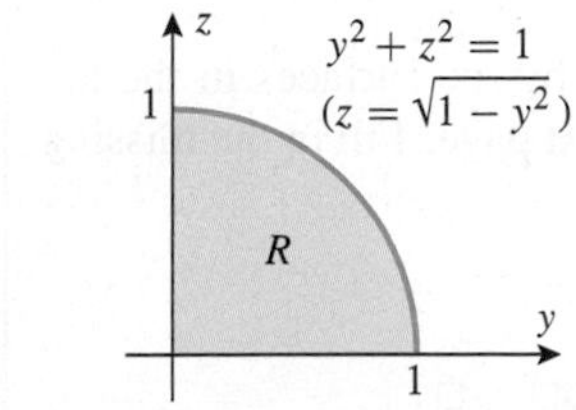


▲ **Figure 14.5.8**

where $R$ is the projection of $G$ on the $yz$-plane (Figure 14.5.8). The integration over $R$ can be performed first with respect to $z$ and then $y$ or vice versa. Performing the $z$-integration first yields

$$\iiint_G z\,dV = \int_0^1 \int_0^{\sqrt{1-y^2}} \int_0^y z\,dx\,dz\,dy = \int_0^1 \int_0^{\sqrt{1-y^2}} zx\Big]_{x=0}^{y} dz\,dy$$

$$= \int_0^1 \int_0^{\sqrt{1-y^2}} zy\,dz\,dy = \int_0^1 \frac{1}{2}z^2y\Big]_{z=0}^{\sqrt{1-y^2}} dy = \int_0^1 \frac{1}{2}(1-y^2)y\,dy = \frac{1}{8}$$

which agrees with the result in Example 2. ◀

## ✓ QUICK CHECK EXERCISES 14.5 *(See page 938 for answers.)*

**1.** The iterated integral

$$\int_1^5 \int_2^4 \int_3^6 f(x, y, z)\, dx\, dz\, dy$$

integrates $f$ over the rectangular box defined by

$\_\_\_\_ \le x \le \_\_\_\_$, $\_\_\_\_ \le y \le \_\_\_\_$,

$\_\_\_\_ \le z \le \_\_\_\_$

**2.** Let $G$ be the solid in the first octant bounded below by the surface $z = y + x^2$ and bounded above by the plane $z = 4$. Supply the missing limits of integration.

(a) $\displaystyle\iiint_G f(x, y, z)\, dA = \int_\square^\square \int_\square^\square \int_{y+x^2}^4 f(x, y, z)\, dz\, dx\, dy$

(b) $\displaystyle\iiint_G f(x, y, z)\, dA = \int_\square^\square \int_\square^\square \int_{y+x^2}^4 f(x, y, z)\, dz\, dy\, dx$

(c) $\displaystyle\iiint_G f(x, y, z)\, dA = \int_\square^\square \int_\square^\square \int_\square^\square f(x, y, z)\, dy\, dz\, dx$

**3.** The volume of the solid $G$ in Quick Check Exercise 2 is ____.

## EXERCISE SET 14.5 [C] CAS

**1–8** Evaluate the iterated integral.

**1.** $\displaystyle\int_{-1}^1 \int_0^2 \int_0^1 (x^2 + y^2 + z^2)\, dx\, dy\, dz$

**2.** $\displaystyle\int_{1/3}^{1/2} \int_0^{\pi} \int_0^1 zx \sin xy\, dz\, dy\, dx$

**3.** $\displaystyle\int_0^2 \int_{-1}^{y^2} \int_{-1}^{z} yz\, dx\, dz\, dy$

**4.** $\displaystyle\int_0^{\pi/4} \int_0^1 \int_0^{x^2} x \cos y\, dz\, dx\, dy$

**5.** $\displaystyle\int_0^3 \int_0^{\sqrt{9-z^2}} \int_0^x xy\, dy\, dx\, dz$

**6.** $\displaystyle\int_1^3 \int_x^{x^2} \int_0^{\ln z} xe^y\, dy\, dz\, dx$

**7.** $\displaystyle\int_0^2 \int_0^{\sqrt{4-x^2}} \int_{-5+x^2+y^2}^{3-x^2-y^2} x\, dz\, dy\, dx$

**8.** $\displaystyle\int_1^2 \int_z^2 \int_0^{\sqrt{3}y} \frac{y}{x^2 + y^2}\, dx\, dy\, dz$

**9–12** Evaluate the triple integral.

**9.** $\displaystyle\iiint_G xy \sin yz\, dV$, where $G$ is the rectangular box defined by the inequalities $0 \le x \le \pi$, $0 \le y \le 1$, $0 \le z \le \pi/6$.

**10.** $\displaystyle\iiint_G y\, dV$, where $G$ is the solid enclosed by the plane $z = y$, the $xy$-plane, and the parabolic cylinder $y = 1 - x^2$.

**11.** $\displaystyle\iiint_G xyz\, dV$, where $G$ is the solid in the first octant that is bounded by the parabolic cylinder $z = 2 - x^2$ and the planes $z = 0$, $y = x$, and $y = 0$.

**12.** $\displaystyle\iiint_G \cos(z/y)\, dV$, where $G$ is the solid defined by the inequalities $\pi/6 \le y \le \pi/2$, $y \le x \le \pi/2$, $0 \le z \le xy$.

[C] **13.** Use the numerical triple integral operation of a CAS to approximate

$$\iiint_G \frac{\sqrt{x + z^2}}{y}\, dV$$

where $G$ is the rectangular box defined by the inequalities $0 \le x \le 3$, $1 \le y \le 2$, $-2 \le z \le 1$.

[C] **14.** Use the numerical triple integral operation of a CAS to approximate

$$\iiint_G e^{-x^2-y^2-z^2}\, dV$$

where $G$ is the spherical region $x^2 + y^2 + z^2 \le 1$.

**15–18** Use a triple integral to find the volume of the solid.

**15.** The solid in the first octant bounded by the coordinate planes and the plane $3x + 6y + 4z = 12$.

**16.** The solid bounded by the surface $z = \sqrt{y}$ and the planes $x + y = 1$, $x = 0$, and $z = 0$.

**17.** The solid bounded by the surface $y = x^2$ and the planes $y + z = 4$ and $z = 0$.

**18.** The wedge in the first octant that is cut from the solid cylinder $y^2 + z^2 \le 1$ by the planes $y = x$ and $x = 0$.

### FOCUS ON CONCEPTS

**19.** Let $G$ be the solid enclosed by the surfaces in the accompanying figure on the next page. Fill in the missing limits of integration.

(a) $\displaystyle\iiint_G f(x, y, z)\, dV$

$\displaystyle= \int_\square^\square \int_\square^\square \int_\square^\square f(x, y, z)\, dz\, dy\, dx$

(b) $\displaystyle\iiint_G f(x, y, z)\, dV$

$\displaystyle= \int_\square^\square \int_\square^\square \int_\square^\square f(x, y, z)\, dz\, dx\, dy$

**20.** Let $G$ be the solid enclosed by the surfaces in the accompanying figure on the next page. Fill in the missing limits of integration.

(a) $\iiint\limits_G f(x, y, z)\, dV$

$$= \int_{\square}^{\square}\int_{\square}^{\square}\int_{\square}^{\square} f(x, y, z)\, dz\, dy\, dx$$

(b) $\iiint\limits_G f(x, y, z)\, dV$

$$= \int_{\square}^{\square}\int_{\square}^{\square}\int_{\square}^{\square} f(x, y, z)\, dz\, dx\, dy$$

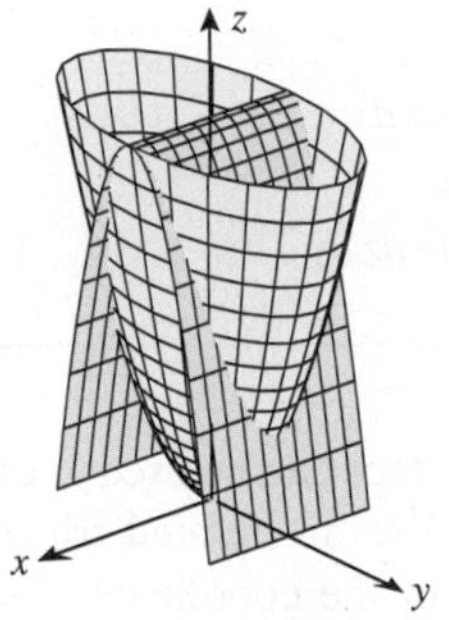


▲ **Figure Ex-19**

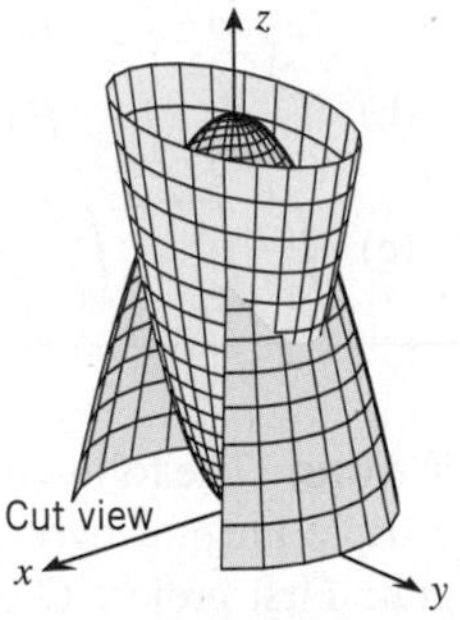


▲ **Figure Ex-20**

**21–24** Set up (but do not evaluate) an iterated triple integral for the volume of the solid enclosed between the given surfaces. ■

**21.** The surfaces in Exercise 19.

**22.** The surfaces in Exercise 20.

**23.** The elliptic cylinder $x^2 + 9y^2 = 9$ and the planes $z = 0$ and $z = x + 3$.

**24.** The cylinders $x^2 + y^2 = 1$ and $x^2 + z^2 = 1$.

**25–26** In each part, sketch the solid whose volume is given by the integral. ■

**25.** (a) $\displaystyle\int_{-1}^{1}\int_{-\sqrt{1-x^2}}^{\sqrt{1-x^2}}\int_{0}^{y+1} dz\, dy\, dx$

(b) $\displaystyle\int_{0}^{9}\int_{0}^{y/3}\int_{0}^{\sqrt{y^2-9x^2}} dz\, dx\, dy$

(c) $\displaystyle\int_{0}^{1}\int_{0}^{\sqrt{1-x^2}}\int_{0}^{2} dy\, dz\, dx$

**26.** (a) $\displaystyle\int_{0}^{3}\int_{x^2}^{9}\int_{0}^{2} dz\, dy\, dx$

(b) $\displaystyle\int_{0}^{2}\int_{0}^{2-y}\int_{0}^{2-x-y} dz\, dx\, dy$

(c) $\displaystyle\int_{-2}^{2}\int_{0}^{4-y^2}\int_{0}^{2} dx\, dz\, dy$

**27–30 True–False** Determine whether the statement is true or false. Explain your answer. ■

**27.** If $G$ is the rectangular solid that is defined by $1 \le x \le 3$, $2 \le y \le 5$, $-1 \le z \le 1$, and if $f(x, y, z)$ is continuous on $G$, then

$$\iiint\limits_G f(x, y, z)\, dV = \int_{1}^{3}\int_{-1}^{1}\int_{2}^{5} f(x, y, z)\, dy\, dz\, dx$$

**28.** If $G$ is a simple $xy$-solid and $f(x, y, z)$ is continuous on $G$, then the triple integral of $f$ over $G$ can be expressed as an iterated integral whose outermost integration is performed with respect to $z$.

**29.** If $G$ is the portion of the unit ball in the first octant, then

$$\iiint\limits_G f(x, y, z)\, dV = \int_{0}^{1}\int_{0}^{1}\int_{0}^{\sqrt{1-x^2-y^2}} f(x, y, z)\, dz\, dy\, dx$$

**30.** If $G$ is a simple $xy$-solid and

$$\text{volume of } G = \iiint\limits_G f(x, y, z)\, dV$$

then $f(x, y, z) = 1$ at every point in $G$.

**31.** Let $G$ be the rectangular box defined by the inequalities $a \le x \le b$, $c \le y \le d$, $k \le z \le l$. Show that

$$\iiint\limits_G f(x)g(y)h(z)\, dV = \left[\int_a^b f(x)\, dx\right]\left[\int_c^d g(y)\, dy\right]\left[\int_k^l h(z)\, dz\right]$$

**32.** Use the result of Exercise 31 to evaluate

(a) $\iiint\limits_G xy^2 \sin z\, dV$, where $G$ is the set of points satisfying $-1 \le x \le 1$, $0 \le y \le 1$, $0 \le z \le \pi/2$;

(b) $\iiint\limits_G e^{2x+y-z}\, dV$, where $G$ is the set of points satisfying $0 \le x \le 1$, $0 \le y \le \ln 3$, $0 \le z \le \ln 2$.

**33–36** The ***average value*** or ***mean value*** of a continuous function $f(x, y, z)$ over a solid $G$ is defined as

$$f_{\text{ave}} = \frac{1}{V(G)}\iiint\limits_G f(x, y, z)\, dV$$

where $V(G)$ is the volume of the solid $G$ (compare to the definition preceding Exercise 61 of Section 14.2). Use this definition in these exercises. ■

**33.** Find the average value of $f(x, y, z) = x + y + z$ over the tetrahedron shown in the accompanying figure.

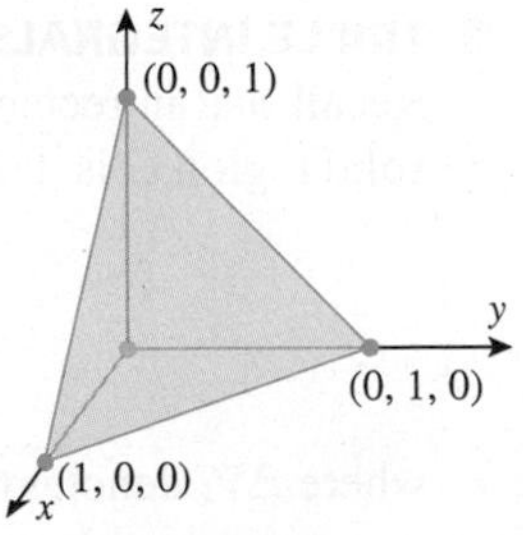


◀ **Figure Ex-33**

**34.** Find the average value of $f(x, y, z) = xyz$ over the spherical region $x^2 + y^2 + z^2 \le 1$.

C **35.** Use the numerical triple integral operation of a CAS to approximate the average distance from the origin to a point in the solid of Example 4.

C **36.** Let $d(x, y, z)$ be the distance from the point $(z, z, z)$ to the point $(x, y, 0)$. Use the numerical triple integral operation of a CAS to approximate the average value of $d$ for

$0 \le x \le 1$, $0 \le y \le 1$, and $0 \le z \le 1$. Write a short explanation as to why this value may be considered to be the average distance between a point on the diagonal from $(0, 0, 0)$ to $(1, 1, 1)$ and a point on the face in the $xy$-plane for the unit cube $0 \le x \le 1$, $0 \le y \le 1$, and $0 \le z \le 1$.

**37.** Let $G$ be the tetrahedron in the first octant bounded by the coordinate planes and the plane

$$\frac{x}{a} + \frac{y}{b} + \frac{z}{c} = 1 \quad (a > 0, b > 0, c > 0)$$

(a) List six different iterated integrals that represent the volume of $G$.

(b) Evaluate any one of the six to show that the volume of $G$ is $\frac{1}{6}abc$.

**38.** Use a triple integral to derive the formula for the volume of the ellipsoid

$$\frac{x^2}{a^2} + \frac{y^2}{b^2} + \frac{z^2}{c^2} = 1$$

**FOCUS ON CONCEPTS**

**39–40** Express each integral as an equivalent integral in which the $z$-integration is performed first, the $y$-integration second, and the $x$-integration last. ■

**39.** (a) $\displaystyle\int_0^5 \int_0^2 \int_0^{\sqrt{4-y^2}} f(x, y, z)\, dx\, dy\, dz$

(b) $\displaystyle\int_0^9 \int_0^{3-\sqrt{x}} \int_0^z f(x, y, z)\, dy\, dz\, dx$

(c) $\displaystyle\int_0^4 \int_y^{8-y} \int_0^{\sqrt{4-y}} f(x, y, z)\, dx\, dz\, dy$

**40.** (a) $\displaystyle\int_0^3 \int_0^{\sqrt{9-z^2}} \int_0^{\sqrt{9-y^2-z^2}} f(x, y, z)\, dx\, dy\, dz$

(b) $\displaystyle\int_0^4 \int_0^2 \int_0^{x/2} f(x, y, z)\, dy\, dz\, dx$

(c) $\displaystyle\int_0^4 \int_0^{4-y} \int_0^{\sqrt{z}} f(x, y, z)\, dx\, dz\, dy$

**41. Writing** The following initial steps can be used to express a triple integral over a solid $G$ as an iterated triple integral: First project $G$ onto one of the coordinate planes to obtain a region $R$, and then project $R$ onto one of the coordinate axes. Describe how you would use these steps to find the limits of integration. Illustrate your discussion with an example.

✓ **QUICK CHECK ANSWERS 14.5** 1. $3 \le x \le 6$, $1 \le y \le 5$, $2 \le z \le 4$ 2. (a) $\displaystyle\int_0^4 \int_0^{\sqrt{4-y}} \int_{y+x^2}^4 f(x, y, z)\, dz\, dx\, dy$ (b) $\displaystyle\int_0^2 \int_0^{4-x^2} \int_{y+x^2}^4 f(x, y, z)\, dz\, dy\, dx$ (c) $\displaystyle\int_0^2 \int_{x^2}^4 \int_0^{z-x^2} f(x, y, z)\, dy\, dz\, dx$ 3. $\dfrac{128}{15}$

## 14.6 TRIPLE INTEGRALS IN CYLINDRICAL AND SPHERICAL COORDINATES

*In Section 14.3 we saw that some double integrals are easier to evaluate in polar coordinates than in rectangular coordinates. Similarly, some triple integrals are easier to evaluate in cylindrical or spherical coordinates than in rectangular coordinates. In this section we will study triple integrals in these coordinate systems.*

### TRIPLE INTEGRALS IN CYLINDRICAL COORDINATES

Recall that in rectangular coordinates the triple integral of a continuous function $f$ over a solid region $G$ is defined as

$$\iiint_G f(x, y, z)\, dV = \lim_{n \to +\infty} \sum_{k=1}^{n} f(x_k^*, y_k^*, z_k^*)\Delta V_k$$

where $\Delta V_k$ denotes the volume of a rectangular parallelepiped interior to $G$ and $(x_k^*, y_k^*, z_k^*)$ is a point in this parallelepiped (see Figure 14.5.1). Triple integrals in cylindrical and spherical coordinates are defined similarly, except that the region $G$ is divided not into rectangular parallelepipeds but into regions more appropriate to these coordinate systems.

In cylindrical coordinates, the simplest equations are of the form

$$r = \text{constant}, \quad \theta = \text{constant}, \quad z = \text{constant}$$

The first equation represents a right circular cylinder centered on the $z$-axis, the second a vertical half-plane hinged on the $z$-axis, and the third a horizontal plane. (See Figure 11.8.3.) These surfaces can be paired up to determine solids called ***cylindrical wedges or***

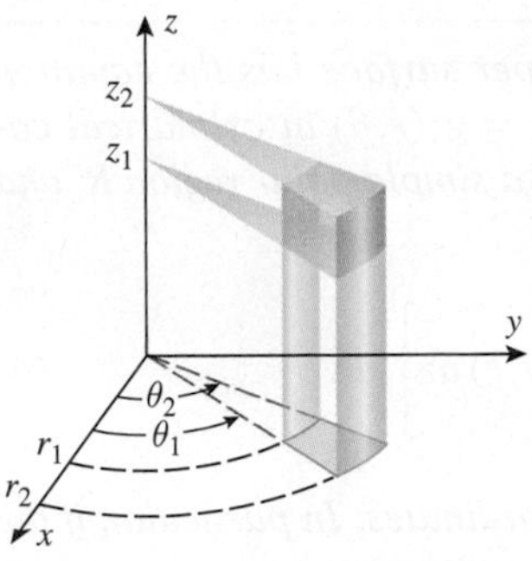


▲ **Figure 14.6.1**

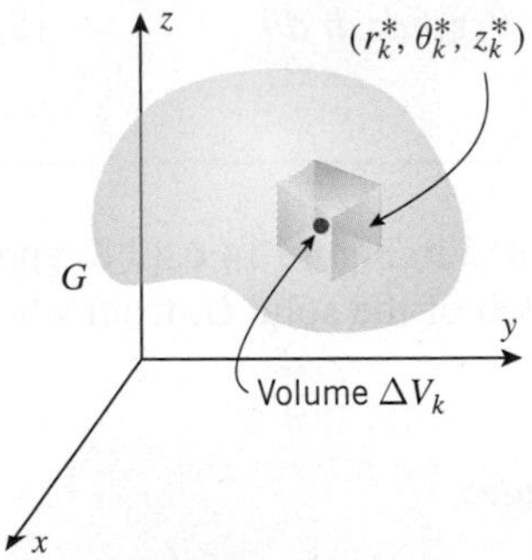


▲ **Figure 14.6.2**

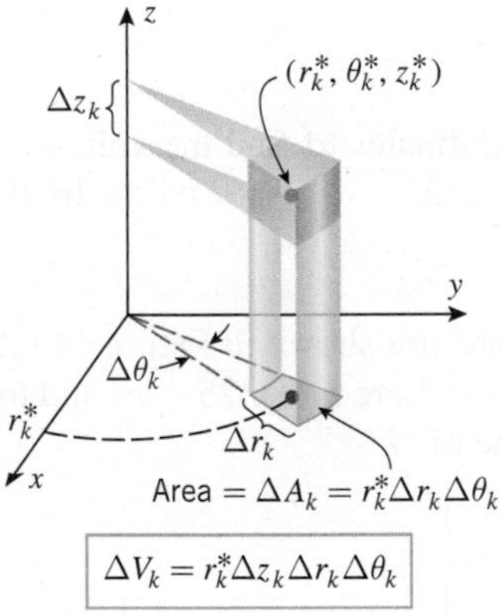


▲ **Figure 14.6.3**

***cylindrical elements of volume***. To be precise, a cylindrical wedge is a solid enclosed between six surfaces of the following form:

| | | | |
|---|---|---|---|
| two cylinders (blue) | $r = r_1$, | $r = r_2$ | $(r_1 < r_2)$ |
| two vertical half-planes (yellow) | $\theta = \theta_1$, | $\theta = \theta_2$ | $(\theta_1 < \theta_2)$ |
| two horizontal planes (gray) | $z = z_1$, | $z = z_2$ | $(z_1 < z_2)$ |

(Figure 14.6.1). The dimensions $\theta_2 - \theta_1, r_2 - r_1$, and $z_2 - z_1$ are called the ***central angle***, ***thickness***, and ***height*** of the wedge.

To define the triple integral over $G$ of a function $f(r, \theta, z)$ in cylindrical coordinates we proceed as follows:

- Subdivide $G$ into pieces by a three-dimensional grid consisting of concentric circular cylinders centered on the $z$-axis, half-planes hinged on the $z$-axis, and horizontal planes. Exclude from consideration all pieces that contain any points outside of $G$, thereby leaving only cylindrical wedges that are subsets of $G$.
- Assume that there are $n$ such cylindrical wedges, and denote the volume of the $k$th cylindrical wedge by $\Delta V_k$. As indicated in Figure 14.6.2, let $(r_k^*, \theta_k^*, z_k^*)$ be any point in the $k$th cylindrical wedge.
- Repeat this process with more and more subdivisions so that as $n$ increases, the height, thickness, and central angle of the cylindrical wedges approach zero. Define

$$\iiint_G f(r, \theta, z)\, dV = \lim_{n \to +\infty} \sum_{k=1}^{n} f(r_k^*, \theta_k^*, z_k^*) \Delta V_k \tag{1}$$

For computational purposes, it will be helpful to express (1) as an iterated integral. Toward this end we note that the volume $\Delta V_k$ of the $k$th cylindrical wedge can be expressed as

$$\Delta V_k = [\text{area of base}] \cdot [\text{height}] \tag{2}$$

If we denote the thickness, central angle, and height of this wedge by $\Delta r_k$, $\Delta\theta_k$, and $\Delta z_k$, and if we choose the arbitrary point $(r_k^*, \theta_k^*, z_k^*)$ to lie above the "center" of the base (Figures 14.3.6 and 14.6.3), then it follows from (5) of Section 14.3 that the base has area $\Delta A_k = r_k^* \Delta r_k \Delta \theta_k$. Thus, (2) can be written as

$$\Delta V_k = r_k^* \Delta r_k \Delta \theta_k \Delta z_k = r_k^* \Delta z_k \Delta r_k \Delta \theta_k$$

Substituting this expression in (1) yields

$$\iiint_G f(r, \theta, z)\, dV = \lim_{n \to +\infty} \sum_{k=1}^{n} f(r_k^*, \theta_k^*, z_k^*) r_k^* \Delta z_k \Delta r_k \Delta \theta_k$$

which suggests that a triple integral in cylindrical coordinates can be evaluated as an iterated integral of the form

$$\iiint_G f(r, \theta, z)\, dV = \iiint_{\substack{\text{appropriate} \\ \text{limits}}} f(r, \theta, z) r\, dz\, dr\, d\theta \tag{3}$$

Note the extra factor of $r$ that appears in the integrand on converting a triple integral to an iterated integral in cylindrical coordinates.

In this formula the integration with respect to $z$ is done first, then with respect to $r$, and then with respect to $\theta$, but any order of integration is allowable.

The following theorem, which we state without proof, makes the preceding ideas more precise.

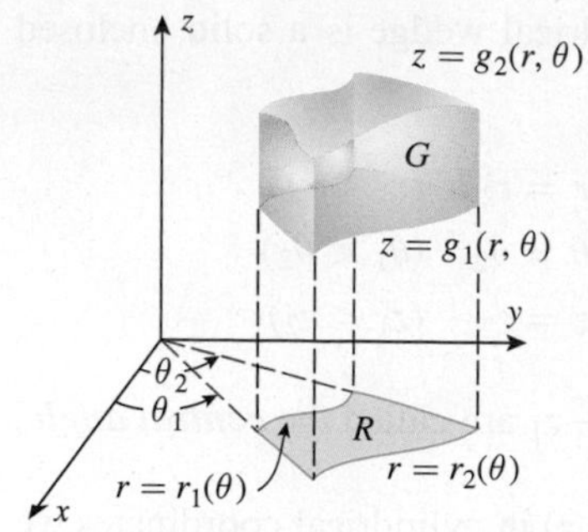


▲ **Figure 14.6.4**

**14.6.1 THEOREM** *Let G be a solid region whose upper surface has the equation $z = g_2(r, \theta)$ and whose lower surface has the equation $z = g_1(r, \theta)$ in cylindrical coordinates. If the projection of the solid on the xy-plane is a simple polar region R, and if $f(r, \theta, z)$ is continuous on G, then*

$$\iiint_G f(r, \theta, z)\, dV = \iint_R \left[ \int_{g_1(r,\theta)}^{g_2(r,\theta)} f(r, \theta, z)\, dz \right] dA \tag{4}$$

*where the double integral over R is evaluated in polar coordinates. In particular, if the projection R is as shown in Figure 14.6.4, then (4) can be written as*

$$\iiint_G f(r, \theta, z)\, dV = \int_{\theta_1}^{\theta_2} \int_{r_1(\theta)}^{r_2(\theta)} \int_{g_1(r,\theta)}^{g_2(r,\theta)} f(r, \theta, z) r\, dz\, dr\, d\theta \tag{5}$$

The type of solid to which Formula (5) applies is illustrated in Figure 14.6.4. To apply (4) and (5) it is best to begin with a three-dimensional sketch of the solid $G$, from which the limits of integration can be obtained as follows:

***Determining Limits of Integration: Cylindrical Coordinates***

**Step 1.** Identify the upper surface $z = g_2(r, \theta)$ and the lower surface $z = g_1(r, \theta)$ of the solid. The functions $g_1(r, \theta)$ and $g_2(r, \theta)$ determine the $z$-limits of integration. (If the upper and lower surfaces are given in rectangular coordinates, convert them to cylindrical coordinates.)

**Step 2.** Make a two-dimensional sketch of the projection $R$ of the solid on the $xy$-plane. From this sketch the $r$- and $\theta$-limits of integration may be obtained exactly as with double integrals in polar coordinates.

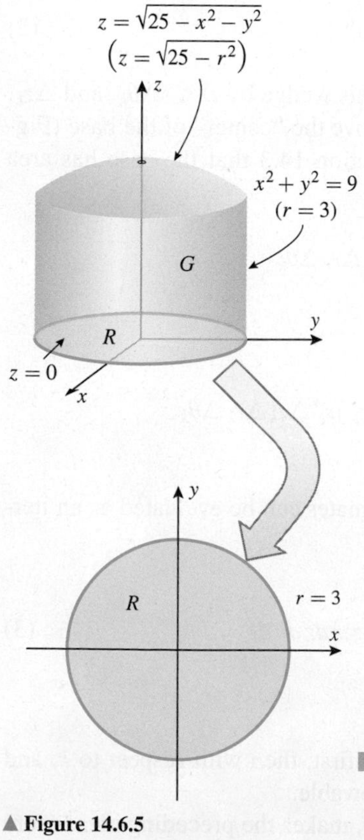


▲ **Figure 14.6.5**

**▶ Example 1** Use triple integration in cylindrical coordinates to find the volume of the solid $G$ that is bounded above by the hemisphere $z = \sqrt{25 - x^2 - y^2}$, below by the $xy$-plane, and laterally by the cylinder $x^2 + y^2 = 9$.

***Solution.*** The solid $G$ and its projection $R$ on the $xy$-plane are shown in Figure 14.6.5. In cylindrical coordinates, the upper surface of $G$ is the hemisphere $z = \sqrt{25 - r^2}$ and the lower surface is the plane $z = 0$. Thus, from (4), the volume of $G$ is

$$V = \iiint_G dV = \iint_R \left[ \int_0^{\sqrt{25-r^2}} dz \right] dA$$

For the double integral over $R$, we use polar coordinates:

$$V = \int_0^{2\pi} \int_0^3 \int_0^{\sqrt{25-r^2}} r\, dz\, dr\, d\theta = \int_0^{2\pi} \int_0^3 [rz]_{z=0}^{\sqrt{25-r^2}}\, dr\, d\theta$$

$$= \int_0^{2\pi} \int_0^3 r\sqrt{25 - r^2}\, dr\, d\theta = \int_0^{2\pi} \left[ -\frac{1}{3}(25 - r^2)^{3/2} \right]_{r=0}^3 d\theta$$

$$u = 25 - r^2$$
$$du = -2r\, dr$$

$$= \int_0^{2\pi} \frac{61}{3}\, d\theta = \frac{122}{3}\pi \ ◀$$

## ■ CONVERTING TRIPLE INTEGRALS FROM RECTANGULAR TO CYLINDRICAL COORDINATES

Sometimes a triple integral that is difficult to integrate in rectangular coordinates can be evaluated more easily by making the substitution $x = r\cos\theta, y = r\sin\theta, z = z$ to convert it to an integral in cylindrical coordinates. Under such a substitution, a rectangular triple integral can be expressed as an iterated integral in cylindrical coordinates as

The order of integration on the right side of (6) can be changed, provided the limits of integration are adjusted accordingly.

$$\iiint_G f(x, y, z)\,dV = \iiint_{\substack{\text{appropriate}\\ \text{limits}}} f(r\cos\theta, r\sin\theta, z)\,r\,dz\,dr\,d\theta \tag{6}$$

▶ **Example 2** Use cylindrical coordinates to evaluate

$$\int_{-3}^{3}\int_{-\sqrt{9-x^2}}^{\sqrt{9-x^2}}\int_{0}^{9-x^2-y^2} x^2\,dz\,dy\,dx$$

***Solution.*** In problems of this type, it is helpful to sketch the region of integration $G$ and its projection $R$ on the $xy$-plane. From the $z$-limits of integration, the upper surface of $G$ is the paraboloid $z = 9 - x^2 - y^2$ and the lower surface is the $xy$-plane $z = 0$. From the $x$- and $y$-limits of integration, the projection $R$ is the region in the $xy$-plane enclosed by the circle $x^2 + y^2 = 9$ (Figure 14.6.6). Thus,

$$\int_{-3}^{3}\int_{-\sqrt{9-x^2}}^{\sqrt{9-x^2}}\int_{0}^{9-x^2-y^2} x^2\,dz\,dy\,dx = \iiint_G x^2\,dV$$

$$= \iint_R \left[\int_0^{9-r^2} r^2\cos^2\theta\,dz\right] dA = \int_0^{2\pi}\int_0^3\int_0^{9-r^2} (r^2\cos^2\theta)\,r\,dz\,dr\,d\theta$$

$$= \int_0^{2\pi}\int_0^3\int_0^{9-r^2} r^3\cos^2\theta\,dz\,dr\,d\theta = \int_0^{2\pi}\int_0^3 \left[zr^3\cos^2\theta\right]_{z=0}^{9-r^2} dr\,d\theta$$

$$= \int_0^{2\pi}\int_0^3 (9r^3 - r^5)\cos^2\theta\,dr\,d\theta = \int_0^{2\pi}\left[\left(\frac{9r^4}{4} - \frac{r^6}{6}\right)\cos^2\theta\right]_{r=0}^{3} d\theta$$

$$= \frac{243}{4}\int_0^{2\pi}\cos^2\theta\,d\theta = \frac{243}{4}\int_0^{2\pi}\frac{1}{2}(1+\cos 2\theta)\,d\theta = \frac{243\pi}{4} \blacktriangleleft$$

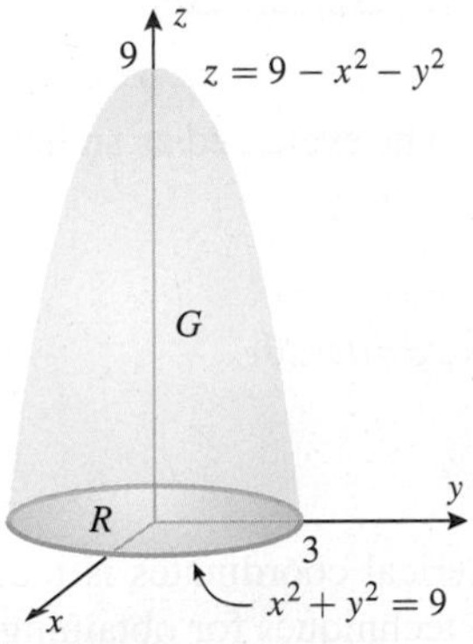

▲ **Figure 14.6.6**

## ■ TRIPLE INTEGRALS IN SPHERICAL COORDINATES

In spherical coordinates, the simplest equations are of the form

$$\rho = \text{constant}, \quad \theta = \text{constant}, \quad \phi = \text{constant}$$

As indicated in Figure 11.8.4, the first equation represents a sphere centered at the origin and the second a half-plane hinged on the $z$-axis. The graph of the third equation is a right circular cone nappe with its vertex at the origin and its line of symmetry along the $z$-axis for $\phi \neq \pi/2$, and is the $xy$-plane if $\phi = \pi/2$. By a ***spherical wedge*** or ***spherical element of volume*** we mean a solid enclosed between six surfaces of the following form:

| | | | |
|---|---|---|---|
| two spheres (green) | $\rho = \rho_1$, | $\rho = \rho_2$ | $(\rho_1 < \rho_2)$ |
| two vertical half-planes (yellow) | $\theta = \theta_1$, | $\theta = \theta_2$ | $(\theta_1 < \theta_2)$ |
| nappes of two circular cones (pink) | $\phi = \phi_1$, | $\phi = \phi_2$ | $(\phi_1 < \phi_2)$ |

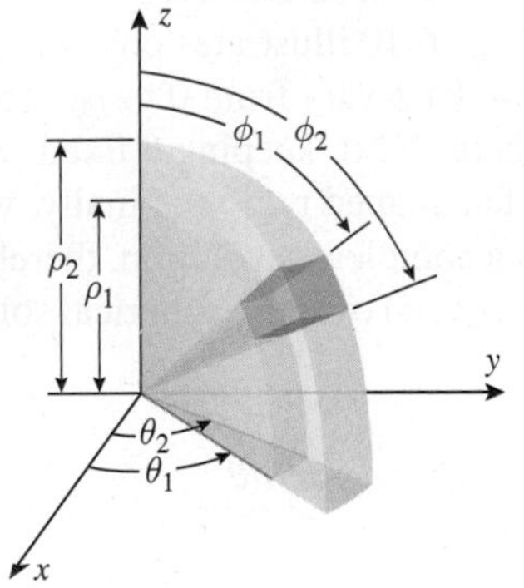

▲ **Figure 14.6.7**

(Figure 14.6.7). We will refer to the numbers $\rho_2 - \rho_1, \theta_2 - \theta_1$, and $\phi_2 - \phi_1$ as the ***dimensions*** of a spherical wedge.

If $G$ is a solid region in three-dimensional space, then the triple integral over $G$ of a continuous function $f(\rho, \theta, \phi)$ in spherical coordinates is similar in definition to the triple integral in cylindrical coordinates, except that the solid $G$ is partitioned into *spherical wedges* by a three-dimensional grid consisting of spheres centered at the origin, half-planes hinged on the $z$-axis, and nappes of right circular cones with vertices at the origin and lines of symmetry along the $z$-axis (Figure 14.6.8).

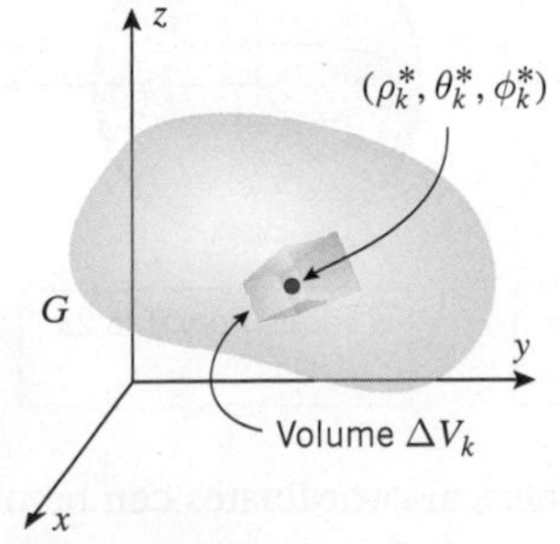

▲ **Figure 14.6.8**

The defining equation of a triple integral in spherical coordinates is

$$\iiint_G f(\rho, \theta, \phi)\, dV = \lim_{n \to +\infty} \sum_{k=1}^{n} f(\rho_k^*, \theta_k^*, \phi_k^*)\Delta V_k \tag{7}$$

where $\Delta V_k$ is the volume of the $k$th spherical wedge that is interior to $G$, $(\rho_k^*, \theta_k^*, \phi_k^*)$ is an arbitrary point in this wedge, and $n$ increases in such a way that the dimensions of each interior spherical wedge tend to zero.

For computational purposes, it will be desirable to express (7) as an iterated integral. In Exercise 30 we will help you to show that if the point $(\rho_k^*, \theta_k^*, \phi_k^*)$ is suitably chosen, then the volume $\Delta V_k$ in (7) can be written as

$$\Delta V_k = \rho_k^{*2} \sin \phi_k^* \Delta\rho_k \Delta\phi_k \Delta\theta_k \tag{8}$$

where $\Delta\rho_k$, $\Delta\phi_k$, and $\Delta\theta_k$ are the dimensions of the wedge (Figure 14.6.9). Substituting this in (7) we obtain

$$\iiint_G f(\rho, \theta, \phi)\, dV = \lim_{n \to +\infty} \sum_{k=1}^{n} f(\rho_k^*, \theta_k^*, \phi_k^*)\rho_k^{*2} \sin \phi_k^* \Delta\rho_k \Delta\phi_k \Delta\theta_k$$

which suggests that a triple integral in spherical coordinates can be evaluated as an iterated integral of the form

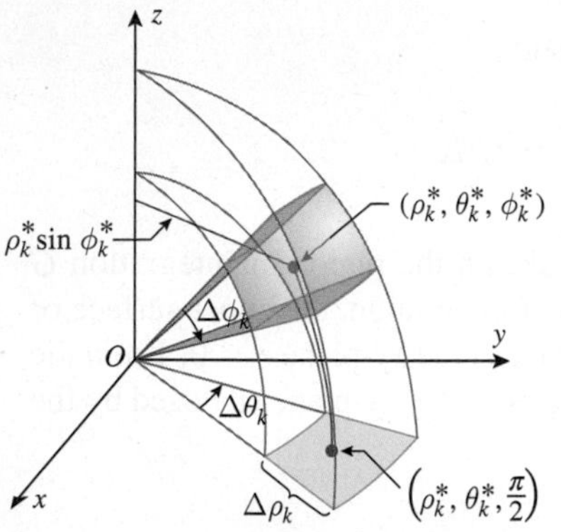


$\Delta V_k = \rho_k^{*2} \sin \phi_k^* \Delta\rho_k \Delta\phi_k \Delta\theta_k$

▲ **Figure 14.6.9**

Note the extra factor of $\rho^2 \sin \phi$ that appears in the integrand on converting a triple integral to an iterated integral in spherical coordinates. This is analogous to the extra factor of $r$ that appears in an iterated integral in cylindrical coordinates.

$$\iiint_G f(\rho, \theta, \phi)\, dV = \iiint_{\substack{\text{appropriate} \\ \text{limits}}} f(\rho, \theta, \phi)\rho^2 \sin \phi \, d\rho \, d\phi \, d\theta \tag{9}$$

The analog of Theorem 14.6.1 for triple integrals in spherical coordinates is tedious to state, so instead we will give some examples that illustrate techniques for obtaining the limits of integration. In all of our examples we will use the same order of integration—first with respect to $\rho$, then $\phi$, and then $\theta$. Once you have mastered the basic ideas, there should be no trouble using other orders of integration.

Suppose that we want to integrate $f(\rho, \theta, \phi)$ over the spherical solid $G$ enclosed by the sphere $\rho = \rho_0$. The basic idea is to choose the limits of integration so that every point of the solid is accounted for in the integration process. Figure 14.6.10 illustrates one way of doing this. Holding $\theta$ and $\phi$ fixed for the first integration, we let $\rho$ vary from 0 to $\rho_0$. This covers a radial line from the origin to the surface of the sphere. Next, keeping $\theta$ fixed, we let $\phi$ vary from 0 to $\pi$ so that the radial line sweeps out a fan-shaped region. Finally, we let $\theta$ vary from 0 to $2\pi$ so that the fan-shaped region makes a complete revolution, thereby sweeping out the entire sphere. Thus, the triple integral of $f(\rho, \theta, \phi)$ over the spherical solid $G$ can be evaluated by writing

$$\iiint_G f(\rho, \theta, \phi)\, dV = \int_0^{2\pi} \int_0^{\pi} \int_0^{\rho_0} f(\rho, \theta, \phi)\rho^2 \sin \phi \, d\rho \, d\phi \, d\theta$$

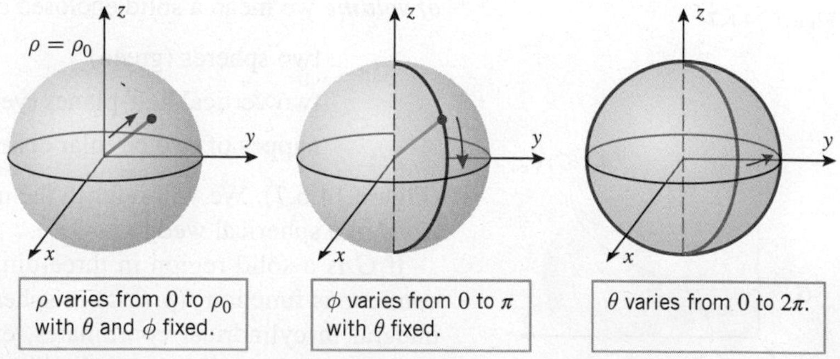


▶ **Figure 14.6.10**

Table 14.6.1 suggests how the limits of integration in spherical coordinates can be obtained for some other common solids.

**Table 14.6.1**

| DETERMINATION OF LIMITS | INTEGRAL |
|---|---|
| This is the portion of the sphere of radius $\rho_0$ that lies in the first octant. | $\int_0^{\pi/2}\int_0^{\pi/2}\int_0^{\rho_0} f(\rho, \theta, \phi)\rho^2 \sin\phi \, d\rho \, d\phi \, d\theta$ |

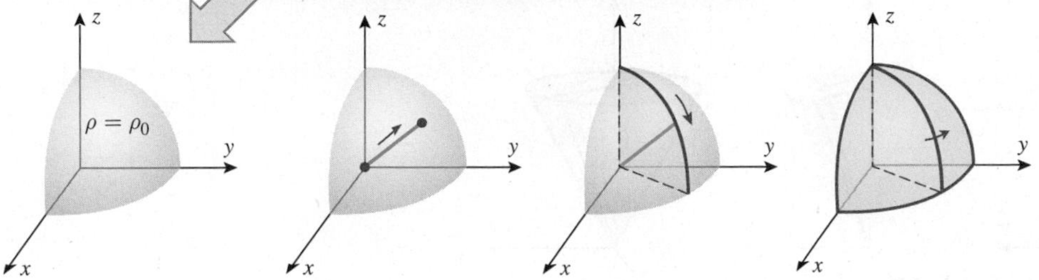


| | | |
|---|---|---|
| $\rho$ varies from 0 to $\rho_0$ with $\theta$ and $\phi$ held fixed. | $\phi$ varies from 0 to $\pi/2$ with $\theta$ held fixed. | $\theta$ varies from 0 to $\pi/2$. |

| DETERMINATION OF LIMITS | INTEGRAL |
|---|---|
| This ice-cream-cone-shaped solid is cut from the sphere of radius $\rho_0$ by the cone $\phi = \phi_0$. | $\int_0^{2\pi}\int_0^{\phi_0}\int_0^{\rho_0} f(\rho, \theta, \phi)\rho^2 \sin\phi \, d\rho \, d\phi \, d\theta$ |

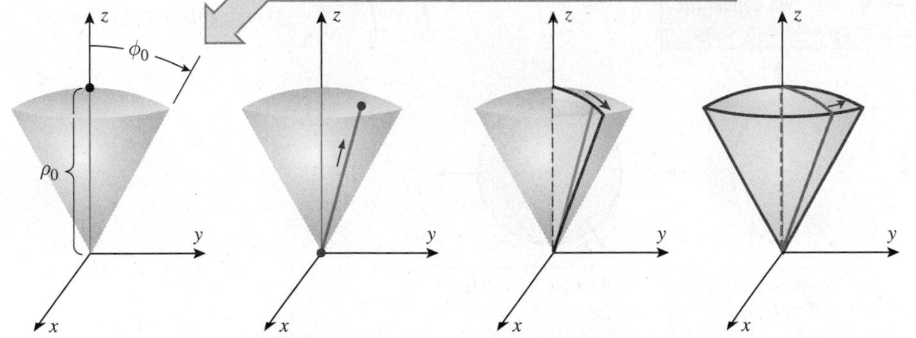


| | | |
|---|---|---|
| $\rho$ varies from 0 to $\rho_0$ with $\theta$ and $\phi$ held fixed. | $\phi$ varies from 0 to $\phi_0$ with $\theta$ held fixed. | $\theta$ varies from 0 to $2\pi$. |

| DETERMINATION OF LIMITS | INTEGRAL |
|---|---|
| This solid is cut from the sphere of radius $\rho_0$ by two cones, $\phi = \phi_1$ and $\phi = \phi_2$, where $\phi_1 < \phi_2$. | $\int_0^{2\pi}\int_{\phi_1}^{\phi_2}\int_0^{\rho_0} f(\rho, \theta, \phi)\rho^2 \sin\phi \, d\rho \, d\phi \, d\theta$ |

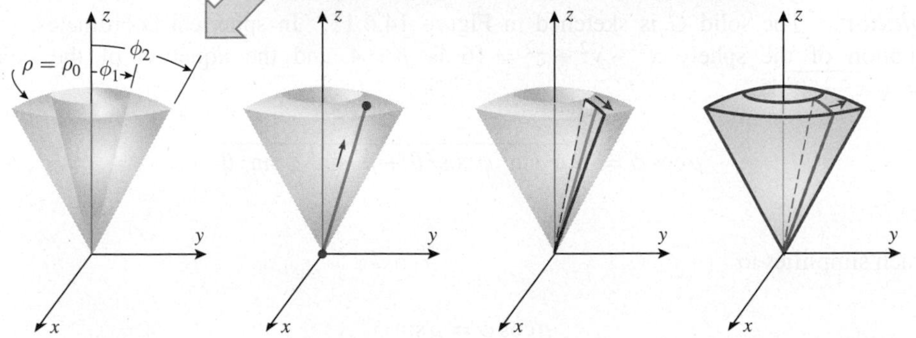


| | | |
|---|---|---|
| $\rho$ varies from 0 to $\rho_0$ with $\theta$ and $\phi$ held fixed. | $\phi$ varies from $\phi_1$ to $\phi_2$ with $\theta$ held fixed. | $\theta$ varies from 0 to $2\pi$. |

**Table 14.6.1** (*continued*)

| DETERMINATION OF LIMITS | INTEGRAL |
|---|---|
| 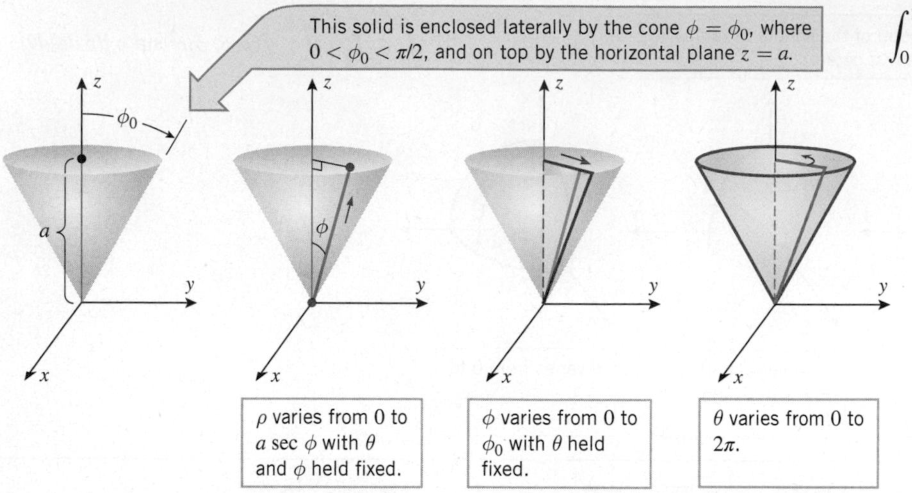 | $\int_0^{2\pi}\int_0^{\phi_0}\int_0^{a \sec\phi} f(\rho, \theta, \phi)\rho^2 \sin\phi \, d\rho \, d\phi \, d\theta$ |
| 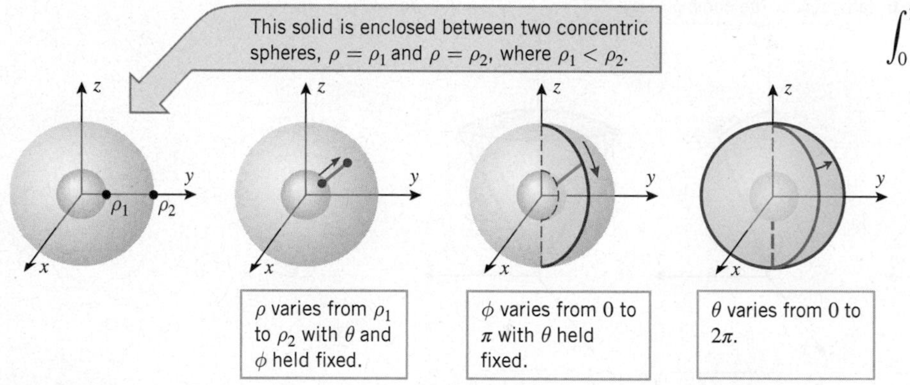 | $\int_0^{2\pi}\int_0^{\pi}\int_{\rho_1}^{\rho_2} f(\rho, \theta, \phi)\rho^2 \sin\phi \, d\rho \, d\phi \, d\theta$ |





▶ **Example 3** Use spherical coordinates to find the volume of the solid $G$ bounded above by the sphere $x^2 + y^2 + z^2 = 16$ and below by the cone $z = \sqrt{x^2 + y^2}$.

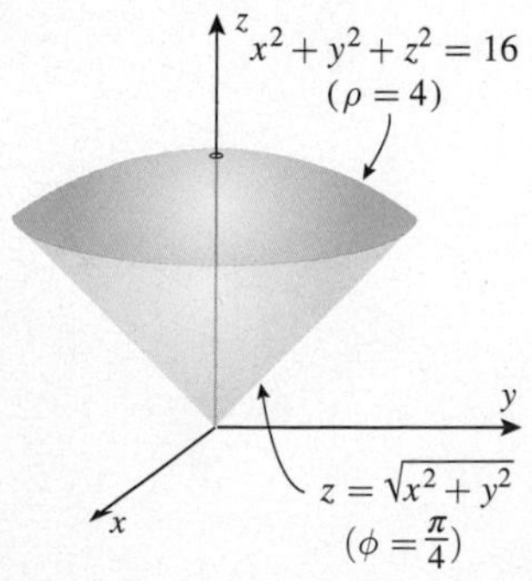


▲ **Figure 14.6.11**

***Solution.*** The solid $G$ is sketched in Figure 14.6.11. In spherical coordinates, the equation of the sphere $x^2 + y^2 + z^2 = 16$ is $\rho = 4$ and the equation of the cone $z = \sqrt{x^2 + y^2}$ is

$$\rho \cos\phi = \sqrt{\rho^2 \sin^2\phi \cos^2\theta + \rho^2 \sin^2\phi \sin^2\theta}$$

which simplifies to

$$\rho \cos\phi = \rho \sin\phi$$

Dividing both sides of this equation by $\rho\cos\phi$ yields $\tan\phi = 1$, from which it follows that

$$\phi = \pi/4$$

Thus, it follows from the second entry in Table 14.6.1 that the volume of $G$ is

$$\begin{aligned} V = \iiint_G dV &= \int_0^{2\pi}\int_0^{\pi/4}\int_0^4 \rho^2 \sin\phi \, d\rho\, d\phi\, d\theta \\ &= \int_0^{2\pi}\int_0^{\pi/4} \left[\frac{\rho^3}{3}\sin\phi\right]_{\rho=0}^4 d\phi\, d\theta \\ &= \int_0^{2\pi}\int_0^{\pi/4} \frac{64}{3}\sin\phi\, d\phi\, d\theta \\ &= \frac{64}{3}\int_0^{2\pi}[-\cos\phi]_{\phi=0}^{\pi/4}\, d\theta = \frac{64}{3}\int_0^{2\pi}\left(1-\frac{\sqrt{2}}{2}\right)d\theta \\ &= \frac{64\pi}{3}(2-\sqrt{2}) \approx 39.26 \blacktriangleleft \end{aligned}$$

## CONVERTING TRIPLE INTEGRALS FROM RECTANGULAR TO SPHERICAL COORDINATES

Referring to Table 11.8.1, triple integrals can be converted from rectangular coordinates to spherical coordinates by making the substitution $x = \rho\sin\phi\cos\theta$, $y = \rho\sin\phi\sin\theta$, $z = \rho\cos\phi$. The two integrals are related by the equation

$$\iiint_G f(x, y, z)\, dV = \iiint_{\substack{\text{appropriate}\\ \text{limits}}} f(\rho\sin\phi\cos\theta, \rho\sin\phi\sin\theta, \rho\cos\phi)\rho^2 \sin\phi\, d\rho\, d\phi\, d\theta \tag{10}$$

**► Example 4** Use spherical coordinates to evaluate

$$\int_{-2}^{2}\int_{-\sqrt{4-x^2}}^{\sqrt{4-x^2}}\int_0^{\sqrt{4-x^2-y^2}} z^2\sqrt{x^2+y^2+z^2}\, dz\, dy\, dx$$

***Solution.*** In problems like this, it is helpful to begin with a sketch of the region $G$ of integration. From the $z$-limits of integration, the upper surface of $G$ is the hemisphere $z = \sqrt{4-x^2-y^2}$ and the lower surface is the $xy$-plane $z = 0$. From the $x$- and $y$-limits of integration, the projection of the solid $G$ on the $xy$-plane is the region enclosed by the circle $x^2 + y^2 = 4$. From this information we obtain the sketch of $G$ in Figure 14.6.12. Thus,

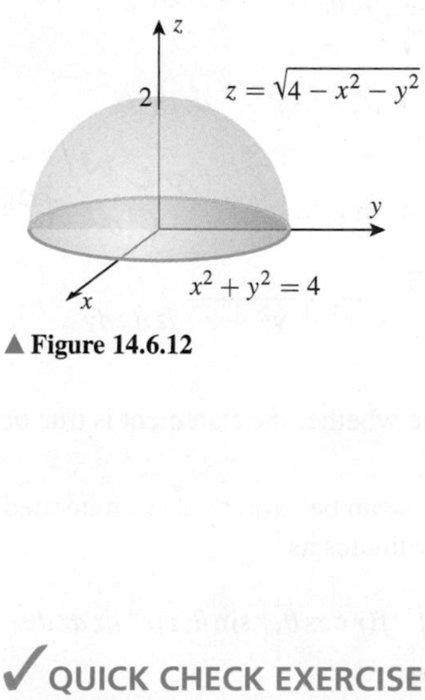

▲ Figure 14.6.12

$$\begin{aligned} &\int_{-2}^{2}\int_{-\sqrt{4-x^2}}^{\sqrt{4-x^2}}\int_0^{\sqrt{4-x^2-y^2}} z^2\sqrt{x^2+y^2+z^2}\, dz\, dy\, dx \\ &= \iiint_G z^2\sqrt{x^2+y^2+z^2}\, dV \\ &= \int_0^{2\pi}\int_0^{\pi/2}\int_0^2 \rho^5\cos^2\phi\sin\phi\, d\rho\, d\phi\, d\theta \\ &= \int_0^{2\pi}\int_0^{\pi/2} \frac{32}{3}\cos^2\phi\sin\phi\, d\phi\, d\theta \\ &= \frac{32}{3}\int_0^{2\pi}\left[-\frac{1}{3}\cos^3\phi\right]_{\phi=0}^{\pi/2} d\theta = \frac{32}{9}\int_0^{2\pi} d\theta = \frac{64}{9}\pi \blacktriangleleft \end{aligned}$$

## ✓ QUICK CHECK EXERCISES 14.6 (See page 947 for answers.)

1. (a) The cylindrical wedge $1 \le r \le 3$, $\pi/6 \le \theta \le \pi/2$, $0 \le z \le 5$ has volume $V =$ ______.
   (b) The spherical wedge $1 \le \rho \le 3$, $\pi/6 \le \theta \le \pi/2$, $0 \le \phi \le \pi/3$ has volume $V =$ ______.

2. Let $G$ be the solid region inside the sphere of radius 2 centered at the origin and above the plane $z = 1$. In each part, supply the missing integrand and limits of integration for the iterated integral in cylindrical coordinates.
(a) The volume of $G$ is

$$\iiint_G dV = \int_{\square}^{\square}\int_{\square}^{\square}\int_{\square}^{\square} \_\_\_\_\_\_ \, dz\, dr\, d\theta$$

(b) $$\iiint_G \frac{z}{x^2+y^2+z^2}\, dV = \int_{\square}^{\square}\int_{\square}^{\square}\int_{\square}^{\square} \_\_\_\_\_\_ \, dz\, dr\, d\theta$$

3. Let $G$ be the solid region described in Quick Check Exercise 2. In each part, supply the missing integrand and limits of integration for the iterated integral in spherical coordinates.
(a) The volume of $G$ is

$$\iiint_G dV = \int_{\square}^{\square}\int_{\square}^{\square}\int_{\square}^{\square} \_\_\_\_\_\_ \, d\rho\, d\phi\, d\theta$$

(b) $$\iiint_G \frac{z}{x^2+y^2+z^2}\, dV = \int_{\square}^{\square}\int_{\square}^{\square}\int_{\square}^{\square} \_\_\_\_\_\_ \, d\rho\, d\phi\, d\theta$$

## EXERCISE SET 14.6 C CAS

**1–4** Evaluate the iterated integral. ■

1. $\displaystyle\int_0^{2\pi}\int_0^{1}\int_0^{\sqrt{1-r^2}} zr\, dz\, dr\, d\theta$

2. $\displaystyle\int_0^{\pi/2}\int_0^{\cos\theta}\int_0^{r^2} r\sin\theta\, dz\, dr\, d\theta$

3. $\displaystyle\int_0^{\pi/2}\int_0^{\pi/2}\int_0^{1} \rho^3 \sin\phi\cos\phi\, d\rho\, d\phi\, d\theta$

4. $\displaystyle\int_0^{2\pi}\int_0^{\pi/4}\int_0^{a\sec\phi} \rho^2 \sin\phi\, d\rho\, d\phi\, d\theta \quad (a > 0)$

**FOCUS ON CONCEPTS**

5. Sketch the region $G$ and identify the function $f$ so that
$$\iiint_G f(r,\theta,z)\, dV$$
corresponds to the iterated integral in Exercise 1.

6. Sketch the region $G$ and identify the function $f$ so that
$$\iiint_G f(r,\theta,z)\, dV$$
corresponds to the iterated integral in Exercise 2.

7. Sketch the region $G$ and identify the function $f$ so that
$$\iiint_G f(\rho,\theta,\phi)\, dV$$
corresponds to the iterated integral in Exercise 3.

8. Sketch the region $G$ and identify the function $f$ so that
$$\iiint_G f(\rho,\theta,\phi)\, dV$$
corresponds to the iterated integral in Exercise 4.

**9–12** Use cylindrical coordinates to find the volume of the solid. ■

9. The solid enclosed by the paraboloid $z = x^2 + y^2$ and the plane $z = 9$.

10. The solid bounded above by the sphere $x^2 + y^2 + z^2 = 1$ and bounded below by the cone $z = \sqrt{x^2 + y^2}$.

11. The solid that is inside the surface $r^2 + z^2 = 20$ but not above the surface $z = r^2$.

12. The solid enclosed between the cone $z = (hr)/a$ and the plane $z = h$.

**13–16** Use spherical coordinates to find the volume of the solid. ■

13. The solid bounded above by the sphere $\rho = 4$ and below by the cone $\phi = \pi/3$.

14. The solid within the cone $\phi = \pi/4$ and between the spheres $\rho = 1$ and $\rho = 2$.

15. The solid enclosed by the sphere $x^2 + y^2 + z^2 = 4a^2$ and the planes $z = 0$ and $z = a$.

16. The solid within the sphere $x^2 + y^2 + z^2 = 9$, outside the cone $z = \sqrt{x^2 + y^2}$, and above the $xy$-plane.

**17–20** Use cylindrical or spherical coordinates to evaluate the integral. ■

17. $\displaystyle\int_0^{a}\int_0^{\sqrt{a^2-x^2}}\int_0^{a^2-x^2-y^2} x^2\, dz\, dy\, dx \quad (a > 0)$

18. $\displaystyle\int_{-1}^{1}\int_0^{\sqrt{1-x^2}}\int_0^{\sqrt{1-x^2-y^2}} e^{-(x^2+y^2+z^2)^{3/2}}\, dz\, dy\, dx$

19. $\displaystyle\int_0^{2}\int_0^{\sqrt{4-y^2}}\int_{\sqrt{x^2+y^2}}^{\sqrt{8-x^2-y^2}} z^2\, dz\, dx\, dy$

20. $\displaystyle\int_{-3}^{3}\int_{-\sqrt{9-y^2}}^{\sqrt{9-y^2}}\int_{-\sqrt{9-x^2-y^2}}^{\sqrt{9-x^2-y^2}} \sqrt{x^2+y^2+z^2}\, dz\, dx\, dy$

**21–24 True–False** Determine whether the statement is true or false. Explain your answer. ■

21. A rectangular triple integral can be expressed as an iterated integral in cylindrical coordinates as
$$\iiint_G f(x,y,z)\, dV = \iiint_{\substack{\text{appropriate}\\ \text{limits}}} f(r\cos\theta, r\sin\theta, z) r^2\, dz\, dr\, d\theta$$

22. If $0 \le \rho_1 < \rho_2$, $0 \le \theta_1 < \theta_2 \le 2\pi$, and $0 \le \phi_1 < \phi_2 \le \pi$, then the volume of the spherical wedge bounded by the

spheres $\rho = \rho_1$ and $\rho = \rho_2$, the half-planes $\theta = \theta_1$ and $\theta = \theta_2$, and the cones $\phi = \phi_1$ and $\phi = \phi_2$ is

$$\int_{\theta_1}^{\theta_2} \int_{\phi_1}^{\phi_2} \int_{\rho_1}^{\rho_2} \rho^2 \sin\phi \, d\rho \, d\phi \, d\theta$$

**23.** Let $G$ be the solid region in 3-space between the spheres of radius 1 and 3 centered at the origin and above the cone $z = \sqrt{x^2 + y^2}$. The volume of $G$ equals

$$\int_0^{\pi/4} \int_0^{2\pi} \int_1^3 \rho^2 \sin\phi \, d\rho \, d\theta \, d\phi$$

**24.** If $G$ is the solid in Exercise 23 and $f(x, y, z)$ is continuous on $G$, then

$$\iiint_G f(x, y, z) \, dV = \int_0^{\pi/4} \int_0^{2\pi} \int_1^3 F(\rho, \theta, \phi)\rho^2 \sin\phi \, d\rho \, d\theta \, d\phi$$

where $F(\rho, \theta, \phi) = f(\rho \sin\phi \sin\theta, \rho \sin\phi \cos\theta, \rho \cos\phi)$.

C **25.** (a) Use a CAS to evaluate

$$\int_{-2}^{2} \int_1^4 \int_{\pi/6}^{\pi/3} \frac{r \tan^3 \theta}{\sqrt{1 + z^2}} \, d\theta \, dr \, dz$$

(b) Find a function $f(x, y, z)$ and sketch a region $G$ in 3-space so that the triple integral in rectangular coordinates

$$\iiint_G f(x, y, z) \, dV$$

matches the iterated integral in cylindrical coordinates given in part (a).

C **26.** Use a CAS to evaluate

$$\int_0^{\pi/2} \int_0^{\pi/4} \int_0^{\cos\theta} \rho^{17} \cos\phi \cos^{19}\theta \, d\rho \, d\phi \, d\theta$$

**27.** Find the volume enclosed by $x^2 + y^2 + z^2 = a^2$ using
(a) cylindrical coordinates
(b) spherical coordinates.

**28.** Let $G$ be the solid in the first octant bounded by the sphere $x^2 + y^2 + z^2 = 4$ and the coordinate planes. Evaluate

$$\iiint_G xyz \, dV$$

(a) using rectangular coordinates
(b) using cylindrical coordinates
(c) using spherical coordinates.

**29.** Find the volume of the solid in the first octant bounded by the sphere $\rho = 2$, the coordinate planes, and the cones $\phi = \pi/6$ and $\phi = \pi/3$.

**30.** In this exercise we will obtain a formula for the volume of the spherical wedge illustrated in Figures 14.6.7 and 14.6.9.
(a) Use a triple integral in cylindrical coordinates to show that the volume of the solid bounded above by a sphere $\rho = \rho_0$, below by a cone $\phi = \phi_0$, and on the sides by $\theta = \theta_1$ and $\theta = \theta_2$ $(\theta_1 < \theta_2)$ is

$$V = \tfrac{1}{3}\rho_0^3(1 - \cos\phi_0)(\theta_2 - \theta_1)$$

[*Hint:* In cylindrical coordinates, the sphere has the equation $r^2 + z^2 = \rho_0^2$ and the cone has the equation $z = r \cot\phi_0$. For simplicity, consider only the case $0 < \phi_0 < \pi/2$.]

(b) Subtract appropriate volumes and use the result in part (a) to deduce that the volume $\Delta V$ of the spherical wedge is

$$\Delta V = \frac{\rho_2^3 - \rho_1^3}{3}(\cos\phi_1 - \cos\phi_2)(\theta_2 - \theta_1)$$

(c) Apply the Mean-Value Theorem to the functions $\cos\phi$ and $\rho^3$ to deduce that the formula in part (b) can be written as

$$\Delta V = \rho^{*2} \sin\phi^* \, \Delta\rho \, \Delta\phi \, \Delta\theta$$

where $\Delta\rho = \rho_2 - \rho_1$, $\Delta\phi = \phi_2 - \phi_1$, $\Delta\theta = \theta_2 - \theta_1$, and $\rho^*$ are between $\rho_1$ and $\rho_2$, $\phi^*$ is between $\phi_1$ and $\phi_2$.

**31. Writing** Suppose that a triple integral is expressed in cylindrical or spherical coordinates in such a way that the outermost variable of integration is $\theta$ and none of the limits of integration involves $\theta$. Discuss what this says about the region of integration for the integral.

✓ **QUICK CHECK ANSWERS 14.6** 1. (a) $\frac{20}{3}\pi$ (b) $\frac{13}{9}\pi$ 2. (a) $\int_0^{2\pi} \int_0^{\sqrt{3}} \int_1^{\sqrt{4-r^2}} r \, dz \, dr \, d\theta$ (b) $\int_0^{2\pi} \int_0^{\sqrt{3}} \int_1^{\sqrt{4-r^2}} \frac{rz}{r^2 + z^2} \, dz \, dr \, d\theta$ 3. (a) $\int_0^{2\pi} \int_0^{\pi/3} \int_{\sec\phi}^{2} \rho^2 \sin\phi \, d\rho \, d\phi \, d\theta$ (b) $\int_0^{2\pi} \int_0^{\pi/3} \int_{\sec\phi}^{2} \rho \cos\phi \sin\phi \, d\rho \, d\phi \, d\theta$

## 14.7 CHANGE OF VARIABLES IN MULTIPLE INTEGRALS; JACOBIANS

*In this section we will discuss a general method for evaluating double and triple integrals by substitution. Most of the results in this section are very difficult to prove, so our approach will be informal and motivational. Our goal is to provide a geometric understanding of the basic principles and an exposure to computational techniques.*

## CHANGE OF VARIABLE IN A SINGLE INTEGRAL

To motivate techniques for evaluating double and triple integrals by substitution, it will be helpful to consider the effect of a substitution $x = g(u)$ on a single integral over an interval $[a, b]$. If $g$ is differentiable and either increasing or decreasing, then $g$ is one-to-one and

$$\int_a^b f(x)\,dx = \int_{g^{-1}(a)}^{g^{-1}(b)} f(g(u))g'(u)\,du$$

In this relationship $f(x)$ and $dx$ are expressed in terms of $u$, and the $u$-limits of integration result from solving the equations

$$a = g(u) \quad \text{and} \quad b = g(u)$$

In the case where $g$ is decreasing we have $g^{-1}(b) < g^{-1}(a)$, which is contrary to our usual convention of writing definite integrals with the larger limit of integration at the top. We can remedy this by reversing the limits of integration and writing

$$\int_a^b f(x)\,dx = -\int_{g^{-1}(b)}^{g^{-1}(a)} f(g(u))g'(u)\,du = \int_{g^{-1}(b)}^{g^{-1}(a)} f(g(u))|g'(u)|\,du$$

where the absolute value results from the fact that $g'(u)$ is negative. Thus, regardless of whether $g$ is increasing or decreasing we can write

$$\int_a^b f(x)\,dx = \int_\alpha^\beta f(g(u))|g'(u)|\,du \tag{1}$$

where $\alpha$ and $\beta$ are the $u$-limits of integration and $\alpha < \beta$.

The expression $g'(u)$ that appears in (1) is called the ***Jacobian*** of the change of variable $x = g(u)$ in honor of C. G. J. Jacobi, who made the first serious study of change of variables in multiple integrals in the mid-1800s. Formula (1) reveals three effects of the change of variable $x = g(u)$:

- The new integrand becomes $f(g(u))$ times the absolute value of the Jacobian.
- $dx$ becomes $du$.
- The $x$-interval of integration is transformed into a $u$-interval of integration.

Our goal in this section is to show that analogous results hold for changing variables in double and triple integrals.

## TRANSFORMATIONS OF THE PLANE

In earlier sections we considered parametric equations of three kinds:

$$x = x(t), \quad y = y(t)$$ A curve in the plane

$$x = x(t), \quad y = y(t), \quad z = z(t)$$ A curve in 3-space

$$x = x(u, v), \quad y = y(u, v), \quad z = z(u, v)$$ A surface in 3-space

Now we will consider parametric equations of the form

$$x = x(u, v), \quad y = y(u, v) \tag{2}$$

Parametric equations of this type associate points in the $xy$-plane with points in the $uv$-plane. These equations can be written in vector form as

$$\mathbf{r} = \mathbf{r}(u, v) = x(u, v)\mathbf{i} + y(u, v)\mathbf{j}$$

where $\mathbf{r} = x\mathbf{i} + y\mathbf{j}$ is a position vector in the $xy$-plane and $\mathbf{r}(u, v)$ is a vector-valued function of the variables $u$ and $v$.

It will also be useful in this section to think of the parametric equations in (2) in terms of inputs and outputs. If we think of the pair of numbers $(u, v)$ as an input, then the two equations, in combination, produce a unique output $(x, y)$, and hence define a function $T$ that associates points in the $xy$-plane with points in the $uv$-plane. This function is described by the formula

$$T(u, v) = (x(u, v), y(u, v))$$

We call $T$ a ***transformation*** from the $uv$-plane to the $xy$-plane and $(x, y)$ the ***image*** of $(u, v)$ under the transformation $T$. We also say that $T$ ***maps*** $(u, v)$ into $(x, y)$. The set $R$ of all images in the $xy$-plane of a set $S$ in the $uv$-plane is called the ***image of S under T***. If distinct points in the $uv$-plane have distinct images in the $xy$-plane, then $T$ is said to be ***one-to-one***. In this case the equations in (2) define $u$ and $v$ as functions of $x$ and $y$, say

$$u = u(x, y), \quad v = v(x, y)$$

These equations, which can often be obtained by solving (2) for $u$ and $v$ in terms of $x$ and $y$, define a transformation from the $xy$-plane to the $uv$-plane that maps the image of $(u, v)$ under $T$ back into $(u, v)$. This transformation is denoted by $T^{-1}$ and is called the ***inverse of T*** (Figure 14.7.1).

Because there are four variables involved, a three-dimensional figure is not very useful for describing the transformation geometrically. The idea here is to use the two planes to get the four dimensions needed.

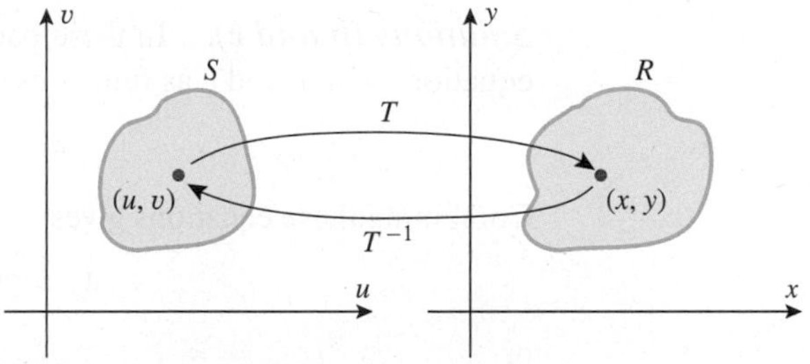


▶ **Figure 14.7.1**

One way to visualize the geometric effect of a transformation $T$ is to determine the images in the $xy$-plane of the vertical and horizontal lines in the $uv$-plane. Following the discussion in Section 14.4, sets of points in the $xy$-plane that are images of horizontal lines ($v$ constant) are called ***constant v-curves***, and sets of points that are images of vertical lines ($u$ constant) are called ***constant u-curves*** (Figure 14.7.2).

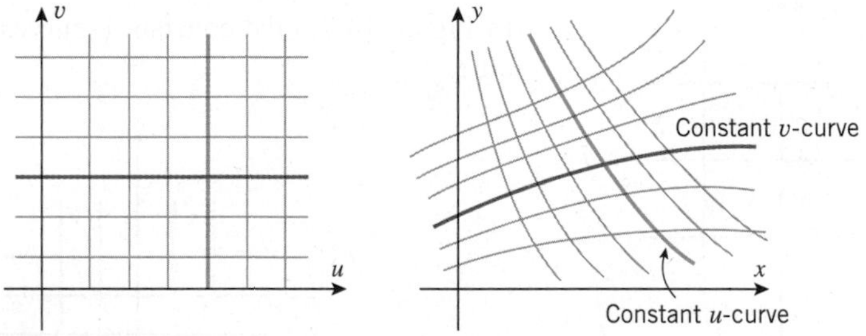


▶ **Figure 14.7.2**

**Carl Gustav Jacob Jacobi (1804–1851)** German mathematician. Jacobi, the son of a banker, grew up in a background of wealth and culture and showed brilliance in mathematics early. He resisted studying mathematics by rote, preferring instead to learn general principles from the works of the masters, Euler and Lagrange. He entered the University of Berlin at age 16 as a student of mathematics and classical studies. However, he soon realized that he could not do both and turned fully to mathematics with a blazing intensity that he would maintain throughout his life. He received his Ph.D. in 1825 and was able to secure a position as a lecturer at the University of Berlin by giving up Judaism and becoming a Christian. However, his promotion opportunities remained limited and he moved on to the University of Königsberg. Jacobi was born to teach—he had a dynamic personality and delivered his lectures with a clarity and enthusiasm that frequently left his audience spellbound. In spite of extensive teaching commitments, he was able to publish volumes of revolutionary mathematical research that eventually made him the leading European mathematician after Gauss. His main body of research was in the area of elliptic functions, a branch of mathematics with important applications in astronomy and physics as well as in other fields of mathematics. Because of his family wealth, Jacobi was not dependent on his teaching salary in his early years. However, his comfortable world eventually collapsed. In 1840 his family went bankrupt and he was wiped out financially. In 1842 he had a nervous breakdown from overwork. In 1843 he became seriously ill with diabetes and moved to Berlin with the help of a government grant to defray his medical expenses. In 1848 he made an injudicious political speech that caused the government to withdraw the grant, eventually resulting in the loss of his home. His health continued to decline and in 1851 he finally succumbed to successive bouts of influenza and smallpox. In spite of all his problems, Jacobi was a tireless worker to the end. When a friend expressed concern about the effect of the hard work on his health, Jacobi replied, "Certainly, I have sometimes endangered my health by overwork, but what of it? Only cabbages have no nerves, no worries. And what do they get out of their perfect well-being?"

*[Image: georgios/Depositphotos]*

**► Example 1** Let $T$ be the transformation from the $uv$-plane to the $xy$-plane defined by the equations

$$x = \tfrac{1}{4}(u + v), \quad y = \tfrac{1}{2}(u - v) \tag{3}$$

(a) Find $T(1, 3)$.

(b) Sketch the constant $v$-curves corresponding to $v = -2, -1, 0, 1, 2$.

(c) Sketch the constant $u$-curves corresponding to $u = -2, -1, 0, 1, 2$.

(d) Sketch the image under $T$ of the square region in the $uv$-plane bounded by the lines $u = -2$, $u = 2$, $v = -2$, and $v = 2$.

***Solution (a).*** Substituting $u = 1$ and $v = 3$ in (3) yields $T(1, 3) = (1, -1)$.

***Solutions (b and c).*** In these parts it will be convenient to express the transformation equations with $u$ and $v$ as functions of $x$ and $y$. From (3)

$$4x = u + v, \quad 2y = u - v$$

Combining these equations gives

$$4x + 2y = 2u, \quad 4x - 2y = 2v$$

or

$$2x + y = u, \quad 2x - y = v$$

Thus, the constant $v$-curves corresponding to $v = -2, -1, 0, 1$, and 2 are

$$2x - y = -2, \quad 2x - y = -1, \quad 2x - y = 0, \quad 2x - y = 1, \quad 2x - y = 2$$

and the constant $u$-curves corresponding to $u = -2, -1, 0, 1$, and 2 are

$$2x + y = -2, \quad 2x + y = -1, \quad 2x + y = 0, \quad 2x + y = 1, \quad 2x + y = 2$$

In Figure 14.7.3 the constant $v$-curves are shown in purple and the constant $u$-curves in blue.

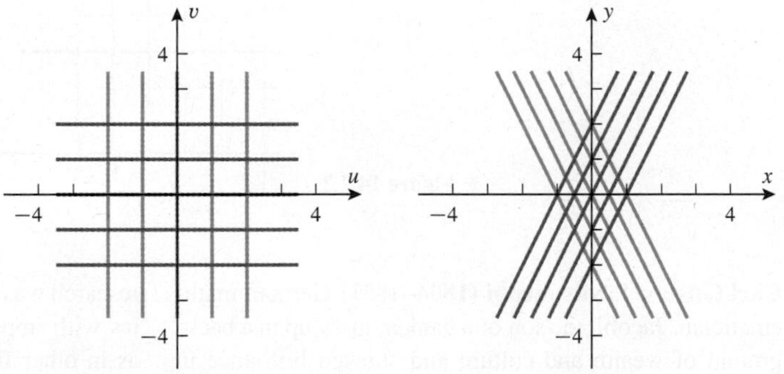


► Figure 14.7.3

***Solution (d).*** The image of a region can often be found by finding the image of its boundary. In this case the images of the boundary lines $u = -2$, $u = 2$, $v = -2$, and $v = 2$ enclose the diamond-shaped region in the $xy$-plane shown in Figure 14.7.4. ◄

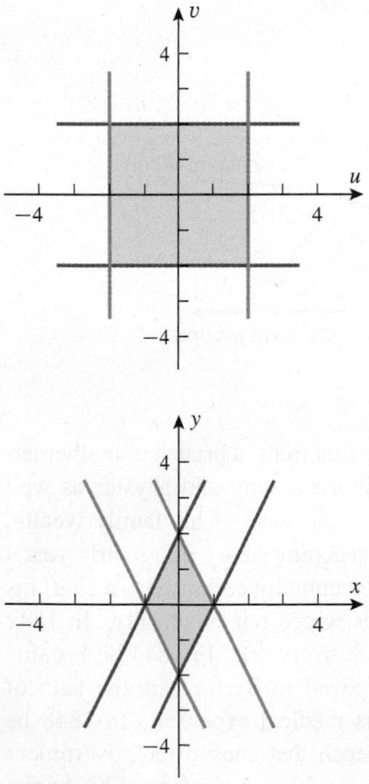


▲ Figure 14.7.4

## JACOBIANS IN TWO VARIABLES

To derive the change of variables formula for double integrals, we will need to understand the relationship between the area of a *small* rectangular region in the $uv$-plane and the area of its image in the $xy$-plane under a transformation $T$ given by the equations

$$x = x(u, v), \quad y = y(u, v)$$

For this purpose, suppose that $\Delta u$ and $\Delta v$ are positive, and consider a rectangular region $S$ in the $uv$-plane enclosed by the lines

$$u = u_0, \quad u = u_0 + \Delta u, \quad v = v_0, \quad v = v_0 + \Delta v$$

If the functions $x(u, v)$ and $y(u, v)$ are continuous, and if $\Delta u$ and $\Delta v$ are not too large, then the image of $S$ in the $xy$-plane will be a region $R$ that looks like a slightly distorted parallelogram (Figure 14.7.5). The sides of $R$ are the constant $u$-curves and $v$-curves that correspond to the sides of $S$.

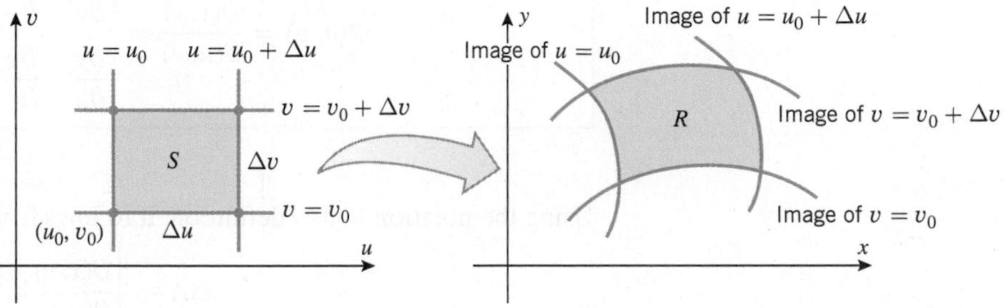

▶ Figure 14.7.5

If we let

$$\mathbf{r} = \mathbf{r}(u, v) = x(u, v)\mathbf{i} + y(u, v)\mathbf{j}$$

be the position vector of the point in the $xy$-plane that corresponds to the point $(u, v)$ in the $uv$-plane, then the constant $v$-curve corresponding to $v = v_0$ and the constant $u$-curve corresponding to $u = u_0$ can be represented in vector form as

$$\mathbf{r}(u, v_0) = x(u, v_0)\mathbf{i} + y(u, v_0)\mathbf{j} \quad \text{Constant } v\text{-curve}$$

$$\mathbf{r}(u_0, v) = x(u_0, v)\mathbf{i} + y(u_0, v)\mathbf{j} \quad \text{Constant } u\text{-curve}$$

Since we are assuming $\Delta u$ and $\Delta v$ to be small, the region $R$ can be approximated by a parallelogram determined by the "secant vectors"

$$\mathbf{a} = \mathbf{r}(u_0 + \Delta u, v_0) - \mathbf{r}(u_0, v_0) \tag{4}$$

$$\mathbf{b} = \mathbf{r}(u_0, v_0 + \Delta v) - \mathbf{r}(u_0, v_0) \tag{5}$$

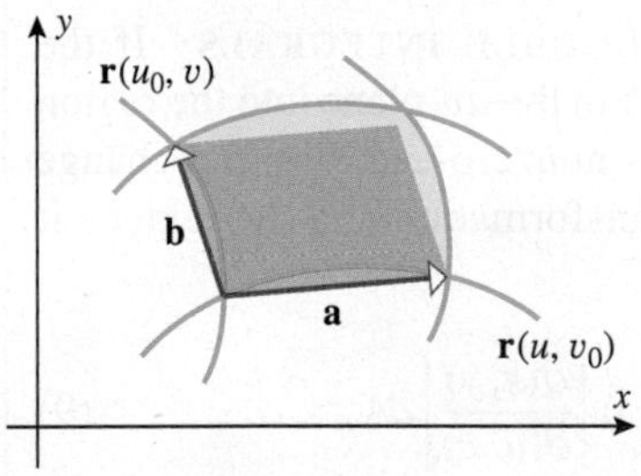

▲ Figure 14.7.6

shown in Figure 14.7.6. A more useful approximation of $R$ can be obtained by using Formulas (7) and (8) of Section 14.4 to approximate these secant vectors by tangent vectors as follows:

$$\mathbf{a} = \frac{\mathbf{r}(u_0 + \Delta u, v_0) - \mathbf{r}(u_0, v_0)}{\Delta u}\Delta u$$

$$\approx \frac{\partial \mathbf{r}}{\partial u}\Delta u = \left(\frac{\partial x}{\partial u}\mathbf{i} + \frac{\partial y}{\partial u}\mathbf{j}\right)\Delta u$$

$$\mathbf{b} = \frac{\mathbf{r}(u_0, v_0 + \Delta v) - \mathbf{r}(u_0, v_0)}{\Delta v}\Delta v$$

$$\approx \frac{\partial \mathbf{r}}{\partial v}\Delta v = \left(\frac{\partial x}{\partial v}\mathbf{i} + \frac{\partial y}{\partial v}\mathbf{j}\right)\Delta v$$

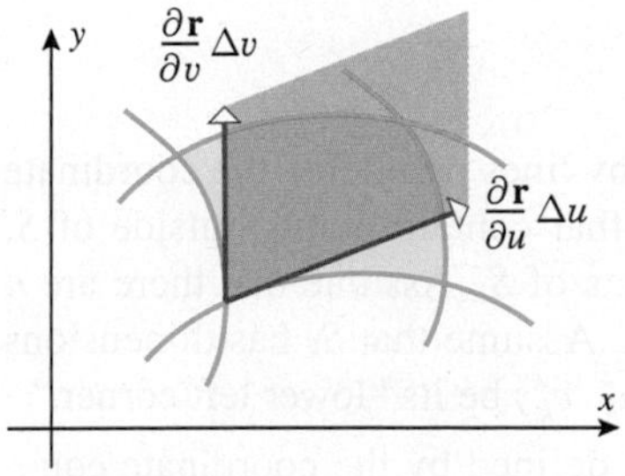

▲ Figure 14.7.7

where the partial derivatives are evaluated at $(u_0, v_0)$ (Figure 14.7.7). Hence, it follows that the area of the region $R$, which we will denote by $\Delta A$, can be approximated by the area of the parallelogram determined by these vectors. Thus, from Theorem 11.4.5($b$) we have

$$\Delta A \approx \left\| \frac{\partial \mathbf{r}}{\partial u}\Delta u \times \frac{\partial \mathbf{r}}{\partial v}\Delta v \right\| = \left\| \frac{\partial \mathbf{r}}{\partial u} \times \frac{\partial \mathbf{r}}{\partial v} \right\| \Delta u \, \Delta v \tag{6}$$

where the derivatives are evaluated at $(u_0, v_0)$. Computing the cross product, we obtain

$$\frac{\partial \mathbf{r}}{\partial u} \times \frac{\partial \mathbf{r}}{\partial v} = \begin{vmatrix} \mathbf{i} & \mathbf{j} & \mathbf{k} \\ \dfrac{\partial x}{\partial u} & \dfrac{\partial y}{\partial u} & 0 \\ \dfrac{\partial x}{\partial v} & \dfrac{\partial y}{\partial v} & 0 \end{vmatrix} = \begin{vmatrix} \dfrac{\partial x}{\partial u} & \dfrac{\partial y}{\partial u} \\ \dfrac{\partial x}{\partial v} & \dfrac{\partial y}{\partial v} \end{vmatrix} \mathbf{k} = \begin{vmatrix} \dfrac{\partial x}{\partial u} & \dfrac{\partial x}{\partial v} \\ \dfrac{\partial y}{\partial u} & \dfrac{\partial y}{\partial v} \end{vmatrix} \mathbf{k} \tag{7}$$

The determinant in (7) is sufficiently important that it has its own terminology and notation.

**14.7.1 DEFINITION** If $T$ is the transformation from the $uv$-plane to the $xy$-plane defined by the equations $x = x(u, v)$, $y = y(u, v)$, then the ***Jacobian of T*** is denoted by $J(u, v)$ or by $\partial(x, y)/\partial(u, v)$ and is defined by

$$J(u,v) = \frac{\partial(x,y)}{\partial(u,v)} = \begin{vmatrix} \dfrac{\partial x}{\partial u} & \dfrac{\partial x}{\partial v} \\[2ex] \dfrac{\partial y}{\partial u} & \dfrac{\partial y}{\partial v} \end{vmatrix} = \frac{\partial x}{\partial u}\frac{\partial y}{\partial v} - \frac{\partial y}{\partial u}\frac{\partial x}{\partial v}$$

Using the notation in this definition, it follows from (6) and (7) that

$$\Delta A \approx \left\| \frac{\partial(x,y)}{\partial(u,v)}\mathbf{k} \right\| \Delta u\, \Delta v$$

or, since $\mathbf{k}$ is a unit vector,

$$\Delta A \approx \left| \frac{\partial(x,y)}{\partial(u,v)} \right| \Delta u\, \Delta v \tag{8}$$

At the point $(u_0, v_0)$ this important formula relates the areas of the regions $R$ and $S$ in Figure 14.7.5; it tells us that *for small values of $\Delta u$ and $\Delta v$, the area of R is approximately the absolute value of the Jacobian times the area of S*. Moreover, it is proved in advanced calculus courses that the relative error in the approximation approaches zero as $\Delta u \to 0$ and $\Delta v \to 0$.

## CHANGE OF VARIABLES IN DOUBLE INTEGRALS

Our next objective is to provide a geometric motivation for the following result.

**14.7.2 CHANGE OF VARIABLES FORMULA FOR DOUBLE INTEGRALS** If the transformation $x = x(u, v)$, $y = y(u, v)$ maps the region $S$ in the $uv$-plane into the region $R$ in the $xy$-plane, and if the Jacobian $\partial(x, y)/\partial(u, v)$ is nonzero and does not change sign on $S$, then with appropriate restrictions on the transformation and the regions it follows that

$$\iint_R f(x,y)\, dA_{xy} = \iint_S f(x(u,v), y(u,v)) \left| \frac{\partial(x,y)}{\partial(u,v)} \right| dA_{uv} \tag{9}$$

where we have attached subscripts to the $dA$'s to help identify the associated variables.

A precise statement of conditions under which Formula (9) holds is beyond the scope of this course. Suffice it to say that the formula holds if $T$ is a one-to-one transformation, $f(x, y)$ is continuous on $R$, the partial derivatives of $x(u, v)$ and $y(u, v)$ exist and are continuous on $S$, and the regions $R$ and $S$ are not complicated.

To motivate Formula (9), we proceed as follows:

- Subdivide the region $S$ in the $uv$-plane into pieces by lines parallel to the coordinate axes, and exclude from consideration any pieces that contain points outside of $S$. This leaves only rectangular regions that are subsets of $S$. Assume that there are $n$ such regions and denote the $k$th such region by $S_k$. Assume that $S_k$ has dimensions $\Delta u_k$ by $\Delta v_k$ and, as shown in Figure 14.7.8*a*, let $(u_k^*, v_k^*)$ be its "lower left corner."
- As shown in Figure 14.7.8*b*, the transformation $T$ defined by the coordinate equations $x = x(u, v)$, $y = y(u, v)$ maps $S_k$ into a curvilinear parallelogram $R_k$ in the $xy$-plane and maps the point $(u_k^*, v_k^*)$ into the point $(x_k^*, y_k^*) = (x(u_k^*, v_k^*), y(u_k^*, v_k^*))$ in $R_k$. Denote the area of $R_k$ by $\Delta A_k$.
- In rectangular coordinates the double integral of $f(x, y)$ over a region $R$ is defined as a limit of Riemann sums in which $R$ is subdivided into *rectangular* subregions. It is proved in advanced calculus courses that under appropriate conditions subdivisions

into *curvilinear* parallelograms can be used instead. Accepting this to be so, we can approximate the double integral of $f(x, y)$ over $R$ as

$$\iint_R f(x,y)\,dA_{xy} \approx \sum_{k=1}^{n} f(x_k^*, y_k^*)\,\Delta A_k$$
$$\approx \sum_{k=1}^{n} f(x(u_k^*, v_k^*), y(u_k^*, v_k^*)) \left|\frac{\partial(x,y)}{\partial(u,v)}\right| \Delta u_k\,\Delta v_k$$

where the Jacobian is evaluated at $(u_k^*, v_k^*)$. But the last expression is a Riemann sum for the integral

$$\iint_S f(x(u,v), y(u,v)) \left|\frac{\partial(x,y)}{\partial(u,v)}\right| dA_{uv}$$

so Formula (9) follows if we assume that the errors in the approximations approach zero as $n \to +\infty$.

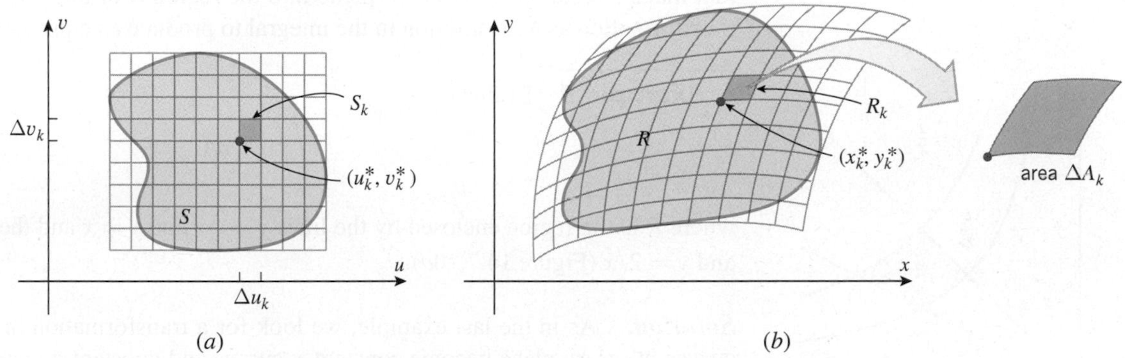


▲ Figure 14.7.8

▶ **Example 2** Evaluate

$$\iint_R \frac{x-y}{x+y}\,dA$$

where $R$ is the region enclosed by $x - y = 0$, $x - y = 1$, $x + y = 1$, and $x + y = 3$ (Figure 14.7.9*a*).

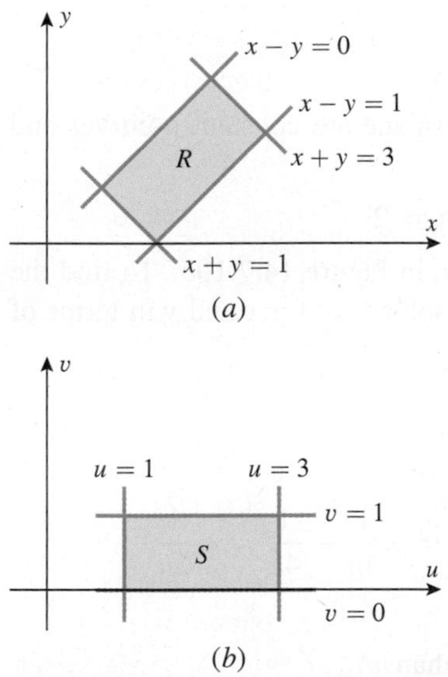


▲ Figure 14.7.9

***Solution.*** This integral would be tedious to evaluate directly because the region $R$ is oriented in such a way that we would have to subdivide it and integrate over each part separately. However, the occurrence of the expressions $x - y$ and $x + y$ in the equations of the boundary suggests that the transformation

$$u = x + y, \quad v = x - y \tag{10}$$

would be helpful, since with this transformation the boundary lines

$$x + y = 1, \quad x + y = 3, \quad x - y = 0, \quad x - y = 1$$

are constant $u$-curves and constant $v$-curves corresponding to the lines

$$u = 1, \quad u = 3, \quad v = 0, \quad v = 1$$

in the $uv$-plane. These lines enclose the rectangular region $S$ shown in Figure 14.7.9*b*. To find the Jacobian $\partial(x, y)/\partial(u, v)$ of this transformation, we first solve (10) for $x$ and $y$ in terms of $u$ and $v$. This yields

$$x = \tfrac{1}{2}(u + v), \quad y = \tfrac{1}{2}(u - v)$$

from which we obtain

$$\frac{\partial(x,y)}{\partial(u,v)} = \begin{vmatrix} \dfrac{\partial x}{\partial u} & \dfrac{\partial x}{\partial v} \\[2ex] \dfrac{\partial y}{\partial u} & \dfrac{\partial y}{\partial v} \end{vmatrix} = \begin{vmatrix} \frac{1}{2} & \frac{1}{2} \\[1ex] \frac{1}{2} & -\frac{1}{2} \end{vmatrix} = -\tfrac{1}{4} - \tfrac{1}{4} = -\tfrac{1}{2}$$

Thus, from Formula (9), but with the notation $dA$ rather than $dA_{xy}$,

$$\iint\limits_R \frac{x-y}{x+y}\,dA = \iint\limits_S \frac{v}{u}\left|\frac{\partial(x,y)}{\partial(u,v)}\right| dA_{uv}$$

$$= \iint\limits_S \frac{v}{u}\left|-\frac{1}{2}\right| dA_{uv} = \frac{1}{2}\int_0^1\int_1^3 \frac{v}{u}\,du\,dv$$

$$= \frac{1}{2}\int_0^1 v\ln|u|\Big]_{u=1}^{3}\,dv$$

$$= \frac{1}{2}\ln 3\int_0^1 v\,dv = \frac{1}{4}\ln 3 \blacktriangleleft$$

The underlying idea illustrated in Example 2 is to find a one-to-one transformation that maps a rectangle $S$ in the $uv$-plane into the region $R$ of integration, and then use that transformation as a substitution in the integral to produce an equivalent integral over $S$.

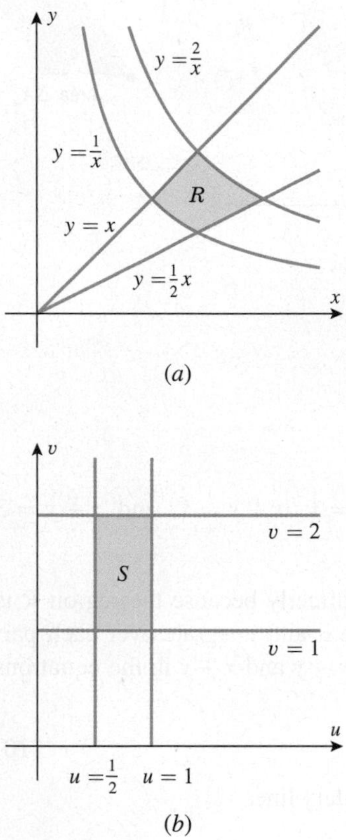

▲ Figure 14.7.10

▶ **Example 3** Evaluate

$$\iint\limits_R e^{xy}\,dA$$

where $R$ is the region enclosed by the lines $y = \frac{1}{2}x$ and $y = x$ and the hyperbolas $y = 1/x$ and $y = 2/x$ (Figure 14.7.10$a$).

***Solution.*** As in the last example, we look for a transformation in which the boundary curves in the $xy$-plane become constant $v$-curves and constant $u$-curves. For this purpose we rewrite the four boundary curves as

$$\frac{y}{x} = \frac{1}{2}, \quad \frac{y}{x} = 1, \quad xy = 1, \quad xy = 2$$

which suggests the transformation

$$u = \frac{y}{x}, \quad v = xy \tag{11}$$

With this transformation the boundary curves in the $xy$-plane are constant $u$-curves and constant $v$-curves corresponding to the lines

$$u = \tfrac{1}{2}, \quad u = 1, \quad v = 1, \quad v = 2$$

in the $uv$-plane. These lines enclose the region $S$ shown in Figure 14.7.10$b$. To find the Jacobian $\partial(x,y)/\partial(u,v)$ of this transformation, we first solve (11) for $x$ and $y$ in terms of $u$ and $v$. This yields

$$x = \sqrt{v/u}, \quad y = \sqrt{uv}$$

from which we obtain

$$\frac{\partial(x,y)}{\partial(u,v)} = \begin{vmatrix} \dfrac{\partial x}{\partial u} & \dfrac{\partial x}{\partial v} \\ \dfrac{\partial y}{\partial u} & \dfrac{\partial y}{\partial v} \end{vmatrix} = \begin{vmatrix} -\dfrac{1}{2u}\sqrt{\dfrac{v}{u}} & \dfrac{1}{2\sqrt{uv}} \\ \dfrac{1}{2}\sqrt{\dfrac{v}{u}} & \dfrac{1}{2}\sqrt{\dfrac{u}{v}} \end{vmatrix} = -\frac{1}{4u} - \frac{1}{4u} = -\frac{1}{2u}$$

Thus, from Formula (9), but with the notation $dA$ rather than $dA_{xy}$,

$$\iint\limits_R e^{xy}\,dA = \iint\limits_S e^{v}\left|-\frac{1}{2u}\right| dA_{uv} = \frac{1}{2}\iint\limits_S \frac{1}{u}e^{v}\,dA_{uv}$$

$$= \frac{1}{2}\int_1^2\int_{1/2}^1 \frac{1}{u}e^{v}\,du\,dv = \frac{1}{2}\int_1^2 e^{v}\ln|u|\Big]_{u=1/2}^{1}\,dv$$

$$= \frac{1}{2}\ln 2\int_1^2 e^{v}\,dv = \frac{1}{2}(e^2 - e)\ln 2 \blacktriangleleft$$

## CHANGE OF VARIABLES IN TRIPLE INTEGRALS

Equations of the form

$$x = x(u, v, w), \quad y = y(u, v, w), \quad z = z(u, v, w) \tag{12}$$

define a ***transformation*** $T$ from $uvw$-space to $xyz$-space. Just as a transformation $x = x(u, v)$, $y = y(u, v)$ in two variables maps small rectangles in the $uv$-plane into curvilinear parallelograms in the $xy$-plane, so (12) maps small rectangular parallelepipeds in $uvw$-space into curvilinear parallelepipeds in $xyz$-space (Figure 14.7.11). The definition of the Jacobian of (12) is similar to Definition 14.7.1.

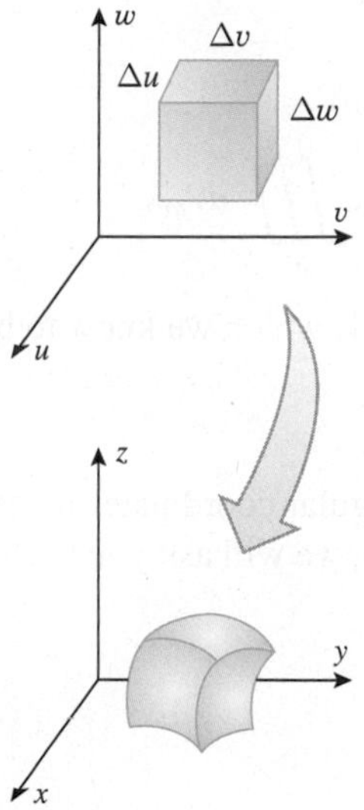

▲ Figure 14.7.11

**14.7.3 DEFINITION** If $T$ is the transformation from $uvw$-space to $xyz$-space defined by the equations $x = x(u, v, w)$, $y = y(u, v, w)$, $z = z(u, v, w)$, then the ***Jacobian of T*** is denoted by $J(u, v, w)$ or $\partial(x, y, z)/\partial(u, v, w)$ and is defined by

$$J(u, v, w) = \frac{\partial(x, y, z)}{\partial(u, v, w)} = \begin{vmatrix} \dfrac{\partial x}{\partial u} & \dfrac{\partial x}{\partial v} & \dfrac{\partial x}{\partial w} \\ \dfrac{\partial y}{\partial u} & \dfrac{\partial y}{\partial v} & \dfrac{\partial y}{\partial w} \\ \dfrac{\partial z}{\partial u} & \dfrac{\partial z}{\partial v} & \dfrac{\partial z}{\partial w} \end{vmatrix}$$

For small values of $\Delta u$, $\Delta v$, and $\Delta w$, the volume $\Delta V$ of the curvilinear parallelepiped in Figure 14.7.11 is related to the volume $\Delta u\, \Delta v\, \Delta w$ of the rectangular parallelepiped by

$$\Delta V \approx \left| \frac{\partial(x, y, z)}{\partial(u, v, w)} \right| \Delta u\, \Delta v\, \Delta w \tag{13}$$

which is the analog of Formula (8). Using this relationship and an argument similar to the one that led to Formula (9), we can obtain the following result.

**14.7.4 CHANGE OF VARIABLES FORMULA FOR TRIPLE INTEGRALS** If the transformation $x = x(u, v, w)$, $y = y(u, v, w)$, $z = z(u, v, w)$ maps the region $S$ in $uvw$-space into the region $R$ in $xyz$-space, and if the Jacobian $\partial(x, y, z)/\partial(u, v, w)$ is nonzero and does not change sign on $S$, then with appropriate restrictions on the transformation and the regions it follows that

$$\iiint_R f(x, y, z)\, dV_{xyz} = \iiint_S f(x(u, v, w), y(u, v, w), z(u, v, w)) \left| \frac{\partial(x, y, z)}{\partial(u, v, w)} \right| dV_{uvw} \tag{14}$$

▶ **Example 4** Find the volume of the region $G$ enclosed by the ellipsoid

$$\frac{x^2}{a^2} + \frac{y^2}{b^2} + \frac{z^2}{c^2} = 1$$

***Solution.*** The volume $V$ is given by the triple integral

$$V = \iiint_G dV$$

To evaluate this integral, we make the change of variables

$$x = au, \quad y = bv, \quad z = cw \tag{15}$$

which maps the region $S$ in $uvw$-space enclosed by a sphere of radius 1 into the region $G$ in $xyz$-space. This can be seen from (15) by noting that

$$\frac{x^2}{a^2} + \frac{y^2}{b^2} + \frac{z^2}{c^2} = 1 \quad \text{becomes} \quad u^2 + v^2 + w^2 = 1$$

The Jacobian of (15) is

$$\frac{\partial(x,y,z)}{\partial(u,v,w)} = \begin{vmatrix} \frac{\partial x}{\partial u} & \frac{\partial x}{\partial v} & \frac{\partial x}{\partial w} \\ \frac{\partial y}{\partial u} & \frac{\partial y}{\partial v} & \frac{\partial y}{\partial w} \\ \frac{\partial z}{\partial u} & \frac{\partial z}{\partial v} & \frac{\partial z}{\partial w} \end{vmatrix} = \begin{vmatrix} a & 0 & 0 \\ 0 & b & 0 \\ 0 & 0 & c \end{vmatrix} = abc$$

Thus, from Formula (14), but with the notation $dV$ rather than $dV_{xyz}$,

$$V = \iiint_G dV = \iiint_S \left| \frac{\partial(x,y,z)}{\partial(u,v,w)} \right| dV_{uvw} = abc \iiint_S dV_{uvw}$$

The last integral is the volume enclosed by a sphere of radius 1, which we know to be $\frac{4}{3}\pi$. Thus, the volume enclosed by the ellipsoid is $V = \frac{4}{3}\pi abc$. ◂

Jacobians also arise in converting triple integrals in rectangular coordinates to iterated integrals in cylindrical and spherical coordinates. For example, we will ask you to show in Exercise 48 that the Jacobian of the transformation

$$x = r\cos\theta, \quad y = r\sin\theta, \quad z = z$$

is

$$\frac{\partial(x,y,z)}{\partial(r,\theta,z)} = r$$

and the Jacobian of the transformation

$$x = \rho\sin\phi\cos\theta, \quad y = \rho\sin\phi\sin\theta, \quad z = \rho\cos\phi$$

is

$$\frac{\partial(x,y,z)}{\partial(\rho,\phi,\theta)} = \rho^2\sin\phi$$

Thus, Formulas (6) and (10) of Section 14.6 can be expressed in terms of Jacobians as

$$\iiint_G f(x,y,z)\,dV = \iiint_{\substack{\text{appropriate}\\ \text{limits}}} f(r\cos\theta, r\sin\theta, z)\frac{\partial(x,y,z)}{\partial(r,\theta,z)}\,dz\,dr\,d\theta \tag{16}$$

The absolute-value signs are omitted from Formulas (16) and (17) because the Jacobians are nonnegative (see the restrictions in Table 11.8.1).

$$\iiint_G f(x,y,z)\,dV = \iiint_{\substack{\text{appropriate}\\ \text{limits}}} f(\rho\sin\phi\cos\theta, \rho\sin\phi\sin\theta, \rho\cos\phi)\frac{\partial(x,y,z)}{\partial(\rho,\phi,\theta)}\,d\rho\,d\phi\,d\theta \tag{17}$$

## ✓ QUICK CHECK EXERCISES 14.7 (See page 959 for answers.)

**1.** Let $T$ be the transformation from the $uv$-plane to the $xy$-plane defined by the equations

$$x = u - 2v, \quad y = 3u + v$$

(a) Sketch the image under $T$ of the rectangle $1 \le u \le 3$, $0 \le v \le 2$.

(b) Solve for $u$ and $v$ in terms of $x$ and $y$:

$u =$ ______, $v =$ ______

**2.** State the relationship between $R$ and $S$ in the change of variables formula

$$\iint_R f(x,y)\,dA_{xy} = \iint_S f(x(u,v), y(u,v)) \left| \frac{\partial(x,y)}{\partial(u,v)} \right| dA_{uv}$$

**3.** Let $T$ be the transformation in Quick Check Exercise 1.

(a) The Jacobian $\partial(x,y)/\partial(u,v)$ of $T$ is ______.

(b) Let $R$ be the region in Quick Check Exercise 1(a). Fill in the missing integrand and limits of integration for the change of variables given by $T$.

$$\iint_R e^{x+2y}\,dA = \int_{\square}^{\square}\int_{\square}^{\square} \underline{\qquad\qquad}\,du\,dv$$

**4.** The Jacobian of the transformation

$$x = uv, \quad y = vw, \quad z = 2w$$

is

$$\frac{\partial(x,y,z)}{\partial(u,v,w)} = \underline{\qquad\qquad}$$

## EXERCISE SET 14.7

**1–4** Find the Jacobian $\partial(x, y)/\partial(u, v)$. ■

**1.** $x = u + 4v,\ y = 3u - 5v$

**2.** $x = u + 2v^2,\ y = 2u^2 - v$

**3.** $x = \sin u + \cos v,\ y = -\cos u + \sin v$

**4.** $x = \dfrac{2u}{u^2 + v^2},\ y = -\dfrac{2v}{u^2 + v^2}$

**5–8** Solve for $x$ and $y$ in terms of $u$ and $v$, and then find the Jacobian $\partial(x, y)/\partial(u, v)$. ■

**5.** $u = 2x - 5y,\ v = x + 2y$

**6.** $u = e^x,\ v = ye^{-x}$

**7.** $u = x^2 - y^2,\ v = x^2 + y^2 \quad (x > 0, y > 0)$

**8.** $u = xy,\ v = xy^3 \quad (x > 0, y > 0)$

**9–12** Find the Jacobian $\partial(x, y, z)/\partial(u, v, w)$. ■

**9.** $x = 3u + v,\ y = u - 2w,\ z = v + w$

**10.** $x = u - uv,\ y = uv - uvw,\ z = uvw$

**11.** $u = xy,\ v = y,\ w = x + z$

**12.** $u = x + y + z,\ v = x + y - z,\ w = x - y + z$

**13–16 True–False** Determine whether the statement is true or false. Explain your answer. ■

**13.** If $\mathbf{r} = x(u, v)\mathbf{i} + y(u, v)\mathbf{j}$, then evaluating $|\partial(x, y)/\partial(u, v)|$ at a point $(u_0, v_0)$ gives the perimeter of the parallelogram generated by the vectors $\partial\mathbf{r}/\partial u$ and $\partial\mathbf{r}/\partial v$ at $(u_0, v_0)$.

**14.** If $\mathbf{r} = x(u, v)\mathbf{i} + y(u, v)\mathbf{j}$ maps the rectangle $0 \le u \le 2$, $1 \le v \le 5$ to a region $R$ in the $xy$-plane, then the area of $R$ is given by

$$\int_1^5 \int_0^2 \left| \frac{\partial(x, y)}{\partial(u, v)} \right| du\, dv$$

**15.** The Jacobian of the transformation $x = r\cos\theta, y = r\sin\theta$ is

$$\frac{\partial(x, y)}{\partial(r, \theta)} = r^2$$

**16.** The Jacobian of the transformation $x = \rho\sin\phi\cos\theta$, $y = \rho\sin\phi\sin\theta$, $z = \rho\cos\phi$ is

$$\frac{\partial(x, y, z)}{\partial(\rho, \phi, \theta)} = \rho^2 \sin\phi$$

**FOCUS ON CONCEPTS**

**17–20** Sketch the image in the $xy$-plane of the set $S$ under the given transformation. ■

**17.**

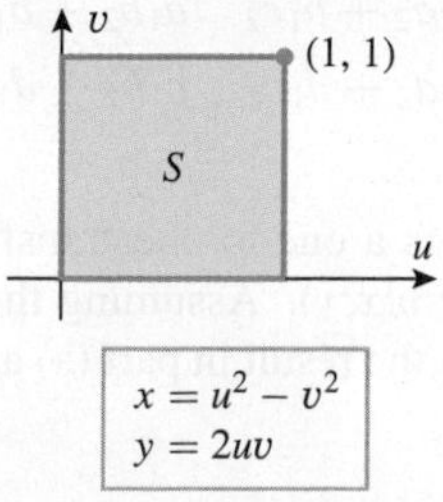


**18.**

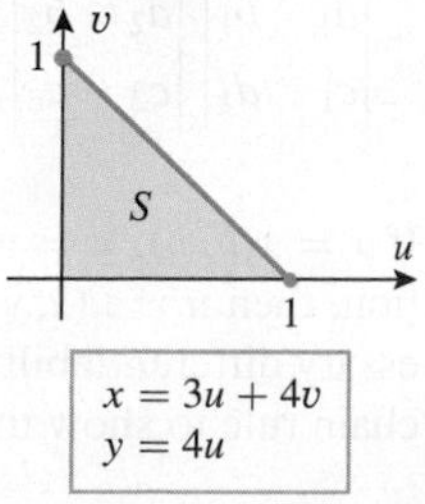


**19.**

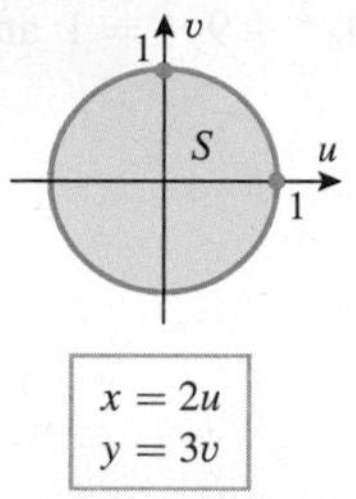


**20.**

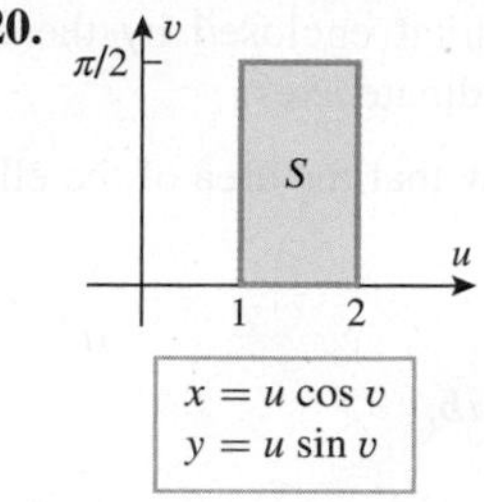


**21.** Use the transformation $u = x - 2y$, $v = 2x + y$ to find

$$\iint_R \frac{x - 2y}{2x + y}\, dA$$

where $R$ is the rectangular region enclosed by the lines $x - 2y = 1$, $x - 2y = 4$, $2x + y = 1$, $2x + y = 3$.

**22.** Use the transformation $u = x + y$, $v = x - y$ to find

$$\iint_R (x - y)e^{x^2 - y^2}\, dA$$

over the rectangular region $R$ enclosed by the lines $x + y = 0$, $x + y = 1$, $x - y = 1$, $x - y = 4$.

**23.** Use the transformation $u = \frac{1}{2}(x + y)$, $v = \frac{1}{2}(x - y)$ to find

$$\iint_R \sin\tfrac{1}{2}(x + y)\cos\tfrac{1}{2}(x - y)\, dA$$

over the triangular region $R$ with vertices $(0, 0)$, $(2, 0)$, $(1, 1)$.

**24.** Use the transformation $u = y/x$, $v = xy$ to find

$$\iint_R xy^3\, dA$$

over the region $R$ in the first quadrant enclosed by $y = x$, $y = 3x$, $xy = 1$, $xy = 4$.

**25–27** The transformation $x = au$, $y = bv$ $(a > 0, b > 0)$ can be rewritten as $x/a = u$, $y/b = v$, and hence it maps the circular region

$$u^2 + v^2 \le 1$$

into the elliptical region

$$\frac{x^2}{a^2} + \frac{y^2}{b^2} \le 1$$

In these exercises, perform the integration by transforming the elliptical region of integration into a circular region of integration and then evaluating the transformed integral in polar coordinates. ■

**25.** $\displaystyle\iint_R \sqrt{16x^2 + 9y^2}\, dA$, where $R$ is the region enclosed by the ellipse $(x^2/9) + (y^2/16) = 1$.

**26.** $\displaystyle\iint_R e^{-(x^2 + 4y^2)}\, dA$, where $R$ is the region enclosed by the ellipse $(x^2/4) + y^2 = 1$.

**27.** $\iint_R \sin(4x^2 + 9y^2)\, dA$, where $R$ is the region in the first quadrant enclosed by the ellipse $4x^2 + 9y^2 = 1$ and the coordinate axes.

**28.** Show that the area of the ellipse

$$\frac{x^2}{a^2} + \frac{y^2}{b^2} = 1$$

is $\pi ab$.

**29–30** If $a, b$, and $c$ are positive constants, then the transformation $x = au$, $y = bv$, $z = cw$ can be rewritten as $x/a = u$, $y/b = v$, $z/c = w$, and hence it maps the spherical region

$$u^2 + v^2 + w^2 \leq 1$$

into the ellipsoidal region

$$\frac{x^2}{a^2} + \frac{y^2}{b^2} + \frac{z^2}{c^2} \leq 1$$

In these exercises, perform the integration by transforming the ellipsoidal region of integration into a spherical region of integration and then evaluating the transformed integral in spherical coordinates. ■

**29.** $\iiint_G x^2\, dV$, where $G$ is the region enclosed by the ellipsoid $9x^2 + 4y^2 + z^2 = 36$.

**30.** $\iiint_G (y^2 + z^2)\, dV$, where $G$ is the region enclosed by the ellipsoid

$$\frac{x^2}{a^2} + \frac{y^2}{b^2} + \frac{z^2}{c^2} = 1$$

**FOCUS ON CONCEPTS**

**31–34** Find a transformation

$$u = f(x, y), \quad v = g(x, y)$$

that when applied to the region $R$ in the $xy$-plane has as its image the region $S$ in the $uv$-plane. ■

**31.**

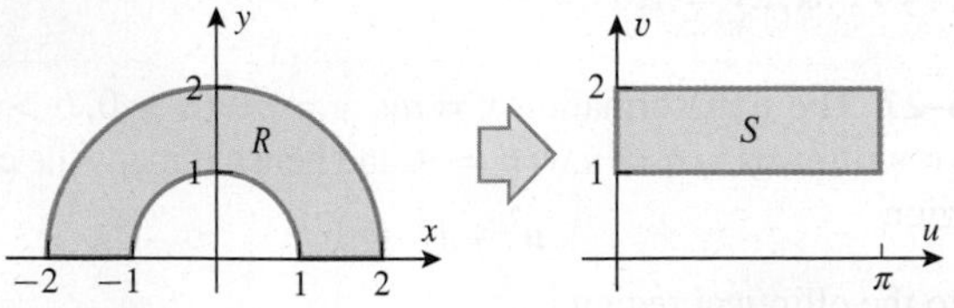


**32.**

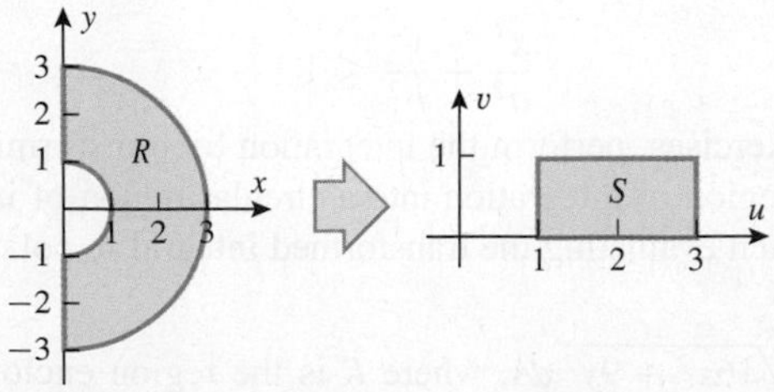


**33.**

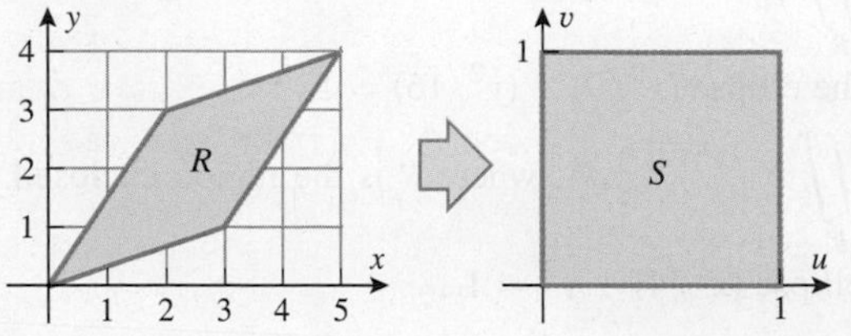


**34.**

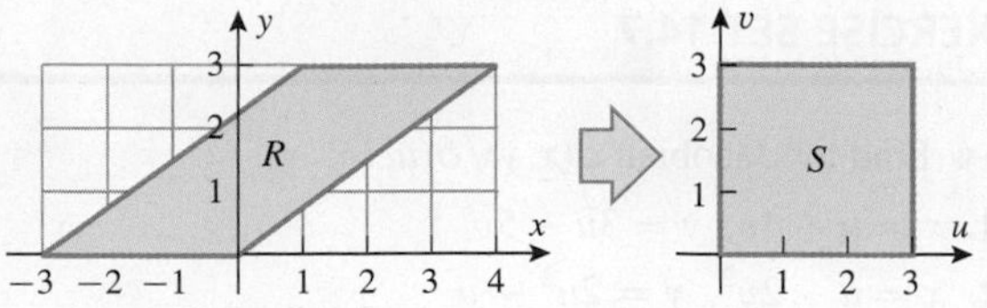


**35–38** Evaluate the integral by making an appropriate change of variables. ■

**35.** $\iint_R \frac{y - 4x}{y + 4x}\, dA$, where $R$ is the region enclosed by the lines $y = 4x$, $y = 4x + 2$, $y = 2 - 4x$, $y = 5 - 4x$.

**36.** $\iint_R (x^2 - y^2)\, dA$, where $R$ is the rectangular region enclosed by the lines $y = -x$, $y = 1 - x$, $y = x$, $y = x + 2$.

**37.** $\iint_R \frac{\sin(x - y)}{\cos(x + y)}\, dA$, where $R$ is the triangular region enclosed by the lines $y = 0$, $y = x$, $x + y = \pi/4$.

**38.** $\iint_R e^{(y-x)/(y+x)}\, dA$, where $R$ is the region in the first quadrant enclosed by the trapezoid with vertices $(0, 1)$, $(1, 0)$, $(0, 4)$, $(4, 0)$.

**39.** Use an appropriate change of variables to find the area of the region in the first quadrant enclosed by the curves $y = x$, $y = 2x$, $x = y^2$, $x = 4y^2$.

**40.** Use an appropriate change of variables to find the volume of the solid bounded above by the plane $x + y + z = 9$, below by the $xy$-plane, and laterally by the elliptic cylinder $4x^2 + 9y^2 = 36$. [*Hint:* Express the volume as a double integral in $xy$-coordinates, then use polar coordinates to evaluate the transformed integral.]

**41.** Use the transformation $u = x$, $v = z - y$, $w = xy$ to find

$$\iiint_G (z - y)^2 xy\, dV$$

where $G$ is the region enclosed by the surfaces $x = 1$, $x = 3$, $z = y$, $z = y + 1$, $xy = 2$, $xy = 4$.

**42.** Use the transformation $u = xy$, $v = yz$, $w = xz$ to find the volume of the region in the first octant that is enclosed by the hyperbolic cylinders $xy = 1$, $xy = 2$, $yz = 1$, $yz = 3$, $xz = 1$, $xz = 4$.

**43.** (a) Verify that

$$\begin{vmatrix} a_1 & b_1 \\ c_1 & d_1 \end{vmatrix} \begin{vmatrix} a_2 & b_2 \\ c_2 & d_2 \end{vmatrix} = \begin{vmatrix} a_1a_2 + b_1c_2 & a_1b_2 + b_1d_2 \\ c_1a_2 + d_1c_2 & c_1b_2 + d_1d_2 \end{vmatrix}$$

(b) If $x = x(u, v)$, $y = y(u, v)$ is a one-to-one transformation, then $u = u(x, y)$, $v = v(x, y)$. Assuming the necessary differentiability, use the result in part (a) and the chain rule to show that

$$\frac{\partial(x, y)}{\partial(u, v)} \cdot \frac{\partial(u, v)}{\partial(x, y)} = 1$$

**44–46** The formula obtained in part (b) of Exercise 43 is useful in integration problems where it is inconvenient or impossible to solve the transformation equations $u = f(x, y)$, $v = g(x, y)$ explicitly for $x$ and $y$ in terms of $u$ and $v$. In these exercises, use the relationship

$$\frac{\partial(x, y)}{\partial(u, v)} = \frac{1}{\partial(u, v)/\partial(x, y)}$$

to avoid solving for $x$ and $y$ in terms of $u$ and $v$. ■

**44.** Use the transformation $u = xy$, $v = xy^4$ to find

$$\iint_R \sin(xy)\, dA$$

where $R$ is the region enclosed by the curves $xy = \pi$, $xy = 2\pi$, $xy^4 = 1$, $xy^4 = 2$.

**45.** Use the transformation $u = x^2 - y^2$, $v = x^2 + y^2$ to find

$$\iint_R xy\, dA$$

where $R$ is the region in the first quadrant that is enclosed by the hyperbolas $x^2 - y^2 = 1$, $x^2 - y^2 = 4$ and the circles $x^2 + y^2 = 9$, $x^2 + y^2 = 16$.

**46.** Use the transformation $u = xy$, $v = x^2 - y^2$ to find

$$\iint_R (x^4 - y^4)e^{xy}\, dA$$

where $R$ is the region in the first quadrant enclosed by the hyperbolas $xy = 1$, $xy = 3$, $x^2 - y^2 = 3$, $x^2 - y^2 = 4$.

**47.** The three-variable analog of the formula derived in part (b) of Exercise 43 is

$$\frac{\partial(x, y, z)}{\partial(u, v, w)} \cdot \frac{\partial(u, v, w)}{\partial(x, y, z)} = 1$$

Use this result to show that the volume $V$ of the oblique parallelepiped that is bounded by the planes $x + y + 2z = \pm 3$, $x - 2y + z = \pm 2$, $4x + y + z = \pm 6$ is $V = 16$.

**48.** (a) Consider the transformation

$$x = r\cos\theta, \quad y = r\sin\theta, \quad z = z$$

from cylindrical to rectangular coordinates, where $r \geq 0$. Show that

$$\frac{\partial(x, y, z)}{\partial(r, \theta, z)} = r$$

(b) Consider the transformation

$$x = \rho\sin\phi\cos\theta, \quad y = \rho\sin\phi\sin\theta, \quad z = \rho\cos\phi$$

from spherical to rectangular coordinates, where $0 \leq \phi \leq \pi$. Show that

$$\frac{\partial(x, y, z)}{\partial(\rho, \phi, \theta)} = \rho^2\sin\phi$$

**49. Writing** For single-variable definite integrals, the technique of substitution was generally used to simplify the integrand. Discuss some motivations for using a change of variables in a multiple integral.

**50. Writing** Suppose that the boundary curves of a region $R$ in the $xy$-plane can be described as level curves of various functions. Discuss how this information can be used to choose an appropriate change of variables for a double integral over $R$. Illustrate your discussion with an example.

---

✓ **QUICK CHECK ANSWERS 14.7** 1. (a) The image is the region in the $xy$-plane enclosed by the parallelogram with vertices $(1, 3)$, $(-3, 5)$, $(-1, 11)$, and $(3, 9)$. (b) $u = \frac{1}{7}(x + 2y)$, $v = \frac{1}{7}(y - 3x)$ 2. $S$ is a region in the $uv$-plane and $R$ is the image of $S$ in the $xy$-plane under the transformation $x = x(u, v)$, $y = y(u, v)$. 3. (a) 7 (b) $\int_0^2\int_1^3 7e^{7u}\, du\, dv$ 4. $2vw$

---

# 14.8 CENTERS OF GRAVITY USING MULTIPLE INTEGRALS

*In Section 6.7 we showed how to find the mass and center of gravity of a homogeneous lamina using single integrals. In this section we will show how double and triple integrals can be used to find the mass and center of gravity of inhomogeneous laminas and three-dimensional solids.*

## ■ DENSITY AND MASS OF AN INHOMOGENEOUS LAMINA

An idealized flat object that is thin enough to be viewed as a two-dimensional plane region is called a ***lamina*** (Figure 14.8.1). A lamina is called ***homogeneous*** if its composition is uniform throughout and ***inhomogeneous*** otherwise. The ***density*** of a *homogeneous* lamina was defined in Section 6.7 to be its mass per unit area. Thus, the density $\delta$ of a homogeneous lamina of mass $M$ and area $A$ is given by $\delta = M/A$.

▲ **Figure 14.8.1**

For an inhomogeneous lamina the composition may vary from point to point, and hence an appropriate definition of "density" must reflect this. To motivate such a definition, suppose that the lamina is placed in an $xy$-plane. The density at a point $(x, y)$ can be specified by a function $\delta(x, y)$, called the ***density function***, which can be interpreted as follows: Construct a small rectangle centered at $(x, y)$ and let $\Delta M$ and $\Delta A$ be the mass and area of the portion of the lamina enclosed by this rectangle (Figure 14.8.2). If the ratio $\Delta M/\Delta A$

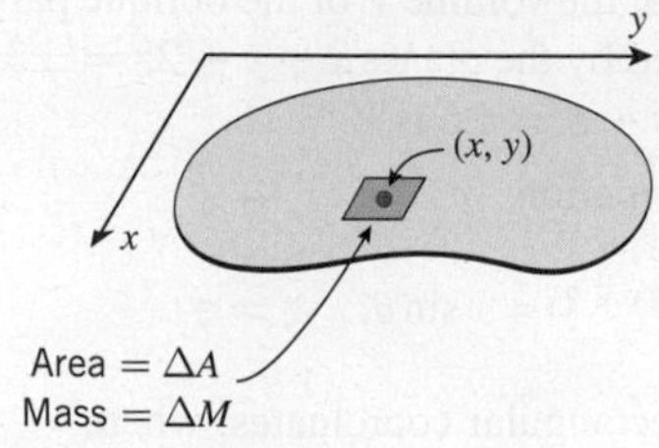


▲ **Figure 14.8.2**

approaches a limiting value as the dimensions (and hence the area) of the rectangle approach zero, then this limit is considered to be the density of the lamina at $(x, y)$. Symbolically,

$$\delta(x, y) = \lim_{\Delta A \to 0} \frac{\Delta M}{\Delta A} \tag{1}$$

From this relationship we obtain the approximation

$$\Delta M \approx \delta(x, y)\Delta A \tag{2}$$

which relates the mass and area of a small rectangular portion of the lamina centered at $(x, y)$. It is assumed that as the dimensions of the rectangle tend to zero, the error in this approximation also tends to zero.

The following result shows how to find the mass of a lamina from its density function.

> **14.8.1 MASS OF A LAMINA** If a lamina with a continuous density function $\delta(x, y)$ occupies a region $R$ in the $xy$-plane, then its total mass $M$ is given by
>
> $$M = \iint_R \delta(x, y)\, dA \tag{3}$$

This formula can be motivated by a limiting process that can be outlined as follows: Imagine the lamina to be subdivided into rectangular pieces using lines parallel to the coordinate axes and excluding from consideration any nonrectangular parts at the boundary (Figure 14.8.3). Assume that there are $n$ such rectangular pieces, and suppose that the $k$th piece has area $\Delta A_k$. If we let $(x_k^*, y_k^*)$ denote the center of the $k$th piece, then from Formula (2), the mass $\Delta M_k$ of this piece can be approximated by

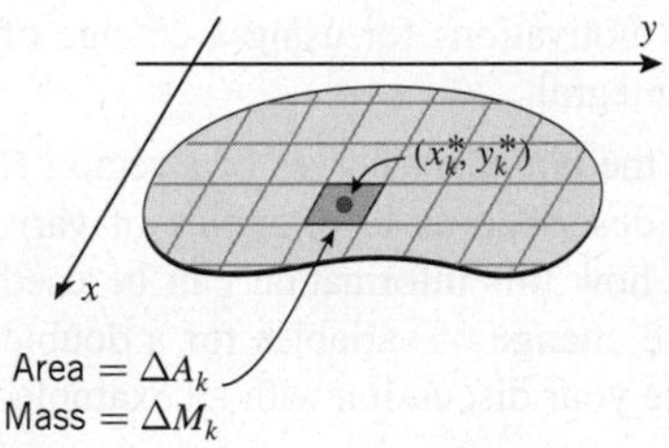


▲ **Figure 14.8.3**

$$\Delta M_k \approx \delta(x_k^*, y_k^*)\Delta A_k \tag{4}$$

and hence the mass $M$ of the entire lamina can be approximated by

$$M \approx \sum_{k=1}^{n} \delta(x_k^*, y_k^*)\Delta A_k$$

If we now increase $n$ in such a way that the dimensions of the rectangles tend to zero, then it is plausible that the errors in our approximations will approach zero, so

$$M = \lim_{n \to +\infty} \sum_{k=1}^{n} \delta(x_k^*, y_k^*)\Delta A_k = \iint_R \delta(x, y)\, dA$$

▶ **Example 1** A triangular lamina with vertices (0, 0), (0, 1), and (1, 0) has density function $\delta(x, y) = xy$. Find its total mass.

***Solution.*** Referring to (3) and Figure 14.8.4, the mass $M$ of the lamina is

$$M = \iint_R \delta(x, y)\, dA = \iint_R xy\, dA = \int_0^1 \int_0^{-x+1} xy\, dy\, dx$$

$$= \int_0^1 \left[\frac{1}{2}xy^2\right]_{y=0}^{-x+1} dx = \int_0^1 \left[\frac{1}{2}x^3 - x^2 + \frac{1}{2}x\right] dx = \frac{1}{24} \text{ (unit of mass)} \blacktriangleleft$$

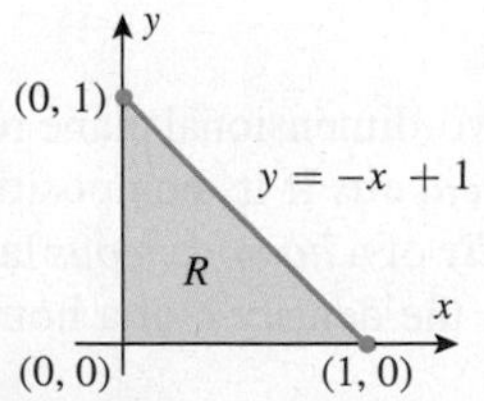


▲ **Figure 14.8.4**

## CENTER OF GRAVITY OF AN INHOMOGENEOUS LAMINA

Recall that the ***center of gravity*** of a lamina occupying a region $R$ in the horizontal $xy$-plane is the point $(\bar{x}, \bar{y})$ such that the effect of gravity on the lamina is "equivalent" to that of a single force acting at $(\bar{x}, \bar{y})$. If $(\bar{x}, \bar{y})$ is in $R$, then the lamina will balance horizontally on a point of support placed at $(\bar{x}, \bar{y})$. In Section 6.7 we showed how to locate the center of gravity of a homogeneous lamina. We now turn to this problem for an inhomogeneous lamina.

> **14.8.2 PROBLEM** Suppose that a lamina with a continuous density function $\delta(x, y)$ occupies a region $R$ in a horizontal $xy$-plane. Find the coordinates $(\bar{x}, \bar{y})$ of the center of gravity.

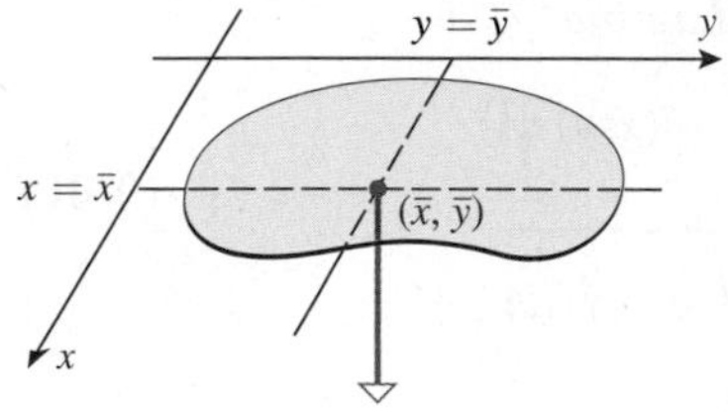

▲ **Figure 14.8.5**

To motivate the solution of Problem 14.8.2, consider what happens if we try to place the lamina in Figure 14.8.5 on a knife-edge running along the line $y = \bar{y}$. Since the lamina behaves as if its entire mass is concentrated at $(\bar{x}, \bar{y})$, the lamina will be in perfect balance. Similarly, the lamina will be in perfect balance if the knife-edge runs along the line $x = \bar{x}$. To find these lines of balance we begin by reviewing some results from Section 6.7 about rotations.

Recall that if a point-mass $m$ is located at the point $(x, y)$, then the moment of $m$ about $x = a$ measures the tendency of the mass to produce a rotation about the line $x = a$, and the moment of $m$ about $y = c$ measures the tendency of the mass to produce a rotation about the line $y = c$. The moments are given by the following formulas:

$$\begin{bmatrix}\text{moment of } m\\ \text{about the}\\ \text{line } x = a\end{bmatrix} = m(x - a) \quad \text{and} \quad \begin{bmatrix}\text{moment of } m\\ \text{about the}\\ \text{line } y = c\end{bmatrix} = m(y - c) \qquad (5\text{–}6)$$

If a number of point-masses are distributed throughout the $xy$-plane, the sum of their moments about $x = a$ is a measure of the tendency of the masses to produce a rotation of the plane (viewed as a weightless sheet) about the line $x = a$. If the sum of these moments is zero, the collective masses will produce no net rotational effect about the line. (Intuitively, this means that the plane would balance on a knife-edge along the line $x = a$. Similarly, if the sum of the moments of the masses about $y = c$ is zero, the plane would balance on a knife-edge along the line $y = c$.)

We are now ready to solve Problem 14.8.2. We imagine the lamina to be subdivided into rectangular pieces using lines parallel to the coordinate axes and excluding from consideration any nonrectangular pieces at the boundary (Figure 14.8.3). We assume that there are $n$ such rectangular pieces and that the $k$th piece has area $\Delta A_k$ and mass $\Delta M_k$. We will let $(x_k^*, y_k^*)$ be the center of the $k$th piece, and we will assume that the entire mass of the $k$th piece is concentrated at its center. From (4), the mass of the $k$th piece can be approximated by

$$\Delta M_k \approx \delta(x_k^*, y_k^*)\Delta A_k$$

Since the lamina balances on the lines $x = \bar{x}$ and $y = \bar{y}$, the sum of the moments of the rectangular pieces about those lines should be close to zero; that is,

$$\sum_{k=1}^{n} (x_k^* - \bar{x})\Delta M_k = \sum_{k=1}^{n} (x_k^* - \bar{x})\delta(x_k^*, y_k^*)\Delta A_k \approx 0$$

$$\sum_{k=1}^{n} (y_k^* - \bar{y})\Delta M_k = \sum_{k=1}^{n} (y_k^* - \bar{y})\delta(x_k^*, y_k^*)\Delta A_k \approx 0$$

If we now increase $n$ in such a way that the dimensions of the rectangles tend to zero, then it is plausible that the errors in our approximations will approach zero, so that

$$\lim_{n\to+\infty} \sum_{k=1}^{n} (x_k^* - \bar{x})\delta(x_k^*, y_k^*)\Delta A_k = 0$$

$$\lim_{n\to+\infty} \sum_{k=1}^{n} (y_k^* - \bar{y})\delta(x_k^*, y_k^*)\Delta A_k = 0$$

from which we obtain

$$\iint_R (x - \bar{x})\delta(x, y)\, dA = \iint_R x\delta(x, y)\, dA - \bar{x} \iint_R \delta(x, y)\, dA = 0 \tag{7}$$

$$\iint_R (y - \bar{y})\delta(x, y)\, dA = \iint_R y\delta(x, y)\, dA - \bar{y} \iint_R \delta(x, y)\, dA = 0 \tag{8}$$

Solving (7) and (8) respectively for $\bar{x}$ and $\bar{y}$ gives formulas for the center of gravity of a lamina:

***Center of Gravity $(\bar{x}, \bar{y})$ of a Lamina***

$$\bar{x} = \frac{\displaystyle\iint_R x\delta(x, y)\, dA}{\displaystyle\iint_R \delta(x, y)\, dA}, \qquad \bar{y} = \frac{\displaystyle\iint_R y\delta(x, y)\, dA}{\displaystyle\iint_R \delta(x, y)\, dA} \tag{9–10}$$

In both formulas the denominator is the mass $M$ of the lamina [see (3)]. The numerator in the formula for $\bar{x}$ is denoted by $M_y$ and is called the ***first moment of the lamina about the y-axis***; the numerator of the formula for $\bar{y}$ is denoted by $M_x$ and is called the ***first moment of the lamina about the x-axis***. Thus, Formulas (9) and (10) can be expressed as

***Alternative Formulas for Center of Gravity $(\bar{x}, \bar{y})$ of a Lamina***

$$\bar{x} = \frac{M_y}{M} = \frac{1}{\text{mass of } R} \iint_R x\delta(x, y)\, dA \tag{11}$$

$$\bar{y} = \frac{M_x}{M} = \frac{1}{\text{mass of } R} \iint_R y\delta(x, y)\, dA \tag{12}$$

---

▶ **Example 2** Find the center of gravity of the triangular lamina with vertices $(0, 0)$, $(0, 1)$, and $(1, 0)$ and density function $\delta(x, y) = xy$.

***Solution.*** The lamina is shown in Figure 14.8.4. In Example 1 we found the mass of the lamina to be

$$M = \iint_R \delta(x, y)\, dA = \iint_R xy\, dA = \frac{1}{24}$$

The moment of the lamina about the $y$-axis is

$$M_y = \iint_R x\delta(x, y)\, dA = \iint_R x^2 y\, dA = \int_0^1 \int_0^{-x+1} x^2 y\, dy\, dx$$

$$= \int_0^1 \left[\frac{1}{2}x^2 y^2\right]_{y=0}^{-x+1} dx = \int_0^1 \left(\frac{1}{2}x^4 - x^3 + \frac{1}{2}x^2\right) dx = \frac{1}{60}$$

and the moment about the $x$-axis is

$$M_x = \iint_R y\delta(x, y)\, dA = \iint_R xy^2\, dA = \int_0^1 \int_0^{-x+1} xy^2\, dy\, dx$$

$$= \int_0^1 \left[\frac{1}{3}xy^3\right]_{y=0}^{-x+1} dx = \int_0^1 \left(-\frac{1}{3}x^4 + x^3 - x^2 + \frac{1}{3}x\right) dx = \frac{1}{60}$$

From (11) and (12),

$$\bar{x} = \frac{M_y}{M} = \frac{1/60}{1/24} = \frac{2}{5}, \quad \bar{y} = \frac{M_x}{M} = \frac{1/60}{1/24} = \frac{2}{5}$$

so the center of gravity is $\left(\frac{2}{5}, \frac{2}{5}\right)$. ◀

Recall that the center of gravity of a *homogeneous* lamina is called the ***centroid of the lamina*** or sometimes the ***centroid of the region R***. Because the density function $\delta$ is constant for a homogeneous lamina, the factor $\delta$ may be moved through the integral signs in (9) and (10) and canceled. Thus, the centroid $(\bar{x}, \bar{y})$ is a geometric property of the region $R$ and is given by the following formulas:

***Centroid of a Region R***

$$\bar{x} = \frac{\iint_R x\,dA}{\iint_R dA} = \frac{1}{\text{area of } R}\iint_R x\,dA \qquad (13)$$

$$\bar{y} = \frac{\iint_R y\,dA}{\iint_R dA} = \frac{1}{\text{area of } R}\iint_R y\,dA \qquad (14)$$

▶ **Example 3** Find the centroid of the semicircular region in Figure 14.8.6.

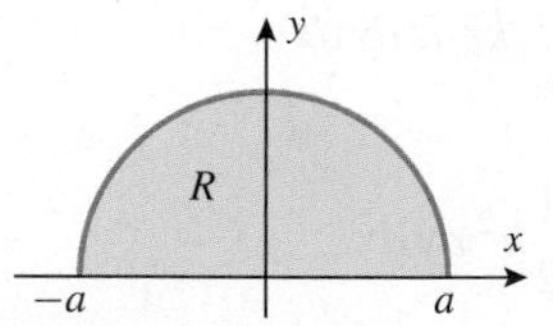


▲ **Figure 14.8.6**

***Solution.*** By symmetry, $\bar{x} = 0$ since the $y$-axis is obviously a line of balance. From (14),

$$\bar{y} = \frac{1}{\text{area of } R}\iint_R y\,dA = \frac{1}{\frac{1}{2}\pi a^2}\iint_R y\,dA$$

$$= \frac{1}{\frac{1}{2}\pi a^2}\int_0^{\pi}\int_0^{a} (r\sin\theta)r\,dr\,d\theta \qquad \text{Evaluating in polar coordinates}$$

$$= \frac{1}{\frac{1}{2}\pi a^2}\int_0^{\pi}\left[\frac{1}{3}r^3\sin\theta\right]_{r=0}^{a} d\theta$$

$$= \frac{1}{\frac{1}{2}\pi a^2}\left(\frac{1}{3}a^3\right)\int_0^{\pi}\sin\theta\,d\theta = \frac{1}{\frac{1}{2}\pi a^2}\left(\frac{2}{3}a^3\right) = \frac{4a}{3\pi}$$

so the centroid is $\left(0, \frac{4a}{3\pi}\right)$. ◀

Compare the calculation in Example 3 to that of Example 3 in Section 6.7.

## CENTER OF GRAVITY AND CENTROID OF A SOLID

For a three-dimensional solid $G$, the formulas for moments, center of gravity, and centroid are similar to those for laminas. If $G$ is *homogeneous*, then its ***density*** is defined to be its mass per unit volume. Thus, if $G$ is a homogeneous solid of mass $M$ and volume $V$, then its density $\delta$ is given by $\delta = M/V$. If $G$ is inhomogeneous and is in an $xyz$-coordinate system, then its density at a general point $(x, y, z)$ is specified by a ***density function*** $\delta(x, y, z)$ whose value at a point can be viewed as a limit:

$$\delta(x, y, z) = \lim_{\Delta V \to 0} \frac{\Delta M}{\Delta V}$$

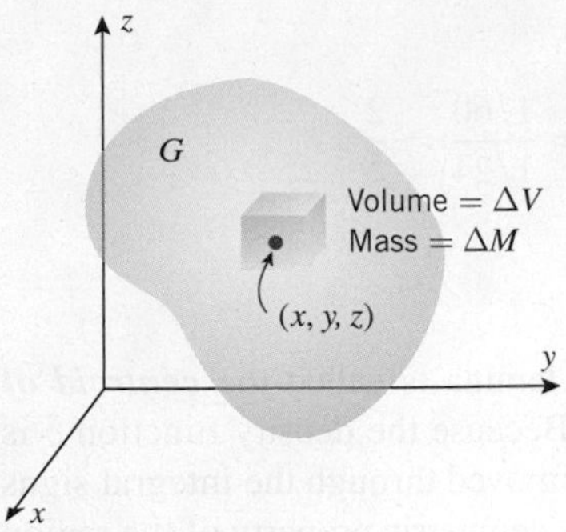

▲ Figure 14.8.7

where $\Delta M$ and $\Delta V$ represent the mass and volume of a rectangular parallelepiped, centered at $(x, y, z)$, whose dimensions tend to zero (Figure 14.8.7).

Using the discussion of laminas as a model, you should be able to show that the mass $M$ of a solid with a continuous density function $\delta(x, y, z)$ is

$$M = \text{mass of } G = \iiint_G \delta(x, y, z)\, dV \tag{15}$$

The formulas for center of gravity and centroid are as follows:

| ***Center of Gravity*** $(\bar{x}, \bar{y}, \bar{z})$ ***of a Solid G*** | ***Centroid*** $(\bar{x}, \bar{y}, \bar{z})$ ***of a Solid G*** |
|---|---|
| $\bar{x} = \frac{1}{M}\iiint_G x\delta(x, y, z)\, dV$ | $\bar{x} = \frac{1}{V}\iiint_G x\, dV$ |
| $\bar{y} = \frac{1}{M}\iiint_G y\delta(x, y, z)\, dV$ | $\bar{y} = \frac{1}{V}\iiint_G y\, dV$ |
| $\bar{z} = \frac{1}{M}\iiint_G z\delta(x, y, z)\, dV$ | $\bar{z} = \frac{1}{V}\iiint_G z\, dV$ |

(16–17)

► **Example 4** Find the mass and the center of gravity of a cylindrical solid of height $h$ and radius $a$ (Figure 14.8.8), assuming that the density at each point is proportional to the distance between the point and the base of the solid.

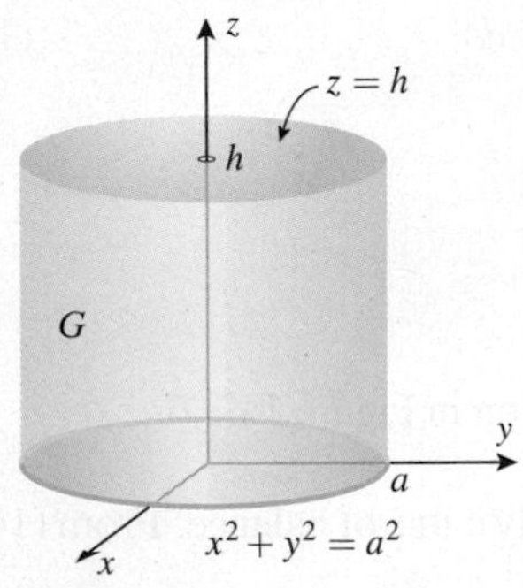

▲ Figure 14.8.8

***Solution.*** Since the density is proportional to the distance $z$ from the base, the density function has the form $\delta(x, y, z) = kz$, where $k$ is some (unknown) positive constant of proportionality. From (15) the mass of the solid is

$$\begin{aligned}
M = \iiint_G \delta(x, y, z)\, dV &= \int_{-a}^{a}\int_{-\sqrt{a^2-x^2}}^{\sqrt{a^2-x^2}}\int_0^h kz\, dz\, dy\, dx \\
&= k\int_{-a}^{a}\int_{-\sqrt{a^2-x^2}}^{\sqrt{a^2-x^2}} \frac{1}{2}h^2\, dy\, dx \\
&= kh^2\int_{-a}^{a}\sqrt{a^2 - x^2}\, dx \\
&= \tfrac{1}{2}kh^2\pi a^2
\end{aligned}$$

Interpret the integral as the area of a semicircle.

Without additional information, the constant $k$ cannot be determined. However, as we will now see, the value of $k$ does not affect the center of gravity.

From (16),

$$\begin{aligned}
\bar{z} = \frac{1}{M}\iiint_G z\delta(x, y, z)\, dV &= \frac{1}{\frac{1}{2}kh^2\pi a^2}\iiint_G z\delta(x, y, z)\, dV \\
&= \frac{1}{\frac{1}{2}kh^2\pi a^2}\int_{-a}^{a}\int_{-\sqrt{a^2-x^2}}^{\sqrt{a^2-x^2}}\int_0^h z(kz)\, dz\, dy\, dx \\
&= \frac{k}{\frac{1}{2}kh^2\pi a^2}\int_{-a}^{a}\int_{-\sqrt{a^2-x^2}}^{\sqrt{a^2-x^2}} \frac{1}{3}h^3\, dy\, dx \\
&= \frac{\frac{1}{3}kh^3}{\frac{1}{2}kh^2\pi a^2}\int_{-a}^{a} 2\sqrt{a^2 - x^2}\, dx \\
&= \frac{\frac{1}{3}kh^3\pi a^2}{\frac{1}{2}kh^2\pi a^2} = \frac{2}{3}h
\end{aligned}$$

Similar calculations using (16) will yield $\bar{x} = \bar{y} = 0$. However, this is evident by inspection, since it follows from the symmetry of the solid and the form of its density function that the center of gravity is on the $z$-axis. Thus, the center of gravity is $\left(0, 0, \frac{2}{3}h\right)$. ◄

► **Example 5** Find the centroid of the solid $G$ bounded below by the cone $z = \sqrt{x^2 + y^2}$ and above by the sphere $x^2 + y^2 + z^2 = 16$.

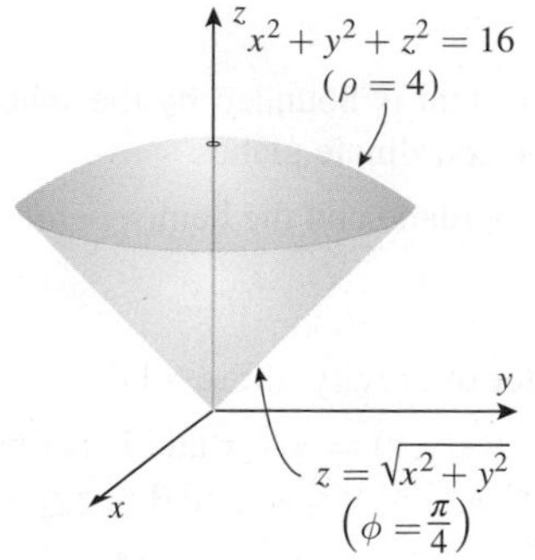


▲ **Figure 14.8.9**

***Solution.*** The solid $G$ is sketched in Figure 14.8.9. In Example 3 of Section 14.6, spherical coordinates were used to find that the volume of $G$ is

$$V = \frac{64\pi}{3}(2 - \sqrt{2})$$

By symmetry, the centroid $(\bar{x}, \bar{y}, \bar{z})$ is on the $z$-axis, so $\bar{x} = \bar{y} = 0$. In spherical coordinates, the equation of the sphere $x^2 + y^2 + z^2 = 16$ is $\rho = 4$ and the equation of the cone $z = \sqrt{x^2 + y^2}$ is $\phi = \pi/4$, so from (17) we have

$$\begin{aligned}\bar{z} &= \frac{1}{V}\iiint_G z\,dV = \frac{1}{V}\int_0^{2\pi}\int_0^{\pi/4}\int_0^4 (\rho\cos\phi)\rho^2\sin\phi\,d\rho\,d\phi\,d\theta \\ &= \frac{1}{V}\int_0^{2\pi}\int_0^{\pi/4}\left[\frac{\rho^4}{4}\cos\phi\sin\phi\right]_{\rho=0}^{4} d\phi\,d\theta \\ &= \frac{64}{V}\int_0^{2\pi}\int_0^{\pi/4}\sin\phi\cos\phi\,d\phi\,d\theta = \frac{64}{V}\int_0^{2\pi}\left[\frac{1}{2}\sin^2\phi\right]_{\phi=0}^{\pi/4} d\theta \\ &= \frac{16}{V}\int_0^{2\pi} d\theta = \frac{32\pi}{V} = \frac{3}{2(2-\sqrt{2})}\end{aligned}$$

The centroid of $G$ is

$$(\bar{x}, \bar{y}, \bar{z}) = \left(0, 0, \frac{3}{2(2-\sqrt{2})}\right) \approx (0, 0, 2.561) \;◄$$

## ✓QUICK CHECK EXERCISES 14.8 (See page 968 for answers.)

1. The total mass of a lamina with continuous density function $\delta(x, y)$ that occupies a region $R$ in the $xy$-plane is given by $M =$ ______.
2. Consider a lamina with mass $M$ and continuous density function $\delta(x, y)$ that occupies a region $R$ in the $xy$-plane. The $x$-coordinate of the center of gravity of the lamina is $M_y/M$, where $M_y$ is called the ______ and is given by the double integral ______.
3. Let $R$ be the region between the graphs of $y = x^2$ and $y = 2 - x$ for $0 \le x \le 1$. The area of $R$ is $\frac{7}{6}$ and the centroid of $R$ is ______.

## EXERCISE SET 14.8 Graphing Utility C CAS

**1–4** Find the mass and center of gravity of the lamina. ■

1. A lamina with density $\delta(x, y) = x + y$ is bounded by the $x$-axis, the line $x = 1$, and the curve $y = \sqrt{x}$.
2. A lamina with density $\delta(x, y) = y$ is bounded by $y = \sin x$, $y = 0$, $x = 0$, and $x = \pi$.
3. A lamina with density $\delta(x, y) = xy$ is in the first quadrant and is bounded by the circle $x^2 + y^2 = a^2$ and the coordinate axes.
4. A lamina with density $\delta(x, y) = x^2 + y^2$ is bounded by the $x$-axis and the upper half of the circle $x^2 + y^2 = 1$.

**FOCUS ON CONCEPTS**

**5–6** For the given density function, make a conjecture about the coordinates of the center of gravity and confirm your conjecture by integrating. ■

5. $\delta(x, y) = |x + y - 1|$

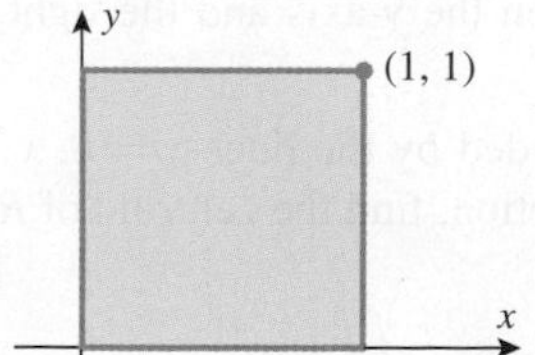

6. $\delta(x, y) = 1 + x^2 + y^2$

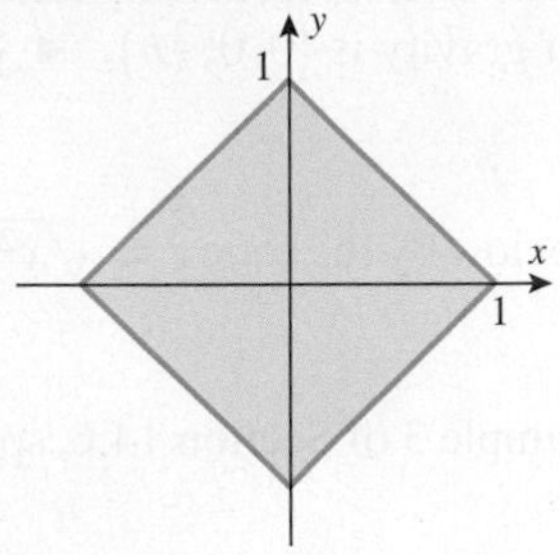


**7–8** Make a conjecture about the coordinates of the centroid of the region and confirm your conjecture by integrating. ■

7.

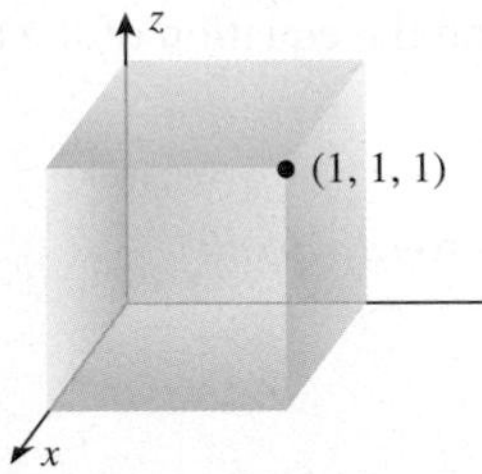


8.

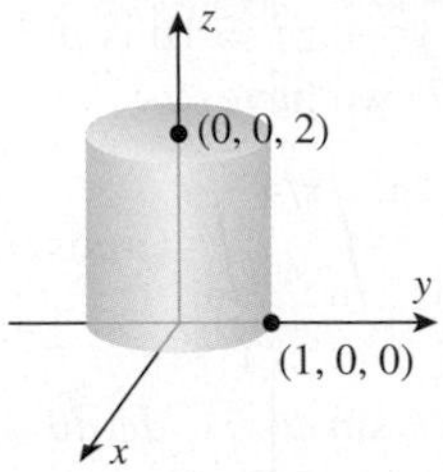


**9–12 True–False** Determine whether the statement is true or false. Explain your answer. ■

9. The center of gravity of a homogeneous lamina in a plane is located at the lamina's centroid.

10. The mass of a two-dimensional lamina is the product of its area and the density of the lamina at its centroid.

11. The coordinates of the center of gravity of a two-dimensional lamina are the lamina's first moments about the $y$- and $x$-axes, respectively.

12. The density of a solid in 3-space is measured in units of mass per unit area.

13. Show that in polar coordinates the formulas for the centroid $(\bar{x}, \bar{y})$ of a region $R$ are

$$\bar{x} = \frac{1}{\text{area of } R} \iint_R r^2 \cos\theta \, dr \, d\theta$$

$$\bar{y} = \frac{1}{\text{area of } R} \iint_R r^2 \sin\theta \, dr \, d\theta$$

**14–17** Use the result of Exercise 13 to find the centroid $(\bar{x}, \bar{y})$ of the region. ■

14. The region enclosed by the cardioid $r = a(1 + \sin\theta)$.

15. The petal of the rose $r = \sin 2\theta$ in the first quadrant.

16. The region above the $x$-axis and between the circles $x^2 + y^2 = a^2$ and $x^2 + y^2 = b^2$ $(a < b)$.

17. The region enclosed between the $y$-axis and the right half of the circle $x^2 + y^2 = a^2$.

18. Let $R$ be the rectangle bounded by the lines $x = 0$, $x = 3$, $y = 0$, and $y = 2$. By inspection, find the centroid of $R$ and use it to evaluate

$$\iint_R x \, dA \quad \text{and} \quad \iint_R y \, dA$$

**19–24** Find the centroid of the solid. ■

19. The tetrahedron in the first octant enclosed by the coordinate planes and the plane $x + y + z = 1$.

20. The solid bounded by the parabolic cylinder $z = 1 - y^2$ and the planes $x + z = 1$, $x = 0$, and $z = 0$.

21. The solid bounded by the surface $z = y^2$ and the planes $x = 0$, $x = 1$, and $z = 1$.

22. The solid in the first octant bounded by the surface $z = xy$ and the planes $z = 0$, $x = 2$, and $y = 2$.

23. The solid in the first octant that is bounded by the sphere $x^2 + y^2 + z^2 = a^2$ and the coordinate planes.

24. The solid enclosed by the $xy$-plane and the hemisphere $z = \sqrt{a^2 - x^2 - y^2}$.

**25–28** Find the mass and center of gravity of the solid. ■

25. The cube that has density $\delta(x, y, z) = a - x$ and is defined by the inequalities $0 \le x \le a$, $0 \le y \le a$, and $0 \le z \le a$.

26. The cylindrical solid that has density $\delta(x, y, z) = h - z$ and is enclosed by $x^2 + y^2 = a^2$, $z = 0$, and $z = h$.

27. The solid that has density $\delta(x, y, z) = yz$ and is enclosed by $z = 1 - y^2$ (for $y \ge 0$), $z = 0$, $y = 0$, $x = -1$, and $x = 1$.

28. The solid that has density $\delta(x, y, z) = xz$ and is enclosed by $y = 9 - x^2$ (for $x \ge 0$), $x = 0$, $y = 0$, $z = 0$, and $z = 1$.

29. Find the center of gravity of the square lamina with vertices $(0, 0)$, $(1, 0)$, $(0, 1)$, and $(1, 1)$ if
    (a) the density is proportional to the square of the distance from the origin;
    (b) the density is proportional to the distance from the $y$-axis.

30. Find the center of gravity of the cube that is determined by the inequalities $0 \le x \le 1$, $0 \le y \le 1$, $0 \le z \le 1$ if
    (a) the density is proportional to the square of the distance to the origin;
    (b) the density is proportional to the sum of the distances to the faces that lie in the coordinate planes.

C 31. Use the numerical triple integral capability of a CAS to approximate the location of the centroid of the solid that is bounded above by the surface $z = 1/(1 + x^2 + y^2)$, below by the $xy$-plane, and laterally by the plane $y = 0$ and the surface $y = \sin x$ for $0 \le x \le \pi$ (see the accompanying figure on the next page).

32. The accompanying figure on the next page shows the solid that is bounded above by the surface $z = 1/(x^2 + y^2 + 1)$, below by the $xy$-plane, and laterally by the surface $x^2 + y^2 = a^2$.
    (a) By symmetry, the centroid of the solid lies on the $z$-axis. Make a conjecture about the behavior of the $z$-coordinate of the centroid as $a \to 0^+$ and as $a \to +\infty$.
    (b) Find the $z$-coordinate of the centroid, and check your conjecture by calculating the appropriate limits.
    (c) Use a graphing utility to plot the $z$-coordinate of the centroid versus $a$, and use the graph to estimate the value of $a$ for which the centroid is $(0, 0, 0.25)$.

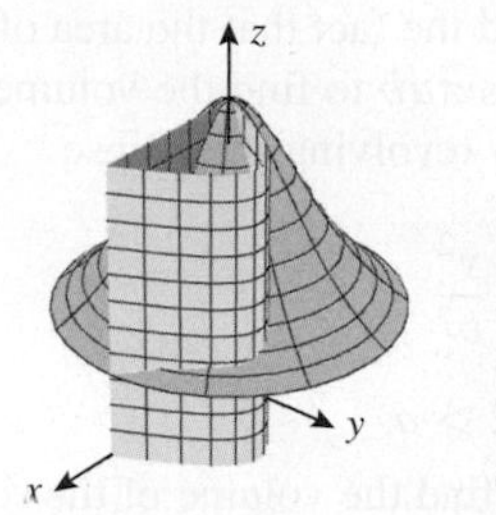


▲ **Figure Ex-31**

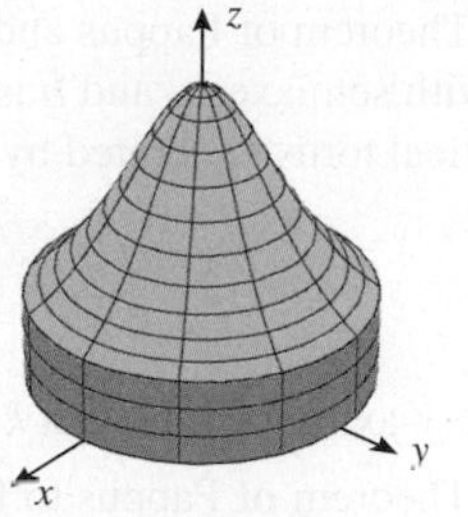


▲ **Figure Ex-32**

**33–34** Use cylindrical coordinates. ■

**33.** Find the mass of the solid with density $\delta(x, y, z) = 3 - z$ that is bounded by the cone $z = \sqrt{x^2 + y^2}$ and the plane $z = 3$.

**34.** Find the mass of a right circular cylinder of radius $a$ and height $h$ if the density is proportional to the distance from the base. (Let $k$ be the constant of proportionality.)

**35–36** Use spherical coordinates. ■

**35.** Find the mass of a spherical solid of radius $a$ if the density is proportional to the distance from the center. (Let $k$ be the constant of proportionality.)

**36.** Find the mass of the solid enclosed between the spheres $x^2 + y^2 + z^2 = 1$ and $x^2 + y^2 + z^2 = 4$ if the density is $\delta(x, y, z) = (x^2 + y^2 + z^2)^{-1/2}$.

**37–38** Use cylindrical coordinates to find the centroid of the solid. ■

**37.** The solid that is bounded above by the sphere
$$x^2 + y^2 + z^2 = 2$$
and below by the paraboloid $z = x^2 + y^2$.

**38.** The solid that is bounded by the cone $z = \sqrt{x^2 + y^2}$ and the plane $z = 2$.

**39–40** Use the Wallis sine and cosine formulas:

$$\int_0^{\pi/2} \sin^n x\,dx = \frac{\pi}{2} \cdot \frac{1 \cdot 3 \cdot 5 \cdots (n-1)}{2 \cdot 4 \cdot 6 \cdots n} \quad \begin{pmatrix} n \text{ even} \\ \text{and} \geq 2 \end{pmatrix}$$

$$\int_0^{\pi/2} \sin^n x\,dx = \frac{2 \cdot 4 \cdot 6 \cdots (n-1)}{3 \cdot 5 \cdot 7 \cdots n} \quad \begin{pmatrix} n \text{ odd} \\ \text{and} \geq 3 \end{pmatrix}$$

$$\int_0^{\pi/2} \cos^n x\,dx = \frac{\pi}{2} \cdot \frac{1 \cdot 3 \cdot 5 \cdots (n-1)}{2 \cdot 4 \cdot 6 \cdots n} \quad \begin{pmatrix} n \text{ even} \\ \text{and} \geq 2 \end{pmatrix}$$

$$\int_0^{\pi/2} \cos^n x\,dx = \frac{2 \cdot 4 \cdot 6 \cdots (n-1)}{3 \cdot 5 \cdot 7 \cdots n} \quad \begin{pmatrix} n \text{ odd} \\ \text{and} \geq 3 \end{pmatrix}$$ ■

**39.** Find the centroid of the solid bounded above by the paraboloid $z = x^2 + y^2$, below by the plane $z = 0$, and laterally by the cylinder $(x - 1)^2 + y^2 = 1$.

**40.** Find the mass of the solid in the first octant bounded above by the paraboloid $z = 4 - x^2 - y^2$, below by the plane $z = 0$, and laterally by the cylinder $x^2 + y^2 = 2x$ and the plane $y = 0$, assuming the density to be $\delta(x, y, z) = z$.

**41–42** Use spherical coordinates to find the centroid of the solid. ■

**41.** The solid in the first octant bounded by the coordinate planes and the sphere $x^2 + y^2 + z^2 = a^2$.

**42.** The solid bounded above by the sphere $\rho = 4$ and below by the cone $\phi = \pi/3$.

**43.** Find the mass of the solid that is enclosed by the sphere $x^2 + y^2 + z^2 = 1$ and lies above the cone $z = \sqrt{x^2 + y^2}$ if the density is $\delta(x, y, z) = \sqrt{x^2 + y^2 + z^2}$.

**44.** Find the center of gravity of the solid bounded by the paraboloid $z = 1 - x^2 - y^2$ and the $xy$-plane, assuming the density to be $\delta(x, y, z) = x^2 + y^2 + z^2$.

**45.** Find the center of gravity of the solid that is bounded by the cylinder $x^2 + y^2 = 1$, the cone $z = \sqrt{x^2 + y^2}$, and the $xy$-plane if the density is $\delta(x, y, z) = z$.

**46.** Find the center of gravity of the solid hemisphere bounded by $z = \sqrt{a^2 - x^2 - y^2}$ and $z = 0$ if the density is proportional to the distance from the origin.

**47.** Find the centroid of the solid that is enclosed by the hemispheres $y = \sqrt{9 - x^2 - z^2}$, $y = \sqrt{4 - x^2 - z^2}$, and the plane $y = 0$.

**48.** Suppose that the density at a point in a gaseous spherical star is modeled by the formula
$$\delta = \delta_0 e^{-(\rho/R)^3}$$
where $\delta_0$ is a positive constant, $R$ is the radius of the star, and $\rho$ is the distance from the point to the star's center. Find the mass of the star.

**49–50** The tendency of a lamina to resist a change in rotational motion about an axis is measured by its ***moment of inertia*** about that axis. If a lamina occupies a region $R$ of the $xy$-plane, and if its density function $\delta(x, y)$ is continuous on $R$, then the moments of inertia about the $x$-axis, the $y$-axis, and the $z$-axis are denoted by $I_x, I_y$, and $I_z$, respectively, and are defined by
$$I_x = \iint_R y^2\,\delta(x, y)\,dA, \quad I_y = \iint_R x^2\,\delta(x, y)\,dA,$$
$$I_z = \iint_R (x^2 + y^2)\,\delta(x, y)\,dA$$
Use these definitions in Exercises 49 and 50. ■

**49.** Consider the rectangular lamina that occupies the region described by the inequalities $0 \leq x \leq a$ and $0 \leq y \leq b$. Assuming that the lamina has constant density $\delta$, show that
$$I_x = \frac{\delta ab^3}{3}, \quad I_y = \frac{\delta a^3 b}{3}, \quad I_z = \frac{\delta ab(a^2 + b^2)}{3}$$

**50.** Consider the circular lamina that occupies the region described by the inequalities $0 \leq x^2 + y^2 \leq a^2$. Assuming that the lamina has constant density $\delta$, show that
$$I_x = I_y = \frac{\delta\pi a^4}{4}, \quad I_z = \frac{\delta\pi a^4}{2}$$

**51–54** The tendency of a solid to resist a change in rotational motion about an axis is measured by its ***moment of inertia*** about that axis. If the solid occupies a region $G$ in an $xyz$-coordinate system, and if its density function $\delta(x, y, z)$ is continuous on $G$, then the moments of inertia about the $x$-axis, the $y$-axis, and the $z$-axis are denoted by $I_x$, $I_y$, and $I_z$, respectively, and are defined by

$$I_x = \iiint_G (y^2 + z^2)\,\delta(x, y, z)\,dV$$

$$I_y = \iiint_G (x^2 + z^2)\,\delta(x, y, z)\,dV$$

$$I_z = \iiint_G (x^2 + y^2)\,\delta(x, y, z)\,dV$$

In these exercises, find the indicated moments of inertia of the solid, assuming that it has constant density $\delta$.

**51.** $I_z$ for the solid cylinder $x^2 + y^2 \le a^2$, $0 \le z \le h$.

**52.** $I_y$ for the solid cylinder $x^2 + y^2 \le a^2$, $0 \le z \le h$.

**53.** $I_z$ for the hollow cylinder $a_1^2 \le x^2 + y^2 \le a_2^2$, $0 \le z \le h$.

**54.** $I_z$ for the solid sphere $x^2 + y^2 + z^2 \le a^2$.

**55–59** These exercises reference the ***Theorem of Pappus***: *If R is a bounded plane region and L is a line that lies in the plane of R such that R is entirely on one side of L, then the volume of the solid formed by revolving R about L is given by*

$$\textit{volume} = (\textit{area of } R) \cdot \begin{pmatrix} \textit{distance traveled} \\ \textit{by the centroid} \end{pmatrix} \quad ■$$

**55.** Perform the following steps to prove the Theorem of Pappus:

(a) Introduce an $xy$-coordinate system so that $L$ is along the $y$-axis and the region $R$ is in the first quadrant. Partition $R$ into rectangular subregions in the usual way and let $R_k$ be a typical subregion of $R$ with center $(x_k^*, y_k^*)$ and area $\Delta A_k = \Delta x_k \Delta y_k$. Show that the volume generated by $R_k$ as it revolves about $L$ is

$$2\pi x_k^* \Delta x_k \Delta y_k = 2\pi x_k^* \Delta A_k$$

(b) Show that the volume generated by $R$ as it revolves about $L$ is

$$V = \iint_R 2\pi x\, dA = 2\pi \cdot \bar{x} \cdot [\text{area of } R]$$

**56.** Use the Theorem of Pappus and the result of Example 3 to find the volume of the solid generated when the region bounded by the $x$-axis and the semicircle $y = \sqrt{a^2 - x^2}$ is revolved about

(a) the line $y = -a$ (b) the line $y = x - a$.

**57.** Use the Theorem of Pappus and the fact that the area of an ellipse with semiaxes $a$ and $b$ is $\pi ab$ to find the volume of the elliptical torus generated by revolving the ellipse

$$\frac{(x-k)^2}{a^2} + \frac{y^2}{b^2} = 1$$

about the $y$-axis. Assume that $k > a$.

**58.** Use the Theorem of Pappus to find the volume of the solid that is generated when the region enclosed by $y = x^2$ and $y = 8 - x^2$ is revolved about the $x$-axis.

**59.** Use the Theorem of Pappus to find the centroid of the triangular region with vertices $(0, 0)$, $(a, 0)$, and $(0, b)$, where $a > 0$ and $b > 0$. [*Hint:* Revolve the region about the $x$-axis to obtain $\bar{y}$ and about the $y$-axis to obtain $\bar{x}$.]

**60.** It can be proved that if a bounded plane region slides along a helix in such a way that the region is always orthogonal to the helix (i.e., orthogonal to the unit tangent vector to the helix), then the volume swept out by the region is equal to the area of the region times the distance traveled by its centroid. Use this result to find the volume of the "tube" in the accompanying figure that is swept out by sliding a circle of radius $\frac{1}{2}$ along the helix

$$x = \cos t, \quad y = \sin t, \quad z = \frac{t}{4} \quad (0 \le t \le 4\pi)$$

in such a way that the circle is always centered on the helix and lies in the plane perpendicular to the helix.

**Figure Ex-60**

**61. Writing** Give a physical interpretation of the "center of gravity" of a lamina.

**✓QUICK CHECK ANSWERS 14.8** 1. $\iint_R \delta(x, y)\, dA$ 2. first moment about the $y$-axis; $\iint_R x\delta(x, y)\, dA$ 3. $\left(\frac{5}{14}, \frac{32}{35}\right)$

## CHAPTER 14 REVIEW EXERCISES

**1.** The double integral over a region $R$ in the $xy$-plane is defined as

$$\iint_R f(x, y)\, dA = \lim_{n \to +\infty} \sum_{k=1}^{n} f(x_k^*, y_k^*)\,\Delta A_k$$

Describe the procedure on which this definition is based.

**2.** The triple integral over a solid $G$ in an $xyz$-coordinate system is defined as

$$\iiint_G f(x, y, z)\, dV = \lim_{n \to +\infty} \sum_{k=1}^{n} f(x_k^*, y_k^*, z_k^*)\,\Delta V_k$$

Describe the procedure on which this definition is based.

**3.** (a) Express the area of a region $R$ in the $xy$-plane as a double integral.

(b) Express the volume of a region $G$ in an $xyz$-coordinate system as a triple integral.

(c) Express the area of the portion of the surface $z = f(x, y)$ that lies above the region $R$ in the $xy$-plane as a double integral.

**4.** (a) Write down parametric equations for a sphere of radius $a$ centered at the origin.
(b) Write down parametric equations for the right circular cylinder of radius $a$ and height $h$ that is centered on the $z$-axis, has its base in the $xy$-plane, and extends in the positive $z$-direction.

**5.** Let $R$ be the region in the accompanying figure. Fill in the missing limits of integration in the iterated integral

$$\int_{\square}^{\square}\int_{\square}^{\square} f(x, y)\,dx\,dy$$

over $R$.

**6.** Let $R$ be the region shown in the accompanying figure. Fill in the missing limits of integration in the sum of the iterated integrals

$$\int_0^2\int_{\square}^{\square} f(x, y)\,dy\,dx + \int_2^3\int_{\square}^{\square} f(x, y)\,dy\,dx$$

over $R$.

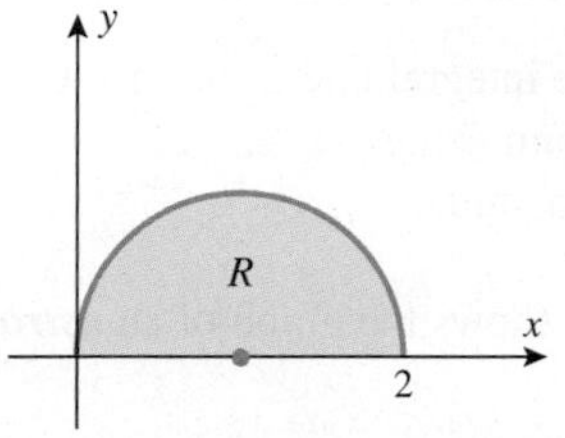


▲ **Figure Ex-5**

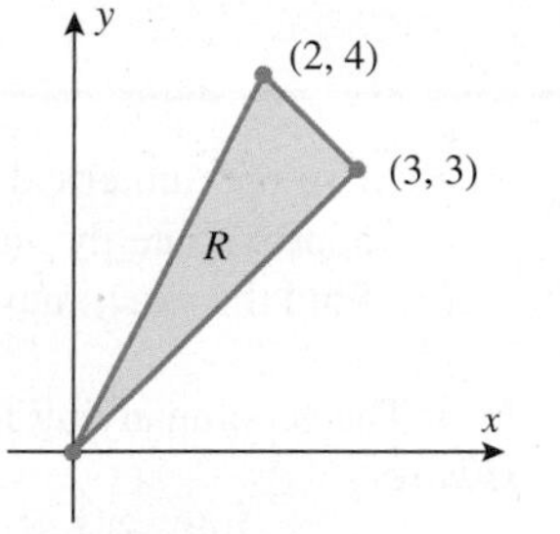


▲ **Figure Ex-6**

**7.** (a) Find constants $a$, $b$, $c$, and $d$ such that the transformation $x = au + bv$, $y = cu + dv$ maps the region $S$ in the accompanying figure into the region $R$.
(b) Find the area of the parallelogram $R$ by integrating over the region $S$, and check your answer using a formula from geometry.

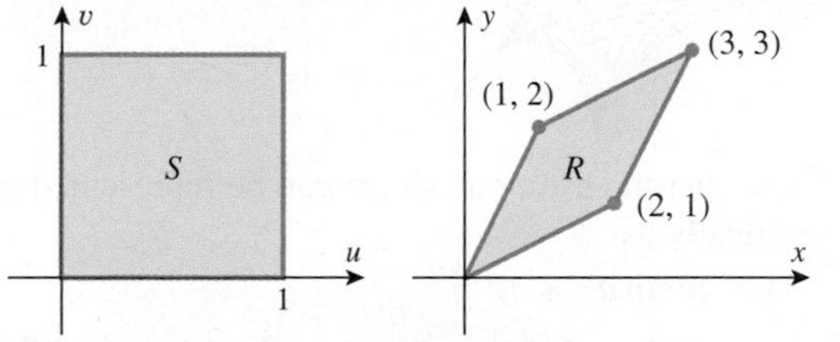


▲ **Figure Ex-7**

**8.** Give a geometric argument to show that

$$0 < \int_0^{\pi}\int_0^{\pi} \sin\sqrt{xy}\,dy\,dx < \pi^2$$

**9–10** Evaluate the iterated integral. ■

**9.** $\displaystyle\int_{1/2}^{1}\int_0^{2x} \cos(\pi x^2)\,dy\,dx$ **10.** $\displaystyle\int_0^2\int_{-y}^{2y} xe^{y^3}\,dx\,dy$

**11–12** Express the iterated integral as an equivalent integral with the order of integration reversed. ■

**11.** $\displaystyle\int_0^2\int_0^{x/2} e^x e^y\,dy\,dx$ **12.** $\displaystyle\int_0^{\pi}\int_y^{\pi} \frac{\sin x}{x}\,dx\,dy$

**13–14** Sketch the region whose area is represented by the iterated integral. ■

**13.** $\displaystyle\int_0^{\pi/2}\int_{\tan(x/2)}^{\sin x} dy\,dx$

**14.** $\displaystyle\int_{\pi/6}^{\pi/2}\int_a^{a(1+\cos\theta)} r\,dr\,d\theta \quad (a > 0)$

**15–16** Evaluate the double integral. ■

**15.** $\displaystyle\iint_R x^2 \sin y^2\,dA$; $R$ is the region that is bounded by $y = x^3$, $y = -x^3$, and $y = 8$.

**16.** $\displaystyle\iint_R (4 - x^2 - y^2)\,dA$; $R$ is the sector in the first quadrant bounded by the circle $x^2 + y^2 = 4$ and the coordinate axes.

**17.** Convert to rectangular coordinates and evaluate:

$$\int_0^{\pi/2}\int_0^{2a\sin\theta} r\sin 2\theta\,dr\,d\theta$$

**18.** Convert to polar coordinates and evaluate:

$$\int_0^{\sqrt{2}}\int_x^{\sqrt{4-x^2}} 4xy\,dy\,dx$$

**19–20** Find the area of the region using a double integral. ■

**19.** The region bounded by $y = 2x^3$, $2x + y = 4$, and the $x$-axis.

**20.** The region enclosed by the rose $r = \cos 3\theta$.

**21.** Convert to cylindrical coordinates and evaluate:

$$\int_{-2}^{2}\int_{-\sqrt{4-x^2}}^{\sqrt{4-x^2}}\int_{(x^2+y^2)^2}^{16} x^2\,dz\,dy\,dx$$

**22.** Convert to spherical coordinates and evaluate:

$$\int_0^1\int_0^{\sqrt{1-x^2}}\int_0^{\sqrt{1-x^2-y^2}} \frac{1}{1 + x^2 + y^2 + z^2}\,dz\,dy\,dx$$

**23.** Let $G$ be the region bounded above by the sphere $\rho = a$ and below by the cone $\phi = \pi/3$. Express

$$\iiint_G (x^2 + y^2)\,dV$$

as an iterated integral in
(a) spherical coordinates (b) cylindrical coordinates
(c) rectangular coordinates.

**24.** Let $G = \{(x, y, z) : x^2 + y^2 \le z \le 4x\}$. Express the volume of $G$ as an iterated integral in
(a) rectangular coordinates (b) cylindrical coordinates.

**25–26** Find the volume of the solid using a triple integral. ■

**25.** The solid bounded below by the cone $\phi = \pi/6$ and above by the plane $z = a$.

**26.** The solid enclosed between the surfaces $x = y^2 + z^2$ and $x = 1 - y^2$.

**27.** Find the area of the portion of the surface $z = 3y + 2x^2 + 4$ that is above the triangular region with vertices $(0, 0)$, $(1, 1)$, and $(1, -1)$.

**28.** Find the surface area of the portion of the hyperbolic paraboloid
$$\mathbf{r}(u, v) = (u + v)\mathbf{i} + (u - v)\mathbf{j} + uv\mathbf{k}$$
for which $u^2 + v^2 \le 4$.

**29–30** Find the equation of the tangent plane to the surface at the specified point. ■

**29.** $\mathbf{r} = u\mathbf{i} + v\mathbf{j} + (u^2 + v^2)\mathbf{k}$; $u = 1, v = 2$

**30.** $x = u\cosh v, y = u\sinh v, z = u^2$; $(-3, 0, 9)$

**31.** Suppose that you have a double integral over a region $R$ in the $xy$-plane and you want to transform that integral into an equivalent double integral over a region $S$ in the $uv$-plane. Describe the procedure you would use.

**32.** Use the transformation $u = x - 3y, v = 3x + y$ to find
$$\iint_R \frac{x - 3y}{(3x + y)^2}\, dA$$
where $R$ is the rectangular region enclosed by the lines $x - 3y = 0, x - 3y = 4, 3x + y = 1$, and $3x + y = 3$.

**33.** Let $G$ be the solid in 3-space defined by the inequalities
$$1 - e^x \le y \le 3 - e^x,\ \ 1 - y \le 2z \le 2 - y,\ \ y \le e^x \le y + 4$$
(a) Using the coordinate transformation
$$u = e^x + y,\quad v = y + 2z,\quad w = e^x - y$$
calculate the Jacobian $\partial(x, y, z)/\partial(u, v, w)$. Express your answer in terms of $u$, $v$, and $w$.
(b) Using a triple integral and the change of variables given in part (a), find the volume of $G$.

**34.** Find the average distance from a point inside a sphere of radius $a$ to the center. [See the definition preceding Exercise 33 of Section 14.5.]

**35–36** Find the centroid of the region. ■

**35.** The region bounded by $y^2 = 4x$ and $y^2 = 8(x - 2)$.

**36.** The upper half of the ellipse $(x/a)^2 + (y/b)^2 = 1$.

**37–38** Find the centroid of the solid. ■

**37.** The solid cone with vertex $(0, 0, h)$ and with base the disk $x^2 + y^2 \le a^2$ in the $xy$-plane.

**38.** The solid bounded by $y = x^2$, $z = 0$, and $y + z = 4$.

## CHAPTER 14 MAKING CONNECTIONS  C CAS

**1.** The integral $\int_0^{+\infty} e^{-x^2}\, dx$, which arises in probability theory, can be evaluated using the following method. Let the value of the integral be $I$. Thus,
$$I = \int_0^{+\infty} e^{-x^2}\, dx = \int_0^{+\infty} e^{-y^2}\, dy$$
since the letter used for the variable of integration in a definite integral does not matter.
(a) Give a reasonable argument to show that
$$I^2 = \int_0^{+\infty}\int_0^{+\infty} e^{-(x^2+y^2)}\, dx\, dy$$
(b) Evaluate the iterated integral in part (a) by converting to polar coordinates.
(c) Use the result in part (b) to show that $I = \sqrt{\pi}/2$.

**2.** Show that
$$\int_0^{+\infty}\int_0^{+\infty} \frac{1}{(1 + x^2 + y^2)^2}\, dx\, dy = \frac{\pi}{4}$$
[*Hint:* See Exercise 1.]

C **3.** (a) Use the numerical integration capability of a CAS to approximate the value of the double integral
$$\int_{-1}^{1}\int_0^{\sqrt{1-x^2}} e^{-(x^2+y^2)^2}\, dy\, dx$$
(b) Compare the approximation obtained in part (a) to the approximation that results if the integral is first converted to polar coordinates.

C **4.** (a) Find the region $G$ over which the triple integral
$$\iiint_G (1 - x^2 - y^2 - z^2)\, dV$$
has its maximum value.
(b) Use the numerical triple integral operation of a CAS to approximate the maximum value.
(c) Find the exact maximum value.

**5–6** The accompanying figure shows the graph of an ***astroidal sphere***
$$x^{2/3} + y^{2/3} + z^{2/3} = a^{2/3} \ ■$$

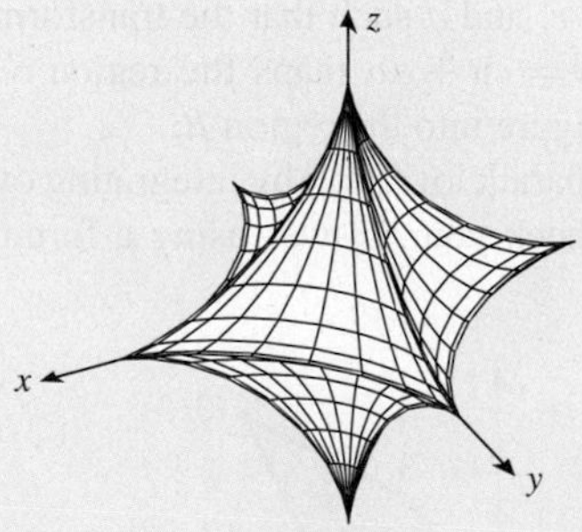


C **5.** (a) Show that the astroidal sphere can be represented parametrically as
$$x = a(\sin u \cos v)^3$$
$$y = a(\sin u \sin v)^3 \qquad (0 \le u \le \pi,\ 0 \le v \le 2\pi)$$
$$z = a(\cos u)^3$$
(b) Use a CAS to approximate the surface area in the case where $a = 1$.

**6.** Find the volume of the astroidal sphere using a triple integral and the transformation
$$x = \rho(\sin\phi\cos\theta)^3$$
$$y = \rho(\sin\phi\sin\theta)^3$$
$$z = \rho(\cos\phi)^3$$
for which $0 \le \rho \le a, 0 \le \phi \le \pi, 0 \le \theta \le 2\pi$.

# 15

# TOPICS IN VECTOR CALCULUS

Hal Pierce/Laboratory for Atmospheres/NASA Goddard Space Flight Center

*Results in this chapter provide tools for analyzing and understanding the behavior of hurricanes and other fluid flows.*

We begin this chapter by introducing the concept of a vector field, an important tool for the study of gravitational and electrostatic force fields, the flow of fluids, and conservation of energy. Next, we will introduce the "line integral," a new type of integral with a variety of applications to the analysis of vector fields. Finally, we conclude with three major theorems, Green's Theorem, the Divergence Theorem, and Stokes' Theorem. These theorems provide deep insight into the nature of vector fields and are the basis for many of the most important principles in physics and engineering.

## 15.1 VECTOR FIELDS

*In this section we will consider functions that associate vectors with points in 2-space or 3-space. We will see that such functions play an important role in the study of fluid flow, gravitational force fields, electromagnetic force fields, and a wide range of other applied problems.*

### VECTOR FIELDS

Consider a *unit* point-mass located at any point in the Universe. According to Newton's Law of Universal Gravitation, the Earth exerts an attractive force on the mass that is directed toward the center of the Earth and has a magnitude that is inversely proportional to the square of the distance from the mass to the Earth's center (Figure 15.1.1). This association of force vectors with points in space is called the Earth's *gravitational field.* A similar association occurs in fluid flow. Imagine a stream in which the water flows horizontally at every level, and consider the layer of water at a specific depth. At each point of the layer, the water has a certain velocity, which we can represent by a vector at that point (Figure 15.1.2). This association of velocity vectors with points in the two-dimensional layer is called the *velocity field* at that layer. These ideas are captured in the following definition.

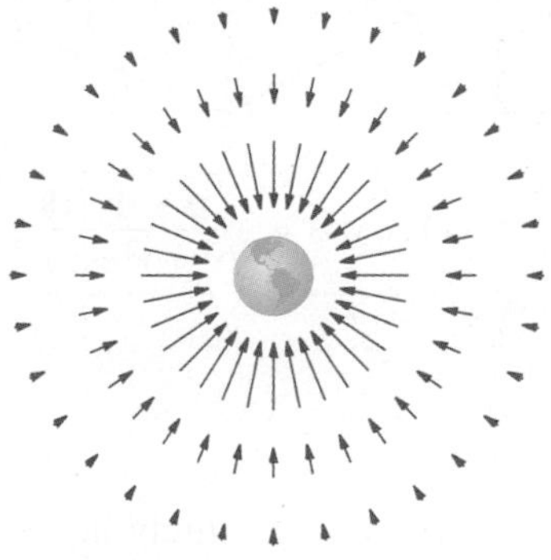

▲ Figure 15.1.1

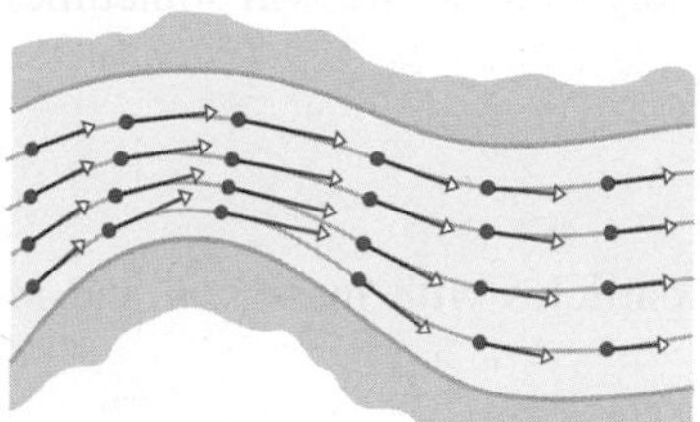

▲ Figure 15.1.2

**15.1.1 DEFINITION** A ***vector field*** in a plane is a function that associates with each point $P$ in the plane a unique vector $\mathbf{F}(P)$ parallel to the plane. Similarly, a vector field in 3-space is a function that associates with each point $P$ in 3-space a unique vector $\mathbf{F}(P)$ in 3-space.

Observe that in this definition there is no reference to a coordinate system. However, for computational purposes it is useful to introduce a coordinate system so that vectors can be assigned components. Specifically, if $\mathbf{F}(P)$ is a vector field in an $xy$-coordinate system, then the point $P$ will have some coordinates $(x, y)$ and the associated vector will have components that are functions of $x$ and $y$. Thus, the vector field $\mathbf{F}(P)$ can be expressed as

$$\mathbf{F}(x, y) = f(x, y)\mathbf{i} + g(x, y)\mathbf{j}$$

Notice that a vector field is really just a vector-valued function. The term "vector field" is commonly used in physics and engineering.

Similarly, in 3-space with an $xyz$-coordinate system, a vector field $\mathbf{F}(P)$ can be expressed as

$$\mathbf{F}(x, y, z) = f(x, y, z)\mathbf{i} + g(x, y, z)\mathbf{j} + h(x, y, z)\mathbf{k}$$

## GRAPHICAL REPRESENTATIONS OF VECTOR FIELDS

A vector field in 2-space can be pictured geometrically by drawing representative field vectors $\mathbf{F}(x, y)$ at some well-chosen points in the $xy$-plane. Such graphical representations can provide useful information about the general behavior of the field if the vectors are chosen appropriately. Figure 15.1.3 shows four computer-generated vector fields. The vector field in part ($a$) might describe the velocity of the current in a stream at various depths. At the bottom of the stream the velocity is zero, but the speed of the current increases as the depth decreases. Points at the same depth have the same speed. The vector field in part ($b$) might describe the velocity at points on a rotating wheel. At the center of the wheel the velocity is zero, but the speed increases with the distance from the center. Points at the same distance from the center have the same speed. The vector field in part ($c$) might describe the repulsive force of an electrical charge—the closer to the charge, the greater the force of repulsion. Part ($d$) shows a vector field in 3-space. Such pictures tend to be cluttered and hence are of lesser value than graphical representations of vector fields in 2-space. Note also that the vectors in parts ($b$) and ($c$) are not to scale—their lengths have been compressed for clarity. We will follow this procedure throughout this chapter.

**TECHNOLOGY MASTERY**

If you have a graphing utility that can generate vector fields, read the relevant documentation and try to make reasonable duplicates of parts ($a$) and ($b$) of Figure 15.1.3.

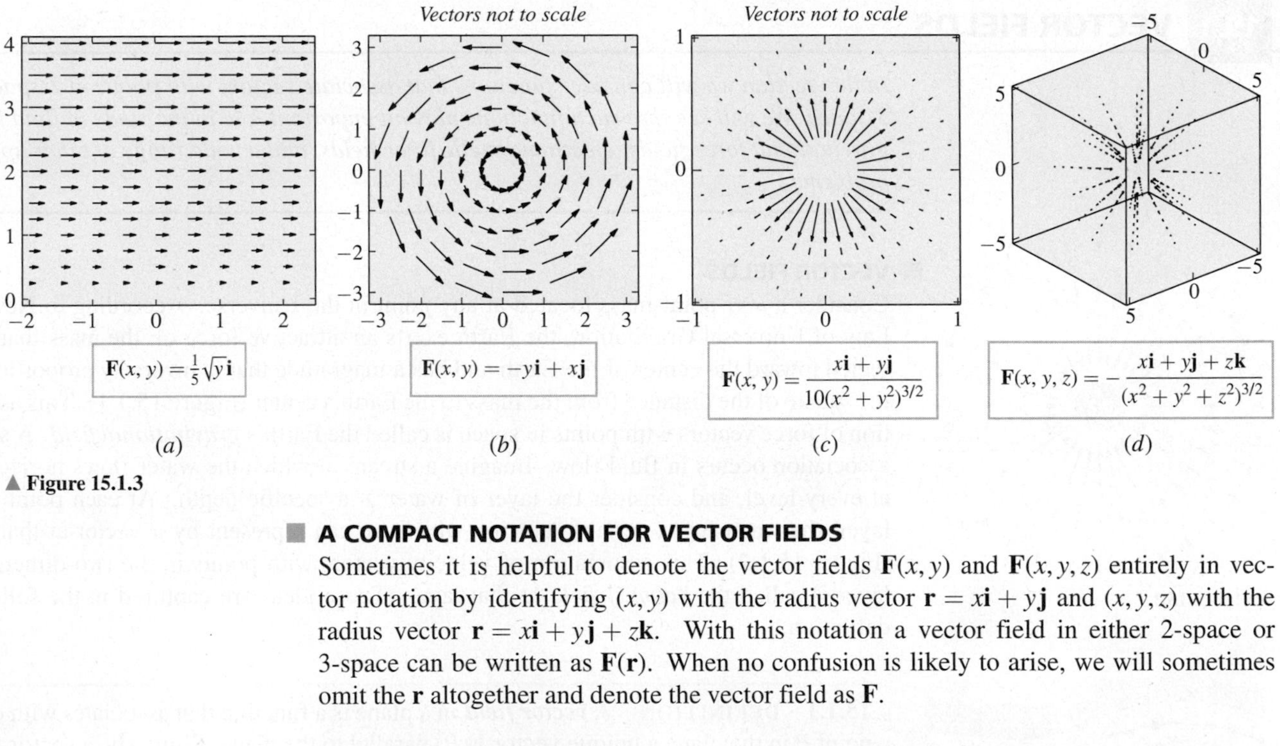


▲ **Figure 15.1.3**

## A COMPACT NOTATION FOR VECTOR FIELDS

Sometimes it is helpful to denote the vector fields $\mathbf{F}(x, y)$ and $\mathbf{F}(x, y, z)$ entirely in vector notation by identifying $(x, y)$ with the radius vector $\mathbf{r} = x\mathbf{i} + y\mathbf{j}$ and $(x, y, z)$ with the radius vector $\mathbf{r} = x\mathbf{i} + y\mathbf{j} + z\mathbf{k}$. With this notation a vector field in either 2-space or 3-space can be written as $\mathbf{F}(\mathbf{r})$. When no confusion is likely to arise, we will sometimes omit the $\mathbf{r}$ altogether and denote the vector field as $\mathbf{F}$.

## INVERSE-SQUARE FIELDS

According to Newton's Law of Universal Gravitation, particles with masses $m$ and $M$ attract each other with a force $\mathbf{F}$ of magnitude

$$\|\mathbf{F}\| = \frac{GmM}{r^2} \tag{1}$$

where $r$ is the distance between the particles and $G$ is a constant. If we assume that the particle of mass $M$ is located at the origin of an $xyz$-coordinate system and $\mathbf{r}$ is the radius vector to the particle of mass $m$, then $r = \|\mathbf{r}\|$, and the force $\mathbf{F}(\mathbf{r})$ exerted by the particle of mass $M$ on the particle of mass $m$ is in the direction of the unit vector $-\mathbf{r}/\|\mathbf{r}\|$. Thus, it follows from (1) that

$$\mathbf{F}(\mathbf{r}) = -\frac{GmM}{\|\mathbf{r}\|^2}\frac{\mathbf{r}}{\|\mathbf{r}\|} = -\frac{GmM}{\|\mathbf{r}\|^3}\mathbf{r} \tag{2}$$

If $m$ and $M$ are constant, and we let $c = -GmM$, then this formula can be expressed as

$$\mathbf{F}(\mathbf{r}) = \frac{c}{\|\mathbf{r}\|^3}\mathbf{r}$$

Vector fields of this form arise in electromagnetic as well as gravitational problems. Such fields are so important that they have their own terminology.

**15.1.2 DEFINITION** If $\mathbf{r}$ is a radius vector in 2-space or 3-space, and if $c$ is a constant, then a vector field of the form

$$\mathbf{F}(\mathbf{r}) = \frac{c}{\|\mathbf{r}\|^3}\mathbf{r} \tag{3}$$

is called an ***inverse-square field***.

Observe that if $c > 0$ in (3), then $\mathbf{F}(\mathbf{r})$ has the same direction as $\mathbf{r}$, so each vector in the field is directed away from the origin; and if $c < 0$, then $\mathbf{F}(\mathbf{r})$ is oppositely directed to $\mathbf{r}$, so each vector in the field is directed toward the origin. In either case the magnitude of $\mathbf{F}(\mathbf{r})$ is inversely proportional to the square of the distance from the terminal point of $\mathbf{r}$ to the origin, since

$$\|\mathbf{F}(\mathbf{r})\| = \frac{|c|}{\|\mathbf{r}\|^3}\|\mathbf{r}\| = \frac{|c|}{\|\mathbf{r}\|^2}$$

We leave it for you to verify that in 2-space Formula (3) can be written in component form as

$$\mathbf{F}(x, y) = \frac{c}{(x^2 + y^2)^{3/2}}(x\mathbf{i} + y\mathbf{j}) \tag{4}$$

and in 3-space as

$$\mathbf{F}(x, y, z) = \frac{c}{(x^2 + y^2 + z^2)^{3/2}}(x\mathbf{i} + y\mathbf{j} + z\mathbf{k}) \tag{5}$$

[see parts (*c*) and (*d*) of Figure 15.1.3].

► **Example 1** *Coulomb's law* states that *the electrostatic force exerted by one charged particle on another is directly proportional to the product of the charges and inversely proportional to the square of the distance between them.* This has the same form as Newton's Law of Universal Gravitation, so the electrostatic force field exerted by a charged particle is an inverse-square field. Specifically, if a particle of charge $Q$ is at the origin of a coordinate system, and if $\mathbf{r}$ is the radius vector to a particle of charge $q$, then the force $\mathbf{F}(\mathbf{r})$ that the particle of charge $Q$ exerts on the particle of charge $q$ is of the form

$$\mathbf{F}(\mathbf{r}) = \frac{qQ}{4\pi\epsilon_0\|\mathbf{r}\|^3}\mathbf{r}$$

where $\epsilon_0$ is a positive constant (called the ***permittivity constant***). This formula is of form (3) with $c = qQ/4\pi\epsilon_0$. ◄

## GRADIENT FIELDS

An important class of vector fields comes from gradients. Recall that if $\phi$ is a function of three variables, then the gradient of $\phi$ is defined as

$$\nabla\phi = \frac{\partial\phi}{\partial x}\mathbf{i} + \frac{\partial\phi}{\partial y}\mathbf{j} + \frac{\partial\phi}{\partial z}\mathbf{k}$$

This formula defines a vector field in 3-space called the ***gradient field of*** $\phi$. Similarly, the gradient of a function of two variables defines a gradient field in 2-space. At each point in a gradient field where the gradient is nonzero, the vector points in the direction in which the rate of increase of $\phi$ is maximum.

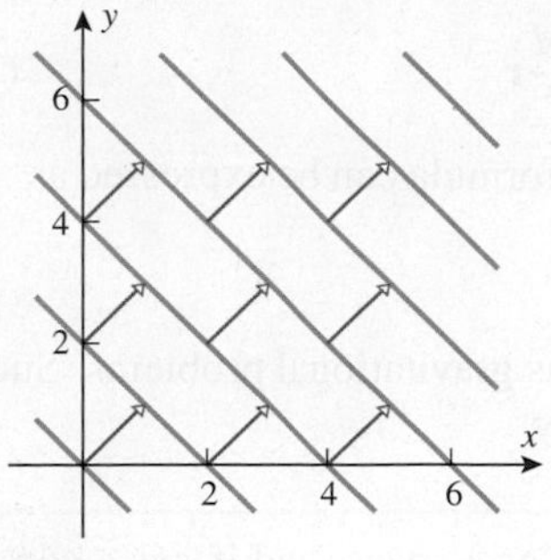

▲ Figure 15.1.4

► **Example 2** Sketch the gradient field of $\phi(x, y) = x + y$.

***Solution.*** The gradient of $\phi$ is

$$\nabla\phi = \frac{\partial\phi}{\partial x}\mathbf{i} + \frac{\partial\phi}{\partial y}\mathbf{j} = \mathbf{i} + \mathbf{j}$$

which is constant [i.e., is the same vector at each point $(x, y)$]. A portion of the vector field is sketched in Figure 15.1.4 together with some level curves of $\phi$. Note that at each point, $\nabla\phi$ is normal to the level curve of $\phi$ through the point (Theorem 13.6.6). ◄

## CONSERVATIVE FIELDS AND POTENTIAL FUNCTIONS

If $\mathbf{F}(\mathbf{r})$ is an arbitrary vector field in 2-space or 3-space, we can ask whether it is the gradient field of some function $\phi$, and if so, how we can find $\phi$. This is an important problem and we will study it in more detail later. However, there is some terminology for such fields that we will introduce now.

**15.1.3 DEFINITION** A vector field $\mathbf{F}$ in 2-space or 3-space is said to be ***conservative*** in a region if it is the gradient field for some function $\phi$ in that region, that is, if

$$\mathbf{F} = \nabla\phi$$

The function $\phi$ is called a ***potential function*** for $\mathbf{F}$ in the region.

► **Example 3** Inverse-square fields are conservative in any region that does not contain the origin. For example, in the two-dimensional case the function

$$\phi(x, y) = -\frac{c}{(x^2 + y^2)^{1/2}} \tag{6}$$

is a potential function for (4) in any region not containing the origin, since

$$\begin{aligned}\nabla\phi(x, y) &= \frac{\partial\phi}{\partial x}\mathbf{i} + \frac{\partial\phi}{\partial y}\mathbf{j} \\ &= \frac{cx}{(x^2 + y^2)^{3/2}}\mathbf{i} + \frac{cy}{(x^2 + y^2)^{3/2}}\mathbf{j} \\ &= \frac{c}{(x^2 + y^2)^{3/2}}(x\mathbf{i} + y\mathbf{j}) \\ &= \mathbf{F}(x, y)\end{aligned}$$ ◄

## DIVERGENCE AND CURL

We will now define two important operations on vector fields in 3-space—the *divergence* and the *curl* of the field. These names originate in the study of fluid flow, in which case the divergence relates to the way in which fluid flows toward or away from a point and the curl relates to the rotational properties of the fluid at a point. We will investigate the physical interpretations of these operations in more detail later, but for now we will focus only on their computation.

**15.1.4 DEFINITION** If $\mathbf{F}(x, y, z) = f(x, y, z)\mathbf{i} + g(x, y, z)\mathbf{j} + h(x, y, z)\mathbf{k}$, then we define the ***divergence of*** $\mathbf{F}$, written div $\mathbf{F}$, to be the function given by

$$\text{div}\,\mathbf{F} = \frac{\partial f}{\partial x} + \frac{\partial g}{\partial y} + \frac{\partial h}{\partial z} \tag{7}$$

**15.1.5 DEFINITION** If $\mathbf{F}(x, y, z) = f(x, y, z)\mathbf{i} + g(x, y, z)\mathbf{j} + h(x, y, z)\mathbf{k}$, then we define the ***curl of* F**, written curl **F**, to be the vector field given by

$$\text{curl } \mathbf{F} = \left(\frac{\partial h}{\partial y} - \frac{\partial g}{\partial z}\right)\mathbf{i} + \left(\frac{\partial f}{\partial z} - \frac{\partial h}{\partial x}\right)\mathbf{j} + \left(\frac{\partial g}{\partial x} - \frac{\partial f}{\partial y}\right)\mathbf{k} \tag{8}$$

**REMARK** Observe that div **F** and curl **F** depend on the point at which they are computed, and hence are more properly written as div $\mathbf{F}(x, y, z)$ and curl $\mathbf{F}(x, y, z)$. However, even though these functions are expressed in terms of $x$, $y$, and $z$, it can be proved that their values at a fixed point depend only on the point and not on the coordinate system selected. This is important in applications, since it allows physicists and engineers to compute the curl and divergence in any convenient coordinate system.

Before proceeding to some examples, we note that div **F** has scalar values, whereas curl **F** has vector values (i.e., curl **F** is itself a vector field). Moreover, for computational purposes it is useful to note that the formula for the curl can be expressed in the determinant form

$$\text{curl } \mathbf{F} = \begin{vmatrix} \mathbf{i} & \mathbf{j} & \mathbf{k} \\ \dfrac{\partial}{\partial x} & \dfrac{\partial}{\partial y} & \dfrac{\partial}{\partial z} \\ f & g & h \end{vmatrix} \tag{9}$$

You should verify that Formula (8) results if the determinant is computed by interpreting a "product" such as $(\partial/\partial x)(g)$ to mean $\partial g/\partial x$. Keep in mind, however, that (9) is just a mnemonic device and not a true determinant, since the entries in a determinant must be numbers, not vectors and partial derivative symbols.

▶ **Example 4** Find the divergence and the curl of the vector field

$$\mathbf{F}(x, y, z) = x^2y\mathbf{i} + 2y^3z\mathbf{j} + 3z\mathbf{k}$$

***Solution.*** From (7)

$$\begin{aligned} \text{div } \mathbf{F} &= \frac{\partial}{\partial x}(x^2y) + \frac{\partial}{\partial y}(2y^3z) + \frac{\partial}{\partial z}(3z) \\ &= 2xy + 6y^2z + 3 \end{aligned}$$

and from (9)

$$\begin{aligned} \text{curl } \mathbf{F} &= \begin{vmatrix} \mathbf{i} & \mathbf{j} & \mathbf{k} \\ \dfrac{\partial}{\partial x} & \dfrac{\partial}{\partial y} & \dfrac{\partial}{\partial z} \\ x^2y & 2y^3z & 3z \end{vmatrix} \\ &= \left[\frac{\partial}{\partial y}(3z) - \frac{\partial}{\partial z}(2y^3z)\right]\mathbf{i} + \left[\frac{\partial}{\partial z}(x^2y) - \frac{\partial}{\partial x}(3z)\right]\mathbf{j} + \left[\frac{\partial}{\partial x}(2y^3z) - \frac{\partial}{\partial y}(x^2y)\right]\mathbf{k} \\ &= -2y^3\mathbf{i} - x^2\mathbf{k} \end{aligned}$$ ◀

**TECHNOLOGY MASTERY**

Most computer algebra systems can compute gradient fields, divergence, and curl. If you have a CAS with these capabilities, read the relevant documentation, and use your CAS to check the computations in Examples 2 and 4.

▶ **Example 5** Show that the divergence of the inverse-square field

$$\mathbf{F}(x, y, z) = \frac{c}{(x^2 + y^2 + z^2)^{3/2}}(x\mathbf{i} + y\mathbf{j} + z\mathbf{k})$$

is zero.

***Solution.*** The computations can be simplified by letting $r = (x^2 + y^2 + z^2)^{1/2}$, in which case **F** can be expressed as

$$\mathbf{F}(x, y, z) = \frac{cx\mathbf{i} + cy\mathbf{j} + cz\mathbf{k}}{r^3} = \frac{cx}{r^3}\mathbf{i} + \frac{cy}{r^3}\mathbf{j} + \frac{cz}{r^3}\mathbf{k}$$

We leave it for you to show that

$$\frac{\partial r}{\partial x} = \frac{x}{r}, \quad \frac{\partial r}{\partial y} = \frac{y}{r}, \quad \frac{\partial r}{\partial z} = \frac{z}{r}$$

Thus

$$\operatorname{div} \mathbf{F} = c\left[\frac{\partial}{\partial x}\left(\frac{x}{r^3}\right) + \frac{\partial}{\partial y}\left(\frac{y}{r^3}\right) + \frac{\partial}{\partial z}\left(\frac{z}{r^3}\right)\right] \tag{10}$$

But

$$\frac{\partial}{\partial x}\left(\frac{x}{r^3}\right) = \frac{r^3 - x(3r^2)(x/r)}{(r^3)^2} = \frac{1}{r^3} - \frac{3x^2}{r^5}$$

$$\frac{\partial}{\partial y}\left(\frac{y}{r^3}\right) = \frac{1}{r^3} - \frac{3y^2}{r^5}$$

$$\frac{\partial}{\partial z}\left(\frac{z}{r^3}\right) = \frac{1}{r^3} - \frac{3z^2}{r^5}$$

Substituting these expressions in (10) yields

$$\operatorname{div} \mathbf{F} = c\left[\frac{3}{r^3} - \frac{3x^2 + 3y^2 + 3z^2}{r^5}\right] = c\left[\frac{3}{r^3} - \frac{3r^2}{r^5}\right] = 0 \blacktriangleleft$$

## THE ∇ OPERATOR

Thus far, the symbol $\nabla$ that appears in the gradient expression $\nabla\phi$ has not been given a meaning of its own. However, it is often convenient to view $\nabla$ as an operator

$$\nabla = \frac{\partial}{\partial x}\mathbf{i} + \frac{\partial}{\partial y}\mathbf{j} + \frac{\partial}{\partial z}\mathbf{k} \tag{11}$$

which when applied to $\phi(x, y, z)$ produces the gradient

$$\nabla\phi = \frac{\partial\phi}{\partial x}\mathbf{i} + \frac{\partial\phi}{\partial y}\mathbf{j} + \frac{\partial\phi}{\partial z}\mathbf{k}$$

We call (11) the ***del operator***. This is analogous to the derivative operator $d/dx$, which when applied to $f(x)$ produces the derivative $f'(x)$.

The del operator allows us to express the divergence of a vector field

$$\mathbf{F} = f(x, y, z)\mathbf{i} + g(x, y, z)\mathbf{j} + h(x, y, z)\mathbf{k}$$

in dot product notation as

$$\operatorname{div} \mathbf{F} = \nabla \cdot \mathbf{F} = \frac{\partial f}{\partial x} + \frac{\partial g}{\partial y} + \frac{\partial h}{\partial z} \tag{12}$$

and the curl of this field in cross-product notation as

$$\operatorname{curl} \mathbf{F} = \nabla \times \mathbf{F} = \begin{vmatrix} \mathbf{i} & \mathbf{j} & \mathbf{k} \\ \dfrac{\partial}{\partial x} & \dfrac{\partial}{\partial y} & \dfrac{\partial}{\partial z} \\ f & g & h \end{vmatrix} \tag{13}$$

## THE LAPLACIAN $\nabla^2$

The operator that results by taking the dot product of the del operator with itself is denoted by $\nabla^2$ and is called the ***Laplacian operator***. This operator has the form

$$\nabla^2 = \nabla \cdot \nabla = \frac{\partial^2}{\partial x^2} + \frac{\partial^2}{\partial y^2} + \frac{\partial^2}{\partial z^2} \tag{14}$$

When applied to $\phi(x, y, z)$ the Laplacian operator produces the function

$$\nabla^2 \phi = \frac{\partial^2 \phi}{\partial x^2} + \frac{\partial^2 \phi}{\partial y^2} + \frac{\partial^2 \phi}{\partial z^2}$$

Note that $\nabla^2 \phi$ can also be expressed as div $(\nabla \phi)$. The equation $\nabla^2 \phi = 0$ or, equivalently,

$$\frac{\partial^2 \phi}{\partial x^2} + \frac{\partial^2 \phi}{\partial y^2} + \frac{\partial^2 \phi}{\partial z^2} = 0$$

is known as ***Laplace's equation***. This partial differential equation plays an important role in a wide variety of applications, resulting from the fact that it is satisfied by the potential function for the inverse-square field.

## ✓QUICK CHECK EXERCISES 15.1 *(See page 979 for answers.)*

1. The function $\phi(x, y, z) = xy + yz + xz$ is a potential for the vector field $\mathbf{F} =$ ________.
2. The vector field $\mathbf{F}(x, y, z) =$ ________, defined for $(x, y, z) \neq (0, 0, 0)$, is always directed toward the origin and is of length equal to the distance from $(x, y, z)$ to the origin.
3. An inverse-square field is one that can be written in the form $\mathbf{F}(\mathbf{r}) =$ ________.
4. The vector field

$$\mathbf{F}(x, y, z) = yz\mathbf{i} + xy^2\mathbf{j} + yz^2\mathbf{k}$$

has divergence ________ and curl ________.

**Pierre-Simon de Laplace (1749–1827)** French mathematician and physicist. Laplace is sometimes referred to as the French Isaac Newton because of his work in celestial mechanics. In a five-volume treatise entitled *Traité de Mécanique Céleste*, he solved extremely difficult problems involving gravitational interactions between the planets. In particular, he was able to show that our solar system is stable and not prone to catastrophic collapse as a result of these interactions. This was an issue of major concern at the time because Jupiter's orbit appeared to be shrinking and Saturn's expanding; Laplace showed that these were expected periodic anomalies. In addition to his work in celestial mechanics, he founded modern probability theory, showed with Lavoisier that respiration is a form of combustion, and developed methods that fostered many new branches of pure mathematics.

Laplace was born to moderately successful parents in Normandy, his father being a farmer and cider merchant. He matriculated in the theology program at the University of Caen at age 16 but left for Paris at age 18 with a letter of introduction to the influential mathematician d'Alembert, who eventually helped him undertake a career in mathematics. Laplace was a prolific writer, and after his election to the Academy of Sciences in 1773, the secretary wrote that the Academy had never received so many important research papers by so young a person in such a short time. Laplace had little interest in pure mathematics—he regarded mathematics merely as a tool for solving applied problems. In his impatience with mathematical detail, he frequently omitted complicated arguments with the statement, "It is easy to show that. . . ." He admitted, however, that as time passed he often had trouble reconstructing the omitted details himself!

At the height of his fame, Laplace served on many government committees and held the posts of Minister of the Interior and Chancellor of the Senate. He barely escaped imprisonment and execution during the period of the Revolution, probably because he was able to convince each opposing party that he sided with them. Napoleon described him as a great mathematician but a poor administrator who "sought subtleties everywhere, had only doubtful ideas, and . . . carried the spirit of the infinitely small into administration." In spite of his genius, Laplace was both egotistic and insecure, attempting to ensure his place in history by conveniently failing to credit mathematicians whose work he used—an unnecessary pettiness since his own work was so brilliant. However, on the positive side he was supportive of young mathematicians, often treating them as his own children. Laplace ranks as one of the most influential mathematicians in history.

## EXERCISE SET 15.1 Graphing Utility C CAS

### FOCUS ON CONCEPTS

**1–2** Match the vector field $\mathbf{F}(x, y)$ with one of the plots, and explain your reasoning. ■

1. (a) $\mathbf{F}(x, y) = x\mathbf{i}$ (b) $\mathbf{F}(x, y) = \sin x\mathbf{i} + \mathbf{j}$

2. (a) $\mathbf{F}(x, y) = \mathbf{i} + \mathbf{j}$
   (b) $\mathbf{F}(x, y) = \dfrac{x}{\sqrt{x^2 + y^2}}\mathbf{i} + \dfrac{y}{\sqrt{x^2 + y^2}}\mathbf{j}$

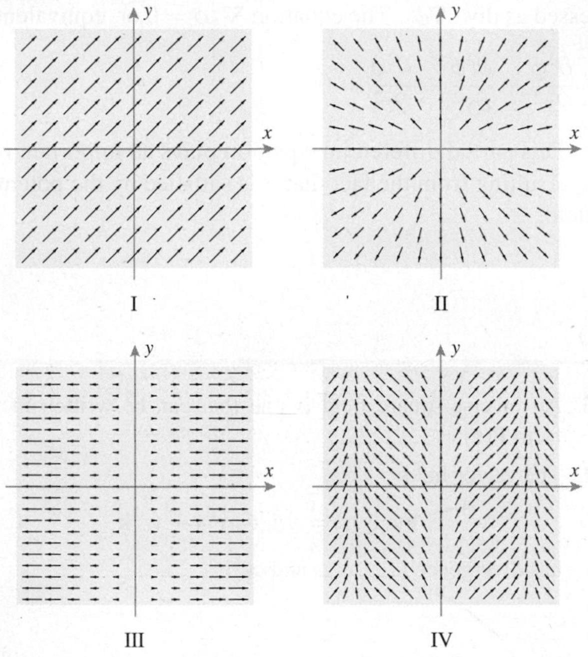


**3–4** Determine whether the statement about the vector field $\mathbf{F}(x, y)$ is true or false. If false, explain why. ■

3. $\mathbf{F}(x, y) = x^2\mathbf{i} - y\mathbf{j}$.
   (a) $\|\mathbf{F}(x, y)\| \to 0$ as $(x, y) \to (0, 0)$.
   (b) If $(x, y)$ is on the positive $y$-axis, then the vector points in the negative $y$-direction.
   (c) If $(x, y)$ is in the first quadrant, then the vector points down and to the right.

4. $\mathbf{F}(x, y) = \dfrac{x}{\sqrt{x^2 + y^2}}\mathbf{i} - \dfrac{y}{\sqrt{x^2 + y^2}}\mathbf{j}$.
   (a) As $(x, y)$ moves away from the origin, the lengths of the vectors decrease.
   (b) If $(x, y)$ is a point on the positive $x$-axis, then the vector points up.
   (c) If $(x, y)$ is a point on the positive $y$-axis, the vector points to the right.

**5–8** Sketch the vector field by drawing some representative nonintersecting vectors. The vectors need not be drawn to scale, but they should be in reasonably correct proportion relative to each other. ■

5. $\mathbf{F}(x, y) = 2\mathbf{i} - \mathbf{j}$ 6. $\mathbf{F}(x, y) = y\mathbf{j}, \quad y > 0$

7. $\mathbf{F}(x, y) = y\mathbf{i} - x\mathbf{j}$. [*Note:* Each vector in the field is perpendicular to the position vector $\mathbf{r} = x\mathbf{i} + y\mathbf{j}$.]

8. $\mathbf{F}(x, y) = \dfrac{x\mathbf{i} + y\mathbf{j}}{\sqrt{x^2 + y^2}}$. [*Note:* Each vector in the field is a unit vector in the same direction as the position vector $\mathbf{r} = x\mathbf{i} + y\mathbf{j}$.]

**9–10** Use a graphing utility to generate a plot of the vector field. ■

9. $\mathbf{F}(x, y) = \mathbf{i} + \cos y\mathbf{j}$ 10. $\mathbf{F}(x, y) = y\mathbf{i} - x\mathbf{j}$

**11–14 True–False** Determine whether the statement is true or false. Explain your answer. ■

11. The vector-valued function
$$\mathbf{F}(x, y) = y\mathbf{i} + x^2\mathbf{j} + xy\mathbf{k}$$
is an example of a vector field in the $xy$-plane.

12. If $\mathbf{r}$ is a radius vector in 3-space, then a vector field of the form
$$\mathbf{F}(\mathbf{r}) = \frac{1}{\|\mathbf{r}\|^2}\mathbf{r}$$
is an example of an inverse-square field.

13. If $\mathbf{F}$ is a vector field, then so is $\nabla \times \mathbf{F}$.

14. If $\mathbf{F}$ is a vector field and $\nabla \cdot \mathbf{F} = \phi$, then $\phi$ is a potential function for $\mathbf{F}$.

**15–16** Confirm that $\phi$ is a potential function for $\mathbf{F}(\mathbf{r})$ on some region, and state the region. ■

15. (a) $\phi(x, y) = \tan^{-1} xy$
   $\mathbf{F}(x, y) = \dfrac{y}{1 + x^2y^2}\mathbf{i} + \dfrac{x}{1 + x^2y^2}\mathbf{j}$
   (b) $\phi(x, y, z) = x^2 - 3y^2 + 4z^2$
   $\mathbf{F}(x, y, z) = 2x\mathbf{i} - 6y\mathbf{j} + 8z\mathbf{k}$

16. (a) $\phi(x, y) = 2y^2 + 3x^2y - xy^3$
   $\mathbf{F}(x, y) = (6xy - y^3)\mathbf{i} + (4y + 3x^2 - 3xy^2)\mathbf{j}$
   (b) $\phi(x, y, z) = x \sin z + y \sin x + z \sin y$
   $\mathbf{F}(x, y, z) = (\sin z + y \cos x)\mathbf{i} + (\sin x + z \cos y)\mathbf{j} + (\sin y + x \cos z)\mathbf{k}$

**17–22** Find div $\mathbf{F}$ and curl $\mathbf{F}$. ■

17. $\mathbf{F}(x, y, z) = x^2\mathbf{i} - 2\mathbf{j} + yz\mathbf{k}$

18. $\mathbf{F}(x, y, z) = xz^3\mathbf{i} + 2y^4x^2\mathbf{j} + 5z^2y\mathbf{k}$

19. $\mathbf{F}(x, y, z) = 7y^3z^2\mathbf{i} - 8x^2z^5\mathbf{j} - 3xy^4\mathbf{k}$

20. $\mathbf{F}(x, y, z) = e^{xy}\mathbf{i} - \cos y\mathbf{j} + \sin^2 z\mathbf{k}$

21. $\mathbf{F}(x, y, z) = \dfrac{1}{\sqrt{x^2 + y^2 + z^2}}(x\mathbf{i} + y\mathbf{j} + z\mathbf{k})$

22. $\mathbf{F}(x, y, z) = \ln x\mathbf{i} + e^{xyz}\mathbf{j} + \tan^{-1}(z/x)\mathbf{k}$

**23–24** Find $\nabla \cdot (\mathbf{F} \times \mathbf{G})$. ■

23. $\mathbf{F}(x, y, z) = 2x\mathbf{i} + \mathbf{j} + 4y\mathbf{k}$
   $\mathbf{G}(x, y, z) = x\mathbf{i} + y\mathbf{j} - z\mathbf{k}$

24. $\mathbf{F}(x, y, z) = yz\mathbf{i} + xz\mathbf{j} + xy\mathbf{k}$
   $\mathbf{G}(x, y, z) = xy\mathbf{j} + xyz\mathbf{k}$

**25–26** Find $\nabla \cdot (\nabla \times \mathbf{F})$. ■

**25.** $\mathbf{F}(x, y, z) = \sin x\mathbf{i} + \cos(x - y)\mathbf{j} + z\mathbf{k}$

**26.** $\mathbf{F}(x, y, z) = e^{xz}\mathbf{i} + 3xe^{y}\mathbf{j} - e^{yz}\mathbf{k}$

**27–28** Find $\nabla \times (\nabla \times \mathbf{F})$. ■

**27.** $\mathbf{F}(x, y, z) = xy\mathbf{j} + xyz\mathbf{k}$

**28.** $\mathbf{F}(x, y, z) = y^2x\mathbf{i} - 3yz\mathbf{j} + xy\mathbf{k}$

C **29.** Use a CAS to check the calculations in Exercises 23, 25, and 27.

C **30.** Use a CAS to check the calculations in Exercises 24, 26, and 28.

**31–38** Let $k$ be a constant, $\mathbf{F} = \mathbf{F}(x, y, z)$, $\mathbf{G} = \mathbf{G}(x, y, z)$, and $\phi = \phi(x, y, z)$. Prove the following identities, assuming that all derivatives involved exist and are continuous. ■

**31.** $\operatorname{div}(k\mathbf{F}) = k \operatorname{div} \mathbf{F}$ **32.** $\operatorname{curl}(k\mathbf{F}) = k \operatorname{curl} \mathbf{F}$

**33.** $\operatorname{div}(\mathbf{F} + \mathbf{G}) = \operatorname{div} \mathbf{F} + \operatorname{div} \mathbf{G}$

**34.** $\operatorname{curl}(\mathbf{F} + \mathbf{G}) = \operatorname{curl} \mathbf{F} + \operatorname{curl} \mathbf{G}$

**35.** $\operatorname{div}(\phi\mathbf{F}) = \phi \operatorname{div} \mathbf{F} + \nabla\phi \cdot \mathbf{F}$

**36.** $\operatorname{curl}(\phi\mathbf{F}) = \phi \operatorname{curl} \mathbf{F} + \nabla\phi \times \mathbf{F}$

**37.** $\operatorname{div}(\operatorname{curl} \mathbf{F}) = 0$ **38.** $\operatorname{curl}(\nabla\phi) = \mathbf{0}$

**39.** Rewrite the identities in Exercises 31, 33, 35, and 37 in an equivalent form using the notation $\nabla \cdot$ for divergence and $\nabla \times$ for curl.

**40.** Rewrite the identities in Exercises 32, 34, 36, and 38 in an equivalent form using the notation $\nabla \cdot$ for divergence and $\nabla \times$ for curl.

**41–42** Verify that the radius vector $\mathbf{r} = x\mathbf{i} + y\mathbf{j} + z\mathbf{k}$ has the stated property. ■

**41.** (a) $\operatorname{curl} \mathbf{r} = \mathbf{0}$ (b) $\nabla\|\mathbf{r}\| = \dfrac{\mathbf{r}}{\|\mathbf{r}\|}$

**42.** (a) $\operatorname{div} \mathbf{r} = 3$ (b) $\nabla \dfrac{1}{\|\mathbf{r}\|} = -\dfrac{\mathbf{r}}{\|\mathbf{r}\|^3}$

**43–44** Let $\mathbf{r} = x\mathbf{i} + y\mathbf{j} + z\mathbf{k}$, let $r = \|\mathbf{r}\|$, let $f$ be a differentiable function of one variable, and let $\mathbf{F}(\mathbf{r}) = f(r)\mathbf{r}$. ■

**43.** (a) Use the chain rule and Exercise 41(b) to show that

$$\nabla f(r) = \frac{f'(r)}{r}\mathbf{r}$$

(b) Use the result in part (a) and Exercises 35 and 42(a) to show that $\operatorname{div} \mathbf{F} = 3f(r) + rf'(r)$.

**44.** (a) Use part (a) of Exercise 43, Exercise 36, and Exercise 41(a) to show that $\operatorname{curl} \mathbf{F} = \mathbf{0}$.

(b) Use the result in part (a) of Exercise 43 and Exercises 35 and 42(a) to show that

$$\nabla^2 f(r) = 2\frac{f'(r)}{r} + f''(r)$$

**45.** Use the result in Exercise 43(b) to show that the divergence of the inverse-square field $\mathbf{F} = \mathbf{r}/\|\mathbf{r}\|^3$ is zero.

**46.** Use the result of Exercise 43(b) to show that if $\mathbf{F}$ is a vector field of the form $\mathbf{F} = f(\|\mathbf{r}\|)\mathbf{r}$ and if $\operatorname{div} \mathbf{F} = 0$, then $\mathbf{F}$ is an inverse-square field. [*Suggestion:* Let $r = \|\mathbf{r}\|$ and multiply $3f(r) + rf'(r) = 0$ through by $r^2$. Then write the result as a derivative of a product.]

**47.** A curve $C$ is called a ***flow line*** of a vector field $\mathbf{F}$ if $\mathbf{F}$ is a tangent vector to $C$ at each point along $C$ (see the accompanying figure).

(a) Let $C$ be a flow line for $\mathbf{F}(x, y) = -y\mathbf{i} + x\mathbf{j}$, and let $(x, y)$ be a point on $C$ for which $y \neq 0$. Show that the flow lines satisfy the differential equation

$$\frac{dy}{dx} = -\frac{x}{y}$$

(b) Solve the differential equation in part (a) by separation of variables, and show that the flow lines are concentric circles centered at the origin.

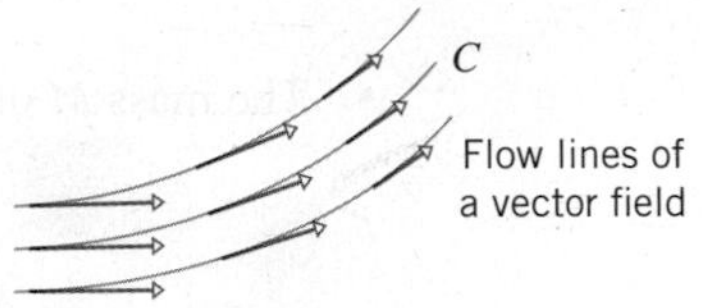


◄ **Figure Ex-47**

**48–50** Find a differential equation satisfied by the flow lines of $\mathbf{F}$ (see Exercise 47), and solve it to find equations for the flow lines of $\mathbf{F}$. Sketch some typical flow lines and tangent vectors. ■

**48.** $\mathbf{F}(x, y) = \mathbf{i} + x\mathbf{j}$ **49.** $\mathbf{F}(x, y) = x\mathbf{i} + \mathbf{j}$, $x > 0$

**50.** $\mathbf{F}(x, y) = x\mathbf{i} - y\mathbf{j}$, $x > 0$ and $y > 0$

**51. Writing** Discuss the similarities and differences between the concepts "vector field" and "slope field."

**52. Writing** In physical applications it is often necessary to deal with vector quantities that depend not only on position in space but also on time. Give some examples and discuss how the concept of a vector field would need to be modified to apply to such situations.

✓ **QUICK CHECK ANSWERS 15.1** 1. $(y + z)\mathbf{i} + (x + z)\mathbf{j} + (x + y)\mathbf{k}$ 2. $-\mathbf{r} = -x\mathbf{i} - y\mathbf{j} - z\mathbf{k}$ 3. $\dfrac{c}{\|\mathbf{r}\|^3}\mathbf{r}$ 4. $2xy + 2yz$; $z^2\mathbf{i} + y\mathbf{j} + (y^2 - z)\mathbf{k}$

# 15.2 LINE INTEGRALS

*In earlier chapters we considered three kinds of integrals in rectangular coordinates: single integrals over intervals, double integrals over two-dimensional regions, and triple integrals over three-dimensional regions. In this section we will discuss integrals along curves in two- or three-dimensional space.*

## LINE INTEGRALS

The first goal of this section is to define what it means to integrate a function along a curve. To motivate the definition we will consider the problem of finding the mass of a very thin wire whose linear density function (mass per unit length) is known. We assume that we can model the wire by a smooth curve $C$ between two points $P$ and $Q$ in 3-space (Figure 15.2.1). Given any point $(x, y, z)$ on $C$, we let $f(x, y, z)$ denote the corresponding value of the density function. To compute the mass of the wire, we proceed as follows:

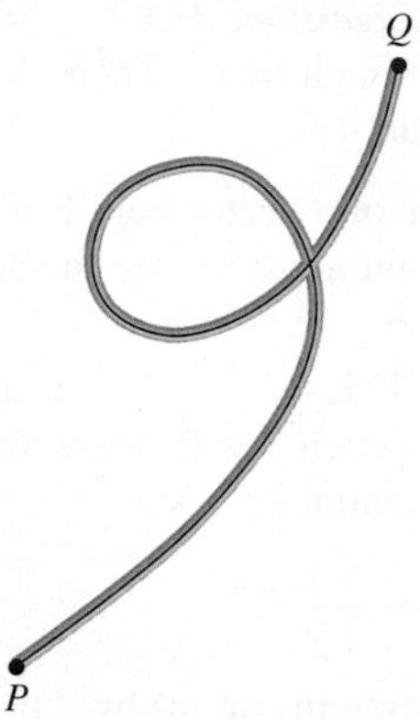


▲ **Figure 15.2.1** A bent thin wire modeled by a smooth curve

- Divide $C$ into $n$ very small sections using a succession of distinct partition points

$$P = P_0, P_1, P_2, \ldots, P_{n-1}, P_n = Q$$

as illustrated on the left side of Figure 15.2.2. Let $\Delta M_k$ be the mass of the $k$th section, and let $\Delta s_k$ be the length of the arc between $P_{k-1}$ and $P_k$.

- Choose an arbitrary sampling point $P_k^*(x_k^*, y_k^*, z_k^*)$ on the $k$th arc, as illustrated on the right side of Figure 15.2.2. If $\Delta s_k$ is very small, the value of $f$ will not vary much along the $k$th section and we can approximate $f$ along this section by the value $f(x_k^*, y_k^*, z_k^*)$. It follows that the mass of the $k$th section can be approximated by

$$\Delta M_k \approx f(x_k^*, y_k^*, z_k^*)\Delta s_k$$

- The mass $M$ of the entire wire can then be approximated by

$$M = \sum_{k=1}^{n} \Delta M_k \approx \sum_{k=1}^{n} f(x_k^*, y_k^*, z_k^*)\Delta s_k \qquad (1)$$

- We will use the expression $\max \Delta s_k \to 0$ to indicate the process of increasing $n$ in such a way that the lengths of all the sections approach 0. It is plausible that the error in (1) will approach 0 as $\max \Delta s_k \to 0$ and the exact value of $M$ will be given by

$$M = \lim_{\max \Delta s_k \to 0} \sum_{k=1}^{n} f(x_k^*, y_k^*, z_k^*)\Delta s_k \qquad (2)$$

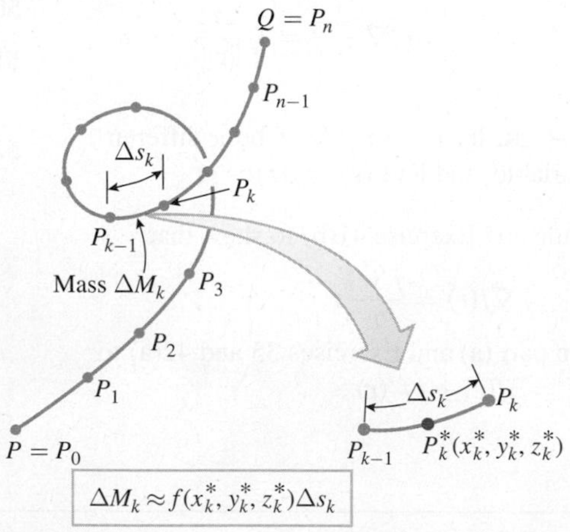


▶ **Figure 15.2.2**

The limit in (2) is similar to the limit of Riemann sums used to define the definite integral of a function over an interval (Definition 5.5.1). With this similarity in mind, we make the following definition.

**15.2.1 DEFINITION** If $C$ is a smooth curve in 2-space or 3-space, then the ***line integral of f with respect to s along C*** is

$$\int_C f(x, y)\,ds = \lim_{\max \Delta s_k \to 0} \sum_{k=1}^{n} f(x_k^*, y_k^*)\Delta s_k \quad \boxed{\text{2-space}} \tag{3}$$

or

$$\int_C f(x, y, z)\,ds = \lim_{\max \Delta s_k \to 0} \sum_{k=1}^{n} f(x_k^*, y_k^*, z_k^*)\Delta s_k \quad \boxed{\text{3-space}} \tag{4}$$

provided this limit exists and does not depend on the choice of partition or on the choice of sample points.

Although the term "curve integrals" is more descriptive, the integrals in Definition 15.2.1 are called "line integrals" for historical reasons.

It is usually impractical to evaluate line integrals directly from Definition 15.2.1. However, the definition is important in the application and interpretation of line integrals. For example:

- If $C$ is a curve in 3-space that models a thin wire, and if $f(x, y, z)$ is the linear density function of the wire, then it follows from (2) and Definition 15.2.1 that the mass $M$ of the wire is given by

$$M = \int_C f(x, y, z)\,ds \tag{5}$$

  That is, to obtain the mass of a thin wire, we integrate the linear density function over the smooth curve that models the wire.

- If $C$ is a smooth curve of arc length $L$, and $f$ is identically 1, then it immediately follows from Definition 15.2.1 that

$$\int_C ds = \lim_{\max \Delta s_k \to 0} \sum_{k=1}^{n} \Delta s_k = \lim_{\max \Delta s_k \to 0} L = L \tag{6}$$

- If $C$ is a curve in the $xy$-plane and $f(x, y)$ is a nonnegative continuous function defined on $C$, then $\int_C f(x, y)\,ds$ can be interpreted as the area $A$ of the "sheet" that is swept out by a vertical line segment that extends upward from the point $(x, y)$ to a height of $f(x, y)$ and moves along $C$ from one endpoint to the other (Figure 15.2.3). To see why this is so, refer to Figure 15.2.4 in which $f(x_k^*, y_k^*)$ is the value of $f$ at an arbitrary point $P_k^*$ on the $k$th arc of the partition and note the approximation

$$\Delta A_k \approx f(x_k^*, y_k^*)\Delta s_k$$

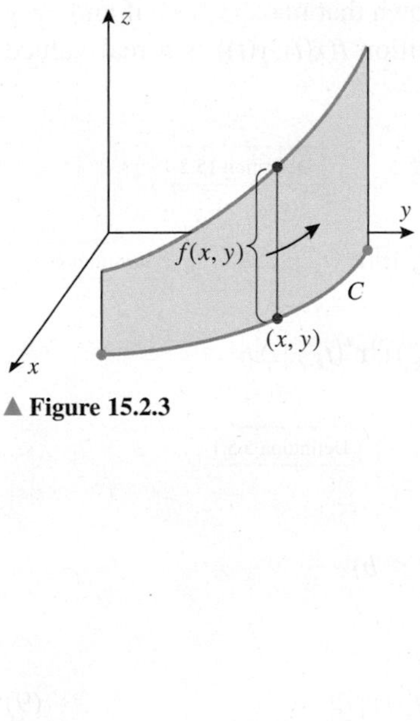

▲ Figure 15.2.3

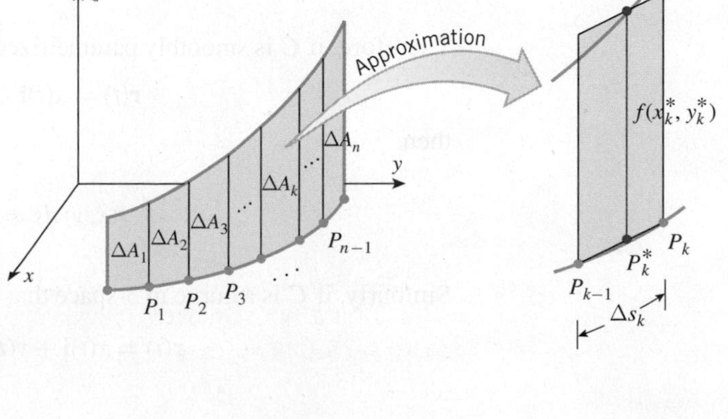

▶ Figure 15.2.4

It follows that

$$A = \sum_{k=1}^{n} \Delta A_k \approx \sum_{k=1}^{n} f(x_k^*, y_k^*)\Delta s_k$$

It is then plausible that

$$A = \lim_{\max \Delta s_k \to 0} \sum_{k=1}^{n} f(x_k^*, y_k^*)\Delta s_k = \int_C f(x, y)\, ds \tag{7}$$

Since Definition 15.2.1 is closely modeled on Definition 5.5.1, line integrals share many of the common properties of ordinary definite integrals. For example, we have

$$\int_C [f(x, y) + g(x, y)]\, ds = \int_C f(x, y)\, ds + \int_C g(x, y)\, ds$$

provided both line integrals on the right-hand side of this equation exist. Similarly, it can be shown that if $f$ is continuous on $C$, then the line integral of $f$ with respect to $s$ along $C$ exists.

## EVALUATING LINE INTEGRALS

Except in simple cases, it will not be feasible to evaluate a line integral directly from (3) or (4). However, we will now show that it is possible to express a line integral as an ordinary definite integral, so that no special methods of evaluation are required. For example, suppose that $C$ is a curve in the $xy$-plane that is smoothly parametrized by

$$\mathbf{r}(t) = x(t)\mathbf{i} + y(t)\mathbf{j} \qquad (a \le t \le b)$$

Moreover, suppose that each partition point $P_k$ of $C$ corresponds to a parameter value of $t_k$ in $[a, b]$. The arc length of $C$ between points $P_{k-1}$ and $P_k$ is then given by

$$\Delta s_k = \int_{t_{k-1}}^{t_k} \|\mathbf{r}'(t)\|\, dt \tag{8}$$

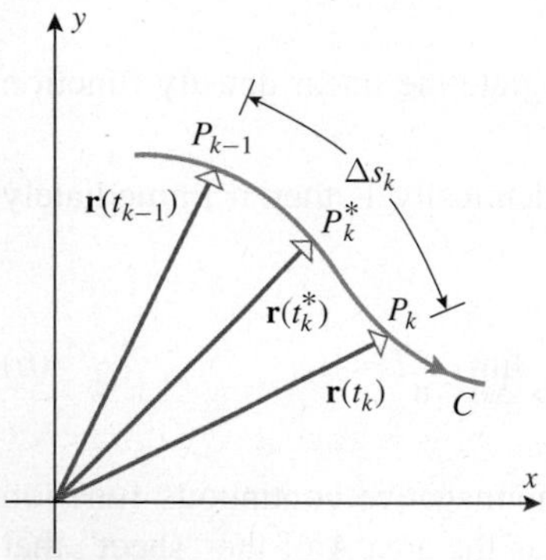


▲ **Figure 15.2.5**

(Theorem 12.3.1). If we let $\Delta t_k = t_k - t_{k-1}$, then it follows from (8) and the Mean-Value Theorem for Integrals (Theorem 5.6.2) that there exists a point $t_k^*$ in $[t_{k-1}, t_k]$ such that

$$\Delta s_k = \int_{t_{k-1}}^{t_k} \|\mathbf{r}'(t)\|\, dt = \|\mathbf{r}'(t_k^*)\|\Delta t_k$$

We let $P_k^*(x_k^*, y_k^*) = P_k^*(x(t_k^*), y(t_k^*))$ correspond to the parameter value $t_k^*$ (Figure 15.2.5). Since the parametrization of $C$ is smooth, it can be shown that $\max \Delta s_k \to 0$ if and only if $\max \Delta t_k \to 0$ (Exercise 57). Furthermore, the composition $f(x(t), y(t))$ is a real-valued function defined on $[a, b]$ and we have

$$\begin{aligned}
\int_C f(x, y)\, ds &= \lim_{\max \Delta s_k \to 0} \sum_{k=1}^{n} f(x_k^*, y_k^*)\, \Delta s_k && \boxed{\text{Definition 15.2.1}} \\
&= \lim_{\max \Delta s_k \to 0} \sum_{k=1}^{n} f(x(t_k^*), y(t_k^*))\|\mathbf{r}'(t_k^*)\|\Delta t_k && \boxed{\text{Substitution}} \\
&= \lim_{\max \Delta t_k \to 0} \sum_{k=1}^{n} f(x(t_k^*), y(t_k^*))\|\mathbf{r}'(t_k^*)\|\Delta t_k \\
&= \int_a^b f(x(t), y(t))\|\mathbf{r}'(t)\|\, dt && \boxed{\text{Definition 5.5.1}}
\end{aligned}$$

Therefore, if $C$ is smoothly parametrized by

$$\mathbf{r}(t) = x(t)\mathbf{i} + y(t)\mathbf{j} \qquad (a \le t \le b)$$

then

$$\int_C f(x, y)\, ds = \int_a^b f(x(t), y(t))\|\mathbf{r}'(t)\|\, dt \tag{9}$$

Similarly, if $C$ is a curve in 3-space that is smoothly parametrized by

$$\mathbf{r}(t) = x(t)\mathbf{i} + y(t)\mathbf{j} + z(t)\mathbf{k} \qquad (a \le t \le b)$$

Explain how Formulas (9) and (10) confirm Formula (6) for arc length.

then

$$\int_C f(x, y, z)\, ds = \int_a^b f(x(t), y(t), z(t))\|\mathbf{r}'(t)\|\, dt \tag{10}$$

► **Example 1** Using the given parametrization, evaluate the line integral $\int_C (1 + xy^2)\, ds$.

(a) $C: \mathbf{r}(t) = t\mathbf{i} + 2t\mathbf{j} \quad (0 \le t \le 1)$ (see Figure 15.2.6*a*)

(b) $C: \mathbf{r}(t) = (1 - t)\mathbf{i} + (2 - 2t)\mathbf{j} \quad (0 \le t \le 1)$ (see Figure 15.2.6*b*)

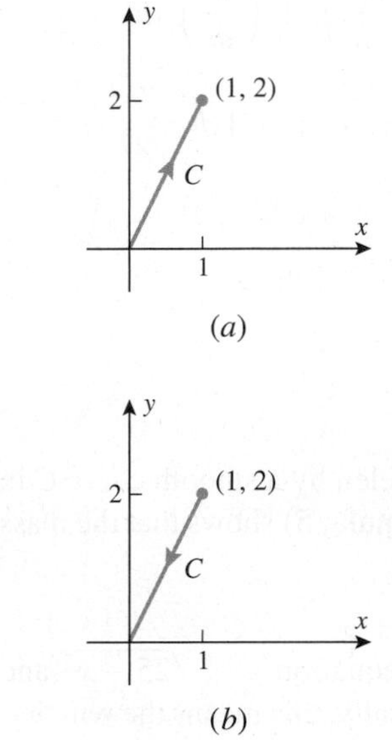


▲ **Figure 15.2.6**

***Solution (a).*** Since $\mathbf{r}'(t) = \mathbf{i} + 2\mathbf{j}$, we have $\|\mathbf{r}'(t)\| = \sqrt{5}$ and it follows from Formula (9) that

$$\int_C (1 + xy^2)\, ds = \int_0^1 [1 + t(2t)^2]\sqrt{5}\, dt$$

$$= \int_0^1 (1 + 4t^3)\sqrt{5}\, dt$$

$$= \sqrt{5}\left[t + t^4\right]_0^1 = 2\sqrt{5}$$

***Solution (b).*** Since $\mathbf{r}'(t) = -\mathbf{i} - 2\mathbf{j}$, we have $\|\mathbf{r}'(t)\| = \sqrt{5}$ and it follows from Formula (9) that

$$\int_C (1 + xy^2)\, ds = \int_0^1 [1 + (1 - t)(2 - 2t)^2]\sqrt{5}\, dt$$

$$= \int_0^1 [1 + 4(1 - t)^3]\sqrt{5}\, dt$$

$$= \sqrt{5}\left[t - (1 - t)^4\right]_0^1 = 2\sqrt{5} \blacktriangleleft$$

Note that the integrals in parts (a) and (b) of Example 1 agree, even though the corresponding parametrizations of $C$ have opposite orientations. This illustrates the important result that the value of a line integral of $f$ with respect to $s$ along $C$ *does not depend on an orientation of* $C$. (This is because $\Delta s_k$ is always positive; therefore, it does not matter in which *direction* along $C$ we list the partition points of the curve in Definition 15.2.1.) Later in this section we will discuss line integrals that are defined only for oriented curves.

Formula (9) has an alternative expression for a curve $C$ in the $xy$-plane that is given by parametric equations

$$x = x(t), \quad y = y(t) \qquad (a \le t \le b)$$

In this case, we write (9) in the expanded form

$$\int_C f(x, y)\, ds = \int_a^b f(x(t), y(t))\sqrt{\left(\frac{dx}{dt}\right)^2 + \left(\frac{dy}{dt}\right)^2}\, dt \tag{11}$$

Similarly, if $C$ is a curve in 3-space that is parametrized by

$$x = x(t), \quad y = y(t), \quad z = z(t) \qquad (a \le t \le b)$$

then we write (10) in the form

$$\int_C f(x, y, z)\, ds = \int_a^b f(x(t), y(t), z(t))\sqrt{\left(\frac{dx}{dt}\right)^2 + \left(\frac{dy}{dt}\right)^2 + \left(\frac{dz}{dt}\right)^2}\, dt \tag{12}$$

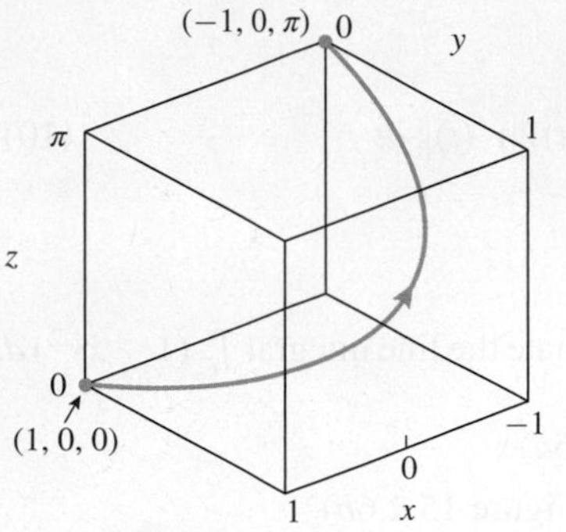

▲ Figure 15.2.7

▶ **Example 2** Evaluate the line integral $\int_C (xy + z^3)\,ds$ from $(1, 0, 0)$ to $(-1, 0, \pi)$ along the helix $C$ that is represented by the parametric equations

$$x = \cos t, \quad y = \sin t, \quad z = t \qquad (0 \le t \le \pi)$$

(Figure 15.2.7).

***Solution.*** From (12)

$$\begin{aligned}\int_C (xy + z^3)\,ds &= \int_0^{\pi} (\cos t \sin t + t^3)\sqrt{\left(\frac{dx}{dt}\right)^2 + \left(\frac{dy}{dt}\right)^2 + \left(\frac{dz}{dt}\right)^2}\,dt \\ &= \int_0^{\pi} (\cos t \sin t + t^3)\sqrt{(-\sin t)^2 + (\cos t)^2 + 1}\,dt \\ &= \sqrt{2}\int_0^{\pi} (\cos t \sin t + t^3)\,dt \\ &= \sqrt{2}\left[\frac{\sin^2 t}{2} + \frac{t^4}{4}\right]_0^{\pi} = \frac{\sqrt{2}\pi^4}{4} \blacktriangleleft\end{aligned}$$

If $\delta(x, y)$ is the linear density function of a wire that is modeled by a smooth curve $C$ in the $xy$-plane, then an argument similar to the derivation of Formula (5) shows that the mass of the wire is given by $\int_C \delta(x, y)\,ds$.

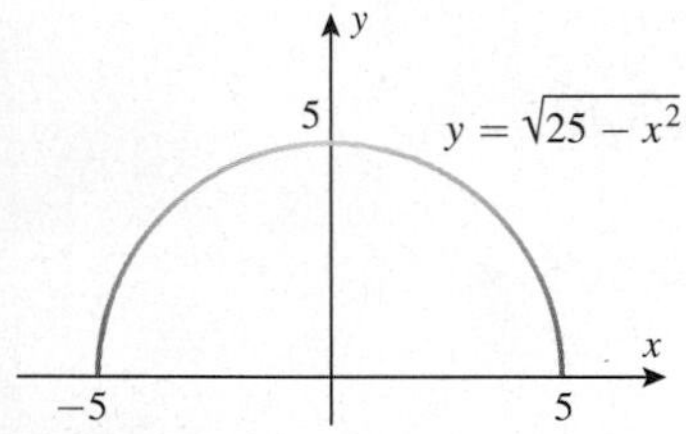

▲ Figure 15.2.8

▶ **Example 3** Suppose that a semicircular wire has the equation $y = \sqrt{25 - x^2}$ and that its mass density is $\delta(x, y) = 15 - y$ (Figure 15.2.8). Physically, this means the wire has a maximum density of 15 units at the base $(y = 0)$ and that the density of the wire decreases linearly with respect to $y$ to a value of 10 units at the top $(y = 5)$. Find the mass of the wire.

***Solution.*** The mass $M$ of the wire can be expressed as the line integral

$$M = \int_C \delta(x, y)\,ds = \int_C (15 - y)\,ds$$

along the semicircle $C$. To evaluate this integral we will express $C$ parametrically as

$$x = 5\cos t, \quad y = 5\sin t \qquad (0 \le t \le \pi)$$

Thus, it follows from (11) that

$$\begin{aligned}M = \int_C (15 - y)\,ds &= \int_0^{\pi} (15 - 5\sin t)\sqrt{\left(\frac{dx}{dt}\right)^2 + \left(\frac{dy}{dt}\right)^2}\,dt \\ &= \int_0^{\pi} (15 - 5\sin t)\sqrt{(-5\sin t)^2 + (5\cos t)^2}\,dt \\ &= 5\int_0^{\pi} (15 - 5\sin t)\,dt \\ &= 5\,[15t + 5\cos t]_0^{\pi} \\ &= 75\pi - 50 \approx 185.6 \text{ units of mass} \blacktriangleleft\end{aligned}$$

In the special case where $t$ is an arc length parameter, say $t = s$, it follows from Formulas (20) and (21) in Section 12.3 that the radicals in (11) and (12) reduce to 1 and the equations simplify to

$$\int_C f(x, y)\,ds = \int_a^b f(x(s), y(s))\,ds \tag{13}$$

and

$$\int_C f(x, y, z)\,ds = \int_a^b f(x(s), y(s), z(s))\,ds \tag{14}$$

respectively.

▶ **Example 4** Find the area of the surface extending upward from the circle $x^2+y^2=1$ in the $xy$-plane to the parabolic cylinder $z=1-x^2$ (Figure 15.2.9).

***Solution.*** It follows from (7) that the area $A$ of the surface can be expressed as the line integral

$$A=\int_C (1-x^2)\,ds \tag{15}$$

where $C$ is the circle $x^2+y^2=1$. This circle can be parametrized in terms of arc length as

$$x=\cos s,\quad y=\sin s\qquad (0\le s\le 2\pi)$$

Thus, it follows from (13) and (15) that

$$\begin{aligned}A&=\int_C (1-x^2)\,ds=\int_0^{2\pi}(1-\cos^2 s)\,ds\\&=\int_0^{2\pi}\sin^2 s\,ds=\frac{1}{2}\int_0^{2\pi}(1-\cos 2s)\,ds=\pi\end{aligned}$$ ◀

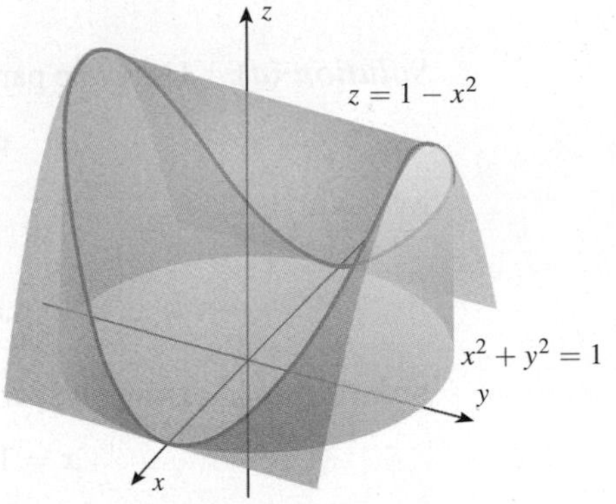

▶ **Figure 15.2.9**

## LINE INTEGRALS WITH RESPECT TO *x*, *y*, AND *z*

We now describe a second type of line integral in which we replace the "$ds$" in the integral by $dx$, $dy$, or $dz$. For example, suppose that $f$ is a function defined on a smooth curve $C$ in the $xy$-plane and that partition points of $C$ are denoted by $P_k(x_k, y_k)$. Letting

$$\Delta x_k = x_k - x_{k-1}\quad\text{and}\quad \Delta y_k = y_k - y_{k-1}$$

we would like to define

$$\int_C f(x,y)\,dx=\lim_{\max\Delta s_k\to 0}\sum_{k=1}^{n} f(x_k^*, y_k^*)\Delta x_k \tag{16}$$

$$\int_C f(x,y)\,dy=\lim_{\max\Delta s_k\to 0}\sum_{k=1}^{n} f(x_k^*, y_k^*)\Delta y_k \tag{17}$$

However, unlike $\Delta s_k$, the values of $\Delta x_k$ and $\Delta y_k$ change sign if the order of the partition points along $C$ is reversed. Therefore, in order to define the line integrals using Formulas (16) and (17), we must restrict ourselves to *oriented* curves $C$ and to partitions of $C$ in which the partition points are ordered in the direction of the curve. With this restriction, if the limit in (16) exists and does not depend on the choice of partition or sampling points, then we refer to (16) as the ***line integral of f with respect to x along C***. Similarly, (17) defines the ***line integral of f with respect to y along C***. If $C$ is a smooth curve in 3-space, we can have ***line integrals of f with respect to x, y, and z along C***. For example,

$$\int_C f(x,y,z)\,dx=\lim_{\max\Delta s_k\to 0}\sum_{k=1}^{n} f(x_k^*, y_k^*, z_k^*)\Delta x_k$$

Explain why Formula (16) implies that $\int_C dx = x_f - x_i$, where $x_f$ and $x_i$ are the respective $x$-coordinates of the final and initial points of $C$. What about $\int_C dy$?

Explain why Formula (16) implies that $\int_C f(x,y)\,dx = 0$ on any oriented segment parallel to the $y$-axis. What can you say about $\int_C f(x,y)\,dy$ on any oriented segment parallel to the $x$-axis?

and so forth. As was the case with line integrals with respect to $s$, line integrals of $f$ with respect to $x$, $y$, and $z$ exist if $f$ is continuous on $C$.

The basic procedure for evaluating these line integrals is to find parametric equations for $C$, say

$$x = x(t), \quad y = y(t), \quad z = z(t) \qquad (a \le t \le b)$$

in which the orientation of $C$ is in the direction of increasing $t$, and then express the integrand in terms of $t$. For example,

$$\int_C f(x,y,z)\,dz = \int_a^b f(x(t), y(t), z(t))z'(t)\,dt$$

[Such a formula is easy to remember—just substitute for $x$, $y$, and $z$ using the parametric equations and recall that $dz = z'(t)\,dt$.]

► **Example 5** Evaluate $\int_C 3xy\,dy$, where $C$ is the line segment joining $(0,0)$ and $(1,2)$ with the given orientation.

(a) Oriented from $(0,0)$ to $(1,2)$ as in Figure 15.2.6$a$.

(b) Oriented from $(1,2)$ to $(0,0)$ as in Figure 15.2.6$b$.

***Solution (a).*** Using the parametrization

$$x = t, \quad y = 2t \qquad (0 \le t \le 1)$$

we have

$$\int_C 3xy\,dy = \int_0^1 3(t)(2t)(2)\,dt = \int_0^1 12t^2\,dt = 4t^3\Big]_0^1 = 4$$

***Solution (b).*** Using the parametrization

$$x = 1 - t, \quad y = 2 - 2t \qquad (0 \le t \le 1)$$

we have

$$\int_C 3xy\,dy = \int_0^1 3(1-t)(2-2t)(-2)\,dt = \int_0^1 -12(1-t)^2\,dt = 4(1-t)^3\Big]_0^1 = -4 \blacktriangleleft$$

In Example 5, note that reversing the orientation of the curve changed the sign of the line integral. This is because reversing the orientation of a curve changes the sign of $\Delta x_k$ in definition (16). Thus, unlike line integrals of functions with respect to $s$ along $C$, reversing the orientation of $C$ changes the sign of a line integral with respect to $x$, $y$, and $z$. If $C$ is a smooth oriented curve, we will let $-C$ denote the oriented curve consisting of the same points as $C$ but with the opposite orientation (Figure 15.2.10). We then have

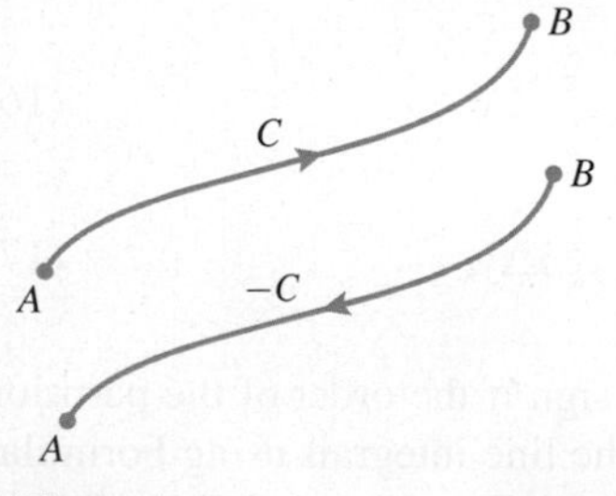

▲ **Figure 15.2.10**

$$\int_{-C} f(x,y)\,dx = -\int_C f(x,y)\,dx \quad \text{and} \quad \int_{-C} g(x,y)\,dy = -\int_C g(x,y)\,dy \qquad (18\text{–}19)$$

while

$$\int_{-C} f(x,y)\,ds = \int_C f(x,y)\,ds \qquad (20)$$

Similar identities hold for line integrals in 3-space. Unless indicated otherwise, we will assume that parametric curves are oriented in the direction of increasing parameter.

Frequently, the line integrals with respect to $x$ and $y$ occur in combination, in which case we will dispense with one of the integral signs and write

$$\int_C f(x,y)\,dx + g(x,y)\,dy = \int_C f(x,y)\,dx + \int_C g(x,y)\,dy \qquad (21)$$

We will use a similar convention for combinations of line integrals with respect to $x$, $y$, and $z$ along curves in 3-space.

▶ **Example 6** Evaluate

$$\int_C 2xy\,dx + (x^2+y^2)\,dy$$

along the circular arc $C$ given by $x = \cos t, y = \sin t\,(0 \le t \le \pi/2)$ (Figure 15.2.11).

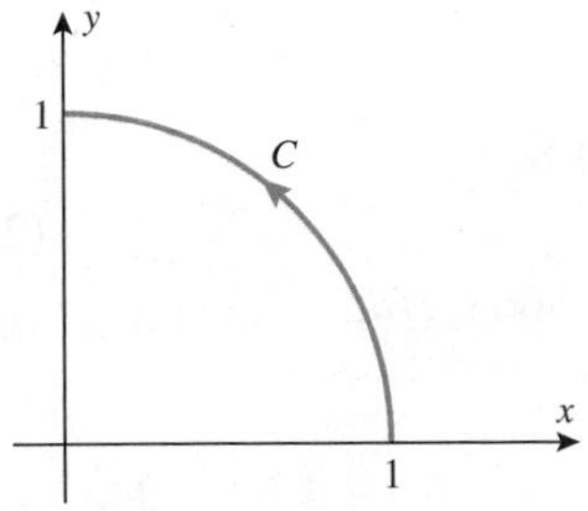

$x = \cos t,\ y = \sin t\ (0 \le t \le \pi/2)$

▲ **Figure 15.2.11**

***Solution.*** We have

$$\int_C 2xy\,dx = \int_0^{\pi/2} (2\cos t \sin t)\left[\frac{d}{dt}(\cos t)\right] dt$$

$$= -2\int_0^{\pi/2} \sin^2 t \cos t\,dt = -\frac{2}{3}\sin^3 t\Big]_0^{\pi/2} = -\frac{2}{3}$$

$$\int_C (x^2+y^2)\,dy = \int_0^{\pi/2} (\cos^2 t + \sin^2 t)\left[\frac{d}{dt}(\sin t)\right] dt$$

$$= \int_0^{\pi/2} \cos t\,dt = \sin t\Big]_0^{\pi/2} = 1$$

Thus, from (21)

$$\int_C 2xy\,dx + (x^2+y^2)\,dy = \int_C 2xy\,dx + \int_C (x^2+y^2)\,dy$$

$$= -\frac{2}{3} + 1 = \frac{1}{3} \blacktriangleleft$$

It can be shown that if $f$ and $g$ are continuous functions on $C$, then combinations of line integrals with respect to $x$ and $y$ can be expressed in terms of a limit and can be evaluated together in a single step. For example, we have

$$\int_C f(x,y)\,dx + g(x,y)\,dy = \lim_{\max\Delta s_k \to 0} \sum_{k=1}^{n} [f(x_k^*, y_k^*)\Delta x_k + g(x_k^*, y_k^*)\,\Delta y_k] \tag{22}$$

and

$$\int_C f(x,y)\,dx + g(x,y)\,dy = \int_a^b [f(x(t),y(t))x'(t) + g(x(t),y(t))y'(t)]\,dt \tag{23}$$

Similar results hold for line integrals in 3-space. The evaluation of a line integral can sometimes be simplified by using Formula (23).

▶ **Example 7** Evaluate

$$\int_C (3x^2+y^2)\,dx + 2xy\,dy$$

along the circular arc $C$ given by $x = \cos t, y = \sin t\,(0 \le t \le \pi/2)$ (Figure 15.2.11).

***Solution.*** From (23) we have

$$\int_C (3x^2+y^2)\,dx + 2xy\,dy = \int_0^{\pi/2} [(3\cos^2 t + \sin^2 t)(-\sin t) + 2(\cos t)(\sin t)(\cos t)]\,dt$$

$$= \int_0^{\pi/2} (-3\cos^2 t \sin t - \sin^3 t + 2\cos^2 t \sin t)\,dt$$

$$= \int_0^{\pi/2} (-\cos^2 t - \sin^2 t)(\sin t)\,dt = \int_0^{\pi/2} -\sin t\,dt$$

$$= \cos t\Big]_0^{\pi/2} = -1 \blacktriangleleft$$

Compare the computations in Example 7 with those involved in computing

$$\int_C (3x^2+y^2)\,dx + \int_C 2xy\,dy$$

It follows from (18) and (19) that

$$\int_{-C} f(x, y)\, dx + g(x, y)\, dy = -\int_{C} f(x, y)\, dx + g(x, y)\, dy \tag{24}$$

so that reversing the orientation of $C$ changes the sign of a line integral in which $x$ and $y$ occur in combination. Similarly,

$$\begin{aligned}\int_{-C} & f(x, y, z)\, dx + g(x, y, z)\, dy + h(x, y, z)\, dz \\ &= -\int_{C} f(x, y, z)\, dx + g(x, y, z)\, dy + h(x, y, z)\, dz\end{aligned} \tag{25}$$

## INTEGRATING A VECTOR FIELD ALONG A CURVE

There is an alternative notation for line integrals with respect to $x$, $y$, and $z$ that is particularly appropriate for dealing with problems involving vector fields. We will interpret $d\mathbf{r}$ as

$$d\mathbf{r} = dx\mathbf{i} + dy\mathbf{j} \quad \text{or} \quad d\mathbf{r} = dx\mathbf{i} + dy\mathbf{j} + dz\mathbf{k}$$

depending on whether $C$ is in 2-space or 3-space. For an oriented curve $C$ in 2-space and a vector field

$$\mathbf{F}(x, y) = f(x, y)\mathbf{i} + g(x, y)\mathbf{j}$$

we will write

$$\int_C \mathbf{F} \cdot d\mathbf{r} = \int_C (f(x, y)\mathbf{i} + g(x, y)\mathbf{j}) \cdot (dx\mathbf{i} + dy\mathbf{j}) = \int_C f(x, y)\, dx + g(x, y)\, dy \tag{26}$$

Similarily, for a curve $C$ in 3-space and vector field

$$\mathbf{F}(x, y, z) = f(x, y, z)\mathbf{i} + g(x, y, z)\mathbf{j} + h(x, y, z)\mathbf{k}$$

we will write

$$\begin{aligned}\int_C \mathbf{F} \cdot d\mathbf{r} &= \int_C (f(x, y, z)\mathbf{i} + g(x, y, z)\mathbf{j} + h(x, y, z)\mathbf{k}) \cdot (dx\mathbf{i} + dy\mathbf{j} + dz\mathbf{k}) \\ &= \int_C f(x, y, z)\, dx + g(x, y, z)\, dy + h(x, y, z)\, dz\end{aligned} \tag{27}$$

With these conventions, we are led to the following definition.

**15.2.2 DEFINITION** If $\mathbf{F}$ is a continuous vector field and $C$ is a smooth oriented curve, then the ***line integral of* F *along* C** is

$$\int_C \mathbf{F} \cdot d\mathbf{r} \tag{28}$$

The notation in Definition 15.2.2 makes it easy to remember the formula for evaluating the line integral of $\mathbf{F}$ along $C$. For example, suppose that $C$ is an oriented curve in the plane given in vector form by

$$\mathbf{r} = \mathbf{r}(t) = x(t)\mathbf{i} + y(t)\mathbf{j} \qquad (a \le t \le b)$$

If we write

$$\mathbf{F}(\mathbf{r}(t)) = f(x(t), y(t))\mathbf{i} + g(x(t), y(t))\mathbf{j}$$

then

$$\int_C \mathbf{F} \cdot d\mathbf{r} = \int_a^b \mathbf{F}(\mathbf{r}(t)) \cdot \mathbf{r}'(t)\, dt \tag{29}$$

Formula (29) is also valid for oriented curves in 3-space.

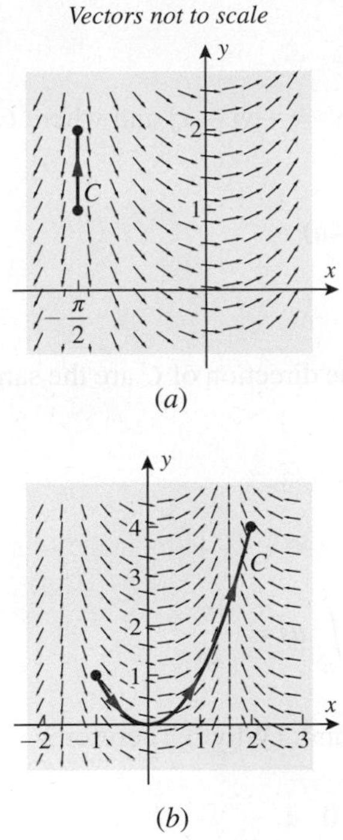

▲ Figure 15.2.12

▶ **Example 8** Evaluate $\int_C \mathbf{F}\cdot d\mathbf{r}$ where $\mathbf{F}(x, y) = \cos x\mathbf{i} + \sin x\mathbf{j}$ and where $C$ is the given oriented curve.

(a) $C: \mathbf{r}(t) = -\frac{\pi}{2}\mathbf{i} + t\mathbf{j} \quad (1 \le t \le 2)$ (see Figure 15.2.12*a*)

(b) $C: \mathbf{r}(t) = t\mathbf{i} + t^2\mathbf{j} \quad (-1 \le t \le 2)$ (see Figure 15.2.12*b*)

***Solution (a).*** Using (29) we have

$$\int_C \mathbf{F}\cdot d\mathbf{r} = \int_1^2 \mathbf{F}(\mathbf{r}(t))\cdot\mathbf{r}'(t)\,dt = \int_1^2 (-\mathbf{j})\cdot\mathbf{j}\,dt = \int_1^2 (-1)\,dt = -1$$

***Solution (b).*** Using (29) we have

$$\begin{aligned}\int_C \mathbf{F}\cdot d\mathbf{r} &= \int_{-1}^2 \mathbf{F}(\mathbf{r}(t))\cdot\mathbf{r}'(t)\,dt = \int_{-1}^2 (\cos t\mathbf{i} + \sin t\mathbf{j})\cdot(\mathbf{i} + 2t\mathbf{j})\,dt \\ &= \int_{-1}^2 (\cos t + 2t\sin t)\,dt = (-2t\cos t + 3\sin t)\Big]_{-1}^2 \\ &= -2\cos 1 - 4\cos 2 + 3(\sin 1 + \sin 2) \approx 5.83629 \blacktriangleleft\end{aligned}$$

If we let $t$ denote an arc length parameter, say $t = s$, with $\mathbf{T} = \mathbf{r}'(s)$ the unit tangent vector field along $C$, then

$$\int_C \mathbf{F}\cdot d\mathbf{r} = \int_a^b \mathbf{F}(\mathbf{r}(s))\cdot\mathbf{r}'(s)\,ds = \int_a^b \mathbf{F}(\mathbf{r}(s))\cdot\mathbf{T}\,ds = \int_C \mathbf{F}\cdot\mathbf{T}\,ds$$

which shows that

$$\int_C \mathbf{F}\cdot d\mathbf{r} = \int_C \mathbf{F}\cdot\mathbf{T}\,ds \tag{30}$$

In words, the integral of a vector field along a curve has the same value as the integral of the tangential component of the vector field along the curve.

We can use (30) to interpret $\int_C \mathbf{F}\cdot d\mathbf{r}$ geometrically. If $\theta$ is the angle between $\mathbf{F}$ and $\mathbf{T}$ at a point on $C$, then at this point

$$\begin{aligned}\mathbf{F}\cdot\mathbf{T} &= \|\mathbf{F}\|\|\mathbf{T}\|\cos\theta && \text{Formula (4) in Section 11.3} \\ &= \|\mathbf{F}\|\cos\theta && \text{Since } \|\mathbf{T}\| = 1\end{aligned}$$

Thus,

$$-\|\mathbf{F}\| \le \mathbf{F}\cdot\mathbf{T} \le \|\mathbf{F}\|$$

and if $\mathbf{F} \ne \mathbf{0}$, then the sign of $\mathbf{F}\cdot\mathbf{T}$ will depend on the angle between the direction of $\mathbf{F}$ and the direction of $C$ (Figure 15.2.13). That is, $\mathbf{F}\cdot\mathbf{T}$ will be positive where $\mathbf{F}$ has the same general direction as $C$, it will be 0 if $\mathbf{F}$ is normal to $C$, and it will be negative where $\mathbf{F}$ and $C$ have more or less opposite directions. The line integral of $\mathbf{F}$ along $C$ can be interpreted

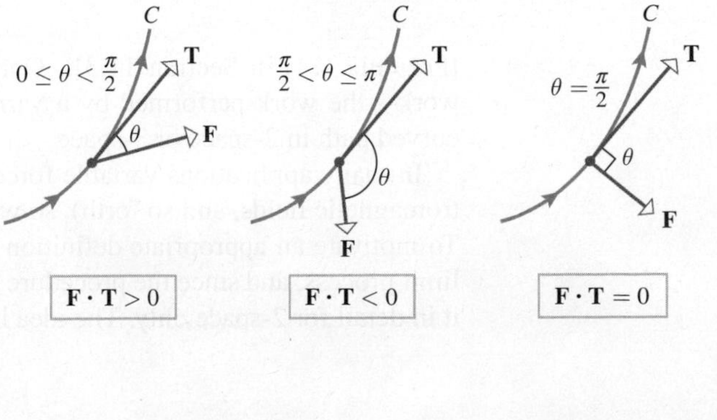

▶ Figure 15.2.13

as the accumulated effect of the magnitude of **F** along $C$, the extent to which **F** and $C$ have the same direction, and the arc length of $C$.

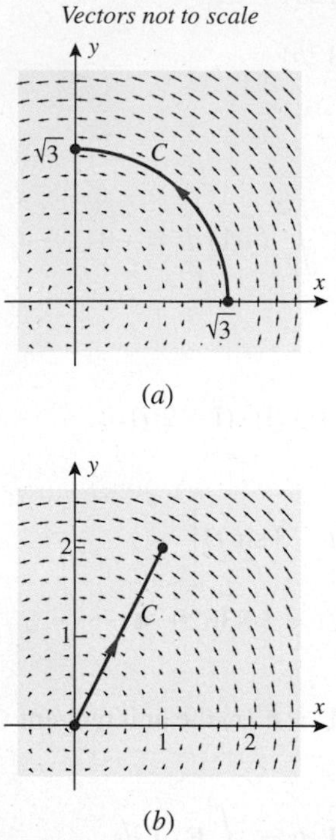

▲ **Figure 15.2.14**

> Refer to Figure 15.2.12 and explain the sign of each line integral in Example 8 geometrically. Exercises 5 and 6 take this geometric analysis further.

► **Example 9** Use (30) to evaluate $\int_C \mathbf{F}\cdot d\mathbf{r}$ where $\mathbf{F}(x, y) = -y\mathbf{i} + x\mathbf{j}$ and where $C$ is the given oriented curve.

(a) $C: x^2 + y^2 = 3 \quad (0 \le x, y;$ oriented as in Figure 15.2.14$a)$

(b) $C: \mathbf{r}(t) = t\mathbf{i} + 2t\mathbf{j} \quad (0 \le t \le 1;$ see Figure 15.2.14$b)$

***Solution (a).*** At every point on $C$ the direction of **F** and the direction of $C$ are the same. (Why?) In addition, at every point on $C$

$$\|\mathbf{F}\| = \sqrt{(-y)^2 + x^2} = \sqrt{x^2 + y^2} = \sqrt{3}$$

Therefore, $\mathbf{F}\cdot\mathbf{T} = \|\mathbf{F}\|\cos(0) = \|\mathbf{F}\| = \sqrt{3}$, and

$$\int_C \mathbf{F}\cdot d\mathbf{r} = \int_C \mathbf{F}\cdot\mathbf{T}\,ds = \int_C \sqrt{3}\,ds = \sqrt{3}\int_C ds = \frac{3\pi}{2}$$

***Solution (b).*** The vector field **F** is normal to $C$ at every point. (Why?) Therefore,

$$\int_C \mathbf{F}\cdot d\mathbf{r} = \int_C \mathbf{F}\cdot\mathbf{T}\,ds = \int_C 0\,ds = 0 \quad ◄$$

In light of (20) and (30), you might expect that reversing the orientation of $C$ in $\int_C \mathbf{F}\cdot d\mathbf{r}$ would have no effect on the value of the line integral. However, reversing the orientation of $C$ reverses the orientation of **T** in the integrand and hence reverses the sign of the integral; that is,

$$\int_{-C} \mathbf{F}\cdot\mathbf{T}\,ds = -\int_C \mathbf{F}\cdot\mathbf{T}\,ds \tag{31}$$

$$\int_{-C} \mathbf{F}\cdot d\mathbf{r} = -\int_C \mathbf{F}\cdot d\mathbf{r} \tag{32}$$

## WORK AS A LINE INTEGRAL

An important application of line integrals with respect to $x, y$, and $z$ is to the problem of defining the work performed by a variable force moving a particle along a curved path. In Section 6.6 we defined the work $W$ performed by a force of constant magnitude acting on an object in the direction of motion (Definition 6.6.1), and later in that section we extended the definition to allow for a force of variable magnitude acting in the direction of motion (Definition 6.6.3). In Section 11.3 we took the concept of work a step further by defining the work $W$ performed by a constant force **F** moving a particle in a straight line from point $P$ to point $Q$. We defined the work to be

$$W = \mathbf{F}\cdot\overrightarrow{PQ} \tag{33}$$

[Formula (14) in Section 11.3]. Our next goal is to define a more general concept of work—the work performed by a variable force acting on a particle that moves along a curved path in 2-space or 3-space.

In many applications variable forces arise from force fields (gravitational fields, electromagnetic fields, and so forth), so we will consider the problem of work in that context. To motivate an appropriate definition for work performed by a force field, we will use a limit process, and since the procedure is the same for 2-space and 3-space, we will discuss it in detail for 2-space only. The idea is as follows:

- Assume that a force field $\mathbf{F} = \mathbf{F}(x, y)$ moves a particle along a smooth curve $C$ from a point $P$ to a point $Q$. Divide $C$ into $n$ arcs using the partition points

$$P = P_0(x_0, y_0), P_1(x_1, y_1), P_2(x_2, y_2), \ldots, P_{n-1}(x_{n-1}, y_{n-1}), P_n(x_n, y_n) = Q$$

directed along $C$ from $P$ to $Q$, and denote the length of the $k$th arc by $\Delta s_k$. Let $(x_k^*, y_k^*)$ be any point on the $k$th arc, and let

$$\mathbf{F}_k^* = \mathbf{F}(x_k^*, y_k^*) = f(x_k^*, y_k^*)\mathbf{i} + g(x_k^*, y_k^*)\mathbf{j}$$

be the force vector at this point (Figure 15.2.15).

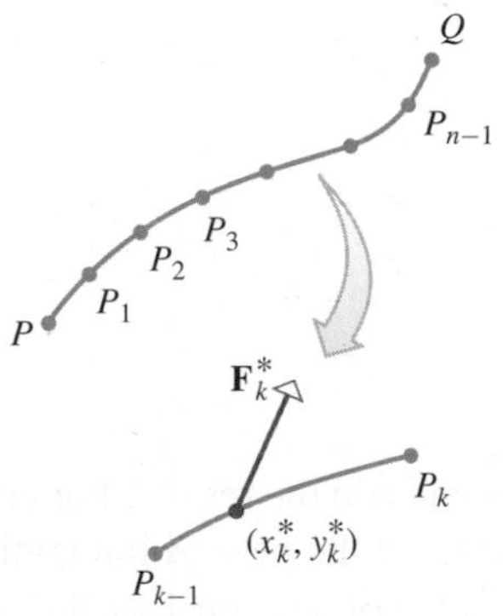

▲ **Figure 15.2.15**

- If the $k$th arc is small, then the force will not vary much, so we can approximate the force by the constant value $\mathbf{F}_k^*$ on this arc. Moreover, the direction of motion will not vary much over this small arc, so we can approximate the movement of the particle by the displacement vector

$$\overrightarrow{P_{k-1}P_k} = (\Delta x_k)\mathbf{i} + (\Delta y_k)\mathbf{j}$$

where $\Delta x_k = x_k - x_{k-1}$ and $\Delta y_k = y_k - y_{k-1}$.

- Since the work done by a constant force $\mathbf{F}_k^*$ moving a particle along a straight line from $P_{k-1}$ to $P_k$ is

$$\begin{aligned}\mathbf{F}_k^* \cdot \overrightarrow{P_{k-1}P_k} &= (f(x_k^*, y_k^*)\mathbf{i} + g(x_k^*, y_k^*)\mathbf{j}) \cdot ((\Delta x_k)\mathbf{i} + (\Delta y_k)\mathbf{j}) \\ &= f(x_k^*, y_k^*)\Delta x_k + g(x_k^*, y_k^*)\Delta y_k\end{aligned}$$

[Formula (33)], the work $\Delta W_k$ performed by the force field along the $k$th arc of $C$ can be approximated by

$$\Delta W_k \approx f(x_k^*, y_k^*)\Delta x_k + g(x_k^*, y_k^*)\Delta y_k$$

The total work $W$ performed by the force moving the particle over the entire curve $C$ can then be approximated as

$$W = \sum_{k=1}^{n} \Delta W_k \approx \sum_{k=1}^{n} [f(x_k^*, y_k^*)\Delta x_k + g(x_k^*, y_k^*)\Delta y_k]$$

- As max $\Delta s_k \to 0$, it is plausible that the error in this approximation approaches 0 and the exact work performed by the force field is

$$\begin{aligned}W &= \lim_{\max \Delta s_k \to 0} \sum_{k=1}^{n} [f(x_k^*, y_k^*)\Delta x_k + g(x_k^*, y_k^*)\Delta y_k] \\ &= \int_C f(x, y)\,dx + g(x, y)\,dy \qquad \boxed{\text{Formula (22)}} \\ &= \int_C \mathbf{F} \cdot d\mathbf{r} \qquad \boxed{\text{Formula (26)}}\end{aligned}$$

Thus, we are led to the following definition.

> Note from Formula (30) that the work performed by a force field on a particle moving along a smooth curve $C$ is obtained by integrating the scalar tangential component of force along $C$. This implies that the component of force orthogonal to the direction of motion of the particle has no effect on the work done.

**15.2.3 DEFINITION** Suppose that under the influence of a continuous force field $\mathbf{F}$ a particle moves along a smooth curve $C$ and that $C$ is oriented in the direction of motion of the particle. Then the ***work performed by the force field*** on the particle is

$$\int_C \mathbf{F} \cdot d\mathbf{r} \tag{34}$$

For example, suppose that force is measured in pounds and distance is measured in feet. It follows from part (a) of Example 9 that the work done by a force $\mathbf{F}(x, y) = -y\mathbf{i} + x\mathbf{j}$ acting on a particle moving along the circle $x^2 + y^2 = 3$ from $(\sqrt{3}, 0)$ to $(0, \sqrt{3})$ is $3\pi/2$ foot-pounds.

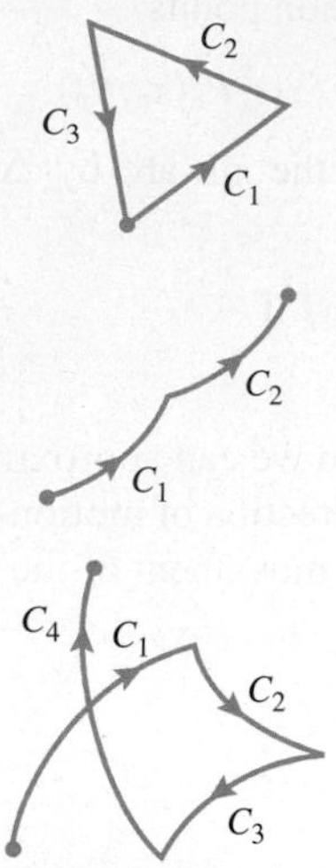


▲ Figure 15.2.16

## LINE INTEGRALS ALONG PIECEWISE SMOOTH CURVES

Thus far, we have only considered line integrals along smooth curves. However, the notion of a line integral can be extended to curves formed from finitely many smooth curves $C_1, C_2, \ldots, C_n$ joined end to end. Such a curve is called ***piecewise smooth*** (Figure 15.2.16). We define a line integral along a piecewise smooth curve $C$ to be the sum of the integrals along the sections:

$$\int_C = \int_{C_1} + \int_{C_2} + \cdots + \int_{C_n}$$

**▶ Example 10** Evaluate

$$\int_C x^2 y\,dx + x\,dy$$

where $C$ is the triangular path shown in Figure 15.2.17.

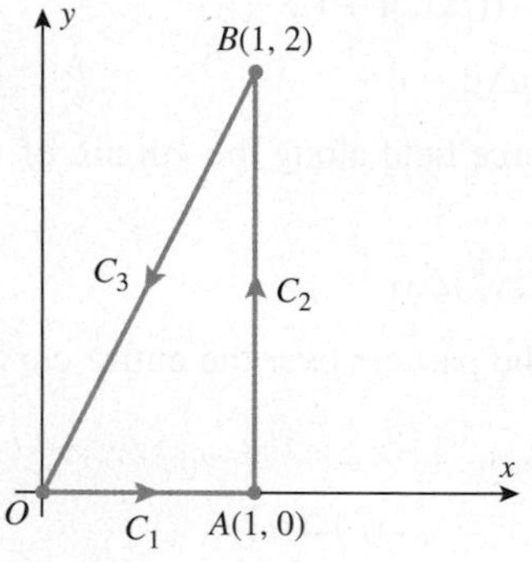


▲ Figure 15.2.17

***Solution.*** We will integrate over $C_1$, $C_2$, and $C_3$ separately and add the results. For each of the three integrals we must find parametric equations that trace the path of integration in the correct direction. For this purpose recall from Formula (7) of Section 12.1 that the graph of the vector-valued function

$$\mathbf{r}(t) = (1-t)\mathbf{r}_0 + t\mathbf{r}_1 \qquad (0 \le t \le 1)$$

is the line segment joining $\mathbf{r}_0$ and $\mathbf{r}_1$, oriented in the direction from $\mathbf{r}_0$ to $\mathbf{r}_1$. Thus, the line segments $C_1$, $C_2$, and $C_3$ can be represented in vector notation as

$$C_1\colon \mathbf{r}(t) = (1-t)\langle 0,0\rangle + t\langle 1,0\rangle = \langle t, 0\rangle$$
$$C_2\colon \mathbf{r}(t) = (1-t)\langle 1,0\rangle + t\langle 1,2\rangle = \langle 1, 2t\rangle$$
$$C_3\colon \mathbf{r}(t) = (1-t)\langle 1,2\rangle + t\langle 0,0\rangle = \langle 1-t, 2-2t\rangle$$

where $t$ varies from 0 to 1 in each case. From these equations we obtain

$$\int_{C_1} x^2 y\,dx + x\,dy = \int_{C_1} x^2 y\,dx = \int_0^1 (t^2)(0)\frac{d}{dt}[t]\,dt = 0$$

$$\int_{C_2} x^2 y\,dx + x\,dy = \int_{C_2} x\,dy = \int_0^1 (1)\frac{d}{dt}[2t]\,dt = 2$$

$$\int_{C_3} x^2 y\,dx + x\,dy = \int_0^1 (1-t)^2(2-2t)\frac{d}{dt}[1-t]\,dt + \int_0^1 (1-t)\frac{d}{dt}[2-2t]\,dt$$
$$= 2\int_0^1 (t-1)^3\,dt + 2\int_0^1 (t-1)\,dt = -\tfrac{1}{2} - 1 = -\tfrac{3}{2}$$

Thus,

$$\int_C x^2 y\,dx + x\,dy = 0 + 2 + \left(-\tfrac{3}{2}\right) = \tfrac{1}{2} \blacktriangleleft$$

## ✔ QUICK CHECK EXERCISES 15.2 

(See page 995 for answers.)

1. The area of the surface extending upward from the line segment $y = x$ $(0 \le x \le 1)$ in the $xy$-plane to the plane $z = 2x + 1$ is ________.

2. Suppose that a wire has equation $y = 1 - x$ $(0 \le x \le 1)$ and that its mass density is $\delta(x, y) = 2 - x$. The mass of the wire is ________.

3. If $C$ is the curve represented by the equations
$$x = \sin t, \quad y = \cos t, \quad z = t \qquad (0 \le t \le 2\pi)$$
then $\int_C y\,dx - x\,dy + dz =$ ________.

4. If $C$ is the unit circle $x^2 + y^2 = 1$ oriented counterclockwise and $\mathbf{F}(x, y) = x\mathbf{i} + y\mathbf{j}$, then
$$\int_C \mathbf{F} \cdot d\mathbf{r} = \text{\_\_\_\_\_\_\_\_}$$

## EXERCISE SET 15.2 Graphing Utility C CAS

**FOCUS ON CONCEPTS**

**1.** Let $C$ be the line segment from $(0,0)$ to $(0,1)$. In each part, evaluate the line integral along $C$ by inspection, and explain your reasoning.

(a) $\int_C ds$ (b) $\int_C \sin xy\, dy$

**2.** Let $C$ be the line segment from $(0,2)$ to $(0,4)$. In each part, evaluate the line integral along $C$ by inspection, and explain your reasoning.

(a) $\int_C ds$ (b) $\int_C e^{xy}\, dx$

**3–4** Evaluate $\int_C \mathbf{F}\cdot d\mathbf{r}$ by inspection for the force field $\mathbf{F}(x,y)=\mathbf{i}+\mathbf{j}$ and the curve $C$ shown in the figure. Explain your reasoning. [*Note:* For clarity, the vectors in the force field are shown at less than true scale.] ■

**3.**

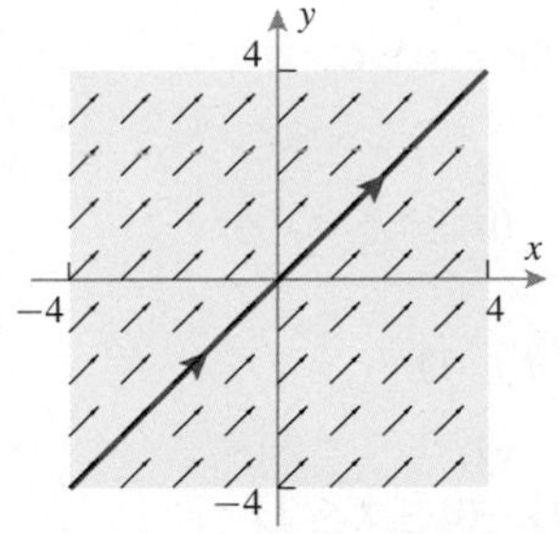


**4.**

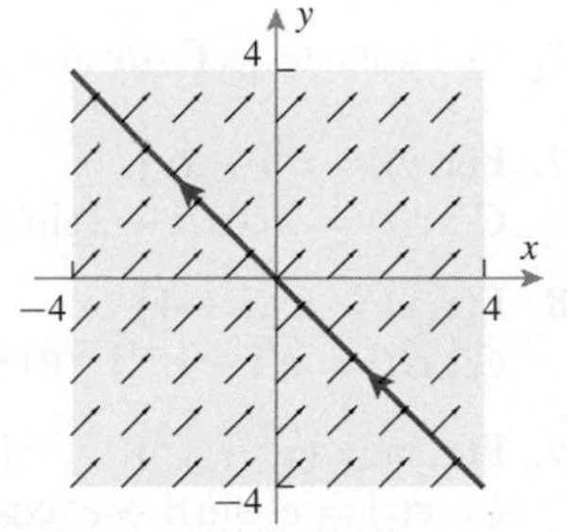


**5.** Use (30) to explain why the line integral in part (a) of Example 8 can be found by multiplying the length of the line segment $C$ by $-1$.

**6.** (a) Use (30) to explain why the line integral in part (b) of Example 8 should be close to, but somewhat less than, the length of the parabolic curve $C$.
(b) Verify the conclusion in part (a) of this exercise by computing the length of $C$ and comparing the length with the value of the line integral.

**7–10** Evaluate $\int_C \mathbf{F}\cdot d\mathbf{r}$ along the line segment $C$ from $P$ to $Q$. ■

**7.** $\mathbf{F}(x,y)=8\mathbf{i}+8\mathbf{j}$; $P(-4,4), Q(-4,5)$

**8.** $\mathbf{F}(x,y)=2\mathbf{i}+5\mathbf{j}$; $P(1,-3), Q(4,-3)$

**9.** $\mathbf{F}(x,y)=2x\mathbf{j}$; $P(-2,4), Q(-2,11)$

**10.** $\mathbf{F}(x,y)=-8x\mathbf{i}+3y\mathbf{j}$; $P(-1,0), Q(6,0)$

**11.** Let $C$ be the curve represented by the equations

$$x=2t, \quad y=t^2 \quad (0\le t\le 1)$$

In each part, evaluate the line integral along $C$.

(a) $\int_C (x-\sqrt{y})\, ds$ (b) $\int_C (x-\sqrt{y})\, dx$

(c) $\int_C (x-\sqrt{y})\, dy$

**12.** Let $C$ be the curve represented by the equations

$$x=t, \quad y=3t^2, \quad z=6t^3 \quad (0\le t\le 1)$$

In each part, evaluate the line integral along $C$.

(a) $\int_C xyz^2\, ds$ (b) $\int_C xyz^2\, dx$

(c) $\int_C xyz^2\, dy$ (d) $\int_C xyz^2\, dz$

**13.** In each part, evaluate the integral

$$\int_C (3x+2y)\,dx+(2x-y)\,dy$$

along the stated curve.
(a) The line segment from $(0,0)$ to $(1,1)$.
(b) The parabolic arc $y=x^2$ from $(0,0)$ to $(1,1)$.
(c) The curve $y=\sin(\pi x/2)$ from $(0,0)$ to $(1,1)$.
(d) The curve $x=y^3$ from $(0,0)$ to $(1,1)$.

**14.** In each part, evaluate the integral

$$\int_C y\,dx+z\,dy-x\,dz$$

along the stated curve.
(a) The line segment from $(0,0,0)$ to $(1,1,1)$.
(b) The twisted cubic $x=t,\ y=t^2,\ z=t^3$ from $(0,0,0)$ to $(1,1,1)$.
(c) The helix $x=\cos \pi t,\ y=\sin \pi t,\ z=t$ from $(1,0,0)$ to $(-1,0,1)$.

**15–18 True–False** Determine whether the statement is true or false. Explain your answer. ■

**15.** If $C$ is a smooth oriented curve in the $xy$-plane and $f(x,y)$ is a continuous function defined on $C$, then

$$\int_C f(x,y)\,ds = -\int_{-C} f(x,y)\,ds$$

**16.** The line integral of a continuous vector field along a smooth curve $C$ is a vector.

**17.** If $\mathbf{F}(x,y)=f(x,y)\mathbf{i}+g(x,y)\mathbf{j}$ along a smooth oriented curve $C$ in the $xy$-plane, then

$$\int_C \mathbf{F}\cdot d\mathbf{r}=\int_C f(x,y)\,dx+g(x,y)\,dy$$

**18.** If a smooth oriented curve $C$ in the $xy$-plane is a contour for a differentiable function $f(x,y)$, then

$$\int_C \nabla f\cdot d\mathbf{r}=0$$

**19–22** Evaluate the line integral with respect to $s$ along the curve $C$. ■

**19.** $\int_C \frac{1}{1+x}\,ds$
$C: \mathbf{r}(t)=t\mathbf{i}+\frac{2}{3}t^{3/2}\mathbf{j} \quad (0\le t\le 3)$

**20.** $\int_C \frac{x}{1+y^2}\,ds$
$C: x=1+2t,\ y=t \quad (0\le t\le 1)$

**21.** $\int_C 3x^2yz\,ds$
$C: x=t,\ y=t^2,\ z=\frac{2}{3}t^3 \quad (0\le t\le 1)$

**22.** $\displaystyle\int_C \frac{e^{-z}}{x^2+y^2}\,ds$
$C: \mathbf{r}(t) = 2\cos t\mathbf{i} + 2\sin t\mathbf{j} + t\mathbf{k} \quad (0 \le t \le 2\pi)$

**23–30** Evaluate the line integral along the curve $C$. ■

**23.** $\displaystyle\int_C (x+2y)\,dx + (x-y)\,dy$
$C: x = 2\cos t,\ y = 4\sin t \quad (0 \le t \le \pi/4)$

**24.** $\displaystyle\int_C (x^2-y^2)\,dx + x\,dy$
$C: x = t^{2/3},\ y = t \quad (-1 \le t \le 1)$

**25.** $\displaystyle\int_C -y\,dx + x\,dy$
$C: y^2 = 3x$ from $(3, 3)$ to $(0, 0)$

**26.** $\displaystyle\int_C (y-x)\,dx + x^2y\,dy$
$C: y^2 = x^3$ from $(1, -1)$ to $(1, 1)$

**27.** $\displaystyle\int_C (x^2+y^2)\,dx - x\,dy$
$C: x^2+y^2 = 1$, counterclockwise from $(1, 0)$ to $(0, 1)$

**28.** $\displaystyle\int_C (y-x)\,dx + xy\,dy$
$C$: the line segment from $(3, 4)$ to $(2, 1)$

**29.** $\displaystyle\int_C yz\,dx - xz\,dy + xy\,dz$
$C: x = e^t,\ y = e^{3t},\ z = e^{-t} \quad (0 \le t \le 1)$

**30.** $\displaystyle\int_C x^2\,dx + xy\,dy + z^2\,dz$
$C: x = \sin t,\ y = \cos t,\ z = t^2 \quad (0 \le t \le \pi/2)$

C **31–32** Use a CAS to evaluate the line integrals along the given curves. ■

**31.** (a) $\displaystyle\int_C (x^3+y^3)\,ds$
$C: \mathbf{r}(t) = e^t\mathbf{i} + e^{-t}\mathbf{j} \quad (0 \le t \le \ln 2)$

(b) $\displaystyle\int_C xe^z\,dx + (x-z)\,dy + (x^2+y^2+z^2)\,dz$
$C: x = \sin t,\ y = \cos t,\ z = t \quad (0 \le t \le \pi/2)$

**32.** (a) $\displaystyle\int_C x^7y^3\,ds$
$C: x = \cos^3 t,\ y = \sin^3 t \quad (0 \le t \le \pi/2)$

(b) $\displaystyle\int_C x^5z\,dx + 7y\,dy + y^2z\,dz$
$C: \mathbf{r}(t) = t\mathbf{i} + t^2\mathbf{j} + \ln t\mathbf{k} \quad (1 \le t \le e)$

**33–34** Evaluate $\int_C y\,dx - x\,dy$ along the curve $C$ shown in the figure. ■

**33.** (a)
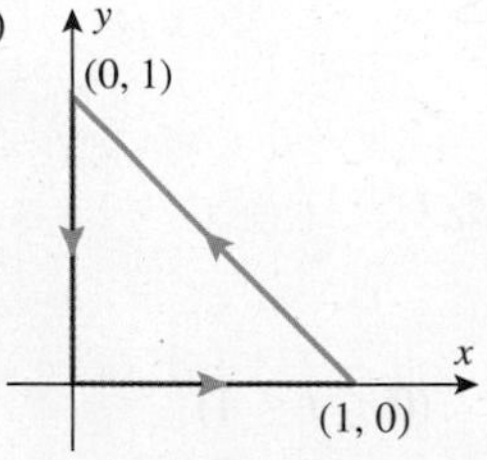


(b)
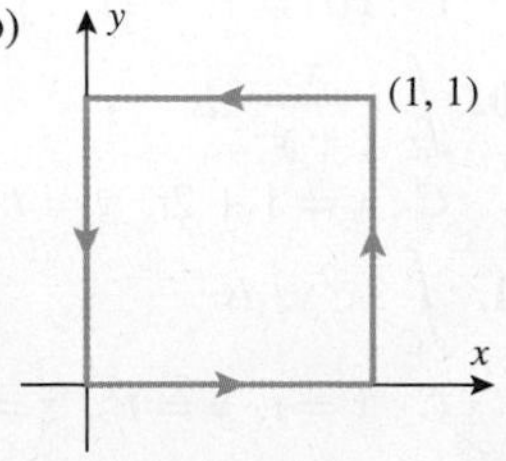


**34.** (a)
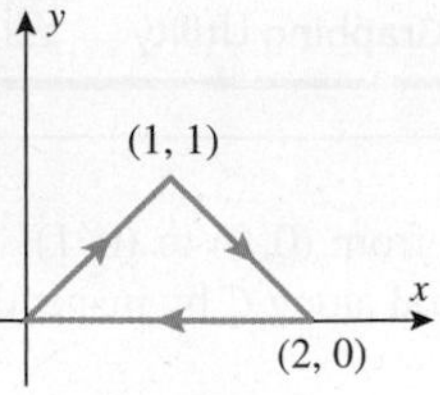


(b)
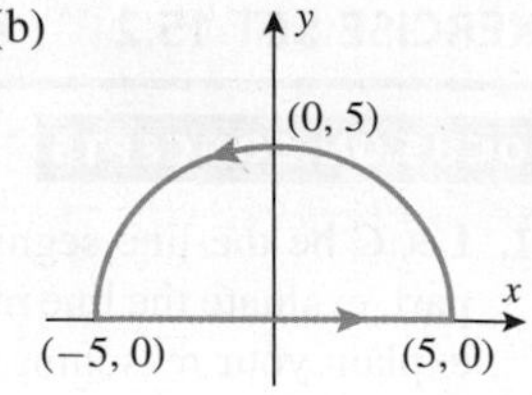


**35–36** Evaluate $\int_C x^2z\,dx - yx^2\,dy + 3\,dz$ along the curve $C$ shown in the figure. ■

**35.**
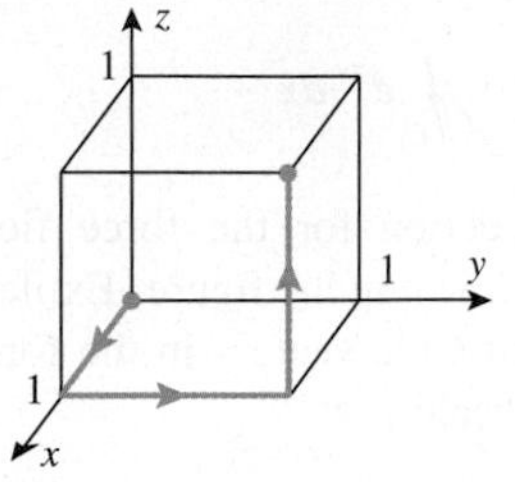


**36.**
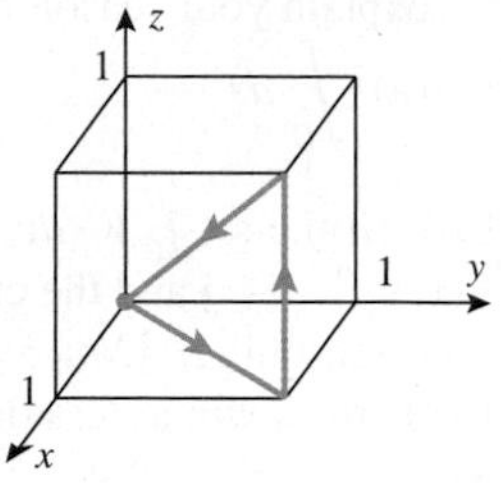


**37–40** Evaluate $\int_C \mathbf{F}\cdot d\mathbf{r}$ along the curve $C$. ■

**37.** $\mathbf{F}(x, y) = x^2\mathbf{i} + xy\mathbf{j}$
$C: \mathbf{r}(t) = 2\cos t\mathbf{i} + 2\sin t\mathbf{j} \quad (0 \le t \le \pi)$

**38.** $\mathbf{F}(x, y) = x^2y\mathbf{i} + 4\mathbf{j}$
$C: \mathbf{r}(t) = e^t\mathbf{i} + e^{-t}\mathbf{j} \quad (0 \le t \le 1)$

**39.** $\mathbf{F}(x, y) = (x^2+y^2)^{-3/2}(x\mathbf{i} + y\mathbf{j})$
$C: \mathbf{r}(t) = e^t\sin t\mathbf{i} + e^t\cos t\mathbf{j} \quad (0 \le t \le 1)$

**40.** $\mathbf{F}(x, y, z) = z\mathbf{i} + x\mathbf{j} + y\mathbf{k}$
$C: \mathbf{r}(t) = \sin t\mathbf{i} + 3\sin t\mathbf{j} + \sin^2 t\mathbf{k} \quad (0 \le t \le \pi/2)$

**41.** Find the mass of a thin wire shaped in the form of the circular arc $y = \sqrt{9-x^2}$ $(0 \le x \le 3)$ if the density function is $\delta(x, y) = x\sqrt{y}$.

**42.** Find the mass of a thin wire shaped in the form of the curve $x = e^t\cos t$, $y = e^t\sin t$ $(0 \le t \le 1)$ if the density function $\delta$ is proportional to the distance from the origin.

**43.** Find the mass of a thin wire shaped in the form of the helix $x = 3\cos t$, $y = 3\sin t$, $z = 4t$ $(0 \le t \le \pi/2)$ if the density function is $\delta = kx/(1+y^2)$ $(k > 0)$.

**44.** Find the mass of a thin wire shaped in the form of the curve $x = 2t$, $y = \ln t$, $z = 4\sqrt{t}$ $(1 \le t \le 4)$ if the density function is proportional to the distance above the $xy$-plane.

**45–48** Find the work done by the force field $\mathbf{F}$ on a particle that moves along the curve $C$. ■

**45.** $\mathbf{F}(x, y) = xy\mathbf{i} + x^2\mathbf{j}$
$C: x = y^2$ from $(0, 0)$ to $(1, 1)$

**46.** $\mathbf{F}(x, y) = (x^2+xy)\mathbf{i} + (y-x^2y)\mathbf{j}$
$C: x = t,\ y = 1/t \quad (1 \le t \le 3)$

**47.** $\mathbf{F}(x, y, z) = xy\mathbf{i} + yz\mathbf{j} + xz\mathbf{k}$
$C: \mathbf{r}(t) = t\mathbf{i} + t^2\mathbf{j} + t^3\mathbf{k} \quad (0 \le t \le 1)$

**48.** $\mathbf{F}(x, y, z) = (x+y)\mathbf{i} + xy\mathbf{j} - z^2\mathbf{k}$
$C$: along line segments from $(0, 0, 0)$ to $(1, 3, 1)$ to $(2, -1, 4)$

**49–50** Find the work done by the force field

$$\mathbf{F}(x, y) = \frac{1}{x^2+y^2}\mathbf{i} + \frac{4}{x^2+y^2}\mathbf{j}$$

on a particle that moves along the curve $C$ shown in the figure. ■

**49.**

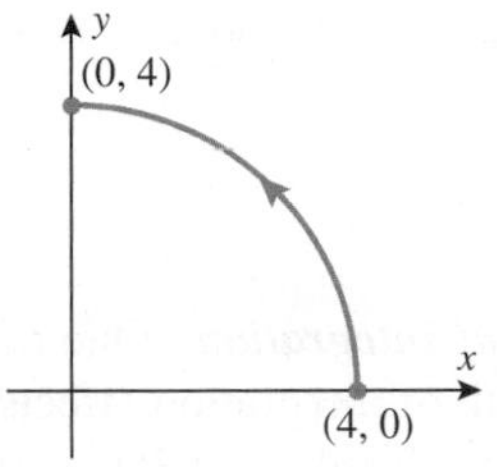


**50.**

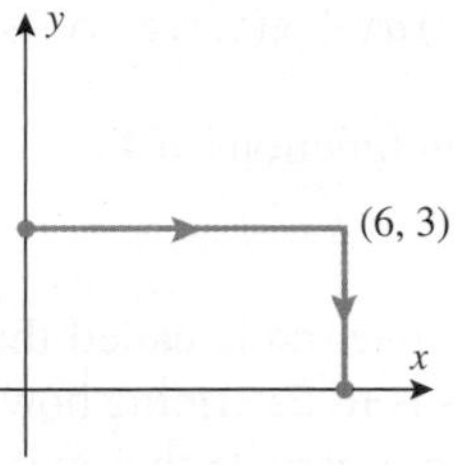


**51–52** Use a line integral to find the area of the surface. ■

**51.** The surface that extends upward from the parabola $y = x^2$ $(0 \le x \le 2)$ in the $xy$-plane to the plane $z = 3x$.

**52.** The surface that extends upward from the semicircle $y = \sqrt{4 - x^2}$ in the $xy$-plane to the surface $z = x^2y$.

**53.** As illustrated in the accompanying figure, a sinusoidal cut is made in the top of a cylindrical tin can. Suppose that the base is modeled by the parametric equations $x = \cos t$, $y = \sin t$, $z = 0$ $(0 \le t \le 2\pi)$, and the height of the cut as a function of $t$ is $z = 2 + 0.5 \sin 3t$.

(a) Use a geometric argument to find the lateral surface area of the cut can.
(b) Write down a line integral for the surface area.
(c) Use the line integral to calculate the surface area.

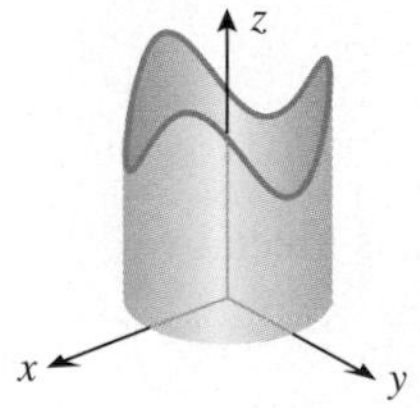


◀ **Figure Ex-53**

**54.** Evaluate the integral $\displaystyle\int_{-C} \frac{x\,dy - y\,dx}{x^2+y^2}$, where $C$ is the circle $x^2 + y^2 = a^2$ traversed counterclockwise.

**55.** Suppose that a particle moves through the force field $\mathbf{F}(x, y) = xy\mathbf{i} + (x - y)\mathbf{j}$ from the point $(0, 0)$ to the point $(1, 0)$ along the curve $x = t, y = \lambda t(1 - t)$. For what value of $\lambda$ will the work done by the force field be 1?

**56.** A farmer weighing 150 lb carries a sack of grain weighing 20 lb up a circular helical staircase around a silo of radius 25 ft. As the farmer climbs, grain leaks from the sack at a rate of 1 lb per 10 ft of ascent. How much work is performed by the farmer in climbing through a vertical distance of 60 ft in exactly four revolutions? [*Hint:* Find a vector field that represents the force exerted by the farmer in lifting his own weight plus the weight of the sack upward at each point along his path.]

**57.** Suppose that a curve $C$ in the $xy$-plane is smoothly parametrized by

$$\mathbf{r}(t) = x(t)\mathbf{i} + y(t)\mathbf{j} \qquad (a \le t \le b)$$

In each part, refer to the notation used in the derivation of Formula (9).

(a) Let $m$ and $M$ denote the respective minimum and maximum values of $\|\mathbf{r}'(t)\|$ on $[a, b]$. Prove that

$$0 \le m\,(\max \Delta t_k) \le \max \Delta s_k \le M\,(\max \Delta t_k)$$

(b) Use part (a) to prove that $\max \Delta s_k \to 0$ if and only if $\max \Delta t_k \to 0$.

**58. Writing** Discuss the similarities and differences between the definition of a definite integral over an interval (Definition 5.5.1) and the definition of the line integral with respect to arc length along a curve (Definition 15.2.1).

**59. Writing** Describe the different types of line integrals, and discuss how they are related.

✓ **QUICK CHECK ANSWERS 15.2** 1. $2\sqrt{2}$ 2. $\dfrac{3\sqrt{2}}{2}$ 3. $4\pi$ 4. 0

## 15.3 INDEPENDENCE OF PATH; CONSERVATIVE VECTOR FIELDS

*In this section we will show that for certain kinds of vector fields* **F** *the line integral of* **F** *along a curve depends only on the endpoints of the curve and not on the curve itself. Vector fields with this property, which include gravitational and electrostatic fields, are of special importance in physics and engineering.*

### WORK INTEGRALS

We saw in the last section that if **F** is a force field in 2-space or 3-space, then the work performed by the field on a particle moving along a parametric curve $C$ from an initial point $P$ to a final point $Q$ is given by the integral

$$\int_C \mathbf{F} \cdot d\mathbf{r} \quad \text{or equivalently} \quad \int_C \mathbf{F} \cdot \mathbf{T}\, ds$$

Accordingly, we call an integral of this type a ***work integral***. Recall that a work integral can also be expressed in scalar form as

$$\int_C \mathbf{F}\cdot d\mathbf{r} = \int_C f(x,y)\,dx + g(x,y)\,dy \quad \boxed{\text{2-space}} \tag{1}$$

$$\int_C \mathbf{F}\cdot d\mathbf{r} = \int_C f(x,y,z)\,dx + g(x,y,z)\,dy + h(x,y,z)\,dz \quad \boxed{\text{3-space}} \tag{2}$$

where $f$, $g$, and $h$ are the component functions of $\mathbf{F}$.

## INDEPENDENCE OF PATH

The parametric curve $C$ in a work integral is called the ***path of integration***. One of the important problems in applications is to determine how the path of integration affects the work performed by a force field on a particle that moves from a fixed point $P$ to a fixed point $Q$. We will show shortly that if the force field $\mathbf{F}$ is conservative (i.e., is the gradient of some potential function $\phi$), then the work that the field performs on a particle that moves from $P$ to $Q$ does not depend on the particular path $C$ that the particle follows. This is illustrated in the following example.

*Vectors not to scale*

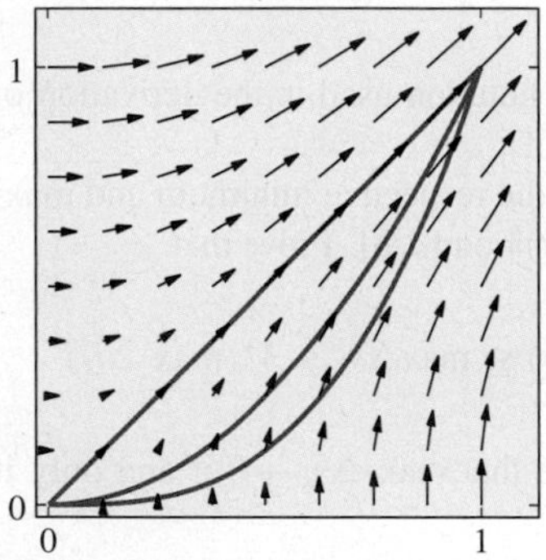


▲ Figure 15.3.1

▶ **Example 1** The force field $\mathbf{F}(x,y) = y\mathbf{i} + x\mathbf{j}$ is conservative since it is the gradient of $\phi(x,y) = xy$ (verify). Thus, the preceding discussion suggests that the work performed by the field on a particle that moves from the point $(0,0)$ to the point $(1,1)$ should be the same along different paths. Confirm that the value of the work integral

$$\int_C \mathbf{F}\cdot d\mathbf{r}$$

is the same along the following paths (Figure 15.3.1):

(a) The line segment $y = x$ from $(0,0)$ to $(1,1)$.
(b) The parabola $y = x^2$ from $(0,0)$ to $(1,1)$.
(c) The cubic $y = x^3$ from $(0,0)$ to $(1,1)$.

***Solution (a).*** With $x = t$ as the parameter, the path of integration is given by

$$x = t, \quad y = t \qquad (0 \le t \le 1)$$

Thus,

$$\int_C \mathbf{F}\cdot d\mathbf{r} = \int_C (y\mathbf{i} + x\mathbf{j})\cdot(dx\mathbf{i} + dy\mathbf{j}) = \int_C y\,dx + x\,dy$$
$$= \int_0^1 2t\,dt = 1$$

***Solution (b).*** With $x = t$ as the parameter, the path of integration is given by

$$x = t, \quad y = t^2 \qquad (0 \le t \le 1)$$

Thus,

$$\int_C \mathbf{F}\cdot d\mathbf{r} = \int_C y\,dx + x\,dy = \int_0^1 3t^2\,dt = 1$$

***Solution (c).*** With $x = t$ as the parameter, the path of integration is given by

$$x = t, \quad y = t^3 \qquad (0 \le t \le 1)$$

Thus,

$$\int_C \mathbf{F}\cdot d\mathbf{r} = \int_C y\,dx + x\,dy = \int_0^1 4t^3\,dt = 1 \blacktriangleleft$$

## THE FUNDAMENTAL THEOREM OF LINE INTEGRALS

Recall from the Fundamental Theorem of Calculus (Theorem 5.6.1) that if $F$ is an antiderivative of $f$, then

$$\int_a^b f(x)\,dx = F(b) - F(a)$$

The following result is the analog of that theorem for line integrals in 2-space.

> The value of
> $$\int_C \mathbf{F}\cdot d\mathbf{r} = \int_C \mathbf{F}\cdot\mathbf{T}\,ds$$
> depends on the magnitude of $\mathbf{F}$ along $C$, the alignment of $\mathbf{F}$ with the direction of $C$ at each point, and the length of $C$. If $\mathbf{F}$ is conservative, these various factors always "balance out" so that the value of $\int_C \mathbf{F}\cdot d\mathbf{r}$ depends only on the initial and final points of $C$.

**15.3.1 THEOREM (*The Fundamental Theorem of Line Integrals*)** *Suppose that*

$$\mathbf{F}(x, y) = f(x, y)\mathbf{i} + g(x, y)\mathbf{j}$$

*is a conservative vector field in some open region $D$ containing the points $(x_0, y_0)$ and $(x_1, y_1)$ and that $f(x, y)$ and $g(x, y)$ are continuous in this region. If*

$$\mathbf{F}(x, y) = \nabla\phi(x, y)$$

*and if $C$ is any piecewise smooth parametric curve that starts at $(x_0, y_0)$, ends at $(x_1, y_1)$, and lies in the region $D$, then*

$$\int_C \mathbf{F}(x, y)\cdot d\mathbf{r} = \phi(x_1, y_1) - \phi(x_0, y_0) \tag{3}$$

*or, equivalently,*

$$\int_C \nabla\phi\cdot d\mathbf{r} = \phi(x_1, y_1) - \phi(x_0, y_0) \tag{4}$$

**PROOF** We will give the proof for a smooth curve $C$. The proof for a piecewise smooth curve, which is left as an exercise, can be obtained by applying the theorem to each individual smooth piece and adding the results. Suppose that $C$ is given parametrically by $x = x(t)$, $y = y(t)$ $(a \le t \le b)$, so that the initial and final points of the curve are

$$(x_0, y_0) = (x(a), y(a)) \quad \text{and} \quad (x_1, y_1) = (x(b), y(b))$$

Since $\mathbf{F}(x, y) = \nabla\phi$, it follows that

$$\mathbf{F}(x, y) = \frac{\partial\phi}{\partial x}\mathbf{i} + \frac{\partial\phi}{\partial y}\mathbf{j}$$

so

$$\begin{aligned}\int_C \mathbf{F}(x, y)\cdot d\mathbf{r} &= \int_C \frac{\partial\phi}{\partial x}dx + \frac{\partial\phi}{\partial y}dy = \int_a^b \left[\frac{\partial\phi}{\partial x}\frac{dx}{dt} + \frac{\partial\phi}{\partial y}\frac{dy}{dt}\right]dt\\ &= \int_a^b \frac{d}{dt}[\phi(x(t), y(t))]\,dt = \phi(x(t), y(t))\Big]_{t=a}^{b}\\ &= \phi(x(b), y(b)) - \phi(x(a), y(a))\\ &= \phi(x_1, y_1) - \phi(x_0, y_0) \quad \blacksquare\end{aligned}$$

Stated informally, this theorem shows that *the value of a line integral of a conservative vector field along a piecewise smooth path is* ***independent of the path***; that is, the value of the integral depends on the endpoints and not on the actual path $C$. Accordingly, for line integrals of conservative vector fields, it is common to express (3) and (4) as

$$\int_{(x_0, y_0)}^{(x_1, y_1)} \mathbf{F}\cdot d\mathbf{r} = \int_{(x_0, y_0)}^{(x_1, y_1)} \nabla\phi\cdot d\mathbf{r} = \phi(x_1, y_1) - \phi(x_0, y_0) \tag{5}$$

If $\mathbf{F}$ is conservative, then you have a choice of methods for evaluating $\int_C \mathbf{F}\cdot d\mathbf{r}$. You can work directly with the curve $C$, you can replace $C$ with another curve that has the same endpoints as $C$, or you can apply Formula (3).

► **Example 2**

We observed in Example 1 that the force field $\mathbf{F}(x, y) = y\mathbf{i} + x\mathbf{j}$ is the gradient of $\phi(x, y) = xy$. Use Formula (5) to evaluate

$$\int_{(0,0)}^{(1,1)} \mathbf{F}\cdot d\mathbf{r}$$

***Solution.*** From (5) we obtain

$$\int_{(0,0)}^{(1,1)} \mathbf{F}\cdot d\mathbf{r} = \phi(1,1) - \phi(0,0) = 1 - 0 = 1$$

which agrees with the results obtained in Example 1 by integrating from $(0, 0)$ to $(1, 1)$ along specific paths. ◄

## LINE INTEGRALS ALONG CLOSED PATHS

Parametric curves that begin and end at the same point play an important role in the study of vector fields, so there is some special terminology associated with them. A parametric curve $C$ that is represented by the vector-valued function $\mathbf{r}(t)$ for $a \le t \le b$ is said to be ***closed*** if the initial point $\mathbf{r}(a)$ and the terminal point $\mathbf{r}(b)$ coincide; that is, $\mathbf{r}(a) = \mathbf{r}(b)$ (Figure 15.3.2).

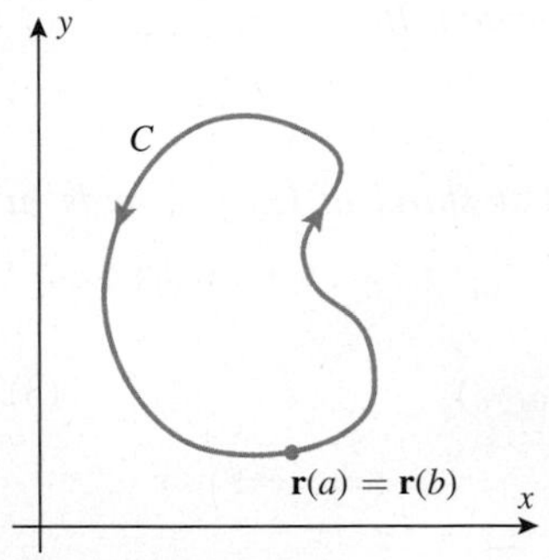

▲ **Figure 15.3.2**

It follows from (5) that the line integral of a conservative vector field along a closed path $C$ that begins and ends at $(x_0, y_0)$ is zero. This is because the point $(x_1, y_1)$ in (5) is the same as $(x_0, y_0)$ and hence

$$\int_C \mathbf{F}\cdot d\mathbf{r} = \phi(x_1, y_1) - \phi(x_0, y_0) = 0$$

Our next objective is to show that the converse of this result is also true. That is, we want to show that under appropriate conditions a vector field whose line integral is zero along *all* closed paths must be conservative. For this to be true we will need to require that the domain $D$ of the vector field be ***connected***, by which we mean that any two points in $D$ can be joined by some piecewise smooth curve that lies entirely in $D$. Stated informally, $D$ is connected if it does not consist of two or more separate pieces (Figure 15.3.3).

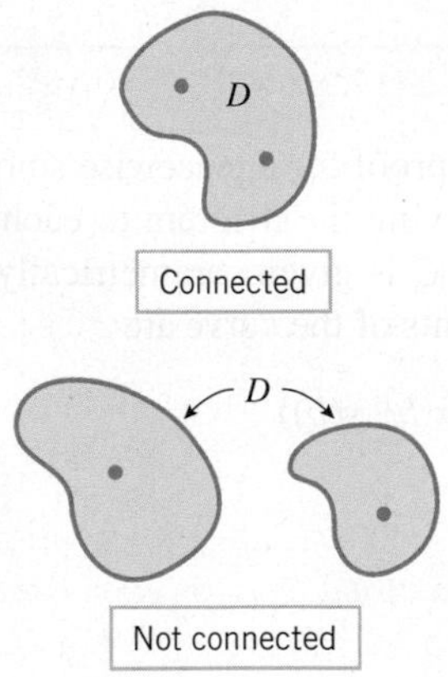

▲ **Figure 15.3.3**

**15.3.2 THEOREM** *If $f(x, y)$ and $g(x, y)$ are continuous on some open connected region $D$, then the following statements are equivalent* (*all true or all false*):

(*a*) $\mathbf{F}(x, y) = f(x, y)\mathbf{i} + g(x, y)\mathbf{j}$ *is a conservative vector field on the region $D$.*

(*b*) $\int_C \mathbf{F}\cdot d\mathbf{r} = 0$ *for every piecewise smooth closed curve $C$ in $D$.*

(*c*) $\int_C \mathbf{F}\cdot d\mathbf{r}$ *is independent of the path from any point $P$ in $D$ to any point $Q$ in $D$ for every piecewise smooth curve $C$ in $D$.*

This theorem can be established by proving three implications: $(a) \Rightarrow (b)$, $(b) \Rightarrow (c)$, and $(c) \Rightarrow (a)$. Since we showed above that $(a) \Rightarrow (b)$, we need only prove the last two implications. We will prove $(c) \Rightarrow (a)$ and leave the other implication as an exercise.

**PROOF** $(c) \Rightarrow (a)$. We are assuming that $\int_C \mathbf{F}\cdot d\mathbf{r}$ is independent of the path for every piecewise smooth curve $C$ in the region, and we want to show that there is a function $\phi = \phi(x, y)$ such that $\nabla\phi = \mathbf{F}(x, y)$ at each point of the region; that is,

$$\frac{\partial \phi}{\partial x} = f(x, y) \quad \text{and} \quad \frac{\partial \phi}{\partial y} = g(x, y) \tag{6}$$

Now choose a fixed point $(a, b)$ in $D$, let $(x, y)$ be any point in $D$, and define

$$\phi(x, y) = \int_{(a,b)}^{(x,y)} \mathbf{F}\cdot d\mathbf{r} \tag{7}$$

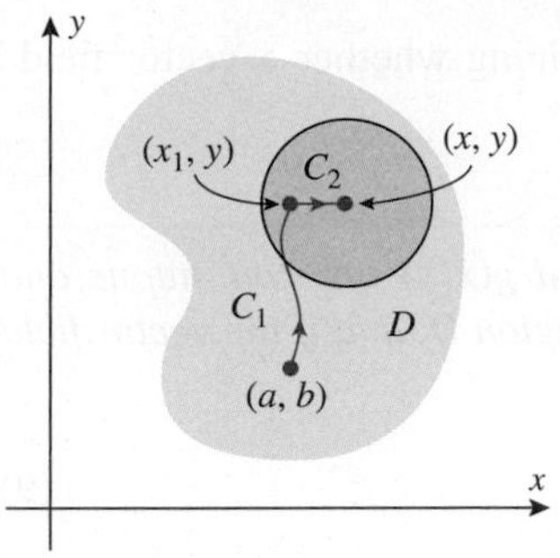


▲ **Figure 15.3.4**

This is an unambiguous definition because we have assumed that the integral is independent of the path. We will show that $\nabla\phi = \mathbf{F}$. Since $D$ is open, we can find a circular disk centered at $(x, y)$ whose points lie entirely in $D$. As shown in Figure 15.3.4, choose any point $(x_1, y)$ in this disk that lies on the same horizontal line as $(x, y)$ such that $x_1 < x$. Because the integral in (7) is independent of path, we can evaluate it by first integrating from $(a, b)$ to $(x_1, y)$ along an arbitrary piecewise smooth curve $C_1$ in $D$, and then continuing along the horizontal line segment $C_2$ from $(x_1, y)$ to $(x, y)$. This yields

$$\phi(x, y) = \int_{C_1} \mathbf{F}\cdot d\mathbf{r} + \int_{C_2} \mathbf{F}\cdot d\mathbf{r} = \int_{(a,b)}^{(x_1,y)} \mathbf{F}\cdot d\mathbf{r} + \int_{C_2} \mathbf{F}\cdot d\mathbf{r}$$

Since the first term does not depend on $x$, its partial derivative with respect to $x$ is zero and hence

$$\frac{\partial\phi}{\partial x} = \frac{\partial}{\partial x}\int_{C_2} \mathbf{F}\cdot d\mathbf{r} = \frac{\partial}{\partial x}\int_{C_2} f(x, y)\,dx + g(x, y)\,dy$$

However, the line integral with respect to $y$ is zero along the horizontal line segment $C_2$, so this equation simplifies to

$$\frac{\partial\phi}{\partial x} = \frac{\partial}{\partial x}\int_{C_2} f(x, y)\,dx \tag{8}$$

To evaluate the integral in this expression, we treat $y$ as a constant and express the line $C_2$ parametrically as

$$x = t, \quad y = y \quad (x_1 \le t \le x)$$

At the risk of confusion, but to avoid complicating the notation, we have used $x$ both as the dependent variable in the parametric equations and as the endpoint of the line segment. With the latter interpretation of $x$, it follows that (8) can be expressed as

$$\frac{\partial\phi}{\partial x} = \frac{\partial}{\partial x}\int_{x_1}^{x} f(t, y)\,dt$$

Now we apply Part 2 of the Fundamental Theorem of Calculus (Theorem 5.6.3), treating $y$ as constant. This yields

$$\frac{\partial\phi}{\partial x} = f(x, y)$$

which proves the first part of (6). The proof that $\partial\phi/\partial y = g(x, y)$ can be obtained in a similar manner by joining $(x, y)$ to a point $(x, y_1)$ with a vertical line segment (Exercise 39). ■

## A TEST FOR CONSERVATIVE VECTOR FIELDS

Although Theorem 15.3.2 is an important characterization of conservative vector fields, it is not an effective computational tool because it is usually not possible to evaluate the line integral over all possible piecewise smooth curves in $D$, as required in parts (*b*) and (*c*). To develop a method for determining whether a vector field is conservative, we will need to introduce some new concepts about parametric curves and connected sets. We will say that a parametric curve is ***simple*** if it does not intersect itself between its endpoints. A simple parametric curve may or may not be closed (Figure 15.3.5). In addition, we will say that a connected set $D$ in 2-space is ***simply connected*** if no simple closed curve in $D$ encloses points that are not in $D$. Stated informally, a connected set $D$ is simply connected if it has no holes; a connected set with one or more holes is said to be ***multiply connected*** (Figure 15.3.6).

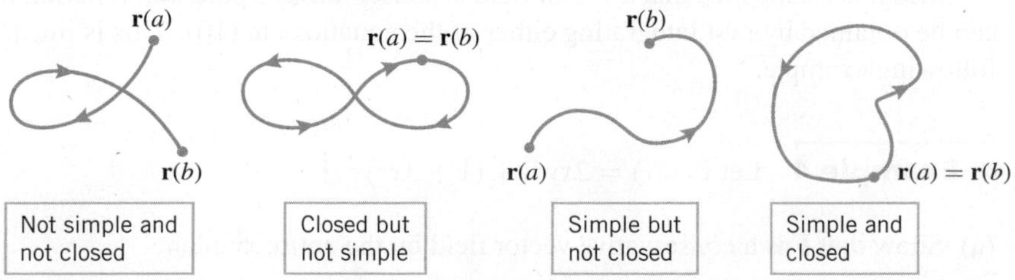


▲ **Figure 15.3.5**

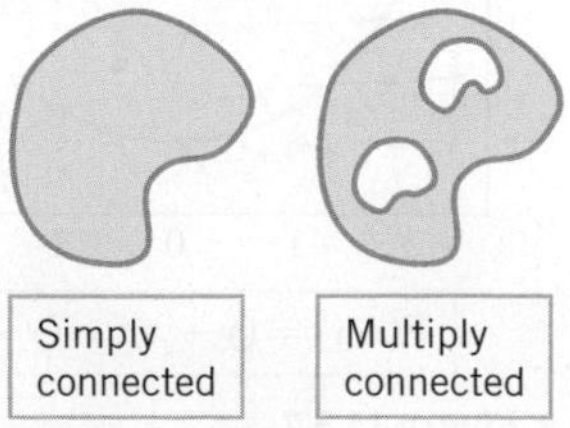


▲ **Figure 15.3.6**

The following theorem is the primary tool for determining whether a vector field in 2-space is conservative.

**WARNING**

In (9), the **i**-component of **F** is differentiated with respect to $y$ and the **j**-component with respect to $x$. It is easy to get this backwards by mistake.

**15.3.3 THEOREM** (*Conservative Field Test*) *If $f(x, y)$ and $g(x, y)$ are continuous and have continuous first partial derivatives on some open region D, and if the vector field $\mathbf{F}(x, y) = f(x, y)\mathbf{i} + g(x, y)\mathbf{j}$ is conservative on D, then*

$$\frac{\partial f}{\partial y} = \frac{\partial g}{\partial x} \tag{9}$$

*at each point in D. Conversely, if D is simply connected and (9) holds at each point in D, then $\mathbf{F}(x, y) = f(x, y)\mathbf{i} + g(x, y)\mathbf{j}$ is conservative.*

A complete proof of this theorem requires results from advanced calculus and will be omitted. However, it is not hard to see why (9) must hold if **F** is conservative. For this purpose suppose that $\mathbf{F} = \nabla\phi$, in which case we can express the functions $f$ and $g$ as

$$\frac{\partial \phi}{\partial x} = f \quad \text{and} \quad \frac{\partial \phi}{\partial y} = g \tag{10}$$

Thus,

$$\frac{\partial f}{\partial y} = \frac{\partial}{\partial y}\left(\frac{\partial \phi}{\partial x}\right) = \frac{\partial^2 \phi}{\partial y \partial x} \quad \text{and} \quad \frac{\partial g}{\partial x} = \frac{\partial}{\partial x}\left(\frac{\partial \phi}{\partial y}\right) = \frac{\partial^2 \phi}{\partial x \partial y}$$

But the mixed partial derivatives in these equations are equal (Theorem 13.3.2), so (9) follows.

▶ **Example 3** Use Theorem 15.3.3 to determine whether the vector field

$$\mathbf{F}(x, y) = (y + x)\mathbf{i} + (y - x)\mathbf{j}$$

is conservative on some open set.

***Solution.*** Let $f(x, y) = y + x$ and $g(x, y) = y - x$. Then

$$\frac{\partial f}{\partial y} = 1 \quad \text{and} \quad \frac{\partial g}{\partial x} = -1$$

Thus, there are no points in the $xy$-plane at which condition (9) holds, and hence **F** is not conservative on any open set. ◀

**REMARK** Since the vector field **F** in Example 3 is not conservative, it follows from Theorem 15.3.2 that there must exist piecewise smooth closed curves in every open connected set in the $xy$-plane on which

$$\int_C \mathbf{F} \cdot d\mathbf{r} = \int_C \mathbf{F} \cdot \mathbf{T}\, ds \neq 0$$

One such curve is the oriented circle shown in Figure 15.3.7. The figure suggests that $\mathbf{F} \cdot \mathbf{T} < 0$ at each point of $C$ (why?), so $\int_C \mathbf{F} \cdot \mathbf{T}\, ds < 0$.

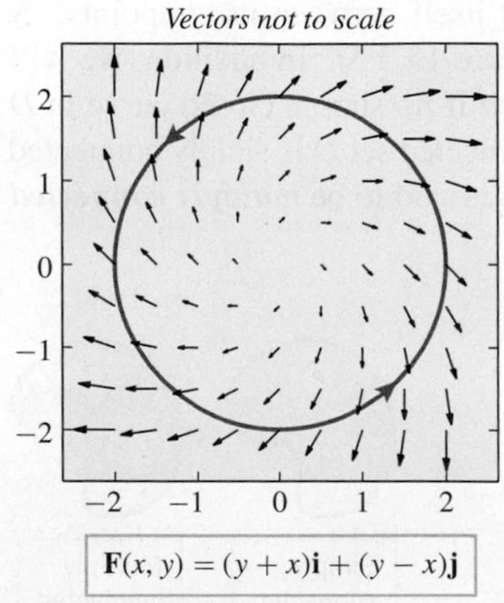


▲ **Figure 15.3.7**

Once it is established that a vector field is conservative, a potential function for the field can be obtained by first integrating either of the equations in (10). This is illustrated in the following example.

▶ **Example 4** Let $\mathbf{F}(x, y) = 2xy^3\mathbf{i} + (1 + 3x^2y^2)\mathbf{j}$.

(a) Show that **F** is a conservative vector field on the entire $xy$-plane.

(b) Find $\phi$ by first integrating $\partial\phi/\partial x$.

(c) Find $\phi$ by first integrating $\partial\phi/\partial y$.

***Solution (a).*** Since $f(x, y) = 2xy^3$ and $g(x, y) = 1 + 3x^2y^2$, we have

$$\frac{\partial f}{\partial y} = 6xy^2 = \frac{\partial g}{\partial x}$$

so (9) holds for all $(x, y)$.

***Solution (b).*** Since the field $\mathbf{F}$ is conservative, there is a potential function $\phi$ such that

$$\frac{\partial \phi}{\partial x} = 2xy^3 \quad \text{and} \quad \frac{\partial \phi}{\partial y} = 1 + 3x^2y^2 \tag{11}$$

Integrating the first of these equations with respect to $x$ (and treating $y$ as a constant) yields

$$\phi = \int 2xy^3\, dx = x^2y^3 + k(y) \tag{12}$$

where $k(y)$ represents the "constant" of integration. We are justified in treating the constant of integration as a function of $y$, since $y$ is held constant in the integration process. To find $k(y)$ we differentiate (12) with respect to $y$ and use the second equation in (11) to obtain

$$\frac{\partial \phi}{\partial y} = 3x^2y^2 + k'(y) = 1 + 3x^2y^2$$

from which it follows that $k'(y) = 1$. Thus,

$$k(y) = \int k'(y)\, dy = \int 1\, dy = y + K$$

where $K$ is a (numerical) constant of integration. Substituting in (12) we obtain

$$\phi = x^2y^3 + y + K$$

The appearance of the arbitrary constant $K$ tells us that $\phi$ is not unique. As a check on the computations, you may want to verify that $\nabla\phi = \mathbf{F}$.

You can also use (7) to find a potential function for a conservative vector field. For example, find a potential function for the vector field in Example 4 by evaluating (7) on the line segment

$$\mathbf{r}(t) = t(x\mathbf{i}) + t(y\mathbf{j}) \quad (0 \le t \le 1)$$

from $(0, 0)$ to $(x, y)$.

***Solution (c).*** Integrating the second equation in (11) with respect to $y$ (and treating $x$ as a constant) yields

$$\phi = \int (1 + 3x^2y^2)\, dy = y + x^2y^3 + k(x) \tag{13}$$

where $k(x)$ is the "constant" of integration. Differentiating (13) with respect to $x$ and using the first equation in (11) yields

$$\frac{\partial \phi}{\partial x} = 2xy^3 + k'(x) = 2xy^3$$

from which it follows that $k'(x) = 0$ and consequently that $k(x) = K$, where $K$ is a numerical constant of integration. Substituting this in (13) yields

$$\phi = y + x^2y^3 + K$$

which agrees with the solution in part (b). ◄

► **Example 5** Use the potential function obtained in Example 4 to evaluate the integral

$$\int_{(1,4)}^{(3,1)} 2xy^3\, dx + (1 + 3x^2y^2)\, dy$$

In the solution to Example 5, note that the constant $K$ drops out. In future integration problems of the type in this example, we will often omit $K$ from the computations. See Exercise 7 for other ways to evaluate this integral.

***Solution.*** The integrand can be expressed as $\mathbf{F}\cdot d\mathbf{r}$, where $\mathbf{F}$ is the vector field in Example 4. Thus, using Formula (3) and the potential function $\phi = y + x^2y^3 + K$ for $\mathbf{F}$, we obtain

$$\int_{(1,4)}^{(3,1)} 2xy^3\,dx + (1+3x^2y^2)\,dy = \int_{(1,4)}^{(3,1)} \mathbf{F}\cdot d\mathbf{r} = \phi(3,1) - \phi(1,4)$$
$$= (10+K) - (68+K) = -58 \blacktriangleleft$$

**▶ Example 6** Let $\mathbf{F}(x,y) = e^y\mathbf{i} + xe^y\mathbf{j}$ denote a force field in the $xy$-plane.

(a) Verify that the force field $\mathbf{F}$ is conservative on the entire $xy$-plane.

(b) Find the work done by the field on a particle that moves from $(1,0)$ to $(-1,0)$ along the semicircular path $C$ shown in Figure 15.3.8.

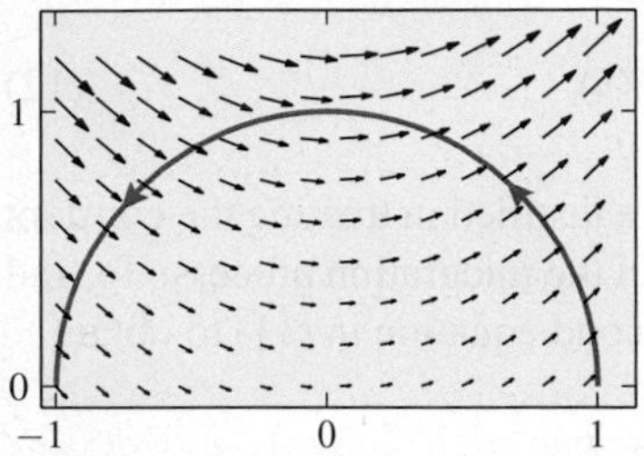

▲ Figure 15.3.8

***Solution (a).*** For the given field we have $f(x,y) = e^y$ and $g(x,y) = xe^y$. Thus,

$$\frac{\partial}{\partial y}(e^y) = e^y = \frac{\partial}{\partial x}(xe^y)$$

so (9) holds for all $(x,y)$ and hence $\mathbf{F}$ is conservative on the entire $xy$-plane.

***Solution (b).*** From Formula (34) of Section 15.2, the work done by the field is

$$W = \int_C \mathbf{F}\cdot d\mathbf{r} = \int_C e^y\,dx + xe^y\,dy \tag{14}$$

However, the calculations involved in integrating along $C$ are tedious, so it is preferable to apply Theorem 15.3.1, taking advantage of the fact that the field is conservative and the integral is independent of path. Thus, we write (14) as

$$W = \int_{(1,0)}^{(-1,0)} e^y\,dx + xe^y\,dy = \phi(-1,0) - \phi(1,0) \tag{15}$$

As illustrated in Example 4, we can find $\phi$ by integrating either of the equations

$$\frac{\partial\phi}{\partial x} = e^y \quad\text{and}\quad \frac{\partial\phi}{\partial y} = xe^y \tag{16}$$

We will integrate the first. We obtain

$$\phi = \int e^y\,dx = xe^y + k(y) \tag{17}$$

Differentiating this equation with respect to $y$ and using the second equation in (16) yields

$$\frac{\partial\phi}{\partial y} = xe^y + k'(y) = xe^y$$

from which it follows that $k'(y) = 0$ or $k(y) = K$. Thus, from (17)

$$\phi = xe^y + K$$

and hence from (15)

$$W = \phi(-1,0) - \phi(1,0) = (-1)e^0 - 1e^0 = -2 \blacktriangleleft$$

## CONSERVATIVE VECTOR FIELDS IN 3-SPACE

All of the results in this section have analogs in 3-space: Theorems 15.3.1 and 15.3.2 can be extended to vector fields in 3-space simply by adding a third variable and modifying the hypotheses appropriately. For example, in 3-space, Formula (3) becomes

$$\int_C \mathbf{F}(x,y,z)\cdot d\mathbf{r} = \phi(x_1,y_1,z_1) - \phi(x_0,y_0,z_0) \tag{18}$$

Theorem 15.3.3 can also be extended to vector fields in 3-space. We leave it for the exercises to show that if $\mathbf{F}(x, y, z) = f(x, y, z)\mathbf{i} + g(x, y, z)\mathbf{j} + h(x, y, z)\mathbf{k}$ is a conservative field, then

$$\frac{\partial f}{\partial y} = \frac{\partial g}{\partial x}, \quad \frac{\partial f}{\partial z} = \frac{\partial h}{\partial x}, \quad \frac{\partial g}{\partial z} = \frac{\partial h}{\partial y} \tag{19}$$

that is, curl $\mathbf{F} = \mathbf{0}$. Conversely, a vector field satisfying these conditions on a suitably restricted region is conservative on that region if $f$, $g$, and $h$ are continuous and have continuous first partial derivatives in the region. Some problems involving Formulas (18) and (19) are given in the review exercises at the end of this chapter.

## CONSERVATION OF ENERGY

If $\mathbf{F}(x,y,z)$ is a conservative force field with a potential function $\phi(x,y,z)$, then we call $V(x, y, z) = -\phi(x, y, z)$ the ***potential energy*** of the field at the point $(x, y, z)$. Thus, it follows from the 3-space version of Theorem 15.3.1 that the work $W$ done by $\mathbf{F}$ on a particle that moves along any path $C$ from a point $(x_0, y_0, z_0)$ to a point $(x_1, y_1, z_1)$ is related to the potential energy by the equation

$$W = \int_C \mathbf{F} \cdot d\mathbf{r} = \phi(x_1, y_1, z_1) - \phi(x_0, y_0, z_0) = -[V(x_1, y_1, z_1) - V(x_0, y_0, z_0)] \tag{20}$$

That is, the work done by the field is the negative of the change in potential energy. In particular, it follows from the 3-space analog of Theorem 15.3.2 that if a particle traverses a piecewise smooth closed path in a conservative vector field, then the work done by the field is zero, and there is no change in potential energy. To take this a step further, suppose that a particle of mass $m$ moves along any piecewise smooth curve (not necessarily closed) in a conservative force field $\mathbf{F}$, starting at $(x_0, y_0, z_0)$ with speed $v_i$ and ending at $(x_1, y_1, z_1)$ with speed $v_f$. If $\mathbf{F}$ is the only force acting on the particle, then an argument similar to the derivation of Equation (6) in Section 6.6 shows that the work done on the particle by $\mathbf{F}$ is equal to the change in kinetic energy $\frac{1}{2}mv_f^2 - \frac{1}{2}mv_i^2$ of the particle. (An argument for smooth curves appears in the Making Connections exercises.) If we let $V_i$ denote the potential energy at the starting point and $V_f$ the potential energy at the final point, then it follows from (20) that

$$\tfrac{1}{2}mv_f^2 - \tfrac{1}{2}mv_i^2 = -[V_f - V_i]$$

which we can rewrite as

$$\tfrac{1}{2}mv_f^2 + V_f = \tfrac{1}{2}mv_i^2 + V_i$$

This equation states that the total energy of the particle (kinetic energy + potential energy) does not change as the particle moves along a path in a conservative vector field. This result, called the ***conservation of energy principle***, explains the origin of the term "conservative vector field."

## ✓ QUICK CHECK EXERCISES 15.3 *(See page 1005 for answers.)*

**1.** If $C$ is a piecewise smooth curve from $(1, 2, 3)$ to $(4, 5, 6)$, then
$$\int_C dx + 2\,dy + 3\,dz = \underline{\hspace{2cm}}$$

**2.** If $C$ is the portion of the circle $x^2 + y^2 = 1$ where $0 \le x$, oriented counterclockwise, and $f(x, y) = ye^x$, then
$$\int_C \nabla f \cdot d\mathbf{r} = \underline{\hspace{2cm}}$$

**3.** A potential function for the vector field
$$\mathbf{F}(x, y, z) = yz\mathbf{i} + (xz + z)\mathbf{j} + (xy + y + 1)\mathbf{k}$$
is $\phi(x, y, z) = \underline{\hspace{2cm}}$.

**4.** If $a$, $b$, and $c$ are nonzero real numbers such that the vector field $x^5y^a\mathbf{i} + x^by^c\mathbf{j}$ is a conservative vector field, then
$a = \underline{\hspace{1.5cm}}$, $b = \underline{\hspace{1.5cm}}$, $c = \underline{\hspace{1.5cm}}$

## EXERCISE SET 15.3 [C] CAS

**1–6** Determine whether $\mathbf{F}$ is a conservative vector field. If so, find a potential function for it. ■

1. $\mathbf{F}(x, y) = x\mathbf{i} + y\mathbf{j}$
2. $\mathbf{F}(x, y) = 3y^2\mathbf{i} + 6xy\mathbf{j}$
3. $\mathbf{F}(x, y) = x^2y\mathbf{i} + 5xy^2\mathbf{j}$
4. $\mathbf{F}(x, y) = e^x \cos y\mathbf{i} - e^x \sin y\mathbf{j}$
5. $\mathbf{F}(x, y) = (\cos y + y \cos x)\mathbf{i} + (\sin x - x \sin y)\mathbf{j}$
6. $\mathbf{F}(x, y) = x \ln y\mathbf{i} + y \ln x\mathbf{j}$
7. In each part, evaluate $\int_C 2xy^3\,dx + (1 + 3x^2y^2)\,dy$ over the curve $C$, and compare your answer with the result of Example 5.
   (a) $C$ is the line segment from $(1, 4)$ to $(3, 1)$.
   (b) $C$ consists of the line segment from $(1, 4)$ to $(1, 1)$, followed by the line segment from $(1, 1)$ to $(3, 1)$.
8. (a) Show that the line integral $\int_C y \sin x\,dx - \cos x\,dy$ is independent of the path.
   (b) Evaluate the integral in part (a) along the line segment from $(0, 1)$ to $(\pi, -1)$.
   (c) Evaluate the integral $\int_{(0,1)}^{(\pi,-1)} y \sin x\,dx - \cos x\,dy$ using Theorem 15.3.1, and confirm that the value is the same as that obtained in part (b).

**9–14** Show that the integral is independent of the path, and use Theorem 15.3.1 to find its value. ■

9. $\displaystyle\int_{(1,2)}^{(4,0)} 3y\,dx + 3x\,dy$
10. $\displaystyle\int_{(0,0)}^{(1,\pi/2)} e^x \sin y\,dx + e^x \cos y\,dy$
11. $\displaystyle\int_{(0,0)}^{(3,2)} 2xe^y\,dx + x^2e^y\,dy$
12. $\displaystyle\int_{(-1,2)}^{(0,1)} (3x - y + 1)\,dx - (x + 4y + 2)\,dy$
13. $\displaystyle\int_{(2,-2)}^{(-1,0)} 2xy^3\,dx + 3y^2x^2\,dy$
14. $\displaystyle\int_{(1,1)}^{(3,3)} \left(e^x \ln y - \frac{e^y}{x}\right) dx + \left(\frac{e^x}{y} - e^y \ln x\right) dy$, where $x$ and $y$ are positive.

**15–18** Confirm that the force field $\mathbf{F}$ is conservative in some open connected region containing the points $P$ and $Q$, and then find the work done by the force field on a particle moving along an arbitrary smooth curve in the region from $P$ to $Q$. ■

15. $\mathbf{F}(x, y) = xy^2\mathbf{i} + x^2y\mathbf{j}$; $P(1, 1), Q(0, 0)$
16. $\mathbf{F}(x, y) = 2xy^3\mathbf{i} + 3x^2y^2\mathbf{j}$; $P(-3, 0), Q(4, 1)$
17. $\mathbf{F}(x, y) = ye^{xy}\mathbf{i} + xe^{xy}\mathbf{j}$; $P(-1, 1), Q(2, 0)$
18. $\mathbf{F}(x, y) = e^{-y} \cos x\mathbf{i} - e^{-y} \sin x\mathbf{j}$; $P(\pi/2, 1), Q(-\pi/2, 0)$

**19–22 True–False** Determine whether the statement is true or false. Explain your answer. ■

19. If $\mathbf{F}$ is a vector field and there exists a closed curve $C$ such that $\int_C \mathbf{F} \cdot d\mathbf{r} = 0$, then $\mathbf{F}$ is conservative.
20. If $\mathbf{F}(x, y) = ay\mathbf{i} + bx\mathbf{j}$ is a conservative vector field, then $a = b$.
21. If $\phi(x, y)$ is a potential function for a constant vector field, then the graph of $z = \phi(x, y)$ is a plane.
22. If $f(x, y)$ and $g(x, y)$ are differentiable functions defined on the $xy$-plane, and if $f_y(x, y) = g_x(x, y)$ for all $(x, y)$, then there exists a function $\phi(x, y)$ such that $\phi_x(x, y) = f(x, y)$ and $\phi_y(x, y) = g(x, y)$.

**23–24** Find the exact value of $\int_C \mathbf{F} \cdot d\mathbf{r}$ using any method. ■

23. $\mathbf{F}(x, y) = (e^y + ye^x)\mathbf{i} + (xe^y + e^x)\mathbf{j}$
    $C: \mathbf{r}(t) = \sin(\pi t/2)\mathbf{i} + \ln t\mathbf{j}\quad (1 \le t \le 2)$
24. $\mathbf{F}(x, y) = 2xy\mathbf{i} + (x^2 + \cos y)\mathbf{j}$
    $C: \mathbf{r}(t) = t\mathbf{i} + t \cos(t/3)\mathbf{j}\quad (0 \le t \le \pi)$
25. [C] Use the numerical integration capability of a CAS or other calculating utility to approximate the value of the integral in Exercise 23 by direct integration. Confirm that the numerical approximation is consistent with the exact value.
26. [C] Use the numerical integration capability of a CAS or other calculating utility to approximate the value of the integral in Exercise 24 by direct integration. Confirm that the numerical approximation is consistent with the exact value.

**FOCUS ON CONCEPTS**

**27–28** Is the vector field conservative? Explain. ■

27.

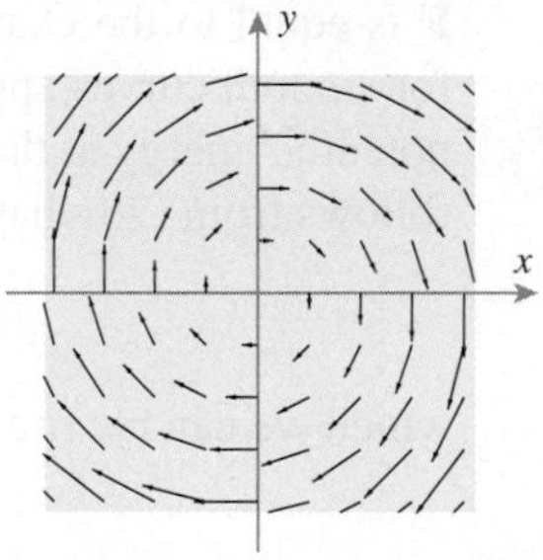


28.

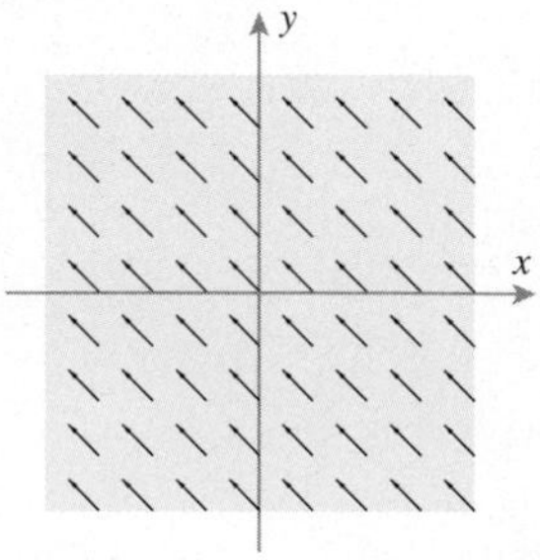


29. Suppose that $C$ is a circle in the domain of a conservative nonzero vector field in the $xy$-plane whose component functions are continuous. Explain why there must be at least two points on $C$ at which the vector field is normal to the circle.
30. Does the result in Exercise 29 remain true if the circle $C$ is replaced by a square? Explain.

31. Prove: If
$$\mathbf{F}(x, y, z) = f(x, y, z)\mathbf{i} + g(x, y, z)\mathbf{j} + h(x, y, z)\mathbf{k}$$
is a conservative field and $f$, $g$, and $h$ are continuous and have continuous first partial derivatives in a region, then
$$\frac{\partial f}{\partial y} = \frac{\partial g}{\partial x}, \quad \frac{\partial f}{\partial z} = \frac{\partial h}{\partial x}, \quad \frac{\partial g}{\partial z} = \frac{\partial h}{\partial y}$$
in the region.

**32.** Use the result in Exercise 31 to show that the integral

$$\int_C yz\,dx + xz\,dy + yx^2\,dz$$

is not independent of the path.

**33.** Find a nonzero function $h$ for which

$$\mathbf{F}(x, y) = h(x)[x \sin y + y \cos y]\mathbf{i} + h(x)[x \cos y - y \sin y]\mathbf{j}$$

is conservative.

**34.** (a) In Example 3 of Section 15.1 we showed that

$$\phi(x, y) = -\frac{c}{(x^2 + y^2)^{1/2}}$$

is a potential function for the two-dimensional inverse-square field

$$\mathbf{F}(x, y) = \frac{c}{(x^2 + y^2)^{3/2}}(x\mathbf{i} + y\mathbf{j})$$

but we did not explain how the potential function $\phi(x, y)$ was obtained. Use Theorem 15.3.3 to show that the two-dimensional inverse-square field is conservative everywhere except at the origin, and then use the method of Example 4 to derive the formula for $\phi(x, y)$.

(b) Use an appropriate generalization of the method of Example 4 to derive the potential function

$$\phi(x, y, z) = -\frac{c}{(x^2 + y^2 + z^2)^{1/2}}$$

for the three-dimensional inverse-square field given by Formula (5) of Section 15.1.

**35–36** Use the result in Exercise 34(b). ■

**35.** In each part, find the work done by the three-dimensional inverse-square field

$$\mathbf{F}(\mathbf{r}) = \frac{1}{\|\mathbf{r}\|^3}\mathbf{r}$$

on a particle that moves along the curve $C$.

(a) $C$ is the line segment from $P(1, 1, 2)$ to $Q(3, 2, 1)$.

(b) $C$ is the curve

$$\mathbf{r}(t) = (2t^2 + 1)\mathbf{i} + (t^3 + 1)\mathbf{j} + (2 - \sqrt{t})\mathbf{k}$$

where $0 \le t \le 1$.

(c) $C$ is the circle in the $xy$-plane of radius 1 centered at $(2, 0, 0)$ traversed counterclockwise.

**36.** Let $\mathbf{F}(x, y) = \dfrac{y}{x^2 + y^2}\mathbf{i} - \dfrac{x}{x^2 + y^2}\mathbf{j}$.

(a) Show that

$$\int_{C_1} \mathbf{F} \cdot d\mathbf{r} \ne \int_{C_2} \mathbf{F} \cdot d\mathbf{r}$$

if $C_1$ and $C_2$ are the semicircular paths from $(1, 0)$ to $(-1, 0)$ given by

$$C_1 : x = \cos t,\ \ y = \sin t \qquad (0 \le t \le \pi)$$
$$C_2 : x = \cos t,\ \ y = -\sin t \qquad (0 \le t \le \pi)$$

(b) Show that the components of $\mathbf{F}$ satisfy Formula (9).

(c) Do the results in parts (a) and (b) contradict Theorem 15.3.3? Explain.

**37.** Prove Theorem 15.3.1 if $C$ is a piecewise smooth curve composed of smooth curves $C_1, C_2, \ldots, C_n$.

**38.** Prove that (*b*) implies (*c*) in Theorem 15.3.2. [*Hint:* Consider any two piecewise smooth oriented curves $C_1$ and $C_2$ in the region from a point $P$ to a point $Q$, and integrate around the closed curve consisting of $C_1$ and $-C_2$.]

**39.** Complete the proof of Theorem 15.3.2 by showing that $\partial\phi/\partial y = g(x, y)$, where $\phi(x, y)$ is the function in (7).

**40. Writing** Describe the different methods available for evaluating the integral of a conservative vector field over a smooth curve.

**41. Writing** Discuss some of the ways that you can show a vector field is *not* conservative.

✓ **QUICK CHECK ANSWERS 15.3** 1. 18 2. 2 3. $xyz + yz + z$ 4. 6, 6, 5

## 15.4 GREEN'S THEOREM

*In this section we will discuss a remarkable and beautiful theorem that expresses a double integral over a plane region in terms of a line integral around its boundary.*

### GREEN'S THEOREM

**15.4.1 THEOREM (*Green's Theorem*)** *Let $R$ be a simply connected plane region whose boundary is a simple, closed, piecewise smooth curve $C$ oriented counterclockwise. If $f(x, y)$ and $g(x, y)$ are continuous and have continuous first partial derivatives on some open set containing $R$, then*

$$\int_C f(x, y)\,dx + g(x, y)\,dy = \iint_R \left(\frac{\partial g}{\partial x} - \frac{\partial f}{\partial y}\right) dA \tag{1}$$

**PROOF** For simplicity, we will prove the theorem for regions that are simultaneously type I and type II (see Definition 14.2.1). Such a region is shown in Figure 15.4.1. The crux of the proof is to show that

$$\int_C f(x,y)\,dx = -\iint_R \frac{\partial f}{\partial y}\,dA \quad \text{and} \quad \int_C g(x,y)\,dy = \iint_R \frac{\partial g}{\partial x}\,dA \tag{2–3}$$

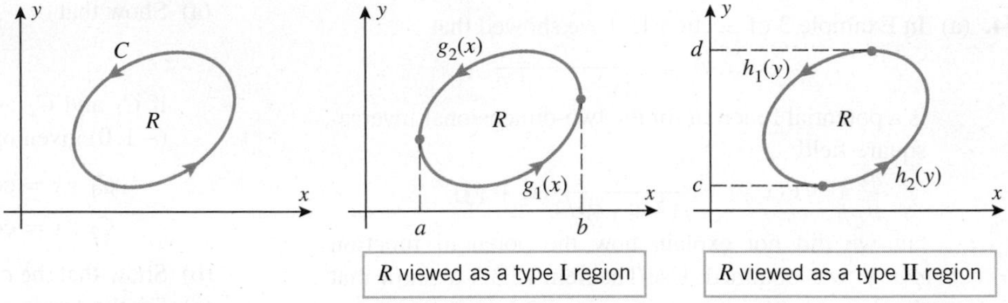


▶ **Figure 15.4.1**

To prove (2), view $R$ as a type I region and let $C_1$ and $C_2$ be the lower and upper boundary curves, oriented as in Figure 15.4.2. Then

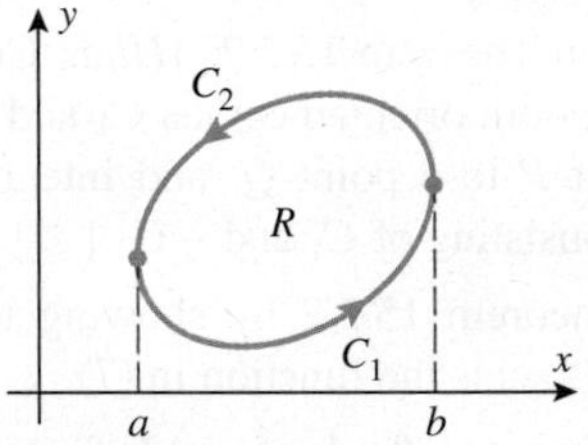


▲ **Figure 15.4.2**

$$\int_C f(x,y)\,dx = \int_{C_1} f(x,y)\,dx + \int_{C_2} f(x,y)\,dx$$

or, equivalently,

$$\int_C f(x,y)\,dx = \int_{C_1} f(x,y)\,dx - \int_{-C_2} f(x,y)\,dx \tag{4}$$

(This step will help simplify our calculations since $C_1$ and $-C_2$ are then both oriented left to right.) The curves $C_1$ and $-C_2$ can be expressed parametrically as

$$C_1 : x = t, \quad y = g_1(t) \quad (a \le t \le b)$$
$$-C_2 : x = t, \quad y = g_2(t) \quad (a \le t \le b)$$

Thus, we can rewrite (4) as

$$\begin{aligned}
\int_C f(x,y)\,dx &= \int_a^b f(t, g_1(t))x'(t)\,dt - \int_a^b f(t, g_2(t))x'(t)\,dt \\
&= \int_a^b f(t, g_1(t))\,dt - \int_a^b f(t, g_2(t))\,dt \\
&= -\int_a^b [f(t, g_2(t)) - f(t, g_1(t))]\,dt \\
&= -\int_a^b \Big[ f(t,y) \Big]_{y=g_1(t)}^{y=g_2(t)} dt = -\int_a^b \left[ \int_{g_1(t)}^{g_2(t)} \frac{\partial f}{\partial y}\,dy \right] dt \\
&= -\int_a^b \int_{g_1(x)}^{g_2(x)} \frac{\partial f}{\partial y}\,dy\,dx = -\iint_R \frac{\partial f}{\partial y}\,dA
\end{aligned}$$

Since $x = t$

Supply the details for the proof of (3).

The proof of (3) is obtained similarly by treating $R$ as a type II region. We omit the details. ■

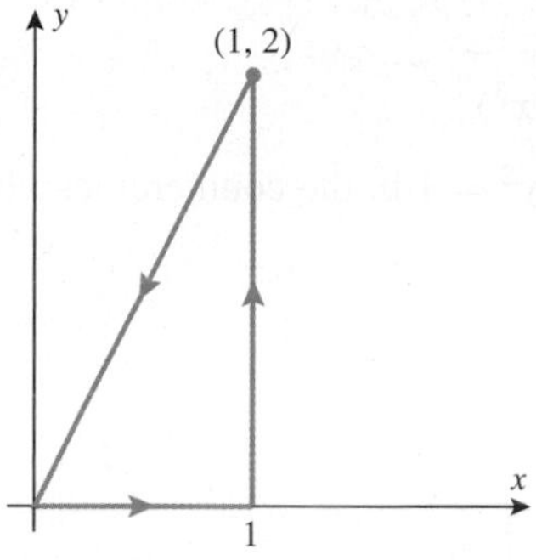

▲ Figure 15.4.3

▶ **Example 1** Use Green's Theorem to evaluate

$$\int_C x^2y\,dx + x\,dy$$

along the triangular path shown in Figure 15.4.3.

***Solution.*** Since $f(x, y) = x^2y$ and $g(x, y) = x$, it follows from (1) that

$$\int_C x^2y\,dx + x\,dy = \iint_R \left[\frac{\partial}{\partial x}(x) - \frac{\partial}{\partial y}(x^2y)\right] dA = \int_0^1 \int_0^{2x} (1 - x^2)\,dy\,dx$$

$$= \int_0^1 (2x - 2x^3)\,dx = \left[x^2 - \frac{x^4}{2}\right]_0^1 = \frac{1}{2}$$

This agrees with the result obtained in Example 10 of Section 15.2, where we evaluated the line integral directly. Note how much simpler this solution is. ◀

## A NOTATION FOR LINE INTEGRALS AROUND SIMPLE CLOSED CURVES

It is common practice to denote a line integral around a simple closed curve by an integral sign with a superimposed circle. With this notation Formula (1) would be written as

$$\oint_C f(x, y)\,dx + g(x, y)\,dy = \iint_R \left(\frac{\partial g}{\partial x} - \frac{\partial f}{\partial y}\right) dA$$

Sometimes a direction arrow is added to the circle to indicate whether the integration is clockwise or counterclockwise. Thus, if we wanted to emphasize the counterclockwise direction of integration required by Theorem 15.4.1, we could express (1) as

$$\oint_C f(x, y)\,dx + g(x, y)\,dy = \iint_R \left(\frac{\partial g}{\partial x} - \frac{\partial f}{\partial y}\right) dA \qquad (5)$$

## FINDING WORK USING GREEN'S THEOREM

It follows from Formula (26) of Section 15.2 that the integral on the left side of (5) is the work performed by the force field $\mathbf{F}(x, y) = f(x, y)\mathbf{i} + g(x, y)\mathbf{j}$ on a particle moving counterclockwise around the simple closed curve $C$. In the case where this vector field is conservative, it follows from Theorem 15.3.2 that the integrand in the double integral on the right side of (5) is zero, so the work performed by the field is zero, as expected. For vector fields that are not conservative, it is often more efficient to calculate the work around simple closed curves by using Green's Theorem than by parametrizing the curve.

**George Green (1793–1841)** English mathematician and physicist. Green left school at an early age to work in his father's bakery and consequently had little early formal education. When his father opened a mill, the boy used the top room as a study in which he taught himself physics and mathematics from library books. In 1828 Green published his most important work, *An Essay on the Application of Mathematical Analysis to the Theories of Electricity and Magnetism.* Although Green's Theorem appeared in that paper, the result went virtually unnoticed because of the small press-run and local distribution. Following the death of his father in 1829, Green was urged by friends to seek a college education. In 1833, after four years of self-study to close the gaps in his elementary education, Green was admitted to Caius College, Cambridge. He graduated four years later, but with a disappointing performance on his final examinations—possibly because he was more interested in his own research. After a succession of works on light and sound, he was named to be Perse Fellow at Caius College. Two years later he died. In 1845, four years after his death, his paper of 1828 was published and the theories developed therein by this obscure, self-taught baker's son helped pave the way to the modern theories of electricity and magnetism.

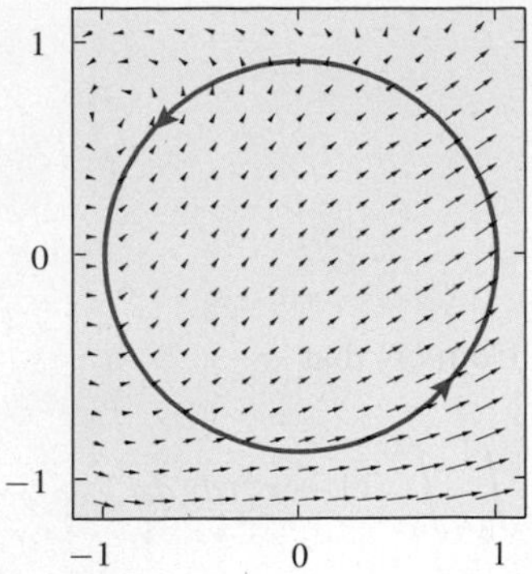

▲ Figure 15.4.4

► **Example 2** Find the work done by the force field

$$\mathbf{F}(x, y) = (e^x - y^3)\mathbf{i} + (\cos y + x^3)\mathbf{j}$$

on a particle that travels once around the unit circle $x^2 + y^2 = 1$ in the counterclockwise direction (Figure 15.4.4).

***Solution.*** The work $W$ performed by the field is

$$\begin{aligned} W &= \oint_C \mathbf{F}\cdot d\mathbf{r} = \oint_C (e^x - y^3)\,dx + (\cos y + x^3)\,dy \\ &= \iint_R \left[\frac{\partial}{\partial x}(\cos y + x^3) - \frac{\partial}{\partial y}(e^x - y^3)\right] dA \qquad \text{Green's Theorem} \\ &= \iint_R (3x^2 + 3y^2)\,dA = 3\iint_R (x^2 + y^2)\,dA \\ &= 3\int_0^{2\pi}\int_0^1 (r^2)r\,dr\,d\theta = \frac{3}{4}\int_0^{2\pi} d\theta = \frac{3\pi}{2} \blacktriangleleft \end{aligned}$$

We converted to polar coordinates.

## FINDING AREAS USING GREEN'S THEOREM

Green's Theorem leads to some useful new formulas for the area $A$ of a region $R$ that satisfies the conditions of the theorem. Two such formulas can be obtained as follows:

$$A = \iint_R dA = \oint_C x\,dy \quad \text{and} \quad A = \iint_R dA = \oint_C (-y)\,dx$$

Set $f(x, y) = 0$ and $g(x, y) = x$ in (1).

Set $f(x, y) = -y$ and $g(x, y) = 0$ in (1).

A third formula can be obtained by adding these two equations together. Thus, we have the following three formulas that express the area $A$ of a region $R$ in terms of line integrals around the boundary:

Although the third formula in (6) looks more complicated than the other two, it often leads to simpler integrations. Each has advantages in certain situations.

$$A = \oint_C x\,dy = -\oint_C y\,dx = \frac{1}{2}\oint_C -y\,dx + x\,dy \tag{6}$$

► **Example 3** Use a line integral to find the area enclosed by the ellipse

$$\frac{x^2}{a^2} + \frac{y^2}{b^2} = 1$$

***Solution.*** The ellipse, with counterclockwise orientation, can be represented parametrically by

$$x = a\cos t, \quad y = b\sin t \qquad (0 \le t \le 2\pi)$$

If we denote this curve by $C$, then from the third formula in (6) the area $A$ enclosed by the ellipse is

$$\begin{aligned} A &= \frac{1}{2}\oint_C -y\,dx + x\,dy \\ &= \frac{1}{2}\int_0^{2\pi} [(-b\sin t)(-a\sin t) + (a\cos t)(b\cos t)]\,dt \\ &= \frac{1}{2}ab\int_0^{2\pi} (\sin^2 t + \cos^2 t)\,dt = \frac{1}{2}ab\int_0^{2\pi} dt = \pi ab \blacktriangleleft \end{aligned}$$

## GREEN'S THEOREM FOR MULTIPLY CONNECTED REGIONS

Recall that a plane region is said to be simply connected if it has no holes and is said to be multiply connected if it has one or more holes (see Figure 15.3.6). At the beginning of this section we stated Green's Theorem for a counterclockwise integration around the boundary of a simply connected region $R$ (Theorem 15.4.1). Our next goal is to extend this theorem to multiply connected regions. To make this extension we will need to assume that *the region lies on the left when any portion of the boundary is traversed in the direction of its orientation*. This implies that the outer boundary curve of the region is oriented counterclockwise and the boundary curves that enclose holes have clockwise orientation (Figure 15.4.5*a*). If all portions of the boundary of a multiply connected region $R$ are oriented in this way, then we say that the boundary of $R$ has ***positive orientation***.

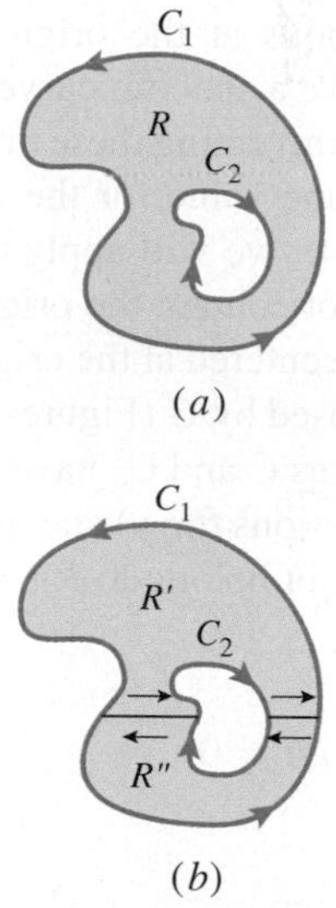

▲ Figure 15.4.5

We will now derive a version of Green's Theorem that applies to multiply connected regions with positively oriented boundaries. For simplicity, we will consider a multiply connected region $R$ with one hole, and we will assume that $f(x, y)$ and $g(x, y)$ have continuous first partial derivatives on some open set containing $R$. As shown in Figure 15.4.5*b*, let us divide $R$ into two regions $R'$ and $R''$ by introducing two "cuts" in $R$. The cuts are shown as line segments, but any piecewise smooth curves will suffice. If we assume that $f$ and $g$ satisfy the hypotheses of Green's Theorem on $R$ (and hence on $R'$ and $R''$), then we can apply this theorem to both $R'$ and $R''$ to obtain

$$\iint_R \left(\frac{\partial g}{\partial x} - \frac{\partial f}{\partial y}\right) dA = \iint_{R'} \left(\frac{\partial g}{\partial x} - \frac{\partial f}{\partial y}\right) dA + \iint_{R''} \left(\frac{\partial g}{\partial x} - \frac{\partial f}{\partial y}\right) dA$$

$$= \oint_{\substack{\text{Boundary}\\ \text{of } R'}} f(x, y)\,dx + g(x, y)\,dy + \oint_{\substack{\text{Boundary}\\ \text{of } R''}} f(x, y)\,dx + g(x, y)\,dy$$

However, the two line integrals are taken in opposite directions along the cuts, and hence cancel there, leaving only the contributions along $C_1$ and $C_2$. Thus,

$$\iint_R \left(\frac{\partial g}{\partial x} - \frac{\partial f}{\partial y}\right) dA = \oint_{C_1} f(x, y)\,dx + g(x, y)\,dy + \oint_{C_2} f(x, y)\,dx + g(x, y)\,dy \tag{7}$$

which is an extension of Green's Theorem to a multiply connected region with one hole. Observe that the integral around the outer boundary is taken counterclockwise and the integral around the hole is taken clockwise. More generally, if $R$ is a multiply connected region with $n$ holes, then the analog of (7) involves a sum of $n + 1$ integrals, one taken counterclockwise around the outer boundary of $R$ and the rest taken clockwise around the holes.

---

▶ **Example 4** Evaluate the integral

$$\oint_C \frac{-y\,dx + x\,dy}{x^2 + y^2}$$

if $C$ is a piecewise smooth simple closed curve oriented counterclockwise such that (a) $C$ does not enclose the origin and (b) $C$ encloses the origin.

***Solution (a).*** Let

$$f(x, y) = -\frac{y}{x^2 + y^2}, \quad g(x, y) = \frac{x}{x^2 + y^2} \tag{8}$$

so that

$$\frac{\partial g}{\partial x} = \frac{y^2 - x^2}{(x^2 + y^2)^2} = \frac{\partial f}{\partial y}$$

if $x$ and $y$ are not both zero. Thus, if $C$ does not enclose the origin, we have

$$\frac{\partial g}{\partial x} - \frac{\partial f}{\partial y} = 0 \tag{9}$$

on the simply connected region enclosed by $C$, and hence the given integral is zero by Green's Theorem.

***Solution (b).*** Unlike the situation in part (a), we cannot apply Green's Theorem directly because the functions $f(x, y)$ and $g(x, y)$ in (8) are discontinuous at the origin. Our problems are further compounded by the fact that we do not have a specific curve $C$ that we can parametrize to evaluate the integral. Our strategy for circumventing these problems will be to replace $C$ with a specific curve that produces the same value for the integral and then use that curve for the evaluation. To obtain such a curve, we will apply Green's Theorem for multiply connected regions to a region that does not contain the origin. For this purpose we construct a circle $C_a$ with *clockwise* orientation, centered at the origin, and with sufficiently small radius $a$ that it lies inside the region enclosed by $C$ (Figure 15.4.6). This creates a multiply connected region $R$ whose boundary curves $C$ and $C_a$ have the orientations required by Formula (7) and such that within $R$ the functions $f(x, y)$ and $g(x, y)$ in (8) satisfy the hypotheses of Green's Theorem (the origin does not belong to $R$). Thus, it follows from (7) and (9) that

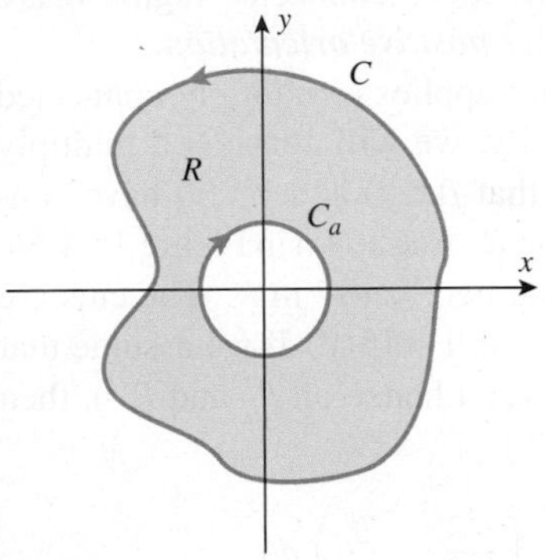


▲ Figure 15.4.6

$$\oint_C \frac{-y\,dx + x\,dy}{x^2+y^2} + \oint_{C_a} \frac{-y\,dx + x\,dy}{x^2+y^2} = \iint_R 0\,dA = 0$$

It follows from this equation that

$$\oint_C \frac{-y\,dx + x\,dy}{x^2+y^2} = -\oint_{C_a} \frac{-y\,dx + x\,dy}{x^2+y^2}$$

which we can rewrite as

$$\oint_C \frac{-y\,dx + x\,dy}{x^2+y^2} = \oint_{-C_a} \frac{-y\,dx + x\,dy}{x^2+y^2}$$

Reversing the orientation of $C_a$ reverses the sign of the integral.

But $C_a$ has clockwise orientation, so $-C_a$ has counterclockwise orientation. Thus, we have shown that the original integral can be evaluated by integrating counterclockwise around a circle of radius $a$ that is centered at the origin and lies within the region enclosed by $C$. Such a circle can be expressed parametrically as $x = a\cos t$, $y = a\sin t$ $(0 \le t \le 2\pi)$; and hence

$$\oint_C \frac{-y\,dx + x\,dy}{x^2+y^2} = \int_0^{2\pi} \frac{(-a\sin t)(-a\sin t)\,dt + (a\cos t)(a\cos t)\,dt}{(a\cos t)^2 + (a\sin t)^2}$$

$$= \int_0^{2\pi} 1\,dt = 2\pi \blacktriangleleft$$

## ✓QUICK CHECK EXERCISES 15.4

(See page 1013 for answers.)

1. If $C$ is the square with vertices $(\pm 1, \pm 1)$ oriented counterclockwise, then

$$\int_C -y\,dx + x\,dy = \underline{\qquad}$$

2. If $C$ is the triangle with vertices $(0, 0)$, $(1, 0)$, and $(1, 1)$ oriented counterclockwise, then

$$\int_C 2xy\,dx + (x^2 + x)\,dy = \underline{\qquad}$$

3. If $C$ is the unit circle centered at the origin and oriented counterclockwise, then

$$\int_C (y^3 - y - x)\,dx + (x^3 + x + y)\,dy = \underline{\qquad}$$

4. What region $R$ and choice of functions $f(x, y)$ and $g(x, y)$ allow us to use Formula (1) of Theorem 15.4.1 to claim that

$$\int_0^1 \int_0^{\sqrt{1-x^2}} (2x + 2y)\,dy\,dx = \int_0^{\pi/2} (\sin^3 t + \cos^3 t)\,dt?$$

## EXERCISE SET 15.4 [C] CAS

**1–2** Evaluate the line integral using Green's Theorem and check the answer by evaluating it directly. ■

1. $\oint_C y^2\,dx + x^2\,dy$, where $C$ is the square with vertices $(0,0)$, $(1,0)$, $(1,1)$, and $(0,1)$ oriented counterclockwise.
2. $\oint_C y\,dx + x\,dy$, where $C$ is the unit circle oriented counterclockwise.

**3–13** Use Green's Theorem to evaluate the integral. In each exercise, assume that the curve $C$ is oriented counterclockwise. ■

3. $\oint_C 3xy\,dx + 2xy\,dy$, where $C$ is the rectangle bounded by $x=-2$, $x=4$, $y=1$, and $y=2$.
4. $\oint_C (x^2-y^2)\,dx + x\,dy$, where $C$ is the circle $x^2+y^2=9$.
5. $\oint_C x\cos y\,dx - y\sin x\,dy$, where $C$ is the square with vertices $(0,0)$, $(\pi/2,0)$, $(\pi/2,\pi/2)$, and $(0,\pi/2)$.
6. $\oint_C y\tan^2 x\,dx + \tan x\,dy$, where $C$ is the circle $x^2+(y+1)^2=1$.
7. $\oint_C (x^2-y)\,dx + x\,dy$, where $C$ is the circle $x^2+y^2=4$.
8. $\oint_C (e^x+y^2)\,dx + (e^y+x^2)\,dy$, where $C$ is the boundary of the region between $y=x^2$ and $y=x$.
9. $\oint_C \ln(1+y)\,dx - \dfrac{xy}{1+y}\,dy$, where $C$ is the triangle with vertices $(0,0)$, $(2,0)$, and $(0,4)$.
10. $\oint_C x^2y\,dx - y^2x\,dy$, where $C$ is the boundary of the region in the first quadrant, enclosed between the coordinate axes and the circle $x^2+y^2=16$.
11. $\oint_C \tan^{-1}y\,dx - \dfrac{y^2x}{1+y^2}\,dy$, where $C$ is the square with vertices $(0,0)$, $(1,0)$, $(1,1)$, and $(0,1)$.
12. $\oint_C \cos x\sin y\,dx + \sin x\cos y\,dy$, where $C$ is the triangle with vertices $(0,0)$, $(3,3)$, and $(0,3)$.
13. $\oint_C x^2y\,dx + (y+xy^2)\,dy$, where $C$ is the boundary of the region enclosed by $y=x^2$ and $x=y^2$.
14. Let $C$ be the boundary of the region enclosed between $y=x^2$ and $y=2x$. Assuming that $C$ is oriented counterclockwise, evaluate the following integrals by Green's Theorem:
    (a) $\oint_C (6xy-y^2)\,dx$ (b) $\oint_C (6xy-y^2)\,dy$.

**15–18 True–False** Determine whether the statement is true or false. Explain your answer. (In Exercises 16–18, assume that $C$ is a simple, smooth, closed curve, oriented counterclockwise.) ■

15. Green's Theorem allows us to replace any line integral by a double integral.
16. If
$$\int_C f(x,y)\,dx + g(x,y)\,dy = 0$$
then $\partial g/\partial x = \partial f/\partial y$ at all points in the region bounded by $C$.
17. It must be the case that
$$\int_C x\,dy > 0$$
18. It must be the case that
$$\int_C e^{x^2}\,dx + \sin y^3\,dy = 0$$

[C] 19. Use a CAS to check Green's Theorem by evaluating both integrals in the equation
$$\oint_C e^y\,dx + ye^x\,dy = \iint_R \left[\frac{\partial}{\partial x}(ye^x) - \frac{\partial}{\partial y}(e^y)\right] dA$$
where
(a) $C$ is the circle $x^2+y^2=1$
(b) $C$ is the boundary of the region enclosed by $y=x^2$ and $x=y^2$.

20. In Example 3, we used Green's Theorem to obtain the area of an ellipse. Obtain this area using the first and then the second formula in (6).
21. Use a line integral to find the area of the region enclosed by the astroid
$$x=a\cos^3\phi,\quad y=a\sin^3\phi \qquad (0\le\phi\le 2\pi)$$
22. Use a line integral to find the area of the triangle with vertices $(0,0)$, $(a,0)$, and $(0,b)$, where $a>0$ and $b>0$.
23. Use the formula
$$A=\frac{1}{2}\oint_C -y\,dx + x\,dy$$
to find the area of the region swept out by the line from the origin to the ellipse $x=a\cos t$, $y=b\sin t$ if $t$ varies from $t=0$ to $t=t_0$ $(0\le t_0\le 2\pi)$.
24. Use the formula
$$A=\frac{1}{2}\oint_C -y\,dx + x\,dy$$
to find the area of the region swept out by the line from the origin to the hyperbola $x=a\cosh t$, $y=b\sinh t$ if $t$ varies from $t=0$ to $t=t_0$ $(t_0\ge 0)$.

**FOCUS ON CONCEPTS**

**25.** Suppose that $\mathbf{F}(x, y) = f(x, y)\mathbf{i} + g(x, y)\mathbf{j}$ is a vector field whose component functions $f$ and $g$ have continuous first partial derivatives. Let $C$ denote a simple, closed, piecewise smooth curve oriented counterclockwise that bounds a region $R$ contained in the domain of $\mathbf{F}$. We can think of $\mathbf{F}$ as a vector field in 3-space by writing it as

$$\mathbf{F}(x, y, z) = f(x, y)\mathbf{i} + g(x, y)\mathbf{j} + 0\mathbf{k}$$

With this convention, explain why

$$\int_C \mathbf{F} \cdot d\mathbf{r} = \iint_R \operatorname{curl} \mathbf{F} \cdot \mathbf{k}\, dA$$

**26.** Suppose that $\mathbf{F}(x, y) = f(x, y)\mathbf{i} + g(x, y)\mathbf{j}$ is a vector field on the $xy$-plane and that $f$ and $g$ have continuous first partial derivatives with $f_y = g_x$ everywhere. Use Green's Theorem to explain why

$$\int_{C_1} \mathbf{F} \cdot d\mathbf{r} = \int_{C_2} \mathbf{F} \cdot d\mathbf{r}$$

where $C_1$ and $C_2$ are the oriented curves in the accompanying figure. [*Note:* Compare this result with Theorems 15.3.2 and 15.3.3.]

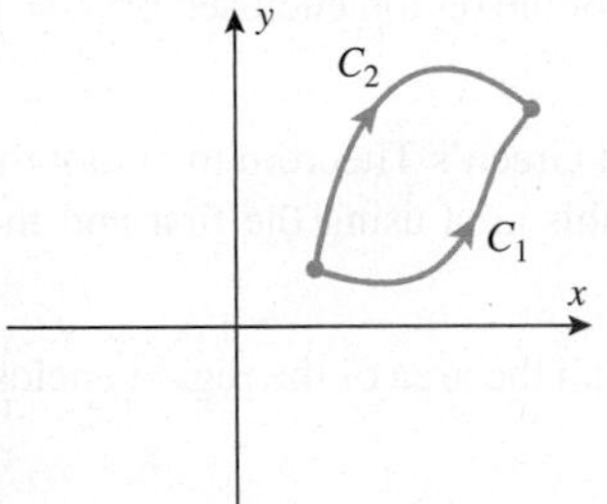


◀ **Figure Ex-26**

**27.** Suppose that $f(x)$ and $g(x)$ are continuous functions with $g(x) \le f(x)$. Let $R$ denote the region bounded by the graph of $f$, the graph of $g$, and the vertical lines $x = a$ and $x = b$. Let $C$ denote the boundary of $R$ oriented counterclockwise. What familiar formula results from applying Green's Theorem to $\int_C (-y)\, dx$?

**28.** In the accompanying figure, $C$ is a smooth oriented curve from $P(x_0, y_0)$ to $Q(x_1, y_1)$ that is contained inside the rectangle with corners at the origin and $Q$ and outside the rectangle with corners at the origin and $P$.

(a) What region in the figure has area $\int_C x\, dy$?

(b) What region in the figure has area $\int_C y\, dx$?

(c) Express $\int_C x\, dy + \int_C y\, dx$ in terms of the coordinates of $P$ and $Q$.

(d) Interpret the result of part (c) in terms of the Fundamental Theorem of Line Integrals.

(e) Interpret the result in part (c) in terms of integration by parts.

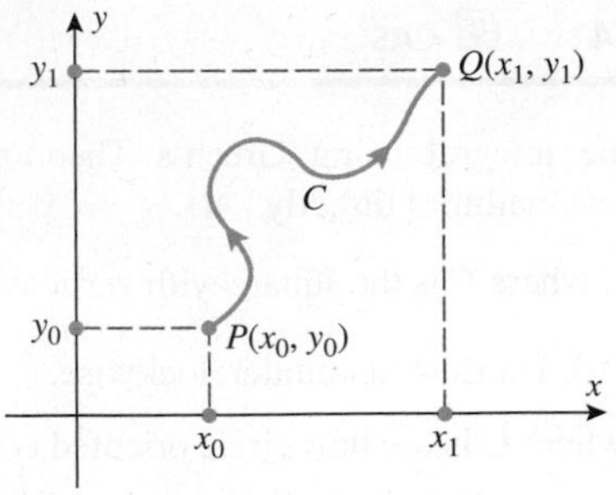


◀ **Figure Ex-28**

**29–30** Use Green's Theorem to find the work done by the force field $\mathbf{F}$ on a particle that moves along the stated path. ■

**29.** $\mathbf{F}(x, y) = xy\mathbf{i} + \left(\frac{1}{2}x^2 + xy\right)\mathbf{j}$; the particle starts at $(5, 0)$, traverses the upper semicircle $x^2 + y^2 = 25$, and returns to its starting point along the $x$-axis.

**30.** $\mathbf{F}(x, y) = \sqrt{y}\,\mathbf{i} + \sqrt{x}\,\mathbf{j}$; the particle moves counterclockwise one time around the closed curve given by the equations $y = 0$, $x = 2$, and $y = x^3/4$.

**31.** Evaluate $\oint_C y\, dx - x\, dy$, where $C$ is the cardioid

$$r = a(1 + \cos\theta) \quad (0 \le \theta \le 2\pi)$$

**32.** Let $R$ be a plane region with area $A$ whose boundary is a piecewise smooth, simple, closed curve $C$. Use Green's Theorem to prove that the centroid $(\bar{x}, \bar{y})$ of $R$ is given by

$$\bar{x} = \frac{1}{2A}\oint_C x^2\, dy, \quad \bar{y} = -\frac{1}{2A}\oint_C y^2\, dx$$

**33–36** Use the result in Exercise 32 to find the centroid of the region. ■

**33.**

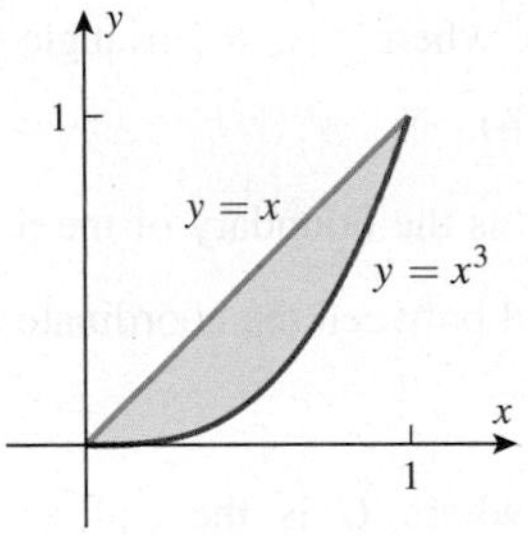


**34.**

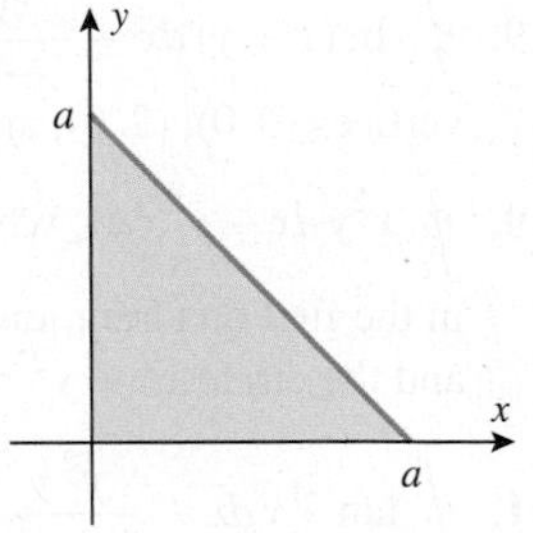


**35.**

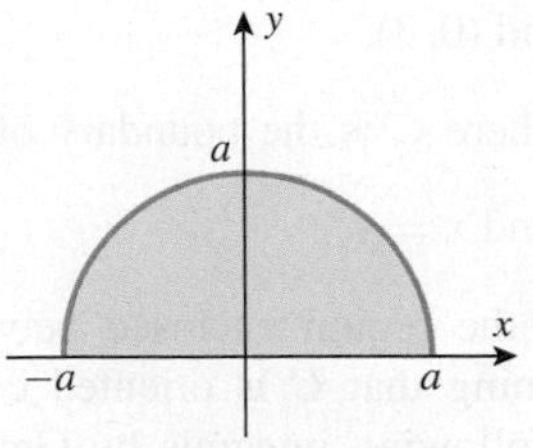


**36.**

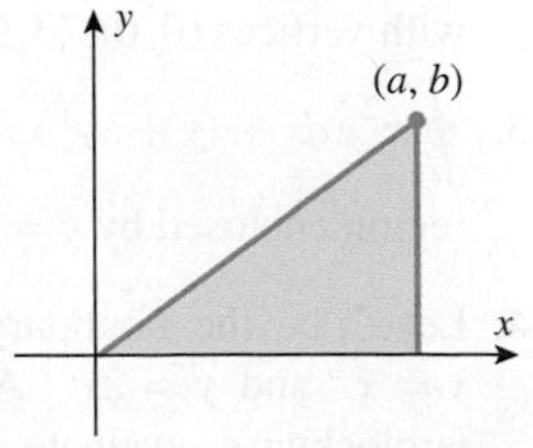


**37.** Find a simple closed curve $C$ with counterclockwise orientation that maximizes the value of

$$\oint_C \tfrac{1}{3}y^3\, dx + \left(x - \tfrac{1}{3}x^3\right) dy$$

and explain your reasoning.

**38.** (a) Let $C$ be the line segment from a point $(a, b)$ to a point $(c, d)$. Show that

$$\int_C -y\,dx + x\,dy = ad - bc$$

(b) Use the result in part (a) to show that the area $A$ of a triangle with successive vertices $(x_1, y_1)$, $(x_2, y_2)$, and $(x_3, y_3)$ going counterclockwise is

$$A = \tfrac{1}{2}[(x_1y_2 - x_2y_1) + (x_2y_3 - x_3y_2) + (x_3y_1 - x_1y_3)]$$

(c) Find a formula for the area of a polygon with successive vertices $(x_1, y_1), (x_2, y_2), \ldots, (x_n, y_n)$ going counterclockwise.

(d) Use the result in part (c) to find the area of a quadrilateral with vertices $(0, 0)$, $(3, 4)$, $(-2, 2)$, $(-1, 0)$.

**39–40** Evaluate the integral $\int_C \mathbf{F} \cdot d\mathbf{r}$, where $C$ is the boundary of the region $R$ and $C$ is oriented so that the region is on the left when the boundary is traversed in the direction of its orientation. ■

**39.** $\mathbf{F}(x, y) = (x^2 + y)\mathbf{i} + (4x - \cos y)\mathbf{j}$; $C$ is the boundary of the region $R$ that is inside the square with vertices $(0, 0)$, $(5, 0)$, $(5, 5)$, $(0, 5)$ but is outside the rectangle with vertices $(1, 1)$, $(3, 1)$, $(3, 2)$, $(1, 2)$.

**40.** $\mathbf{F}(x, y) = (e^{-x} + 3y)\mathbf{i} + x\mathbf{j}$; $C$ is the boundary of the region $R$ inside the circle $x^2 + y^2 = 16$ and outside the circle $x^2 - 2x + y^2 = 3$.

**41. Writing** Discuss the role of the Fundamental Theorem of Calculus in the proof of Green's Theorem.

**42. Writing** Use the Internet or other sources to find information about "planimeters," and then write a paragraph that describes the relationship between these devices and Green's Theorem.

✓ **QUICK CHECK ANSWERS 15.4** 1. 8 2. $\frac{1}{2}$ 3. $2\pi$ 4. $R$ is the region $x^2 + y^2 \le 1$ $(0 \le x, 0 \le y)$ and $f(x, y) = -y^2$, $g(x, y) = x^2$.

## 15.5 SURFACE INTEGRALS

*In this section we will discuss integrals over surfaces in three-dimensional space. Such integrals occur in problems involving fluid and heat flow, electricity, magnetism, mass, and center of gravity.*

### DEFINITION OF A SURFACE INTEGRAL

In this section we will define what it means to integrate a function $f(x, y, z)$ over a smooth parametric surface $\sigma$. To motivate the definition we will consider the problem of finding the mass of a curved lamina whose density function (mass per unit area) is known. Recall that in Section 6.7 we defined a *lamina* to be an idealized flat object that is thin enough to be viewed as a plane region. Analogously, a ***curved lamina*** is an idealized object that is thin enough to be viewed as a surface in 3-space. A curved lamina may look like a bent plate, as in Figure 15.5.1, or it may enclose a region in 3-space, like the shell of an egg. We will model the lamina by a smooth parametric surface $\sigma$. Given any point $(x, y, z)$ on $\sigma$, we let $f(x, y, z)$ denote the corresponding value of the density function. To compute the mass of the lamina, we proceed as follows:

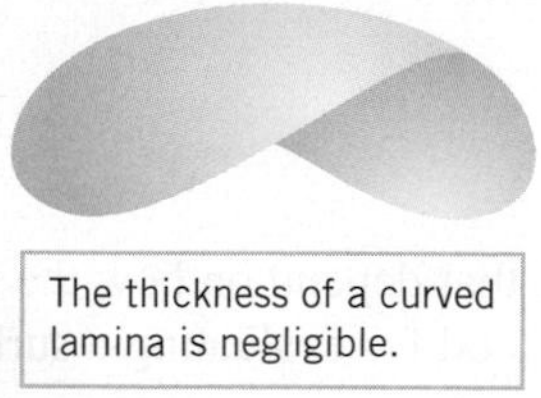

▲ Figure 15.5.1

- As shown in Figure 15.5.2, we divide $\sigma$ into $n$ very small patches $\sigma_1, \sigma_2, \ldots, \sigma_n$ with areas $\Delta S_1, \Delta S_2, \ldots, \Delta S_n$, respectively. Let $(x_k^*, y_k^*, z_k^*)$ be a sample point in the $k$th patch with $\Delta M_k$ the mass of the corresponding section.
- If the dimensions of $\sigma_k$ are very small, the value of $f$ will not vary much along the $k$th section and we can approximate $f$ along this section by the value $f(x_k^*, y_k^*, z_k^*)$. It follows that the mass of the $k$th section can be approximated by

$$\Delta M_k \approx f(x_k^*, y_k^*, z_k^*)\Delta S_k$$

- The mass $M$ of the entire lamina can then be approximated by

$$M = \sum_{k=1}^{n} \Delta M_k \approx \sum_{k=1}^{n} f(x_k^*, y_k^*, z_k^*)\Delta S_k \tag{1}$$

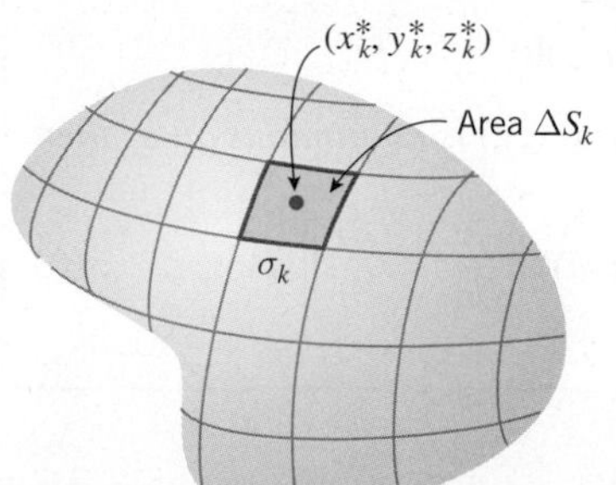

▲ Figure 15.5.2

- We will use the expression $n \to \infty$ to indicate the process of increasing $n$ in such a way that the maximum dimension of each patch approaches 0. It is plausible that the error in (1) will approach 0 as $n \to \infty$ and the exact value of $M$ will be given by

$$M = \lim_{n \to \infty} \sum_{k=1}^{n} f(x_k^*, y_k^*, z_k^*)\Delta S_k \tag{2}$$

The limit in (2) is very similar to the limit used to find the mass of a thin wire [Formula (2) in Section 15.2]. By analogy to Definition 15.2.1, we make the following definition.

**15.5.1 DEFINITION** If $\sigma$ is a smooth parametric surface, then the ***surface integral*** of $f(x, y, z)$ over $\sigma$ is

$$\iint_{\sigma} f(x, y, z)\, dS = \lim_{n \to \infty} \sum_{k=1}^{n} f(x_k^*, y_k^*, z_k^*)\Delta S_k \tag{3}$$

provided this limit exists and does not depend on the way the subdivisions of $\sigma$ are made or how the sample points $(x_k^*, y_k^*, z_k^*)$ are chosen.

It can be shown that the integral of $f$ over $\sigma$ exists if $f$ is continuous on $\sigma$.

We see from (2) and Definition 15.5.1 that if $\sigma$ models a lamina and if $f(x, y, z)$ is the density function of the lamina, then the mass $M$ of the lamina is given by

$$M = \iint_{\sigma} f(x, y, z)\, dS \tag{4}$$

That is, to obtain the mass of a lamina, we integrate the density function over the smooth surface that models the lamina.

Note that if $\sigma$ is a smooth surface of surface area $S$, and $f$ is identically 1, then it immediately follows from Definition 15.5.1 that

$$\iint_{\sigma} dS = \lim_{n \to \infty} \sum_{k=1}^{n} \Delta S_k = \lim_{n \to \infty} S = S \tag{5}$$

## EVALUATING SURFACE INTEGRALS

There are various procedures for evaluating surface integrals that depend on how the surface $\sigma$ is represented. The following theorem provides a method for evaluating a surface integral when $\sigma$ is represented parametrically.

**15.5.2 THEOREM** *Let $\sigma$ be a smooth parametric surface whose vector equation is*

$$\mathbf{r} = x(u, v)\mathbf{i} + y(u, v)\mathbf{j} + z(u, v)\mathbf{k}$$

*where $(u, v)$ varies over a region $R$ in the $uv$-plane. If $f(x, y, z)$ is continuous on $\sigma$, then*

$$\iint_{\sigma} f(x, y, z)\, dS = \iint_{R} f(x(u, v), y(u, v), z(u, v)) \left\| \frac{\partial \mathbf{r}}{\partial u} \times \frac{\partial \mathbf{r}}{\partial v} \right\| dA \tag{6}$$

Explain how to use Formula (6) to confirm Formula (5).

To motivate this result, suppose that the parameter domain $R$ is subdivided as in Figure 14.4.14, and suppose that the point $(x_k^*, y_k^*, z_k^*)$ in (3) corresponds to parameter values of $u_k^*$ and $v_k^*$. If we use Formula (11) of Section 14.4 to approximate $\Delta S_k$, and if we assume that the errors in the approximations approach zero as $n \to +\infty$, then it follows from (3) that

$$\iint_\sigma f(x, y, z)\, dS = \lim_{n \to +\infty} \sum_{k=1}^{n} f(x(u_k^*, v_k^*), y(u_k^*, v_k^*), z(u_k^*, v_k^*)) \left\| \frac{\partial \mathbf{r}}{\partial u} \times \frac{\partial \mathbf{r}}{\partial v} \right\| \Delta A_k$$

which suggests Formula (6).

Although Theorem 15.5.2 is stated for *smooth* parametric surfaces, Formula (6) remains valid even if $\partial \mathbf{r}/\partial u \times \partial \mathbf{r}/\partial v$ is allowed to equal $\mathbf{0}$ on the boundary of $R$.

▶ **Example 1** Evaluate the surface integral $\iint_\sigma x^2\, dS$ over the sphere $x^2 + y^2 + z^2 = 1$.

***Solution.*** As in Example 11 of Section 14.4 (with $a = 1$), the sphere is the graph of the vector-valued function

$$\mathbf{r}(\phi, \theta) = \sin\phi\cos\theta\,\mathbf{i} + \sin\phi\sin\theta\,\mathbf{j} + \cos\phi\,\mathbf{k} \quad (0 \le \phi \le \pi,\ 0 \le \theta \le 2\pi) \tag{7}$$

and

$$\left\| \frac{\partial \mathbf{r}}{\partial \phi} \times \frac{\partial \mathbf{r}}{\partial \theta} \right\| = \sin\phi$$

Explain why the function $\mathbf{r}(\phi, \theta)$ given in (7) fails to be smooth on its domain.

From the $\mathbf{i}$-component of $\mathbf{r}$, the integrand in the surface integral can be expressed in terms of $\phi$ and $\theta$ as $x^2 = \sin^2\phi\cos^2\theta$. Thus, it follows from (6) with $\phi$ and $\theta$ in place of $u$ and $v$ and $R$ as the rectangular region in the $\phi\theta$-plane determined by the inequalities in (7) that

$$\begin{aligned}
\iint_\sigma x^2\, dS &= \iint_R (\sin^2\phi\cos^2\theta) \left\| \frac{\partial \mathbf{r}}{\partial \phi} \times \frac{\partial \mathbf{r}}{\partial \theta} \right\| dA \\
&= \int_0^{2\pi} \int_0^{\pi} \sin^3\phi\cos^2\theta\, d\phi\, d\theta \\
&= \int_0^{2\pi} \left[ \int_0^{\pi} \sin^3\phi\, d\phi \right] \cos^2\theta\, d\theta \\
&= \int_0^{2\pi} \left[ \frac{1}{3}\cos^3\phi - \cos\phi \right]_0^{\pi} \cos^2\theta\, d\theta && \text{Formula (11), Section 7.3} \\
&= \frac{4}{3} \int_0^{2\pi} \cos^2\theta\, d\theta \\
&= \frac{4}{3} \left[ \frac{1}{2}\theta + \frac{1}{4}\sin 2\theta \right]_0^{2\pi} = \frac{4\pi}{3} && \text{Formula (8), Section 7.3}
\end{aligned}$$

◀

## ■ SURFACE INTEGRALS OVER $z = g(x, y)$, $y = g(x, z)$, AND $x = g(y, z)$

In the case where $\sigma$ is a surface of the form $z = g(x, y)$, we can take $x = u$ and $y = v$ as parameters and express the equation of the surface as

$$\mathbf{r} = u\mathbf{i} + v\mathbf{j} + g(u, v)\mathbf{k}$$

in which case we obtain

$$\left\| \frac{\partial \mathbf{r}}{\partial u} \times \frac{\partial \mathbf{r}}{\partial v} \right\| = \sqrt{\left(\frac{\partial z}{\partial x}\right)^2 + \left(\frac{\partial z}{\partial y}\right)^2 + 1}$$

(verify). Thus, it follows from (6) that

$$\iint_{\sigma} f(x, y, z)\, dS = \iint_{R} f(x, y, g(x, y))\sqrt{\left(\frac{\partial z}{\partial x}\right)^2 + \left(\frac{\partial z}{\partial y}\right)^2 + 1}\, dA$$

Note that in this formula the region $R$ lies in the $xy$-plane because the parameters are $x$ and $y$. Geometrically, this region is the projection of $\sigma$ on the $xy$-plane. The following theorem summarizes this result and gives analogous formulas for surface integrals over surfaces of the form $y = g(x, z)$ and $x = g(y, z)$.

**15.5.3 THEOREM**

(a) *Let $\sigma$ be a surface with equation $z = g(x, y)$ and let $R$ be its projection on the xy-plane. If g has continuous first partial derivatives on $R$ and $f(x, y, z)$ is continuous on $\sigma$, then*

$$\iint_{\sigma} f(x, y, z)\, dS = \iint_{R} f(x, y, g(x, y))\sqrt{\left(\frac{\partial z}{\partial x}\right)^2 + \left(\frac{\partial z}{\partial y}\right)^2 + 1}\, dA \tag{8}$$

(b) *Let $\sigma$ be a surface with equation $y = g(x, z)$ and let $R$ be its projection on the xz-plane. If g has continuous first partial derivatives on $R$ and $f(x, y, z)$ is continuous on $\sigma$, then*

$$\iint_{\sigma} f(x, y, z)\, dS = \iint_{R} f(x, g(x, z), z)\sqrt{\left(\frac{\partial y}{\partial x}\right)^2 + \left(\frac{\partial y}{\partial z}\right)^2 + 1}\, dA \tag{9}$$

(c) *Let $\sigma$ be a surface with equation $x = g(y, z)$ and let $R$ be its projection on the yz-plane. If g has continuous first partial derivatives on $R$ and $f(x, y, z)$ is continuous on $\sigma$, then*

$$\iint_{\sigma} f(x, y, z)\, dS = \iint_{R} f(g(y, z), y, z)\sqrt{\left(\frac{\partial x}{\partial y}\right)^2 + \left(\frac{\partial x}{\partial z}\right)^2 + 1}\, dA \tag{10}$$

Formulas (9) and (10) can be recovered from Formula (8). Explain how.

▶ **Example 2** Evaluate the surface integral

$$\iint_{\sigma} xz\, dS$$

where $\sigma$ is the part of the plane $x + y + z = 1$ that lies in the first octant.

***Solution.*** The equation of the plane can be written as

$$z = 1 - x - y$$

Consequently, we can apply Formula (8) with $z = g(x, y) = 1 - x - y$ and $f(x, y, z) = xz$. We have

$$\frac{\partial z}{\partial x} = -1 \quad \text{and} \quad \frac{\partial z}{\partial y} = -1$$

so (8) becomes

$$\iint_{\sigma} xz\, dS = \iint_{R} x(1 - x - y)\sqrt{(-1)^2 + (-1)^2 + 1}\, dA \tag{11}$$

where $R$ is the projection of $\sigma$ on the $xy$-plane (Figure 15.5.3). Rewriting the double integral in (11) as an iterated integral yields

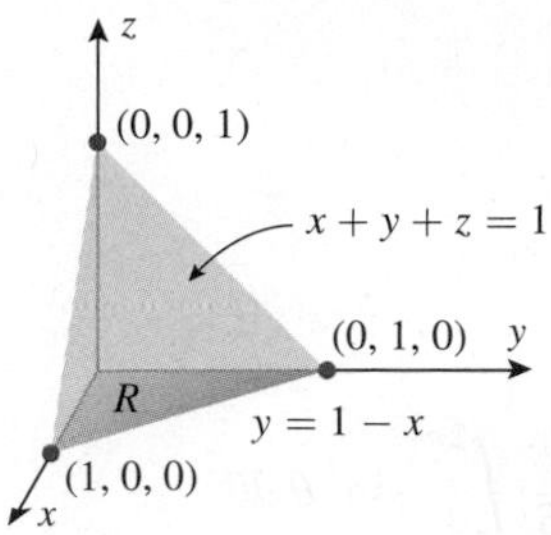

▲ Figure 15.5.3

$$\begin{aligned}\iint_\sigma xz\,dS &= \sqrt{3}\int_0^1\int_0^{1-x}(x-x^2-xy)\,dy\,dx\\ &= \sqrt{3}\int_0^1\left[xy-x^2y-\frac{xy^2}{2}\right]_{y=0}^{1-x}dx\\ &= \sqrt{3}\int_0^1\left(\frac{x}{2}-x^2+\frac{x^3}{2}\right)dx\\ &= \sqrt{3}\left[\frac{x^2}{4}-\frac{x^3}{3}+\frac{x^4}{8}\right]_0^1=\frac{\sqrt{3}}{24}\end{aligned}$$ ◀

▶ **Example 3** Evaluate the surface integral

$$\iint_\sigma y^2z^2\,dS$$

where $\sigma$ is the part of the cone $z=\sqrt{x^2+y^2}$ that lies between the planes $z=1$ and $z=2$ (Figure 15.5.4).

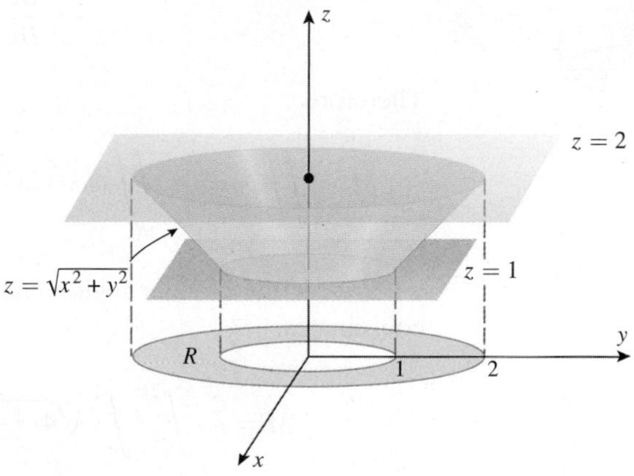

▶ Figure 15.5.4

***Solution.*** We will apply Formula (8) with

$$z=g(x,y)=\sqrt{x^2+y^2}\quad\text{and}\quad f(x,y,z)=y^2z^2$$

Thus,

$$\frac{\partial z}{\partial x}=\frac{x}{\sqrt{x^2+y^2}}\quad\text{and}\quad\frac{\partial z}{\partial y}=\frac{y}{\sqrt{x^2+y^2}}$$

so

$$\sqrt{\left(\frac{\partial z}{\partial x}\right)^2+\left(\frac{\partial z}{\partial y}\right)^2+1}=\sqrt{2}$$

(verify), and (8) yields

$$\iint_\sigma y^2z^2\,dS=\iint_R y^2\left(\sqrt{x^2+y^2}\right)^2\sqrt{2}\,dA=\sqrt{2}\iint_R y^2(x^2+y^2)\,dA$$

where $R$ is the annulus enclosed between $x^2 + y^2 = 1$ and $x^2 + y^2 = 4$ (Figure 15.5.4). Using polar coordinates to evaluate this double integral over the annulus $R$ yields

$$\iint_\sigma y^2 z^2\, dS = \sqrt{2}\int_0^{2\pi}\int_1^2 (r\sin\theta)^2(r^2) r\, dr\, d\theta$$

$$= \sqrt{2}\int_0^{2\pi}\int_1^2 r^5 \sin^2\theta\, dr\, d\theta$$

$$= \sqrt{2}\int_0^{2\pi}\left[\frac{r^6}{6}\sin^2\theta\right]_{r=1}^2 d\theta = \frac{21}{\sqrt{2}}\int_0^{2\pi}\sin^2\theta\, d\theta$$

$$= \frac{21}{\sqrt{2}}\left[\frac{1}{2}\theta - \frac{1}{4}\sin 2\theta\right]_0^{2\pi} = \frac{21\pi}{\sqrt{2}}$$

Formula (7), Section 7.3 ◄

Evaluate the integral in Example 3 with the help of Formula (6) and the parametrization

$\mathbf{r} = \langle r\cos\theta, r\sin\theta, r\rangle$

$(1 \le r \le 2, 0 \le \theta \le 2\pi)$

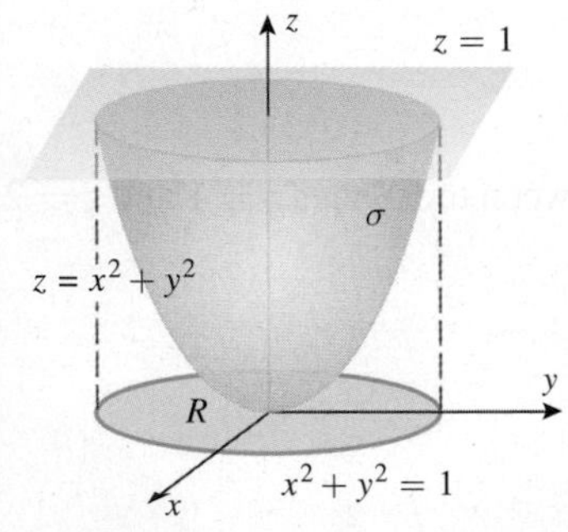


▲ Figure 15.5.5

► **Example 4** Suppose that a curved lamina $\sigma$ with constant density $\delta(x, y, z) = \delta_0$ is the portion of the paraboloid $z = x^2 + y^2$ below the plane $z = 1$ (Figure 15.5.5). Find the mass of the lamina.

***Solution.*** Since $z = g(x, y) = x^2 + y^2$, it follows that

$$\frac{\partial z}{\partial x} = 2x \quad \text{and} \quad \frac{\partial z}{\partial y} = 2y$$

Therefore,

$$M = \iint_\sigma \delta_0\, dS = \iint_R \delta_0\sqrt{(2x)^2 + (2y)^2 + 1}\, dA = \delta_0\iint_R \sqrt{4x^2 + 4y^2 + 1}\, dA \qquad (12)$$

where $R$ is the circular region enclosed by $x^2 + y^2 = 1$. To evaluate (12) we use polar coordinates:

$$M = \delta_0\int_0^{2\pi}\int_0^1 \sqrt{4r^2 + 1}\, r\, dr\, d\theta = \frac{\delta_0}{12}\int_0^{2\pi}\left[(4r^2 + 1)^{3/2}\right]_{r=0}^1 d\theta$$

$$= \frac{\delta_0}{12}\int_0^{2\pi}(5^{3/2} - 1)\, d\theta = \frac{\pi\delta_0}{6}(5\sqrt{5} - 1) \quad ◄$$

## ✓ QUICK CHECK EXERCISES 15.5 *(See page 1021 for answers.)*

1. Consider the surface integral $\iint_\sigma f(x, y, z)\, dS$.
   (a) If $\sigma$ is a parametric surface whose vector equation is
   $$\mathbf{r} = x(u, v)\mathbf{i} + y(u, v)\mathbf{j} + z(u, v)\mathbf{k}$$
   to evaluate the integral replace $dS$ by ______.
   (b) If $\sigma$ is the graph of a function $z = g(x, y)$ with continuous first partial derivatives, to evaluate the integral replace $dS$ by ______.
2. If $\sigma$ is the triangular region with vertices $(1, 0, 0)$, $(0, 1, 0)$, and $(0, 0, 1)$, then
   $$\iint_\sigma (x + y + z)\, dS = \_\_\_\_\_\_$$
3. If $\sigma$ is the sphere of radius 2 centered at the origin, then
   $$\iint_\sigma (x^2 + y^2 + z^2)\, dS = \_\_\_\_\_\_$$
4. If $f(x, y, z)$ is the mass density function of a curved lamina $\sigma$, then the mass of $\sigma$ is given by the integral ______.

## EXERCISE SET 15.5 C CAS

**1–8** Evaluate the surface integral

$$\iint_{\sigma} f(x, y, z)\, dS$$

1. $f(x, y, z) = z^2$; $\sigma$ is the portion of the cone $z = \sqrt{x^2 + y^2}$ between the planes $z = 1$ and $z = 2$.
2. $f(x, y, z) = xy$; $\sigma$ is the portion of the plane $x + y + z = 1$ lying in the first octant.
3. $f(x, y, z) = x^2y$; $\sigma$ is the portion of the cylinder $x^2 + z^2 = 1$ between the planes $y = 0$, $y = 1$, and above the $xy$-plane.
4. $f(x, y, z) = (x^2 + y^2)z$; $\sigma$ is the portion of the sphere $x^2 + y^2 + z^2 = 4$ above the plane $z = 1$.
5. $f(x, y, z) = x - y - z$; $\sigma$ is the portion of the plane $x + y = 1$ in the first octant between $z = 0$ and $z = 1$.
6. $f(x, y, z) = x + y$; $\sigma$ is the portion of the plane $z = 6 - 2x - 3y$ in the first octant.
7. $f(x, y, z) = x + y + z$; $\sigma$ is the surface of the cube defined by the inequalities $0 \le x \le 1, 0 \le y \le 1, 0 \le z \le 1$. [*Hint:* Integrate over each face separately.]
8. $f(x, y, z) = x^2 + y^2$; $\sigma$ is the surface of the sphere $x^2 + y^2 + z^2 = a^2$.

**9–12 True–False** Determine whether the statement is true or false. Explain your answer.

9. If $f(x, y, z) \ge 0$ on $\sigma$, then
$$\iint_{\sigma} f(x, y, z)\, dS \ge 0$$
10. If $\sigma$ has surface area $S$, and if
$$\iint_{\sigma} f(x, y, z)\, dS = S$$
then $f(x, y, z)$ is equal to 1 identically on $\sigma$.
11. If $\sigma$ models a curved lamina, and if $f(x, y, z)$ is the density function of the lamina, then
$$\iint_{\sigma} f(x, y, z)\, dS$$
represents the total density of the lamina.
12. If $\sigma$ is the portion of a plane $z = c$ over a region $R$ in the $xy$-plane, then
$$\iint_{\sigma} f(x, y, z)\, dS = \iint_{R} f(x, y, c)\, dA$$
for every continuous function $f$ on $\sigma$.

**13–14** Sometimes evaluating a surface integral results in an improper integral. When this happens, one can either attempt to determine the value of the integral using an appropriate limit or one can try another method. These exercises explore both approaches.

13. Consider the integral of $f(x, y, z) = z + 1$ over the upper hemisphere $\sigma$: $z = \sqrt{1 - x^2 - y^2}$ $(0 \le x^2 + y^2 \le 1)$.
    (a) Explain why evaluating this surface integral using (8) results in an improper integral.
    (b) Use (8) to evaluate the integral of $f$ over the surface $\sigma_r$ : $z = \sqrt{1 - x^2 - y^2}$ $(0 \le x^2 + y^2 \le r^2 < 1)$. Take the limit of this result as $r \to 1^-$ to determine the integral of $f$ over $\sigma$.
    (c) Parametrize $\sigma$ using spherical coordinates and evaluate the integral of $f$ over $\sigma$ using (6). Verify that your answer agrees with the result in part (b).
14. Consider the integral of $f(x, y, z) = \sqrt{x^2 + y^2 + z^2}$ over the cone $\sigma : z = \sqrt{x^2 + y^2}$ $(0 \le z \le 1)$.
    (a) Explain why evaluating this surface integral using (8) results in an improper integral.
    (b) Use (8) to evaluate the integral of $f$ over the surface $\sigma_r : z = \sqrt{x^2 + y^2}$ $(0 < r^2 \le x^2 + y^2 \le 1)$. Take the limit of this result as $r \to 0^+$ to determine the integral of $f$ over $\sigma$.
    (c) Parametrize $\sigma$ using spherical coordinates and evaluate the integral of $f$ over $\sigma$ using (6). Verify that your answer agrees with the result in part (b).

### FOCUS ON CONCEPTS

**15–18** In some cases it is possible to use Definition 15.5.1 along with symmetry considerations to evaluate a surface integral without reference to a parametrization of the surface. In these exercises, $\sigma$ denotes the unit sphere centered at the origin.

15. (a) Explain why it is possible to subdivide $\sigma$ into patches and choose corresponding sample points $(x_k^*, y_k^*, z_k^*)$ such that (i) the dimensions of each patch are as small as desired and (ii) for each sample point $(x_k^*, y_k^*, z_k^*)$, there exists a sample point $(x_j^*, y_j^*, z_j^*)$ with
$$x_k = -x_j, \quad y_k = y_j, \quad z_k = z_j$$
and with $\Delta S_k = \Delta S_j$.
    (b) Use Definition 15.5.1, the result in part (a), and the fact that surface integrals exist for continuous functions to prove that $\iint_{\sigma} x^n\, dS = 0$ for $n$ an odd positive integer.
16. Use the argument in Exercise 15 to prove that if $f(x)$ is a continuous odd function of $x$, and if $g(y, z)$ is a continuous function, then
$$\iint_{\sigma} f(x)g(y, z)\, dS = 0$$
17. (a) Explain why
$$\iint_{\sigma} x^2\, dS = \iint_{\sigma} y^2\, dS = \iint_{\sigma} z^2\, dS$$
    (b) Conclude from part (a) that
$$\iint_{\sigma} x^2\, dS = \frac{1}{3}\left[\iint_{\sigma} x^2\, dS + \iint_{\sigma} y^2\, dS + \iint_{\sigma} y^2\, dS\right]$$

*(cont.)*

(c) Use part (b) to evaluate

$$\iint_\sigma x^2\, dS$$

without performing an integration.

**18.** Use the results of Exercises 16 and 17 to evaluate

$$\iint_\sigma (x-y)^2\, dS$$

without performing an integration.

**19–20** Set up, but do not evaluate, an iterated integral equal to the given surface integral by projecting $\sigma$ on (a) the $xy$-plane, (b) the $yz$-plane, and (c) the $xz$-plane. ■

**19.** $\iint_\sigma xyz\, dS$, where $\sigma$ is the portion of the plane $2x+3y+4z=12$ in the first octant.

**20.** $\iint_\sigma xz\, dS$, where $\sigma$ is the portion of the sphere $x^2+y^2+z^2=a^2$ in the first octant.

C **21.** Use a CAS to confirm that the three integrals you obtained in Exercise 19 are equal, and find the exact value of the surface integral.

C **22.** Try to confirm with a CAS that the three integrals you obtained in Exercise 20 are equal. If you did not succeed, what was the difficulty?

**23–24** Set up, but do not evaluate, two different iterated integrals equal to the given integral. ■

**23.** $\iint_\sigma xyz\, dS$, where $\sigma$ is the portion of the surface $y^2=x$ between the planes $z=0$, $z=4$, $y=1$, and $y=2$.

**24.** $\iint_\sigma x^2 y\, dS$, where $\sigma$ is the portion of the cylinder $y^2+z^2=a^2$ in the first octant between the planes $x=0$, $x=9$, $z=y$, and $z=2y$.

C **25.** Use a CAS to confirm that the two integrals you obtained in Exercise 23 are equal, and find the exact value of the surface integral.

C **26.** Use a CAS to find the value of the surface integral

$$\iint_\sigma x^2 yz\, dS$$

where the surface $\sigma$ is the portion of the elliptic paraboloid $z=5-3x^2-2y^2$ that lies above the $xy$-plane.

**27–28** Find the mass of the lamina with constant density $\delta_0$. ■

**27.** The lamina that is the portion of the circular cylinder $x^2+z^2=4$ that lies directly above the rectangle $R=\{(x,y): 0\le x\le 1, 0\le y\le 4\}$ in the $xy$-plane.

**28.** The lamina that is the portion of the paraboloid $2z=x^2+y^2$ inside the cylinder $x^2+y^2=8$.

**29.** Find the mass of the lamina that is the portion of the surface $y^2=4-z$ between the planes $x=0$, $x=3$, $y=0$, and $y=3$ if the density is $\delta(x,y,z)=y$.

**30.** Find the mass of the lamina that is the portion of the cone $z=\sqrt{x^2+y^2}$ between $z=1$ and $z=4$ if the density is $\delta(x,y,z)=x^2z$.

**31.** If a curved lamina has constant density $\delta_0$, what relationship must exist between its mass and surface area? Explain your reasoning.

**32.** Show that if the density of the lamina $x^2+y^2+z^2=a^2$ at each point is equal to the distance between that point and the $xy$-plane, then the mass of the lamina is $2\pi a^3$.

**33–34** The centroid of a surface $\sigma$ is defined by

$$\bar{x}=\frac{\iint_\sigma x\, dS}{\text{area of } \sigma},\quad \bar{y}=\frac{\iint_\sigma y\, dS}{\text{area of } \sigma},\quad \bar{z}=\frac{\iint_\sigma z\, dS}{\text{area of } \sigma}$$

Find the centroid of the surface. ■

**33.** The portion of the paraboloid $z=\frac{1}{2}(x^2+y^2)$ below the plane $z=4$.

**34.** The portion of the sphere $x^2+y^2+z^2=4$ above the plane $z=1$.

**35–38** Evaluate the integral $\iint_\sigma f(x,y,z)\, dS$ over the surface $\sigma$ represented by the vector-valued function $\mathbf{r}(u,v)$. ■

**35.** $f(x,y,z)=xyz$; $\mathbf{r}(u,v)=u\cos v\mathbf{i}+u\sin v\mathbf{j}+3u\mathbf{k}$ $(1\le u\le 2, 0\le v\le \pi/2)$

**36.** $f(x,y,z)=\dfrac{x^2+z^2}{y}$; $\mathbf{r}(u,v)=2\cos v\mathbf{i}+u\mathbf{j}+2\sin v\mathbf{k}$ $(1\le u\le 3, 0\le v\le 2\pi)$

**37.** $f(x,y,z)=\dfrac{1}{\sqrt{1+4x^2+4y^2}}$; $\mathbf{r}(u,v)=u\cos v\mathbf{i}+u\sin v\mathbf{j}+u^2\mathbf{k}$ $(0\le u\le \sin v, 0\le v\le \pi)$

**38.** $f(x,y,z)=e^{-z}$; $\mathbf{r}(u,v)=2\sin u\cos v\mathbf{i}+2\sin u\sin v\mathbf{j}+2\cos u\mathbf{k}$ $(0\le u\le \pi/2, 0\le v\le 2\pi)$

C **39.** Use a CAS to approximate the mass of the curved lamina $z=e^{-x^2-y^2}$ that lies above the region in the $xy$-plane enclosed by $x^2+y^2=9$ given that the density function is $\delta(x,y,z)=\sqrt{x^2+y^2}$.

C **40.** The surface $\sigma$ shown in the accompanying figure on the next page, called a ***Möbius strip***, is represented by the parametric equations

$$x=(5+u\cos(v/2))\cos v$$
$$y=(5+u\cos(v/2))\sin v$$
$$z=u\sin(v/2)$$

where $-1\le u\le 1$ and $0\le v\le 2\pi$.

(a) Use a CAS to generate a reasonable facsimile of this surface.

(b) Use a CAS to approximate the location of the centroid of $\sigma$ (see the definition preceding Exercise 33).

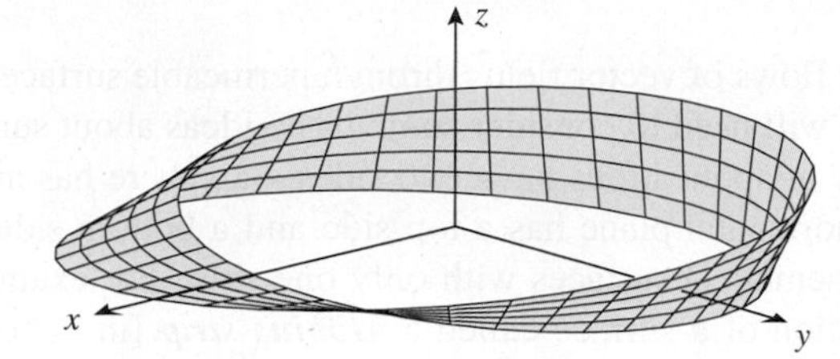


▲ **Figure Ex-40**

41. **Writing** Discuss the similarities and differences between the definition of a surface integral and the definition of a double integral.

42. **Writing** Suppose that a surface $\sigma$ in 3-space and a function $f(x, y, z)$ are described geometrically. For example, $\sigma$ might be the sphere of radius 1 centered at the origin and $f(x, y, z)$ might be the distance from the point $(x, y, z)$ to the $z$-axis. How would you explain to a classmate a procedure for evaluating the surface integral of $f$ over $\sigma$?

✓ QUICK CHECK ANSWERS 15.5 1. (a) $\left\|\frac{\partial \mathbf{r}}{\partial u} \times \frac{\partial \mathbf{r}}{\partial v}\right\| dA$ (b) $\sqrt{\left(\frac{\partial z}{\partial x}\right)^2 + \left(\frac{\partial z}{\partial y}\right)^2 + 1}\, dA$ 2. $\frac{\sqrt{3}}{2}$ 3. $64\pi$ 4. $\iint\limits_{\sigma} f(x, y, z)\, dS$

## 15.6 APPLICATIONS OF SURFACE INTEGRALS; FLUX

*In this section we will discuss applications of surface integrals to vector fields associated with fluid flow and electrostatic forces. However, the ideas that we will develop will be general in nature and applicable to other kinds of vector fields as well.*

### FLOW FIELDS

We will be concerned in this section with vector fields in 3-space that involve some type of "flow"—the flow of a fluid or the flow of charged particles in an electrostatic field, for example. In the case of fluid flow, the vector field $\mathbf{F}(x, y, z)$ represents the velocity of a fluid particle at the point $(x, y, z)$, and the fluid particles flow along "streamlines" that are tangential to the velocity vectors (Figure 15.6.1*a*). In the case of an electrostatic field, $\mathbf{F}(x, y, z)$ is the force that the field exerts on a small unit of positive charge at the point $(x, y, z)$, and such charges have acceleration in the directions of "electric lines" that are tangential to the force vectors (Figures 15.6.1*b* and 15.6.1*c*).

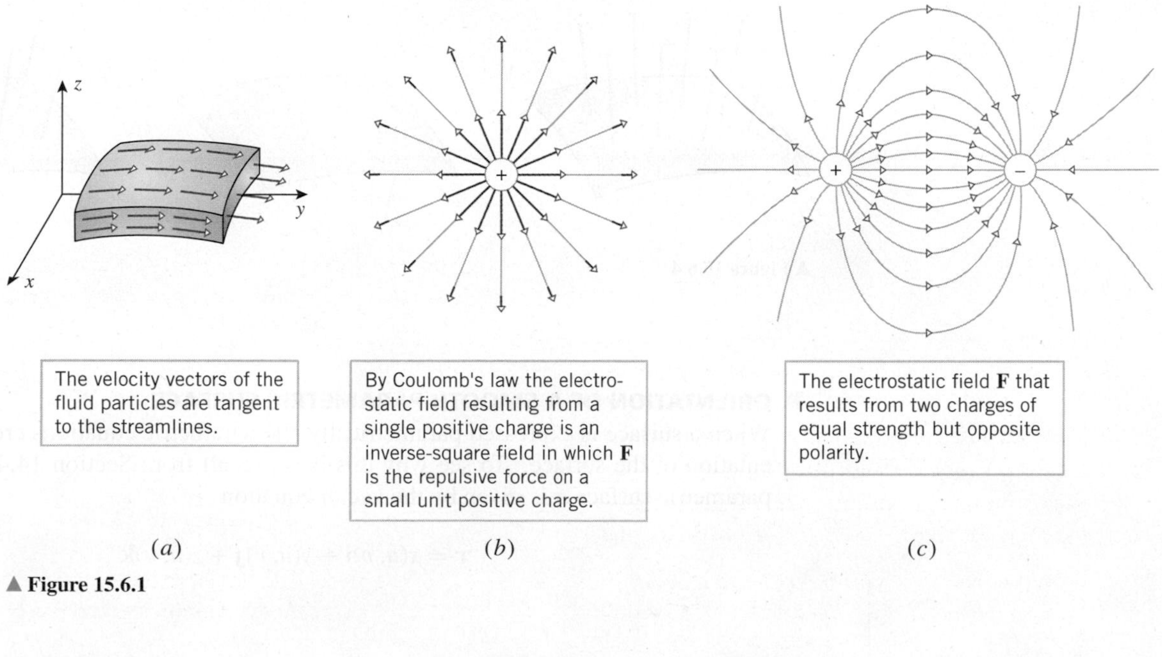


▲ **Figure 15.6.1**

## ORIENTED SURFACES

Our main goal in this section is to study flows of vector fields through permeable surfaces placed in the field. For this purpose we will need to consider some basic ideas about surfaces. Most surfaces that we encounter in applications have two sides—a sphere has an inside and an outside, and an infinite horizontal plane has a top side and a bottom side, for example. However, there exist mathematical surfaces with only one side. For example, Figure 15.6.2$a$ shows the construction of a surface called a ***Möbius strip*** [in honor of the German mathematician August Möbius (1790–1868)]. The Möbius strip has only one side in the sense that a bug can traverse the *entire* surface without crossing an edge (Figure 15.6.2$b$). In contrast, a sphere is two-sided in the sense that a bug walking on the sphere can traverse the inside surface or the outside surface but cannot traverse both without somehow passing through the sphere. A two-sided surface is said to be ***orientable***, and a one-sided surface is said to be ***nonorientable***. In the rest of this text we will only be concerned with orientable surfaces.

If a bug starts at $P$ with its back facing you and makes one circuit around the strip, then its back will face away from you when it returns to $P$.

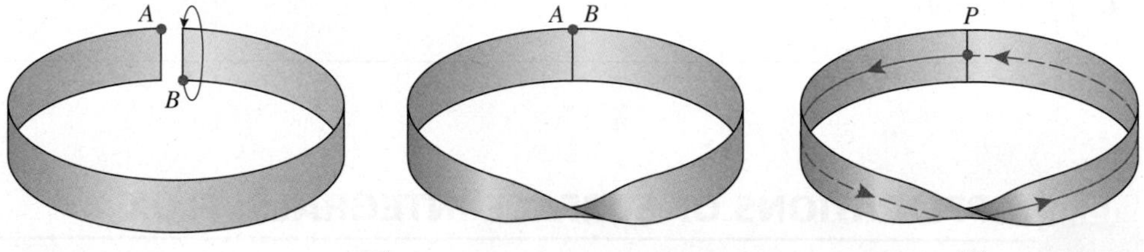


▲ Figure 15.6.2

In applications, it is important to have some way of distinguishing between the two sides of an orientable surface. For this purpose let us suppose that $\sigma$ is an orientable surface that has a unit normal vector $\mathbf{n}$ at each point. As illustrated in Figure 15.6.3, the vectors $\mathbf{n}$ and $-\mathbf{n}$ point to opposite sides of the surface and hence serve to distinguish between the two sides. It can be proved that if $\sigma$ is a smooth orientable surface, then it is always possible to choose the direction of $\mathbf{n}$ at each point so that $\mathbf{n} = \mathbf{n}(x, y, z)$ varies continuously over the surface. These unit vectors are then said to form an ***orientation*** of the surface. It can also be proved that a smooth orientable surface has only two possible orientations. For example, the surface in Figure 15.6.4 is oriented up by the purple vectors and down by the green vectors. However, we cannot create a third orientation by mixing the two since this produces points on the surface at which there is an abrupt change in direction (across the black curve in the figure, for example).

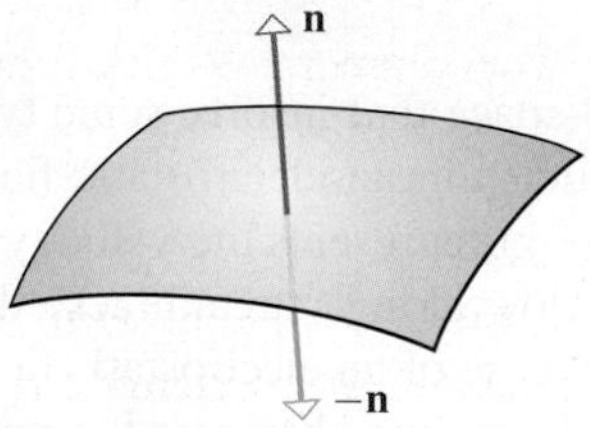


▲ Figure 15.6.3

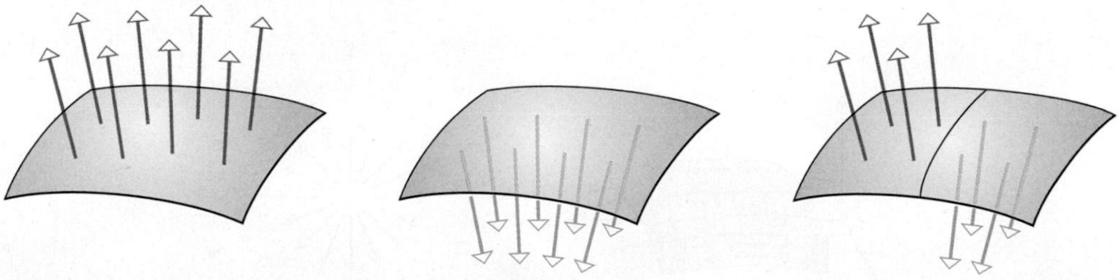

▲ Figure 15.6.4

## ORIENTATION OF A SMOOTH PARAMETRIC SURFACE

When a surface is expressed parametrically, the parametric equations create a natural orientation of the surface. To see why this is so, recall from Section 14.4 that if a smooth parametric surface $\sigma$ is given by the vector equation

$$\mathbf{r} = x(u, v)\mathbf{i} + y(u, v)\mathbf{j} + z(u, v)\mathbf{k}$$

then the unit normal

$$\mathbf{n} = \mathbf{n}(u, v) = \frac{\dfrac{\partial \mathbf{r}}{\partial u} \times \dfrac{\partial \mathbf{r}}{\partial v}}{\left\| \dfrac{\partial \mathbf{r}}{\partial u} \times \dfrac{\partial \mathbf{r}}{\partial v} \right\|} \tag{1}$$

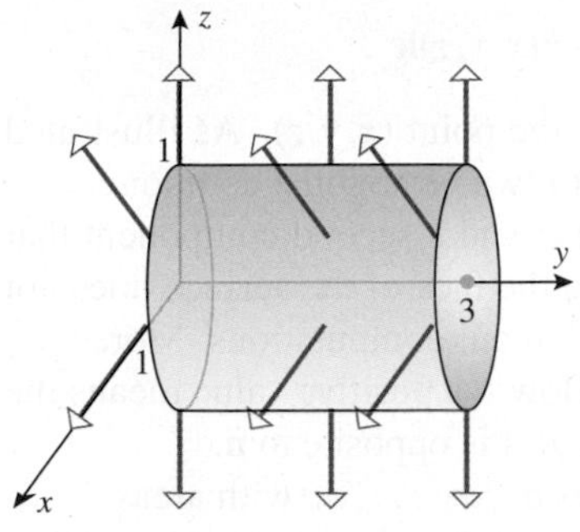

▲ Figure 15.6.5

See if you can find a parametrization of the cylinder in which the positive direction is inward.

is a continuous vector-valued function of $u$ and $v$. Thus, Formula (1) defines an orientation of the surface; we call this the ***positive orientation*** of the parametric surface and we say that $\mathbf{n}$ points in the ***positive direction*** from the surface. The orientation determined by $-\mathbf{n}$ is called the ***negative orientation*** of the surface and we say that $-\mathbf{n}$ points in the ***negative direction*** from the surface. For example, consider the cylinder that is represented parametrically by the vector equation

$$\mathbf{r}(u, v) = \cos u\mathbf{i} + v\mathbf{j} - \sin u\mathbf{k} \qquad (0 \le u \le 2\pi,\ 0 \le v \le 3)$$

Then

$$\frac{\partial \mathbf{r}}{\partial u} \times \frac{\partial \mathbf{r}}{\partial v} = \cos u\mathbf{i} - \sin u\mathbf{k}$$

has unit length, so that Formula (1) becomes

$$\mathbf{n} = \frac{\partial \mathbf{r}}{\partial u} \times \frac{\partial \mathbf{r}}{\partial v} = \cos u\mathbf{i} - \sin u\mathbf{k}$$

Since $\mathbf{n}$ has the same **i**- and **k**-components as $\mathbf{r}$, the positive orientation of the cylinder is *outward* and the negative orientation is *inward* (Figure 15.6.5).

## FLUX

In physics, the term *fluid* is used to describe both liquids and gases. Liquids are usually regarded to be ***incompressible***, meaning that the liquid has a uniform density (mass per unit volume) that cannot be altered by compressive forces. Gases are regarded to be ***compressible***, meaning that the density may vary from point to point and can be altered by compressive forces. In this text we will be concerned primarily with incompressible fluids. Moreover, we will assume that the velocity of the fluid at a fixed point does not vary with time. Fluid flows with this property are said to be in a ***steady state***.

Our next goal in this section is to define a fundamental concept of physics known as *flux* (from the Latin word *fluxus*, meaning "flowing"). This concept is applicable to any vector field, but we will motivate it in the context of steady-state incompressible fluid flow. Imagine that fluid is flowing freely through a permeable surface, from one side of the surface to the other. In this context, you can think of flux as:

*The volume of fluid that passes through the surface in one unit of time.*

This idea is illustrated in Figure 15.6.6, which suggests that the volume of fluid that flows through a portion of the surface depends on three factors:

- The speed of the fluid; the greater the speed, the greater the volume (Figure 15.6.6*a*).
- How the surface is oriented relative to the flow; the more nearly orthogonal the flow is to the surface, the greater the volume (Figure 15.6.6*b*).
- The area of the portion of the surface; the greater the area, the greater the volume (Figure 15.6.6*c*).

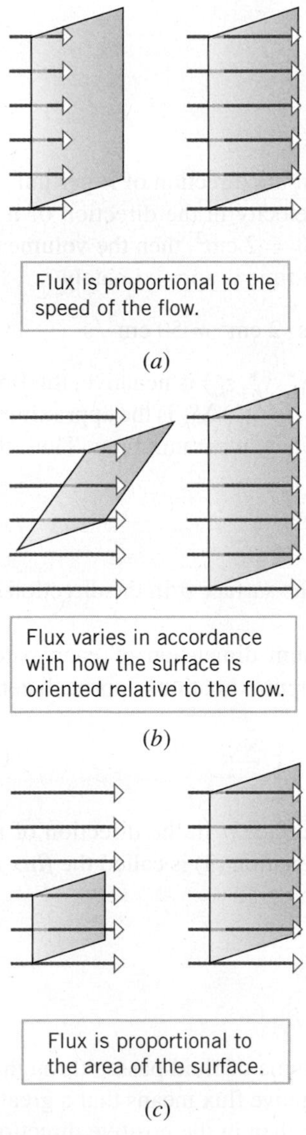

▲ Figure 15.6.6

These ideas lead us to the following problem.

**15.6.1 PROBLEM** Suppose that an oriented surface $\sigma$ is immersed in an incompressible, steady-state fluid flow and that the surface is permeable so that the fluid can flow through it freely in either direction. Find the net volume of fluid $\Phi$ that passes through the surface per unit of time, where the net volume is interpreted to mean the volume that passes through the surface in the positive direction minus the volume that passes through the surface in the negative direction.

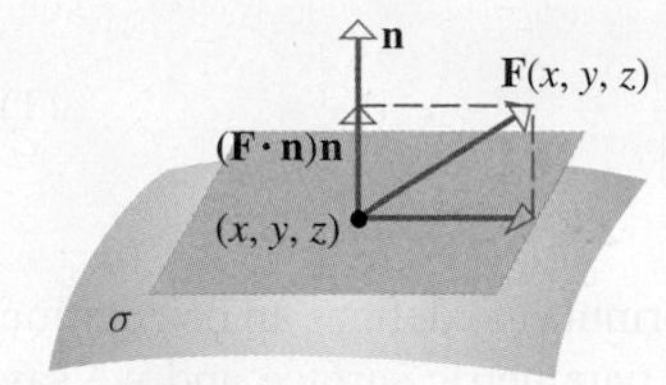


▲ Figure 15.6.7

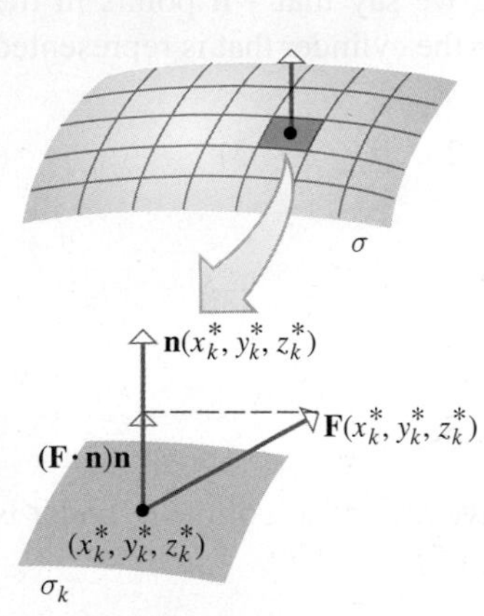


▲ Figure 15.6.8

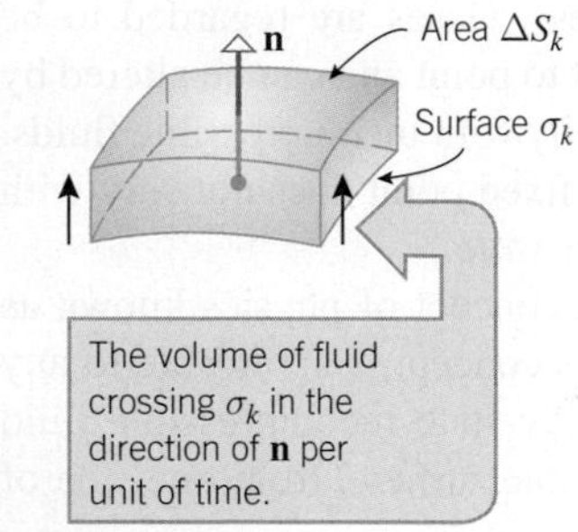


▲ Figure 15.6.9

To solve this problem, suppose that the velocity of the fluid at a point $(x, y, z)$ on the surface $\sigma$ is given by

$$\mathbf{F}(x, y, z) = f(x, y, z)\mathbf{i} + g(x, y, z)\mathbf{j} + h(x, y, z)\mathbf{k}$$

Let $\mathbf{n}$ be the unit normal toward the positive side of $\sigma$ at the point $(x, y, z)$. As illustrated in Figure 15.6.7, the velocity vector $\mathbf{F}$ can be resolved into two orthogonal components—a component $(\mathbf{F}\cdot\mathbf{n})\mathbf{n}$ that is perpendicular to the surface $\sigma$ and a second component that is along the "face" of $\sigma$. The component of velocity along the face of the surface does not contribute to the flow through $\sigma$ and hence can be ignored in our computations. Moreover, observe that the sign of $\mathbf{F}\cdot\mathbf{n}$ determines the direction of flow—a positive value means the flow is in the direction of $\mathbf{n}$ and a negative value means that it is opposite to $\mathbf{n}$.

To solve Problem 15.6.1, we subdivide $\sigma$ into $n$ patches $\sigma_1, \sigma_2, \ldots, \sigma_n$ with areas

$$\Delta S_1, \Delta S_2, \ldots, \Delta S_n$$

If the patches are small and the flow is not too erratic, it is reasonable to assume that the velocity does not vary much on each patch. Thus, if $(x_k^*, y_k^*, z_k^*)$ is any point in the $k$th patch, we can assume that $\mathbf{F}(x, y, z)$ is constant and equal to $\mathbf{F}(x_k^*, y_k^*, z_k^*)$ throughout the patch and that the component of velocity across the surface $\sigma_k$ is

$$\mathbf{F}(x_k^*, y_k^*, z_k^*)\cdot\mathbf{n}(x_k^*, y_k^*, z_k^*) \tag{2}$$

(Figure 15.6.8). Thus, we can interpret

$$\mathbf{F}(x_k^*, y_k^*, z_k^*)\cdot\mathbf{n}(x_k^*, y_k^*, z_k^*)\Delta S_k$$

as the approximate volume of fluid crossing the patch $\sigma_k$ in the direction of $\mathbf{n}$ per unit of time (Figure 15.6.9). For example, if the component of velocity in the direction of $\mathbf{n}$ is $\mathbf{F}(x_k^*, y_k^*, z_k^*)\cdot\mathbf{n} = 25$ cm/s, and the area of the patch is $\Delta S_k = 2$ cm$^2$, then the volume of fluid $\Delta V_k$ crossing the patch in the direction of $\mathbf{n}$ per unit of time is approximately

$$\Delta V_k \approx \mathbf{F}(x_k^*, y_k^*, z_k^*)\cdot\mathbf{n}(x_k^*, y_k^*, z_k^*)\Delta S_k = 25\text{ cm/s}\cdot 2\text{ cm}^2 = 50\text{ cm}^3/\text{s}$$

In the case where the velocity component $\mathbf{F}(x_k^*, y_k^*, z_k^*)\cdot\mathbf{n}(x_k^*, y_k^*, z_k^*)$ is negative, the flow is in the direction opposite to $\mathbf{n}$, so that $-\mathbf{F}(x_k^*, y_k^*, z_k^*)\cdot\mathbf{n}(x_k^*, y_k^*, z_k^*)\Delta S_k$ is the approximate volume of fluid crossing the patch $\sigma_k$ in the direction opposite to $\mathbf{n}$ per unit time. Thus, the sum

$$\sum_{k=1}^{n} \mathbf{F}(x_k^*, y_k^*, z_k^*)\cdot\mathbf{n}(x_k^*, y_k^*, z_k^*)\Delta S_k$$

measures the approximate net volume of fluid that crosses the surface $\sigma$ in the direction of its orientation $\mathbf{n}$ per unit of time.

If we now increase $n$ in such a way that the maximum dimension of each patch approaches zero, then it is plausible that the errors in the approximations approach zero, and the limit

$$\Phi = \lim_{n\to+\infty} \sum_{k=1}^{n} \mathbf{F}(x_k^*, y_k^*, z_k^*)\cdot\mathbf{n}(x_k^*, y_k^*, z_k^*)\Delta S_k \tag{3}$$

represents the exact net volume of fluid that crosses the surface $\sigma$ in the direction of its orientation $\mathbf{n}$ per unit of time. The quantity $\Phi$ defined by Equation (3) is called the ***flux of F across σ***. The flux can also be expressed as the surface integral

$$\Phi = \iint_{\sigma} \mathbf{F}(x, y, z)\cdot\mathbf{n}(x, y, z)\, dS \tag{4}$$

If the fluid has mass density $\delta$, then $\Phi\delta$ (volume/time × density) represents the net mass of fluid that passes through $\sigma$ per unit of time.

A positive flux means that in one unit of time a greater volume of fluid passes through $\sigma$ in the positive direction than in the negative direction, a negative flux means that a greater volume passes through the surface in the negative direction than in the positive direction, and a zero flux means that the same volume passes through the surface in each direction. Integrals of form (4) arise in other contexts as well and are called ***flux integrals***.

## EVALUATING FLUX INTEGRALS

An effective formula for evaluating flux integrals can be obtained by applying Theorem 15.5.2 and using Formula (1) for **n**. This yields

$$\iint_{\sigma} \mathbf{F}\cdot\mathbf{n}\,dS = \iint_{R} \mathbf{F}\cdot\mathbf{n}\left\|\frac{\partial\mathbf{r}}{\partial u}\times\frac{\partial\mathbf{r}}{\partial v}\right\| dA$$

$$= \iint_{R} \mathbf{F}\cdot\frac{\dfrac{\partial\mathbf{r}}{\partial u}\times\dfrac{\partial\mathbf{r}}{\partial v}}{\left\|\dfrac{\partial\mathbf{r}}{\partial u}\times\dfrac{\partial\mathbf{r}}{\partial v}\right\|}\left\|\frac{\partial\mathbf{r}}{\partial u}\times\frac{\partial\mathbf{r}}{\partial v}\right\| dA$$

$$= \iint_{R} \mathbf{F}\cdot\left(\frac{\partial\mathbf{r}}{\partial u}\times\frac{\partial\mathbf{r}}{\partial v}\right) dA$$

In summary, we have the following result.

**15.6.2 THEOREM** *Let $\sigma$ be a smooth parametric surface represented by the vector equation $\mathbf{r}=\mathbf{r}(u,v)$ in which $(u,v)$ varies over a region $R$ in the $uv$-plane. If the component functions of the vector field $\mathbf{F}$ are continuous on $\sigma$, and if $\mathbf{n}$ determines the positive orientation of $\sigma$, then*

$$\Phi = \iint_{\sigma} \mathbf{F}\cdot\mathbf{n}\,dS = \iint_{R} \mathbf{F}\cdot\left(\frac{\partial\mathbf{r}}{\partial u}\times\frac{\partial\mathbf{r}}{\partial v}\right) dA \tag{5}$$

*where it is understood that the integrand on the right side of the equation is expressed in terms of $u$ and $v$.*

Although Theorem 15.6.2 was derived for smooth parametric surfaces, Formula (5) is valid more generally. For example, as long as $\sigma$ has a continuous normal vector field **n** and the component functions of $\mathbf{r}(u,v)$ have continuous first partial derivatives, Formula (5) can be applied whenever $\partial\mathbf{r}/\partial u\times\partial\mathbf{r}/\partial v$ is a positive multiple of **n** in the *interior* of $R$. (That is, $\partial\mathbf{r}/\partial u\times\partial\mathbf{r}/\partial v$ is allowed to equal **0** on the boundary of $R$.)

▶ **Example 1** Find the flux of the vector field $\mathbf{F}(x,y,z)=z\mathbf{k}$ across the outward-oriented sphere $x^2+y^2+z^2=a^2$.

***Solution.*** The sphere with outward positive orientation can be represented by the vector-valued function

$$\mathbf{r}(\phi,\theta)=a\sin\phi\cos\theta\,\mathbf{i}+a\sin\phi\sin\theta\,\mathbf{j}+a\cos\phi\,\mathbf{k} \qquad (0\le\phi\le\pi,\ 0\le\theta\le 2\pi)$$

From this formula we obtain (see Example 11 of Section 14.4 for the computations)

$$\frac{\partial\mathbf{r}}{\partial\phi}\times\frac{\partial\mathbf{r}}{\partial\theta}=a^2\sin^2\phi\cos\theta\,\mathbf{i}+a^2\sin^2\phi\sin\theta\,\mathbf{j}+a^2\sin\phi\cos\phi\,\mathbf{k}$$

Moreover, for points on the sphere we have $\mathbf{F}=z\mathbf{k}=a\cos\phi\,\mathbf{k}$; hence,

$$\mathbf{F}\cdot\left(\frac{\partial\mathbf{r}}{\partial\phi}\times\frac{\partial\mathbf{r}}{\partial\theta}\right)=a^3\sin\phi\cos^2\phi$$

> Solve Example 1 using symmetry: First argue that the vector fields $x\mathbf{i}$, $y\mathbf{j}$, and $z\mathbf{k}$ will have the same flux across the sphere. Then define
>
> $$\mathbf{H} = x\mathbf{i} + y\mathbf{j} + z\mathbf{k}$$
>
> and explain why
>
> $$\mathbf{H} \cdot \mathbf{n} = a$$
>
> Use this to compute $\Phi$.

Thus, it follows from (5) with the parameters $u$ and $v$ replaced by $\phi$ and $\theta$ that

$$\begin{aligned}\Phi &= \iint_{\sigma} \mathbf{F} \cdot \mathbf{n}\, dS \\ &= \iint_{R} \mathbf{F} \cdot \left(\frac{\partial \mathbf{r}}{\partial \phi} \times \frac{\partial \mathbf{r}}{\partial \theta}\right) dA \\ &= \int_0^{2\pi} \int_0^{\pi} a^3 \sin\phi \cos^2\phi \, d\phi\, d\theta \\ &= a^3 \int_0^{2\pi} \left[-\frac{\cos^3\phi}{3}\right]_0^{\pi} d\theta \\ &= \frac{2a^3}{3} \int_0^{2\pi} d\theta = \frac{4\pi a^3}{3} \quad \blacktriangleleft \end{aligned}$$

**REMARK** Reversing the orientation of the surface $\sigma$ in (5) reverses the sign of $\mathbf{n}$, hence the sign of $\mathbf{F} \cdot \mathbf{n}$, and hence reverses the sign of $\Phi$. This can also be seen physically by interpreting the flux integral as the volume of fluid per unit time that crosses $\sigma$ in the positive direction minus the volume per unit time that crosses in the negative direction—reversing the orientation of $\sigma$ changes the sign of the difference. Thus, in Example 1 an inward orientation of the sphere would produce a flux of $-4\pi a^3/3$.

## ORIENTATION OF NONPARAMETRIC SURFACES

Nonparametric surfaces of the form $z = g(x, y)$, $y = g(z, x)$, and $x = g(y, z)$ can be expressed parametrically using the independent variables as parameters. More precisely, these surfaces can be represented by the vector equations

$$\mathbf{r} = u\mathbf{i} + v\mathbf{j} + g(u, v)\mathbf{k}, \quad \mathbf{r} = v\mathbf{i} + g(u, v)\mathbf{j} + u\mathbf{k}, \quad \mathbf{r} = g(u, v)\mathbf{i} + u\mathbf{j} + v\mathbf{k} \tag{6–8}$$

$z = g(x, y)$ $\quad$ $y = g(z, x)$ $\quad$ $x = g(y, z)$

These representations impose positive and negative orientations on the surfaces in accordance with Formula (1). We leave it as an exercise to calculate $\mathbf{n}$ and $-\mathbf{n}$ in each case and to show that the positive and negative orientations are as shown in Table 15.6.1. (To assist with perspective, each graph is pictured as a portion of the surface of a small solid region.)

**Table 15.6.1**

| $z = g(x, y)$ | $y = g(z, x)$ | $x = g(y, z)$ |
|---|---|---|
| 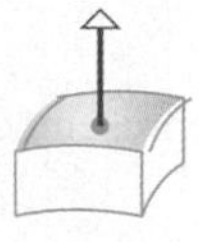 $\mathbf{n} = \dfrac{-\frac{\partial z}{\partial x}\mathbf{i} - \frac{\partial z}{\partial y}\mathbf{j} + \mathbf{k}}{\sqrt{\left(\frac{\partial z}{\partial x}\right)^2 + \left(\frac{\partial z}{\partial y}\right)^2 + 1}}$ <br> Positive **k**-component; Positive orientation | 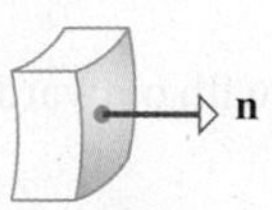 $\mathbf{n} = \dfrac{-\frac{\partial y}{\partial x}\mathbf{i} + \mathbf{j} - \frac{\partial y}{\partial z}\mathbf{k}}{\sqrt{\left(\frac{\partial y}{\partial x}\right)^2 + \left(\frac{\partial y}{\partial z}\right)^2 + 1}}$ <br> Positive **j**-component; Positive orientation |  $\mathbf{n} = \dfrac{\mathbf{i} - \frac{\partial x}{\partial y}\mathbf{j} - \frac{\partial x}{\partial z}\mathbf{k}}{\sqrt{\left(\frac{\partial x}{\partial y}\right)^2 + \left(\frac{\partial x}{\partial z}\right)^2 + 1}}$ <br> Positive **i**-component; Positive orientation |
| 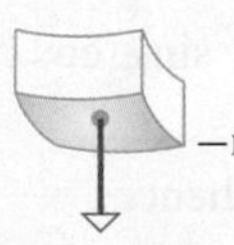 $-\mathbf{n} = \dfrac{\frac{\partial z}{\partial x}\mathbf{i} + \frac{\partial z}{\partial y}\mathbf{j} - \mathbf{k}}{\sqrt{\left(\frac{\partial z}{\partial x}\right)^2 + \left(\frac{\partial z}{\partial y}\right)^2 + 1}}$ <br> Negative **k**-component; Negative orientation | 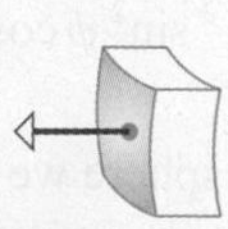 $-\mathbf{n} = \dfrac{\frac{\partial y}{\partial x}\mathbf{i} - \mathbf{j} + \frac{\partial y}{\partial z}\mathbf{k}}{\sqrt{\left(\frac{\partial y}{\partial x}\right)^2 + \left(\frac{\partial y}{\partial z}\right)^2 + 1}}$ <br> Negative **j**-component; Negative orientation | 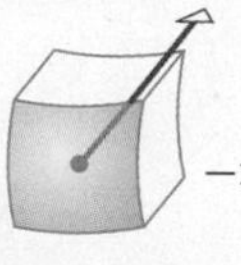 $-\mathbf{n} = \dfrac{-\mathbf{i} + \frac{\partial x}{\partial y}\mathbf{j} + \frac{\partial x}{\partial z}\mathbf{k}}{\sqrt{\left(\frac{\partial x}{\partial y}\right)^2 + \left(\frac{\partial x}{\partial z}\right)^2 + 1}}$ <br> Negative **i**-component; Negative orientation |

The dependent variable will increase as you move away from a surface

$$z = g(x, y), \quad y = g(z, x)$$

or

$$x = g(y, z)$$

in the direction of positive orientation.

The results in Table 15.6.1 can also be obtained using gradients. To see how this can be done, rewrite the equations of the surfaces as

$$z - g(x, y) = 0, \quad y - g(z, x) = 0, \quad x - g(y, z) = 0$$

Each of these equations has the form $G(x, y, z) = 0$ and hence can be viewed as a level surface of a function $G(x, y, z)$. Since the gradient of $G$ is normal to the level surface, it follows that the unit normal $\mathbf{n}$ is either $\nabla G/\|\nabla G\|$ or $-\nabla G/\|\nabla G\|$. However,if $G(x, y, z) = z - g(x, y)$, then $\nabla G$ has a **k**-component of 1; if $G(x, y, z) = y - g(z, x)$, then $\nabla G$ has a **j**-component of 1; and if $G(x, y, z) = x - g(y, z)$, then $\nabla G$ has an **i**-component of 1. Thus, it is evident from Table 15.6.1 that in all three cases we have

$$\mathbf{n} = \frac{\nabla G}{\|\nabla G\|} \tag{9}$$

Moreover, we leave it as an exercise to show that if the surfaces $z = g(x, y)$, $y = g(z, x)$, and $x = g(y, z)$ are expressed in vector forms (6), (7), and (8), then

$$\nabla G = \frac{\partial \mathbf{r}}{\partial u} \times \frac{\partial \mathbf{r}}{\partial v} \tag{10}$$

[compare (1) and (9)]. Thus, we are led to the following version of Theorem 15.6.2 for non-parametric surfaces.

**15.6.3 THEOREM** *Let $\sigma$ be a smooth surface of the form $z = g(x, y)$, $y = g(z, x)$, or $x = g(y, z)$, and suppose that the component functions of the vector field* **F** *are continuous on $\sigma$. Suppose also that the equation for $\sigma$ is rewritten as $G(x, y, z) = 0$ by taking $g$ to the left side of the equation, and let $R$ be the projection of $\sigma$ on the coordinate plane determined by the independent variables of $g$. If $\sigma$ has positive orientation, then*

$$\Phi = \iint_{\sigma} \mathbf{F} \cdot \mathbf{n}\, dS = \iint_{R} \mathbf{F} \cdot \nabla G\, dA \tag{11}$$

Formula (11) can either be used directly for computations or to derive some more specific formulas for each of the three surface types. For example, if $z = g(x, y)$, then we have $G(x, y, z) = z - g(x, y)$, so

$$\nabla G = -\frac{\partial g}{\partial x}\mathbf{i} - \frac{\partial g}{\partial y}\mathbf{j} + \mathbf{k} = -\frac{\partial z}{\partial x}\mathbf{i} - \frac{\partial z}{\partial y}\mathbf{j} + \mathbf{k}$$

Substituting this expression for $\nabla G$ in (11) and taking $R$ to be the projection of the surface $z = g(x, y)$ on the $xy$-plane yields

$$\iint_{\sigma} \mathbf{F} \cdot \mathbf{n}\, dS = \iint_{R} \mathbf{F} \cdot \left(-\frac{\partial z}{\partial x}\mathbf{i} - \frac{\partial z}{\partial y}\mathbf{j} + \mathbf{k}\right) dA \tag{12}$$

$\sigma$ of the form $z = g(x, y)$ and oriented up

$$\iint_{\sigma} \mathbf{F} \cdot \mathbf{n}\, dS = \iint_{R} \mathbf{F} \cdot \left(\frac{\partial z}{\partial x}\mathbf{i} + \frac{\partial z}{\partial y}\mathbf{j} - \mathbf{k}\right) dA \tag{13}$$

$\sigma$ of the form $z = g(x, y)$ and oriented down

The derivations of the corresponding formulas when $y = g(z, x)$ and $x = g(y, z)$ are left as exercises.

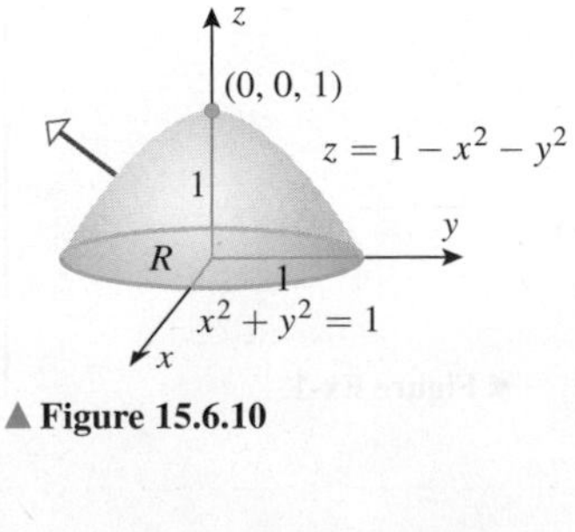

▲ Figure 15.6.10

▶ **Example 2** Let $\sigma$ be the portion of the surface $z = 1 - x^2 - y^2$ that lies above the $xy$-plane, and suppose that $\sigma$ is oriented up, as shown in Figure 15.6.10. Find the flux of the vector field $\mathbf{F}(x, y, z) = x\mathbf{i} + y\mathbf{j} + z\mathbf{k}$ across $\sigma$.

***Solution.*** From (12) the flux $\Phi$ is given by

$$\Phi = \iint_{\sigma} \mathbf{F}\cdot\mathbf{n}\,dS = \iint_{R} \mathbf{F}\cdot\left(-\frac{\partial z}{\partial x}\mathbf{i} - \frac{\partial z}{\partial y}\mathbf{j} + \mathbf{k}\right) dA$$

$$= \iint_{R} (x\mathbf{i} + y\mathbf{j} + z\mathbf{k})\cdot(2x\mathbf{i} + 2y\mathbf{j} + \mathbf{k})\,dA$$

$$= \iint_{R} (x^2 + y^2 + 1)\,dA$$

Since $z = 1 - x^2 - y^2$ on the surface

$$= \int_0^{2\pi}\int_0^1 (r^2 + 1)r\,dr\,d\theta$$

Using polar coordinates to evaluate the integral

$$= \int_0^{2\pi} \left(\frac{3}{4}\right) d\theta = \frac{3\pi}{2} \blacktriangleleft$$

## ✓QUICK CHECK EXERCISES 15.6 *(See page 1030 for answers.)*

In these exercises, $\mathbf{F}(x, y, z)$ denotes a vector field defined on a surface $\sigma$ oriented by a unit normal vector field $\mathbf{n}(x, y, z)$, and $\Phi$ denotes the flux of $\mathbf{F}$ across $\sigma$.

**1.** (a) $\Phi$ is the value of the surface integral ________.
(b) If $\sigma$ is the unit sphere and $\mathbf{n}$ is the outward unit normal, then the flux of

$$\mathbf{F}(x, y, z) = x\mathbf{i} + y\mathbf{j} + z\mathbf{k}$$

across $\sigma$ is $\Phi =$ ________.

**2.** (a) Assume that $\sigma$ is parametrized by a vector-valued function $\mathbf{r}(u, v)$ whose domain is a region $R$ in the $uv$-plane and that $\mathbf{n}$ is a positive multiple of

$$\frac{\partial \mathbf{r}}{\partial u} \times \frac{\partial \mathbf{r}}{\partial v}$$

Then the double integral over $R$ whose value is $\Phi$ is ________.
(b) Suppose that $\sigma$ is the parametric surface

$$\mathbf{r}(u, v) = u\mathbf{i} + v\mathbf{j} + (u + v)\mathbf{k} \quad (0 \le u^2 + v^2 \le 1)$$

and that $\mathbf{n}$ is a positive multiple of

$$\frac{\partial \mathbf{r}}{\partial u} \times \frac{\partial \mathbf{r}}{\partial v}$$

Then the flux of $\mathbf{F}(x, y, z) = x\mathbf{i} + y\mathbf{j} + z\mathbf{k}$ across $\sigma$ is $\Phi =$ ________.

**3.** (a) Assume that $\sigma$ is the graph of a function $z = g(x, y)$ over a region $R$ in the $xy$-plane and that $\mathbf{n}$ has a positive $\mathbf{k}$-component for every point on $\sigma$. Then a double integral over $R$ whose value is $\Phi$ is ________.
(b) Suppose that $\sigma$ is the triangular region with vertices $(1, 0, 0)$, $(0, 1, 0)$, and $(0, 0, 1)$ with upward orientation. Then the flux of

$$\mathbf{F}(x, y, z) = x\mathbf{i} + y\mathbf{j} + z\mathbf{k}$$

across $\sigma$ is $\Phi =$ ________.

**4.** In the case of steady-state incompressible fluid flow, with $\mathbf{F}(x, y, z)$ the fluid velocity at $(x, y, z)$ on $\sigma$, $\Phi$ can be interpreted as ________.

## EXERCISE SET 15.6 [C] CAS

**FOCUS ON CONCEPTS**

**1.** Suppose that the surface $\sigma$ of the unit cube in the accompanying figure has an outward orientation. In each part, determine whether the flux of the vector field $\mathbf{F}(x, y, z) = z\mathbf{j}$ across the specified face is positive, negative, or zero.
(a) The face $x = 1$ (b) The face $x = 0$
(c) The face $y = 1$ (d) The face $y = 0$
(e) The face $z = 1$ (f) The face $z = 0$




◀ **Figure Ex-1**

**2.** Find the flux of the constant vector field $\mathbf{F}(x, y, z) = 2\mathbf{i} - 2\mathbf{j} - 2\mathbf{k}$ across the entire surface $\sigma$ in Figure Ex-1. Explain your reasoning.

**3.** Find the flux of $\mathbf{F}(x, y, z) = x\mathbf{i}$ through a square of side 4 in the plane $x = -5$ oriented in the positive $x$-direction.

**4.** Find the flux of $\mathbf{F}(x, y, z) = (y + 1)\mathbf{j}$ through a square of side 5 in the $xz$-plane oriented in the negative $y$-direction.

**5.** Find the flux of $\mathbf{F}(x, y, z) = x\mathbf{i} + y\mathbf{j} + (z^2 + 4)\mathbf{k}$ through a $2 \times 3$ rectangle in the plane $z = 1$ oriented in the positive $z$-direction.

**6.** Find the flux of $\mathbf{F}(x, y, z) = 2\mathbf{i} + 3\mathbf{j}$ through a disk of radius 5 in the plane $y = 3$ oriented in the direction of increasing $y$.

**7.** Find the flux of $\mathbf{F}(x, y, z) = 9\mathbf{j} + 8\mathbf{k}$ through a disk of radius 5 in the plane $z = 2$ oriented in the upward direction.

**8.** Let $\sigma$ be the cylindrical surface that is represented by the vector-valued function $\mathbf{r}(u, v) = \cos v\mathbf{i} + \sin v\mathbf{j} + u\mathbf{k}$ with $0 \le u \le 1$ and $0 \le v \le 2\pi$.

(a) Find the unit normal $\mathbf{n} = \mathbf{n}(u, v)$ that defines the positive orientation of $\sigma$.

(b) Is the positive orientation inward or outward? Justify your answer.

**9–16** Find the flux of the vector field $\mathbf{F}$ across $\sigma$. ■

**9.** $\mathbf{F}(x, y, z) = x\mathbf{k}$; $\sigma$ is the square $0 \le x \le 2, 0 \le y \le 2$ in the $xy$-plane, oriented in the upward direction.

**10.** $\mathbf{F}(x, y, z) = 5z\mathbf{i} + y\mathbf{j} + 2x\mathbf{k}$; $\sigma$ is the rectangle $0 \le x \le 2$, $0 \le y \le 3$ in the plane $z = 2$, oriented in the positive $z$-direction.

**11.** $\mathbf{F}(x, y, z) = x\mathbf{i} + y\mathbf{j} + 2z\mathbf{k}$; $\sigma$ is the portion of the surface $z = 1 - x^2 - y^2$ above the $xy$-plane, oriented by upward normals.

**12.** $\mathbf{F}(x, y, z) = x^2\mathbf{i} + (x + e^y)\mathbf{j} - \mathbf{k}$; $\sigma$ is the vertical rectangle $0 \le x \le 2, 0 \le z \le 4$ in the plane $y = -1$, oriented in the negative $y$-direction.

**13.** $\mathbf{F}(x, y, z) = x\mathbf{i} + y\mathbf{j} + 2z\mathbf{k}$; $\sigma$ is the portion of the cone $z^2 = x^2 + y^2$ between the planes $z = 1$ and $z = 2$, oriented by upward unit normals.

**14.** $\mathbf{F}(x, y, z) = y\mathbf{j} + \mathbf{k}$; $\sigma$ is the portion of the paraboloid $z = x^2 + y^2$ below the plane $z = 4$, oriented by downward unit normals.

**15.** $\mathbf{F}(x, y, z) = x\mathbf{k}$; the surface $\sigma$ is the portion of the paraboloid $z = x^2 + y^2$ below the plane $z = y$, oriented by downward unit normals.

**16.** $\mathbf{F}(x, y, z) = x^2\mathbf{i} + yx\mathbf{j} + zx\mathbf{k}$; $\sigma$ is the portion of the plane $6x + 3y + 2z = 6$ in the first octant, oriented by unit normals with positive components.

**17–20** Find the flux of the vector field $\mathbf{F}$ across $\sigma$ in the direction of positive orientation. ■

**17.** $\mathbf{F}(x, y, z) = x\mathbf{i} + y\mathbf{j} + \mathbf{k}$; $\sigma$ is the portion of the paraboloid

$$\mathbf{r}(u, v) = u\cos v\mathbf{i} + u\sin v\mathbf{j} + (1 - u^2)\mathbf{k}$$

with $1 \le u \le 2, 0 \le v \le 2\pi$.

**18.** $\mathbf{F}(x, y, z) = e^{-y}\mathbf{i} - y\mathbf{j} + x\sin z\mathbf{k}$; $\sigma$ is the portion of the elliptic cylinder

$$\mathbf{r}(u, v) = 2\cos v\mathbf{i} + \sin v\mathbf{j} + u\mathbf{k}$$

with $0 \le u \le 5, 0 \le v \le 2\pi$.

**19.** $\mathbf{F}(x, y, z) = \sqrt{x^2 + y^2}\,\mathbf{k}$; $\sigma$ is the portion of the cone

$$\mathbf{r}(u, v) = u\cos v\mathbf{i} + u\sin v\mathbf{j} + 2u\mathbf{k}$$

with $0 \le u \le \sin v, 0 \le v \le \pi$.

**20.** $\mathbf{F}(x, y, z) = x\mathbf{i} + y\mathbf{j} + z\mathbf{k}$; $\sigma$ is the portion of the sphere

$$\mathbf{r}(u, v) = 2\sin u\cos v\mathbf{i} + 2\sin u\sin v\mathbf{j} + 2\cos u\mathbf{k}$$

with $0 \le u \le \pi/3, 0 \le v \le 2\pi$.

**21.** Let $\sigma$ be the surface of the cube bounded by the planes $x = \pm 1$, $y = \pm 1$, $z = \pm 1$, oriented by outward unit normals. In each part, find the flux of $\mathbf{F}$ across $\sigma$.

(a) $\mathbf{F}(x, y, z) = x\mathbf{i}$

(b) $\mathbf{F}(x, y, z) = x\mathbf{i} + y\mathbf{j} + z\mathbf{k}$

(c) $\mathbf{F}(x, y, z) = x^2\mathbf{i} + y^2\mathbf{j} + z^2\mathbf{k}$

**22.** Let $\sigma$ be the closed surface consisting of the portion of the paraboloid $z = x^2 + y^2$ for which $0 \le z \le 1$ and capped by the disk $x^2 + y^2 \le 1$ in the plane $z = 1$. Find the flux of the vector field $\mathbf{F}(x, y, z) = z\mathbf{j} - y\mathbf{k}$ in the outward direction across $\sigma$.

**23–26 True–False** Determine whether the statement is true or false. Explain your answer. ■

**23.** The Möbius strip is a surface that has two orientations.

**24.** The flux of a vector field is another vector field.

**25.** If the net volume of fluid that passes through a surface per unit time in the positive direction is zero, then the velocity of the fluid is everywhere tangent to the surface.

**26.** If a surface $\sigma$ is oriented by a unit normal vector field $\mathbf{n}$, the flux of $\mathbf{n}$ across $\sigma$ is numerically equal to the surface area of $\sigma$.

**27–28** Find the flux of $\mathbf{F}$ across the surface $\sigma$ by expressing $\sigma$ parametrically. ■

**27.** $\mathbf{F}(x, y, z) = \mathbf{i} + \mathbf{j} + \mathbf{k}$; the surface $\sigma$ is the portion of the cone $z = \sqrt{x^2 + y^2}$ between the planes $z = 1$ and $z = 2$, oriented by downward unit normals.

**28.** $\mathbf{F}(x, y, z) = 3\mathbf{i} - 7\mathbf{j} + z\mathbf{k}$; $\sigma$ is the portion of the cylinder $x^2 + y^2 = 16$ between the planes $z = -2$ and $z = 2$, oriented by outward unit normals.

**29.** Let $x$, $y$, and $z$ be measured in meters, and suppose that $\mathbf{F}(x, y, z) = 2x\mathbf{i} - 3y\mathbf{j} + z\mathbf{k}$ is the velocity vector (in m/s) of a fluid particle at the point $(x, y, z)$ in a steady-state incompressible fluid flow.

(a) Find the net volume of fluid that passes in the upward direction through the portion of the plane $x + y + z = 1$ in the first octant in 1 s.

(b) Assuming that the fluid has a mass density of 806 kg/m$^3$, find the net mass of fluid that passes in the upward direction through the surface in part (a) in 1 s.

**30.** Let $x$, $y$, and $z$ be measured in meters, and suppose that $\mathbf{F}(x, y, z) = -y\mathbf{i} + z\mathbf{j} + 3x\mathbf{k}$ is the velocity vector (in m/s) of a fluid particle at the point $(x, y, z)$ in a steady-state incompressible fluid flow.

(a) Find the net volume of fluid that passes in the upward direction through the hemisphere $z = \sqrt{9 - x^2 - y^2}$ in 1 s.

(b) Assuming that the fluid has a mass density of 1060 $\text{kg/m}^3$, find the net mass of fluid that passes in the upward direction through the surface in part (a) in 1 s.

**31.** (a) Derive the analogs of Formulas (12) and (13) for surfaces of the form $x = g(y, z)$.

(b) Let $\sigma$ be the portion of the paraboloid $x = y^2 + z^2$ for $x \leq 1$ and $z \geq 0$ oriented by unit normals with negative $x$-components. Use the result in part (a) to find the flux of
$$\mathbf{F}(x, y, z) = y\mathbf{i} - z\mathbf{j} + 8\mathbf{k}$$
across $\sigma$.

**32.** (a) Derive the analogs of Formulas (12) and (13) for surfaces of the form $y = g(z, x)$.

(b) Let $\sigma$ be the portion of the paraboloid $y = z^2 + x^2$ for $y \leq 1$ and $z \geq 0$ oriented by unit normals with positive $y$-components. Use the result in part (a) to find the flux of
$$\mathbf{F}(x, y, z) = x\mathbf{i} + y\mathbf{j} + z\mathbf{k}$$
across $\sigma$.

**33.** Let $\mathbf{F} = \|\mathbf{r}\|^k\mathbf{r}$, where $\mathbf{r} = x\mathbf{i} + y\mathbf{j} + z\mathbf{k}$ and $k$ is a constant. (Note that if $k = -3$, this is an inverse-square field.) Let $\sigma$ be the sphere of radius $a$ centered at the origin and oriented by the outward normal $\mathbf{n} = \mathbf{r}/\|\mathbf{r}\| = \mathbf{r}/a$.

(a) Find the flux of $\mathbf{F}$ across $\sigma$ without performing any integrations. [*Hint:* The surface area of a sphere of radius $a$ is $4\pi a^2$.]

(b) For what value of $k$ is the flux independent of the radius of the sphere?

C **34.** Let
$$\mathbf{F}(x, y, z) = a^2x\mathbf{i} + (y/a)\mathbf{j} + az^2\mathbf{k}$$
and let $\sigma$ be the sphere of radius 1 centered at the origin and oriented outward. Use a CAS to find all values of $a$ such that the flux of $\mathbf{F}$ across $\sigma$ is $3\pi$.

C **35.** Let
$$\mathbf{F}(x, y, z) = \left(\frac{6}{a} + 1\right)x\mathbf{i} - 4ay\mathbf{j} + a^2z\mathbf{k}$$
and let $\sigma$ be the sphere of radius $a$ centered at the origin and oriented outward. Use a CAS to find all values of $a$ such that the flux of $\mathbf{F}$ across $\sigma$ is zero.

**36. Writing** Discuss the similarities and differences between the flux of a vector field across a surface and the line integral of a vector field along a curve.

**37. Writing** Write a paragraph explaining the concept of flux to someone unfamiliar with its meaning.

✓ **QUICK CHECK ANSWERS 15.6** 1. (a) $\iint_\sigma \mathbf{F}\cdot\mathbf{n}\,dS$ (b) $4\pi$ 2. (a) $\iint_R \mathbf{F}\cdot\left(\frac{\partial\mathbf{r}}{\partial u}\times\frac{\partial\mathbf{r}}{\partial v}\right)dA$ (b) 0 3. (a) $\iint_R \mathbf{F}\cdot\left(-\frac{\partial z}{\partial x}\mathbf{i} - \frac{\partial z}{\partial y}\mathbf{j} + \mathbf{k}\right)dA$ (b) $\frac{1}{2}$ 4. the net volume of fluid crossing $\sigma$ in the positive direction per unit time

## 15.7 THE DIVERGENCE THEOREM

*In this section we will be concerned with flux across surfaces, such as spheres, that "enclose" a region of space. We will show that the flux across such surfaces can be expressed in terms of the divergence of the vector field, and we will use this result to give a physical interpretation of the concept of divergence.*

### ORIENTATION OF PIECEWISE SMOOTH CLOSED SURFACES

In the last section we studied flux across general surfaces. Here we will be concerned exclusively with surfaces that are boundaries of finite solids—the surface of a solid sphere, the surface of a solid box, or the surface of a solid cylinder, for example. Such surfaces are said to be ***closed***. A closed surface may or may not be smooth, but most of the surfaces that arise in applications are ***piecewise smooth***; that is, they consist of finitely many smooth surfaces joined together at the edges (a box, for example). We will limit our discussion to piecewise smooth surfaces that can be assigned an ***inward orientation*** (toward the interior of the solid) and an ***outward orientation*** (away from the interior). It is difficult to make this concept mathematically precise, but the basic idea is that each piece of the surface is orientable, and oriented pieces fit together in such a way that the entire surface can be assigned an orientation (Figure 15.7.1).

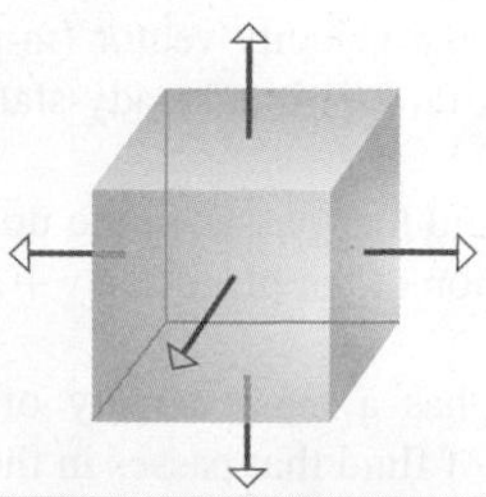


▲ **Figure 15.7.1**

### THE DIVERGENCE THEOREM

In Section 15.1 we defined the divergence of a vector field
$$\mathbf{F}(x, y, z) = f(x, y, z)\mathbf{i} + g(x, y, z)\mathbf{j} + h(x, y, z)\mathbf{k}$$

as

$$\operatorname{div} \mathbf{F} = \frac{\partial f}{\partial x} + \frac{\partial g}{\partial y} + \frac{\partial h}{\partial z}$$

but we did not attempt to give a physical explanation of its meaning at that time. The following result, known as the ***Divergence Theorem*** or ***Gauss's Theorem***, will provide us with a physical interpretation of divergence in the context of fluid flow.

**15.7.1 THEOREM (*The Divergence Theorem*)** *Let $G$ be a solid whose surface $\sigma$ is oriented outward. If*

$$\mathbf{F}(x, y, z) = f(x, y, z)\mathbf{i} + g(x, y, z)\mathbf{j} + h(x, y, z)\mathbf{k}$$

*where $f$, $g$, and $h$ have continuous first partial derivatives on some open set containing $G$, and if $\mathbf{n}$ is the outward unit normal on $\sigma$, then*

$$\iint_{\sigma} \mathbf{F} \cdot \mathbf{n} \, dS = \iiint_{G} \operatorname{div} \mathbf{F} \, dV \tag{1}$$

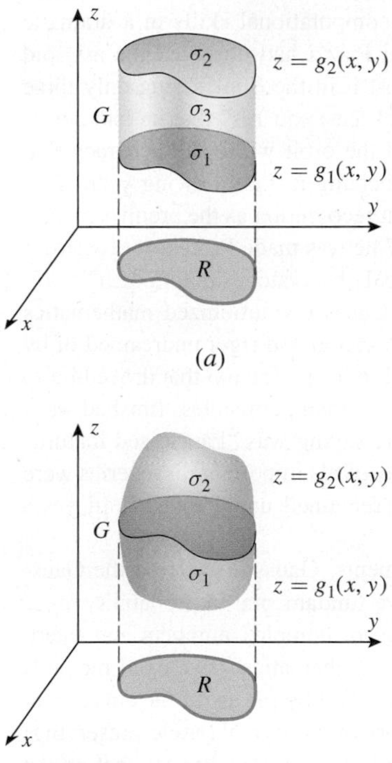

▲ **Figure 15.7.2**

We will give a proof for the special case where $G$ is simultaneously a simple $xy$-solid, a simple $yz$-solid, and a simple $zx$-solid (see Figure 14.5.3 and the related discussion for terminology).

**PROOF** Formula (1) can be expressed as

$$\iint_{\sigma} [f(x, y, z)\mathbf{i} + g(x, y, z)\mathbf{j} + h(x, y, z)\mathbf{k}] \cdot \mathbf{n} \, dS = \iiint_{G} \left( \frac{\partial f}{\partial x} + \frac{\partial g}{\partial y} + \frac{\partial h}{\partial z} \right) dV$$

so it suffices to prove the three equalities

$$\iint_{\sigma} f(x, y, z)\mathbf{i} \cdot \mathbf{n} \, dS = \iiint_{G} \frac{\partial f}{\partial x} \, dV \tag{2a}$$

$$\iint_{\sigma} g(x, y, z)\mathbf{j} \cdot \mathbf{n} \, dS = \iiint_{G} \frac{\partial g}{\partial y} \, dV \tag{2b}$$

$$\iint_{\sigma} h(x, y, z)\mathbf{k} \cdot \mathbf{n} \, dS = \iiint_{G} \frac{\partial h}{\partial z} \, dV \tag{2c}$$

Since the proofs of all three equalities are similar, we will prove only the third.

Suppose that $G$ has upper surface $z = g_2(x, y)$, lower surface $z = g_1(x, y)$, and projection $R$ on the $xy$-plane. Let $\sigma_1$ denote the lower surface, $\sigma_2$ the upper surface, and $\sigma_3$ the lateral surface (Figure 15.7.2*a*). If the upper surface and lower surface meet as in Figure 15.7.2*b*, then there is no lateral surface $\sigma_3$. Our proof will allow for both cases shown in those figures.

It follows from Theorem 14.5.2 that

$$\iiint_{G} \frac{\partial h}{\partial z} \, dV = \iint_{R} \left[ \int_{g_1(x,y)}^{g_2(x,y)} \frac{\partial h}{\partial z} \, dz \right] dA = \iint_{R} \left[ h(x, y, z) \right]_{z=g_1(x,y)}^{g_2(x,y)} dA$$

so

$$\iiint_{G} \frac{\partial h}{\partial z} \, dV = \iint_{R} [h(x, y, g_2(x, y)) - h(x, y, g_1(x, y))] \, dA \tag{3}$$

Next we will evaluate the surface integral in (2c) by integrating over each surface of $G$ separately. If there is a lateral surface $\sigma_3$, then at each point of this surface $\mathbf{k} \cdot \mathbf{n} = 0$ since $\mathbf{n}$ is horizontal and $\mathbf{k}$ is vertical. Thus,

$$\iint_{\sigma_3} h(x, y, z)\mathbf{k} \cdot \mathbf{n}\, dS = 0$$

Therefore, regardless of whether $G$ has a lateral surface, we can write

$$\iint_{\sigma} h(x, y, z)\mathbf{k} \cdot \mathbf{n}\, dS = \iint_{\sigma_1} h(x, y, z)\mathbf{k} \cdot \mathbf{n}\, dS + \iint_{\sigma_2} h(x, y, z)\mathbf{k} \cdot \mathbf{n}\, dS \tag{4}$$

**Carl Friedrich Gauss (1777–1855)** German mathematician and scientist. Sometimes called the "prince of mathematicians," Gauss ranks with Newton and Archimedes as one of the three greatest mathematicians who ever lived. His father, a laborer, was an uncouth but honest man who would have liked Gauss to take up a trade such as gardening or bricklaying; but the boy's genius for mathematics was not to be denied. In the entire history of mathematics there may never have been a child so precocious as Gauss—by his own account he worked out the rudiments of arithmetic before he could talk. One day, before he was even three years old, his genius became apparent to his parents in a very dramatic way. His father was preparing the weekly payroll for the laborers under his charge while the boy watched quietly from a corner. At the end of the long and tedious calculation, Gauss informed his father that there was an error in the result and stated the answer, which he had worked out in his head. To the astonishment of his parents, a check of the computations showed Gauss to be correct!

For his elementary education Gauss was enrolled in a squalid school run by a man named Büttner whose main teaching technique was thrashing. Büttner was in the habit of assigning long addition problems which, unknown to his students, were arithmetic progressions that he could sum up using formulas. On the first day that Gauss entered the arithmetic class, the students were asked to sum the numbers from 1 to 100. But no sooner had Büttner stated the problem than Gauss turned over his slate and exclaimed in his peasant dialect, "Ligget se'." (Here it lies.) For nearly an hour Büttner glared at Gauss, who sat with folded hands while his classmates toiled away. When Büttner examined the slates at the end of the period, Gauss's slate contained a single number, 5050—the only correct solution in the class. To his credit, Büttner recognized the genius of Gauss and with the help of his assistant, John Bartels, had him brought to the attention of Karl Wilhelm Ferdinand, Duke of Brunswick. The shy and awkward boy, who was then fourteen, so captivated the Duke that he subsidized him through preparatory school, college, and the early part of his career.

From 1795 to 1798 Gauss studied mathematics at the University of Göttingen, receiving his degree in absentia from the University of Helmstadt. For his dissertation, he gave the first complete proof of the fundamental theorem of algebra, which states that every polynomial equation has as many solutions as its degree. At age 19 he solved a problem that baffled Euclid, inscribing a regular polygon of 17 sides in a circle using straightedge and compass; and in 1801, at age 24, he published his first masterpiece, *Disquisitiones Arithmeticae*, considered by many to be one of the most brilliant achievements in mathematics. In that book Gauss systematized the study of number theory (properties of the integers) and formulated the basic concepts that form the foundation of that subject.

In the same year that the *Disquisitiones* was published, Gauss again applied his phenomenal computational skills in a dramatic way. The astronomer Giuseppi Piazzi had observed the asteroid Ceres for $\frac{1}{40}$ of its orbit, but lost it in the Sun. Using only three observations and the "method of least squares" that he had developed in 1795, Gauss computed the orbit with such accuracy that astronomers had no trouble relocating it the following year. This achievement brought him instant recognition as the premier mathematician in Europe, and in 1807 he was made Professor of Astronomy and head of the astronomical observatory at Göttingen.

In the years that followed, Gauss revolutionized mathematics by bringing to it standards of precision and rigor undreamed of by his predecessors. He had a passion for perfection that drove him to polish and rework his papers rather than publish less finished work in greater numbers—his favorite saying was "Pauca, sed matura" (Few, but ripe). As a result, many of his important discoveries were squirreled away in diaries that remained unpublished until years after his death.

Among his myriad achievements, Gauss discovered the Gaussian or "bell-shaped" error curve fundamental in probability, gave the first geometric interpretation of complex numbers and established their fundamental role in mathematics, developed methods of characterizing surfaces intrinsically by means of the curves that they contain, developed the theory of conformal (angle-preserving) maps, and discovered non-Euclidean geometry 30 years before the ideas were published by others. In physics he made major contributions to the theory of lenses and capillary action, and with Wilhelm Weber he did fundamental work in electromagnetism. Gauss invented the heliotrope, bifilar magnetometer, and an electrotelegraph.

Gauss was deeply religious and aristocratic in demeanor. He mastered foreign languages with ease, read extensively, and enjoyed mineralogy and botany as hobbies. He disliked teaching and was usually cool and discouraging to other mathematicians, possibly because he had already anticipated their work. It has been said that if Gauss had published all of his discoveries, the current state of mathematics would be advanced by 50 years. He was without a doubt the greatest mathematician of the modern era.

*[Image: georgios/Depositphotos]*

On the upper surface $\sigma_2$, the outer normal is an upward normal, and on the lower surface $\sigma_1$, the outer normal is a downward normal. Thus, Formulas (12) and (13) of Section 15.6 imply that

$$\iint_{\sigma_2} h(x,y,z)\mathbf{k}\cdot\mathbf{n}\,dS = \iint_R h(x,y,g_2(x,y))\mathbf{k}\cdot\left(-\frac{\partial z}{\partial x}\mathbf{i} - \frac{\partial z}{\partial y}\mathbf{j} + \mathbf{k}\right) dA$$
$$= \iint_R h(x,y,g_2(x,y))\,dA \tag{5}$$

and

$$\iint_{\sigma_1} h(x,y,z)\mathbf{k}\cdot\mathbf{n}\,dS = \iint_R h(x,y,g_1(x,y))\mathbf{k}\cdot\left(\frac{\partial z}{\partial x}\mathbf{i} + \frac{\partial z}{\partial y}\mathbf{j} - \mathbf{k}\right) dA$$
$$= -\iint_R h(x,y,g_1(x,y))\,dA \tag{6}$$

Substituting (5) and (6) into (4) and combining the terms into a single integral yields

$$\iint_{\sigma} h(x,y,z)\mathbf{k}\cdot\mathbf{n}\,dS = \iint_R [h(x,y,g_2(x,y)) - h(x,y,g_1(x,y))]\,dA \tag{7}$$

Explain how the derivation of (2c) should be modified to yield a proof of (2a) or (2b).

Equation (2c) now follows from (3) and (7). ■

The flux of a vector field across a closed surface with outward orientation is sometimes called the ***outward flux*** across the surface. In words, the Divergence Theorem states:

*The outward flux of a vector field across a closed surface is equal to the triple integral of the divergence over the region enclosed by the surface.*

## USING THE DIVERGENCE THEOREM TO FIND FLUX

Sometimes it is easier to find the flux across a closed surface by using the Divergence Theorem than by evaluating the flux integral directly.

**▶ Example 1** Use the Divergence Theorem to find the outward flux of the vector field $\mathbf{F}(x,y,z) = z\mathbf{k}$ across the sphere $x^2 + y^2 + z^2 = a^2$.

***Solution.*** Let $\sigma$ denote the outward-oriented spherical surface and $G$ the region that it encloses. The divergence of the vector field is

$$\text{div}\,\mathbf{F} = \frac{\partial z}{\partial z} = 1$$

so from (1) the flux across $\sigma$ is

$$\Phi = \iint_{\sigma} \mathbf{F}\cdot\mathbf{n}\,dS = \iiint_G dV = \text{volume of } G = \frac{4\pi a^3}{3}$$

Note how much simpler this calculation is than that in Example 1 of Section 15.6. ◀

The Divergence Theorem is usually the method of choice for finding the flux across closed piecewise smooth surfaces with multiple sections, since it eliminates the need for a separate integral evaluation over each section. This is illustrated in the next three examples.

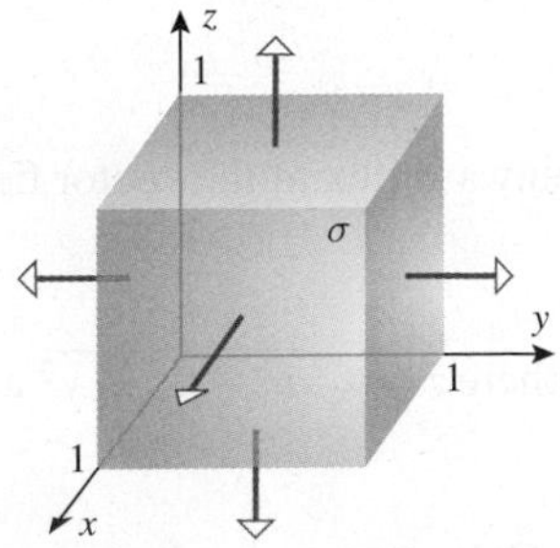

▲ Figure 15.7.3

**▶ Example 2** Use the Divergence Theorem to find the outward flux of the vector field

$$\mathbf{F}(x,y,z) = 2x\mathbf{i} + 3y\mathbf{j} + z^2\mathbf{k}$$

across the unit cube in Figure 15.7.3.

***Solution.*** Let $\sigma$ denote the outward-oriented surface of the cube and $G$ the region that it encloses. The divergence of the vector field is

$$\operatorname{div} \mathbf{F} = \frac{\partial}{\partial x}(2x) + \frac{\partial}{\partial y}(3y) + \frac{\partial}{\partial z}(z^2) = 5 + 2z$$

so from (1) the flux across $\sigma$ is

> Let $\mathbf{F}(x, y, z)$ be the vector field in Example 2 and show that $\mathbf{F} \cdot \mathbf{n}$ is constant on each of the six faces of the cube in Figure 15.7.3. Use your computations to confirm the result in Example 2.

$$\Phi = \iint_{\sigma} \mathbf{F} \cdot \mathbf{n}\, dS = \iiint_{G} (5 + 2z)\, dV = \int_0^1 \int_0^1 \int_0^1 (5 + 2z)\, dz\, dy\, dx$$

$$= \int_0^1 \int_0^1 \left[5z + z^2\right]_{z=0}^{1} dy\, dx = \int_0^1 \int_0^1 6\, dy\, dx = 6 \blacktriangleleft$$

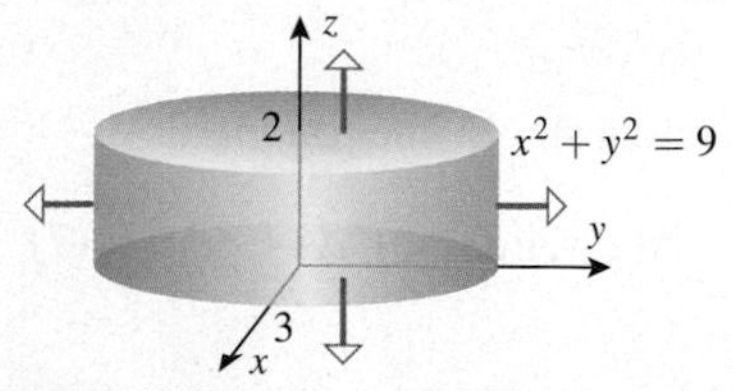

▲ **Figure 15.7.4**

► **Example 3** Use the Divergence Theorem to find the outward flux of the vector field

$$\mathbf{F}(x, y, z) = x^3\mathbf{i} + y^3\mathbf{j} + z^2\mathbf{k}$$

across the surface of the region that is enclosed by the circular cylinder $x^2 + y^2 = 9$ and the planes $z = 0$ and $z = 2$ (Figure 15.7.4).

***Solution.*** Let $\sigma$ denote the outward-oriented surface and $G$ the region that it encloses. The divergence of the vector field is

$$\operatorname{div} \mathbf{F} = \frac{\partial}{\partial x}(x^3) + \frac{\partial}{\partial y}(y^3) + \frac{\partial}{\partial z}(z^2) = 3x^2 + 3y^2 + 2z$$

so from (1) the flux across $\sigma$ is

$$\Phi = \iint_{\sigma} \mathbf{F} \cdot \mathbf{n}\, dS = \iiint_{G} (3x^2 + 3y^2 + 2z)\, dV$$

$$= \int_0^{2\pi} \int_0^3 \int_0^2 (3r^2 + 2z) r\, dz\, dr\, d\theta \quad \text{Using cylindrical coordinates}$$

$$= \int_0^{2\pi} \int_0^3 \left[3r^3 z + z^2 r\right]_{z=0}^{2} dr\, d\theta$$

$$= \int_0^{2\pi} \int_0^3 (6r^3 + 4r)\, dr\, d\theta$$

$$= \int_0^{2\pi} \left[\frac{3r^4}{2} + 2r^2\right]_0^3 d\theta$$

$$= \int_0^{2\pi} \frac{279}{2}\, d\theta = 279\pi \blacktriangleleft$$

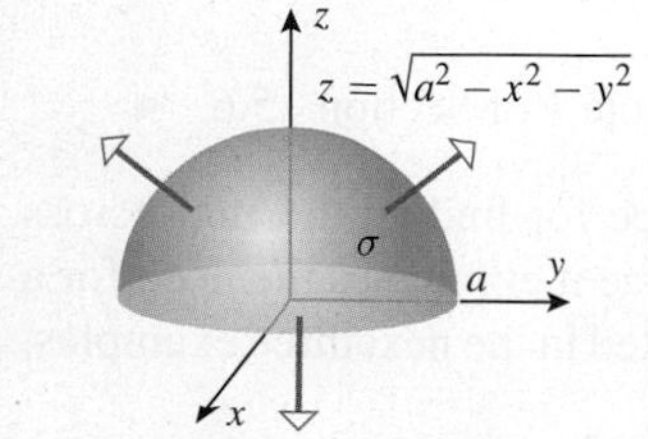

▲ **Figure 15.7.5**

► **Example 4** Use the Divergence Theorem to find the outward flux of the vector field

$$\mathbf{F}(x, y, z) = x^3\mathbf{i} + y^3\mathbf{j} + z^3\mathbf{k}$$

across the surface of the region that is enclosed by the hemisphere $z = \sqrt{a^2 - x^2 - y^2}$ and the plane $z = 0$ (Figure 15.7.5).

***Solution.*** Let $\sigma$ denote the outward-oriented surface and $G$ the region that it encloses. The divergence of the vector field is

$$\operatorname{div} \mathbf{F} = \frac{\partial}{\partial x}(x^3) + \frac{\partial}{\partial y}(y^3) + \frac{\partial}{\partial z}(z^3) = 3x^2 + 3y^2 + 3z^2$$

so from (1) the flux across $\sigma$ is

$$\Phi = \iint_{\sigma} \mathbf{F}\cdot\mathbf{n}\,dS = \iiint_{G} (3x^2+3y^2+3z^2)\,dV$$

$$= \int_0^{2\pi}\int_0^{\pi/2}\int_0^{a} (3\rho^2)\rho^2 \sin\phi\,d\rho\,d\phi\,d\theta$$

Using spherical coordinates

$$= 3\int_0^{2\pi}\int_0^{\pi/2}\int_0^{a} \rho^4 \sin\phi\,d\rho\,d\phi\,d\theta$$

$$= 3\int_0^{2\pi}\int_0^{\pi/2}\left[\frac{\rho^5}{5}\sin\phi\right]_{\rho=0}^{a} d\phi\,d\theta$$

$$= \frac{3a^5}{5}\int_0^{2\pi}\int_0^{\pi/2} \sin\phi\,d\phi\,d\theta$$

$$= \frac{3a^5}{5}\int_0^{2\pi} [-\cos\phi]_0^{\pi/2}\,d\theta$$

$$= \frac{3a^5}{5}\int_0^{2\pi} d\theta = \frac{6\pi a^5}{5} \blacktriangleleft$$

## DIVERGENCE VIEWED AS FLUX DENSITY

The Divergence Theorem provides a way of interpreting the divergence of a vector field **F**. Suppose that $G$ is a *small* spherical region centered at the point $P_0$ and that its surface, denoted by $\sigma(G)$, is oriented outward. Denote the volume of the region by vol($G$) and the flux of **F** across $\sigma(G)$ by $\Phi(G)$. If div **F** is continuous on $G$, then across the small region $G$ the value of div **F** will not vary much from its value div $\mathbf{F}(P_0)$ at the center, and we can reasonably approximate div **F** by the constant div $\mathbf{F}(P_0)$ on $G$. Thus, the Divergence Theorem implies that the flux $\Phi(G)$ of **F** across $\sigma(G)$ can be approximated by

$$\Phi(G) = \iint_{\sigma(G)} \mathbf{F}\cdot\mathbf{n}\,dS = \iiint_{G} \operatorname{div}\mathbf{F}\,dV \approx \operatorname{div}\mathbf{F}(P_0)\iiint_{G} dV = \operatorname{div}\mathbf{F}(P_0)\operatorname{vol}(G)$$

from which we obtain the approximation

$$\operatorname{div}\mathbf{F}(P_0) \approx \frac{\Phi(G)}{\operatorname{vol}(G)} \tag{8}$$

The expression on the right side of (8) is called the ***outward flux density of* F *across G***. If we now let the radius of the sphere approach zero [so that vol($G$) approaches zero], then it is plausible that the error in this approximation will approach zero, and the divergence of **F** at the point $P_0$ will be given exactly by

$$\operatorname{div}\mathbf{F}(P_0) = \lim_{\operatorname{vol}(G)\to 0} \frac{\Phi(G)}{\operatorname{vol}(G)}$$

which we can express as

$$\operatorname{div}\mathbf{F}(P_0) = \lim_{\operatorname{vol}(G)\to 0} \frac{1}{\operatorname{vol}(G)} \iint_{\sigma(G)} \mathbf{F}\cdot\mathbf{n}\,dS \tag{9}$$

Formula (9) is sometimes taken as the definition of divergence. This is a useful alternative to Definition 15.1.4 because it does not require a coordinate system.

This limit, which is called the ***outward flux density of* F *at* $P_0$**, tells us that if **F** denotes the velocity field of a fluid, then *in a steady-state fluid flow* div **F** *can be interpreted as the limiting flux per unit volume at a point.* Moreover, it follows from (8) that for a small spherical region $G$ centered at a point $P_0$ in the flow, the outward flux across the surface of $G$ can be approximated by

$$\Phi(G) \approx (\operatorname{div}\mathbf{F}(P_0))(\operatorname{vol}(G)) \tag{10}$$

## SOURCES AND SINKS

If $P_0$ is a point in an incompressible fluid at which div $\mathbf{F}(P_0) > 0$, then it follows from (8) that $\Phi(G) > 0$ for a sufficiently small sphere $G$ centered at $P_0$. Thus, there is a greater volume of fluid going out through the surface of $G$ than coming in. But this can only happen if there is some point *inside* the sphere at which fluid is entering the flow (say by condensation, melting of a solid, or a chemical reaction); otherwise the net outward flow through the surface would result in a decrease in density within the sphere, contradicting the incompressibility assumption. Similarly, if div $\mathbf{F}(P_0) < 0$, there would have to be a point *inside* the sphere at which fluid is leaving the flow (say by evaporation); otherwise the net inward flow through the surface would result in an increase in density within the sphere. In an incompressible fluid, points at which div $\mathbf{F}(P_0) > 0$ are called ***sources*** and points at which div $\mathbf{F}(P_0) < 0$ are called ***sinks***. Fluid enters the flow at a source and drains out at a sink. In an incompressible fluid without sources or sinks we must have

$$\operatorname{div} \mathbf{F}(P) = 0$$

at every point $P$. In hydrodynamics this is called the ***continuity equation for incompressible fluids*** and is sometimes taken as the defining characteristic of an incompressible fluid.

## GAUSS'S LAW FOR INVERSE-SQUARE FIELDS

The Divergence Theorem applied to inverse-square fields (see Definition 15.1.2) produces a result called ***Gauss's Law for Inverse-Square Fields***. This result is the basis for many important principles in physics.

**15.7.2 GAUSS'S LAW FOR INVERSE-SQUARE FIELDS** If

$$\mathbf{F}(\mathbf{r}) = \frac{c}{\|\mathbf{r}\|^3}\mathbf{r}$$

is an inverse-square field in 3-space, and if $\sigma$ is a closed orientable surface that surrounds the origin, then the outward flux of $\mathbf{F}$ across $\sigma$ is

$$\Phi = \iint_{\sigma} \mathbf{F}\cdot\mathbf{n}\,dS = 4\pi c \tag{11}$$

To derive this result, recall from Formula (5) of Section 15.1 that $\mathbf{F}$ can be expressed in component form as

$$\mathbf{F}(x, y, z) = \frac{c}{(x^2+y^2+z^2)^{3/2}}(x\mathbf{i}+y\mathbf{j}+z\mathbf{k}) \tag{12}$$

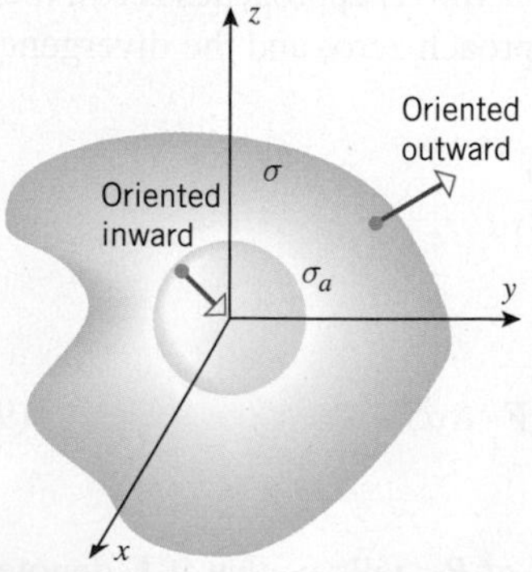


▲ **Figure 15.7.6**

Since the components of $\mathbf{F}$ are not continuous at the origin, we cannot apply the Divergence Theorem across the solid enclosed by $\sigma$. However, we can circumvent this difficulty by constructing a sphere of radius $a$ centered at the origin, where the radius is sufficiently small that the sphere lies entirely within the region enclosed by $\sigma$ (Figure 15.7.6). We will denote the surface of this sphere by $\sigma_a$. The solid $G$ enclosed between $\sigma_a$ and $\sigma$ is an example of a three-dimensional solid with an internal "cavity." Just as we were able to extend Green's Theorem to multiply connected regions in the plane (regions with holes), so it is possible to extend the Divergence Theorem to solids in 3-space with internal cavities, provided the surface integral in the theorem is taken over the *entire* boundary with the outside boundary of the solid oriented outward and the boundaries of the cavities oriented inward. Thus, if $\mathbf{F}$ is the inverse-square field in (12), and if $\sigma_a$ is oriented inward, then the Divergence Theorem yields

$$\iiint_G \operatorname{div}\mathbf{F}\,dV = \iint_{\sigma} \mathbf{F}\cdot\mathbf{n}\,dS + \iint_{\sigma_a} \mathbf{F}\cdot\mathbf{n}\,dS \tag{13}$$

But we showed in Example 5 of Section 15.1 that div $\mathbf{F} = 0$, so (13) yields

$$\iint_{\sigma} \mathbf{F}\cdot\mathbf{n}\,dS = -\iint_{\sigma_a} \mathbf{F}\cdot\mathbf{n}\,dS \tag{14}$$

We can evaluate the surface integral over $\sigma_a$ by expressing the integrand in terms of components; however, it is easier to leave it in vector form. At each point on the sphere the unit normal $\mathbf{n}$ points inward along a radius from the origin, and hence $\mathbf{n} = -\mathbf{r}/\|\mathbf{r}\|$. Thus, (14) yields

$$\begin{aligned}
\iint_{\sigma} \mathbf{F}\cdot\mathbf{n}\,dS &= -\iint_{\sigma_a} \frac{c}{\|\mathbf{r}\|^3}\mathbf{r}\cdot\left(-\frac{\mathbf{r}}{\|\mathbf{r}\|}\right) dS \\
&= \iint_{\sigma_a} \frac{c}{\|\mathbf{r}\|^4}(\mathbf{r}\cdot\mathbf{r})\,dS \\
&= \iint_{\sigma_a} \frac{c}{\|\mathbf{r}\|^2}\,dS \\
&= \frac{c}{a^2}\iint_{\sigma_a} dS \\
&= \frac{c}{a^2}(4\pi a^2) \\
&= 4\pi c
\end{aligned}$$

$\|\mathbf{r}\| = a$ on $\sigma_a$

The integral is the surface area of the sphere.

which establishes (11).

## GAUSS'S LAW IN ELECTROSTATICS

It follows from Example 1 of Section 15.1 with $q = 1$ that a single charged particle of charge $Q$ located at the origin creates an inverse-square field

$$\mathbf{F}(\mathbf{r}) = \frac{Q}{4\pi\epsilon_0\|\mathbf{r}\|^3}\mathbf{r}$$

in which $\mathbf{F}(\mathbf{r})$ is the electrical force exerted by $Q$ on a unit positive charge ($q = 1$) located at the point with position vector $\mathbf{r}$. In this case Gauss's law (15.7.2) states that the outward flux $\Phi$ across any closed orientable surface $\sigma$ that surrounds $Q$ is

$$\Phi = \iint_{\sigma} \mathbf{F}\cdot\mathbf{n}\,dS = 4\pi\left(\frac{Q}{4\pi\epsilon_0}\right) = \frac{Q}{\epsilon_0}$$

This result, which is called ***Gauss's Law for Electric Fields***, can be extended to more than one charge. It is one of the fundamental laws in electricity and magnetism.

## ✓ QUICK CHECK EXERCISES 15.7 (See page 1039 for answers.)

**1.** Let $G$ be a solid whose surface $\sigma$ is oriented outward by the unit normal $\mathbf{n}$, and let $\mathbf{F}(x, y, z)$ denote a vector field whose component functions have continuous first partial derivatives on some open set containing $G$. The Divergence Theorem states that the surface integral ________ and the triple integral ________ have the same value.

**2.** The outward flux of $\mathbf{F}(x, y, z) = x\mathbf{i} + y\mathbf{j} + z\mathbf{k}$ across any unit cube is ________.

**3.** If $\mathbf{F}(x, y, z)$ is the velocity vector field for a steady-state incompressible fluid flow, then a point at which div $\mathbf{F}$ is positive is called a ________ and a point at which div $\mathbf{F}$ is negative is called a ________. The continuity equation for an incompressible fluid states that ________.

**4.** If

$$\mathbf{F}(\mathbf{r}) = \frac{c}{\|\mathbf{r}\|^3}\mathbf{r}$$

is an inverse-square field, and if $\sigma$ is a closed orientable surface that surrounds the origin, then Gauss's law states that the outward flux of $\mathbf{F}$ across $\sigma$ is ________. On the other hand, if $\sigma$ does not surround the origin, then it follows from the Divergence Theorem that the outward flux of $\mathbf{F}$ across $\sigma$ is ________.

## EXERCISE SET 15.7 C CAS

**1–4** Verify Formula (1) in the Divergence Theorem by evaluating the surface integral and the triple integral. ■

1. $\mathbf{F}(x, y, z) = x\mathbf{i} + y\mathbf{j} + z\mathbf{k}$; $\sigma$ is the surface of the cube bounded by the planes $x = 0, x = 1, y = 0, y = 1, z = 0, z = 1$.
2. $\mathbf{F}(x, y, z) = 5\mathbf{j} + 7\mathbf{k}$; $\sigma$ is the sphere $x^2 + y^2 + z^2 = 1$.
3. $\mathbf{F}(x, y, z) = 2x\mathbf{i} - yz\mathbf{j} + z^2\mathbf{k}$; the surface $\sigma$ is the paraboloid $z = x^2 + y^2$ capped by the disk $x^2 + y^2 \le 1$ in the plane $z = 1$.
4. $\mathbf{F}(x, y, z) = xy\mathbf{i} + yz\mathbf{j} + xz\mathbf{k}$; $\sigma$ is the surface of the cube bounded by the planes $x = 0$, $x = 2$, $y = 0$, $y = 2$, $z = 0$, $z = 2$.

**5–8 True–False** Determine whether the statement is true or false. Explain your answer. ■

5. The Divergence Theorem equates a surface integral and a line integral.
6. If $G$ is a solid whose surface $\sigma$ is oriented outward, and if $\operatorname{div} \mathbf{F} > 0$ at all points of $G$, then the flux of $\mathbf{F}$ across $\sigma$ is positive.
7. The continuity equation for incompressible fluids states that the divergence of the velocity vector field of the fluid is zero.
8. Since the divergence of an inverse-square field is zero, the flux of an inverse-square field across any closed orientable surface must be zero as well.

**9–19** Use the Divergence Theorem to find the flux of $\mathbf{F}$ across the surface $\sigma$ with outward orientation. ■

9. $\mathbf{F}(x, y, z) = (x^2 + y)\mathbf{i} + z^2\mathbf{j} + (e^y - z)\mathbf{k}$; $\sigma$ is the surface of the rectangular solid bounded by the coordinate planes and the planes $x = 3$, $y = 1$, and $z = 2$.
10. $\mathbf{F}(x, y, z) = z^3\mathbf{i} - x^3\mathbf{j} + y^3\mathbf{k}$, where $\sigma$ is the spherical surface $x^2 + y^2 + z^2 = a^2$.
11. $\mathbf{F}(x, y, z) = (x - z)\mathbf{i} + (y - x)\mathbf{j} + (z - y)\mathbf{k}$; $\sigma$ is the surface of the cylindrical solid bounded by $x^2 + y^2 = a^2$, $z = 0$, and $z = 1$.
12. $\mathbf{F}(x, y, z) = x\mathbf{i} + y\mathbf{j} + z\mathbf{k}$; $\sigma$ is the surface of the solid bounded by the paraboloid $z = 1 - x^2 - y^2$ and the $xy$-plane.
13. $\mathbf{F}(x, y, z) = x^3\mathbf{i} + y^3\mathbf{j} + z^3\mathbf{k}$; $\sigma$ is the surface of the cylindrical solid bounded by $x^2 + y^2 = 4$, $z = 0$, and $z = 3$.
14. $\mathbf{F}(x, y, z) = (x^2 + y)\mathbf{i} + xy\mathbf{j} - (2xz + y)\mathbf{k}$; $\sigma$ is the surface of the tetrahedron in the first octant bounded by $x + y + z = 1$ and the coordinate planes.
15. $\mathbf{F}(x, y, z) = (x^3 - e^y)\mathbf{i} + (y^3 + \sin z)\mathbf{j} + (z^3 - xy)\mathbf{k}$, where $\sigma$ is the surface of the solid bounded above by $z = \sqrt{4 - x^2 - y^2}$ and below by the $xy$-plane. [*Hint:* Use spherical coordinates.]
16. $\mathbf{F}(x, y, z) = 2xz\mathbf{i} + yz\mathbf{j} + z^2\mathbf{k}$, where $\sigma$ is the surface of the solid bounded above by $z = \sqrt{a^2 - x^2 - y^2}$ and below by the $xy$-plane.
17. $\mathbf{F}(x, y, z) = x^2\mathbf{i} + y^2\mathbf{j} + z^2\mathbf{k}$; $\sigma$ is the surface of the conical solid bounded by $z = \sqrt{x^2 + y^2}$ and $z = 1$.
18. $\mathbf{F}(x, y, z) = x^2y\mathbf{i} - xy^2\mathbf{j} + (z + 2)\mathbf{k}$; $\sigma$ is the surface of the solid bounded above by the plane $z = 2x$ and below by the paraboloid $z = x^2 + y^2$.
19. $\mathbf{F}(x, y, z) = x^3\mathbf{i} + x^2y\mathbf{j} + xy\mathbf{k}$; $\sigma$ is the surface of the solid bounded by $z = 4 - x^2$, $y + z = 5$, $z = 0$, and $y = 0$.
20. Prove that if $\mathbf{r} = x\mathbf{i} + y\mathbf{j} + z\mathbf{k}$ and $\sigma$ is the surface of a solid $G$ oriented by outward unit normals, then
$$\operatorname{vol}(G) = \frac{1}{3}\iint_{\sigma} \mathbf{r} \cdot \mathbf{n}\, dS$$
where $\operatorname{vol}(G)$ is the volume of $G$.
21. Use the result in Exercise 20 to find the outward flux of the vector field $\mathbf{F}(x, y, z) = x\mathbf{i} + y\mathbf{j} + z\mathbf{k}$ across the surface $\sigma$ of the cylindrical solid bounded by $x^2 + 4x + y^2 = 5$, $z = -1$, and $z = 4$.

**FOCUS ON CONCEPTS**

22. Let $\mathbf{F}(x, y, z) = a\mathbf{i} + b\mathbf{j} + c\mathbf{k}$ be a constant vector field and let $\sigma$ be the surface of a solid $G$. Use the Divergence Theorem to show that the flux of $\mathbf{F}$ across $\sigma$ is zero. Give an informal physical explanation of this result.
23. Find a vector field $\mathbf{F}(x, y, z)$ that has
(a) positive divergence everywhere
(b) negative divergence everywhere.
24. In each part, the figure shows a horizontal layer of the vector field of a fluid flow in which the flow is parallel to the $xy$-plane at every point and is identical in each layer (i.e., is independent of $z$). For each flow, what can you say about the sign of the divergence at the origin? Explain your reasoning.

(a)

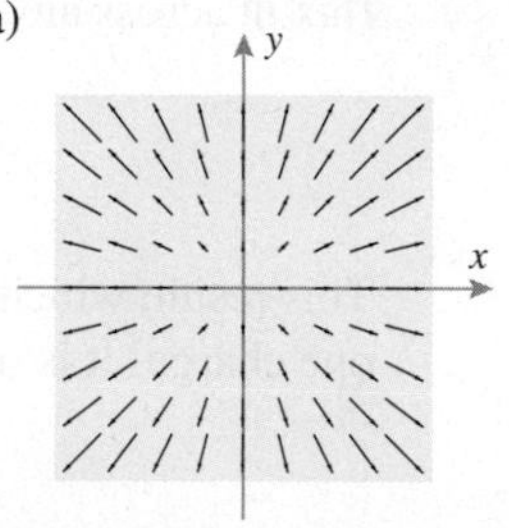


(b)

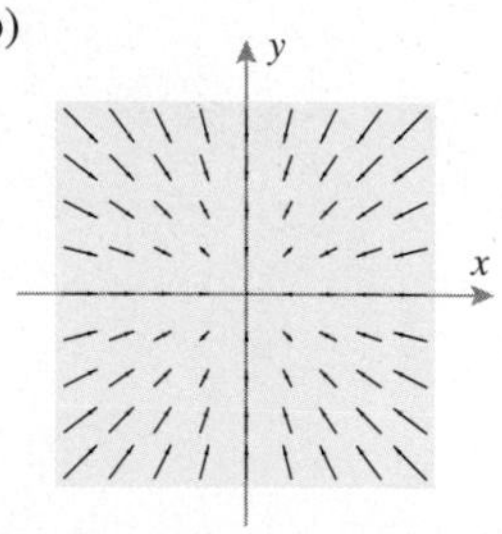


25. Let $\mathbf{F}(x, y, z)$ be a nonzero vector field in 3-space whose component functions have continuous first partial derivatives, and assume that $\operatorname{div} \mathbf{F} = 0$ everywhere. If $\sigma$ is any sphere in 3-space, explain why there are infinitely many points on $\sigma$ at which $\mathbf{F}$ is tangent to the sphere.
26. Does the result in Exercise 25 remain true if the sphere $\sigma$ is replaced by a cube? Explain.

**27–31** Prove the identity, assuming that $\mathbf{F}$, $\sigma$, and $G$ satisfy the hypotheses of the Divergence Theorem and that all necessary differentiability requirements for the functions $f(x, y, z)$ and $g(x, y, z)$ are met. ■

27. $\iint_{\sigma} \operatorname{curl} \mathbf{F} \cdot \mathbf{n}\, dS = 0$ [*Hint:* See Exercise 37, Section 15.1.]

28. $\iint_{\sigma} \nabla f \cdot \mathbf{n}\, dS = \iiint_{G} \nabla^2 f\, dV$
$\left(\nabla^2 f = \dfrac{\partial^2 f}{\partial x^2} + \dfrac{\partial^2 f}{\partial y^2} + \dfrac{\partial^2 f}{\partial z^2}\right)$

29. $\iint_{\sigma} (f\nabla g) \cdot \mathbf{n}\, dS = \iiint_{G} (f\nabla^2 g + \nabla f \cdot \nabla g)\, dV$

30. $\iint_{\sigma} (f\nabla g - g\nabla f) \cdot \mathbf{n}\, dS = \iiint_{G} (f\nabla^2 g - g\nabla^2 f)\, dV$
[*Hint:* Interchange $f$ and $g$ in Exercise 29.]

31. $\iint_{\sigma} (f\mathbf{n}) \cdot \mathbf{v}\, dS = \iiint_{G} \nabla f \cdot \mathbf{v}\, dV$ ($\mathbf{v}$ a fixed vector)

32. Use the Divergence Theorem to find all positive values of $k$ such that
$$\mathbf{F}(\mathbf{r}) = \frac{\mathbf{r}}{\|\mathbf{r}\|^k}$$
satisfies the condition div $\mathbf{F} = 0$ when $\mathbf{r} \neq \mathbf{0}$.
[*Hint:* Modify the proof of (11).]

**33–36** Determine whether the vector field $\mathbf{F}(x, y, z)$ is free of sources and sinks. If it is not, locate them. ■

33. $\mathbf{F}(x, y, z) = (y + z)\mathbf{i} - xz^3\mathbf{j} + (x^2 \sin y)\mathbf{k}$

34. $\mathbf{F}(x, y, z) = xy\mathbf{i} - xy\mathbf{j} + y^2\mathbf{k}$

35. $\mathbf{F}(x, y, z) = x^3\mathbf{i} + y^3\mathbf{j} + z^3\mathbf{k}$

36. $\mathbf{F}(x, y, z) = (x^3 - x)\mathbf{i} + (y^3 - y)\mathbf{j} + (z^3 - z)\mathbf{k}$

C 37. Let $\sigma$ be the surface of the solid $G$ that is enclosed by the paraboloid $z = 1 - x^2 - y^2$ and the plane $z = 0$. Use a CAS to verify Formula (1) in the Divergence Theorem for the vector field
$$\mathbf{F} = (x^2 y - z^2)\mathbf{i} + (y^3 - x)\mathbf{j} + (2x + 3z - 1)\mathbf{k}$$
by evaluating the surface integral and the triple integral.

38. **Writing** Discuss what it means to say that the divergence of a vector field is independent of a coordinate system. Explain how we know this to be true.

39. **Writing** Describe some geometrical and physical applications of the Divergence Theorem.

✓ **QUICK CHECK ANSWERS 15.7** 1. $\iint_{\sigma} \mathbf{F} \cdot \mathbf{n}\, dS$; $\iiint_{G} \operatorname{div} \mathbf{F}\, dV$ 2. 3 3. source; sink; div $\mathbf{F} = 0$ 4. $4\pi c$; 0

## 15.8 STOKES' THEOREM

*In this section we will discuss a generalization of Green's Theorem to three dimensions that has important applications in the study of vector fields, particularly in the analysis of rotational motion of fluids. This theorem will also provide us with a physical interpretation of the curl of a vector field.*

### RELATIVE ORIENTATION OF CURVES AND SURFACES

We will be concerned in this section with oriented surfaces in 3-space that are bounded by simple closed parametric curves (Figure 15.8.1*a*). If $\sigma$ is an oriented surface bounded by a simple closed parametric curve $C$, then there are two possible relationships between the orientations of $\sigma$ and $C$, which can be described as follows. Imagine a person walking along the curve $C$ with his or her head in the direction of the orientation of $\sigma$. The person is said to be walking in the ***positive direction*** of $C$ relative to the orientation of $\sigma$ if the surface is on the person's left (Figure 15.8.1*b*), and the person is said to be walking in the ***negative direction*** of $C$ relative to the orientation of $\sigma$ if the surface is on the person's right (Figure 15.8.1*c*). The positive direction of $C$ establishes a right-hand relationship between

The oriented surface $\sigma$ is bounded by the simple closed curve $C$. (*a*)

The positive direction of $C$ relative to the orientation of $\sigma$. (*b*)

The negative direction of $C$ relative to the orientation of $\sigma$. (*c*)

▲ **Figure 15.8.1**

the orientations of $\sigma$ and $C$ in the sense that if the fingers of the right hand are curled from the direction of $C$ toward $\sigma$, then the thumb points (roughly) in the direction of the orientation of $\sigma$.

## STOKES' THEOREM

In Section 15.1 we defined the curl of a vector field

$$\mathbf{F}(x, y, z) = f(x, y, z)\mathbf{i} + g(x, y, z)\mathbf{j} + h(x, y, z)\mathbf{k}$$

as

$$\text{curl } \mathbf{F} = \left(\frac{\partial h}{\partial y} - \frac{\partial g}{\partial z}\right)\mathbf{i} + \left(\frac{\partial f}{\partial z} - \frac{\partial h}{\partial x}\right)\mathbf{j} + \left(\frac{\partial g}{\partial x} - \frac{\partial f}{\partial y}\right)\mathbf{k} = \begin{vmatrix} \mathbf{i} & \mathbf{j} & \mathbf{k} \\ \dfrac{\partial}{\partial x} & \dfrac{\partial}{\partial y} & \dfrac{\partial}{\partial z} \\ f & g & h \end{vmatrix} \tag{1}$$

but we did not attempt to give a physical explanation of its meaning at that time. The following result, known as ***Stokes' Theorem***, will provide us with a physical interpretation of the curl in the context of fluid flow.

**15.8.1 THEOREM** (*Stokes' Theorem*) *Let $\sigma$ be a piecewise smooth oriented surface that is bounded by a simple, closed, piecewise smooth curve $C$ with positive orientation. If the components of the vector field*

$$\mathbf{F}(x, y, z) = f(x, y, z)\mathbf{i} + g(x, y, z)\mathbf{j} + h(x, y, z)\mathbf{k}$$

*are continuous and have continuous first partial derivatives on some open set containing $\sigma$, and if $\mathbf{T}$ is the unit tangent vector to $C$, then*

$$\oint_C \mathbf{F} \cdot \mathbf{T}\, ds = \iint_\sigma (\text{curl } \mathbf{F}) \cdot \mathbf{n}\, dS \tag{2}$$

The proof of this theorem is beyond the scope of this text, so we will focus on its applications.

Recall from Formulas (30) and (34) in Section 15.2 that if $\mathbf{F}$ is a force field, the integral on the left side of (2) represents the work performed by the force field on a particle that traverses the curve $C$. Thus, loosely phrased, Stokes' Theorem states:

*The work performed by a force field on a particle that traverses a simple, closed, piecewise smooth curve $C$ in the positive direction can be obtained by integrating the normal component of the curl over an oriented surface $\sigma$ bounded by $C$.*

## USING STOKES' THEOREM TO CALCULATE WORK

For computational purposes it is usually preferable to use Formula (30) in Section 15.2 to rewrite the formula in Stokes' Theorem as

$$\oint_C \mathbf{F} \cdot d\mathbf{r} = \iint_\sigma (\text{curl } \mathbf{F}) \cdot \mathbf{n}\, dS \tag{3}$$

Stokes' Theorem is usually the method of choice for calculating work around piecewise smooth curves with multiple sections, since it eliminates the need for a separate integral evaluation over each section.

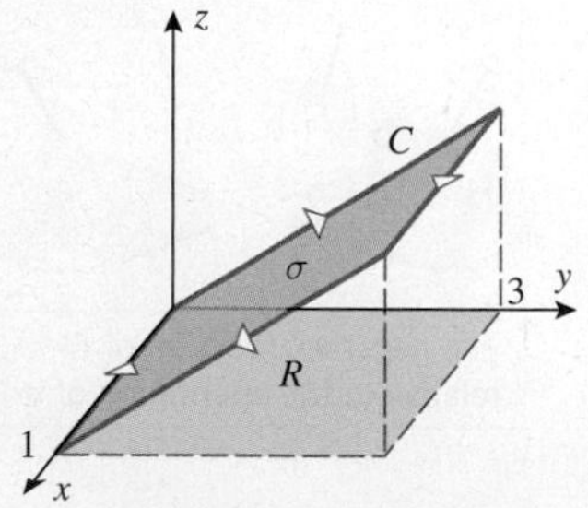

▲ Figure 15.8.2

▶ **Example 1** Find the work performed by the force field

$$\mathbf{F}(x, y, z) = x^2\mathbf{i} + 4xy^3\mathbf{j} + y^2x\mathbf{k}$$

on a particle that traverses the rectangle $C$ in the plane $z = y$ shown in Figure 15.8.2.

***Solution.*** The work performed by the field is

$$W = \oint_C \mathbf{F} \cdot d\mathbf{r}$$

However, to evaluate this integral directly would require four separate integrations, one over each side of the rectangle. Instead, we will use Formula (3) to express the work as the surface integral

$$W = \iint_{\sigma} (\text{curl } \mathbf{F}) \cdot \mathbf{n}\, dS$$

in which the plane surface $\sigma$ enclosed by $C$ is assigned a *downward* orientation to make the orientation of $C$ positive, as required by Stokes' Theorem.

Since the surface $\sigma$ has equation $z = y$ and

$$\text{curl } \mathbf{F} = \begin{vmatrix} \mathbf{i} & \mathbf{j} & \mathbf{k} \\ \dfrac{\partial}{\partial x} & \dfrac{\partial}{\partial y} & \dfrac{\partial}{\partial z} \\ x^2 & 4xy^3 & xy^2 \end{vmatrix} = 2xy\mathbf{i} - y^2\mathbf{j} + 4y^3\mathbf{k}$$

it follows from Formula (13) of Section 15.6 with curl $\mathbf{F}$ replacing $\mathbf{F}$ that

$$\begin{aligned} W = \iint_{\sigma} (\text{curl } \mathbf{F}) \cdot \mathbf{n}\, dS &= \iint_R (\text{curl } \mathbf{F}) \cdot \left( \frac{\partial z}{\partial x}\mathbf{i} + \frac{\partial z}{\partial y}\mathbf{j} - \mathbf{k} \right) dA \\ &= \iint_R (2xy\mathbf{i} - y^2\mathbf{j} + 4y^3\mathbf{k}) \cdot (0\mathbf{i} + \mathbf{j} - \mathbf{k})\, dA \\ &= \int_0^1 \int_0^3 (-y^2 - 4y^3)\, dy\, dx \\ &= -\int_0^1 \left[ \frac{y^3}{3} + y^4 \right]_{y=0}^{3} dx \\ &= -\int_0^1 90\, dx = -90 \blacktriangleleft \end{aligned}$$

Explain how the result in Example 1 shows that the given force field is not conservative.

**George Gabriel Stokes (1819–1903)** Irish mathematician and physicist. Born in Skreen, Ireland, Stokes came from a family deeply rooted in the Church of Ireland. His father was a rector, his mother the daughter of a rector, and three of his brothers took holy orders. He received his early education from his father and a local parish clerk. In 1837, he entered Pembroke College and after graduating with top honors accepted a fellowship at the college. In 1847 he was appointed Lucasian professor of mathematics at Cambridge, a position once held by Isaac Newton (and now held by the British physicist, Stephen Hawking), but one that had lost its esteem through the years. By virtue of his accomplishments, Stokes ultimately restored the position to the eminence it once held. Unfortunately, the position paid very little and Stokes was forced to teach at the Government School of Mines during the 1850s to supplement his income.

Stokes was one of several outstanding nineteenth century scientists who helped turn the physical sciences in a more empirical direction. He systematically studied hydrodynamics, elasticity of solids, behavior of waves in elastic solids, and diffraction of light. For Stokes, mathematics was a tool for his physical studies. He wrote classic papers on the motion of viscous fluids that laid the foundation for modern hydrodynamics; he elaborated on the wave theory of light; and he wrote papers on gravitational variation that established him as a founder of the modern science of geodesy.

Stokes was honored in his later years with degrees, medals, and memberships in foreign societies. He was knighted in 1889. Throughout his life, Stokes gave generously of his time to learned societies and readily assisted those who sought his help in solving problems. He was deeply religious and vitally concerned with the relationship between science and religion.

*[Image: photos.com/Getty Images]*

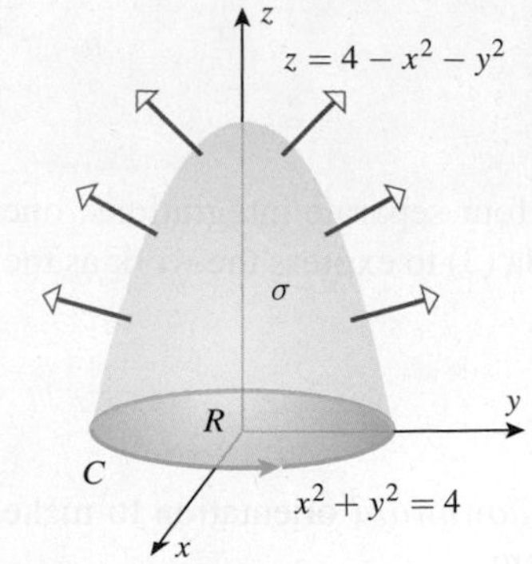

▲ **Figure 15.8.3**

▶ **Example 2** Verify Stokes' Theorem for the vector field $\mathbf{F}(x, y, z) = 2z\mathbf{i} + 3x\mathbf{j} + 5y\mathbf{k}$, taking $\sigma$ to be the portion of the paraboloid $z = 4 - x^2 - y^2$ for which $z \geq 0$ with upward orientation, and $C$ to be the positively oriented circle $x^2 + y^2 = 4$ that forms the boundary of $\sigma$ in the $xy$-plane (Figure 15.8.3).

***Solution.*** We will verify Formula (3). Since $\sigma$ is oriented up, the positive orientation of $C$ is counterclockwise looking down the positive $z$-axis. Thus, $C$ can be represented parametrically (with positive orientation) by

$$x = 2\cos t, \quad y = 2\sin t, \quad z = 0 \qquad (0 \leq t \leq 2\pi) \tag{4}$$

Therefore,

$$\begin{aligned}\oint_C \mathbf{F} \cdot d\mathbf{r} &= \oint_C 2z\,dx + 3x\,dy + 5y\,dz \\ &= \int_0^{2\pi} [0 + (6\cos t)(2\cos t) + 0]\,dt \\ &= \int_0^{2\pi} 12\cos^2 t\,dt = 12\left[\frac{1}{2}t + \frac{1}{4}\sin 2t\right]_0^{2\pi} = 12\pi\end{aligned}$$

To evaluate the right side of (3), we start by finding curl $\mathbf{F}$. We obtain

$$\operatorname{curl}\mathbf{F} = \begin{vmatrix} \mathbf{i} & \mathbf{j} & \mathbf{k} \\ \dfrac{\partial}{\partial x} & \dfrac{\partial}{\partial y} & \dfrac{\partial}{\partial z} \\ 2z & 3x & 5y \end{vmatrix} = 5\mathbf{i} + 2\mathbf{j} + 3\mathbf{k}$$

Since $\sigma$ is oriented up and is expressed in the form $z = g(x, y) = 4 - x^2 - y^2$, it follows from Formula (12) of Section 15.6 with curl $\mathbf{F}$ replacing $\mathbf{F}$ that

$$\begin{aligned}\iint_\sigma (\operatorname{curl}\mathbf{F}) \cdot \mathbf{n}\,dS &= \iint_R (\operatorname{curl}\mathbf{F}) \cdot \left(-\frac{\partial z}{\partial x}\mathbf{i} - \frac{\partial z}{\partial y}\mathbf{j} + \mathbf{k}\right) dA \\ &= \iint_R (5\mathbf{i} + 2\mathbf{j} + 3\mathbf{k}) \cdot (2x\mathbf{i} + 2y\mathbf{j} + \mathbf{k})\,dA \\ &= \iint_R (10x + 4y + 3)\,dA \\ &= \int_0^{2\pi}\int_0^2 (10r\cos\theta + 4r\sin\theta + 3)r\,dr\,d\theta \\ &= \int_0^{2\pi}\left[\frac{10r^3}{3}\cos\theta + \frac{4r^3}{3}\sin\theta + \frac{3r^2}{2}\right]_{r=0}^2 d\theta \\ &= \int_0^{2\pi}\left(\frac{80}{3}\cos\theta + \frac{32}{3}\sin\theta + 6\right) d\theta \\ &= \left[\frac{80}{3}\sin\theta - \frac{32}{3}\cos\theta + 6\theta\right]_0^{2\pi} = 12\pi\end{aligned}$$

As guaranteed by Stokes' Theorem, the value of this surface integral is the same as the value obtained for the line integral. Note, however, that the line integral was simpler to evaluate and hence would be the method of choice in this case. ◀

**REMARK** Observe that in Formula (3) the only relationships required between $\sigma$ and $C$ are that $C$ be the boundary of $\sigma$ and that $C$ be positively oriented relative to the orientation of $\sigma$. Thus, if $\sigma_1$ and $\sigma_2$ are *different* oriented surfaces but have the *same* positively oriented boundary curve $C$, then it follows from (3) that

$$\iint_{\sigma_1} \operatorname{curl} \mathbf{F} \cdot \mathbf{n}\, dS = \iint_{\sigma_2} \operatorname{curl} \mathbf{F} \cdot \mathbf{n}\, dS$$

For example, the parabolic surface in Example 2 has the same positively oriented boundary $C$ as the disk $R$ in Figure 15.8.3 with upper orientation. Thus, the value of the surface integral in that example would not change if $\sigma$ is replaced by $R$ (or by any other oriented surface that has the positively oriented circle $C$ as its boundary). This can be useful in computations because it is sometimes possible to circumvent a difficult integration by changing the surface of integration.

## RELATIONSHIP BETWEEN GREEN'S THEOREM AND STOKES' THEOREM

It is sometimes convenient to regard a vector field

$$\mathbf{F}(x, y) = f(x, y)\mathbf{i} + g(x, y)\mathbf{j}$$

in 2-space as a vector field in 3-space by expressing it as

$$\mathbf{F}(x, y) = f(x, y)\mathbf{i} + g(x, y)\mathbf{j} + 0\mathbf{k} \tag{5}$$

If $R$ is a region in the $xy$-plane enclosed by a simple, closed, piecewise smooth curve $C$, then we can treat $R$ as a *flat* surface, and we can treat a surface integral over $R$ as an ordinary double integral over $R$. Thus, if we orient $R$ up and $C$ counterclockwise looking down the positive $z$-axis, then Formula (3) applied to (5) yields

$$\oint_C \mathbf{F} \cdot d\mathbf{r} = \iint_R \operatorname{curl} \mathbf{F} \cdot \mathbf{k}\, dA \tag{6}$$

But

$$\operatorname{curl} \mathbf{F} = \begin{vmatrix} \mathbf{i} & \mathbf{j} & \mathbf{k} \\ \dfrac{\partial}{\partial x} & \dfrac{\partial}{\partial y} & \dfrac{\partial}{\partial z} \\ f & g & 0 \end{vmatrix} = -\frac{\partial g}{\partial z}\mathbf{i} + \frac{\partial f}{\partial z}\mathbf{j} + \left(\frac{\partial g}{\partial x} - \frac{\partial f}{\partial y}\right)\mathbf{k} = \left(\frac{\partial g}{\partial x} - \frac{\partial f}{\partial y}\right)\mathbf{k}$$

since $\partial g/\partial z = \partial f/\partial z = 0$. Substituting this expression in (6) and expressing the integrals in terms of components yields

$$\oint_C f\, dx + g\, dy = \iint_R \left(\frac{\partial g}{\partial x} - \frac{\partial f}{\partial y}\right) dA$$

which is Green's Theorem [Formula (1) of Section 15.4]. Thus, we have shown that Green's Theorem can be viewed as a special case of Stokes' Theorem.

## CURL VIEWED AS CIRCULATION

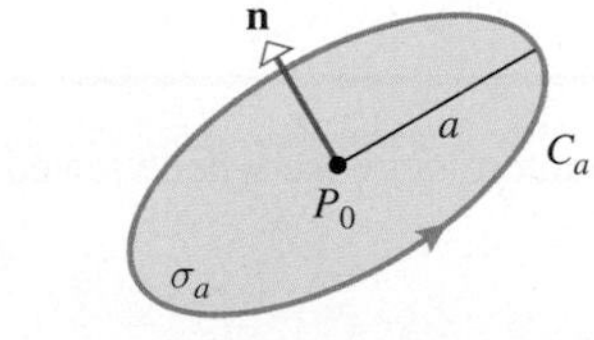

▲ **Figure 15.8.4**

Stokes' Theorem provides a way of interpreting the curl of a vector field $\mathbf{F}$ in the context of fluid flow. For this purpose let $\sigma_a$ be a small oriented disk of radius $a$ centered at a point $P_0$ in a steady-state fluid flow, and let $\mathbf{n}$ be a unit normal vector at the center of the disk that points in the direction of orientation. Let us assume that the flow of liquid past the disk causes it to spin around the axis through $\mathbf{n}$, and let us try to find the direction of $\mathbf{n}$ that will produce the maximum rotation rate in the positive direction of the boundary curve $C_a$ (Figure 15.8.4). For convenience, we will denote the area of the disk $\sigma_a$ by $A(\sigma_a)$; that is, $A(\sigma_a) = \pi a^2$.

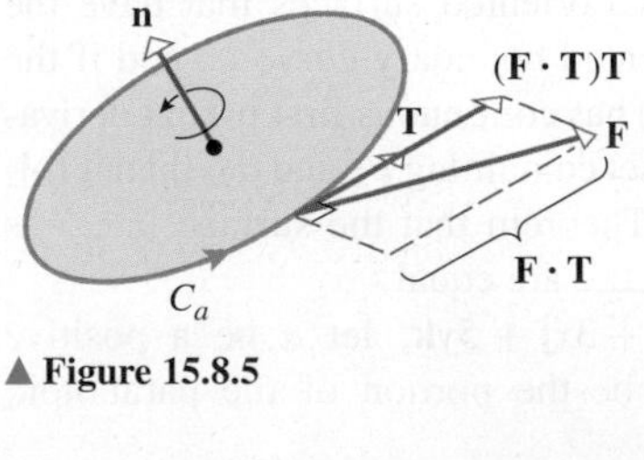

▲ **Figure 15.8.5**

If the direction of $\mathbf{n}$ is fixed, then at each point of $C_a$ the only component of $\mathbf{F}$ that contributes to the rotation of the disk about $\mathbf{n}$ is the component $\mathbf{F} \cdot \mathbf{T}$ tangent to $C_a$ (Figure 15.8.5). Thus, for a fixed $\mathbf{n}$ the integral

$$\oint_{C_a} \mathbf{F} \cdot \mathbf{T}\, ds \tag{7}$$

can be viewed as a measure of the tendency for the fluid to flow in the positive direction around $C_a$. Accordingly, (7) is called the ***circulation of* F *around* $C_a$**. For example, in the extreme case where the flow is normal to the circle at each point, the circulation around $C_a$ is zero, since $\mathbf{F}\cdot\mathbf{T} = 0$ at each point. The more closely that **F** aligns with **T** along the circle, the larger the value of $\mathbf{F}\cdot\mathbf{T}$ and the larger the value of the circulation.

To see the relationship between circulation and curl, suppose that curl **F** is continuous on $\sigma_a$, so that when $\sigma_a$ is small the value of curl **F** at any point of $\sigma_a$ will not vary much from the value of curl $\mathbf{F}(P_0)$ at the center. Thus, for a small disk $\sigma_a$ we can reasonably approximate curl **F** on $\sigma_a$ by the constant value curl $\mathbf{F}(P_0)$. Moreover, because the surface $\sigma_a$ is flat, the unit normal vectors that orient $\sigma_a$ are all equal. Thus, the vector quantity **n** in Formula (3) can be treated as a constant, and we can write

$$\oint_{C_a} \mathbf{F}\cdot\mathbf{T}\,ds = \iint_{\sigma_a} (\text{curl}\,\mathbf{F})\cdot\mathbf{n}\,dS \approx \text{curl}\,\mathbf{F}(P_0)\cdot\mathbf{n}\iint_{\sigma_a} dS$$

where the line integral is taken in the positive direction of $C_a$. But the last double integral in this equation represents the surface area of $\sigma_a$, so

$$\oint_{C_a} \mathbf{F}\cdot\mathbf{T}\,ds \approx [\text{curl}\,\mathbf{F}(P_0)\cdot\mathbf{n}]A(\sigma_a)$$

from which we obtain

$$\text{curl}\,\mathbf{F}(P_0)\cdot\mathbf{n} \approx \frac{1}{A(\sigma_a)}\oint_{C_a} \mathbf{F}\cdot\mathbf{T}\,ds \tag{8}$$

Formula (9) is sometimes taken as a definition of curl. This is a useful alternative to Definition 15.1.5 because it does not require a coordinate system.

The quantity on the right side of (8) is called the ***circulation density of* F *around* $C_a$**. If we now let the radius $a$ of the disk approach zero (with **n** fixed), then it is plausible that the error in this approximation will approach zero and the exact value of curl $\mathbf{F}(P_0)\cdot\mathbf{n}$ will be given by

$$\text{curl}\,\mathbf{F}(P_0)\cdot\mathbf{n} = \lim_{a\to 0}\frac{1}{A(\sigma_a)}\oint_{C_a} \mathbf{F}\cdot\mathbf{T}\,ds \tag{9}$$

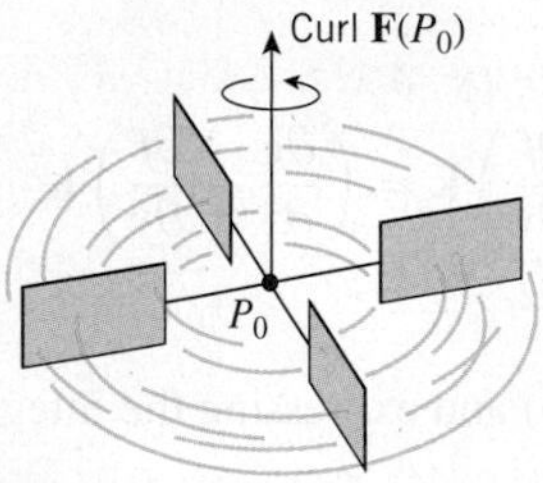

▲ **Figure 15.8.6**

We call curl $\mathbf{F}(P_0)\cdot\mathbf{n}$ the ***circulation density of* F *at* $P_0$ *in the direction of* n**. This quantity has its maximum value when **n** is in the same direction as curl $\mathbf{F}(P_0)$; this tells us that *at each point in a steady-state fluid flow the maximum circulation density occurs in the direction of the curl.* Physically, this means that if a small paddle wheel is immersed in the fluid so that the pivot point is at $P_0$, then the paddles will turn most rapidly when the spindle is aligned with curl $\mathbf{F}(P_0)$ (Figure 15.8.6). If curl $\mathbf{F} = \mathbf{0}$ at each point of a region, then **F** is said to be ***irrotational*** in that region, since no circulation occurs about any point of the region.

## ✓ QUICK CHECK EXERCISES 15.8

*(See page 1046 for answers.)*

**1.** Let $\sigma$ be a piecewise smooth oriented surface that is bounded by a simple, closed, piecewise smooth curve $C$ with positive orientation. If the component functions of the vector field $\mathbf{F}(x, y, z)$ have continuous first partial derivatives on some open set containing $\sigma$, and if **T** is the unit tangent vector to $C$, then Stokes' Theorem states that the line integral ________ and the surface integral ________ are equal.

**2.** We showed in Example 2 that the vector field

$$\mathbf{F}(x, y, z) = 2z\mathbf{i} + 3x\mathbf{j} + 5y\mathbf{k}$$

satisfies the equation curl $\mathbf{F} = 5\mathbf{i} + 2\mathbf{j} + 3\mathbf{k}$. It follows from Stokes' Theorem that if $C$ is any circle of radius $a$ in the $xy$-plane that is oriented counterclockwise when viewed from the positive $z$-axis, then

$$\int_C \mathbf{F}\cdot\mathbf{T}\,ds = \underline{\qquad\qquad}$$

where **T** denotes the unit tangent vector to $C$.

**3.** (a) If $\sigma_1$ and $\sigma_2$ are two oriented surfaces that have the same positively oriented boundary curve $C$, and if the vector field $\mathbf{F}(x, y, z)$ has continuous first partial derivatives on some open set containing $\sigma_1$ and $\sigma_2$, then it follows from Stokes' Theorem that the surface integrals ________ and ________ are equal.

(b) Let $\mathbf{F}(x, y, z) = 2z\mathbf{i} + 3x\mathbf{j} + 5y\mathbf{k}$, let $a$ be a positive number, and let $\sigma$ be the portion of the paraboloid

$z = a^2 - x^2 - y^2$ for which $z \geq 0$ with upward orientation. Using part (a) and Quick Check Exercise 2, it follows that

$$\iint_{\sigma} (\text{curl } \mathbf{F}) \cdot \mathbf{n}\, dS = \underline{\hspace{2cm}}$$

4. For steady-state flow, the maximum circulation density occurs in the direction of the ______ of the velocity vector field for the flow.

## EXERCISE SET 15.8 C CAS

**1–4** Verify Formula (2) in Stokes' Theorem by evaluating the line integral and the surface integral. Assume that the surface has an upward orientation. ■

1. $\mathbf{F}(x, y, z) = (x - y)\mathbf{i} + (y - z)\mathbf{j} + (z - x)\mathbf{k}$; $\sigma$ is the portion of the plane $x + y + z = 1$ in the first octant.
2. $\mathbf{F}(x, y, z) = x^2\mathbf{i} + y^2\mathbf{j} + z^2\mathbf{k}$; $\sigma$ is the portion of the cone $z = \sqrt{x^2 + y^2}$ below the plane $z = 1$.
3. $\mathbf{F}(x, y, z) = x\mathbf{i} + y\mathbf{j} + z\mathbf{k}$; $\sigma$ is the upper hemisphere $z = \sqrt{a^2 - x^2 - y^2}$.
4. $\mathbf{F}(x, y, z) = (z - y)\mathbf{i} + (z + x)\mathbf{j} - (x + y)\mathbf{k}$; $\sigma$ is the portion of the paraboloid $z = 9 - x^2 - y^2$ above the $xy$-plane.

**5–12** Use Stokes' Theorem to evaluate $\oint_C \mathbf{F} \cdot d\mathbf{r}$. ■

5. $\mathbf{F}(x, y, z) = z^2\mathbf{i} + 2x\mathbf{j} - y^3\mathbf{k}$; $C$ is the circle $x^2 + y^2 = 1$ in the $xy$-plane with counterclockwise orientation looking down the positive $z$-axis.
6. $\mathbf{F}(x, y, z) = xz\mathbf{i} + 3x^2y^2\mathbf{j} + yx\mathbf{k}$; $C$ is the rectangle in the plane $z = y$ shown in Figure 15.8.2.
7. $\mathbf{F}(x, y, z) = 3z\mathbf{i} + 4x\mathbf{j} + 2y\mathbf{k}$; $C$ is the boundary of the paraboloid shown in Figure 15.8.3.
8. $\mathbf{F}(x, y, z) = -3y^2\mathbf{i} + 4z\mathbf{j} + 6x\mathbf{k}$; $C$ is the triangle in the plane $z = \frac{1}{2}y$ with vertices $(2, 0, 0)$, $(0, 2, 1)$, and $(0, 0, 0)$ with a counterclockwise orientation looking down the positive $z$-axis.
9. $\mathbf{F}(x, y, z) = xy\mathbf{i} + x^2\mathbf{j} + z^2\mathbf{k}$; $C$ is the intersection of the paraboloid $z = x^2 + y^2$ and the plane $z = y$ with a counterclockwise orientation looking down the positive $z$-axis.
10. $\mathbf{F}(x, y, z) = xy\mathbf{i} + yz\mathbf{j} + zx\mathbf{k}$; $C$ is the triangle in the plane $x + y + z = 1$ with vertices $(1, 0, 0)$, $(0, 1, 0)$, and $(0, 0, 1)$ with a counterclockwise orientation looking from the first octant toward the origin.
11. $\mathbf{F}(x, y, z) = (x - y)\mathbf{i} + (y - z)\mathbf{j} + (z - x)\mathbf{k}$; $C$ is the circle $x^2 + y^2 = a^2$ in the $xy$-plane with counterclockwise orientation looking down the positive $z$-axis.
12. $\mathbf{F}(x, y, z) = (z + \sin x)\mathbf{i} + (x + y^2)\mathbf{j} + (y + e^z)\mathbf{k}$; $C$ is the intersection of the sphere $x^2 + y^2 + z^2 = 1$ and the cone $z = \sqrt{x^2 + y^2}$ with counterclockwise orientation looking down the positive $z$-axis.

**13–16 True–False** Determine whether the statement is true or false. Explain your answer. ■

13. Stokes' Theorem equates a line integral and a surface integral.
14. Stokes' Theorem is a special case of Green's Theorem.
15. The circulation of a vector field $\mathbf{F}$ around a closed curve $C$ is defined to be

$$\int_C (\text{curl } \mathbf{F}) \cdot \mathbf{T}\, ds$$

16. If $\mathbf{F}(x, y, z)$ is defined everywhere in 3-space, and if curl $\mathbf{F}$ has no $\mathbf{k}$-component at any point in the $xy$-plane, then

$$\int_C \mathbf{F} \cdot \mathbf{T}\, ds = 0$$

for every smooth, simple, closed curve in the $xy$-plane.

17. Consider the vector field given by the formula

$$\mathbf{F}(x, y, z) = (x - z)\mathbf{i} + (y - x)\mathbf{j} + (z - xy)\mathbf{k}$$

(a) Use Stokes' Theorem to find the circulation around the triangle with vertices $A(1, 0, 0)$, $B(0, 2, 0)$, and $C(0, 0, 1)$ oriented counterclockwise looking from the origin toward the first octant.
(b) Find the circulation density of $\mathbf{F}$ at the origin in the direction of $\mathbf{k}$.
(c) Find the unit vector $\mathbf{n}$ such that the circulation density of $\mathbf{F}$ at the origin is maximum in the direction of $\mathbf{n}$.

**FOCUS ON CONCEPTS**

18. (a) Let $\sigma$ denote the surface of a solid $G$ with $\mathbf{n}$ the outward unit normal vector field to $\sigma$. Assume that $\mathbf{F}$ is a vector field with continuous first-order partial derivatives on $\sigma$. Prove that

$$\iint_{\sigma} (\text{curl } \mathbf{F}) \cdot \mathbf{n}\, dS = 0$$

[*Hint:* Let $C$ denote a simple closed curve on $\sigma$ that separates the surface into two subsurfaces $\sigma_1$ and $\sigma_2$ that share $C$ as their common boundary. Apply Stokes' Theorem to $\sigma_1$ and to $\sigma_2$ and add the results.]
(b) The vector field curl($\mathbf{F}$) is called the ***curl field*** of $\mathbf{F}$. In words, interpret the formula in part (a) as a statement about the flux of the curl field.

**19–20** The figures in these exercises show a horizontal layer of the vector field of a fluid flow in which the flow is parallel to the $xy$-plane at every point and is identical in each layer (i.e., is independent of $z$). For each flow, state whether you believe that the curl is nonzero at the origin, and explain your reasoning. If you believe that it is nonzero, then state whether it points in the positive or negative $z$-direction. ■

**19.** (a) (b)

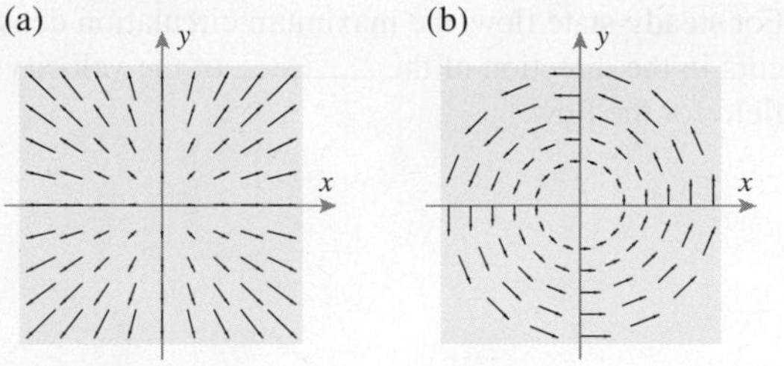


**20.** (a) (b)

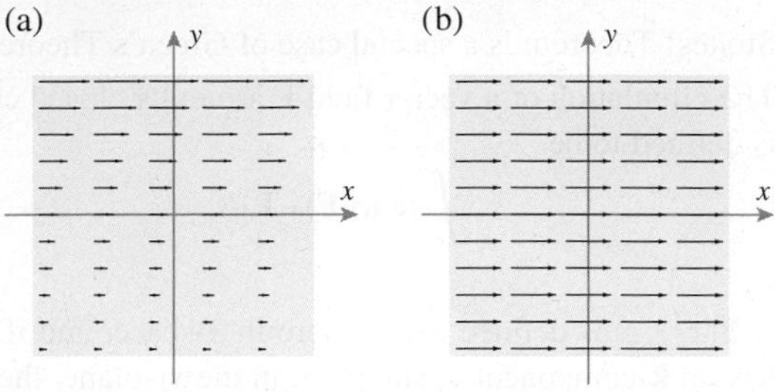


**21.** Let $\mathbf{F}(x, y, z)$ be a conservative vector field in 3-space whose component functions have continuous first partial derivatives. Explain how to use Formula (9) to prove that curl $\mathbf{F} = \mathbf{0}$.

**22.** In 1831 the physicist Michael Faraday discovered that an electric current can be produced by varying the magnetic flux through a conducting loop. His experiments showed that the electromotive force $\mathbf{E}$ is related to the magnetic induction $\mathbf{B}$ by the equation

$$\oint_C \mathbf{E} \cdot d\mathbf{r} = -\iint_\sigma \frac{\partial \mathbf{B}}{\partial t} \cdot \mathbf{n}\, dS$$

Use this result to make a conjecture about the relationship between curl $\mathbf{E}$ and $\mathbf{B}$, and explain your reasoning.

C **23.** Let $\sigma$ be the portion of the paraboloid $z = 1 - x^2 - y^2$ for which $z \geq 0$, and let $C$ be the circle $x^2 + y^2 = 1$ that forms the boundary of $\sigma$ in the $xy$-plane. Assuming that $\sigma$ is oriented up, use a CAS to verify Formula (2) in Stokes' Theorem for the vector field

$$\mathbf{F} = (x^2y - z^2)\mathbf{i} + (y^3 - x)\mathbf{j} + (2x + 3z - 1)\mathbf{k}$$

by evaluating the line integral and the surface integral.

**24. Writing** Discuss what it means to say that the curl of a vector field is independent of a coordinate system. Explain how we know this to be true.

**25. Writing** Compare and contrast the Fundamental Theorem of Line Integrals, the Divergence Theorem, and Stokes' Theorem.

✓ **QUICK CHECK ANSWERS 15.8** 1. $\int_C \mathbf{F} \cdot \mathbf{T}\, ds$; $\iint_\sigma (\text{curl } \mathbf{F}) \cdot \mathbf{n}\, dS$ 2. $3\pi a^2$ 3. (a) $\iint_{\sigma_1} (\text{curl } \mathbf{F}) \cdot \mathbf{n}\, dS$; $\iint_{\sigma_2} (\text{curl } \mathbf{F}) \cdot \mathbf{n}\, dS$ (b) $3\pi a^2$ 4. curl

## CHAPTER 15 REVIEW EXERCISES

**1.** In words, what is a vector field? Give some physical examples of vector fields.

**2.** (a) Give a physical example of an inverse-square field $\mathbf{F}(\mathbf{r})$ in 3-space.
(b) Write a formula for a general inverse-square field $\mathbf{F}(\mathbf{r})$ in terms of the radius vector $\mathbf{r}$.
(c) Write a formula for a general inverse-square field $\mathbf{F}(x, y, z)$ in 3-space using rectangular coordinates.

**3.** Find an explicit coordinate expression for the vector field $\mathbf{F}(x, y)$ that at every point $(x, y) \neq (1, 2)$ is the unit vector directed from $(x, y)$ to $(1, 2)$.

**4.** Find $\nabla\left(\dfrac{x + y}{x - y}\right)$.

**5.** Find $\text{curl}(z\mathbf{i} + x\mathbf{j} + y\mathbf{k})$.

**6.** Let

$$\mathbf{F}(x, y, z) = \frac{x}{x^2 + y^2}\mathbf{i} + \frac{y}{x^2 + y^2}\mathbf{j} + \frac{z}{x^2 + y^2}\mathbf{k}$$

Sketch the level surface div $\mathbf{F} = 1$.

**7.** Assume that $C$ is the parametric curve $x = x(t)$, $y = y(t)$, where $t$ varies from $a$ to $b$. In each part, express the line integral as a definite integral with variable of integration $t$.
(a) $\int_C f(x, y)\, dx + g(x, y)\, dy$ (b) $\int_C f(x, y)\, ds$

**8.** (a) Express the mass $M$ of a thin wire in 3-space as a line integral.
(b) Express the length of a curve as a line integral.

**9.** Give a physical interpretation of $\int_C \mathbf{F} \cdot \mathbf{T}\, ds$.

**10.** State some alternative notations for $\int_C \mathbf{F} \cdot \mathbf{T}\, ds$.

**11–13** Evaluate the line integral. ■

**11.** $\int_C (x - y)\, ds$; $C: x^2 + y^2 = 1$

**12.** $\int_C x\, dx + z\, dy - 2y^2\, dz$;
$C: x = \cos t,\ y = \sin t,\ z = t \quad (0 \leq t \leq 2\pi)$

**13.** $\int_C \mathbf{F} \cdot d\mathbf{r}$ where $\mathbf{F}(x, y) = (x/y)\mathbf{i} - (y/x)\mathbf{j}$;
$\mathbf{r}(t) = t\mathbf{i} + 2t\mathbf{j} \quad (1 \le t \le 2)$

**14.** Find the work done by the force field

$$\mathbf{F}(x, y) = y^2\mathbf{i} + xy\mathbf{j}$$

moving a particle from $(0, 0)$ to $(1, 1)$ along the parabola $y = x^2$.

**15.** State the Fundamental Theorem of Line Integrals, including all required hypotheses.

**16.** Evaluate $\int_C \nabla f \cdot d\mathbf{r}$ where $f(x, y, z) = xy^2z^3$ and

$$\mathbf{r}(t) = t\mathbf{i} + (t^2 + t)\mathbf{j} + \sin(3\pi t/2)\mathbf{k} \quad (0 \le t \le 1)$$

**17.** Let $\mathbf{F}(x, y) = y\mathbf{i} - 2x\mathbf{j}$.
(a) Find a nonzero function $h(x)$ such that $h(x)\mathbf{F}(x, y)$ is a conservative vector field.
(b) Find a nonzero function $g(y)$ such that $g(y)\mathbf{F}(x, y)$ is a conservative vector field.

**18.** Let $\mathbf{F}(x, y) = (ye^{xy} - 1)\mathbf{i} + xe^{xy}\mathbf{j}$.
(a) Show that $\mathbf{F}$ is a conservative vector field.
(b) Find a potential function for $\mathbf{F}$.
(c) Find the work performed by the force field on a particle that moves along the sawtooth curve represented by the parametric equations

$$x = t + \sin^{-1}(\sin t), \quad y = (2/\pi)\sin^{-1}(\sin t) \quad (0 \le t \le 8\pi)$$

(see the accompanying figure).

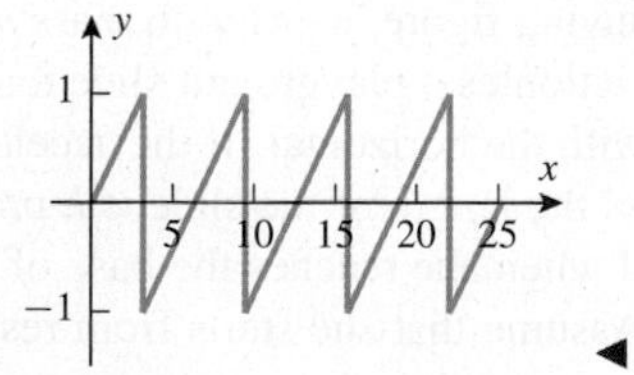

◀ **Figure Ex-18**

**19.** State Green's Theorem, including all of the required hypotheses.

**20.** Express the area of a plane region as a line integral.

**21.** Let $\alpha$ and $\beta$ denote angles that satisfy $0 < \beta - \alpha \le 2\pi$ and assume that $r = f(\theta)$ is a smooth polar curve with $f(\theta) > 0$ on the interval $[\alpha, \beta]$. Use the formula

$$A = \frac{1}{2}\int_C -y\,dx + x\,dy$$

to find the area of the region $R$ enclosed by the curve $r = f(\theta)$ and the rays $\theta = \alpha$ and $\theta = \beta$.

**22.** (a) Use Green's Theorem to prove that

$$\int_C f(x)\,dx + g(y)\,dy = 0$$

if $f$ and $g$ are differentiable functions and $C$ is a simple, closed, piecewise smooth curve.
(b) What does this tell you about the vector field $\mathbf{F}(x, y) = f(x)\mathbf{i} + g(y)\mathbf{j}$?

**23.** Assume that $\sigma$ is the parametric surface

$$\mathbf{r} = x(u, v)\mathbf{i} + y(u, v)\mathbf{j} + z(u, v)\mathbf{k}$$

where $(u, v)$ varies over a region $R$. Express the surface integral

$$\iint_\sigma f(x, y, z)\,dS$$

as a double integral with variables of integration $u$ and $v$.

**24.** Evaluate $\iint_\sigma z\,dS$; $\sigma : x^2 + y^2 = 1\ (0 \le z \le 1)$.

**25.** Do you think that the surface in the accompanying figure is orientable? Explain your reasoning.

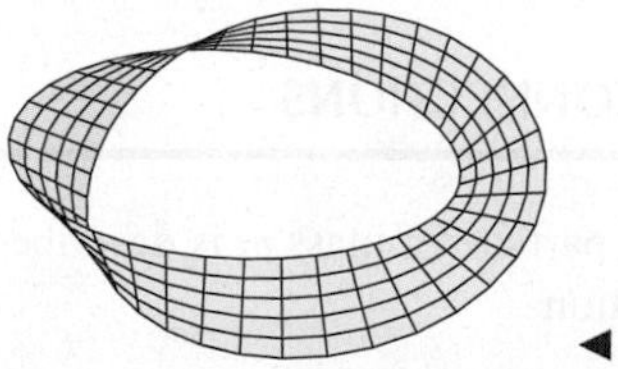
◀ **Figure Ex-25**

**26.** Give a physical interpretation of $\iint_\sigma \mathbf{F} \cdot \mathbf{n}\,dS$.

**27.** Find the flux of $\mathbf{F}(x, y, z) = x\mathbf{i} + y\mathbf{j} + 2z\mathbf{k}$ through the portion of the paraboloid $z = 1 - x^2 - y^2$ that is on or above the $xy$-plane, with upward orientation.

**28.** Find the flux of $\mathbf{F}(x, y, z) = x\mathbf{i} + 2y\mathbf{j} + 3z\mathbf{k}$ through the unit sphere centered at the origin with outward orientation.

**29.** State the Divergence Theorem and Stokes' Theorem, including all required hypotheses.

**30.** Let $G$ be a solid with the surface $\sigma$ oriented by outward unit normals, suppose that $\phi$ has continuous first and second partial derivatives in some open set containing $G$, and let $D_\mathbf{n}\phi$ be the directional derivative of $\phi$, where $\mathbf{n}$ is an outward unit normal to $\sigma$. Show that

$$\iint_\sigma D_\mathbf{n}\phi\,dS = \iiint_G \left[\frac{\partial^2\phi}{\partial x^2} + \frac{\partial^2\phi}{\partial y^2} + \frac{\partial^2\phi}{\partial z^2}\right] dV$$

**31.** Let $\sigma$ be the sphere $x^2 + y^2 + z^2 = 1$, let $\mathbf{n}$ be an inward unit normal, and let $D_\mathbf{n}f$ be the directional derivative of $f(x, y, z) = x^2 + y^2 + z^2$. Use the result in Exercise 30 to evaluate the surface integral

$$\iint_\sigma D_\mathbf{n}f\,dS$$

**32.** Use Stokes' Theorem to evaluate $\iint_\sigma \text{curl}\,\mathbf{F} \cdot \mathbf{n}\,dS$ where $\mathbf{F}(x, y, z) = (z - y)\mathbf{i} + (x + z)\mathbf{j} - (x + y)\mathbf{k}$ and $\sigma$ is the portion of the paraboloid $z = 2 - x^2 - y^2$ on or above the plane $z = 1$, with upward orientation.

**33.** Let $\mathbf{F}(x, y, z) = f(x, y, z)\mathbf{i} + g(x, y, z)\mathbf{j} + h(x, y, z)\mathbf{k}$ and suppose that $f$, $g$, and $h$ are continuous and have continuous first partial derivatives in a region. It was shown in Exercise 31 of Section 15.3 that if $\mathbf{F}$ is conservative in the region, then

$$\frac{\partial f}{\partial y} = \frac{\partial g}{\partial x}, \quad \frac{\partial f}{\partial z} = \frac{\partial h}{\partial x}, \quad \frac{\partial g}{\partial z} = \frac{\partial h}{\partial y}$$

there. Use this result to show that if $\mathbf{F}$ is conservative in an open spherical region, then curl $\mathbf{F} = \mathbf{0}$ in that region.

**34–35** With the aid of Exercise 33, determine whether $\mathbf{F}$ is conservative. ■

**34.** (a) $\mathbf{F}(x, y, z) = z^2\mathbf{i} + e^{-y}\mathbf{j} + 2xz\mathbf{k}$
(b) $\mathbf{F}(x, y, z) = xy\mathbf{i} + x^2\mathbf{j} + \sin z\mathbf{k}$

**35.** (a) $\mathbf{F}(x, y, z) = \sin x\mathbf{i} + z\mathbf{j} + y\mathbf{k}$
(b) $\mathbf{F}(x, y, z) = z\mathbf{i} + 2yz\mathbf{j} + y^2\mathbf{k}$

**36.** As discussed in Example 1 of Section 15.1, *Coulomb's law* states that the electrostatic force $\mathbf{F}(\mathbf{r})$ that a particle of charge $Q$ exerts on a particle of charge $q$ is given by the formula

$$\mathbf{F}(\mathbf{r}) = \frac{qQ}{4\pi\epsilon_0\|\mathbf{r}\|^3}\mathbf{r}$$

where $\mathbf{r}$ is the radius vector from $Q$ to $q$ and $\epsilon_0$ is the permittivity constant.
(a) Express the vector field $\mathbf{F}(\mathbf{r})$ in coordinate form $\mathbf{F}(x, y, z)$ with $Q$ at the origin.
(b) Find the work performed by the force field $\mathbf{F}$ on a charge $q$ that moves along a straight line from $(3, 0, 0)$ to $(3, 1, 5)$.

## CHAPTER 15 MAKING CONNECTIONS

Assume that the motion of a particle of mass $m$ is described by a smooth vector-valued function

$$\mathbf{r}(t) = x(t)\mathbf{i} + y(t)\mathbf{j} + z(t)\mathbf{k} \quad (a \le t \le b)$$

where $t$ denotes time. Let $C$ denote the graph of the vector-valued function and let $v(t)$ and $\mathbf{a}(t)$ denote the respective speed and acceleration of the particle at time $t$.

**1.** We will say that the particle is moving "freely" under the influence of a force field $\mathbf{F}(x, y, z)$, provided $\mathbf{F}$ is the *only* force acting on the particle. In this case Newton's Second Law of Motion becomes

$$\mathbf{F}(x(t), y(t), z(t)) = m\mathbf{a}(t)$$

Use Theorem 12.6.2 to prove that when the particle is moving freely

$$\begin{aligned}\int_C \mathbf{F} \cdot \mathbf{T}\, ds &= \int_C m\left(\frac{dv}{dt}\right) ds = m\int_a^b v(t)\left(\frac{dv}{dt}\right) dt\\ &= m\int_a^b \frac{d}{dt}\left(\frac{1}{2}[v(t)]^2\right) dt\\ &= \frac{1}{2}m[v(b)]^2 - \frac{1}{2}m[v(a)]^2\end{aligned}$$

This tells us that the work performed by $\mathbf{F}$ on the particle is equal to the change in kinetic energy of the particle.

**2.** Suppose that the particle moves along a *prescribed* curve $C$ under the influence of a force field $\mathbf{F}(x, y, z)$. In addition to $\mathbf{F}$, the particle will experience a concurrent "support force" $\mathbf{S}(x(t), y(t), z(t))$ from the curve. (Imagine a roller-coaster car falling without friction under the influence of the gravitational force $\mathbf{F}$. The tracks of the coaster provide the support force $\mathbf{S}$.) In this case we will say that the particle has a "constrained" motion under the influence of $\mathbf{F}$. Prove that the work performed by $\mathbf{F}$ on a particle with constrained motion is also equal to the change in kinetic energy of the particle. [*Hint:* Apply the argument of Exercise 1 to the resultant force $\mathbf{F} + \mathbf{S}$ on the particle. Use the fact that at each point on $C$, $\mathbf{S}$ will be normal to the curve.]

**3.** Suppose that $\mathbf{F}$ is a conservative force field. Use Exercises 1 and 2, along with the discussion in Section 15.3, to develop the conservation of energy principle for both free and constrained motion under $\mathbf{F}$.

**4.** As shown in the accompanying figure, a girl with mass $m$ is sliding down a smooth (frictionless) playground slide that is inclined at an angle of $\theta$ with the horizontal. If the acceleration due to gravity is $g$ and the length of the slide is $l$, prove that the speed of the child when she reaches the base of the slide is $v = \sqrt{2gl\sin\theta}$. Assume that she starts from rest at the top of the slide.

◀ **Figure Ex-4**

## EXPANDING THE CALCULUS HORIZON

To learn how the topics in this chapter can be used to model hurricane behavior, see the module entitled **Hurricane Modeling** at:

www.wiley.com/college/anton

# A

# TRIGONOMETRY REVIEW (SUMMARY)

*This reference summary highlights key facts and results concerning trigonometric functions. A more detailed discussion, including exercises, is contained in Web Appendix A,* Trigonometry Review.

## ANGLES

Angles in the plane can be generated by rotating a ray about its endpoint. The starting position of the ray is called the ***initial side*** of the angle, the final position is called the ***terminal side*** of the angle, and the point at which the initial and terminal sides meet is called the ***vertex*** of the angle. We allow for the possibility that the ray may make more than one complete revolution. Angles are considered to be ***positive*** if generated counterclockwise and ***negative*** if generated clockwise (Figure A.1).

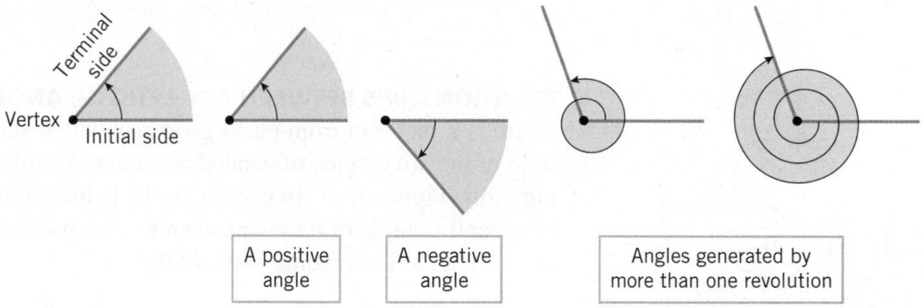


▶ **Figure A.1**

There are two standard measurement systems for describing the size of an angle: ***degree measure*** and ***radian measure***. In degree measure, one degree (written $1^\circ$) is the measure of an angle generated by $1/360$ of one revolution. Thus, there are $360^\circ$ in an angle of one revolution, $180^\circ$ in an angle of one-half revolution, $90^\circ$ in an angle of one-quarter revolution (a *right angle*), and so forth. Degrees are divided into sixty equal parts, called ***minutes***, and minutes are divided into sixty equal parts, called ***seconds***. Thus, one minute (written $1'$) is $1/60$ of a degree, and one second (written $1''$) is $1/60$ of a minute. Smaller subdivisions of a degree are expressed as fractions of a second.

In radian measure, angles are measured by the length of the arc that the angle subtends on a circle of radius 1 when the vertex is at the center. One unit of arc on a circle of radius 1 is called one ***radian*** (written 1 radian or 1 rad) (Figure A.2), and hence the entire circumference of a circle of radius 1 is $2\pi$ radians. It follows that an angle of $360^\circ$ subtends an arc of $2\pi$ radians, an angle of $180^\circ$ subtends an arc of $\pi$ radians, an angle of $90^\circ$ subtends an arc of $\pi/2$ radians, and so forth. Figure A.3 and Table A.1 show the relationship between degree measure and radian measure for some important positive angles.

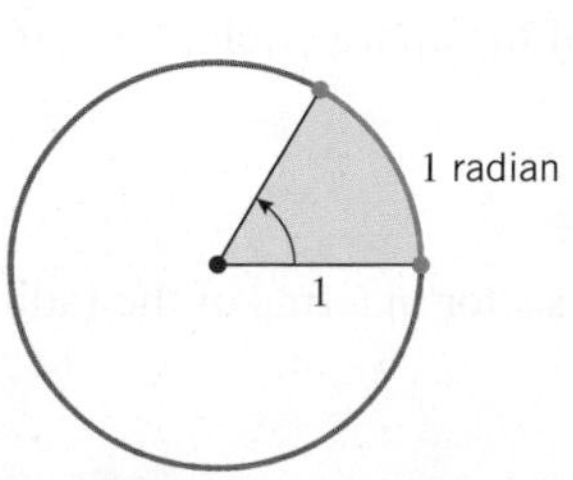


▲ **Figure A.2**

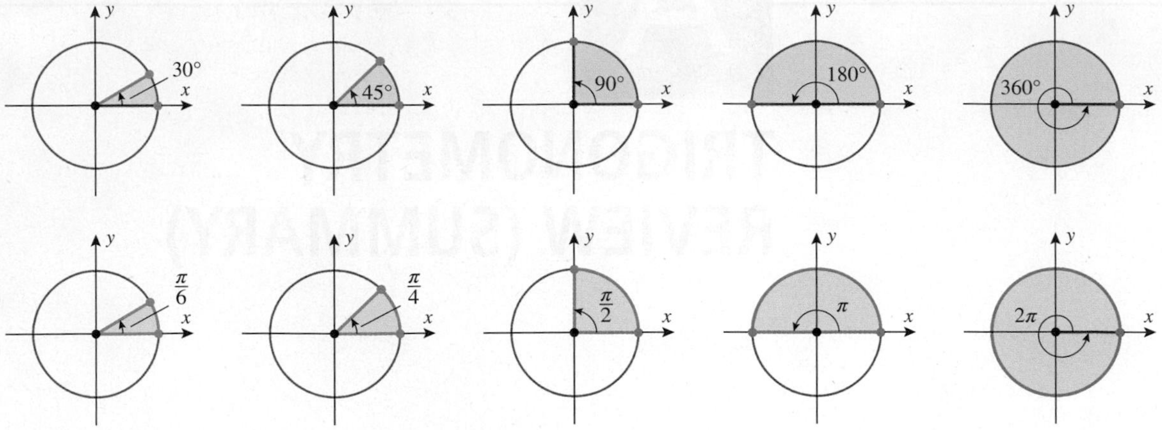


▲ **Figure A.3**

**Table A.1**

| DEGREES | 30° | 45° | 60° | 90° | 120° | 135° | 150° | 180° | 270° | 360° |
|---|---|---|---|---|---|---|---|---|---|---|
| RADIANS | $\frac{\pi}{6}$ | $\frac{\pi}{4}$ | $\frac{\pi}{3}$ | $\frac{\pi}{2}$ | $\frac{2\pi}{3}$ | $\frac{3\pi}{4}$ | $\frac{5\pi}{6}$ | $\pi$ | $\frac{3\pi}{2}$ | $2\pi$ |

Observe that in Table A.1, angles in degrees are designated by the degree symbol, but angles in radians have no units specified. This is standard practice—when no units are specified for an angle, it is understood that the units are radians.

From the fact that $\pi$ radians corresponds to 180°, we obtain the following formulas, which are useful for converting from degrees to radians and conversely.

$$1^\circ = \frac{\pi}{180} \text{ rad} \approx 0.01745 \text{ rad} \quad (1)$$

$$1 \text{ rad} = \left(\frac{180}{\pi}\right)^\circ \approx 57^\circ 17' 44.8'' \quad (2)$$

## RELATIONSHIPS BETWEEN ARC LENGTH, ANGLE, RADIUS, AND AREA

There is a theorem from plane geometry which states that for two concentric circles, the ratio of the arc lengths subtended by a central angle is equal to the ratio of the corresponding radii (Figure A.4). In particular, if $s$ is the arc length subtended on a circle of radius $r$ by a central angle of $\theta$ radians, then by comparison with the arc length subtended by that angle on a circle of radius 1 we obtain

$$\frac{s}{\theta} = \frac{r}{1}$$

from which we obtain the following relationships between the central angle $\theta$, the radius $r$, and the subtended arc length $s$ when $\theta$ is in radians (Figure A.5):

$$\theta = s/r \quad \text{and} \quad s = r\theta \quad (3\text{–}4)$$

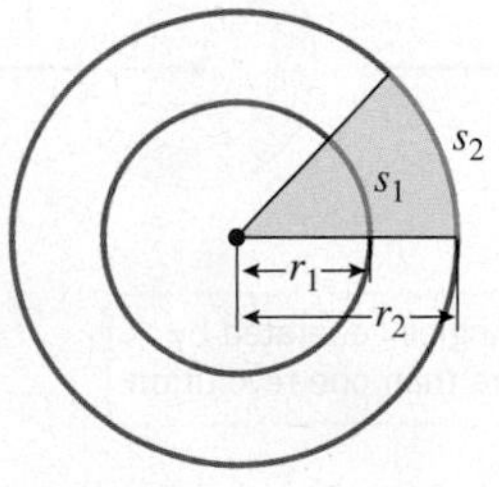


$\frac{s_1}{s_2} = \frac{r_1}{r_2}$

▲ **Figure A.4**

The shaded region in Figure A.5 is called a ***sector***. It is a theorem from plane geometry that the ratio of the area $A$ of this sector to the area of the entire circle is the same as the ratio of the central angle of the sector to the central angle of the entire circle; thus, if the angles are in radians, we have

$$\frac{A}{\pi r^2} = \frac{\theta}{2\pi}$$

Solving for $A$ yields the following formula for the area of a sector in terms of the radius $r$ and the angle $\theta$ in radians:

$$A = \tfrac{1}{2}r^2\theta \quad (5)$$

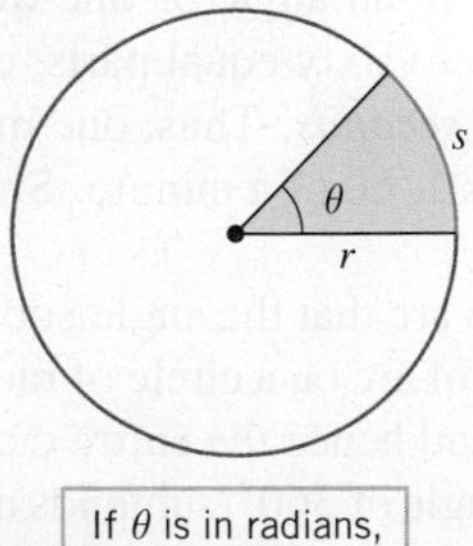


If $\theta$ is in radians, then $\theta = s/r$.

▲ **Figure A.5**

## TRIGONOMETRIC FUNCTIONS FOR RIGHT TRIANGLES

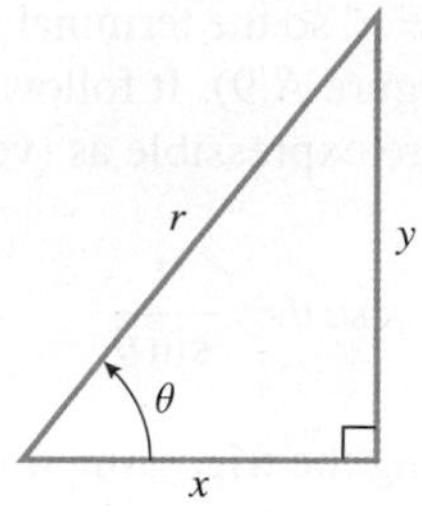


▲ Figure A.6

The ***sine***, ***cosine***, ***tangent***, ***cosecant***, ***secant***, and ***cotangent*** of a positive acute angle $\theta$ can be defined as ratios of the sides of a right triangle. Using the notation from Figure A.6, these definitions take the following form:

$$\begin{aligned} \sin\theta &= \frac{\text{side opposite } \theta}{\text{hypotenuse}} = \frac{y}{r}, & \csc\theta &= \frac{\text{hypotenuse}}{\text{side opposite } \theta} = \frac{r}{y} \\ \cos\theta &= \frac{\text{side adjacent to } \theta}{\text{hypotenuse}} = \frac{x}{r}, & \sec\theta &= \frac{\text{hypotenuse}}{\text{side adjacent to } \theta} = \frac{r}{x} \\ \tan\theta &= \frac{\text{side opposite } \theta}{\text{side adjacent to } \theta} = \frac{y}{x}, & \cot\theta &= \frac{\text{side adjacent to } \theta}{\text{side opposite } \theta} = \frac{x}{y} \end{aligned} \tag{6}$$

We will call sin, cos, tan, csc, sec, and cot the ***trigonometric functions***. Because similar triangles have proportional sides, the values of the trigonometric functions depend only on the size of $\theta$ and not on the particular right triangle used to compute the ratios. Moreover, in these definitions it does not matter whether $\theta$ is measured in degrees or radians.

## ANGLES IN RECTANGULAR COORDINATE SYSTEMS

Because the angles of a right triangle are between 0° and 90°, the formulas in (6) are not directly applicable to negative angles or to angles greater than 90°. To extend the trigonometric functions to include these cases, it will be convenient to consider angles in rectangular coordinate systems. An angle is said to be in ***standard position*** in an $xy$-coordinate system if its vertex is at the origin and its initial side is on the positive $x$-axis (Figure A.7).

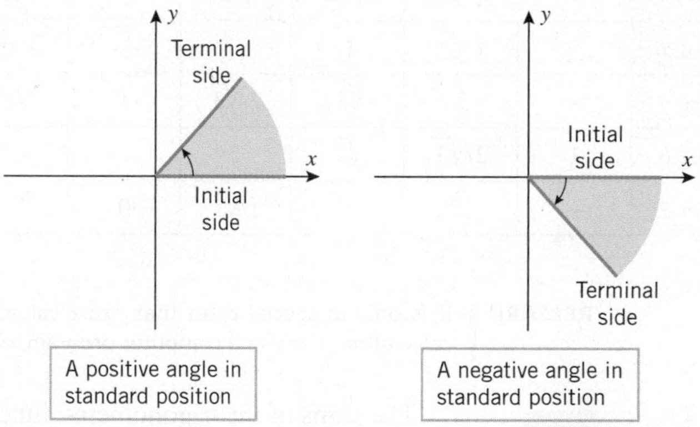


▶ Figure A.7

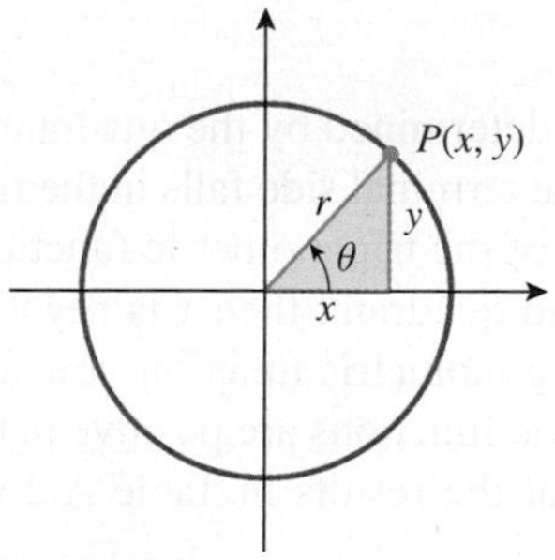


▲ Figure A.8

To define the trigonometric functions of an angle $\theta$ in standard position, construct a circle of radius $r$, centered at the origin, and let $P(x, y)$ be the intersection of the terminal side of $\theta$ with this circle (Figure A.8). We make the following definition.

**A.1 DEFINITION**

$$\sin\theta = \frac{y}{r}, \quad \cos\theta = \frac{x}{r}, \quad \tan\theta = \frac{y}{x}$$

$$\csc\theta = \frac{r}{y}, \quad \sec\theta = \frac{r}{x}, \quad \cot\theta = \frac{x}{y}$$

Note that the formulas in this definition agree with those in (6), so there is no conflict with the earlier definition of the trigonometric functions for triangles. However, this definition applies to all angles (except for cases where a zero denominator occurs).

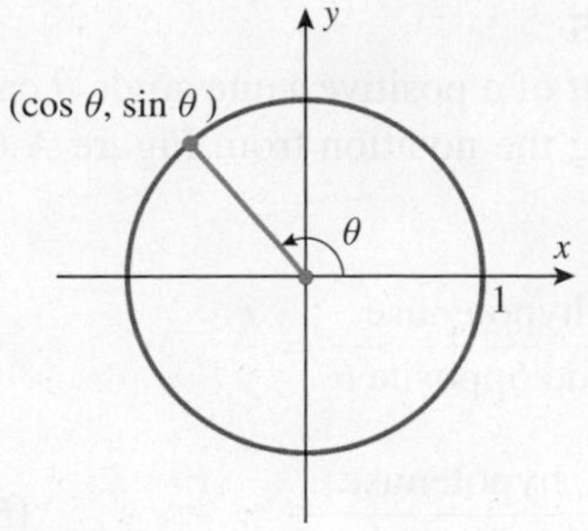


▲ Figure A.9

In the special case where $r = 1$, we have $\sin\theta = y$ and $\cos\theta = x$, so the terminal side of the angle $\theta$ intersects the unit circle at the point $(\cos\theta, \sin\theta)$ (Figure A.9). It follows from Definition A.1 that the remaining trigonometric functions of $\theta$ are expressible as (verify)

$$\tan\theta = \frac{\sin\theta}{\cos\theta}, \quad \cot\theta = \frac{\cos\theta}{\sin\theta} = \frac{1}{\tan\theta}, \quad \sec\theta = \frac{1}{\cos\theta}, \quad \csc\theta = \frac{1}{\sin\theta} \qquad (7\text{–}10)$$

These observations suggest the following procedure for evaluating the trigonometric functions of common angles:

- Construct the angle $\theta$ in standard position in an $xy$-coordinate system.
- Find the coordinates of the intersection of the terminal side of the angle and the unit circle; the $x$- and $y$-coordinates of this intersection are the values of $\cos\theta$ and $\sin\theta$, respectively.
- Use Formulas (7) through (10) to find the values of the remaining trigonometric functions from the values of $\cos\theta$ and $\sin\theta$.

You should be able to obtain all of the results in Table A.2. The dashes indicate quantities that are undefined.

**Table A.2**

| | $\theta = 0$ (0°) | $\pi/6$ (30°) | $\pi/4$ (45°) | $\pi/3$ (60°) | $\pi/2$ (90°) | $2\pi/3$ (120°) | $3\pi/4$ (135°) | $5\pi/6$ (150°) | $\pi$ (180°) | $3\pi/2$ (270°) | $2\pi$ (360°) |
|---|---|---|---|---|---|---|---|---|---|---|---|
| $\sin\theta$ | 0 | 1/2 | $1/\sqrt{2}$ | $\sqrt{3}/2$ | 1 | $\sqrt{3}/2$ | $1/\sqrt{2}$ | 1/2 | 0 | −1 | 0 |
| $\cos\theta$ | 1 | $\sqrt{3}/2$ | $1/\sqrt{2}$ | 1/2 | 0 | −1/2 | $-1/\sqrt{2}$ | $-\sqrt{3}/2$ | −1 | 0 | 1 |
| $\tan\theta$ | 0 | $1/\sqrt{3}$ | 1 | $\sqrt{3}$ | — | $-\sqrt{3}$ | −1 | $-1/\sqrt{3}$ | 0 | — | 0 |
| $\csc\theta$ | — | 2 | $\sqrt{2}$ | $2/\sqrt{3}$ | 1 | $2/\sqrt{3}$ | $\sqrt{2}$ | 2 | — | −1 | — |
| $\sec\theta$ | 1 | $2/\sqrt{3}$ | $\sqrt{2}$ | 2 | — | −2 | $-\sqrt{2}$ | $-2/\sqrt{3}$ | −1 | — | 1 |
| $\cot\theta$ | — | $\sqrt{3}$ | 1 | $1/\sqrt{3}$ | 0 | $-1/\sqrt{3}$ | −1 | $-\sqrt{3}$ | — | 0 | — |

**REMARK** It is only in special cases that exact values for trigonometric functions can be obtained; usually, a calculating utility or a computer program will be required.

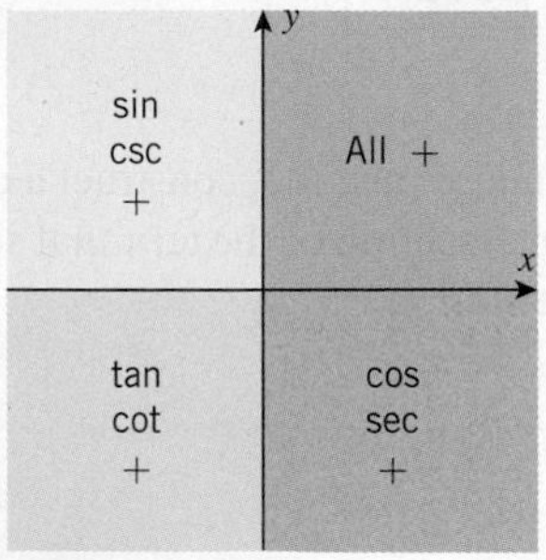


▲ Figure A.10

The signs of the trigonometric functions of an angle are determined by the quadrant in which the terminal side of the angle falls. For example, if the terminal side falls in the first quadrant, then $x$ and $y$ are positive in Definition A.1, so all of the trigonometric functions have positive values. If the terminal side falls in the second quadrant, then $x$ is negative and $y$ is positive, so sin and csc are positive, but all other trigonometric functions are negative. The diagram in Figure A.10 shows which trigonometric functions are positive in the various quadrants. You will find it instructive to check that the results in Table A.2 are consistent with Figure A.10.

## TRIGONOMETRIC IDENTITIES

A ***trigonometric identity*** is an equation involving trigonometric functions that is true for all angles for which both sides of the equation are defined. One of the most important identities in trigonometry can be derived by applying the Theorem of Pythagoras to the triangle in Figure A.8 to obtain

$$x^2 + y^2 = r^2$$

Dividing both sides by $r^2$ and using the definitions of $\sin\theta$ and $\cos\theta$ (Definition A.1), we obtain the following fundamental result:

$$\sin^2\theta + \cos^2\theta = 1 \qquad (11)$$

The following identities can be obtained from (11) by dividing through by $\cos^2\theta$ and $\sin^2\theta$, respectively, then applying Formulas (7) through (10):

$$\tan^2\theta + 1 = \sec^2\theta \tag{12}$$

$$1 + \cot^2\theta = \csc^2\theta \tag{13}$$

If $(x, y)$ is a point on the unit circle, then the points $(-x, y)$, $(-x, -y)$, and $(x, -y)$ also lie on the unit circle (why?), and the four points form corners of a rectangle with sides parallel to the coordinate axes (Figure A.11*a*). The $x$- and $y$-coordinates of each corner represent the cosine and sine of an angle in standard position whose terminal side passes through the corner; hence we obtain the identities in parts (*b*), (*c*), and (*d*) of Figure A.11 for sine and cosine. Dividing those identities leads to identities for the tangent. In summary:

$$\sin(\pi-\theta) = \sin\theta, \quad \sin(\pi+\theta) = -\sin\theta, \quad \sin(-\theta) = -\sin\theta \qquad (14\text{–}16)$$

$$\cos(\pi-\theta) = -\cos\theta, \quad \cos(\pi+\theta) = -\cos\theta, \quad \cos(-\theta) = \cos\theta \qquad (17\text{–}19)$$

$$\tan(\pi-\theta) = -\tan\theta, \quad \tan(\pi+\theta) = \tan\theta, \quad \tan(-\theta) = -\tan\theta \qquad (20\text{–}22)$$

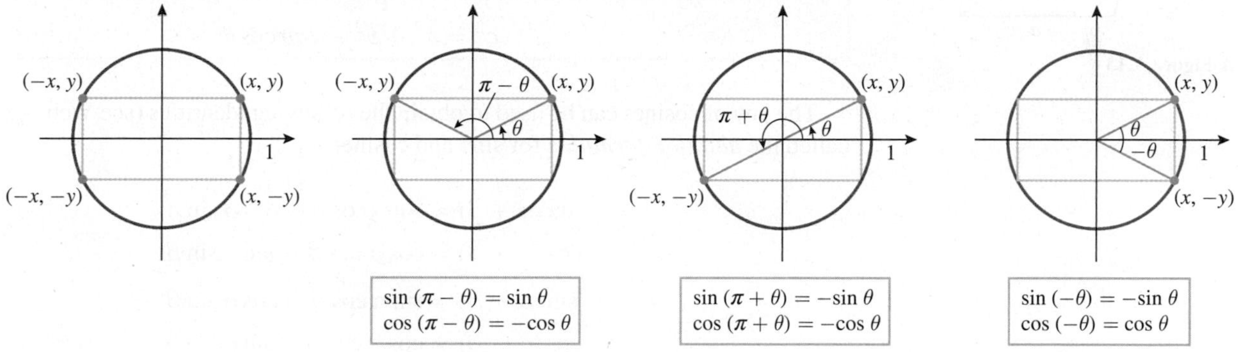


(*a*) (*b*) (*c*) (*d*)

▲ **Figure A.11**

Two angles in standard position that have the same terminal side must have the same values for their trigonometric functions since their terminal sides intersect the unit circle at the same point. In particular, two angles whose radian measures differ by a multiple of $2\pi$ have the same terminal side and hence have the same values for their trigonometric functions. This yields the identities

$$\sin\theta = \sin(\theta + 2\pi) = \sin(\theta - 2\pi) \tag{23}$$

$$\cos\theta = \cos(\theta + 2\pi) = \cos(\theta - 2\pi) \tag{24}$$

and more generally,

$$\sin\theta = \sin(\theta \pm 2n\pi), \quad n = 0, 1, 2, \ldots \tag{25}$$

$$\cos\theta = \cos(\theta \pm 2n\pi), \quad n = 0, 1, 2, \ldots \tag{26}$$

Identity (21) implies that

$$\tan\theta = \tan(\theta + \pi) \quad \text{and} \quad \tan\theta = \tan(\theta - \pi) \qquad (27\text{–}28)$$

Identity (27) is just (21) with the terms in the sum reversed, and identity (28) follows from (21) by substituting $\theta - \pi$ for $\theta$. These two identities state that adding or subtracting $\pi$ from an angle does not affect the value of the tangent of the angle. It follows that the same is true for any multiple of $\pi$; thus,

$$\tan\theta = \tan(\theta \pm n\pi), \quad n = 0, 1, 2, \ldots \tag{29}$$

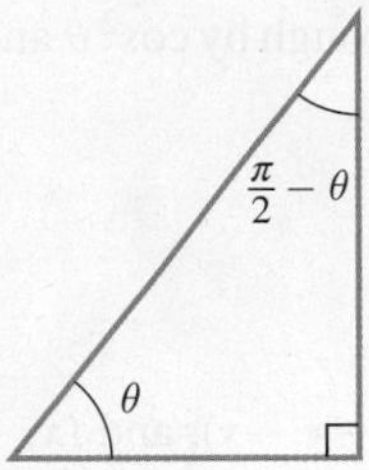

▲ Figure A.12

Figure A.12 shows complementary angles $\theta$ and $(\pi/2) - \theta$ of a right triangle. It follows from (6) that

$$\sin\theta = \frac{\text{side opposite } \theta}{\text{hypotenuse}} = \frac{\text{side adjacent to } (\pi/2) - \theta}{\text{hypotenuse}} = \cos\left(\frac{\pi}{2} - \theta\right)$$

$$\cos\theta = \frac{\text{side adjacent to } \theta}{\text{hypotenuse}} = \frac{\text{side opposite } (\pi/2) - \theta}{\text{hypotenuse}} = \sin\left(\frac{\pi}{2} - \theta\right)$$

which yields the identities

$$\sin\left(\frac{\pi}{2} - \theta\right) = \cos\theta, \quad \cos\left(\frac{\pi}{2} - \theta\right) = \sin\theta, \quad \tan\left(\frac{\pi}{2} - \theta\right) = \cot\theta \tag{30–32}$$

where the third identity results from dividing the first two. These identities are also valid for angles that are not acute and for negative angles as well.

## THE LAW OF COSINES

The next theorem, called the ***law of cosines***, generalizes the Theorem of Pythagoras.

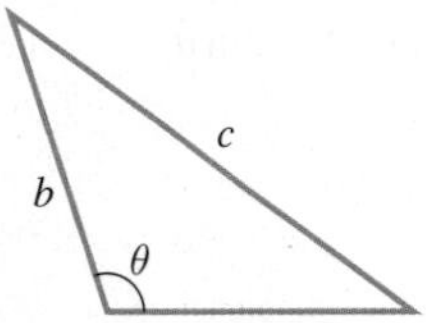

▲ Figure A.13

**A.2 THEOREM** (*Law of Cosines*) *If the sides of a triangle have lengths a, b, and c, and if $\theta$ is the angle between the sides with lengths a and b (Figure A.13), then*

$$c^2 = a^2 + b^2 - 2ab\cos\theta \tag{33}$$

The law of cosines can be used to obtain the following identities (see Web Appendix A), called the ***addition formulas*** for sine and cosine:

$$\sin(\alpha + \beta) = \sin\alpha\cos\beta + \cos\alpha\sin\beta \tag{34}$$

$$\cos(\alpha + \beta) = \cos\alpha\cos\beta - \sin\alpha\sin\beta \tag{35}$$

$$\sin(\alpha - \beta) = \sin\alpha\cos\beta - \cos\alpha\sin\beta \tag{36}$$

$$\cos(\alpha - \beta) = \cos\alpha\cos\beta + \sin\alpha\sin\beta \tag{37}$$

The addition formula for tangent follows from those for sine and cosine.

$$\tan(\alpha + \beta) = \frac{\tan\alpha + \tan\beta}{1 - \tan\alpha\tan\beta} \qquad \tan(\alpha - \beta) = \frac{\tan\alpha - \tan\beta}{1 + \tan\alpha\tan\beta} \tag{38–39}$$

In the special case where $\alpha = \beta$, identities (34), (35), and (38) yield the ***double-angle formulas***

$$\sin 2\alpha = 2\sin\alpha\cos\alpha \tag{40}$$

$$\cos 2\alpha = \cos^2\alpha - \sin^2\alpha \tag{41}$$

$$\tan 2\alpha = \frac{2\tan\alpha}{1 - \tan^2\alpha} \tag{42}$$

By using the identity $\sin^2\alpha + \cos^2\alpha = 1$, (41) can be rewritten in the alternative forms

$$\cos 2\alpha = 2\cos^2\alpha - 1 \quad \text{and} \quad \cos 2\alpha = 1 - 2\sin^2\alpha \tag{43–44}$$

Exercises in Web Appendix A provide guidance for deriving ***half-angle formulas***

$$\cos^2\frac{\alpha}{2} = \frac{1 + \cos\alpha}{2} \quad \text{and} \quad \sin^2\frac{\alpha}{2} = \frac{1 - \cos\alpha}{2} \tag{45–46}$$

***product-to-sum formulas***

$$\sin\alpha\cos\beta = \frac{1}{2}[\sin(\alpha-\beta)+\sin(\alpha+\beta)] \tag{47}$$

$$\sin\alpha\sin\beta = \frac{1}{2}[\cos(\alpha-\beta)-\cos(\alpha+\beta)] \tag{48}$$

$$\cos\alpha\cos\beta = \frac{1}{2}[\cos(\alpha-\beta)+\cos(\alpha+\beta)] \tag{49}$$

and ***sum-to-product formulas***

$$\sin\alpha+\sin\beta = 2\sin\frac{\alpha+\beta}{2}\cos\frac{\alpha-\beta}{2} \tag{50}$$

$$\sin\alpha-\sin\beta = 2\cos\frac{\alpha+\beta}{2}\sin\frac{\alpha-\beta}{2} \tag{51}$$

$$\cos\alpha+\cos\beta = 2\cos\frac{\alpha+\beta}{2}\cos\frac{\alpha-\beta}{2} \tag{52}$$

$$\cos\alpha-\cos\beta = -2\sin\frac{\alpha+\beta}{2}\sin\frac{\alpha-\beta}{2} \tag{53}$$

## ANGLE OF INCLINATION

The slope of a nonvertical line $L$ is related to the angle that $L$ makes with the positive $x$-axis. If $\phi$ is the smallest positive angle measured counterclockwise from the $x$-axis to $L$, then the slope of the line can be expressed as

$$m = \tan\phi \tag{54}$$

(Figure A.14*a*). The angle $\phi$, which is called the ***angle of inclination*** of the line, satisfies $0^\circ \le \phi < 180^\circ$ in degree measure (or, equivalently, $0 \le \phi < \pi$ in radian measure). If $\phi$ is an acute angle, then $m = \tan\phi$ is positive and the line slopes up to the right, and if $\phi$ is an obtuse angle, then $m = \tan\phi$ is negative and the line slopes down to the right. For example, a line whose angle of inclination is $45^\circ$ has slope $m = \tan 45^\circ = 1$, and a line whose angle of inclination is $135^\circ$ has a slope of $m = \tan 135^\circ = -1$ (Figure A.14*b*). Figure A.15 shows a convenient way of using the line $x = 1$ as a "ruler" for visualizing the relationship between lines of various slopes.

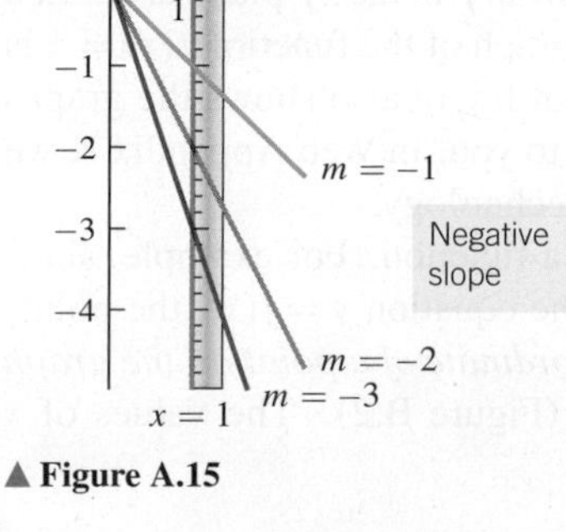


▲ **Figure A.15**

▲ **Figure A.14**

# B

# FUNCTIONS (SUMMARY)

*This reference summary highlights key facts and results concerning the concept of a "function." A more detailed discussion, including exercises, is contained in Web Appendix B,* Functions.

## DEFINITION OF A FUNCTION

**B.1 DEFINITION** If a variable $y$ depends on a variable $x$ in such a way that each value of $x$ determines exactly one value of $y$, then we say that ***y is a function of x***.

Four common methods for representing functions are:

- Numerically by tables
- Geometrically by graphs
- Algebraically by formulas
- Verbally

**B.2 DEFINITION** A ***function*** $f$ is a rule that associates a unique output with each input. If the input is denoted by $x$, then the output is denoted by $f(x)$ (read "$f$ of $x$").

## INDEPENDENT AND DEPENDENT VARIABLES

For a given input $x$, the output of a function $f$ is called the ***value*** of $f$ at $x$ or the ***image*** of $x$ under $f$. Sometimes we will want to denote the output by a single letter, say $y$, and write

$$y = f(x)$$

This equation expresses $y$ as a function of $x$; the variable $x$ is called the ***independent variable*** (or ***argument***) of $f$, and the variable $y$ is called the ***dependent variable*** of $f$. This terminology is intended to suggest that $x$ is free to vary, but that once $x$ has a specific value a corresponding value of $y$ is determined. For now we will only consider functions in which the independent and dependent variables are real numbers, in which case we say that $f$ is a ***real-valued function of a real variable***.

## GRAPHS OF FUNCTIONS

Figure B.1 shows only portions of the graphs. Where appropriate, and unless indicated otherwise, it is understood that graphs shown in this text extend indefinitely beyond the boundaries of the displayed figure.

If $f$ is a real-valued function of a real variable, then the ***graph*** of $f$ in the $xy$-plane is defined to be the graph of the equation $y = f(x)$. For example, the graph of the function $f(x) = x$ is the graph of the equation $y = x$, shown in Figure B.1. That figure also shows the graphs of some other basic functions that may already be familiar to you. In Web Appendix K we discuss techniques for graphing functions using graphing technology.

Graphs can provide valuable visual information about a function. For example, since the graph of a function $f$ in the $xy$-plane is the graph of the equation $y = f(x)$, the points on the graph of $f$ are of the form $(x, f(x))$; that is, *the y-coordinate of a point on the graph of f is the value of f at the corresponding x-coordinate* (Figure B.2). The values of $x$

for which $f(x) = 0$ are the $x$-coordinates of the points where the graph of $f$ intersects the $x$-axis (Figure B.3). These values are called the ***zeros*** of $f$, the ***roots*** of $f(x) = 0$, or the ***x-intercepts*** of the graph of $y = f(x)$.

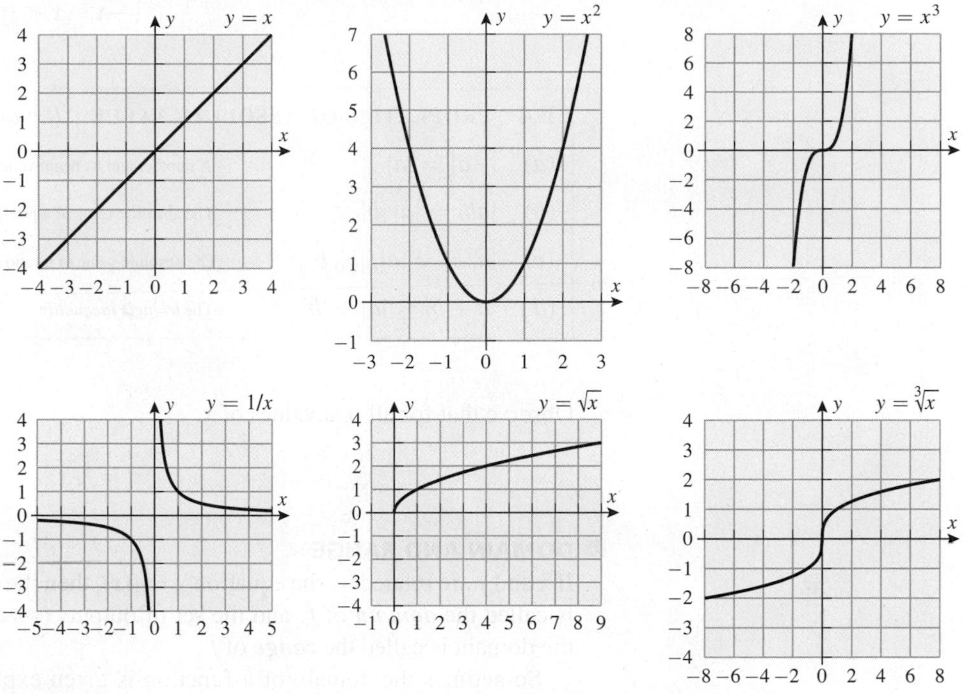


▲ **Figure B.1**

Since $\sqrt{x}$ is imaginary for negative values of $x$, there are no points on the graph of $y = \sqrt{x}$ in the region where $x < 0$.

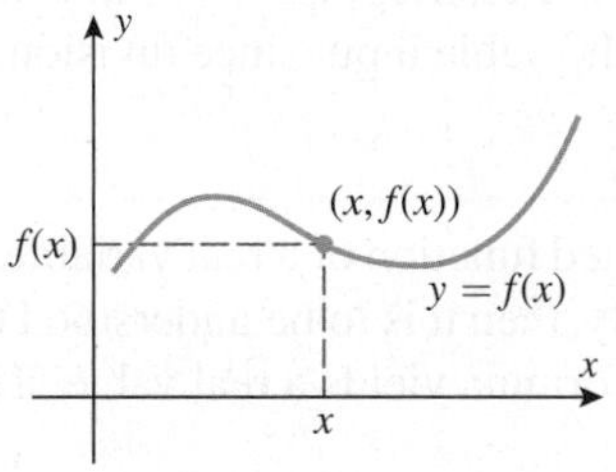


▲ **Figure B.2** The $y$-coordinate of a point on the graph of $y = f(x)$ is the value of $f$ at the corresponding $x$-coordinate.

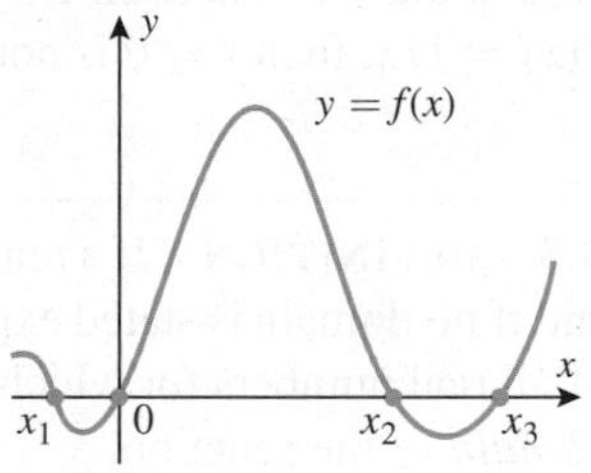


▲ **Figure B.3** $f$ has zeros at $x_1$, 0, $x_2$, and $x_3$.

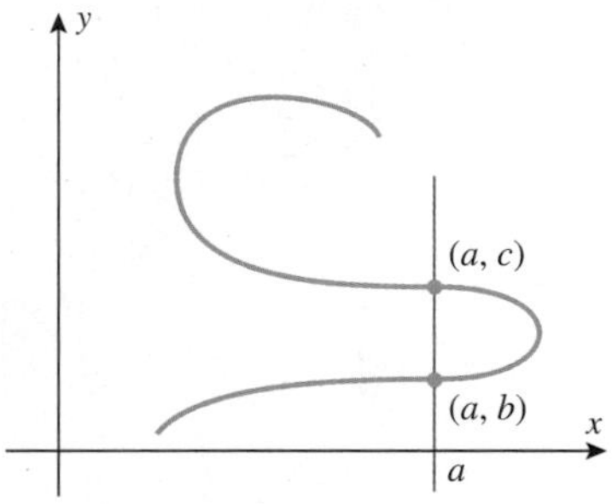


▲ **Figure B.4** This curve cannot be the graph of a function.

## THE VERTICAL LINE TEST

Not every curve in the $xy$-plane is the graph of a function. For example, consider the curve in Figure B.4, which is cut at two distinct points, $(a, b)$ and $(a, c)$, by a vertical line. This curve cannot be the graph of $y = f(x)$ for any function $f$; otherwise, we would have

$$f(a) = b \quad \text{and} \quad f(a) = c$$

which is impossible, since $f$ cannot assign two different values to $a$. Thus, there is no function $f$ whose graph is the given curve. This illustrates the following general result, which we will call the ***vertical line test***.

> **B.3 THE VERTICAL LINE TEST** *A curve in the xy-plane is the graph of some function f if and only if no vertical line intersects the curve more than once.*

## THE ABSOLUTE VALUE FUNCTION

Recall that the ***absolute value*** or ***magnitude*** of a real number $x$ is defined by

$$|x| = \begin{cases} x, & x \geq 0 \\ -x, & x < 0 \end{cases}$$

**B.4 PROPERTIES OF ABSOLUTE VALUE** *If a and b are real numbers, then:*

(*a*) $|-a| = |a|$ — A number and its negative have the same absolute value.

(*b*) $|ab| = |a|\,|b|$ — The absolute value of a product is the product of the absolute values.

(*c*) $|a/b| = |a|/|b|, b \neq 0$ — The absolute value of a ratio is the ratio of the absolute values.

(*d*) $|a+b| \leq |a| + |b|$ — The ***triangle inequality***

Observe that for all real values of $x$,

$$|x| = \sqrt{x^2} \tag{1}$$

## DOMAIN AND RANGE

If $x$ and $y$ are related by the equation $y = f(x)$, then the set of all allowable inputs ($x$-values) is called the ***domain*** of $f$, and the set of outputs ($y$-values) that result when $x$ varies over the domain is called the ***range*** of $f$.

Sometimes the domain of a function is given explicitly, but at other times it may be derived from context. For example, the area of a square of side $x$ is given by the function $A(x) = x^2$. Here, the geometric context of "length" of a side of a square imposes the requirement that $x \geq 0$ for the domain of A. When a function is defined by a mathematical formula, the formula itself may impose restrictions on the allowable inputs. For example, if $f(x) = 1/x$, then $x = 0$ is not an allowable input since division by zero is undefined.

**B.5 DEFINITION** If a real-valued function of a real variable is defined by a formula, and if no domain is stated explicitly, then it is to be understood that the domain consists of all real numbers for which the formula yields a real value. This is called the ***natural domain*** of the function.

C

# NEW FUNCTIONS FROM OLD (SUMMARY)

*This reference summary highlights key facts and results concerning operations on functions. A more detailed discussion, including exercises, is contained in Web Appendix C,* New Functions from Old.

## ARITHMETIC OPERATIONS ON FUNCTIONS

Two functions, $f$ and $g$, can be added, subtracted, multiplied, and divided in a natural way to form new functions $f+g$, $f-g$, $fg$, and $f/g$. For example, $f+g$ is defined by the formula

$$(f+g)(x) = f(x) + g(x) \tag{1}$$

which states that for each input the value of $f+g$ is obtained by adding the values of $f$ and $g$. Equation (1) provides a formula for $f+g$ but does not say anything about the domain of $f+g$. However, for the right side of this equation to be defined, $x$ must lie in the domains of both $f$ and $g$, so we define the domain of $f+g$ to be the intersection of these two domains. More generally, we make the following definition.

If $f$ is a constant function, that is, $f(x) = c$ for all $x$, then the product of $f$ and $g$ is $cg$, so multiplying a function by a constant is a special case of multiplying two functions.

**C.1 DEFINITION** Given functions $f$ and $g$, we define

$$(f+g)(x) = f(x) + g(x)$$
$$(f-g)(x) = f(x) - g(x)$$
$$(fg)(x) = f(x)g(x)$$
$$(f/g)(x) = f(x)/g(x)$$

For the functions $f+g$, $f-g$, and $fg$ we define the domain to be the intersection of the domains of $f$ and $g$, and for the function $f/g$ we define the domain to be the intersection of the domains of $f$ and $g$ but with the points where $g(x) = 0$ excluded (to avoid division by zero).

## COMPOSITION OF FUNCTIONS

We now consider an operation on functions, called *composition*, which has no direct analog in ordinary arithmetic. Informally stated, the operation of composition is performed by substituting some function for the independent variable of another function. For example, suppose that

$$f(x) = x^2 \quad \text{and} \quad g(x) = x + 1$$

If we substitute $g(x)$ for $x$ in the formula for $f$, we obtain a new function

$$f(g(x)) = [g(x)]^2 = (x+1)^2$$

which we denote by $f \circ g$. Thus,

$$(f \circ g)(x) = f(g(x)) = [g(x)]^2 = (x+1)^2$$

In general, we make the following definition.

Although the domain of $f \circ g$ may seem complicated at first glance, it makes sense intuitively: To compute $f(g(x))$ one needs $x$ in the domain of $g$ to compute $g(x)$, and one needs $g(x)$ in the domain of $f$ to compute $f(g(x))$.

**C.2 DEFINITION** Given functions $f$ and $g$, the ***composition*** of $f$ with $g$, denoted by $f \circ g$, is the function defined by

$$(f \circ g)(x) = f(g(x))$$

The domain of $f \circ g$ is defined to consist of all $x$ in the domain of $g$ for which $g(x)$ is in the domain of $f$.

## EXPRESSING A FUNCTION AS A COMPOSITION

Many problems in mathematics are solved by "decomposing" functions into compositions of simpler functions. For example, consider the function $h$ given by

$$h(x) = (x+1)^2$$

To evaluate $h(x)$ for a given value of $x$, we would first compute $x+1$ and then square the result. These two operations are performed by the functions

$$g(x) = x+1 \quad \text{and} \quad f(x) = x^2$$

We can express $h$ in terms of $f$ and $g$ by writing

$$h(x) = (x+1)^2 = [g(x)]^2 = f(g(x))$$

so we have succeeded in expressing $h$ as the composition $h = f \circ g$.

The thought process in this example suggests a general procedure for decomposing a function $h$ into a composition $h = f \circ g$:

- Think about how you would evaluate $h(x)$ for a specific value of $x$, trying to break the evaluation into two steps performed in succession.
- The first operation in the evaluation will determine a function $g$ and the second a function $f$.
- The formula for $h$ can then be written as $h(x) = f(g(x))$.

For descriptive purposes, we will refer to $g$ as the "inside function" and $f$ as the "outside function" in the expression $f(g(x))$. The inside function performs the first operation and the outside function performs the second.

Table C.1 gives some more examples of decomposing functions into compositions.

**Table C.1**
COMPOSING FUNCTIONS

| FUNCTION | $g(x)$ INSIDE | $f(x)$ OUTSIDE | COMPOSITION |
|---|---|---|---|
| $(x^2+1)^{10}$ | $x^2+1$ | $x^{10}$ | $(x^2+1)^{10} = f(g(x))$ |
| $\sin^3 x$ | $\sin x$ | $x^3$ | $\sin^3 x = f(g(x))$ |
| $\tan(x^5)$ | $x^5$ | $\tan x$ | $\tan(x^5) = f(g(x))$ |
| $\sqrt{4-3x}$ | $4-3x$ | $\sqrt{x}$ | $\sqrt{4-3x} = f(g(x))$ |
| $8+\sqrt{x}$ | $\sqrt{x}$ | $8+x$ | $8+\sqrt{x} = f(g(x))$ |
| $\dfrac{1}{x+1}$ | $x+1$ | $\dfrac{1}{x}$ | $\dfrac{1}{x+1} = f(g(x))$ |

**REMARK** There is always more than one way to express a function as a composition. For example, here are two ways to express $(x^2+1)^{10}$ as a composition that differ from that in Table C.1:

$$(x^2+1)^{10} = [(x^2+1)^2]^5 = f(g(x)) \qquad \boxed{g(x) = (x^2+1)^2 \text{ and } f(x) = x^5}$$

$$(x^2+1)^{10} = [(x^2+1)^3]^{10/3} = f(g(x)) \qquad \boxed{g(x) = (x^2+1)^3 \text{ and } f(x) = x^{10/3}}$$

## TRANSLATIONS

Table C.2 illustrates the geometric effect on the graph of $y = f(x)$ of adding or subtracting a *positive* constant $c$ to $f$ or to its independent variable $x$. For example, the first result in the table illustrates that adding a positive constant $c$ to a function $f$ adds $c$ to each $y$-coordinate of its graph, thereby shifting the graph of $f$ up by $c$ units. Similarly, subtracting $c$ from $f$ shifts the graph down by $c$ units. On the other hand, if a positive constant $c$ is added to $x$, then the value of $y = f(x+c)$ at $x - c$ is $f(x)$; and since the point $x - c$ is $c$ units to the left of $x$ on the $x$-axis, the graph of $y = f(x+c)$ must be the graph of $y = f(x)$ shifted left by $c$ units. Similarly, subtracting $c$ from $x$ shifts the graph of $y = f(x)$ right by $c$ units.

**Table C.2**
**TRANSLATION PRINCIPLES**

| OPERATION ON $y = f(x)$ | Add a positive constant $c$ to $f(x)$ | Subtract a positive constant $c$ from $f(x)$ | Add a positive constant $c$ to $x$ | Subtract a positive constant $c$ from $x$ |
|---|---|---|---|---|
| NEW EQUATION | $y = f(x) + c$ | $y = f(x) - c$ | $y = f(x+c)$ | $y = f(x-c)$ |
| GEOMETRIC EFFECT | Translates the graph of $y = f(x)$ up $c$ units | Translates the graph of $y = f(x)$ down $c$ units | Translates the graph of $y = f(x)$ left $c$ units | Translates the graph of $y = f(x)$ right $c$ units |
| EXAMPLE | 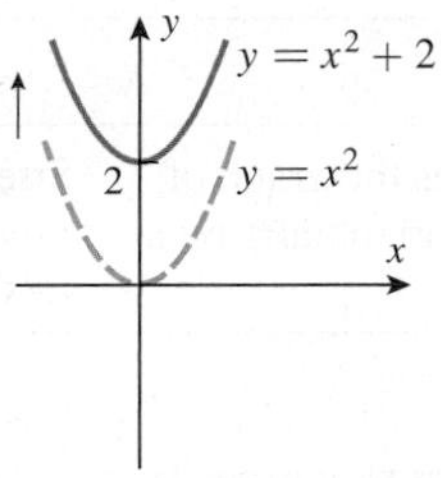 | 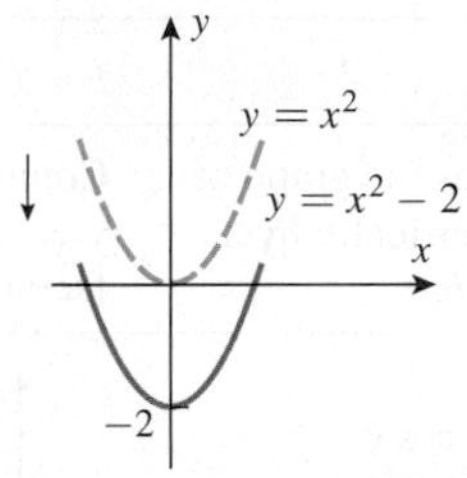 | 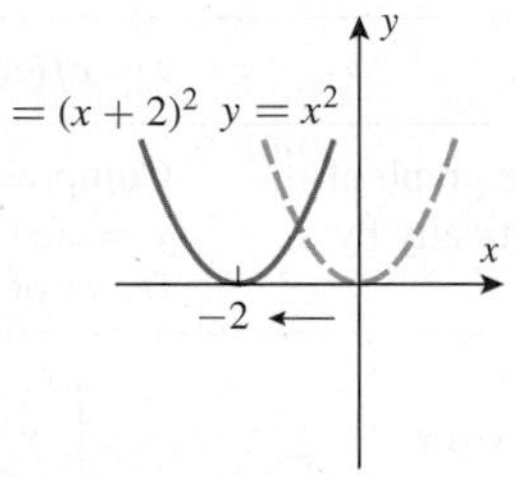 | 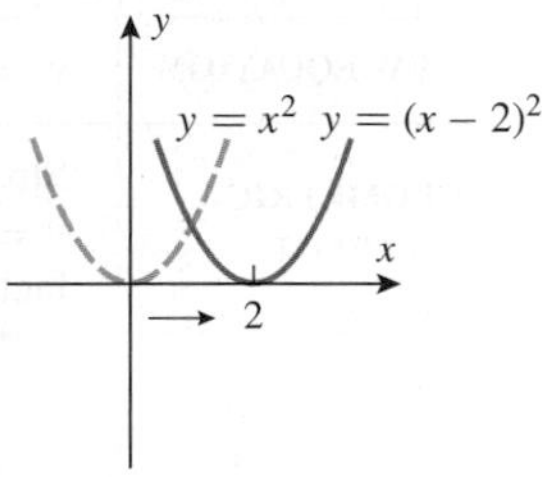 |

## REFLECTIONS

The graph of $y = f(-x)$ is the reflection of the graph of $y = f(x)$ about the $y$-axis because the point $(x, y)$ on the graph of $f(x)$ is replaced by $(-x, y)$. Similarly, the graph of $y = -f(x)$ is the reflection of the graph of $y = f(x)$ about the $x$-axis because the point $(x, y)$ on the graph of $f(x)$ is replaced by $(x, -y)$ [the equation $y = -f(x)$ is equivalent to $-y = f(x)$]. This is summarized in Table C.3.

## STRETCHES AND COMPRESSIONS

Describe the geometric effect of multiplying a function $f$ by a *negative* constant in terms of reflection and stretching or compressing. What is the geometric effect of multiplying the independent variable of a function $f$ by a *negative* constant?

Multiplying $f(x)$ by a *positive* constant $c$ has the geometric effect of stretching the graph of $y = f(x)$ in the $y$-direction by a factor of $c$ if $c > 1$ and compressing it in the $y$-direction by a factor of $1/c$ if $0 < c < 1$. For example, multiplying $f(x)$ by 2 doubles each $y$-coordinate, thereby stretching the graph vertically by a factor of 2, and multiplying by $\frac{1}{2}$ cuts each $y$-coordinate in half, thereby compressing the graph vertically by a factor of 2. Similarly, multiplying $x$ by a *positive* constant $c$ has the geometric effect of compressing the graph of $y = f(x)$ by a factor of $c$ in the $x$-direction if $c > 1$ and stretching it by a factor of $1/c$ if $0 < c < 1$. [If this seems backwards to you, then think of it this way: The value of $2x$ changes twice as fast as $x$, so a point moving along the $x$-axis from the origin will only have to move half as far for $y = f(2x)$ to have the same value as $y = f(x)$, thereby creating a horizontal compression of the graph.] All of this is summarized in Table C.4.

**Table C.3**
**REFLECTION PRINCIPLES**

| OPERATION ON $y = f(x)$ | Replace $x$ by $-x$ | Multiply $f(x)$ by $-1$ |
|---|---|---|
| NEW EQUATION | $y = f(-x)$ | $y = -f(x)$ |
| GEOMETRIC EFFECT | Reflects the graph of $y = f(x)$ about the $y$-axis | Reflects the graph of $y = f(x)$ about the $x$-axis |
| EXAMPLE | 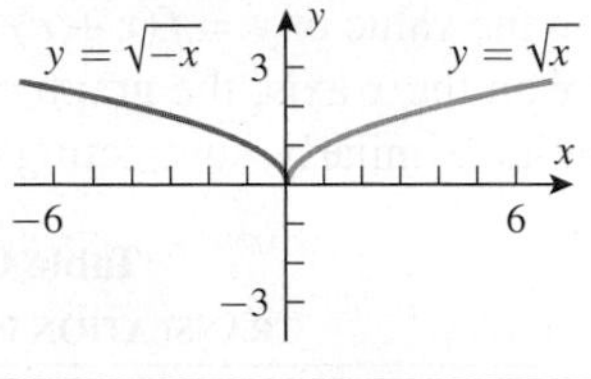  | 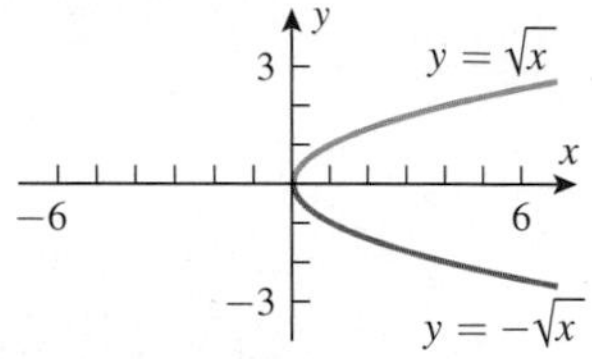  |

**Table C.4**
**STRETCHING AND COMPRESSING PRINCIPLES**

| OPERATION ON $y = f(x)$ | Multiply $f(x)$ by $c$ $(c > 1)$ | Multiply $f(x)$ by $c$ $(0 < c < 1)$ | Multiply $x$ by $c$ $(c > 1)$ | Multiply $x$ by $c$ $(0 < c < 1)$ |
|---|---|---|---|---|
| NEW EQUATION | $y = cf(x)$ | $y = cf(x)$ | $y = f(cx)$ | $y = f(cx)$ |
| GEOMETRIC EFFECT | Stretches the graph of $y = f(x)$ vertically by a factor of $c$ | Compresses the graph of $y = f(x)$ vertically by a factor of $1/c$ | Compresses the graph of $y = f(x)$ horizontally by a factor of $c$ | Stretches the graph of $y = f(x)$ horizontally by a factor of $1/c$ |
| EXAMPLE | 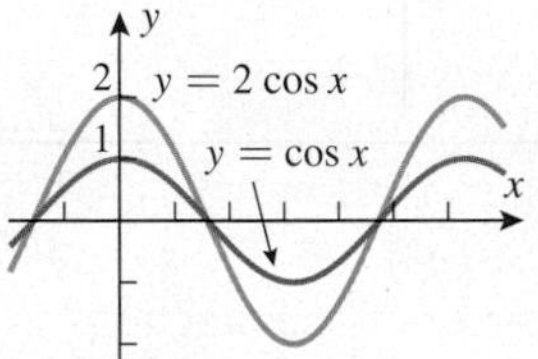  | 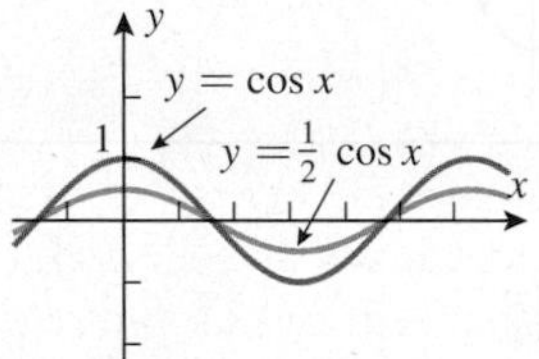  | 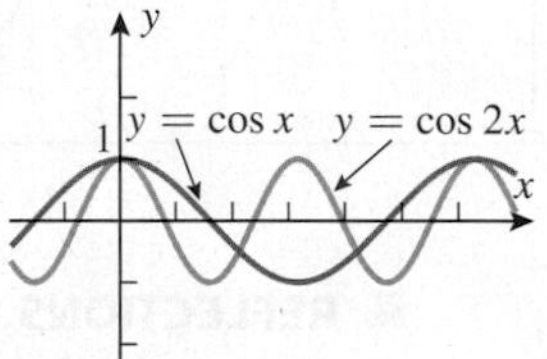  | 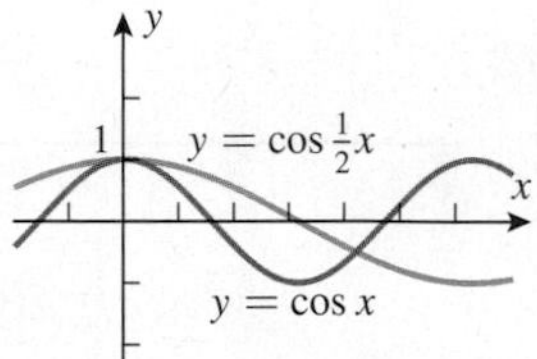  |

## SYMMETRY

Figure C.1 illustrates three types of symmetries: ***symmetry about the x-axis***, ***symmetry about the y-axis***, and ***symmetry about the origin***. As illustrated in the figure, a curve is symmetric about the $x$-axis if for each point $(x, y)$ on the graph the point $(x, -y)$ is also on the graph, and it is symmetric about the $y$-axis if for each point $(x, y)$ on the graph the point $(-x, y)$ is also on the graph. A curve is symmetric about the origin if for each point $(x, y)$ on the graph, the point $(-x, -y)$ is also on the graph. (Equivalently, a graph is symmetric about the origin if rotating the graph 180° about the origin leaves it unchanged.) This suggests the following symmetry tests.

Explain why the graph of a nonzero function cannot be symmetric about the $x$-axis.

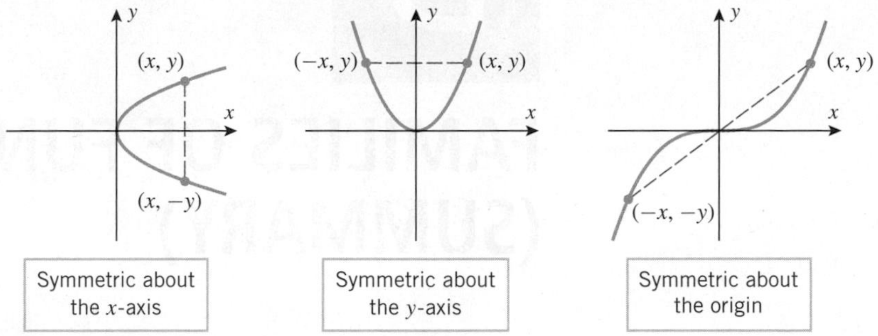


► **Figure C.1**

**C.3 THEOREM** (*Symmetry Tests*)

(*a*) *A plane curve is symmetric about the y-axis if and only if replacing x by −x in its equation produces an equivalent equation.*

(*b*) *A plane curve is symmetric about the x-axis if and only if replacing y by −y in its equation produces an equivalent equation.*

(*c*) *A plane curve is symmetric about the origin if and only if replacing both x by −x and y by −y in its equation produces an equivalent equation.*

## EVEN AND ODD FUNCTIONS

A function $f$ is said to be an ***even function*** if

$$f(-x) = f(x) \tag{2}$$

and is said to be an ***odd function*** if

$$f(-x) = -f(x) \tag{3}$$

Geometrically, the graphs of even functions are symmetric about the $y$-axis because replacing $x$ by $-x$ in the equation $y = f(x)$ yields $y = f(-x)$, which is equivalent to the original equation $y = f(x)$ by (2) (see Figure C.2). Similarly, it follows from (3) that graphs of odd functions are symmetric about the origin (see Figure C.3). Some examples of even functions are $x^2, x^4, x^6$, and $\cos x$; and some examples of odd functions are $x^3, x^5, x^7$, and $\sin x$.

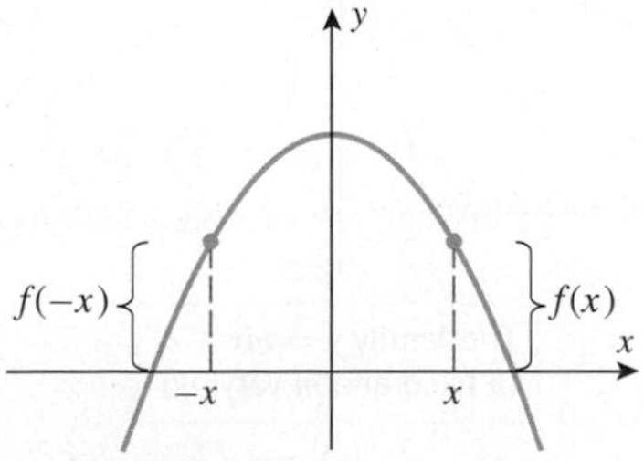


▲ **Figure C.2** This is the graph of an even function since $f(-x) = f(x)$.

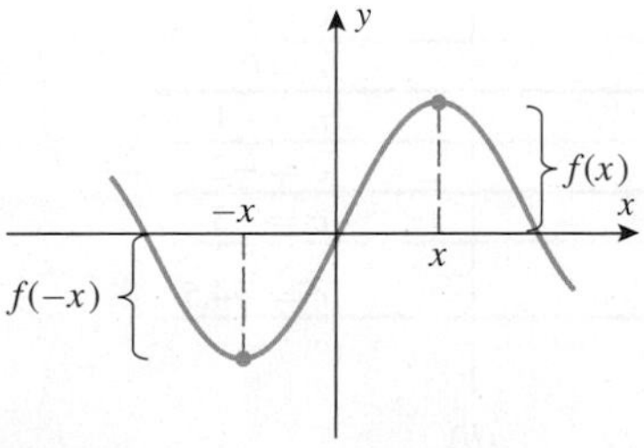


▲ **Figure C.3** This is the graph of an odd function since $f(-x) = -f(x)$.

D

# FAMILIES OF FUNCTIONS (SUMMARY)

*This reference summary highlights key facts and results concerning some basic families of functions. A more detailed discussion, including exercises, is contained in Web Appendix D,* Families of Functions.

## FAMILIES OF CURVES

The graph of a constant function $f(x) = c$ is the graph of the equation $y = c$, which is the horizontal line shown in Figure D.1*a*. If we vary *c*, then we obtain a set or ***family*** of horizontal lines such as those in Figure D.1*b*.

Constants that are varied to produce families of curves are called ***parameters***. For example, recall that an equation of the form $y = mx + b$ represents a line of slope $m$ and $y$-intercept $b$. If we keep $b$ fixed and treat $m$ as a parameter, then we obtain a family of lines whose members all have $y$-intercept $b$ (Figure D.2*a*), and if we keep $m$ fixed and treat $b$ as a parameter, we obtain a family of parallel lines whose members all have slope $m$ (Figure D.2*b*).

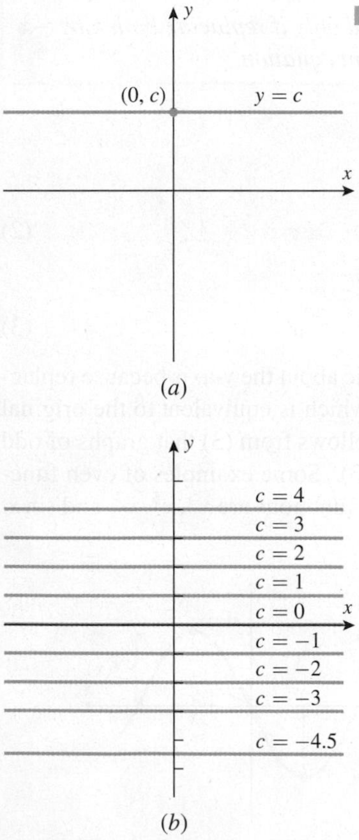

▲ **Figure D.1**

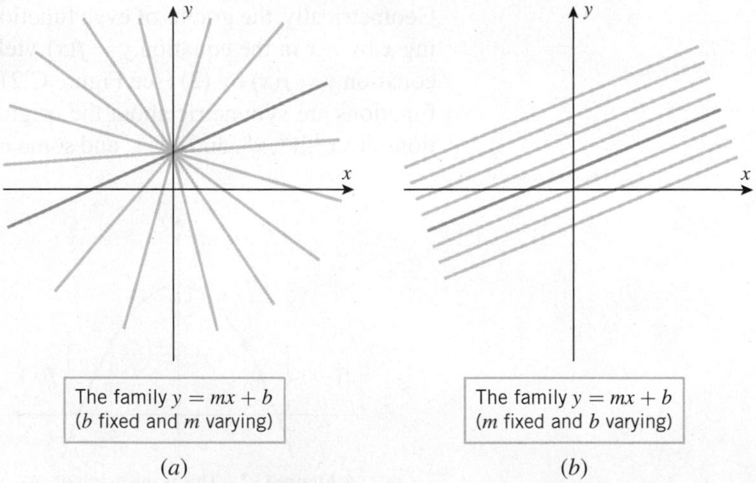

▶ **Figure D.2**

## POWER FUNCTIONS; THE FAMILY $y = x^n$

A function of the form $f(x) = x^p$, where $p$ is constant, is called a ***power function***. For the moment, let us consider the case where $p$ is a positive integer, say $p = n$. The graphs of the curves $y = x^n$ for $n = 1, 2, 3, 4$, and 5 are shown in Figure D.3. The first graph is the line with slope 1 that passes through the origin, and the second is a parabola that opens up and has its vertex at the origin (see Web Appendix I).

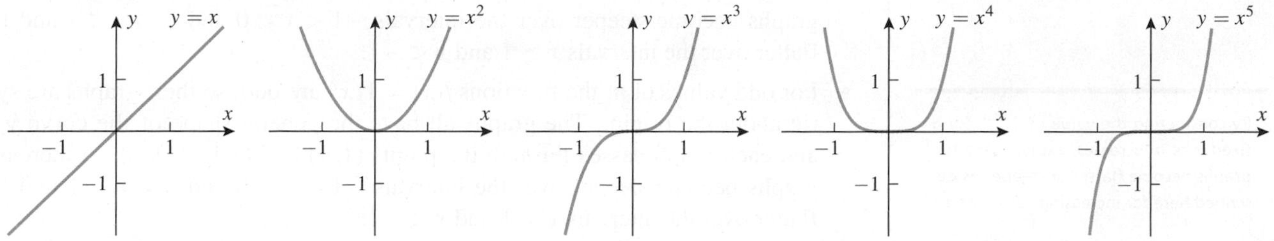


▲ **Figure D.3**

For $n \geq 2$ the shape of the curve $y = x^n$ depends on whether $n$ is even or odd (Figure D.4):

- For even values of $n$, the functions $f(x) = x^n$ are even, so their graphs are symmetric about the $y$-axis. The graphs all have the general shape of the graph of $y = x^2$, and each graph passes through the points $(-1, 1)$, $(0, 0)$, and $(1, 1)$. As $n$ increases, the graphs become flatter over the interval $-1 < x < 1$ and steeper over the intervals $x > 1$ and $x < -1$.
- For odd values of $n$, the functions $f(x) = x^n$ are odd, so their graphs are symmetric about the origin. The graphs all have the general shape of the curve $y = x^3$, and each graph passes through the points $(-1, -1)$, $(0, 0)$, and $(1, 1)$. As $n$ increases, the graphs become flatter over the interval $-1 < x < 1$ and steeper over the intervals $x > 1$ and $x < -1$.

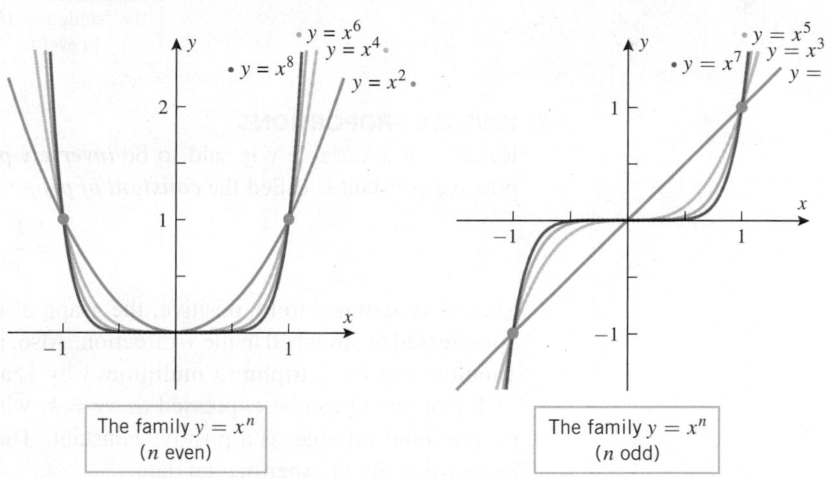


► **Figure D.4**

**REMARK** The flattening and steepening effects can be understood by considering what happens when a number $x$ is raised to higher and higher powers: If $-1 < x < 1$, then the absolute value of $x^n$ *decreases* as $n$ increases, thereby causing the graphs to become flatter on this interval as $n$ increases (try raising $\frac{1}{2}$ or $-\frac{1}{2}$ to higher and higher powers). On the other hand, if $x > 1$ or $x < -1$, then the absolute value of $x^n$ *increases* as $n$ increases, thereby causing the graphs to become steeper on these intervals as $n$ increases (try raising 2 or $-2$ to higher and higher powers).

## THE FAMILY $y = x^{-n}$

If $p$ is a negative integer, say $p = -n$, then the power functions $f(x) = x^p$ have the form $f(x) = x^{-n} = 1/x^n$. Figure D.5 shows the graphs of $y = 1/x$ and $y = 1/x^2$. The graph of $y = 1/x$ is called an ***equilateral hyperbola***.

As illustrated in Figure D.5, the shape of the curve $y = 1/x^n$ depends on whether $n$ is even or odd:

- For even values of $n$, the functions $f(x) = 1/x^n$ are even, so their graphs are symmetric about the $y$-axis. The graphs all have the general shape of the curve $y = 1/x^2$, and each graph passes through the points $(-1, 1)$ and $(1, 1)$. As $n$ increases, the graphs become steeper over the intervals $-1 < x < 0$ and $0 < x < 1$ and become flatter over the intervals $x > 1$ and $x < -1$.

By considering the value of $1/x^n$ for a fixed $x$ as $n$ increases, explain why the graphs become flatter or steeper as described here for increasing values of $n$.

- For odd values of $n$, the functions $f(x) = 1/x^n$ are odd, so their graphs are symmetric about the origin. The graphs all have the general shape of the curve $y = 1/x$, and each graph passes through the points $(1, 1)$ and $(-1, -1)$. As $n$ increases, the graphs become steeper over the intervals $-1 < x < 0$ and $0 < x < 1$ and become flatter over the intervals $x > 1$ and $x < -1$.
- For both even and odd values of $n$ the graph $y = 1/x^n$ has a break at the origin (called a ***discontinuity***), which occurs because division by zero is undefined.

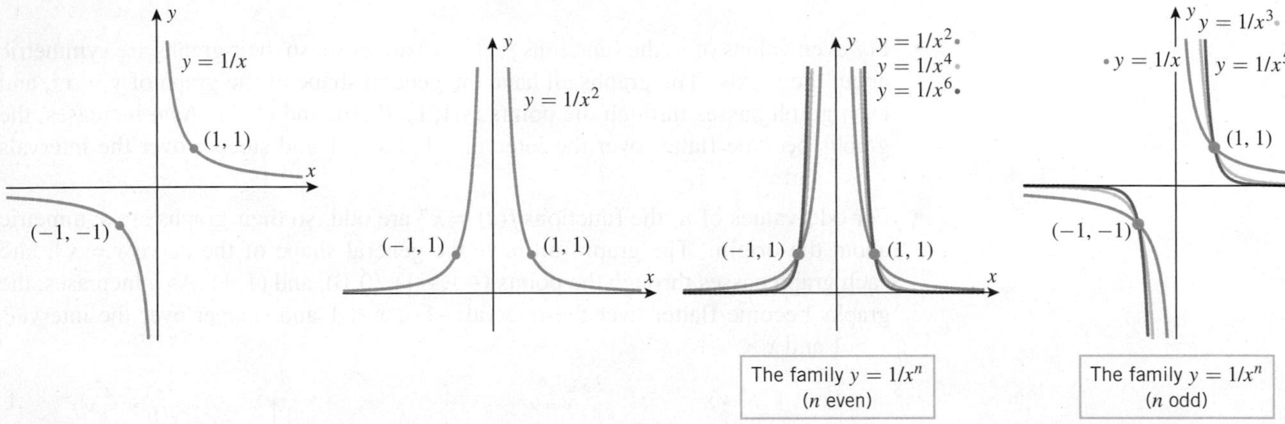


▲ **Figure D.5**

## INVERSE PROPORTIONS

Recall that a variable $y$ is said to be ***inversely proportional to a variable x*** if there is a positive constant $k$, called the ***constant of proportionality***, such that

$$y = \frac{k}{x} \tag{1}$$

Since $k$ is assumed to be positive, the graph of (1) has the same shape as $y = 1/x$ but is compressed or stretched in the $y$-direction. Also, it should be evident from (1) that doubling $x$ multiplies $y$ by $\frac{1}{2}$, tripling $x$ multiplies $y$ by $\frac{1}{3}$, and so forth.

Equation (1) can be expressed as $xy = k$, which tells us that the product of inversely proportional variables is a positive constant. This is a useful form for identifying inverse proportionality in experimental data.

## POWER FUNCTIONS WITH NONINTEGER EXPONENTS

If $p = 1/n$, where $n$ is a positive integer, then the power functions $f(x) = x^p$ have the form

$$f(x) = x^{1/n} = \sqrt[n]{x}$$

In particular, if $n = 2$, then $f(x) = \sqrt{x}$, and if $n = 3$, then $f(x) = \sqrt[3]{x}$. The graphs of these functions are shown in parts $(a)$ and $(b)$ of Figure D.6.

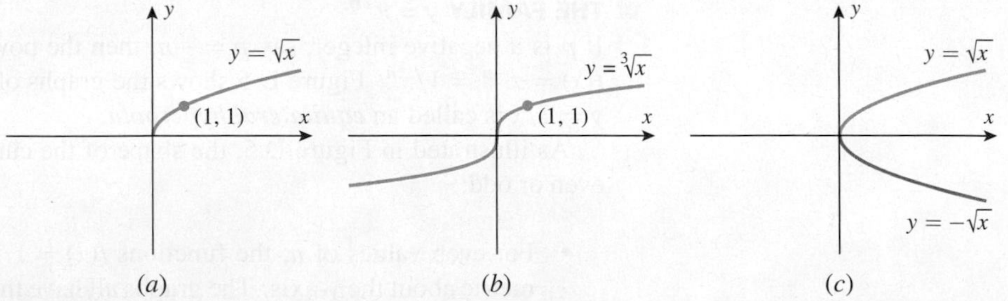


▲ **Figure D.6**

Since every real number has a real cube root, the domain of the function $f(x) = \sqrt[3]{x}$ is $(-\infty, +\infty)$, and hence the graph of $y = \sqrt[3]{x}$ extends over the entire $x$-axis. In contrast, the graph of $y = \sqrt{x}$ extends only over the interval $[0, +\infty)$ because $\sqrt{x}$ is imaginary for negative $x$. As illustrated in Figure D.6*c*, the graphs of $y = \sqrt{x}$ and $y = -\sqrt{x}$ form the upper and lower halves of the parabola $x = y^2$. In general, the graph of $y = \sqrt[n]{x}$ extends over the entire $x$-axis if $n$ is odd, but extends only over the interval $[0, +\infty)$ if $n$ is even.

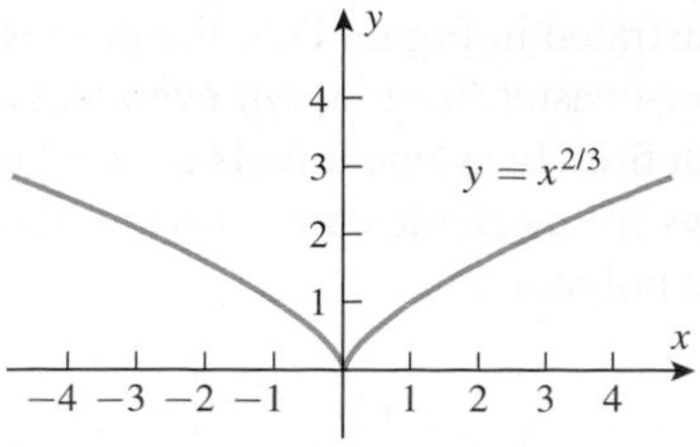

▲ **Figure D.7**

Power functions can have other fractional exponents. Some examples are

$$f(x) = x^{2/3}, \quad f(x) = \sqrt[5]{x^3}, \quad f(x) = x^{-7/8} \tag{2}$$

The graph of $f(x) = x^{2/3}$ is shown in Figure D.7. We discuss expressions involving irrational exponents elsewhere in this text.

**TECHNOLOGY MASTERY**

Graphing utililties sometimes omit portions of the graph of a function involving fractional exponents (or radicals). If $f(x) = x^{p/q}$, where $p/q$ is a positive fraction in *lowest terms*, then you can circumvent this problem as follows:

- If $p$ is even and $q$ is odd, then graph $g(x) = |x|^{p/q}$ instead of $f(x)$.
- If $p$ is odd and $q$ is odd, then graph $g(x) = (|x|/x)|x|^{p/q}$ instead of $f(x)$.

Use a graphing utility to generate graphs of $f(x) = \sqrt[5]{x^3}$ and $f(x) = x^{-7/8}$ that show all of their significant features.

## POLYNOMIALS

A ***polynomial in x*** is a function that is expressible as a sum of finitely many terms of the form $cx^n$, where $c$ is a constant and $n$ is a nonnegative integer. Some examples of polynomials are

$$2x + 1, \quad 3x^2 + 5x - \sqrt{2}, \quad x^3, \quad 4\,(= 4x^0), \quad 5x^7 - x^4 + 3$$

The function $(x^2 - 4)^3$ is also a polynomial because it can be expanded by the binomial formula (see the inside front cover) and expressed as a sum of terms of the form $cx^n$:

$$(x^2 - 4)^3 = (x^2)^3 - 3(x^2)^2(4) + 3(x^2)(4^2) - (4^3) = x^6 - 12x^4 + 48x^2 - 64 \tag{3}$$

A more detailed review of polynomials appears in Web Appendix K.

A general polynomial can be written in either of the following forms, depending on whether one wants the powers of $x$ in ascending or descending order:

$$c_0 + c_1x + c_2x^2 + \cdots + c_nx^n$$
$$c_nx^n + c_{n-1}x^{n-1} + \cdots + c_1x + c_0$$

The constants $c_0, c_1, \ldots, c_n$ are called the ***coefficients*** of the polynomial. When a polynomial is expressed in one of these forms, the highest power of $x$ that occurs with a nonzero coefficient is called the ***degree*** of the polynomial. Nonzero constant polynomials are considered to have degree 0, since we can write $c = cx^0$. Polynomials of degree 1, 2, 3, 4, and 5 are described as ***linear***, ***quadratic***, ***cubic***, ***quartic***, and ***quintic***, respectively. For example,

The constant 0 is a polynomial called the ***zero polynomial***. In this text we will take the degree of the zero polynomial to be undefined. Other texts may use different conventions for the degree of the zero polynomial.

| | | |
|---|---|---|
| $3 + 5x$ | $x^2 - 3x + 1$ | $2x^3 - 7$ |
| Has degree 1 (linear) | Has degree 2 (quadratic) | Has degree 3 (cubic) |
| $8x^4 - 9x^3 + 5x - 3$ | $\sqrt{3} + x^3 + x^5$ | $(x^2 - 4)^3$ |
| Has degree 4 (quartic) | Has degree 5 (quintic) | Has degree 6 [see (3)] |

The natural domain of a polynomial in $x$ is $(-\infty, +\infty)$, since the only operations involved are multiplication and addition; the range depends on the particular polynomial. We already know that the graphs of polynomials of degree 0 and 1 are lines and that the graphs of polynomials of degree 2 are parabolas. Figure D.8 shows the graphs of some typical polynomials of higher degree. We discuss polynomial graphs in detail in the text, but for now it suffices to observe that graphs of polynomials are very well behaved in the sense that they have no discontinuities or sharp corners. As illustrated in Figure D.8, the graphs of polynomials wander up and down for awhile in a roller-coaster fashion, but eventually that behavior stops and the graphs steadily rise or fall indefinitely as one travels along the curve in either the positive or negative direction. It follows from calculus methods that the number of peaks and valleys is less than the degree of the polynomial.

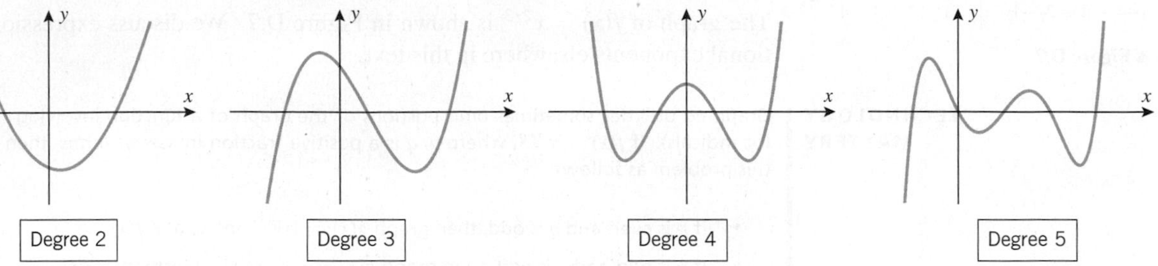


▲ **Figure D.8**

## RATIONAL FUNCTIONS

A function that can be expressed as a ratio of two polynomials is called a ***rational function***. If $P(x)$ and $Q(x)$ are polynomials, then the domain of the rational function

$$f(x) = \frac{P(x)}{Q(x)}$$

consists of all values of $x$ such that $Q(x) \neq 0$. For example, the domain of the rational function

$$f(x) = \frac{x^2 + 2x}{x^2 - 1}$$

consists of all values of $x$, except $x = 1$ and $x = -1$. Its graph is shown in Figure D.9 along with the graphs of two other typical rational functions.

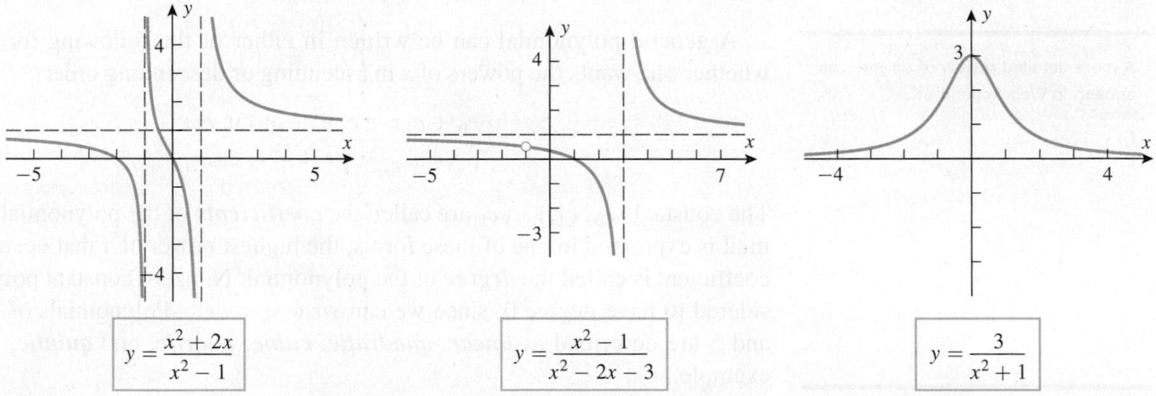


▲ **Figure D.9**

The graphs of rational functions with nonconstant denominators differ from the graphs of polynomials in some essential ways:

- Unlike polynomials whose graphs are continuous (unbroken) curves, the graphs of rational functions have discontinuities at the points where the denominator is zero.
- Unlike polynomials, rational functions may have numbers at which they are not defined. Near such points, many rational functions have graphs that closely approximate a vertical line, called a ***vertical asymptote***. These are represented by the dashed vertical lines in Figure D.9.

- Unlike the graphs of nonconstant polynomials, which eventually rise or fall indefinitely, the graphs of many rational functions eventually get closer and closer to some horizontal line, called a ***horizontal asymptote***, as one traverses the curve in either the positive or negative direction. The horizontal asymptotes are represented by the dashed horizontal lines in the first two parts of Figure D.9. In the third part of the figure the $x$-axis is a horizontal asymptote.

## ALGEBRAIC FUNCTIONS

Functions that can be constructed from polynomials by applying finitely many algebraic operations (addition, subtraction, multiplication, division, and root extraction) are called ***algebraic functions***. Some examples are

$$f(x) = \sqrt{x^2 - 4}, \quad f(x) = 3\sqrt[3]{x}(2 + x), \quad f(x) = x^{2/3}(x + 2)^2$$

As illustrated in Figure D.10, the graphs of algebraic functions vary widely, so it is difficult to make general statements about them. Elsewhere in this text we develop general calculus methods for analyzing such functions.

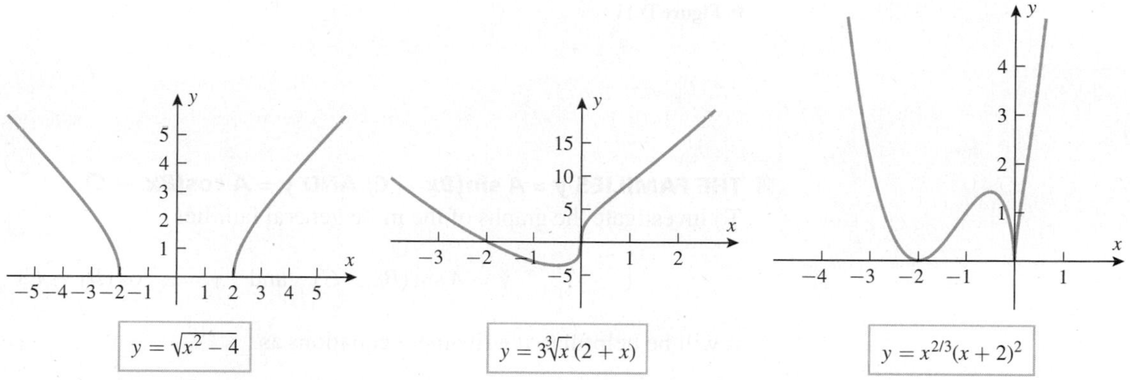


▲ **Figure D.10**

## THE FAMILIES $y = A \sin Bx$ AND $y = A \cos Bx$

Many important applications lead to trigonometric functions of the form

$$f(x) = A \sin(Bx - C) \quad \text{and} \quad g(x) = A \cos(Bx - C) \tag{4}$$

In this text we will assume that the independent variable of a trigonometric function is in radians unless otherwise stated. A review of trigonometric functions can be found in Appendix A.

where $A$, $B$, and $C$ are nonzero constants. The graphs of such functions can be obtained by stretching, compressing, translating, and reflecting the graphs of $y = \sin x$ and $y = \cos x$ appropriately. To see why this is so, let us start with the case where $C = 0$ and consider how the graphs of the equations

$$y = A \sin Bx \quad \text{and} \quad y = A \cos Bx$$

relate to the graphs of $y = \sin x$ and $y = \cos x$. If $A$ and $B$ are positive, then the effect of the constant $A$ is to stretch or compress the graphs of $y = \sin x$ and $y = \cos x$ vertically and the effect of the constant $B$ is to compress or stretch the graphs of $\sin x$ and $\cos x$ horizontally. For example, the graph of $y = 2 \sin 4x$ can be obtained by stretching the graph of $y = \sin x$ vertically by a factor of 2 and compressing it horizontally by a factor of 4. (Recall from Appendix C that the multiplier of $x$ *stretches* when it is less than 1 and *compresses* when it is greater than 1.) Thus, as shown in Figure D.11, the graph of $y = 2 \sin 4x$ varies between $-2$ and 2, and repeats every $2\pi/4 = \pi/2$ units.

In general, if $A$ and $B$ are positive numbers, then the graphs of

$$y = A \sin Bx \quad \text{and} \quad y = A \cos Bx$$

oscillate between $-A$ and $A$ and repeat every $2\pi/B$ units, so we say that these functions have ***amplitude*** $A$ and ***period*** $2\pi/B$. In addition, we define the ***frequency*** of these functions to be the reciprocal of the period, that is, the frequency is $B/(2\pi)$. If $A$ or $B$ is negative, then these constants cause reflections of the graphs about the axes as well as compressing or stretching them; and in this case the amplitude, period, and frequency are given by

$$\text{amplitude} = |A|, \quad \text{period} = \frac{2\pi}{|B|}, \quad \text{frequency} = \frac{|B|}{2\pi}$$

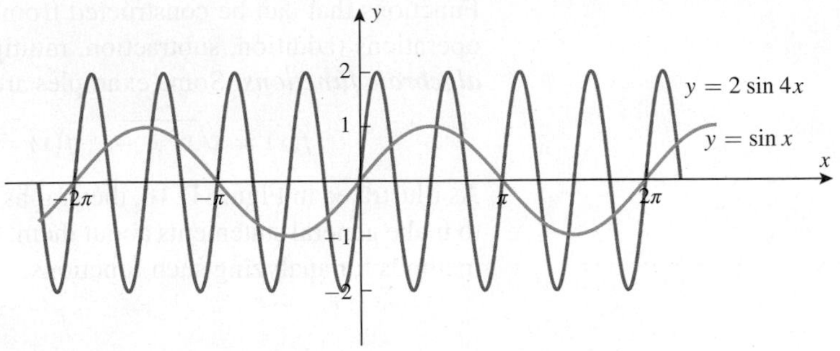


▶ **Figure D.11**

## THE FAMILIES *y* = *A* sin(*Bx* − *C*) AND *y* = *A* cos(*Bx* − *C*)

To investigate the graphs of the more general families

$$y = A\sin(Bx - C) \quad \text{and} \quad y = A\cos(Bx - C)$$

it will be helpful to rewrite these equations as

$$y = A\sin\left[B\left(x - \frac{C}{B}\right)\right] \quad \text{and} \quad y = A\cos\left[B\left(x - \frac{C}{B}\right)\right]$$

In this form we see that the graphs of these equations can be obtained by translating the graphs of $y = A\sin Bx$ and $y = A\cos Bx$ to the left or right, depending on the sign of $C/B$. For example, if $C/B > 0$, then the graph of

$$y = A\sin\left[B\left(x - \frac{C}{B}\right)\right] = A\sin(Bx - C)$$

can be obtained by translating the graph of $y = A\sin Bx$ to the right by $C/B$ units (Figure D.12). If $C/B < 0$, the graph of $y = A\sin(Bx - C)$ is obtained by translating the graph of $y = A\sin Bx$ to the left by $|C/B|$ units.

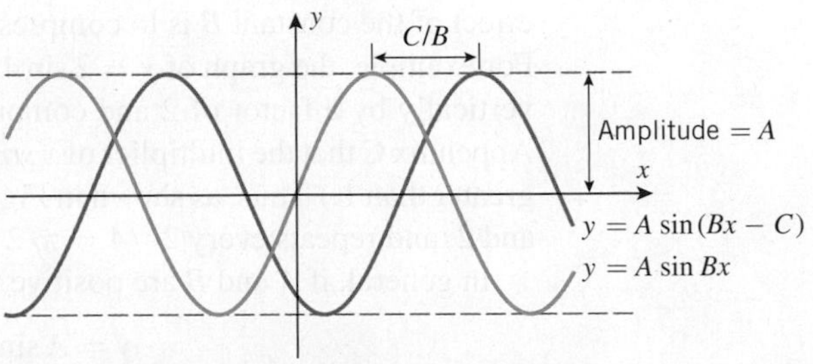


▶ **Figure D.12**

# E

# INVERSE FUNCTIONS (SUMMARY)

*This reference summary highlights key facts and results concerning inverse functions. A more detailed discussion, including exercises, is contained in Web Appendix E,* Inverse Functions.

## INVERSE FUNCTIONS

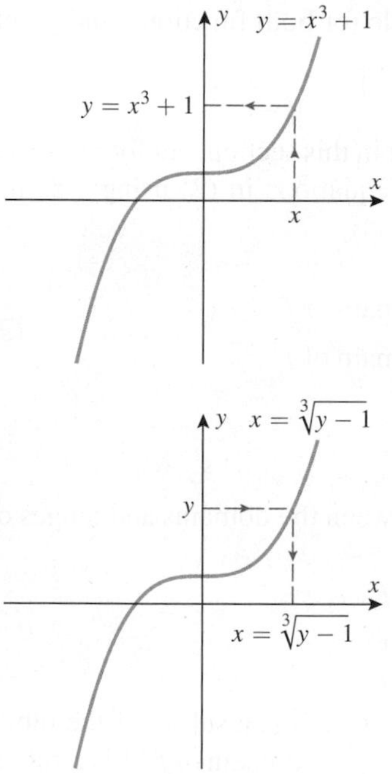

▲ Figure E.1

The idea of solving an equation $y = f(x)$ for $x$ as a function of $y$, say $x = g(y)$, is one of the most important ideas in mathematics. Sometimes, solving an equation is a simple process; for example, using basic algebra the equation

$$y = x^3 + 1 \qquad \boxed{y = f(x)}$$

can be solved for $x$ as a function of $y$:

$$x = \sqrt[3]{y-1} \qquad \boxed{x = g(y)}$$

The first equation is better for computing $y$ if $x$ is known, and the second is better for computing $x$ if $y$ is known (Figure E.1).

Our primary interest in this section is to identify relationships that may exist between the functions $f$ and $g$ when an equation $y = f(x)$ is expressed as $x = g(y)$, or conversely. For example, consider the functions $f(x) = x^3 + 1$ and $g(y) = \sqrt[3]{y-1}$ discussed above. When these functions are composed in either order, they cancel out the effect of one another in the sense that

$$\begin{aligned} g(f(x)) &= \sqrt[3]{f(x) - 1} = \sqrt[3]{(x^3+1) - 1} = x \\ f(g(y)) &= [g(y)]^3 + 1 = (\sqrt[3]{y-1})^3 + 1 = y \end{aligned} \tag{1}$$

Pairs of functions with these two properties are so important that there is special terminology for them.

> **E.1 DEFINITION** If the functions $f$ and $g$ satisfy the two conditions
>
> $$g(f(x)) = x \text{ for every } x \text{ in the domain of } f$$
> $$f(g(y)) = y \text{ for every } y \text{ in the domain of } g$$
>
> then we say that ***f* is an inverse of *g*** and ***g* is an inverse of *f*** or that ***f* and *g* are inverse functions**.

**WARNING**

If $f$ is a function, then the $-1$ in the symbol $f^{-1}$ always denotes an inverse and *never* an exponent. That is,

$$f^{-1}(x) \quad \textit{never means} \quad \frac{1}{f(x)}$$

It can be shown that if a function $f$ has an inverse, then that inverse is unique. Thus, if a function $f$ has an inverse, then we are entitled to talk about "the" inverse of $f$, in which case we denote it by the symbol $f^{-1}$.

▶ **Example 1** The computations in (1) show that $g(y) = \sqrt[3]{y-1}$ is the inverse of $f(x) = x^3 + 1$. Thus, we can express $g$ in inverse notation as

$$f^{-1}(y) = \sqrt[3]{y-1}$$

and we can express the equations in Definition E.1 as

$$\begin{aligned} f^{-1}(f(x)) &= x \quad \text{for every } x \text{ in the domain of } f \\ f(f^{-1}(y)) &= y \quad \text{for every } y \text{ in the domain of } f^{-1} \end{aligned} \tag{2}$$

In general, if a function $f$ has an inverse and $f(a) = b$, then the cancellation equations show that $a = f^{-1}(b)$; that is, $f^{-1}$ maps each output of $f$ back into the corresponding input (Figure E.2).

We will call these the ***cancellation equations*** for $f$ and $f^{-1}$. ◀

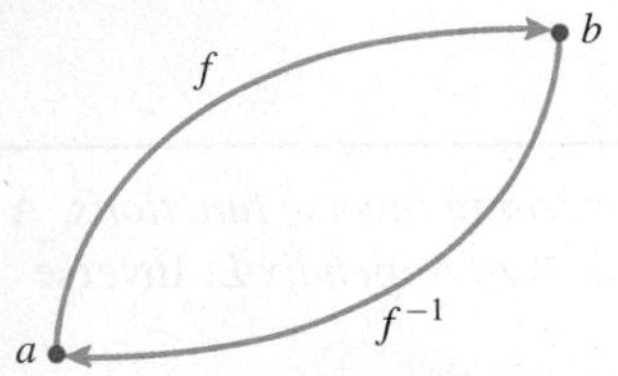

▲ **Figure E.2** If $f$ maps $a$ to $b$, then $f^{-1}$ maps $b$ back to $a$.

## CHANGING THE INDEPENDENT VARIABLE

The formulas in (2) use $x$ as the independent variable for $f$ and $y$ as the independent variable for $f^{-1}$. Although it is often convenient to use different independent variables for $f$ and $f^{-1}$, there will be occasions on which it is desirable to use the same independent variable for both. For example, if we want to graph the functions $f$ and $f^{-1}$ together in the same $xy$-coordinate system, then we would want to use $x$ as the independent variable and $y$ as the dependent variable for both functions. Thus, to graph the functions $f(x) = x^3 + 1$ and $f^{-1}(y) = \sqrt[3]{y-1}$ of Example 1 in the same $xy$-coordinate system, we would change the independent variable $y$ to $x$, use $y$ as the dependent variable for both functions, and graph the equations

$$y = x^3 + 1 \quad \text{and} \quad y = \sqrt[3]{x-1}$$

We will talk more about graphs of inverse functions later in this section, but for reference we give the following reformulation of the cancellation equations in (2) using $x$ as the independent variable for both $f$ and $f^{-1}$:

$$\begin{aligned} f^{-1}(f(x)) &= x \quad \text{for every } x \text{ in the domain of } f \\ f(f^{-1}(x)) &= x \quad \text{for every } x \text{ in the domain of } f^{-1} \end{aligned} \tag{3}$$

## DOMAIN AND RANGE OF INVERSE FUNCTIONS

The equations in (3) imply the following relationships between the domains and ranges of $f$ and $f^{-1}$:

$$\begin{aligned} \text{domain of } f^{-1} &= \text{range of } f \\ \text{range of } f^{-1} &= \text{domain of } f \end{aligned} \tag{4}$$

One way to show that two sets are the same is to show that each is a subset of the other. Thus we can establish the first equality in (4) by showing that the domain of $f^{-1}$ is a subset of the range of $f$ and that the range of $f$ is a subset of the domain of $f^{-1}$. We do this as follows: The first equation in (3) implies that $f^{-1}$ is defined at $f(x)$ for all values of $x$ in the domain of $f$, and this implies that the range of $f$ is a subset of the domain of $f^{-1}$. Conversely, if $x$ is in the domain of $f^{-1}$, then the second equation in (3) implies that $x$ is in the range of $f$ because it is the image of $f^{-1}(x)$. Thus, the domain of $f^{-1}$ is a subset of the range of $f$. We leave the proof of the second equation in (4) as an exercise.

## A METHOD FOR FINDING INVERSE FUNCTIONS

At the beginning of this section we observed that solving $y = f(x) = x^3 + 1$ for $x$ as a function of $y$ produces $x = f^{-1}(y) = \sqrt[3]{y-1}$. The following theorem shows that this is not accidental.

**E.2 THEOREM** *If an equation $y = f(x)$ can be solved for $x$ as a function of $y$, say $x = g(y)$, then $f$ has an inverse and that inverse is $g(y) = f^{-1}(y)$.*

PROOF Substituting $y = f(x)$ into $x = g(y)$ yields $x = g(f(x))$, which confirms the first equation in Definition E.1, and substituting $x = g(y)$ into $y = f(x)$ yields $y = f(g(y))$, which confirms the second equation in Definition E.1. ■

Theorem E.2 provides us with the following procedure for finding the inverse of a function.

***A Procedure for Finding the Inverse of a Function f***

**Step 1.** Write down the equation $y = f(x)$.

**Step 2.** If possible, solve this equation for $x$ as a function of $y$.

**Step 3.** The resulting equation will be $x = f^{-1}(y)$, which provides a formula for $f^{-1}$ with $y$ as the independent variable.

**Step 4.** If $y$ is acceptable as the independent variable for the inverse function, then you are done, but if you want to have $x$ as the independent variable, then you need to interchange $x$ and $y$ in the equation $x = f^{-1}(y)$ to obtain $y = f^{-1}(x)$.

An alternative way to obtain a formula for $f^{-1}(x)$ with $x$ as the independent variable is to reverse the roles of $x$ and $y$ at the outset and solve the equation $x = f(y)$ for $y$ as a function of $x$.

## EXISTENCE OF INVERSE FUNCTIONS

The procedure we gave above for finding the inverse of a function $f$ was based on solving the equation $y = f(x)$ for $x$ as a function of $y$. This procedure can fail for two reasons—the function $f$ may not have an inverse, or it may have an inverse but the equation $y = f(x)$ cannot be solved explicitly for $x$ as a function of $y$. Thus, it is important to establish conditions that ensure the existence of an inverse, even if it cannot be found explicitly.

If a function $f$ has an inverse, then it must assign distinct outputs to distinct inputs. For example, the function $f(x) = x^2$ cannot have an inverse because it assigns the same value to $x = 2$ and $x = -2$, namely,

$$f(2) = f(-2) = 4$$

Thus, if $f(x) = x^2$ were to have an inverse, then the equation $f(2) = 4$ would imply that $f^{-1}(4) = 2$, and the equation $f(-2) = 4$ would imply that $f^{-1}(4) = -2$. But this is impossible because $f^{-1}(4)$ cannot have two different values. Another way to see that $f(x) = x^2$ has no inverse is to attempt to find the inverse by solving the equation $y = x^2$ for $x$ as a function of $y$. We run into trouble immediately because the resulting equation $x = \pm\sqrt{y}$ does not express $x$ as a *single* function of $y$.

A function that assigns distinct outputs to distinct inputs is said to be ***one-to-one*** or ***invertible***, so we know from the preceding discussion that if a function $f$ has an inverse, then it must be one-to-one. The converse is also true, thereby establishing the following theorem.

**E.3 THEOREM** *A function has an inverse if and only if it is one-to-one.*

Stated algebraically, a function $f$ is one-to-one if and only if $f(x_1) \neq f(x_2)$ whenever $x_1 \neq x_2$; stated geometrically, a function $f$ is one-to-one if and only if the graph of $y = f(x)$ is cut at most once by any horizontal line (Figure E.3). The latter statement together with Theorem E.3 provides the following geometric test for determining whether a function has an inverse.

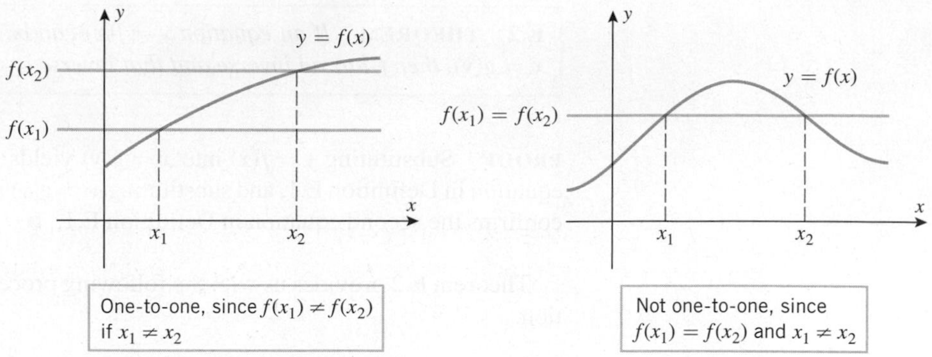


▶ **Figure E.3**

> **E.4 THEOREM** (*The Horizontal Line Test*) *A function has an inverse function if and only if its graph is cut at most once by any horizontal line.*

## INCREASING OR DECREASING FUNCTIONS ARE INVERTIBLE

A function whose graph is always rising as it is traversed from left to right is said to be an ***increasing function***, and a function whose graph is always falling as it is traversed from left to right is said to be a ***decreasing function***. If $x_1$ and $x_2$ are points in the domain of a function $f$, then $f$ is increasing if

$$f(x_1) < f(x_2) \quad \text{whenever } x_1 < x_2$$

and $f$ is decreasing if

$$f(x_1) > f(x_2) \quad \text{whenever } x_1 < x_2$$

(Figure E.4). It is evident geometrically that increasing and decreasing functions pass the horizontal line test and hence are invertible.

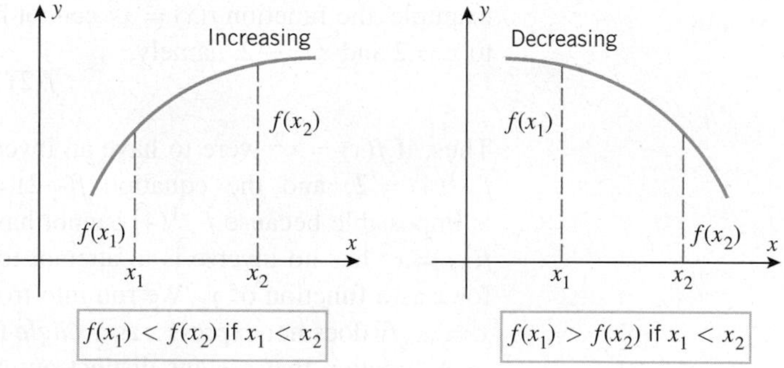


▶ **Figure E.4**

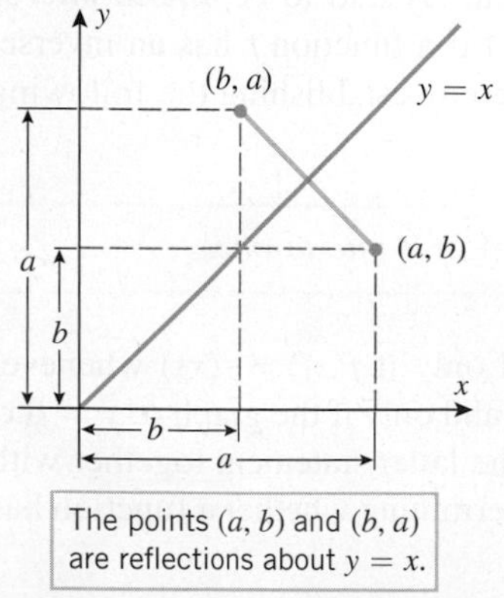


▲ **Figure E.5**

## GRAPHS OF INVERSE FUNCTIONS

Our next objective is to explore the relationship between the graphs of $f$ and $f^{-1}$. For this purpose, it will be desirable to use $x$ as the independent variable for both functions so we can compare the graphs of $y = f(x)$ and $y = f^{-1}(x)$.

If $(a, b)$ is a point on the graph $y = f(x)$, then $b = f(a)$. This is equivalent to the statement that $a = f^{-1}(b)$, which means that $(b, a)$ is a point on the graph of $y = f^{-1}(x)$. In short, reversing the coordinates of a point on the graph of $f$ produces a point on the graph of $f^{-1}$. Similarly, reversing the coordinates of a point on the graph of $f^{-1}$ produces a point on the graph of $f$ (verify). However, the geometric effect of reversing the coordinates of a point is to reflect that point about the line $y = x$ (Figure E.5), and hence the graphs of $y = f(x)$ and $y = f^{-1}(x)$ are reflections of one another about this line (Figure E.6). In summary, we have the following result.

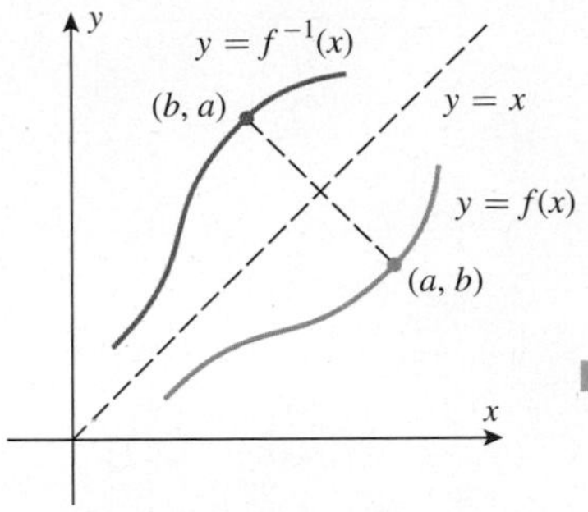


The graphs of $f$ and $f^{-1}$ are reflections about $y = x$.

▲ **Figure E.6**

**E.5 THEOREM** *If $f$ has an inverse, then the graphs of $y = f(x)$ and $y = f^{-1}(x)$ are reflections of one another about the line $y = x$; that is, each graph is the mirror image of the other with respect to that line.*

## RESTRICTING DOMAINS FOR INVERTIBILITY

If a function $g$ is obtained from a function $f$ by placing restrictions on the domain of $f$, then $g$ is called a ***restriction*** of $f$. Thus, for example, the function

$$g(x) = x^3, \quad x \geq 0$$

is a restriction of the function $f(x) = x^3$. More precisely, it is called the restriction of $x^3$ to the interval $[0, +\infty)$.

Sometimes it is possible to create an invertible function from a function that is not invertible by restricting the domain appropriately. For example, we showed earlier that $f(x) = x^2$ is not invertible. However, consider the restricted functions

$$f_1(x) = x^2, \quad x \geq 0 \quad \text{and} \quad f_2(x) = x^2, \quad x \leq 0$$

the union of whose graphs is the complete graph of $f(x) = x^2$ (Figure E.7). These restricted functions are each one-to-one (hence invertible), since their graphs pass the horizontal line test. As illustrated in Figure E.8, their inverses are

$$f_1^{-1}(x) = \sqrt{x} \quad \text{and} \quad f_2^{-1}(x) = -\sqrt{x}$$

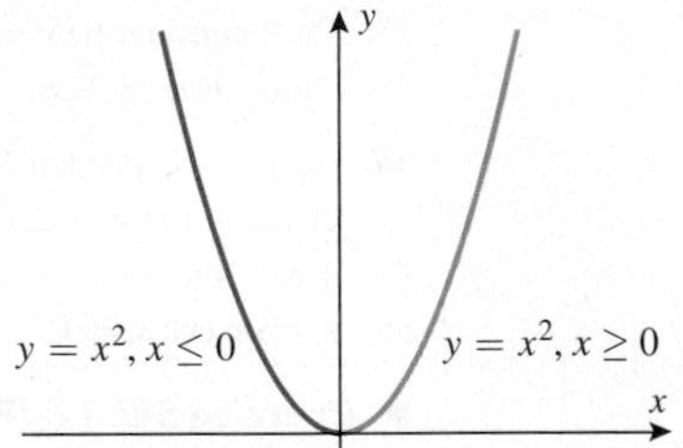


▲ **Figure E.7**

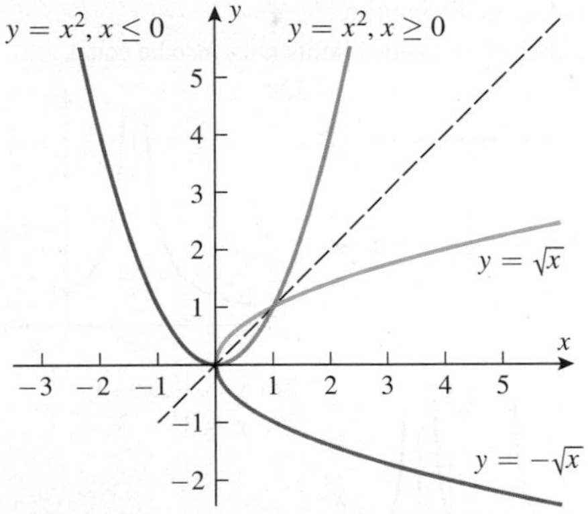


▲ **Figure E.8**

# ANSWERS TO ODD-NUMBERED EXERCISES

## ▶ Exercise Set 1.1 (Page 10)

1. (a) 3 (b) 3 (c) 3 (d) 3
3. (a) $-1$ (b) 3 (c) does not exist (d) 1
5. (a) 0 (b) 0 (c) 0 (d) 3
7. (a) $-\infty$ (b) $-\infty$ (c) $-\infty$ (d) 1
9. (a) $+\infty$ (b) $+\infty$ (c) 2 (d) 2 (e) $-\infty$ (f) the lines $x = -2$, $x = 0, x = 2$
11. (i)

| $x$ | $-0.1$ | $-0.01$ | $-0.001$ | 0.001 | 0.01 | 0.1 |
|---|---|---|---|---|---|---|
| $f(x)$ | 1.9866933 | 1.9998667 | 1.9999987 | 1.9999987 | 1.9998667 | 1.9866933 |

The limit appears to be 2.

13. (a) $\frac{1}{3}$ (b) $+\infty$ (c) $-\infty$ 15. (a) 3 (b) does not exist

Responses to True–False questions may be abridged to save space.

17. False; see Example 6.
19. False; the one-sided limits must also be equal.

21.
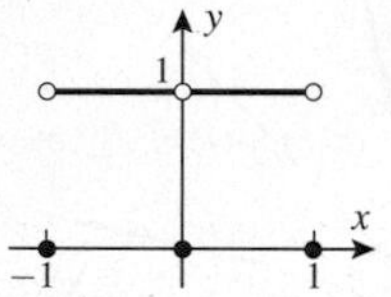


23.
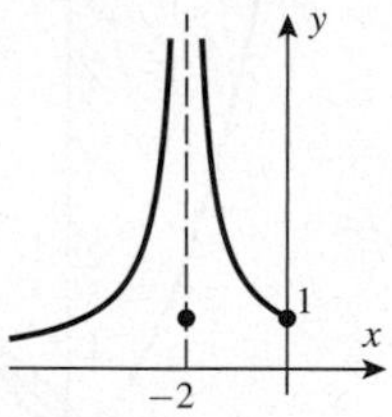


25.
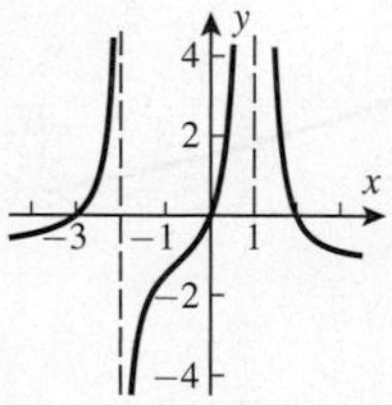


27. $y = -2x - 1$
29. $y = 4x - 3$
31. (a) rest length (b) 0. As speed approaches $c$, length shrinks to zero.

## ▶ Exercise Set 1.2 (Page 20)

1. (a) $-6$ (b) 13 (c) $-8$ (d) 16 (e) 2 (f) $-\frac{1}{2}$
3. 6 5. $\frac{3}{4}$ 7. 4 9. $-\frac{4}{5}$ 11. $-3$ 13. $\frac{3}{2}$ 15. $+\infty$
17. does not exist 19. $-\infty$ 21. $+\infty$ 23. does not exist 25. $+\infty$
27. $+\infty$ 29. 6 31. (a) 2 (b) 2 (c) 2

Responses to True–False questions may be abridged to save space.

33. True; this is Theorem 1.2.2(*a*). 35. False; see Example 9. 37. $\frac{1}{4}$
39. (a) 3 (b)

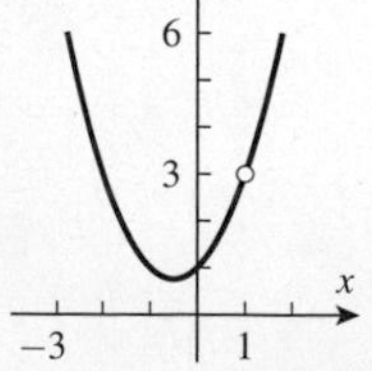


41. (a) Theorem 1.2.2(*a*) does not apply.
(b) $\lim_{x\to 0^+}\left(\frac{1}{x} - \frac{1}{x^2}\right) = \lim_{x\to 0^+}\left(\frac{x-1}{x^2}\right) = -\infty$ 43. $a = 2$
45. The left and/or right limits could be $\pm\infty$; or the limit could exist and equal any preassigned real number.

## ▶ Exercise Set 1.3 (Page 28)

1. (a) $-\infty$ (b) $+\infty$ 3. (a) 0 (b) $-1$
5. (a) $-12$ (b) 21 (c) $-15$ (d) 25 (e) 2 (f) $-\frac{3}{5}$ (g) 0
7. (a)

| $x$ | 10 | 100 | 1000 | 10,000 | 100,000 | 1,000,000 |
|---|---|---|---|---|---|---|
| $f(x)$ | 0.9534626 | 0.9950372 | 0.9995004 | 0.9999500 | 0.9999950 | 0.9999995 |

The limit appears to be 1.

9. $-\infty$ 11. $+\infty$ 13. $\frac{3}{2}$ 15. 0 17. 0 19. $-\infty$ 21. $-\frac{1}{7}$
23. $\dfrac{-\sqrt[3]{5}}{2}$ 25. $-\sqrt{5}$ 27. $1/\sqrt{6}$ 29. $\sqrt{3}$ 31. 0

Responses to True–False questions may be abridged to save space.

33. False; the limit is $+\infty$.
35. True; consider $f(x) = (\sin x)/x$.
37. $\lim_{t\to+\infty} n(t) = +\infty$; $\lim_{t\to+\infty} e(t) = c$ 39. (a) $+\infty$ (b) $-5$
43. (a) no (b) yes; $\tan x$ and $\sec x$ at $x = n\pi + \pi/2$, and $\cot x$ and $\csc x$ at $x = n\pi, n = 0, \pm 1, \pm 2, \ldots$
47. $+\infty$ 49. $+\infty$ 51. $y = x + 2; x = 2$ 53. $y = 1 - x^2; x = 3$
55. $y = \sin(x); x = 1$

## ▶ Exercise Set 1.4 (Page 37)

1. (a) $|x| < 0.1$ (b) $|x - 3| < 0.0025$ (c) $|x - 4| < 0.000124$
3. (a) $x_0 = 3.8025, x_1 = 4.2025$ (b) $\delta = 0.1975$
5. $\delta = 0.0442$ 7. $\delta = 0.13$ 9. $\delta = 0.05$ 11. $\delta = 0.05$

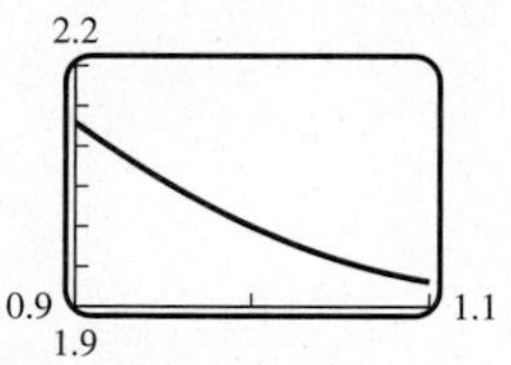


13. $\delta = \sqrt[3]{8.001} - 2 \approx 8.332986 \cdot 10^{-5}$ 15. $\delta = 1$
17. any $\delta$ 19. $\delta = \frac{1}{3}\epsilon$ 21. $\delta = \epsilon/2$ 23. $\delta = \epsilon$ 25. $\delta = \epsilon$
29. (b) 65 (c) $\epsilon/65$; 65; 65; $\epsilon/65$ 31. $\delta = \min\left(1, \frac{1}{6}\epsilon\right)$
33. $\delta = \min\left(\frac{1}{2}, \frac{\epsilon}{2}\right)$ 35. $\delta = 2\epsilon$
39. (a) $\sqrt{10}$ (b) 99 (c) $-10$ (d) $-101$
41. (a) $-\sqrt{\frac{1-\epsilon}{\epsilon}}$; $\sqrt{\frac{1-\epsilon}{\epsilon}}$ (b) $\sqrt{\frac{1-\epsilon}{\epsilon}}$ (c) $-\sqrt{\frac{1-\epsilon}{\epsilon}}$
43. 10 45. 999 47. $-202$ 49. $-57.5$ 51. $N = \dfrac{1}{\sqrt{\epsilon}}$
53. $N = -\dfrac{5}{2} - \dfrac{11}{2\epsilon}$ 55. $N = (1 + 2/\epsilon)^2$

57. **(a)** $|x| < \frac{1}{10}$ **(b)** $|x-1| < \frac{1}{1000}$ **(c)** $|x-3| < \frac{1}{10\sqrt{10}}$ **(d)** $|x| < \frac{1}{10}$

59. $\delta = 1/\sqrt{M}$ 61. $\delta = 1/M$ 63. $\delta = 1/(-M)^{1/4}$ 65. $\delta = \epsilon$ 67. $\delta = \epsilon^2$ 69. $\delta = \epsilon$ 71. **(a)** $\delta = -1/M$ **(b)** $\delta = 1/M$

73. **(a)** $N = M - 1$ **(b)** $N = M - 1$

75. **(a)** 0.4 amps **(b)** about 0.39474 to 0.40541 amps **(c)** $3/(7.5+\delta)$ to $3/(7.5-\delta)$ **(d)** $\delta \approx 0.01870$ **(e)** current approaches $+\infty$

## ▶ Exercise Set 1.5 (Page 48)

1. **(a)** not continuous, $x = 2$ **(b)** not continuous, $x = 2$ **(c)** not continuous, $x = 2$ **(d)** continuous **(e)** continuous **(f)** continuous

3. **(a)** not continuous, $x = 1, 3$ **(b)** continuous **(c)** not continuous, $x = 1$ **(d)** continuous **(e)** not continuous, $x = 3$ **(f)** continuous

5. **(a)** no **(b)** no **(c)** no **(d)** yes **(e)** yes **(f)** no **(g)** yes

7. **(a)**

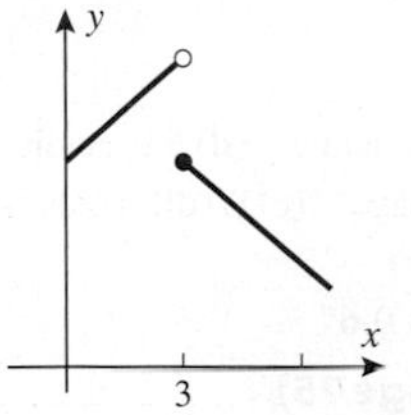


**(b)**

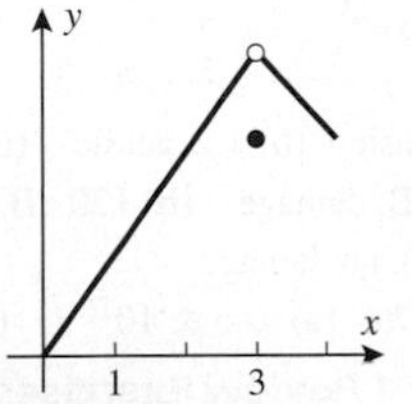


**(c)**

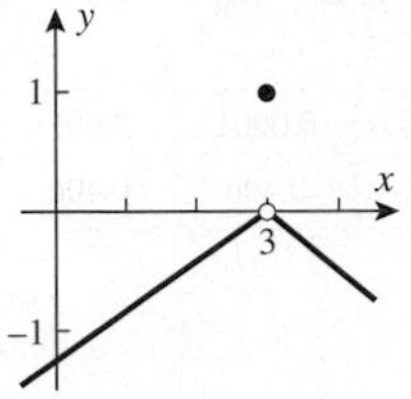


**(d)**

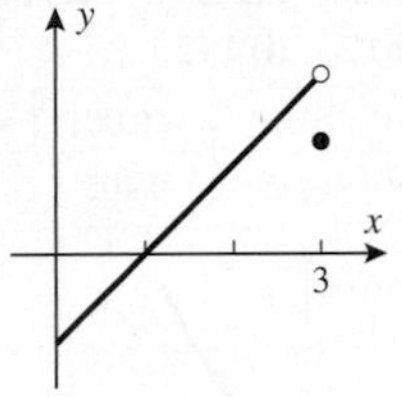


9. **(a)**

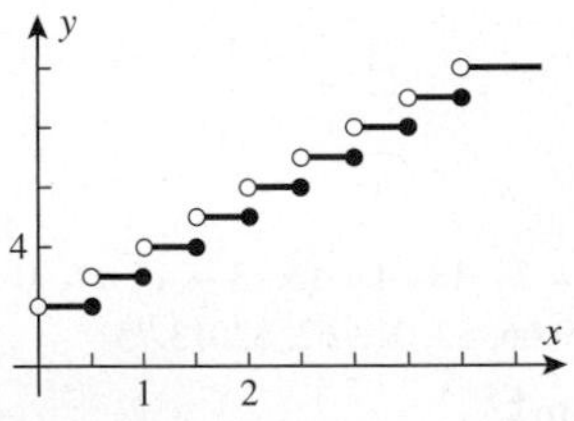


**(b)** One second could cost you one dollar.

11. none 13. none 15. $-1/2, 0$ 17. $-1, 0, 1$ 19. none 21. none

Responses to True–False questions may be abridged to save space.

23. True; the composition of continuous functions is continuous.

25. False; let $f$ and $g$ be the functions in Exercise 6.

27. True; $f(x) = \sqrt{f(x)} \cdot \sqrt{f(x)}$

29. **(a)** $k = 5$ **(b)** $k = \frac{4}{3}$ 31. $k = 4, m = 5/3$

33. **(a)**

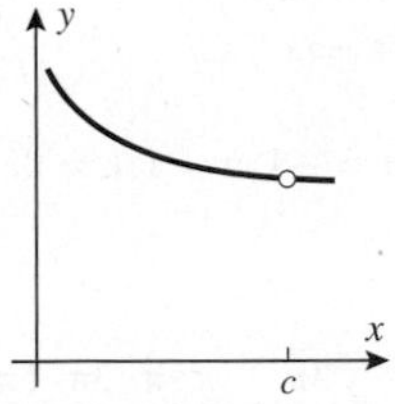


**(b)**

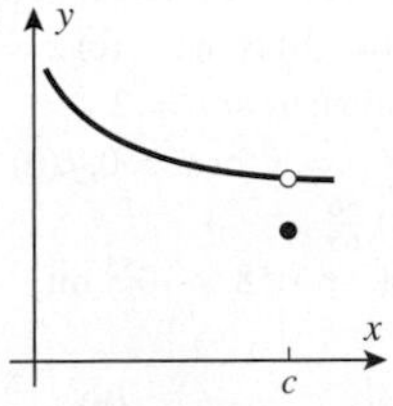


35. **(a)** $x = 0$, not removable **(b)** $x = -3$, removable **(c)** $x = 2$, removable; $x = -2$, not removable

37. **(a)** $x = \frac{1}{2}$, not removable; at $x = -3$, removable **(b)** $(2x-1)(x+3)$

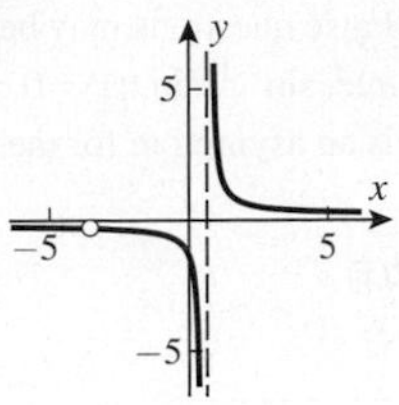


45. $f(x) = 1$ for $0 \le x < 1$, $f(x) = -1$ for $1 \le x \le 2$

49. $x = -1.25, x = 0.75$ 51. $x = 2.24$

## ▶ Exercise Set 1.6 (Page 54)

1. none 3. $x = n\pi, n = 0, \pm 1, \pm 2, \ldots$

5. $x = n\pi, n = 0, \pm 1, \pm 2, \ldots$

7. $2n\pi + (\pi/6), 2n\pi + (5\pi/6), n = 0, \pm 1, \pm 2, \ldots$

9. **(a)** $\sin x, x^3 + 7x + 1$ **(b)** $|x|, \sin x$ **(c)** $x^3, \cos x, x + 1$

11. 1 13. 3 15. $-3$ 17. $+\infty$ 19. $\frac{7}{3}$ 21. 0 23. 0 25. 1 27. 2 29. does not exist 31. $a/b$

33. **(a)**

| $x$ | 4 | 4.5 | 4.9 | 5.1 | 5.5 | 6 |
|---|---|---|---|---|---|---|
| $f(x)$ | 0.093497 | 0.100932 | 0.100842 | 0.098845 | 0.091319 | 0.076497 |

The limit appears to be $\frac{1}{10}$. **(b)** $\frac{1}{10}$

Responses to True–False questions may be abridged to save space.

35. True; use the Squeezing Theorem.

37. True; see the Remark after Example 3.

39. **(b)** $\pi/180$ 41. $k = \frac{1}{2}$ 43. **(a)** 1 **(b)** 0 **(c)** 1 45. $-\pi$

47. $-|x| \le x\cos(50\pi/x) \le |x|$ 49. $\lim_{x\to 0} \sin(1/x)$ does not exist

51. The limit is 0.

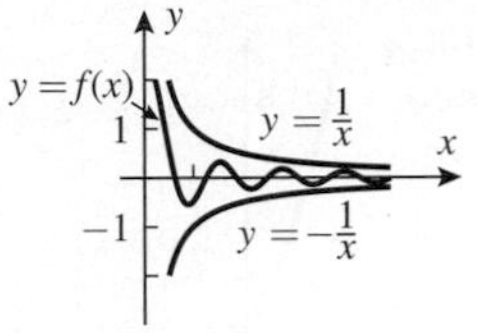


53. **(b)**

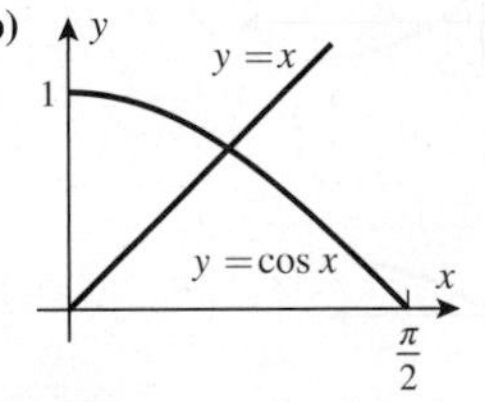


**(c)** 0.739

55. **(a)** Gravity is strongest at the poles and weakest at the equator.

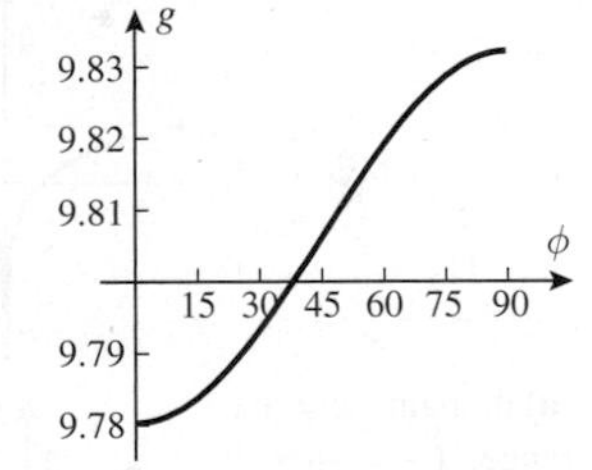


## ▶ Exercise Set 1.7 (Page 61)

1. $[-\frac{1}{2}, \frac{1}{2}]$ 3. $(0, 3) \cup (3, +\infty)$ 5. $\frac{4}{5}, \frac{3}{5}, \frac{3}{4}, \frac{5}{3}, \frac{5}{4}$

7. **(a)** $0 \le x \le \pi$ **(b)** $-1 \le x \le 1$ **(c)** $-\pi/2 < x < \pi/2$ **(d)** $-\infty < x < +\infty$ 9. $\frac{24}{25}$

11. **(a)** $\dfrac{1}{\sqrt{1+x^2}}$ **(b)** $\dfrac{\sqrt{1-x^2}}{x}$ **(c)** $\dfrac{\sqrt{x^2-1}}{x}$ **(d)** $\dfrac{1}{\sqrt{x^2-1}}$

13. **(a)**

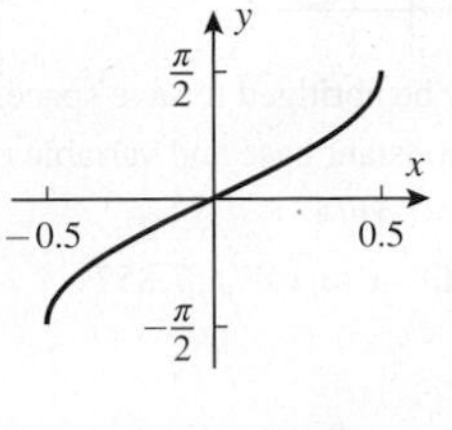


**(b)**

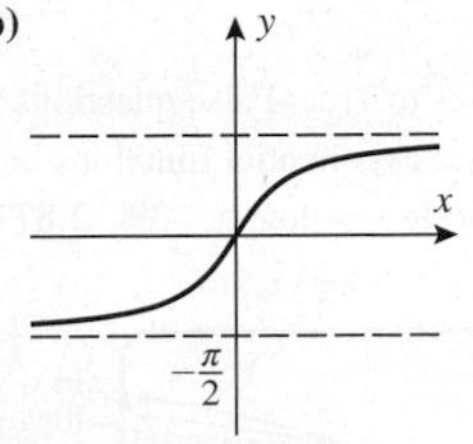


15. **(a)** $x = 2.76258$ rad **(b)** $\theta = 217.59°$

17. **(a)** 0.25545, error **(b)** $|x| \le \sin 1$

19. $-\pi/6$

Responses to True–False questions may be abridged to save space.

21. False; for example, $\sin^{-1}(\sin \pi) = 0 \neq \pi$.

23. True; $y = \pi/2$ is an asymptote for the graph of $y = \sec^{-1} x$.

25. 1 27. 5

29. (a)

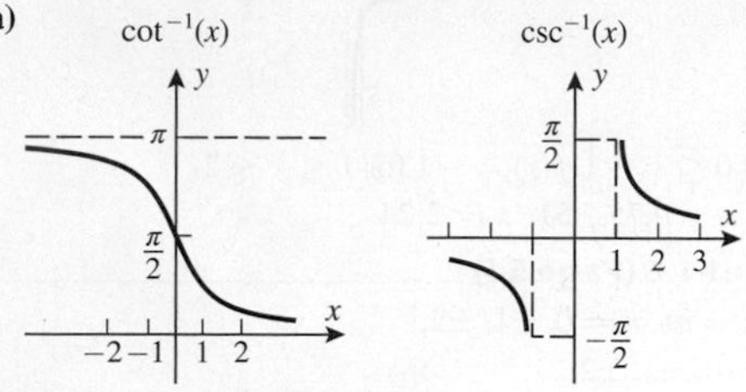


(b) $\cot^{-1} x$: all $x$, $0 < y < \pi$
$\csc^{-1} x$: $|x| \geq 1$, $0 < |y| \leq \pi/2$

31. (a) 55.0° (b) 33.6° (c) 25.8°

33. (a) 21.1 hours (b) 2.9 hours 35. 29°

## ▶ Exercise Set 1.8 (Page 72)

1. (a) −4 (b) 4 (c) $\frac{1}{4}$ 3. (a) 2.9690 (b) 0.0341

5. (a) 4 (b) −5 (c) 1 (d) $\frac{1}{2}$ 7. (a) 1.3655 (b) −0.3011

9. (a) $2r + \dfrac{s}{2} + \dfrac{t}{2}$ (b) $s - 3r - t$

11. (a) $1 + \log x + \frac{1}{2}\log(x-3)$
(b) $2\ln|x| + 3\ln(\sin x) - \frac{1}{2}\ln(x^2+1)$

13. $\log \frac{256}{3}$ 15. $\ln \dfrac{\sqrt[3]{x}(x+1)^2}{\cos x}$ 17. 0.01 19. $e^2$ 21. 4

23. $\sqrt{3/2}$ 25. $-\dfrac{\ln 3}{2\ln 5}$ 27. $\frac{1}{3}\ln\frac{7}{2}$ 29. −2

31. (a) domain: $(-\infty, +\infty)$;
range: $(-1, +\infty)$

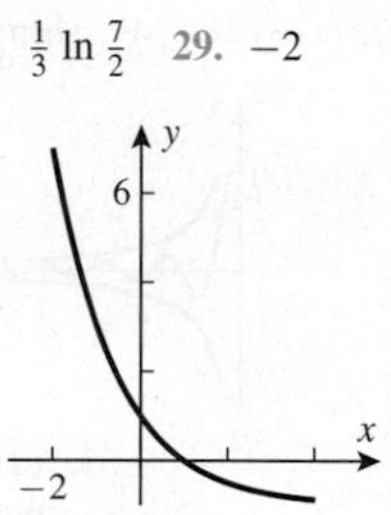


(b) domain: $x \neq 0$;
range: $(-\infty, +\infty)$

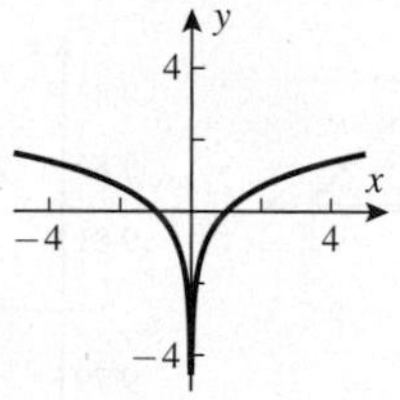


33. (a) domain: $x \neq 0$;
range: $(-\infty, +\infty)$

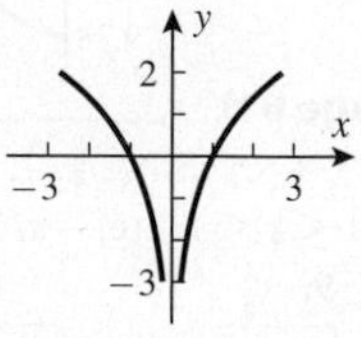


(b) domain: $(-\infty, +\infty)$;
range: $(0, 1]$

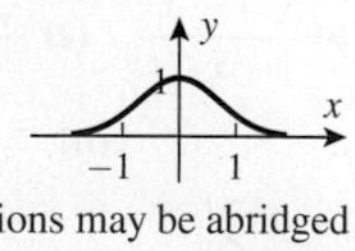


Responses to True–False questions may be abridged to save space.

35. False; exponential functions have constant base and variable exponent.

37. True; $\ln x = \log_e x$ 39. 2.8777, −0.3174

41.

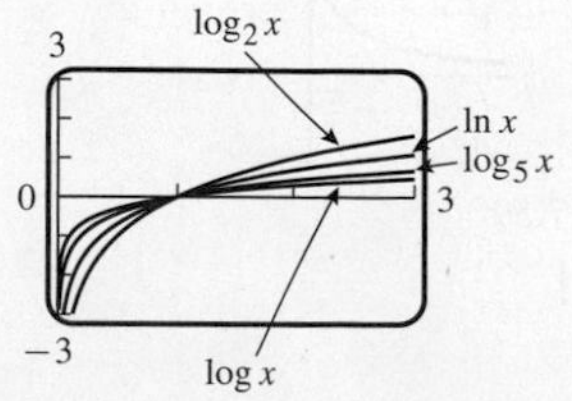


43. $x \approx 1.471, 7.857$

45. (a) no
(b) $y = 2^{x/4}$
(c) $y = 2^{-x}$
(d) $y = (\sqrt{5})^x$

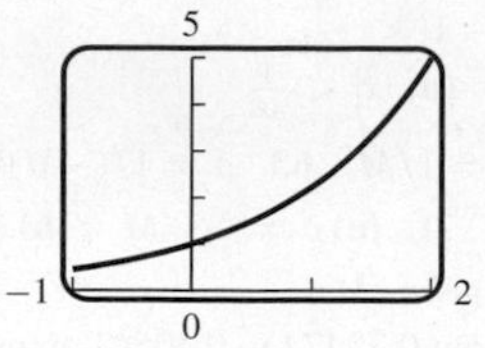


47. $\log \frac{1}{2} < 0$, so $3\log\frac{1}{2} < 2\log\frac{1}{2}$ 49. 1 51. 1 53. $-\infty$ 55. $e$

57. $+\infty$ 59. $+\infty$ 61. 1 63. $e$

67. (a)

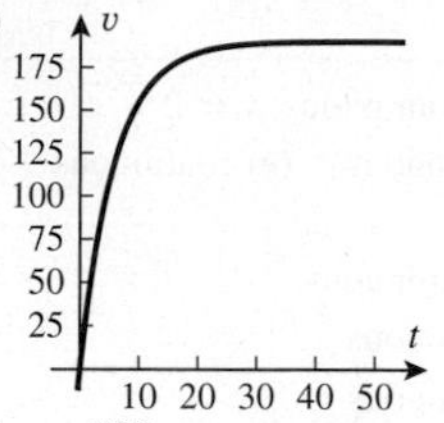


(b) $c = 190$
(c) It is the terminal velocity of the skydiver.

69. (a) $e$ (c) $e^a$

71. 201 days

73. (a) 7.4, basic (b) 4.2, acidic (c) 6.4, acidic (d) 5.9, acidic

75. (a) 140 dB, damage (b) 120 dB, damage (c) 80 dB, no damage
(d) 75 dB, no damage

77. $\approx 200$ 79. (a) $\approx 5 \times 10^{16}$ J (b) $\approx 0.67$

## ▶ Chapter 1 Review Exercises (Page 75)

1. (a) 1 (b) does not exist (c) does not exist (d) 1 (e) 3 (f) 0
(g) 0 (h) 2 (i) 1/2

3. (a)

| $x$ | −0.01 | −0.001 | −0.0001 | 0.0001 | 0.001 | 0.01 |
|---|---|---|---|---|---|---|
| $f(x)$ | 0.402 | 0.405 | 0.405 | 0.406 | 0.406 | 0.409 |

(b)

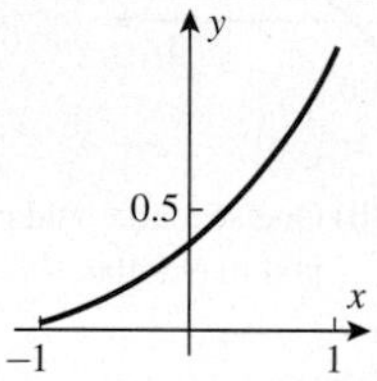


5. 1 7. $-\frac{3}{2}$ 9. $\frac{32}{3}$

11. (a) $y = 0$ (b) None (c) $y = 2$ 13. 1 15. $3 - k$ 17. 0

19. $e^{-3}$ 21. \$2,001.60, \$2,009.66, \$2,013.62, \$2013.75.

23. (a) $f(x) = 2x/(x-1)$ (b)

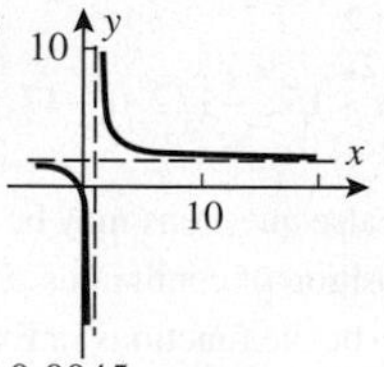


25. (a) $\lim_{x\to 2} f(x) = 5$ (b) $\delta = 0.0045$

27. (a) $\delta = 0.0025$ (b) $\delta = 0.025$
(c) $\delta = 1/9000$ (Some larger values also work.)

31. (a) $x = \pm 1$ (b) None (c) $x = 0, x = -3$

33. no; not continuous at $x = 2$

35. Consider $f(x) = x$ for $x \neq 0$, $f(0) = 1$, $a = -1$, $b = 1$, $k = 0$.

39. (a) $\frac{33}{65}$ (b) $\frac{56}{65}$

41. $10^{60}/63360 \approx 1.58 \times 10^{55}$ mi

43. $15x + 2$

45. (a)

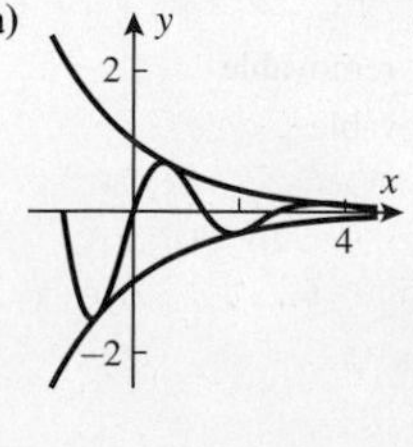


(b) $-\dfrac{\pi}{2}, 0, \dfrac{\pi}{2}, \pi, \dfrac{3\pi}{2}; -\dfrac{\pi}{4}, \dfrac{\pi}{4}, \dfrac{3\pi}{4}, \dfrac{5\pi}{4}$

47. **(a)**

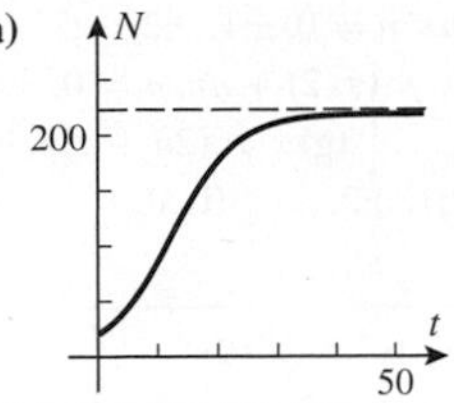


**(b)** about 10 years **(c)** 220 sheep

49. **(b)** 3.654, 332105.108

51. **(a)** $f$ is increasing **(b)** asymptotes for $f$: $x = 0$ and $x = \pi/2$; asymptotes for $f^{-1}$: $y = 0$ (as $x \to -\infty$) and $y = \pi/2$ (as $x \to +\infty$)

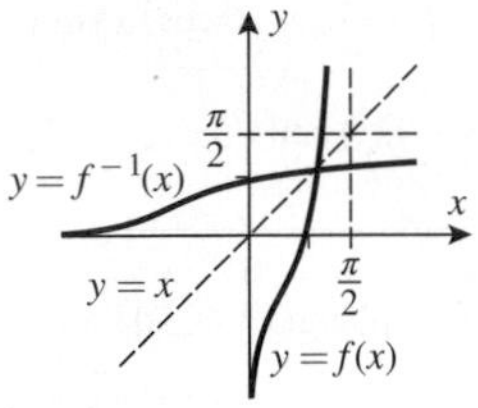


## ▶ Chapter 1 Making Connections (Page 78)

Where correct answers to a Making Connections exercise may vary, no answer is listed. Sample answers for these questions are available on the Book Companion Site.

4. **(a)** The circle through the origin with center $\left(0, \frac{1}{8}\right)$
**(b)** The circle through the origin with center $\left(0, \frac{1}{2}\right)$
**(c)** The circle does not exist.
**(d)** The circle through the origin with center $\left(0, \frac{1}{2}\right)$
**(e)** The circle through (0, 1) with center at the origin.
**(f)** The circle through the origin with center $\left(0, \dfrac{1}{2g(0)}\right)$
**(g)** The circle does not exist.

## ▶ Exercise Set 2.1 (Page 87)

1. **(a)** 4 m/s **(b)**

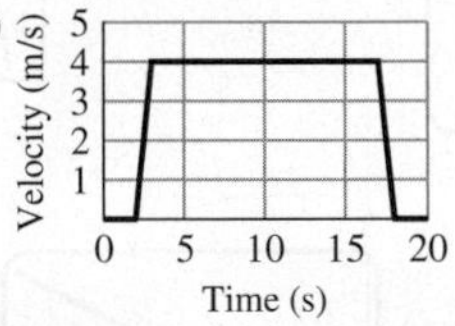


3. **(a)** 0 cm/s **(b)** $t = 0, t = 2$, and $t = 4.2$ **(c)** maximum: $t = 1$; minimum: $t = 3$ **(d)** $-7.5$ cm/s
5. straight line with slope equal to the velocity.
7. Answers may vary.

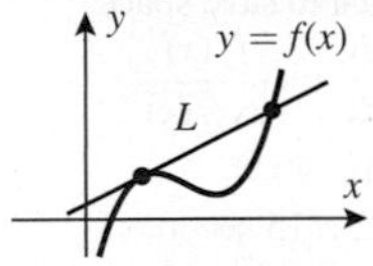


9. Answers may vary.

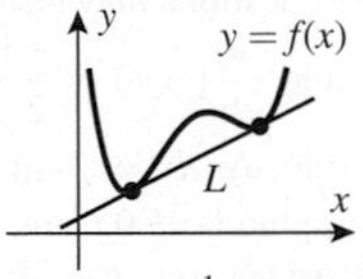


11. **(a)** 2 **(b)** 0 **(c)** $4x_0$
**(d)**

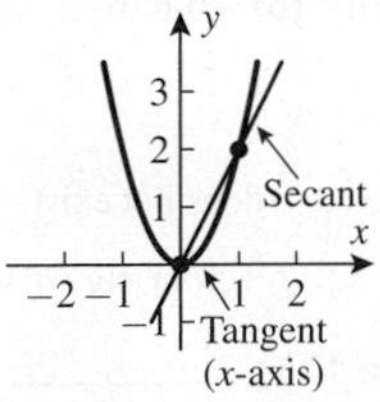


13. **(a)** $-\frac{1}{6}$ **(b)** $-\frac{1}{4}$ **(c)** $-1/x_0^2$
**(d)**

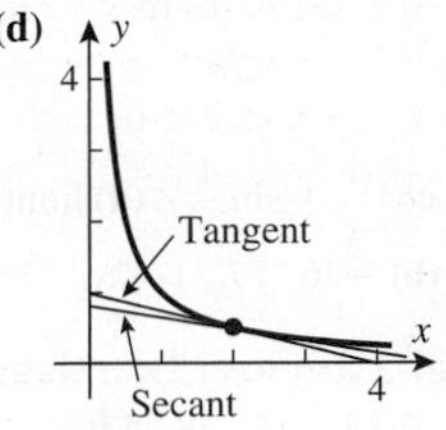


15. **(a)** $2x_0$ **(b)** $-2$ 17. **(a)** $1 + \dfrac{1}{2\sqrt{x_0}}$ **(b)** $\frac{3}{2}$

Responses to True–False questions may be abridged to save space.

19. True; set $h = x - 1$, so $x = 1 + h$ and $h \to 0$ is equivalent to $x \to 1$.
21. False; velocity is a ratio of change in position to change in time.
23. **(a)** 72° F at about 4:30 P.M. **(b)** 4° F/h **(c)** −7° F/h at about 9 P.M.
25. **(a)** first year
**(b)** 6 cm/year
**(c)** 10 cm/year at about age 14
**(d)**

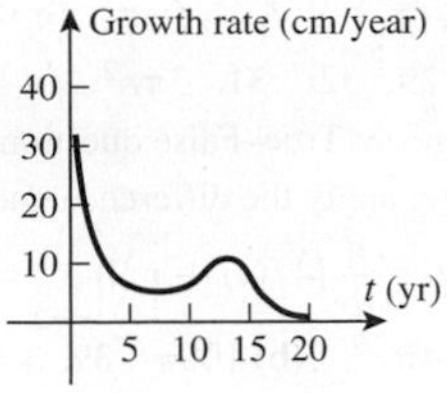


27. **(a)** 19,200 ft **(b)** 480 ft/s **(c)** 66.94 ft/s **(d)** 1440 ft/s
29. **(a)** 720 ft/min **(b)** 192 ft/min

## ▶ Exercise Set 2.2 (Page 97)

1. 2, 0, −2, −1
3. **(b)** 3 **(c)** 3
5.

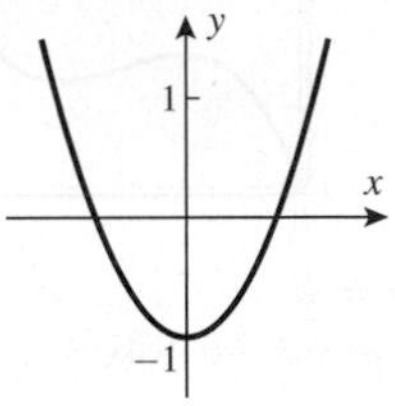


7. $y = 5x - 16$
9. $4x, y = 4x - 2$
11. $3x^2; y = 0$
13. $\dfrac{1}{2\sqrt{x+1}}; y = \frac{1}{6}x + \frac{5}{3}$ 15. $-1/x^2$ 17. $2x - 1$
19. $-1/(2x^{3/2})$ 21. $8t + 1$
23. **(a)** D **(b)** F **(c)** B **(d)** C **(e)** A **(f)** E
25. **(a)**

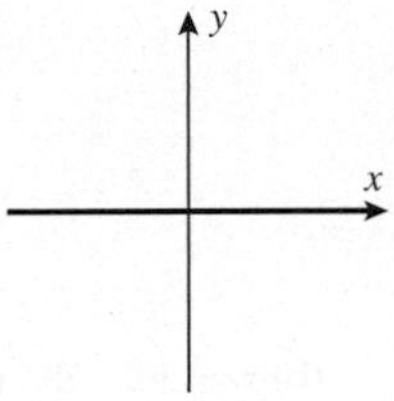


**(b)**

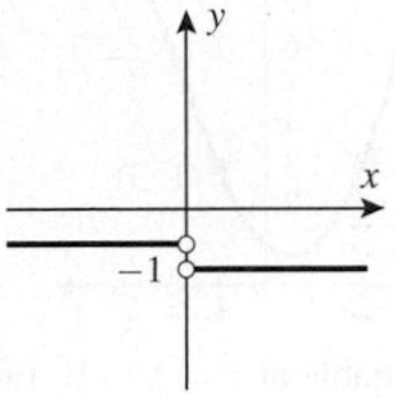


**(c)**

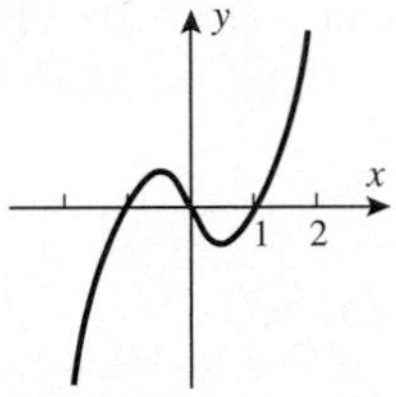


Responses to True–False questions may be abridged to save space.

27. False; $f'(a) = 0$ 29. False; for example, $f(x) = |x|$
31. **(a)** $\sqrt{x}$, 1 **(b)** $x^2$, 3 33. −2
35. $y = -2x + 1$

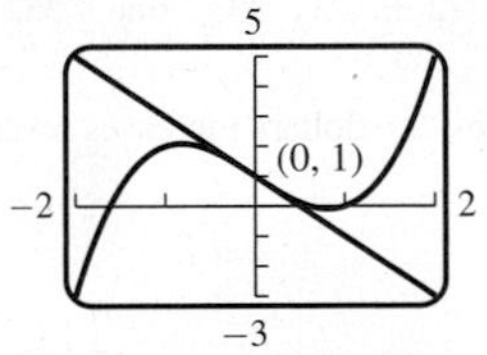


37. **(b)**

| $w$ | 1.5 | 1.1 | 1.01 | 1.001 | 1.0001 | 1.00001 |
|---|---|---|---|---|---|---|
| $[f(w) - f(1)]/(w - 1)$ | 1.6569 | 1.4355 | 1.3911 | 1.3868 | 1.3863 | 1.3863 |

39. **(a)** 0.04, 0.22, 0.88 **(b)** best: $\dfrac{f(2) - f(0)}{2 - 0}$; worst: $\dfrac{f(3) - f(1)}{3 - 1}$
41. **(a)** dollars per foot **(b)** the price per additional foot **(c)** positive **(d)** \$1000
43. **(a)** $F \approx 200$ lb, $dF/d\theta \approx 50$ lb/rad **(b)** $\mu = 0.25$
45. **(a)** $T \approx 115°$ F, $dT/dt \approx -3.35°$ F/min **(b)** $k = -0.084$

## ▶ Exercise Set 2.3 (Page 106)

1. $28x^6$ 3. $24x^7 + 2$ 5. 0 7. $-\frac{1}{3}(7x^6 + 2)$
9. $-3x^{-4} - 7x^{-8}$ 11. $24x^{-9} + (1/\sqrt{x})$
13. $f'(x) = ex^{e-1} - \dfrac{\sqrt{10}}{x^{(1+\sqrt{10})}}$

15. $12x(3x^2+1)$ 17. 7 19. $2t-1$ 21. 15 23. $-8$ 25. 0
27. 0 29. $32t$ 31. $3\pi r^2$

Responses to True–False questions may be abridged to save space.

33. True; apply the difference and constant multiple rules.

35. False; $\left.\frac{d}{dx}[4f(x)+x^3]\right|_{x=2} = \left.[4f'(x)+3x^2]\right|_{x=2} = 32$

37. (a) $4\pi r^2$ (b) $100\pi$ 39. $y = 5x + 17$

41. (a) $42x - 10$ (b) 24 (c) $2/x^3$ (d) $700x^3 - 96x$

43. (a) $-210x^{-8} + 60x^2$ (b) $-6x^{-4}$ (c) $6a$

45. (a) 0 (b) 112 (c) 360 49. $\left(1, \frac{5}{6}\right)$ $\left(2, \frac{2}{3}\right)$

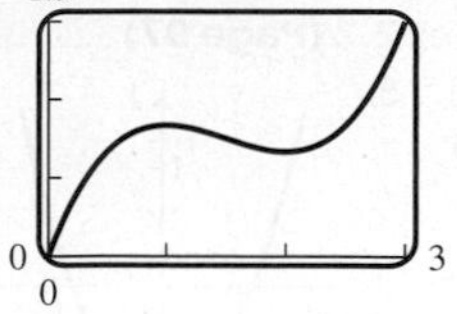


51. $y = 3x^2 - x - 2$ 53. $x = \frac{1}{2}$

55. $(2+\sqrt{3}, -6-4\sqrt{3}), (2-\sqrt{3}, -6+4\sqrt{3})$

57. $-2x_0$ 61. $-\dfrac{2GmM}{r^3}$ 63. 0.0755 s/m

65. $f'(x) > 0$ for all $x \neq 0$

67. yes, 3

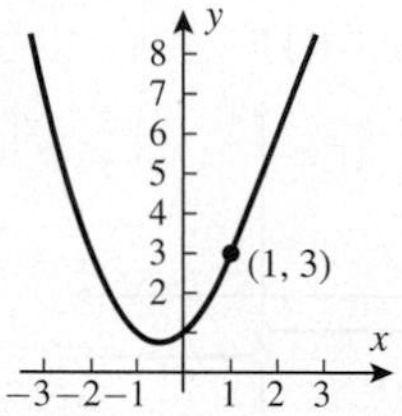


69. not differentiable at $x = 1$ 71. (a) $x = \frac{2}{3}$ (b) $x = \pm 2$ 73. (b) yes

75. (a) $n(n-1)(n-2)\cdots 1$ (b) 0 (c) $a_n n(n-1)(n-2)\cdots 1$

81. $-12/(2x+1)^3$ 83. $-2/(x+1)^3$

## ▶ Exercise Set 2.4 (Page 112)

1. $4x+1$ 3. $4x^3$ 5. $18x^2 - \frac{3}{2}x + 12$

7. $-15x^{-2} - 14x^{-3} + 48x^{-4} + 32x^{-5}$ 9. $3x^2$

11. $\dfrac{-3x^2-8x+3}{(x^2+1)^2}$ 13. $\dfrac{3x^2-8x}{(3x-4)^2}$ 15. $\dfrac{x^{3/2}+10x^{1/2}+4-3x^{-1/2}}{(x+3)^2}$

17. $2(1+x^{-1})(x^{-3}+7) + (2x+1)(-x^{-2})(x^{-3}+7) + (2x+1)(1+x^{-1})(-3x^{-4})$ 19. $3(7x^6+2)(x^7+2x-3)^2$ 21. $\frac{7}{16}$

23. $-29$ 25. 0 27. (a) $-\frac{37}{4}$ (b) $-\frac{23}{16}$

29. (a) 10 (b) 19 (c) 9 (d) $-1$ 31. $-2 \pm \sqrt{3}$ 33. none 35. $-2$

39. $F''(x) = xf''(x) + 2f'(x)$

41. $R'(120) = 1800$; increasing the price by $\Delta p$ dollars increases revenue by approximately 1800 $\Delta p$ dollars.

43. $f'(x) = -nx^{-n-1}$

## ▶ Exercise Set 2.5 (Page 116)

1. $-4\sin x + 2\cos x$ 3. $4x^2\sin x - 8x\cos x$

5. $(1+5\sin x - 5\cos x)/(5+\sin x)^2$ 7. $\sec x\tan x - \sqrt{2}\sec^2 x$

9. $-4\csc x\cot x + \csc^2 x$ 11. $\sec^3 x + \sec x\tan^2 x$ 13. $-\dfrac{\csc x}{1+\csc x}$

15. 0 17. $\dfrac{1}{(1+x\tan x)^2}$ 19. $-x\cos x - 2\sin x$

21. $-x\sin x + 5\cos x$ 23. $-4\sin x\cos x$

25. (a) $y = x$ (b) $y = 2x - (\pi/2) + 1$ (c) $y = 2x + (\pi/2) - 1$

29. (a) $x = \pm\pi/2, \pm 3\pi/2$ (b) $x = -3\pi/2, \pi/2$ (c) no horizontal tangent line (d) $x = \pm 2\pi, \pm\pi, 0$

31. 0.087 ft/deg 33. 1.75 m/deg

Responses to True–False questions may be abridged to save space.

35. False; by the product rule, $g'(x) = f(x)\cos x + f'(x)\sin x$.

37. True; $f(x) = (\sin x)/(\cos x) = \tan x$, so $f'(x) = \sec^2 x$.

39. $-\cos x$ 41. 3, 7, 11, ...

43. (a) all $x$ (b) all $x$ (c) $x \neq (\pi/2) + n\pi, n = 0, \pm 1, \pm 2, \ldots$ (d) $x \neq n\pi, n = 0, \pm 1, \pm 2, \ldots$ (e) $x \neq (\pi/2) + n\pi, n = 0, \pm 1, \pm 2, \ldots$ (f) $x \neq n\pi, n = 0, \pm 1, \pm 2, \ldots$ (g) $x \neq (2n+1)\pi, n = 0, \pm 1, \pm 2, \ldots$ (h) $x \neq n\pi/2, n = 0, \pm 1, \pm 2, \ldots$ (i) all $x$

## ▶ Exercise Set 2.6 (Page 122)

1. 6 3. (a) $(2x-3)^5, 10(2x-3)^4$ (b) $2x^5 - 3, 10x^4$

5. (a) $-7$ (b) $-8$ 7. $37(x^3+2x)^{36}(3x^2+2)$

9. $-2\left(x^3 - \frac{7}{x}\right)^{-3}\left(3x^2 + \frac{7}{x^2}\right)$ 11. $\dfrac{24(1-3x)}{(3x^2-2x+1)^4}$

13. $\dfrac{3}{4\sqrt{3x}\sqrt{4+\sqrt{3x}}}$ 15. $-\dfrac{2}{x^3}\cos\left(\dfrac{1}{x^2}\right)$ 17. $-20\cos^4 x\sin x$

19. $-\dfrac{3}{\sqrt{x}}\cos(3\sqrt{x})\sin(3\sqrt{x})$ 21. $28x^6\sec^2(x^7)\tan(x^7)$

23. $-\dfrac{5\sin(5x)}{2\sqrt{\cos(5x)}}$

25. $-3[x+\csc(x^3+3)]^{-4}[1 - 3x^2\csc(x^3+3)\cot(x^3+3)]$

27. $10x^3\sin 5x\cos 5x + 3x^2\sin^2 5x$

29. $-x^3\sec\left(\frac{1}{x}\right)\tan\left(\frac{1}{x}\right) + 5x^4\sec\left(\frac{1}{x}\right)$

31. $\sin(\cos x)\sin x$ 33. $-6\cos^2(\sin 2x)\sin(\sin 2x)\cos 2x$

35. $35(5x+8)^6(1-\sqrt{x})^6 - \dfrac{3}{\sqrt{x}}(5x+8)^7(1-\sqrt{x})^5$

37. $\dfrac{33(x-5)^2}{(2x+1)^4}$ 39. $-\dfrac{2(2x+3)^2(52x^2+96x+3)}{(4x^2-1)^9}$

41. $5[x\sin 2x + \tan^4(x^7)]^4[2x\cos 2x + \sin 2x + 28x^6\tan^3(x^7)\sec^2(x^7)]$

43. $y = -x$ 45. $y = -1$ 47. $y = 8\sqrt{\pi}x - 8\pi$ 49. $y = \frac{7}{2}x - \frac{3}{2}$

51. $-25x\cos(5x) - 10\sin(5x) - 2\cos(2x)$ 53. $4(1-x)^{-3}$

55. $3\cot^2\theta\csc^2\theta$ 57. $\pi(b-a)\sin 2\pi\omega$

59. (a)

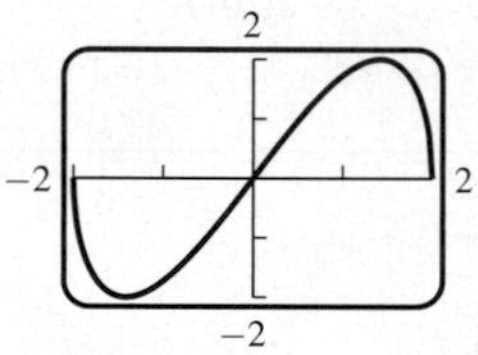


(c) $\dfrac{4-2x^2}{\sqrt{4-x^2}}$

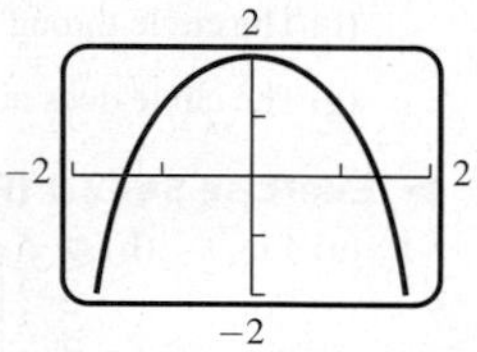


(d) $y - \sqrt{3} = \frac{2}{\sqrt{3}}(x-1)$

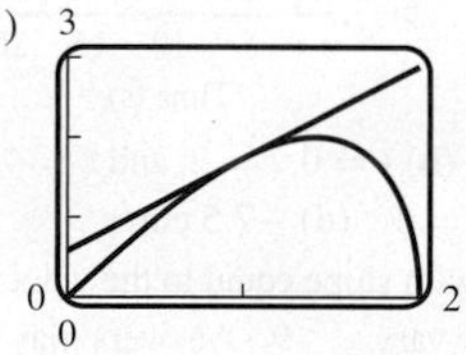


Responses to True–False questions may be abridged to save space.

61. False; by the chain rule, $\dfrac{d}{dx}[\sqrt{y}] = \dfrac{1}{2\sqrt{y}}\cdot\dfrac{dy}{dx} = \dfrac{f'(x)}{2\sqrt{f(x)}}$.

63. False; by the chain rule, $dy/dx = (-\sin[g(x)])\cdot g'(x)$.

65. (c) $f = 1/T$ (d) amplitude = 0.6 cm, $T = 2\pi/15$ seconds per oscillation, $f = 15/(2\pi)$ oscillations per second

67. $\frac{7}{24}\sqrt{6}$ 69. (a) 10 lb/in², −2 lb/in²/mi (b) −0.6 lb/in²/s

71. $\begin{cases} \cos x, & 0 < x < \pi \\ -\cos x, & -\pi < x < 0 \end{cases}$

73. (c) $-\dfrac{1}{x}\cos\dfrac{1}{x} + \sin\dfrac{1}{x}$ (d) limit as $x$ goes to 0 does not exist

75. (a) 21 (b) $-36$ 77. $1/(2x)$ 79. $\frac{2}{3}x$ 83. $f'(g(h(x)))g'(h(x))h'(x)$

## ▶ Chapter 2 Review Exercises (Page 125)

3. (a) $2x$ (b) 4 5. 58.75 ft/s 7. (a) 13 mi/h (b) 7 mi/h

9. (a) $-2/\sqrt{9-4x}$ (b) $1/(x+1)^2$

11. (a) $x = -2, -1, 1, 3$ (b) $(-\infty, -2), (-1, 1), (3, +\infty)$ (c) $(-2, -1), (1, 3)$ (d) 4

13. (a) 78 million people per year (b) 1.3% per year

15. (a) $x^2\cos x + 2x\sin x$ (c) $4x\cos x + (2-x^2)\sin x$

17. (a) $(6x^2+8x-17)/(3x+2)^2$ (c) $118/(3x+2)^3$

19. (a) 2000 gal/min (b) 2500 gal/min 21. (a) 3.6 (b) $-0.777778$
23. $f(1) = 0, f'(1) = 5$ 25. $y = -16x, y = -145x/4$
29. (a) $8x^7 - \dfrac{3}{2\sqrt{x}} - 15x^{-4}$ (b) $(2x+1)^{100}(1030x^2 + 10x - 1414)$
31. (a) $\dfrac{(x-1)(15x+1)}{2\sqrt{3x+1}}$ (b) $-3(3x+1)^2(3x+2)/x^7$
33. $x = -\frac{7}{2}, -\frac{1}{2}, 2$ 35. $y = \pm 2x$
37. $x = n\pi \pm (\pi/4), n = 0, \pm 1, \pm 2, \ldots$ 39. $y = -3x + (1 + 9\pi/4)$
41. (a) $40\sqrt{3}$ (b) 7500

**▶ Chapter 2 Making Connections (Page 128)**

Where correct answers to a Making Connections exercise may vary, no answer is listed. Sample answers for these questions are available on the Book Companion Site.

2. (c) $k = 2$ (d) $h'(x) = 0$
3. (b) $f' \cdot g \cdot h \cdot k + f \cdot g' \cdot h \cdot k + f \cdot g \cdot h' \cdot k + f \cdot g \cdot h \cdot k'$
4. (c) $\dfrac{f' \cdot g \cdot h - f \cdot g' \cdot h + f \cdot g \cdot h'}{g^2}$

**▶ Exercise Set 3.1 (Page 133)**

1. (a) $(6x^2 - y - 1)/x$ (b) $4x - 2/x^2$ 3. $-\dfrac{x}{y}$ 5. $\dfrac{1 - 2xy - 3y^3}{x^2 + 9xy^2}$
7. $\dfrac{-y^{3/2}}{x^{3/2}}$ 9. $\dfrac{1 - 2xy^2\cos(x^2y^2)}{2x^2y\cos(x^2y^2)}$
11. $\dfrac{1 - 3y^2\tan^2(xy^2+y)\sec^2(xy^2+y)}{3(2xy+1)\tan^2(xy^2+y)\sec^2(xy^2+y)}$ 13. $-\dfrac{8}{9y^3}$ 15. $\dfrac{2y}{x^2}$
17. $\dfrac{\sin y}{(1+\cos y)^3}$ 19. $-1/\sqrt{3}, 1/\sqrt{3}$

Responses to True–False questions may be abridged to save space.

21. False; the graph of $f$ need only coincide with a portion of the graph of the equation in $x$ and $y$.
23. False; the equation is equivalent to $x^2 = y^2$ and $y = |x|$ satisfies this equation.
25. $-15^{-3/4} \approx -0.1312$ 27. $-\frac{9}{13}$ 29. $\dfrac{2t^3 + 3a^2}{2a^3 - 6at}$ 31. $-\dfrac{b^2\lambda}{a^2\omega}$
35. (a)

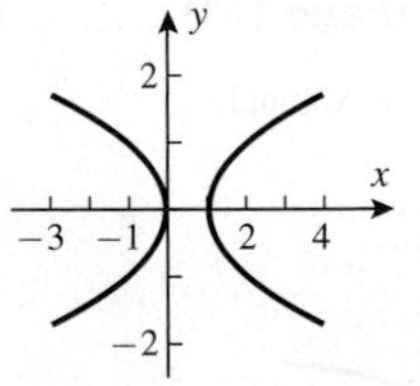


(c) $x = -y^2$ or $x = y^2 + 1$

37. $a = \frac{1}{4}, b = \frac{5}{4}$
41. (a)

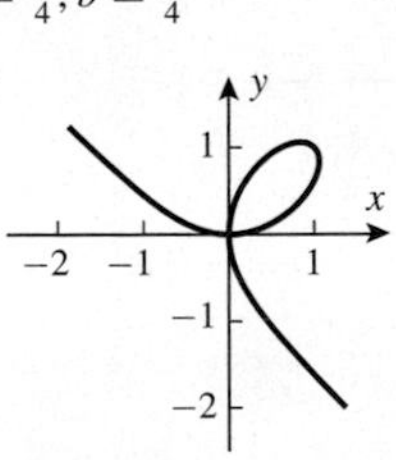


(c) $2\sqrt[3]{2}/3$ 43. $-\dfrac{2y^3 + 3t^2y}{(6ty^2 + t^3)\cos t}$

**▶ Exercise Set 3.2 (Page 138)**

1. $1/x$ 3. $1/(1+x)$ 5. $2x/(x^2-1)$ 7. $\dfrac{1-x^2}{x(1+x^2)}$ 9. $2/x$
11. $\dfrac{1}{2x\sqrt{\ln x}}$ 13. $1 + \ln x$ 15. $2x\log_2(3-2x) - \dfrac{2x^2}{(\ln 2)(3-2x)}$
17. $\dfrac{2x(1+\log x) - x/(\ln 10)}{(1+\log x)^2}$ 19. $1/(x\ln x)$ 21. $2\csc 2x$
23. $-\dfrac{1}{x}\sin(\ln x)$ 25. $2\cot x/(\ln 10)$ 27. $\dfrac{3}{x-1} + \dfrac{8x}{x^2+1}$
29. $-\tan x + \dfrac{3x}{4 - 3x^2}$

Responses to True–False questions may be abridged to save space.

31. True; $\lim\limits_{x \to 0^+} \dfrac{1}{x} = +\infty$ 33. True; $1/x$ is an odd function.
35. $x\sqrt[3]{1+x^2}\left[\dfrac{1}{x} + \dfrac{2x}{3(1+x^2)}\right]$
37. $\dfrac{(x^2-8)^{1/3}\sqrt{x^3+1}}{x^6 - 7x + 5}\left[\dfrac{2x}{3(x^2-8)} + \dfrac{3x^2}{2(x^3+1)} - \dfrac{6x^5 - 7}{x^6 - 7x + 5}\right]$
39. (a) $-\dfrac{1}{x(\ln x)^2}$ (b) $-\dfrac{\ln 2}{x(\ln x)^2}$
41. $y = ex - 2$ 43. $y = -x/e$ 45. (a) $y = x/e$ 47. $A(w) = w/2$
51. $f(x) = \ln(x+1)$ 53. (a) 3 (b) $-5$ 55. (a) 0 (b) $\sqrt{2}$

**▶ Exercise Set 3.3 (Page 144)**

1. (b) $\frac{1}{9}$ 3. $-2/x^2$ 5. (a) no (b) yes (c) yes (d) yes
7. $\dfrac{1}{15y^2 + 1}$ 9. $\dfrac{1}{10y^4 + 3y^2}$ 13. $f(x) + g(x), f(g(x))$
15. $7e^{7x}$ 17. $x^2e^x(x+3)$ 19. $\dfrac{4}{(e^x + e^{-x})^2}$
21. $(x\sec^2 x + \tan x)e^{x\tan x}$ 23. $(1 - 3e^{3x})e^{x - e^{3x}}$
25. $\dfrac{x-1}{e^x - x}$ 27. $2^x \ln 2$ 29. $\pi^{\sin x}(\ln \pi)\cos x$
31. $(x^3 - 2x)^{\ln x}\left[\dfrac{3x^2 - 2}{x^3 - 2x}\ln x + \dfrac{1}{x}\ln(x^3 - 2x)\right]$
33. $(\ln x)^{\tan x}\left[\dfrac{\tan x}{x\ln x} + (\sec^2 x)\ln(\ln x)\right]$
35. $(\ln x)^{\ln x}\left[\dfrac{\ln(\ln x)}{x} + \dfrac{1}{x}\right]$ 37. $(x^3 + x^2 - 4x + 1)e^x$
39. $((\ln 3)x^2 + 2x + (\ln 3)\sqrt{x} + 1/(2\sqrt{x}))3^x$
41. $(\ln 4)(3\cos x - e^x)4^{3\sin x - e^x}$ 43. $3/\sqrt{1 - 9x^2}$
45. $-\dfrac{1}{|x|\sqrt{x^2 - 1}}$ 47. $3x^2/(1 + x^6)$ 49. $-\dfrac{\sec^2 x}{\tan^2 x} = -\csc^2 x$
51. $\dfrac{e^x}{|x|\sqrt{x^2 - 1}} + e^x\sec^{-1} x$ 53. 0 55. 0 57. $-\dfrac{1}{2\sqrt{x}(1+x)}$

Responses to True–False questions may be abridged to save space.

59. False; consider $y = Ae^x$. 61. True; use the chain rule.
65. $\dfrac{(3x^2 + \tan^{-1} y)(1 + y^2)}{(1 + y^2)e^y - x}$ 67. (b) $1 - (\sqrt{3}/3)$
69. (b) $y = (88x - 89)/7$
75. (a)

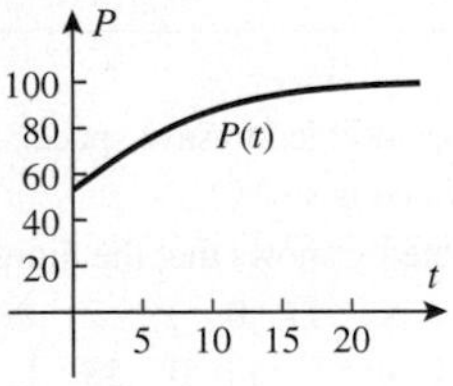


(b) $P(t) \to 100\%$
(c) $P'(t) \to 0$

77. 3 79. ln 10 81. $12\pi$ 83. $9.8t$; if the fluid offers no resistance, then the speed will increase at a constant rate of 9.8 m/s.

**▶ Exercise Set 3.4 (Page 150)**

1. (a) 6 (b) $-\frac{1}{3}$ 3. (a) $-2$ (b) $6\sqrt{5}$
5. (b) $A = x^2$ (c) $\dfrac{dA}{dt} = 2x\dfrac{dx}{dt}$ (d) 12 ft²/min
7. (a) $\dfrac{dV}{dt} = \pi\left(r^2\dfrac{dh}{dt} + 2rh\dfrac{dr}{dt}\right)$ (b) $-20\pi$ in³/s; decreasing
9. (a) $\dfrac{d\theta}{dt} = \dfrac{\cos^2\theta}{x^2}\left(x\dfrac{dy}{dt} - y\dfrac{dx}{dt}\right)$ (b) $-\frac{5}{16}$ rad/s; decreasing
11. $\dfrac{4\pi}{15}$ in²/min 13. $\dfrac{1}{\sqrt{\pi}}$ mi/h 15. $4860\pi$ cm³/min 17. $\frac{5}{6}$ ft/s
19. $\dfrac{125}{\sqrt{61}}$ ft/s 21. 704 ft/s
23. (a) 500 mi, 1716 mi (b) 1354 mi; 27.7 mi/min
25. $\dfrac{9}{20\pi}$ ft/min 27. $125\pi$ ft³/min 29. 250 mi/h
31. $\dfrac{36\sqrt{69}}{25}$ ft/min 33. $\dfrac{8\pi}{5}$ km/s 35. $600\sqrt{7}$ mi/h

**37.** **(a)** $-\frac{60}{7}$ units per second **(b)** falling **39.** $-4$ units per second

**41.** $x = \pm\sqrt{\dfrac{-5+\sqrt{33}}{2}}$ **43.** 4.5 cm/s; away **47.** $\dfrac{20}{9\pi}$ cm/s

## ▶ Exercise Set 3.5 (Page 158)

**1.** **(a)** $f(x) \approx 1 + 3(x-1)$ **(b)** $f(1+\Delta x) \approx 1 + 3\Delta x$ **(c)** 1.06

**3.** **(a)** $1 + \frac{1}{2}x$, 0.95, 1.05 **17.** $|x| < 1.692$

**(b)**

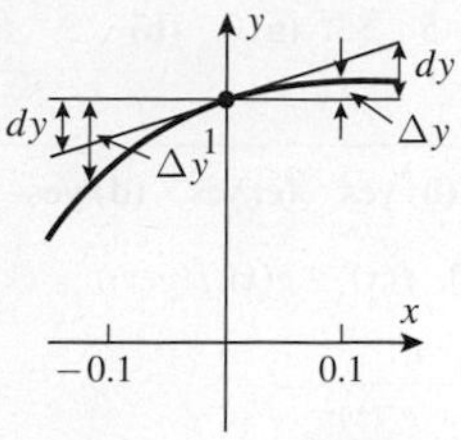


**19.** $|x| < 0.3158$ **21.** **(a)** 0.0174533 **(b)** $x_0 = 45°$ **(c)** 0.694765
**23.** 83.16 **25.** 8.0625 **27.** 8.9944 **29.** 0.1 **31.** 0.8573
**33.** 0.780398 **37.** **(a)** 0.5, 1 **(b)**

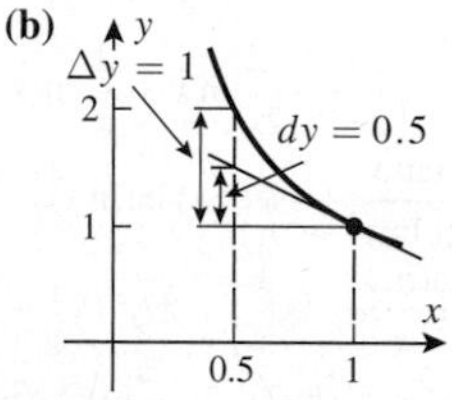


**39.** $3x^2\,dx,\ 3x^2\Delta x + 3x(\Delta x)^2 + (\Delta x)^3$
**41.** $(2x-2)\,dx,\ 2x\Delta x + (\Delta x)^2 - 2\Delta x$
**43.** **(a)** $(12x^2 - 14x)\,dx$ **(b)** $(-x\sin x + \cos x)\,dx$
**45.** **(a)** $\dfrac{2-3x}{2\sqrt{1-x}}\,dx$ **(b)** $-17(1+x)^{-18}\,dx$

Responses to True–False questions may be abridged to save space.

**47.** False; $dy = (dy/dx)\,dx$ **49.** False; consider any linear function.
**51.** 0.0225 **53.** 0.0048 **55.** **(a)** $\pm 2$ ft$^2$ **(b)** side: $\pm 1\%$; area: $\pm 2\%$
**57.** **(a)** opposite: $\pm 0.151$ in; adjacent: $\pm 0.087$ in
**(b)** opposite: $\pm 3.0\%$; adjacent: $\pm 1.0\%$
**59.** $\pm 10\%$ **61.** $\pm 0.017$ cm$^2$ **63.** $\pm 6\%$ **65.** $\pm 0.5\%$ **67.** $15\pi/2$ cm$^3$

## ▶ Exercise Set 3.6 (Page 167)

**1.** **(a)** $\frac{2}{3}$ **(b)** $\frac{2}{3}$

Responses to True–False questions may be abridged to save space.

**3.** True; the expression $(\ln x)/x$ is undefined if $x \le 0$.
**5.** False; applying L'Hôpital's rule repeatedly shows that the limit is 0.
**7.** 1 **9.** 1 **11.** $-1$ **13.** 0 **15.** $-\infty$ **17.** 0 **19.** 2 **21.** 0
**23.** $\pi$ **25.** $-\frac{5}{3}$ **27.** $e^{-3}$ **29.** $e^2$ **31.** $e^{2/\pi}$ **33.** 0 **35.** $\frac{1}{2}$
**37.** $+\infty$ **39.** 1 **41.** 1 **43.** 1 **45.** 1 **47.** **(b)** 2
**49.** 0

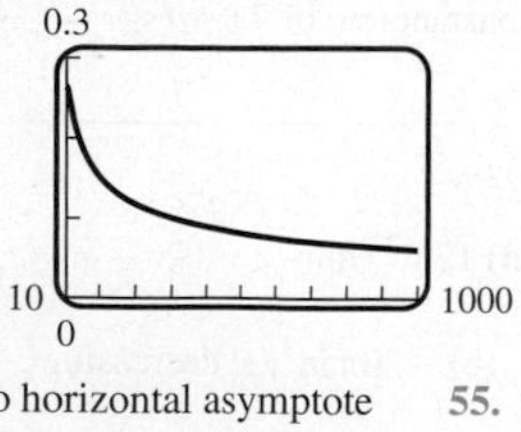


**51.** $e^3$

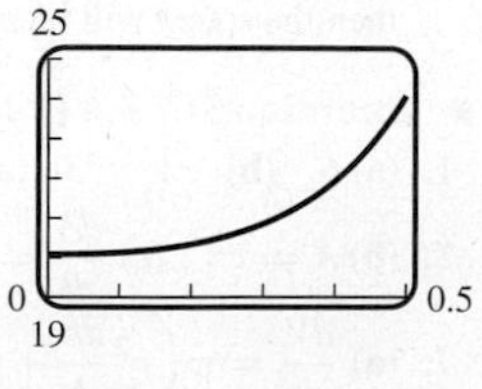


**53.** no horizontal asymptote

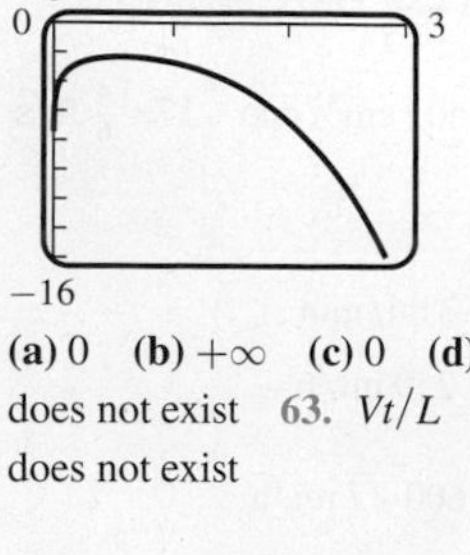


**55.** $y = 1$

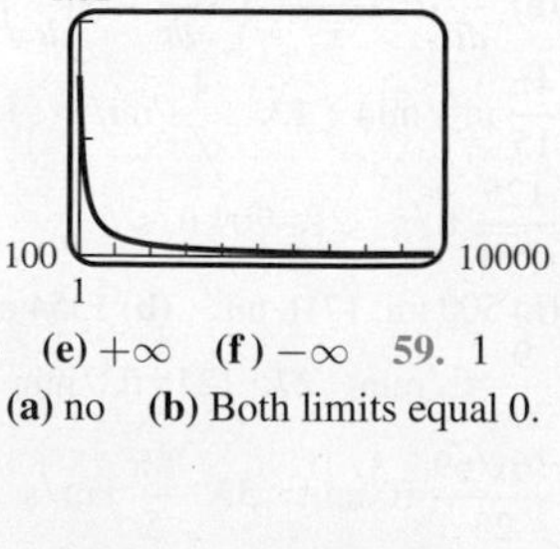


**57.** **(a)** 0 **(b)** $+\infty$ **(c)** 0 **(d)** $-\infty$ **(e)** $+\infty$ **(f)** $-\infty$ **59.** 1
**61.** does not exist **63.** $Vt/L$ **67.** **(a)** no **(b)** Both limits equal 0.
**69.** does not exist

## ▶ Chapter 3 Review Exercises (Page 169)

**1.** **(a)** $\dfrac{2-3x^2-y}{x}$ **(b)** $-\dfrac{1}{x^2} - 2x$ **3.** $-\dfrac{y^2}{x^2}$
**5.** $\dfrac{y\sec(xy)\tan(xy)}{1 - x\sec(xy)\tan(xy)}$ **7.** $-\dfrac{21}{16y^3}$
**9.** $2/(2-\pi)$ **13.** $(\sqrt[3]{4}/3,\ \sqrt[3]{2}/3)$
**15.** $\dfrac{1}{x+1} + \dfrac{2}{x+2} - \dfrac{3}{x+3} - \dfrac{4}{x+4}$ **17.** $\dfrac{1}{x}$ **19.** $\dfrac{1}{3x(\ln x + 1)^{2/3}}$
**21.** $\dfrac{1}{(\ln 10)x\ln x}$ **23.** $\dfrac{3}{2x} + \dfrac{2x^3}{1+x^4}$ **25.** $2x$ **27.** $e^{\sqrt{x}}(2+\sqrt{x})$
**29.** $\dfrac{2}{\pi(1+4x^2)}$ **31.** $e^x x^{(e^x)}\left(\ln x + \dfrac{1}{x}\right)$ **33.** $\dfrac{1}{|2x+1|\sqrt{x^2+x}}$
**35.** $\dfrac{x^3}{\sqrt{x^2+1}}\left(\dfrac{3}{x} - \dfrac{x}{x^2+1}\right)$
**37.** **(b)**

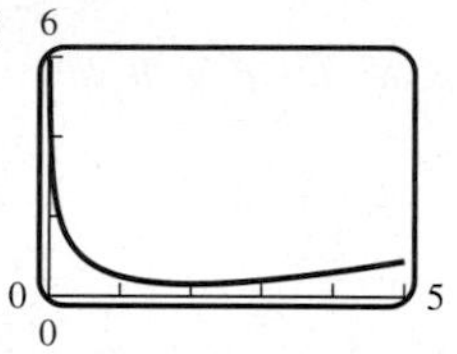


**(d)** curve must have a horizontal tangent line between $x = 1$ and $x = e$
**(e)** $x = 2$

**39.** $e^2$ **41.** $e^{1/e}$ **43.** No; for example, $f(x) = x^3$. **45.** $\left(\frac{1}{3}, e\right)$

**51.** **(a)**

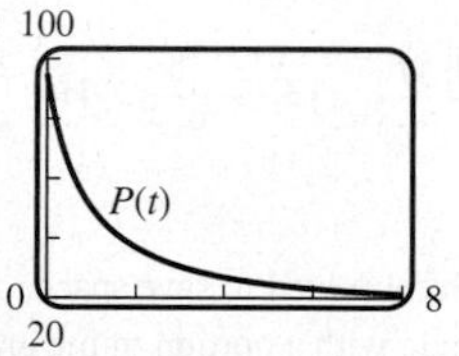


**(b)** $P(t) \to 19$
**(c)** $P'(t) \to 0$

**53.** $+\infty, +\infty$: yes; $+\infty, -\infty$: no; $-\infty, +\infty$: no; $-\infty, -\infty$: yes
**55.** $+\infty$ **57.** $\frac{1}{9}$ **59.** $500\pi$ m$^2$/min
**61.** **(a)** $-0.5, 1, 0.5$ **(b)** $\pi/4, 1, \pi/2$ **(c)** $3, -1.0$
**63.** **(a)** between 139.48 m and 144.55 m **(c)** $|d\phi| \le 0.98°$

## ▶ Chapter 3 Making Connections (Page 171)

Answers are provided in the Student Solutions Manual.

## ▶ Exercise Set 4.1 (Page 180)

**1.** **(a)** $f' > 0, f'' > 0$ **(b)** $f' > 0, f'' < 0$

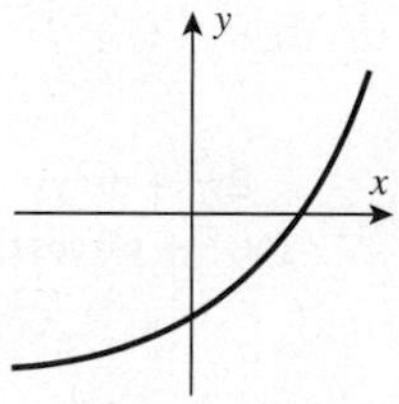


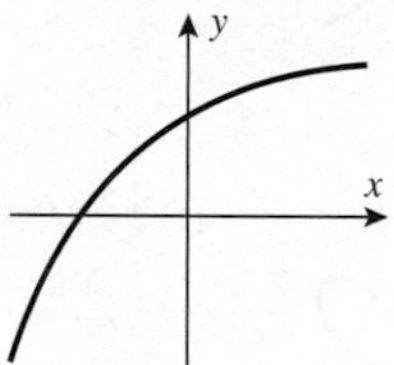


**(c)** $f' < 0, f'' > 0$ **(d)** $f' < 0, f'' < 0$

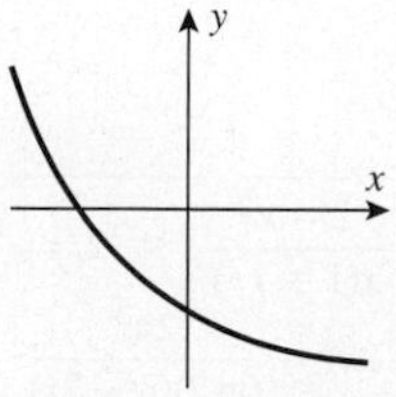


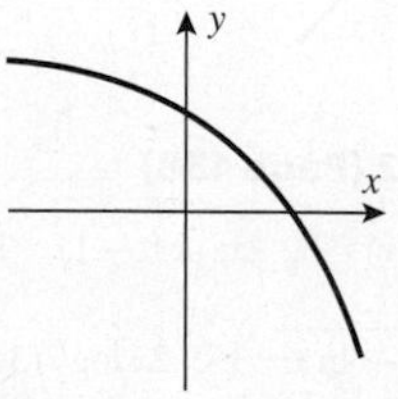


**3.** $A$: $dy/dx < 0,\ d^2y/dx^2 > 0$; $B$: $dy/dx > 0,\ d^2y/dx^2 < 0$;
$C$: $dy/dx < 0,\ d^2y/dx^2 < 0$ **5.** $x = -1, 0, 1, 2$
**7.** **(a)** $[4, 6]$ **(b)** $[1, 4], [6, 7]$ **(c)** $(1, 2), (3, 5)$ **(d)** $(2, 3), (5, 7)$
**(e)** $x = 2, 3, 5$
**9.** **(a)** $[1, 3]$ **(b)** $(-\infty, 1], [3, +\infty)$ **(c)** $(-\infty, 2), (4, +\infty)$
**(d)** $(2, 4)$ **(e)** $x = 2, 4$

Responses to True–False questions may be abridged to save space.

11. True; see definition of decreasing: $f(x_1) > f(x_2)$ whenever $0 \le x_1 < x_2 \le 2$.

13. False; for example, $f(x) = (x-1)^3$ is increasing on $[0, 2]$ and $f'(1) = 0$.

15. **(a)** $[3/2, +\infty)$ **(b)** $(-\infty, 3/2]$ **(c)** $(-\infty, +\infty)$ **(d)** none **(e)** none

17. **(a)** $(-\infty, +\infty)$ **(b)** none **(c)** $(-1/2, +\infty)$ **(d)** $(-\infty, -1/2)$ **(e)** $-1/2$

19. **(a)** $[1, +\infty)$ **(b)** $(-\infty, 1]$ **(c)** $(-\infty, 0), \left(\frac{2}{3}, +\infty\right)$ **(d)** $\left(0, \frac{2}{3}\right)$ **(e)** $0, \frac{2}{3}$

21. **(a)** $\left[\frac{3-\sqrt{5}}{2}, \frac{3+\sqrt{5}}{2}\right]$ **(b)** $\left(-\infty, \frac{3-\sqrt{5}}{2}\right], \left[\frac{3+\sqrt{5}}{2}, +\infty\right)$
**(c)** $\left(0, \frac{4-\sqrt{6}}{2}\right), \left(\frac{4+\sqrt{6}}{2}, +\infty\right)$
**(d)** $(-\infty, 0), \left(\frac{4-\sqrt{6}}{2}, \frac{4+\sqrt{6}}{2}\right)$ **(e)** $0, \frac{4 \pm \sqrt{6}}{2}$

23. **(a)** $[-1/2, +\infty)$ **(b)** $(-\infty, -1/2]$ **(c)** $(-2, 1)$ **(d)** $(-\infty, -2), (1, +\infty)$ **(e)** $-2, 1$

25. **(a)** $[-1, 0], [1, +\infty)$ **(b)** $(-\infty, -1], [0, 1]$ **(c)** $(-\infty, 0), (0, +\infty)$ **(d)** none **(e)** none

27. **(a)** $(-\infty, 0]$ **(b)** $[0, +\infty)$ **(c)** $(-\infty, -1), (1, +\infty)$ **(d)** $(-1, 1)$ **(e)** $-1, 1$

29. **(a)** $[0, +\infty)$ **(b)** $(-\infty, 0]$ **(c)** $(-2, 2)$ **(d)** $(-\infty, 2), (2, +\infty)$ **(e)** $-2, 2$

31. **(a)** $[0, +\infty)$ **(b)** $(-\infty, 0]$ **(c)** $\left(-\sqrt{\frac{1+\sqrt{7}}{3}}, \sqrt{\frac{1+\sqrt{7}}{3}}\right)$
**(d)** $\left(-\infty, -\sqrt{\frac{1+\sqrt{7}}{3}}\right), \left(\sqrt{\frac{1+\sqrt{7}}{3}}, +\infty\right)$
**(e)** $\pm\sqrt{\frac{1+\sqrt{7}}{3}}$

33. increasing: $[-\pi/4, 3\pi/4]$; decreasing: $[-\pi, -\pi/4], [3\pi/4, \pi]$; concave up: $(-3\pi/4, \pi/4)$; concave down: $(-\pi, -3\pi/4), (\pi/4, \pi)$; inflection points: $-3\pi/4, \pi/4$

35. increasing: none; decreasing: $(-\pi, \pi)$; concave up: $(-\pi, 0)$; concave down: $(0, \pi)$; inflection point: 0

37. increasing: $[-\pi, -3\pi/4], [-\pi/4, \pi/4], [3\pi/4, \pi]$; decreasing: $[-3\pi/4, -\pi/4], [\pi/4, 3\pi/4]$; concave up: $(-\pi/2, 0), (\pi/2, \pi)$; concave down: $(-\pi, -\pi/2), (0, \pi/2)$; inflection points: $0, \pm\pi/2$

39. **(a)**
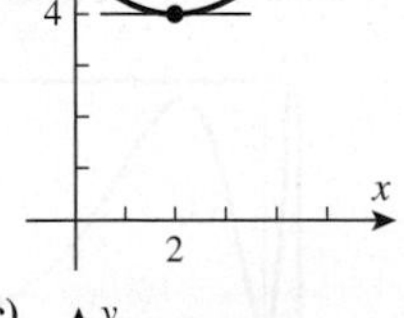
**(b)**
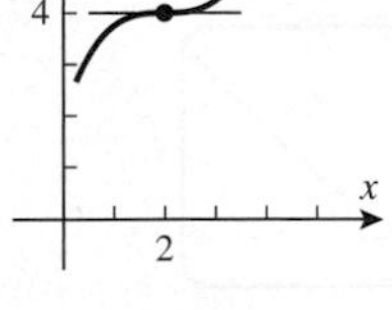
**(c)**
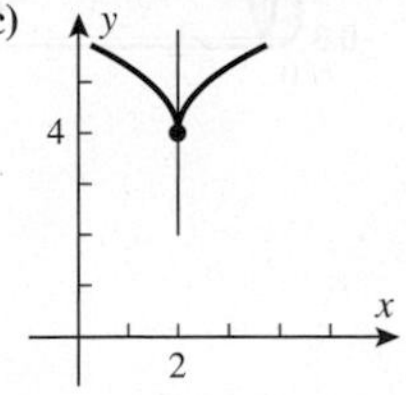

41. $1 + \frac{1}{3}x - \sqrt[3]{1+x} \ge 0$ if $x > 0$
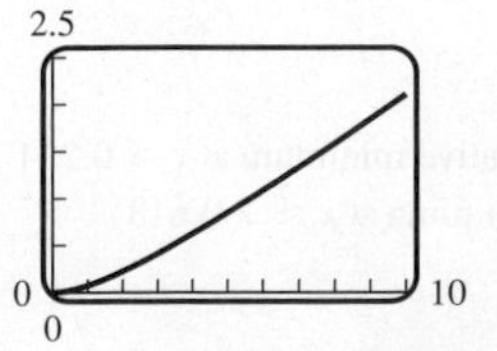

43. $x \ge \sin x$
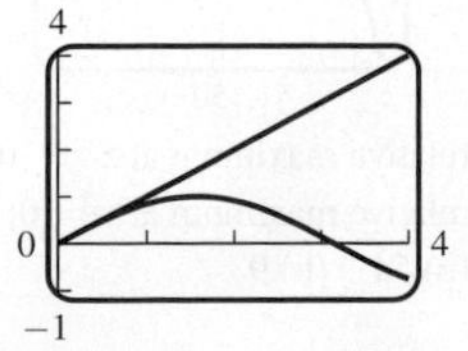

47.
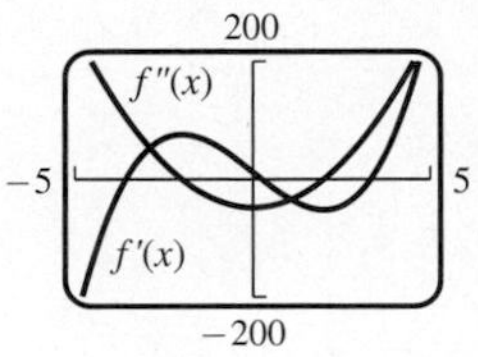

points of inflection at $x = -2, 2$; concave up on $[-5, -2], [2, 5]$; concave down on $[-2, 2]$; increasing on $[-3.5829, 0.2513]$ and $[3.3316, 5]$; decreasing on $[-5, -3.5829]$, $[0.2513, 3.3316]$

49. $-2.464202, 0.662597, 2.701605$

53. **(a)** true **(b)** false

57. **(c)** inflection point $(1, 0)$; concave up on $(1, +\infty)$; concave down on $(-\infty, 1)$

63.
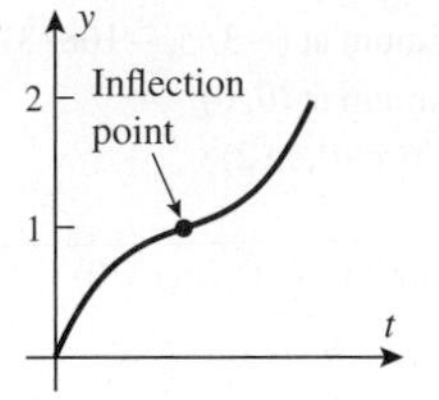


65.
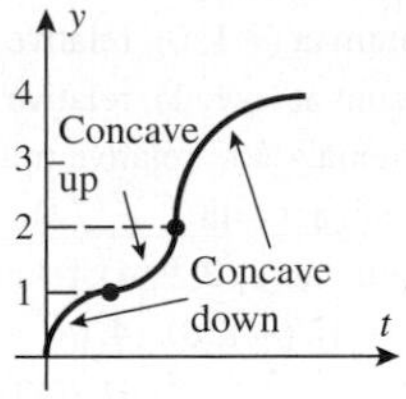


67. **(a)** $\frac{LAk}{(1+A)^2}$ **(c)** $\frac{1}{k}\ln A$

69. the eighth day
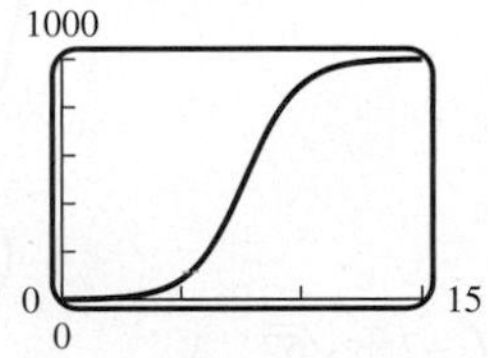

## ► Exercise Set 4.2 (Page 190)

1. **(a)**
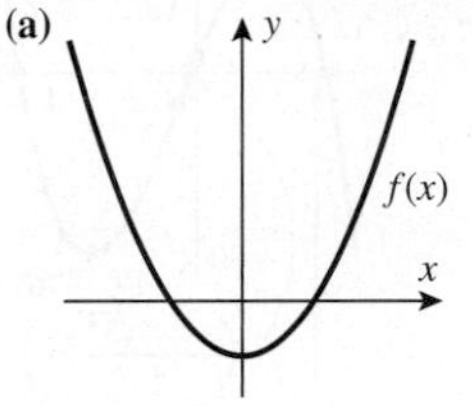
**(b)**
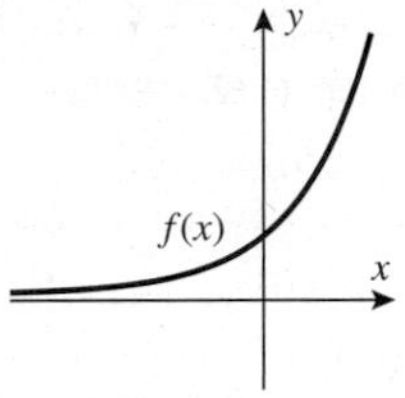
**(c)**
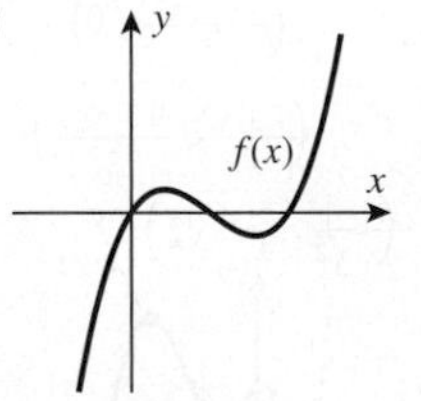
**(d)**
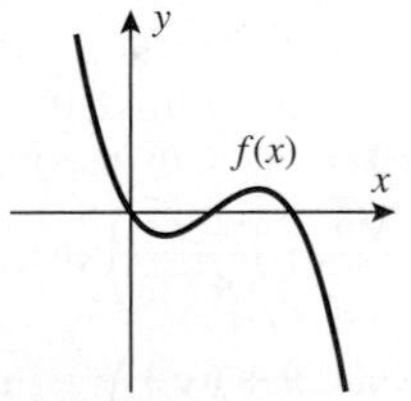

5. **(b)** nothing **(c)** $f$ has a relative minimum at $x = 1$, $g$ has no relative extremum at $x = 1$.

7. critical: $0, \pm\sqrt{2}$; stationary: $0, \pm\sqrt{2}$

9. critical: $-3, 1$; stationary: $-3, 1$

11. critical: $0, \pm 5$; stationary: 0

13. critical: $n\pi/2$ for every integer $n$; stationary: $n\pi + \pi/2$ for every integer $n$

Responses to True–False questions may be abridged to save space.

15. False; for example, $f(x) = (x-1)^2(x-1.5)$ has a relative maximum at $x = 1$, but $f(2) = 0.5 > 0 = f(1)$.

17. False; to apply the second derivative test (Theorem 4.2.4) at $x = 1$, $f'(1)$ must equal 0.

19.
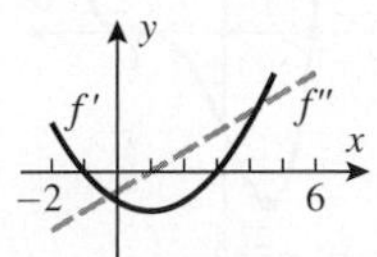

21. **(a)** none **(b)** $x = 1$ **(c)** none **(d)**
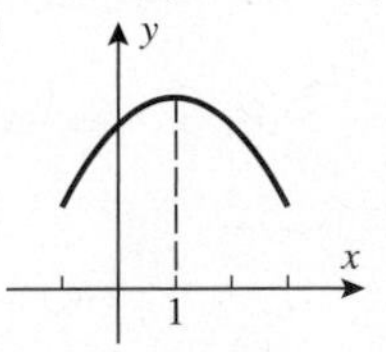

**23.** **(a)** 2 **(b)** 0 **(c)** 1, 3
**(d)**

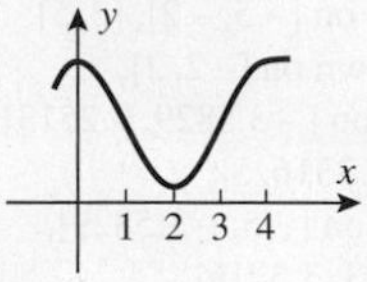


**25.** 0 (neither), $\sqrt[3]{5}$ (min) **27.** $-2$ (min), $2/3$ (max) **29.** 0 (min)
**31.** $-1$ (min), 1 (max) **33.** relative maximum at $(4/3, 19/3)$
**35.** relative maximum at $(\pi/4, 1)$; relative minimum at $(3\pi/4, -1)$
**37.** relative maximum at $(1, 1)$; relative minima at $(0, 0)$, $(2, 0)$
**39.** relative maximum at $(-1, 0)$; relative minimum at $(-3/5, -108/3125)$
**41.** relative maximum at $(-1, 1)$; relative minimum at $(0, 0)$
**43.** no relative extrema **45.** relative minimum at $(0, \ln 2)$
**47.** relative minimum at $(-\ln 2, -1/4)$
**49.** relative maximum at $(3/2, 9/4)$; relative minima at $(0, 0)$, $(3, 0)$
**51.** intercepts: $(0, -4)$, $(-1, 0)$, $(4, 0)$;
stationary point: $(3/2, -25/4)$ (min);
inflection points: none

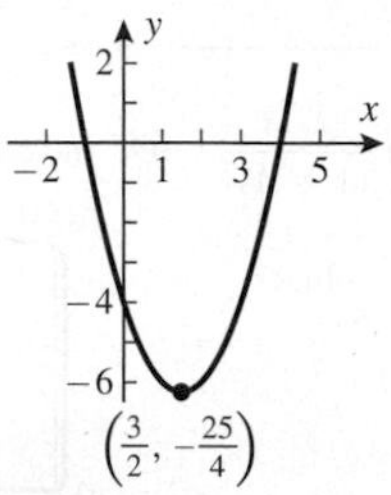


**53.** intercepts: $(0, 5)$, $\left(\dfrac{-7 \pm \sqrt{57}}{4}, 0\right)$, $(5, 0)$;
stationary points: $(-2, 49)$ (max),
$(3, -76)$ (min);
inflection point: $(1/2, -27/2)$

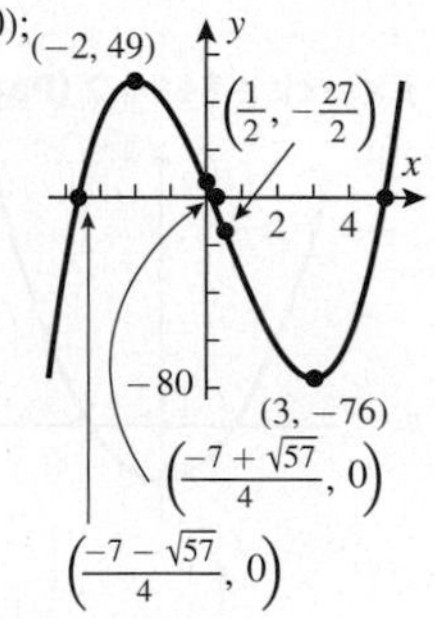


**55.** intercepts: $(-1, 0)$, $(0, 0)$, $(2, 0)$;
stationary points: $(-1, 0)$ (max),
$\left(\dfrac{1-\sqrt{3}}{2}, \dfrac{9-6\sqrt{3}}{4}\right)$ (min),
$\left(\dfrac{1+\sqrt{3}}{2}, \dfrac{9+6\sqrt{3}}{4}\right)$ (max);
inflection points: $\left(-\dfrac{1}{\sqrt{2}}, \dfrac{5}{4} - \sqrt{2}\right)$,
$\left(\dfrac{1}{\sqrt{2}}, \dfrac{5}{4} + \sqrt{2}\right)$,

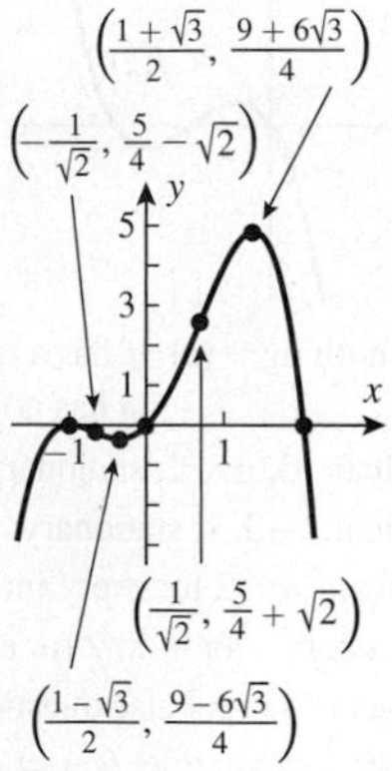


**57.** intercepts: $(0, -1)$, $(-1, 0)$, $(1, 0)$;
stationary points: $(-1/2, -27/16)$ (min),
$(1, 0)$ (neither);
inflection points: $(0, -1)$, $(1, 0)$

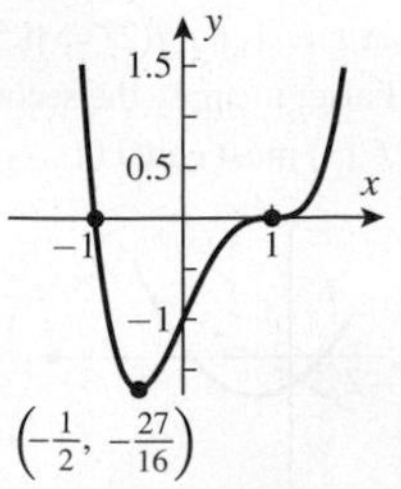


**59.** intercepts: $(-1, 0)$, $(0, 0)$, $(1, 0)$;
stationary points: $(-1, 0)$ (max),
$\left(-\dfrac{1}{\sqrt{5}}, -\dfrac{16}{25\sqrt{5}}\right)$ (min),
$\left(\dfrac{1}{\sqrt{5}}, \dfrac{16}{25\sqrt{5}}\right)$ (max), $(1, 0)$ (min);
inflection points: $\left(-\sqrt{\dfrac{3}{5}}, -\dfrac{4}{25}\sqrt{\dfrac{3}{5}}\right)$,
$(0, 0)$, $\left(\sqrt{\dfrac{3}{5}}, \dfrac{4}{25}\sqrt{\dfrac{3}{5}}\right)$

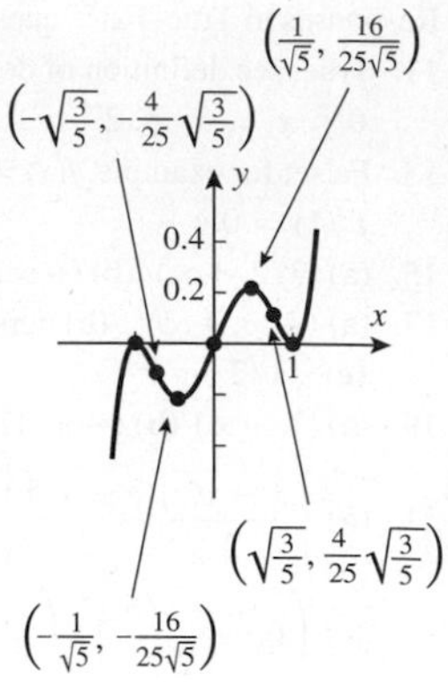


**61.** **(a)**

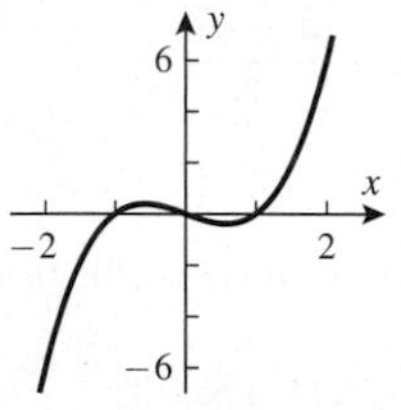


**(b)**

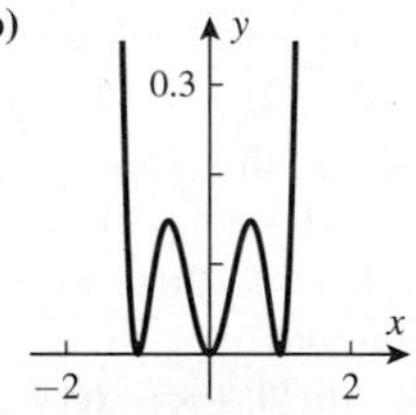


**(c)**

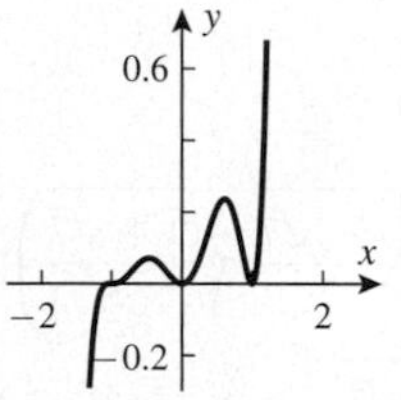


**(d)**

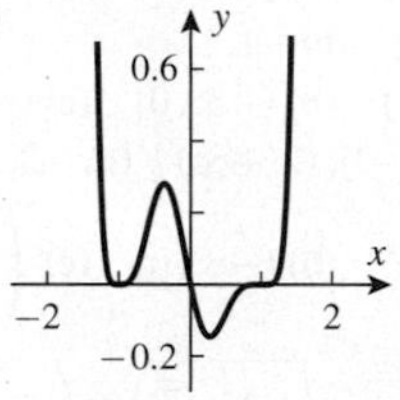


**63.** relative min of 0 at $x = \pi/2, \pi, 3\pi/2$;
relative max of 1 at $x = \pi/4, 3\pi/4,$
$5\pi/4, 7\pi/4$

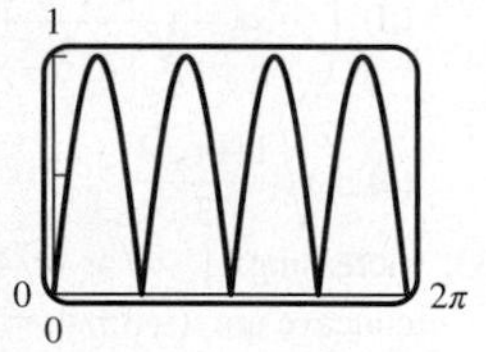


**65.** relative min of 0 at $x = \pi/2, 3\pi/2$;
relative max of 1 at $x = \pi$

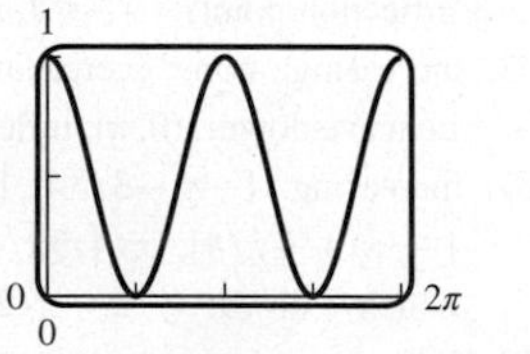


**67.** relative min of $-1/e$ at $x = 1/e$

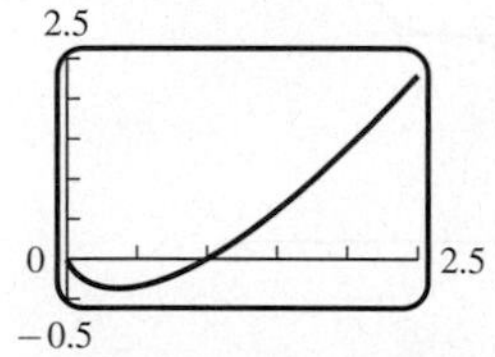


**69.** relative min of 0 at $x = 0$;
relative max of $1/e^2$ at $x = 1$

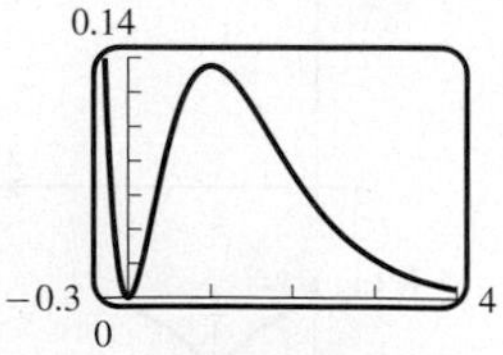


**71.** relative minima at $x = -3.58, 3.33$;
relative max at $x = 0.25$

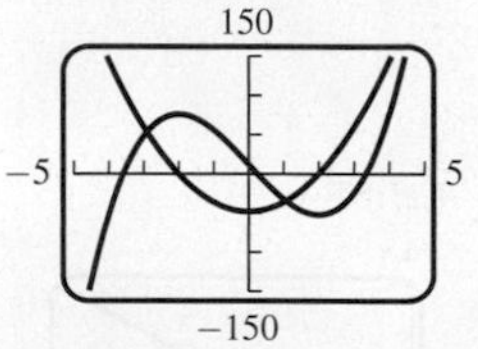


**73.** relative maximum at $x \approx -0.272$; relative minimum at $x \approx 0.224$
**75.** relative maximum at $x = 0$; relative minima at $x \approx \pm 0.618$
**77.** **(a)** 54 **(b)** 9

79. **(b)**

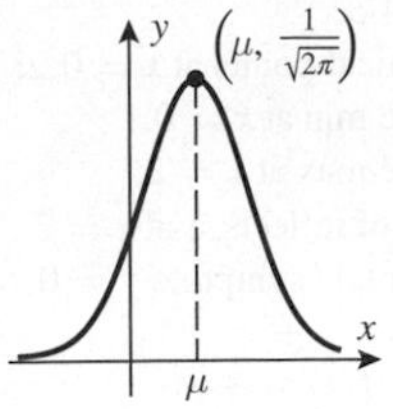


## ▶ Exercise Set 4.3 (Page 202)

1. stationary points: none; inflection points: none; asymptotes: $x = 4, y = -2$; asymptote crossings: none

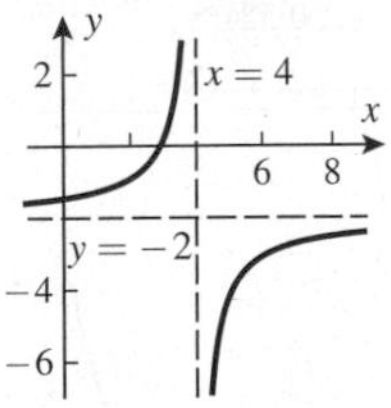


3. stationary points: none; inflection point: $(0, 0)$; asymptotes: $x = \pm 2, y = 0$; asymptote crossings: $(0, 0)$

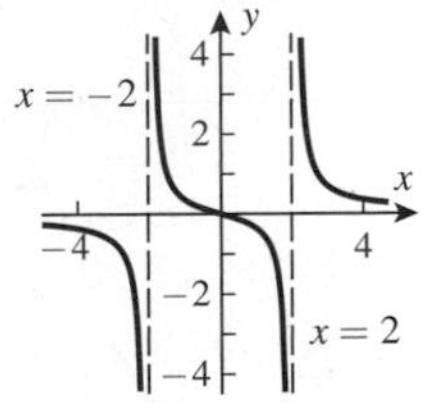


5. stationary point: $(0, 0)$; inflection points: $\left(\pm\frac{2}{\sqrt{3}}, \frac{1}{4}\right)$; asymptote: $y = 1$; asymptote crossings: none

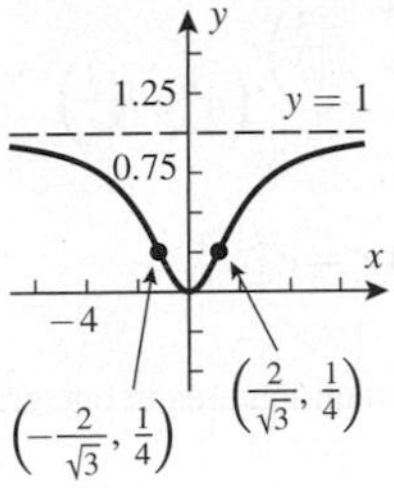


7. stationary point: $(0, -1)$; inflection points: $(0, -1)$, $\left(-\frac{1}{\sqrt[3]{2}}, -\frac{1}{3}\right)$; asymptotes: $x = 1, y = 1$; asymptote crossings: none

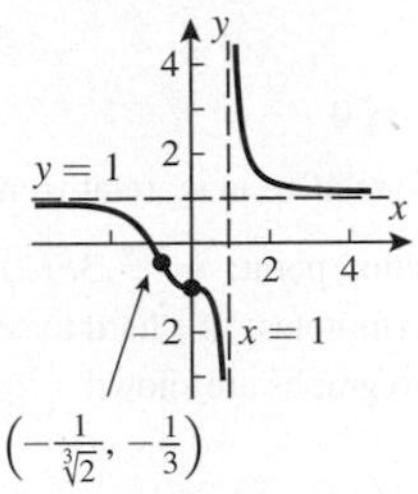


9. stationary point: $(4, 11/4)$; inflection point: $(6, 25/9)$; asymptotes: $x = 0, y = 3$; asymptote crossing: $(2, 3)$

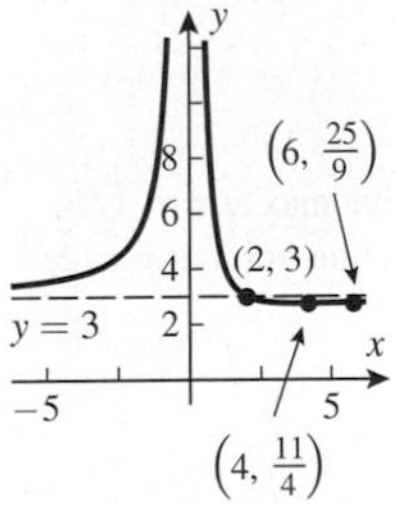


11. stationary point: $(-1/3, 0)$; inflection point: $(-1, 1)$; asymptotes: $x = 1, y = 9$; asymptote crossing: $(1/3, 9)$

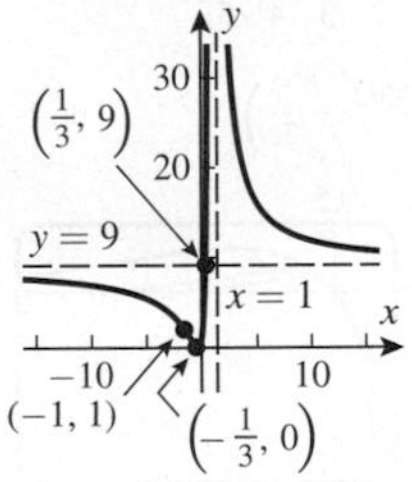


13. stationary points: none; inflection points: none; asymptotes: $x = 1, y = -1$; asymptote crossings: none

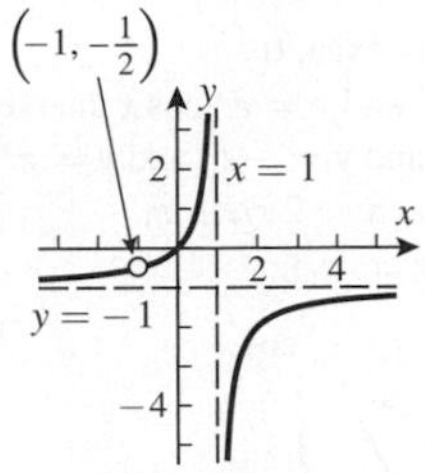


15. **(a)**

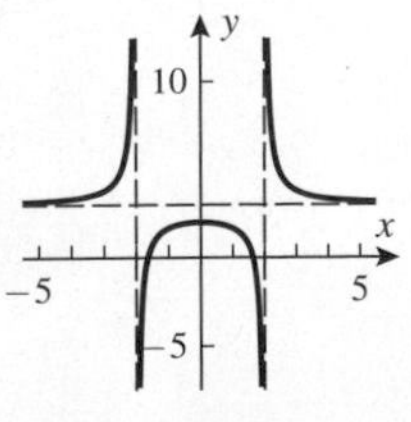


**(b)**

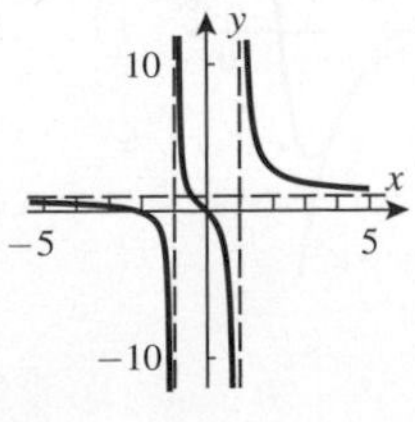


17.

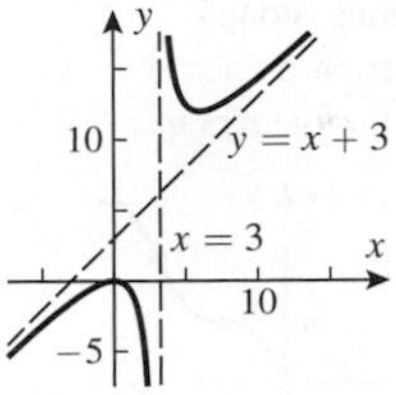


19. stationary point: $\left(-\frac{1}{\sqrt[3]{2}}, \frac{3}{2}\sqrt[3]{2}\right)$; inflection point: $(1, 0)$; asymptotes: $y = x^2, x = 0$; asymptote crossings: none

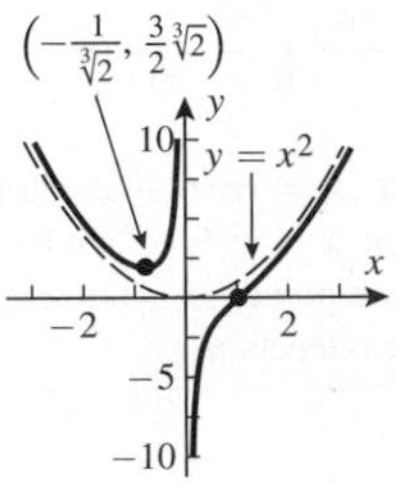


21. stationary points: $(-4, -27/2), (2, 0)$; inflection point: $(2, 0)$; asymptotes: $x = 0, y = x - 6$; asymptote crossing: $(2/3, -16/3)$

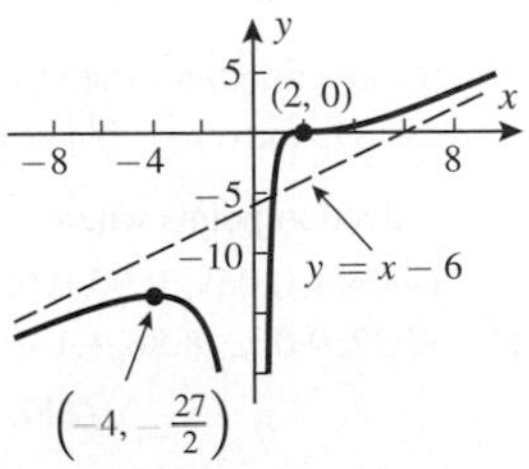


23. stationary points: $(-3, 23), (0, -4)$; inflection point: $(0, -4)$; asymptotes: $x = -2, y = x^2 - 2x$; asymptote crossings: none

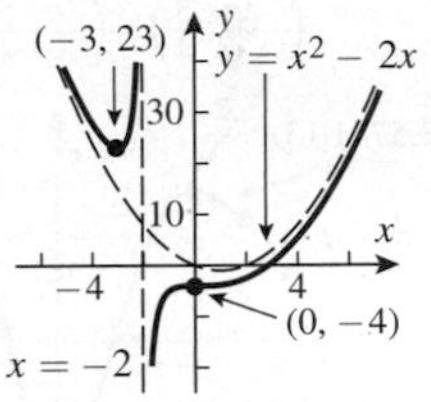


25. **(a)** VI **(b)** I **(c)** III **(d)** V **(e)** IV **(f)** II

Responses to True–False questions may be abridged to save space.

27. True; if deg $P >$ deg $Q$, then $f(x)$ is unbounded as $x \to \pm\infty$; if deg $P <$ deg $Q$, then $f(x) \to 0$ as $x \to \pm\infty$.

29. False; for example, $f(x) = (x - 1)^{1/3}$ is continuous (with vertical tangent line) at $x = 1$, but $f'(x) = \dfrac{1}{3(x - 1)^{2/3}}$ has a vertical asymptote at $x = 1$.

31. critical points: $(\pm 1/2, 0)$; inflection points: none

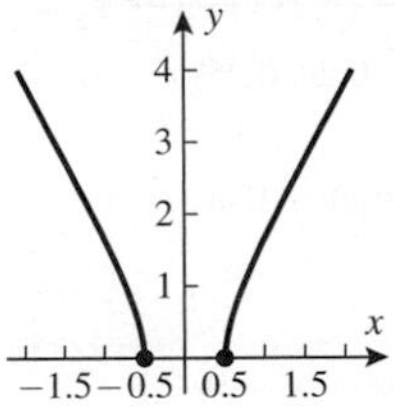


33. critical points: $(-1, 1), (0, 0)$; inflection points: none

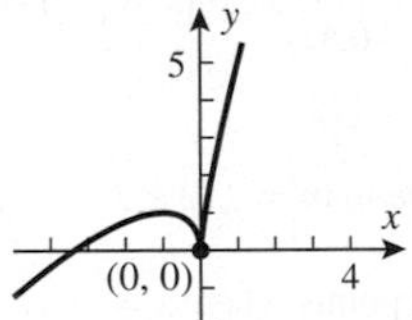


35. critical points: $(0, 0), (1, 3)$; inflection points: $(0, 0), (-2, -6\sqrt[3]{2})$. It's hard to see all the important features in one graph, so two graphs are shown:

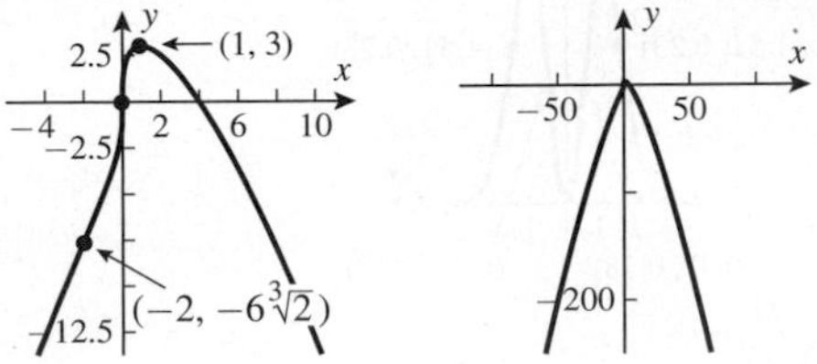

**37.** critical points: (0, 4), (1, 3); inflection points: (0, 4), (8, 4)

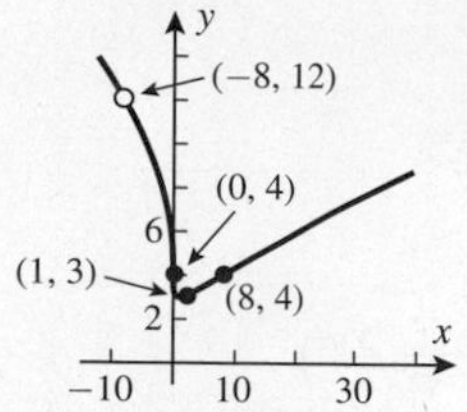


**39.** extrema: none; inflection points: $x = \pi n$ for integers $n$

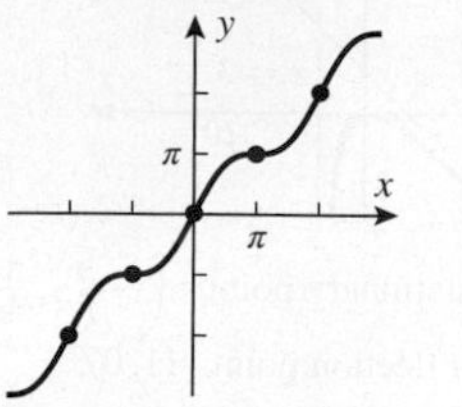


**41.** minima: $x = 7\pi/6 + 2\pi n$ for integers $n$; maxima: $x = \pi/6 + 2\pi n$ for integers $n$; inflection points: $x = 2\pi/3 + \pi n$ for integers $n$

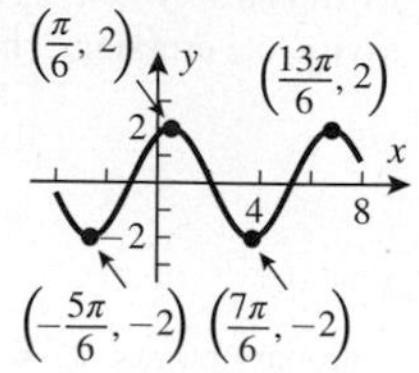


**43.** relative minima: 1 at $x = \pi$; −1 at $x = 0, 2\pi$; relative maxima: 5/4 at $x = -2\pi/3, 2\pi/3, 4\pi/3, 8\pi/3$; inflection points where $\cos x = \dfrac{-1 \pm \sqrt{33}}{8}$: (−2.57, 1.13), (−0.94, 0.06), (0.94, 0.06), (2.57, 1.13), (3.71, 1.13), (5.35, 0.06), (7.22, 0.06), (8.86, 1.13)

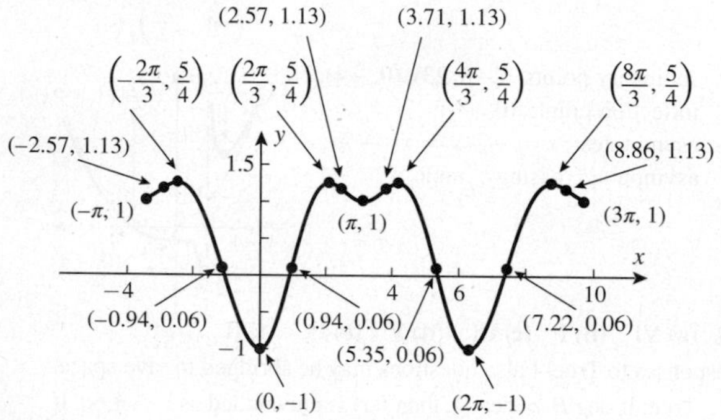


**45.** **(a)** $+\infty, 0$
**(b)**

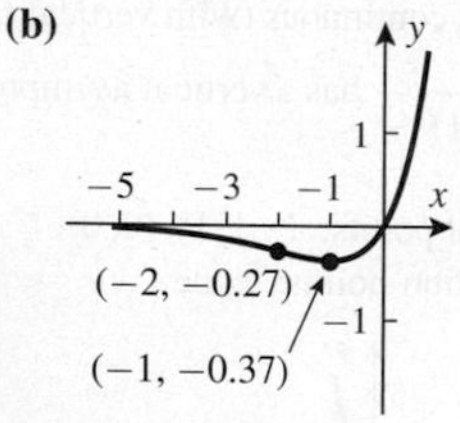


**47.** **(a)** $0, +\infty$
**(b)**

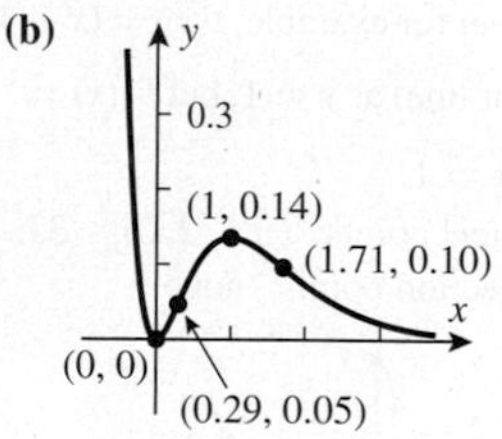


**49.** **(a)** 0, 0
**(b)** relative max $= 1/e$ at $x = \pm 1$; relative min $= 0$ at $x = 0$;

inflection points where $x = \pm\sqrt{\dfrac{5 \pm \sqrt{17}}{4}}$:

about (±0.47, 0.18), (±1.51, 0.23); asymptote: $y = 0$

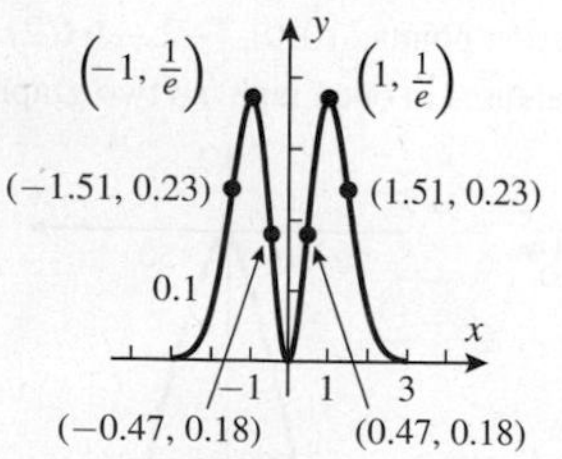


**51.** **(a)** $-\infty, 0$
**(b)** relative max $= -e^2$ at $x = 2$; no relative min; no inflection points; asymptotes: $y = 0, x = 1$

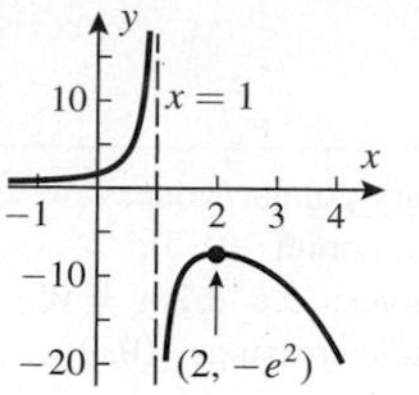


**53.** **(a)** $0, +\infty$
**(b)** critical points at $x = 0.2$; relative min at $x = 0$, relative max at $x = 2$; points of inflection at $x = 2 \pm \sqrt{2}$; horizontal asymptote $y = 0$ as $x \to +\infty$

$\lim_{x \to -\infty} f(x) = +\infty$

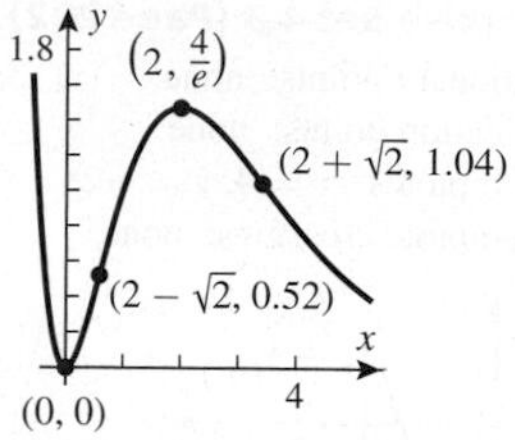


**55.** **(a)** $+\infty, 0$
**(b)**

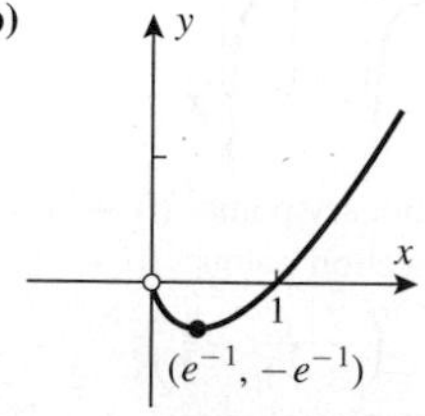


**57.** **(a)** $+\infty, 0$
**(b)**

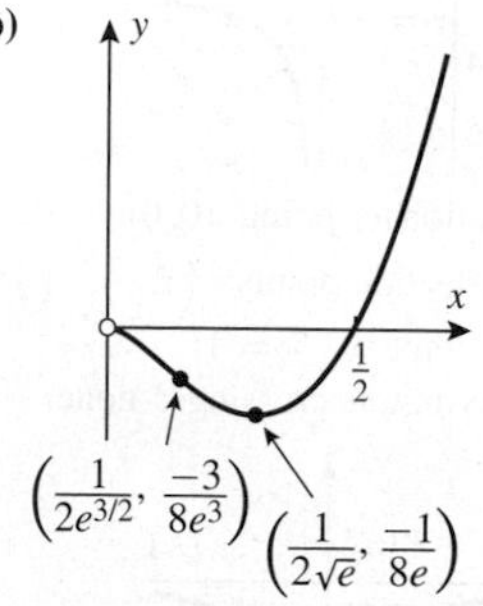


**59.** **(a)** $+\infty, 0$
**(b)** no relative max; relative min $= -\dfrac{3}{2e}$ at $x = e^{-3/2}$;
inflection point: $(e^{3/2}, 3e/2)$;
no asymptotes. It's hard to see all the important features in one graph, so two graphs are shown:

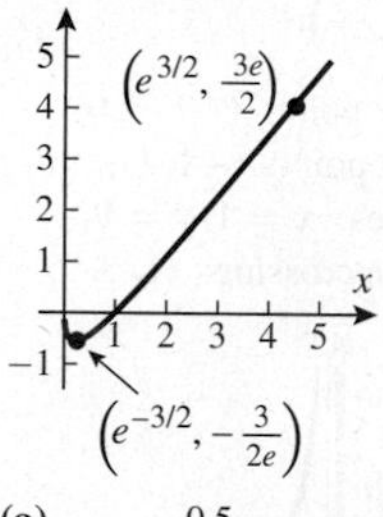


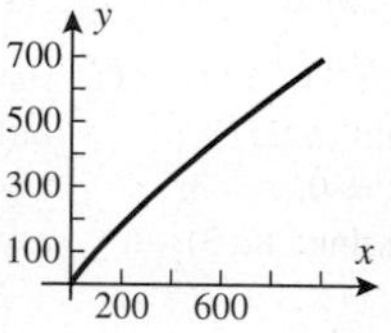


**61.** **(a)**

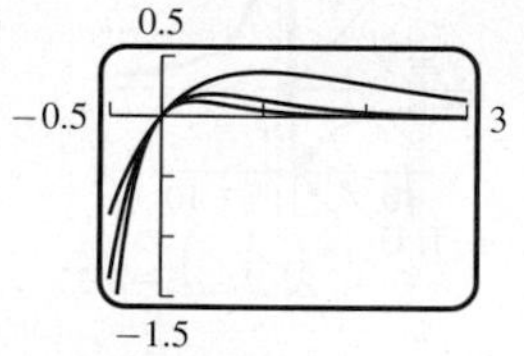


**(b)** relative max at $x = 1/b$; inflection point at $x = 2/b$

**63.** **(a)** does not exist, 0
**(b)** $y = e^x$ and $y = e^x \cos x$ intersect for $x = 2\pi n$, and $y = -e^x$ and $y = e^x \cos x$ intersect for $x = 2\pi n + \pi$, for all integers $n$.

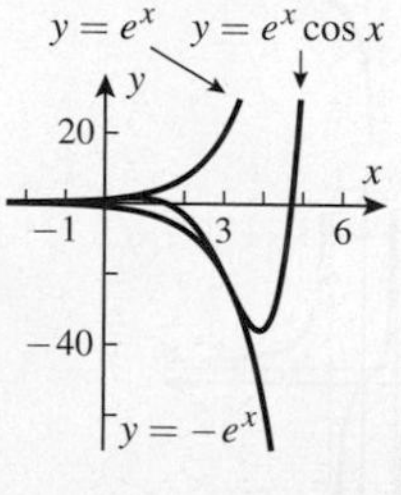


**(c)** Graphs for $a = 1$:

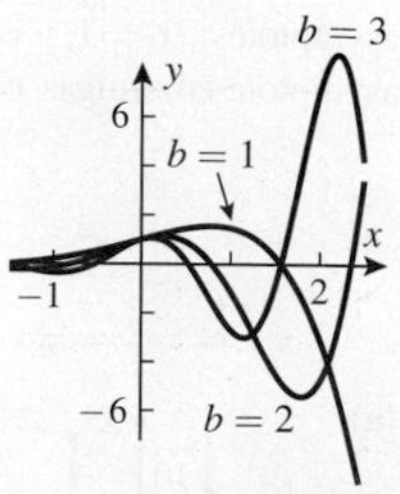

65. **(a)** $x = 1, 2.5, 3, 4$ **(b)** $(-\infty, 1]$, $[2.5, 3]$
**(c)** relative max at $x = 1, 3$;
relative min at $x = 2.5$ **(d)** $x \approx 0.6, 1.9, 4$

67.

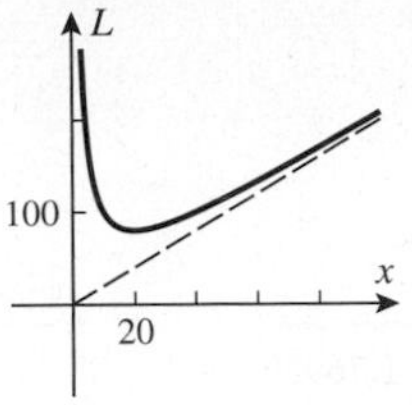


69. Graph misses zeros at $x = 0, 1$ and min at $x = 5/6$.

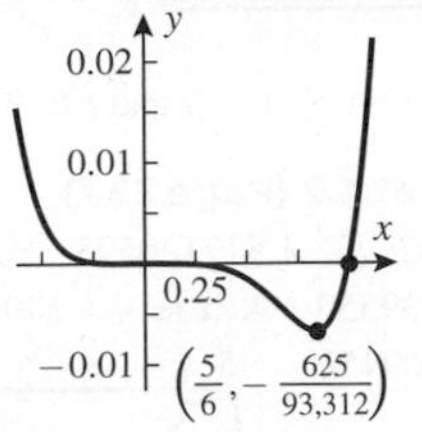


## ▶ Exercise Set 4.4 (Page 210)

1. relative maxima at $x = 2, 6$; absolute max at $x = 6$; relative min at $x = 4$; absolute minima at $x = 0, 4$

3. **(a)**

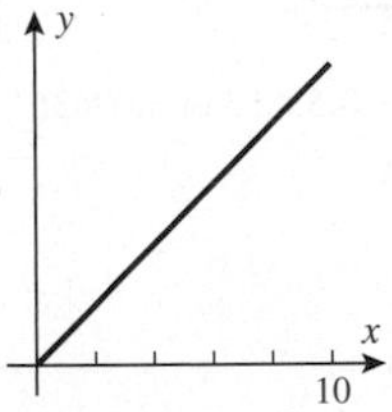


**(b)**

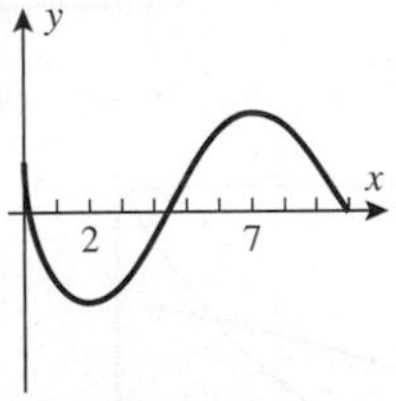


**(c)**

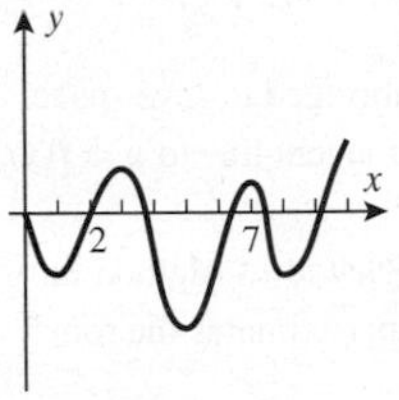


7. max $= 2$ at $x = 1, 2$; min $= 1$ at $x = 3/2$
9. max $= 8$ at $x = 4$; min $= -1$ at $x = 1$
11. maximum value $3/\sqrt{5}$ at $x = 1$; minimum value $-3/\sqrt{5}$ at $x = -1$
13. max $= \sqrt{2} - \pi/4$ at $x = -\pi/4$; min $= \pi/3 - \sqrt{3}$ at $x = \pi/3$
15. maximum value 17 at $x = -5$; minimum value 1 at $x = -3$.

Responses to True–False questions may be abridged to save space.

17. True; see the Extreme-Value Theorem (4.4.2).
19. True; see Theorem 4.4.3.
21. no maximum; min $= -9/4$ at $x = 1/2$
23. maximum value $f(1) = 1$; no minimum
25. no maximum or minimum
27. max $= -2 - 2\sqrt{2}$ at $x = -1 - \sqrt{2}$; no minimum
29. no maximum; min $= 0$ at $x = 0, 2$
31. maximum value 48 at $x = 8$; minimum value 0 at $x = 0, 20$

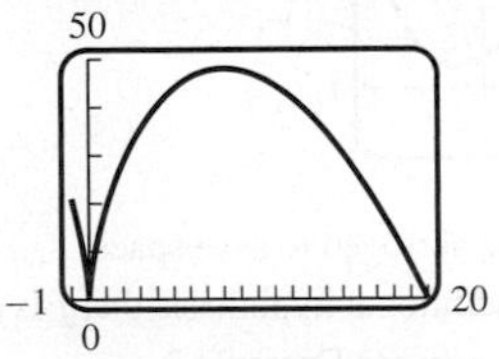


33. no maximum or minimum

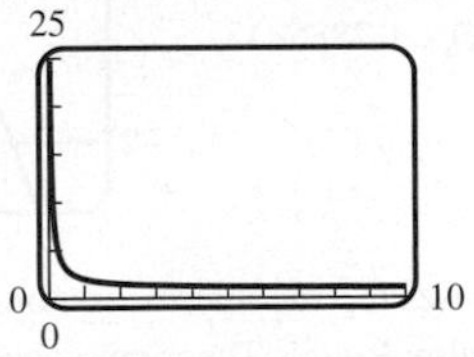


35. max $= 2\sqrt{2} + 1$ at $x = 3\pi/4$; min $= \sqrt{3}$ at $x = \pi/3$

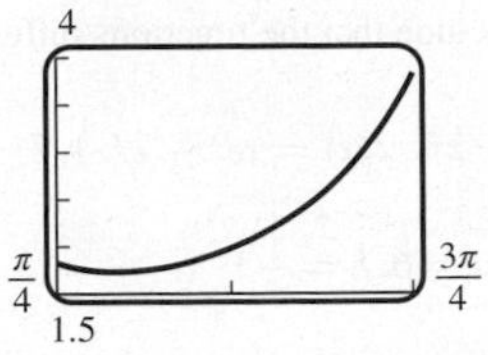


37. maximum value $\frac{27}{8}e^{-3}$ at $x = \frac{3}{2}$; minimum value $64/e^8$ at $x = 4$

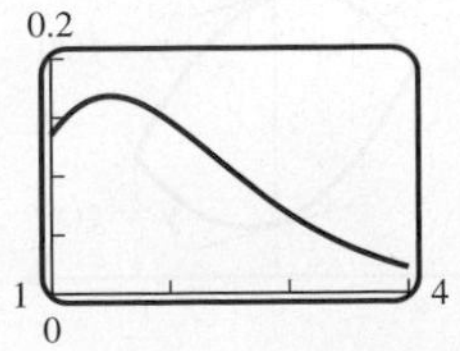


39. max $= 5 \ln 10 - 9$ at $x = 3$; min $= 5 \ln(10/9) - 1$ at $x = 1/3$

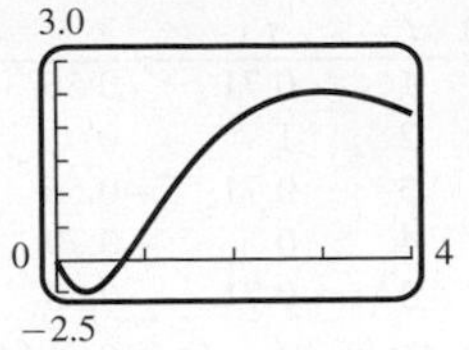


41. maximum value $\sin(1) \approx 0.84147$; minimum value $-\sin(1) \approx -0.84147$

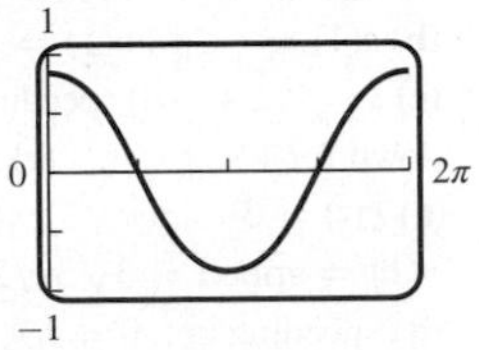


43. maximum value 2; minimum value $-\frac{1}{4}$
45. max $= 3$ at $x = 2n\pi$; min $= -3/2$ at $x = \pm 2\pi/3 + 2n\pi$ for any integer $n$ 49. 2, at $x = 1$
53. $x = 20$; 20 in $\times$ 35 in 55. $3\sqrt{3}$ ft (at $x = 2$ ft)
57. maximum $y = 4$ at $t = \pi, 3\pi$; minimum $y = 0$ at $t = 0, 2\pi$

## ▶ Exercise Set 4.5 (Page 221)

1. **(a)** 1 **(b)** $\frac{1}{2}$ 3. 500 ft parallel to stream, 250 ft perpendicular
5. 500 ft (\$3 fencing) $\times$ 750 ft (\$2 fencing) 7. 5 in $\times$ $\frac{12}{5}$ in
9. $10\sqrt{2} \times 10\sqrt{2}$ 11. 80 ft (\$1 fencing), 40 ft (\$2 fencing)
15. maximum area is 108 when $x = 2$
17. maximum area is 144 when $x = 2$
19. 11,664 in$^3$ 21. $\frac{200}{27}$ ft$^3$ 23. base 10 cm square, height 20 cm
25. ends $\sqrt[3]{3V/4}$ units square, length $\frac{4}{3}\sqrt[3]{3V/4}$
27. height $= 2R/\sqrt{3}$, radius $= \sqrt{2/3}R$
31. height $=$ radius $= \sqrt[3]{500/\pi}$ cm 33. $L/12$ by $L/12$ by $L/12$
35. height $= L/\sqrt{3}$, radius $= \sqrt{2/3}L$
37. height $= 2\sqrt[3]{75/\pi}$ cm, radius $= \sqrt{2}\sqrt[3]{75/\pi}$ cm
39. height $= 4R$, radius $= \sqrt{2}R$
41. $R(x) = 225x - 0.25x^2$; $R'(x) = 225 - 0.5x$; 450 tons
43. **(a)** 7000 units **(b)** yes **(c)** \$15 45. 13,722 lb 47. $3\sqrt{3}$
49. height $= r/\sqrt{2}$ 51. $1/\sqrt{5}$ 53. $\left(\sqrt{2}, \frac{1}{2}\right)$ 55. $\left(-1/\sqrt{3}, \frac{3}{4}\right)$
57. **(a)** $\pi$ mi **(b)** $2\sin^{-1}(1/4)$ mi 59. $4(1 + 2^{2/3})^{3/2}$ ft
61. 30 cm from the weaker source 63. $\sqrt{24} = 2\sqrt{6}$ ft

## ▶ Exercise Set 4.6 (Page 231)

1. **(a)** positive, negative, slowing down
**(b)** positive, positive, speeding up
**(c)** negative, positive, slowing down

3. **(a)** left
**(b)** negative
**(c)** speeding up
**(d)** slowing down

5.

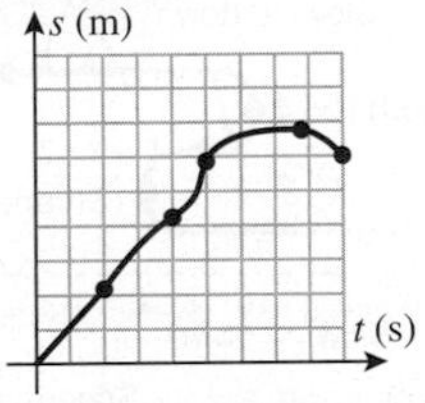


7.

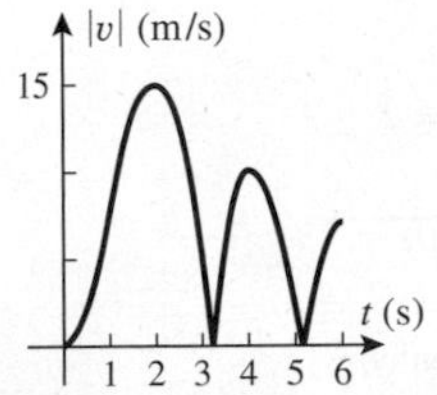


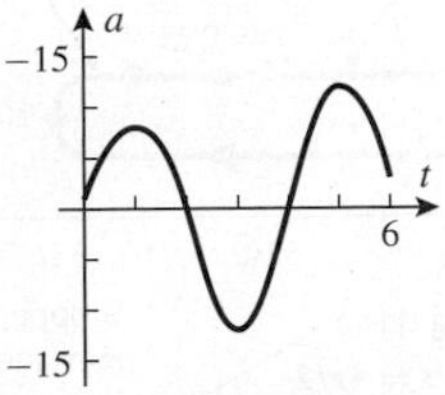


Responses to True–False questions may be abridged to save space.

9. False; a particle has positive velocity when its position versus time graph is increasing; if that positive velocity is decreasing, the particle would be slowing down.
11. False; acceleration is the derivative of velocity (with respect to time); speed is the absolute value of velocity.
13. **(a)** 6.2 ft/s$^2$ **(b)** $t = 0$ s

15. (a)

| $t$ | $s$ | $v$ | $a$ |
|---|---|---|---|
| 1 | 0.71 | 0.56 | −0.44 |
| 2 | 1 | 0 | −0.62 |
| 3 | 0.71 | −0.56 | −0.44 |
| 4 | 0 | −0.79 | 0 |
| 5 | −0.71 | −0.56 | 0.44 |

(b) stopped at $t = 2$; moving right at $t = 1$; moving left at $t = 3, 4, 5$ (c) speeding up at $t = 3$; slowing down at $t = 1, 5$; neither at $t = 2, 4$

17. (a) $v(t) = 3t^2 - 6t$, $a(t) = 6t - 6$
(b) $s(1) = -2$ ft, $v(1) = -3$ ft/s, $|v(1)| = 3$ ft/s, $a(1) = 0$ ft/s$^2$
(c) $t = 0, 2$ s (d) speeding up for $0 < t < 1$ and $2 < t$, slowing down for $1 < t < 2$ (e) 58 ft

19. (a) $v(t) = 3\pi \sin(\pi t/3)$, $a(t) = \pi^2 \cos(\pi t/3)$ (b) $s(1) = 9/2$ ft, $v(1) = \text{speed} = 3\sqrt{3}\pi/2$ ft/s, $a(1) = \pi^2/2$ ft/s$^2$ (c) $t = 0$ s, 3 s
(d) speeding up: $0 < t < 1.5, 3 < t < 4.5$; slowing down: $1.5 < t < 3, 4.5 < t < 5$ (e) 31.5 ft

21. (a) $v(t) = -\frac{1}{3}(t^2 - 6t + 8)e^{-t/3}$, $a(t) = \frac{1}{9}(t^2 - 12t + 26)e^{-t/3}$
(b) $s(1) = 9e^{-1/3}$ ft, $v(1) = -e^{-1/3}$ ft/s, speed $= e^{-1/3}$ ft/s, $a(1) = \frac{5}{3}e^{-1/3}$ ft/s$^2$ (c) $t = 2$ s, 4 s
(d) speeding up: $2 < t < 6 - \sqrt{10}, 4 < t < 6 + \sqrt{10}$; slowing down: $0 < t < 2, 6 - \sqrt{10} < t < 4, 6 + \sqrt{10} < t$
(e) $8 - 24e^{-2/3} + 48e^{-4/3} - 33e^{-5/3}$

23. (a) $\sqrt{5}$ (b) $\sqrt{5}/10$

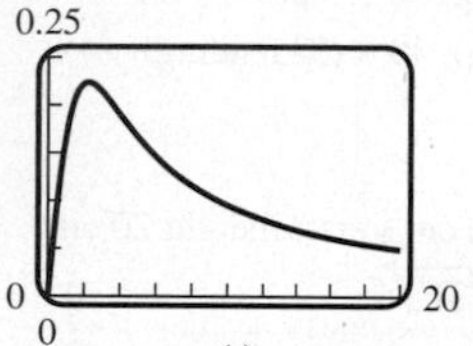

$s(t)$

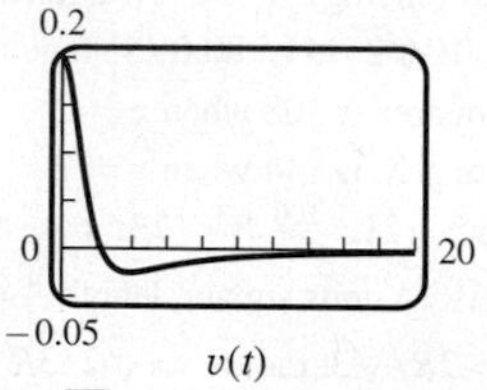

$v(t)$

(c) speeding up for $\sqrt{5} < t < \sqrt{15}$; slowing down for $0 < t < \sqrt{5}$ and $\sqrt{15} < t$

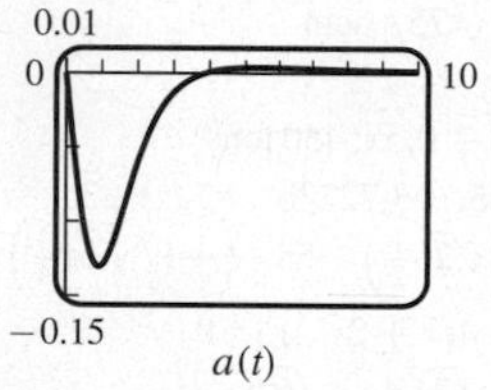

$a(t)$

25.

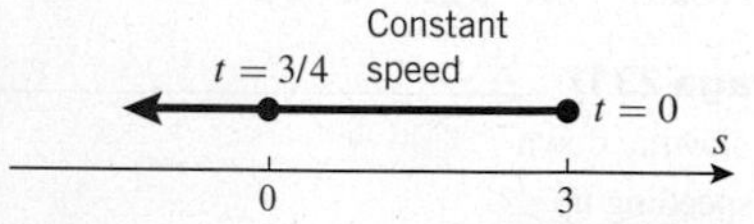


27.

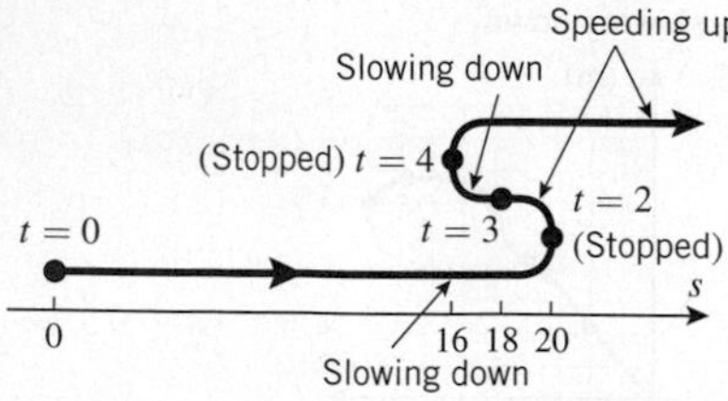


29.

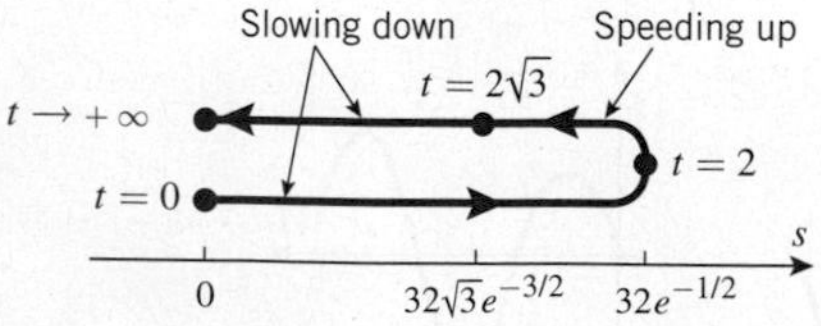


31.

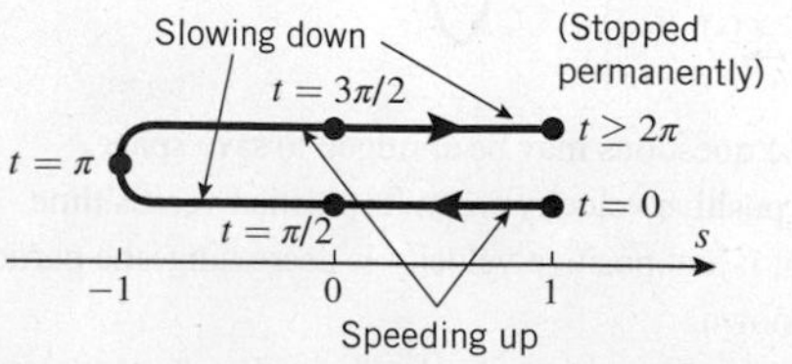


33. (a) 12 ft/s (b) $t = 2.2$ s, $s = -24.2$ ft

35. (a) $t = 2 \pm 1/\sqrt{3}, s = \ln 2, v = \pm\sqrt{3}$ (b) $t = 2, s = 0, a = 6$

37. (a) (b) $\sqrt{2}$

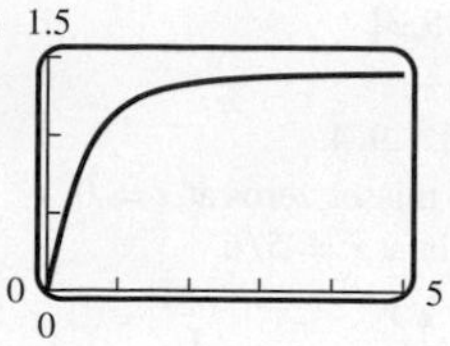


39. (b) $\frac{2}{3}$ unit (c) $0 \le t < 1$ and $t > 2$

## ▶ Exercise Set 4.7 (Page 237)

1. 1.414213562 3. 1.817120593 5. $x \approx 1.76929$
7. $x \approx 1.224439550$ 9. $x \approx -1.24962$ 11. $x \approx 1.02987$
13. $x \approx 4.493409458$ 15. $x \approx 0.68233$

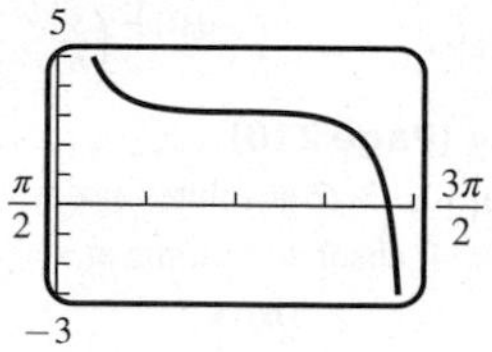


17. −0.474626618, 1.395336994 19. $x \approx 0.58853$ or 3.09636

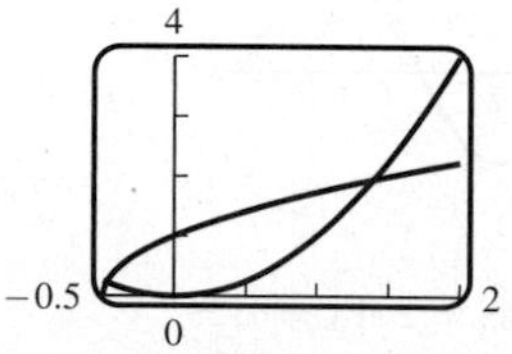


Responses to True–False questions may be abridged to save space.

21. True; $x = x_{n+1}$ is the $x$-intercept of the tangent line to $y = f(x)$ at $x = x_n$.

23. False; for example, if $f(x) = x(x-3)^2$, Newton's Method fails (analogous to Figure 4.7.4) with $x_1 = 1$ and approximates the root $x = 3$ for $x_1 > 1$.

25. (b) 3.162277660 27. −4.098859132

29. $x = -1$ or $x \approx 0.17951$ 31. (0.589754512, 0.347810385)

33. (b) $\theta \approx 2.99156$ rad or 171°

35. (2.24551022, 1.32626189); distance ≈ 40.832 meters

37. −1.220744085, 0.724491959

39. $i = 0.053362$ or 5.33% 41. (a) The values do not converge.

## ▶ Exercise Set 4.8 (Page 245)

1. $c = 4$ 3. $c = \pi$ 5. $c = 1$ 7. $c = -\sqrt{5}$

9. (a) $[-2, 1]$
(b) $c \approx -1.29$
(c) −1.2885843

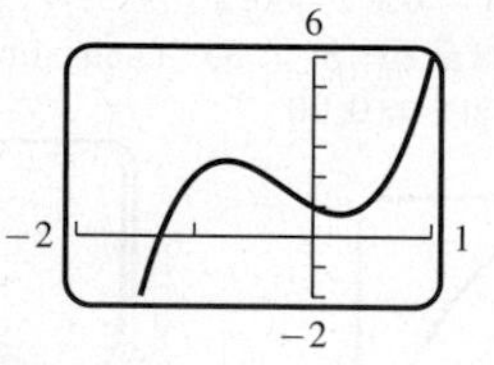


Responses to True–False questions may be abridged to save space.

11. False; Rolle's Theorem requires the additional hypothesis that $f$ is differentiable on $(a, b)$ and $f(a) = f(b) = 0$; see Example 2.

13. False; the Constant Difference Theorem applies to two functions with equal derivatives on an interval to conclude that the functions differ by a constant on the interval.

15. (b) $\tan x$ is not continuous on $[0, \pi]$. 25. $f(x) = xe^x - e^x + 2$

35. (b) $f(x) = \sin x$, $g(x) = \cos x$

37.

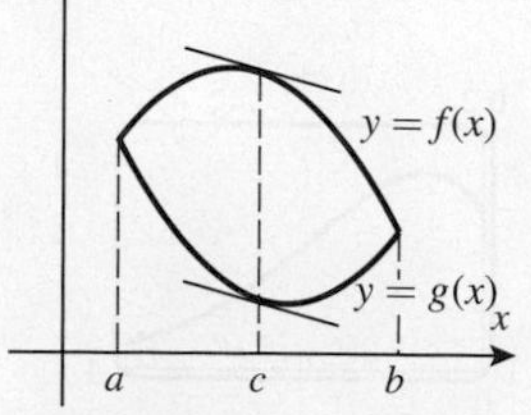


41. $a = 6, b = -3$

## ▶ Chapter 4 Review Exercises (Page 247)

1. (a) $f(x_1) < f(x_2)$; $f(x_1) > f(x_2)$; $f(x_1) = f(x_2)$
   (b) $f' > 0$; $f' < 0$; $f' = 0$

3. (a) $\left[\frac{5}{2}, +\infty\right)$ (b) $\left(-\infty, \frac{5}{2}\right]$ (c) $(-\infty, +\infty)$ (d) none (e) none

5. (a) $[0, +\infty)$ (b) $(-\infty, 0]$ (c) $(-\sqrt{2/3}, \sqrt{2/3})$
   (d) $(-\infty, -\sqrt{2/3}), (\sqrt{2/3}, +\infty)$ (e) $-\sqrt{2/3}, \sqrt{2/3}$

7. (a) $[-1, +\infty)$ (b) $(-\infty, -1]$ (c) $(-\infty, 0), (2, +\infty)$
   (d) $(0, 2)$ (e) $0, 2$

9. (a) $(-\infty, 0]$ (b) $[0, +\infty)$ (c) $(-\infty, -1/\sqrt{2}), (1/\sqrt{2}, +\infty)$
   (d) $(-1/\sqrt{2}, 1/\sqrt{2})$ (e) $\pm 1/\sqrt{2}$

11. increasing on $[\pi, 2\pi]$;
    decreasing on $[0, \pi]$;
    concave up on $(\pi/2, 3\pi/2)$;
    concave down on $(0, \pi/2), (3\pi/2, 2\pi)$;
    inflection points: $(\pi/2, 0), (3\pi/2, 0)$

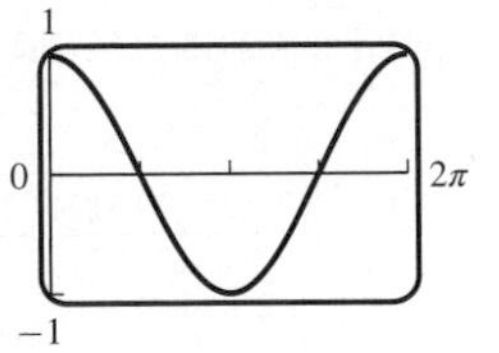


13. increasing on $[0, \pi/4], [3\pi/4, \pi]$;
    decreasing on $[\pi/4, 3\pi/4]$;
    concave up on $(\pi/2, \pi)$;
    concave down on $(0, \pi/2)$;
    inflection point: $(\pi/2, 0)$

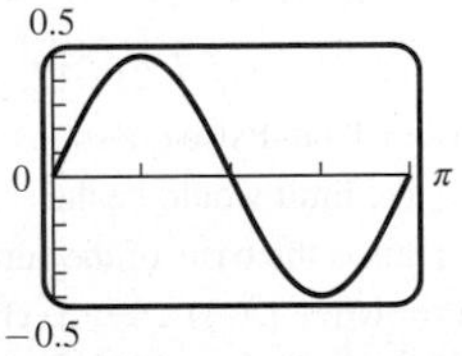


15. (a) (b) (c)

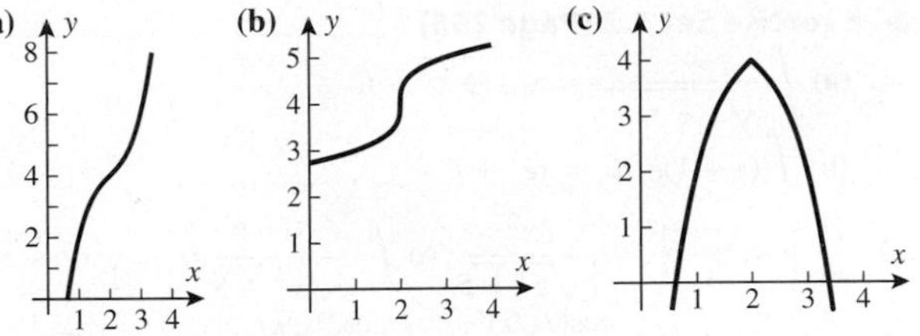


17. $-\dfrac{b}{2a} \le 0$ 19. $x = -1$ 21. (a) at an inflection point

25. (a) $x = \pm\sqrt{2}$ (stationary points) (b) $x = 0$ (stationary point)

27. (a) relative max at $x = 1$, relative min at $x = 7$, neither at $x = 0$
    (b) relative max at $x = \pi/2, 3\pi/2$; relative min at $x = 7\pi/6, 11\pi/6$
    (c) relative max at $x = 5$

29. $\lim_{x\to-\infty} f(x) = +\infty$, $\lim_{x\to+\infty} f(x) = +\infty$;
    relative min at $x = 0$;
    points of inflection at $x = \frac{1}{2}, 1$;
    no asymptotes

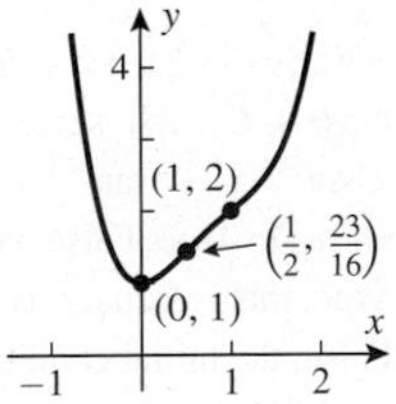


31. $\lim_{x\to\pm\infty} f(x)$ does not exist; critical point at $x = 0$; relative min at $x = 0$; point of inflection when $1 + 4x^2 \tan(x^2 + 1) = 0$; vertical asymptotes at $x = \pm\sqrt{\pi\left(n + \frac{1}{2}\right) - 1}$, $n = 0, 1, 2, \ldots$

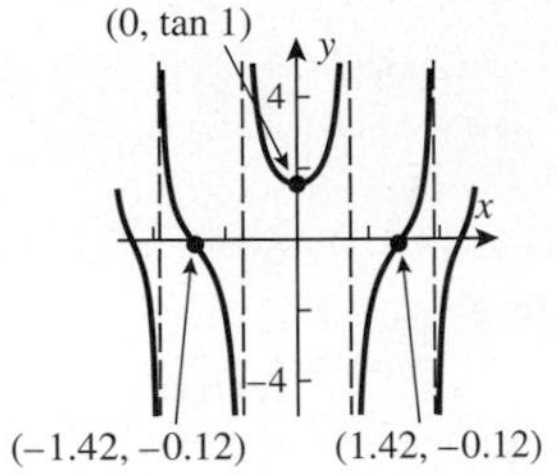


33. critical points at $x = -5, 0$; relative max at $x = -5$, relative min at $x = 0$; points of inflection at $x \approx -7.26, -1.44, 1.20$; horizontal asymptote $y = 1$ for $x \to \pm\infty$

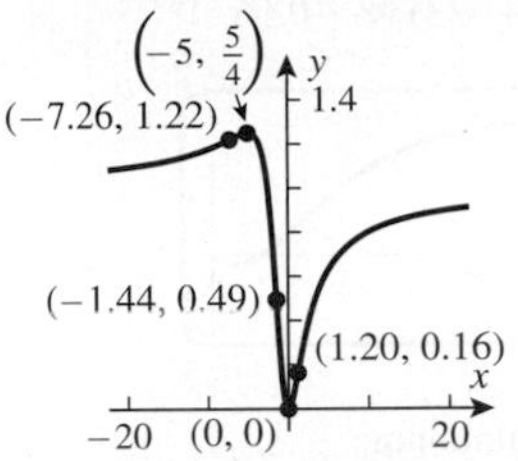


35. $\lim_{x\to-\infty} f(x) = +\infty$, $\lim_{x\to+\infty} f(x) = -\infty$;
    critical point at $x = 0$;
    no extrema;
    inflection point at $x = 0$
    ($f$ changes concavity);
    no asymptotes

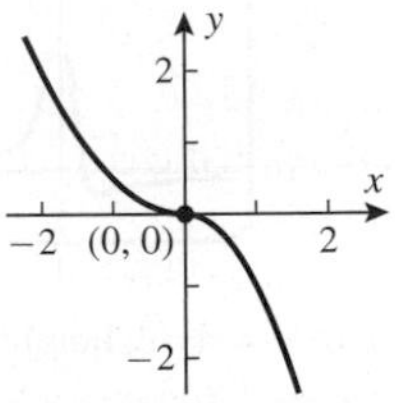


37. no relative extrema 39. relative min of 0 at $x = 0$

41. relative min of 0 at $x = 0$ 43. relative min of 0 at $x = 0$

45. (a)

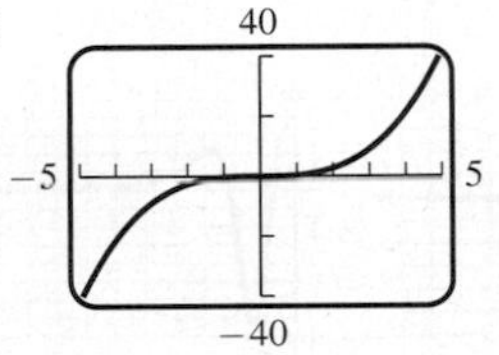


(b) relative max at $x = -\frac{1}{20}$; relative min at $x = \frac{1}{20}$

(c) The finer details can be seen when graphing over a much smaller $x$-window.

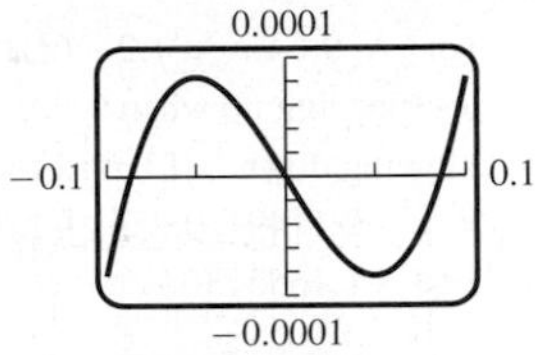


47. (a)

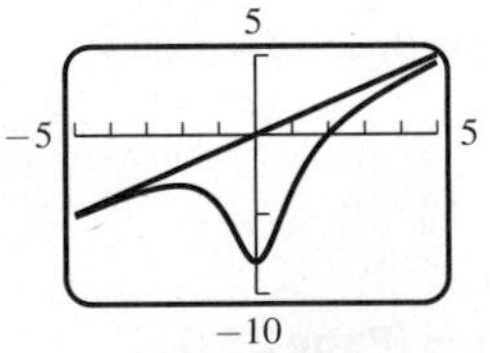


49. $f(x) = \dfrac{x^2 + x - 7}{3x^2 + x - 1}, x \neq \dfrac{1}{2}$

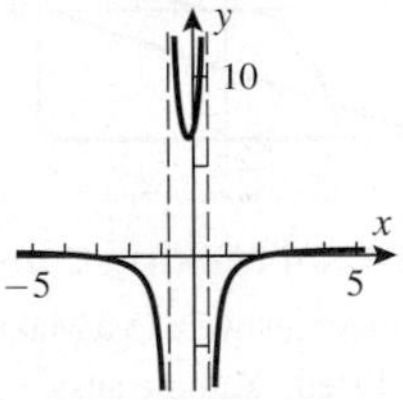


horizontal asymptote $y = 1/3$
vertical asymptotes at
$x = (-1 \pm \sqrt{13})/6$

53. (a) true (b) false

55. (a) no max; min $= -13/4$ at $x = 3/2$ (b) no max or min
    (c) no max; min $m = e^2/4$ at $x = 2$
    (d) no max; min $m = e^{-1/e}$ at $x = 1/e$

57. (a) minimum value 0 for $x = \pm 1$; no maximum (b) max $= 1/2$ at $x = 1$; min $= 0$ at $x = 0$

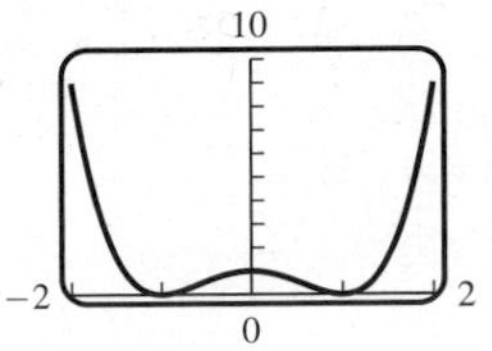


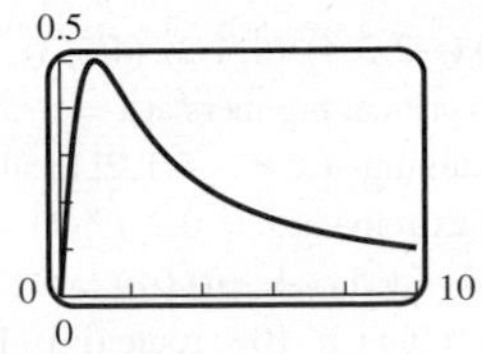

**(c)** maximum value 2 at $x = 0$; minimum value $\sqrt{3}$ at $x = \pi/6$

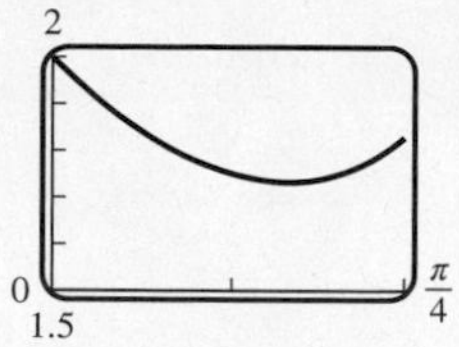


**(d)** maximum value $f(-2-\sqrt{3}) \approx 0.84$; minimum value $f(-2+\sqrt{3}) \approx -0.06$

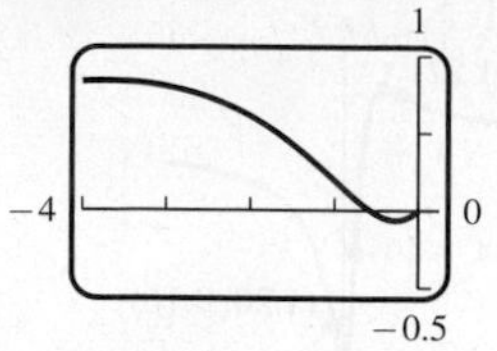


**59.** **(a)**

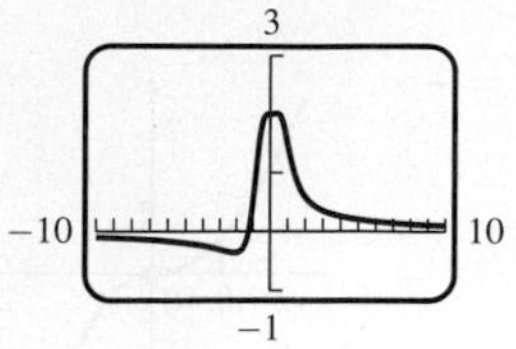


**(b)** minimum: $(-2.111985, -0.355116)$; maximum: $(0.372591, 2.012931)$

**61.** width $= 4\sqrt{2}$, height $= 3\sqrt{2}$ **63.** 2 in square

**65.** **(a)** yes **(b)** yes

**67.** **(a)** $v = -2\dfrac{t(t^4+2t^2-1)}{(t^4+1)^2}$, $a = 2\dfrac{3t^8+10t^6-12t^4-6t^2+1}{(t^4+1)^3}$

**(b)**

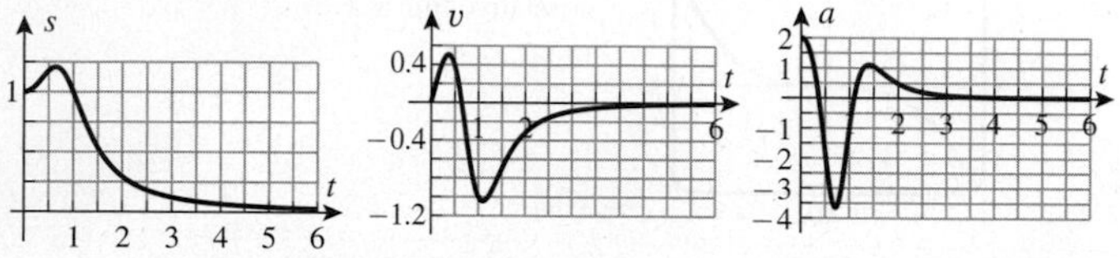


**(c)** $t \approx 0.64, s \approx 1.2$ **(d)** $0 \le t \le 0.64$

**(e)** speeding up when $0 \le t < 0.36$ and $0.64 < t < 1.1$, otherwise slowing down **(f)** maximum speed $\approx 1.05$ when $t \approx 1.10$

**69.** $x \approx -2.11491, 0.25410, 1.86081$

**71.** $x \approx -1.165373043$

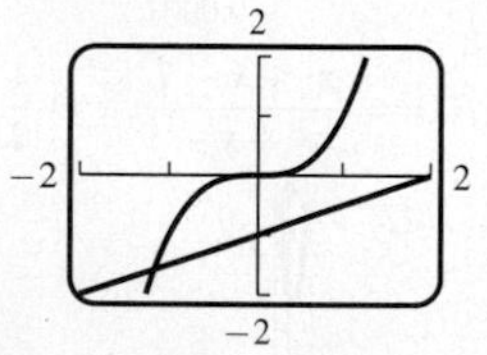


**73.** $249 \times 10^6$ km

**75.** **(a)** yes, $c = 0$ **(b)** no **(c)** yes, $c = \sqrt{\pi/2}$

**77.** use Rolle's Theorem

## ▶ Chapter 4 Making Connections (Page 251)

Where correct answers to a Making Connections exercise may vary, no answer is listed. Sample answers for these questions are available on the Book Companion Site.

**1.** **(a)** no zeros **(b)** one **(c)** $\lim_{x\to+\infty} g'(x) = 0$

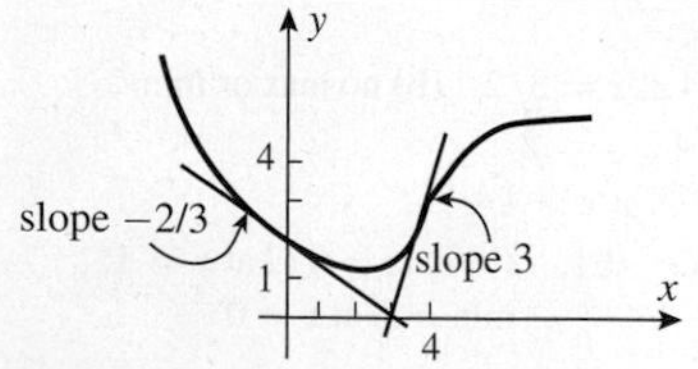


**2.** **(a)** $(-2.2, 4), (2, 1.2), (4.2, 3)$

**(b)** critical numbers at $x = -5.1, -2, 0.2, 2$; local min at $x = -5.1, 2$; local max at $x = -2$; no extrema at $x = 0.2$; $f''(1) \approx -1.2$

**3.** $x = -4, 5$ **4.** **(d)** $f(c) = 0$

**6.** **(a)** route (i): 10 s; route (iv): 10 s

**(b)** $2 \le x \le 5$; $\dfrac{4\sqrt{10}}{2.1} + \dfrac{5}{0.7} \approx 13.166$ s

**(c)** $0 \le x \le 2$; 10 s

**(d)** route (i) or (iv); 10 s

## ▶ Exercise Set 5.1 (Page 257)

**1.**

| $n$ | 2 | 5 | 10 | 50 | 100 |
|---|---|---|---|---|---|
| $A_n$ | 0.853553 | 0.749739 | 0.710509 | 0.676095 | 0.671463 |

**3.**

| $n$ | 2 | 5 | 10 | 50 | 100 |
|---|---|---|---|---|---|
| $A_n$ | 1.57080 | 1.93376 | 1.98352 | 1.99935 | 1.99984 |

**5.**

| $n$ | 2 | 5 | 10 | 50 | 100 |
|---|---|---|---|---|---|
| $A_n$ | 0.583333 | 0.645635 | 0.668771 | 0.688172 | 0.690653 |

**7.**

| $n$ | 2 | 5 | 10 | 50 | 100 |
|---|---|---|---|---|---|
| $A_n$ | 0.433013 | 0.659262 | 0.726130 | 0.774567 | 0.780106 |

**9.**

| $n$ | 2 | 5 | 10 | 50 | 100 |
|---|---|---|---|---|---|
| $A_n$ | 3.71828 | 2.85174 | 2.59327 | 2.39772 | 2.37398 |

**11.**

| $n$ | 2 | 5 | 10 | 50 | 100 |
|---|---|---|---|---|---|
| $A_n$ | 1.04720 | 0.75089 | 0.65781 | 0.58730 | 0.57894 |

**13.** $3(x-1)$ **15.** $x(x+2)$ **17.** $(x+3)(x-1)$

Responses to True–False questions may be abridged to save space.

**19.** False; the limit would be the area of the circle $4\pi$.

**21.** True; this is the basis of the antiderivative method.

**23.** area $= A(6) - A(3)$ **27.** $f(x) = 2x$; $a = 2$

## ▶ Exercise Set 5.2 (Page 265)

**1.** **(a)** $\displaystyle\int \frac{x}{\sqrt{1+x^2}}\,dx = \sqrt{1+x^2} + C$

**(b)** $\displaystyle\int (x+1)e^x\,dx = xe^x + C$

**5.** $\dfrac{d}{dx}\left[\sqrt{x^3+5}\right] = \dfrac{3x^2}{2\sqrt{x^3+5}}$, so $\displaystyle\int \frac{3x^2}{2\sqrt{x^3+5}}\,dx = \sqrt{x^3+5} + C.$

**7.** $\dfrac{d}{dx}[\sin(2\sqrt{x})] = \dfrac{\cos(2\sqrt{x})}{\sqrt{x}}$, so $\displaystyle\int \frac{\cos(2\sqrt{x})}{\sqrt{x}}\,dx = \sin(2\sqrt{x}) + C.$

**9.** **(a)** $(x^9/9) + C$ **(b)** $\frac{7}{12}x^{12/7} + C$ **(c)** $\frac{2}{9}x^{9/2} + C$

**11.** $\dfrac{5}{2}x^2 - \dfrac{1}{6x^4} + C$ **13.** $-\dfrac{1}{2}x^{-2} - \dfrac{12}{5}x^{5/4} + \dfrac{8}{3}x^3 + C$

**15.** $(x^2/2) + (x^5/5) + C$ **17.** $3x^{4/3} - \frac{12}{7}x^{7/3} + \frac{3}{10}x^{10/3} + C$

**19.** $\dfrac{x^2}{2} - \dfrac{2}{x} + \dfrac{1}{3x^3} + C$ **21.** $2\ln|x| + 3e^x + C$

**23.** $-3\cos x - 2\tan x + C$ **25.** $\tan x + \sec x + C$

**27.** $\tan\theta + C$ **29.** $\sec x + C$ **31.** $\theta - \cos\theta + C$

**33.** $\frac{1}{2}\sin^{-1}x - 3\tan^{-1}x + C$ **35.** $\tan x - \sec x + C$

Responses to True–False questions may be abridged to save space.

**37.** True; this is Equations (1) and (2).

**39.** False; the initial condition is not satisfied since $y(0) = 2$.

**41.**

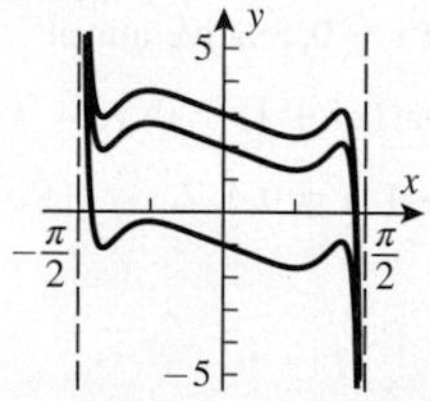


**43.** **(a)** $y(x) = \frac{3}{4}x^{4/3} + \frac{5}{4}$

**(b)** $y = -\cos t + t + 1 - \pi/3$

**(c)** $y(x) = \frac{2}{3}x^{3/2} + 2x^{1/2} - \frac{8}{3}$

**45.** **(a)** $y = 4e^x - 3$ **(b)** $y = \ln|t| + 5$

**47.** $s(t) = 16t^2 + 20$ **49.** $s(t) = 2t^{3/2} - 15$

**51.** $f(x) = \frac{4}{15}x^{5/2} + C_1x + C_2$ **53.** $y = x^2 + x - 6$

**55.** $f(x) = \cos x + 1$ **57.** $y = x^3 - 6x + 7$

**59.** **(a)**

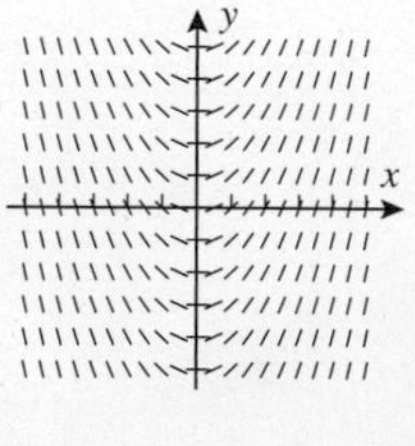


**(b)**

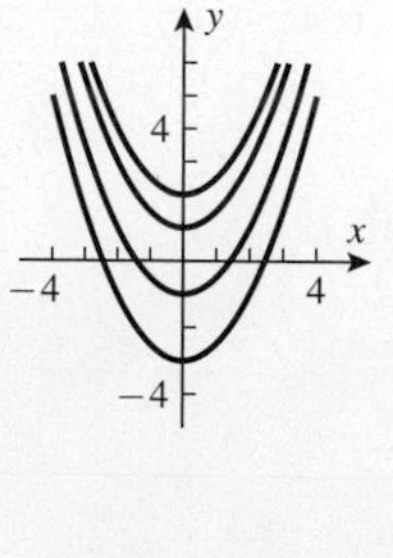


**(c)** $f(x) = \dfrac{x^2}{2} - 1$

61. **(b)**

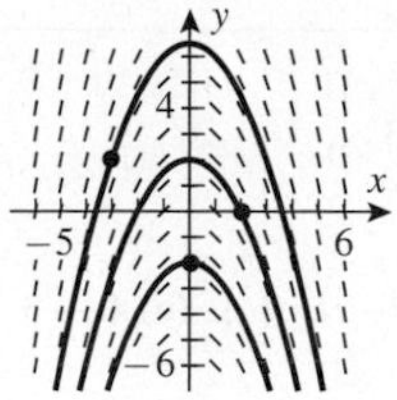


63. **(c)**

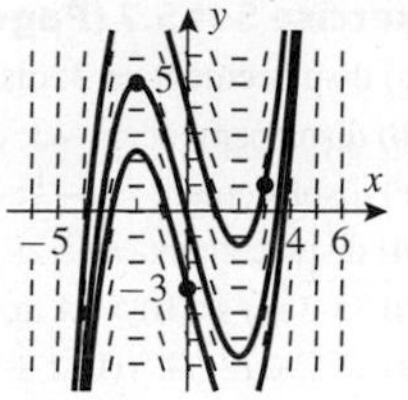


65. **(b)** $\pi/2$ 67. $\tan x - x + C$
69. **(a)** $\frac{1}{2}(x - \sin x) + C$ **(b)** $\frac{1}{2}(x + \sin x) + C$
71. $v = \dfrac{1087}{\sqrt{273}} T^{1/2}$ ft/s 73. $T = 1.2x + 25$

## ▶ Exercise Set 5.3 (Page 273)

1. **(a)** $\dfrac{(x^2+1)^{24}}{24} + C$ **(b)** $-\dfrac{\cos^4 x}{4} + C$
3. **(a)** $\frac{1}{4}\tan(4x+1) + C$ **(b)** $\frac{1}{6}(1 + 2y^2)^{3/2} + C$
5. **(a)** $-\frac{1}{2}\cot^2 x + C$ **(b)** $\frac{1}{10}(1 + \sin t)^{10} + C$
7. **(a)** $\frac{2}{7}(1+x)^{7/2} - \frac{4}{5}(1+x)^{5/2} + \frac{2}{3}(1+x)^{3/2} + C$
**(b)** $-\cot(\sin x) + C$
9. **(a)** $\ln|\ln x| + C$ **(b)** $-\frac{1}{5}e^{-5x} + C$
11. **(a)** $\frac{1}{3}\tan^{-1}(x^3) + C$ **(b)** $\sin^{-1}(\ln x) + C$
15. $\frac{1}{40}(4x-3)^{10} + C$ 17. $-\frac{1}{7}\cos 7x + C$ 19. $\frac{1}{4}\sec 4x + C$
21. $\frac{1}{2}e^{2x} + C$ 23. $\frac{1}{2}\sin^{-1}(2x) + C$ 25. $\frac{1}{21}(7t^2+12)^{3/2} + C$
27. $\dfrac{3}{2(1-2x)^2} + C$ 29. $-\dfrac{1}{40(5x^4+2)^2} + C$ 31. $e^{\sin x} + C$
33. $-\frac{1}{6}e^{-2x^3} + C$ 35. $\tan^{-1} e^x + C$ 37. $\frac{1}{5}\cos(5/x) + C$
39. $-\frac{1}{15}\cos^5 3t + C$ 41. $\frac{1}{2}\tan(x^2) + C$ 43. $-\frac{1}{6}(2 - \sin 4\theta)^{3/2} + C$
45. $\sin^{-1}(\tan x) + C$ 47. $\frac{1}{6}\sec^3 2x + C$ 49. $-e^{-x} + C$
51. $-e^{-2\sqrt{x}} + C$ 53. $\frac{1}{6}(2y+1)^{3/2} - \frac{1}{2}(2y+1)^{1/2} + C$
55. $-\frac{1}{2}\cos 2\theta + \frac{1}{6}\cos^3 2\theta + C$ 57. $t + \ln|t| + C$
59. $\int [\ln(e^x) + \ln(e^{-x})]\,dx = C$
61. **(a)** $\sin^{-1}\left(\frac{1}{3}x\right) + C$ **(b)** $\frac{1}{\sqrt{5}}\tan^{-1}\left(\frac{x}{\sqrt{5}}\right) + C$
**(c)** $\dfrac{1}{\sqrt{\pi}}\sec^{-1}\left(\dfrac{x}{\sqrt{\pi}}\right) + C$
63. $\dfrac{1}{b}\dfrac{(a+bx)^{n+1}}{n+1} + C$ 65. $\dfrac{1}{b(n+1)}\sin^{n+1}(a+bx) + C$
67. **(a)** $\frac{1}{2}\sin^2 x + C_1$; $-\frac{1}{2}\cos^2 x + C_2$ **(b)** They differ by a constant.
69. $\frac{2}{15}(5x+1)^{3/2} - \frac{158}{15}$ 71. $y = -\frac{1}{2}e^{2t} + \frac{13}{2}$
73. **(a)** $\sqrt{x^2+1} + C$ 75. $f(x) = \frac{2}{9}(3x+1)^{3/2} + \frac{7}{9}$
**(b)** 77. 1280

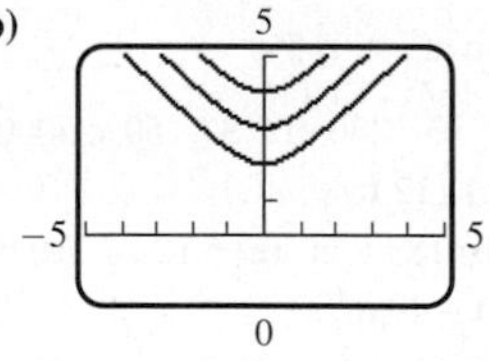


## ▶ Exercise Set 5.4 (Page 283)

1. **(a)** 36 **(b)** 55 **(c)** 40 **(d)** 6 **(e)** 11 **(f)** 0 3. $\sum_{k=1}^{10} k$
5. $\sum_{k=1}^{10} 2k$ 7. $\sum_{k=1}^{6} (-1)^{k+1}(2k-1)$ 9. **(a)** $\sum_{k=1}^{50} 2k$ **(b)** $\sum_{k=1}^{50} (2k-1)$
11. 5050 13. 2870 15. 214,365 17. $\frac{3}{2}(n+1)$ 19. $\frac{1}{4}(n-1)^2$

Responses to True–False questions may be abridged to save space.

21. True; by parts (*a*) and (*c*) of Theorem 5.4.2.
23. False; consider $[a, b] = [-1, 0]$.
25. **(a)** $\left(2 + \frac{3}{n}\right)^4 \cdot \frac{3}{n}, \left(2 + \frac{6}{n}\right)^4 \cdot \frac{3}{n}, \left(2 + \frac{9}{n}\right)^4 \cdot \frac{3}{n}$,
$\left(2 + \frac{3(n-1)}{n}\right)^4 \cdot \frac{3}{n}, (2+3)^4 \cdot \frac{3}{n}$ **(b)** $\sum_{k=0}^{n-1} \left(2 + k \cdot \frac{3}{n}\right)^4 \frac{3}{n}$

27. **(a)** 46 **(b)** 52 **(c)** 58 29. **(a)** $\frac{\pi}{4}$ **(b)** 0 **(c)** $-\frac{\pi}{4}$
31. **(a)** 0.7188, 0.7058, 0.6982 **(b)** 0.6928, 0.6931, 0.6931
**(c)** 0.6688, 0.6808, 0.6882
33. **(a)** 4.8841, 5.1156, 5.2488 **(b)** 5.3471, 5.3384, 5.3346
**(c)** 5.6841, 5.5156, 5.4088
35. $\frac{15}{4}$ 37. 18 39. 320 41. $\frac{15}{4}$ 43. 18 45. 16 47. $\frac{1}{3}$ 49. 0
51. $\frac{2}{3}$ 53. **(b)** $\frac{1}{4}(b^4 - a^4)$
55. $\dfrac{n^2+2n}{4}$ if $n$ is even; $\dfrac{(n+1)^2}{4}$ if $n$ is odd 57. $3^{17} - 3^4$ 59. $-\frac{399}{400}$
61. **(b)** $\frac{1}{2}$ 65. **(a)** yes **(b)** yes

## ▶ Exercise Set 5.5 (Page 292)

1. **(a)** $\frac{71}{6}$ **(b)** 2 3. **(a)** $-\frac{117}{16}$ **(b)** 3 5. $\int_{-1}^{2} x^2\,dx$
7. $\int_{-3}^{3} 4x(1-3x)\,dx$
9. **(a)** $\lim_{\max \Delta x_k \to 0} \sum_{k=1}^{n} 2x_k^* \Delta x_k$; $a = 1, b = 2$
**(b)** $\lim_{\max \Delta x_k \to 0} \sum_{k=1}^{n} \dfrac{x_k^*}{x_k^* + 1}\Delta x_k$; $a = 0, b = 1$
13. **(a)** $A = \frac{9}{2}$ **(b)** $-A = -\frac{3}{2}$

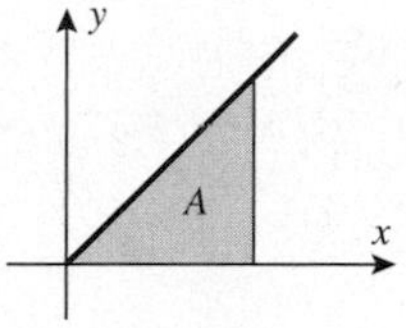


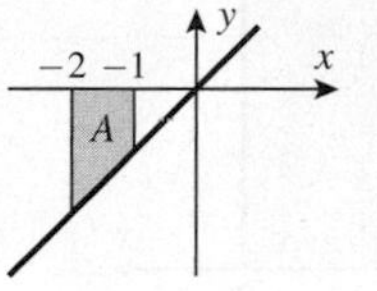


**(c)** $-A_1 + A_2 = \frac{15}{2}$ **(d)** $-A_1 + A_2 = 0$

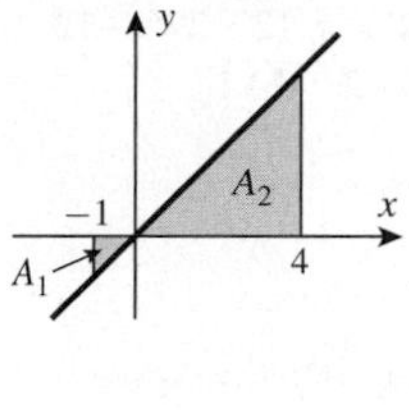


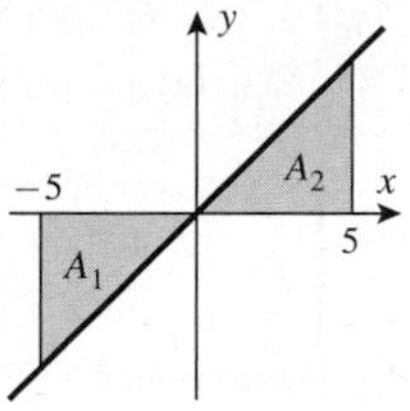


15. **(a)** $A = 10$ **(b)** $A_1 - A_2 = 0$ by symmetry

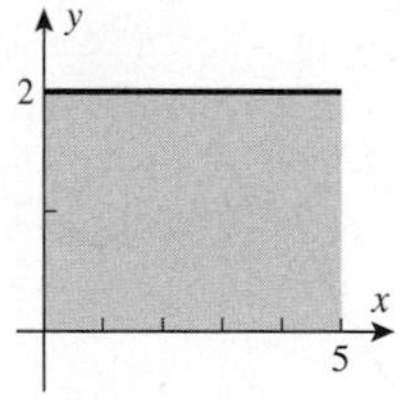


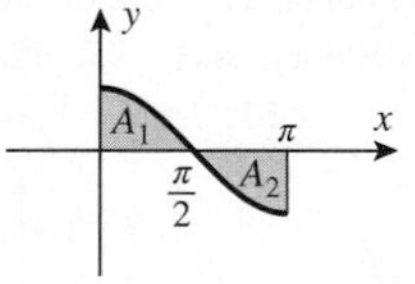


**(c)** $A_1 + A_2 = \frac{13}{2}$ **(d)** $\pi/2$

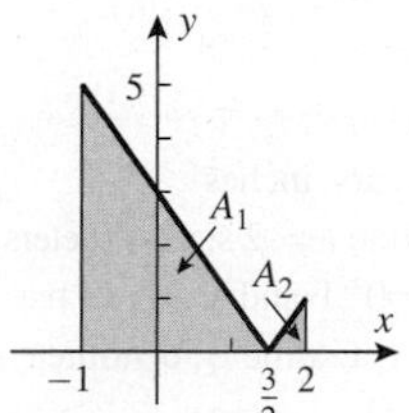


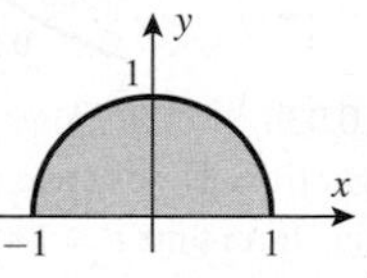


17. **(a)** 2 **(b)** 4 **(c)** 10 **(d)** 10
19. **(a)** 0.8 **(b)** −2.6 **(c)** −1.8 **(d)** −0.3
21. −1 23. 3 25. −4 27. $(1 + \pi)/2$

Responses to True–False questions may be abridged to save space.

29. False; see Theorem 5.5.8(*a*).

31. False; consider $f(x) = x - 2$ on $[0, 3]$.

33. **(a)** negative **(b)** positive 37. $\frac{25}{2}\pi$ 39. $\frac{5}{2}$

45. **(a)** integrable **(b)** integrable **(c)** not integrable **(d)** integrable

## ▶ Exercise Set 5.6 (Page 303)

1. **(a)** $\int_0^2 (2 - x)\,dx = 2$ **(b)** $\int_{-1}^{1} 2\,dx = 4$ **(c)** $\int_1^3 (x + 1)\,dx = 6$

3. **(a)** $x^* = f(x^*) = 1$ **(b)** $x^*$ is any point in $[-1, 1], f(x^*) = 2$

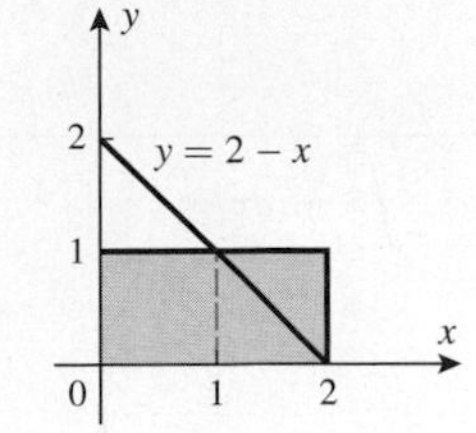


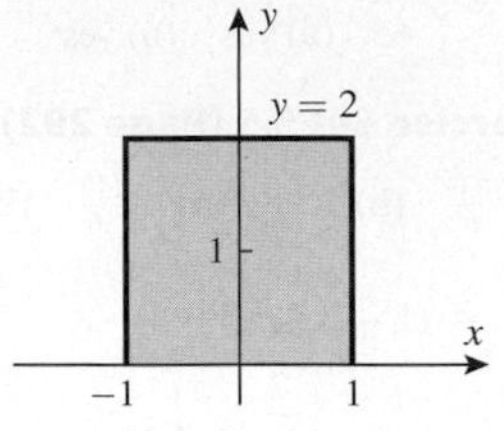


**(c)** $x^* = 2, f(x^*) = 3$

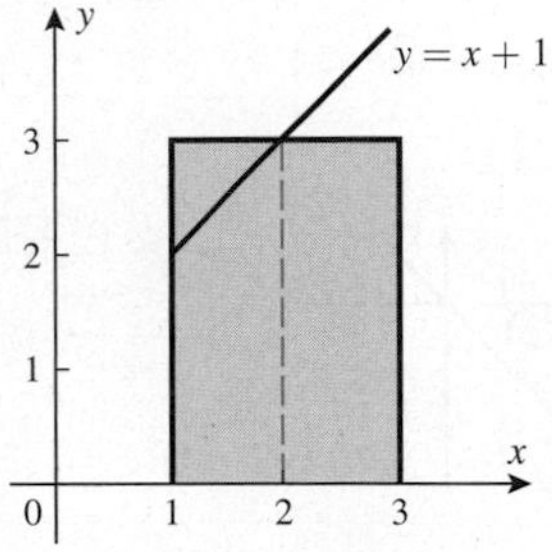


5. $\frac{65}{4}$ 7. 14 9. $\frac{3}{2}$ 11. **(a)** $\frac{4}{3}$ **(b)** $-7$ 13. 48 15. 3 17. $\frac{844}{5}$

19. 0 21. $\sqrt{2}$ 23. $5e^3 - 10$ 25. $\pi/4$ 27. $\pi/12$ 29. $-12$

31. **(a)** $5/2$ **(b)** $2 - \frac{\sqrt{2}}{2}$ 33. **(a)** $e + (1/e) - 2$ **(b)** 1

35. **(a)** $\frac{17}{6}$ **(b)** $F(x) = \begin{cases} \dfrac{x^2}{2}, & x \le 1 \\ \dfrac{x^3}{3} + \dfrac{1}{6}, & x > 1 \end{cases}$

Responses to True–False questions may be abridged to save space.

37. False; since $|x|$ is continuous, it has an antiderivative.

39. True; by the Fundamental Theorem of Calculus.

41. 0.6659; $\frac{2}{3}$ 43. 3.1060; 2 tan 1 45. 12 47. $\frac{9}{2}$

49. area $= 1$ 51. area $= e + e^{-1} - 2$

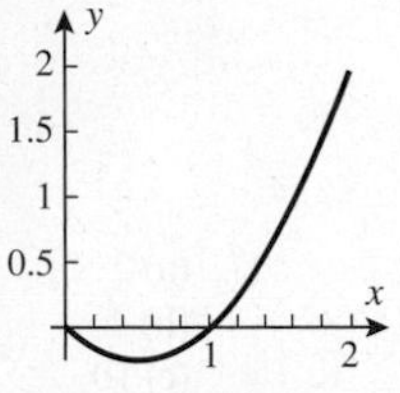

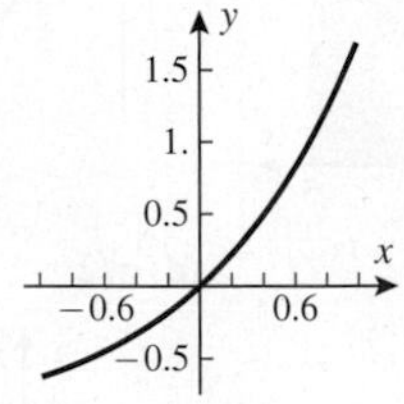

53. **(b)** degree mode, 0.93

55. **(a)** change in height from age 0 to age 10 years; inches
**(b)** change in radius from time $t = 1$ s to time $t = 2$ s; centimeters
**(c)** difference between speed of sound at 100° F and at 32° F; feet per second **(d)** change in position from time $t_1$ to time $t_2$; centimeters

57. **(a)** $3x^2 - 3$ 59. **(a)** $\sin(x^2)$ **(b)** $e^{\sqrt{x}}$ 61. $-x \sec x$

63. **(a)** 0 **(b)** 5 **(c)** $\frac{4}{5}$

65. **(a)** $x = 3$ **(b)** increasing on $[3, +\infty)$, decreasing on $(-\infty, 3]$
**(c)** concave up on $(-1, 7)$, concave down on $(-\infty, -1)$ and $(7, +\infty)$

67. **(a)** $(-\pi/2, \pi/2)$ **(b)** $x = 0$

69. **(a)** 120 gal **(b)** 420 gal **(c)** 2076.36 gal 71. 14 students 73. 1

## ▶ Exercise Set 5.7 (Page 312)

1. **(a)** displacement $= 3$; distance $= 3$
**(b)** displacement $= -3$; distance $= 3$
**(c)** displacement $= -\frac{1}{2}$; distance $= \frac{3}{2}$
**(d)** displacement $= \frac{3}{2}$; distance $= 2$

3. **(a)** 35.3 m/s **(b)** 51.4 m/s 5. **(a)** $t^3 - t^2 + 1$ **(b)** $4t + 3 - \frac{1}{3}\sin 3t$

7. **(a)** $\frac{3}{2}t^2 + t - 4$ **(b)** $t + 1 - \ln t$

9. **(a)** displacement $= 1$ m; distance $= 1$ m
**(b)** displacement $= -1$ m; distance $= 3$ m

11. **(a)** displacement $= \frac{9}{4}$ m; distance $= \frac{11}{4}$ m
**(b)** displacement $= 2\sqrt{3} - 6$ m; distance $= 6 - 2\sqrt{3}$ m

13. 4, 13/3 15. 296/27, 296/27

17. **(a)** $s = 2/\pi, v = 1, |v| = 1, a = 0$
**(b)** $s = \frac{1}{2}, v = -\frac{3}{2}, |v| = \frac{3}{2}, a = -3$ 19. $t \approx 1.27$ s

21.

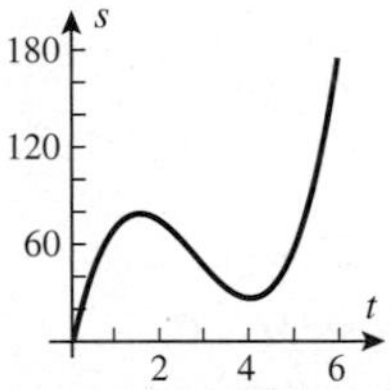

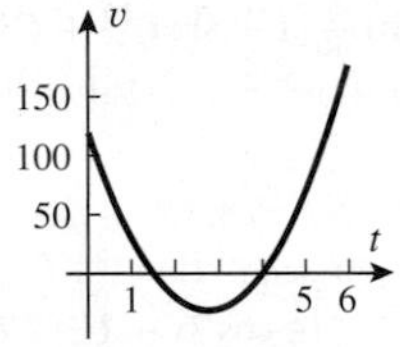

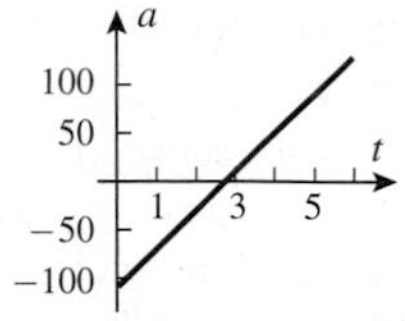

Responses to True–False questions may be abridged to save space.

23. True; if $a(t) = a_0$, then $v(t) = a_0 t + v_0$.

25. False; consider $v(t) = \sin t$ on $[0, 2\pi]$.

27. **(a)**

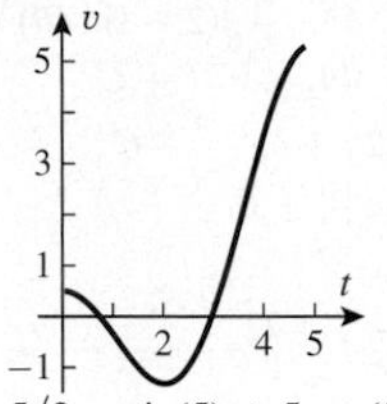

**(b)** $5/2 - \sin(5) + 5\cos(5)$

29. **(a)**

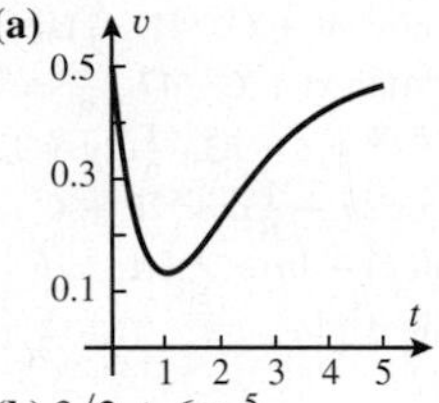

**(b)** $3/2 + 6e^{-5}$

31. **(a)**

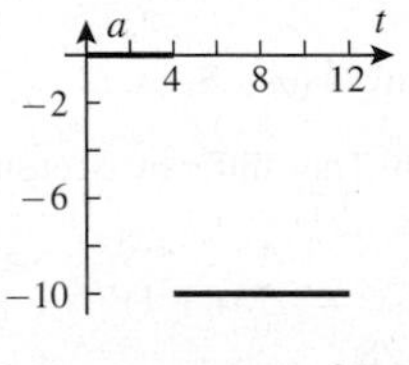

**(b)**

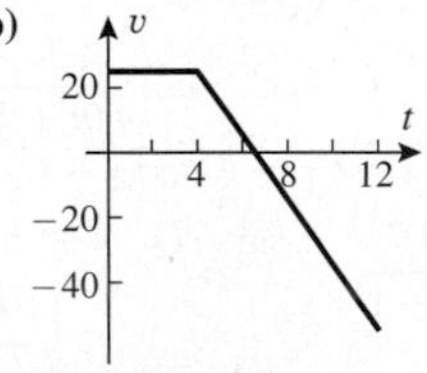

**(c)** 120 cm, −20 cm **(d)** 131.25 cm at $t = 6.5$ s

33. **(a)** $-\frac{121}{5}$ ft/s$^2$ **(b)** $\frac{70}{33}$ s **(c)** $\frac{60}{11}$ s 35. 280 m 37. 50 s, 5000 ft

39. **(a)** 16 ft/s, −48 ft/s **(b)** 196 ft **(c)** 112 ft/s

41. **(a)** 1 s **(b)** $\frac{1}{2}$ s 43. **(a)** 6.122 s **(b)** 183.7 m **(c)** 6.122 s **(d)** 60 m/s

45. **(a)** 5 s **(b)** 272.5 m **(c)** 10 s **(d)** −49 m/s
**(e)** 12.46 s **(f)** 73.1 m/s

## ▶ Exercise Set 5.8 (Page 317)

1. **(a)** 4 **(b)** 2 **(c)**

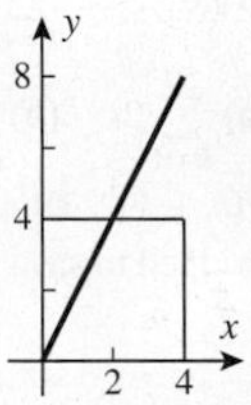

3. 6

5. $2/\pi$

7. $\dfrac{1}{e - 1}$

9. $\dfrac{\pi}{12(\sqrt{3} - 1)}$

11. $\dfrac{1 - e^{-8}}{8}$ 13. **(a)** 5.28 **(b)** 4.305 **(c)** 4 15. **(a)** $-\frac{1}{6}$ **(b)** $\frac{1}{2}$

Responses to True–False questions may be abridged to save space.

19. False; let $g(x) = \cos x$; $f(x) = 0$ on $[0, 3\pi/2]$.

21. True; see Theorem 5.5.4(*b*).
23. **(a)** $\frac{263}{4}$ **(b)** 31 25. $1404\pi$ lb 27. 97 cars/min
31. 466.8 wolves

## ▶ Exercise Set 5.9 (Page 322)

1. **(a)** $\frac{1}{2}\int_1^5 u^3\,du$ **(b)** $\frac{3}{2}\int_9^{25}\sqrt{u}\,du$ **(c)** $\frac{1}{\pi}\int_{-\pi/2}^{\pi/2}\cos u\,du$
**(d)** $\int_1^2 (u+1)u^5\,du$ 3. **(a)** $\frac{1}{2}\int_{-1}^{1} e^u\,du$ **(b)** $\int_1^2 u\,du$
5. 10 7. 0 9. $\frac{1192}{15}$ 11. $8-(4\sqrt{2})$ 13. $-\frac{1}{48}$ 15. $\ln\frac{21}{13}$
17. $\pi/6$ 19. $25\pi/6$ 21. $\pi/8$ 23. $2/\pi$ m 25. 6 27. $\pi/18$
29. $1/21$ 31. 2 33. $\frac{2}{3}(\sqrt{10}-2\sqrt{2})$ 35. $2(\sqrt{7}-\sqrt{3})$ 37. 1
39. 0 41. $(\sqrt{3}-1)/3$ 43. $\frac{106}{405}$ 45. $(\ln 3)/2$ 47. $\pi/(6\sqrt{3})$
49. $\pi/9$ 51. **(a)** $\frac{23}{4480}$ 53. **(a)** $\frac{5}{3}$ **(b)** $\frac{5}{3}$ **(c)** $-\frac{1}{2}$ 57. Method 2
59. Method 1 61. $\approx$ 48,233,500,000 63. **(a)** 0.45 **(b)** 0.461
65. $(\ln 7)/2$ 67. **(a)** $2/\pi$ 71. **(b)** $\frac{3}{2}$ **(c)** $\pi/4$

## ▶ Exercise Set 5.10 (Page 334)

1. **(a)**
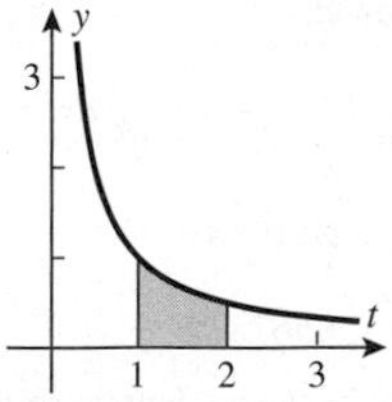


**(b)**
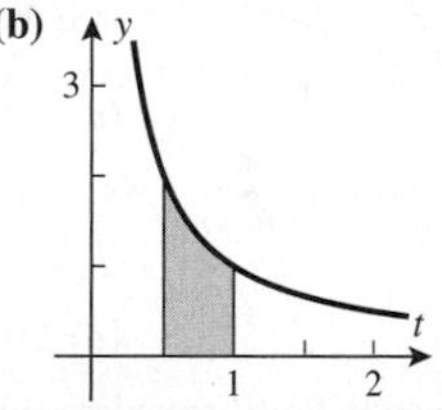


**(c)**
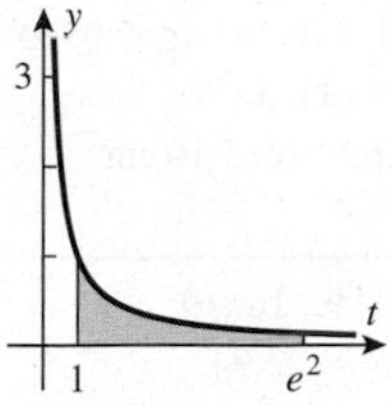


3. **(a)** 7 **(b)** −5 **(c)** −3 **(d)** 6
5. 1.603210678; magnitude of error is < 0.0063
7. **(a)** $x^{-1}, x>0$ **(b)** $x^2, x\neq 0$ **(c)** $-x^2, -\infty<x<+\infty$
**(d)** $-x, -\infty<x<+\infty$ **(e)** $x^3, x>0$ **(f)** $\ln x + x, x>0$
**(g)** $x-\sqrt[3]{x}, -\infty<x<+\infty$ **(h)** $e^x/x, x>0$
9. **(a)** $e^{\pi\ln 3}$ **(b)** $e^{\sqrt{2}\ln 2}$ 11. **(a)** $\sqrt{e}$ **(b)** $e^2$ 13. $x^2-x$
15. **(a)** $3/x$ **(b)** 1 17. **(a)** 0 **(b)** 0 **(c)** 1

Responses to True–False questions may be abridged to save space.

19. True; both equal $-\ln a$.
21. False; the integrand is unbounded on $[-1, e]$ and thus the integrand is undefined.
23. **(a)** $2x^3\sqrt{1+x^2}$ **(b)** $-\frac{2}{3}(x^2+1)^{3/2}+\frac{2}{5}(x^2+1)^{5/2}-\frac{4\sqrt{2}}{15}$
25. **(a)** $-\cos(x^3)$ **(b)** $-\tan^2 x$ 27. $-3\dfrac{3x-1}{9x^2+1}+2x\dfrac{x^2-1}{x^4+1}$
29. **(a)** $3x^2\sin^2(x^3)-2x\sin^2(x^2)$ **(b)** $\dfrac{2}{1-x^2}$
31. **(a)** $F(0)=0, F(3)=0, F(5)=6, F(7)=6, F(10)=3$
**(b)** increasing on $\left[\frac{3}{2},6\right]$ and $\left[\frac{37}{4},10\right]$, decreasing on $\left[0,\frac{3}{2}\right]$ and $\left[6,\frac{37}{4}\right]$
**(c)** maximum $\frac{15}{2}$ at $x=6$, minimum $-\frac{9}{4}$ at $x=\frac{3}{2}$
**(d)**
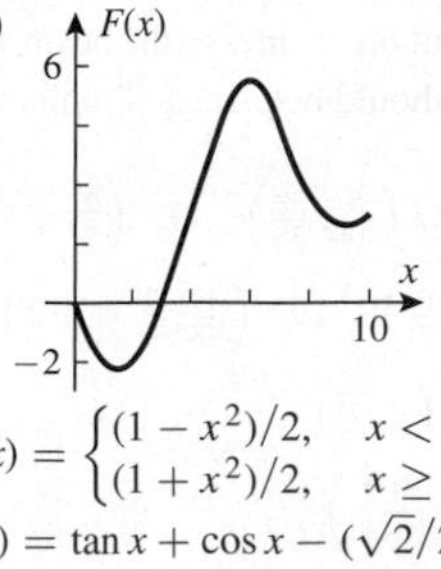


33. $F(x)=\begin{cases}(1-x^2)/2, & x<0\\ (1+x^2)/2, & x\geq 0\end{cases}$ 35. $y(x)=x^2+\ln x+1$
37. $y(x)=\tan x+\cos x-(\sqrt{2}/2)$
39. $P(x)=P_0+\int_0^x r(t)\,dt$ individuals 41. I is the derivative of II.
43. **(a)** $t=3$ **(b)** $t=1, 5$
**(c)** $t=5$ **(d)** $t=3$
**(e)** $F$ is concave up on $\left(0,\frac{1}{2}\right)$ and $(2,4)$, concave down on $\left(\frac{1}{2},2\right)$ and $(4,5)$.
**(f)**
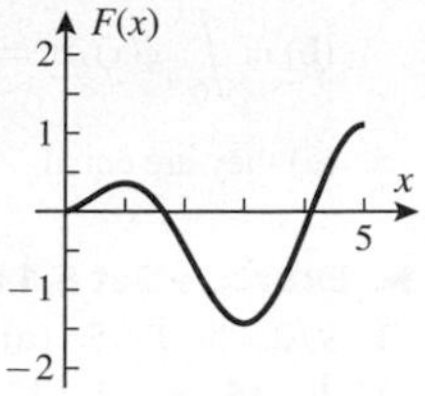


45. **(a)** relative maxima at $x=\pm\sqrt{4k+1}, k=0,1,\ldots$; relative minima at $x=\pm\sqrt{4k-1}, k=1,2,\ldots$
**(b)** $x=\pm\sqrt{2k}, k=1,2,\ldots$, and at $x=0$
47. $f(x)=2e^{2x}, a=\ln 2$ 49. 0.06
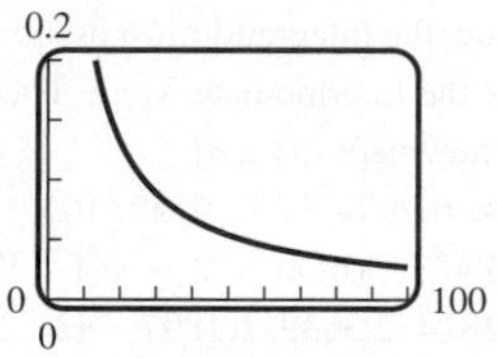


## ▶ Chapter 5 Review Exercises (Page 337)

1. $-\dfrac{1}{4x^2}+\dfrac{8}{3}x^{3/2}+C$ 3. $-4\cos x+2\sin x+C$
5. $3x^{1/3}-5e^x+C$ 7. $\tan^{-1}x+2\sin^{-1}x+C$
9. **(a)** $y(x)=2\sqrt{x}-\frac{2}{3}x^{3/2}-\frac{4}{3}$ **(b)** $y(x)=\sin x-5e^x+5$
**(c)** $y(x)=\frac{5}{4}+\frac{3}{4}x^{4/3}$ **(d)** $y(x)=\frac{1}{2}e^{x^2}-\frac{1}{2}$
13. $\frac{1}{2}\sec^{-1}(x^2-1)+C$ 15. $\frac{1}{3}\sqrt{5+2\sin 3x}+C$
17. $-\dfrac{1}{3a}\dfrac{1}{ax^3+b}+C$
19. **(a)** $\sum_{k=0}^{14}(k+4)(k+1)$ **(b)** $\sum_{k=5}^{19}(k-1)(k-4)$
21. $\frac{32}{3}$ 23. 0.35122, 0.42054, 0.38650
27. **(a)** $\frac{3}{4}$ **(b)** $-\frac{3}{2}$ **(c)** $-\frac{35}{4}$ **(d)** −2 **(e)** not enough information
**(f)** not enough information
29. **(a)** $2+(\pi/2)$ **(b)** $\dfrac{1}{3}(10^{3/2}-1)-\dfrac{9\pi}{4}$ **(c)** $\pi/8$
31. 48 33. $\frac{2}{3}$ 35. $\frac{3}{2}-\sec 1$ 37. $\frac{5}{2}$ 39. $\frac{52}{3}$ 41. $e^3-e$
43. area $=\frac{1}{6}$
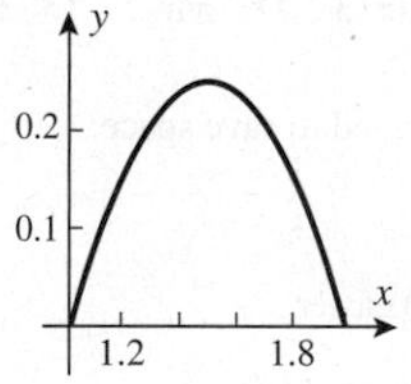


45. $\frac{22}{3}$
47. **(a)** $x^3+1$
49. $e^{x^2}$
51. $|x-1|$
53. $\dfrac{\cos x}{1+\sin^3 x}$
57. **(b)** $\dfrac{\pi}{2}$; $\tan^{-1}x+\tan^{-1}\left(\dfrac{1}{x}\right)=\dfrac{\pi}{2}$
59. **(a)** $F(x)$ is 0 if $x=1$, positive if $x>1$, and negative if $x<1$.
**(b)** $F(x)$ is 0 if $x=-1$, positive if $-1<x\leq 2$, and negative if $-2\leq x<-1$.
61. **(a)** $\frac{4}{3}$ **(b)** $e-1$ 63. $\frac{3}{10}$ 67. $\frac{1}{4}t^4-\frac{2}{3}t^3+t+1$
69. $t^2-3t+7$ 71. 12 m, 20 m 73. $\frac{1}{3}$ m, $\frac{10}{3}-2\sqrt{2}$ m
75. displacement $=-6$ m; distance $=\frac{13}{2}$ m
77. **(a)** 2.2 s **(b)** 387.2 ft 79. $v_0/2$ ft/s 81. $\frac{121}{5}$ 83. $\frac{2}{3}$ 85. 0
87. $2-2/\sqrt{e}$ 89. **(a)** $e^2$ **(b)** $e^{1/3}$

## ▶ Chapter 5 Making Connections (Page 340)

Where correct answers to a Making Connections exercise may vary, no answer is listed. Sample answers for these questions are available on the Book Companion Site.

1. **(b)** $b^2-a^2$ 2. $16/3$ 3. 12

4. (a) the sum for $f$ is $m$ times that for $g$
(b) $m\int_0^1 g(x)\,dx = \int_0^m f(x)\,du$

5. (a) they are equal (b) $\int_2^3 g(x)\,dx = \int_4^9 f(u)\,du$

## ▶ Exercise Set 6.1 (Page 347)

1. $9/2$ 3. 1 5. (a) $4/3$ (b) $4/3$ 7. $49/192$ 9. $1/2$ 11. $\sqrt{2}$
13. $\frac{1}{2}$ 15. $\pi - 1$ 17. 24 19. $37/12$ 21. $4\sqrt{2}$ 23. $\frac{1}{2}$
25. $\ln 2 - \frac{1}{2}$

Responses to True–False questions may be abridged to save space.

27. True; use area Formula (1) with $f(x) = g(x) + c$.
29. True; the integrand must assume both positive and negative values. By the Intermediate-Value Theorem, the integrand must be equal to 0 somewhere in $[a, b]$.
31. $k \approx 0.9973$ 33. $9152/105$ 35. $9/\sqrt[3]{4}$
37. (a) $4/3$ (b) $m = 2 - \sqrt[3]{4}$ 39. 1.180898334
41. 0.4814, 2.3639, 1.1897 43. 2.54270
45. racer 1's lead over racer 2 at time $t = 0$
47. the increase in population from 1960 to 2010 49. $a^2/6$

## ▶ Exercise Set 6.2 (Page 355)

1. $8\pi$ 3. $13\pi/6$ 5. $(1 - \sqrt{2}/2)\pi$ 7. $8\pi$ 9. $32/5$ 11. $256\pi/3$
13. $2048\pi/15$ 15. $4\pi$ 17. $\pi^2/4$ 19. $3/5$ 21. $2\pi$
23. $72\pi/5$ 25. $\frac{\pi}{2}(e^2 - 1)$

Responses to True–False questions may be abridged to save space.

27. False; see the solids associated with Exercises 9 and 10.
29. False; see Example 2 where the cross-sectional area is a linear function of $x$.
31. $4\pi ab^2/3$ 33. $\pi$ 35. $\int_a^b \pi[f(x) - k]^2\,dx$ 37. (b) $40\pi/3$
39. $648\pi/5$ 41. $\pi/2$ 43. $\pi/15$ 45. $40{,}000\pi\,\text{ft}^3$ 47. $1/30$
49. (a) $2\pi/3$ (b) $16/3$ (c) $4\sqrt{3}/3$ 51. 0.710172176 53. $\pi$
57. (b) left $\approx 11.157$; right $\approx 11.771$; $V \approx$ average $= 11.464\ \text{cm}^3$
59. $V = \begin{cases} 3\pi h^2, & 0 \le h < 2 \\ \frac{1}{3}\pi(12h^2 - h^3 - 4), & 2 \le h \le 4 \end{cases}$ 61. $\frac{2}{3}r^3\tan\theta$ 63. $16r^3/3$

## ▶ Exercise Set 6.3 (Page 363)

1. $15\pi/2$ 3. $\pi/3$ 5. $2\pi/5$ 7. $4\pi$ 9. $20\pi/3$ 11. $\pi\ln 2$ 13. $\pi/2$
15. $\pi/5$

Responses to True–False questions may be abridged to save space.

17. True; this is a restatement of Formula (1).
19. True; see Formula (2).
21. $2\pi e^2$ 23. 1.73680 25. (a) $7\pi/30$ (b) easier
27. (a) $\int_0^1 2\pi(1 - x)x\,dx$ (b) $\int_0^1 2\pi(1 + y)(1 - y)\,dy$
29. $7\pi/4$ 31. $\pi r^2 h/3$ 33. $V = \frac{4}{3}\pi(L/2)^3$ 35. $b = 1$

## ▶ Exercise Set 6.4 (Page 367)

1. $L = \sqrt{5}$ 3. $(85\sqrt{85} - 8)/243$ 5. $\frac{1}{27}(80\sqrt{10} - 13\sqrt{13})$ 7. $\frac{17}{6}$

Responses to True–False questions may be abridged to save space.

9. False; $f'$ is undefined at the endpoints $\pm 1$.
11. True; if $f(x) = mx + c$ over $[a, b]$, then $L = \sqrt{1 + m^2}(b - a)$, which is equal to the given sum.
13. $L = \ln(1 + \sqrt{2})$
15. (a)

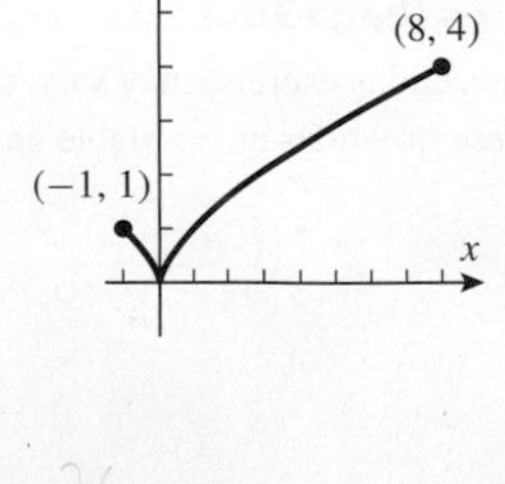


(b) $dy/dx$ does not exist at $x = 0$.
(c) $L = (13\sqrt{13} + 80\sqrt{10} - 16)/27$

17. (a) They are mirror images across the line $y = x$.

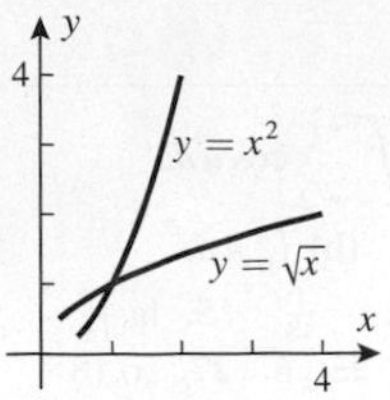


(b) $\int_{1/2}^{2} \sqrt{1 + 4x^2}\,dx$, $\int_{1/4}^{4} \sqrt{1 + \frac{1}{4x}}\,dx$
$x = \sqrt{u}$ transforms the first integral into the second.
(c) $\int_{1/4}^{4} \sqrt{1 + \frac{1}{4y}}\,dy$, $\int_{1/2}^{2} \sqrt{1 + 4y^2}\,dy$
(d) 4.0724, 4.0716
(e) The first: Both are underestimates of the arc length, so the larger one is more accurate.
(f) 4.0724, 4.0662 (g) 4.0729

19. (a) They are mirror images across the line $y = x$.

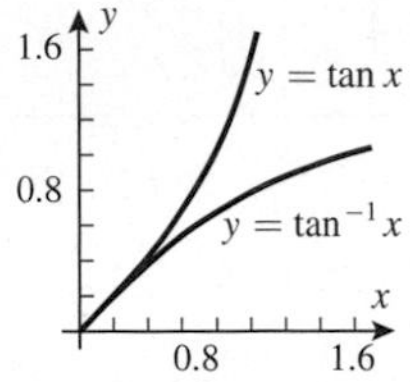


(b) $\int_0^{\pi/3} \sqrt{1 + \sec^4 x}\,dx$,
$\int_0^{\sqrt{3}} \sqrt{1 + \frac{1}{(1 + x^2)^2}}\,dx$,
$x = \tan^{-1} u$ transforms the first integral into the second.
(c) $\int_0^{\sqrt{3}} \sqrt{1 + \frac{1}{(1 + y^2)^2}}\,dy$,
$\int_0^{\pi/3} \sqrt{1 + \sec^4 y}\,dy$
(d) 2.0566, 2.0567
(e) The second: Both are underestimates of the arc length, so the larger one is more accurate. (f) 2.0509, 2.0571 (g) 2.0570

23. 4354 ft 25. 196.31 yards 27. $(2\sqrt{2} - 1)/3$
29. $\pi$ 31. $L = \sqrt{2}(e^{\pi/2} - 1)$ 33. (b) 9.69 (c) 5.16 cm

## ▶ Exercise Set 6.5 (Page 373)

1. $35\pi\sqrt{2}$ 3. $8\pi$ 5. $40\pi\sqrt{82}$ 7. $24\pi$ 9. $16\pi/9$
11. $16{,}911\pi/1024$ 13. $S \approx 14.42$ 15. $S \approx 22.94$

Responses to True–False questions may be abridged to save space.

17. True; use Formula (1) with $r_1 = 0, r_2 = r, l = \sqrt{r^2 + h^2}$.
19. True; the sum telescopes to the surface area of a cylinder.
21. 14.39 23. $S = \int_a^b 2\pi[f(x) + k]\sqrt{1 + [f'(x)]^2}\,dx$
33. $\frac{8}{3}\pi(17\sqrt{17} - 1)$ 35. $\frac{\pi}{24}(17\sqrt{17} - 1)$

## ▶ Exercise Set 6.6 (Page 381)

1. 7.5 ft·lb 3. $d = 7/4$ 5. 100 ft·lb 7. 160 J 9. 20 lb/ft

Responses to True–False questions may be abridged to save space.

11. False; the work done is the same.
13. True; joules 15. $47{,}385\pi$ ft·lb 17. 261,600 J
19. (a) 926,640 ft·lb (b) hp of motor = 0.468 21. 75,000 ft·lb
23. 120,000 ft·tons 25. (a) $2{,}400{,}000{,}000/x^2$ lb
(b) $(9.6 \times 10^{10})/(x + 4000)^2$ lb (c) $2.5344 \times 10^{10}$ ft·lb
27. $v_f = 100$ m/s
29. (a) decrease of $4.5 \times 10^{14}$ J (b) $\approx 0.107$ (c) $\approx 8.24$ bombs

## ▶ Exercise Set 6.7 (Page 390)

1. (a) positive: $m_2$ is at the fulcrum, so it can be ignored; masses $m_1$ and $m_3$ are equidistant from position 5, but $m_1 < m_3$, so the beam will rotate clockwise. (b) The fulcrum should be placed $\frac{50}{7}$ units to the right of $m_1$.
3. $\left(\frac{1}{2}, \frac{1}{2}\right)$ 5. $\left(1, \frac{1}{2}\right)$ 7. $\left(\frac{2}{3}, \frac{1}{3}\right)$ 9. $\left(\frac{5}{14}, \frac{38}{35}\right)$ 11. $\left(\frac{2}{3}, \frac{1}{3}\right)$
13. $\left(-\frac{1}{2}, 4\right)$ 15. $\left(\frac{1}{2}, \frac{8}{5}\right)$ 17. $\left(\frac{9}{20}, \frac{9}{20}\right)$ 19. $\left(\frac{49}{48}, \frac{7}{3} - \ln 2\right)$
23. $\frac{4}{3}$; $\left(\frac{3}{5}, \frac{3}{8}\right)$ 25. 3; $\left(0, \frac{2}{3}\right)$ 27. 8; $\left(\frac{\pi}{2}, \frac{\pi}{8}\right)$
29. $\ln 4 - 1$; $\left(\frac{4\ln 4 - 3}{4\ln 4 - 4}, \frac{(\ln 2)^2 + 1 - \ln 4}{\ln 4 - 1}\right)$

Responses to True–False questions may be abridged to save space.

31. True; use symmetry. 33. True; use symmetry.

35. $\left(\dfrac{2a}{3}, 0\right)$ 37. $(\bar{x}, \bar{y}) = \left(0, \dfrac{(a+2b)c}{3(a+b)}\right)$

41. $2\pi^2 abk$ 43. $(a/3, b/3)$

## ▶ Exercise Set 6.8 (Page 397)

1. (a) $F = 31{,}200$ lb; $P = 312$ lb/ft$^2$
(b) $F = 2{,}452{,}500$ N; $P = 98.1$ kPa

3. 499.2 lb 5. $8.175 \times 10^5$ N 7. 1,098,720 N 9. yes

11. $\rho a^3/\sqrt{2}$ lb

Responses to True–False questions may be abridged to save space.

13. True; this is a consequence of inequalities (4).

15. False; by Equation (7) the force can be arbitrarily large for a fixed volume of water.

17. 61,748 lb 19. $9.81 \times 10^9$ N 21. (b) $80\rho_0$ lb/min

## ▶ Exercise Set 6.9 (Page 407)

1. (a) $\approx 10.0179$ (b) $\approx 3.7622$ (c) $15/17 \approx 0.8824$
(d) $\approx -1.4436$ (e) $\approx 1.7627$ (f) $\approx 0.9730$

3. (a) $\dfrac{4}{3}$ (b) $\dfrac{5}{4}$ (c) $\dfrac{312}{313}$ (d) $-\dfrac{63}{16}$

5.

| | $\sinh x_0$ | $\cosh x_0$ | $\tanh x_0$ | $\coth x_0$ | $\operatorname{sech} x_0$ | $\operatorname{csch} x_0$ |
|---|---|---|---|---|---|---|
| (a) | 2 | $\sqrt{5}$ | $2/\sqrt{5}$ | $\sqrt{5}/2$ | $1/\sqrt{5}$ | 1/2 |
| (b) | 3/4 | 5/4 | 3/5 | 5/3 | 4/5 | 4/3 |
| (c) | 4/3 | 5/3 | 4/5 | 5/4 | 3/5 | 3/4 |

9. $4\cosh(4x-8)$ 11. $-\dfrac{1}{x}\operatorname{csch}^2(\ln x)$

13. $\dfrac{1}{x^2}\operatorname{csch}\left(\dfrac{1}{x}\right)\coth\left(\dfrac{1}{x}\right)$ 15. $\dfrac{2+5\cosh(5x)\sinh(5x)}{\sqrt{4x+\cosh^2(5x)}}$

17. $x^{5/2}\tanh(\sqrt{x})\operatorname{sech}^2(\sqrt{x}) + 3x^2\tanh^2(\sqrt{x})$

19. $\dfrac{1}{\sqrt{9+x^2}}$ 21. $\dfrac{1}{(\cosh^{-1}x)\sqrt{x^2-1}}$ 23. $-\dfrac{(\tanh^{-1}x)^{-2}}{1-x^2}$

25. $\dfrac{\sinh x}{|\sinh x|} = \begin{cases} 1, & x>0 \\ -1, & x<0 \end{cases}$ 27. $-\dfrac{e^x}{2x\sqrt{1-x}} + e^x \operatorname{sech}^{-1} x$

29. $\frac{1}{7}\sinh^7 x + C$ 31. $\frac{2}{3}(\tanh x)^{3/2} + C$ 33. $\ln(\cosh x) + C$

35. $37/375$ 37. $\frac{1}{3}\sinh^{-1}3x + C$ 39. $-\operatorname{sech}^{-1}(e^x) + C$

41. $-\operatorname{csch}^{-1}|2x| + C$ 43. $\frac{1}{2}\ln 3$

Responses to True–False questions may be abridged to save space.

45. True; see Figure 6.9.1 47. True; $f(x) = \sinh x$

49. 16/9 51. $5\pi$ 53. $\frac{3}{4}$

55. (a) $+\infty$ (b) $-\infty$ (c) 1 (d) $-1$ (e) $+\infty$ (f) $+\infty$

63. $|u| < 1$: $\tanh^{-1} u + C$; $|u| > 1$: $\tanh^{-1}(1/u) + C$

65. (a) ln 2 (b) 1/2 71. 405.9 ft

73. (a)

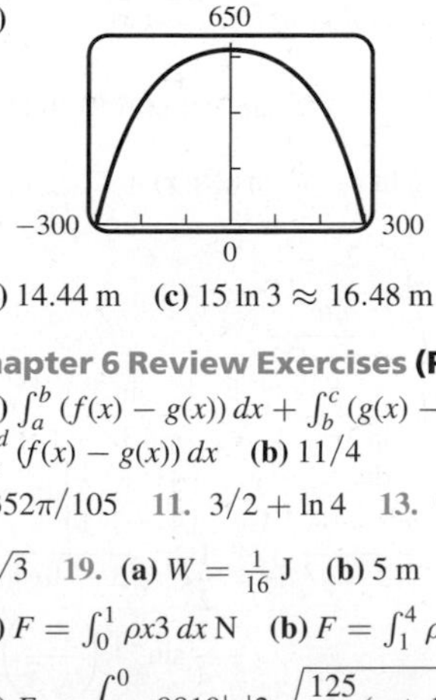


(b) 1480.2798 ft
(c) ±283.6249 ft
(d) 82°

75. (b) 14.44 m (c) $15\ln 3 \approx 16.48$ m

## ▶ Chapter 6 Review Exercises (Page 409)

7. (a) $\int_a^b (f(x)-g(x))\,dx + \int_b^c (g(x)-f(x))\,dx + \int_c^d (f(x)-g(x))\,dx$ (b) 11/4

9. $4352\pi/105$ 11. $3/2 + \ln 4$ 13. 9 15. $\dfrac{\pi}{6}\left(65^{3/2} - 37^{3/2}\right)$

17. $3\sqrt{3}$ 19. (a) $W = \frac{1}{16}$ J (b) 5 m 21. $\left(\frac{8}{5}, 0\right)$

23. (a) $F = \int_0^1 \rho x 3\,dx$ N (b) $F = \int_1^4 \rho(1+x)2x\,dx$ lb/ft$^2$

(c) $F = \displaystyle\int_{-10}^{0} 9810|y|2\sqrt{\frac{125}{8}}(y+10)\,dy$ N

## ▶ Chapter 6 Making Connections (Page 411)

Where correct answers to a Making Connections exercise may vary, no answer is listed. Sample answers for these questions are available on the Book Companion Site.

1. (a) $\pi A_1$ (b) $a = \dfrac{A_1}{2A_2}$ 2. 1,010,807 ft·lb 3. $\displaystyle\int_0^a 2\pi r f(r)\,dr$

## ▶ Exercise Set 7.1 (Page 414)

1. $-2(x-2)^4 + C$ 3. $\frac{1}{2}\tan(x^2) + C$ 5. $-\frac{1}{3}\ln(2+\cos 3x) + C$

7. $\cosh(e^x) + C$ 9. $e^{\tan x} + C$ 11. $-\frac{1}{30}\cos^6 5x + C$

13. $\ln(e^x + \sqrt{e^{2x}+4}) + C$ 15. $2e^{\sqrt{x-1}} + C$ 17. $2\sinh\sqrt{x} + C$

19. $-\dfrac{2}{\ln 3}3^{-\sqrt{x}} + C$ 21. $\dfrac{1}{2}\coth\dfrac{2}{x} + C$ 23. $-\dfrac{1}{4}\ln\left|\dfrac{2+e^{-x}}{2-e^{-x}}\right| + C$

25. $\sin^{-1}(e^x) + C$ 27. $-\frac{1}{2}\cos(x^2) + C$ 29. $-\dfrac{1}{\ln 16}4^{-x^2} + C$

31. (a) $\frac{1}{2}\sin^2 x + C$ (b) $-\frac{1}{4}\cos 2x + C$

33. (b) $\ln\left|\tan\dfrac{x}{2}\right| + C$ (c) $\ln\left|\cot\left(\dfrac{\pi}{4} - \dfrac{x}{2}\right)\right| + C$

## ▶ Exercise Set 7.2 (Page 421)

1. $-e^{-2x}\left(\dfrac{x}{2} + \dfrac{1}{4}\right) + C$ 3. $x^2e^x - 2xe^x + 2e^x + C$

5. $-\frac{1}{3}x\cos 3x + \frac{1}{9}\sin 3x + C$ 7. $x^2\sin x + 2x\cos x - 2\sin x + C$

9. $\dfrac{x^2}{2}\ln x - \dfrac{x^2}{4} + C$ 11. $x(\ln x)^2 - 2x\ln x + 2x + C$

13. $x\ln(3x-2) - x - \frac{2}{3}\ln(3x-2) + C$ 15. $x\sin^{-1}x + \sqrt{1-x^2} + C$

17. $x\tan^{-1}(3x) - \frac{1}{6}\ln(1+9x^2) + C$ 19. $\frac{1}{2}e^x(\sin x - \cos x) + C$

21. $(x/2)[\sin(\ln x) - \cos(\ln x)] + C$ 23. $x\tan x + \ln|\cos x| + C$

25. $\frac{1}{2}x^2e^{x^2} - \frac{1}{2}e^{x^2} + C$ 27. $\frac{1}{4}(3e^4+1)$ 29. $(2e^3+1)/9$

31. $3\ln 3 - 2$ 33. $\dfrac{5\pi}{6} - \sqrt{3} + 1$ 35. $-\pi/2$

37. $\dfrac{1}{3}\left(2\sqrt{3}\pi - \dfrac{\pi}{2} - 2 + \ln 2\right)$

Responses to True–False questions may be abridged to save space.

39. True; see the subsection "Guidelines for Integration by Parts."

41. False; $e^x$ isn't a factor of the integrand.

43. $2(\sqrt{x}-1)e^{\sqrt{x}} + C$ 47. $-(3x^2+5x+7)e^{-x} + C$

49. $(4x^3-6x)\sin 2x - (2x^4-6x^2+3)\cos 2x + C$

51. $\dfrac{e^{ax}}{a^2+b^2}(a\sin bx - b\cos bx) + C$ 53. (a) $\frac{1}{2}\sin^2 x + C$

55. (a) $A = 1$ (b) $V = \pi(e-2)$ 57. $V = 2\pi^2$ 59. $\pi^3 - 6\pi$

61. (a) \$86,173.41 (b) \$7817.48

63. (a) \$183,580.44 (b) \$111,347.17

65. (a) \$133,805.80 (b) \$60,122.82

67. (a) $2\pi x\,d(x)\,\Delta x = 6\pi x e^{-0.25x}\,\Delta x$ thousand ants
(b) 133.357 thousand ants

69. (a) $-\frac{1}{4}\sin^3 x\cos x - \frac{3}{8}\sin x\cos x + \frac{3}{8}x + C$ (b) 8/15

73. (a) $\frac{1}{3}\tan^3 x - \tan x + x + C$ (b) $\frac{1}{3}\sec^2 x\tan x + \frac{2}{3}\tan x + C$
(c) $x^3e^x - 3x^2e^x + 6xe^x - 6e^x + C$

77. $(x+1)\ln(x+1) - x + C$ 79. $\frac{1}{2}(x^2+1)\tan^{-1}x - \frac{1}{2}x + C$

## ▶ Exercise Set 7.3 (Page 429)

1. $-\frac{1}{4}\cos^4 x + C$ 3. $\dfrac{\theta}{2} - \dfrac{1}{20}\sin 10\theta + C$

5. $\dfrac{1}{3a}\cos^3(a\theta) - \dfrac{1}{a}\cos(a\theta) + C$ 7. $\dfrac{1}{2a}\sin^2 ax + C$

9. $\frac{1}{3}\sin^3 t - \frac{1}{5}\sin^5 t + C$ 11. $\frac{1}{8}x - \frac{1}{32}\sin 4x + C$

13. $-\frac{1}{10}\cos 5x + \frac{1}{2}\cos x + C$ 15. $-\frac{1}{3}\cos(3x/2) - \cos(x/2) + C$

17. 2/3 19. 0 21. 7/24 23. $\frac{1}{2}\tan(2x-1) + C$

25. $\ln|\cos(e^{-x})| + C$ 27. $\frac{1}{4}\ln|\sec 4x + \tan 4x| + C$

29. $\frac{1}{3}\tan^3 x + C$ 31. $\frac{1}{16}\sec^4 4x + C$ 33. $\frac{1}{7}\sec^7 x - \frac{1}{5}\sec^5 x + C$

35. $\frac{1}{4}\sec^3 x\tan x - \frac{5}{8}\sec x\tan x + \frac{3}{8}\ln|\sec x + \tan x| + C$

37. $\frac{1}{3}\sec^3 t + C$ 39. $\tan x + \frac{1}{3}\tan^3 x + C$

41. $\frac{1}{8}\tan^2 4x + \frac{1}{4}\ln|\cos 4x| + C$ 43. $\frac{2}{3}\tan^{3/2} x + \frac{2}{7}\tan^{7/2} x + C$

45. $\frac{1}{2} - \frac{\pi}{8}$ 47. $-\frac{1}{2} + \ln 2$ 49. $-\frac{1}{5}\csc^5 x + \frac{1}{3}\csc^3 x + C$

51. $-\frac{1}{2}\csc^2 x - \ln|\sin x| + C$

Responses to True–False questions may be abridged to save space.

53. True; $\int \sin^5 x \cos^8 x\, dx = \int \sin x(1-\cos^2 x)^2 \cos^8 x\, dx = -\int (1-u^2)^2 u^8\, du = -\int (u^8 - 2u^{10} + u^{12})\, du$

55. False; use this identity to help evaluate integrals of the form $\int \sin mx \cos nx\, dx$.

59. $L = \ln(\sqrt{2}+1)$ 61. $V = \pi/2$

67. $-\frac{1}{\sqrt{a^2+b^2}} \ln\left[\frac{\sqrt{a^2+b^2} + a\cos x - b\sin x}{a\sin x + b\cos x}\right] + C$

69. **(a)** $\frac{2}{3}$ **(b)** $3\pi/16$ **(c)** $\frac{8}{15}$ **(d)** $5\pi/32$

## ▶ Exercise Set 7.4 (Page 436)

1. $2\sin^{-1}(x/2) + \frac{1}{2}x\sqrt{4-x^2} + C$ 3. $8\sin^{-1}\left(\frac{x}{4}\right) - \frac{x\sqrt{16-x^2}}{2} + C$

5. $\frac{1}{16}\tan^{-1}(x/2) + \frac{x}{8(4+x^2)} + C$ 7. $\sqrt{x^2-9} - 3\sec^{-1}(x/3) + C$

9. $-(x^2+2)\sqrt{1-x^2} + C$ 11. $\frac{\sqrt{9x^2-4}}{4x} + C$ 13. $\frac{x}{\sqrt{1-x^2}} + C$

15. $\ln|\sqrt{x^2-9} + x| + C$ 17. $\frac{-x}{9\sqrt{4x^2-9}} + C$

19. $\frac{1}{2}\sin^{-1}(e^x) + \frac{1}{2}e^x\sqrt{1-e^{2x}} + C$ 21. $2/3$ 23. $(\sqrt{3}-\sqrt{2})/2$

25. $\frac{10\sqrt{3}+18}{243}$

Responses to True–False questions may be abridged to save space.

27. True; with the restriction $-\pi/2 \le \theta \le \pi/2$, this substitution gives $\sqrt{a^2-x^2} = a\cos\theta$ and $dx = a\cos\theta\, d\theta$.

29. False; use the substitution $x = a\sec\theta$ with $0 \le \theta < \pi/2\ (x \ge a)$ or $\pi/2 \le \theta < \pi\ (x \le -a)$.

31. $\frac{1}{2}\ln(x^2+4) + C$

33. $L = \sqrt{5} - \sqrt{2} + \ln\frac{2+2\sqrt{2}}{1+\sqrt{5}}$ 35. $S = \frac{\pi}{32}\left[18\sqrt{5} - \ln(2+\sqrt{5})\right]$

37. $\tan^{-1}(x-2) + C$ 39. $\sin^{-1}\left(\frac{x-1}{2}\right) + C$

41. $\ln(x-3+\sqrt{(x-3)^2+1}) + C$

43. $2\sin^{-1}\left(\frac{x+1}{2}\right) + \frac{1}{2}(x+1)\sqrt{3-2x-x^2} + C$

45. $\frac{1}{\sqrt{10}}\tan^{-1}\sqrt{\frac{2}{5}}(x+1) + C$ 47. $\pi/6$

49. $u = \sin^2 x,\ \frac{1}{2}\int \sqrt{1-u^2}\, du$
$= \frac{1}{4}[\sin^2 x\sqrt{1-\sin^4 x} + \sin^{-1}(\sin^2 x)] + C$

51. **(a)** $\sinh^{-1}(x/3) + C$ **(b)** $\ln\left(\frac{\sqrt{x^2+9}}{3} + \frac{x}{3}\right) + C$

## ▶ Exercise Set 7.5 (Page 444)

1. $\frac{A}{x-3} + \frac{B}{x+4}$ 3. $\frac{A}{x} + \frac{B}{x^2} + \frac{C}{x-1}$

5. $\frac{A}{x} + \frac{B}{x^2} + \frac{C}{x^3} + \frac{Dx+E}{x^2+2}$ 7. $\frac{Ax+B}{x^2+5} + \frac{Cx+D}{(x^2+5)^2}$

9. $\frac{1}{5}\ln\left|\frac{x-4}{x+1}\right| + C$ 11. $\frac{5}{2}\ln|2x-1| + 3\ln|x+4| + C$

13. $\ln\left|\frac{x(x+3)^2}{x-3}\right| + C$ 15. $\frac{x^2}{2} - 3x + \ln|x+3| + C$

17. $3x + 12\ln|x-2| - \frac{2}{x-2} + C$

19. $\ln|x^2-3x-10| + C$

21. $x + \frac{x^3}{3} + \ln\left|\frac{(x-1)^2(x+1)}{x^2}\right| + C$

23. $3\ln|x| - \ln|x-1| - \frac{5}{x-1} + C$

25. $\frac{2}{x-3} + \ln|x-3| + \ln|x+1| + C$

27. $\frac{2}{x+1} - \frac{1}{2(x+1)^2} + \ln|x+1| + C$

29. $-\frac{7}{34}\ln|4x-1| + \frac{6}{17}\ln(x^2+1) + \frac{3}{17}\tan^{-1} x + C$

31. $3\tan^{-1} x + \frac{1}{2}\ln(x^2+3) + C$

33. $\frac{x^2}{2} - 2x + \frac{1}{2}\ln(x^2+1) + C$

Responses to True–False questions may be abridged to save space.

35. True; partial fractions rewrites proper rational functions $P(x)/Q(x)$ as a sum of terms of the form $\frac{A}{(Bx+C)^k}$ and/or $\frac{Dx+E}{(Fx^2+Gx+H)^k}$.

37. True; $\frac{2x+3}{x^2} = \frac{2x}{x^2} + \frac{3}{x^2} = \frac{2}{x} + \frac{3}{x^2}$.

39. $\frac{1}{6}\ln\left(\frac{1-\sin\theta}{5+\sin\theta}\right) + C$ 41. $e^x - 2\tan^{-1}\left(\frac{1}{2}e^x\right) + C$

43. $V = \pi\left(\frac{19}{5} - \frac{9}{4}\ln 5\right)$ 45. $\frac{1}{\sqrt{2}}\tan^{-1}\left(\frac{x+1}{\sqrt{2}}\right) + \frac{1}{x^2+2x+3} + C$

47. $\frac{1}{8}\ln|x-1| - \frac{1}{5}\ln|x-2| + \frac{1}{12}\ln|x-3| - \frac{1}{120}\ln|x+3| + C$

## ▶ Exercise Set 7.6 (Page 452)

1. Formula (60): $\frac{4}{3}x + \frac{4}{9}\ln|3x-1| + C$

3. Formula (65): $\frac{1}{5}\ln\left|\frac{x}{5+2x}\right| + C$

5. Formula (102): $\frac{1}{5}(x-1)(2x+3)^{3/2} + C$

7. Formula (108): $\frac{1}{2}\ln\left|\frac{\sqrt{4-3x}-2}{\sqrt{4-3x}+2}\right| + C$

9. Formula (69): $\frac{1}{8}\ln\left|\frac{x+4}{x-4}\right| + C$

11. Formula (73): $\frac{x}{2}\sqrt{x^2-3} - \frac{3}{2}\ln|x+\sqrt{x^2-3}| + C$

13. Formula (95): $\frac{x}{2}\sqrt{x^2+4} - 2\ln(x+\sqrt{x^2+4}) + C$

15. Formula (74): $\frac{x}{2}\sqrt{9-x^2} + \frac{9}{2}\sin^{-1}\frac{x}{3} + C$

17. Formula (79): $\sqrt{4-x^2} - 2\ln\left|\frac{2+\sqrt{4-x^2}}{x}\right| + C$

19. Formula (38): $-\frac{\sin 7x}{14} + \frac{1}{2}\sin x + C$

21. Formula (50): $\frac{x^4}{16}[4\ln x - 1] + C$

23. Formula (42): $\frac{e^{-2x}}{13}[-2\sin(3x) - 3\cos(3x)] + C$

25. Formula (62): $\frac{1}{2}\int\frac{u\, du}{(4-3u)^2} = \frac{1}{18}\left[\frac{4}{4-3e^{2x}} + \ln\left|4-3e^{2x}\right|\right] + C$

27. Formula (68): $\frac{2}{3}\int\frac{du}{u^2+4} = \frac{1}{3}\tan^{-1}\frac{3\sqrt{x}}{2} + C$

29. Formula (76): $\frac{1}{2}\int\frac{du}{\sqrt{u^2-9}} = \frac{1}{2}\ln|2x+\sqrt{4x^2-9}| + C$

31. Formula (81): $\frac{1}{4}\int\frac{u^2}{\sqrt{2-u^2}}\, du = -\frac{1}{4}x^2\sqrt{2-4x^4}$
$+ \frac{1}{4}\sin^{-1}\left(\sqrt{2}x^2\right) + C$

33. Formula (26): $\int \sin^2 u\, du = \frac{1}{2}\ln x - \frac{1}{4}\sin(2\ln x) + C$

35. Formula (51): $\frac{1}{4}\int ue^u\, du = \frac{1}{4}(-2x-1)e^{-2x} + C$

37. $u = \sin 3x$, Formula (67): $\frac{1}{3}\int\frac{du}{u(u+1)^2}$
$= \frac{1}{3}\left(\frac{1}{\sin 3x + 1} + \ln\left|\frac{\sin 3x}{\sin 3x + 1}\right|\right) + C$

39. $u = 4x^2$, Formula (70): $\frac{1}{8}\int\frac{du}{u^2-1} = \frac{1}{16}\ln\left|\frac{4x^2-1}{4x^2+1}\right| + C$

41. $u = 2e^x$, Formula (74): $\frac{1}{2}\int\sqrt{3-u^2}\, du = \frac{1}{2}e^x\sqrt{3-4e^{2x}}$
$+ \frac{3}{4}\sin^{-1}\left(\frac{2e^x}{\sqrt{3}}\right) + C$

43. $u = 3x$, Formula (112): $\frac{1}{3}\int\sqrt{\frac{5}{3}u - u^2}\,du = \frac{18x-5}{36}\sqrt{5x-9x^2} + \frac{25}{216}\sin^{-1}\left(\frac{18x-5}{5}\right) + C$

45. $u = 2x$, Formula (44): $\int u \sin u\, du = \sin 2x - 2x\cos 2x + C$

47. $u = -\sqrt{x}$, Formula (51): $2\int ue^u\,du = -2(\sqrt{x}+1)e^{-\sqrt{x}} + C$

49. $x^2 + 6x - 7 = (x+3)^2 - 16$, $u = x+3$, Formula (70): $\int \frac{du}{u^2-16} = \frac{1}{8}\ln\left|\frac{x-1}{x+7}\right| + C$

51. $x^2 - 4x - 5 = (x-2)^2 - 9$, $u = x-2$, Formula (77): $\int \frac{u+2}{\sqrt{9-u^2}}\,du = -\sqrt{5+4x-x^2} + 2\sin^{-1}\left(\frac{x-2}{3}\right) + C$

53. $u = \sqrt{x-2}$, $\frac{2}{5}(x-2)^{5/2} + \frac{4}{3}(x-2)^{3/2} + C$

55. $u = \sqrt{x^3+1}$, $\frac{2}{3}\int u^2(u^2-1)\,du = \frac{2}{15}(x^3+1)^{5/2} - \frac{2}{9}(x^3+1)^{3/2} + C$

57. $u = x^{1/3}$, $\int \frac{3u^2}{u^3-u}\,du = \frac{3}{2}\ln|x^{2/3}-1| + C$

59. $u = x^{1/4}$, $4\int \frac{1}{u(1-u)}\,du = 4\ln\frac{x^{1/4}}{|1-x^{1/4}|} + C$

61. $u = x^{1/6}$, $6\int \frac{u^3}{u-1}\,du = 2x^{1/2} + 3x^{1/3} + 6x^{1/6} + 6\ln|x^{1/6}-1| + C$

63. $u = \sqrt{1+x^2}$, $\int (u^2-1)\,du = \frac{1}{3}(1+x^2)^{3/2} - (1+x^2)^{1/2} + C$

65. $\int \frac{1}{1+\frac{2u}{1+u^2}+\frac{1-u^2}{1+u^2}}\,\frac{2}{1+u^2}\,du = \int \frac{1}{u+1}\,du = \ln|\tan(x/2)+1| + C$

67. $\int \frac{d\theta}{1-\cos\theta} = \int \frac{1}{u^2}\,du = -\cot(\theta/2) + C$

69. $\int \frac{1}{\frac{2u}{1+u^2}+\frac{2u}{1+u^2}\cdot\frac{1+u^2}{1-u^2}}\cdot\frac{2}{1+u^2}\,du = \int \frac{1-u^2}{2u}\,du = \frac{1}{2}\ln|\tan(x/2)| - \frac{1}{4}\tan^2(x/2) + C$

71. $x = \frac{4e^2}{1+e^2}$ 73. $A = 6 + \frac{25}{2}\sin^{-1}\frac{4}{5}$ 75. $A = \frac{1}{40}\ln 9$

77. $V = \pi(\pi - 2)$ 79. $V = 2\pi(1-4e^{-3})$

81. $L = \sqrt{65} + \frac{1}{8}\ln(8+\sqrt{65})$ 83. $S = 2\pi\left[\sqrt{2} + \ln(1+\sqrt{2})\right]$

85.
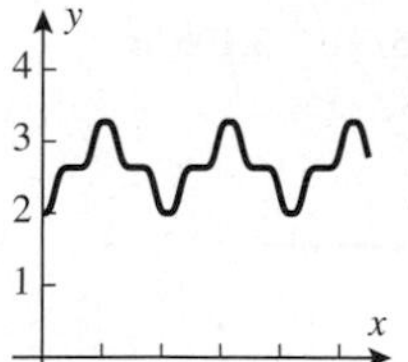


89. $\frac{2}{\sqrt{3}}\tan^{-1}\left(\frac{1}{\sqrt{3}} + \frac{2}{\sqrt{3}}\tanh\frac{x}{2}\right) + C$

91. $\frac{1}{31}\cos^{31}x\sin^{31}x + C$

93. $-\frac{1}{9}\ln|1+x^{-9}| + C$

## ▶ Exercise Set 7.7 (Page 464)

1. $\int_0^3 \sqrt{x+1}\,dx = \frac{14}{3} \approx 4.66667$
(a) $M_{10} = 4.66760$; $|E_M| \approx 0.000933996$
(b) $T_{10} = 4.66480$; $|E_T| \approx 0.00187099$
(c) $S_{20} = 4.66667$; $|E_S| \approx 9.98365 \times 10^{-7}$

3. $\int_0^{\pi/2} \cos x\,dx = 1$
(a) $M_{10} = 1.00103$; $|E_M| \approx 0.00102882$
(b) $T_{10} = 0.997943$; $|E_T| \approx 0.00205701$
(c) $S_{20} = 1.00000$; $|E_S| \approx 2.11547 \times 10^{-7}$

5. $\int_1^3 e^{-2x}\,dx = \frac{-1+e^4}{2e^6} \approx 0.0664283$
(a) $M_{10} = 0.0659875$; $|E_M| \approx 0.000440797$
(b) $T_{10} = 0.0673116$; $|E_T| \approx 0.000883357$
(c) $S_{20} = 0.0664289$; $|E_S| \approx 5.87673 \times 10^{-7}$

7. (a) $|E_M| \le \frac{9}{3200} = 0.0028125$
(b) $|E_T| \le \frac{9}{1600} = 0.005625$
(c) $|E_S| \le \frac{81}{10{,}240{,}000} \approx 7.91016 \times 10^{-6}$

9. (a) $|E_M| \le \frac{\pi^3}{19{,}200} \approx 0.00161491$
(b) $|E_T| \le \frac{\pi^3}{9600} \approx 0.00322982$
(c) $|E_S| \le \frac{\pi^5}{921{,}600{,}000} \approx 3.32053 \times 10^{-7}$

11. (a) $|E_M| \le \frac{1}{75e^2} \approx 0.00180447$
(b) $|E_T| \le \frac{2}{75e^2} \approx 0.00360894$
(c) $|E_S| \le \frac{1}{56{,}250e^2} \approx 2.40596 \times 10^{-6}$

13. (a) $n = 24$ (b) $n = 34$ (c) $n = 8$

15. (a) $n = 13$ (b) $n = 18$ (c) $n = 4$

17. (a) $n = 43$ (b) $n = 61$ (c) $n = 8$

Responses to True–False questions may be abridged to save space.

19. False; $T_n$ is the average of $L_n$ and $R_n$.

21. False; $S_{50} = \frac{2}{3}M_{25} + \frac{1}{3}T_{25}$

23. $g(x) = \frac{1}{24}x^2 - \frac{3}{8}x + \frac{13}{12}$

25. $S_{10} = 1.49367$; $\int_{-1}^{1} e^{-x^2}\,dx \approx 1.49365$

27. $S_{10} = 3.80678$; $\int_{-1}^{2} x\sqrt{2+x^3}\,dx \approx 3.80554$

29. $S_{10} = 0.904524$; $\int_0^1 \cos x^2\,dx \approx 0.904524$

31. (a) $M_{10} = 3.14243$; error $E_M \approx -0.000833331$
(b) $T_{10} = 3.13993$; error $E_T \approx 0.00166666$
(c) $S_{20} = 3.14159$; error $E_S \approx 6.20008 \times 10^{-10}$

33. $S_{14} = 0.693147984$, $|E_S| \approx 0.000000803 = 8.03 \times 10^{-7}$

35. $n = 116$ 39. 3.82019 41. 3975 ft 43. 37.9 mi 45. 9.3 L

47. (a) max $|f''(x)| \approx 3.844880$ (b) $n = 18$ (c) 0.904741

49. (a) The maximum value of $|f^{(4)}(x)|$ is approximately 12.4282.
(b) $n = 6$ (c) $S_6 = 0.983347$

## ▶ Exercise Set 7.8 (Page 474)

1. (a) improper; infinite discontinuity at $x = 3$ (b) not improper
(c) improper; infinite discontinuity at $x = 0$
(d) improper; infinite interval of integration
(e) improper; infinite interval of integration and infinite discontinuity at $x = 1$ (f) not improper

3. $\frac{1}{2}$ 5. $\ln 2$ 7. $\frac{1}{2}$ 9. $-\frac{1}{4}$ 11. $\frac{1}{3}$ 13. divergent 15. 0

17. divergent 19. divergent 21. $\pi/2$ 23. 1 25. divergent

27. $\frac{9}{2}$ 29. divergent 31. $\pi/2$

Responses to True–False questions may be abridged to save space.

33. True; see Theorem 7.8.2 with $p = \frac{4}{3} > 1$.

35. False; the integrand $\frac{1}{x(x-3)}$ is continuous on $[1, 2]$.

37. 2 39. 2 41. $\frac{1}{2}$

43. (a) 2.726585 (b) 2.804364 (c) 0.219384 (d) 0.504067 45. 12

47. $-1$ 49. $\frac{1}{3}$ 51. (a) $V = \pi/2$ (b) $S = \pi[\sqrt{2} + \ln(1+\sqrt{2})]$

53. (b) $1/e$ (c) It is convergent. 55. $V = \pi$

59. $\frac{2\pi NI}{kr}\left(1 - \frac{a}{\sqrt{r^2+a^2}}\right)$ 61. Method 1

63. (b) $2.4 \times 10^7$ mi·lb 65. (a) $\frac{1}{s^2}$ (b) $\frac{2}{s^3}$ (c) $\frac{e^{-3s}}{s}$

69. (a) 1.047 73. 1.809

## ▶ Chapter 7 Review Exercises (Page 477)

1. $\frac{2}{27}(4+9x)^{3/2}+C$ 3. $-\frac{2}{3}\cos^{3/2}\theta+C$ 5. $\frac{1}{6}\tan^3(x^2)+C$
7. (a) $2\sin^{-1}(\sqrt{x}/2)+C$; $-2\sin^{-1}(\sqrt{2-x}/\sqrt{2})+C$; $\sin^{-1}(x-1)+C$
9. $-xe^{-x}-e^{-x}+C$ 11. $x\ln(2x+3)-x+\frac{3}{2}\ln(2x+3)+C$
13. $(4x^4-12x^2+6)\sin(2x)+(8x^3-12x)\cos(2x)+C$
15. $\frac{1}{2}\theta-\frac{1}{20}\sin 10\theta+C$ 17. $-\frac{1}{6}\cos 3x+\frac{1}{2}\cos x+C$
19. $-\frac{1}{8}\sin^3(2x)\cos 2x-\frac{3}{16}\cos 2x\sin 2x+\frac{3}{8}x+C$
21. $\frac{9}{2}\sin^{-1}(x/3)-\frac{1}{2}x\sqrt{9-x^2}+C$ 23. $\ln|x+\sqrt{x^2-1}|+C$
25. $\dfrac{x\sqrt{x^2+9}}{2}-\dfrac{9\ln(|\sqrt{x^2+9}+x|)}{2}+C$ 27. $\dfrac{1}{5}\ln\left|\dfrac{x-1}{x+4}\right|+C$
29. $\frac{1}{2}x^2-2x+6\ln|x+2|+C$
31. $\ln|x+2|+\dfrac{4}{x+2}-\dfrac{2}{(x+2)^2}+C$
33. (a) $\ln\dfrac{\sqrt{x^2-1}}{|x|}+C,\ |x|>1$ (b) $\ln\dfrac{\sqrt{1-x^2}}{|x|}+C,\ 0<|x|<1$
(c) $-\ln|x|+\frac{1}{2}\ln|x^2-1|+C,\ x\neq 0,\pm 1$
35. Formula (40): $-\dfrac{\cos 16x}{32}+\dfrac{\cos 2x}{4}+C$
37. Formula (113): $\frac{1}{24}(8x^2-2x-3)\sqrt{x-x^2}+\frac{1}{16}\sin^{-1}(2x-1)+C$
39. Formula (28): $\frac{1}{2}\tan 2x-x+C$
41. $\displaystyle\int_1^3\frac{1}{\sqrt{x+1}}=4-2\sqrt{2}\approx 1.17157$
(a) $M_{10}=1.17138$; $|E_M|\approx 0.000190169$
(b) $T_{10}=1.17195$; $|E_T|\approx 0.000380588$
(c) $S_{20}=1.17157$; $|E_S|\approx 8.35151\times 10^{-8}$
43. (a) $|E_M|\leq\dfrac{1}{1600\sqrt{2}}\approx 0.000441942$
(b) $|E_T|\leq\dfrac{1}{800\sqrt{2}}\approx 0.000883883$
(c) $|E_S|\leq\dfrac{7}{15{,}360{,}000\sqrt{2}}\approx 3.22249\times 10^{-7}$
45. (a) $n=22$ (b) $n=30$ (c) $n=6$ 47. 1 49. 6
51. $e^{-1}$ 53. $a=\pi/2$ 55. $\dfrac{x}{3\sqrt{3+x^2}}+C$ 57. $\frac{5}{12}-\frac{1}{2}\ln 2$
59. $\frac{1}{6}\sin^3 2x-\frac{1}{10}\sin^5 2x+C$
61. $\frac{2}{13}e^{2x}\cos 3x+\frac{3}{13}e^{2x}\sin 3x+C$
63. $-\frac{1}{6}\ln|x-1|+\frac{1}{15}\ln|x+2|+\frac{1}{10}\ln|x-3|+C$
65. $4-\pi$ 67. $\ln\dfrac{\sqrt{e^x+1}-1}{\sqrt{e^x+1}+1}+C$ 69. $\dfrac{\pi}{12}+\dfrac{\sqrt{3}}{2}-1$
71. $\sqrt{x^2+2x+2}+2\ln(\sqrt{x^2+2x+2}+x+1)+C$ 73. $\dfrac{1}{2(a^2+1)}$

## ▶ Chapter 7 Making Connections (Page 479)

Where correct answers to a Making Connections exercise may vary, no answer is listed. Sample answers for these questions are available on the Book Companion Site.

3. (a) $\Gamma(1)=1$ (c) $\Gamma(2)=1,\ \Gamma(3)=2,\ \Gamma(4)=6$
5. (b) 1.37078 seconds

## ▶ Exercise Set 8.1 (Page 486)

3. (a) first order (b) second order

Responses to True–False questions may be abridged to save space.

5. False; only first-order derivatives appear.
7. True; it is third order.
15. $y(x)=e^{-2x}-2e^x$ 17. $y(x)=2e^{2x}-2xe^{2x}$
19. $y(x)=\sin 2x+\cos 2x$ 21. $y(x)=-2x^2+2x+3$
23. $y(x)=2/(3-2x)$ 25. $y(x)=2/x^2$
27. (a) $\dfrac{dy}{dt}=ky^2,\ y(0)=y_0\ (k>0)$
(b) $\dfrac{dy}{dt}=-ky^2,\ y(0)=y_0\ (k>0)$
29. (a) $\dfrac{ds}{dt}=\dfrac{1}{2}s$ (b) $\dfrac{d^2s}{dt^2}=2\dfrac{ds}{dt}$ 33. (b) $L/2$

## ▶ Exercise Set 8.2 (Page 494)

1. $y=Cx$ 3. $y=Ce^{-\sqrt{1+x^2}}-1,\ C\neq 0$
5. $2\ln|y|+y^2=e^x+C$ 7. $y=\ln(\sec x+C)$
9. $y=\dfrac{1}{1-C(\csc x-\cot x)},\ y=0$
11. $y^2+\sin y=x^3+\pi^2$ 13. $y^2-2y=t^2+t+3$
15. (a)

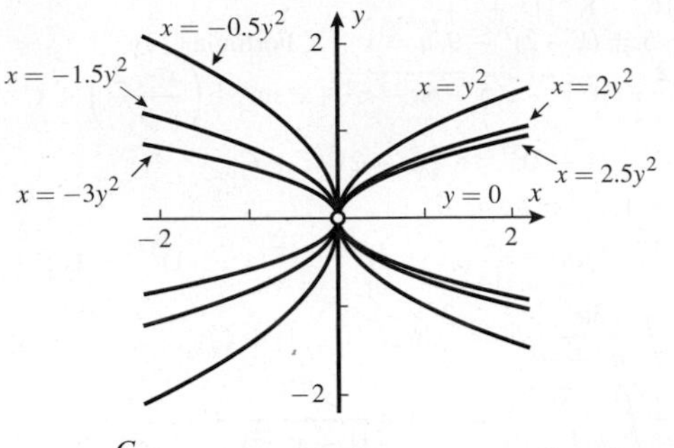


(b) $y^2=x/2$

17. $y=\dfrac{C}{\sqrt{x^2+4}}$

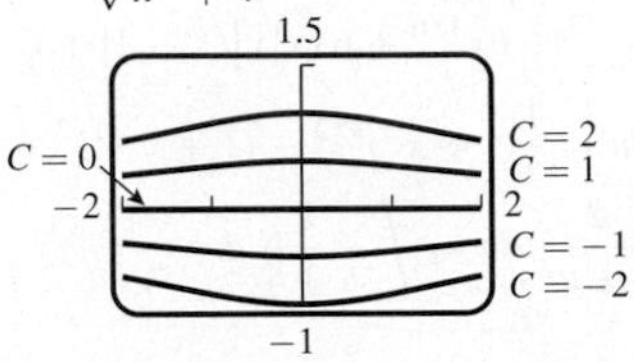


19. $x^3+y^3-3y=C$

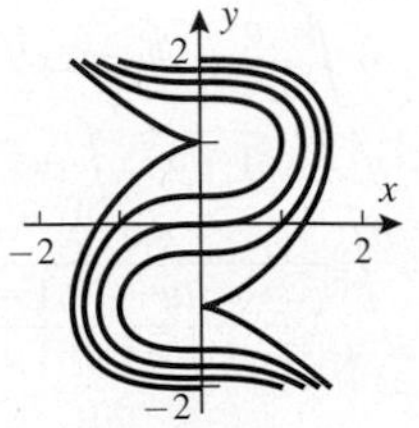


Responses to True–False questions may be abridged to save space.

21. True; since $\dfrac{1}{f(y)}\,dy=dx$. 23. True; since $\left(\frac{1}{2}\right)^5 32=1$.
27. $y=\ln\left(\dfrac{x^2}{2}-1\right)$
29. (a) $y'(t)=y(t)/50,\ y(0)=10{,}000$ (b) $y(t)=10{,}000e^{t/50}$
(c) $50\ln 2\approx 34.66$ hr (d) $50\ln(4.5)\approx 75.20$ hr
31. (a) $\dfrac{dy}{dt}=-ky,\ k\approx 0.1810$ (b) $y=5.0\times 10^7e^{-0.181t}$
(c) $\approx 219{,}000$ atoms (d) 12.72 days
33. $50\ln(100)\approx 230.26$ days 35. 3.30 days
39. (b) 70 years (c) 20 years (d) 7%
43. (a) no (b) same, $r$% 45. (b) $\ln(2)/\ln(5/4)\approx 3.106$ hr
47. (a) \$1491.82 (b) \$4493.29 (c) 8.7 years
51. (a)

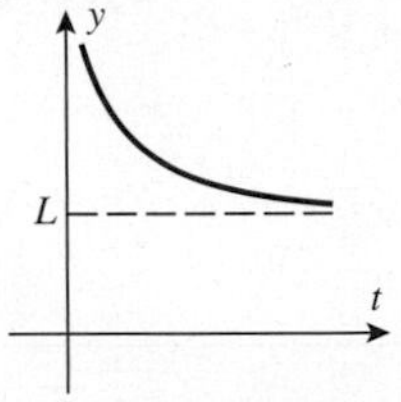


(b)

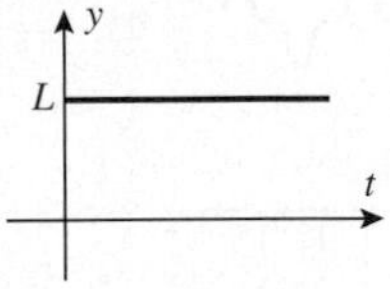


(c)

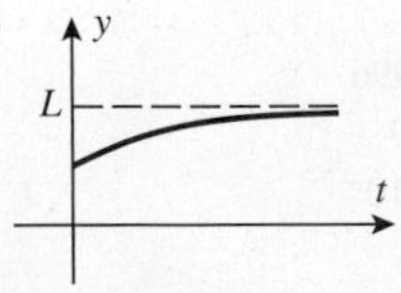


(d)

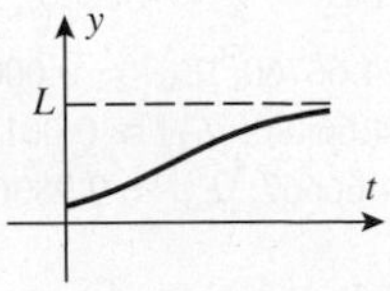


53. $y_0\approx 2,\ L\approx 8,\ k\approx 0.5493$
55. (a) $y_0=5$ (b) $L=12$ (c) $k=1$ (d) $t=0.3365$
(e) $\dfrac{dy}{dt}=\dfrac{1}{12}y(12-y),\ y(0)=5$
57. (a) $y=\dfrac{1000}{1+49e^{-0.115t}}$

**(b)**

| $t$ | 0 | 1 | 2 | 3 | 4 | 5 | 6 | 7 |
|---|---|---|---|---|---|---|---|---|
| $y(t)$ | 20 | 22 | 25 | 28 | 31 | 35 | 39 | 44 |

| $t$ | 8 | 9 | 10 | 11 | 12 | 13 | 14 | |
|---|---|---|---|---|---|---|---|---|
| $y(t)$ | 49 | 54 | 61 | 67 | 75 | 83 | 93 | |

**(c)**

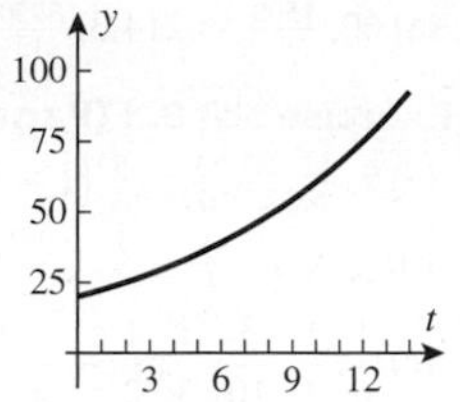


59. **(a)** $T = 21 + 74e^{-kt}$ **(b)** 6.22 min
61. **(a)** $v = c \ln \dfrac{m_0}{m_0 - kt} - gt$ **(b)** 3044 m/s
63. **(a)** $h \approx (2 - 0.003979t)^2$ **(b)** 8.4 min
65. **(a)** $v = 128/(4t+1), x = 32\ln(4t+1)$

## ▶ Exercise Set 8.3 (Page 502)

1.

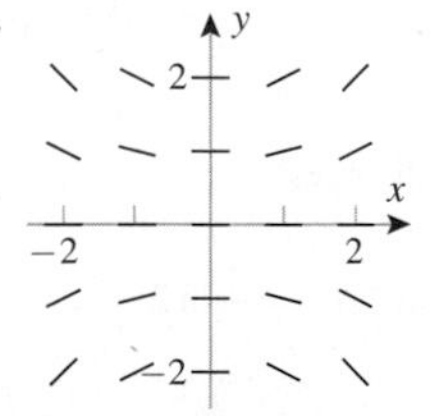


3.

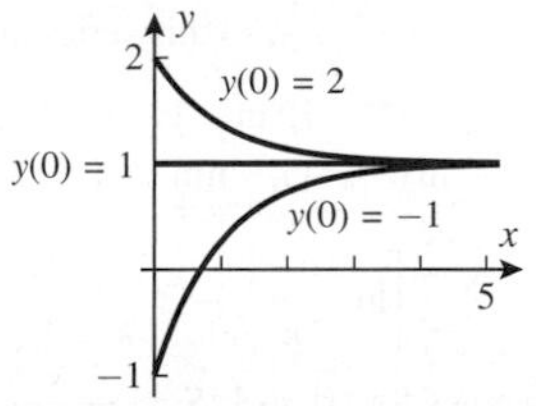


5. $y \to 1$ as $x \to +\infty$

7.

| $n$ | 0 | 1 | 2 | 3 | 4 | 5 | 6 | 7 | 8 |
|---|---|---|---|---|---|---|---|---|---|
| $x_n$ | 0 | 0.5 | 1 | 1.5 | 2 | 2.5 | 3 | 3.5 | 4 |
| $y_n$ | 1.00 | 1.50 | 2.07 | 2.71 | 3.41 | 4.16 | 4.96 | 5.82 | 6.72 |

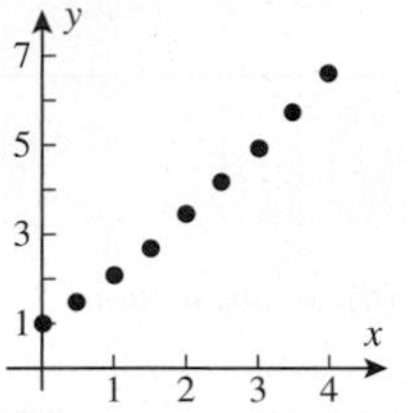


9.

| $n$ | 0 | 1 | 2 | 3 | 4 |
|---|---|---|---|---|---|
| $t_n$ | 0.00 | 0.50 | 1.00 | 1.50 | 2.00 |
| $y_n$ | 1.00 | 1.27 | 1.42 | 1.49 | 1.53 |

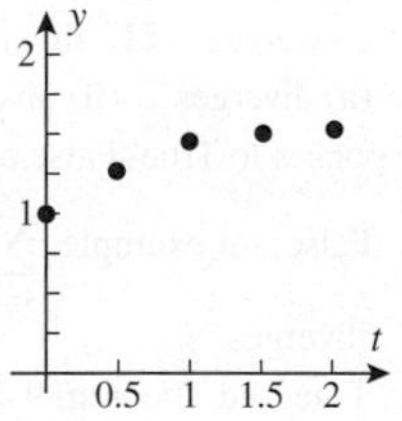


11. 0.62

Responses to True–False questions may be abridged to save space.

13. True; the derivative is positive.
15. True; $y = y_0$ is a solution if $y_0$ is a root of $p$.
17. **(b)** $y(1/2) = \sqrt{3}/2$ 19. **(b)** The $x$-intercept is ln 2.
23. **(a)** $y' = \dfrac{2xy - y^3}{3xy^2 - x^2}$ **(c)** $xy^3 - x^2y = 2$
25. **(b)** $\lim\limits_{n\to+\infty} y_n = \lim\limits_{n\to+\infty} \left(\dfrac{n+1}{n}\right)^n = e$

## ▶ Exercise Set 8.4 (Page 509)

1. $y = e^{-3x} + Ce^{-4x}$ 3. $y = e^{-x}\sin(e^x) + Ce^{-x}$
5. $y = \dfrac{C}{\sqrt{x^2+1}}$ 7. $y = \dfrac{x}{2} + \dfrac{3}{2x}$ 9. $y = 4e^{x^2} - 1$

Responses to True–False questions may be abridged to save space.

11. False; $y = x^2$ is a solution to $dy/dx = 2x$, but $y + y = 2x^2$ is not.
13. True; it will approach the concentration of the entering fluid.

15.

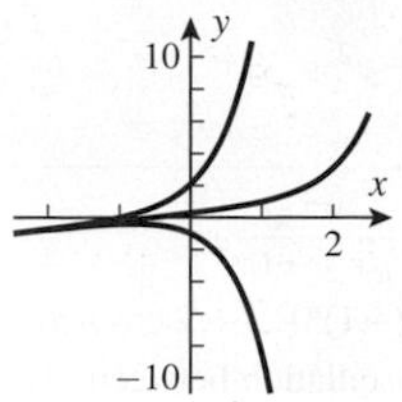


17. $\lim\limits_{x\to+\infty} y = \begin{cases} +\infty & \text{if } y_0 \ge 1/4 \\ -\infty, & \text{if } y_0 < 1/4 \end{cases}$

19. **(a)**

| $n$ | 0 | 1 | 2 | 3 | 4 | 5 |
|---|---|---|---|---|---|---|
| $x_n$ | 0 | 0.2 | 0.4 | 0.6 | 0.8 | 1.0 |
| $y_n$ | 1 | 1.20 | 1.48 | 1.86 | 2.35 | 2.98 |

**(b)** $y = -(x+1) + 2e^x$

| $x_n$ | 0 | 0.2 | 0.4 | 0.6 | 0.8 | 1.0 |
|---|---|---|---|---|---|---|
| $y(x_n)$ | 1 | 1.24 | 1.58 | 2.04 | 2.65 | 3.44 |
| Absolute error | 0 | 0.04 | 0.10 | 0.19 | 0.30 | 0.46 |
| Percentage error | 0 | 3 | 6 | 9 | 11 | 13 |

21. **(a)** $200 - 175e^{-t/25}$ oz **(b)** 136 oz
23. **(a)** $dy/dt = 145 - 0.09y, y_0 = 300$
**(b)** $y(t) = \left[14{,}500 - 11{,}800e^{-0.09t}\right]/9$
**(c)** $\lim\limits_{t\to\infty} y(t) = 14{,}500/9 \approx 1611\ \mu$g. The man should modify his diet.
27. **(a)** $I(t) = 2 - 2e^{-2t}$ A **(b)** $I(t) \to 2$ A

## ▶ Chapter 8 Review Exercises (Page 511)

1. **(a)** linear **(b)** both **(c)** separable **(d)** neither
3. $y = \tan(x^3/3 + C)$ 5. $\ln|y| + y^2/2 = e^x + C$ and $y = 0$
7. $y^{-4} + 4\ln(x/y) = 1$

9.

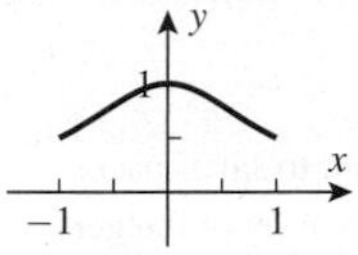


11.

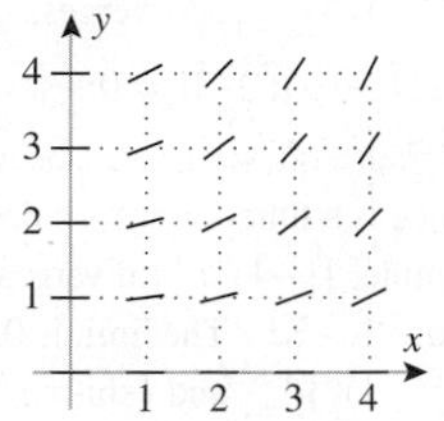


13.

| $n$ | 0 | 1 | 2 | 3 | 4 | 5 | 6 | 7 | 8 |
|---|---|---|---|---|---|---|---|---|---|
| $x_n$ | 0 | 0.5 | 1 | 1.5 | 2 | 2.5 | 3 | 3.5 | 4 |
| $y_n$ | 1 | 1.50 | 2.11 | 2.84 | 3.68 | 4.64 | 5.72 | 6.91 | 8.23 |

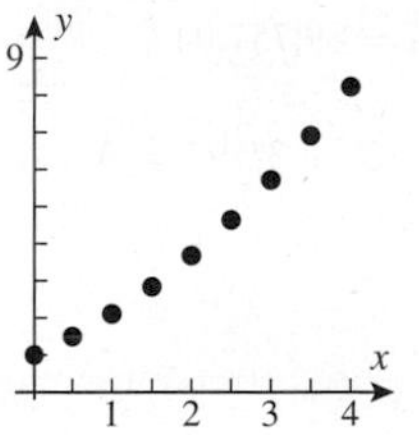


15. $y(1) \approx 1.00$

| $n$ | 0 | 1 | 2 | 3 | 4 | 5 |
|---|---|---|---|---|---|---|
| $t_n$ | 0 | 0.2 | 0.4 | 0.6 | 0.8 | 1.0 |
| $y_n$ | 1.00 | 1.20 | 1.26 | 1.10 | 0.94 | 1.00 |

17. **(a)** $y \approx 2e^{0.1386t}$ **(b)** $y = 5e^{0.015t}$ **(c)** $y \approx 0.5995e^{0.5117t}$
**(d)** $y \approx 0.8706e^{0.1386t}$ 19. $y = e^{-2x} + Ce^{-3x}$
21. $y = -1 + 4e^{x^2/2}$ 23. $y = 2\,\text{sech}\,x + \frac{1}{2}(x\,\text{sech}\,x + \sinh x)$
25. about 646 oz

## ▶ Chapter 8 Making Connections (Page 512)

Where correct answers to a Making Connections exercise may vary, no answer is listed. Sample answers for these questions are available on the Book Companion Site.

1. **(b)** $y = 2 - 3e^{-2x}$
3. **(a)** $du/dx = (f(u) - u)/x$ **(b)** $x^2 - 2xy - y^2 = C$

## ▶ Exercise Set 9.1 (Page 522)

1. **(a)** $\dfrac{1}{3^{n-1}}$ **(b)** $\dfrac{(-1)^{n-1}}{3^{n-1}}$ **(c)** $\dfrac{2n-1}{2n}$ **(d)** $\dfrac{n^2}{\pi^{1/(n+1)}}$
3. **(a)** $2, 0, 2, 0$ **(b)** $1, -1, 1, -1$ **(c)** $2(1 + (-1)^n); 2 + 2\cos n\pi$
5. **(a)** The limit doesn't exist due to repeated oscillation between $-1$ and 1. **(b)** $-1; 1; -1; 1; -1$ **(c)** no
7. $\frac{1}{3}, \frac{2}{4}, \frac{3}{5}, \frac{4}{6}, \frac{5}{7}$; converges, $\lim_{n\to+\infty} \dfrac{n}{n+2} = 1$
9. $2, 2, 2, 2, 2$; converges, $\lim_{n\to+\infty} 2 = 2$
11. $\dfrac{\ln 1}{1}, \dfrac{\ln 2}{2}, \dfrac{\ln 3}{3}, \dfrac{\ln 4}{4}, \dfrac{\ln 5}{5}$; converges, $\lim_{n\to+\infty} \dfrac{\ln n}{n} = 0$
13. $0, 2, 0, 2, 0$; diverges 15. $-1, \frac{16}{9}, -\frac{54}{28}, \frac{128}{65}, -\frac{250}{126}$; diverges
17. $\frac{6}{2}, \frac{12}{8}, \frac{20}{18}, \frac{30}{32}, \frac{42}{50}$; converges, $\lim_{n\to+\infty} \dfrac{1}{2}\left(1 + \dfrac{1}{n}\right)\left(1 + \dfrac{2}{n}\right) = \dfrac{1}{2}$
19. $e^{-1}, 4e^{-2}, 9e^{-3}, 16e^{-4}, 25e^{-5}$; converges, $\lim_{n\to+\infty} n^2 e^{-n} = 0$
21. $2, \left(\dfrac{5}{3}\right)^2, \left(\dfrac{6}{4}\right)^3, \left(\dfrac{7}{5}\right)^4, \left(\dfrac{8}{6}\right)^5$; converges, $\lim_{n\to+\infty} \left[\dfrac{n+3}{n+1}\right]^n = e^2$
23. $\left\{\dfrac{2n-1}{2n}\right\}_{n=1}^{+\infty}$; converges, $\lim_{n\to+\infty} \dfrac{2n-1}{2n} = 1$
25. $\left\{(-1)^{n+1}\dfrac{1}{3^n}\right\}_{n=1}^{+\infty}$; converges, $\lim_{n\to+\infty} (-1)^{n+1}\dfrac{1}{3^n} = 0$
27. $\left\{(-1)^{n+1}\left(\dfrac{1}{n} - \dfrac{1}{n+1}\right)\right\}_{n=1}^{+\infty}$; converges, $\lim_{n\to+\infty} (-1)^{n+1}\left(\dfrac{1}{n} - \dfrac{1}{n+1}\right) = 0$
29. $\{\sqrt{n+1} - \sqrt{n+2}\}_{n=1}^{+\infty}$; converges, $\lim_{n\to+\infty} (\sqrt{n+1} - \sqrt{n+2}) = 0$

Responses to True–False questions may be abridged to save space.

31. True; a sequence is a function whose domain is a set of integers.
33. False; for example, $\{(-1)^{n+1}\}$ diverges with terms that oscillate between 1 and $-1$. 35. The limit is 0.
37. for example, $\{(-1)^n\}_{n=1}^{+\infty}$ and $\{\sin(\pi n/2) + 1/n\}_{n=1}^{+\infty}$
39. **(a)** $1, 2, 1, 4, 1, 6$ **(b)** $a_n = \begin{cases} n, & n \text{ odd} \\ 1/2^n, & n \text{ even} \end{cases}$
 **(c)** $a_n = \begin{cases} 1/n, & n \text{ odd} \\ 1/(n+1); & n \text{ even} \end{cases}$
 **(d)** (a) diverges; (b) diverges; (c) $\lim_{n\to+\infty} a_n = 0$
43. **(a)** $a_{n+1} = 1.1a_n + 20, a_0 = 20$ **(b)** $a_{40} = \$9{,}757.04$
45. **(a)** $p_{10} = 6002$ **(b)** $p_0 = 6000$
47. **(a)**

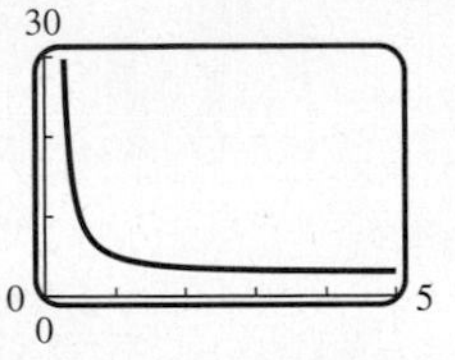


**(b)** $\lim_{n\to+\infty} (2^n + 3^n)^{1/n} = 3$

51. **(a)** $N = 4$ **(b)** $N = 10$ **(c)** $N = 1000$

## ▶ Exercise Set 9.2 (Page 530)

1. strictly decreasing 3. strictly increasing 5. strictly decreasing
7. strictly increasing 9. strictly decreasing 11. strictly increasing

Responses to True–False questions may be abridged to save space.

13. True; $a_{n+1} - a_n > 0$ for all $n$ is equivalent to $a_1 < a_2 < a_3 < \cdots < a_n < \cdots$.
15. False; for example, $\{(-1)^{n+1}\} = \{1, -1, 1, -1, \ldots\}$ is bounded but diverges.
17. strictly increasing 19. strictly increasing
21. eventually strictly increasing 23. eventually strictly increasing
25. Yes; the limit lies in the interval $[1, 2]$.
27. **(a)** $\sqrt{2}, \sqrt{2 + \sqrt{2}}, \sqrt{2 + \sqrt{2 + \sqrt{2}}}$ **(e)** $L = 2$
29. **(a)** $60, \frac{1500}{7} \approx 214.3, \frac{3750}{13} \approx 288.5, \frac{75{,}000}{251} \approx 298.8$ **(d)** $L = 300$

## ▶ Exercise Set 9.3 (Page 537)

1. **(a)** $2, \frac{12}{5}, \frac{62}{25}, \frac{312}{125}; \frac{5}{2}\left(1 - \left(\frac{1}{5}\right)^n\right)$; $\lim_{n\to+\infty} s_n = \frac{5}{2}$ (converges)
 **(b)** $\frac{1}{4}, \frac{3}{4}, \frac{7}{4}, \frac{15}{4}; -\frac{1}{4}(1 - 2^n)$; $\lim_{n\to+\infty} s_n = +\infty$ (diverges)
 **(c)** $\dfrac{1}{6}, \dfrac{1}{4}, \dfrac{3}{10}, \dfrac{1}{3}; \dfrac{1}{2} - \dfrac{1}{n+2}$; $\lim_{n\to+\infty} s_n = \dfrac{1}{2}$ (converges)
3. $\frac{4}{7}$ 5. 6 7. $\frac{1}{3}$ 9. $\frac{1}{6}$ 11. diverges 13. $\frac{448}{3}$
15. **(a)** Exercise 5 **(b)** Exercise 3 **(c)** Exercise 7 **(d)** Exercise 9

Responses to True–False questions may be abridged to save space.

17. False; an infinite series converges if its sequence of *partial sums* converges.
19. True; the sequence of partial sums $\{s_n\}$ for the harmonic series satisfies $s_{2^n} > \dfrac{n+1}{2}$, so this series diverges.
21. 1 23. $\frac{532}{99}$ 27. 70 m 29. **(a)** $1/4$
31. **(a)** $S_n = -\ln(n+1)$; $\lim_{n\to+\infty} S_n = -\infty$ (diverges)
 **(b)** $S_n = \displaystyle\sum_{k=2}^{n+1}\left[\ln\frac{k-1}{k} - \ln\frac{k}{k+1}\right]$, $\lim_{n\to+\infty} S_n = -\ln 2$
33. **(a)** converges for $|x| < 1$; $S = \dfrac{x}{1+x^2}$
 **(b)** converges for $|x| > 2$; $S = \dfrac{1}{x^2 - 2x}$
 **(c)** converges for $x > 0$; $S = \dfrac{1}{e^x - 1}$
35. $a_n = \dfrac{1}{2^{n-1}}a_1 + \dfrac{1}{2^{n-1}} + \dfrac{1}{2^{n-2}} + \cdots + \dfrac{1}{2}$, $\lim_{n\to+\infty} a_n = 1$

## ▶ Exercise Set 9.4 (Page 545)

1. **(a)** $\frac{4}{3}$ **(b)** $-\frac{3}{4}$
3. **(a)** $p = 3$, converges **(b)** $p = \frac{1}{2}$, diverges
 **(c)** $p = 1$, diverges **(d)** $p = \frac{2}{3}$, diverges
5. **(a)** diverges **(b)** diverges **(c)** diverges **(d)** no information
7. **(a)** diverges **(b)** converges
9. diverges 11. diverges 13. diverges 15. diverges 17. diverges
19. converges 21. diverges 23. converges 25. converges for $p > 1$
29. **(a)** diverges **(b)** diverges

Responses to True–False questions may be abridged to save space.

31. False; for example, $\displaystyle\sum_{k=0}^{\infty} 2^{-k}$ converges to 2, but $\displaystyle\sum \frac{1}{2^{-k}} = \sum 2^k$ diverges.
33. True; see Theorem 9.4.4.
35. **(a)** $(\pi^2/2) - (\pi^4/90)$ **(b)** $(\pi^2/6) - (5/4)$ **(c)** $\pi^4/90$
37. **(d)** $\frac{1}{11} < \frac{1}{6}\pi^2 - s_{10} < \frac{1}{10}$
39. **(a)** $\displaystyle\int_n^{+\infty} \frac{1}{x^4}\,dx = \frac{1}{3n^3}$; apply Exercise 36(b) **(b)** $n = 6$
 **(c)** $\dfrac{\pi^4}{90} \approx 1.08238$
41. converges

## ▶ Exercise Set 9.5 (Page 551)

1. **(a)** converges **(b)** diverges 5. converges 7. converges
9. diverges 11. converges 13. inconclusive 15. diverges
17. diverges 19. converges

Responses to True–False questions may be abridged to save space.

21. False; the limit comparison test uses a limit of the quotient of corresponding terms taken from two different sequences.
23. True; use the limit comparison test with the convergent series $\sum(1/k^2)$.
25. converges 27. converges 29. converges 31. converges
33. diverges 35. converges 37. diverges 39. converges
41. converges 43. diverges 45. converges 47. converges
49. converges

51. $u_k = \dfrac{k!}{1 \cdot 3 \cdot 5 \cdots (2k-1)}$; $\rho = \lim_{k \to +\infty} \dfrac{k+1}{2k+1} = \dfrac{1}{2}$; converges
53. (a) converges (b) diverges 55. (a) converges

## ▶ Exercise Set 9.6 (Page 561)

3. diverges 5. converges 7. converges absolutely 9. diverges
11. converges absolutely 13. conditionally convergent 15. divergent
17. conditionally convergent 19. conditionally convergent
21. divergent 23. conditionally convergent 25. converges absolutely
27. converges absolutely

Responses to True–False questions may be abridged to save space.

29. False; an alternating series has terms that alternate between positive and negative.
31. True; if a series converges but diverges absolutely, then it converges conditionally.
33. $|\text{error}| < 0.125$ 35. $|\text{error}| < 0.1$ 37. $n = 9999$
39. $n = 39{,}999$ 41. $|\text{error}| < 0.00074$; $s_{10} \approx 0.4995$; $S = 0.5$
43. 0.84 45. 0.41 47. (c) $n = 50$
49. (a) If $a_k = \dfrac{(-1)^k}{\sqrt{k}}$, then $\sum a_k$ converges and $\sum a_k^2$ diverges.
If $a_k = \dfrac{(-1)^k}{k}$, then $\sum a_k$ converges and $\sum a_k^2$ also converges.
(b) If $a_k = \dfrac{1}{k}$, then $\sum a_k^2$ converges and $\sum a_k$ diverges. If $a_k = \dfrac{1}{k^2}$, then $\sum a_k^2$ converges and $\sum a_k$ also converges.

## ▶ Exercise Set 9.7 (Page 572)

1. (a) $1 - x + \frac{1}{2}x^2,\ 1 - x$ (b) $1 - \frac{1}{2}x^2,\ 1$
3. (a) $1 + \frac{1}{2}(x-1) - \frac{1}{8}(x-1)^2$ (b) 1.04875 5. 1.80397443
7. $p_0(x) = 1, p_1(x) = 1 - x, p_2(x) = 1 - x + \frac{1}{2}x^2,$
$p_3(x) = 1 - x + \dfrac{1}{2}x^2 - \dfrac{1}{3!}x^3,$
$p_4(x) = 1 - x + \dfrac{1}{2}x^2 - \dfrac{1}{3!}x^3 + \dfrac{1}{4!}x^4; \sum_{k=0}^{n} \dfrac{(-1)^k}{k!}x^k$
9. $p_0(x) = 1, p_1(x) = 1, p_2(x) = 1 - \dfrac{\pi^2}{2!}x^2, p_3(x) = 1 - \dfrac{\pi^2}{2!}x^2,$
$p_4(x) = 1 - \dfrac{\pi^2}{2!}x^2 + \dfrac{\pi^4}{4!}x^4; \sum_{k=0}^{\lfloor n/2 \rfloor} \dfrac{(-1)^k \pi^{2k}}{(2k)!}x^{2k}$ (See Exercise 74 of Section 0.2.)
11. $p_0(x) = 0, p_1(x) = x, p_2(x) = x - \frac{1}{2}x^2, p_3(x) = x - \frac{1}{2}x^2 + \frac{1}{3}x^3,$
$p_4(x) = x - \frac{1}{2}x^2 + \frac{1}{3}x^3 - \frac{1}{4}x^4; \sum_{k=1}^{n} \dfrac{(-1)^{k+1}}{k}x^k$
13. $p_0(x) = 1, p_1(x) = 1, p_2(x) = 1 + \dfrac{x^2}{2},$
$p_3(x) = 1 + \dfrac{x^2}{2}, p_4(x) = 1 + \dfrac{x^2}{2} + \dfrac{x^4}{4!}; \sum_{k=0}^{\lfloor n/2 \rfloor} \dfrac{1}{(2k)!}x^{2k}$
(See Exercise 74 of Section 0.2.)
15. $p_0(x) = 0, p_1(x) = 0, p_2(x) = x^2, p_3(x) = x^2,$
$p_4(x) = x^2 - \frac{1}{6}x^4; \sum_{k=0}^{\lfloor n/2 \rfloor - 1} \dfrac{(-1)^k}{(2k+1)!}x^{2k+2}$ (See Exercise 74 of Section 0.2.)
17. $p_0(x) = e, p_1(x) = e + e(x-1),$
$p_2(x) = e + e(x-1) + \dfrac{e}{2}(x-1)^2,$
$p_3(x) = e + e(x-1) + \dfrac{e}{2}(x-1)^2 + \dfrac{e}{3!}(x-1)^3,$
$p_4(x) = e + e(x-1) + \dfrac{e}{2}(x-1)^2 + \dfrac{e}{3!}(x-1)^3 + \dfrac{e}{4!}(x-1)^4;$
$\sum_{k=0}^{n} \dfrac{e}{k!}(x-1)^k$
19. $p_0(x) = -1, p_1(x) = -1 - (x+1),$
$p_2(x) = -1 - (x+1) - (x+1)^2,$
$p_3(x) = -1 - (x+1) - (x+1)^2 - (x+1)^3,$
$p_4(x) = -1 - (x+1) - (x+1)^2 - (x+1)^3 - (x+1)^4;$
$\sum_{k=0}^{n} (-1)(x+1)^k$
21. $p_0(x) = p_1(x) = 1, p_2(x) = p_3(x) = 1 - \dfrac{\pi^2}{2}\left(x - \dfrac{1}{2}\right)^2,$
$p_4(x) = 1 - \dfrac{\pi^2}{2}\left(x - \dfrac{1}{2}\right)^2 + \dfrac{\pi^4}{4!}\left(x - \dfrac{1}{2}\right)^4;$
$\sum_{k=0}^{\lfloor n/2 \rfloor} \dfrac{(-1)^k \pi^{2k}}{(2k)!}\left(x - \dfrac{1}{2}\right)^{2k}$ (See Exercise 74 of Section 0.2.)
23. $p_0(x) = 0, p_1(x) = (x-1), p_2(x) = (x-1) - \frac{1}{2}(x-1)^2,$
$p_3(x) = (x-1) - \frac{1}{2}(x-1)^2 + \frac{1}{3}(x-1)^3,$
$p_4(x) = (x-1) - \frac{1}{2}(x-1)^2 + \frac{1}{3}(x-1)^3 - \frac{1}{4}(x-1)^4;$
$\sum_{k=1}^{n} \dfrac{(-1)^{k-1}}{k}(x-1)^k$
25. (a) $p_3(x) = 1 + 2x - x^2 + x^3$
(b) $p_3(x) = 1 + 2(x-1) - (x-1)^2 + (x-1)^3$
27. $p_0(x) = 1, p_1(x) = 1 - 2x,$
$p_2(x) = 1 - 2x + 2x^2,$
$p_3(x) = 1 - 2x + 2x^2 - \frac{4}{3}x^3$

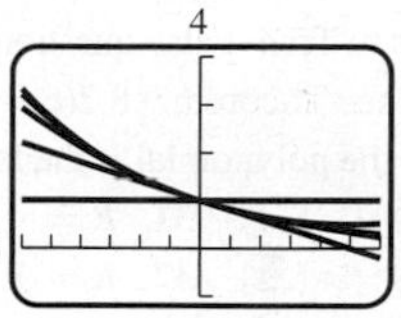


29. $p_0(x) = -1, p_2(x) = -1 + \frac{1}{2}(x-\pi)^2,$
$p_4(x) = -1 + \frac{1}{2}(x-\pi)^2 - \frac{1}{24}(x-\pi)^4,$
$p_6(x) = -1 + \frac{1}{2}(x-\pi)^2 - \frac{1}{24}(x-\pi)^4 + \frac{1}{720}(x-\pi)^6$

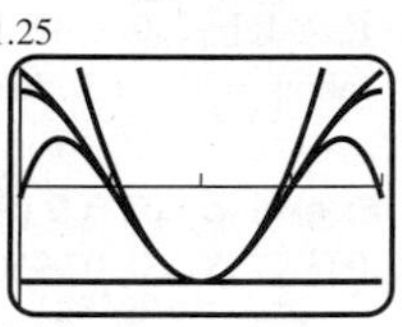


Responses to True–False questions may be abridged to save space.

31. True; $y = f(x_0) + f'(x_0)(x - x_0)$ is the first-degree Taylor polynomial for $f$ about $x = x_0$.
33. False; $p_6^{(4)}(x_0) = f^{(4)}(x_0)$ 35. 1.64870 37. IV
39. (a)

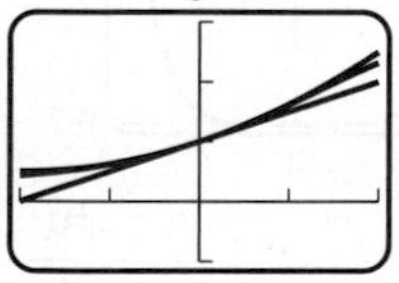


(b)

| $x$ | −1.000 | −0.750 | −0.500 | −0.250 | 0.000 | 0.250 | 0.500 | 0.750 | 1.000 |
|---|---|---|---|---|---|---|---|---|---|
| $f(x)$ | 0.431 | 0.506 | 0.619 | 0.781 | 1.000 | 1.281 | 1.615 | 1.977 | 2.320 |
| $p_1(x)$ | 0.000 | 0.250 | 0.500 | 0.750 | 1.000 | 1.250 | 1.500 | 1.750 | 2.000 |
| $p_2(x)$ | 0.500 | 0.531 | 0.625 | 0.781 | 1.000 | 1.281 | 1.625 | 2.031 | 2.500 |

(c) $|e^{\sin x} - (1 + x)| < 0.01$ for $-0.14 < x < 0.14$

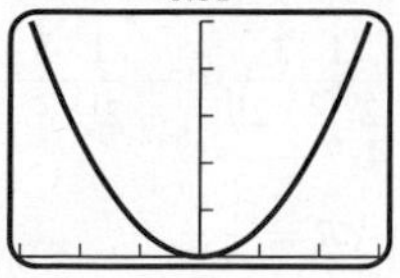


(d) $\left|e^{\sin x} - \left(1 + x + \dfrac{x^2}{2}\right)\right| < 0.01$ for $-0.50 < x < 0.50$

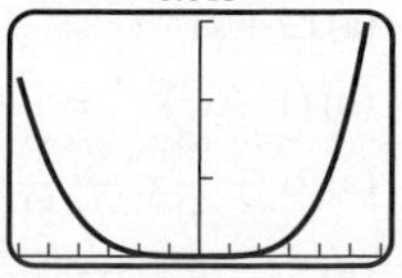

41. (a) $[0, 0.137]$ (b)

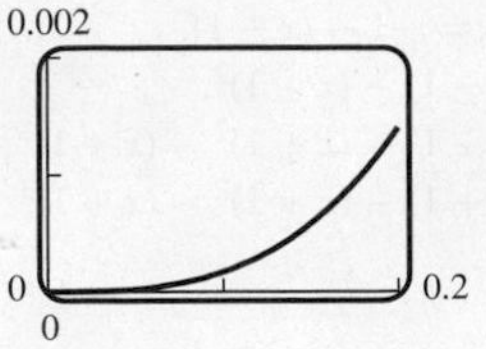


43. $(-0.569, 0.569)$ 45. $(-0.281, 0.281)$

### ▶ Exercise Set 9.8 (Page 581)

1. $\sum_{k=0}^{\infty} \frac{(-1)^k}{k!} x^k$ 3. $\sum_{k=0}^{\infty} \frac{(-1)^k \pi^{2k}}{(2k)!} x^{2k}$ 5. $\sum_{k=1}^{\infty} \frac{(-1)^{k+1}}{k} x^k$

7. $\sum_{k=0}^{\infty} \frac{1}{(2k)!} x^{2k}$ 9. $\sum_{k=0}^{\infty} \frac{(-1)^k}{(2k+1)!} x^{2k+2}$ 11. $\sum_{k=0}^{\infty} \frac{e}{k!}(x-1)^k$

13. $\sum_{k=0}^{\infty} (-1)(x+1)^k$ 15. $\sum_{k=0}^{\infty} \frac{(-1)^k \pi^{2k}}{(2k)!}\left(x - \frac{1}{2}\right)^{2k}$

17. $\sum_{k=1}^{\infty} \frac{(-1)^{k-1}}{k}(x-1)^k$ 19. $-1 < x < 1; \frac{1}{1+x}$

21. $1 < x < 3; \frac{1}{3-x}$ 23. (a) $-2 < x < 2$ (b) $f(0) = 1; f(1) = \frac{2}{3}$

Responses to True–False questions may be abridged to save space.

25. True; see Theorem 9.8.2(*c*).

27. True; the polynomial *is* the Maclaurin series and converges for all $x$.

29. $R = 1; [-1, 1)$ 31. $R = +\infty; (-\infty, +\infty)$ 33. $R = \frac{1}{5}; \left[-\frac{1}{5}, \frac{1}{5}\right]$

35. $R = 1; [-1, 1]$ 37. $R = 1; (-1, 1]$ 39. $R = +\infty; (-\infty, +\infty)$

41. $R = 1; [-1, 1]$ 43. $R = \frac{4}{3}; \left(-\frac{19}{3}, -\frac{11}{3}\right)$ 45. $R = 1; (-2, 0]$

47. $R = 1; [-2, 0]$ 49. $R = +\infty; (-\infty, +\infty)$ 51. $(-\infty, +\infty)$

57. radius $= R$ 63. (a) $n = 5$; $s_5 \approx 1.1026$ (b) $\zeta(3.7) \approx 1.10629$

### ▶ Exercise Set 9.9 (Page 589)

3. 0.069756 5. 0.99500 7. 0.99619 9. 0.5208

11. (a) $\sum_{k=1}^{\infty} 2\frac{(1/9)^{2k-1}}{2k-1}$ (b) 0.223

13. (a) 0.4635; 0.3218 (b) 3.1412 (c) no

15. (a) error $\le 9 \times 10^{-8}$ (b)

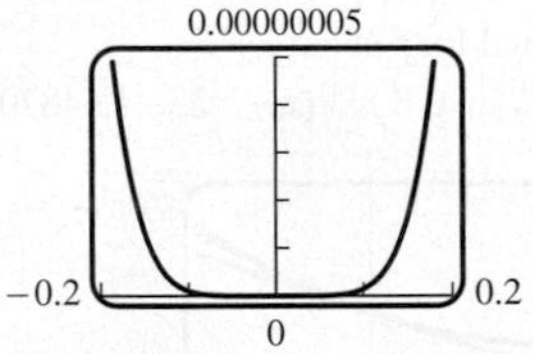


17. (a) $\sum_{k=0}^{\infty} (-1)^k x^k$ (b) $1 + \frac{x}{3} + \sum_{k=2}^{\infty} (-1)^{k-1} \frac{2 \cdot 5 \cdots (3k-4)}{3^k k!} x^k$

(c) $\sum_{k=0}^{\infty} (-1)^k \frac{(k+2)(k+1)}{2} x^k$ 23. 23.406%

### ▶ Exercise Set 9.10 (Page 599)

1. (a) $1 - x + x^2 - \cdots + (-1)^k x^k + \cdots; R = 1$

(b) $1 + x^2 + x^4 + \cdots + x^{2k} + \cdots; R = 1$

(c) $1 + 2x + 4x^2 + \cdots + 2^k x^k + \cdots; R = \frac{1}{2}$

(d) $\frac{1}{2} + \frac{1}{2^2}x + \frac{1}{2^3}x^2 + \cdots + \frac{1}{2^{k+1}}x^k + \cdots; R = 2$

3. (a) $(2+x)^{-1/2} = \frac{1}{2^{1/2}} - \frac{1}{2^{5/2}}x + \frac{1 \cdot 3}{2^{9/2} \cdot 2!}x^2 - \frac{1 \cdot 3 \cdot 5}{2^{13/2} \cdot 3!}x^3 + \cdots$

(b) $(1 - x^2)^{-2} = 1 + 2x^2 + 3x^4 + 4x^6 + \cdots$

5. (a) $2x - \frac{2^3}{3!}x^3 + \frac{2^5}{5!}x^5 - \frac{2^7}{7!}x^7 + \cdots; R = +\infty$

(b) $1 - 2x + 2x^2 - \frac{4}{3}x^3 + \cdots; R = +\infty$

(c) $1 + x^2 + \frac{1}{2!}x^4 + \frac{1}{3!}x^6 + \cdots; R = +\infty$

(d) $x^2 - \frac{\pi^2}{2}x^4 + \frac{\pi^4}{4!}x^6 - \frac{\pi^6}{6!}x^8 + \cdots; R = +\infty$

7. (a) $x^2 - 3x^3 + 9x^4 - 27x^5 + \cdots; R = \frac{1}{3}$

(b) $2x^2 + \frac{2^3}{3!}x^4 + \frac{2^5}{5!}x^6 + \frac{2^7}{7!}x^8 + \cdots; R = +\infty$

(c) $x - \frac{3}{2}x^3 + \frac{3}{8}x^5 + \frac{1}{16}x^7 + \cdots; R = 1$

9. (a) $x^2 - \frac{2^3}{4!}x^4 + \frac{2^5}{6!}x^6 - \frac{2^7}{8!}x^8 + \cdots$

(b) $12x^3 - 6x^6 + 4x^9 - 3x^{12} + \cdots$

11. (a) $1 - (x-1) + (x-1)^2 - \cdots + (-1)^k(x-1)^k + \cdots$ (b) $(0, 2)$

13. (a) $x + x^2 + \frac{x^3}{3} - \frac{x^5}{30} + \cdots$ (b) $x - \frac{x^3}{24} + \frac{x^4}{24} - \frac{71}{1920}x^5 + \cdots$

15. (a) $1 + \frac{1}{2}x^2 + \frac{5}{24}x^4 + \frac{61}{720}x^6 + \cdots$

(b) $x - x^2 + \frac{1}{3}x^3 - \frac{1}{30}x^5 + \cdots$

19. $2 - 4x + 2x^2 - 4x^3 + 2x^4 + \cdots$

25. $[-1, 1]; [-1, 1)$ 27. (a) $\sum_{k=0}^{\infty} x^{2k+1}$ (b) $f^{(5)}(0) = 5!, f^{(6)}(0) = 0$

(c) $f^{(n)}(0) = n! c_n = \begin{cases} n! & \text{if } n \text{ odd} \\ 0 & \text{if } n \text{ even} \end{cases}$

29. (a) 1 (b) $-\frac{1}{3}$ 31. 0.3103 33. 0.200

35. (a) $\sum_{k=0}^{\infty} \frac{x^{4k}}{k!}; R = +\infty$ 37. (a) $3/4$ (b) $\ln(4/3)$

39. (a) $x - \frac{1}{6}x^3 + \frac{3}{40}x^5 - \frac{5}{112}x^7 + \cdots$

(b) $x + \sum_{k=1}^{\infty} (-1)^k \frac{1 \cdot 3 \cdot 5 \cdots (2k-1)}{2^k k!(2k+1)} x^{2k+1}$ (c) $R = 1$

41. (a) $y(t) = y_0 \sum_{k=0}^{\infty} \frac{(-1)^k (0.000121)^k t^k}{k!}$ (c) $0.9998790073 y_0$

43. $2\pi\sqrt{\frac{L}{g}}\left(1 + \frac{k^2}{4} + \frac{9k^4}{64}\right)$

### ▶ Chapter 9 Review Exercises (Page 602)

9. (a) true (b) sometimes false (c) sometimes false (d) true (e) sometimes false (f) sometimes false (g) false (h) sometimes false (i) true (j) true (k) sometimes false (l) sometimes false

11. (a) $\left\{\frac{n+2}{(n+1)^2 - n^2}\right\}_{n=1}^{+\infty}$; converges, $\lim_{n \to +\infty} \frac{n+2}{(n+1)^2 - n^2} = \frac{1}{2}$

(b) $\left\{(-1)^{n+1}\frac{n}{2n+1}\right\}_{n=1}^{+\infty}$; diverges

15. (a) converges (b) converges 17. (a) converges (b) diverges

19. (a) diverges (b) converges 21. $\frac{1}{4 \cdot 5^{99}}$

23. (a) 2 (b) diverges (c) $3/4$ (d) $\pi/4$ 25. $p > 1$

29. (a) $p_0(x) = 1, p_1(x) = 1 - 7x, p_2(x) = 1 - 7x + 5x^2,$ $p_3(x) = 1 - 7x + 5x^2 + 4x^3, p_4(x) = 1 - 7x + 5x^2 + 4x^3$

33. (a) $e^2 - 1$ (b) 0 (c) $\cos e$ (d) $\frac{1}{3}$

37. (a) $x - \frac{2}{3}x^3 + \frac{2}{15}x^5 - \frac{4}{315}x^7$ (b) $x - \frac{2}{3}x^3 + \frac{2}{15}x^5 - \frac{4}{315}x^7$

### ▶ Chapter 9 Making Connections (Page 604)

Where correct answers to a Making Connections exercise may vary, no answer is listed. Sample answers for these questions are available on the Book Companion Site.

1. (a) $\frac{a \sin\theta}{1 - \cos\theta}$ (b) $a \csc\theta$ (c) $a \cot\theta$

2. (a) $A = 1, B = -2$ (b) $s_n = 2 - \frac{2^{n+1}}{3^{n+1} - 2^{n+1}}; 2$

4. (a) $124.58 < d < 124.77$ (b) $1243 < s < 1424$

6. (b) $v(t) \approx v_0 - \left(\frac{cv_0}{m} + g\right)t + \frac{c^2}{2m^2}\left(v_0 + \frac{mg}{c}\right)t^2$

## ▶ Exercise Set 10.1 (Page 613)

1. **(a)** $y = x + 2\,(-1 \le x \le 4)$

**(c)**

| $t$ | 0 | 1 | 2 | 3 | 4 | 5 |
|---|---|---|---|---|---|---|
| $x$ | −1 | 0 | 1 | 2 | 3 | 4 |
| $y$ | 1 | 2 | 3 | 4 | 5 | 6 |

**(d)**

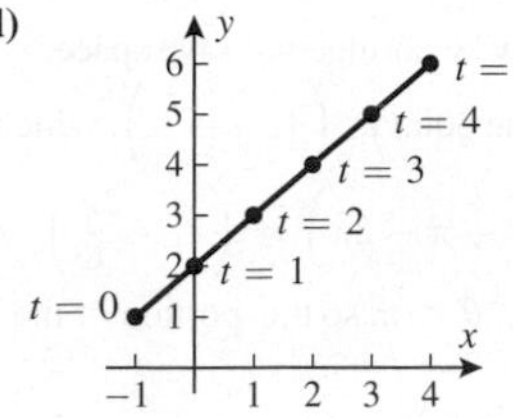


3.

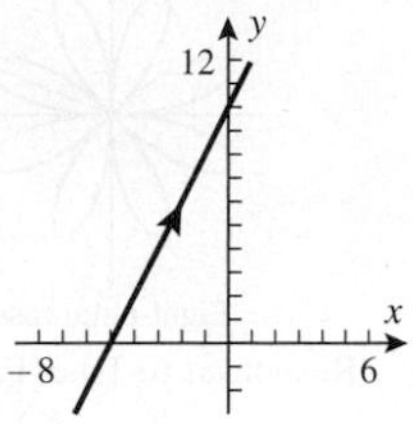


5.

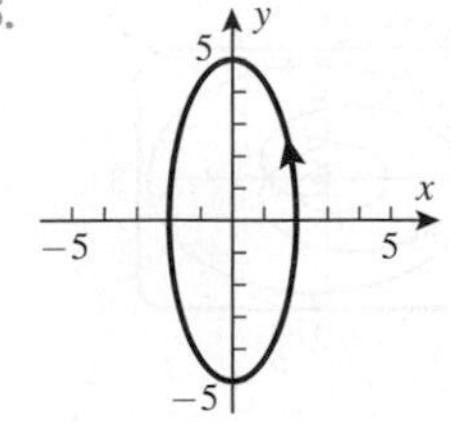


7.

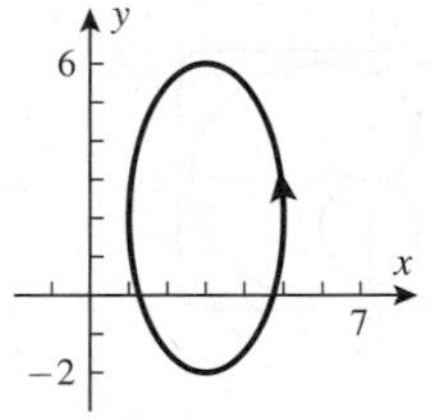


9.

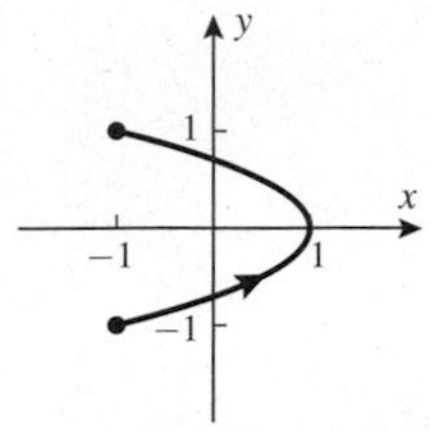


11.

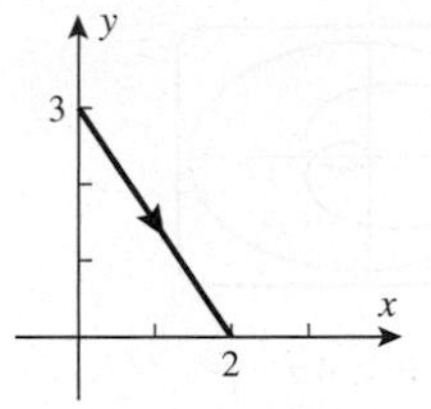


13. $x = 5\cos t, y = -5\sin t\,(0 \le t \le 2\pi)$ 15. $x = 2, y = t$

17. $x = t^2, y = t\,(-1 \le t \le 1)$

19. **(a)**

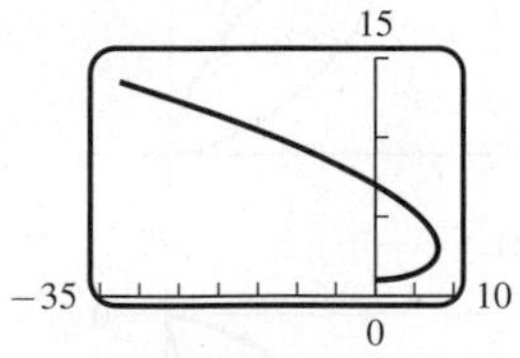


**(b)**

| $t$ | 0 | 1 | 2 | 3 | 4 | 5 |
|---|---|---|---|---|---|---|
| $x$ | 0 | 5.5 | 8 | 4.5 | −8 | −32.5 |
| $y$ | 1 | 1.5 | 3 | 5.5 | 9 | 13.5 |

**(c)** $t = 0, 2\sqrt{3}$ **(d)** $0 < t < 2\sqrt{2}$ **(e)** $t = 2$

21. **(a)**

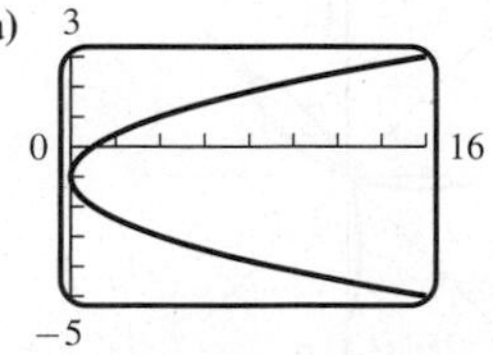


**(b)**

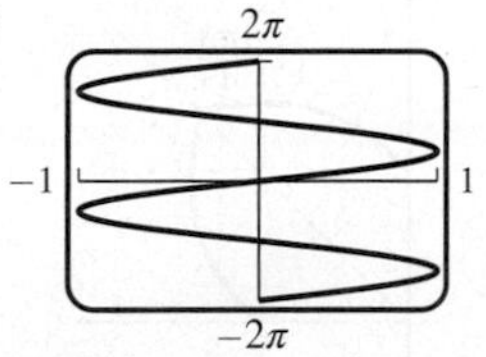


23. **(a)** IV **(b)** II **(c)** V **(d)** VI **(e)** III **(f)** I 25. **(b)** $\frac{1}{2}$ **(c)** $\frac{3}{4}$

27. **(b)** from $(x_0, y_0)$ to $(x_1, y_1)$
**(c)** $x = 3 - 2(t - 1), y = -1 + 5(t - 1)$

29.

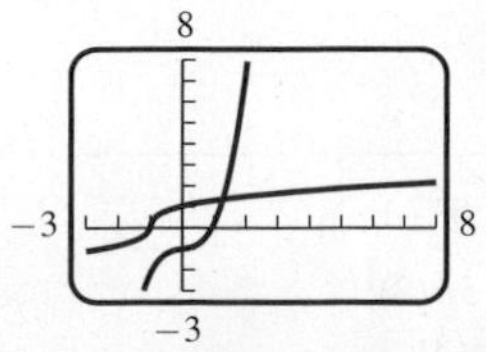


31.

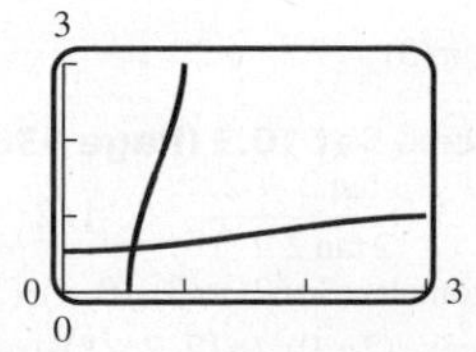


Responses to True–False questions may be abridged to save space.

33. False; $x = \sin t, y = \cos^2 t$ describe only the portion of the parabola $y = 1 - x^2$ with $-1 \le x \le 1$.

35. True; $\dfrac{dy}{dx} = \dfrac{dy/dt}{dx/dt} = \dfrac{12t^3 - 6t^2}{x'(t)}$ 37.

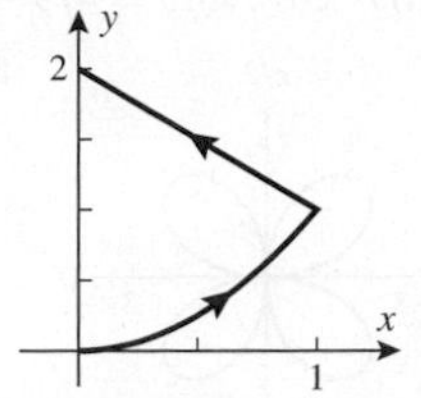


39. **(a)** $x = 4\cos t, y = 3\sin t$ **(b)** $x = -1 + 4\cos t, y = 2 + 3\sin t$

41. −4, 4 43. both are positive 45. 4, 4 47. $2/\sqrt{3}, -1/(3\sqrt{3})$

49. $\sqrt{3}, 4$ 51. $y = -e^{-2}x + 2e^{-1}$

53. **(a)** $0, \pi, 2\pi$ **(b)** $\pi/2, 3\pi/2$

55. **(a)** **(b)** $y = -2x, y = 2x$

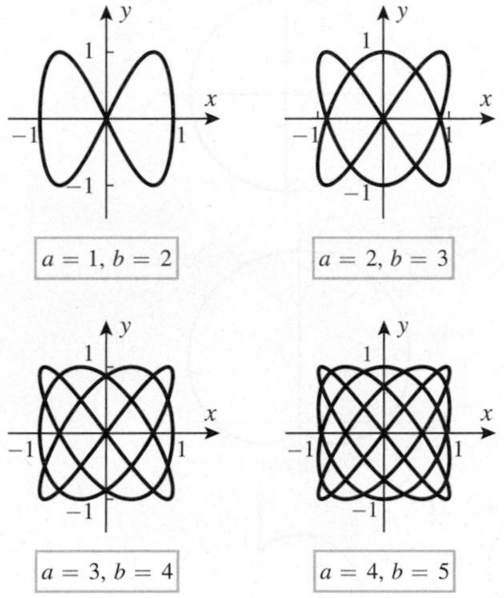


57. $y = 2x - 8, y = -2x + 8$ 59.

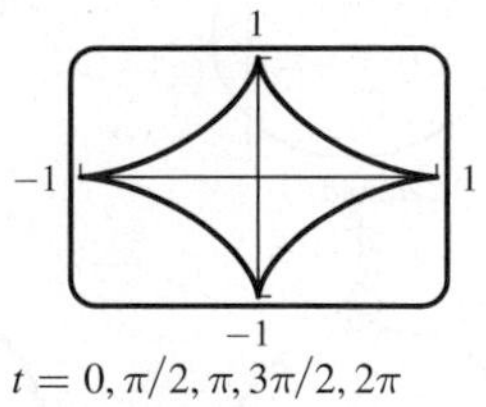


$t = 0, \pi/2, \pi, 3\pi/2, 2\pi$

61. **(a)** $\dfrac{dy}{dx} = \dfrac{3\sin t}{1 - 3\cos t}$ **(b)** $\theta \approx -0.4345$

63. **(a)** ellipses with fixed center, varying shapes and sizes
**(b)** ellipses with varying center, fixed shape, size, and orientation
**(c)** circles of radius 1 with centers on line $y = x - 1$

65. $\frac{1}{3}(5\sqrt{5} - 8)$ 67. $3\pi$ 69. $\frac{\sqrt{10}}{2}(e^2 - e^{-2})$

73. **(b)** $x = \cos t + \cos 2t, y = \sin t + \sin 2t$ **(c)** yes

75. $S = 49\pi$ 77. $S = \sqrt{2}\pi$

## ▶ Exercise Set 10.2 (Page 627)

1.

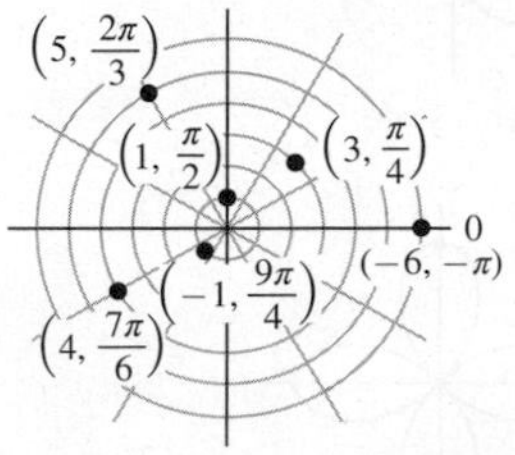


3. **(a)** $(3\sqrt{3}, 3)$
**(b)** $(-7/2, 7\sqrt{3}/2)$
**(c)** $(3\sqrt{3}, 3)$
**(d)** $(0, 0)$
**(e)** $(-7\sqrt{3}/2, 7/2)$
**(f)** $(-5, 0)$

5. **(a)** $(5, \pi), (5, -\pi)$ **(b)** $(4, 11\pi/6), (4, -\pi/6)$
**(c)** $(2, 3\pi/2), (2, -\pi/2)$ **(d)** $(8\sqrt{2}, 5\pi/4), (8\sqrt{2}, -3\pi/4)$
**(e)** $(6, 2\pi/3), (6, -4\pi/3)$ **(f)** $(\sqrt{2}, \pi/4), (\sqrt{2}, -7\pi/4)$

7. **(a)** $(5, 0.92730)$ **(b)** $(10, -0.92730)$ **(c)** $(1.27155, 2.47582)$
9. **(a)** circle **(b)** line **(c)** circle **(d)** line
11. **(a)** $r = 3\sec\theta$ **(b)** $r = \sqrt{7}$ **(c)** $r = -6\sin\theta$
**(d)** $r^2\cos\theta\sin\theta = 4/9$

13.
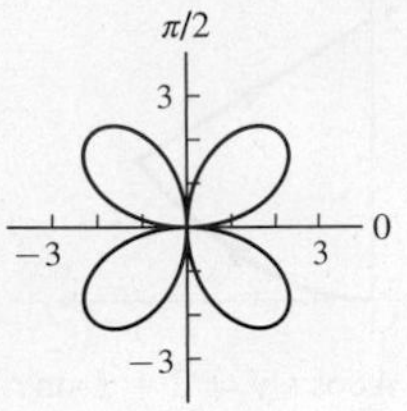


15.
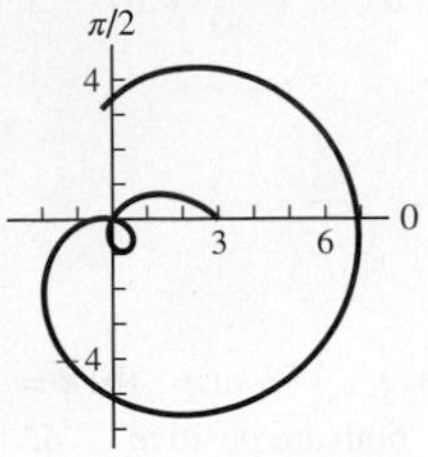


17. **(a)** $r = 5$ **(b)** $r = 6\cos\theta$ **(c)** $r = 1 - \cos\theta$
19. **(a)** $r = 3\sin 2\theta$ **(b)** $r = 3 + 2\sin\theta$ **(c)** $r^2 = 9\cos 2\theta$

21.
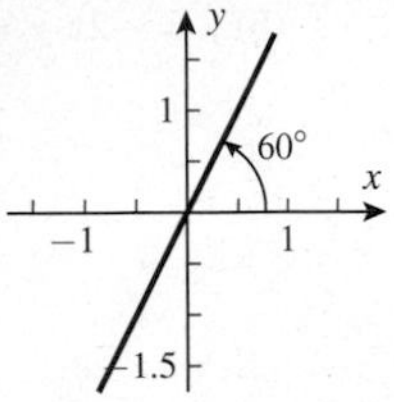


23.
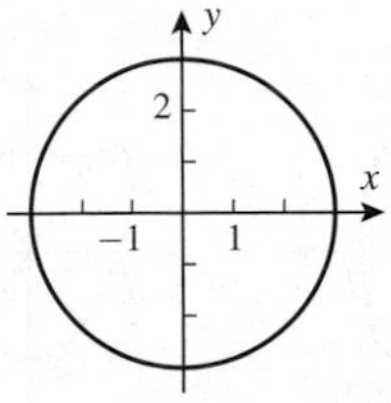


25.
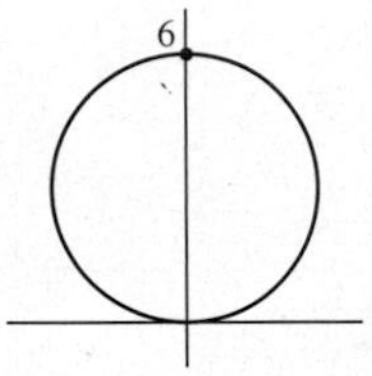


Circle

27.
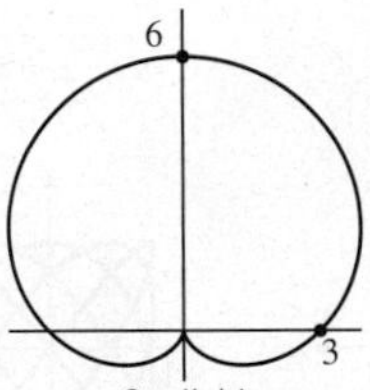


Cardioid

29.
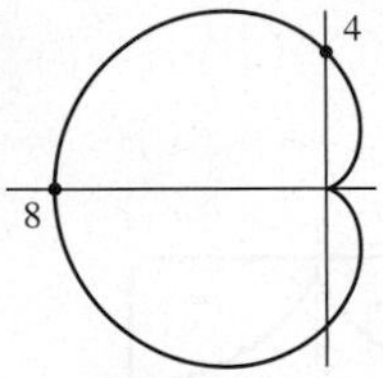


Cardioid

31.
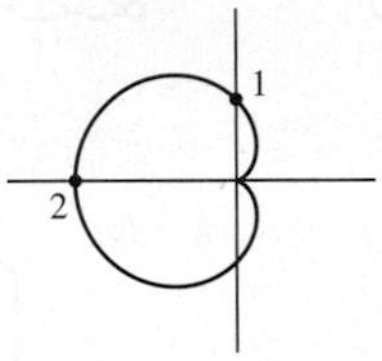


Cardioid

33.
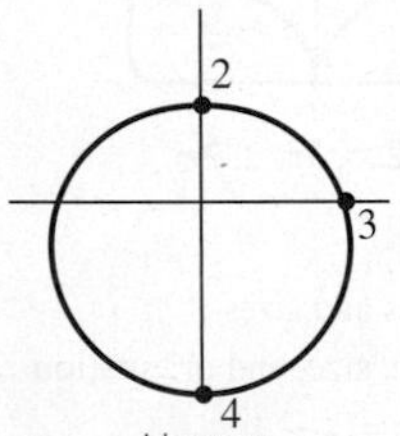


Limaçon

35.
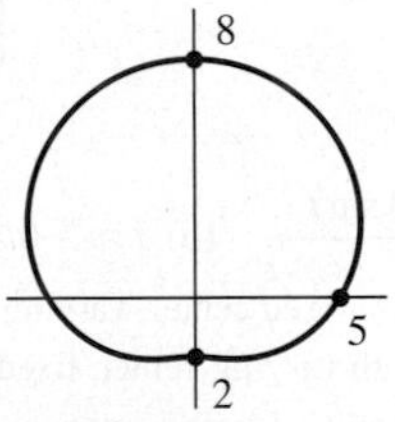


Limaçon

37.
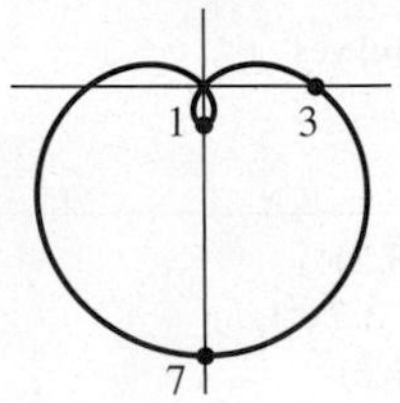


Limaçon

39.
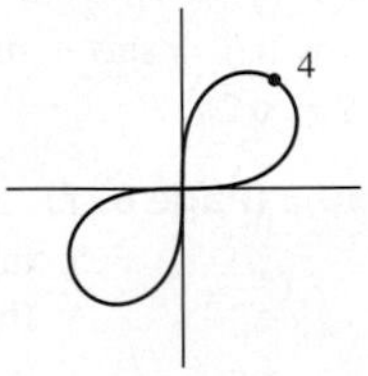


Lemniscate

41.
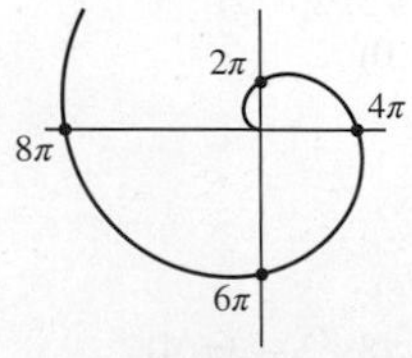


Spiral

43.
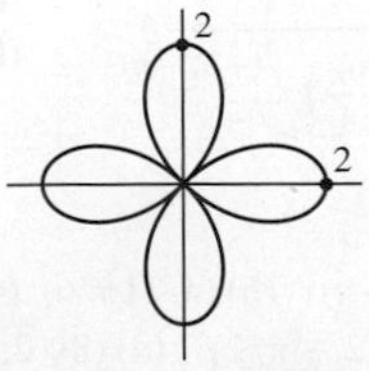


Four-petal rose

45.

Eight-petal rose

Responses to True–False questions may be abridged to save space.

47. True; $\left(-1, \dfrac{\pi}{3}\right)$ describes the same point as $\left(1, \dfrac{\pi}{3} + \pi\right)$, which describes the same point as $\left(1, \dfrac{\pi}{3} + \pi - 2\pi\right) = \left(1, -\dfrac{2\pi}{3}\right)$.
49. False; $-1 < \sin 2\theta < 0$ for $\pi/2 < \theta < \pi$, so this portion of the graph is in the fourth quadrant.

51. $0 \le \theta \le 4\pi$
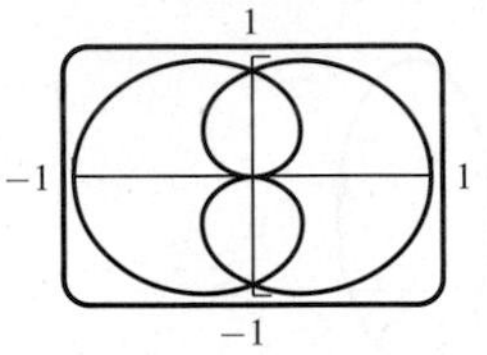


53. $0 \le \theta \le 8\pi$
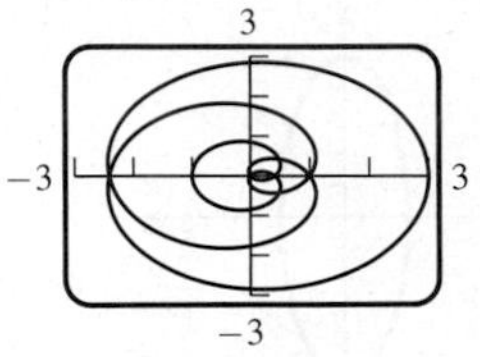


55. $0 \le \theta \le 5\pi$
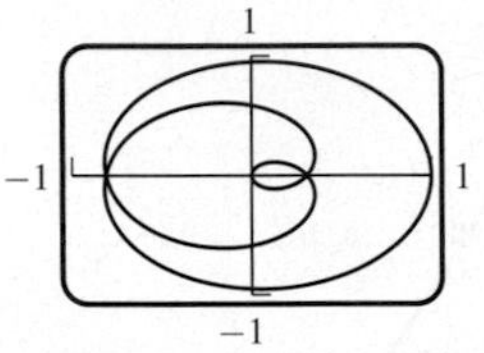


57. **(a)** $-4\pi < \theta < 4\pi$

61. **(a)**
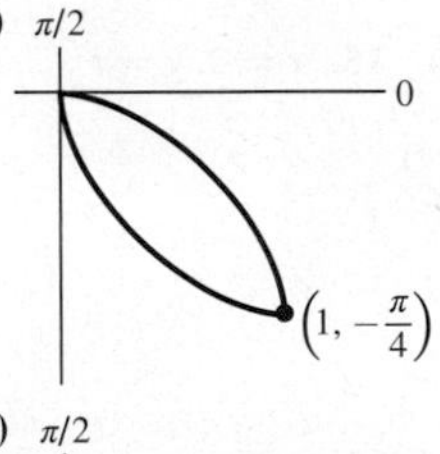


**(b)**
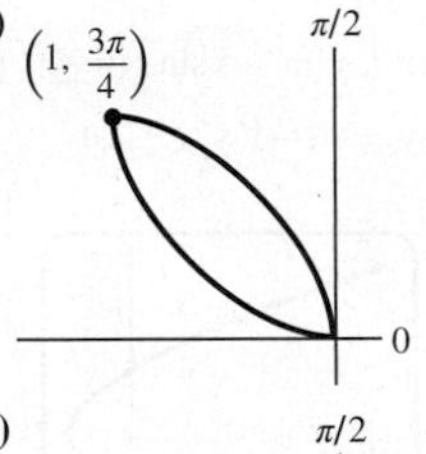


**(c)**
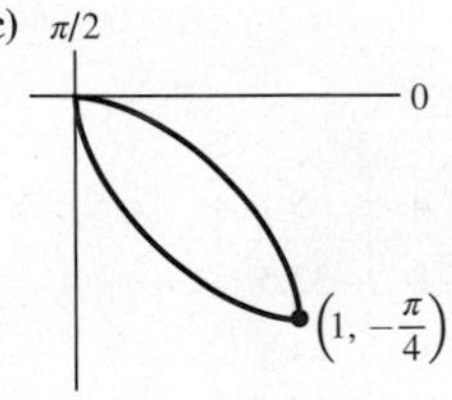


**(d)**
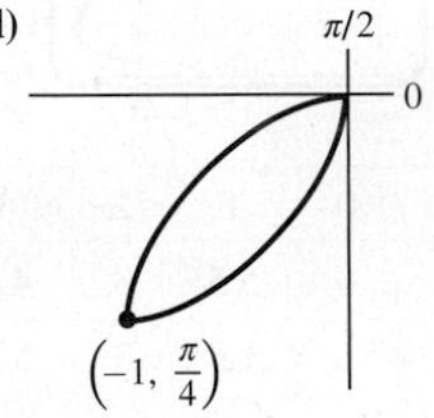


63. **(a)**
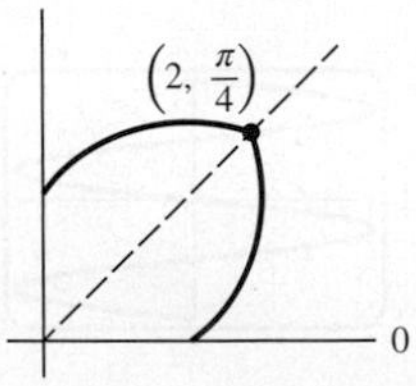


**(b)**
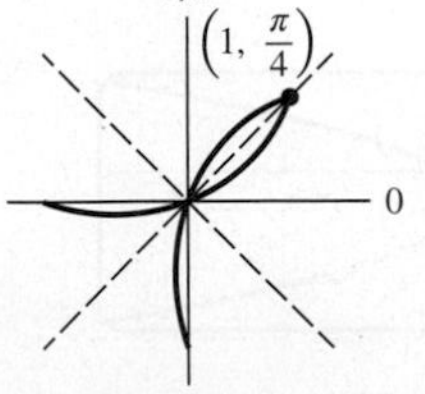


67. **(a)** $r = 1 + \dfrac{\sqrt{2}}{2}(\cos\theta + \sin\theta)$ **(b)** $r = 1 + \sin\theta$
**(c)** $r = 1 - \cos\theta$ **(d)** $r = 1 - \dfrac{\sqrt{2}}{2}(\cos\theta + \sin\theta)$
69. $(3/2, \pi/3)$ 73. $\sqrt{2}$

## ▶ Exercise Set 10.3 (Page 636)

1. $\sqrt{3}$ 3. $\dfrac{\tan 2 - 2}{2\tan 2 + 1}$ 5. $1/2$ 7. $1, 0, -1$
9. horizontal: $(3a/2, \pi/3), (0, \pi), (3a/2, 5\pi/3)$;
vertical: $(2a, 0), (a/2, 2\pi/3), (a/2, 4\pi/3)$

11. $(0,0), (\sqrt{2}/4, \pi/4), (\sqrt{2}/4, 3\pi/4)$

13.
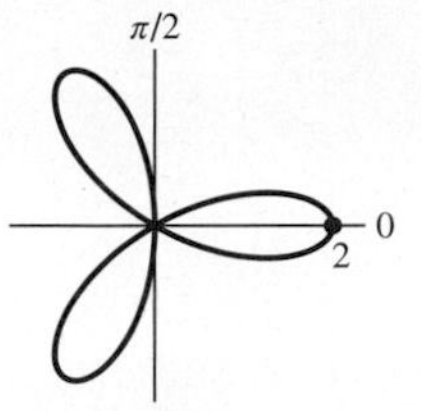


$\theta = \pi/2, \pm\pi/6$

15.
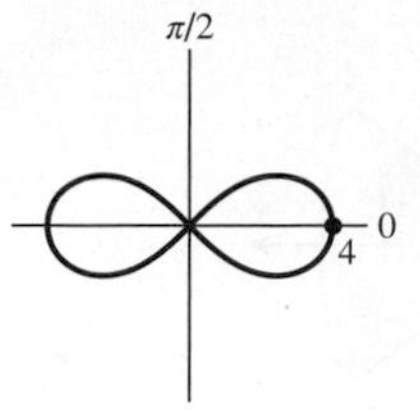


$\theta = \pm\pi/4$

17.
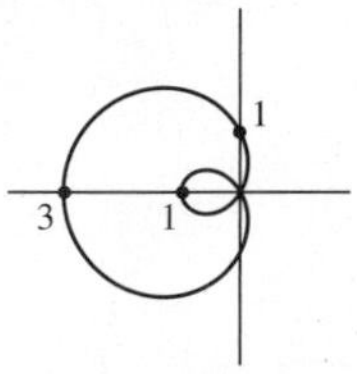


$\theta = \pm\pi/3$

19. $L = 2\pi a$ 21. $L = 8a$

23. (b) $\approx 2.42$

(c)

| $n$ | 2 | 3 | 4 | 5 | 6 | 7 |
|---|---|---|---|---|---|---|
| $L$ | 2.42211 | 2.22748 | 2.14461 | 2.10100 | 2.07501 | 2.05816 |

| $n$ | 8 | 9 | 10 | 11 | 12 | 13 | 14 |
|---|---|---|---|---|---|---|---|
| $L$ | 2.04656 | 2.03821 | 2.03199 | 2.02721 | 2.02346 | 2.02046 | 2.01802 |

| $n$ | 15 | 16 | 17 | 18 | 19 | 20 |
|---|---|---|---|---|---|---|
| $L$ | 2.01600 | 2.01431 | 2.01288 | 2.01167 | 2.01062 | 2.00971 |

25. (a) $\displaystyle\int_{\pi/2}^{\pi} \tfrac{1}{2}(1-\cos\theta)^2\,d\theta$ (b) $\displaystyle\int_0^{\pi/2} 2\cos^2\theta\,d\theta$

(c) $\displaystyle\int_0^{\pi/2} \tfrac{1}{2}\sin^2 2\theta\,d\theta$ (d) $\displaystyle\int_0^{2\pi} \tfrac{1}{2}\theta^2\,d\theta$

(e) $\displaystyle\int_{-\pi/2}^{\pi/2} \tfrac{1}{2}(1-\sin\theta)^2\,d\theta$ (f) $\displaystyle\int_0^{\pi/4} \cos^2 2\theta\,d\theta$

27. (a) $\pi a^2$ (b) $\pi a^2$ 29. $6\pi$ 31. $4\pi$ 33. $\pi - 3\sqrt{3}/2$

35. $\pi/2 - \frac{1}{4}$ 37. $10\pi/3 - 4\sqrt{3}$ 39. $\pi$ 41. $9\sqrt{3}/2 - \pi$

43. $(\pi + 3\sqrt{3})/4$ 45. $\pi - 2$

Responses to True–False questions may be abridged to save space.

47. True; apply Theorem 10.3.1: $\cos\left.\dfrac{\theta}{2}\right|_{\theta=3\pi} = 0$ and $\left.\dfrac{dr}{d\theta}\right|_{\theta=3\pi} = \dfrac{1}{2} \neq 0$, so the line $\theta = 3\pi$ (the $x$-axis) is tangent to the curve at the origin.

49. False; the area of the sector is $\dfrac{\theta}{2\pi}\cdot\pi r^2 = \dfrac{1}{2}\theta r^2$.

51. (b) $a^2$ (c) $2\sqrt{3} - \dfrac{2\pi}{3}$ 53. $8\pi^3 a^2$

59. $\pi/16$
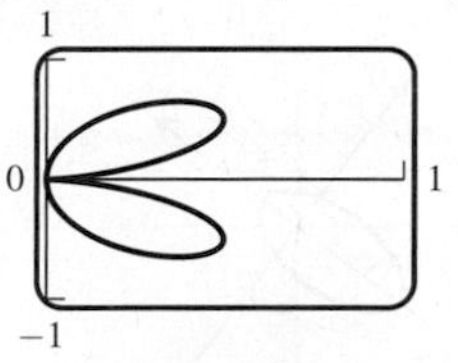


65. $\pi^2$
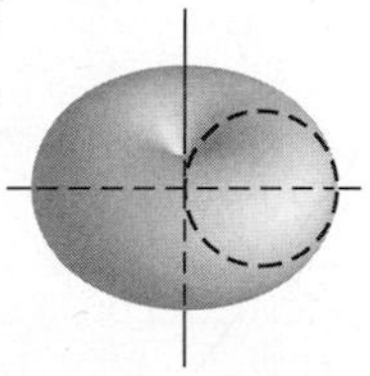

67. $32\pi/5$
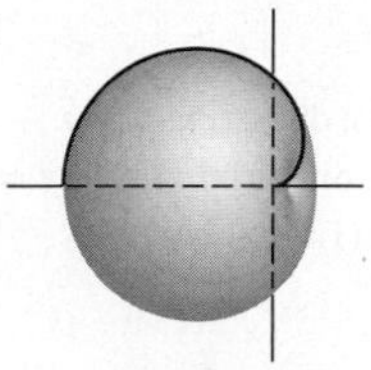

## ▶ Exercise Set 10.4 (Page 652)

1. (a) $x = y^2$ (b) $-3y = x^2$ (c) $\dfrac{x^2}{9} + \dfrac{y^2}{4} = 1$ (d) $\dfrac{x^2}{4} + \dfrac{y^2}{9} = 1$

(e) $y^2 - x^2 = 1$ (f) $\dfrac{x^2}{4} - \dfrac{y^2}{4} = 1$

3. (a) focus: $(1, 0)$; vertex: $(0, 0)$; directrix: $x = -1$

(b) focus: $(0, -2)$; vertex: $(0, 0)$; directrix: $y = 2$

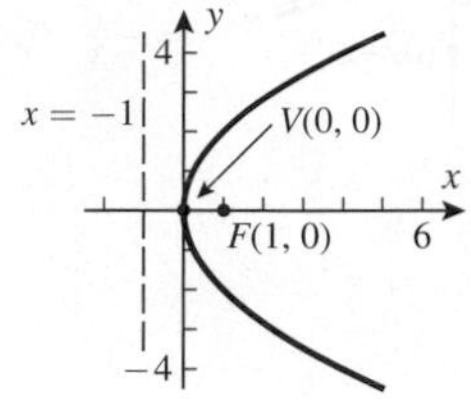


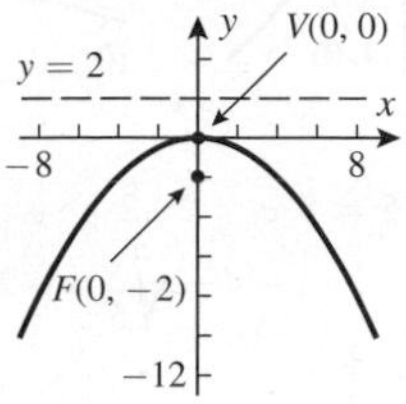


5. (a)
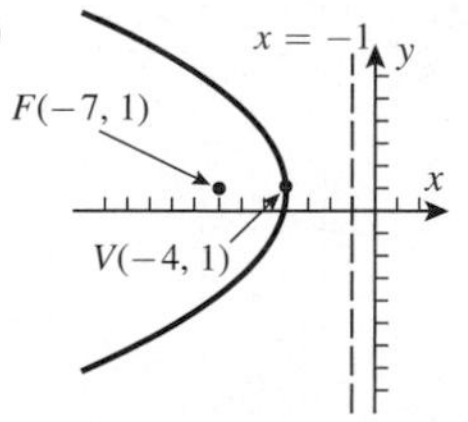


(b)
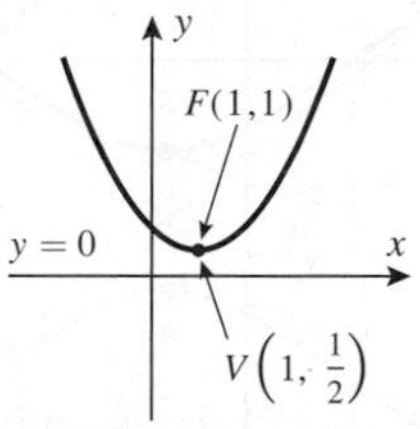


7. (a)
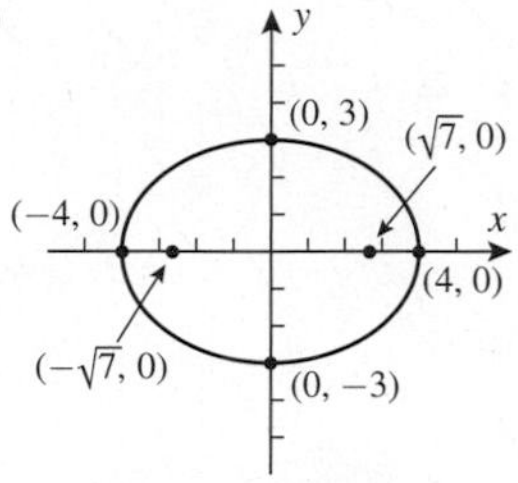


(b)
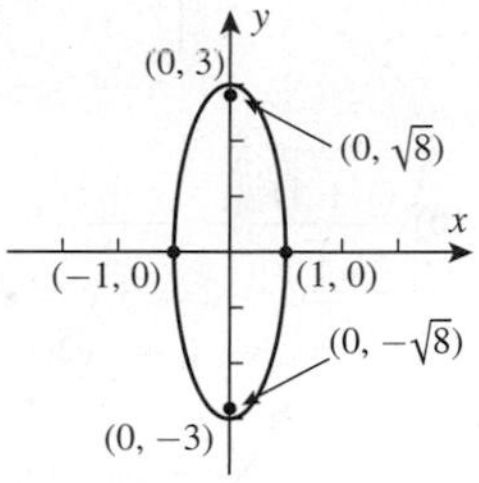


9. (a) $\dfrac{(x+3)^2}{16} + \dfrac{(y-5)^2}{4} = 1$

$c^2 = 16 - 4 = 12, c = 2\sqrt{3}$

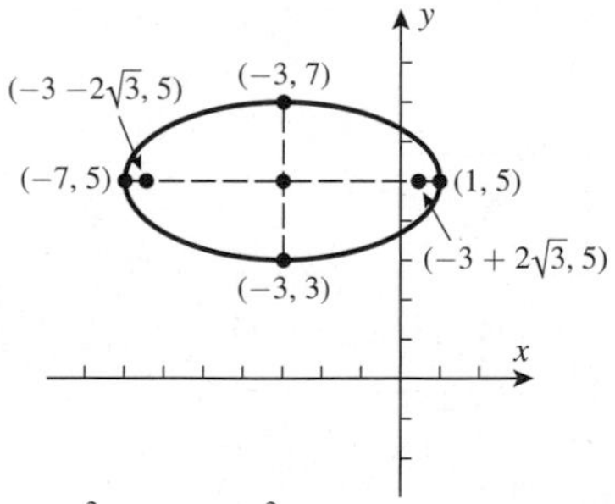


(b) $\dfrac{x^2}{4} + \dfrac{(y+2)^2}{9} = 1$

$c^2 = 9 - 4 = 5, c = \sqrt{5}$

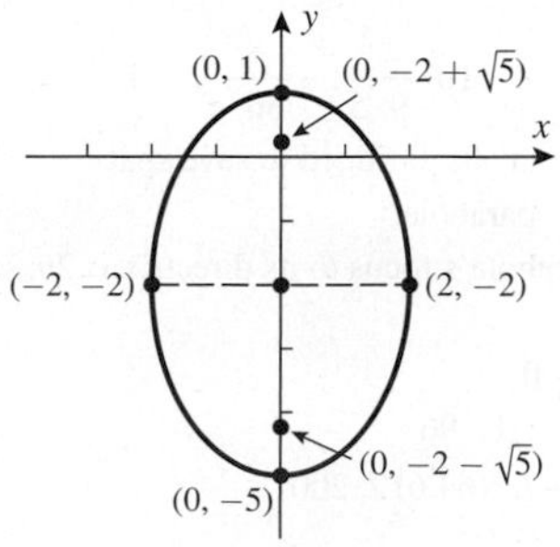

11. **(a)** vertices: $(\pm 4, 0)$; foci: $(\pm 5, 0)$; asymptotes: $y = \pm 3x/4$

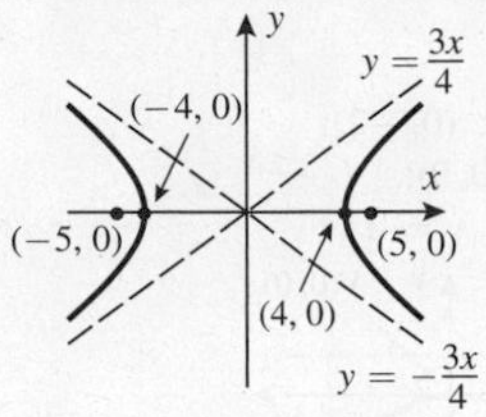


**(b)** vertices: $(0, \pm 2)$; foci: $(0, \pm 2\sqrt{10})$; asymptotes: $y = \pm x/3$

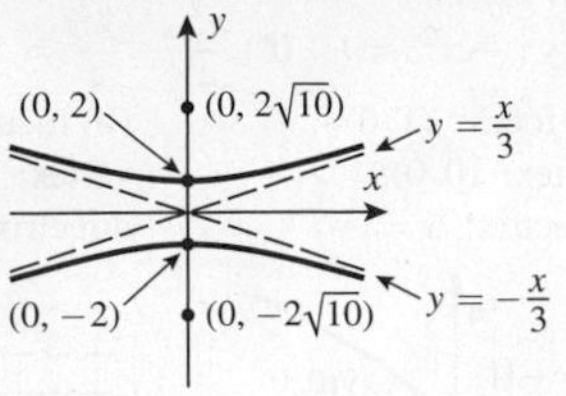


13. **(a)** $c^2 = 3 + 5 = 8, c = 2\sqrt{2}$

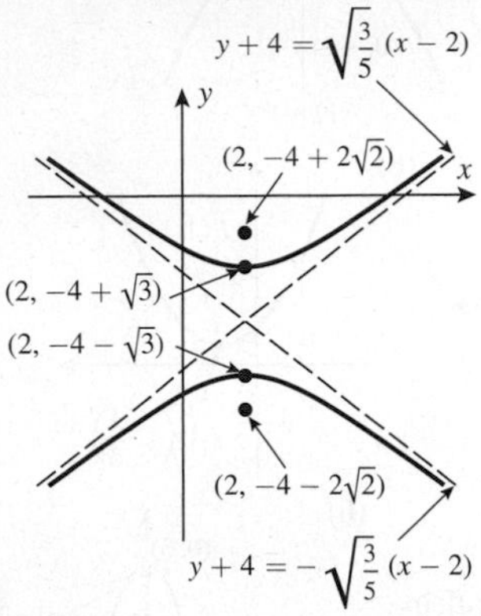


**(b)** $\dfrac{(x+1)^2}{1} - \dfrac{(y-3)^2}{2} = 1$
$c^2 = 1 + 2 = 3, c = \sqrt{3}$

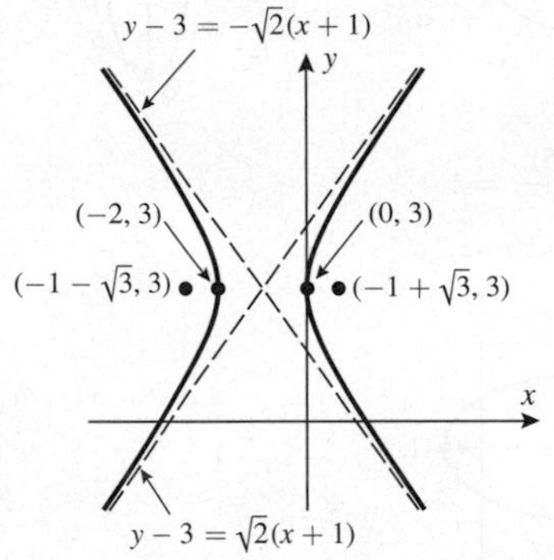


15. **(a)** $y^2 = 12x$ **(b)** $x^2 = -y$ 17. $y^2 = 2(x - 1)$

19. **(a)** $\dfrac{x^2}{9} + \dfrac{y^2}{4} = 1$ **(b)** $\dfrac{x^2}{16} + \dfrac{y^2}{25} = 1$

21. **(a)** $\dfrac{x^2}{81/8} + \dfrac{y^2}{36} = 1$ **(b)** $\dfrac{(x+1)^2}{4} + \dfrac{(y-2)^2}{5} = 1$

23. **(a)** $\dfrac{x^2}{4} - \dfrac{y^2}{5} = 1$ **(b)** $\dfrac{y^2}{4} - \dfrac{x^2}{9} = 1$

25. **(a)** $\dfrac{y^2}{9} - \dfrac{x^2}{16} = 1, \dfrac{x^2}{16} - \dfrac{y^2}{9} = 1$ **(b)** $\dfrac{x^2}{9/5} - \dfrac{y^2}{36/5} = 1$

Responses to True–False questions may be abridged to save space.

27. False; the description matches a parabola.

29. False; the distance from the parabola's focus to its directrix is $2p$; see Figure 10.4.6.

31. **(a)** 16 ft **(b)** $8\sqrt{3}$ ft 35. $\frac{1}{16}$ ft

39. $\frac{1}{32}(x-4)^2 + \frac{1}{36}(y-3)^2 = 1$ 41. 96

45. $L = D\sqrt{1+p^2}, T = \frac{1}{2}pD$ 47. (64.612, 200)

49. **(a)** $V = \dfrac{\pi b^2}{3a^2}(b^2 - 2a^2)\sqrt{a^2+b^2} + \dfrac{2}{3}ab^2\pi$

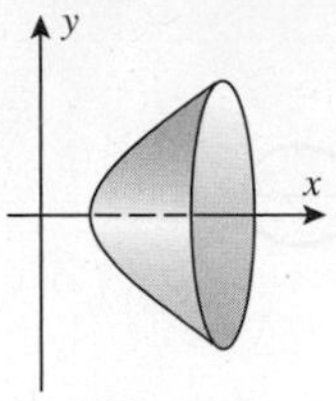


**(b)** $V = \dfrac{2b^4}{3a}\pi$

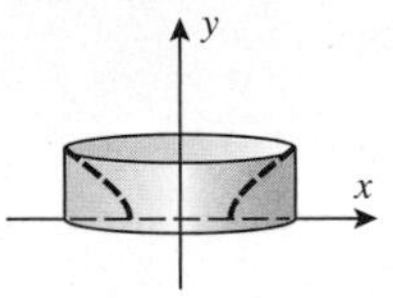


55. $k = \pm 4$; $(2, 1), (-2, -1)$

57. $\left(\pm\dfrac{3\sqrt{13}}{2}, -9\right)$

59. **(a)** $(x-1)^2 - 5(y+1)^2 = 5$, hyperbola
**(b)** $x^2 - 3(y+1)^2 = 0, x = \pm\sqrt{3}(y+1)$, two lines
**(c)** $4(x+2)^2 + 8(y+1)^2 = 4$, ellipse
**(d)** $3(x+2)^2 + (y+1)^2 = 0$, the point $(-2, -1)$ (degenerate case)
**(e)** $(x+4)^2 + 2y = 2$, parabola
**(f)** $5(x+4)^2 + 2y = -14$, parabola

## ▶ Exercise Set 10.5 (Page 660)

1. **(a)** $x' = -1 + 3\sqrt{3}, y' = 3 + \sqrt{3}$
**(b)** $3x'^2 - y'^2 = 12$
**(c)**

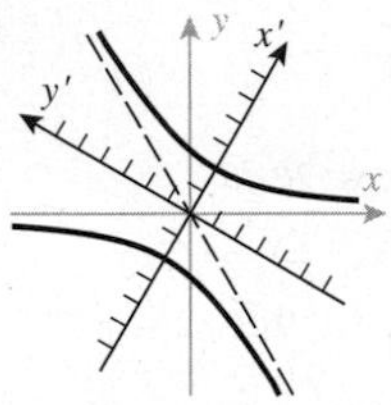


3. $y'^2 - x'^2 = 18$, hyperbola

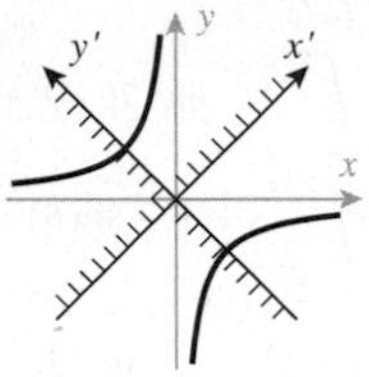


5. $\frac{1}{3}x'^2 - \frac{1}{2}y'^2 = 1$, hyperbola

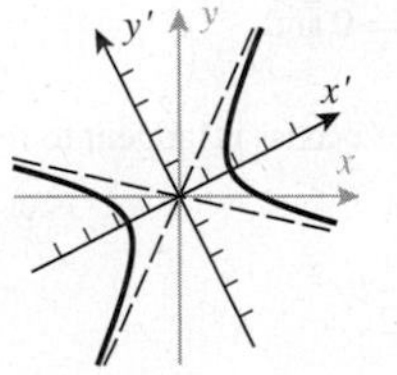


7. $y' = x'^2$, parabola

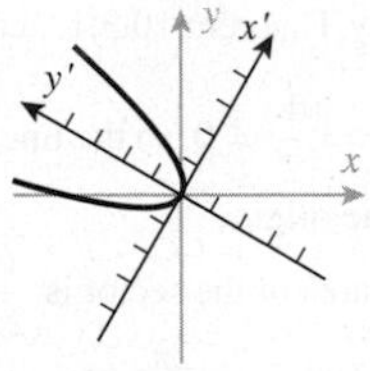


9. $y'^2 = 4(x' - 1)$, parabola

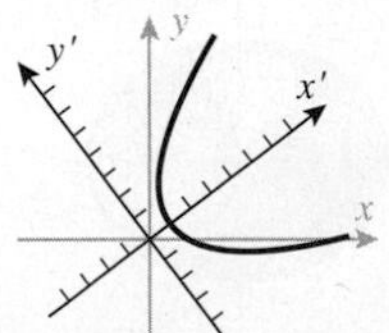


11. $\frac{1}{4}(x' + 1)^2 + y'^2 = 1$, ellipse

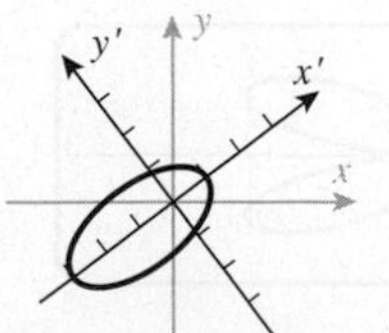


13. $x^2 + xy + y^2 = 3$

19. vertex: $(0, 0)$; focus: $(-1/\sqrt{2}, 1/\sqrt{2})$; directrix: $y = x - \sqrt{2}$

21. vertex: $(4/5, 3/5)$; focus: $(8/5, 6/5)$; directrix: $4x + 3y = 0$

23. foci: $\pm(4\sqrt{7}/5, 3\sqrt{7}/5)$; vertices: $\pm(16/5, 12/5)$; ends: $\pm(-9/5, 12/5)$

25. foci: $(1-\sqrt{5}/2, -\sqrt{3}+\sqrt{15}/2), (1+\sqrt{5}/2, -\sqrt{3}-\sqrt{15}/2)$; vertices: $(-1/2, \sqrt{3}/2), (5/2, -5\sqrt{3}/2)$; ends: $(1+\sqrt{3}, 1-\sqrt{3}), (1-\sqrt{3}, -1-\sqrt{3})$

27. foci: $\pm(\sqrt{15}, \sqrt{5})$; vertices: $\pm(2\sqrt{3}, 2)$; asymptotes: $y = \dfrac{5\sqrt{3}\pm 8}{11}x$

29. foci: $\left(-\dfrac{4}{\sqrt{5}} \pm 2\sqrt{\dfrac{13}{5}}, \dfrac{8}{\sqrt{5}} \pm \sqrt{\dfrac{13}{5}}\right)$; vertices: $(2/\sqrt{5}, 11/\sqrt{5}), (-2\sqrt{5}, \sqrt{5})$; asymptotes: $y = 7x/4 + 3\sqrt{5}, y = -x/8 + 3\sqrt{5}/2$

## Exercise Set 10.6 (Page 668)

1. (a) $e = 1, d = \frac{3}{2}$ (b) $e = \frac{1}{2}, d = 3$

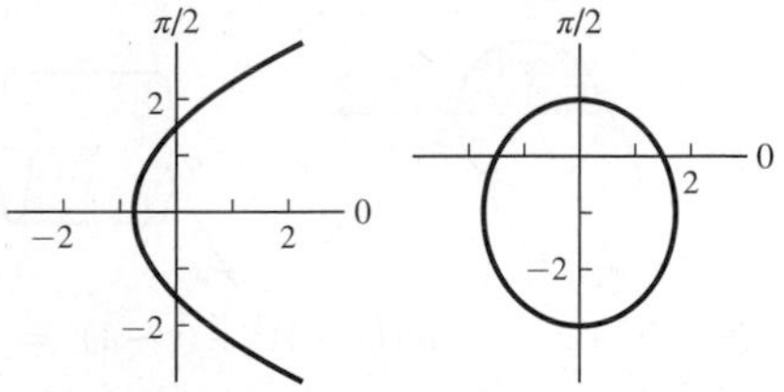

3. (a) parabola, opens up (b) ellipse, directrix above the pole

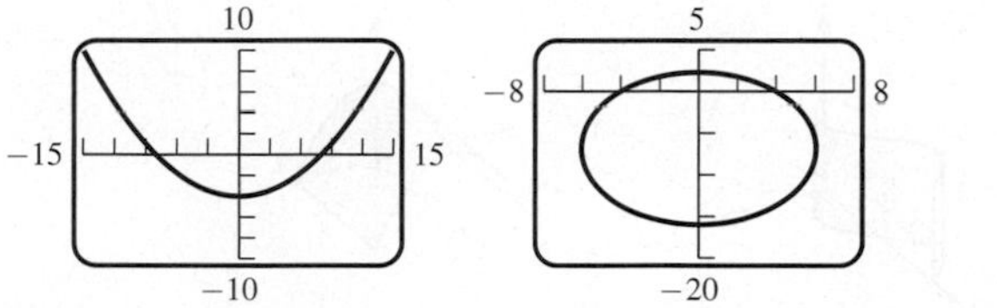

5. (a) $r = \dfrac{6}{4+3\cos\theta}$ (b) $r = \dfrac{1}{1+\cos\theta}$ (c) $r = \dfrac{12}{3+4\sin\theta}$

7. (a) $r_0 = 2, r_1 = 6; \frac{1}{12}x^2 + \frac{1}{16}(y+2)^2 = 1$
(b) $r_0 = \frac{1}{3}, r_1 = 1; \frac{9}{4}\left(x-\frac{1}{3}\right)^2 + 3y^2 = 1$

9. (a) $r_0 = 1, r_1 = 3; (y-2)^2 - \dfrac{x^2}{3} = 1$
(b) $r_0 = 1, r_1 = 5; \dfrac{(x+3)^2}{4} - \dfrac{y^2}{5} = 1$

11. (a) $r = \dfrac{12}{2+\cos\theta}$ (b) $r = \dfrac{64}{25-15\sin\theta}$

13. $r = \dfrac{5\sqrt{2}+5}{1+\sqrt{2}\cos\theta}$ or $r = \dfrac{5\sqrt{2}-5}{1+\sqrt{2}\cos\theta}$

Responses to True–False questions may be abridged to save space.

19. True; the eccentricity $e$ of an ellipse satisfies $0 < e < 1$ (Theorem 10.6.1).

21. False; eccentricity correlates to the "flatness" of an ellipse, which is independent of the distance between its foci.

23. (a) $T \approx 248$ yr
(b) $r_0 = 29.6645$ AU $\approx$ 4,449,675,000 km, $r_1 = 49.3355$ AU $\approx$ 7,400,325,000 km
(c) $r \approx \dfrac{37.05}{1+0.249\cos\theta}$ AU (d)

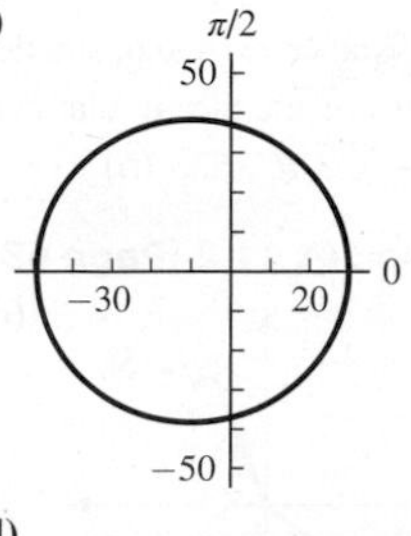

25. (a) $a \approx 178.26$ AU
(b) $r_0 \approx 0.8735$ AU, $r_1 \approx 355.64$ AU
(c) $r \approx \dfrac{1.74}{1+0.9951\cos\theta}$ AU
(d)

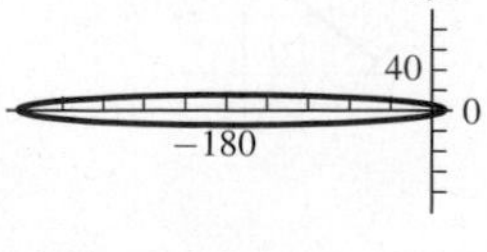

27. 563 km, 4286 km

## Chapter 10 Review Exercises (Page 670)

1. $x = \sqrt{2}\cos t, y = -\sqrt{2}\sin t\ (0 \le t \le 3\pi/2)$ 3. (a) $-1/4, 1/4$

5. (a) $t = \pi/2 + n\pi$ for $n = 0, \pm 1, \ldots$ (b) $t = n\pi$ for $n = 0, \pm 1, \ldots$

7. (a) $(-4\sqrt{2}, -4\sqrt{2})$ (b) $(7/\sqrt{2}, -7/\sqrt{2})$ (c) $(4\sqrt{2}, 4\sqrt{2})$ (d) $(5, 0)$ (e) $(0, -2)$ (f) $(0, 0)$

9. (a) $(5, 0.6435)$ (b) $(\sqrt{29}, 5.0929)$ (c) $(1.2716, 0.6658)$

11. (a) parabola (b) hyperbola (c) line (d) circle

13. 15. 17.

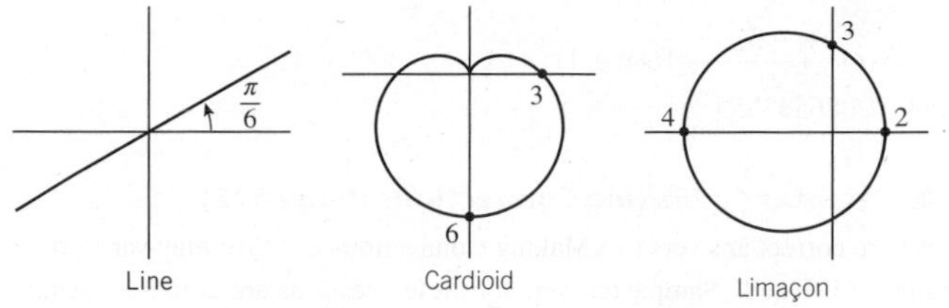


19. (a) $-2, 1/4$ (b) $-3\sqrt{3}/4, 3\sqrt{3}/4$

21. (a) The top is traced from right to left as $t$ goes from 0 to $\pi$. The bottom is traced from right to left as $t$ goes from $\pi$ to $2\pi$, except for the loop, which is traced counterclockwise as $t$ goes from $\pi + \sin^{-1}(1/4)$ to $2\pi - \sin^{-1}(1/4)$. (b) $y = 1$
(c) horizontal: $t = \pi/2, 3\pi/2$; vertical: $t = \pi + \sin^{-1}(1/\sqrt[3]{4})$, $2\pi - \sin^{-1}(1/\sqrt[3]{4})$
(d) $r = 4 + \csc\theta, \theta = \pi + \sin^{-1}(1/4), \theta = 2\pi - \sin^{-1}(1/4)$

23. $A = 6\pi$ 25. $A = \dfrac{5\pi}{12} - \dfrac{\sqrt{3}}{2}$ 27.

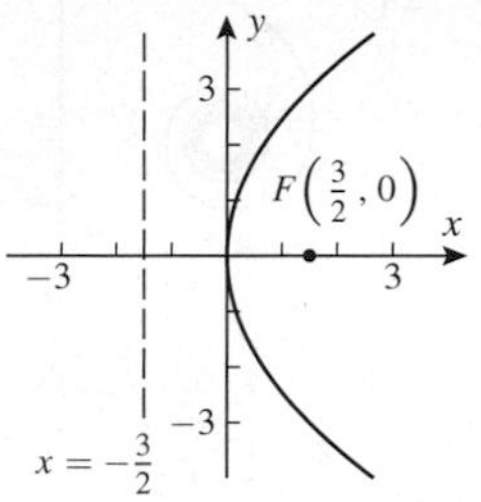

29.

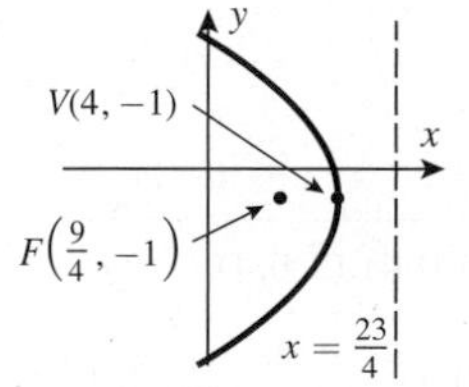

focus: $(9/4, -1)$; vertex: $(4, -1)$; directrix: $x = 23/4$

31.

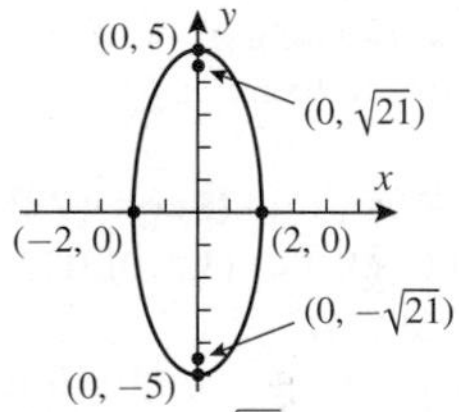

foci: $(0, \pm\sqrt{21})$; vertices: $(0, \pm 5)$; ends: $(\pm 2, 0)$

33.

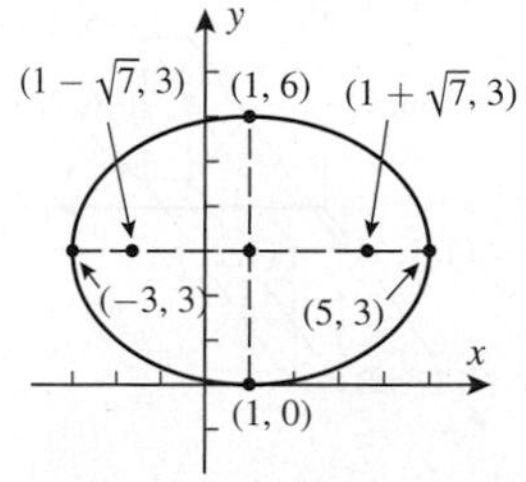

35.

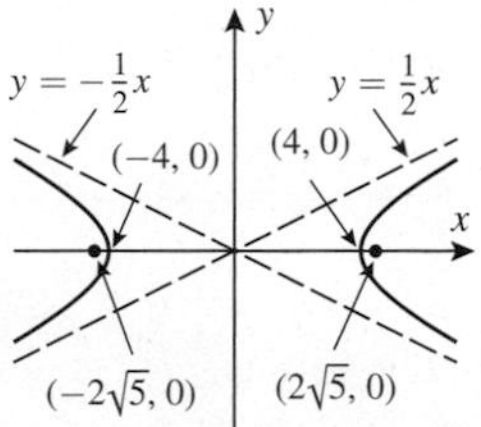

37.

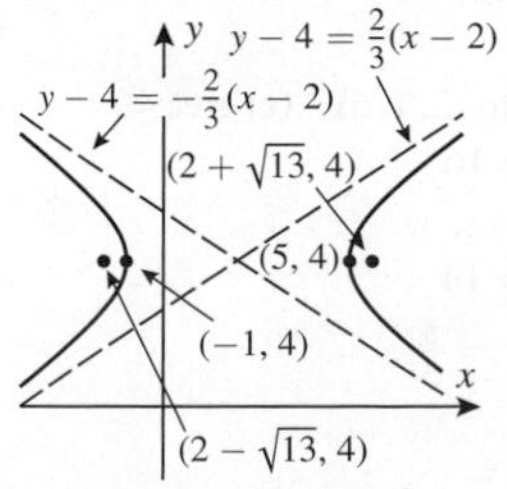

39. $x^2 = -16y$ 41. $y^2 - x^2 = 9$

43. **(b)** $x = \dfrac{v_0^2}{g}\sin\alpha\cos\alpha;\ y = y_0 + \dfrac{v_0^2\sin^2\alpha}{2g}$
45. $\theta = \pi/4$; $5(y')^2 - (x')^2 = 6$; hyperbola
47. $\theta = \tan^{-1}(1/2)$; $y' = (x')^2$; parabola
49. **(a)** (i) ellipse; (ii) right; (iii) 1 **(b)** (i) hyperbola; (ii) left; (iii) $1/3$ **(c)** (i) parabola; (ii) above; (iii) $1/3$ **(d)** (i) parabola; (ii) below; (iii) 3
51. **(a)** $\dfrac{(x+3)^2}{25} + \dfrac{(y-2)^2}{9} = 1$ **(b)** $(x+2)^2 = -8y$
**(c)** $\dfrac{(y-5)^2}{4} - 16(x+1)^2 = 1$
53. 15.86543959

## ▶ Chapter 10 Making Connections (Page 672)

Where correct answers to a Making Connections exercise may vary, no answer is listed. Sample answers for these questions are available on the Book Companion Site.

1. **(a)**

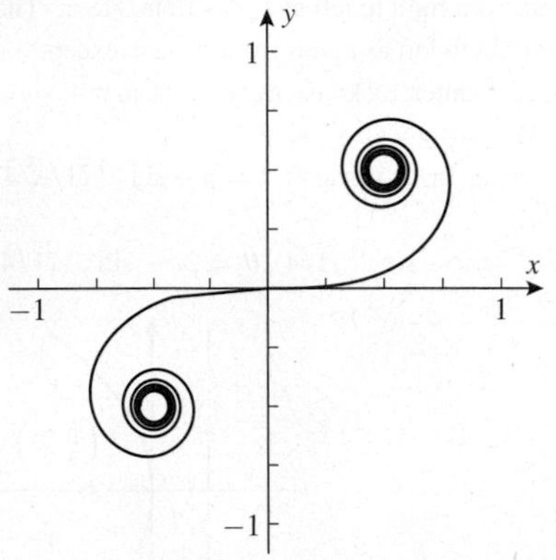


**(c)** $L = \displaystyle\int_{-1}^{1}\left[\cos^2\left(\frac{\pi t^2}{2}\right) + \sin^2\left(\frac{\pi t^2}{2}\right)\right]dt = 2$

2. **(a)** $P: (b\cos t, b\sin t)$; $Q: (a\cos t, a\sin t)$; $R: (a\cos t, b\sin t)$

## ▶ Exercise Set 11.1 (Page 678)

1. **(a)** (0, 0, 0), (3, 0, 0), (3, 5, 0), (0, 5, 0), (0, 0, 4), (3, 0, 4), (3, 5, 4), (0, 5, 4)
**(b)** (0, 1, 0), (4, 1, 0), (4, 6, 0), (0, 6, 0), (0, 1, −2), (4, 1, −2), (4, 6, −2), (0, 6, −2)
3. (4, 2, −2), (4, 2, 1), (4, 1, 1), (4, 1, −2), (−6, 1, 1), (−6, 2, 1), (−6, 2, −2), (−6, 1, −2)

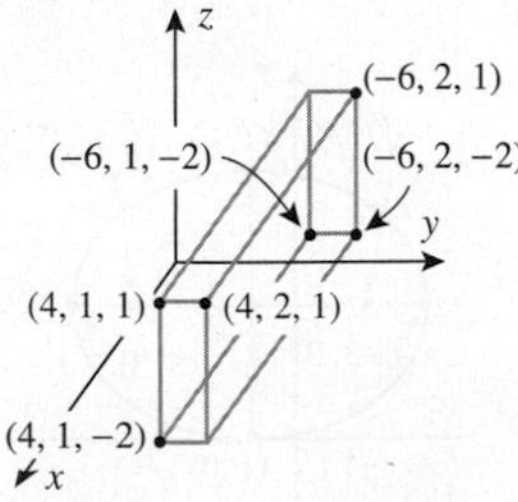


5. **(a)** point **(b)** line parallel to the $y$-axis
**(c)** plane parallel to the $yz$-plane
9. radius $\sqrt{74}$, center (2, 1, −4) 11. **(b)** (2, 1, 6) **(c)** area 49
13. **(a)** $(x-7)^2 + (y-1)^2 + (z-1)^2 = 16$
**(b)** $(x-1)^2 + y^2 + (z+1)^2 = 16$
**(c)** $(x+1)^2 + (y-3)^2 + (z-2)^2 = 14$
**(d)** $\left(x+\frac{1}{2}\right)^2 + (y-2)^2 + (z-2)^2 = \frac{5}{4}$
15. $(x-2)^2 + (y+1)^2 + (z+3)^2 = r^2$;
**(a)** $r^2 = 9$ **(b)** $r^2 = 1$ **(c)** $r^2 = 4$

Responses to True–False questions may be abridged to save space.

19. False; see Figure 11.1.6.
21. True; see Figure 11.1.3.
23. sphere, center (−5, −2, −1), radius 7
25. sphere; center $\left(\frac{1}{2}, \frac{3}{4}, -\frac{5}{4}\right)$, radius $\dfrac{3\sqrt{6}}{4}$
27. no graph
29. **(a)** **(b)** **(c)**

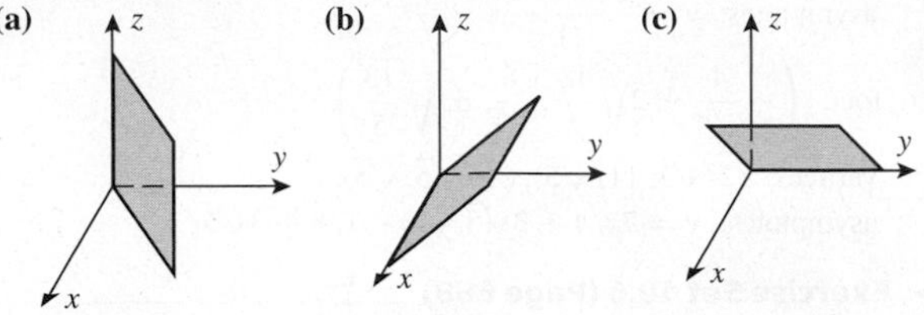

31. **(a)** **(b)** **(c)**

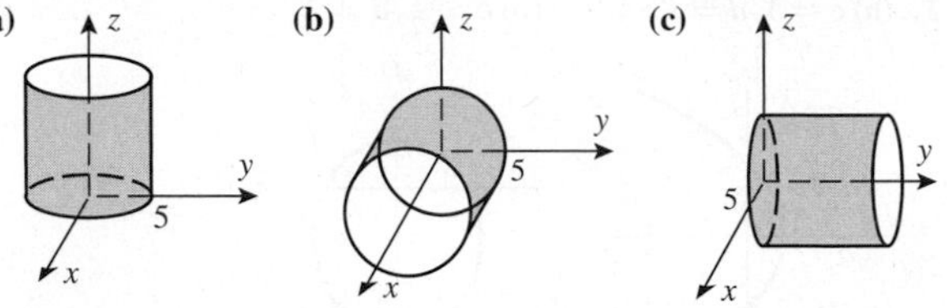

33. **(a)** $-2y + z = 0$ **(b)** $-2x + z = 0$ **(c)** $(x-1)^2 + (y-1)^2 = 1$
**(d)** $(x-1)^2 + (z-1)^2 = 1$

35.

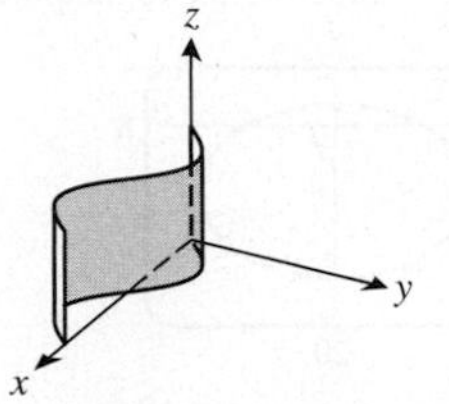

37.

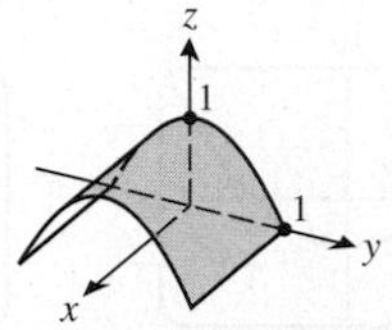

39.

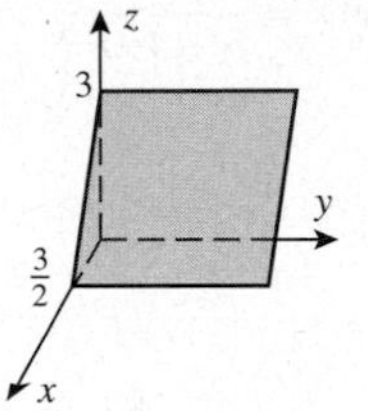

41.

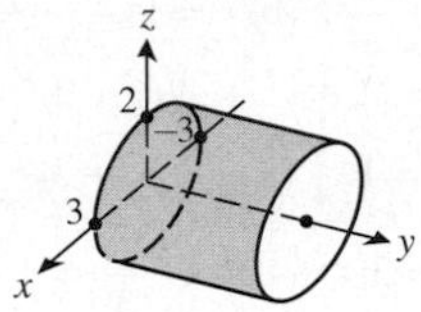

43.

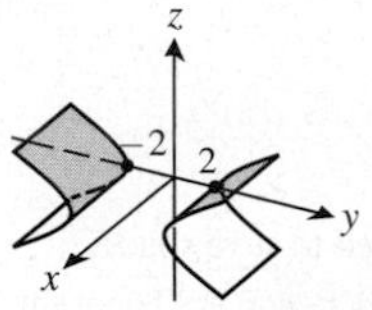

45.

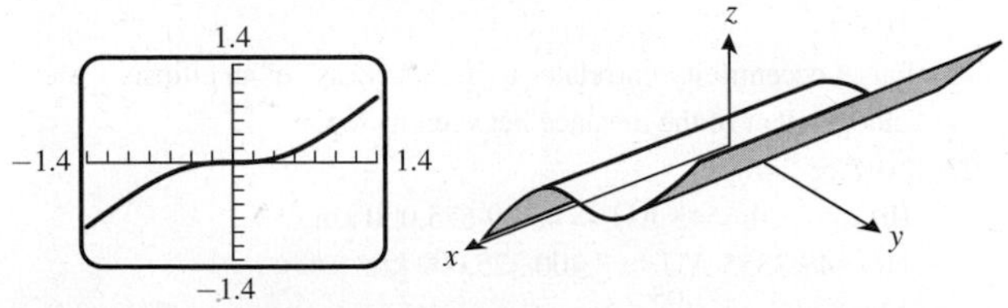


47. largest distance, $3 + \sqrt{6}$; smallest distance, $3 - \sqrt{6}$
49. all points outside the circular cylinder $(y+3)^2 + (z-2)^2 = 16$
51. $r = (2 - \sqrt{3})R$ 53. **(b)** $y^2 + z^2 = e^{2x}$

## ▶ Exercise Set 11.2 (Page 688)

1. **(a-c)**

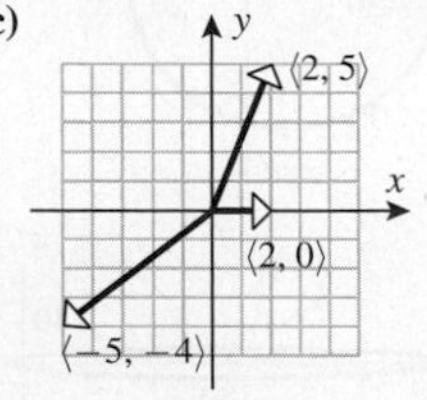


**(d-f)**

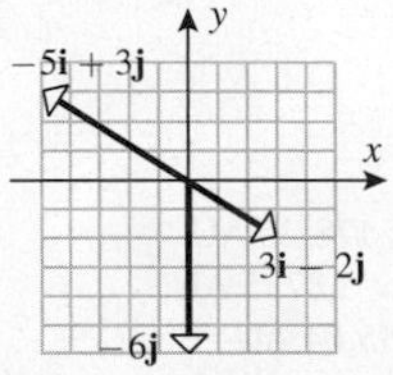

3. **(a,b)**

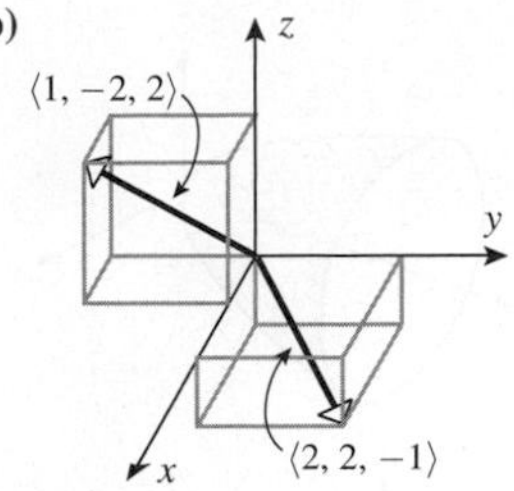


**(c,d)**

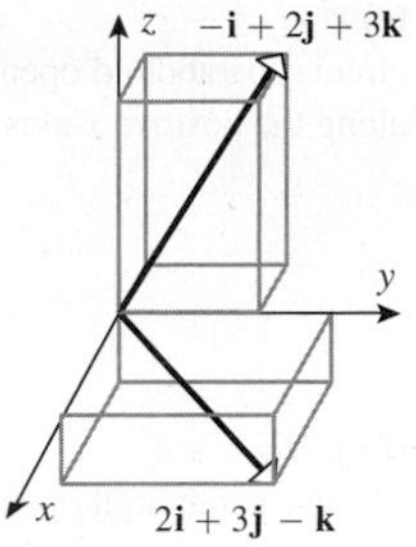


5. **(a)** $\langle 3, -4\rangle$

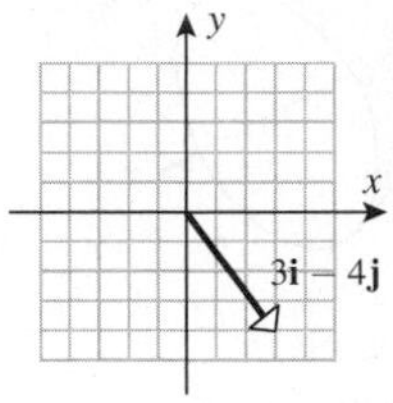


**(b)** $\langle -2, -3, 4\rangle$

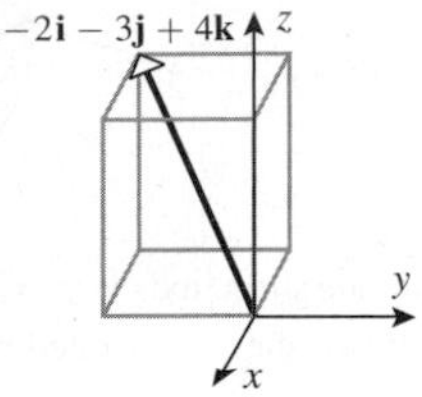


7. **(a)** $\langle -1, 3\rangle$ **(b)** $\langle -7, 2\rangle$ **(c)** $\langle -3, 6, 1\rangle$
9. **(a)** $(4, -4)$ **(b)** $(8, -1, -3)$
11. **(a)** $-\mathbf{i} + 4\mathbf{j} - 2\mathbf{k}$ **(b)** $18\mathbf{i} + 12\mathbf{j} - 6\mathbf{k}$ **(c)** $-\mathbf{i} - 5\mathbf{j} - 2\mathbf{k}$ **(d)** $40\mathbf{i} - 4\mathbf{j} - 4\mathbf{k}$ **(e)** $-2\mathbf{i} - 16\mathbf{j} - 18\mathbf{k}$ **(f)** $-\mathbf{i} + 13\mathbf{j} - 2\mathbf{k}$
13. **(a)** $\sqrt{2}$ **(b)** $5\sqrt{2}$ **(c)** $\sqrt{21}$ **(d)** $\sqrt{14}$
15. **(a)** $2\sqrt{3}$ **(b)** $\sqrt{14} + \sqrt{2}$ **(c)** $2\sqrt{14} + 2\sqrt{2}$ **(d)** $2\sqrt{37}$ **(e)** $(1/\sqrt{6})\mathbf{i} + (1/\sqrt{6})\mathbf{j} - (2/\sqrt{6})\mathbf{k}$ **(f)** 1

Responses to True–False questions may be abridged to save space.

17. False; $\|\mathbf{i} + \mathbf{j}\| = \sqrt{2} \neq 1 + 1 = 2$
19. True; one in the same direction and one in the opposite direction.
21. **(a)** $(-1/\sqrt{17})\mathbf{i} + (4/\sqrt{17})\mathbf{j}$ **(b)** $(-3\mathbf{i} + 2\mathbf{j} - \mathbf{k})/\sqrt{14}$ **(c)** $(4\mathbf{i} + \mathbf{j} - \mathbf{k})/(3\sqrt{2})$
23. **(a)** $\left\langle -\frac{3}{2}, 2\right\rangle$ **(b)** $\dfrac{1}{\sqrt{5}}\langle 7, 0, -6\rangle$
25. **(a)** $\langle 3\sqrt{2}/2, 3\sqrt{2}/2\rangle$ **(b)** $\langle 0, 2\rangle$ **(c)** $\langle -5/2, 5\sqrt{3}/2\rangle$ **(d)** $\langle -1, 0\rangle$
27. $\langle(\sqrt{3} - \sqrt{2})/2, (1 + \sqrt{2})/2\rangle$
29. **(a)** $\langle -2, 5\rangle$

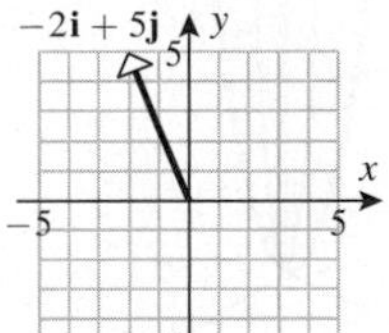


**(b)** $\langle 3, -8\rangle$

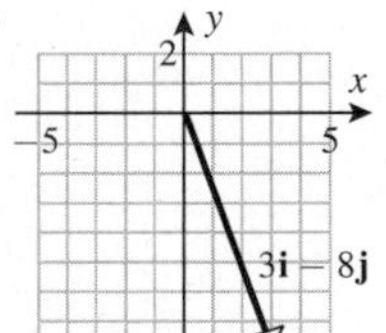


31. $\left\langle -\frac{2}{3}, 1\right\rangle$ 33. $\mathbf{u} = \frac{5}{7}\mathbf{i} + \frac{2}{7}\mathbf{j} + \frac{1}{7}\mathbf{k}, \mathbf{v} = \frac{8}{7}\mathbf{i} - \frac{1}{7}\mathbf{j} - \frac{4}{7}\mathbf{k}$
35. $\sqrt{5}, 3$ 37. **(a)** $\pm\frac{5}{3}$ **(b)** 3
39. **(a)** $\langle 1/\sqrt{10}, 3/\sqrt{10}\rangle, \langle -1/\sqrt{10}, -3/\sqrt{10}\rangle$ **(b)** $\langle 1/\sqrt{2}, -1/\sqrt{2}\rangle, \langle -1/\sqrt{2}, 1/\sqrt{2}\rangle$ **(c)** $\pm\dfrac{1}{\sqrt{26}}\langle 5, 1\rangle$
41. **(a)** the circle of radius 1 about the origin **(b)** the closed disk of radius 1 about the origin **(c)** all points outside the closed disk of radius 1 about the origin
43. **(a)** the (hollow) sphere of radius 1 about the origin **(b)** the closed ball of radius 1 about the origin **(c)** all points outside the closed ball of radius 1 about the origin
45. magnitude $= 30\sqrt{5}$ lb, $\theta \approx 26.57°$
47. magnitude $\approx 207.06$ N, $\theta = 45°$
49. magnitude $\approx 94.995$ N, $\theta \approx 28.28°$
51. magnitude $\approx 9.165$ lb, angle $\approx -70.890°$
53. $\approx 183.02$ lb, 224.13 lb 55. $450\sqrt{2} + 150\sqrt{6}$ lb, $300 + 300\sqrt{3}$ lb
57. **(a)** $c_1 = -2, c_2 = 1$

## ▶ Exercise Set 11.3 (Page 698)

1. **(a)** $-10$; $\cos\theta = -1/\sqrt{5}$ **(b)** $-3$; $\cos\theta = -3/\sqrt{58}$ **(c)** 0; $\cos\theta = 0$ **(d)** $-20$; $\cos\theta = -20/(3\sqrt{70})$
3. **(a)** obtuse **(b)** acute **(c)** obtuse **(d)** orthogonal
5. $\sqrt{2}/2, 0, -\sqrt{2}/2, -1, -\sqrt{2}/2, 0, \sqrt{2}/2$
7. **(a)** vertex $B$ **(b)** $82°, 60°, 38°$
9. **(b)** Yes, we can scalar multiply a vector by a number. **(d)** Yes, we can add two numbers. **(f)** Yes, we can multiply two numbers.
11. Total time to complete all three events. 13. $r = 7/5$
15. **(a)** $\alpha = \beta \approx 55°, \gamma \approx 125°$ **(b)** $\alpha \approx 48°, \beta \approx 132°, \gamma \approx 71°$
19. **(a)** $\approx 35°$ **(b)** $90°$
21. $64°, 41°, 60°$ 23. $71°, 61°, 36°$
25. **(a)** $\left\langle \frac{2}{3}, \frac{4}{3}, \frac{4}{3}\right\rangle, \left\langle \frac{4}{3}, -\frac{7}{3}, \frac{5}{3}\right\rangle$ **(b)** $\left\langle -\frac{74}{49}, -\frac{111}{49}, \frac{222}{49}\right\rangle, \left\langle \frac{270}{49}, \frac{62}{49}, \frac{121}{49}\right\rangle$
27. **(a)** $\langle 1, 1\rangle + \langle -4, 4\rangle$ **(b)** $\left\langle 0, -\frac{8}{5}, \frac{4}{5}\right\rangle + \left\langle -2, \frac{13}{5}, \frac{26}{5}\right\rangle$ **(c)** $\mathbf{v} = \langle 1, 4, 1\rangle$ is orthogonal to $\mathbf{b}$.

Responses to True–False questions may be abridged to save space.

29. True; $\mathbf{v} + \mathbf{w} = \mathbf{0}$ implies $0 = \mathbf{v}\cdot(\mathbf{v} + \mathbf{w}) = \|\mathbf{v}\|^2 \neq 0$, a contradiction.
31. True; see Equation (12). 33. $\sqrt{564/29}$ 35. 169.8 N
37. 375 ft·lb 39. $-5\sqrt{3}$ J 47. **(a)** $40°$ **(b)** $x \approx -0.682328$

## ▶ Exercise Set 11.4 (Page 708)

1. **(a)** $-\mathbf{j} + \mathbf{k}$ 3. $\langle 7, 10, 9\rangle$ 5. $\langle -4, -6, -3\rangle$
7. **(a)** $\langle -20, -67, -9\rangle$ **(b)** $\langle -78, 52, -26\rangle$ **(c)** $\langle 0, -56, -392\rangle$ **(d)** $\langle 0, 56, 392\rangle$
9. $\dfrac{1}{\sqrt{2}}, -\dfrac{1}{\sqrt{2}}, 0$ 11. $\pm\dfrac{1}{\sqrt{6}}\langle 2, 1, 1\rangle$

Responses to True–False questions may be abridged to save space.

13. True; see Theorem 11.4.5($c$).
15. False; let $\mathbf{v} = \mathbf{u} = \mathbf{i}$ and let $\mathbf{w} = 2\mathbf{i}$.
17. $\sqrt{59}$ 19. $\sqrt{374}/2$
21. 80 23. $-3$ 25. 16 27. **(a)** yes **(b)** yes **(c)** no
29. **(a)** 9 **(b)** $\sqrt{122}$ **(c)** $\sin^{-1}\left(\frac{9}{14}\right)$
31. **(a)** $2\sqrt{141/29}$ **(b)** $6/\sqrt{5}$ 33. $\frac{2}{3}$ 37. $\theta = \pi/4$
39. **(a)** $10\sqrt{2}$ lb·ft, direction of rotation about $P$ is counterclockwise looking along $\overrightarrow{PQ} \times \mathbf{F} = -10\mathbf{i} + 10\mathbf{k}$ toward its initial point **(b)** 10 lb·ft, direction of rotation about $P$ is counterclockwise looking along $-10\mathbf{i}$ toward its initial point **(c)** 0 lb·ft, no rotation about $P$
41. $\approx 36.19$ N·m 45. $-8\mathbf{i} - 20\mathbf{j} + 2\mathbf{k}, -8\mathbf{i} - 8\mathbf{k}$ 49. 1.887850

## ▶ Exercise Set 11.5 (Page 714)

1. **(a)** $L_1: x = 1, y = t, L_2: x = t, y = 1, L_3: x = t, y = t$ **(b)** $L_1: x = 1, y = 1, z = t, L_2: x = t, y = 1, z = 1, L_3: x = 1, y = t, z = 1, L_4: x = t, y = t, z = t$
3. **(a)** $x = 3 + 2t, y = -2 + 3t$; line segment: $0 \le t \le 1$ **(b)** $x = 5 - 3t, y = -2 + 6t, z = 1 + t$; line segment: $0 \le t \le 1$
5. **(a)** $x = 2 + t, y = -3 - 4t$ **(b)** $x = t, y = -t, z = 1 + t$
7. **(a)** $P(2, -1), \mathbf{v} = 4\mathbf{i} - \mathbf{j}$ **(b)** $P(-1, 2, 4), \mathbf{v} = 5\mathbf{i} + 7\mathbf{j} - 8\mathbf{k}$
9. **(a)** $\langle -3, 4\rangle + t\langle 1, 5\rangle; -3\mathbf{i} + 4\mathbf{j} + t(\mathbf{i} + 5\mathbf{j})$ **(b)** $\langle 2, -3, 0\rangle + t\langle -1, 5, 1\rangle; 2\mathbf{i} - 3\mathbf{j} + t(-\mathbf{i} + 5\mathbf{j} + \mathbf{k})$

Responses to True–False questions may be abridged to save space.

11. False; the lines could be skew.
13. False; see part (b) of the solution to Example 3.
15. $x = -5 + 2t, y = 2 - 3t$ 17. $x = 3 + 4t, y = -4 + 3t$
19. $x = -1 + 3t, y = 2 - 4t, z = 4 + t$
21. $x = -2 + 2t, y = -t, z = 5 + 2t$
23. **(a)** $x = 7$ **(b)** $y = \frac{7}{3}$ **(c)** $x = \dfrac{-1 \pm \sqrt{85}}{6}, y = \dfrac{43 \mp \sqrt{85}}{18}$
25. $(-2, 10, 0)$; $(-2, 0, -5)$; the line does not intersect the $yz$-plane.
27. $(0, 4, -2), (4, 0, 6)$ 29. $(1, -1, 2)$ 33. The lines are parallel.
35. The points do not lie on the same line.
39. $\langle x, y\rangle = \langle -1, 2\rangle + t\langle 1, 1\rangle$

41. the point $1/n$ of the way from $(-2, 0)$ to $(1, 3)$
43. the line segment joining the points $(1, 0)$ and $(-3, 6)$
45. $(5, 2)$ 47. $2\sqrt{5}$ 49. distance $= \sqrt{35/6}$
51. **(a)** $x = x_0 + (x_1 - x_0)t, y = y_0 + (y_1 - y_0)t, z = z_0 + (z_1 - z_0)t$
**(b)** $x = x_1 + at, y = y_1 + bt, z = z_1 + ct$
53. **(b)** $\langle x, y, z\rangle = \langle 1 + 2t, -3 + 4t, 5 + t\rangle$
55. **(b)** $84°$ **(c)** $x = 7 + t, y = -1, z = -2 + t$
57. $x = t, y = 2 + t, z = 1 - t$
59. **(a)** $\sqrt{17}$ cm **(b)** 10

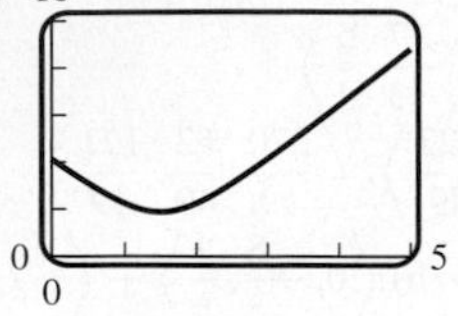


**(d)** $\sqrt{14}/2$ cm

## ▶ Exercise Set 11.6 (Page 722)

1. $x = 3, y = 4, z = 5$ 3. $x + 4y + 2z = 28$ 5. $z = 0$
7. $x - y = 0$ 9. $y + z = 1$ 11. $2y - z = 1$
13. **(a)** parallel **(b)** perpendicular **(c)** neither
15. **(a)** parallel **(b)** neither **(c)** perpendicular
17. **(a)** point of intersection is $\left(\frac{5}{2}, \frac{5}{2}, \frac{5}{2}\right)$ **(b)** no intersection
19. $35°$

Responses to True–False questions may be abridged to save space.

21. True; each will be the negative of the other.
23. True; the direction vector of $L$ must be orthogonal to both normal vectors.
25. $4x - 2y + 7z = 0$ 27. $4x - 13y + 21z = -14$
29. $x + y - 3z = 6$ 31. $x + 5y + 3z = -6$
33. $x + 2y + 4z = \frac{29}{2}$ 35. $x = 5 - 2t, y = 5t, z = -2 + 11t$
37. $7x + y + 9z = 25$ 39. yes
41. $x = -\frac{11}{7} - 23t, y = -\frac{12}{7} + t, z = -7t$
43. $\frac{5}{3}$ 45. $5/\sqrt{54}$ 47. $25/\sqrt{126}$
49. $(x - 2)^2 + (y - 1)^2 + (z + 3)^2 = \frac{121}{14}$ 51. $5/\sqrt{12}$

## ▶ Exercise Set 11.7 (Page 733)

1. **(a)** elliptic paraboloid, $a = 2, b = 3$
**(b)** hyperbolic paraboloid, $a = 1, b = 5$
**(c)** hyperboloid of one sheet, $a = b = c = 4$
**(d)** circular cone, $a = b = 1$ **(e)** elliptic paraboloid, $a = 2, b = 1$
**(f)** hyperboloid of two sheets, $a = b = c = 1$
3. **(a)** $-z = x^2 + y^2$, circular paraboloid opening down the negative $z$-axis

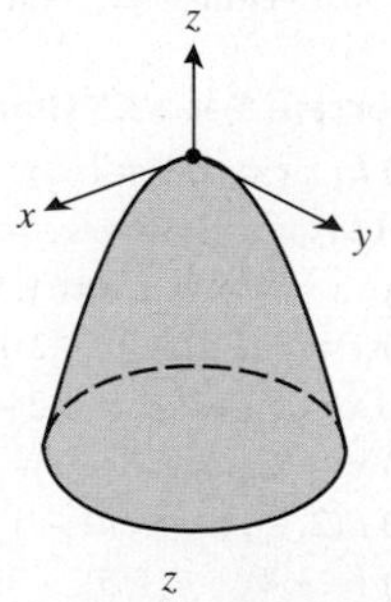


**(b)** $z = x^2 + y^2$, circular paraboloid, no change
**(c)** $z = x^2 + y^2$, circular paraboloid, no change
**(d)** $z = x^2 + y^2$, circular paraboloid, no change

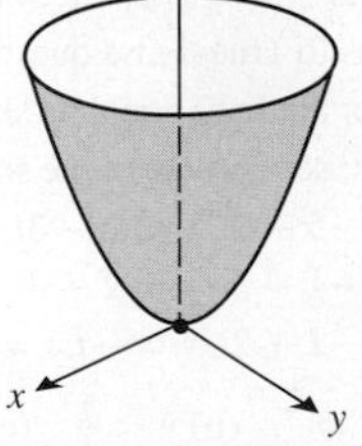


**(e)** $x = y^2 + z^2$, circular paraboloid opening along the positive $x$-axis

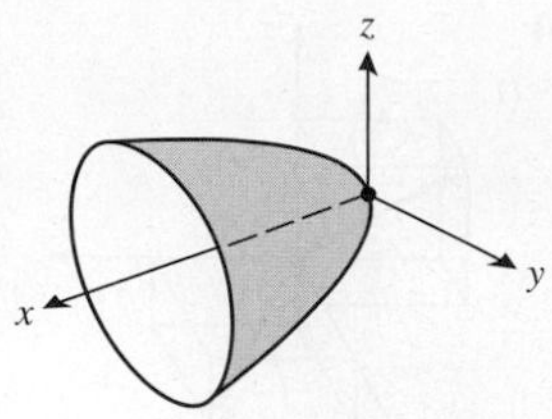


**(f)** $y = x^2 + z^2$, circular paraboloid opening along the positive $y$-axis

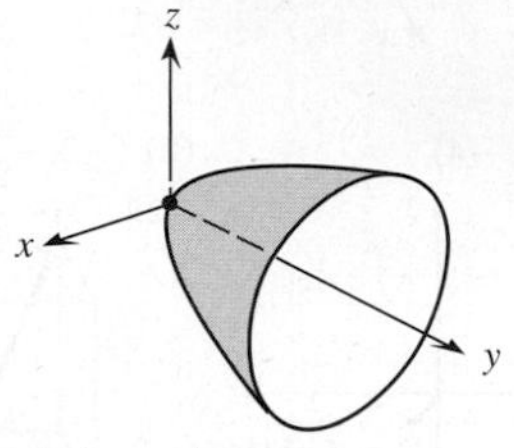


5. **(a)** hyperboloid of one sheet, axis is $y$-axis
**(b)** hyperboloid of two sheets separated by $yz$-plane
**(c)** elliptic paraboloid opening along the positive $x$-axis
**(d)** elliptic cone with $x$-axis as axis
**(e)** hyperbolic paraboloid straddling the $x$-axis
**(f)** paraboloid opening along the negative $y$-axis
7. **(a)** $x = 0$: $\dfrac{y^2}{25} + \dfrac{z^2}{4} = 1$;
$y = 0$: $\dfrac{x^2}{9} + \dfrac{z^2}{4} = 1$;
$z = 0$: $\dfrac{x^2}{9} + \dfrac{y^2}{25} = 1$

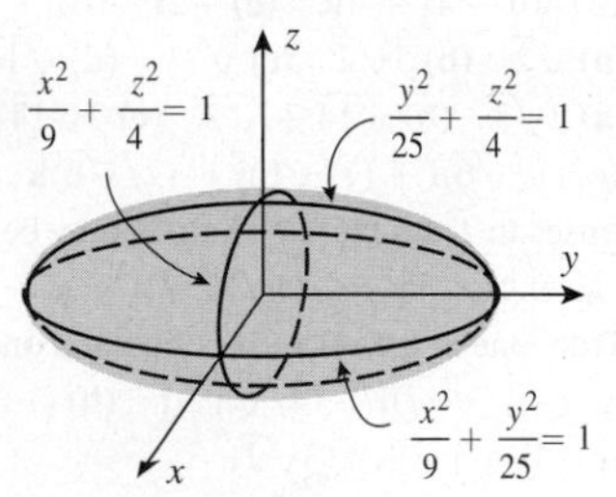


**(b)** $x = 0$: $z = 4y^2$;
$y = 0$: $z = x^2$;
$z = 0$: $x = y = 0$

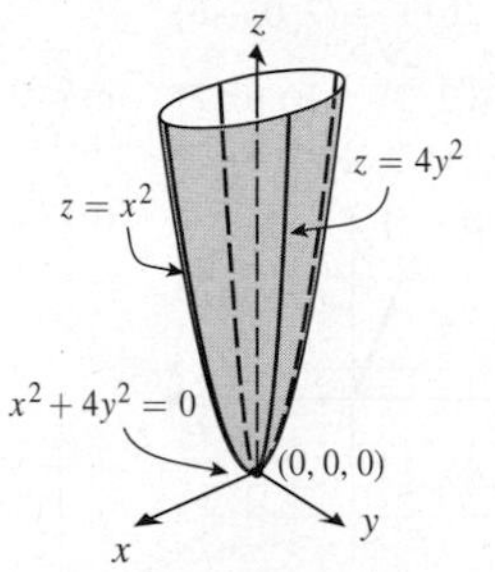


**(c)** $x = 0$: $\dfrac{y^2}{16} - \dfrac{z^2}{4} = 1$;
$y = 0$: $\dfrac{x^2}{9} - \dfrac{z^2}{4} = 1$;
$z = 0$: $\dfrac{x^2}{9} + \dfrac{y^2}{16} = 1$

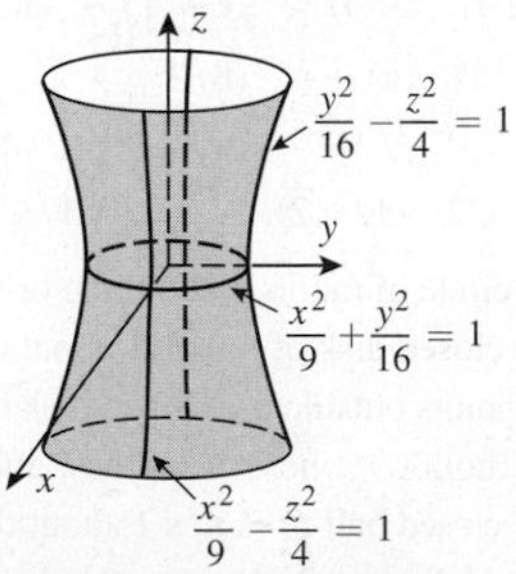


9. **(a)** $4x^2 + z^2 = 3$; ellipse **(b)** $y^2 + z^2 = 3$; circle
**(c)** $y^2 + z^2 = 20$; circle **(d)** $9x^2 - y^2 = 20$; hyperbola
**(e)** $z = 9x^2 + 16$; parabola **(f)** $9x^2 + 4y^2 = 4$; ellipse

Responses to True–False questions may be abridged to save space.

11. False; "quadric" refers to second powers.
13. False; none of the cross sections need be circles.

15.

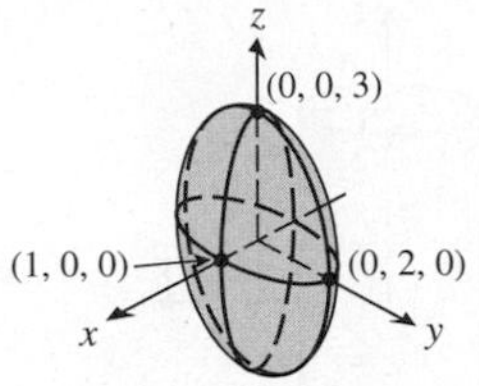


Ellipsoid

17.

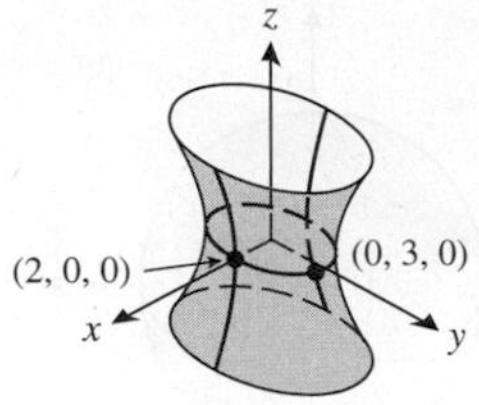


Hyperboloid of one sheet

19.

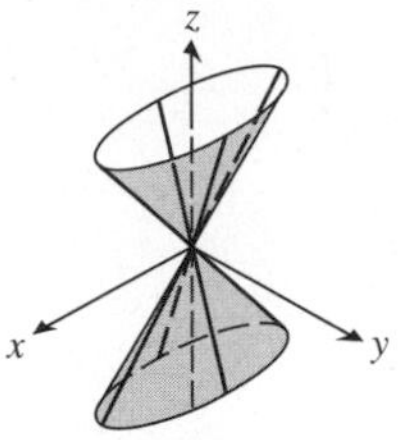


Elliptic cone

21.

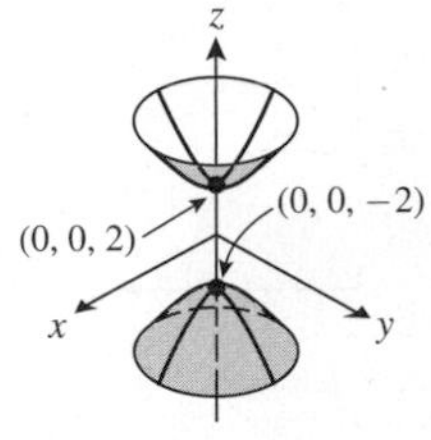


Hyperboloid of two sheets

23.

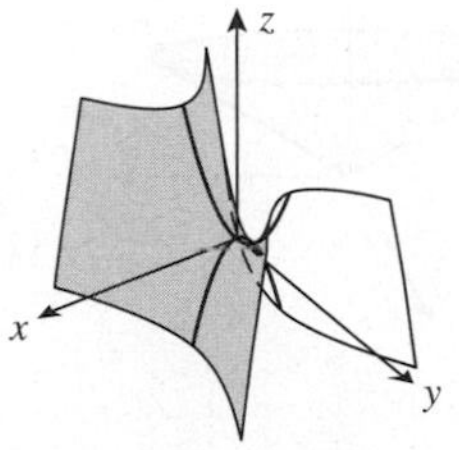


Hyperbolic paraboloid

25.

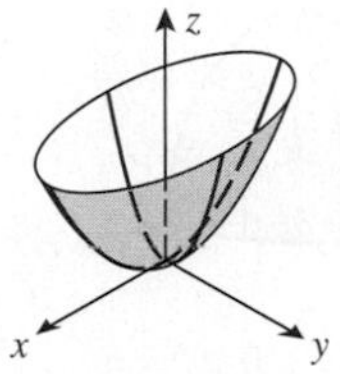


Elliptic paraboloid

27.

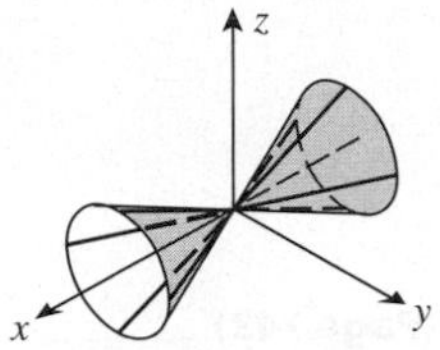


Circular cone

29.

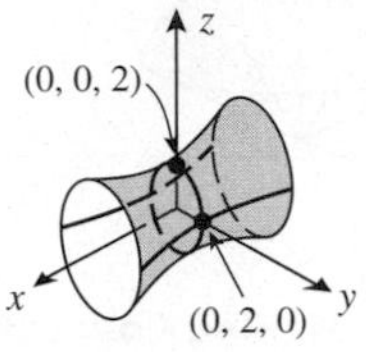


Hyperboloid of one sheet

31.

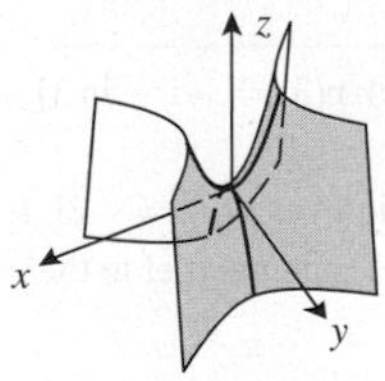


Hyperbolic paraboloid

33.

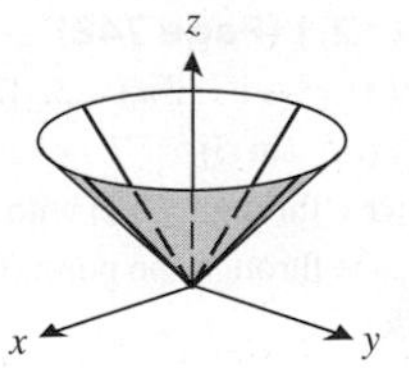


35.

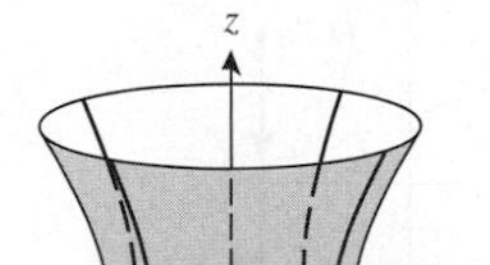


37.

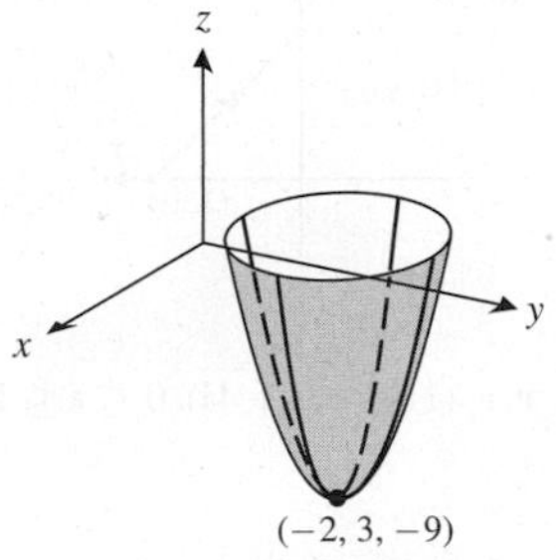


Circular paraboloid

39.

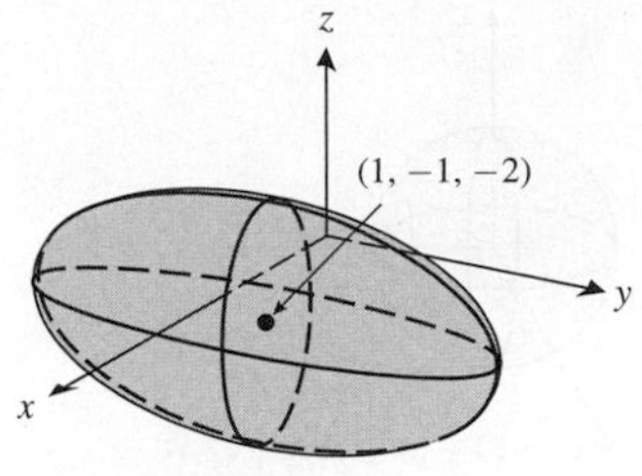


Ellipsoid

41. **(a)** $\dfrac{x^2}{9}+\dfrac{y^2}{4}=1$ **(b)** 6, 4 **(c)** $(\pm\sqrt{5}, 0, \sqrt{2})$
**(d)** The focal axis is parallel to the $x$-axis.

43. **(a)** $\dfrac{y^2}{4}-\dfrac{x^2}{4}=1$ **(b)** $(0, \pm 2, 4)$ **(c)** $(0, \pm 2\sqrt{2}, 4)$
**(d)** The focal axis is parallel to the $y$-axis.

45. **(a)** $z+4=y^2$ **(b)** $(2, 0, -4)$ **(c)** $\left(2, 0, -\frac{15}{4}\right)$
**(d)** The focal axis is parallel to the $z$-axis.

47. circle of radius $\sqrt{2}$ in the plane $z=2$, centered at $(0, 0, 2)$

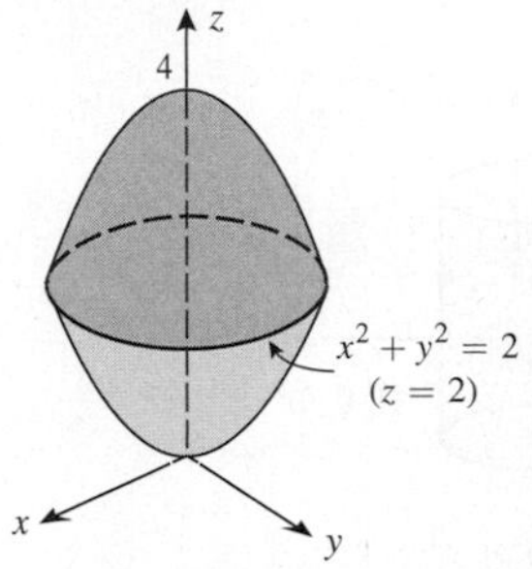


49. $y=4(x^2+z^2)$ 51. $z=(x^2+y^2)/4$ (circular paraboloid)

## ▶ Exercise Set 11.8 (Page 740)

1. **(a)** $(8, \pi/6, -4)$ **(b)** $(5\sqrt{2}, 3\pi/4, 6)$
**(c)** $(2, \pi/2, 0)$ **(d)** $(8, 5\pi/3, 6)$
3. **(a)** $(2\sqrt{3}, 2, 3)$ **(b)** $(-4\sqrt{2}, 4\sqrt{2}, -2)$
**(c)** $(5, 0, 4)$ **(d)** $(-7, 0, -9)$
5. **(a)** $(2\sqrt{2}, \pi/3, 3\pi/4)$ **(b)** $(2, 7\pi/4, \pi/4)$
**(c)** $(6, \pi/2, \pi/3)$ **(d)** $(10, 5\pi/6, \pi/2)$
7. **(a)** $(5\sqrt{6}/4, 5\sqrt{2}/4, 5\sqrt{2}/2)$ **(b)** $(7, 0, 0)$
**(c)** $(0, 0, 1)$ **(d)** $(0, -2, 0)$
9. **(a)** $(2\sqrt{3}, \pi/6, \pi/6)$ **(b)** $(\sqrt{2}, \pi/4, 3\pi/4)$
**(c)** $(2, 3\pi/4, \pi/2)$ **(d)** $(4\sqrt{3}, 1, 2\pi/3)$
11. **(a)** $(5\sqrt{3}/2, \pi/4, -5/2)$ **(b)** $(0, 7\pi/6, -1)$
**(c)** $(0, 0, 3)$ **(d)** $(4, \pi/6, 0)$

Responses to True–False questions may be abridged to save space.

15. True; see Figure 11.8.1*b*.
17. True; see Figures 11.8.3 and 11.8.4.

19.

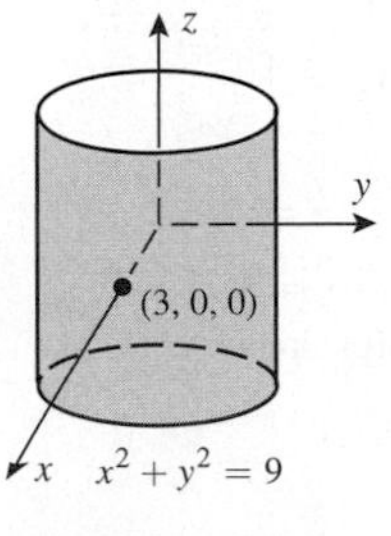


21.

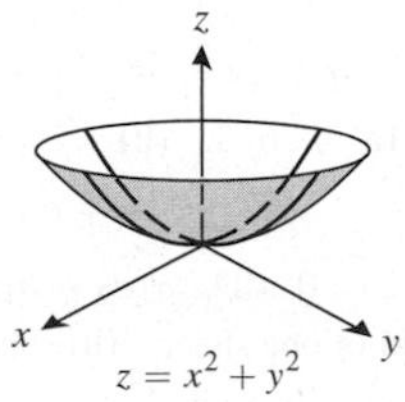

23.

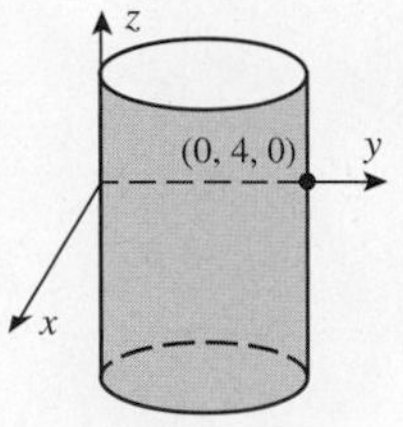


$x^2 + (y-2)^2 = 4$

25.

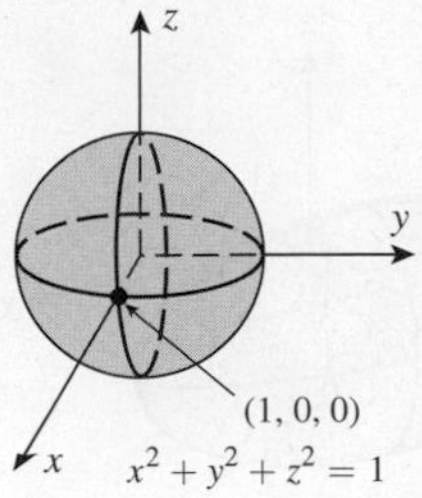


$x^2 + y^2 + z^2 = 1$

27.

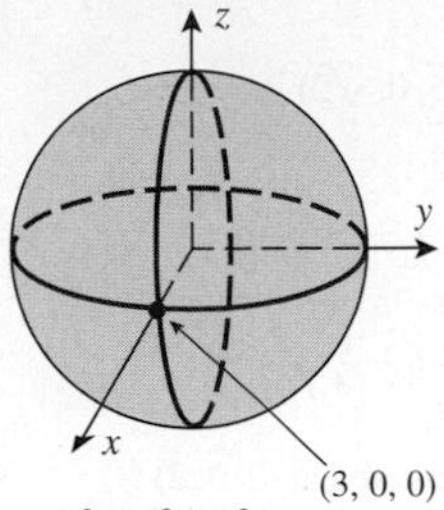


$x^2 + y^2 + z^2 = 9$

29.

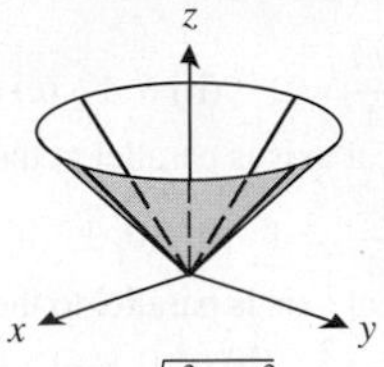


$z = \sqrt{x^2 + y^2}$

31.

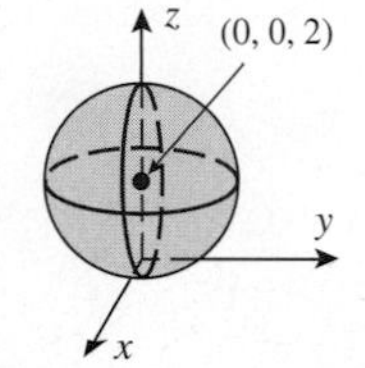


$x^2 + y^2 + (z-2)^2 = 4$

33.

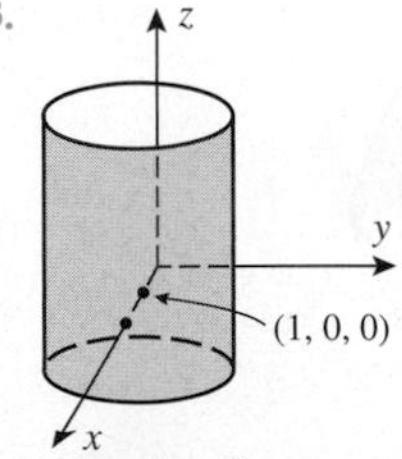


$(x-1)^2 + y^2 = 1$

35. **(a)** $z = 3$ **(b)** $\rho = 3 \sec \phi$ 37. **(a)** $z = 3r^2$ **(b)** $\rho = \frac{1}{3} \csc \phi \cot \phi$
39. **(a)** $r = 2$ **(b)** $\rho = 2 \csc \phi$ 41. **(a)** $r^2 + z^2 = 9$ **(b)** $\rho = 3$
43. **(a)** $2r \cos \theta + 3r \sin \theta + 4z = 1$
**(b)** $2\rho \sin \phi \cos \theta + 3\rho \sin \phi \sin \theta + 4\rho \cos \phi = 1$
45. **(a)** $r^2 \cos^2 \theta = 16 - z^2$ **(b)** $\rho^2(1 - \sin^2 \phi \sin^2 \theta) = 16$
47. all points on or above the paraboloid $z = x^2 + y^2$ that are also on or below the plane $z = 4$
49. all points on or between concentric spheres of radii 1 and 3 centered at the origin
51. spherical: $(4000, \pi/6, \pi/6)$; rectangular: $(1000\sqrt{3}, 1000, 2000\sqrt{3})$
53. **(a)** $(10, \pi/2, 1)$ **(b)** $(0, 10, 1)$ **(c)** $(\sqrt{101}, \pi/2, \tan^{-1} 10)$
55. 23,936 $\text{m}^2$

## ▶ Chapter 11 Review Exercises (Page 741)

3. **(b)** $-1/2, \pm\sqrt{3}/2$ **(d)** true
5. $(x+3)^2 + (y-5)^2 + (z+4)^2 = r^2$;
**(a)** $r^2 = 16$ **(b)** $r^2 = 25$ **(c)** $r^2 = 9$
7. $(7, 5)$
9. **(a)** $-\frac{3}{4}$ **(b)** $\frac{1}{7}$ **(c)** $(48 \pm 25\sqrt{3})/11$ **(d)** $c = \frac{4}{3}$
13. 13 ft·lb 15. **(a)** $\sqrt{26}/2$ **(b)** $\sqrt{26}/3$
17. **(a)** 29 **(b)** $\dfrac{29}{\sqrt{65}}$ 19. $x = 4 + t, y = 1 - t, z = 2$
21. $x + 5y - z - 2 = 0$ 23. $a_1a_2 + b_1b_2 + c_1c_2 = 0$
25. **(a)** hyperboloid of one sheet **(b)** sphere **(c)** circular cone
27. **(a)** $z = x^2 - y^2$ **(b)** $xz = 1$

29. **(a)**

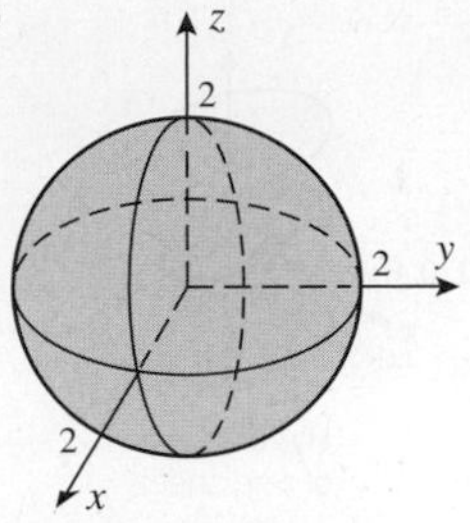


**(b)**

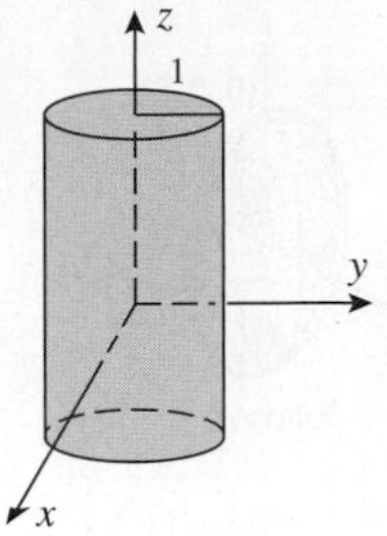


**(c)**

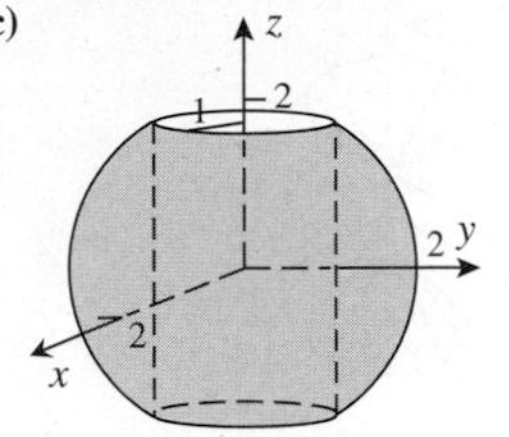


31. **(a)**

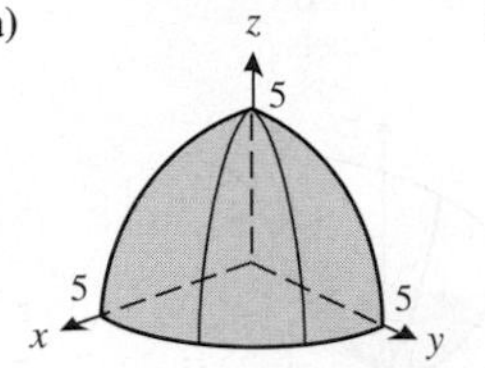


**(b)**

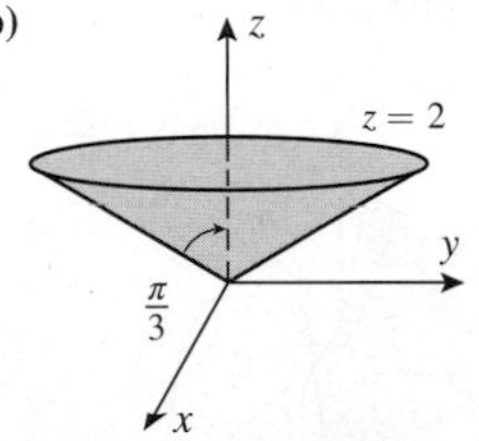


**(c)**

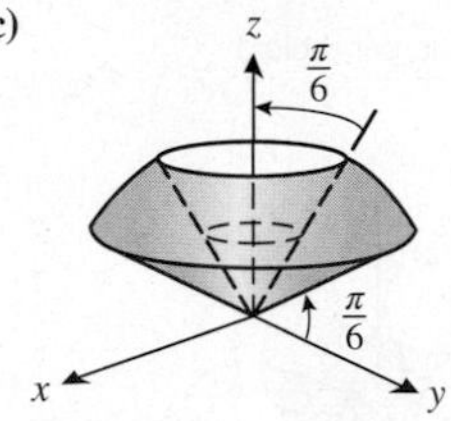


## ▶ Chapter 11 Making Connections (Page 743)

Answers are provided in the Student Solutions Manual.

## ▶ Exercise Set 12.1 (Page 748)

1. $(-\infty, +\infty)$; $\mathbf{r}(\pi) = -\mathbf{i} - 3\pi\mathbf{j}$ 3. $[2, +\infty)$; $\mathbf{r}(3) = -\mathbf{i} - \ln 3\mathbf{j} + \mathbf{k}$
5. $\mathbf{r} = 3 \cos t\mathbf{i} + (t + \sin t)\mathbf{j}$ 7. $x = 3t^2, y = -2$
9. the line in 2-space through $(3, 0)$ with direction vector $\mathbf{a} = -2\mathbf{i} + 5\mathbf{j}$
11. the line in 3-space through the point $(0, -3, 1)$ and parallel to the vector $2\mathbf{i} + 3\mathbf{k}$
13. an ellipse centered at $(0, 0, 1)$ in the plane $z = 1$
15. **(a)** slope $-\frac{3}{2}$ **(b)** $\left(\frac{5}{2}, 0, \frac{3}{2}\right)$
17. **(a)**

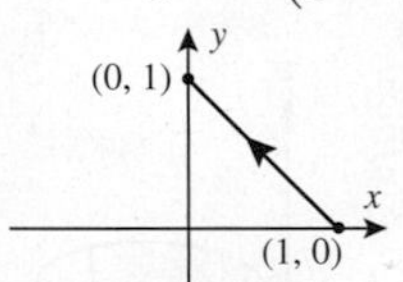


**(b)**

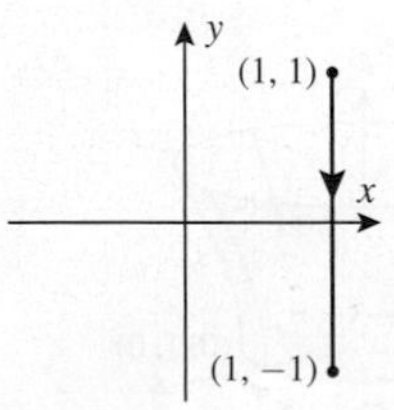


19. $\mathbf{r} = (1 - t)(3\mathbf{i} + 4\mathbf{j}), 0 \le t \le 1$

21. $x = 2$

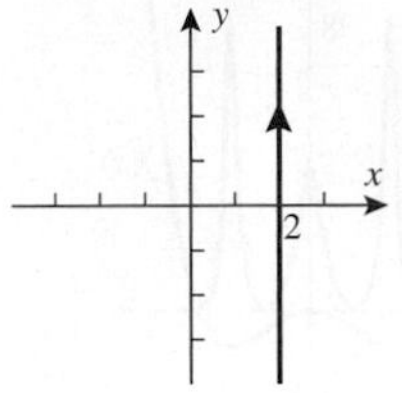


23. $(x-1)^2 + (y-3)^2 = 1$

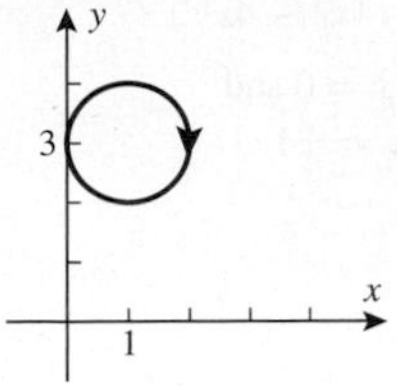


25. $x^2 - y^2 = 1, x \geq 1$

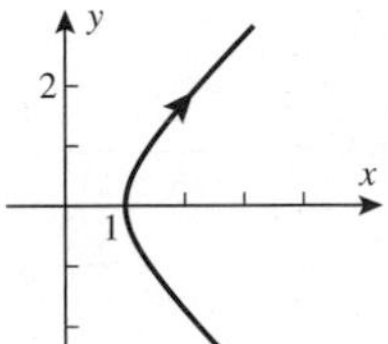


27.

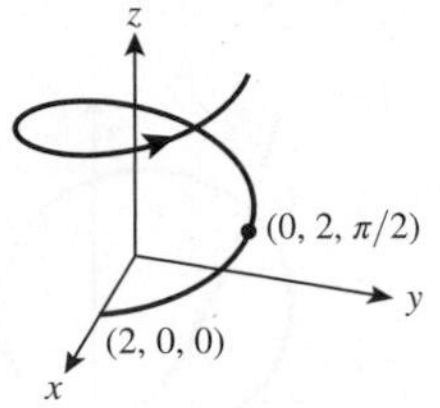


29.

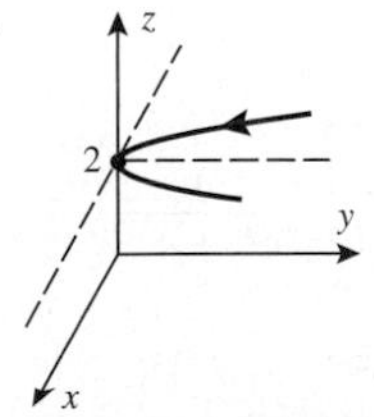


Responses to True–False questions may be abridged to save space.

31. False; the natural domain of a vector-valued function is the *intersection* of the domains of its component functions.

33. True; $\mathbf{r}(t) = (1-t)\mathbf{r}_0 + t\mathbf{r}_1 (0 \leq t \leq 1)$ represents the line segment in 3-space that is traced from $\mathbf{r}_0$ to $\mathbf{r}_1$.

35. $x = t, y = t, z = 2t^2$

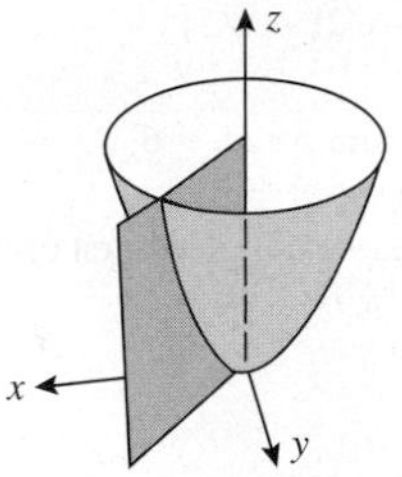


37. $\mathbf{r}(t) = t\mathbf{i} + t^2\mathbf{j} \pm \frac{1}{3}\sqrt{81 - 9t^2 - t^4}\,\mathbf{k}$  43. $c = 3/(2\pi)$

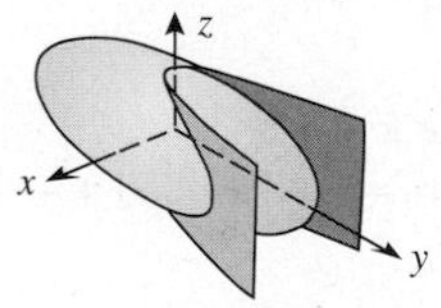


47. **(a)** III, since the curve is a subset of the plane $y = -x$
**(b)** IV, since only $x$ is periodic in $t$ and $y$, $z$ increase without bound
**(c)** II, since all three components are periodic in $t$
**(d)** I, since the projection onto the $yz$-plane is a circle and the curve increases without bound in the $x$-direction

49. **(a)** $x = 3\cos t, y = 3\sin t, z = 9\cos^2 t$
**(b)**

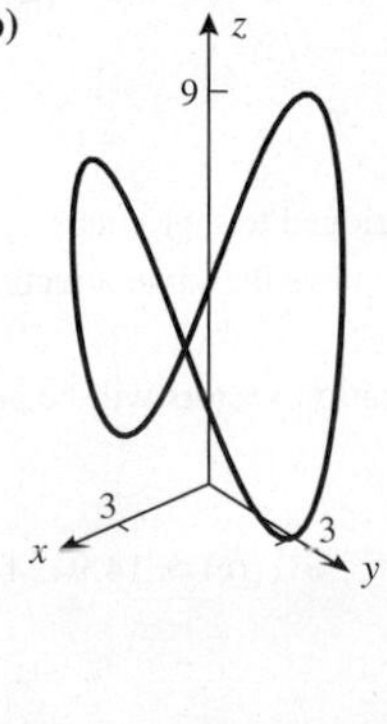


## ▸ Exercise Set 12.2 (Page 757)

1. $\left\langle \frac{1}{3}, 0 \right\rangle$  3. $2\mathbf{i} - 3\mathbf{j} + 4\mathbf{k}$  5. **(a)** continuous  **(b)** not continuous

7.

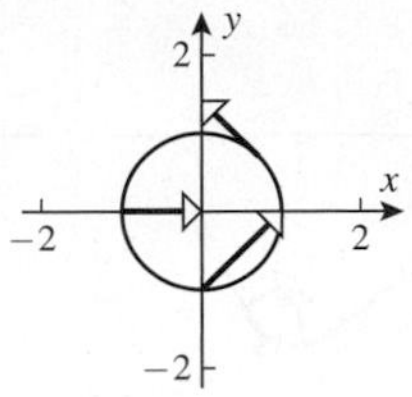


9. $(\sin t)\mathbf{j}$  11. $\mathbf{r}'(2) = \langle 1, 4 \rangle$

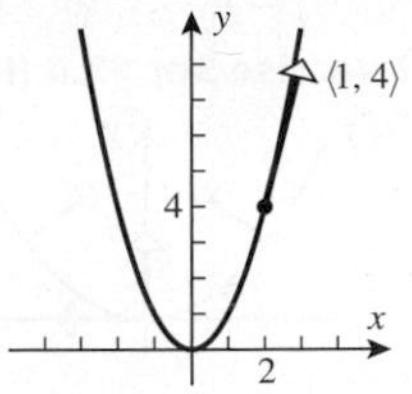


13. $\mathbf{r}'(0) = \mathbf{j}$

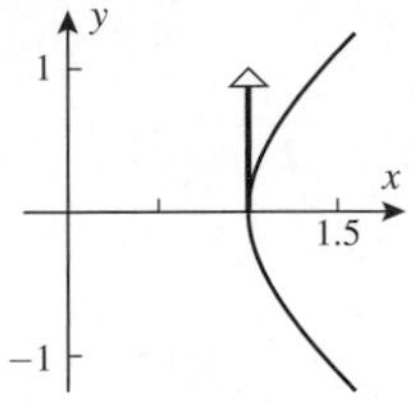


15. $\mathbf{r}'(\pi/2) = -2\mathbf{k}$

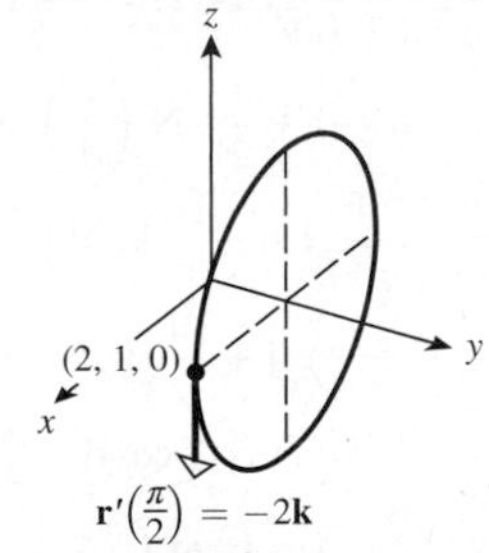


17.

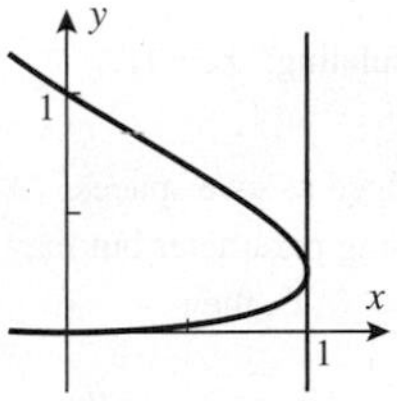


19. $x = 1 + 2t, y = 2 - t$
21. $x = 1 - \sqrt{3}\pi t, y = \sqrt{3} + \pi t, z = 1 + 3t$
23. $\mathbf{r} = (-\mathbf{i} + 2\mathbf{j}) + t\left(2\mathbf{i} + \frac{3}{4}\mathbf{j}\right)$
25. $\mathbf{r} = (4\mathbf{i} + \mathbf{j}) + t(-4\mathbf{i} + \mathbf{j} + 4\mathbf{k})$
27. **(a)** $\mathbf{i} - \mathbf{j} + \mathbf{k}$  **(b)** $-\mathbf{i} + \mathbf{k}$  **(c)** $0$
29. $7t^6$; $18t^5\mathbf{i} - 10t^4\mathbf{j}$
31. $3t\mathbf{i} + 2t^2\mathbf{j} + \mathbf{C}$

33. $\langle te^t - e^t, t\ln t - t \rangle + \mathbf{C}$  35. $\mathbf{j}$  37. $(5\sqrt{5} - 1)/3$
39. $\frac{52}{3}\mathbf{i} + 4\mathbf{j}$

Responses to True–False questions may be abridged to save space.

41. False; for example, $\mathbf{r}(t) = \langle t, |t| \rangle$ is continuous at $t = 0$, but the specified limit doesn't exist at $t = 0$.

43. True; see the definition of $\int_a^b \mathbf{r}(t)\,dt$.

45. $(t^2 + 1)\mathbf{i} + (t^3 - 1)\mathbf{j}$
47. $\mathbf{y}(t) = \left(\frac{1}{2}t^2 + 2\right)\mathbf{i} + (e^t - 1)\mathbf{j}$
49. **(a)** $(-2, 4, 6)$ and $(1, 1, -3)$  **(b)** $76°, 71°$  51. $68°$

## ▸ Exercise Set 12.3 (Page 766)

1. smooth  3. not smooth, $\mathbf{r}'(1) = \mathbf{0}$  5. $L = \frac{3}{2}$  7. $L = e - e^{-1}$
9. $L = 28$  11. $L = 2\pi\sqrt{10}$  13. $\mathbf{r}'(\tau) = 4\mathbf{i} + 8(4\tau + 1)\mathbf{j}$
15. $\mathbf{r}'(\tau) = 2\tau e^{\tau^2}\mathbf{i} - 8\tau e^{-\tau^2}\mathbf{j}$

Responses to True–False questions may be abridged to save space.

17. False; $\int_a^b \|\mathbf{r}'(t)\|\,dt$ is a scalar that represents the arc length of the curve in 2-space traced by $\mathbf{r}(t)$ from $t = a$ to $t = b$ (Theorem 12.3.1).

19. False; $\mathbf{r}'$ isn't defined at the point corresponding to the origin.

21. **(a)** $x = \dfrac{s}{\sqrt{2}}, y = \dfrac{s}{\sqrt{2}}$  **(b)** $x = y = z = \dfrac{s}{\sqrt{3}}$

23. **(a)** $x = 1 + \dfrac{s}{3}, y = 3 - \dfrac{2s}{3}, z = 4 + \dfrac{2s}{3}$  **(b)** $\left\langle \frac{28}{3}, -\frac{41}{3}, \frac{62}{3} \right\rangle$

25. $x = 3 + \cos s, y = 2 + \sin s, 0 \leq s \leq 2\pi$

27. $x = \frac{1}{3}[(3s+1)^{2/3} - 1]^{3/2}, y = \frac{1}{2}[(3s+1)^{2/3} - 1], s \geq 0$

29. $x = \left(\dfrac{s}{\sqrt{2}} + 1\right)\cos\left[\ln\left(\dfrac{s}{\sqrt{2}} + 1\right)\right],$
$0 \leq s \leq \sqrt{2}(e^{\pi/2} - 1)$
$y = \left(\dfrac{s}{\sqrt{2}} + 1\right)\sin\left[\ln\left(\dfrac{s}{\sqrt{2}} + 1\right)\right],$

33. $x = 2a\cos^{-1}[1 - s/(4a)]$
$- 2a(1 - [1 - s/(4a)]^2)^{1/2}(2[1 - s/(4a)]^2 - 1),$
$y = \dfrac{s(8a - s)}{8a}$ for $0 \leq s \leq 8a$

35. (a) $9/2$ (b) $9-2\sqrt{6}$ 37. (a) $\sqrt{3}(1-e^{-2})$ (b) $4\sqrt{5}$
39. (a) $g(\tau)=\pi(\tau)$ (b) $g(\tau)=\pi(1-\tau)$ 41. 44 in
43. (a) $2t+\dfrac{1}{t}$ (b) $2t+\dfrac{1}{t}$ (c) $8+\ln 3$

## ▶ Exercise Set 12.4 (Page 772)

1. (a)

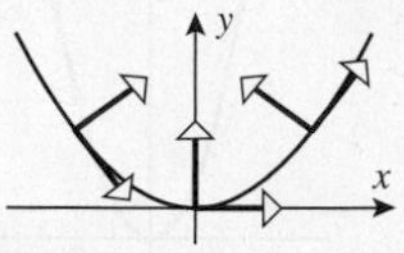


(b)

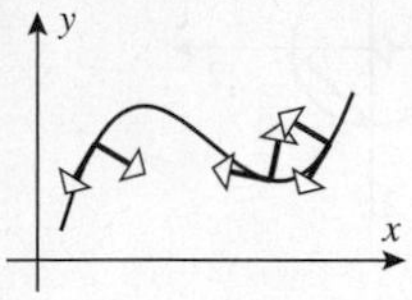


5. $\mathbf{T}(1)=\dfrac{2}{\sqrt{5}}\mathbf{i}+\dfrac{1}{\sqrt{5}}\mathbf{j}, \mathbf{N}(1)=\dfrac{1}{\sqrt{5}}\mathbf{i}-\dfrac{2}{\sqrt{5}}\mathbf{j}$

7. $\mathbf{T}\left(\dfrac{\pi}{3}\right)=-\dfrac{\sqrt{3}}{2}\mathbf{i}+\dfrac{1}{2}\mathbf{j}, \mathbf{N}\left(\dfrac{\pi}{3}\right)=-\dfrac{1}{2}\mathbf{i}-\dfrac{\sqrt{3}}{2}\mathbf{j}$

9. $\mathbf{T}\left(\dfrac{\pi}{2}\right)=-\dfrac{4}{\sqrt{17}}\mathbf{i}+\dfrac{1}{\sqrt{17}}\mathbf{k}, \mathbf{N}\left(\dfrac{\pi}{2}\right)=-\mathbf{j}$

11. $\mathbf{T}(0)=\dfrac{1}{\sqrt{3}}\mathbf{i}+\dfrac{1}{\sqrt{3}}\mathbf{j}+\dfrac{1}{\sqrt{3}}\mathbf{k}, \mathbf{N}(0)=-\dfrac{1}{\sqrt{2}}\mathbf{i}+\dfrac{1}{\sqrt{2}}\mathbf{j}$

13. $x=s, y=1$ 15. $\mathbf{B}=\frac{4}{5}\cos t\mathbf{i}-\frac{4}{5}\sin t\mathbf{j}-\frac{3}{5}\mathbf{k}$ 17. $\mathbf{B}=-\mathbf{k}$

19. $\mathbf{T}\left(\dfrac{\pi}{4}\right)=\dfrac{\sqrt{2}}{2}(-\mathbf{i}+\mathbf{j}), \mathbf{N}\left(\dfrac{\pi}{4}\right)=-\dfrac{\sqrt{2}}{2}(\mathbf{i}+\mathbf{j})$,
$\mathbf{B}\left(\dfrac{\pi}{4}\right)=\mathbf{k}$; rectifying: $x+y=\sqrt{2}$; osculating: $z=1$;
normal: $-x+y=0$

Responses to True–False questions may be abridged to save space.

21. False; $\mathbf{T}(t)$ points in the direction of increasing parameter but may not be orthogonal to $\mathbf{r}(t)$. For example, if $\mathbf{r}(t)=\langle t,t\rangle$, then $\mathbf{T}(t)=\langle 1/\sqrt{2}, 1/\sqrt{2}\rangle$ is parallel to $\mathbf{r}(t)$.

23. True; $\mathbf{T}(s)=\mathbf{r}'(s)$, the unit tangent vector, and $\mathbf{N}(s)=\dfrac{\mathbf{r}''(s)}{\|\mathbf{r}''(s)\|}$, the unit normal vector, are orthogonal, so $\mathbf{r}'(s)$ and $\mathbf{r}''(s)$ are orthogonal.

## ▶ Exercise Set 12.5 (Page 778)

1. $\kappa\approx 2$ 3. (a) I is the curvature of II. (b) I is the curvature of II.

5. $\dfrac{6}{|t|(4+9t^2)^{3/2}}$ 7. $\dfrac{12e^{2t}}{(9e^{6t}+e^{-2t})^{3/2}}$ 9. $\frac{4}{17}$ 11. $\dfrac{1}{2\cosh^2 t}$

13. $\kappa=\frac{2}{5}, \rho=\frac{5}{2}$ 15. $\kappa=\dfrac{\sqrt{2}}{3}, \rho=\dfrac{3\sqrt{2}}{2}$ 17. $\kappa=\frac{1}{4}$

Responses to True–False questions may be abridged to save space.

19. True; see Example 1: a circle of radius $a$ has constant curvature $1/a$.

21. False; see Definition 12.5.1: the curvature of the graph of $\mathbf{r}(s)$ is $\|\mathbf{r}''(s)\|$, the length of $\mathbf{r}''(s)$.

25. 1 27. $\dfrac{e^{-1}}{(1+e^{-2})^{3/2}}$ 29. $\frac{96}{125}$ 31. $\dfrac{1}{\sqrt{2}}$

33. (a)

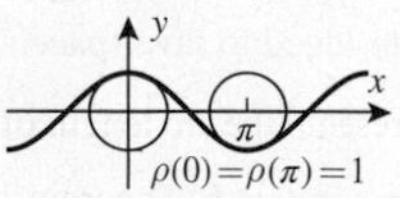


(b)

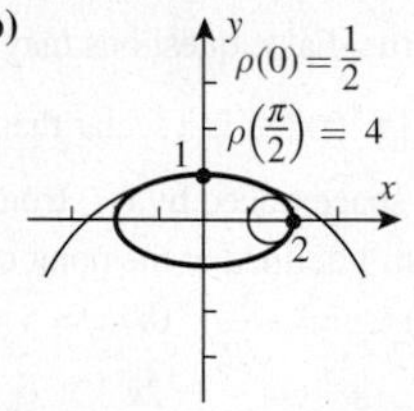


35.

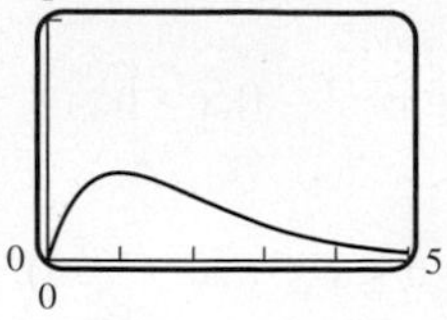


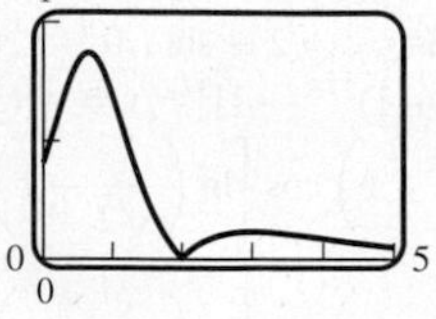


37. (a) $\kappa=\dfrac{|12x^2-4|}{[1+(4x^3-4x)^2]^{3/2}}$
(c) $\rho=\frac{1}{4}$ for $x=0$ and $\rho=\frac{1}{8}$ when $x=\pm 1$

(b)

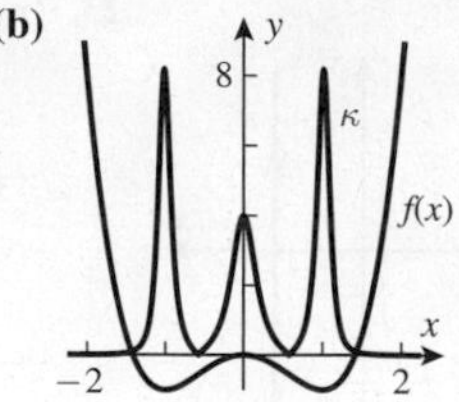


41. $\dfrac{3}{2\sqrt{2}}$ 43. $\frac{2}{3}$ 45. $\rho=2|p|$ 47. $(3,0),(-3,0)$

51. (b) $\rho=\sqrt{2}$ (c)

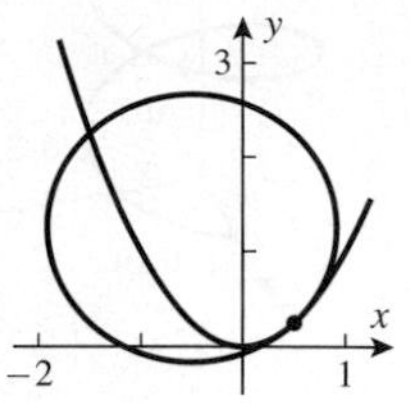


55. $a=\dfrac{1}{2r}$

63. $\tau=\dfrac{2}{(t^2+2)^2}$

65. $\tau=-\dfrac{\sqrt{2}}{(e^t+e^{-t})^2}$

## ▶ Exercise Set 12.6 (Page 790)

1. $\mathbf{v}(t)=-3\sin t\mathbf{i}+3\cos t\mathbf{j}$
$\mathbf{a}(t)=-3\cos t\mathbf{i}-3\sin t\mathbf{j}$
$\|\mathbf{v}(t)\|=3$

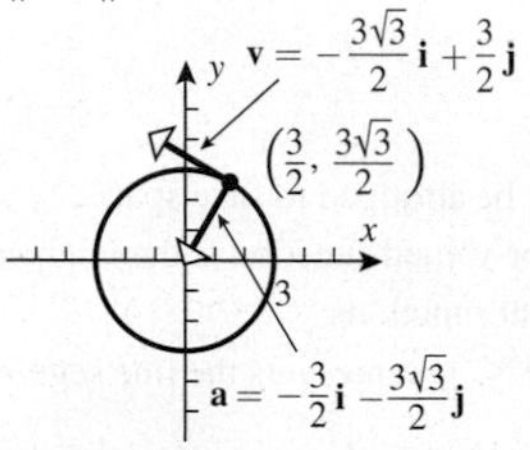


3. $\mathbf{v}(t)=e^t\mathbf{i}-e^{-t}\mathbf{j}$
$\mathbf{a}(t)=e^t\mathbf{i}+e^{-t}\mathbf{j}$
$\|\mathbf{v}(t)\|=\sqrt{e^{2t}+e^{-2t}}$

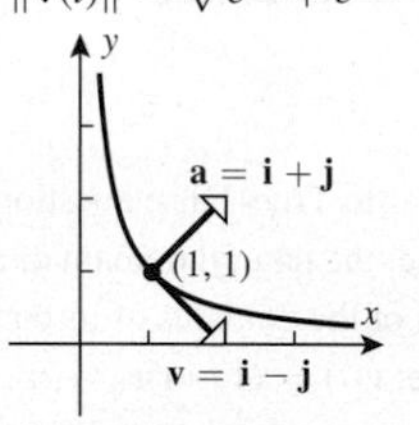


5. $\mathbf{v}=\mathbf{i}+\mathbf{j}+\mathbf{k}, \|\mathbf{v}\|=\sqrt{3}, \mathbf{a}=\mathbf{j}+2\mathbf{k}$
7. $\mathbf{v}=-\sqrt{2}\mathbf{i}+\sqrt{2}\mathbf{j}+\mathbf{k}, \|\mathbf{v}\|=\sqrt{5}, \mathbf{a}=-\sqrt{2}\mathbf{i}-\sqrt{2}\mathbf{j}$
13. minimum speed $3\sqrt{2}$ when $\mathbf{r}=24\mathbf{i}+8\mathbf{j}$
15. (a)

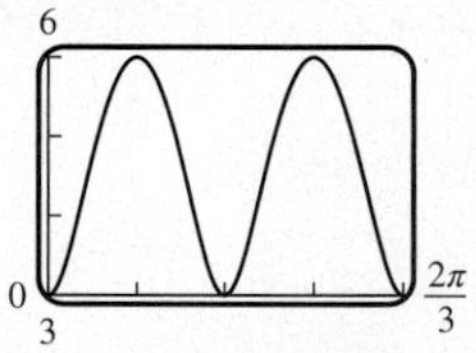


(b) maximum speed = 6, minimum speed = 3
(d) The maximum speed first occurs when $t=\pi/6$.

17. $\mathbf{v}(t)=(1-\sin t)\mathbf{i}+(\cos t-1)\mathbf{j}$;
$\mathbf{r}(t)=(t+\cos t-1)\mathbf{i}+(\sin t-t+1)\mathbf{j}$
19. $\mathbf{v}(t)=(1-\cos t)\mathbf{i}+\sin t\mathbf{j}+e^t\mathbf{k}$;
$\mathbf{r}(t)=(t-\sin t-1)\mathbf{i}+(1-\cos t)\mathbf{j}+e^t\mathbf{k}$
21. $15^\circ$ 23. (a) $0.7\mathbf{i}+2.7\mathbf{j}-3.4\mathbf{k}$ (b) $\mathbf{r}_0=-0.7\mathbf{i}-2.9\mathbf{j}+4.8\mathbf{k}$
25. $\Delta\mathbf{r}=8\mathbf{i}+\frac{26}{3}\mathbf{j}, s=(13\sqrt{13}-5\sqrt{5})/3$
27. $\Delta\mathbf{r}=2\mathbf{i}-\frac{2}{3}\mathbf{j}+\sqrt{2}\ln 3\mathbf{k}; s=\frac{8}{3}$
31. (a) $a_T=0, a_N=\sqrt{2}$ (b) $a_T\mathbf{T}=\mathbf{0}, a_N\mathbf{N}=\mathbf{i}+\mathbf{j}$ (c) $1/\sqrt{2}$
33. (a) $a_T=2\sqrt{5}, a_N=2\sqrt{5}$ (b) $a_T\mathbf{T}=2\mathbf{i}+4\mathbf{j}, a_N\mathbf{N}=4\mathbf{i}-2\mathbf{j}$
(c) $2/\sqrt{5}$
35. (a) $a_T=-7/\sqrt{6}, a_N=\sqrt{53/6}$
(b) $a_T\mathbf{T}=-\frac{7}{6}(\mathbf{i}-2\mathbf{j}+\mathbf{k}), a_N\mathbf{N}=\frac{13}{6}\mathbf{i}+\frac{5}{3}\mathbf{j}+\frac{7}{6}\mathbf{k}$ (c) $\dfrac{\sqrt{53}}{6\sqrt{6}}$
37. $a_T=-3, a_N=2, \mathbf{T}=-\mathbf{j}, \mathbf{N}=\mathbf{i}$ 39. $-3/2$
41. $a_N=8.41\times 10^{10}\ \mathrm{km/s^2}$
43. $a_N=18/(1+4x^2)^{3/2}$ 45. $a_N=0$

Responses to True–False questions may be abridged to save space.

47. True; the velocity and unit tangent vectors have the same direction, so are parallel.
49. False; in this case the velocity and acceleration vectors will be parallel, but they may have opposite direction.
53. $\approx 257.20$ N
55. $40\sqrt{3}$ ft 57. 800 ft/s 59. $15^\circ$ or $75^\circ$ 61. (c) $\approx 14.942$ ft

63. **(a)** $\rho \approx 176.78$ m **(b)** $\frac{125}{4}$ m
65. **(b)** $R$ is maximum when $\alpha = 45°$, maximum value $v_0^2/g$
67. **(a)** 2.62 s **(b)** 181.5 ft
69. **(a)** $v_0 \approx 83$ ft/s, $\alpha \approx 8°$ **(b)** 268.76 ft

## ▶ Exercise Set 12.7 (Page 799)

7. 7.75 km/s 9. 10.88 km/s
11. **(a)** minimum distance $= 220{,}680$ mi, maximum distance $= 246{,}960$ mi **(b)** 27.5 days
13. **(a)** 17,224 mi/h **(b)** $e \approx 0.071$, apogee altitude $= 819$ mi

## ▶ Chapter 12 Review Exercises (Page 801)

3. the circle of radius 3 in the $xy$-plane, with center at the origin
5. a parabola in the plane $x = -2$, vertex at $(-2, 0, -1)$, opening upward
11. $x = 1 + t, y = -t, z = t$ 13. $(\sin t)\mathbf{i} - (\cos t)\mathbf{j} + \mathbf{C}$
15. $y(t) = \left(\frac{1}{3}t^3 + 1\right)\mathbf{i} + (t^2 + 1)\mathbf{j}$ 17. 15/4
19. $\mathbf{r}(s) = \dfrac{s-3}{3}\mathbf{i} + \dfrac{12-2s}{3}\mathbf{j} + \dfrac{9+2s}{3}\mathbf{k}$ 25. 3/5 27. 0
29. **(a)** speed **(b)** distance traveled **(c)** distance of the particle from the origin
33. **(a)** $\mathbf{r}(t) = \left(\frac{1}{6}t^4 + t\right)\mathbf{i} + \left(\frac{1}{2}t^2 + 2t\right)\mathbf{j} - \left(\frac{1}{4}\cos 2t + t - \frac{1}{4}\right)\mathbf{k}$ **(b)** 3.475 35. 10.65 km/s 37. 24.78 ft

## ▶ Chapter 12 Making Connections (Page 802)

Where correct answers to a Making Connections exercise may vary, no answer is listed. Sample answers for these questions are available on the Book Companion Site.

1. **(c)** (i) $\mathbf{N} = \frac{1}{\sqrt{5}}\mathbf{i} - \frac{2}{\sqrt{5}}\mathbf{j}$ (ii) $\mathbf{N} = -\mathbf{j}$
2. **(b)** (i) $\mathbf{N} = -\sin t\mathbf{i} - \cos t\mathbf{j}$

(ii) $\mathbf{N} = \dfrac{-(4t + 18t^3)\mathbf{i} + (2 - 18t^4)\mathbf{j} + (6t + 12t^3)\mathbf{k}}{2\sqrt{81t^8 + 117t^6 + 54t^4 + 13t^2 + 1}}$

3. **(c)** $\kappa(s) \to +\infty$, so the spiral winds ever tighter.
4. semicircle: 53.479 ft; quarter-circle: 60.976 ft; point: 64.001 ft

## ▶ Exercise Set 13.1 (Page 812)

1. **(a)** 5 **(b)** 3 **(c)** 1 **(d)** $-2$ **(e)** $9a^3 + 1$ **(f)** $a^3b^2 - a^2b^3 + 1$
3. **(a)** $x^2 - y^2 + 3$ **(b)** $3x^3y^4 + 3$ 5. $x^3e^{x^3(3y+1)}$
7. **(a)** $t^2 + 3t^{10}$ **(b)** 0 **(c)** 3076
9. **(a)** 2.5 mg/L **(b)** $C(100, t) = 20(e^{-0.2t} - e^{-t})$ **(c)** $C(x, 1) = 0.2x(e^{-0.2} - e^{-1}) \approx 0.09x$
11. **(a)** WCI $= 17.8°$F **(b)** WCI $= 22.6°$F 13. **(a)** 30°F **(b)** 22.5°F
15. **(a)** 66% **(b)** 73.5% **(c)** 60.6%
17. **(a)** 19 **(b)** $-9$ **(c)** 3 **(d)** $a^6 + 3$ **(e)** $-t^8 + 3$ **(f)** $(a + b)(a - b)^2b^3 + 3$
19. $(y + 1)e^{x^2(y+1)z^2}$ 21. **(a)** $80\sqrt{\pi}$ **(b)** $n(n + 1)/2$

23.

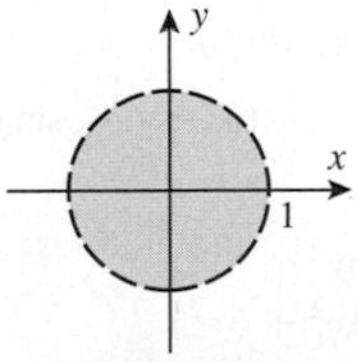


25.

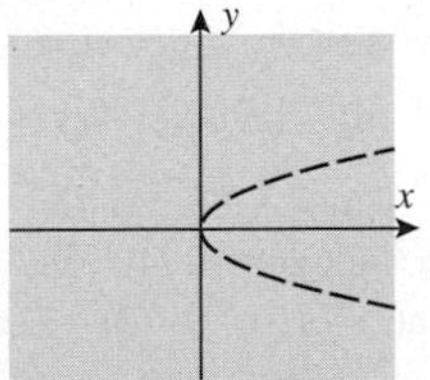


27. **(a)** all points above or on the line $y = -2$ **(b)** all points on or within the sphere $x^2 + y^2 + z^2 = 25$ **(c)** all points in 3-space

Responses to True–False questions may be abridged to save space.

29. True; the interval [0, 1] is the intersection of the domains of $\sin^{-1} t$ and $\sqrt{t}$.
31. False; the natural domain is an infinite solid cylinder.

33.

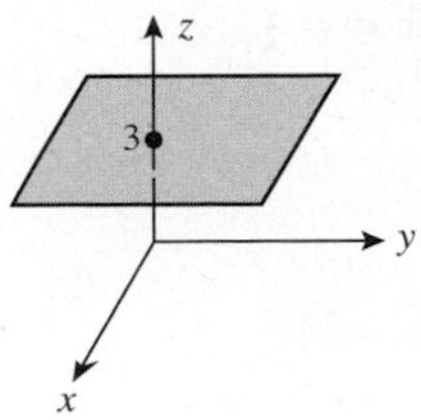


35.

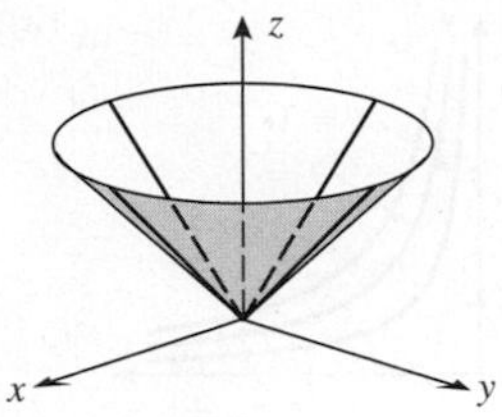


37.

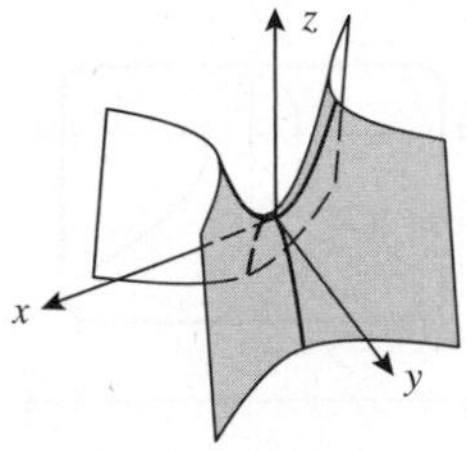


39.

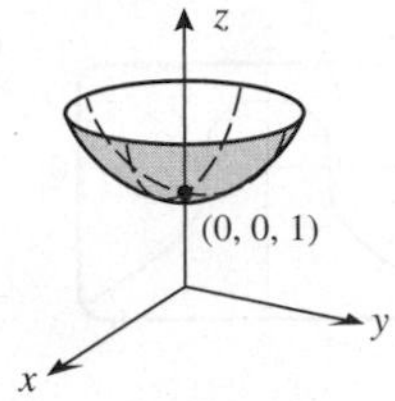


41.

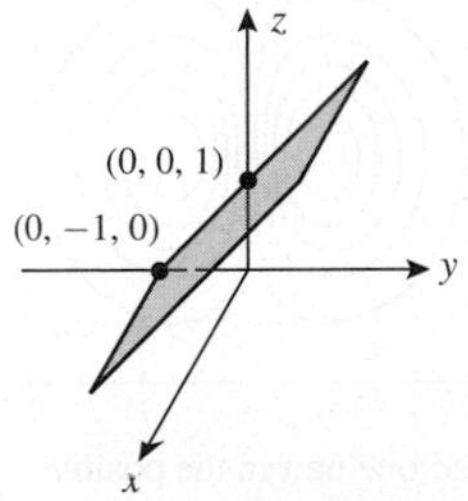


43. **(a)** hyperbolas **(b)** parabolas **(c)** noncircular ellipses **(d)** lines
45. **(a)** \$130 **(b)** \$275
47. **(a)** $1 - x^2 - y^2$ **(b)** $\sqrt{x^2 + y^2}$ **(c)** $x^2 + y^2$
49. **(a)** $A$ **(b)** $B$ **(c)** increase **(d)** decrease **(e)** increase **(f)** decrease

51.

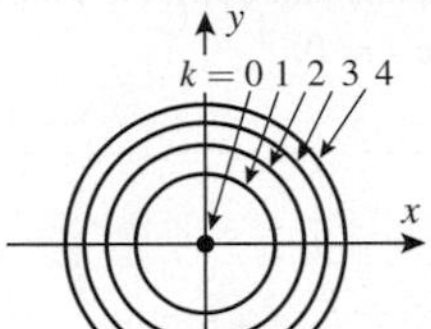


53.

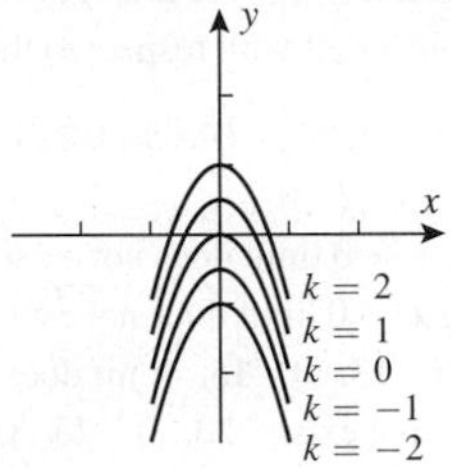


55.

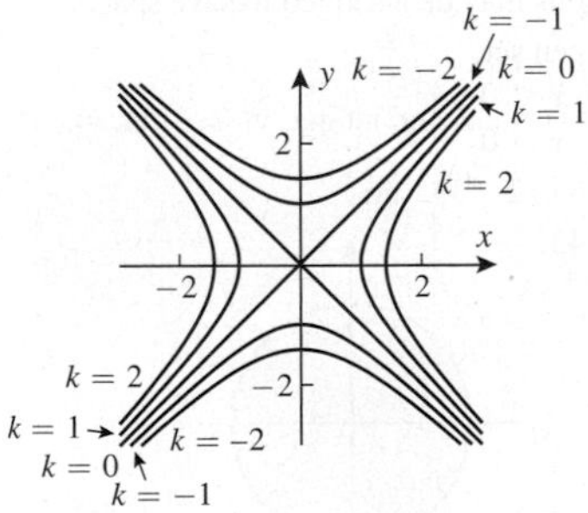


57.

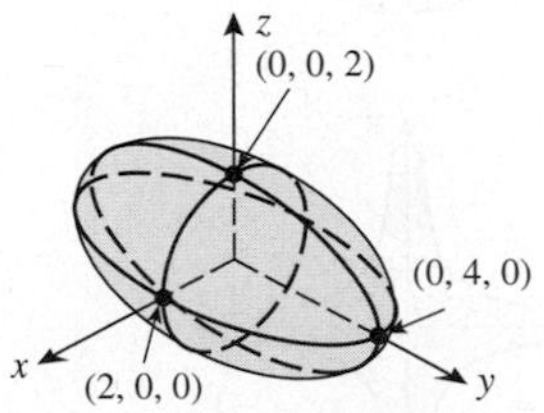


59.

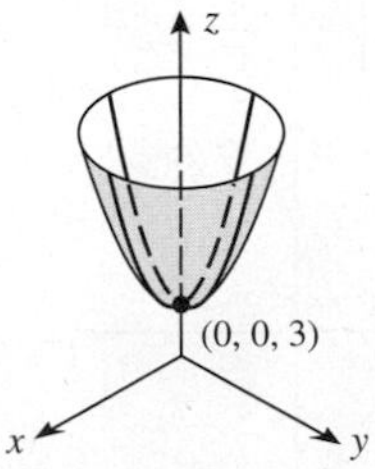


61. concentric spheres, common center at (2, 0, 0)
63. concentric cylinders, common axis the $y$-axis
65. **(a)** $x^2 - 2x^3 + 3xy = 0$ **(b)** $x^2 - 2x^3 + 3xy = 0$ **(c)** $x^2 - 2x^3 + 3xy = -18$
67. **(a)** $x^2 + y^2 - z = 5$ **(b)** $x^2 + y^2 - z = -2$ **(c)** $x^2 + y^2 - z = 0$

**69.** **(a)**

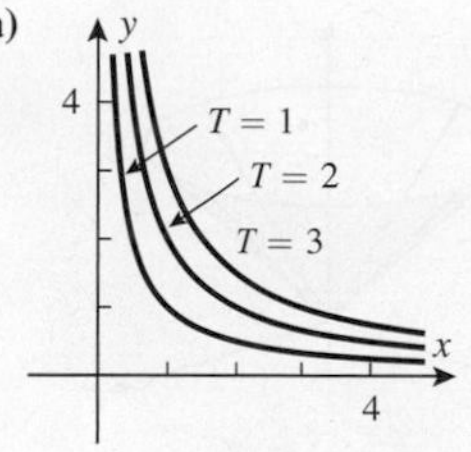


**(b)** the path $xy = 4$

**71.** **(a)**

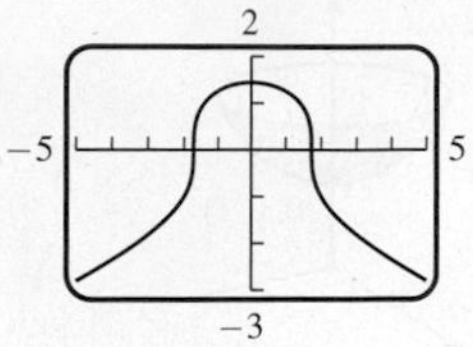


**(b)**

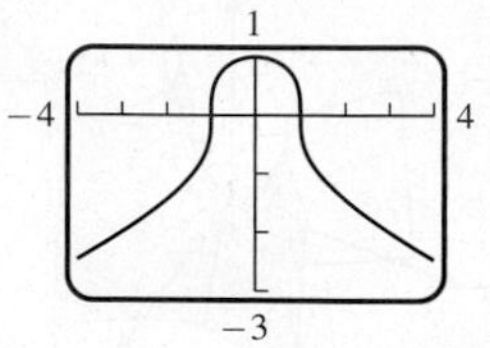


**73.** **(a)**

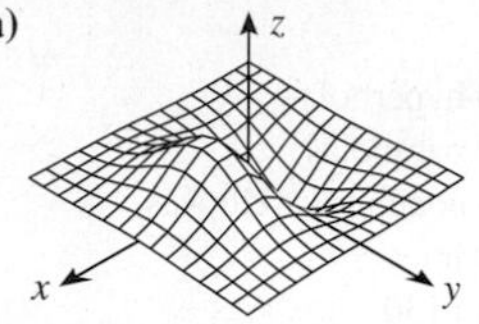


**(b)**

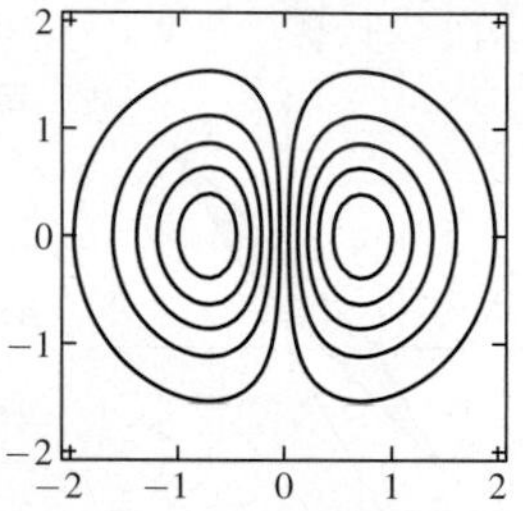


**75.** **(a)** The graph of $g$ is the graph of $f$ shifted one unit in the positive $x$-direction.
**(b)** The graph of $g$ is the graph of $f$ shifted one unit up the $z$-axis.
**(c)** The graph of $g$ is the graph of $f$ shifted one unit down the $y$-axis and then inverted with respect to the plane $z = 0$.

## ▶ Exercise Set 13.2 (Page 823)

**1.** 35 **3.** −8 **5.** 0
**7.** **(a)** along $x = 0$ limit does not exist
**(b)** along $x = 0$ limit does not exist
**9.** 1 **11.** 0 **13.** 0 **15.** limit does not exist **17.** $\frac{8}{3}$ **19.** 0
**21.** limit does not exist **23.** 0 **25.** 0 **27.** 0

Responses to True–False questions may be abridged to save space.

**29.** True; by the definition of open set.
**31.** False; let $f(x, y) = \begin{cases} 1, & x \le 0 \\ -1, & x > 0 \end{cases}$ and let $g(x, y) = -f(x, y)$.
**33.** **(a)** no **(d)** no; yes **37.** $-\pi/2$ **39.** no

**41.**

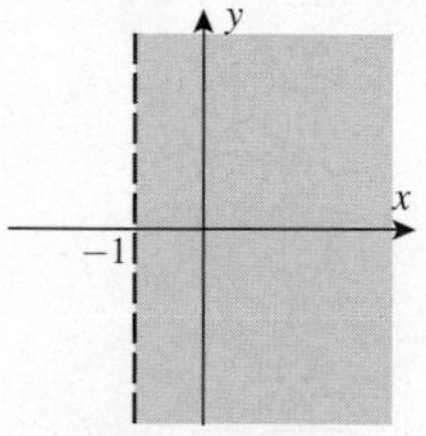


**43.**

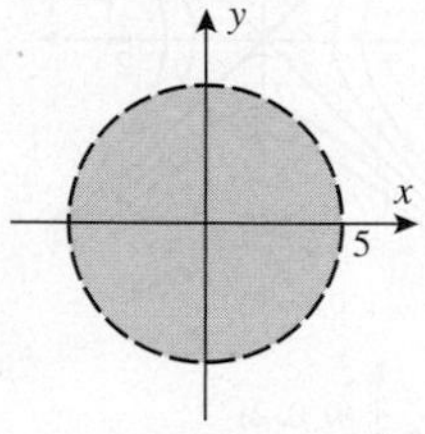


**45.**

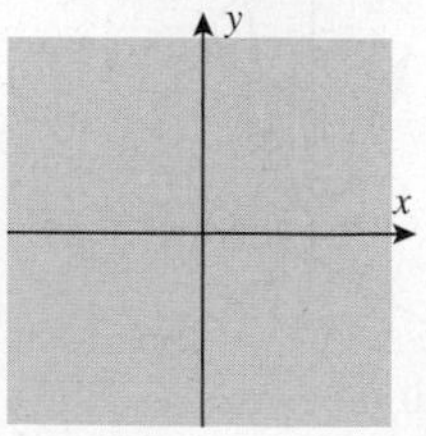


**47.**

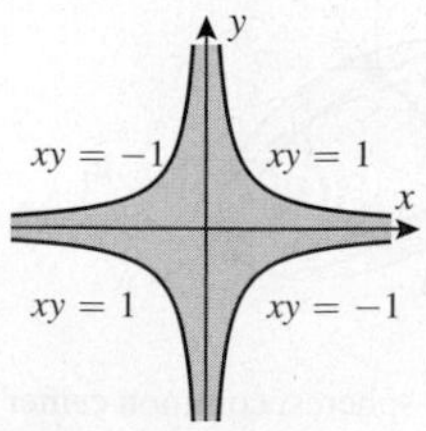


**49.** all of 3-space **51.** all points not on the cylinder $x^2 + z^2 = 1$

## ▶ Exercise Set 13.3 (Page 833)

**1.** **(a)** $9x^2y^2$ **(b)** $6x^3y$ **(c)** $9y^2$ **(d)** $9x^2$ **(e)** $6y$ **(f)** $6x^3$ **(g)** 36 **(h)** 12
**3.** $18xy - 15x^4y, 9x^2 - 3x^5$
**5.** $(16x + 40)(x^2 + 5x - 2y)^7, -16(x^2 + 5x - 2y)^7$
**7.** $-\dfrac{7}{q}e^{-7p/q}, \dfrac{7p}{q^2}e^{-7p/q}$
**9.** $(15x^2y + 7y^2)\cos(5x^3y + 7xy^2), (5x^3 + 14xy)\cos(5x^3y + 7xy^2)$
**11.** **(a)** $\frac{3}{8}$ **(b)** $\frac{1}{4}$ **13.** **(a)** $-4\cos 7$ **(b)** $2\cos 7$
**15.** $\partial z/\partial x = -4$; $\partial z/\partial y = \frac{1}{2}$ **17.** **(a)** 4.9 **(b)** 1.2
**19.** $z = f(x, y)$ has II as its graph, $f_x$ has I as its graph, and $f_y$ has III as its graph.

Responses to True–False questions may be abridged to save space.

**21.** True; on $y = 2$, $f(x, 2) = c$ is a constant function of $x$.
**23.** True; $z$ must be a linear function of $x$ and $y$.
**25.** $8xy^3e^{x^2y^3}, 12x^2y^2e^{x^2y^3}$
**27.** $x^3/(y^{3/5} + x) + 3x^2\ln(1 + xy^{-3/5}), -\frac{3}{5}x^4/(y^{8/5} + xy)$
**29.** $-\dfrac{y(x^2 - y^2)}{(x^2 + y^2)^2}, \dfrac{x(x^2 - y^2)}{(x^2 + y^2)^2}$
**31.** $(3/2)x^2y(5x^2 - 7)(3x^5y - 7x^3y)^{-1/2}$
$(1/2)x^3(3x^2 - 7)(3x^5y - 7x^3y)^{-1/2}$
**33.** $\dfrac{y^{-1/2}}{y^2 + x^2}, -\dfrac{xy^{-3/2}}{y^2 + x^2} - \dfrac{3}{2}y^{-5/2}\tan^{-1}\left(\dfrac{x}{y}\right)$
**35.** $-\frac{4}{3}y^2\sec^2 x(y^2\tan x)^{-7/3}, -\frac{8}{3}y\tan x(y^2\tan x)^{-7/3}$
**37.** $-6, -21$ **39.** $1/\sqrt{17}, 8/\sqrt{17}$
**41.** **(a)** $2xy^4z^3 + y$ **(b)** $4x^2y^3z^3 + x$ **(c)** $3x^2y^4z^2 + 2z$
**(d)** $2y^4z^3 + y$ **(e)** $32z^3 + 1$ **(f)** 438
**43.** $2z/x, z/y, \ln(x^2y\cos z) - z\tan z$
**45.** $-y^2z^3/(1 + x^2y^4z^6), -2xyz^3/(1 + x^2y^4z^6),$
$-3xy^2z^2/(1 + x^2y^4z^6)$
**47.** $yze^z\cos(xz), e^z\sin(xz), ye^z(\sin(xz) + x\cos(xz))$
**49.** $x/\sqrt{x^2 + y^2 + z^2}, y/\sqrt{x^2 + y^2 + z^2}, z/\sqrt{x^2 + y^2 + z^2}$
**51.** **(a)** $e$ **(b)** $2e$ **(c)** $e$
**53.** **(a)**

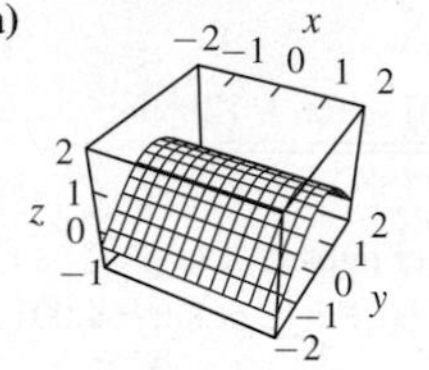


**(b)**

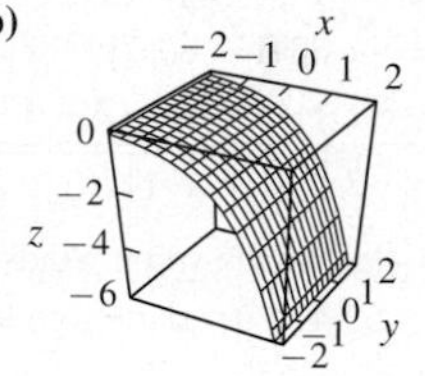


**55.** 4 **57.** −2

**59.** **(a)** $\partial V/\partial r = 2\pi rh$ **(b)** $\partial V/\partial h = \pi r^2$ **(c)** $48\pi$ **(d)** $64\pi$
**61.** **(a)** $\dfrac{1}{5}\dfrac{\text{lb}}{\text{in}^2\cdot\text{K}}$ **(b)** $-\dfrac{25}{8}\dfrac{\text{in}^5}{\text{lb}}$
**63.** **(a)** $\dfrac{\partial V}{\partial l} = 6$ **(b)** $\dfrac{\partial V}{\partial w} = 15$ **(c)** $\dfrac{\partial V}{\partial h} = 10$
**67.** **(a)** $\pm\sqrt{6}/4$ **69.** $-x/z, -y/z$
**71.** $-\dfrac{2x + yz^2\cos(xyz)}{xyz\cos(xyz) + \sin(xyz)}; -\dfrac{xz^2\cos(xyz)}{xyz\cos(xyz) + \sin(xyz)}$
**73.** $-x/w, -y/w, -z/w$
**75.** $-\dfrac{yzw\cos(xyz)}{2w + \sin(xyz)}, -\dfrac{xzw\cos(xyz)}{2w + \sin(xyz)}, -\dfrac{xyw\cos(xyz)}{2w + \sin(xyz)}$
**77.** $e^{x^2}, -e^{y^2}$
**79.** $f_x(x, y) = 2xy^3\sin(x^6y^9), f_y(x, y) = 3x^2y^2\sin(x^6y^9)$
**81.** **(a)** $-\dfrac{\cos y}{4\sqrt{x^3}}$ **(b)** $-\sqrt{x}\cos y$ **(c)** $-\dfrac{1}{2\sqrt{x}}\sin y$ **(d)** $-\dfrac{1}{2\sqrt{x}}\sin y$
**83.** **(a)** $6\cos(3x^2 + 6y^2) - 36x^2\sin(3x^2 + 6y^2)$
**(b)** $12\cos(3x^2 + 6y^2) - 144y^2\sin(3x^2 + 6y^2)$
**(c)** $-72xy\sin(3x^2 + 6y^2)$ **(d)** $-72xy\sin(3x^2 + 6y^2)$
**85.** $-32y^3$ **87.** $-e^x\sin y$ **89.** $\dfrac{20}{(4x - 5y)^2}$ **91.** $\dfrac{2(x - y)}{(x + y)^3}$
**93.** **(a)** $\dfrac{\partial^3 f}{\partial x^3}$ **(b)** $\dfrac{\partial^3 f}{\partial y^2\partial x}$ **(c)** $\dfrac{\partial^4 f}{\partial x^2\partial y^2}$ **(d)** $\dfrac{\partial^4 f}{\partial y^3\partial x}$
**95.** **(a)** $30xy^4 - 4$ **(b)** $60x^2y^3$ **(c)** $60x^3y^2$
**97.** **(a)** −30 **(b)** −125 **(c)** 150
**99.** **(a)** $15x^2y^4z^7 + 2y$ **(b)** $35x^3y^4z^6 + 3y^2$ **(c)** $21x^2y^5z^6$
**(d)** $42x^3y^5z^5$ **(e)** $140x^3y^3z^6 + 6y$ **(f)** $30xy^4z^7$ **(g)** $105x^2y^4z^6$
**(h)** $210xy^4z^6$

107. $\dfrac{\partial f}{\partial v} = 8vw^3x^4y^5$, $\dfrac{\partial f}{\partial w} = 12v^2w^2x^4y^5$, $\dfrac{\partial f}{\partial x} = 16v^2w^3x^3y^5$, $\dfrac{\partial f}{\partial y} = 20v^2w^3x^4y^4$

109. $\dfrac{\partial f}{\partial v_1} = \dfrac{2v_1}{v_3^2+v_4^2}$, $\dfrac{\partial f}{\partial v_2} = \dfrac{-2v_2}{v_3^2+v_4^2}$, $\dfrac{\partial f}{\partial v_3} = \dfrac{-2v_3(v_1^2-v_2^2)}{(v_3^2+v_4^2)^2}$, $\dfrac{\partial f}{\partial v_4} = \dfrac{-2v_4(v_1^2-v_2^2)}{(v_3^2+v_4^2)^2}$

111. **(a)** 0 **(b)** 0 **(c)** 0 **(d)** 0 **(e)** $2(1+yw)e^{yw}\sin z\cos z$ **(f)** $2xw(2+yw)e^{yw}\sin z\cos z$

113. $-i\sin(x_1+2x_2+\cdots+nx_n)$

115. **(a)** $xy$-plane, $12x^2+6x$ **(b)** $y\neq 0, -3x^2/y^2$

117. $f_x(2,-1)=11, f_y(2,-1)=-8$

119. **(b)** does not exist if $y\neq 0$ and $x=-y$

## ▶ Exercise Set 13.4 (Page 843)

1. 5.04 3. 4.14 9. $dz = 7\,dx - 2\,dy$ 11. $dz = 3x^2y^2\,dx + 2x^3y\,dy$ 13. $dz = \dfrac{y}{1+x^2y^2}dx + \dfrac{x}{1+x^2y^2}dy$ 15. $dw = 8\,dx - 3\,dy + 4\,dz$

17. $dw = 3x^2y^2z\,dx + 2x^3yz\,dy + x^3y^2\,dz$

19. $dw = \dfrac{yz}{1+x^2y^2z^2}dx + \dfrac{xz}{1+x^2y^2z^2}dy + \dfrac{xy}{1+x^2y^2z^2}dz$

21. $df = 0.10, \Delta f = 0.1009$ 23. $df = 0.03, \Delta f \approx 0.029412$

25. $df = 0.96, \Delta f \approx 0.97929$

Responses to True–False questions may be abridged to save space.

27. False; see the discussion at the beginning of this section.

29. True; see Theorems 13.4.3 and 13.4.4.

31. The increase in the area of the rectangle is given by the sum of the areas of the three small rectangles, and the total differential is given by the sum of the areas of the upper left and lower right rectangles.

33. **(a)** $L = \frac{1}{5} - \frac{4}{125}(x-4) - \frac{3}{125}(y-3)$ **(b)** 0.000176603

35. **(a)** $L=0$ **(b)** 0.0024

37. **(a)** $L = 6+6(x-1)+3(y-2)+2(z-3)$ **(b)** $-0.00481$

39. **(a)** $L = e+e(x-1)-e(y+1)-e(z+1)$ **(b)** 0.01554

45. 0.5 47. 1, 1, −1, 2 49. (−1, 1) 51. (1, 0, 1) 53. 8%

55. 0.3% 57. 1.2%

59. **(a)** $(r+s)\%$ **(b)** $(r+s)\%$ **(c)** $(2r+3s)\%$ **(d)** $\left(3r+\dfrac{s}{2}\right)\%$

61. $\approx 39$ ft$^2$

## ▶ Exercise Set 13.5 (Page 852)

1. $42t^{13}$ 3. $3t^{-2}\sin(1/t)$ 5. $-\frac{10}{3}t^{7/3}e^{1-t^{10/3}}$ 7. $\dfrac{dw}{dt} = 165t^{32}$

9. $-2t\cos t^2$ 11. 3264 13. 0

17. $24u^2v^2 - 16uv^3 - 2v + 3,\ 16u^3v - 24u^2v^2 - 2u - 3$

19. $-\dfrac{2\sin u}{3\sin v}, -\dfrac{2\cos u\cos v}{3\sin^2 v}$ 21. $e^u, 0$

23. $3r^2\sin\theta\cos^2\theta - 4r^3\sin^3\theta\cos\theta,$
$-2r^3\sin^2\theta\cos\theta + r^4\sin^4\theta + r^3\cos^3\theta - 3r^4\sin^2\theta\cos^2\theta$

25. $\dfrac{x^2+y^2}{4x^2y^3}, \dfrac{y^2-3x^2}{4xy^4}$ 27. $\dfrac{\partial z}{\partial r} = \dfrac{2r\cos^2\theta}{r^2\cos^2\theta+1}, \dfrac{\partial z}{\partial \theta} = \dfrac{-2r^2\cos\theta\sin\theta}{r^2\cos^2\theta+1}$

29. $\dfrac{dw}{d\rho} = 2\rho(4\sin^2\phi+\cos^2\phi), \dfrac{\partial w}{\partial\phi} = 6\rho^2\sin\phi\cos\phi, \dfrac{dw}{d\theta} = 0$

31. $-\pi$ 33. $\sqrt{3}e^{\sqrt{3}}, (2-4\sqrt{3})e^{\sqrt{3}}$ 35. $-0.779$ rad/s

Responses to True–False questions may be abridged to save space.

37. False; the symbols $\partial z$ and $\partial x$ have no individual meaning.

39. False; consider $z = xy, x = t, y = t$.

41. $-\dfrac{2xy^3}{3x^2y^2 - \sin y}$

43. $-\dfrac{ye^{xy}}{xe^{xy}+ye^y+e^y}$ 45. $\dfrac{2x+yz}{6yz-xy}, \dfrac{xz-3z^2}{6yz-xy}$

47. $\dfrac{ye^x}{15\cos 3z+3}, \dfrac{e^x}{15\cos 3z+3}$

61. $\dfrac{\partial w}{\partial\rho} = (\sin\phi\cos\theta)\dfrac{\partial w}{\partial x} + (\sin\phi\sin\theta)\dfrac{\partial w}{\partial y} + (\cos\phi)\dfrac{\partial w}{\partial z}$,
$\dfrac{\partial w}{\partial\phi} = (\rho\cos\phi\cos\theta)\dfrac{\partial w}{\partial x} + (\rho\cos\phi\sin\theta)\dfrac{\partial w}{\partial y} - (\rho\sin\phi)\dfrac{\partial w}{\partial z}$,
$\dfrac{\partial w}{\partial\theta} = -(\rho\sin\phi\sin\theta)\dfrac{\partial w}{\partial x} + (\rho\sin\phi\cos\theta)\dfrac{\partial w}{\partial y}$

65. **(a)** $\dfrac{dw}{dt} = \displaystyle\sum_{i=1}^{4}\dfrac{\partial w}{\partial x_i}\dfrac{dx_i}{dt}$ **(b)** $\dfrac{\partial w}{\partial v_j} = \displaystyle\sum_{i=1}^{4}\dfrac{\partial w}{\partial x_i}\dfrac{\partial x_i}{\partial v_j}, j = 1, 2, 3$

## ▶ Exercise Set 13.6 (Page 863)

1. $6\sqrt{2}$ 3. $-3/\sqrt{10}$ 5. $-320$ 7. $-314/741$ 9. 0 11. $-8\sqrt{2}$

13. $\sqrt{2}/4$ 15. $5/\sqrt{3}$ 17. $-8/63$ 19. $1/2+\sqrt{3}/8$ 21. $2\sqrt{2}$

23. $1/\sqrt{5}$ 25. $-\frac{3}{2}e$ 27. $3/\sqrt{11}$ 29. **(a)** 5 **(b)** 10 **(c)** $-5\sqrt{5}$

31. III 33. $\cos(7y^2-7xy)(-7y\mathbf{i}+(14y-7x)\mathbf{j})$

35. $\left(\dfrac{-84y}{(6x-7y)^2}\right)\mathbf{i} + \left(\dfrac{84x}{(6x-7y)^2}\right)\mathbf{j}$ 37. $-9x^8\mathbf{i} - 3y^2\mathbf{j} + 12z^{11}\mathbf{k}$

39. $\nabla w = \dfrac{x}{x^2+y^2+z^2}\mathbf{i} + \dfrac{y}{x^2+y^2+z^2}\mathbf{j} + \dfrac{z}{x^2+y^2+z^2}\mathbf{k}$

41. $40\mathbf{i}+32\mathbf{j}$ 43. $-36\mathbf{i}-12\mathbf{j}$ 45. $4(\mathbf{i}+\mathbf{j}+\mathbf{k})$

47.

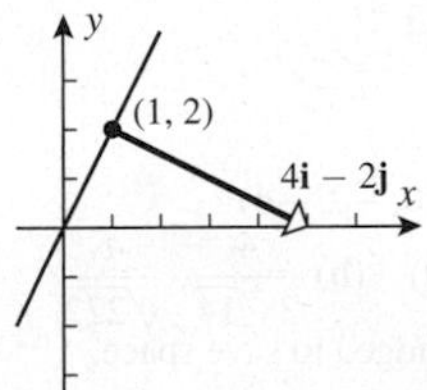


49.

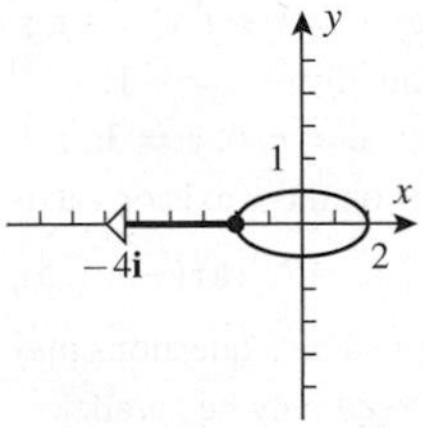


51. $\pm(-4\mathbf{i}+\mathbf{j})/\sqrt{17}$ 53. $\mathbf{u} = (3\mathbf{i}-2\mathbf{j})/\sqrt{13}, \|\nabla f(-1,1)\| = 4\sqrt{13}$

55. $\mathbf{u} = (4\mathbf{i}-3\mathbf{j})/5, \|\nabla f(4,-3)\| = 1$ 57. $\dfrac{1}{\sqrt{2}}(\mathbf{i}-\mathbf{j}), 3\sqrt{2}$

59. $\dfrac{1}{\sqrt{2}}(-\mathbf{i}+\mathbf{j}), \dfrac{1}{\sqrt{2}}$

61. $\mathbf{u} = -(\mathbf{i}+3\mathbf{j})/\sqrt{10}, -\|\nabla f(-1,-3)\| = -2\sqrt{10}$

63. $\mathbf{u} = (3\mathbf{i}-\mathbf{j})/\sqrt{10}, -\|\nabla f(\pi/6,\pi/4)\| = -\sqrt{5}$

65. $(\mathbf{i}-11\mathbf{j}+12\mathbf{k})/\sqrt{266}, -\sqrt{266}$

Responses to True–False questions may be abridged to save space.

67. False; they are equal. 69. False; let $\mathbf{u} = \mathbf{i}$ and let $f(x, y) = y$.

71. $8/\sqrt{29}$

73. **(a)** $\approx 1/\sqrt{2}$ **(b)**

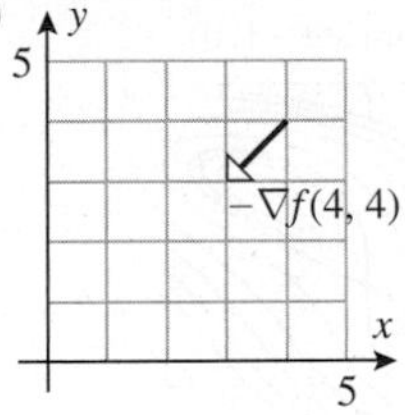


75. $9x^2+y^2=9$

77. $36/\sqrt{17}$

79. **(a)** $2e^{-\pi/2}\mathbf{i}$

81. $-\frac{5}{3}(2\mathbf{i}-\mathbf{j}-2\mathbf{k})$

87. $x(t) = e^{-8t}, y(t) = 4e^{-2t}$

89.

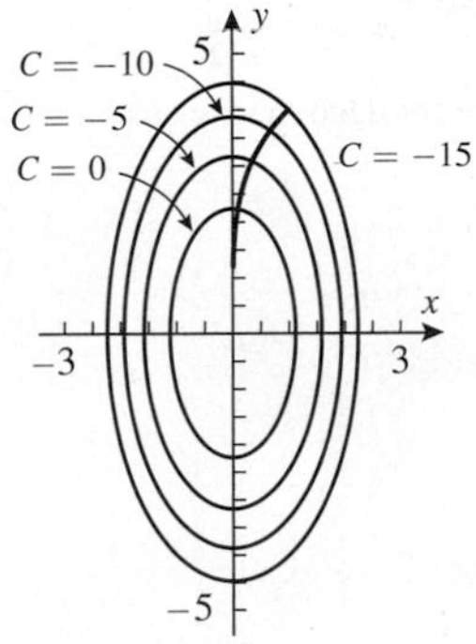

91. (a)

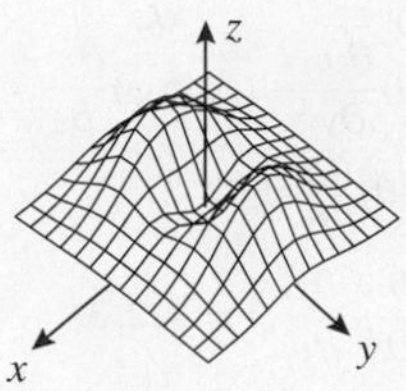


(c) $\nabla f = [2x - 2x(x^2 + 3y^2)]e^{-(x^2+y^2)}\mathbf{i} + [6y - 2y(x^2 + 3y^2)]e^{-(x^2+y^2)}\mathbf{j}$
(d) $x = y = 0$ or $x = 0, y = \pm 1$ or $x = \pm 1, y = 0$

## ► Exercise Set 13.7 (Page 870)

1. (a) $x + y + 2z = 6$ (b) $x = 2 + t, y = 2 + t, z = 1 + 2t$ (c) $35.26°$
3. tangent plane: $3x - 4z = -25$; normal line: $x = -3 + (3t/4), y = 0, z = 4 - t$
5. tangent plane: $9x - 4y - 10z = -76$; normal line: $x = -4 + 9t, y = 5 - 4t, z = 2 - 10t$
7. tangent plane: $48x - 14y - z = 64$; normal line: $x = 1 + 48t, y = -2 - 14t, z = 12 - t$
9. tangent plane: $x - y - z = 0$; normal line: $x = 1 + t, y = -t, z = 1 - t$
11. tangent plane: $3y - z = -1$; normal line: $x = \pi/6, y = 3t, z = 1 - t$
13. (a) all points on the $x$-axis or $y$-axis (b) $(0, -2, -4)$
15. $\left(\frac{1}{2}, -2, -\frac{3}{4}\right)$ 17. (a) $(-2, 1, 5), (0, 3, 9)$ (b) $\frac{4}{3\sqrt{14}}, \frac{4}{\sqrt{222}}$

Responses to True–False questions may be abridged to save space.

19. False; they need only be parallel.
21. True; see Formula (15) of Section 13.4.
23. $\pm\frac{1}{\sqrt{227}}(\mathbf{i} - \mathbf{j} - 15\mathbf{k})$ 27. $(1, 2/3, 2/3), (-1, -2/3, -2/3)$
29. $x = 1 + 8t, y = -1 + 5t, z = 2 + 6t$
31. $x = 3 + 4t, y = -3 - 4t, z = 4 - 3t$

## ► Exercise Set 13.8 (Page 879)

1. (a) minimum at $(2, -1)$, no maxima (b) maximum at $(0, 0)$, no minima (c) no maxima or minima
3. minimum at $(3, -2)$, no maxima 5. relative minimum at $(0, 0)$
7. relative minimum at $(0, 0)$; saddle points at $(\pm 2, 1)$
9. saddle point at $(1, -2)$ 11. relative minimum at $(2, -1)$
13. relative minima at $(-1, -1)$ and $(1, 1)$ 15. saddle point at $(0, 0)$
17. no critical points 19. relative maximum at $(-1, 0)$
21. saddle point at $(0, 0)$; relative minima at $(1, 1)$ and $(-1, -1)$

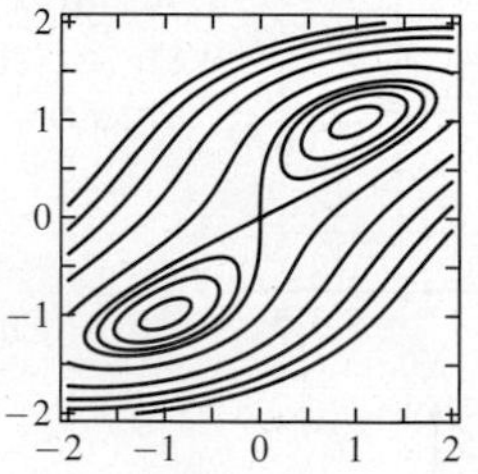


Responses to True–False questions may be abridged to save space.

23. False; let $f(x, y) = y$.
25. True; this follows from Theorem 13.8.6.
27. (b) relative minimum at $(0, 0)$
31. absolute maximum 0, absolute minimum $-12$
33. absolute maximum 3, absolute minimum $-1$
35. absolute maximum $\frac{33}{4}$, absolute minimum $-\frac{1}{4}$
37. 16, 16, 16
39. maximum at $(1, 2, 2)$
41. $2a/\sqrt{3}, 2a/\sqrt{3}, 2a/\sqrt{3}$
43. length and width 2 ft, height 4 ft
45. (a) $x = 0$: minimum $-3$, maximum 0; $x = 1$: minimum 3, maximum $13/3$; $y = 0$: minimum 0, maximum 4; $y = 1$: minimum $-3$, maximum 3 (b) $y = x$: minimum 0, maximum 3; $y = 1 - x$: maximum 4, minimum $-3$ (c) minimum $-3$, maximum $13/3$
47. length and width $\sqrt[3]{2V}$, height $\sqrt[3]{2V}/2$ 51. $y = \frac{3}{4}x + \frac{19}{12}$
53. $y = 0.5x + 0.8$
55. (a) $y = 79.22 + 0.1571t$ (b)

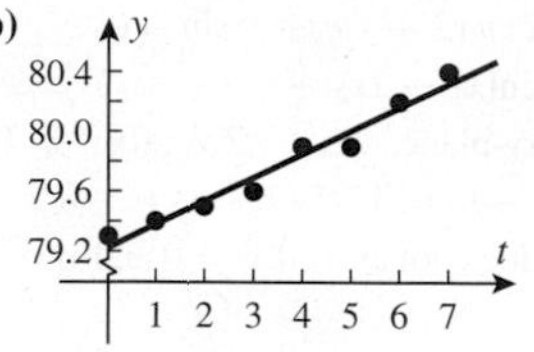


(c) about 81.6 years

57. (a) $P = \frac{2798}{21} + \frac{171}{350}T$ (b)

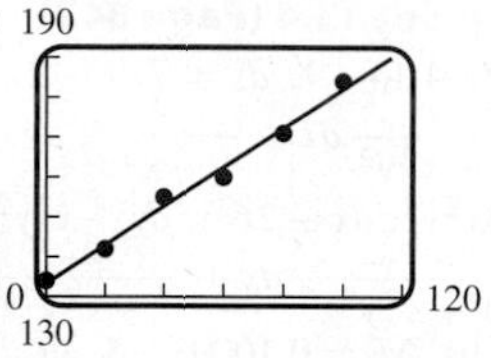


(c) $T \approx -272.7096°$ C

## ► Exercise Set 13.9 (Page 889)

1. (a) 4 3. (a)

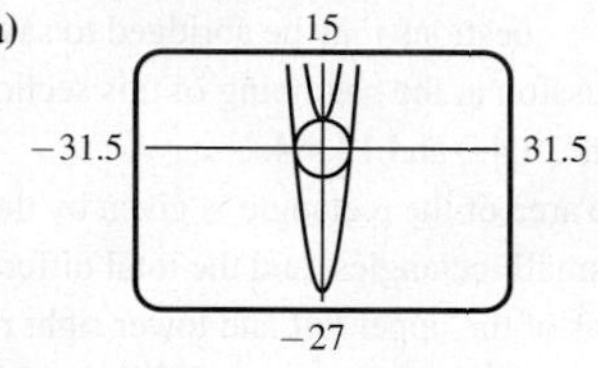


(c) maximum $\frac{101}{4}$, minimum $-5$

5. maximum $\sqrt{2}$ at $(-\sqrt{2}, -1)$ and $(\sqrt{2}, 1)$, minimum $-\sqrt{2}$ at $(-\sqrt{2}, 1)$ and $(\sqrt{2}, -1)$
7. maximum $\sqrt{2}$ at $(1/\sqrt{2}, 0)$, minimum $-\sqrt{2}$ at $(-1/\sqrt{2}, 0)$
9. maximum 6 at $\left(\frac{4}{3}, \frac{2}{3}, -\frac{4}{3}\right)$, minimum $-6$ at $\left(-\frac{4}{3}, -\frac{2}{3}, \frac{4}{3}\right)$
11. maximum is $1/(3\sqrt{3})$ at $(1/\sqrt{3}, 1/\sqrt{3}, 1/\sqrt{3})$, $(1/\sqrt{3}, -1/\sqrt{3}, -1/\sqrt{3})$, $(-1/\sqrt{3}, 1/\sqrt{3}, -1/\sqrt{3})$, and $(-1/\sqrt{3}, -1/\sqrt{3}, 1/\sqrt{3})$; minimum is $-1/(3\sqrt{3})$ at $(1/\sqrt{3}, 1/\sqrt{3}, -1/\sqrt{3})$, $(1/\sqrt{3}, -1/\sqrt{3}, 1/\sqrt{3})$, $(-1/\sqrt{3}, 1/\sqrt{3}, 1/\sqrt{3})$, and $(-1/\sqrt{3}, -1/\sqrt{3}, -1/\sqrt{3})$

Responses to True–False questions may be abridged to save space.

13. False; a Lagrange multiplier is a scalar.
15. False; we must solve three equations in three unknowns.
17. $\left(\frac{3}{10}, -\frac{3}{5}\right)$ 19. $\left(\frac{1}{6}, \frac{1}{3}, \frac{1}{6}\right)$
21. $(3, 6)$ is closest and $(-3, -6)$ is farthest 23. $5(\mathbf{i} + \mathbf{j} + \mathbf{k})/\sqrt{3}$
25. 9, 9, 9 27. $(\pm\sqrt{5}, 0, 0)$ 29. length and width 2 ft, height 4 ft
33. (a) $\alpha = \beta = \gamma = \pi/3$, maximum $1/8$ (b)

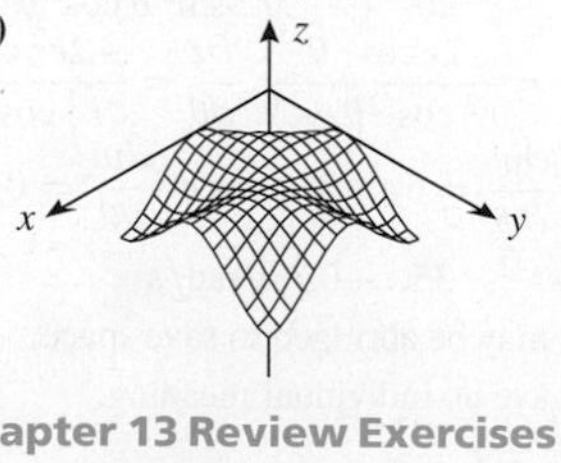


## ► Chapter 13 Review Exercises (Page 891)

1. (a) $xy$ (b) $e^{r+s}\ln(rs)$
5. (a) not defined on line $y = x$ (b) not continuous
9. (a) 12 Pa/min (b) 240 Pa/min
15. $df$ (the differential of $f$) is an approximation for $\Delta f$ (the change in $f$)
17. $dV = -0.06667\text{ m}^3$; $\Delta V = -0.07267\text{ m}^3$ 19. 2
21. $\frac{-f_y^2 f_{xx} + 2f_x f_y f_{xy} - f_x^2 f_{yy}}{f_y^3}$ 25. $\frac{7}{2} + \frac{4}{5}\ln 2$ 27. $-7/\sqrt{5}$

29. $(0,0,2),(1,1,1),(-1,-1,1)$ 31. $\left(-\frac{1}{3},-\frac{1}{2},2\right)$
33. relative minimum at $(15,-8)$
35. saddle point at $(0,0)$, relative minimum at $(3,9)$
37. absolute maximum of 4 at $(\pm 1,\pm 2)$, absolute minimum of 0 at $(\pm\sqrt{2},0)$ and $(0,\pm 2\sqrt{2})$
39. $I_1 : I_2 : I_3 = \dfrac{1}{R_1} : \dfrac{1}{R_2} : \dfrac{1}{R_3}$
41. (a) $\partial P/\partial L = c\alpha L^{\alpha-1}K^{\beta}, \partial P/\partial K = c\beta L^{\alpha}K^{\beta-1}$

## ▶ Chapter 13 Making Connections (Page 893)

Answers are provided in the Student Solutions Manual.

## ▶ Exercise Set 14.1 (Page 900)

1. 7 3. 2 5. 2 7. 3 9. $1-\ln 2$ 11. $\dfrac{1-\ln 2}{2}$ 13. 0 15. $\frac{1}{3}$
17. (a) $37/4$ (b) exact value $= 28/3$; differ by $1/12$
19. 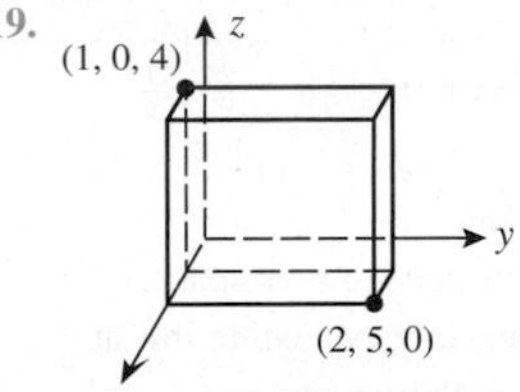

Volume = 20
21. 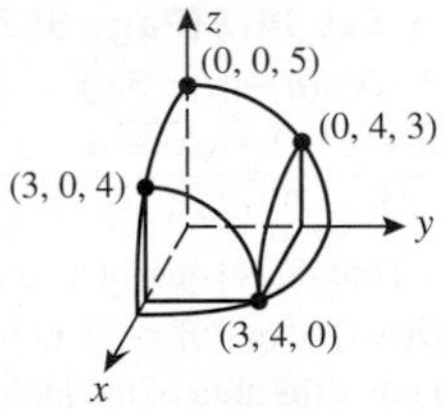


Responses to True–False questions may be abridged to save space.
23. False; $\Delta A_k$ is the area of such a rectangular region.
25. False; $\displaystyle\iint_R f(x,y)\,dA = \int_1^5\int_2^4 f(x,y)\,dy\,dx.$
29. 19 31. 8 33. $\dfrac{1}{3\pi}$ 35. 48 37. $1-\dfrac{2}{\pi}$ 39. $\frac{14}{3}\,^{\circ}$C
41. 1.381737122 43. first integral equals $\frac{1}{2}$, second equals $-\frac{1}{2}$; no

## ▶ Exercise Set 14.2 (Page 908)

1. $\frac{1}{40}$ 3. 9 5. $\dfrac{\pi}{2}$ 7. $\frac{1}{12}$
9. (a) $\displaystyle\int_0^2\int_0^{x^2} f(x,y)\,dy\,dx$ (b) $\displaystyle\int_0^4\int_{\sqrt{y}}^2 f(x,y)\,dx\,dy$
11. (a) $\displaystyle\int_1^2\int_{-2x+5}^3 f(x,y)\,dy\,dx + \int_2^4\int_1^3 f(x,y)\,dy\,dx + \int_4^5\int_{2x-7}^3 f(x,y)\,dy\,dx$
(b) $\displaystyle\int_1^3\int_{(5-y)/2}^{(y+7)/2} f(x,y)\,dx\,dy$
13. (a) $\frac{16}{3}$ (b) 38 15. 576 17. 0 19. $\dfrac{\sqrt{17}-1}{2}$ 21. $\frac{50}{3}$
23. $-\frac{7}{60}$ 25. $\dfrac{1-\cos 8}{3}$
27. (a) 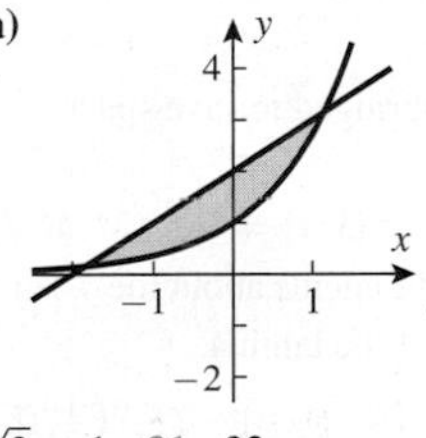

(b) $(-1.8414, 0.1586), (1.1462, 3.1462)$
(c) $-0.4044$
(d) $-0.4044$
29. $\sqrt{2}-1$ 31. 32
Responses to True–False questions may be abridged to save space.
33. False; $\displaystyle\int_0^1\int_{x^2}^{2x} f(x,y)\,dy\,dx$ integrates $f(x,y)$ over the region between the graphs of $y=x^2$ and $y=2x$ for $0\le x\le 1$ and results in a number, but $\displaystyle\int_{x^2}^{2x}\int_0^1 f(x,y)\,dx\,dy$ produces an expression involving $x$.
35. False; although $R$ is symmetric across the $x$-axis, the integrand may not be.
37. 12 39. $27\pi$ 41. 170 43. $\dfrac{27\pi}{2}$ 45. $\dfrac{\pi}{2}$
47. $\displaystyle\int_0^{\sqrt{2}}\int_{y^2}^2 f(x,y)\,dx\,dy$ 49. $\displaystyle\int_1^{e^2}\int_{\ln x}^2 f(x,y)\,dy\,dx$
51. $\displaystyle\int_0^{\pi/2}\int_0^{\sin x} f(x,y)\,dy\,dx$ 53. $\dfrac{1-e^{-16}}{8}$ 55. $\dfrac{e^8-1}{3}$
57. (a) 0 (b) tan 1 59. 0 61. $\dfrac{\pi}{2}-\ln 2$ 63. $\frac{2}{3}\,^{\circ}$C 65. 0.676089

## ▶ Exercise Set 14.3 (Page 916)

1. $\frac{1}{6}$ 3. $\frac{2}{9}a^3$ 5. 0 7. $\dfrac{3\pi}{2}$ 9. $\dfrac{\pi}{16}$ 11. $\displaystyle\int_{\pi/6}^{5\pi/6}\int_2^{4\sin\theta} f(r,\theta)r\,dr\,d\theta$
13. $\displaystyle 8\int_0^{\pi/2}\int_1^3 r\sqrt{9-r^2}\,dr\,d\theta$ 15. $\displaystyle 2\int_0^{\pi/2}\int_0^{\cos\theta}(1-r^2)r\,dr\,d\theta$
17. $\dfrac{64\sqrt{2}}{3}\pi$ 19. $\dfrac{5\pi}{32}$ 21. $\dfrac{27\pi}{16}$ 23. $(1-\cos 9)\pi$ 25. $\dfrac{\pi}{8}\ln 5$ 27. $\dfrac{\pi}{8}$
29. $\frac{16}{9}$ 31. $\dfrac{\pi}{2}\left(1-\dfrac{1}{\sqrt{1+a^2}}\right)$ 33. $\dfrac{\pi}{4}(\sqrt{5}-1)$
Responses to True–False questions may be abridged to save space.
35. True; the disk is given in polar coordinates by $0\le r\le 2, 0\le\theta\le 2\pi$.
37. False; the integrand is missing a factor of $r$:
$$\iint_R f(r,\theta)\,dA = \int_0^{\pi/2}\int_1^2 f(r,\theta)r\,dr\,d\theta$$
39. $\dfrac{1}{5}+\dfrac{\pi}{2}$
41. (a) $\dfrac{4}{3}\pi a^2 c$ (b) $\approx 1.0831682\times 10^{21}$ m$^3$ 43. $2a^2$

## ▶ Exercise Set 14.4 (Page 927)

1. $6\pi$ 3. $\dfrac{\sqrt{5}}{6}$ 5. $\sqrt{2}\pi$ 7. $\dfrac{(10\sqrt{10}-1)\pi}{18}$ 9. $8\pi$
11. (a) 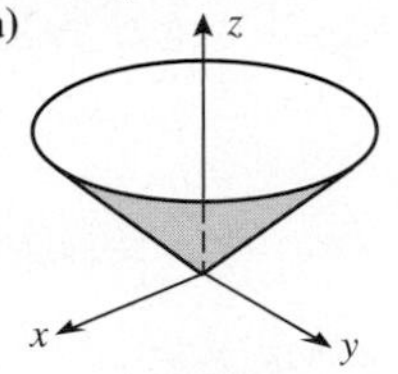

(b) 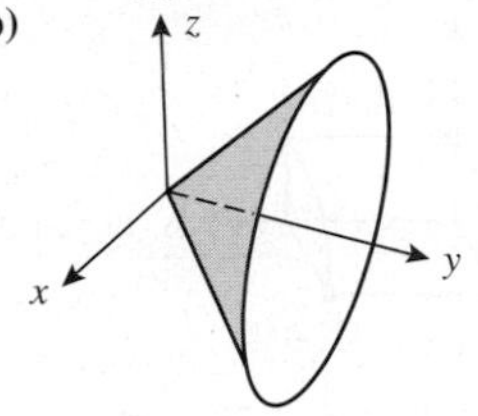

(c) 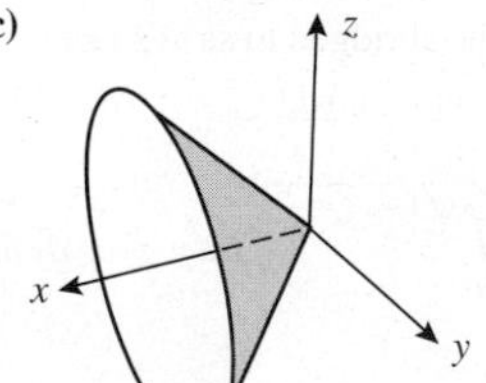

13. (a) $x=u, y=v, z=\frac{5}{2}+\frac{3}{2}u-2v$ (b) $x=u, y=v, z=u^2$
15. (a) $x=\sqrt{5}\cos u, y=\sqrt{5}\sin u, z=v; 0\le u\le 2\pi, 0\le v\le 1$
(b) $x=2\cos u, y=v, z=2\sin u; 0\le u\le 2\pi, 1\le v\le 3$
17. $x=u, y=\sin u\cos v, z=\sin u\sin v$
19. $x=r\cos\theta, y=r\sin\theta, z=\dfrac{1}{1+r^2}$
21. $x=r\cos\theta, y=r\sin\theta, z=2r^2\cos\theta\sin\theta$
23. $x=r\cos\theta, y=r\sin\theta, z=\sqrt{9-r^2}; r\le\sqrt{5}$
25. $x=\dfrac{1}{2}\rho\cos\theta, y=\dfrac{1}{2}\rho\sin\theta, z=\dfrac{\sqrt{3}}{2}\rho$ 27. $z=x-2y$; a plane
29. $(x/3)^2+(y/2)^2=1; 2\le z\le 4$; part of an elliptic cylinder
31. $(x/3)^2+(y/4)^2=z^2; 0\le z\le 1$; part of an elliptic cone
33. (a) $x=r\cos\theta, y=r\sin\theta, z=r, 0\le r\le 2$; $x=u, y=v, z=\sqrt{u^2+v^2}, 0\le u^2+v^2\le 4$
35. (a) $0\le u\le 3, 0\le v\le\pi$ (b) $0\le u\le 4, -\pi/2\le v\le\pi/2$
37. (a) $0\le\phi\le\pi/2, 0\le\theta\le 2\pi$ (b) $0\le\phi\le\pi, 0\le\theta\le\pi$
39. $2x+4y-z=5$ 41. $z=0$ 43. $x-y+\dfrac{\sqrt{2}}{2}z=\dfrac{\pi\sqrt{2}}{8}$
45. $\dfrac{(17\sqrt{17}-5\sqrt{5})\pi}{6}$

Responses to True–False questions may be abridged to save space.

47. False; the surface area is $S = \iint_R \sqrt{[f_x(x,y)]^2 + [f_y(x,y)]^2 + 1}\, dA$.

49. True; see the discussion preceding Definition 14.4.1.

51. $4\pi a^2$ 55. $4\pi^2 ab$ 57. 9.099

59. $(x/a)^2 + (y/b)^2 + (z/c)^2 = 1$; ellipsoid

61. $(x/a)^2 + (y/b)^2 - (z/c)^2 = -1$; hyperboloid of two sheets

## ▶ Exercise Set 14.5 (Page 936)

1. 8 3. $\frac{47}{3}$ 5. $\frac{81}{5}$ 7. $\frac{128}{15}$ 9. $\pi(\pi - 3)/2$ 11. $\frac{1}{6}$ 13. 9.425

15. 4 17. $\frac{256}{15}$

19. (a) $\displaystyle\int_{-1}^{1}\int_{-\sqrt{1-x^2}}^{\sqrt{1-x^2}}\int_{4x^2+y^2}^{4-3y^2} f(x,y,z)\,dz\,dy\,dx$

(b) $\displaystyle\int_{-1}^{1}\int_{-\sqrt{1-y^2}}^{\sqrt{1-y^2}}\int_{4x^2+y^2}^{4-3y^2} f(x,y,z)\,dz\,dx\,dy$

21. $\displaystyle 4\int_{0}^{1}\int_{0}^{\sqrt{1-x^2}}\int_{4x^2+y^2}^{4-3y^2} dz\,dy\,dx$

23. $\displaystyle 2\int_{-3}^{3}\int_{0}^{\frac{1}{3}\sqrt{9-x^2}}\int_{0}^{x+3} dz\,dy\,dx$

25. (a)

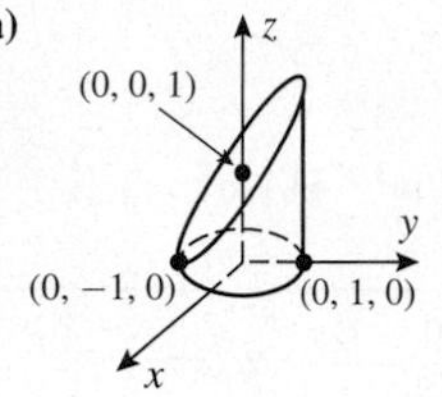


(b)

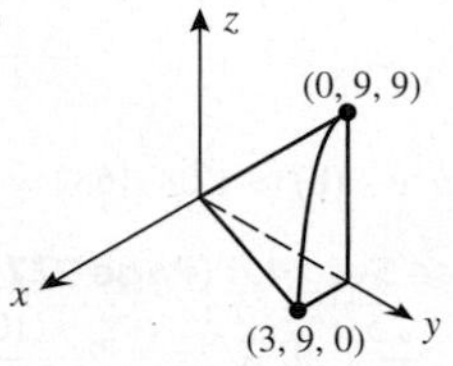


(c)

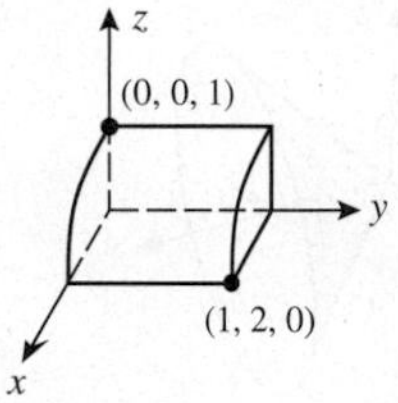


Responses to True–False questions may be abridged to save space.

27. True; apply Fubini's Theorem (Theorem 14.5.1).

29. False;

$$\iiint_G f(x,y,z)\,dV = \int_0^1\int_0^{\sqrt{1-x^2}}\int_0^{\sqrt{1-x^2-y^2}} f(x,y,z)\,dz\,dy\,dx.$$

33. $\frac{3}{4}$ 35. 3.291

37. (a) $\displaystyle\int_0^a\int_0^{b(1-x/a)}\int_0^{c(1-x/a-y/b)} dz\,dy\,dx$ is one example.

39. (a) $\displaystyle\int_0^2\int_0^{\sqrt{4-x^2}}\int_0^5 f(x,y,z)\,dz\,dy\,dx$

(b) $\displaystyle\int_0^9\int_0^{3-\sqrt{x}}\int_y^{3-\sqrt{x}} f(x,y,z)\,dz\,dy\,dx$

(c) $\displaystyle\int_0^2\int_0^{4-x^2}\int_y^{8-y} f(x,y,z)\,dz\,dy\,dx$

## ▶ Exercise Set 14.6 (Page 946)

1. $\dfrac{\pi}{4}$ 3. $\dfrac{\pi}{16}$

5. The region is bounded by the $xy$-plane and the upper half of a sphere of radius 1 centered at the origin; $f(r,\theta,z) = z$.

7. The region is the portion of the first octant inside a sphere of radius 1 centered at the origin; $f(\rho,\theta,\phi) = \rho\cos\phi$.

9. $\dfrac{81\pi}{2}$ 11. $\frac{152}{3}\pi$ 13. $\dfrac{64\pi}{3}$ 15. $\dfrac{11\pi a^3}{3}$ 17. $\dfrac{\pi a^6}{48}$

19. $\dfrac{32(2\sqrt{2}-1)\pi}{15}$

Responses to True–False questions may be abridged to save space.

21. False; the factor $r^2$ should be $r$ [Formula (6)]:

$$\iiint_G f(x,y,z)\,dV = \iiint_{\substack{\text{appropriate}\\ \text{limits}}} f(r\cos\theta, r\sin\theta, z)r\,dz\,dr\,d\theta.$$

23. True; $G$ is the spherical wedge bounded by the spheres $\rho = 1$ and $\rho = 3$, the half-planes $\theta = 0$ and $\theta = 2\pi$, and above the cone $\phi = \pi/4$, so

$$(\text{volume of } G) = \iiint_G dV = \int_0^{\pi/4}\int_0^{2\pi}\int_1^3 \rho^2\sin\phi\,d\rho\,d\theta\,d\phi.$$

25. (a) $\frac{5}{2}(-8 + 3\ln 3)\ln(\sqrt{5} - 2)$ (b) $f(x,y,z) = \dfrac{y^3}{x^3\sqrt{1+z^2}}$; $G$ is the cylindrical wedge $1 \le r \le 4$, $\dfrac{\pi}{6} \le \theta \le \dfrac{\pi}{3}$, $-2 \le z \le 2$

27. $\dfrac{4\pi a^3}{3}$ 29. $\dfrac{2(\sqrt{3}-1)\pi}{3}$

## ▶ Exercise Set 14.7 (Page 957)

1. −17 3. $\cos(u - v)$ 5. $x = \frac{2}{9}u + \frac{5}{9}v$, $y = -\frac{1}{9}u + \frac{2}{9}v$; $\frac{1}{9}$

7. $x = \dfrac{\sqrt{u+v}}{\sqrt{2}}$, $y = \dfrac{\sqrt{v-u}}{\sqrt{2}}$; $\dfrac{1}{4\sqrt{v^2-u^2}}$ 9. 5 11. $\dfrac{1}{v}$

Responses to True–False questions may be abridged to save space.

13. False; $|\partial(x,y)/\partial(u,v)| = \|\partial\mathbf{r}/\partial u \times \partial\mathbf{r}/\partial v\|$; evaluating this at $(u_0, v_0)$ gives the area of the indicated parallelogram.

15. False; $\partial(x,y)/\partial(r,\theta) = r$.

17.

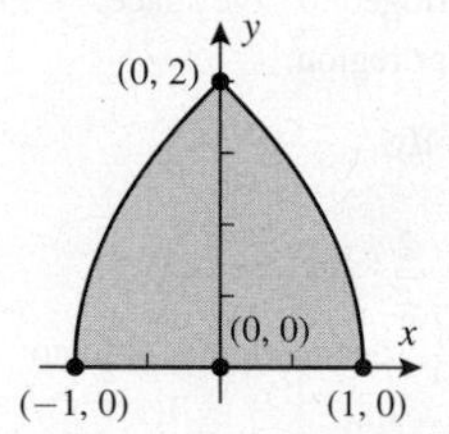


19.

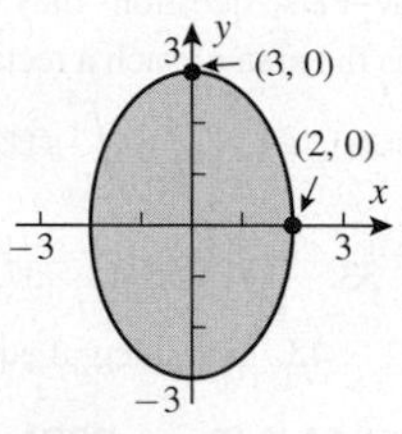


21. $\frac{3}{2}\ln 3$ 23. $1 - \frac{1}{2}\sin 2$ 25. $96\pi$ 27. $\dfrac{\pi}{24}(1 - \cos 1)$ 29. $\frac{192}{5}\pi$

31. $u = \begin{cases} \cot^{-1}(x/y), & y \ne 0 \\ 0, & y = 0 \text{ and } x > 0 \\ \pi, & y = 0 \text{ and } x < 0 \end{cases}$

$v = \sqrt{x^2 + y^2}$; other answers possible

33. $u = (3/7)x - (2/7)y$, $v = (-1/7)x + (3/7)y$; other answers possible

35. $\frac{1}{4}\ln\frac{5}{2}$

37. $\dfrac{1}{2}\left[\ln(\sqrt{2}+1) - \dfrac{\pi}{4}\right]$ 39. $\frac{35}{256}$ 41. $2\ln 3$ 45. 21/8

## ▶ Exercise Set 14.8 (Page 965)

1. $M = \frac{13}{20}$, center of gravity $\left(\frac{190}{273}, \frac{6}{13}\right)$

3. $M = a^4/8$, center of gravity $(8a/15, 8a/15)$

5. $\left(\frac{1}{2}, \frac{1}{2}\right)$ 7. $\left(\frac{1}{2}, \frac{1}{2}, \frac{1}{2}\right)$

Responses to True–False questions may be abridged to save space.

9. True; recall this from Section 6.7.

11. False; the center of gravity of the lamina is $(\bar{x}, \bar{y}) = (M_y/M, M_x/M)$, where $M_y$ and $M_x$ are the lamina's first moments about the $y$- and $x$-axes, respectively, and $M$ is the mass of the lamina.

15. $\left(\dfrac{128}{105\pi}, \dfrac{128}{105\pi}\right)$ 17. $\left(\dfrac{4a}{3\pi}, 0\right)$ 19. $\left(\frac{1}{4}, \frac{1}{4}, \frac{1}{4}\right)$ 21. $\left(\frac{1}{2}, 0, \frac{3}{5}\right)$

23. $(3a/8, 3a/8, 3a/8)$

25. $M = a^4/2$, center of gravity $(a/3, a/2, a/2)$

27. $M = \frac{1}{6}$, center of gravity $\left(0, \frac{16}{35}, \frac{1}{2}\right)$ 29. (a) $\left(\frac{5}{8}, \frac{5}{8}\right)$ (b) $\left(\frac{2}{3}, \frac{1}{2}\right)$

31. $(1.177406, 0.353554, 0.231557)$

33. $\dfrac{27\pi}{4}$ 35. $\pi k a^4$ 37. $\left(0, 0, \dfrac{7}{16\sqrt{2}-14}\right)$ 39. $\left(\frac{4}{3}, 0, \frac{10}{9}\right)$

41. $(3a/8, 3a/8, 3a/8)$ 43. $(2 - \sqrt{2})\pi/4$ 45. $(0, 0, 8/15)$

47. $(0, 195/152, 0)$ 51. $\frac{1}{2}\delta\pi a^4 h$ 53. $\frac{1}{2}\delta\pi h(a_2^4 - a_1^4)$ 57. $2\pi^2 abk$

59. $(a/3, b/3)$

### ▶ Chapter 14 Review Exercises (Page 968)

3. **(a)** $\iint_R dA$ **(b)** $\iiint_G dV$ **(c)** $\iint_R \sqrt{1+\left(\frac{\partial z}{\partial x}\right)^2+\left(\frac{\partial z}{\partial y}\right)^2}\,dA$

5. $\int_0^1 \int_{1-\sqrt{1-y^2}}^{1+\sqrt{1-y^2}} f(x,y)\,dx\,dy$

7. **(a)** $a=2, b=1, c=1, d=2$ or $a=1, b=2, c=2, d=1$ **(b)** 3

9. $-\frac{1}{\sqrt{2\pi}}$

11. $\int_0^1 \int_{2y}^{2} e^x e^y\,dx\,dy$

13.

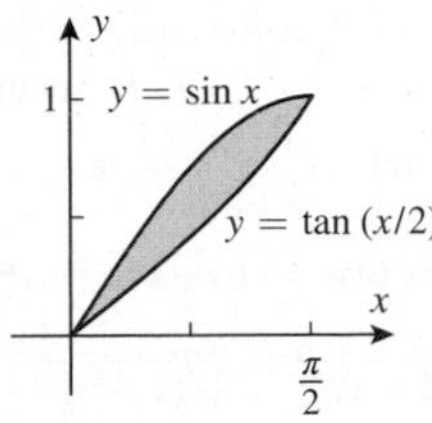


15. $\frac{1}{3}(1-\cos 64)$ 17. $a^2$ 19. $\frac{3}{2}$ 21. $32\pi$

23. **(a)** $\int_0^{2\pi}\int_0^{\pi/3}\int_0^a \rho^4\sin^3\phi\,d\rho\,d\phi\,d\theta$

**(b)** $\int_0^{2\pi}\int_0^{\sqrt{3}a/2}\int_{r/\sqrt{3}}^{\sqrt{a^2-r^2}} r^3\,dz\,dr\,d\theta$

**(c)** $\int_{-\sqrt{3}a/2}^{\sqrt{3}a/2}\int_{-\sqrt{(3a^2/4)-x^2}}^{\sqrt{(3a^2/4)-x^2}}\int_{\sqrt{x^2+y^2}/\sqrt{3}}^{\sqrt{a^2-x^2-y^2}} (x^2+y^2)\,dz\,dy\,dx$

25. $\frac{\pi a^3}{9}$ 27. $\frac{1}{24}(26^{3/2}-10^{3/2}) \approx 4.20632$ 29. $2x+4y-z=5$

33. **(a)** $\frac{1}{2(u+w)}$ **(b)** $\frac{1}{2}(7\ln 7-5\ln 5-3\ln 3)$ 35. $\left(\frac{8}{5},0\right)$

37. $(0,0,h/4)$

### ▶ Chapter 14 Making Connections (Page 970)

Where correct answers to a Making Connections exercise may vary, no answer is listed. Sample answers for these questions are available on the Book Companion Site.

1. **(b)** $\frac{\pi}{4}$ 3. **(a)** 1.173108605 **(b)** 1.173108605

4. **(a)** the sphere $0 \le x^2+y^2+z^2 \le 1$ **(b)** 4.934802202 **(c)** $\pi^2/2$

5. **(b)** 4.4506 6. $\frac{4}{35}\pi a^3$

### ▶ Exercise Set 15.1 (Page 978)

1. **(a)** III **(b)** IV 3. **(a)** true **(b)** true **(c)** true

5.

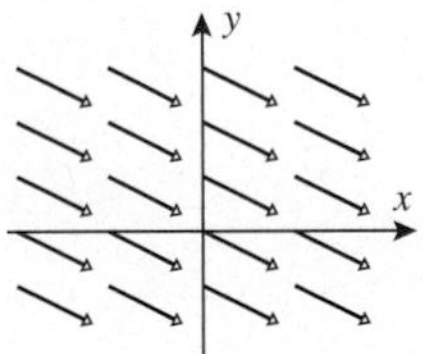


7.

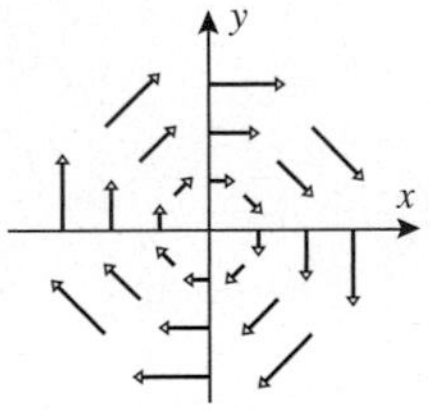


9.

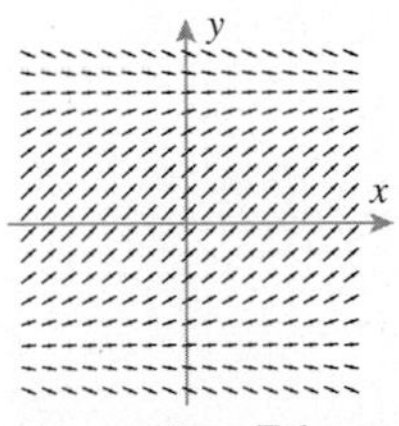


Responses to True–False questions may be abridged to save space.

11. False; the vector field has a nonzero **k**-component.

13. True; this is the curl of **F**.

15. **(a)** all $x, y$ **(b)** all $x, y$ 17. div $\mathbf{F} = 2x+y$, curl $\mathbf{F} = z\mathbf{i}$

19. div $\mathbf{F} = 0$, curl $\mathbf{F} = (40x^2z^4 - 12xy^3)\mathbf{i} + (14y^3z + 3y^4)\mathbf{j} - (16xz^5 + 21y^2z^2)\mathbf{k}$

21. div $\mathbf{F} = \frac{2}{\sqrt{x^2+y^2+z^2}}$, curl $\mathbf{F} = \mathbf{0}$ 23. $4x$ 25. 0

27. $(1+y)\mathbf{i} + x\mathbf{j}$

39. $\nabla\cdot(k\mathbf{F}) = k\nabla\cdot\mathbf{F}$, $\nabla\cdot(\mathbf{F}+\mathbf{G}) = \nabla\cdot\mathbf{F}+\nabla\cdot\mathbf{G}$, $\nabla\cdot(\phi\mathbf{F}) = \phi\nabla\cdot\mathbf{F}+\nabla\phi\cdot\mathbf{F}$, $\nabla\cdot(\nabla\times\mathbf{F}) = 0$

47. **(b)** $x^2+y^2 = K$

49. $\frac{dy}{dx} = \frac{1}{x}$, $y = \ln x + K$

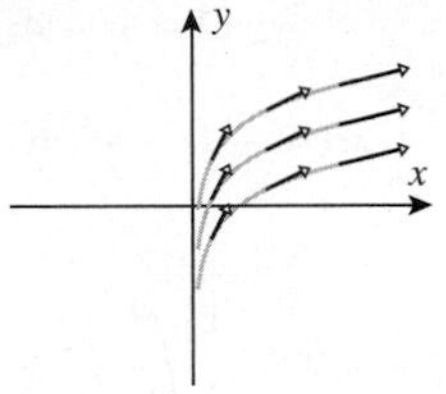


### ▶ Exercise Set 15.2 (Page 993)

1. **(a)** 1 **(b)** 0 3. 16 7. 8 9. $-28$

11. **(a)** $\frac{4\sqrt{2}-2}{3}$ **(b)** 1 **(c)** $\frac{2}{3}$

13. **(a)** 3 **(b)** 3 **(c)** 3 **(d)** 3

Responses to True–False questions may be abridged to save space.

15. False; line integrals of functions are independent of the orientation of the curve. 17. True; this is Equation (26).

19. 2 21. $\frac{13}{20}$ 23. $1-\pi$ 25. 3 27. $-1-(\pi/4)$ 29. $1-e^3$

31. **(a)** $\frac{63\sqrt{17}}{64} + \frac{1}{4}\ln(4+\sqrt{17}) - \frac{1}{8}\ln\frac{\sqrt{17}+1}{\sqrt{17}-1} - \frac{1}{4}\ln(\sqrt{2}+1) + \frac{1}{8}\ln\frac{\sqrt{2}+1}{\sqrt{2}-1}$ **(b)** $\frac{\pi^3}{24} + \frac{e^{\pi/2}}{5} + \frac{\pi}{4} + \frac{6}{5}$

33. **(a)** $-1$ **(b)** $-2$ 35. $\frac{5}{2}$ 37. 0 39. $1-e^{-1}$ 41. $6\sqrt{3}$

43. $5k\tan^{-1}3$ 45. $\frac{3}{5}$ 47. $\frac{27}{28}$ 49. $\frac{3}{4}$ 51. $\frac{17\sqrt{17}-1}{4}$

53. **(b)** $S = \int_C z(t)\,dt$ **(c)** $4\pi$ 55. $\lambda = -12$

### ▶ Exercise Set 15.3 (Page 1004)

1. conservative, $\phi = \frac{x^2}{2}+\frac{y^2}{2}+K$ 3. not conservative

5. conservative, $\phi = x\cos y + y\sin x + K$

9. $-6$ 11. $9e^2$ 13. 32 15. $W = -\frac{1}{2}$ 17. $W = 1-e^{-1}$

Responses to True–False questions may be abridged to save space.

19. False; the integral must be 0 for *all* closed curves $C$.

21. True; if $\nabla\phi$ is constant, then $\phi$ must be a linear function.

23. $\ln 2 - 1$ 25. $\approx -0.307$ 27. no 33. $h(x) = Ce^x$

35. **(a)** $W = -\frac{1}{\sqrt{14}}+\frac{1}{\sqrt{6}}$ **(b)** $W = -\frac{1}{\sqrt{14}}+\frac{1}{\sqrt{6}}$ **(c)** $W = 0$

### ▶ Exercise Set 15.4 (Page 1011)

1. 0 3. 0 5. 0 7. $8\pi$ 9. $-4$ 11. $-1$ 13. 0

Responses to True–False questions may be abridged to save space.

15. False; Green's Theorem applies to closed curves.

17. True; the integral is the area of the region bounded by $C$.

19. **(a)** $\approx -3.550999378$ **(b)** $\approx -0.269616482$ 21. $\frac{3}{8}a^2\pi$ 23. $\frac{1}{2}abt_0$

27. Formula (1) of Section 6.1 29. $\frac{250}{3}$ 31. $-3\pi a^2$ 33. $\left(\frac{8}{15},\frac{8}{21}\right)$

35. $\left(0,\frac{4a}{3\pi}\right)$ 37. the circle $x^2+y^2=1$ 39. 69

### ▶ Exercise Set 15.5 (Page 1019)

1. $\frac{15}{2}\pi\sqrt{2}$ 3. $\frac{\pi}{4}$ 5. $-\frac{\sqrt{2}}{2}$ 7. 9

Responses to True–False questions may be abridged to save space.

9. True; this follows from the definition.

11. False; the integral is the total mass of the lamina.

13. **(b)** $2\pi\left[1-\sqrt{1-r^2}+\frac{r^2}{2}\right] \to 3\pi$ as $r \to 1^-$

**(c)** $\mathbf{r}(\phi,\theta) = \sin\phi\cos\theta\mathbf{i} + \sin\phi\sin\theta\mathbf{j} + \cos\phi\mathbf{k}$, $0 \le \theta \le 2\pi, 0 \le \phi \le \pi/2$;

$$\iint_\sigma (1+z)\,dS = \int_0^{2\pi}\int_0^{\pi/2} (1+\cos\phi)\sin\phi\,d\phi\,d\theta = 3\pi$$

17. (c) $4\pi/3$

19. (a) $\dfrac{\sqrt{29}}{16}\displaystyle\int_0^6\int_0^{(12-2x)/3} xy(12-2x-3y)\,dy\,dx$

(b) $\dfrac{\sqrt{29}}{4}\displaystyle\int_0^3\int_0^{(12-4z)/3} yz(12-3y-4z)\,dy\,dz$

(c) $\dfrac{\sqrt{29}}{9}\displaystyle\int_0^3\int_0^{6-2z} xz(12-2x-4z)\,dx\,dz$

21. $\dfrac{18\sqrt{29}}{5}$

23. $\displaystyle\int_0^4\int_1^2 y^3z\sqrt{4y^2+1}\,dy\,dz;\ \frac{1}{2}\int_0^4\int_1^4 xz\sqrt{1+4x}\,dx\,dz$

25. $\dfrac{391\sqrt{17}}{15}-\dfrac{5\sqrt{5}}{3}$ 27. $\frac{4}{3}\pi\delta_0$ 29. $\frac{1}{4}(37\sqrt{37}-1)$ 31. $M=\delta_0 S$

33. $(0,0,149/65)$ 35. $\dfrac{93}{\sqrt{10}}$ 37. $\dfrac{\pi}{4}$ 39. 57.895751

## ▶ Exercise Set 15.6 (Page 1028)

1. (a) zero (b) zero (c) positive (d) negative (e) zero (f) zero
3. $-80$ 5. 30 7. $200\pi$ 9. 4 11. $2\pi$ 13. $\dfrac{14\pi}{3}$ 15. 0
17. $18\pi$ 19. $\frac{4}{9}$ 21. (a) 8 (b) 24 (c) 0

Responses to True–False questions may be abridged to save space.

23. False; the Möbius strip has no orientation.
25. False; the net volume can be zero because as much fluid passes through the surface in the negative direction as in the positive direction.
27. $-3\pi$ 29. (a) $0\ \text{m}^3/\text{s}$ (b) $0\ \text{kg/s}$ 31. (b) $32/3$
33. (a) $4\pi a^{k+3}$ (b) $k=-3$ 35. $a=2,3$

## ▶ Exercise Set 15.7 (Page 1038)

1. 3 3. $\dfrac{4\pi}{3}$

Responses to True–False questions may be abridged to save space.

5. False; it equates a surface integral and a triple integral.
7. True; see subsection entitled Sources and Sinks.
9. 12 11. $3\pi a^2$ 13. $180\pi$ 15. $\dfrac{192\pi}{5}$ 17. $\dfrac{\pi}{2}$ 19. $\dfrac{4608}{35}$
21. $135\pi$ 23. (a) $\mathbf{F}=x\mathbf{i}+y\mathbf{j}+z\mathbf{k}$ (b) $\mathbf{F}=-x\mathbf{i}-y\mathbf{j}-z\mathbf{k}$
33. no sources or sinks
35. sources at all points except the origin, no sinks 37. $\dfrac{7\pi}{4}$

## ▶ Exercise Set 15.8 (Page 1045)

1. $\frac{3}{2}$ 3. 0 5. $2\pi$ 7. $16\pi$ 9. 0 11. $\pi a^2$

Responses to True–False questions may be abridged to save space.

13. True; see Theorem 15.8.1. 15. False; the circulation is $\int_C \mathbf{F}\cdot\mathbf{T}\,ds$.
17. (a) $\frac{3}{2}$ (b) $-1$ (c) $-\dfrac{1}{\sqrt{2}}\mathbf{j}-\dfrac{1}{\sqrt{2}}\mathbf{k}$ 23. $-\dfrac{5\pi}{4}$

## ▶ Chapter 15 Review Exercises (Page 1046)

3. $\dfrac{1-x}{\sqrt{(1-x)^2+(2-y)^2}}\mathbf{i}+\dfrac{2-y}{\sqrt{(1-x)^2+(2-y)^2}}\mathbf{j}$ 5. $\mathbf{i}+\mathbf{j}+\mathbf{k}$

7. (a) $\displaystyle\int_a^b\left[f(x(t),y(t))\frac{dx}{dt}+g(x(t),y(t))\frac{dy}{dt}\right]dt$

(b) $\displaystyle\int_a^b f(x(t),y(t))\sqrt{x'(t)^2+y'(t)^2}\,dt$

11. 0 13. $-7/2$ 17. (a) $h(x)=Cx^{-3/2}$ (b) $g(y)=C/y^3$

21. $A=\dfrac{1}{2}\displaystyle\int_\alpha^\beta r^2\,d\theta$

23. $\displaystyle\iint_R f(x(u,v),y(u,v),z(u,v))\|\mathbf{r}_u\times\mathbf{r}_v\|\,du\,dv$ 25. yes 27. $2\pi$

31. $-8\pi$ 35. (a) conservative (b) not conservative

## ▶ Chapter 15 Making Connections (Page 1048)

Answers are provided in the Student Solutions Manual.

# INDEX

## RATIONAL FUNCTIONS CONTAINING POWERS OF $a + bu$ IN THE DENOMINATOR

60. $\displaystyle\int \frac{u\,du}{a+bu} = \frac{1}{b^2}[bu - a\ln|a+bu|] + C$

61. $\displaystyle\int \frac{u^2\,du}{a+bu} = \frac{1}{b^3}\left[\frac{1}{2}(a+bu)^2 - 2a(a+bu) + a^2\ln|a+bu|\right] + C$

62. $\displaystyle\int \frac{u\,du}{(a+bu)^2} = \frac{1}{b^2}\left[\frac{a}{a+bu} + \ln|a+bu|\right] + C$

63. $\displaystyle\int \frac{u^2\,du}{(a+bu)^2} = \frac{1}{b^3}\left[bu - \frac{a^2}{a+bu} - 2a\ln|a+bu|\right] + C$

64. $\displaystyle\int \frac{u\,du}{(a+bu)^3} = \frac{1}{b^2}\left[\frac{a}{2(a+bu)^2} - \frac{1}{a+bu}\right] + C$

65. $\displaystyle\int \frac{du}{u(a+bu)} = \frac{1}{a}\ln\left|\frac{u}{a+bu}\right| + C$

66. $\displaystyle\int \frac{du}{u^2(a+bu)} = -\frac{1}{au} + \frac{b}{a^2}\ln\left|\frac{a+bu}{u}\right| + C$

67. $\displaystyle\int \frac{du}{u(a+bu)^2} = \frac{1}{a(a+bu)} + \frac{1}{a^2}\ln\left|\frac{u}{a+bu}\right| + C$

## RATIONAL FUNCTIONS CONTAINING $a^2 \pm u^2$ IN THE DENOMINATOR ($a > 0$)

68. $\displaystyle\int \frac{du}{a^2+u^2} = \frac{1}{a}\tan^{-1}\frac{u}{a} + C$

69. $\displaystyle\int \frac{du}{a^2-u^2} = \frac{1}{2a}\ln\left|\frac{u+a}{u-a}\right| + C$

70. $\displaystyle\int \frac{du}{u^2-a^2} = \frac{1}{2a}\ln\left|\frac{u-a}{u+a}\right| + C$

71. $\displaystyle\int \frac{bu+c}{a^2+u^2}\,du = \frac{b}{2}\ln(a^2+u^2) + \frac{c}{a}\tan^{-1}\frac{u}{a} + C$

## INTEGRALS OF $\sqrt{a^2+u^2}$, $\sqrt{a^2-u^2}$, $\sqrt{u^2-a^2}$ AND THEIR RECIPROCALS ($a > 0$)

72. $\displaystyle\int \sqrt{u^2+a^2}\,du = \frac{u}{2}\sqrt{u^2+a^2} + \frac{a^2}{2}\ln(u+\sqrt{u^2+a^2}) + C$

73. $\displaystyle\int \sqrt{u^2-a^2}\,du = \frac{u}{2}\sqrt{u^2-a^2} - \frac{a^2}{2}\ln|u+\sqrt{u^2-a^2}| + C$

74. $\displaystyle\int \sqrt{a^2-u^2}\,du = \frac{u}{2}\sqrt{a^2-u^2} + \frac{a^2}{2}\sin^{-1}\frac{u}{a} + C$

75. $\displaystyle\int \frac{du}{\sqrt{u^2+a^2}} = \ln(u+\sqrt{u^2+a^2}) + C$

76. $\displaystyle\int \frac{du}{\sqrt{u^2-a^2}} = \ln|u+\sqrt{u^2-a^2}| + C$

77. $\displaystyle\int \frac{du}{\sqrt{a^2-u^2}} = \sin^{-1}\frac{u}{a} + C$

## POWERS OF $u$ MULTIPLYING OR DIVIDING $\sqrt{a^2-u^2}$ OR ITS RECIPROCAL

78. $\displaystyle\int u^2\sqrt{a^2-u^2}\,du = \frac{u}{8}(2u^2-a^2)\sqrt{a^2-u^2} + \frac{a^4}{8}\sin^{-1}\frac{u}{a} + C$

79. $\displaystyle\int \frac{\sqrt{a^2-u^2}\,du}{u} = \sqrt{a^2-u^2} - a\ln\left|\frac{a+\sqrt{a^2-u^2}}{u}\right| + C$

80. $\displaystyle\int \frac{\sqrt{a^2-u^2}\,du}{u^2} = -\frac{\sqrt{a^2-u^2}}{u} - \sin^{-1}\frac{u}{a} + C$

81. $\displaystyle\int \frac{u^2\,du}{\sqrt{a^2-u^2}} = -\frac{u}{2}\sqrt{a^2-u^2} + \frac{a^2}{2}\sin^{-1}\frac{u}{a} + C$

82. $\displaystyle\int \frac{du}{u\sqrt{a^2-u^2}} = -\frac{1}{a}\ln\left|\frac{a+\sqrt{a^2-u^2}}{u}\right| + C$

83. $\displaystyle\int \frac{du}{u^2\sqrt{a^2-u^2}} = -\frac{\sqrt{a^2-u^2}}{a^2u} + C$

## POWERS OF $u$ MULTIPLYING OR DIVIDING $\sqrt{u^2 \pm a^2}$ OR THEIR RECIPROCALS

84. $\displaystyle\int u\sqrt{u^2+a^2}\,du = \frac{1}{3}(u^2+a^2)^{3/2} + C$

85. $\displaystyle\int u\sqrt{u^2-a^2}\,du = \frac{1}{3}(u^2-a^2)^{3/2} + C$

86. $\displaystyle\int \frac{du}{u\sqrt{u^2+a^2}} = -\frac{1}{a}\ln\left|\frac{a+\sqrt{u^2+a^2}}{u}\right| + C$

87. $\displaystyle\int \frac{du}{u\sqrt{u^2-a^2}} = \frac{1}{a}\sec^{-1}\left|\frac{u}{a}\right| + C$

88. $\displaystyle\int \frac{\sqrt{u^2-a^2}\,du}{u} = \sqrt{u^2-a^2} - a\sec^{-1}\left|\frac{u}{a}\right| + C$

89. $\displaystyle\int \frac{\sqrt{u^2+a^2}\,du}{u} = \sqrt{u^2+a^2} - a\ln\left|\frac{a+\sqrt{u^2+a^2}}{u}\right| + C$

90. $\displaystyle\int \frac{du}{u^2\sqrt{u^2\pm a^2}} = \mp\frac{\sqrt{u^2\pm a^2}}{a^2u} + C$

91. $\displaystyle\int u^2\sqrt{u^2+a^2}\,du = \frac{u}{8}(2u^2+a^2)\sqrt{u^2+a^2} - \frac{a^4}{8}\ln(u+\sqrt{u^2+a^2}) + C$

92. $\displaystyle\int u^2\sqrt{u^2-a^2}\,du = \frac{u}{8}(2u^2-a^2)\sqrt{u^2-a^2} - \frac{a^4}{8}\ln|u+\sqrt{u^2-a^2}| + C$

93. $\displaystyle\int \frac{\sqrt{u^2+a^2}}{u^2}\,du = -\frac{\sqrt{u^2+a^2}}{u} + \ln(u+\sqrt{u^2+a^2}) + C$

94. $\displaystyle\int \frac{\sqrt{u^2-a^2}}{u^2}\,du = -\frac{\sqrt{u^2-a^2}}{u} + \ln|u+\sqrt{u^2-a^2}| + C$

95. $\displaystyle\int \frac{u^2}{\sqrt{u^2+a^2}}\,du = \frac{u}{2}\sqrt{u^2+a^2} - \frac{a^2}{2}\ln(u+\sqrt{u^2+a^2}) + C$

96. $\displaystyle\int \frac{u^2}{\sqrt{u^2-a^2}}\,du = \frac{u}{2}\sqrt{u^2-a^2} + \frac{a^2}{2}\ln|u+\sqrt{u^2-a^2}| + C$

## INTEGRALS CONTAINING $(a^2+u^2)^{3/2}$, $(a^2-u^2)^{3/2}$, $(u^2-a^2)^{3/2}$ ($a > 0$)

97. $\displaystyle\int \frac{du}{(a^2-u^2)^{3/2}} = \frac{u}{a^2\sqrt{a^2-u^2}} + C$

98. $\displaystyle\int \frac{du}{(u^2\pm a^2)^{3/2}} = \pm\frac{u}{a^2\sqrt{u^2\pm a^2}} + C$

99. $\displaystyle\int (a^2-u^2)^{3/2}\,du = -\frac{u}{8}(2u^2-5a^2)\sqrt{a^2-u^2} + \frac{3a^4}{8}\sin^{-1}\frac{u}{a} + C$

100. $\displaystyle\int (u^2+a^2)^{3/2}\,du = \frac{u}{8}(2u^2+5a^2)\sqrt{u^2+a^2} + \frac{3a^4}{8}\ln(u+\sqrt{u^2+a^2}) + C$

101. $\displaystyle\int (u^2-a^2)^{3/2}\,du = \frac{u}{8}(2u^2-5a^2)\sqrt{u^2-a^2} + \frac{3a^4}{8}\ln|u+\sqrt{u^2-a^2}| + C$